We've been saving money for years. And years. And years.

The Absa Group Museum houses the biggest collection of coins, notes, moneyboxes and related artefacts in the country, and traces the history of South African banking back to its inception. Come visit us. And while you may not always know where your money goes to, you'll certainly be able to see where it comes from.

Absa Group Museum: Ground Floor, 187 Fox Street, Johannesburg. Open 9:00 – 16:00 weekdays
Phone (011) 350 4167/6889, fax (011) 350 3435

ABSA
Today Tomorrow Together

ABSA Bank Ltd, Reg no 1986/004794/06

Y&R Gitam 123925

FROM **MEDIEVAL** TO **REGENCY**

OLD MASTERS IN THE COLLECTION OF THE FERENS ART GALLERY

A complete survey of British and foreign old masters in one of Britain's most outstanding collections

22nd June – 6th October 2002

Mon – Sat 10am – 5pm
Sun 1.30 – 4.30pm
Admission Free

Fully illustrated catalogue by
CHRISTOPHER WRIGHT

Ferens Art Gallery,
Queen Victoria Square, Hull, England HU1 3RA
Tel: 00 44 (0) 1482 613902 Museums@hullcc.gov.uk

Catalogue supported by the Paul Mellon Centre for Studies in British Art,
the Friends of the Ferens Art Gallery, Yorkshire Museums Council and Hull City Council

Jean-Auguste Dominique Ingres: An Unknown Lady, c.1804

Handbook of International Documentation and Information

Volume 16

Vol. I
Afghanistan
—
Swaziland

Vol. II
Sweden
—
Zimbabwe

Indices

Neues Stadtmuseum Landsberg am Lech

Von-Helfensteingasse 426 · 86899 Landsberg · Tel. 0 81 91/ 94 23 26 · Fax: 0 81 91/ 94 23 27
BAB München-Lindau, Ausfahrt 26
e-mail : neues_stadtmuseum@landsberg.de
Geöffnet täglich, außer montags von 14 bis 17 Uhr, Februar und März geschlossen.

Museums of the World

9th revised and
enlarged edition

Volume II
Sweden – Zimbabwe
Indices

K · G · Saur München 2002

Editor/Redaktion:
Michael Zils

Editorial Office/Redaktionsbüro:
Luppenstr. 1b
D-04177 Leipzig (Germany)
Tel. +49 341 4869911
Fax +49 341 4869913

Die Deutsche Bibliothek - CIP-Einheitsaufnahme

Museums of the world
/ [ed.: Michael Zils]. - 9., rev and enl. ed. - München : Saur
(Handbook of international documentation and information ; Vol.16)
ISBN 3-598-20610-0

Vol. 2. Sweden - Zimbabwe; Indices. - 2002

Printed on acid-free paper

© 2002 by K. G. Saur Verlag GmbH, München

Printed in Germany

Data preparation and automatic data processing by
bsix information exchange, Braunschweig
Printed and bound by Strauss Offsetdruck, Mörlenbach

Cover Art by William Pownall

ISSN 0939-1959 (Handbook)
ISBN 3-598-20610-0 (2 volumes)

Contents

Volume I

Volume II

Museums
of the World

Volume II

Homo Pictor

Edited by Gottfried Boehm, sub-editor: Stephan E. Hauser

2001. XIII, 390 pages and 61 plates. Hardbound
€ 57.00. ISBN 3-598-77418-4
(Colloquium Rauricum, volume 7)

Homo Pictor unites the contributions of the seventh sequel of the biennial Colloquia Raurica, regularly held by the distinguished of the Colloquium Rauricum on Castelen in Augst near Basel. The volume offers twenty essays written by experts who discuss the subject of man as creator of images. Their viewpoints primarily reflect arthistorical, philosophical, archaeological and historical ideas, while taking into account German language and literature. The space of time considered extends from prehistory to the present, guiding the reader through the major periods of human history.

Firmly resting on the experience of a periodically very successful and predominant „Science of Language", the authors explore the grammar and syntax of visual modes of expression. They examine the possibilities of a „Science of Image," which lends itself to anthropological reasoning, yet stands apart from any intention to subvert or dislodge historiographic analytical approaches. Amid the tension of the images' reality and their discursive evasiveness, these essays present which both accept the function of the image as a guiding category and define it as a point of departure toward rethinking the obligations of science in a growing image environment.

The publication is of particular interest to those attracted by the questions which arise from the images' ambiguity, to be past and present simultaneously.

 **K·G·Saur Verlag**
A Gale Group/Thomson Learning Company
Postfach 70 16 20 · 81316 München · Germany · Tel. +49 (0)89 7 69 02-232
Fax +49 (0)89 7 69 02-250 · e-mail: info@saur.de · http://www.saur.de

Sweden

Älvängen

Repslagarmuseet, Tågvirkesgränd, 446 37 Älvängen - T: (0303) 749910, Fax: 749915, Internet: http://www.repslagbanan.se
Science&Tech Museum - 1995 30013

Älvdalen

Hembygdsgården Rots Skans, Holen, Rot, 796 02 Älvdalen
Open Air Museum - 1911
Ethnography, 20 different houses 30014

Porfyrmuseet, Dalg 81b, 796 31 Älvdalen - T: (0251) 41035
Natural History Museum
Porphyr artefacts 30015

Ängelholm

Hantverksmuseet, Tingstorget, 262 80 Ängelholm - T: (0431) 87503, 87097
Historical Museum 30016

Åhus

Åhus Museum, Torget, 296 31 Åhus - T: (044) 135800, Fax: 214902, E-mail: info@regionmuseet.m.se, Internet: http://www.regionmuseet.m.se. Head: Agne Furingsten
Local Museum 30017

Alingsås

Alingsås Museum, Lilla Torget, 441 01 Alingsås, mail addr: Box 2, 441 81 Alingsås - T: (0322) 75596, Fax: 13516
Local Museum
Prehistory, textiles 30018

Nolhaga Slott, Nolhaga Allé, 441 55 Alingsås - T: (0322) 75598
Historical Museum 30019

Alvesta

Kronobergs Lantbruksmuseum, Hjärtenholm, 342 00 Alvesta - T: (0472) 40130
Agriculture Museum 30020

Åmål

Åmål Konsthall, Kungsg 20, 662 00 Åmål
Fine Arts Museum - 1968 30021

Åmåls Hembygdsmuseum (Åmåls Heritage Museum), Hamngatan 7, 662 31 Åmål - T: (0532) 15820, 13815, Internet: http://www.amal.se/foreningar/hembygdsmuseum. Head: Karl Erik Waern
Local Museum
Local hist 30022

Angered

Museihallen Blå Stället, Angereds Centrum, 424 65 Angered - T: (031) 317473
Local Museum 30023

Arboga

Arboga Museum, Nyg 37, 732 30 Arboga, mail addr: Box 98, 732 22 Arboga - T: (0589) 14210, Fax: 15970. Head: Magnus Hagberg
Local Museum - 1923
Local hist, ethnology 30024

Bryggerimuseum, Skandiag, 732 33 Arboga - T: (0589) 14210
Historical Museum 30025

Årjäng

Nordiska Travmuseet i Årjäng, Marknaasvägen, 672 23 Årjäng - T: (0573) 711800, Fax: 711018, E-mail: travmuseet@telia.com, Internet: http://www.travmuseet.com. Head: Åke Larsson
Special Museum
History of the trotting sport 30026

Arjeplog

Silvermuseet, Torget, 930 90 Arjeplog - T: (0961) 11290, Fax: 11313. Head: Ingela Bergman
Decorative Arts Museum / Folklore Museum - 1965
Lapp culture, silver, ethnography 30027

Årsunda

Årsunda Viking Museum, STorsjövägen 1, 810 22 Årsunda - T: (026) 290116, Fax: 290116, Internet: http://www.sandviken.se/viking
Local Museum / Open Air Museum 30028

Arvika

Arvika Konsthall, Storg 22, 671 00 Arvika - T: (0570) 81842
Fine Arts Museum 30029

Arvika Museum, Sågudden, 671 21 Arvika - T: (0570) 13795, Fax: 17420, E-mail: info@sagudden.com, Internet: http://www.sagudden.com. Head: Else Marie Svensson
Local Museum
Archaeological finds, ethnography, open air museum 30030

Åsarp

Ekehagens Forntidsby, 520 43 Åsarp - T: (0515) 50060, Fax: 50062
Ethnology Museum / Historical Museum
Domestic item since stone age, handicrafts, domestic animals, wildlife 30031

Åsele

Stiftelsen Kvarnbäcken i Torvsjö, 910 60 Åsele - T: (0941) 53025. Head: Bernhard Westman
Local Museum 30032

Askersund

Stjernsunds Slott, 696 00 Askersund
Decorative Arts Museum - 1951
Interiors 30033

Avesta

Carl Jularbo Museum, Badhusg 2, 774 60 Avesta - T: (0226) 645122. Head: Lars-Åke Everbrand
Music Museum 30034

Bengtfors

Gammelgården, 666 00 Bengtfors
Local Museum
Local history 30035

Bergsjö

Bergsjö Konsthall, Hundskinnsvägen 1, 820 70 Bergsjö, mail addr: Box 3, 820 70 Bergsjö - T: (0652) 36200
Fine Arts Museum 30036

Bjärnum

Bjärnums Museum, Alg 1, 280 20 Bjärnum - T: (0451) 20091
Local Museum
Local history, school, technic 30037

Björkö

Birka Vikingastaden, 760 42 Björkö - T: (08) 56051445, Fax: 56051411, E-mail: birka@wineasy.se, Internet: http://www.raa.se/birka
Open Air Museum 30038

Boden

Garnisonsmuseet, Sveavägen 10, 961 19 Boden - T: (0921) 68399
Military Museum 30039

Borås

Biblioteksmuseet (Library Museum), Stureg 36, 501 15 Borås - T: (033) 353345, Fax: 357675, E-mail: bimu@bimu.net, Internet: http://www.bimu.net. Head: Ingemar Rosberg
Library with Exhibitions
Library objects 30040

Borås Idrottsmuseum, Boråshallen, Bockasjög 2, 504 30 Borås - T: (033) 353939, Fax: 353940, E-mail: bis@bihs.se
Science&Tech Museum 30041

Borås Konstmuseum, P.A. Halls Terrass, 504 02 Borås - T: (033) 357671/72, Fax: 357689
Fine Arts Museum 30042

Borås Museum, Ramnaparken, 504 39 Borås - T: (033) 358580, Fax: 358587, E-mail: oveeriksson@boras.se, Internet: http://www.boras.se/kultur/museer/bormus. Head: Margaretha Persson
Local Museum / Open Air Museum - 1904
Archaeology, ethnography, local hist, open air museum - archives, photos 30043

Immigrant-institutets Museum, Katrinedalsg 43, 504 51 Borås - T: (033) 136070, Fax: 136075, E-mail: migrant@immi.se, Internet: http://www.immi.se/museum.htm
Fine Arts Museum 30044

Textilmuseet (The Swedish Museum of Textile History), Druveforsvägen 8, 504 33 Borås - T: (033) 358950, Fax: 358963, E-mail: marie.pihlang@boras.se, Internet: http://www.boras.se/kultur. Head: Rolf Danielsson
Science&Tech Museum - 1974
Weaving, textile manufacturing, textile industry, textile technology, industrial archaeology, textile machines, textile samples and fashion 30045

Borgholm

Ölands Forngard, Badhusg, 380 70 Borgholm
Archaeological Museum
Archaeology, local history 30046

Borgsjöbyn

Hembygdsgården, Erikslund, 910 53 Borgsjöbyn
Local Museum
Local history 30047

Borlänge

Jussi Björlingmuseet, Borganäsvägen 25, 784 33 Borlänge - T: (0243) 74240, Fax: 74241, E-mail: harald.henrysson@borlange.se, Internet: http://www.borlange.se/kommun/jussi. Head: Harald Henrysson
Special Museum
Opera singers life 30048

Tunabygdens Gammelgård, Gammelgårdsvägen 2, 784 44 Borlänge - T: (0243) 211024, Fax: 211024, E-mail: gammel_tant@hotmail.com
Local Museum / Open Air Museum
Local heritage, mainly 19th c folklore 30049

Broby

Göinge Hembygdsmuseum, Göinge Hembygdspark, 280 60 Broby
Local Museum
Local history 30050

Dala-Husby

Djusa Indianmuseum, Djusa, 776 96 Dala-Husby - Fax: (0225) 41231
Ethnology Museum 30051

Degerhamn

Eketorps Borg, 38065 Degerhamn - T: (0485) 662000, Fax: 662156, E-mail: Eketorp@raa.se, Internet: http://www.raa.se/eketorp
Archaeological Museum / Open Air Museum 30052

Ottenby Naturum, 380 65 Degerhamn - T: (0485) 661200, Fax: 661322, Internet: http://www.sofnet.org. Head: Gösta Friberg
Natural History Museum
Birds and bird migration 30053

Delsbo

Delsbo Forngård Hillgrenmuseet, Hembygdsgård i Åsby, 820 60 Delsbo
Local Museum
Local history, ethnography 30054

Drottningholm

Drottningholm Slott, 178 02 Drottningholm - T: (08) 4026280, Fax: 4026281, E-mail: info.drottningholms-slott@royalcourt.se, Internet: http://www.royalcourt.se. Head: Jacob Lagerkrans
Decorative Arts Museum / Fine Arts Museum
Baroque rooms, interiors in rococo style, royal portraits, tapestries, furniture (18th cent.), sculptures 30055

Kina Slott, Ekerö, 178 02 Drottningholm - T: (08) 4026270, Fax: 4026281, E-mail: info.kina-slott@royalcourt.se, Internet: http://www.royalcourt.se. Head: Jacob Lagerkrans
Decorative Arts Museum
Rococo interiors, 18th c chinoiserie 30056

Ed

Edstraktens Fornminnes- och Hembygdsförenings Museum, Dals-Ed, 668 00 Ed
Local Museum
Archaeology, local history 30057

Edsbyn

Ovanakers Hembygdsgard, Fack 28, 828 22 Edsbyn - T: (0271) 20581. Head: Elisabeth Eriksson
Ethnology Museum
Ethnography 30058

Eksjö

Eksjö Museum med Albert Engströms Samlingarna, Österlångg 31, 575 31 Eksjö - T: (0381) 36170, Fax: 17755, E-mail: museum@eksjo.se, Internet: http://www.eksjo.se/museer. Head: Pia Lofgren
Local Museum / Fine Arts Museum - 1969
Works by Albert Engström and contemporary art exhibitions, town hist (15th-late 19th c) - library 30059

Fornminnesgården, Arent Byggmästareg 24, 575 00 Eksjö
Local Museum - 1923
Local hist, domestic products, machines, motorcycles, bicycles 30060

Eldsberga

Oppenheimers Konsthall, Tönnersjö, 310 31 Eldsberga - T: (035) 43082. Head: Jonny Oppenheimer
Fine Arts Museum
17th c still-life paintings 30061

Enköping

Sydvästra Upplands Kulturhistoriska Museum, 199 00 Enköping
Historical Museum
Local cultural history, ethnography 30062

Eskilstuna

Eskilstuna Konstmuseet, Kyrkog 9, 632 20 Eskilstuna - T: (016) 101369
Fine Arts Museum - 1937
Sculpture, painting, drawing (mainly Swedish or Scandinavian) 30063

Faktorimuseet (Factory Museum), Faktoriholmarna, 631 86 Eskilstuna - T: (016) 102375, Fax: 138710. Head: Lena Bergils
Science&Tech Museum - 1979
Industrial history, weapon technology, steam engines, still in operation, reconstruction of a Remington workshop ca. 1869, archaeology, furniture (from Baroque to Art Nouveau) - lecture room 30064

Rademachersmedjorna (Rademacher Forges), Rademacherg 50, 631 86 Eskilstuna - T: (016) 101371, Fax: 138710. Head: Ulla Fjaestad
Science&Tech Museum - 1906
Preserved forges and dwellings from the 17th c, items produced at the Rademacher forges during three centuries, metal handicrafts 30065

Sörmlandsgården, Faktoriholmarna, 631 86 Eskilstuna - T: (016) 101370, Fax: 138710. Head: Ulla Fjaestad
Open Air Museum - 1924/1932
Sörmlandian homestead from the preindustrial period 30066

Vapentekniska Museet (Weapons Museum), 631 86 Eskilstuna - T: (016) 101721, Fax: 138710. Head: Lena Bergils
Military Museum - 1979
Weapons from the 17th-20th c 30067

Eslöv

Eslövs Stadtsmuseum, Österg 5, 241 39 Eslöv - T: (0413) 62759, Internet: http://www.eslov.se
Local Museum
Local history 30068

Falkenberg

Falkenbergs Museum, Sankt Lars Kyrkog 8, 311 31 Falkenberg - T: (0346) 10504, Fax: 86128. Head: Claes Hederstierna
Local Museum - 1991
Local history, concentrating on the 20th c, shoe- and leather manufacturing - library 30069

Hindströmsgården, Storg 69, 311 31 Falkenberg - T: (0346) 10504
Local Museum 30070

Sjöbergsgårdens Laxrökerimuseum, Sankt Lars Kyrkog 12, 311 31 Falkenberg - T: (0346) 10504
Special Museum 30071

Falköping

Falbygdens Museum, Sankt Olofsg 23, 521 81 Falköping - T: (0515) 85050, Fax: 14492, E-mail: kerstin.arnesson@falkoping.se, Internet: http://www.falkoping.se/museer. Head: Kerstin Arnesson
Ethnology Museum / Archaeological Museum - 1961
Archaeology, ethnography 30072

Falsterbo

Falsterbo Museum, Sjög, 239 40 Falsterbo - T: (040) 470513, E-mail: falsterbomuseum@mail.bip.net, Internet: http://www.foteviken.se/falsterbo. Head: Douglas Åhsberger
Local Museum - 1940
Archaeology, ethnography, maritime coll 30073

Falun

Dalarnas Museum, Stigareg 2-4, 791 21 Falun, mail addr: Box 22, 791 21 Falun - T: (023) 765500, Fax: 28358, E-mail: dalarnas.museum@ltdalarna.se, Internet: http://www.dalarnasmuseum.se. Head: Jan Raihle
Archaeological Museum / Fine Arts Museum / Ethnology Museum / Decorative Arts Museum - 1962
Archaeology, art, ethnography, peasant paintings, peasant furniture 30074

Kopparberget Museum, Berghauptmansg 58, 791 80 Falun - T: (023) 711475, Fax: 782673, E-mail: museum@kopparberget.com, Internet: http://www.kopparberget.com
Local Museum / Science&Tech Museum / Decorative Arts Museum - 1922
Hist of mining, Falun coppermine, minerals, coins, technology and art, industrial history 30075

Farösund

Kulturhistoriska Museet i Bunge, Bunge, 620 35 Farösund - T: (0498) 221018, Fax: 221018, E-mail: bunge.museet@swipnet.se, Internet: http://www.guteinfo.com/bungemuseet. Head: Anders Lundkvist, M.G. Blomberg
Open Air Museum - 1907

4 stone paintings (8th c), 3 farmsteads (17th-19th c) fully furnished, sawmills, smithies, limekilns, sheds for half-wild horses and sheep, fishermen's cottages and boats - 18th c manorhouse 30076

Skolmuseum Bunge, Bunge, 620 35 Farösund - T: (0498) 221018, Fax: 221018, E-mail: bunge.museet@swipnet.se, Internet: http://www.guteinfo.com/bungemuseet. Head: M.G. Blomberg, Anders Lundkvist
Historical Museum 30077

Farsta

Sveriges Riksidrottsmuseum (Swedish Sportsmuseum), Idrotens Hus, 123 87 Farsta - T: (08) 6056000, Fax: 6056101, E-mail: info@rm.rf.se, Internet: http://www.svenskidrott.se/riksidrottsmuseet
Special Museum - 1992
Sports 30078

Filipstad

Filipstads Bergslags Hembygdsmuseum, Hembygdsgarden pa Munkeberg, 682 00 Filipstad - T: (0590) 4028. Head: Per Sakholm
Local Museum
Local history 30079

Långbans Gruvby, Långban, 682 92 Filipstad - T: (0590) 22115, 22181, Fax: 22156, E-mail: jorgen.langhof@wermlandsmuseum.se, Internet: http://www.wermlandsmuseum.se. Head: Jörgen Langhof
Open Air Museum / Science&Tech Museum 30080

Museet Kvarnen, Kvarntorget 2, 682 00 Filipstad - T: (0590) 15198
Local Museum 30081

Forshaga

Dyvelstens Flottningsmuseum, Flottarev, 667 91 Forshaga - T: (054) 871226
Historical Museum 30082

Forsvik

Forsviks Industriminnen (Forsvik's Industrial Heritage), Bruksvägen 2, 546 73 Forsvik - T: (0505) 41327, 41352, Fax: 41440, E-mail: info@forsvik.com, Internet: http://www.forsvik.com. Head: Lars Bergström
Historical Museum 30083

Funäsdalen

Fornminnesparken → Härjedalens Fjällmuseum

Härjedalens Fjällmuseum, 840 95 Funäsdalen - T: (0684) 16425/24, Fax: 29026, E-mail: fornminnes@mail.herjedalen.se, Internet: http://www.herjedalen.se/fjellmuseum. Head: Tage Person
Archaeological Museum
Archaeology 30084

Gävle

Joe Hill-Museet, Nedre Bergsg 28, 802 51 Gävle - T: (026) 612022
Special Museum 30085

Länsmuseet Gävleborg, S Strandg 20, 801 28 Gävle - T: (026) 655600, Fax: 655629, E-mail: rettig@xlm.se, Internet: http://www.lansmusee-tgavleborg.se. Head: Lars Sjösvärd
Local Museum - 1940
Archaeology, ethnography, art, handicrafts, furnishings, maritime coll 30086

Silvanum Skogsmuseet (Silvanum Forestmuseum), Kungsbäcksvägen 32, 801 31 Gävle - T: (026) 614100, Fax: 610299, E-mail: silvanum@silvanum.x.se, Internet: http://www.silvanum.x.se. Head: Jarl Holmström
Natural History Museum - 1961
Forestry, forest industry 30087

Soldat-Museet, Kungsbäcksvägen, 801 26 Gävle
Military Museum - 1957
Old Uniforms, weapons, photographs 30088

Sveriges Järnvägsmuseum (Swedish Railway Museum), Rälsg 1, 801 05 Gävle, mail addr: Box 407, 801 05 Gävle - T: (026) 144615, Fax: 144598, E-mail: museum@stab.sj.se, Internet: http://www.sj.se/museum. Head: Robert Sjöö
Science&Tech Museum - 1915
Original locomotives and carriages dating back to 1854, coll of models (scale 1:10), uniforms, tickets - library 30089

Gammelstad

Hägnan Friluftsmuseet i Gammelstad (Hägnan Open Air Museum), 954 33 Gammelstad - T: (0920) 294866, 293809, Fax: 293830, E-mail: hagnan@kulturen.lulea.se, Internet: http://www.lulea.se. Head: Kaj Bergman
Open Air Museum - 1918
Ethnography, peasant furniture, 40 peasant buildings 30090

Gnosjö

Gnosjö Industrimuseum, 335 31 Gnosjö - T: (0370) 99106, Fax: 99272, Internet: http://www.gnosjo.se/kultfritid/museer.htm
Historical Museum
Töllstorp, Gåröström, Hyltén 30091

Hylténs Industrimuseet, Gåröström, 33580 Gnosjö - T: (0370) 91700, Fax: 331130
Science&Tech Museum
Technical and industrial hist 30092

Göteborg

Äventyret Ostindiefararen Götheborg, Terra Nova, Eriksberg, 417 64 Göteborg - T: (031) 7793450, Fax: 7793455
Special Museum 30093

Antikenmuseet (Museum of the Department of Classical Archaeology and Ancient History, Göteborg University), Olof Wijksg 6, 412 55 Göteborg - T: (031) 7734656, 7734906, Fax: 7735290. Head: Prof. Margareta Strandberg Olofsson
Museum of Classical Antiquities / University Museum - 1960
Antiquities from Cyprus, Greece and Italy 30094

Erna och Victor Hasselblads Fotografiska Centrum, Ekmansgatan 8, 412 56 Göteborg - T: (031) 203530, Fax: 203480, E-mail: info@hasselbladcenter.se, Internet: http://www.hasselbladcenter.se. Head: Gunilla Knape
Fine Arts Museum 30095

Göteborgs Konstmuseum (Museum of Art), Götapl, 412 56 Göteborg - T: (031) 611000, Fax: 184119, E-mail: information@konstmuseum.goteborg.se, Internet: http://www.konstmuseum.goteborg.se. Head: Dr. Björn Fredlund
Fine Arts Museum - 1861
European painting since 1500, sculpture, drawings, graphic art, French impressionists, Nordic art - library 30096

Göteborgs Stadsmuseum (City Museum of Gothenburg), Norra Hamng 12-14, 411 14 Göteborg - T: (031) 612770, Fax: 7740358, E-mail: kulturnemuden@goteborg.se. Head: Anders Clason
Local Museum - 1861
Hist and social life of Gothenburg, hist of the East India Company of Sweden, folk life of Western Sweden, handicrafts, interior decoration, dresses, medals and coins, archaeological finds from the western part of Sweden and the Gothenburg area - library 30097

Idrottsmuseet, Anders Pesonsg 18, 416 64 Göteborg - T: (031) 801120, Fax: 158135
Local Museum
Sports, cultural hist 30098

Medicinhistoriska Museet (Medical History Museum), Oterdahlska Huset, Östra Hamng 11, 411 10 Göteborg - T: (031) 7112331/88, Fax: 7112388. Head: Inger Wikström Haugen
Historical Museum 30099

Militärmuseet Skansen Kronan, Box 7135, 402 33 Göteborg - T: (031) 145000, 612770
Military Museum - 1897
Military history 30100

Naturhistoriska Museet i Göteborg, Natural History Museum of Göteborg, Slottsskogen, 402 35 Göteborg - T: (031) 7752400, Fax: 129807, E-mail: info@gnm.se, Internet: http://www.gnm.se/default.htm. Head: Göran Andersson
Natural History Museum - 1833
Natural history, marine fauna from the west coast of Sweden, Southern Swedish terrestrial invertebrate fauna, mammals, birds, osteological coll, vertebrates, molluscs, insects, invertebrates, geological and mineralogical coll - library 30101

Radiomuseet i Göteborg (Gothenburg Radio Museum), Anders Carlsson g 2, 417 55 Göteborg - T: (031) 7792101, Fax: 7792101, E-mail: radiomuseet@swipnet.se, Internet: http://hotel.telemuseum.se/radiomuseet. Head: Prof. Dr. Karl-Gustav Strid
Science&Tech Museum
Coll of broadcast related objects, maritime, land-mobile, military and amateur radio applications - library 30102

Röhsska Museet (Röhss Museum of Arts and Crafts), Vasag 37-39, 400 15 Göteborg - T: (031) 613850, Fax: 184692, E-mail: info@designmuseum.se, Internet: http://www.designmuseum.se. Head: Elsebeth Welander-Berggren
Decorative Arts Museum - 1916
Furniture, ceramics, textiles, bookbinding, glass, metalwork, decorative arts from Greece, China, Japan and the Near East - library 30103

Sjöfartsmuseet (Maritime Museum), Karl Johansg 1-3, 414 59 Göteborg - T: (031) 612900, Fax: 246182, Internet: http://www.sjofartsmuseum.goteborg.se. Head: Thomas Thieme
Natural History Museum - 1917
Swedish maritime hist - aquarium 30104

Smetanamuseet, Dicksonska Palatset, Parkg 2, 411 38 Göteborg - T: (031) 611009, Fax: 611069. Head: Björn Alm
Music Museum
Musical hist 30105

Världskulturmuseet (National Museum of World Cultures) (reopening in June 2003), Ebbe-Lieberath-Gatan 18b, 402 27 Göteborg, mail addr: Box 5303, 402 27 Göteborg - T: (031) 7037730, Fax: 7037740, E-mail: info@worldcultures.se, Internet: http://www.worldcultures.se. Head: Jette Sandahl
Ethnology Museum - 1891
Ethnography, archaeology, coll from Central and South America, Saami coll, archaeological textiles from South America - library 30106

Grängesberg

Bergslagens Motor Museum, efter Riksväg 60, 772 00 Grängesberg - T: (0240) 21332
Science&Tech Museum
Cars 30107

Lokmuseet, Malmbangården, 772 00 Grängesberg - T: (0240) 20493
Science&Tech Museum 30108

Gränna

Andréemuseet, Stiftelsen Grännamuseerna, Brahega 38, 563 22 Gränna - T: (0390) 41015, Fax: 10275, E-mail: andreemuseet@grm.se, Internet: http://www.grm.se. Head: Håkan Jorikson
Historical Museum
Memorial coll of polar explorer and balloonist Salomon Andrée (1854-1897), finds from White Island 30109

Grimslöv

Huseby Bruk, 340 32 Grimslöv - T: (0470) 752097, Fax: 752141, Internet: http://www.husebybruk.com
Science&Tech Museum
Ironwork, mill, wagons, cotter, Archimedes' screw 30110

Grisslehamn

Albert Engström-Museerna, Hamnplan, 760 45 Grisslehamn - T: (0175) 30890, Fax: 30445, Internet: http://www.netg.se/aes
Fine Arts Museum
Drawings, publishing, garden with atelier 30111

Gustavsberg

Gustavsbergs Porslinmuseum, Keramiskt Centrum, Odelbergs Väg 5b, 134 40 Gustavsberg - T: (08) 57035658, Fax: 57036708, E-mail: info@porslinsmuseum.net, Internet: http://www.porslinsmuseum.net. Head: Inger Nordgren
Decorative Arts Museum 30112

Gyttorp

Nora Museum, Nora Bengtstorp, 713 92 Gyttorp - T: (0587) 311420, Internet: http://hem2.passagen.se/leli8697. Head: Håkan Carlestam
Historical Museum
Crafts in the mountains, hunting 30113

Härnösand

Länsmuseet Västernorrland, Murberget, 871 02 Härnösand - T: (0611) 88600, Fax: 18730, E-mail: museet@ylm.se. Head: Tommy Puktörne
Local Museum - 1880
Archaeology, cultural history, ethnography, handicrafts, religious art, medieval sculpture, textiles, old town hall, school, farmhouses, fishing sheds 30114

Hässleholm

Västra Göinge Hembygdsmuseum, Hembygdsparken, 281 00 Hässleholm
Local Museum
Archaeology, ethnography 30115

Hagfors

Järnvägs- och Industrimuseum, Uvedsvägen, 683 01 Hagfors - T: (0563) 17475, 14900
Science&Tech Museum 30116

Hallstahammar

Kanalmuseet Skantzen, 734 40 Hallstahammar - T: (0220) 17409, Fax: 14835, E-mail: kanalmuseet@swipnet.se
Local Museum - 1976 30117

Halmstad

Friluftmuseet Hallandsgården, Länsmuseet Halmstad, Tollsg, 302 31 Halmstad - T: (035) 162300, Fax: 162318, E-mail: kansli@hallmus.org, Internet: http://www.hallmus.org. Head: Sven Lundström
Historical Museum
Hallandic buildings (17th-18th c), water- and windmills, old schoolhouse (1843) 30118

Länsmuseet Halmstad, Tollsg, 302 31 Halmstad - T: (035) 162300, Fax: 162318, E-mail: kansli@hallmus.org, Internet: http://www.hallmus.org. Head: Sven Lundström
Local Museum - 1886
Archaeology, maritime coll, late and contemporary regional art, wooden religious objects, peasant tapestry paintings, figureheads from old sailing vessels, ceramic model of old Halmstad - library, archives 30119

Mjellby Konstgård (Mjellby Art Centre), 305 91 Halmstad - T: (035) 31619, Fax: 32262
Fine Arts Museum 30120

Haparanda

Kukkola Fiskemuseum, Kukkolaforsen 184, 953 91 Haparanda - T: (0922) 31000, Fax: 31030, E-mail: info@kukkolaforsen.se, Internet: http://www.kukkolaforsen.se
Special Museum / Open Air Museum 30121

Havdhem

Gotlands Landsbruksmuseum, 620 11 Havdhem - T: (0497) 81324
Agriculture Museum 30122

Kattlunds Museigård, 620 11 Havdhem - T: (0497) 86013
Local Museum 30123

Petes Museigård, Hablingbo, 620 11 Havdhem - T: (0497) 87054
Local Museum 30124

Hedemora

Gammelgården, Åsg 15-17, 776 00 Hedemora - T: (0225) 13540
Local Museum 30125

Helsingborg

Dunkers Kulturhus, Kungsg 11, 252 21 Helsingborg - T: (042) 107400, Fax: 105988, Internet: http://www.dunkerskulturhus.com. Head: Magnus Jensner
Decorative Arts Museum / Fine Arts Museum - 1909 30126

Fredriksdals Friluftsmuseum, Hävertg, 250 07 Helsingborg, mail addr: Box 7123, 250 07 Helsingborg - T: (042) 104500, Fax: 104510, E-mail: helsingborgs.museum@helsingborg.se, Internet: http://www.museum.helsingborg.se. Head: Per Lindahl
Local Museum / Open Air Museum - 1909
Local hist, archaeology, applied arts, crafts, different types of buildings, kitchen garden - botanical garden, open air theatre 30127

Vikingbergs Konstmuseum → Dunkers Kulturhus

Höganäs

Höganäs Museum with Art Gallery, Polhemsg 1, 263 37 Höganäs - T: (042) 341335, Fax: 349940, E-mail: hoganas.museum@telia.com, Internet: http://www.hoganas.se/kultur/museum. Head: Annette Jansson
Local Museum / Fine Arts Museum 30128

Höllviken

Bärnstensmuseet (Swedish Amber Museum), Södra Mariav 4, 236 35 Höllviken - T: (040) 454504, Fax: 450861, E-mail: brost@brost.se, Internet: http://www.brost.se. Head: Leif Brost
Decorative Arts Museum 30129

Fotevikens Museum, Halörsv, 236 91 Höllviken - T: (040) 456840, Fax: 455507, E-mail: info@foteviken.se, Internet: http://www.foteviken.se. Head: Björn M. Jakobsen
Ethnology Museum
Viking life 30130

Hörby

Hörby Museum, Vallg 5, 242 31 Hörby - T: (0415) 18449, Fax: 10031, Internet: http://www.horby.se
Local Museum
Cultural hist 30131

Hudiksvall

Hälsinglands Museum, Storg 31, 824 30 Hudiksvall - T: (0650) 19600, Fax: 19601, E-mail: halsinglands.museum@hudiksvall.se, Internet: http://www.hudiksvall.se/hudiksvall/museum.htm
Local Museum / Decorative Arts Museum - 1859
Archaeology, art, cultural history, 16th-18th c tapestries, furniture, folk art, fishing, religious art, pewter, silver, paintings (eg by John Sten) - library 30132

Hudiksvalls Bruksminnen, 824 80 Hudiksvall - T: (0653) 61035, Internet: http://www.hudiksvall.se/hudiksvall/turism/bruksmin.htm
Science&Tech Museum 30133

Hunnebostrand

Nordens Ark, Åby Säteri, 45046 Hunnebostrand - T: (0523) 79590, Fax: 52087, E-mail: nordensark@nordensark.se, Internet: http://www.nordensark.se. Head: Lena M. Lindeh
Open Air Museum / Natural History Museum
Natural hist 30134

Huskvarna

Huskvarna Stadsmuseum, Grannavägen, 561 00 Huskvarna - T: (036) 132286. Head: Eric Y.W. Skoglund
Local Museum
Archaeology, ethnography, history, technology 30135

Svenska Transportmuseet, Gisebo, 561 90 Huskvarna
Science&Tech Museum
Technology, motorcars 30136

Vätterbygdens Automobil-Museum, Gisebo, 56190 Huskvarna - T: (036) 50388
Science&Tech Museum 30137

Iggesund

Iggesunds Bruksmuseum, Iggesund Paperboard, 825 00 Iggesund - T: (0650) 28000
Science&Tech Museum 30138

Jönköping

Friluftsmuseet, Stadspark, 550 02 Jönköping, mail addr: Box 2133, 550 02 Jönköping - T: (036) 301800, Fax: 301818, E-mail: info@jkpglm.se, Internet: http://www.jkpglm.se. Head: Per-Olof Millberg
Open Air Museum 30139

Jönköpings Läns Museum (Jönköping County Museum), Dag Hammarskjöldspl 1, 550 02 Jönköping, mail addr: Box 2133, 550 02 Jönköping - T: (036) 301800, Fax: 301818, E-mail: info@kpglm.se, Internet: http://www.jkpglm.se. Head: Per-Olof Millberg
Local Museum / Fine Arts Museum - 1901
Cultural history of Småland, modern art, John Bauer coll, Swedish art of the last hundred years - library, archive, cinema, open air museum, restorer 30140

Radiomuseet i Jönköping, Tändsticksgränd 16, 553 15 Jönköping - T: (036) 713959, 714654, Fax: 713959, E-mail: radiomuseet@telia.com, Internet: http://www.radiomuseum.home.se
Science&Tech Museum 30141

Tändsticksmuseet (Match Museum), Tändsticksgränd 27, 553 15 Jönköping - T: (036) 105543, Fax: 105541, E-mail: matchmuseum@kn.jonkoping.se, Internet: http://www.jonkoping.se/kultur/matchmus. Head: Annika Blixth
Special Museum - 1948
Labels, matchboxes, photos, fire-making tools 30142

Jokkmokk

Ájtte - Svenskt Fjäll- och Samemuseum (Ájtte - Swedish Mountain and Sami Museum), Kyrkog 3, 962 23 Jokkmokk - T: (0971) 17070, Fax: 12057, E-mail: info@ajtte.com, Internet: http://www.ajtte.com. Head: Dr. Inga-Maria Mulk
Ethnology Museum / Natural History Museum - 1983
Sami culture 30143

Jukkasjärvi

Jukkasjärvi Hembygdsgård, Marknadsvägen, 981 91 Jukkasjärvi - T: (0980) 21422, 21329
Ethnology Museum / Folklore Museum
Ethnography, Lapp coll 30144

Jukkasjärvi Museet, 980 21 Jukkasjärvi
Local Museum / Folklore Museum
Lapp culture 30145

Julita

Julita Museums, Julita Gård, 640 25 Julita - T: (036) 91290. Head: Sune Zachrisson
Open Air Museum / Decorative Arts Museum
Furnishings, decorative arts, open air museum with an ethnographic coll 30146

Kalix

Kalix Flottningsmuseum, Nyg 4, 952 81 Kalix - T: (0923) 65000, Fax: 1696, E-mail: stig.stromback@kommun.kalix.se, Internet: http://www.kalix.se. Head: Stig Strömbäck
Local Museum - 1967
Log-driving museum 30147

Kalmar

Kalmar Konstmuseum (Kalmar Art Museum), Slottsvägen 1d, 392 33 Kalmar - T: (0480) 426282, Fax: 426280, E-mail: info@kalmarkonstmuseum.nu, Internet: http://www.kalmarkonstmuseum.nu. Head: Klas Börjesson
Fine Arts Museum - 1942
Swedish art (19th-20th c), national coll of sketches for Swedish craft and design from the 20th c 30148

Kalmar Slott (Kalmar Castle), Kungsg 1, 392 33 Kalmar - T: (0480) 451490, 451491, Fax: 451499, E-mail: info@slottet.kalmar.se, Internet: http://www.kalmarslott.kalmar.se. Head: Odd Zschiedrich
Historical Museum 30149

Krusenstjernska Gården, Kalmar Läns Museum, Stora Dammg 11, 391 21 Kalmar - T: (0480) 11552
Decorative Arts Museum - 1940
18th-19th c interiors, Chinese porcelain, Swedish household utensils (18th cent.), furniture, clothes 30150

Sjöfartsmuseum, Södra Långg 81, 392 31 Kalmar - T: (0480) 15875, 86690, Internet: http://www.kalmar.se/turism/sjofart.htm
Historical Museum - 1942 30151

Karlsborg

Fästningsmuseet Karlsborg (The Fortress Museum Karlsborg), Fästning, 546 81 Karlsborg - T: (0505) 451826, Fax: 85554, E-mail: nadja.eriksson@k3.mil.se, Internet: http://www.k3.mil.se. Head: Nadja Eriksson
Military Museum
Uniforms, seaponds and other items since the 17th c, fortress history, Life Regiment Hussars 30152

Karlsborgs Museum → Fästningsmuseet Karlsborg

Karlshamn

Karlshamns Museum, Vinkelg 8, 374 38 Karlshamn - T: (0454) 14868, Fax: 306460, E-mail: - karlshamnsmuseum@telia.com, Internet: http://www.karlhamnsmuseum.k.se. Head: Bengt Gabrielson
Local Museum - 1964
Local hist, ethnography, maritime hist, type writers, punsch factory 30153

Karlskoga

Bofors Industrimuseum, c/o Stiftelsen Alfred Nobels Björkborn, Box 1894, 691 33 Karlskoga - T: (0586) 81894, Fax: 35220
Science&Tech Museum 30154

Gråbo Arbetarmuseum, Korpkullsvägen, 691 53 Karlskoga - T: (0586) 33180
Historical Museum 30155

Nobelmuseet, Björkborns Herrgård, 691 33 Karlskoga, mail addr: c/o Stiftelsen Alfred Nobels Björkborn, Box 1894, 691 33 Karlskoga - T: (0586) 81894, Fax: 35220. Head: Gertie Ågren
Special Museum 30156

Karlskrona

Båtsmanskasernen, Bastionsg 8, 371 32 Karlskrona - T: (0455) 303422, Fax: 303423, E-mail: blehmus@algonet.se, Internet: http://www.blekingemuseum.k.se. Head: Tullan Gunér
Fine Arts Museum 30157

Blekinge Museum, Grevagården, Fisktorget 2, 371 22 Karlskrona - T: (0455) 304960, Fax: 304973, E-mail: blekingemuseum@karlskrona.se, Internet: http://www.blekingemuseum.se. Head: Tullan Gunér
Local Museum
Local hist, archaeology, prehistory, ethnography, fishing, boatbuilding 30158

Marinmuseum (Naval Museum), Stumholmen, 371 32 Karlskrona - T: (0455) 53900, Fax: 53949, E-mail: marinmuseum@sshm.se, Internet: http://www.marinmuseum.se. Head: Per-Inge Lindqvist
Science&Tech Museum / Military Museum - 1752
Swedish naval development, shipbuilding and machinery (18th-20th c), figureheads from the 18th c, weapons), shipmodels made by Sheldon and Chapman, figureheads from the late 18th c made by Johan Törnström, minesweeper Bremön from the 40-ies, torpedoboat Spica, motor-torpedoboat T38, full-rigged training ship Jarramas - library, archives 30159

Vämöparken (Open-Air-Museum), Hästövägen, 371 22 Karlskrona, mail addr: Box 111, 371 22 Karlskrona - T: (0455) 304960, Fax: 304973, E-mail: blekingemuseum@karlskrona.se, Internet: http://www.blekingemuseum.se. Head: Tullan Gunér
Local Museum / Open Air Museum 30160

Karlstad

Alsters Herrgård, 656 39 Karlstad - T: (054) 834081, Fax: 834081, E-mail: birgitta@collvin@wermlandsmuseum.se, Internet: http://www.wermlandsmuseum.se
Special Museum 30161

Långbans Gruvby (Långban Mining Village), 65105 Karlstad - T: (054) 111419
Open Air Museum / Science&Tech Museum 30162

Värmlands Museum, Sandgrundsudden, 651 08 Karlstad, mail addr: Box 335, 651 08 Karlstad - T: (054) 143100, Fax: 143198, E-mail: museet@wermlandsmuseum.se, Internet: http://www.wermlandsmuseum.se. Head: Tomas Jönsson
Local Museum / Ethnology Museum / Archaeological Museum - 1839
Archaeology, local hist, art, handicrafts, 18th c textile coll - library 30163

Katrineholm

Dock- och Textilmuseum, Djulög 51, 641 21 Katrineholm - T: (0150) 57643
Science&Tech Museum 30164

Sveriges VVS Museum, Gjuterig 2, 641 30 Katrineholm - T: (0150) 14980, Fax: 14980, E-mail: vvs.museum@telia.com
Local Museum 30165

Kiruna

LKAB Gruvmuseum, 981 86 Kiruna - T: (0980) 71000
Science&Tech Museum 30166

Kisa

Emigrantmuseet, Storg 10, 590 40 Kisa - T: (0494) 12505
Historical Museum 30167

Köping

Friluftsmuseet Gammelgården, Otto Hallströms väg 11, 731 30 Köping - T: (0221) 23386. Head: Annchristine Sigurdson
Open Air Museum 30168

Köpings Museum, Östra Langg 37, 731 30 Köping - T: (0221) 25341/42, 25387, Fax: 17945. Head: Annchristine Sigurdson
Local Museum
Local history, crafts, fire safety, old farmhouse 30169

Kristianstad

Filmmuseet, Regionmuseet i Skåne, Östra Storg 53, 291 32 Kristianstad, mail addr: Box 134, 291 22 - T: (044) 135729, 135800, 135727, Fax: 214902, E-mail: info@regionmuseet.m.se, Internet: http://www.regionmuseet.m.se. Head: Agne Furingsten
Special Museum 30170

Järnvägsmuseet, Regionmuseet i Skåne, Hammarslundsvägen 4, 291 32 Kristianstad - T: (044) 135800, Fax: 214902, Internet: http://www.klm.se
Science&Tech Museum
Railway museum 30171

Regionmuseet i Skåne (Regional Museum of Scania), Stora Torg, 291 22 Kristianstad - T: (044) 135800, Fax: 214902, E-mail: info@regionmuseet.m.se, Internet: http://www.regionmuseet.m.se. Head: Agne Furingsten
Local Museum - 1877/1915
Archaeology, art, ethnography, local peasant culture, natural hist, military hist, regional textiles, regional hist - library 30172

Skolmuseet, Djurröds Byaväg, 291 32 Kristianstad - T: (044) 135245
Special Museum 30173

Kristinehamn

Kristinehamns Kunstmuseum (Kristinehamn Museum of Art), Doktor Enwalls väg 13c, 681 38 Kristinehamn - T: (0550) 18029, 18001, Fax: 18099, E-mail: stefan.konstmuseum@kristinehamn.se, Internet: http://www.kristine-hamnskonstmuseum.com. Head: Stefan Westling
Public Gallery 30174

Kristinehamns Museum (County Museum of Värmland), Mariebergsklinikema, 681 84 Kristinehamn - T: (0550) 20250, Fax: 15258. Head: Inga-Lill Magnusson
Local Museum - 1925
Local hist, archaeology, photo coll (350 000 pieces) - photo coll archive 30175

MuséETT → Kristinehamns Kunstmuseum

Kumla

Skoindustrimuseet (Museum of Swedish Shoe Industry), Sveavägen 19, 692 34 Kumla - T: (019) 588187, E-mail: skoindustrimuseet@telia.com, Internet: http://www.websamba.com/skoindustrimuseet. Head: Lars Andersson
Special Museum
Shoe manufacturing 30176

Kungsbacka

Nordhallands Hembygdsförening, Box 10094, 434 21 Kungsbacka - T: (0300) 10844, Fax: 72600. Head: Leif Ahlberg
Local Museum
Local history 30177

Kungsgården

Rosenlöfs Tryckerimuseum (Printing Museum), Korsikavägen 26, 812 93 Kungsgården - T: (0290) 37618, Fax: 38014, E-mail: maritha.hansson@sandviken.se
Science&Tech Museum 30178

Kungsör

Kungsör Museum, 736 00 Kungsör
Local Museum
Local history 30179

Lagan

Laganland Bilmuseum, 340 14 Lagan - T: (0372) 30425
Local Museum 30180

Laholm

Södra Hallands Hembygdsmuseum, 312 00 Laholm
Local Museum
Archaeology, local history, ethnography, art 30181

Landskrona

Landskrona Konsthall, Slottsg, 261 31 Landskrona - T: (0418) 473115, Fax: 473110, E-mail: birthe.wibrand@kn.landskrona.se, Internet: http://www.landskrona.kn.se. Head: Christin Nielsen
Fine Arts Museum - 1963 30182

Landskrona Museum, Slottsg, 261 31 Landskrona - T: (0418) 473120, Fax: 473110, Internet: http://www.landskrona.se. Head: Christin Nielsen
Decorative Arts Museum / Historical Museum / Archaeological Museum / Science&Tech Museum - 1911
Archaeology, technology, aircraft coll, art, glass paintings, ethnography, interiors, workshops - library 30183

Laxå

Laxå Bruks- och Hembygdsmuseum, 695 00 Laxå
Local Museum
Local history 30184

Sekelskiftesmuseét, Villa Hamilton, Porla Brunn, 695 91 Laxå - T: (0584) 30018. Head: Charlotte von Mahlsdorf
Special Museum
Furniture, household things (1880-1900) 30185

Lessebo

Rolf Bergendorffs Radio Museum, Strömbergshyttan, 360 50 Lessebo - T: (070) 7557575, E-mail: radiomuseum@mailcity.com, Internet: http://home1.swipnet.se/~w-12206/radio
Science&Tech Museum 30186

Lidingö

Millesgården, Carl Milles väg 2, 181 34 Lidingö - T: (08) 4467590/94, Fax: 7670902, E-mail: info@millesgarden.se, Internet: http://www.millesgarden.se. Head: Staffan Carlén
Fine Arts Museum
Work and memorabilia of Swedish sculptor Carl Milles (1875-1955) in his former residence, medieval sculpture, European painting, Chinese statuettes, Greco-Roman antiquities 30187

Lidköping

Läckö Slott, Kållandsö, 531 99 Lidköping - T: (0510) 10320, Fax: 10838
Decorative Arts Museum 30188

Lidköpings Hantverks- och Sjöfartsmuseum, Mellbyg 9, 531 02 Lidköping - T: (0510) 83065, Fax: 28260. Head: P.E. Ullberg Ornell
Science&Tech Museum 30189

Lidköpings Konsthall, Gamla Stadens Torg 2, 531 88 Lidköping - T: (0510) 83010. Head: Helén Forhaug
Public Gallery 30190

Stola Säteri, Läckö slott, 531 99 Lidköping - T: (0510) 18030
Special Museum 30191

Lindesberg

Lindesbergsmuseum, Kvarng 5, 71180 Lindesberg - T: (0581) 81158, Fax: 81159. Head: Lars Hagström
Local Museum
Cultural hist 30192

Linköping

Gamla Linköping, Kryddbodtorget 1, 582 46 Linköping - T: (013) 121110, Fax: 123029, E-mail: gunelf@galalinkoping.unkoping.se, Internet: http://www.unkoping.se/gamlalinkoping. Head: Gunnar Elfström
Open Air Museum
Cultural hist 30193

Medicinhistoriska Museet (Museum of Medical History), Raoul Wallenberg pl, 581 02 Linköping - T: (013) 230300, 230369, Fax: 140562, E-mail: ml.ojesjo@lansmus.linkoping.se, Internet: http://www.ostergotlandslansmuseum.se. Head: Mona Lisa Öjesjö
Historical Museum / Science&Tech Museum
Medical hist 30194

Östergötlands Länsmuseum, Raoul Wallenberg pl, Vasavägen 16, 581 02 Linköping - T: (013) 230300, Fax: 140562. Head: M. Östergren, Elisabet Jonsson, Jonna Stewenius, Marietta Douglas, Gunnel Mörkfors
Local Museum / Archaeological Museum / Ethnology Museum / Fine Arts Museum / Decorative Arts Museum - 1884
Local history, archaeology, ethnography, international and Swedish art (13th-20th cent.), textiles - library 30195

Onkel Adamsgården, Hunnebergsg 30a, 582 34 Linköping - T: (013) 230300
Local Museum 30196

Ljungby

Ljungbergmuseet, Strandg 5, 341 30 Ljungby - T: (0372) 11036
Local Museum 30197

Ljungby Gamla Torg Hembygdsmuseum, 341 00 Ljungby - T: (0372) 83402
Local Museum
Local history 30198

Ljusdal

Ljusdalsbygdens Museum, Museivägen 5, 827 30 Ljusdal - T: (0651) 711675, Fax: 15990
Local Museum 30199

Ljusterö

Museum Åsättra, Björklidsvägen 18, 184 95 Ljusterö - T: (070) 7737035, Internet: http://hem1.passagen.se/xhapr998/museum.html. Head: Magnus Thörnberg
Local Museum 30200

Lödöse

Lödöse Museum, Museivägen, 463 71 Lödöse - T: (0520) 661010, Fax: 660047, E-mail: lodose.museum@alvlanmus.se, Internet: http://www.alvlanmus.se/lodose. Head: Jan Johansson
Local Museum - 1994
Finds from medieval town Lödöse (11th-17th cent.), history 30201

Lövånger

Lövångers Sockenmuseum, Fack 13, 930 10 Lövånger - T: (0913) 10259
Special Museum 30202

Ludvika

Ludvika Gammelgård och Gruvmuseum (Ludvika Old Homestead and Museum of Mining), Nils Nils g 7, 771 53 Ludvika - T: (0240) 10019, Fax: 17845
Open Air Museum / Science&Tech Museum - 1920
Ethnography, mining machinery, wooden water wheel with reciprocating beam transmission - library 30203

Luleå

Norrbottens Järnvägsmuseum, c/o Notviksv. 45, Arcusvägen 1, Karlsvik, 973 42 Luleå - T: (0920) 250016, Internet: http://www.lulea.se/mbv. Head: Bertil Persson
Science&Tech Museum
Seven historical buildings, several locomotives and trains, snow handling equipment, rotary ploughs, other vehicles, goods cars, ore hoppers, 3 model railways 30204

Norrbottensmuseum, Storg 2, 951 08 Luleå, mail addr: Box 266, 971 08 Luleå - T: (0920) 243500, 243502, Fax: 243560/61. Head: Majlis Granström
Local Museum - 1886
Archeology, ethnography, Samii culture, handicrafts, costumes - library, archives 30205

Teknikens Hus (House of Technology), Universitetsområdet, 971 87 Luleå - T: (0920) 72200, Fax: 72202, E-mail: info@teknikens-hus.se, Internet: http://www.teknikens-hus.se. Head: Lena Embertsén
Science&Tech Museum 30206

Lund

Antikmuseet (Museum of Classical Antiquities, Lund University), c/o Lunds Universitet, Sölveg 2, 223 62 Lund - T: (046) 2228375, Fax: 2224227, E-mail: eva.rystedt@klass.lu.se. Head: Prof. Eva Rystedt
Museum of Classical Antiquities / University Museum
Greek and Italic antiquities, plaster casts of ancient sculpture 30207

Botaniska Museet (Botanical Museum), Östra Vallg 18, 223 61 Lund - T: (046) 2229558/59, Fax: 2224234, E-mail: ingvar.karnefelt@botmus.lu.se, Internet: http://www.sysbot.lu.se/web/botmus.html. Head: Prof. Ingvar Kärnefelt
Natural History Museum 30208

Historiska Museet (Historical Museum), c/o Lunds Universitet, Krafts Torg 1, 223 50 Lund - T: (046) 2227944, Fax: 2224021, E-mail: anders.odman@ark.lu.se, Internet: http://www.luhm.lu.se. Head: Dr. Anders Ödman
Historical Museum / Archaeological Museum / University Museum
Prehist, medieval archaeology, religious art, liturgical objects, wooden sculpture, coins and medals, bronze, early medieval crafts 30209

Konstmuseum, Universitetshuset, Paradisg, 221 00 Lund, mail addr: c/o Lunds Universitet, Box 117, 221 00 Lund - T: (046) 2228388. Head: Prof. Sten Åke Nilsson, F.L. Ulla Melander
Fine Arts Museum / University Museum 30210

Kulturhistoriska Museet (Museum of Cultural History), Tegnérspl, 221 04 Lund, mail addr: Box 1095, 221 04 Lund - T: (046) 350400, Fax: 350470, E-mail: info@kulturen.com, Internet: http://www.kulturen.com. Head: Margareta Alin
Historical Museum - 1882
Hist of Southern Sweden, town and country houses representing different classes, applied arts (ceramics, textiles, silver, glass), archaeological finds from medieval Lund, at Östarp, old Scanian farm with inn (30 km from Lund) - library 30211

Lunds Konsthall, Mårtenstorget 3, 220 02 Lund - T: (046) 355295, Fax: 184521. Head: Cecilia Nelsson
Fine Arts Museum - 1957 30212

Medicinhistoriska Museet, Sankt Larsparken, 221 85 Lund, mail addr: Box 907, 220 09 Lund - T: (046) 151739, Fax: 151872, E-mail: medicinhistoriska.museet@telia.com. Head: Pia Michélsen
Special Museum
Medicine and psychiatric care 30213

Skissernas Museum (Museum of Sketches, Lund University), c/o Lunds Universitet, Finng 2, 223 62 Lund - T: (046) 107283/85/86, Fax: 104981. Head: J.T. Ahlstrand
Fine Arts Museum / University Museum - 1934
Sketches and models of monumental art in Sweden, Denmark, Norway, Finland, Iceland, France, Mexico, West Africa - library, archives 30214

Zoologiska Museet (Museum of Zoology), c/o Lunds Universitet, Helgonavägen 3, 223 62 Lund - T: (046) 2229330, Fax: 2227541, E-mail: zoomus@zool.lu.se, Internet: http://darwin.biol.lu.se/systzool/zoomus/index.html. Head: Prof. S.A. Bengtson
Natural History Museum / University Museum - 1735
Zoology, entomology, 19th c coll of insects, fossils, Scandinavian insects, vertebrates, invertebrates, scientific expedition coll from South Africa, Azores, Ceylon, Chile, Canada, Iceland, Afghanistan 30215

Lycksele

Skogsmuseet i Lycksele, Gammplatsen, 921 23 Lycksele, mail addr: Box 176, 921 23 Lycksele - T: (0950) 37945, Fax: 13260, E-mail: skogsmuseet@epost.lycksele.se, Internet: http://www.lycksele.se/skogsmuseet. Head: Maarit Kalela-Brundin
Local Museum 30216

Malmköping

Museet Malmahed, 640 32 Malmköping - T: (0157) 21925
Local Museum 30217

Museispårvägen Malmköping, Järnvägsg 4, 640 32 Malmköping - T: (0157) 20430, Fax: 20450, E-mail: danne70@ss.se, Internet: http://www.swetramway.org
Local Museum 30218

Malmö

Ebbas Hus, Malmö Museer, Snapperupsg 10, 201 24 Malmö - T: (040) 341000, E-mail: malmomuseer@malmo.se, Internet: http://www.malmo.se/museer. Head: Kennet Johansson
Historical Museum
Home of Olsson family 30219

Idrottsmuseet (Museum of Sports), Malmö Stadion, 217 62 Malmö - T: (040) 342688, Fax: 342652, E-mail: idrottsmuseet@malmo.se. Head: Anders Hammer
Special Museum 30220

Limhamns Museum, Limhamnsvägen 102, 216 13 Malmö - T: (040) 157810
Special Museum 30221

Malmö Konsthall, Sankt Johannesg 7, 200 10 Malmö, mail addr: Box 17127, 200 10 Malmö - T: (040) 341293/86, Fax: 301507, E-mail: info@konsthall.malmo.se, Internet: http://www.konsthall.malmo.se. Head: Bera Nordal
Fine Arts Museum - 1975
Schyl collection 30222

Malmö Konstmuseum, Malmöhusvägen, 201 24 Malmö, mail addr: Box 406, 201 24 Malmö - T: (040) 341000, Fax: 124097, E-mail: info@malmomuseer.malmo.se, Internet: http://www.malmomuseer.malmo.se. Head: Goran Christenson
Fine Arts Museum 30223

Malmö Museer, Malmöhusvägen, 201 24 Malmö - T: (040) 341000, Fax: 40124097, E-mail: malmomuseer@museer.malmo.se, Internet: http://www.malmo.se/museer. Head: Kennet Johansson
Local Museum
Archeology, cultural, natural, industrial and maritime history, science and technology - tropicarium, aquarium 30224

Naturhistoriska Museet, Malmö Museer, Slotet Malmöhus, Malmöhusvägen, 201 24 Malmö - T: (040) 341000, Fax: 124097, E-mail: info@malmomuseer.malmo.se, Internet: http://www.malmo.se/museer. Head: Kennet Johansson
Natural History Museum
Natural hist 30225

Rooseum, Center for Contemporary Art, Gasverksg 22, 211 29 Malmö - T: (040) 121716, Fax: 304561, E-mail: office@rooseum.se, Internet: http://www.rooseum.se. Head: Bo Nilsson
Fine Arts Museum 30226

Teknikens och Sjöfartens Hus, Malmö Museer, Malmöhusvägen, 201 24 Malmö - T: (040) 341000, Fax: 124097, E-mail: malmomuseer@malmo.se, Internet: http://www.malmo.se/museer. Head: Kennet Johansson
Science&Tech Museum 30227

Vagnmuseet, Malmö Museer, Drottingtorget, 201 24 Malmö - T: (040) 341000, Internet: http://www.malmo.se/museer. Head: Kennet Johansson
Science&Tech Museum 30228

Malung

Malungs Gammelgård, 782 00 Malung
Local Museum
Local history 30229

Mariefred

Grafikens Hus, Gripsholms Kungsladugård, 150 30 Mariefred - T: (0159) 23160, Fax: 23170, E-mail: info@grafikenshus.se, Internet: http://www.grafikenshus.se. Head: Urban Engström
Fine Arts Museum
Contemporary and classical graphics 30230

Mariefredsbygdens Hembygdsmuseum, Callanderska Gården, Klosterg 5, 150 30 Mariefred
Local Museum
Local history 30231

Svenska Statens Porträttsamling (Swedish National Portrait Collection), Gripsholms Slott, 150 30 Mariefred, mail addr: Box 14, 150 30 Mariefred - T: (0159) 6664250, Fax: 6113719. Head: Magnus Olavsson
Fine Arts Museum - 1822
Portraits 16th-20th c, interiors 16th-19th c, in royal castle 30232

Mariestad

Vadsbo Museum, Marieholm, 542 00 Mariestad - T: (0501) 63214, Fax: 63072. Head: Elisabeth Göthberg
Local Museum
Local history, archaeology, ethnography 30233

Markaryd

Markarydsortens Hembygdsmuseum, Kungsg 48, 285 00 Markaryd - T: (0433) 10211. Head: Gösta Svensson
Local Museum
Local history 30234

Mölndal

Gunnebo House, Christina Halls väg, 431 36 Mölndal - T: (031) 677777, Fax: 871905, E-mail: gunnebo@molndal.se, Internet: http://www.molndal.se/kof/gunnebo. Head: Lena Vikström
Historic Site
Interior decoration, furniture, wall panels, tiled stoves, drawings and plans, in an 18th c manor house - historic gardens 30235

Mölndals Museum, Kvarnbyg 12, 431 82 Mölndal - T: (031) 677576, Fax: 873958, Internet: http://www.museum.molndal.se. Head: Mari-Louise Olsson
Local Museum
Cultural hist 30236

Mönsterås

Stranda Hembygdsförening (Folk Museum of Stranda), Kvarng, 383 23 Mönsterås - T: (0499) 10001. Head: Sigvard Nelsson
Open Air Museum - 1959
13 buildings incl pharmacy museum (19th c) 30237

Mörbylånga

Per Ekström-Museet, Storg 1, 380 62 Mörbylånga - T: (0485) 40403
Special Museum 30238

Mora

Siljansfors Skogsmuseum (Forestry Museum), Siljanfors, 792 92 Mora - T: (0250) 20331, 16773, Fax: 38214, Internet: http://www.afp.slu.se/fparker/siljansfors__skogsmuseum.html
Natural History Museum 30239

Zornsamlingarna (Zorn Collections), Vasag 36, 792 21 Mora - T: (0250) 16560, Fax: 18460, E-mail: info@zorn.se, Internet: http://www.zorn.se. Head: Birgitta Sandström
Fine Arts Museum - 1939
Paintings, sculptures and prints by Anders Zorn (1860-1920) and others, peasant paintings, applied arts, crafts, silver, textiles 30240

Motala

Kanal- och Sjöfartsmuseet, Hamnen, 591 21 Motala - T: (0141) 202050, Fax: 215550, E-mail: info@gotakanal.se, Internet: http://www.gotakanal.se
Science&Tech Museum 30241

Motala Museum, Charlottenborgs Slott, 581 46 Motala - T: (0141) 233591, Fax: 233591. Head: Tina Tybring
Local Museum - 1984
Local history, natural history 30242

Sveriges Rundradiomuseum, Radiovägen, 591 35 Motala - T: (0141) 225254, Internet: http://www.teracom.se/rundradio/motala
Science&Tech Museum 30243

Nacka

Drottningholms Teatermuseum → Sveriges Teatermuseum

Sveriges Teatermuseum, Kvarnholmsvägen 56, 131 01 Nacka, mail addr: Box 15417, 104 65 Stockholm - T: (08) 55693111, Fax: 55693101, E-mail: dtm@dtm.se, Internet: http://www.sverigesteatermuseum.se. Head: Inga Lewenhaupt
Performing Arts Museum - 1922
History of stage scenery, stage machinery, costumes, drawings, engravings, paintings, records of the Royal Theaters of Sweden, photographic coll - archives, library, Drottingholms castle theatre 30244

Nässjö

Gamla Brukets Museum Hembygdsparken, 571 00 Nässjö, mail addr: Box 503, 684 01 Munkfors - T: (0563) 16260
Local Museum
Local history 30245

Norberg

Norbergs Kommuns Museer, Box 25, 738 21 Norberg - T: (0223) 29111, Fax: 20778
Local Museum
Cultural, industrial and technical history 30246

Nordmaling

Olofsfors Bruksmuseum, Olofsfors, 914 91 Nordmaling - T: (0930) 13196, Fax: 13196, E-mail: sirpa@of1762.com, Internet: http://www.olofsfors.nu. Head: Kärki
Local Museum / Open Air Museum 30247

Norrköping

Arbetets Museum (Museum of Work), Laxholmen, 602 21 Norrköping - T: (011) 189800, Fax: 182290, E-mail: info@arbetetsmuseum.se, Internet: http://www.arbetetsmuseum.se. Head: Anders Lindh
Special Museum - 1991
Social conditions, industry, photography - library, research department 30248

Färgargården, Norrköpings Stadsmuseum, Värdshusg 8, 602 33 Norrköping - T: (011) 152620, 152640, Fax: 107601. Head: Tomas Jönsson
Special Museum - 1932
Dye-house with dying instruments and equipment - library 30249

Hällristningsmuseet vid Brunnssalongen, Himmelstalund, 602 36 Norrköping - T: (011) 165545, Fax: 162340
Local Museum 30250

Himmel och Hav (closed) 30251

Löfstad Slott, Östergötlands Museum, Löfstad, 605 90 Norrköping
Historic Site
Manor from 17th c preserved as historical monument - library 30252

Norrköpings Konstmuseum (Norrköping Museum of Art), Kristinapl, 602 34 Norrköping - T: (011) 152600, Fax: 135897, E-mail: konstmuseet@norrkoping.se, Internet: http://www.norrkoping/konstmuseet. Head: Brigitta Flensburg
Fine Arts Museum - 1913
17th-20th c Swedish art, international graphic art - library 30253

Norrköpings Stadsmuseum (City Museum of Norrköping), Västgöteg 21, 602 21 Norrköping - T: (011) 152620, Fax: 107601, E-mail: stadsmuseum@norrkoping.se, Internet: http://www.norrkoping.se/stadsmuseet. Head: Ewa Bergdahl
Local Museum - 1981
Textile industry, crafts, local archaeology and history - library, photographic archive 30254

Norrtälje

Museum Kasper, Lilla Brog, 761 30 Norrtälje - T: (0176) 71409, Fax: 55236. Head: Karin Johansson
Fine Arts Museum - 1980
Satiric drawings and cartoons - library, archive of drawings 30255

Norrtälje Konsthall, Lilla Brog 2, 761 30 Norrtälje - T: (0176) 71674, Fax: 55236, E-mail: konsthallen@norrtalje.se, Internet: http://www.norrtalje.se/konsthall. Head: Torun Ekstrand
Fine Arts Museum 30256

Norrtälje Skolmuseum, Hantverkareg 23, 761 30 Norrtälje - T: (0176) 11630
Special Museum 30257

Roslagsmuseet, Faktorig 1, 761 30 Norrtälje - T: (0176) 57630, Fax: 17947, E-mail: roslagsmuseet@swipnet.se, Internet: http://www.roslagsmuseet.se. Head: Christina Karman Ohlberger
Ethnology Museum 30258

Nybro

Nybro Hembygdsgård, 382 00 Nybro
Local Museum
Local history 30259

Nyköping

Gripes Modeltheatremuseum, Prästg 12, 611 83 Nyköping - T: (0155) 248907, Fax: 248974, E-mail: gripesmuseum@nykoping.se, Internet: http://www.nykoping.se/culturum. Head: Eva Josephsson
Performing Arts Museum
Toy theatre 30260

Sörmlands Museum, Nyköpingshus, Brunnsg 2, 611 26 Nyköping - T: (0155) 245700, Fax: 285542, E-mail: diariet.kuf@kuf.dll.se, Internet: http://www.sormlandsmuseum.sormland.se. Head: Karin Lindvall
Fine Arts Museum / Local Museum - 1913
Scandinavian art (17th-20th c), painting, cultural hist, interiors, furniture, costumes, archaeology, military hist, in 16th c tower - archives, library 30261

Nynäshamn

Nynäshamns Järnvägsmuseum (Railway Museum), Nickstabadsvägen 13, 149 43 Nynäshamn - T: (08) 52013955, Internet: http://www.ettnet.se/~tw/nynas
Science&Tech Museum 30262

Öjebyn

Grans Lantbruksmuseum, 940 20 Öjebyn - T: 60033
Agriculture Museum 30263

Örebro

Konsthallen, Olaig 7, 703 61 Örebro - T: (019) 154215
Fine Arts Museum 30264

Lantbruksmuseet, Kvarnen, 705 90 Örebro - T: (019) 272120
Agriculture Museum 30265

Örebro Läns Museum (County Museum of Örebro), Engelbrektsg 3, 701 46 Örebro - T: (019) 6028700, Fax: 168049, E-mail: david.damell@orebrolansmuseum.se, Internet: http://www.orebrolansmuseum.se. Head: David Damell
Local Museum - 1856
Art, history, archaeology, religious art, ethnography, crafts and industries, coins, medals, Coll of art handicrafts from China - library, archives 30266

Tekniska Museet, Hamnplan 1, 702 12 Örebro - T: (019) 139920, 139938
Science&Tech Museum 30267

Örnsköldsvik

Gene Fornby, 891 41 Örnsköldsvik, mail addr: Bäckagården, 892 43 Domsjö - T: (0660) 53710, Fax: 53720, E-mail: genefornbyinfo@jobbet.utfors.se, Internet: http://www.ornskoldsvik.se/genefornby. Head: Gustaf Lefvert
Archaeological Museum / Open Air Museum 30268

Gösta Werner-Museet → Konstmuseum Gösta Werner

Konstmuseum Gösta Werner, Rådmusg 1, 891 35 Örnsköldsvik - T: (0660) 88608, Fax: 88598, Internet: http://www.ornskoldsvik.se/kulofri/museer/radhuset
Fine Arts Museum 30269

Örnsköldsviks Museum, Läroverksg 1, 891 33 Örnsköldsvik - T: (0660) 88601, Fax: 88640, E-mail: lenanordstrom@ovik.se, Internet: http://www.ovik.se/kulofri/museer. Head: Lena Nordström
Local Museum - 1979
Local art, history and ethnography, peasant handicraft and art, archaeology - library 30270

Österbymo

Smedstorps Gård, 570 60 Österbymo - T: (0140) 92019
Open Air Museum 30271

Östersund

Jämtlands Läns Museum, 831 28 Östersund - T: (063) 150100, Fax: 106168/67, E-mail: lansmuseet@jamtli.com, Internet: http://www.jamtli.com. Head: Sten Rentzhog
Local Museum - 1912
Cultural hist 30272

Jamtli Historieland, Box 709, 831 28 Östersund - T: (063) 150100, Fax: 106167/68, E-mail: lansmuseet@jamtli.com, Internet: http://www.jamtli.com. Head: Sten Rentzhog
Open Air Museum - 1912
Ethnography, 15th c pilgrim's hut, 18th c farm 30273

Stadsmuseet och Olof Ahlbergshallen (Östersund City Museum), Ahlbergshallen, Rådhusg 42-44, 831 36 Östersund - T: (063) 144252
Local Museum
Local history, art coll 30274

Osby

Fotomuséet i Osby, Esplanadgatan 5, 283 21 Osby - T: (0479) 10118, Fax: 10118, E-mail: info@studiosos.m.se, Internet: http://www.fotomuseetiosby.nu. Head: Sven-Olov Sundin
Fine Arts Museum
Photographic coll 30275

Oskarshamn

Döderhultarmuseet (Döderhultar Museum), Hantverksg 18, 572 28 Oskarshamn - T: (0491) 88040, Fax: 83245, E-mail: doderhultarmuseet@oskarshamn.se, Internet: http://www.oskarshamn.se. Head: Ingbritt Jerner
Fine Arts Museum - 1976
Permanent exhibition of Axel Petersson's Döderhultarn art, more than 200 sculptures 30276

Frederiksberg Hus (Frederiksberg Manor), Frederiksberg Gård, 572 00 Oskarshamn - T: (0491) 12677. Head: Rose Hasting
Decorative Arts Museum / Fine Arts Museum
Mansion in Gustavian style, stoves, paintings, interiors, local history 30277

Sjöfartmuseum (Maritime Museum), Hantverksg 18-20, 572 00 Oskarshamn - T: (0491) 88045. Head: Nils E. Jacobsson
Science&Tech Museum - 1940
Maritime Coll - archives 30278

Pålsboda

Holmgrens Volkswagenmuseum, 697 22 Pålsboda - T: (0582) 40010, Fax: 40001, Internet: http://www.algonet.se/~linkan/holmgren.htm. Head: Bengt Holmgren
Science&Tech Museum
Cars 30279

Påskallavik

Masonry Museum Vånevik and Näset, 570 90 Påskallavik - T: (0491) 88188. Head: Willy Karlsson
Local Museum - 1990
Local history 30280

Pengsjö

Pengsjö Same- o Nybyggarmuseum, 911 00 Pengsjö - T: (0935) 23001
Local Museum 30281

Piteå

Piteå Museum, Rådhuset, Storg 40, 941 23 Piteå - T: (0911) 12615, Fax: 92694
Local Museum
Cultural hist 30282

Rättvik

Rättviks Konstmuseum → Rättviks Kulturhus med Konstmuseum och Naturmuseum

Rättviks Kulturhus med Konstmuseum och Naturmuseum, Storg 2, 795 21 Rättvik - T: (0248) 70195, Fax: 70199, E-mail: kultur@rattvik.se, Internet: http://www.rattvik.se
Fine Arts Museum / Natural History Museum 30283

Robertsfors

Robertsfors Bruksmuseum, Herrgårdsvägen, 915 00 Robertsfors - T: (0934) 10045
Local Museum 30284

Romakloster

Albatrossmuseet, Östergarns Bygdegård, 620 23 Romakloster - T: (0498) 53051, E-mail: Svante.Hedin@swipnet.se. Head: Svante Hedin
Special Museum 30285

Rosersberg

Rosersbergs Slott, 195 95 Rosersberg - T: (08) 59035039, Fax: 59035039, E-mail: info.rosersbergs-slott@royalcourt.se, Internet: http://www.royalcourt.se. Head: Jacob Lagercrantz
Historical Museum 30286

Rottneros

Rottneros Park, 686 94 Rottneros - T: (0565) 60295, Fax: 60035, E-mail: rottnerospark@varmland.nu, Internet: http://www.rottnerospark.se. Head: Lasse Karlsson
Public Gallery 30287

Rydal

Rydals Museum, Boråsvägen 237, 511 05 Rydal - T: (0320) 93300, Fax: 93494, E-mail: rydalsmuseum@mark.se, Internet: http://www.mark.se. Head: Ulrika Kullenberg
Local Museum / Science&Tech Museum - 1985
Hist of textile industry, spinning machines 30288

Säffle

Marinmotor Museum, Harafjordens Sydspets, 661 80 Säffle - T: (0533) 12780, Internet: http://home2.swipnet.se/~w-22815/museum.htm
Science&Tech Museum 30289

Säter

Säters Biografmuseum, Järnvägsg 26, 783 00 Säter - T: (0225) 53375, 50158
Local Museum 30290

Säters Hembygdsmuseum, Asgardarna, 783 00 Säter - T: (0225) 51459
Local Museum
Ethnography, history, open air museum 30291

Sala

Aguélimuseet, Norra Esplanaden 7, 733 38 Sala - T: (0224) 13820. Head: Katarina Almquist
Fine Arts Museum 30292

Gruvmuseet (Mining Museum), Sala Silvergruva, Dr. Christinas väg, 733 36 Sala - T: (0224) 19541, Fax: 19548, E-mail: silvergruva@sala.se, Internet: http://www.sala.se/salasilvergruva
Science&Tech Museum
Silver mining, tools and earthenware from the mining village 30293

Väsby Kungsgård, Museig 2, 733 38 Sala - T: (0224) 10637, Fax: 10637. Head: Goeran Ax
Local Museum - 1946
Local history 30294

Sandviken

Bruksmuseet Smedsgården, Smedsg 2, 811 80 Sandviken - T: (026) 258685, Fax: 274105
Local Museum 30295

Dalälvarnas Flottningsmuseum, Gysinge, 811 80 Sandviken - T: (026) 21027
Historical Museum 30296

Sandvikens Konsthall, Köpmang 3, 811 80 Sandviken - T: (026) 241490, Fax: 2411418, E-mail: konsthallen@sandviken.se, Internet: http://www.sandviken.se/konsthallen. Head: Louise Ljungberg
Fine Arts Museum 30297

Sigtuna

Lundströmska Gården, Storag 39, 193 30 Sigtuna - T: (08) 59783870, Fax: 59783883, E-mail: sim@nordm.se, Internet: http://www.sigtuna.se/museer. Head: Sten Tesch
Special Museum 30298

Sigtuna Museer, Storag 55, 193 30 Sigtuna - T: (08) 59783870, Fax: 59783883, E-mail: sim@nordm.se, Internet: http://www.sigtuna.se/museer. Head: Sten Tesch
Archaeological Museum / Local Museum - 1916
Local history, crafts, medieval archaeology - archives 30299

Simrishamn

Garverimuseet, Strömmens Strädde, 272 22 Simrishamn - T: (0414) 19000. Head: Bernt-A. Åkesson
Special Museum 30300

Gislöfs Smidesmuseum, Gamla Skolan, 272 92 Simrishamn - T: (0414) 25050
Science&Tech Museum 30301

Hantverksloftet, Bergengrenska Gården, 272 22 Simrishamn - T: (0414) 19000. Head: Bernt-A. Åkesson
Historical Museum 30302

Österlens Museum, Storg 24, 272 22 Simrishamn - T: (0414) 19000, Fax: 19249. Head: Bernt-A. Åkesson
Local Museum - 1917
Archaeology, ethnography, peasant furniture, history of fishing, agriculture, maritime commerce, in an old granary 30303

Sjöbo

Stickmaskinsmuseum, Sövdeborg, 275 93 Sjöbo - T: (0416) 16025, Internet: http://www.swipnet.se/~w-60308/museum.html
Science&Tech Museum
Embroidery 30304

Skärhamn

Nordiska Akvarellmuseet, Södra Hamnen 10, 471 32 Skärhamn - T: (0304) 674492, Fax: 674491, E-mail: info@akvarellmuseet.org, Internet: http://www.akvarellmuseet.org
Fine Arts Museum 30305

Skara

Skara Järnvägsmuseum (Skara Railway Museum), Lundsbrunn, 532 23 Skara
Science&Tech Museum 30306

Västergötlands Museum, Stadsträdgården, 532 31 Skara - T: (0511) 26000, Fax: 26099. Head: Birgitta Hjolman
Local Museum / Archaeological Museum / Open Air Museum / Fine Arts Museum / Decorative Arts Museum - 1919 (1750)
Archaeology, local history, art, medieval sculpture in stone, textiles, metalwork 30307

Veterinärhistoriska Museet, Brogården, 532 23 Skara, mail addr: Box 234, 532 23 Skara - T: (0511) 67247, 67000, Fax: 67243, E-mail: vetmus@slu.se. Head: Lars Garmer
Science&Tech Museum / Historical Museum 30308

Skellefteå

Museum Anna Nordlander, Kanalg 73, 931 78 Skellefteå - T: (0910) 735000
Special Museum 30309

Skellefteå Museum, Nordanå, 931 22 Skellefteå - T: (0910) 735510, Fax: 735542, E-mail: museum@skelleftea.se. Head: Pia Lidvall
Local Museum
Archaeology, religious art, cultural history, ethnography, fishing, hunting, handicrafts, costumes, textiles, also open-air-museum 30310

Skövde

Skövde Konsthall och Konstmuseum, Trädgårdsg 9, 541 22 Skövde - T: (0500) 468560, Fax: 468573, E-mail: konsthall.konstmuseum@skovde.se, Internet: http://www.skovde.se. Head: Stefan Hammenbeck
Fine Arts Museum - 1931/1995 30311

Skövde Stadsmuseum, Rådhusg 9, 541 83 Skövde - T: (0500) 468069, Fax: 413871, E-mail: stadsmuseet@skovde.se, Internet: http://www.stadsmuseet.se. Head: Göran Lundh
Local Museum - 1946
Archaeology, ethnography, local history 30312

Skokloster

Motormuseum, 190 64 Skokloster
Science&Tech Museum
Motorcars 30313

Skoklosters Slott (Skokloster Castle), 746 96 Skokloster - T: (018) 386077, Fax: 386446, E-mail: skokloster@lsh.se, Internet: http://www.skoklostersslott.nu. Head: Carin Bergström
Decorative Arts Museum / Fine Arts Museum - 1654/76
17th-18th c interiors, furniture, tapestry, silver, glass, ceramics, ivory, fine handicrafts, bookbinder's art, textiles, Swedish and Dutch paintings, armoury, in 17th c castle - library 30314

Skurup

Svaneholms Slott, 274 91 Skurup - T: (0411) 40012. Head: Clara von Arnold
Decorative Arts Museum / Folklore Museum / Archaeological Museum - 1935
Livingrooms (18th-19th c), regional folklore, archaeology, textiles 30315

Smedjebacken

Ekomuseum Bergslagen, Kyrkog 2, 777 30 Smedjebacken - T: (0240) 663082, Fax: 74860, E-mail: info@ekomuseum.se, Internet: http://www.ekomuseum.se. Head: Mats Hulander
Science&Tech Museum - 1986
Cultural, technical and industrial hist, 50 historical sites concerning the iron production 30316

Söderhamn

Söderhamns Museum, Oxtorgsg, Ängsvägen 9, 826 00 Söderhamn - T: (0270) 12125. Head: Ingvar Oremark
Local Museum
Technology 30317

Södertälje

Biologiska Museet, Erik Dahlbergs väg 1-3, 151 89 Södertälje - T: (08) 55021422, Fax: 55022188, E-mail: info@torekallberget.sodertalje.se, Internet: http://www.torekallberget.org. Head: Stefan Sundblad
Natural History Museum 30318

Länskonstmuseet, Nyg 23b, 151 89 Södertälje - T: (08) 55022243, Fax: 55022314
Fine Arts Museum
Art 30319

Södertälje Konsthall, Sankta Ragnhildsg 3, 151 89 Södertälje - T: (08) 55022260, Fax: 55023416, E-mail: konsthall@sodertalje.se, Internet: http://www.konsthall.sodertalje.se. Head: Kristina Möller
Fine Arts Museum 30320

Tom Tits Experiment, Storg 33, 151 36 Södertälje - T: (08) 52252500, Fax: 52252510, E-mail: info@tomtit.se, Internet: http://www.tomtit.se. Head: Klas Fresk
Science&Tech Museum
350 experiments with water, light, sound etc, mechanics, the human being, perception 30321

Torekällbergets Museum, Torekällberget, 151 89 Södertälje - T: (08) 55021422, Fax: 55022188, E-mail: info@torekallberget.sodertalje.se, Internet: http://www.torekallberget.org. Head: Stefan Sundblad
Open Air Museum - 1918
Local history - Biological museum 30322

Sölvesborg

Gammelgården → Sölvesborgs Museum

Sölvesborgs Museum, Skeppsbrog, 294 80 Sölvesborg - T: (0456) 16070, Fax: 13777, E-mail: ingrid.jonsson@solvesborg.se, Internet: http://www.solvesborg.se. Head: Ingrid Jonsson
Local Museum
Archaeology, local history 30323

Solna

Gustav III.'s Paviljong, Haga Parken, 171 64 Solna, mail addr: 111 30 Stockholm - T: (08) 4026130, Fax: 4026167, E-mail: info.stockholms-slott@royalcourt.se, Internet: http://www.royalcourt.se. Head: Dr. Agneta Lundström
Decorative Arts Museum
Interior decoration and furniture in an 18th c building 30324

Olle Olsson-Huset, Furug vid Hagalundsg 50, 171 21 Solna - T: (08) 839744, Fax: 833921, E-mail: olleolssonhuset@solna.se, Internet: http://www.solna.se/olleolssonhuset. Head: Yvonne Norlund
Fine Arts Museum 30325

Polistekniska Museet (Museum of Police Techniques), Polishögskolan, Sörentorp, 170 82 Solna - T: (08) 4016692, Fax: 4015711, E-mail: - polistekniskamuseet@rps.police.se, Internet: http://www.policen.se. Head: Jan Huzell
Special Museum / Science&Tech Museum 30326

Ulriksdals Slott (Ulriksdal Palace), Bergshamra, 170 73 Solna, mail addr: Kungl. Slottet, 111 30 Stockholm - T: (08) 4026130, Fax: 4026167, E-mail: info.stockholms-slott@royalcourt.se, Internet: http://www.royalcourt.se. Head: Agneta Lundström
Local Museum 30327

Sparreholm

Kareum - Gamla Bilsalongen, Sparreholms Slott, 640 34 Sparreholm - T: (0157) 30562, Fax: 30538, E-mail: karinen@telia.com, Internet: http://www.sparreholmsslott.nu. Head: Helge Karinen
Science&Tech Museum - 1968
Motorcars, cameras, music boxes, typewriters, jukeboxes, grammophones, horsewagons, bicycles, tricycles and many other early technical products 30328

Stenstorp

Dalénmuseet, 520 50 Stenstorp - T: (0500) 457165, Fax: 457165, E-mail: claudia.feistner@aga.se
Local Museum 30329

Stenungsund

Hogia PC-Museum - Persondatormuseet, Hakenas Gård, 444 28 Stenungsund - T: (0303) 69648, Fax: 81997, E-mail: pc.museum@hogia.se, Internet: http://www.hogia.se/pcmuseum. Head: Åse Hogsved
Science&Tech Museum - 1993
Computer hist 30330

Stockholm

Almgrens Sidenväveri & Museum, Repslagarg 15, 118 46 Stockholm - T: (08) 6425616, Fax: 6413427
Decorative Arts Museum 30331

Aquaria Vattenmuseum, Falkenbergsg 2, 115 21 Stockholm - T: (08) 6609089, Fax: 6607003, E-mail: info@aquaria.se, Internet: http://www.aquaria.se. Head: Göran Flodin
Natural History Museum - 1991
Natural hist, living rainforest, shark aquarium with live corals, salmon ladder to Baltic 30332

Arkitekturmuseet (Swedish Museum of Architecture), Skeppsholmen, 111 49 Stockholm - T: (08) 58727000, Fax: 58727070, E-mail: info@arkitekturmuseet.se, Internet: http://www.arkitekturmuseet.se. Head: Bitte Nygren
Fine Arts Museum - 1962
Photos and drawings of 19th and 20th c architecture, archives 30333

Armémuseum (Army Museum), Riddarg 13, 104 41 Stockholm - T: (08) 7889530, Fax: 6626831, E-mail: info@armemuseum.sfhm.se, Internet: http://www.armemuseum.org. Head: Johan Engström
Military Museum - 1879
11th-20th c military history, weapons, vehicles, engineering and signalling material, standards, uniforms, sugery and veterinary material, musical instruments, badges for merit, reproductions and models of forts, coll of trophies 30334

Bankmuseet, Svenska Handelsbanken, Stureg 38, 114 36 Stockholm - T: (08) 229020. Head: Ernst Nathorst Böös
Special Museum 30335

Bellmanmuseet, Stora Henriksvik, 117 33 Stockholm - T: (08) 6696969
Special Museum 30336

Bernadottebiblioteket (Bernadotte Library), Kungliga Slottet, 111 30 Stockholm - T: (08) 4026130, Fax: 4026167, E-mail: info.stockholms-slott@royalcourt.se, Internet: http://www.royalcourt.se. Head: Göran Alm
Library with Exhibitions 30337

Berzeliusmuseet, c/o Kungl. Vetenskapsakademien, 104 05 Stockholm - T: (08) 6739500, Fax: 155670
Special Museum 30338

Biologiska Museet, Stiftelsen Skansen (Biological Museum), Djurgården, 115 93 Stockholm - T: (08) 4428215, Fax: 4428283, E-mail: visning@skansen.se, Internet: http://www.skansen.se. Head: Lars-Erik Larsson
Natural History Museum - 1893
Biology, animals 30339

Carl Eldhs Ateljémuseum, Lögebodavägen 10, 113 47 Stockholm - T: (08) 6126560, Fax: 6126560, E-mail: eldhsatelje@swipnet.se, Internet: http://hotel.telemuseum.se/carleldhsatelje. Head: Åsa Cavalli Björkman
Fine Arts Museum - 1963
Sketches, studies and plaster, originals for Carl Eldh's sculptures, his art coll, furniture and personal belongings 30340

Dansmuseet (Dance Museum), Gustav Adolfs torg 22-24, 111 52 Stockholm - T: (08) 4417650/55, Fax: 200602, E-mail: info@dansmuseet.nu, Internet: http://www.dansmuseet.nu. Head: Erik Näslund
Performing Arts Museum - 1953
Hist of dance and ballet, theater and dancing in Asia, coll from India, Ceylon, Indonesia, Siam, China and Japan, costumes, masks, musical instruments, shadow plays, puppet theater, films, photos, recordings, decor and costume design - archive, videotheque, folk dance archive 30341

Ersta Diakonimuseum, Erstag 1m, 116 28 Stockholm - T: (08) 7146348, Fax: 7149327, E-mail: birgitta.wendt@ersta.se, Internet: http://www.ersta.se. Head: Thorbjörn Larsson
Special Museum
Development of the Swedish medical and social care 30342

Etnografiska Museet, Statens Museer för Världskultur (National Museum of Ethnography), Djurgårdsbrunnsvägen 34, 102 52 Stockholm, mail addr: Box 27140, 102 52 Stockholm - T: (08) 51955000, Fax: 51955070, E-mail: info@etnografiska.se, Internet: http://www.etnografiska.se. Head: Anne Murray
Ethnology Museum - 1880
Coll from Cook's voyages, old ethnographical objects from North America, Central Asia, Japan, lower Congo, mask coll from Sri Lanka, the Akamba coll from Kenya, archaeological coll from Mexico - library, archives 30343

Fjärilshuset Haga Tradgard (Butterfly and Bird Museum), Haga Trädgård, 171 53 Stockholm - T: (08) 7303981, Fax: 834818, E-mail: fjaril@fjarilshuset.se, Internet: http://www.fjarilshuset.se. Head: S. Fried
Natural History Museum - 1989
Natural hist - Butterfly house 30344

Folkens Museum Etnografiska → Etnografiska Museet

Friluftmuseet Skansen (Skansen Open Air Museum), Djurgården, 115 93 Stockholm - T: (08) 4428000, Fax: 4428280, E-mail: skansenchefen@skansen.se, Internet: http://www.skansen.se. Head: Anna-Greta Leijon
Open Air Museum - 1891
125 fully furnished and equipped buildings, farmsteads and craftmen's workshops, folklore, natural history, zoology, traditional building techniques 30345

Gustav III.'s Antikmuseum (Gustav III's Museum of Antiquities), Kungl. Slottet, 111 30 Stockholm - T: (08) 4026130, Fax: 4026167, E-mail: info.stockholms-slott@royalcourt.se, Internet: http://www.royalcourt.se. Head: Agneta Lundström
Museum of Classical Antiquities - 1792
Antiquities, mostly classical sculpture 30346

Hallwylska Museet, Hamng 4, 111 47 Stockholm - T: (08) 51955599, Fax: 51955585, E-mail: hallwyl@lsh.se, Internet: http://www.hallwylskamuseet.nu. Head: Eva Helena Cassel-Pihl
Decorative Arts Museum - 1938
Patrician residence with coll of furniture, Dutch and Flemish paintings, silver, European and Oriental ceramics, arms 30347

Historiska Museet, Narvavägen 13-17, 114 84 Stockholm - T: (08) 51955600, Fax: 6676578, E-mail: info@historiska.se, Internet: http://www.historiska.se. Head: Jane Cederqvist
Historical Museum
National antiquities 30348

Hobby- och Leksaksmuseum (Toy Museum), Mariatorget 1c, 118 48 Stockholm - T: (08) 6416100, Fax: 6404492, Internet: http://hotel.telemuseum.se/leksaksmuseet. Head: Mike von Matuska
Special Museum - 1981
Toy hist, Walt Disney, dolls, mechanical musical instruments, cars, motorcycles, trains, tin soldiers, robots, boats, planes 30349

Ivar Lo-Museet, Bastug 21, 118 25 Stockholm - T: (08) 6582584
Special Museum 30350

Judiska Museet i Stockholm (Jewish Museum of Stockholm), Hälsingeg 2, 102 35 Stockholm, mail addr: Box 6299, 102 34 Stockholm - T: (08) 310143, Fax: 318404, E-mail: info@judiska-museet.a.se, Internet: http://www.judiska-museet.a.se. Head: Erika Aronowitsch
Historical Museum
Jewish hist, Judaica 30351

Kulturhuset, Sergels Torg 3, 103 27 Stockholm, mail addr: Box 16414, 103 27 Stockholm - T: (08) 50831400, Fax: 50831409, E-mail: info@kulturhuset.stockholm.se, Internet: http://www.kulturhuset.stockholm.se. Head: Uwe BYdewadt
Fine Arts Museum 30352

Kungliga Akademien för de Fria Konsterna (The Royal Academy of Fine Arts), Fredsg 12, 111 52 Stockholm, mail addr: Box 16317, 103 26 Stockholm - T: (08) 232945, Fax: 7905924, Internet: http://www.konstakademien.se. Head: Mats Edblommery
Fine Arts Museum - 1735
Coll of Swedish paintings (17th-20th c), coll of Swedish and international drawings and graphics 17th-20th c) - library 30353

Kungliga Myntkabinettet (The Royal Coin Cabinet), Slottsbacken 6, 114 84 Stockholm, mail addr: Box 5428, 114 84 Stockholm - T: (08) 51955300, Fax: 4112214, E-mail: info@myntkabinettet.se, Internet: http://www.myntkabinettet.se. Head: Ian Wiséhn
Special Museum - 1572
Coll of Swedish coins, banknotes, medals from the entire world and from all periods and bonds, shares and tokens - library 30354

Långholmens Fängelsemuseum (Långholmen Prison Museum), Kronohäktet Långholmen, Långholmsmuren 20, 118 58 Stockholm - T: (08) 6680500, Fax: 7208590, E-mail: museum@langholmen.com, Internet: http://www.langholmen.com. Head: Ola Nyman
Special Museum
Hist of the prison Långholmen 30355

Leksaksmuseet, Mariatorget 1, 116 48 Stockholm - T: (08) 6416100
Special Museum 30356

Liljevalchs Konsthall (Liljevalch's Art Gallery), Djurgårdsvägen 60, 115 93 Stockholm - T: (08) 50831330, Fax: 50831326, Internet: http://www.liljevalchs.com. Head: Bo Nilsson
Public Gallery - 1916 30357

Livrustkammaren (Royal Armoury), Kungliga Slottet, Slottsbacken 3, 111 30 Stockholm - T: (08) 51955500, Fax: 51955511, E-mail: livrustkammaren@lsh.se, Internet: http://www.lsh.se. Head: Barbro Bursell
Military Museum - 1628
Royal coll of arms and armours, costumes, coaches - library, archives 30358

Måleriyrkets Museum, Brännkyrkag 71, 104 62 Stockholm - T: (08) 6686619, Fax: 6686619
Local Museum / Decorative Arts Museum
Cultural hist 30359

Marionettmuseet (The International Puppet Theatre Museum), Brunnsg 6, 111 38 Stockholm - T: (08) 103061, Fax: 103061, E-mail: marionettmuseet@marionetteatern.com, Internet: http://www.marionetteatern.com. Head: Prof. Michael Meschke, Helena Alvarez
Performing Arts Museum - 1973
Hist of puppet theatre - library, archives and documentation on Swedish and international puppet theatre 30360

Medelhavsmuseet (Museum of Mediterranean and Near Eastern Antiquities), Fredsg 2, Stockholm, mail addr: Box 16008, 103 21 Stockholm - T: (08) 51955300, Fax: 51955370, E-mail: info@medelhavsmuseet.se, Internet: http://www.medelhavsmuseet.se. Head: Dr. Sanne Houby-Nielsen
Archaeological Museum / Museum of Classical Antiquities - 1954
Greek, Roman, Cypriot and Egyptian archaeology, antiquities from the mediterranean area incl Islamic art - library 30361

Medeltidsmuseet, Strömparterren, 100 12 Stockholm - T: (08) 50831790, Fax: 50831799, E-mail: smm-org@nordm.se, Internet: http://www.medeltidsmuseet.stockholm.se. Head: Dr. Solbritt Benneth
Archaeological Museum / Historical Museum 30362

Moderna Museet (Modern Museum), Skeppsholmen, 103 27 Stockholm, mail addr: Box 16382, 103 27 Stockholm - T: (08) 51955200, Fax: 51955210/250, E-mail: info@modernamuseet.se, Internet: http://www.modernamuseet.se. Head: Lars Nittve
Fine Arts Museum - 1958
Modern art incl P. Picasso, H. Matisse, F. Léger, J. Gris, W. Kandinsky, paintings, sculptures, photographs (about 200 000 prints and negatives from 1845 to the present day), prints and drawings, American art from the 50s and 60s, 'The New York Collection' - photo library, archive 30363

Museum Tre Kronor, Kungl. Slottet, 111 30 Stockholm - T: (08) 4026130, Fax: 4026167, E-mail: info.stockholms-slott@royalcourt.se, Internet: http://www.royalcourt.se. Head: Agneta Lundström
Historical Museum / Archaeological Museum
Archaeology, history art 30364

Musikmuseet, Sibylleg 2, 103 26 Stockholm - T: (08) 51955490, Fax: 6639181, E-mail: museum@musikmuseet.se, Internet: http://www.musikmuseet.se. Head: Stefan Bohman
Music Museum - 1899
Musical instruments, including those of India, Africa and the Far East, Swedish folk music, folk music instruments, art 30365

National Museum of Fine Arts, Södra Blasieholmshamnen, 103 24 Stockholm, mail addr: Box 16176, 103 24 Stockholm - T: (08) 51954300, Fax: 51954450, E-mail: info@nationalmuseum.se, Internet: http://www.nationalmuseum.se. Head: Hans Henrik Brummer
Fine Arts Museum / Decorative Arts Museum - 1792
17th c Dutch and Flemish paintings, 18th-19th c French paintings, 17th-19th c Swedish art: paintings, drawings, sculptures, prints, decorative arts and modern design - library, archives 30366

Nationalmuseum → National Museum of Fine Arts

Naturens Hus, Stora Skuggans väg 22, 115 42 Stockholm - T: (08) 167030
Natural History Museum
Natural hist, environment - workshop 30367

Naturhistoriska Riksmuseet (Swedish Museum of Natural History), Frescativägen 40, 104 05 Stockholm - T: (08) 51954000, Fax: 51954085, E-mail: nrm@nrm.se, Internet: http://www.nrm.se. Head: Stefan Claesson
Natural History Museum - 1819
Natural hist, vertebrates, invertebrates, entomology, palaeozoology, phanerogamic botany, cryptogamic botany, palaeobotany, mineralogy 30368

Nobel Museum, Stortorget 2, 103 16 Stockholm, mail addr: Box 2245, 103 16 Stockholm - T: (08) 51954280, Fax: 51954290, E-mail: nobelmuseum@nobel.se, Internet: http://www.nobel.se/nobel/nobelmuseum/index.html. Head: Svante Lindqvist
Special Museum - 2001
Exhibition of the Nobel prize 30369

Nordiska Museet, Djurgårdsvägen 6-16, 115 93 Stockholm - T: (08) 51956000, Fax: 51954580, E-mail: nordiska@nordm.se, Internet: http://www.nordm.se. Head: Christina Mattsson
Folklore Museum / Ethnology Museum / Historical Museum - 1873
Cultural hist, ethnology, folk art, Lapp coll, crafts, trades, guilds, industrial arts, glass, textiles, folk costumes, fashion dresses 1700-1940, furniture, household objects - library, archive 30370

Observatoriemuseet (Observatory Museum), Drottningg 120, 113 60 Stockholm - T: (08) 315810, Fax: 315810, E-mail: observatoriemuseet@swipnet.se, Internet: http://www.observatoriet.kva.se. Head: Inga Elmqvist
Science&Tech Museum - 1991
Cultural hist 30371

Østasiatiska Museet (Museum of Far Eastern Antiquities), Skeppsholmen, 103 24 Stockholm - T: (08) 51955750, Fax: 51955755, E-mail: info@ostasiatiska.se, Internet: http://www.ostasiatiska.se. Head: Dr. Magnus Fiskesjö
Fine Arts Museum / Decorative Arts Museum / Archaeological Museum - 1926
Far Eastern antiquities, Chinese ceramics, Chinese bronzes, Chinese applied arts, Chinese sculpture and paintings, Korean and Japanes art, Southeast Asian art and archaeology, Indian sculptures and archaeological coll - library 30372

Photography Museum → Moderna Museet

Polishistoriska Museet, Polhemsg 30, 102 26 Stockholm - T: (08) 4019064, Fax: 4019932, E-mail: polishhistorikamuseet@rps.police.se, Internet: http://www.polisen.se. Head: Carl-Johan Cronlund
Special Museum - 1910
Police, criminology 30373

Postal Museum, Lilla Nyg 6, Gamla Stan, 103 11 Stockholm, mail addr: PO Box 2002, 10311 Stockholm - T: (08) 7811755, Fax: 209021, E-mail: postmuseum@posten.se, Internet: http://www.posten.se/museum. Head: Gunnar Nordlinder
Special Museum - 1906
Permanent exhibition of Swedish and Nordic Stamps and postal history subjects, 1847 Mauritius stamps, several donated collections from Hans Lagerloef and others - library, archive 30374

Prins Eugens Waldemarsudde, Prins Eugens väg 6, 103 24 Stockholm, mail addr: Box 16176, 103 24 Stockholm - T: (08) 54583700, Fax: 6677459, Internet: http://www.waldemarsudde.com. Head: Hans Henrik Brummer
Fine Arts Museum - 1948
Art, mainly of Swedish origin (19th c) 30375

Riddarholmskyrkan (Riddarholmen Church), Riddarholmen, 111 30 Stockholm, mail addr: Kungl. Slottet, 111 30 Stockholm - T: (08) 4026130, Fax: 4026167, E-mail: info.stockholms-slott@royalcourt.se, Internet: http://www.royalcourt.se. Head: Agneta Lundström
Historical Museum
Former monastery now the burial place of Swedish Kings, the last Swedish King that was buried in the church was Gustav V (died in 1950), church built in 1270 30376

Riddarhuset, Riddarhustorget 10, 111 28 Stockholm - T: (08) 7233990, Fax: 105760, E-mail: kansli@riddarhuset.se, Internet: http://www.riddarhuset.se. Head: Baron Otto von Schwerin
Local Museum / Decorative Arts Museum
16th c house with 2,325 nobles' blazons 30377

Riksutställningar, Alsnög 7, 116 41 Stockholm, mail addr: Box 4715, 116 92 Stockholm - T: (08) 6916000, Fax: 6916020, E-mail: ru@riksutstallningar.se, Internet: http://www.riksutstallningar.se
Public Gallery 30378

Rosendals Slott (Rosendal Palace), Djurgården, 111 30 Stockholm, mail addr: Kungl. Slottet, 111 30 Stockholm - T: (08) 4026130, Fax: 4026167, E-mail: info.stockholms-slott@royalcourt.se, Internet: http://www.royalcourt.se. Head: Agneta

Lundström
Decorative Arts Museum - 1913
Interior decoration and furniture in a early 19th c building 30379

Sjöhistoriska Museet (The National Maritime Museum), Djurgårdsbrunnvägen 24, 102 52 Stockholm, mail addr: Box 27131, 102 52 Stockholm - T: (08) 51954900, Fax: 51954949, E-mail: sshm@sshm.se, Internet: http://www.sjohistoriska.nu. Head: Anders Björklund
Science&Tech Museum / Historical Museum - 1938
Swedish shipbuilding, 17th-18th c models, merchant shipping and naval defence, full-size boats, figure-heads, uniforms, paintings, drawings, figure-heads, and the original stern of the schooner 'Amphion' (owned by King Gustav III) - library, archives, photos 30380

Skattkammaren (The Treasury), Kungliga Slottet, 111 30 Stockholm - T: (08) 4026130, Fax: 4026167, E-mail: info.stockholms-slott@royalcourt.se, Internet: http://www.royalcourt.se. Head: Agneta Lundström
Decorative Arts Museum 30381

Skulpturens Hus, Vinterviksvägen 60, 117 65 Stockholm - T: (08) 196200
Fine Arts Museum
Sculptures in Alfred Nobel's old factory 30382

Spårvägsmuseet (Transport Museum), Tegelviksg 22, 116 41 Stockholm - T: (08) 55903180, Fax: 55903190, E-mail: spumuseet@sl.se, Internet: http://www.sparvagsmuseet.sl.se. Head: Stefan Sundblad
Science&Tech Museum - 1944
Tramway vehicles, fare-collecting methods, signalling, uniforms, equipment 30383

State Apartments of the Royal Palace, Kungl. Slottet, 111 30 Stockholm - T: (08) 4026000, Fax: 4026115. Head: Bo Vahlne
Decorative Arts Museum / Fine Arts Museum
Baroque interiors, rococo decorations, art coll, tapestries, furniture, Meissen and Sèvres porcelain, Swedish silver 30384

Statens Historiska Museum (Museum of National Antiquities), Narvavägen 17, 114 84 Stockholm - T: (08) 7839400, Fax: 6676578, E-mail: info@historika.se, Internet: http://www.historiska.se. Head: Kristian Berg
Historical Museum - 1630
Prehistory, late iron age, Vikings, medieval archaeology and art, gold treasures of the Migration period, the Vendel Finds, Viking age hoards, medieval wooden sculptures, church textiles - library 30385

Stiftelsen Musikkulturens Främjande, Riddarg 35-37, 114 57 Stockholm - T: (08) 6617171, Fax: 6617171, E-mail: smf@nydahlcoll.se, Internet: http://www.nydahlcoll.se. Head: Göran Grahn
Music Museum - 1920 30386

Stockholms Länsmuseum, Sabbatsbergvägen 6, 113 21 Stockholm - T: (08) 6906970
Local Museum
Cultural hist, art 30387

Stockholms Medeltidsmuseum (Museum of Medieval Stockholm), Strömparterren, Norrbro, 100 12 Stockholm - T: (08) 50831790, Fax: 50831799, E-mail: medeltidsmuseet@smf.stockholm.se, Internet: http://www.medeltidsmusee-t.stockholm.se. Head: Dr. Solbritt Benneth
Archaeological Museum / Historical Museum - 1986
Archaeological remains of Stockholm, reflecting its foundation and history from c 1250-1550 30388

Stockholms Skolmuseum, Stockholms Stadsmuseum (Stockholm School Museum), Ryssgården, Slussen, 104 65 Stockholm - T: (08) 50831649/35, Fax: 50831665, E-mail: ebba.moden@smf.stockholm.se, bjorn.curman@smf.stockholm.se, Internet: http://www.stadsmuseum.stockholm.se/skolmus/_start.htm. Head: Lena Högberg
Historical Museum 30389

Stockholms Stadsmuseum (Stockholm City Museum), Ryssgården, Slussen, 104 65 Stockholm - T: (08) 50831600, Fax: 50831699, E-mail: stadsmuseum@smf.stockholm.se, Internet: http://www.stadsmuseum.stockholm.se. Head: Berit Svedberg
Historical Museum - 1937
Hist of the Stockholm area, archaeological finds, town models, paintings, engravings, photographs, silver treasure 30390

Stockholms Universitet Konstsamlingar, Spökslottet, Drottningg 116-118, 106 91 Stockholm - T: (08) 162000, 164707, Fax: 339022, E-mail: nina.weibull@tb.su.se
Fine Arts Museum / University Museum 30391

Strindbergsmuseet Blå Tornet, Drottningg 85, 111 60 Stockholm - T: (08) 4115354, Fax: 4110141, E-mail: info@strindbergsmuseet.se, Internet: http://www.strindbergsmuseet.se. Head: Katarina Ek-Nilsson
Special Museum / Fine Arts Museum - 1973
Memorial to dramatist August Strindberg (1849-1912), his study with all details and the completely furnished flat of his last residence, coll of cuttings and theatre posters and programmes, paintings and photos by Strindberg - library 30392

Tekniska Museet (National Museum of Science and Technology), Museivägen 7, 115 93 Stockholm - T: (08) 4505600, Fax: 4505601, E-mail: info@tekmu.se, Internet: http://www.tekmu.se. Head: Anne Louise Kemdal
Science&Tech Museum - 1924
Steam engines, water turbines, internal combustion engines, automobiles, motorcycles, aeroplanes, mining, metallurgy, electricity, telecommunication, nuclear physics, atomic energy - archive, library 30393

Telemuseum, Museivägen 7, 115 93 Stockholm - T: (08) 6708100, Fax: 6708127, E-mail: angel@telemuseum.se, Internet: http://www.telemuseum.se. Head: Lars Johannesson
Science&Tech Museum - 1937
Telecommunication techniques, telegraph constructions, telephon sets, radio equipment, drawings, photographs 30394

Thielska Galleriet, Sjötullsbacken 6-8, 115 25 Stockholm - T: (08) 6625884, 6638960, Fax: 6625884, E-mail: thielska-galleriet@telia.com, Internet: http://www.thielska-galleriet.a.se
Fine Arts Museum - 1924
19th and 20th c Scandinavian and French art (Munch, Zorn, Larsson) 30395

Tobaksmuseet (Tobacco Museum), Skansen, 118 84 Stockholm - T: (08) 4428026, Fax: 6696446. Head: Inga Junhem
Special Museum - 1938
History of tobacco in Sweden, packages, pipes, snuffboxes, manufacture of cigarettes 30396

Tullmuseum (Customs Museum), Alströmerg 39, 11 298 Stockholm - T: (08) 6530503, Fax: 208012, E-mail: tullmuseet@tullverket.se, Internet: http://www.tullverket.se. Head: Jan Berggten
Historical Museum - 1927
Commerce, communication, customs 30397

Vasamuseet, Statens Sjöhistoriska Museer (Vasa Museum), Galärvarvet, Djurgården, 102 52 Stockholm - T: (08) 51954800, Fax: 51954888, E-mail: vasamuseet@sshm.se, Internet: http://www.vasamuseum.com. Head: Klas Helmerson
Archaeological Museum / Fine Arts Museum / Historical Museum - 1962
Warship Vasa which capsized in 1628 and was raised in 1961, marine archaeology, non-religious art, history 30398

Vin- och Sprithistoriska Museet Stiftelsen (Foundation Wine and Spirits Historical Museum), Dalag 100, 113 43 Stockholm - T: (08) 7447070, Fax: 313928, Internet: http://www.vinosprithi-storiska.a.se. Head: Mirja Lausson
Historical Museum - 1967
Hist of the wine and liquor industry, Swedish legislation concerning alcoholic beverages since the Middle Ages, wine and liquor labels, old price lists, archives of distilleries and wine companies, photos 30399

Storvik

Ovensjö Sockens, Gammelgård, Backvägen, 812 00 Storvik
Local Museum
Local history, national costumes 30400

Strängnäs

Grassagården, Kvarng 2, 645 80 Strängnäs - T: (0152) 13400
Open Air Museum 30401

Roggenmuseet, Roggenborgen, 152 00 Strängnäs - T: (0152) 80
Local Museum
Local hist, religious art 30402

Strängnäs Museum, Gyllenhjelmsg 2, 645 80 Strängnäs - T: (0152) 29683, Fax: 29675. Head: Kerstin Pettersson
Local Museum - 1976
Ancient greek vases from Alexandria - Grassagården (homestead in the very town) 30403

Sundborn

Carl Larsson-Gården, 790 15 Sundborn - T: (023) 60053, Fax: 60653, E-mail: info@clg.se, Internet: http://www.clg.se. Head: Marianne Nilsson
Fine Arts Museum
Home of the artist Carl Larsson and his family, original furnishings, paintings, watercolours and memorabilia of Carl Larsson (1853-1919), painter of family life and the Swedish countryside 30404

Sundbyberg

Sundbybergs Museum, Fredsg 4, 172 33 Sundbyberg - T: (08) 7068178, Fax: 280389, E-mail: info@sbg-museum.se, Internet: http://www.sbg-museum.se. Head: Lena. A Löfström
Local Museum 30405

Sundsvall

Bildens Hus (Swedish House of Photography), Magasinsg 12, 852 34 Sundsvall - T: (060) 192534, Fax: 610798, E-mail: bildenshus@sundsvall.se, Internet: http://www.fotomuseet.sundsvall.se. Head: Petter Österlund
Fine Arts Museum 30406

Medelpads Fornminnesförening, Norra Stadsberget, 856 40 Sundsvall - T: (060) 111748. Head: Karin Strömberg
Open Air Museum / Ethnology Museum / Historical Museum
Ethnography, history, open air museum 30407

Sundsvalls Hantverksmuseum, 852 50 Sundsvall
Historical Museum 30408

Sundsvalls Museum, Packhusg 4, 851 96 Sundsvall - T: (060) 191803, Fax: 615894, E-mail: -sundsvalls.museum@sundsvall.se, Internet: http://www.sundsvall.se. Head: Mona Bornecrantz
Local Museum
Archaeology, 6th c grave finds, technology, forest industry, handicrafts, art, photography, contemporary art, hist of first industry 30409

Sunne

Mårbacka Manor, Home of Selma Lagerlöf, Mårbacka, 686 26 Sunne - T: (0565) 31027, Fax: 31029, E-mail: information@marbacka.s.se, Internet: http://www.marbacka.s.se. Head: Britt Wendling
Special Museum
Memorabilia on Selma Lagerlöf (1858-1940), in her former home, local history 30410

Skogs- och Motorsågsmuseum, Södra Viken, 686 00 Sunne - T: (0565) 770071
Science&Tech Museum 30411

Sundsbergs Gård Museum och Konsthall, Ekebyvägen, 686 00 Sunne - T: (0565) 10363, Fax: 10363, E-mail: sundsberg@varmland.nu, Internet: http://www.varmland.nu/sundsberg
Local Museum / Public Gallery
Local history, arts and crafts 30412

Tandläkarmuseum (Dentist Museum), Villa Helios, Skäggebergsvägen 2, 686 00 Sunne - T: (0565) 103631, Fax: 10363
Historical Museum 30413

Surahammar

Gyllene Hjulet MC-Museum, Bruksg, 735 00 Surahammar - T: (0220) 36870
Local Museum 30414

Surahammars Bruksmuseum, Box 74, 735 22 Surahammar - T: (0220) 39070, 39069, Fax: 39075. Head: Carl-Gustav Hjorth
Decorative Arts Museum
Applied arts 30415

Surte

Glasbruksmuseet i Surte, Kvarnvägen 6, 445 55 Surte - T: (0303) 330106, 330939, Fax: 330720, E-mail: info@glasbruksmuseet.nu, Internet: http://www.glasbruksmuseet.nu. Head: Ragnhild Kappelmark
Science&Tech Museum
Technical and industrial hist 30416

Sysslebäck

Nordvärmlands Jakt och Fiskemuseum, Gammelvägen 44, 680 60 Sysslebäck - T: (0564) 43105, Fax: 43205, Internet: http://www.tordata.se/vadig/svenska/ramar.htm
Special Museum
Hunting, fishery 30417

Täby

Karby Gård, Täbyvägen, 183 43 Täby - T: (0762) 11548
Open Air Museum 30418

Tärnaby

Samegården, Tärnafors, 920 64 Tärnaby - T: (0954) 10440
Open Air Museum 30419

Tanumshede

Vitlycke Museum - Rock Art Centre (Rock Art Museum), Vitlycke, 457 93 Tanumshede - T: (0525) 20950, Fax: 29362, E-mail: vitlycke.museum@bohusmus.se, Internet: http://www.vitlycke.-bohusmus.se. Head: Anita Larsson Modin
Open Air Museum / Archaeological Museum 30420

Tibro

Tibro Museum, Borgarg 27, 543 30 Tibro - T: (0504) 10923, Fax: 10523
Local Museum
Cultural hist 30421

Tidaholm

Tidaholms Konsthall, Turbinhuset, Museig, 522 83 Tidaholm - T: (0502) 16191, Internet: http://www.tidaholm.se
Fine Arts Museum 30422

Tidaholms Museum, Vulcanön, 522 83 Tidaholm - T: (0502) 16192, 16195, Fax: 14329, E-mail: tidaholms.museum@tidaholm.se, Internet: http://www.tidaholm.se. Head: Monika Gyllkrans
Local Museum - 1968
Remains of match factory, Vulcan, and of Tidaholms Bruk production of furniture, horse wagons and cars - archive 30423

Tomelilla

Tomelilla Konsthall, Centralg 13, 273 30 Tomelilla - T: (0417) 18194, Fax: 18116, E-mail: konsthallen@tomelilla.se, Internet: http://www.tomelilla-konsthall.se. Head: Marie Johansson
Fine Arts Museum 30424

Torekov

Torekovs Sjöfartsmuseum, Hamnbacken, 260 93 Torekov - T: (0431) 63137
Science&Tech Museum 30425

Trelleborg

Axel Ebbes Konsthall, Hesekilleg 1, 231 53 Trelleborg - T: (0410) 53056, 53045, Fax: 18290, E-mail: museum@trelleborg.se, Internet: http://www.trelleborg.se
Fine Arts Museum 30426

Trelleborgs Museum, Österg 58, 231 45 Trelleborg - T: (0410) 53045, 53050, Fax: 18290, E-mail: museum@trelleborg.se, Internet: http://www.trelleborg.se. Head: Ulla Ahnfelt
Local Museum - 1908/1934
History, archaeology, ethnography, art gallery 30427

Trollhättan

Forngården, 461 00 Trollhättan
Archaeological Museum 30428

Innovatum Kunskapens Hus, Åkerssjövägen 10, 461 55 Trollhättan - T: (0520) 488480, Fax: 488491
Science&Tech Museum 30429

Kanalmuseet, Sjöfartsverket, 461 29 Trollhättan - T: (0520) 472207, 472251, Fax: 428559, E-mail: sonny.johansson@sjofartsverket.se, Internet: http://www.sjofartsverket.se. Head: Sonny Johansson
Science&Tech Museum 30430

Trollhättans Museum, Magasinsg 15, 461 30 Trollhättan - T: (0520) 31420
Local Museum 30431

Trosa

Trosa Stadsmuseum, Garvaregården, 619 00 Trosa - T: (0156) 12220
Local Museum 30432

Tyresö

Tyresö Slott, 135 00 Tyresö - T: (08) 7700178
Decorative Arts Museum
18th and 19th c interiors, in a 17th c castle 30433

Uddevalla

Båtsamlingarna på Bassholmen, Box 6046, 451 06 Uddevalla - T: (0522) 52422
Fine Arts Museum 30434

Bohusläns Museum, Museig 1, 451 19 Uddevalla - T: (0522) 656500, Fax: 656505, E-mail: museum@bohusmus.se, Internet: http://www.bohusmus.se. Head: Dr. Hans Manneby
Local Museum - 1861
Archaeology, regional hist, 17th c art from the Netherlands, 19th-20th c art of Scandinavia - library 30435

Ugglarp-Slöinge

Svedinos Bil- och Flygmuseum (Svedino's Automobile and Aviation Museum), 310 50 Ugglarp-Slöinge - T: (0346) 43187, Fax: (031) 144848, E-mail: info@svedinos.se, Internet: http://www.svedinos.se. Head: Bjorn Svedfeldt
Science&Tech Museum - 1961
Veteran cars, aircrafts, bicycles, motorbikes 30436

Ulricehamn

Ulricehamns Museum, Jägareg 1, 523 86 Ulricehamn - T: (0321) 27239, Fax: 10980, E-mail: nina.wiklund@ulricehamn.se, Internet: http://www.ulricehamn.se
Local Museum 30437

Umeå

Bildmuseet, c/o Ulmeå Universitet, 901 87 Umeå - T: (090) 165227, Fax: 167733
Fine Arts Museum / University Museum
Art and massproduced pictures 30438

Umeå Energicentrum, Umeå Energi AB, 901 05 Umeå - T: (090) 48028
Science&Tech Museum 30439

Västerbottens Museum med Svenska Skidmuseet, Gammlia, 906 03 Umeå - T: (090) 171800, Fax: 779000, E-mail: info@vasterbottensmuseum.se, Internet: http://www.vasterbottensmuseum.se. Head: Gull-Mari Rosén
Local Museum - 1943
Local history, archaeology, ethnography, open air museum, Swedish Skimuseum, regional fine arts, Lappish coll - library 30440

Uppsala

Biologiska Museet, Vasag 4, 752 24 Uppsala - T: (018) 276370, Fax: 695507, Internet: http://www.uppsala.se/svenska/kultur-fritid/Kultur/museum/biolog.htm
Natural History Museum 30441

Botaniksektionen Utställingar, Evolutionsmuseet Uppsala Universitet (Botany Section, Museum of Evolution), Norbyvägen 16, 752 36 Uppsala - T: (018) 4712790/91, Fax: 4122794, E-mail: barbro.rahm@evolmuseum.uu.se, Internet: http://www-hotel.uu.se/evolmuseum/fytotek. Head: Dr. Roland Moberg
Natural History Museum / University Museum 30442

Bror Hjorths Hus, Norbyvägen 26, 752 39 Uppsala - T: (018) 535724
Fine Arts Museum
Art, handicraft 30443

Disagården, Upplandsmuseet, Sankt Eriks gränd 6, 753 10 Uppsala - T: (018) 169100, Fax: 692509, E-mail: info@uppmus.se, Internet: http://www.uppmus.se. Head: Håkan Liby
Ethnology Museum
Ethnography 30444

Linnémuseet (Linnaeus Museum), Svartbäcksg 27, 751 45 Uppsala - T: (018) 136540, Fax: 126547, E-mail: linnemuseet@linnaeus.uu.se, Internet: http://info.uu.se/popvet.nsf/sida/linne. Head: Inger Estham
Special Museum - 1937
Costumes, books, furniture, household items, scientific equipment of Linné 30445

Linnés Hammarby, 755 98 Uppsala - T: (018) 326094, Fax: 326094, E-mail: -Kristofer.de_Korostenski@linnaeus.uu.se, Internet: http://www.hammarby.uu.se. Head: Magnus Lideń
Natural History Museum / University Museum / Open Air Museum
Linnaeus 18th cent summer residence 30446

Medicinhistoriska Museet i Uppsala, Ewa Lagerwall väg, 750 17 Uppsala - T: (018) 662610
Natural History Museum / Historical Museum 30447

Museum Gustavianum (Uppsala University Museum), Akademig 3, 753 10 Uppsala - T: (018) 4717571, Fax: 4717572, E-mail: museum@gustavianum.uu.se, Internet: http://www.gustavianum.uu.se. Head: Ing-Marie Munktell
Historical Museum / Archaeological Museum / Museum of Classical Antiquities / University Museum
Egyptian antiquities, classical antiquities, pottery, national antiquities, grave artifacts from Valsgärde, anatomy, university hist, Linnæus, Celsius - The Physics Cabinet, The Augsburg Art Cabinet 30448

Paleontologiska Utställingar, Evolutionsmuseet Uppsala Universitet (Paleontology Section, Museum of Evolution), Norbyvägen 22, 752 36 Uppsala - T: (018) 4712739, Fax: 4712794, E-mail: evolmuseum@evolmuseum.uu.se, Internet: http://www.ebc.uu.se/evolmuseum. Head: Prof. John S. Peel
Natural History Museum 30449

Psykiatrihistoriska Museet, Ewa Lagerwall väg 10, 750 17 Uppsala - T: (018) 6112048/50, Fax: 6112038, E-mail: inga-lill.westerberg@psyk.nas.lul.se, Internet: http://www1.nas.se/lul/nas/psyk/serv/ext/museet.htm. Head: Bengt Ekblom
Natural History Museum / Historical Museum 30450

Skattkammaren - Uppsala Domkyrkas Museum (Treasury - Uppsala Cathedral Museum), Domkyrkan, Domkyrkoplan 2, 753 10 Uppsala - T: (018) 187201, Fax: 101695, E-mail: uppsala.domkyrka@svenskakyrkan.se, Internet: http://www.uppsaladomkyrka.nu
Religious Arts Museum
Textiles from the Middles Ages, gold and silver relics 30451

Sveriges Geologiska Undersökning (Geological Survey of Sweden), Villavägen 18, 751 28 Uppsala - T: (018) 179000, Fax: 179210. Head: Jan Olof Carlsson
Natural History Museum - 1858
Swedish rocks, minerals and fossils, coll of ores and ore minerals from Sweden - library 30452

Upplandsmuseet, Sankt Erikstorg 10, 753 10 Uppsala - T: (018) 169100, Fax: 692509, E-mail: info@uppmus.se, Internet: http://www.uppmus.se. Head: Håkan Liby
Local Museum - 1959
Local hist, ethnography, peasant art, handicrafts - library 30453

Uppsala Konstmuseum, Slottet, Ing. E, 752 37 Uppsala - T: (018) 272482, Fax: 507690, E-mail: konstinfo@konstmuseum.uppsala.se, Internet: http://www.uppsala.se/konstmuseum. Head: Deborah Thompson
Fine Arts Museum - 1982
Prints, ceramics 30454

Uppsala Universitet Konstsamling, Slottet, 752 37 Uppsala - T: (018) 181830. Head: Thomas Heinemann
Fine Arts Museum / University Museum
Art, religious art 30455

Uppsala Universitet Myntkabinett, Universitetshuset, Uppsala, mail addr: Box 256, 751 05 Uppsala - T: (018) 4711722, Fax: 4717569, E-mail: harald.nilsson@coin.uu.se. Head: Harald Nilsson
Special Museum / University Museum 30456

Walmstedtska Gårdens Museivåning, Sysslomansg 1, 752 20 Uppsala - T: (018) 169100, Fax: 692509, E-mail: info@uppmus.se, Internet: http://www.uppmus.se. Head: Håkan Liby
Historical Museum 30457

Zoologiska Utställingar, Evolutionsmuseet Uppsala Universitet (Zoology Section, Museum of Evolution), Villavägen 9, 751 36 Uppsala - T: (018) 4712739, Fax: 4712794, E-mail: evolmuseum@evolmuseum.uu.se, Internet: http://www.ebc.uu.se/evolmuseum. Head: Prof. John S. Peel
Natural History Museum / University Museum (Linnaean Museum Acedemicum: 1743) 2500 zoological specimens, invertebrates, amphibians, reptiles, mammals, Linnaean coll 30458

Vadstena

Gottfrid Larsson-Gården, Skänningeg 9, 592 00 Vadstena - T: (0143) 15125
Special Museum 30459

Hospitalsmuseet, Lastköpingsg, 592 32 Vadstena - T: (0143) 31570, Fax: 31579, E-mail: info@tourist.vadstena.se, Internet: http://www.vadstena.se/turism
Historical Museum 30460

Vadstena Stadsmuseum, Rådhustorget, 592 30 Vadstena - T: (0143) 31570. Head: Hans Lundbergh
Historical Museum 30461

Väddö

Roslagens Sjöfartsmuseum, Kaplansbacken, 760 40 Väddö - T: (0176) 50259, Fax: 50259, Internet: http://www.roslagen.com/vaddo/sjofart. Head: Lars Nylén
Science&Tech Museum - 1938
Maritime coll 30462

Vänersborg

Älvsborgs Länsmuseum → Regionmuseum Västra Götaland

Regionmuseum Västra Götaland, Niklasbergsvägen 15, 462 21 Vänersborg - T: (0521) 264100, Fax: 19782, E-mail: kansli@alvlanmus.se, Internet: http://www.alvlanmus.se. Head: Karin Rex Svensson
Local Museum 30463

Vänersborgs Museum, Östra Plantaget, 462 23 Vänersborg - T: (0521) 60060, Fax: 19782, E-mail: kansli@alvlanmus.se, Internet: http://www.alvlanmus.se. Head: Karin Rex Svansson
Local Museum - 1891
Local history, archaeology, ethnography, art, natural history, coll of birds from Botswana and Namibia, Egyptian antiquities, prehistorical finds from Vänersborg and the vicinity 30464

Värnamo

Friluftsmuseet i Apladalen, 331 00 Värnamo - T: (0370) 10460
Open Air Museum 30465

Smålands Konstarkiv, Malmövägen, 331 42 Värnamo - T: (0370) 14800
Fine Arts Museum 30466

Västerås

Västerås Konstmuseum, Fiskartorget 2, 721 87 Västerås, mail addr: Box 717, 721 20 Västerås - T: (021) 161300, Fax: 418120, E-mail: konstmuseet@vasteras.se, Internet: http://www.zon.se/konstmuseet. Head: Christina Rimmö
Fine Arts Museum - 1972
Paintings, sculpture, graphics, drawings 30467

Västmanlands Läns Museum, Slottet, 722 11 Västerås - T: (021) 195480, Fax: 132076. Head: Eva Alström, Karin Thorsen
Local Museum / Folklore Museum
Archaeology, regional history, ethnography, crafts, religious art 30468

Vallby Friluftsmuseum, Vallby, 724 80 Västerås - T: (021) 161670, Fax: 357674, E-mail: -vallby.friluftsmuseum@vasteras.se, Internet: http://www.vasteras.se
Open Air Museum 30469

Västervik

Almviks Tegelbruksmuseum, Hasselbacken, Almvik, 593 95 Västervik - T: (0490) 40204
Local Museum 30470

Kulbackens Museum, Kulbacken, 593 23 Västervik - T: (0490) 21177, Fax: 10671
Local Museum - 1933
Local history, maritime coll 30471

Växjö

Smålands Museum, Södra Järnvägsg 2, 351 04 Växjö - T: (0470) 45145, Fax: 39744
Local Museum - 1867
History of glass making, religious art, weapons, ethnology, archaeology, coins, local history, forest industry - library 30472

Utvandrarnas Hus, Vilhelm Mobergs g 4, 351 04 Växjö - T: (0470) 20120, Fax: 39416, E-mail: info@svenskaemigrantinstitutet.g.se, Internet: http://www.svenskaemigrantinstitutet.g.se. Head: Dr. Ulf Beijbom
Special Museum 30473

Varberg

Hallands Länsmuseer (Halland's Country Museum), Fästningen, 432 44 Varberg - T: (0340) 18520, Fax: 14722. Head: Thomas Thieme
Local Museum - 1916
Ethnography, local history, crafts, the Bocksten find (complete medieval dress about 1360), in a 13th c castle and a fortress from the 17th c - library 30474

Vårgårda

Nårungabygdens Missionshistoriska Museum, Ljurhalla 4189, 447 94 Vårgårda - T: (0322) 660130. Head: Seth Sjöblom
Religious Arts Museum - 1935
Missionary history, religious objects 30475

Vaxholm

Vaxholms Fästnings Museum (Vaxholm Fortress Museum), Vaxholms Kastell, 185 99 Vaxholm - T: (08) 54172157, Fax: 57012552, E-mail: kastellet@epsilon.telenordia.se, Internet: http://www.biogate.com/kastellet. Head: Erik Himmelstrand
Military Museum - 1947
Military hist, models of fortresses, pictures, weapons - library 30476

Vetlanda

Forngården-Hembygds- och Fornminnes-föreningen Njudung, Forngården, 574 00 Vetlanda
Local Museum
Ethnography, local history, open air museum 30477

Njudungs Hembygdsmuseum, Forngården, 574 91 Vetlanda - T: (0383) 761969, Internet: http://www.vetlanda.se/turism/mus_ut/njudung.htm
Local Museum 30478

Vetlanda Museum, Kyrkog 31, 574 31 Vetlanda - T: (0383) 97352, Fax: 15995
Local Museum
Cultural hist 30479

Viken

Paul Jönska Gården, Skepparg 18, 260 40 Viken - T: (042) 236121, Internet: http://www.viken.cc. Head: Märta Braun
Special Museum 30480

Virserum

Virserums Möbelindustrimuseum (Virserum Furniture Industry Museum), Kyrkog, 570 80 Virserum - T: (0495) 30024, 31460, E-mail: -traarbetarnas.museum@swipnet.se
Science&Tech Museum / Local Museum 30481

Visby

Gotlands Fornsal, Strandg 12-14, 621 02 Visby - T: (0498) 247010, Fax: 248325. Head: Sven-Olof Lindquist
Archaeological Museum / Historical Museum - 1875
Archaeology, 5th-11th c stone paintings, Viking treasures, religious art, medieval sculpture, stained glass, weapons and armour, coins, regional history and ethnography, coll illustrating peasant and urban life - library 30482

Gotlands Konstmuseum, Sankt Hansg 21, 621 56 Visby - T: (0498) 292775, Fax: 292785, E-mail: konstmuseet@gotmus.i.se, Internet: http://www.gotmus.i.se
Fine Arts Museum 30483

Gotlands Naturmuseum (Gotland's Museum of Natural History), Hästg 1, 621 56 Visby - T: (0498) 247095, Fax: 248325, E-mail: naturmus.gotland@gotland.mail.telia.com. Head: Sara Eliason
Natural History Museum - 1980
Nature and fossils - library, children department, aquariums 30484

Helge Ands Kyrkormin, Norra Kyrkog, 621 02 Visby - T: (0498) 47010
Special Museum 30485

Sankta Karins Klosterruin, Sankta Katarinag, 621 02 Visby - T: (0498) 47010
Religious Arts Museum 30486

Ystad

Charlotte Berlins Museum, Dammg 23, 271 42 Ystad - T: (0411) 77286. Head: Håkan Nilsson
Decorative Arts Museum - 1918
Furnished 19th c burgher house, decorative arts 30487

Dragonmuseet, Sankt Knuts torg, 271 80 Ystad - T: (0411) 77000, Fax: 19107. Head: Henrik Jern
Military Museum
Military history 30488

Eriksborg Vagnmuseum (Eriksborg Carriage Museum), Eriksborg, 271 91 Ystad - T: (0411) 71040, E-mail: eriksbor@hem2.passagen.se, Internet: http://hem2.passagen.se/eriksbor. Head: Allan Rasmusson
Special Museum 30489

Stadsmuseet i Gråbrödraklostret (Franciscan Monastery), Sankt Petri Kyrkoplan, 271 34 Ystad - T: (0411) 577286, Fax: 12359, E-mail: klostret@ystad.se, Internet: http://www.ystad.se/Text/Service/Kultur/kloster.htm. Head: Håkan Nilsson
Religious Arts Museum
Archaeology, ethnography, local history 30490

Ystads Konstmuseum, Sankt Knuts torg, 271 80 Ystad - T: (0411) 77285, Fax: 19107, E-mail: thomas.millroth@ystad.se. Head: Thomas Millroth
Fine Arts Museum - 1936
Swedish and Danish art, special coll of art from Skåne 30491

Switzerland

Aarau

Aargauer Kunsthaus, Aargauer Pl, 5001 Aarau - T: 0628352330, Fax: 0628352329, E-mail: kunsthaus@ag.ch, Internet: http://www.ag.ch/kunsthaus. Head: Beat Wismer
Fine Arts Museum - 1860
Swiss paintings, graphics and sculptures (18th-20th c) including works by C. Wolf, A. Stäbli, C. Amiet, R. Auberjonois, G. Giacometti, F. Hodler, O. Meyer-Amden, L. Soutter, Varlin, regional folk art, French masters, Theodor Bally donation 30492

Forum Schloßplatz, Laurenzenvorstadt 3, 5000 Aarau - T: 0628556511
Public Gallery 30493

Kunstraum Aarau, Tellistr 118, 5001 Aarau - T: 0628444616, Internet: http://www.echo.ch/kunstraum
Fine Arts Museum 30494

Naturama Aargau, Bahnhofpl, 5001 Aarau - T: 0628327200, Fax: 0628327210, E-mail: uhalder@naturama.ch, Internet: http://www.naturama.ch. Head: Dr. U. Halder
Natural History Museum - 1922
Zoology, geology of the Swiss Jurassic mountains, mineralogy, plateosaurus (Frick), environmental protection, nature conservation, ecosystems of Switzerland, paintings of European orchideae - herbarium argovieuse 30495

Polizeimuseum, Kantonales Polizeikommando, Tellistr 85, 5004 Aarau - T: 0628358181, Fax: 0628358244
Special Museum - 1992 30496

Stadtmuseum Aarau, Schloßpl 23, 5000 Aarau - T: 0628360517, Fax: 0628360630
Local Museum - 1919
Local history, tools and implements, tin figures, weapons, castle (11th c) 30497

Aarburg

Heimatmuseum Aarburg, Im Städtchen 35, 4663 Aarburg - T: 0629715788
Local Museum - 1960
Local history, weapons, uniforms, paintings, domestic utensils, tools, furniture, piano 30498

Aathal-Seegräben

Sauriermuseum Aathal, Zürichstr 202, 8607 Aathal-Seegräben - T: 019321418, Fax: 019321488, E-mail: sauriermuseum@blue-win.ch, Internet: http://www.sauriermuseum.ch. Head: Hans Jakob Siber
Natural History Museum - 1992
Footprints of dinosaurs, Hans Jakob Siber 30499

Adelboden

Heimatmuseum Adelboden, Ehemalige englische Kirche, 3715 Adelboden, mail addr: c/o Ch. Künzi, Mattenweg 8, 3715 Adelboden - T: 0336731656
Local Museum - 1983 30500

Adligenswil

Feuerwehrmuseum, Bei der alten Mühle, 6043 Adligenswil - T: 0413701252
Science&Tech Museum - 1958
History of firefighting, implements and tools 30501

Aesch, Basel-Land

Heimatmuseum, Kesslerhaus, Hauptstr 27, 4147 Aesch, Basel-Land - T: 0617567741, 0617513869
Local Museum - 1975
Local history, farm implements, memorabilia on the poet Traugott Meyer 30502

Affoltern am Albis

Spielzeugeisenbahn- und Zweiradmuseum, Obere Bahnhofstr 7, 8910 Affoltern am Albis - T: 017614686
Special Museum / Science&Tech Museum 30503

Agno

Museo Plebano, Casa del Beneficio parrocchiale, 6982 Agno - T: 0916053360, Fax: 0916046463. Head: Guiseppe Albisetti
Archaeological Museum - 1955
Etruscan, Roman, Langobardian and Byzantian tombs from Agno and surrounding areas, Roman coins 30504

Aigle

Château, CP 453, 1860 Aigle - T: 0244662130, Fax: 0244662131. Head: Suzanne Jotterand
Decorative Arts Museum - 1976 30505

Musée de la Vigne et du Vin, Château, 1860 Aigle, mail addr: CP 453, 1860 Aigle - T: 0244662130, Fax: 0244662131. Head: Pierre Sauter
Agriculture Museum - 1971
Hist of wine cultivation and trade, tools and implements used in viticulture, bottles and glasses 30506

Musée International de l'Etiquette, Maison de la Dime, Château, 1860 Aigle, mail addr: CP 453, 1860 Aigle - T: 0244662130, Fax: 0244662131, E-mail: info@chateauaigle.ch, Internet: http://www.chateauaigle.ch. Head: Florence Winteler
Special Museum - 1990
Hist of wine labels all around the world 30507

Musée Suisse du Sel, 1 Rue du Midi, 1860 Aigle - T: 0244661759. Head: Albert Hahling
Special Museum - 1975 30508

Airolo

Esposizione Forte Airolo, Sulla Strada Cantonale che porta al Passo del San Gottardo, 6780 Airolo - T: 0918737111
Historical Museum - 1989 30509

Alberswil

Bienenmuseum, c/o Edi Kurmann, Burgrain, 6248 Alberswil - T: 0419802259
Natural History Museum 30510

Schweizerisches Museum für Landwirtschaft und Agrartechnik Burgrain, Burgrain, 6248 Alberswil - T: 0419802810, Fax: 0419806911, E-mail: museumburgrain@bluewin.ch, Internet: http://www.museumburgrain.ch. Head: Dr. Hans Burger
Agriculture Museum / Folklore Museum - 1974
Coll of graphics - library 30511

Allschwil

Allschwiler Kunst-Zentrum, Spitzwaldstr 211a, 4123 Allschwil - T: 0613028794
Fine Arts Museum 30512

Heimatmuseum Allschwil, Basler Str 48, 4123 Allschwil - T: 0614815187, Internet: http://www.allschwil.ch/Heimatmuseum
Local Museum - 1968
Furniture and furnishings (17th-19th c), farm implements and tools, palaeolithic to early medieval artifacts, ceramics, coll of tiles, pre- and early hist findings in Allschwil, local hist from 17th c till 1945 30513

Altdorf, Uri

Historisches Museum Uri, Gotthardstr 18, 6460 Altdorf, Uri - T: 0418703236, Internet: http://www.museen-uri.ch. Head: Rolf Gisler-Sauch
Historical Museum - 1906
Cultural hist of the canton Uri, ecclesiastical art, archaeological finds, weapons and banners, textiles and costumes, furnishings 30514

Kirchenschatz-Museum Sankt Martin, Kirchpl 7, 6460 Altdorf, Uri - T: 0418747044, Fax: 0418747045, E-mail: - kath.kirchgemeinde.altdorf@nol.ch. Head: Arnold Furrer
Religious Arts Museum 30515

Naturkundemuseum Kollegium Karl Borromäus, Klausenstr 2, 6460 Altdorf, Uri - T: 0418702242
Natural History Museum 30516

Altenrhein

Fliegermuseum, Beim Flugplatz, 9423 Altenrhein - T: 0794305151, Fax: 0797448260, E-mail: info@fliegermuseum.ch, Internet: http://www.hyperion.ch. Head: Walter Waltenspül
Science&Tech Museum - 1995 30517

Altishofen

Schreinermuseum, Schloß, 6246 Altishofen - T: 062812264. Head: Hermann Bühler
Science&Tech Museum - 1978
Joiner's tools, 16th c castle 30518

Altstätten

Heimatmuseum Prestegg, Rabengasse, 9450 Altstätten - T: 0717551838
Local Museum - 1895
Local history, ecclesiastical and profane art, furniture, coats of arms, documents, weapons, utensils 30519

Altstetten

Ortsmuseum Altstetten, Dachslernstr 20, 8048 Altstetten - T: 019451050
Local Museum
Communal kitchen, farmhouse parlours and chambers, shoemaker's workshop 30520

Amden

Museum Amden, Rüti, 8873 Amden - T: 0556111089
Local Museum - 1991 30521

Amriswil

Bohlenständerhaus, Schrofen, 8580 Amriswil - T: 0714112675. Head: Heini Giezendanner
Folklore Museum - 1989 30522

Kutschensammlung Robert Sallmann, Sankt-Galler-Str 12, 8580 Amriswil - T: 0714116527, Fax: 0714116527
Science&Tech Museum - 1974
18th-19th c carriages, coaches and sledges, harness 30523

Ortsmuseum, Im alten Pfarrhaus, Bahnhofstr 3, 8580 Amriswil - T: 0714141111, Fax: 0714141155, E-mail: info@amriswil.ch, Internet: http://www.amriswil.ch
Local Museum - 1989
Leather and shoe manufacture, shoemaking trade, smith trade, textile industry, book printing, Dino Larese (writer) 30524

Andermatt

Talmuseum Ursern, Gottardstr 113, 6490 Andermatt - T: 0418870624. Head: Hans-Werner Nager
Local Museum - 1991 30525

Andwil

Ortsmuseum, Müliweierstr 9, 9204 Andwil - T: 0713851215, Fax: 0713851590
Local Museum - 1991 30526

Anzère

Musée Alpin d'Anzère, Musée des Bisses, Pl du Village, 1972 Anzère - T: 0273992800, Fax: 0273992805, E-mail: info@anzere.ch, Internet: http://www.anzere.ch. Head: Lydia Fournier
Local Museum 30527

Appenzell

Kulturzentrum Ziegelhütte (closed) 30528

Museum Appenzell, Hauptgasse 4, 9050 Appenzell - T: 0717889631, Fax: 0717889649, E-mail: museum@appenzell.ch, Internet: http://www.ai.ch. Head: Roland Inauen
Local Museum - 1879
Prehistorical finds, antiquities, furnishings, folk art, ecclesiastical art, 16th c house, embroidery from Appenzell 30529

Museum Liner Appenzell, Unterrainstr 5, 9050 Appenzell - T: 0717881800, Fax: 0717881801, E-mail: info@museumliner.ch, Internet: http://www.museumliner.ch. Head: Dr. Peter Dering
Fine Arts Museum
20th c art, contemporary art 30530

Privatmuseum IM BLAUEN HAUS, c/o Hermann Fässler Söhne Kunstschreinerei, Weissbadstr 33, 9050 Appenzell - T: 0717871284, Fax: 0717874790, E-mail: info@faessler-appenzell.ch, Internet: http://www.imblauenhaus.ch. Head: Klaus Fässler
Fine Arts Museum / Folklore Museum - 1981
Conrad Starck (furniture painting), local painters 30531

Arbon

Historisches Museum Arbon, Schloß, 9320 Arbon, mail addr: Postfach, 9320 Arbon - T: 0714466010, Fax: 0714461058. Head: Hans Geisser
Historical Museum - 1912
Local pre- and protohistory, furnishings, crafts and guilds, pictures and documents on contemporary history, history of local trades and industries, textiles, automobiles, arms and armor, weapons, 16th c castle 30532

Kunsthalle Prisma, Grabenstr 6, 9320 Arbon - T: 0714469444, Fax: 0714469444
Fine Arts Museum 30533

Oldtimer-Museum, c/o Oldtimer-Club Saurer, Grabenstr 6, 9320 Arbon - T: 0714468486, Fax: 0718600617, E-mail: r.baer@bsg.ch, Internet: http://www.saureroldtimer.ch. Head: Dr. Rudolf Baer
Science&Tech Museum - 1981 30534

Arlesheim

Ortsmuseum Trotte, Eremitagestr 19, 4144 Arlesheim - T: 0617069555, 0617015656, Fax: 0617069565
Local Museum - 1981 30535

Arosa

Heimatmuseum Schanfigg, Eggahaus, Kirchliweg, 7050 Arosa - T: 0813771731
Local Museum - 1949
Furnishings, agriculture and crafts, weaving, ornithology, wood and stone coll, mining, weapons, hunting, history of winter sports 30536

Ascona

Museo Comunale d'Arte Moderna di Ascona, Via Borgo 34, 6612 Ascona - T: 0917805100, Fax: 0917805102, E-mail: museo@cultura-ascona.ch, Internet: http://www.cultura-ascona.ch. Head: Paola Cerutti
Fine Arts Museum - 1981
Werefkin and Seewald foundations with paintings by Paul Klee, Maurice Utrillo, Franz Marc, Alexej Jawlensky, Alfred Kubin 30537

Museo Epper, Via Albarelle 14, 6612 Ascona - T: 0917911942, Fax: 0917918250, E-mail: info@museoepper.ch, Internet: http://www.museoepper.ch. Head: A. Soldini
Local Museum - 1980 30538

Museum Casa Anatta, Casa Selma und Klarwelt der Seligen, Monte Verità, 6612 Ascona - T: 0917910181, Fax: 0917805135, E-mail: reception@csf-mv.ti-edu.ch, Internet: http://www.csf.mv.ethz.ch. Head: L. Albertini
Special Museum - 1981
Philosophy, theosophy, literature, art, poetry, dance 30539

Assens

Musée de l'Histore Estudiantine, Rue du Moulin, 1042 Assens - T: 0318397655. Head: Dr. Marco A.R. Leutenegger
Historical Museum - 1997 30540

Attiswil

Heimatmuseum, Dorfstr 5, 4536 Attiswil - T: 0326371943, E-mail: gisslerm@post.ch
Local Museum - 1961
Local history, farm implements, craft tools, antiquities 30541

Au, Zürich

Weinbaumuseum am Zürichsee, Vordere Au, 8804 Au, Zürich - T: 017813565, Fax: 017813565, E-mail: info@weinbaumuseum.ch, Internet: http://www.weinbaumuseum.ch. Head: Peter Weissenbach
Agriculture Museum - 1978
Presentation of wine cultivation and the wine grower's tasks, tools and implements, wine storage and subsequent treatment 30542

L'Auberson

Musée Baud, 23 Grand-Rue, 1454 L'Auberson - T: 0244542484, 0244542763, Fax: 0244544166, E-mail: musee-baud@bluewin.ch. Head: Arlette Rustichelli
Music Museum - 1955
Mechanical apparati, musical instruments and automata, hand organs, phonographs 30543

Musée de Musiques, 23 Grand Rue, 1454 L'Auberson - T: 0244542484, Fax: 0244544166, E-mail: musee-baud@bluewin.ch. Head: Arlette Rustichelli
Music Museum 30544

Aubonne

Musée du Bois, En Plan, 1170 Aubonne - T: 0218085183, Fax: 0218086601. Head: Jean-Mario Fischlin
Agriculture Museum - 1977
Wood processing, implements and tools, domestic utensils and farm implements 30545

Augst

Römermuseum Augst, Augusta Raurica, Giebenacherstr 17, 4302 Augst - T: 0618162222, Fax: 0618162261, E-mail: mail@augusta-raurica.ch, Internet: http://www.augusta-raurica.ch. Head: Dr. Beat Rütti
Archaeological Museum / Open Air Museum / Historic Site - 1955/57
Finds and architectural remains from the Roman town Augusta Raurica and from the late Roman fortification, reconstructed Roman house and interiors - archives, restoration laboratory 30546

Avenches

Musée de la Naissance de l'Aviation Suisse, Château d'Avenches, 1580 Avenches - T: 0266751159, Fax: 0266753393. Head: Michel Gilliand
Science&Tech Museum - 1982 30547

Musée Romain, CP 237, 1580 Avenches - T: 0266764200, Fax: 0266764215, E-mail: anne.hochuli@MUSRAV.vd.ch, Internet: http://www.avenches.ch. Head: Dr. Anne Hochuli-Gysel
Archaeological Museum - 1824
Finds from the Roman site Aventicum, Roman ruins, medieval defence tower - library, laboratory 30548

Bad Ragaz

Museum Altes Bad Pfäfers, Pfäfers, 7310 Bad Ragaz - T: 0813027161. Head: Edith Staub
Historical Museum - 1985
Theophrastus Paracelsus, history of the monastery of Pfäfers, balneology 30549

Baden

Elektro Museum, Im Roggebode 19, 5401 Baden - T: 0562002200, Fax: 0562100344, E-mail: museum@regionalwerke.ch, Internet: http://www.regionalwerke.ch. Head: Kurt Scherer
Science&Tech Museum - 1977
Electrotechnical instruments, switchkeys, motors, generator 30550

Hans Trudel-Haus Stiftung, Obere Halde 36, 5400 Baden - T: 0562226418
Fine Arts Museum 30551

Historisches Museum der Stadt Baden, Landvogteischloß, 5401 Baden - T: 0562227574, Fax: 0562227271, E-mail: hist.museum@baden.ag.ch, Internet: http://www.baden-schweiz.ch. Head: Barbara Welter
Historical Museum - 1876
Finds from the Roman colony Aquae Helveticae, pre- and protohist, Roman archaeology, hist of the town, period interiors, weapons, ironwork, glass painting, Dutch tiles, ecclesiastical art, photograph coll, cliché coll, stone coll, industrial culture, hist of balneology, everyday ojects 30552

Kirchenschatz-Museum, Katholische Stadtpfarrkirche, Sakristei, 5400 Baden, mail addr: Rathausgasse 5, 5402 Baden - T: 0562227083. Head: Max Dreier
Religious Arts Museum - 1958
Church treasure, crosses (14th-17th c), monstrance, reliquaries, chandeliers, chalices, ecclesiastical artifacts and vestments (15th-18th c) 30553

Kleines technisches Museum → Elektro Museum

Museum Langmatt Sidney und Jenny Brown, Römerstr 30, 5400 Baden - T: 0562225842, Fax: 0562226227, E-mail: info@langmatt.ch, Internet: http://www.langmatt.ch. Head: Dr. Eva-Maria Preiswerk-Lösel
Fine Arts Museum - 1990
French Impressionism, furniture, clocks, porcelain, silver, ceramics 30554

Schweizer Kindermuseum, Oelrainstr 29, 5400 Baden, mail addr: Postfach 1466, 5401 Baden - T: 0562221444, 0562251919, Fax: 0562226862, Internet: http://kindermuseum.ch. Head: Dr. Roger Kaysel
Special Museum - 1985
Toys and games, education 30555

Städtische Galerie im Amtshimmel, Rathausgasse 3, 5400 Baden - T: 0562008267, Fax: 0562224836, E-mail: galerie.amtshimmel@baden.ag.ch, Internet: http://www.amtshimmel.baden.ch. Head: Stefi Binder
Public Gallery 30556

Stiftung Langmatt Sidney und Jenny Brown → Museum Langmatt Sidney und Jenny Brown

Bäretswil

Textilmaschinenmuseum Neuthal, Ehem. Spinnerei Neuthal, 8344 Bäretswil, mail addr: Postfach 118, 8344 Bäretswil - T: 0523863103. Head: Rico Trümpler
Science&Tech Museum - 1994 30557

Balgach

Heimatmuseum, Steigstr 17, 9436 Balgach - T: 0717221002, Fax: 0717225269
Local Museum - 1969
Local history, farm implements and tools, wine growing, 16th c bulkhead painting, 14th c farmhouse 30558

Balsthal

Heimatmuseum Alt-Falkenstein, Burg, 4710 Balsthal - T: 06226829, 062713224
Local Museum - 1919
Ceramics from local manufactures, peasant furniture and utensils, coins, weapons, 11th c castle 30559

Bardonnex

Musée de l'Ordre de Malte, Commanderie de Compesières, 1257 Bardonnex
Historical Museum - 1973 30560

Basel

Anatomisches Museum Basel, Pestalozzistr 20, 4056 Basel - T: 0612673535, Fax: 0612673939, E-mail: museum-anatomie@unibas.ch, Internet: http://www.unibas.ch/anatomie/museum. Head: Dr. Hugo Kurz

Natural History Museum - 1824
Hist of anatomy, skeleton preparations incl the oldest preserved skeleton (Andreas Vesalius, 1543) embryological preparations and models, Felix Platter, preparations to show how human organs are built 30561

Antikenmuseum Basel und Sammlung Ludwig, Sankt Albangraben 5, 4010 Basel - T: 0612712202, Fax: 0612721861, E-mail: office@antikenmuseumbasel.ch, Internet: http://www.antikenmuseumbasel.ch. Head: Prof. Peter Blome
Archaeological Museum - 1961
Egyptian, Greek, Italian, Etruscan, Roman art, sculptures, ceramics, terracottas, gold jewellery, bronzes - restoration workshops, photo laboratory 30562

Architekturmuseum, Pfluggässlein 3, 4001 Basel - T: 0612611413, Fax: 0612611428, E-mail: am@architekturmuseum.ch, Internet: http://www.architekturmuseum.ch. Head: Dr. Ulrike Jehle-Schulte Strathaus
Special Museum - 1984 30563

Ausstellungsraum Klingental, Kasernenstr 23, 4058 Basel - T: 0616816698. Head: Robert Schiess
Public Gallery 30564

Basler Papiermühle, Schweizerisches Museum für Papier, Schrift und Druck, Sankt-Alban-Tal 37, 4052 Basel - T: 0612729652, Fax: 0612720993, E-mail: info@papiermuseum.ch, Internet: http://www.papiermuseum.ch. Head: Dr. Peter Tschudin, Stefan Meier, Markus Müller
Science&Tech Museum - 1954
Paper manufacturing in various techniques and during diverse periods, other writing materials, history of the different kinds of types, type foundry, typography, printing, book binding, Gallician paper mill (1180/1453), Dr. W.Fr. Tschudin donation - library 30565

Haus zum Kirschgarten, Historisches Museum Basel, Elisabethenstr 27, 4051 Basel, mail addr: Verwaltung, Steinenberg 4, 4051 Basel - T: 0612058600, Fax: 0612058601, E-mail: -historisches.museum@bs.ch, Internet: http://www.historischesmuseumbasel.ch. Head: Dr. Burkard von Roda
Decorative Arts Museum - 1951
18th-19th c interiors, arts and crafts, 17th-19th c costumes, 16th-19th c timepieces, ceramics and porcelain, ironwork, 17th-19th c children's toys 30566

Historisches Museum Basel, Barfüsserkirche, Barfüsserpl 7, 4051 Basel, mail addr: Verwaltung, Steinenberg 4, 4051 Basel - T: 0612058600, Fax: 0612058601, E-mail: historisches.museum@bs.ch, Internet: http://www.historischesmuseumbasel.ch. Head: Dr. Burkard von Roda, Dr. Veronika Gutmann
Historical Museum - 1894
Cultural hist, Gallic, Roman and Alemannic finds, ecclesiastical and profane art, Romanic and late Gothic stone and wood sculptures, big altar by Yvo Striegel, religious goldsmith work, chalices, crosses and monstrances (14th-15th c), tapestry (15th), coins and medals, 15th to 17th c period rooms - library 30567

Jüdisches Museum der Schweiz, Kornhausgasse 8, 4051 Basel - T: 0612619514. Head: Dr. Katia Guth-Dreyfus
Historical Museum - 1966
Jewish life and dogma, Jewish year, documents pertaining to the history of Jews in Switzerland, tombstones from the Jewish cemetery in Basel, ceramics from scriptural times 30568

Karikatur und Cartoon Museum Basel, Sankt-Alban-Vorstadt 28, 4052 Basel, mail addr: Postfach, 4002 Basel - T: 0612711288, 0612711336, Fax: 0612711271, E-mail: cmsbasel@swissonline.ch, cartoonmuseumbasel@cmsbas.ch. Head: Daniel Bolsinger
Fine Arts Museum - 1979
Cartoons, caricatures, Ronald Searle, Chas Addams, Saul Steinberg etc. - library 30569

Kunstforum Bâloise, Aeschengraben 21, 4051 Basel - T: 0612858467
Fine Arts Museum 30570

Kunsthalle Basel, Steinenberg 7, 4051 Basel - T: 0612069900, Fax: 0612069919, E-mail: info@kunsthallebasel.ch, Internet: http://www.kunsthallebasel.ch. Head: Peter Pakesch
Fine Arts Museum 30571

Kunstmuseum Basel, Öffentliche Kunstsammlung Basel, Sankt-Alban-Graben 16, 4010 Basel - T: 0612066262, Fax: 0612066252, E-mail: pressoffice@kunstmuseumbasel.ch, Internet: http://www.kunstmuseumbasel.ch. Head: Dr. Bernhard Mendes Bürgi
Fine Arts Museum - 1661
B. Amerbach coll (16th c), Faeschisches Museum (1823), Birmann coll (1847), Dienast coll (1860), Bachofen-Burckhardt donation (1920), Emanuel Hoffmann donation (1952), gifts from artists and meacenas, art work from the 15th c to the present, works by Konrad Witz and Hans Holbein d.J., German School and Upper Rhine paintings (15th-16th c), Dutch paintings (16th-17th c), German and Swiss paintings (18th-19th c), Classicism, Romanticism, Biedermeier, French naturalism and impressionism, cubism, German expressionism, abstract art, modern European art and Postwar American art 30572

Kupferstichkabinett, Öffentliche Kunstsammlung Basel, Sankt-Alban-Graben 16, 4010 Basel - T: 0612066262, Fax: 0612066252. Head: Dr. Christian Müller
Fine Arts Museum - 1661
One of the world largest coll of prints and drawings, with works originating from the Amerbach Cabinet, which was composed in the second half of the 16th c and important coll by 20th c and contemporary artists, extensive groups are formed by Holbein the Younger, Urs Graf, Martin Schongauer, Hans Baldung, Niklaus Manuel, Albrecht Dürer, Upper Rhenish Goldsmiths and Stained Glass preliminary drawings, sketchbooks and drawings by Paul Cézanne, Cubist collages by Picasso and Braque, drawings by Paul Klee, early drawings from Claes Oldenburg, Joseph Beuys, A.R. Penk and Georg Baselitz, prints, progressive proofs and drawings by Jasper Johns, drawings by Frank Stella and watercolours by Francesco Clemente 30573

Museum der Kulturen Basel, Augustinergasse 2, 4051 Basel, mail addr: Postfach, 4001 Basel - T: 0612665500, Fax: 0612665605, E-mail: info@mkb.ch, Internet: http://www.mkb.ch. Head: Dr. Clara B. Wilpert
Ethnology Museum - 1849
Anthropology and ethnology, Oceania, Southeast Asia, Bali, Indonesia, musical ethnology, East Asia, textiles, South and Central Asia and Tibet, non-European prehist, Precolumbian Art, America, Africa, textiles, European prehist, Swiss ethnography - library, archives, restoration workshop, photo laboratory 30574

Museum für Gegenwartskunst, Öffentliche Kunstsammlung Basel, Sankt-Alban-Rheinweg 60, 4010 Basel - T: 0612066262, 0612728183, Fax: 0612066253, E-mail: info@mgk.basel.ch, Internet: http://www.mkgbasel.ch. Head: Dr. Bernhard Mendes Bürgi
Fine Arts Museum - 1980
Coll of the Öffentliche Kunstsammlung Basel and the Emanuel Hoffmann-Foundation incl works by Beuys, Alighiero e Boetti, Borofsky, Clemente, Cucchi, Disler, Fischli/Weiss, Judd, Kabakov, LeWitt, Mangold, Nauman, Dieter Roth, Ruff, Ryman, J.-F. Schnyder, Stella, Tinguely, Trockel, Twombly, Jeff Wall, Warhol, Zaugg 30575

Museum für Gestaltung Basel, Klosterberg 11, 4051 Basel - T: 0612733595, Fax: 0612733596, E-mail: mfg@museum-gestaltung-basel.ch, Internet: http://www.museum-gestaltung-basel.ch. Head: Matthias Götz, Bruno Halödner
Decorative Arts Museum - 1893 30576

Museum Jean Tinguely, Paul-Sacher-Anlage 1, 4002 Basel - T: 0616819320, Fax: 0616819321, E-mail: infos@tinguely.ch, Internet: http://www.tinguely.ch. Head: Guido Magnaguagno
Fine Arts Museum 30577

Museum Kleines Klingental, Sammlung Basler Münsterskulpturen, Kloster Klingental, Unterer Rheinweg 26, 4058 Basel - T: 0612676625, Fax: 0612676644, E-mail: baslerdenkmalpflege@bs.ch, Internet: http://www.museenbasel.ch. Head: Alexander Schlatter
Fine Arts Museum / Historical Museum / Historic Site - 1939/1997
Original sculptures from the cathedral in Basel (12th-16th c), model of the town, model of the medieval monastery Klingental 30578

Musikmuseum, Historisches Museum Basel, Im Lohnhof 9, 4051 Basel, mail addr: Verwaltung, Steinenberg 4, 4051 Basel - T: 0612058600, Fax: 0612058601, E-mail: historisches.museum@bs.ch, Internet: http://www.musikmuseum.ch. Head: Dr. Veronika Gutmann
Music Museum - 1957/2000
Musical instruments, woodwind and brass wind instruments, organs, keyboard instruments, plucked and bowed string instruments, drums and other percussion instruments 30579

Naturhistorisches Museum Basel, Augustinergasse 2, 4001 Basel, mail addr: Postfach 1048, 4001 Basel - T: 0612665500, Fax: 0612665546, E-mail: nmb@bs.ch, Internet: http://www.nmb.bs.ch. Head: Dr. Christian A. Meyer
Natural History Museum - 1821
Anthropology, entomology (ants and coleoptera), mineralogy, fossils, mammals, zoology (mammals, ornithology, acarology, herpetology), Jurassic ammonites, Tertiary molluscs, Western European center for Ocean drilling program micropaleontological reference coll - library, bookbindery, photo and preparation laboratories 30580

Öffentliche Bibliothek der Universität Basel, Schönbeinstr 18-20, 4056 Basel - T: 0612673111, Fax: 0612673103, E-mail: sekretariat-ub@unibas.ch, Internet: http://www.ub.unibas.ch. Head: Hannes Hug
Library with Exhibitions / University Museum 30581

Pharmazie-Historisches Museum der Universität Basel, Apothekenmuseum, Totengässlein 3, 4051 Basel - T: 0612649111, Fax: 0612649112, E-mail: info@pharmaziemuseum.ch, Internet: http://www.pharmaziemuseum.ch. Head: Dr. Michael Kessler
Special Museum - 1924
Obsolete medicaments from Europe, Asia and Africa, 16th-19th c laboratories, microscopes, healing-amulets, 18th c apothecary's interiors, receptacles, graphics - historic library 30582

Puppenhausmuseum, Steinenvorstadt 1, 4051 Basel - T: 0612259595, Fax: 0612259596, Internet: http://www.puppenhausmuseum.ch. Head: Laura Sinanovitch
Special Museum - 1998
Teddy bears, grocery shops, doll's houses, dolls and miniatures to scale (1:12) 30583

Sammlungen der Schule für Gestaltung Basel, Spalenvorstadt 2, 4003 Basel - T: 0612613006, Fax: 0612616941, Internet: http://www.sfgbasel.ch. Head: Dorothea Flury
Special Museum / Library with Exhibitions - 1893 30584

Schweizer Filmmuseum, Blauenstr 49, 4054 Basel - T: 0616415224. Head: Dieter Dürrenmatt
Special Museum 30585

Schweizerisches Feuerwehrmuseum, Kornhausgasse 18, 4003 Basel - T: 0612681557, Fax: 0612681559, E-mail: fw-museum@pmd.ch, Internet: http://www.berufsfeuerwehr.basel.ch. Head: Hanspeter Frey
Science&Tech Museum - 1957
History and technical development of fire fighting from the 13th c to the present, Lützelhof (12th c monastery) - library 30586

Schweizerisches Sportmuseum (Swiss Sports Museum), Missionsstr 28, 4055 Basel - T: 0612611221, Fax: 0612611247, E-mail: info@swiss-sports-museum.ch, Internet: http://www.swiss-sports-museum.ch. Head: Dr. Max Triet
Special Museum - 1945
Development of all kinds of sports from all over the world, rare sports equipment, posters and pictorial documents - library, picture archives 30587

Skulpturhalle Basel, Abguss-Sammlung des Antikenmuseums, Mittlere Str 17, 4056 Basel - T: 0612615245, Fax: 0612615042, E-mail: info@skulpturhalle.ch, Internet: http://www.skulpturhalle.ch. Head: Dr. Tomas Lochman
Archaeological Museum - 1849
Casts of Greek and Roman sculptures, special exhibition of copies from all intact sculptures and fragments of the Parthenon 30588

Baulmes

Musée du Vieux-Baulmes, Rue du Theu, 1446 Baulmes - T: 0244591372
Local Museum - 1978 30589

Bazenheid

Toggenburger Schmiede- und Handwerksmuseum, Wilerstr 69, 9602 Bazenheid - T: 0719311029, 0719110541. Head: Rupert Meier
Science&Tech Museum - 1990 30590

Bellach

Dorfmuseum Bellach, Dorfstr 3, 4512 Bellach - T: 0326181396
Local Museum - 1974 30591

Bellinzona

Centro d'Arte Contemporanea Ticino, Via Tamaro 3, 6500 Bellinzona - T: 0918254072, Fax: 0918254085, E-mail: cacticino@hotmail.com, Internet: http://www.cacticino.net. Head: Mario Casanova Salvioni
Fine Arts Museum 30592

Civica Galleria d'Arte Villa dei Cedri, Piazza San Biagio 9, 6500 Bellinzona - T: 0918218518/20, Fax: 0918218546, E-mail: museo@villacedri.ch, Internet: http://www.villacedri.ch. Head: Matteo Bianchi
Fine Arts Museum 30593

Montebello Castle, Archaeological Museum, Salita ad Artore, 6500 Bellinzona - T: 0918251342, Fax: 0918253817, E-mail: ett@www.tourismo-ticino.ch, Internet: http://www.bellinzona.ch
Historical Museum 30594

Museo di Castelgrande, Historical Museum, Collina di San Michele, 6500 Bellinzona - T: 0918252131, 0918258145, Fax: 0918252131, E-mail: info@bellinzonaturismo.ch, Internet: http://www.bellinzona.ch
Local Museum - 1991
Archaeology, especially Roman finds, local history, 13th c citadel 30595

Museo Villa dei Cedri, Piazza San Biagio 5, 6501 Bellinzona - T: 0918218518
Fine Arts Museum 30596

Belmont-sur-Lausanne

Musée d'Art Contemporain et Moderne, Fondation Deutsch, 12 Rte Mont de Lavaux, 1092 Belmont-sur-Lausanne - T: 0217283625, Fax: 0217289917. Head: Dr. J. Deutsch, Prof. Dr. H. Deutsch
Fine Arts Museum 30597

Belp

Ortsmuseum Kefiturm, Rubigenstr, 3123 Belp - T: 0318182222, Fax: 0318182299
Local Museum - 1994 30598

Bennwil

Dorfmuseum, Hauptstr 22, 4431 Bennwil
Local Museum - 1972
Local history, paintings, tools, implements for textile manufacture, memorabilia of the poet Carl Spitteler, minerals from the region 30599

Bergün

Ortsmuseum, Hauptstr 113, 7482 Bergün - T: 0814071277
Local Museum - 1991 30600

Beringen

Ortsmuseum Beringen, 8222 Beringen - T: 0526872424
Local Museum - 1950
Local hist, farm implements, domestic utensils, hemp and flax manufacture, scales, coll, painters Alexander and Elise Wolf 30601

Berlingen

Adolf-Dietrich-Haus, Seestr 26, 8267 Berlingen - T: 0527611333, Fax: 0527611333, E-mail: ursoskarkeller@bluewin.ch, Internet: http://www.kunstmuseum.ch/sammlung/dietrich/Dietr4.htw. Head: Urs Oskar Keller
Fine Arts Museum - 1958
Memorabilia of the painter Adolf Dietrich (1877-1957), original paintings and reproductions, originally furnished room 30602

Bern

Antikensammlung, Länggass-Quartier, Hallerstr 12, 3012 Bern, mail addr: c/o Institut für Klassische Archäologie, Länggasstr 10, 3012 Bern - T: 0316318992, Fax: 0316314905, E-mail: lilian.raselli@arch.unibe.ch, Internet: http://www.klassischearchaeologie.unibe.ch. Head: Prof. Dietrich Willers
Archaeological Museum - 1974 30603

Bernisches Historisches Museum, Helvetiapl 5, 3005 Bern - T: 0313507711, Fax: 0313507799, E-mail: info@bhm.ch, Internet: http://www.bhm.ch. Head: Peter Jezler, Prof. Dr. Felix Müller
Historical Museum / Ethnology Museum / Local Museum / Archaeological Museum - 1881
History and applied arts, textiles, national costumes, military items, ceramics, fayence, paintings, graphics, sculptures, glass painting, folklore, treasures from Lausanne cathedral and from monastery Königsfelden, Dr. Albert Kocher porcelain, Islamic coll, American Indian coll, ethnographical coll, coins and medals - library, restoration and photo laboratory 30604

Blasinstrumentensammlung Karl Burri, Morillonstr 11, 3007 Bern - T: 0313718378. Head: Karl Burri
Music Museum - 1964 30605

Einstein-Haus, Kramgasse 49, 3011 Bern, mail addr: Postfach 638, 3000 Bern 8 - T: 0313120091, Fax: 0313120041, E-mail: webmaster@einstein-bern.ch., Internet: http://www.einstein-bern.ch.. Head: Prof. Hermann Bürki
Special Museum - 1979
Memorabilia of the physicist Albert Einstein, photos and documents 30606

Forum für Medien und Gestaltung → Kornhausforum

Fotogalerie, Rathausgasse 2, 3011 Bern - T: 0313114335, Fax: 0313114335, E-mail: kontakt@stadtgalerie.ch, Internet: http://www.stadtgalerie.ch. Head: Beate Engel
Public Gallery
Photography, Video 30607

Kornhausforum, Kornhauspl 18, 3000 Bern 7 - T: 0313129110, Fax: 0313129113, E-mail: forum@kornhaus.org, Internet: http://www.kornhaus.org. Head: Dr. Claudia Rosiny, Peter Eichenberger
Local Museum 30608

Kunsthalle Bern, Helvetiapl 1, 3005 Bern - T: 0313510031, Fax: 0313525385, E-mail: kunsthalle@bluewin.ch, Internet: http://www.kunsthallebern.ch. Head: Dr. Bernhard Fibicher
Public Gallery - 1918 30609

Kunstmuseum Bern, Hodlerstr 8-12, 3011 Bern 7 - T: 0313280944, Fax: 0313280955, E-mail: kmbadmin@kmb.unibe.ch, Internet: http://www.kunstmuseumbern.ch. Head: Dr. Felix A. Baumann
Fine Arts Museum - 1809
European, especially Swiss paintings, sculptures and graphics from 14th c till nowadays; Italian masters of the 14-16th c (Daddi, Gaddi, Fra Angelico), Cubism, Paul-Klee-coll - library 30610

Martin-Lauterburg-Stiftung, Schloss Jegenstorf, c/o Kunstmuseum Bern, Hodlerstr 8, 3000 Bern 7 - T: 0313280944, Fax: 0313280955, E-mail: kmbadmin@kmb.unibe.ch, Internet: http://www.kunstmuseumbern.ch. Head: Dr. Ralf Beil
Fine Arts Museum - 1974 30611

Museum für Kommunikation, Helvetiastr 16, 3000 Bern 6 - T: 0313575555, Fax: 0313575599, E-mail: communication@mfk.ch, Internet: http://www.mfk.ch. Head: Dr. Thomas Dominik Meier
Special Museum - 1907
Hist of postal services, philately, transport, communications and media culture 30612

HISTORISCHES MUSEUM BASEL

Steinenberg 4, CH-4051 Basel
T +41 (0)61 205 86 00 , F +41 (0)61 205 86 01
www.historischesmuseumbasel.ch

BARFÜSSERKIRCHE
Barfüsserplatz
Mon, Wed–Sun 10–17 h

HAUS ZUM KIRSCHGARTEN
Elisabethenstrasse 27/29
Tues, Thur, Fri, Sun 10–17 h,
Wed 10–20 h, Sat 13–17 h

MUSIKMUSEUM
Im Lohnhof 9
Tues, Wed, Fri 14–19 h,
Thur 14–20 h, Sun 11–16 h

KUTSCHENMUSEUM
Brüglingen/St. Jakob
Wed, Sat, Sun 14–17 h

Naturhistorisches Museum der Burgergemeinde Bern, Bernastr 15, 3005 Bern - T: 0313507111, Fax: 0313507499, E-mail: contact@nmbe.unibe.ch, Internet: http://www.nmbe.ch. Head: Prof. Dr. Marcel Güntert
Natural History Museum - 1832
Geology, mineralogy, palaeontology, vertebrates and invertebrates, largest diorama show in Europe - library, archives 30613

Pferdekuranstalt, Länggass-Quartier, Bus 12 Endstation, 3012 Bern, mail addr: Länggasstr 124, 3012 Bern - T: 0316312243, Fax: 0316312620, E-mail: urs.schatzmann@knp.unibe.ch. Head: Prof. Urs Schatzmann
Special Museum - 1995
Farrier's workshop, horseshoes, horse's hospital 30614

Psychiatrie-Museum, c/o Universitäre Psychiatrische Dienste, Pfründerhaus, 3000 Bern 60 - T: 0319309622, Fax: 0319309404, Internet: http://www.cx.uni.be.ch/puk/calture.html. Head: Wolfgang Böker
Special Museum / University Museum - 1993
Psychiatry 30615

Schweizerische Landesbibliothek, Hallwylstr 15, 3003 Bern - T: 0313228911, Fax: 0313228463, E-mail: IZ-Helvetica@slb.admin.ch, Internet: http://www.snl.ch. Head: Dr. J.-F. Jauslin
Library with Exhibitions 30616

Schweizerische Theatersammlung, Schanzenstr 15, 3008 Bern - T: 0313015252, Fax: 0313028525, E-mail: martin.dreier@sts.unibe.ch. Head: Prof. Martin Dreier
Performing Arts Museum - 1927
Documentation of theatrical hist in Switzerland, designs of stage pictures and costumes, masks, marionettes and costumes, memorabilia of famous persons - library 30617

Schweizerisches Alpines Museum, Helvetiapl 4, 3005 Bern - T: 0313510434, Fax: 0313510751, E-mail: info@alpinesmuseum.ch, Internet: http://www.alpinesmuseum.ch. Head: Dr. Urs Kneubühl
Historical Museum / Natural History Museum - 1903/05
Development of equipment for mountaineering, hist of mountaineering, map coll and hist of cartography, relief coll, folklore of the alps, coll of photographs, touristic posters - library 30618

Schweizerisches Schützenmuseum, Bernastr 5, 3000 Bern - T: 0313510127, Fax: 0313510804. Head: Ferdinand Piller
Historical Museum - 1885
Weapons, ammunition, trophies, documentation about the Swiss rifle associations 30619

Stadtgalerie Bern, Rathausgasse 22, 3011 Bern - T: 0313114335, Fax: 0313114335
Fine Arts Museum 30620

Berneck

Haus zum Torggel, Weierbüntstr 2, 9442 Berneck - T: 0717474477, Fax: 0717474488, E-mail: gemeindeamt@berneck.ch. Head: Jakob Schegg
Historical Museum 30621

Radiomuseum, Kirchgasse 3, 9442 Berneck - T: 0717441838
Science&Tech Museum 30622

Beromünster

Heimatmuseum und Buchdruckerstube, Schloß, 6215 Beromünster - T: 0419321030
Local Museum / Science&Tech Museum - 1928
Reconstructed printing room of Helias Helye (1470), prehistorical finds, furnished period rooms, stained glass, ecclesiastical folk art, jewelry, old card games and toys, craftmen's tools and farm implements, music room and poet's room including memorabilia on poets from Münster, 12th c tower 30623

Kirchenschatz des Chorherrenstiftes, Stiftskirche, 6215 Beromünster - T: 0419303585
Religious Arts Museum - 1981
Medieval ecclesiastical art, 7-15th c goldsmith work, early and late medieval textiles, baroque goldsmith work, Baroque embroidery and silks 30624

Stiftung Dr. Edmund Müller, Haus zum Dolder, 6215 Beromünster - T: 0419172464, 0419301626, E-mail: info@hauszumdolder.ch, Internet: http://www.hauszumdolder.ch. Head: Robert Galliker-Tönz, Dr. Helene Büchler-Mattmann
Decorative Arts Museum / Fine Arts Museum - 1969
Art and decorative arts, fayences, painted glass, Flühli-glass, furniture, tin, jewelry, graphics, religious art, portaits, medical history - library 30625

Bex

Mine de Sel du Bouillet, Le Bouillet, 1887 Bex - T: 0244630330, Fax: 0244630332, E-mail: info@mines.ch, Internet: http://www.mines.ch. Head: P. Goin
Science&Tech Museum / Historic Site
Oldest Swiss salt mine (16th c) 30626

Musée du Vieux-Bex, Pl du Marché, 1880 Bex - T: 0244633710, Fax: 0244634426. Head: P. Zwicky
Local Museum - 1975
Local history, documents, tools, costumes, paintings - library 30627

Biberist

Schlößchen Vorder Bleichenberg Biberist, Niesenstr 9, 4562 Biberist - T: 0326722825. Head: Grety Zimmermann
Association with Coll / Fine Arts Museum 30628

Biel, Kanton Bern

Kunsthaus Centre PasquArt, Seevorstadt 71-75, 2502 Biel, Kanton Bern - T: 0323225586, Fax: 0323226181, E-mail: info@pasquart.ch, Internet: http://pasquart.ch. Head: Dolores Denaro
Fine Arts Museum - 1990 30629

Museum Neuhaus, Schüsspromenade 26, 2501 Biel, Kanton Bern - T: 0323287030/31, Fax: 0323287035, E-mail: info@mn-giel.ch, Internet: http://www.mn-giel.ch. Head: Dr. Pietro Scandola
Local Museum - 1975
Watercolour of plants and animals, Karl and Robert Walser coll, regional daily and industrial hist, cinematographic coll 30630

Museum Omega, Jakob-Stämpfli-Str 96, 2500 Biel, Kanton Bern 4 - T: 0323439211, Fax: 0323439870, E-mail: marco.richon@omega.ch, Internet: http://www.omega.ch. Head: Marco Richon
Special Museum
History of clock manufacture 30631

Museum Schwab, Museum für Urgeschichte und Archäologie, Seevorstadt 50, 2502 Biel, Kanton Bern - T: 0323227603, Fax: 0323233768, E-mail: muschwab@bielstar.ch, Internet: http://www.bielstar.ch/culture/musee. Head: Madeleine Betschart, Fabienne Rouvinez
Archaeological Museum / Historical Museum - 1865
Neolithic, Bronze Age, Iron Age and Roman (especially Petinesca) finds from the environ of the Bieler See, Oberst Friedrich Schwab lake-dwelling coll - library 30632

Binn

Regionalmuseum Binn, 3996 Binn - T: 0279714620, 0279714550
Local Museum 30633

Binningen

Monteverdi Car Collection, Schweizer Automuseum, Oberwiler Str 20, 4102 Binningen - T: 0614214545, Fax: 0614214524. Head: Paul Berger
Science&Tech Museum
Complete coll of production models by Peter Monteverdi 30634

Ortsmuseum, Holeerain 20, 4102 Binningen - T: 0614255151, Fax: 0614255208, Internet: http://www.binningen.ch
Local Museum - 1987
Carnival-masks by artists, pin factory 30635

Birmensdorf

Dorfmuseum, Mühlemattstr 7, 8903 Birmensdorf - T: 017372711
Local Museum - 1976 30636

Birr

Dorfmuseum, Im Dorfzentrum, 5242 Birr - T: 0564440111, Fax: 0564448639, E-mail: gdebirr@brugg-online.ch, Internet: http://www.brugg-online.ch
Local Museum - 1980 30637

Birsfelden

Birsfelder Museum, Schulstr 29, 4127 Birsfelden - T: 0613114830, Internet: http://www.birsfelden.ch
Local Museum / Folklore Museum / Public Gallery
Local hist and art 30638

Bischofszell

Kirchenschatz Sankt Pelagius Kirche, Schottengasse 2, 9220 Bischofszell - T: 0714221580, Fax: 0714221656
Religious Arts Museum - 1968
Church treasure, including chalices, chandeliers, monstrances, late Renaissance, baroque and rococo reliquaries from Germany and Switzerland, St. Pelagius Church (14th c) 30639

Museum Bischofszell, Marktgasse 46, 9220 Bischofszell - T: 0714223891. Head: Beat Frei
Local Museum - 1925
Local hist, documents, documents pertaining to the Reformation period, Gothic to 20th c interiors, crafts and guilds, cartography from the 10th-20th c 30640

Bönigen

Dorfmuseum, Interlaknerstr 2, 3806 Bönigen
Local Museum - 1985 30641

Boll

Ortsmuseum Vechingen, Bei der Kirche, 3067 Boll - T: 0318393537
Local Museum - 1981 30642

Bolligen

Ortsstube, Kirchpl, 3065 Bolligen - T: 0319210615
Local Museum - 1976 30643

Bosco/Gurin

Walserhaus Gurin, 6685 Bosco/Gurin - T: 0917541819. Head: Leonhard Tomamichel
Folklore Museum - 1936
16th c wooden house, local hist artifacts, furnishings, textiles, folk costumes, tools 30644

Boswil

Stiftung Künstlerhaus Boswil, Flurstr 21, 5623 Boswil - T: 0566661285, Fax: 0566663032, E-mail: arts.boswil@spectraweb.ch, Internet: http://www.meet.ch/arts.boswil. Head: Pedro Zimmermann
Fine Arts Museum 30645

Bottmingen

Dorfmuseum, Therwiler Str 16-18, 4103 Bottmingen - T: 0614215452
Local Museum - 1978
Local history, farm implements, tools, carriages, workshops, domestic utensils, documents and pictures, wine-vault and distillery 30646

Boudry

Musée de l'Areuse, Près de l'arrêt du tram, 2017 Boudry - T: 0328461916, E-mail: ph.beguin@bluewin.ch. Head: Pierre Henri Béguin
Local Museum - 1866
Local history, ethnography, prehistoric finds, mammals and birds of the region, documents, archaeology, arms, numismatics 30647

Bourg-Saint-Pierre

Musée et Trésor de l'Hospice, Hospice du Grand-Saint-Bernard, 1946 Bourg-Saint-Pierre - T: 7871236, Fax: 78712367871107. Head: Jacques Clerc
Historical Museum - 1987/89 30648

Brè sopra Lugano

Museo Wilhelm Schmid, Contrada Pro 22, 6979 Brè sopra Lugano - T: 0918007201, 0919716693, Fax: 0918007497, E-mail: cultura@lugano.ch, Internet: http://www.lugano.ch. Head: Dr. Rudy Chiappini
Fine Arts Museum 30649

Bremgarten (Aargau)

Kirchenschatz, Pfarrgasse 4, 5620 Bremgarten (Aargau) - T: 05751454
Religious Arts Museum - 1970
Monstrances, chalices, vessels, chandeliers, crosses, statues and wood sculptures, reliquaries and reliquary statues, missals, pictures and paintings 30650

Brienz, Bern

Ausstellung der Kantonalen Schnitzerschule, 3855 Brienz, Bern - T: 0339521751, Fax: 0339521750. Head: Urban Hauser
Decorative Arts Museum - 1884
Wood carvings 30651

Ausstellung der Schweizerischen Geigenbauschule, 3855 Brienz, Bern - T: 0339511861, Fax: 0339521750, E-mail: Geigenbauschule@bluewin.ch
Music Museum - 1944
String instruments and the manufacture of violins, tools, documents, Swiss musical instruments (18th-20th c), Prof. Dr. H. Hanselmann donation of violins 30652

Schweizerisches Freilichtmuseum für ländliche Kultur, Ballenberg, 3855 Brienz, Bern - T: 0339521030, Fax: 0339521039, E-mail: info@ballenberg.ch, Internet: http://www.ballenberg.ch. Head: Walter Trauffer
Open Air Museum - 1978
Peasant architecture and interiors of dwelling houses and outhouses, building materials, construction types, furnishings, tools and implements, ornaments, inscriptions, paintings, farm animals - library 30653

Brig

Museum im Stockalperschloß, Alte Simplonstr 28, 3900 Brig - T: 0279232567, Fax: 0279224159. Head: Arthur Huber
Local Museum - 1970
Local history documents, silver, works of art, ethnography, 17th c castle - library 30654

Brittnau

Ortsmuseum Brittnau, Gemeindehaus, 4805 Brittnau - T: 0627511207, 0627519879
Local Museum 30655

Broc

Electrobroc, Fabrique, Centrale Electrique, 1636 Broc - T: 0269211537, Fax: 0263526580, E-mail: Electrobroc@EEF.ch, Internet: http://www.electrobroc.ch
Science&Tech Museum - 1990
Electricity - production, transport, distribution - play exhibition 30656

Brüglingen

Kutschenmuseum, Historisches Museum Basel, Beim Botanischen Garten, 4052 Brüglingen, mail addr: Verwaltung, Steinenberg 4, 4051 Basel - T: 0612058600, Fax: 0612058601, E-mail: - historisches.museum@bs.ch, Internet: http://www.historischesmuseumbasel.ch. Head: Dr. Burkard von Roda
Historical Museum 30657

Mühlenmuseum, Brüglingerstr 6, 4052 Brüglingen - T: 0612711288, 0613117214
Science&Tech Museum - 1961 30658

Brugg

Heimatmuseum, Altes Zeughaus, Untere Hofstatt 23, 5200 Brugg - T: 0564414742, Fax: 0564414742, E-mail: info@brugg.ch, Internet: http://www.stadt-brugg.ch/leben/heimatmuseum.htm
Local Museum - 1963
Local hist, weapons, domestic utensils, pewter items, weights, fire engines, photos 30659

Vindonissa-Museum, Aargauische Kantonsarchäologie, Museumsstr 1, 5200 Brugg - T: 0564412184, Fax: 0564624815, E-mail: vindonissa@ag.ch, Internet: http://www.ag.ch/vindonissa. Head: René Hänggi
Archaeological Museum - 1912
Roman finds, archaeological finds from the camp Vindonissa, weapons, tools, coins, ceramics, documentation about the excavations, erotic reliefs - library 30660

Bubikon

Hasenmuseum, Dorfstr 20, 8608 Bubikon, mail addr: c/o Gertrud Pürro, Postfach 13, 8608 Bubikon - T: 0552432900, Fax: 0552432909, E-mail: hasenmuseum@ymail.ch, Internet: http://www.hasenmuseum.ch. Head: Gertrud Pürro
Special Museum - 1991
More than 4 500 exhibits on the subject 'rabbit', hare, (various objects made from a range of different materials), toys, books, jewellery, dishes, pictures, rare objects from the 20s and 30s 30661

Johannitermuseum, Ritterhaus, 8608 Bubikon - T: 0552433974, Fax: 0552433977, E-mail: ritterhaus@active.ch, Internet: http://www.ritterhaus.ch. Head: Hans-Peter Frei
Religious Arts Museum / Historical Museum - 1936
Hist of ecclesiastical orders of knighthood, esp Johanniter, 12th-18th c weapons, 12th-16th c architecture and interiors - library 30662

Buch

Freilichtmuseum Säge Buch, Biberbrücke, 8263 Buch. Head: Arthur Meister
Open Air Museum - 1976 30663

Buchegg

Heimatmuseum Bucheggberg, Schloss, 4586 Buchegg - T: 0319718318, Fax: 0319718318, E-mail: peterlaett@bluewin.ch
Local Museum - 1956
Farm implements, peasant interiors, tools, archaeological finds from the area, 17th c prison tower 30664

Buchs, Zürich

Quarzsandbergwerk-Museum, c/o Restaurant Bergwerk, Kraehstelstr 29, 8107 Buchs, Zürich - T: 018441750
Science&Tech Museum 30665

Bülach

Ortsmuseum, Brunngasse 1, 8186 Bülach - T: 018610716
Local Museum - 1984 30666

Büren an der Aare

Heimatmuseum Spittel, Spittelgasse 36, 3294 Büren an der Aare - T: 0323512707, 0323512130, Fax: 0323512753
Local Museum - 1975
Local history, archaeological finds, coins, coats of arms, weights, domestic utensils, chandeliers, carpenter's and weaver's implements and tools, 15th c circular wall building - library 30667

Bürglen

Tell-Museum, Postpl, 6463 Bürglen - T: 0418704155, Fax: 0418710702, E-mail: info@tellmuseum.ch, Internet: http://www.tellmuseum.ch. Head: Thomas Christen
Historical Museum - 1966
Documentation on Wilhelm Tell and the Tell games 30668

Bütschwil

Ortsmuseum, Eichelstock-Pl, 9606 Bütschwil - T: 0719831323
Local Museum - 1983 30669

Bützberg

Bauernmuseum im Holz, Thunstetten, 4922 Bützberg - T: 0629632507
Agriculture Museum 30670

Bulle

Musée Gruérien, Rue de la Condémine 25, 1630 Bulle 1, mail addr: CP 204, 1630 Bulle - T: 0269127260, Fax: 0269127254, E-mail: Museegruerien@fr.ch, Internet: http://www.bulle.ch/culture/musee.htm. Head: Denis Buchs
Local Museum - 1917
Hist of Gruyère and neighbouring areas, folk art, ecclesiastical art, ethnography, exhibition about cheese production, Swiss and French paintings, numismatics, memorabilia on the writer Victor Tissot - library 30671

Buonas

Heimatmuseum Seehof, Dersbachstr, 6343 Buonas - T: 0417902112
Local Museum - 1965 30672

Burgdorf

Museum für Völkerkunde, Im Schloss, 3402 Burgdorf - T: 0344230214, Fax: 0344230448, Internet: http://www.schloss-burgdorf-ch. Head: Andrea Mordasini, Erika Burki
Ethnology Museum - 1909
Ethnography from nearly everywhere outside Europe 30673

Schlossmuseum, Schloss, 3402 Burgdorf, mail addr: PF 153, 3402 Burgdorf - T: 0344230214, Fax: 0344230214, E-mail: schlossmuseum@schloss-burgdorf.ch, Internet: http://www.schloss-burgdorf.ch. Head: Heinz Fankhauser
Local Museum / Historic Site - 1886
Historical coll from Emmental: prehist, militaria, crafts, agriculture, cheese dairy, potter's workshop, picture coll, memorial room to Heinrich Pestalozzi (1947-1827) und 'General' Johann August Sutter (1803-1880), coins and seals, medieval castle - library 30674

Schweizerisches Zentrum für Volkskultur, Kornhausgasse 16, 3400 Burgdorf, mail addr: Postfach 810, 3401 Burgdorf - T: 0344231010, Fax: 0344231013, E-mail: kornhaus-burgdorf@bluewin.ch, Internet: http://www.kornhaus-burgdorf.ch. Head: Cornelia Weber
Ethnology Museum / Folklore Museum / Music Museum
Hist of folk music, costumes, phonographs, grammophones, various musical instruments and books 30675

Busswil (Thurgau)

Greb Jagd-Museum, Hauptstr, 9572 Busswil (Thurgau) - T: 0719232121
Special Museum 30676

Buus

Ständerhaus, Rickenbacher Str, 4463 Buus - T: 0618412911. Head: Werner Graf
Historical Museum - 1973 30677

La Caquerelle

Musée du Mont-Repais, Hôtel de la Caquerelle, 2954 La Caquerelle - T: 0324266656, Fax: 0324267317. Head: Jacques Bourquard
Local Museum - 1993 30678

Carouge

Musée de Carouge, 2 Pl de Sardaigne, 1227 Carouge - T: 0223423383, Fax: 0223423381, E-mail: musee@carouge.ch, Internet: http://www.carouge.ch. Head: Jean M. Marquis
Local Museum - 1984
Faience from Carouge (1800-1930) 30679

Caslano

Museo della Pesca, Via Campagna, 6987 Caslano, mail addr: CP 254, 6987 Caslano - T: 0916066363, E-mail: musmalc@bluewin.ch, Internet: http://www.tinet.ch/malcantone/. Head: Franco Chiesa
Special Museum - 1993 30680

Schokoland Alprose, Via Rompada 36, 6987 Caslano, mail addr: c/o Chocolat Alprose, CP 165, 6987 Caslano - T: 0916118856, Fax: 0916065185, E-mail: info@alprose.ch, Internet: http://www.alprose.ch. Head: Paul Nussbaumer
Special Museum 30681

Castagnola

Fondazione Thyssen-Bornemisza, Villa Favorita, 6976 Castagnola - T: 0919721741, 0919716152, Fax: 0919716151, E-mail: ftbch@swissonline.ch. Head: Dr. Hans A. Lüthy
Public Gallery - 1948
Paintings and water-colours of European and American artists (19th-20th c) 30682

Museo delle Culture Extraeuropee, Via Cortivo 24, 6976 Castagnola - T: 0918007201, 0919717353, Fax: 0918007497, E-mail: cultura@lugano.ch, Internet: http://www.lugano.ch/cultura. Head: Dr. Rudy Chiappini
Ethnology Museum - 1989 30683

Castaneda

Collezione Preistorica, Scuola Elementare, 6540 Castaneda - T: 0918271381
Archaeological Museum 30684

Cevio

Museo di Valmaggia, Palazza Franzoni e Casa Respini-Moretti, 6678 Cevio - T: 0917541340, 0917542368, E-mail: museovm@bluewin.ch. Head: Prof. Bruno Donati
Archaeological Museum / Historical Museum - 1963 30685

Le Châble

Musée de Bagnes, 1934 Le Châble - T: 0277761525
Local Museum - 1985 30686

Musée du Vieux-Pays, Villette, 1934 Le Châble - T: 0277761386
Local Museum - 1977 30687

Cham

Ziegelei-Museum, Riedstr 9, 6330 Cham, mail addr: Postfach 5343, 6330 Cham, Zug - T: 0417413624, Fax: 0417400155, E-mail: tonezzer@ziegelei-museum.ch, Internet: http://www.ziegelei-museum.ch. Head: Jürg Goll
Science&Tech Museum - 1982
Brickworks - library 30688

Chamoson

Musée Suisse de Spéléologie, Au-dessus du Village, 1955 Chamoson - T: 0273063581, Fax: 0273063581, E-mail: jeff@lestaupes.ch, Internet: http://www.chamoson.ch/speleo. Head: Jean-François Crittin
Special Museum - 1994 30689

Charmey (Gruyère)

Musée du Pays et Val de Charmey, Pl de la Télécabine, 1637 Charmey (Gruyère) - T: 0269272447, Fax: 0269272395. Head: Patrick Rudaz
Local Museum - 1991
Folk art, farming, cheese production 30690

Château-d'Oex

Musée d'Architecture, Châlet de l'Etambeau, Rte du Mont, 1837 Château-d'Oex - T: 0269246914, Fax: 0269246914
Fine Arts Museum 30691

Musée du Vieux-Pays d'Enhaut, Bossons, 1660 Château-d'Oex - T: 0269246520, Fax: 0269246914
Folklore Museum - 1922
16-19th c folk art and interiors, cheese-dairy, smithy, tools, paintings, decorative arts, J.J. Hauswirth 30692

Châtel-Saint-Denis

Musée du Bois, Grand-Rue, 1618 Châtel-Saint-Denis
Special Museum 30693

La Chaux-de-Fonds

Musée des Beaux-Arts, 33 Rue des Musées, 2300 La Chaux-de-Fonds - T: 0329130444, Fax: 0329136193, E-mail: Edmond.Charrière@ne.ch. Head: Edmond Charrière
Fine Arts Museum - 1864
19th-20th c paintings and sculpture, Léopold Robert room (1794-1835), Coll René and Madeleine Junod (Liotard, Constable, Delacroix, Matisse etc.) 30694

Musée d'Histoire, 31 Rue des Musées, 2300 La Chaux-de-Fonds - T: 0329135010, Fax: 0329134445, E-mail: museehistoire.vch@ne.ch, Internet: http://www.chaux-de-fonds.ch. Head: Sylviane Musy-Ramseyer
Historical Museum - 1876
Local history, 17th-18th c interiors, 19th c weapons, coins, medals, pictures, glass, furniture - museum library 30695

Musée d'Histoire Naturelle, 63 Av Léopold-Robert, 2300 La Chaux-de-Fonds - T: 0329133976, Fax: 0329133976, E-mail: mhnc@ne.ch, Internet: http://www.mhnc.ch. Head: Marcel S. Jacquat
Natural History Museum - 1845
Zoology, mammalogy, ornithology, herpetology, botany, paleontology, geology, entomology, dioramas, marine biology, Angolan zoology, history of sciences - laboratory, auditorium 30696

Musée International d'Horlogerie, Institut l'Homme et le Temps, 29 Rue des Musées, 2301 La Chaux-de-Fonds 1 - T: 0329676861, Fax: 0329676889, E-mail: mih.vch@ne.ch, Internet: http://www.mih.ch. Head: Dr. Ludwig Oechslin
Science&Tech Museum - 1902
History of timekeeping, coll of clocks and automatons, musical clocks and chronometres since the 16th c - library, workshop 30697

Musée Paysan et Artisanal, 148 Crêtets, 2300 La Chaux-de-Fonds - T: 0329267189, Fax: 0329267139, E-mail: - musee.paysan.artisanal@ne.ch, Internet: http://www.chaux-de-fonds.ch/fr/culture/musees.htm. Head: Diane Skartsounis Schwab
Local Museum - 1971
Local hist, farm and crafts, interiors, bakehouse, furnished rooms, smithy incl tools and implements, watchmaker's shop 30698

Chur

Bündner Kunstmuseum, Postpl, 7002 Chur - T: 0812572868, Fax: 0812572172, E-mail: info@bkm.gr.ch, Internet: http://www.bkm.gr.ch. Head: Dr. Beat Stutzer
Fine Arts Museum - 1900
18-20th c paintings (E.L. Kirchner, Angelika Kauffmann, Giovanni, Augusto and Alberto Giacometti), sculptures from Grisons, graphics, Swiss 19-20th c art 30699

Bündner Natur-Museum, Masanser Str 31, 7000 Chur - T: 0812572841, Fax: 0812572850, E-mail: info@bnm.gr.ch. Head: Dr. Jürg P. Müller
Natural History Museum - 1929
Zoology, botany, geology, mineralogy, geography of the canton Graubünden 30700

Didaktische Ausstellung Urgeschichte, Tittwiesenstr 100, 7000 Chur, mail addr: c/o Christian Foppa, Aspermontstr 9, 7000 Chur - T: 0812847205, Fax: 0812847205. Head: Christian Foppa
Archaeological Museum - 1987
Prehistory 30701

Dommuseum, Hof 18, 7000 Chur - T: 0812522312, Fax: 0812536140, E-mail: kanzlei@bistum-chur.ch, Internet: http://www.bistum-chur.ch
Religious Arts Museum - 1943
Medieval cathedral treasure including 14-18th c ecclesiastical art, late classical and early medieval ivory, textiles, sculptures 30702

Rätisches Museum, Archäologische, historische und volkskundliche Sammlung Graubünden, Hofstr 1, 7000 Chur, mail addr: Quaderstr 15, 7000 Chur - T: 0812572888/89, Fax: 0812572890, E-mail: info@rm-gr.ch, Internet: http://www.rm-gr.ch. Head: Dr. Ingrid R. Metzger
Archaeological Museum / Historical Museum / Folklore Museum - 1872
Archaeology, including finds from the canton Graubünden, numismatics, cultural history, ethnography - restoration and carpenter's workshops, photo laboratory 30703

Römische Ausgrabungen, Markthallenpl/ Seilerbahnweg, 7000 Chur - T: 0812572781, Fax: 0813535448
Archaeological Museum / Open Air Museum 30704

Weinbau-Museum, Neubruchtorkel, 7000 Chur - T: 0812523555, Fax: 0812521915
Agriculture Museum - 1987
Viticulture 30705

Clarens

Villa Kruger, 17 Villa Dubochet, 1815 Clarens - T: 0219641781. Head: Marie-C. Perrottet
Special Museum - 1904
Memorabilia on the South African president of Transvaal Paul Kruger (1825-1904), villa where he spent his last years during exile (1900-1904) 30706

Coffrane

Musée Agricole, 30 Rue du Musée, 2207 Coffrane - T: 0328571512, Internet: http://www.rpn.ch/epcoffrane/musee.htm. Head: Raymond Perrenoud
Agriculture Museum - 1956
Local history, farm implements and agricultural machinery, peasant artifacts, tools for hemp production 30707

Collombey

Centre Culturel-Exposition d'Artistes et d'Artisans, 24 Rue de la Charmette, 1868 Collombey - T: 0244721540
Public Gallery 30708

Cologny

Fondation Martin Bodmer, 19-21 Rte du Guignard, 1223 Cologny - T: 0227074433, Fax: 0227074430, E-mail: info@fondationbodmer.ch. Head: Prof. Dr. Martin Bircher, Prof. Dr. Charles Mila
Library with Exhibitions - 1971
Significant manuscripts and editions of world literature, papyri, oriental writings and palm leaf manuscripts, incunabula and first editions, decorative arts, classical reliefs, sculptures, vases, coins, tapestries, drawings - Bibliotheca Bodmeriana 30709

Musée Militaire Genevois, Chateau de Penthes, Prégny-Chambésy, 1223 Cologny, mail addr: CP 5118 Chateau des Hauts-Créts, 1223 Cologny - T: 0227352406
Military Museum 30710

Colombier

Musée des Toiles Peintes, Château, 2013 Colombier - T: 0328439700, Fax: 0328412950. Head: Alain Geiser
Historical Museum / Ethnology Museum - 1953
Printed cotton cloths, wooden models, designs, memorabilia of the founder of the Boudry textile factory Claude Bovet 30711

Musée Militaire, Château, 2013 Colombier - T: 0328439700, Fax: 0328412950, Internet: http://www.infoform.ch/SwissArmy/EIM. Head: Alain Geiser
Military Museum - 1952
Military art and science, arms and armor, uniforms, armours, flags and banners, memorabilia of the Meuron regiment, 15th c castle 30712

Compesières

Musée sur l'Ordre de Malte, Commanderie de Compesières, 2 km de Bardonnex, 1208 Compesières, mail addr: c/o M. Zanetta, 18 Rue François Grast, 1208 Genève - T: 0227353381, Fax: 0792025564, E-mail: zanetta@isoft.ch, Internet: http://www.isoftch/GenevaGuide/malta/. Head: Jaques Chamay
Religious Arts Museum - 1973 30713

Conches

Musée d'Ethnographie, 7 Ch Calandrini, 1231 Conches - T: 0223460125, Fax: 0227891540. Head: L. Necker
Ethnology Museum 30714

Coppet

Château de Coppet, 1296 Coppet - T: 0227761028, Fax: 0227766532. Head: Comte d' Haussonville
Decorative Arts Museum / Fine Arts Museum - 1948
18th c castle, memorabilia of the Geneva banker Jacques Necker and of his daughter Madame de Staël, 18th-19th c furnishings, porcelain, tapestry, portraits and busts 30715

Musée Régional du Vieux-Coppet, 30 Grand-Rue, 1296 Coppet - T: 0229608700, Fax: 0229608709
Local Museum - 1935
16th c mansion, local history, late 19th c interiors, decorative and applied arts, historical documents 30716

Cornol

Musée de la Radio, Rte Cantonale, 2952 Cornol - T: 0324622774, Fax: 0324622061, E-mail: - gerard.schnoebelen@span.ch, Internet: http://www.schnoebelen.com.ch. Head: Gérard Schnoebelen
Science&Tech Museum - 1991
600 radios and telegraphs 30717

Corseaux

Petite Maison de Le Corbusier, 21 Rte Lavaux, 1802 Corseaux - T: 0219254011, Fax: 0219214019
Special Museum 30718

Curio

Museo del Malcantone, 6985 Curio - T: 0916063172, E-mail: musmalc@bluewin.ch, Internet: http://www.tinet.ch/malcantone
Local Museum 30719

Davos

Heimatmuseum Davos, Museumstr 1, 7260 Davos - T: 0814162666, 0814136117
Local Museum - 1942 30720

Davos Platz

Bergbaumuseum Graubünden mit Schaubergwerk, Schmelzboden Davos, Silberberg, 7270 Davos Platz 1 - T: 0814137603, Fax: 0814137754, E-mail: OS.Hirzel@bluewin.ch
Science&Tech Museum - 1979
History of mining, tools and implements 30721

Kirchner Museum Davos, Ernst-Ludwig-Kirchner-Pl, 7270 Davos Platz - T: 0814132202, Fax: 0814132210, E-mail: kirchnermuseum@spin.ch, Internet: http://www.kirchnermuseum.ch. Head: Bruno Gerber
Fine Arts Museum - 1982 30722

Puppen- und Spielzeugmuseum, Promenade 83, 7270 Davos Platz - T: 0814132848, Fax: 0814132848. Head: Angela Prader
Special Museum - 1996
Art historical coll of rare, originally kept dolls (18th-20th c), doll accessoires, doll's houses, toys, miniature dolls, miniature furniture and other miniatures related to this theme, model of the Sanatorium Berghof (from Th. Mann's "The Magic Mountain") 30723

Wintersport-Museum, Promenade 43, 7270 Davos Platz - T: 0814132484, Fax: 0814134736, E-mail: morningcorner@dplanet.ch, Internet: http://www.wintersportmuseum.ch. Head: Jürg Kaufmann
Special Museum - 1992 30724

Delémont

Musée Jurassien d'Art et d'Histoire, 52 Rue du 23-Juin, 2800 Delémont, mail addr: CP 2206, 2800 Delémont - T: 0324228077, Fax: 0324228074, E-mail: mjah@freesurf.ch, Internet: http://www.jura.ch/musees/arthist.htm. Head: Pierre Philippe
Archaeological Museum / Fine Arts Museum / Historical Museum - 1909
Prehistoric and Roman finds, Merowingian items, history of the old bishopric Basel and of the Jura, ecclesiastical art, coins and medals, peasant interiors, weapons - library 30725

Develier

Musée Cappuis-Fähndrich, 2802 Develier - T: 0324222332
Historical Museum - 1991 30726

Diesbach

Museum im Thomas Legler-Haus, 8777 Diesbach, 8, 8777 - T: 0556432088, 0556404652. Head: Dr. Hans Jakob Streiff
Historical Museum - 1991
Everyday life in the 18-19th c, tin figures 30727

Diessenhofen

Hausmuseum Sankt Katharinental, Am Rheinufer, 8253 Diessenhofen - T: 0526462333
Religious Arts Museum - 1982 30728

Ortsmuseum Diessenhofen, Im oberen Amtshaus, 8253 Diessenhofen - T: 0526464242, Fax: 0526464210, E-mail: diessenhofen-stadt@bluewin.ch
Local Museum - 1961
Dye plants, cloth-printing and cloth-printing techniques in Thurgau during the 19th c, works by the local artist Carl Roesch, 16th c building - library 30729

Dietikon

Ortsmuseum Dietikon, Schöneggstr 20, 8953 Dietikon - T: 017404854
Local Museum - 1931
Roman finds from Dietikon, finds from the medieval castles Schönenwerd and Glanzenberg, coll of stove tiles, local history artifacts - archives 30730

Disentis

Klostermuseum Disentis, Benediktinerabtei, 7180 Disentis - T: 0819296900, Fax: 0819296901
Religious Arts Museum / Natural History Museum / Folklore Museum - 1992
Religious art and folk art, textiles, crystals, fauna 30731

Donzhausen

Heimatmuseum, 8583 Donzhausen - T: 0716421201
Local Museum - 1968
Local history, farm implements, domestic utensils, interiors, weapons, glass, ceramics, fire engines, toys 30732

Dornach

Heimatmuseum Schwarzbubenland, Alte Mauritiuskirche, Hauptstr Oberdornach, 4143 Dornach, mail addr: Postfach 140, 4143 Dornach 2 - T: 0617013154
Local Museum - 1941/49
Local hist, archaeological finds, ecclesiastical art, farm implements, documents on the battle of Dornach (1499), memorabilia of the geologist A. Gressl, tomb of the French scientist Pierre Louis Moreau de Maupertuis (1698-1759), tomb of the German commander-in-chief in the battle of Dornach Graf von Fürstenberg 30733

Dübendorf

Flieger-Flab-Museum, Überlandstr 255, 8600 Dübendorf - T: 018232324, Fax: 018232653, E-mail: ausstellung@flieger-museum.com, Internet: http://www.airforcecenter.ch. Head: Kurt Waldmeier
Military Museum / Science&Tech Museum - 1978
Military aviation in Switzerland, documentation on the development of military aviation, aircraft engines, power units, propellers, aircraft (1910-70), special devices and constructions, aircraft cameras, navigation, wireless sets, uniforms, AAA guns, Radar Systems 30734

Museum der schweizerischen Luftwaffe → Flieger-Flab-Museum

Dulliken

Heimatmuseum Arnold Bärtschi, Lehmgrubenstr 4, 4657 Dulliken - T: 0622954945
Local Museum - 1977
Domestic and agricultural implements, Arnold Bärtschi sel. 30735

Ebikon

Tierwelt-Panorama, Luzerner Str 63, 6030 Ebikon - T: 0414201531. Head: Dr. Walter Linsenmaier
Natural History Museum - 1950
Dioramas of Middle European and exotic animal kingdom, coll of birds of paradise, insects, especially chrysididae, animal paintings, drawings by Walter Linsenmaier 30736

Ebnat-Kappel

Heimatmuseum der Albert-Edelmann-Stiftung, Ackerhusweg 16, 9642 Ebnat-Kappel - T: 0719931905
Music Museum - 1952
Historical musical instruments, peasant furniture, folk costumes, domestic utensils, paintings by Hans Brühlmann, Karl Hofer and Albert Edelmann, 18th c house 30737

Echallens

La Maison du Blé et du Pain, Pl de l'Hôtel de Ville, 1040 Echallens - T: 0218815071, Fax: 0218821096, E-mail: maison-ble-pain@bluewin.ch, Internet: http://www.maison-ble-pain.com. Head: Marc-Etienne Piot
Local Museum - 1988
Agriculture, millery, backery 30738

Ederswiler

Museum Löwenburg, Christoph Merian Stiftung, Hofgut Löwenburg, 2813 Ederswiler - T: 0324311220, Fax: 0324312220, E-mail: a.stade@merianstiftung.ch, Internet: http://www.merianstiftung.ch. Head: Elisabeth Schmid
Local Museum - 1970
Local history, archaeological finds, fossils, medieval to modern history, agriculture 30739

Eglisau

Ortsmuseum Eglisau, Weierbach-Huus, 8193 Eglisau - T: 018674200
Local Museum - 1958
Architectural history of Eglisau, fishing in the upper Rhine, domestic utensils 30740

Einsiedeln

Diorama Bethlehem, Benziger Str 23, 8840 Einsiedeln - T: 0554122617, E-mail: diorama@gmx.net, Internet: http://www.diorama.ch. Head: Beatrice Eberle-Scherer
Religious Arts Museum 30741

Panorama Kreuzigung Christi, Benzigerstr, 8840 Einsiedeln - T: 0554121174, Fax: 0554223043, E-mail: maxfuchs@freesurf.ch, Internet: http://www.einsiedeln-online.ch. Head: Max Fuchs
Religious Arts Museum - 1893 30742

Stiftsbibliothek, Benediktinerabtei, 8840 Einsiedeln - T: 0554186314, Fax: 0554186112. Head: Dr. Odo Lang
Library with Exhibitions 30743

Streichinstrumentemsammlung, Benediktinerabtei, 8840 Einsiedeln - T: 0554186111, Fax: 0554186112, E-mail: lukas.helg@bluewin.ch. Head: Lukas Helg
Music Museum - 1992
Hillel string coll, violines and cellos 19th c 30744

Elgg

Heimatmuseum Elgg, Humperg-Trotte, 8353 Elgg
Local Museum - 1943 30745

Emmenbrücke

Galerie Gersag Emmen, Rüeggisingerstr 22, 6020 Emmenbrücke - T: 0412680396, Fax: 0412680963, E-mail: galerie@emmen.ch, Internet: http://www.emmen.ch. Head: Isolde Bühlmann
Public Gallery - 1972 30746

Endingen

Feuerwehrmuseum, Im Weiler Schöntal, 5304 Endingen - T: 0562410151
Science&Tech Museum - 1992 30747

Engelberg

Altertumssammlung der Benediktinerabtei, Benediktinerabtei, 6390 Engelberg - T: 0416396132, 0416396161. Head: Bernhard Mathis
Religious Arts Museum
Sacral objects worked from precious metals, chasuble of the reformator Ulrich Zwingli - Library, scriptorium 30748

Tal-Museum, Dorfstr 6, 6390 Engelberg - T: 0416370414, E-mail: talmuseum@diopter.cc, Internet: http://www.kulturfenster.ch/tme. Head: Markus Britschgi
Local Museum / Fine Arts Museum - 1988 30749

Eptingen

August-Suter-Museum, Im Friedheim, 4458 Eptingen - T: 0612991262
Fine Arts Museum - 1997
40 sculptures from August Suter (1887-1965) 30750

Erlenbach im Simmental

Agensteinhaus und Simmentaler Hausweg, Dorf, 3762 Erlenbach im Simmental - T: 0336811844. Head: Max Bratschi-Tschirren
Local Museum 30751

Erlenbach (Zürich)

Ortsmuseum Erlenbach, Kirchgemeindehaus, Schulhausstr 40, 8703 Erlenbach (Zürich) - T: 019100931
Local Museum - 1966 30752

Ermatingen

Fischereimuseum, 8272 Ermatingen - T: 0716641938
Special Museum 30753

Werkzeugmuseum Zur Eisenbahn, 8272 Ermatingen - T: 0716642264
Science&Tech Museum 30754

Ernen

Kirchenmuseum, 3995 Ernen - T: 0279711129, 0279711562, Fax: 0279713683, E-mail: gemeinde@ernen.ch. Head: Herbert Heiss
Religious Arts Museum - 1975/1999 30755

Museum im Jost-Sigristen-Haus, 3995 Ernen - T: 0279712336, Fax: 0279713578, E-mail: berglandorder@rhone.ch. Head: Ingrid Schmid-Birri
Historical Museum - 1995 30756

Museum im Zendenrathaus, Dorfpl, 3995 Ernen - T: 0279711428, Fax: 0279713683, E-mail: gemeinde@ernen.ch. Head: Williy Clausen
Local Museum 30757

Eschlikon

Ortsmuseum Eschlikon, Blumenaustr 7, 8360 Eschlikon - T: 0719711083. Head: Peter Jezler
Local Museum - 1984 30758

Estavayer-le-Lac

Musée de Grenouille (Frog Museum), 13 Rue du Musée, 1470 Estavayer-le-Lac - T: 0266631040, E-mail: commune@estavayer-le-lac.ch, Internet: http://www.estavayer-le-lac.ch
Natural History Museum 30759

Musée d'Estavayer, Rue du Musée, 1470 Estavayer-le-Lac - T: 0266632448, 0266633105, Fax: 0266639250, E-mail: administration-estavayer-le-lac@urbanet.ch, Internet: http://www.estavayer-le-lac.ch
Local Museum - 1925
Local hist, prehistoric finds, Roman coins, weapons, craftmen's tools, domestic utensils and 17th c kitchen, interiors, old railway lanterns 30760

Ettingen

Dorfmuseum, Schanzengasse, Guggerhuus, 4107 Ettingen - Internet: http://www.leimental.ch
Local Museum - 1980 30761

Ettiswil

Museum Klösterli, Schloss Wyher, 6218 Ettiswil - T: 0419800174, E-mail: klussi@hmluzern.ch, Internet: http://www.museum.com/jb/museum?id=17673. Head: Kurt Lussi
Folklore Museum - 1997 30762

Schreinermuseum, Im Schloh, 6218 Ettiswil - T: 0419702264
Science&Tech Museum 30763

Feldbrunnen

Dorfmuseum, Möslistr 7a, 4532 Feldbrunnen - T: 0326373251
Local Museum - 1991 30764

Museum Schloss Waldegg, Waldeggstr, 4532 Feldbrunnen - T: 0326223867, Fax: 0326234832, E-mail: info@schloss-waldegg.ch, Internet: http://www.schloss-waldegg.ch. Head: Dr. André Schluchter
Decorative Arts Museum / Fine Arts Museum - 1991
Summer residence for Mayor Johann Viktor von Besenval (1638-1713) and his wife Maria-Margaritha von Sury (1649-1713), period furniture and pictures from the 17th-19th c 30765

Fislisbach

Dorfmuseum, Gemeindehaus, 5442 Fislisbach - T: 0564932134
Local Museum - 1991 30766

Flawil

Ortsmuseum Flawil, Sankt Galler-Str 81, 9230 Flawil - T: 0713932329, 0713932064
Local Museum 30767

Fleurier

Musée Industriel du Val-de-Travers, CP 313, 2114 Fleurier. Head: Elisabeth Spahr
Science&Tech Museum - 1996 30768

Flims Waldhaus

Hotelmuseum, Parkhotel Waldhaus, 7018 Flims Waldhaus - T: 0819284848, Fax: 0819284858, E-mail: phw@bluewin.ch
Special Museum - 1992 30769

Flirns Dorf

Das Gelbe Haus, Museum Flims, Hauptstr 60, 7017 Flirns Dorf, mail addr: Postfach 220, 7017 Flims Dorf - T: 0819367414, Fax: 0819367415, E-mail: dasgelbehaus@kns.ch, Internet: http://www.dasgelbehaus.ch. Head: Luciano Fasciati, Armon Fontana
Local Museum
Architecture, ordinary life, design 30770

Flüh

Forum Flüh, Talstr 42a, 4112 Flüh - T: 0617313109
Local Museum 30771

Frauenfeld

Historisches Museum des Kantons Thurgau, Schloß Frauenfeld, 8510 Frauenfeld - T: 0527241767, 0527242369, Fax: 0527242397, E-mail: rene.schiffmann@kttg.ch, Internet: http://www.kttg.ch/museen/htm/histo1.htm. Head: Dr. René Schiffmann
Historical Museum - 1859
Ecclesiastical art, bourgeois and peasant interiors, glass paintings, clocks, numismatics, weapons, ceramics, graphics of different parts of the canton, state antiquities - library, restoration workshop 30772

Museum für Archäologie, Freiestr 26, 8510 Frauenfeld - T: 0527242219, Fax: 0527202588, E-mail: urs.leuzinger@aa.tg.ch, Internet: http://www.kttg.ch/museen. Head: Dr. Urs Leuzinger
Archaeological Museum - 1996
Neolithic Age, Bronze Age, Roman epoch, early Middle Ages, Middle Ages, modern times 30773

Shed im Eisenwerk, Ausstellungsraum für zeitgenössische Kunst, Industriestr 23, 8500 Frauenfeld - T: 0527288920, Fax: 0527288909. Head: Sabine Schaschl
Fine Arts Museum 30774

Freienbach

Druckereimuseum, Pfarrmatte 6, 8807 Freienbach - T: 0554153434, Fax: 0554153499, E-mail: info@bruhin-druck.ch, Internet: http://www.bruhin-druck.ch. Head: Felix Bruhin
Science&Tech Museum 30775

Frenkendorf

Ortsmuseum Frenkendorf, Schulstr 10a, 4402 Frenkendorf - T: 0619018376, 0619018727
Local Museum - 1978 30776

Fribourg

Espace Jean Tinguely - Niki de Saint-Phalle, 2 Rue de Morat, 1700 Fribourg - T: 0263055140, Fax: 0263055141, E-mail: mahf@fr.ch, Internet: http://www.fr.ch/mahf. Head: Dr. Yvonne Lehnherr
Fine Arts Museum - 1998 30777

Ethnographische Sammlung, c/o Ethnologisches Seminar der Universität, 11 Rte des Bonnesfontaines, 1700 Fribourg - T: 0263007841/42, Fax: 0263009664, E-mail: christian.giordano@unifr.ch, Internet: http://www.unifr.ch/ethnologie. Head: Prof. Christian Giordano
Ethnology Museum - 1941
Objects from New Guinea, Northern Africa, North and South America and India 30778

Fri-Art, Centre d'Art Contemporain, 22 Petites-Rames, 1700 Fribourg - T: 0263232351, Fax: 0263231534, E-mail: fri-art@culture.mcnet.ch, Internet: http://www.fri-art.ch. Head: Michel Ritter
Fine Arts Museum 30779

Gutenberg Museum, Schweizerisches Museum der graphischen Industrie und der Kommunikation, Liebfrauenpl 16, 1701 Fribourg - T: 0263473828, Fax: 0263473829, E-mail: info@gutenbergmuseum.ch, Internet: http://www.gutenbergmuseum.ch. Head: Bruno Glusstein
Science&Tech Museum - 1994
Exhibits about the development of printing, including instruments and books 30780

Musée d'Art et d'Histoire, 12 Rue de Morat, 1700 Fribourg - T: 0263055140, 0263055167, Fax: 0263055141, E-mail: mahf@fr.ch, Internet: http://www.fr.ch/mahf. Head: Dr. Yvonne Lehnherr
Fine Arts Museum / Historical Museum - 1823
Archaeology, art and hist of the canton Fribourg, prehistoric, Roman and medieval finds, 11-20th c sculpture and painting incl works by Hans Fries, H. Gieng, G. Locher, pewter, tapestry, 15-18th c stained glass windows, largest coll in Switzerland of wooden sculpture from first half of 16th c 30781

Musée d'Histoire Naturelle, 6 Chemin du Musée, 1700 Fribourg - T: 0263009040, Fax: 0263009760, E-mail: museehn@fr.ch, Internet: http://www.fr.ch/mhn. Head: André Fasel
Natural History Museum - 1823
Mineralogy, geography, geology and paleontology, zoology, coll of minerals of the Binnental 30782

Musée Suisse de la Machine à Coudre, 58 Grand'Rue, 1700 Fribourg - T: 0264752433, Fax: 0264752434, E-mail: edwassme@mail.mcnet.ch, Internet: http://www.museewassmer.com. Head: Edouard Wassmer
Science&Tech Museum - 1975 30783

Musée Suisse de la Marionette, 2 Derrière les Jardins, 1700 Fribourg - T: 0263228513, Fax: 0263228513, E-mail: -MuseeSuisseMarionette@mcnet.ch, Internet: http://www.mcnet.ch/marionettes. Head: Mares Jans
Performing Arts Museum - 1983 30784

PAC - Poste d'Arte Contemporain, 14 Rte du Criblet, 1700 Fribourg - T: 0263222740
Fine Arts Museum 30785

Trésor de la Cathédrale Saint-Nicolas, Chapitre de Saint-Nicolas, Rue des Chanoines 3, 1702 Fribourg - T: 0263471040, Fax: 0263471059, E-mail: -cathedrale.fribourg@bluewin.ch
Religious Arts Museum 30786

Frick

Saurier-Museum, Primarschulhaus, Schulstr 22, 5070 Frick - T: 0628652806, Fax: 0628715391, E-mail: ruembeli@swissonline.ch, Internet: http://www.sauriermuseum-frick.ch
Natural History Museum - 1978
Plateosaurs, Jurafossils 30787

Gaiserwald

Ortsmuseum Gaiserwald, Altes Pfarrhaus, Josefen-Spisegg-Str 27, 9030 Gaiserwald - T: 0712785171, E-mail: gemeinde.gaiserwald@swissonline.ch, Internet: http://www.gaiserwald.ch
Local Museum - 1994 30788

Gandria

Museo Doganale Svizzero, Schweizerisches Landesmuseum, Cantine di Gandria, 6978 Gandria, mail addr: Postfach 6789, 8023 Zürich - T: 0919239843, Internet: http://www.slmnet.ch. Head: Andres Furger
Historical Museum / Special Museum - 1935
History of customs in Switzerland, smuggling, arms 30789

Gelfingen

Schloßmuseum Heidegg, 6284 Gelfingen - T: 0419171325, Fax: 0419171308, E-mail: info@heidegg.ch, Internet: http://www.heidegg.ch. Head: Dieter Ruckstuhl
Historical Museum - 1950/98
Family Pfyffer von Heidegg estate, hist of Hochdorf 30790

Genève

Asia-Africa Museum, 30 Grand-Rue, 1204 Genève - T: 0223117190, Fax: 0227358904. Head: T.P. Nguyên
Fine Arts Museum / Archaeological Museum - 1961
African and Oriental art, primitive art, Chinese porcelain, far east antiques 30791

attitudes, 5 Av Rosemont, 1208 Genève - T: 0227003421, Fax: 0227003429, E-mail: attitudes@worldcom.ch, Internet: http://www.attitudes.ch. Head: Jean-Paul Felley, Olivier Kaeser
Public Gallery 30792

Bibliothèque d'Art et d'Archéologie des Musées d'Art et d'Histoire de la Ville de Genève, 5 Promenade du Pin, 1204 Genève - T: 0224182700, Fax: 0224182701, E-mail: info.baa@ville-ge.ch. Head: Véronique Goncerut-Estèbe
Library with Exhibitions 30793

Bibliothèque d'Histoire de l'Art, 22 Blvd des Philosophes, 1211 Genève 4 - T: 0227057440, Fax: 0227810171, E-mail: Biblio-Hist-Art@Lettres.UniGE.ch, Internet: http://www.unige.ch/lettres/armus/istar/biblio.html. Head: Jean-Christophe Curtet
Library with Exhibitions 30794

Bibliothèque Publique et Universitaire, Salle Ami Lullin, Promenade des Bastions, 1211 Genève 4 - T: 0224182800, Fax: 0224182801, E-mail: info.bpu@ville-ge.ch, Internet: http://www.ville-ge.ch/bpu/. Head: Alain Jacquesson
Library with Exhibitions - 1905
Portraits from well-known Geneva personalities, history of Reformation, manuscripts, precious books and paintings, autographs, iconographic coll, Ami Lullin (1695-1756) bequest 30795

Cabinet des Estampes du Musée d'Art et d'Histoire, 5 Promenade du Pin, 1204 Genève - T: 0224182770, Fax: 0224182771, E-mail: cde@ville-ge.ch, Internet: http://www.ville-ge.ch/musinfo/mahg/cde/estampes.htm. Head: Rainer Michael Mason
Fine Arts Museum - 1886
Graphic prints from Italy (Piranesi), Germany, the Netherlands, France, England, Spain, Russia and Hungaria, contemporary graphic prints (Bram van Velde, Saura, Baselitz, Malevitch, Lüthi, Raetz, Robert Morrir) 30796

Centre d'Art Contemporain, 10 Rue des Vieux-Grenadiers, 1205 Genève - T: 0223291842, Fax: 0223291886
Fine Arts Museum 30797

Centre de la Photographie Genéve, 16 Rue du Général Dufour, 1204 Genève - T: 0223292835, Fax: 0223292835, E-mail: cenphoto@worldcom.ch, Internet: http://www.bartok.jstechno.ch. Head: Joerg Bader
Fine Arts Museum - 1984 30798

Centre d'Edition Contemporaine, 18 Saint-Léger, 1204 Genève - T: 0223105170, Fax: 0223105262, E-mail: edition@vtx.ch. Head: Veronique Bacchetta
Fine Arts Museum
Contemporary and graphic art 30799

Centre d'Iconographie Genevoise, 2 Passage de la Tour, 1205 Genève - T: 0224184670, Fax: 0224184671. Head: Cäsar Menz
Special Museum 30800

Centre pour l'Image Contemporain Saint-Gervais, 5 Rue du Temple, 1201 Genève - T: 0229082000, Fax: 0229082001, E-mail: cic@sgg.ch, Internet: http://www.centreimage.ch. Head: André Iten
Fine Arts Museum 30801

Collection de la Fondation in memoriam Comtesse Tatiana Zoubov, 2 Rue des Granges, 1204 Genève - T: 0223119255. Head: Nadia Bot
Decorative Arts Museum - 1973
Interiors, furnishings, Régence, Louis XV, Louis XVI, Chippendale, paintings, portraits, 18th c decorative arts, porcelain, busts, vases, tapestry, art objects from China, Hôtel de Sellon (18th c) 30802

Collections Baur, Fondation Alfred et Eugénie Baur-Duret Collections, 8 Rue Munier-Romilly, 1206 Genève - T: 0223461729, Fax: 0227891845, E-mail: email@collections-baur.ch, Internet: http://www.collections-baur.ch. Head: Frank Dunand
Decorative Arts Museum - 1964
Chinese and Japanese art since 7th c collected by Alfred Baur (1865-1951) 30803

Institut et Musée Voltaire, 25 Rue des Délices, 1203 Genève - T: 0223447133, E-mail: institut.voltaire@ville-ge.ch, Internet: http://www.ville-ge.ch/bpu/institut/f/imv.htm. Head: Charles Wirz
Special Museum - 1952
Voltaire (1694-1778) and the 18th c, printed books, manuscripts and iconographic coll - library 30804

Maison Tavel, 6 Rue des Puits-Saint-Pierre, 1204 Genève - T: 0223102900, Fax: 0223102908, Internet: http://www.ville-ge.ch/musinfo/mahg/presse/. Head: Cäsar Menz
Local Museum 30805

Mamco, Musée d'Art Moderne et Contemporain, 10 Rue des Vieux-Grenadiers, 1205 Genève - T: 0223206122, Fax: 0227815681, E-mail: mamco@mamco.ch, Internet: http://www.mamco.ch. Head: Christian Bernard
Fine Arts Museum - 1994 30806

Musée Ariana, Musée Suisse de la Céramique et du Verre, 10 Av de la Paix, 1202 Genève - T: 0224185450, Fax: 0224185451, E-mail: ariana@ville-ge.ch, Internet: http://www.mah.ville-ge.ch. Head: Cäsar Menz
Decorative Arts Museum - 1884/1934
16-20th c ceramics (pottery, faience, stoneware, porcelain) and glass from Europe, China, Japan and the Islamic sphere, Neoclassic villa Ariana (1877-1884) 30807

Musée Automobile, 3 Rue Pestalozzi, 1202 Genève - T: 0227333184
Science&Tech Museum 30808

Musée Barbier-Mueller, 10 Rue Jean-Calvin, 1204 Genève - T: 0223120270, Fax: 0223120190, E-mail: musee@barbier-mueller.ch, Internet: http://www.barbier-mueller.ch. Head: Laurence Mattet
Fine Arts Museum
Primitive art from Africa, The Americas and Oceania 30809

Musée d'Art et d'Histoire, 2 Rue Charles-Galland, 1206 Genève - T: 0224182600, Fax: 0224182601, E-mail: mah@ville-ge.ch, Internet: http://mah.ville-ge.ch. Head: Cäsar Menz
Fine Arts Museum / Historical Museum - 1910
Archaeology, fine arts (Liotard, Hodler), Italian, German, Flemish, French and English paintings, sculpture, applied arts, European decorative arts - library, photo and restoration laboratories 30810

Musée de l'Horlogerie et de l'Emaillerie, 15 Rte de Malagnou, 1208 Genève - T: 0224186470, Fax: 0224186471, E-mail: mhe@mah.ville-ge.ch, Internet: http://www.ville-ge.ch. Head: Cäsar Menz
Science&Tech Museum / Decorative Arts Museum - 1972
Development of horology in Geneva and Europe since the 16th c, 17th-19th c enamel paintings, jewelry 30811

Musée d'Ethnographie, 65-67 Blvd Carl-Vogt, 1205 Genève, mail addr: CP 191, 1211 Genéve - T: 0224184550, Fax: 0224184551, E-mail: -musée.ethnographie@ville-ge.ch, Internet: http://www.ville-ge.ch/eth. Head: Dr. Louis Necker
Ethnology Museum - 1901
Ethnography from five continents esp Australia, Nepal, Peru, Central Africa, musical instruments, ceramics and pottery - library 30812

Musée d'Histoire des Sciences, Villa Bartholoni, 128 Rue de Lausanne, 1202 Genève - T: 0224185060, Fax: 0224185061, E-mail: mhs@ville-ge.ch. Head: Dr. Ninian Hubert van Blyenburgh
Science&Tech Museum / Natural History Museum - 1964
Hist of science in Geneva: astronomical instruments (telescopes, orreries, sundials), physics (instruments by H.B. de Saussure and J.D. Colladon), barometers, hygrometers, microscopes, medicine 30813

Musée Historique de la Réformation, c/o Bibliothèque Publique et Universitaire, Promenade des Bastions, 1211 Genève 4 - T: 0224182800, Fax: 0224182801, E-mail: info.bpu@ville-ge.ch, Internet: http://www.ville-ge.ch/bpu/. Head: Olivier Labarthe
Religious Arts Museum 30814

Musée International de la Croix-Rouge et du Croissant-Rouge (International Red Cross and Red Crescent Museum), 17 Av de la Paix, 1202 Genève - T: 0227489511, Fax: 0227489528, E-mail: admin@micr.org, Internet: http://www.micr.org. Head: Roger Mayou, Bernard Koechlin
Historical Museum - 1988
The Wall of Time (major events in history of humanitarian endeavour since 1863), articles made by prisoners, posters, video documents, multimedia area - photo library, library, archives 30815

Musée Jean-Jacques Rousseau, c/o Bibliothèque Publique et Universitaire, Promenade des Bastions, 1211 Genève 4 - T: 0224182800, Fax: 0224182801, E-mail: info.bpu@ville-ge.ch, Internet: http://www.ville-ge.ch/bpu/. Head: Charles Wirz
Special Museum - 1916
Work and life of Jean-Jacques Rousseau (1712-78), especially manuscripts, first editions, statues, paintings, etchings 30816

Musée Jean Tua, 28-30 Rue des Bains, 1205 Genève - T: 0223213637, Fax: 0223218384. Head: Jean Tua
Science&Tech Museum - 1994
Automobiles 30817

Musée Rath, 4 Pl Neuve, 1204 Genève - T: 0224183340, Fax: 0224183341. Head: Dr. Cäsar Menz
Fine Arts Museum 30818

Muséum d'Histoire Naturelle, 1 Rte de Malagnou, 1208 Genève 6, mail addr: CP 6434, 1211 Genève 6 - T: 0224186300, Fax: 0224186301, E-mail: volker.mahnert@mhn.ville-ge.ch, Internet: http://www.ville-ge.ch/musinfo/mhng/index.htm. Head: Volker Mahnert
Natural History Museum - 1820
Natural history, geology and mineralogy, sediments, precious stones, fluorescent minerals, paleontology, fossils of vertebrates and invertebrates, especially finds from the Argentinian Pampas, zoology, mammalogy, ornithology, entomology, herpetology, ichthyology - library 30819

Patek Philippe Museum, 7 Rue des Vieux-Grenadiers, 1205 Genève - T: 0228070910, Fax: 0228070920, E-mail: info@patekmuseum.com, Internet: http://www.patekmuseum.com. Head: Arnaud Tellier
Special Museum / Decorative Arts Museum / Science&Tech Museum - 2001
Watches, clocks and enamal miniatures 16th-20th c 30820

Petit Palais, Musée d'Art Moderne de Renoir à Picasso, 2 Terrasse Saint-Victor, 1206 Genève - T: 0223461433, Fax: 0223465315, E-mail: petitpalais@vtx.ch. Head: Prof. Claude Ghez
Fine Arts Museum - 1968
French paintings 1880-1930: impressionism, neo-impressionism, Fauves, Montmartre painters, school of Paris, naive painting 30821

Philatelistisches Museum der Vereinten Nationen, Palais des Nations, 1211 Genève 10 - T: 0229174882, Fax: 0229170024, E-mail: wwezenberg@unog.ch, Internet: http://www.musum.com/jb/museum?id= 17154. Head: P. Torelli
Special Museum - 1962
Stamps, envelopes, postcards and documents, League of Nations (1919-1945) and United Nations incl its Specialized Agencies - audio-visual equipment 30822

Les Genevez

Musée Rural Jurassien, 9 Haut du Village, 2714 Les Genevez, mail addr: CP 41, 2714 Les Genevez - T: 0324840080, Fax: 0324840081. Head: Daniel Gerber
Folklore Museum / Agriculture Museum 30823

Gersau

Heimatmuseum Gersau, Dorfstr 14, 6442 Gersau - T: 0418281974
Local Museum - 1984 30824

Gingins

Fondation Neumann, Ecuries du Château, 1276 Gingins - T: 0223693653, Fax: 0223693172, E-mail: info@fondation-neumann.ch, Internet: http://www.fondation-neumann.ch. Head: Helen Bieri Thomson
Decorative Arts Museum - 1994
Art Nouveau and simbolism glass art (Gallé, Daum, Tiffany) 30825

Musée Romand de la Machine Agricole, Moulin de Chiblins, 1276 Gingins, mail addr: c/o Centre Historique de l'Agriculture, 109 Rte du Mandement, 1242 Satigny - T: 0223693311. Head: Victor Bertschi
Agriculture Museum / Science&Tech Museum - 1991 30826

Giornico

Haus für Relief und Halbfiguren von Hans Josephsohn, Stiftung La Congiunta, La Congiunta, 6745 Giornico, mail addr: Walo Huber, Hegibachstr 62, 8032 Zürich - T: 014226107, E-mail: walo.huber@bluewin.ch. Head: Renzo Bretscher
Fine Arts Museum - 1992
Works of the artist Hans Josephsohn, architecture by Peter Märkli 30827

Museo di Leventina, Casa Stanga, 6745 Giornico - T: 0918642522
Folklore Museum - 1966
Local hist, folklore, weights and measures, coins, 16th c building 30828

Giumaglio

Museo di Vallemaggia, Antica Casa Franzoni, 6671 Giumaglio - T: 0917541340. Head: Bruno Donati
Local Museum - 1963
Farm implements, folk art and folk costumes, local history, works by the painter Giovanni A. Vanoni (1810-86) 30829

Glarus

Kirchenschatz, Kath. Pfarramt Sankt Fridolin, Friedhofstr 8, 8750 Glarus - T: 0556402277, Fax: 0556408981, E-mail: pfarramt.glarus@bluewin.ch. Head: Josef Schwitter
Religious Arts Museum
Liturgical objects: chalice (13th c), monstrance (1518), Brandis crucifix (ca. 1400) altar and procession statue "Fridolin and Ursus" (1638) 30830

Kunsthaus Glarus, Im Volksgarten, 8750 Glarus, mail addr: Postfach 665, 8750 Glarus - T: 0556402535, Fax: 0556402519, E-mail: office@kunsthausglarus.ch, Internet: http://www.kunsthausglarus.ch. Head: Nadja Schneider
Fine Arts Museum - 1952
19-20th c paintings and sculptures by Swiss artists 30831

Suworow-Museum, Schwertgasse 2, 8750 Glarus - T: 0556406233, Fax: 0556406450. Head: Walter Gähler
Historical Museum - 1986 30832

Glattfelden

EKZ-Museum Glattfelden, Stromhaus Burenwisen, Turbinenstr, 8192 Glattfelden, mail addr: Postfach, 8022 Zürich - T: 012075256, Fax: 012075399, E-mail: info@ekz.ch, Internet: http://www.ekz.ch. Head: J. Walty
Science&Tech Museum - 1983 30833

Gottfried Keller-Zentrum, Gottfried-Keller-Str 8, 8192 Glattfelden - T: 018672804, 018672232, Fax: 018672804, Internet: http://www.gkz.ch
Special Museum 30834

Goldau

Bergsturz-Museum Goldau, Parkstr 46, 6410 Goldau - T: 0794781105, Fax: 0418551546, E-mail: bergsturz@arth-online.ch, Internet: http://www.arth-online.ch/bergsturz
Local Museum / Natural History Museum - 1956 30835

Gontenschwil

Dorfmuseum, Im alten Pfarrhaus, 5728 Gontenschwil - T: 0627731704, Fax: 0627731704, E-mail: k.gautschi@bluewin.ch, Internet: http://www.geocities.com/Athens/Ithaca/3765
Local Museum - 1972
Local history, peasant interiors, carpenter's and cooper's tools, memorabilia on the poet Jakob Frey, pewter, porcelain, glass, brass, tobacco pipes, furniture, weapons, 15th c parsonage 30836

Gossau (Sankt Gallen)

Burgenkundliche Sammlung im Burgenmuseum, Schloß Oberberg, Oberdorf, 9200 Gossau (Sankt Gallen) - T: 0713852318. Head: Dr. Urs J. Cavelti
Historical Museum - 1972
15th c castle, castles in Eastern Switzerland, photos, models, torturechamber containing instruments of torture 30837

Motorradmuseum, Kirchstr 43, 9200 Gossau (Sankt Gallen) - T: 0713851656. Head: Joseph Hilti
Science&Tech Museum - 1973
140 Motos, 70 Marken aus 12 Ländern, ab 1898 30838

Grächen

Heimatmuseum Grächen, Altes Gemeindehaus, 3925 Grächen - T: 0279562727
Local Museum - 1991 30839

Gränichen

Museum Chornhuus, 5722 Gränichen - T: 0628558877
Local Museum - 1976
Local history, farm implements, dairy industry, craft trades, domestic utensils, weapons, handicrafts, distilling utensils, archaeological finds 30840

Le Grand-Saconnex

Musée International de l'Automobile, Halle 7 du Palexpo, près de l'Aéroport Genève-Cointrin, 1218 Le Grand-Saconnex, mail addr: Voie des Traz 40, 1218 Le Grand-Saconnex - T: 0227888484/82, Fax: 0227888481, Internet: http://www.fastnet.ch/lsne/artcul/musee/musau. Head: Domenico de Bernardinis
Science&Tech Museum - 1995 30841

Le Grand-Saint-Bernard

Musée du Grand Saint-Bernard, 1946 Le Grand-Saint-Bernard - T: 0277871236, Fax: 0277871107. Head: P. Prieur
Local Museum - 1900
Local history, Roman finds, statues, votive tablets, inscriptions, Gallic and Roman coins, ecclesiastical gold jewellery, pewter, pictorial documents, local minerals and insects 30842

Grandson

Château de Grandson, Pl du Château, 1422 Grandson - T: 0244452926, Fax: 0244454289, E-mail: chateau@grandson.ch, Internet: http://www.grandson.ch. Head: Johanna Ehrenberg
Local Museum - 1961
13th-16th c interiors and furniture, family history of the Grandson barons, 15th c arms, torture chamber, models of castles, motocar museum, documentation on the battle of Grandson (1476) 30843

Grandvaux

Maison Buttin-de Loës, Pl du Village, 1603 Grandvaux - T: 0217991412. Head: Gustave Apothéloz
Local Museum - 1941
Local history, 17th-19th c interiors and utensils, M. and Mme. Louis Buttin-de Loës private coll 30844

Grenchen

Kultur-Historisches Museum Grenchen, Absyte 3, 2540 Grenchen - T: 0326520979, Fax: 0326520979. Head: Tanja Leutenegger-Kröni
Historical Museum - 1974
Town hist, hist of the clock industry 30845

Kunsthaus, Freiestr 2, 2540 Grenchen - T: 0326525022, Fax: 0326525003, E-mail: - kunsthaus.grenchen@bluewin.ch, Internet: http://www.kunsthausgrenchen.ch. Head: Dolores Denaro
Fine Arts Museum 30846

Mazzini-Gedenkstätte, Bachtelenstr 24, 2540 Grenchen, mail addr: Postfach 664, 2540 Grenchen - T: 0326527741, Fax: 0326524966. Head: Dr. Anton Meinrad-Meier
Historical Museum - 1992 30847

Grindelwald

Heimatmuseum, Talhaus, 3818 Grindelwald - T: 0338532226, E-mail: admin@grindelwald.ch, Internet: http://www.grindelwald.ch
Local Museum - 1963
Local history, tools, furniture, alpine economy, winter sports and mountaineering 30848

Grüningen

Heimatmuseum, Schloß, 8627 Grüningen - T: 019351900, Fax: 019361508
Local Museum - 1947
Local history, historical artifacts from the bailliff Grüningen, documents, graphics, models, tools and implements, 13th c castle 30849

Zinnfigurenmuseum, In der Müli, 8627 Grüningen - T: 019351803, Fax: 019355668, E-mail: e.gehri@bluewin.ch. Head: Emil Gehri
Decorative Arts Museum - 1988 30850

Grüsch

Heimatmuseum Prättigau, Haus zum Rosengarten, Landstr, 7214 Grüsch, mail addr: Postfach 123, 7214 Grüsch - T: 0813251682
Local Museum - 1969
Local hist, archaeological finds, agricultural and crafts implements and tools domestic utensils 30851

Gruyères

Château, 1663 Gruyères - T: 0269212102, Fax: 0269213802, E-mail: chateau@grzyeres.ch, Internet: http://www.gruyeres.ch/chateau. Head: Raoul Blanchard
Local Museum - 1938
13-15th c castle, interiors, furniture, glasscases, tapestry, weapons, bailiff hall, paintings by C. Corot, H.-C.-A. Baron, F. Furet, B. Menn, works by the sculptor A. Bovy, paintings by A. Baud-Bovy and André Valetin, memorabilia of the artists 30852

Gurbü

Bauernmuseum Althus, Jerisberghof, 3208 Gurbü - T: 0317555326, Fax: 0317555326
Agriculture Museum - 1970
Local history, peasant interiors, tools and implements for cattle breeding and tillage, craftsmen's tools 30853

Guttannen

Kristallgrotte, Grimselpass, 3864 Guttannen - T: 0279731177, Fax: 0279731422
Natural History Museum 30854

Kristallmuseum, Wirzen, 3864 Guttannen - T: 0339731247
Natural History Museum - 1975
Local minerals, quartz, fluorites, amethysts, iron pyrites from the Grimselgebiet 30855

Häggenschwil

Ortsmuseum, Alte Konstanzer Str 7, 9312 Häggenschwil - T: 0712985670, Fax: 0712984791, E-mail: info@haeggenschwil.ch, Internet: http://www.haeggenschwil.ch
Local Museum - 1997 30856

Hallau

Heimatmuseum, Kirchschulhaus, 8215 Hallau
Local Museum - 1858
Local history, archaeological finds, documents, coins, jewelry, weapons, peasant and bourgeois domestic utensils 30857

Schaffhauser Weinbaumuseum, Zur Krone, Hauptstr, 8215 Hallau - T: 0526811688
Agriculture Museum 30858

Halten

Museum Wasseramt, Turm in Halten, 4566 Halten, mail addr: c/o A. Müller, Grossacker 11, 4566 Halten - T: 0326752504, E-mail: rp@cybersystems.ch, Internet: http://www.cyberweb.ch/halten
Science&Tech Museum - 1965
13th c tower, 16th-18th c attics, peasant interiors, craft trades, weights and measures, scales and weights, the development of lighting, farm implements, bricks and tiles, weaving chamber, folk costumes, furnished house with oven 30859

Les Haudères

Musée des Haudères, Hôtel Georges, 1984 Les Haudères - T: 0272831137. Head: Joseph Georges
Local Museum 30860

Hauptwil

Textilmuseum, c/o Gottlob Lutz, Zetag AG, Sorntal, 9213 Hauptwil - T: 0714246211, Fax: 0714246262, E-mail: zetag@compuserve.com. Head: Gottlob Lutz
Science&Tech Museum - 1979 30861

Hauterive

Fondation La Tène, c/o Latenium, Parc et Musée d'Archéologie de Neuchâtel, Espace Paul Vouga, 2068 Hauterive - T: 0328896910, Fax: 0328896286, E-mail: - service.museearcheologie@ne.ch, Internet: http://www.Latenium.ch. Head: René Felber
Archaeological Museum 30862

LATENIUM, Parc et Musée d'Archéologie de Neuchâtel, Espace Paul Vouga, 2068 Hauterive - T: 0328896917, Fax: 0328896286, E-mail: - service.museearcheologie@ne.ch, Internet: http://www.latenium.ch. Head: Prof. Dr. Michel Egloff
Archaeological Museum - 1952
Prehistoric finds, Gallo-Roman and medieval archaeology, lake-dwellings, La Tène culture coll 30863

Heiden

Henry-Dunant-Museum, Asylstr 2, 9410 Heiden - T: 0718914404, Fax: 0718914813, E-mail: info@dunant-museum.ch, Internet: http://www.dunant-museum.ch. Head: Hermann Bergundthal
Special Museum - 1969
Documents on the founder of the Red Cross, Henry Dunant, house where he died, his visions, philantrophy 30864

Historisches Museum Heiden, Postgebäude, 9410 Heiden - T: 0718911956, Fax: 0718911956. Head: Rudolf Rohner
Historical Museum - 1874
Local history, peasant interiors, domestic utensils, pictures, documents, weapons, uniforms, domestic musical instruments 30865

Naturhistorisches Museum, Postgebäude, 9410 Heiden - T: 0718911956, Fax: 0718911956. Head: Rudolf Rohner
Natural History Museum - 1859
Minerals from Alps, local animals life, artefacts from indonesia 30866

Heimisbach

Simon Gfeller-Gedenkstube, Altes Schulhaus, Thal, 3453 Heimisbach, mail addr: c/o W. Herren, Kreuzwegacker 18, 3110 Münsingen - T: 0317211350, Fax: 0317218533, E-mail: w.herren@bluewin.ch. Head: Walter Herren
Special Museum
Memorabilia on the teacher and poet 30867

Hergiswil, Nidwalden

Glasmuseum, c/o Hergiswiler Glas, Seestr 12, 6052 Hergiswil, Nidwalden - T: 0416301223, Fax: 0416302157, Internet: http://www.glasi.ch. Head: Robert Niederer
Decorative Arts Museum - 1992 30868

Herisau

Museum Herisau, Altes Rathaus, 9100 Herisau - T: 0713524823, E-mail: Peter.Witschi@kk.ar.ch. Head: Dr. Peter Witschi
Local Museum - 1946
Weapons, ethnology, painted peasant furniture, embroidery and weaving, music, politics, history of Appenzell, graphics 30869

Hilterfingen

Museum für Wohnkultur des Historismus und des Jugendstils, Schloß Hünegg, 3652 Hilterfingen, mail addr: Staatsstr 52, 3652 Hilterfingen - T: 0332431982, Fax: 0332431882, Internet: http://www.schlosshuenegg.ch
Historical Museum
Interior and furnishings of the 2nd half of the 19th c (historism and modern style), Albert Emil Otto Baron von Parpart, Adelheid Sophie Margaritha von Bonstetten 30870

Hinwil

Ortsmuseum Hinwil, Oberdorfstr 11, 8340 Hinwil - T: 019372952, Fax: 019772626, E-mail: kael@active.ch, Internet: http://www.ortsmuseum.ch
Local Museum - 1925
18th c peasant interiors, craftsmen's tools, farm implements, uniforms and weapons, local history, 18th c farm building - library 30871

Hirzel

Johanna-Spyri-Museum im Alten Schulhaus, Dorfstr 48, 8816 Hirzel - T: 017299566, Fax: 017299758, Internet: http://www.johanna-spyri-museum.ch. Head: Doris Sameli-Erne
Special Museum - 1981
Hist of the literary figure of "Heidi" 30872

Hochfelden

Parfummuseum, c/o Marianne Maag-Riesen, Chäslenstr 7, 8182 Hochfelden - T: 018608008, Fax: 018608001
Special Museum - 1995 30873

Hombrechtikon

Dorfmuseum Stricklerhuus, Langenrietstr 6, 8634 Hombrechtikon - T: 0552441930, Fax: 0552441930, E-mail: therese.schmid@swissonline.ch, Internet: http://www.hombrechtikon.ch/prohon.htm
Local Museum - 1990 30874

Horgen

Bergbaumuseum, Bergwerkstr 27, 8810 Horgen, mail addr: Postfach, 8810 Horgen - T: 017253935, Fax: 017250639, E-mail: cschluep@bluewin.ch, Internet: http://www.horgen.net/bergwerk. Head: Charlotte Schluep
Science&Tech Museum - 1982 30875

Ortsmuseum Sust, Bahnhofstr 27, Sust, 8810 Horgen - T: 017251558
Local Museum - 1954
16th c building, prehistoric finds, local history, coll of 18th-20th c weapons 30876

Hüntwangen

Dorfmuseum, Dorfstr 19, 8194 Hüntwangen - T: 018691222/23, Fax: 018692030
Local Museum - 1988 30877

Huttwil

Museum Salzbütte, Spitalstr 14, 4950 Huttwil - T: 0629622079, 0629622505. Head: Rosmarie Burkhardt-Aebi
Local Museum - 1959
Local history, documents, weapons, uniforms, folk costumes, craftmen's tools and implements 30878

Ibach

Schreinereimuseum, Gotthardstr 24, 6438 Ibach - T: 0418115252, Fax: 0418116429. Head: Bernhard Reichmuth
Science&Tech Museum 30879

Ilanz

Museum Regiunal Surselva Casa Carniec, Städtlistr 10, 7130 Ilanz - T: 0819254181, Fax: 0819254181. Head: Prof. Alfons Maissen
Local Museum - 1988
Handicraft, peasant tools 30880

Intragna

Museo Regionale della Centovalli e del Pedemonte, 6655 Intragna - T: 0917962577. Head: Mario Manfrina
Local Museum - 1989 30881

Isérables

Musée Isérables, Station du Téléphérique, 1914 Isérables - T: 0273062762, 0273062622, Fax: 0273062762, E-mail: musee-iserables@bluemail.ch, Internet: http://www.iserables.ch. Head: Jean-Maximin Gillioz
Local Museum - 1967
Local history, crystals from Valais, craftsmen's and farmers' tools and implements 30882

Islikon

Museum im Greuterhof, Greuterhof, 8546 Islikon - T: 0523751235, Fax: 0523752595, E-mail: greuterhof@leunet.ch, Internet: http://www.greuterhof.ch. Head: Johann Lassnig
Historical Museum - 1983
Factory hist 30883

Telefonmuseum im Greuterhof, Greuterhof, 8546 Islikon, mail addr: Hauptstr 15, 8546 Islikon - T: 0523752727, Fax: 0523752595. Head: Max Bollhalder
Science&Tech Museum - 1995 30884

Jegenstorf

Schloß, General-Guisan-Str 5, 3303 Jegenstorf - T: 0317610159, Fax: 0317613506, E-mail: schloss.jegi@bluewin.ch, Internet: http://www.schloss-jegenstorf.ch. Head: Heinz Witschi
Historic Site - 1936
Interiors, Renaissance to 19th c furnishings, documents, memorabilia of the writer Rudolf von Tavel (1866-1934), medieval castle 30885

Jenins

Weinbaumuseum Jenins, Hauptstr, 7307 Jenins - T: 0813221517
Agriculture Museum - 1974 30886

Jona

Ortsmuseum, Neuhof, 8645 Jona - T: 0552125268, 0552252727, Internet: http://www.jona.ch
Local Museum 30887

Kaltbrunn

Ortsmuseum, Rickenstr 8, 8722 Kaltbrunn - T: 0552831641
Local Museum - 1976
Local history, domestic utensils and farm implements, crafts, manufacture of hemp and flax, ecclesiastical items, finds from the historical ruin Bibiton, coal mining 30888

Kiesen

Milchwirtschaftliches Museum, Bernstr, 3117 Kiesen, mail addr: Postfach 651, 3000 Bern 25 - T: 0317811844, 0313351919, Fax: 0313351910. Head: R. Seiler
Agriculture Museum - 1965
Interiors of an old cheese dairy, pictures, artifacts, audiovisual presentation of cheese production 30889

Kilchberg, Zürich

Ortsmuseum Kilchberg, Alte Landstr 170, 8802 Kilchberg, Zürich - T: 017153140, Internet: http://www.kilchberg.ch/freizeit/kultur/ortsmuseum.htm. Head: Dr. Elisabeth Lott-Büttiker
Local Museum - 1943
Porcelain, fine pottery and ceramics from the Zurich factory at 'Schooren' in Kilchberg and nearby factories, objects and documentation about fishing and shipping on the Lake of Zurich, local winegrowing, study of the poet Conrad Ferdinand Meyer, show-room about the Mann family at Kilchberg 30890

Kippel

Lötschentaler Museum, 3917 Kippel, mail addr: Postfach, 3917 Kippel - T: 0279391871. Head: Marcus Seeberger
Local Museum 30891

Klosters

Heimatmuseum Nutli-Hüschi, Monbielerstr, 7250 Klosters - T: 0814222153
Local Museum - 1918
16th c farmhouse, cultural history of Prättigau, furniture, domestic utensils, farm implements, wood-working tools, ceramics 30892

Kloten

Büecheler-Hus, Dorfstr 47, 8302 Kloten - T: 018135514
Local Museum 30893

Klus

Heimatmuseum Klus, Burg Alt-Falkenstein, 4710 Klus, mail addr: Postfach 4, 4710 Klus - T: 0623915432
Local Museum - 1929
Ceramics 30894

Kölliken

Strohhaus und Dorfmuseum, Hauptstr 43, 5742 Kölliken - T: 0627238407, 0627232076, Fax: 0627232076. Head: Peter Diem
Local Museum / Agriculture Museum 30895

Konolfingen

Dorfmuseum, Burgdorfstr 85, 3510 Konolfingen - T: 0317910098
Local Museum - 1978
Crafts, arms, fire fighting, toys, textiles, distillery, cheese-factory, engines, music instruments 30896

Naturhistorisches Museum, Alte Post, 3510 Konolfingen - T: 0317911031
Natural History Museum 30897

Kradolf

Feuerwehrmuseum Kradolf-Schönenberg, Bahnhofstr 19, 9214 Kradolf, mail addr: Postfach 10, 9214 Kradolf - T: 0716424492, 0716421367, Fax: 0716423479
Science&Tech Museum - 1956 30898

Krauchthal

Gemeindemuseum, Altes Schulhaus, 3326 Krauchthal - T: 0344111040
Local Museum - 1981 30899

Kreuzlingen

Bodensee-Museum, Seeburgpark, 8280 Kreuzlingen
Local Museum 30900

Feuerwehrmuseum, Löwenstr 7, 8280 Kreuzlingen - T: 0716776370, Fax: 0716723473, E-mail: ordnungsdienste@kreuzlingen.ch. Head: Werner Ilg
Science&Tech Museum - 1956
Firefighting, several 19th-20th c fire engines and manual apparatuses, tools and implements, pictures and documents 30901

Hausmuseum Kloster Kreuzlingen, Hauptstr 96, 8280 Kreuzlingen - T: 0716722218, Fax: 0716722254. Head: Alois Bachmann
Historical Museum / Religious Arts Museum - 1993 30902

Heimatmuseum Kreuzlingen, Roseneggschulhaus, Bärenstr 6, 8280 Kreuzlingen - T: 0716724993
Local Museum 30903

Puppenmuseum Jeannine, Schloßgut Girsberg, 8280 Kreuzlingen - T: 0716725914, 0716724655, Fax: 0716724655
Decorative Arts Museum - 1973
memorial room Count Zeppelin 30904

Seemuseum in der Kornschütte, Seeburgpark, Seeweg 3, 8280 Kreuzlingen, mail addr: Postfach 111, 8280 Kreuzlingen 2 - T: 0716885242, Fax: 0716885243, Internet: http://www.seemuseum.ch. Head: Dr. Hans-Ulrich Wepfer
Special Museum - 1993
Fishing and shipping on the Lake Constance, hydrography 30905

Kriens

Museum im Bellpark, Luzerner Str 21, 6010 Kriens - T: 0413103381, Fax: 0413109381. Head: Hilar Stadler
Local Museum - 1991
Local hist, photography, fine and contemporary art 30906

Küsnacht

Ortsmuseum Küsnacht, Tobelweg 1, 8700 Küsnacht - T: 019105970, Fax: 019101880, E-mail: ch.schweiss@ortsmuseum-kuesnacht.ch, Internet: http://www.ortsmuseum-kuesnacht.ch. Head: Christoph Schweiss
Local Museum - 1983
Local hist, coiffeur, costume (ca. 1870-1970) 30907

Küssnacht am Rigi

Heimatmuseum, Beim Kirchturm, 6403 Küssnacht am Rigi, mail addr: c/o W.Lüönd, Haldenweg 12, 6403 Küssnacht am Rigi - T: 0418504482, 0418540235, Fax: 0418501549, E-mail: w.lueoend@kuessnacht.ch, Internet: http://www.kuessnacht.ch
Local Museum - 1951
Local history, prehistory, documentation on the Tell tale, customs and traditions, ecclesiastical 30908

Kyburg

Museum Schloss Kyburg, 8314 Kyburg - T: 0522324664, Fax: 0522326935, E-mail: museum@schlosskyburg.ch, Internet: http://www.schlosskyburg.ch. Head: Ueli Stauffacher
Historical Museum - 1917
12th-13th and 16th c castle, 15th and 17th c wall paintings, 16th-18th c interiors, 16th-18th c glass paintings, arms and armour 30909

Laax

Ortsmuseum, Via Principala 62, 7031 Laax, mail addr: Center Communal, 7031 Laax - T: 0819215366, 0819214702
Local Museum 30910

Le Landeron

Musée, Hôtel de Ville, 2525 Le Landeron, mail addr: Administration communale, 2 Rue du Centre, 2525 Le Landeron - T: 0327523570, Fax: 0327523571
Local Museum - 1981
Local history, Roman archeological finds, pictures and photos, goldsmith art (15th-18th c), interiors, birds, uniforms, arms 30911

Langendorf

Dorfmuseum, Schulhausstr 2, 4513 Langendorf - T: 0326220904
Local Museum - 1984 30912

Langenthal

Museum Langenthal, Bahnhofstr 11, 4900 Langenthal - T: 0629227181, Fax: 0629236705, E-mail: samherrmann@datacomm.ch, Internet: http://www.museums.ch/vms-ams. Head: Samuel Herrmann
Local Museum - 1984
Geography, natural and prehist, linen weavery 30913

Laufen

Brauereichäller Kulturforum, Delsberger Str 82, 4242 Laufen - T: 0617617148
Public Gallery 30914

Museum Laufental, Am Helye-Pl 59, 4242 Laufen - T: 0617614189. Head: Robert Kamber
Local Museum - 1945
Geology, documents on regional history, crafts and industries, religious art, Roman farmhouse 'Müschhag', memorabilia of the book printer Helyas Helye, works of the local painter August Cueni (1883-1966), prehistory of Laufental 30915

Laufenburg

Museum zum Schiff, Fluhgasse, 5080 Laufenburg - T: 0628742243. Head: Gabi Strittmatter
Local Museum - 1978
Local hist, the Rhine in its original course, fishing industry, tools 30916

Lausanne

Cabinet des Médailles Cantonal, Palais de Rumine, 6 Pl de la Riponne, 1014 Lausanne - T: 0213163990, Fax: 0213163999, E-mail: Anne.Geiser@SERAC.vd.ch, Internet: http://www.lausanne.ch/musees/medaille.htm. Head: Anne Geiser
Special Museum
Coins and medals from Switzerland and neighbouring countries, Gallo-Roman and Greek coins, weights, scales - library 30917

Chemin de Fer-Musée Blonay-Chamby, CP 366, 1001 Lausanne - T: 0219432121, Fax: 0219432221, E-mail: info@blonay-chamby.ch, Internet: http://www.blonay-chamby.ch. Head: M. Friederich
Science&Tech Museum - 1968
Coll of steam trains, trams, wagons (19-20th c) 30918

Collection de l'Art Brut, 11 Av des Bergières, 1004 Lausanne - T: 0216475435, Fax: 0216485521, E-mail: art.brut@lausanne.ch, Internet: http://www.artbrut.ch. Head: Lucienne Peiry
Fine Arts Museum - 1976
Outsider art 30919

Espace Arlaud, 2bis Pl de la Riponne, 1005 Lausanne - T: 0213163850
Natural History Museum 30920

Espace Lausannoise d'Art Contemporain, 19 Rue de Genève, 1003 Lausanne - T: 0213112240, Fax: 0213112241, E-mail: pierre.keller@dfj.vd.ch, Internet: http://www.ecal.ch. Head: Pierre Keller
Fine Arts Museum 30921

Fondation de l'Hermitage, 2 Rte du Signal, 1000 Lausanne 8 - T: 0213205001, Fax: 0213205071, E-mail: info@fondation-hermitage.ch, Internet: http://www.fondation-hermitage.ch. Head: Juliane Cosandier
Fine Arts Museum - 1984 30922

Musée Cantonal d'Archéologie et d'Histoire, Palais de Rumine, 6 Pl de la Riponne, 1005 Lausanne - T: 0213163430, Fax: 0213163431, E-mail: musee.archeologie@serac.vd.ch, Internet: http://www.lausanne.ch/archeo. Head: Gilbert Kaenel
Archaeological Museum / Historical Museum - 19th c
Regional archaeology: Mesolithic, Neolithic, Bronze Age, Iron Age, Gallo-Roman times, Middle ages, hist, classical archaeology, egyptology - library, phototheque 30923

Musée Cantonal de Géologie, UNIL, BFSH-2, 1015 Lausanne - T: 0216924470, Fax: 0216924475, E-mail: aymon.baud@sst.unil.ch, Internet: http://www-sst.unil.ch/musee. Head: Dr. A. Baud
Natural History Museum - 1900
Mineralogy, paleontology, geology 30924

Musée Cantonal de Zoologie, Palais de Rumine, 6 Pl de la Riponne, 1005 Lausanne, mail addr: CP 448, 1000 Lausanne 17 - T: 0213163460, Fax: 0213163479, E-mail: musee.zoologie@serac.vd.ch. Head: Dr. Michel Sartori
Natural History Museum - 1833
Zoology, extinct birds, local fauna, Swiss vertebrates, entomology, cryptozoology, O.Forel/V.Nabokov colls 30925

Musée de Botanique, 14bis Av de Cour, 1007 Lausanne - T: 0213169988, Fax: 0216164665, E-mail: gino.muller@dfj.unil.ch, Internet: http://www.lausanne.ch/musees/botaniq.htm. Head: Dr. Gino Müller
Natural History Museum 30926

Musée de Design et d'Arts Appliqués Contemporains, 6 Pl de la Cathédrale, 1005 Lausanne - T: 0213152530, Fax: 0213152539, E-mail: mu.dac@lausanne.ch, Internet: http://www.lausanne.ch/mudac. Head: Chantal Prod'Hom
Decorative Arts Museum - 1862
Contemporary arts and crafts, very important coll of contemporary international (European, American and Japanese) glass sculptures, design 30927

Musée de la Main, Fondation Claude Verdan, 21 Rue du Bugnon, 1005 Lausanne - T: 0213144955, Fax: 0213144963, E-mail: mmain@hospvd.ch, Internet: http://verdan.hospvd.ch. Head: Dr. Ninian Hubert von Blyenburgh
Special Museum - 1981
Science, art, hand 30928

Musée de l'Elysée, 18 Av de l'Elysée, 1014 Lausanne - T: 0216174821, Fax: 0216170783, E-mail: dgirardin@pingnet.ch. Head: William A. Ewing
Fine Arts Museum 30929

Musée des Beaux-Arts Cantonal, Palais de Rumine, 6 Pl de la Riponne, 1014 Lausanne - T: 0213163445, Fax: 0213163446, E-mail: musee.beaux-arts@serac.vd.ch, Internet: http://www.lausanne.ch/musees/beauxarts.htm. Head: Yves Aupetitallot
Fine Arts Museum - 1841
Collections of the cantonal departments of paintings, prints, drawings and sculpture. The emphasis is on Swiss paintings from 1750 through to 20th c art. These works are permanently exhibited in the first three galleries. The museum has the world's largest collections of works by the watercolourist Louis Ducros (1748-1810), the academic painter Charles Gleyre (1806-1874), the wood engraver and painter Félix Valloton (1865-1925) and the Art Brut artist Louis Soutter (1871-1942) - library, phototheque 30930

Musée Historique de Lausanne, Collection du Vieux-Lausanne, 4 Pl de la Cathédrale, 1005 Lausanne - T: 0213310353, 0213121368, Fax: 0213124268, E-mail: musee.historique@lausanne.ch, Internet: http://www.lausanne.ch. Head: Olivier Pavillon
Historical Museum - 1918
Local history, archeological finds from the Roman period and the Middle Ages, history of the bishopric, interiors (17th-19th c), tin, silver, furniture, wood carving, paintings and drawings, plans relating to town development - library 30931

Musée Olympique, 1 Quai d'Ouchy, 1006 Lausanne, mail addr: CP, 1001 Lausanne - T: 0216216511, Fax: 0216216512, E-mail: fsi@olympic.org, Internet: http://www.olympic.org. Head: Françoise Zweifel
Historical Museum - 1982
Olympic games, collections of posters, art, flags, sport equipement, pins, medals, souvenirs, torches, clothes or accessoires, furniture - library (16,000 vol.200 periodicals, photo and video library) 30932

Musée Romain, 24 Chemin du Bois-de-Vaux, 1007 Lausanne - T: 0216251084, Fax: 0216251135, E-mail: mrv@lausanne.ch, Internet: http://www.lausanne.ch/mrv. Head: Laurent Flutsch
Archaeological Museum - 1993
Archaeological finds from the Roman site of Lousonna (Lausanne) 30933

Lauterbrunnen

Heimatmuseum der Talschaft Lauterbrunnen, Mühle, 3822 Lauterbrunnen - T: 0338553586, 0338551388
Local Museum - 1976 30934

Lens

Musée du Grand-Lens, 3962 Lens - T: 0274832451. Head: Sylvie Doriot
Local Museum - 1992 30935

Lenzburg

Historisches Museum Aargau, Schloß, 5600 Lenzburg - T: 0628884840, Fax: 0628884841, E-mail: daniela.ball@ag.ch, Internet: http://www.AG.CH/LENZBURG. Head: Dr. Daniela Ball
Historical Museum - 1868
Housing (15th-19th c), European handicraft, local history 30936

Museum Burghalde, Schlossgasse 23, 5600 Lenzburg - T: 0628916670, 0628917565. Head: Alfred Huber
Historical Museum
Local, pre- and early history 30937

Leuk Stadt

Heimatmuseum Leuk Stadt, Bischofsschloß, 3953 Leuk Stadt - T: 0274731223
Local Museum - 1977 30938

Lichtensteig

Fredy's Mechanisches Musikmuseum, Bürgistr 5, 9620 Lichtensteig - T: 0719883766, Fax: 0719883766, Internet: http://www.kaufurs.ch/fredysmechmusi. Head: Fredy Künzle
Music Museum
Mechanical musical instruments 30939

Toggenburger Museum, Hauptgasse 1, 9620 Lichtensteig - T: 0719888181, 0719883585, E-mail: hans.buechler@bluewin.ch. Head: Dr. Hans Büchler
Local Museum - 1896
History and cultural history of the region, esp arts and crafts, painted furniture, Alpine folk art, early cotton industry 30940

Liesberg

Ortsmuseum, Ehemaliges Pfarrhaus, 4253 Liesberg - T: 0617710754
Local Museum - 1997 30941

Liestal

Dichter- und Stadtmuseum/ Herwegh-Archiv, Rathausstr 30, 4410 Liestal - T: 0619237015, Fax: 0619237016, E-mail: mail@dichtermuseum.ch, Internet: http://www.dichtermuseum.ch. Head: Dr. Hans Schneider
Local Museum - 1946
Memorabilia of Georg Herwegh, Carl Spitteler, Josef Viktor Widmann, Hugo Marti, Theodor Opitz' coll of autographs, town hist - Herwegh archives 30942

Erzgebirgisches Spielzeugmuseum, Seltisbergerstr 18, 4410 Liestal - T: 0619222324, Fax: 0619222304. Head: Kathrin Grauwiller-Straub
Decorative Arts Museum - 1994 30943

Harmonium-Museum, Widmannstr 9a, 4410 Liestal - T: 0619216410, E-mail: dstalder@datacomm.ch, Internet: http://www.datacomm.ch/~dstalder/harmoniummuseum.html. Head: Dieter Stalder
Music Museum - 1992 30944

Kantonsmuseum Baselland, Zeughauspl 28, 4410 Liestal - T: 0619255986, 0619255088, Fax: 0619256956, E-mail: kantonsmuseum@ekd.bl.ch, Internet: http://www.kantons-museum.bl.ch. Head: Pascale Meyer
Local Museum - 1837
Archeology (pre- and early history, Middle Ages), numismatics, arms, folklore, graphic arts, natural history, zoology, geology, paleontology, mineralogy - library, archives, photo library 30945

Kunsthalle Palazzo, Poststr 2, 4410 Liestal - T: 0619215062, Fax: 0619220548, E-mail: kunsthalle@palazzo.ch, Internet: http://www.palazzo.ch. Head: Esther Maria Jungo
Fine Arts Museum 30946

Ligerz

Rebbaumuseum am Bielersee, Hof, Neuenburgstr, 2514 Ligerz, mail addr: Postfach, 2514 Ligerz - T: 0323152132, Fax: 0323157278, E-mail: hof@bielersee-events.ch, Internet: http://www.bielersee-events.ch. Head: Urs Wendling, Heidi Lüdi
Agriculture Museum - 1963
Viticulture - library, index of archives about viticulture 30947

Ligornetto

Museo Vela, Largo Vela, 6853 Ligornetto - T: 0916407044, Fax: 0916473241, E-mail: museo.vela@bak.admin.ch, Internet: http://www.museo-vela.CH. Head: Dr. Gianna A. Mina
Fine Arts Museum - 1898
Works by the sculptor Vincenzo Vela (1820-1891) and documents on his life, contemporary Italian painting and sculpture, historical residency 30948

Linthal

Ortsmuseum Linthal, Landvogtei, Schiesserhaus, 8783 Linthal - T: 0556431693
Local Museum 30949

Locarno

Alexej von Jawlensky-Archiv, Via delle Monache 16, 6600 Locarno - T: 0917514982, Fax: 0917512665, E-mail: jawlensky.archivio@ticino.com
Fine Arts Museum 30950

Museo Civico e Archeologico, Castello Visconteo, Via al Castello, 6600 Locarno, mail addr: c/o Servizi Culturali, Direzione, Via B. Rusca 5, 6600 Locarno - T: 0917563170, 0917563180, Fax: 0917519871, E-mail: servizi.culturali@locarno.ch. Head: Riccardo Carazzetti
Archaeological Museum - 1900
Archaeology, regional history 30951

Pinacoteca Comunale Casa Rusca, Piazza San Antonio, 6600 Locarno, mail addr: c/o Servizi Culturali, Direzione, Via B. Rusca 5, 6600 Locarno - T: 0917563185/86, 0917563170, Fax: 0917519871, E-mail: servizi.culturali@locarno.ch. Head: Riccardo Carazzetti
Fine Arts Museum - 1987
Collezione Hans Arp, Lascito Nesto Jacometti, Donazione Giovanni Bianconi, Donazione Rudolf Mumprecht, Collezione Filippo Franzoni, Donazione Rosalda Gilaroi-Bernocco - videoteca documentaria 30952

Le Locle

Collection d'Histoire Naturelle, 5 Rue de l'Hôtel de Ville, 2400 Le Locle
Natural History Museum 30953

Moulins Souterrains du Col-des-Roches, Col-des-Roches 23, 2400 Le Locle, mail addr: Fondation des Moulins Souterrains du Col-des-Roches 23 - T: 0329318989, Fax: 0329318915, E-mail: col-des-roches@lesmoulins.ch, Internet: http://www.lesmoulins.ch. Head: Caroline Calame
Science&Tech Museum - 1987 30954

Musée des Beaux-Arts, 6 Rue Marie-Anne-Calame, 2400 Le Locle - T: 0329311333, Fax: 0329313257, E-mail: mbal@bluewin.ch. Head: Jean Grédy
Fine Arts Museum - 1880
Coll of art from Neuchâtel and Switzerland, printing press (19th-20th c) 30955

Musée d'Horlogerie du Locle, Château des Monts, 65 Rte des Monts, 2400 Le Locle - T: 0329311680, Fax: 0329311670, E-mail: mhl.monts@bluewin.ch. Head: Pierre Buser
Science&Tech Museum - 1959
Chronometry from its early beginnings to the present, M. and E.M. Sandoz coll - library 30956

Loco

Museo Onsernonese, Casa Geo de Giorgi, Strada Cantonale, 6661 Loco - T: 0917971070, Fax: 0917519871, E-mail: riccardo.carazzetti@bluewin.ch. Head: Prof. Riccardo Carazzetti
Local Museum - 1966
Regional history, furniture, costumes, industries, religious art, works of the painter Carlo Meletta 30957

Lottigna

Museo di Blenio, Casa dei Landfogti, 6711 Lottigna - T: 0918711977
Local Museum - 1950
Regional history, agriculture, viticulture, forestry, folklore, arms (15th c to present) 30958

Lourtier

Musée des Glaciers, Maison Jean-Pierre Perraudin, Centre du Village, 1948 Lourtier - T: 0267781288, 0267771100. Head: Marguerite Perraudin
Natural History Museum - 1993
Memorabilia of Jean-Pierre Perraudin, glaziologist 30959

Lucens

Musée Sherlock Holmes, Château, 1522 Lucens
Special Museum 30960

Lützelflüh

Gotthelf-Stube, Schriftsteller-Museum, Beim Pfarrhaus, 3432 Lützelflüh - T: 0344601611, Fax: 0344601600, Internet: http://www.luetzelflueh.ch/Gotthelf. Head: Hans Messerli
Special Museum - 1954
Memorabilia of Jeremias Gotthelf (1797-1854), pictures and documents concerning the poet, furniture and peasants' implements - archives 30961

Kulturmühle Lützelflüh, Stiftung Jolanda Rodio, Mühlegasse 29, 3432 Lützelflüh - T: 0344613623
Local Museum 30962

Lugano

Fondazione Galleria Gottardo, Viale Stefano Franscini 12, 6900 Lugano - T: 0918081988, Fax: 0918082447, E-mail: galleria@gottardo.ch, Internet: http://www.gottardo.ch/galleria. Head: Luca Patocchi
Public Gallery 30963

Museo Cantonale d'Arte, Via Canova 10, 6900 Lugano - T: 0919104780, Fax: 0919104789, E-mail: dic-mca@ti.ch, Internet: http://www.museo-cantonale-arte.ch. Head: Marco Franciolli
Fine Arts Museum 30964

Museo Cantonale di Storia Naturale, 4 Viale C. Cattaneo, 6900 Lugano - T: 0919115380, Fax: 0919115389, E-mail: dt-mcsn@ti.ch, Internet: http://www.ti.ch/dt/da/museo. Head: Filippo Rampazzi
Natural History Museum - 1854
Minerals, geology, fossils, regional flora and fauna - library 30965

Museo Civico di Belle Arti, Villa Ciani, 6900 Lugano, mail addr: Dicastero attività culturali, CP 2110, 6900 Lugano - T: 0918007201, 0918007196, Fax: 0918007497, E-mail: cultura@lugano.ch, Internet: http://www.lugano.ch. Head: Dr. Rudy Chiappini
Fine Arts Museum - 1933
Municipal collection with works by the great impressionists and modern masters (Monet, Rousseau, Matisse), and works by principal Ticino artists from every era (Serodine, Mola, Carloni, Vela, Ciseri, Rossi, Berta) 30966

Museo d'Arte Moderna, Villa Malpensata, Riva Caccia 5, 6900 Lugano, mail addr: CP 2110, 6901 Lugano - T: 0918007201, 0919944370, Fax: 0918007497, E-mail: info@mdam.ch, Internet: http://www.mdam.ch. Head: Dr. Rudy Chiappini
Fine Arts Museum - 1973 30967

Museo di Santa Maria degli Angioli, Chiesa Santa Maria degli Angioli, Piazza Luini, 6900 Lugano - T: 0919220112, Fax: 0919220112. Head: Dr. Andrzej Rogalski
Religious Arts Museum - 1974
Religious art 30968

Museo Storico, Villa Saroli, Viale Stefano Franscini 9, 6900 Lugano, mail addr: Strada di Gandria 4, 6976 Castagnola - T: 0919710271, Fax: 0919703825. Head: Dr. Antonio Gili
Historical Museum - 1994 30969

Luzern

Alpineum, 3D-Alpenpanorama/ Diorama, Denkmalstr 11, 6006 Luzern - T: 0414104064, 0414106266, Fax: 0414104745, E-mail: info@alpineum.ch, Internet: http://www.alpineum.ch. Head: Daniel E. Hodel
Special Museum - 1901
Stereoskopie, 3D-photography, the Alps, tourism 30970

Archäologische Sammlung des Natur-Museums Luzern, Kasernenpl 6, 6003 Luzern - T: 0412285411, Fax: 0412105140, E-mail: juerg.manser@lu.ch, Internet: http://www.naturmuseum.ch. Head: Dr. Peter Herger, Jurg Manser
Archaeological Museum / Natural History Museum 30971

Architekturgalerie Luzern, Denkmalstr 15, 6005 Luzern - T: 0412492018, Fax: 0412492017, E-mail: info@architekturgalerieluzern.ch, Internet: http://www.architekturgalerie.ch. Head: Toni Häflinger, Luca Oeon
Fine Arts Museum - 1983 30972

Bourbaki-Panorama, Löwenpl 11, 6328 Luzern, mail addr: CP, 6004 Luzern - T: 0414123030, Fax: 0414123031, E-mail: info@panorama-luzern.ch, Internet: http://www.bourbaki.ch. Head: Bernadette Burger
Special Museum 30973

Gletschergarten, Stiftung Amrein-Troller, Denkmalstr 4, 6006 Luzern - T: 0414104340, Fax: 0414104310, E-mail: wick@gletschergarten.ch, Internet: http://www.gletschergarten.ch. Head: Peter Wick
Natural History Museum / Local Museum - 1873
Natural monument from the Ice Age (discovered 1873) models of Swiss and other mountain ranges, town views, finds from the cave 'Steiglfadbalm', minerals, fossils, personal possessions of the founder of the museum Amrein Troller, hall of mirrors (maze) 30974

Hans Erni Museum, Hans Erni-Stiftung, Lidostr 5, 6006 Luzern - T: 0413708280, Fax: 0413708288, Internet: http://www.hans-erni.ch
Fine Arts Museum
Paintings from Hans, Erni 30975

Historisches Museum Luzern, Pfistergasse 24, 6000 Luzern 7, mail addr: Postfach 7437, 6000 Luzern 7 - T: 0412285424, Fax: 0412285418, E-mail: info@hmluzern.ch, Internet: http://www.hmluzern.ch. Head: Dr. Heinz Horat
Historical Museum - 1875
Costumes and textiles, glass painting (15th-17th c), coins and arms 30976

Kornschütte, Kornmarkt 3, 6004 Luzern - T: 0414102875
Public Gallery 30977

Kunstmuseum Luzern, Europapl 1, 6002 Luzern - T: 0412267800, Fax: 0412267801, E-mail: kml@kunstmuseumluzern.ch, Internet: http://www.kunstmuseumluzern.ch. Head: Peter Fischer
Fine Arts Museum - 1819
Swiss art (15th-20th c), European art (20th c), German expressionists, international contemporary art 30978

Kunstpanorama im Bourbaki, Löwenpl 11, 6004 Luzern - T: 0414120809, E-mail: info@panorama-luzern.ch, Internet: http://www.panorama-luzern.ch
Fine Arts Museum - 2000 30979

Natur-Museum Luzern, Kasernenpl 6, 6003 Luzern - T: 0412285411, Fax: 0412285406, E-mail: luzern@naturmuseum.ch, Internet: http://www.naturmuseum.ch. Head: Dr. Peter Herger
Natural History Museum - 1825
Geology, paleontology, mineralogy, botany, entomology, zoology, prehistorical regional finds - library 30980

Picasso-Museum, Donation Rosengart, Rhyn-Haus, Furrengasse 21, 6004 Luzern - T: 0414103533. Head: Heidi Rothen
Fine Arts Museum - 1978
Works by Pablo Picasso (1881-1973), paintings, drawings, graphic art, sculpture 'Femme au chapeau' (1963), ceramics 30981

Richard Wagner-Museum, Städtische Sammlung alter Musikinstrumente Tribschen, Richard-Wagner-Weg 27, 6005 Luzern - T: 0413602370, Fax: 0413602370, E-mail: HabeggU@stadtluzern.ch. Head: Dr. Ueli Habegger
Music Museum - 1933
Memorabilia of the composer Richard Wagner (1813-1883), European and non-European musical instruments 30982

Verkehrshaus der Schweiz, Schweizerisches Museum für Verkehr und Kommunikation, Lidostr 5, 6006 Luzern - T: 0413704444, Fax: 0413706168, E-mail: mail@verkehrshaus.org, Internet: http://www.verkehrshaus.org. Head: Dr. Heinrich Zemp, Daniel Suter
Science&Tech Museum / Special Museum - 1959
Aviation and space technology, railway, navigation, post and telecommunications, Hans Erni-Museum, road transport, cableways and tourism - library, archive, restoration workshop, planetarium 30983

Männedorf

Zürichsee-Schiffahrtsmuseum, Heimethuus, Villa Liebegg, Alte Landstraße 220, 8708 Männedorf - T: 019202002, Fax: 017402250, E-mail: lentylerconsulting@bluewin.ch. Head: Wolfgang Benninghoff
Science&Tech Museum 30984

Malix

Musik-Instrumenten-Sammlung, Oberdorf 113, 7074 Malix - T: 0812520052
Music Museum 30985

Maloja

Atelier Segantini, 7516 Maloja - T: 081824388, Fax: 0818243637. Head: Dr. Frank Lohmann
Fine Arts Museum - 1985
Biographical docs related to Siovanni, Segantinis 30986

Marbach (Sankt Gallen)

Ortsmuseum Oberes Bad, Obergasse 25, 9437 Marbach (Sankt Gallen) - T: 0717772486, Fax: 0717758199, E-mail: gemeindeverwaltung@marbach.ch, Internet: http://www.marbach.ch
Local Museum - 1985 30987

Marin-Epagnier

Papiliorama-Nocturama Foundation, Marin-Centre, 2074 Marin-Epagnier, mail addr: CP 31, 2074 Marin-Epagnier - T: 0327534344, 0327534350, Fax: 0327534675, E-mail: contact@papiliorama.ch, Internet: http://www.papiliorama.ch. Head: Caspar Bijleveld van Lexmond
Natural History Museum
Exotic butterflies and other tropical fauna and flora incl birds, fishes and reptiles, South-american nocturnal fauna 30988

Marthalen

Orts- und Wohnmuseum, Hirschenpl, 8460 Marthalen - T: 0523191227, 0523054444
Local Museum - 1978
Peasant tools and implements, domestic utensils and furnished farm house, viticulture, village blacksmith, firefighting instruments 30989

Martigny

Fondation Louis Moret, 33 Chemin des Barrières, 1920 Martigny - T: 0277222347, Fax: 0277222347. Head: Marie-F. Aymon
Fine Arts Museum 30990

Fondation Pierre Gianadda, 59 Rue du Forum, 1920 Martigny - T: 0277223978, Fax: 0277223163, E-mail: info@gianadda.ch, Internet: http://www.gianadda.ch. Head: Léonard Gianadda
Fine Arts Museum - 1978
Art exhibitions 30991

Manoir de la Ville de Martigny, 1 Pl du Manoir, 1920 Martigny - T: 0277212230, Fax: 0277212232, E-mail: jmg@omedia.ch. Head: Jean-Michel Gard
Public Gallery - 1971 30992

Mazot-Musée de Plan-Cerisier, c/o Café Restaurant de Plan-Cerisier, 1921 Martigny - T: 0277222960
Special Museum - 1978 30993

Musée de l'Automobile, Rue du Forum, 1920 Martigny - T: 0277223978, Fax: 0277225285, E-mail: info@gianadda.ch, Internet: http://www.gianadda.ch. Head: Léonard Gianadda
Science&Tech Museum - 1978
Automobiles 30994

Musée Gallo-Romain d'Octodure, Rue du Forum, 1920 Martigny - T: 0277223978, Fax: 0277223163, E-mail: info@gianadda.ch, Internet: http://www.gianadda.ch. Head: Léonard Gianadda
Archaeological Museum - 1978
Roman finds, finds from Octodorus Forum Claudii Vallensium, coins, historical development of Martigny as a Roman point of support on the Great-Saint-Bernhard road, furnishing and interiors 30995

Maschwanden

Dorfmuseum Maschwanden, Unterdorf 288, 8933 Maschwanden - T: 017670555
Local Museum - 1972 30996

Matzendorf

Thaler Keramikmuseum und Maria-Felchin-Sammlung, Pfarrheim, 4713 Matzendorf - T: 0623941167
Decorative Arts Museum - 1968
Ceramics from Matzendorf and Ädermannsdorf, ceramics by Urs Studer (1787-1846) 30997

Maur

Herrliberger-Sammlung, Burgstr 8, 8124 Maur - T: 019802221, E-mail: museenmaur@swissonline.ch, Internet: http://www.museenmaur.ch. Head: Christine Bozzone
Special Museum - 1976
Works of engraver and publisher David Herrliberger (1697-1777), local history, religious objects, stove ceramics 30998

Meilen

Ortsmuseum, Kirchgasse 14, 8706 Meilen - T: 019234727
Local Museum - 1927
Regional history, prehistory, farm implements, cellarman's shop, interiors, graphic arts 30999

Meiringen

Museum der Landschaft Hasli, Bei der Kirche, 3860 Meiringen - T: 0339712501, 0339712058. Head: Andreas Würgler
Local Museum - 1967 31000

Sherlock Holmes-Museum, Conan-Doyle-Pl, 3860 Meiringen, mail addr: Bahnhofstr 26, 3860 Meiringen - T: 0339714141, Fax: 0339714300, E-mail: sauvage@bluewin.ch, Internet: http://www.parkhotel-du-sauvage.ch. Head: Jürg Musfeld
Special Museum - 1991 31001

Melide

Swissminiatur, 6815 Melide - T: 0916497951, Fax: 0916499070. Head: J.L. Vuigner
Open Air Museum - 1959
120 models (1:25) of historic buildings 31002

Mellingen

Historische Sammlung im Zeitturm, 5507 Mellingen - T: 0564912058. Head: Pius Zimmermann
Historical Museum - 1954
Regional history, lamps - archives 31003

Mendrisio

Museo d'Arte Mendrisio, Piazza San Giovanni, 6850 Mendrisio, mail addr: CP 142, 6850 Mendrisio - T: 0916467649, Fax: 0916465675. Head: Alessandro Guglielmetti
Fine Arts Museum - 1982 31004

Merenschwand

Ortsmuseum, Postlonzihus, 5634 Merenschwand - T: 0566641894
Local Museum - 1987 31005

Meride

Museo dei Fossili, Nel centro del Villaggio, 6866 Meride, mail addr: Comune di Meride, 6866 Meride - T: 0916463780, Fax: 0916460854, E-mail: comunemeride@bluewin.ch. Head: Pascal Cattaneo
Natural History Museum - 1973
Fossils, Triassic original finds, reproductions and pictures of saurians, fishes and molluscs 31006

Minusio

Museo Elisarion, Via R. Simen 3, 6648 Minusio - T: 0917436671, Fax: 0917436603, E-mail: centro.elisarion@minusio.ch. Head: Claudio Berger
Local Museum - 1981 31007

Möhlin

Dorfmuseum Melihus, Bachstr 20, 4313 Möhlin - T: 0618512346, 0618513875
Local Museum - 1985
Style of home décor, housekeeping, early and pre-history 31008

Mollis

Ortsmuseum Mollis, Altersheim, 8753 Mollis, mail addr: c/o H.-R. Gallati-Berlinger, Seelmessgasse 16, 8753 Mollis - T: 0556121032, Fax: 0556121032
Local Museum - 1975 31009

Montagnola

Museo Hermann Hesse, Torre Camuzzi, 6926 Montagnola - T: 0919933770, Fax: 0919933772, E-mail: hesse.museo@ticino.com, Internet: http://www.hessemontagnola.ch. Head: Regina Bucher
Special Museum - 1997 31010

Monthey

Musée du Vieux-Monthey, Nouveau Château, 1870 Monthey - T: 0244715661, 0244722870, Fax: 0244715661. Head: Raymond Delacoste
Local Museum - 1939
Local hist, interiors, pictures and documents on village hist, crafts and industries 31011

Montreux

Château du Châtelard, 1820 Montreux
Local Museum 31012

Maison Visinand, Centre Culturel, 32 Rue Pont, 1820 Montreux - T: 0219630726, Fax: 0219630585, E-mail: maisonvisinand@centreculturelmontreux.ch, Internet: http://www.centreculturelmontreux.ch. Head: Françoise Burkhalter, Susanne Hilpert Stuber
Local Museum 31013

Musée du Vieux-Montreux, 40 Rue de la Gare, 1820 Montreux, mail addr: CP, 1820 Montreux 3 - T: 0219631353, Fax: 0219631353, E-mail: museemontreux@bluewin.ch, Internet: http://www.museemontreux.ch. Head: Monique Riwar
Local Museum - 1874
Hist, local artifacts, tourism, climate, nature, collection of thimbles 31014

Musée National Suisse de l'Audiovisuel, 74 Av de Chillon, 1820 Montreux - T: 0219632233, Fax: 0219630294. Head: Gilbert Grandchamp
Science&Tech Museum 31015

Morcote

Parco Scherrer, Riva di Pilastri, 6922 Morcote, mail addr: Cancelleria Comunale, 6922 Morcote - T: 0919962125, 0919860000, Fax: 0919860009
Open Air Museum / Ethnology Museum 31016

Morges

Musée Alexis Forel, 54 Grand Rue, 1110 Morges, mail addr: CP 160, 1110 Morges - T: 0218012647, Fax: 0218012626, Internet: http://www.morges.ch. Head: Pietro Sarto
Decorative Arts Museum - 1918
Applied art, wood carving (16th-19th c), complete works of the engraver Alexis Forel (1852-1922), engravings by Dürer and Rembrandt, interiors (15th-19th c), glass, porcelain, toys, dolls coll from 18th c to 1940 31017

Musée Militaire Vaudois, Château, Pl du Port, 1110 Morges - T: 0218048556, Fax: 0218012621, Internet: http://www.swisscastles.ch/vaud/morges.html, http://www.chateau-morge.ch. Head: Albert Dutoit
Military Museum - 1932
Arms (15th-20th c), uniforms, banners, documents, tin figures, artillery museum 31018

Musée Paderewski, 1 Pl du Casino, 1110 Morges - T: 0218049727, 0218035926, Fax: 0218035926, Internet: http://www.multimania.com/phonotheque. Head: Rita Rosenstiel
Music Museum - 1991 31019

Musée Suisse de la Figurine Historique, Château, Pl du Port, 1110 Morges - T: 0218048556, Fax: 0218012621, Internet: http://www.swisscatles.ch/vaud/morges.html, http://www.chateau-morges.ch
Special Museum 31020

Môtiers

Musée Jean-Jacques Rousseau, c/o Association Jean-Jacques Rousseau, Neuchâtel, Rue Jean-Jacques Rousseau, 2112 Môtiers - T: 0328611318. Head: Prof. François Matthey
Special Museum - 1969
Works and life of Jean-Jacques Rousseau (1712-1778), iconographic documents, rooms where Rousseau lived during his exile 1762-1765 - library 31021

Musée Léon Perrin, Château, 2112 Môtiers, mail addr: 22 Rue des Musées, 2300 La Chaux-de-Fonds - T: 0329133010, 0327211391
Fine Arts Museum - 1975 31022

Musée Régional d'Histoire et d'Artisanat du Val-de-Travers, 14 Grand-Rue, 2112 Môtiers - T: 0328613551, E-mail: musee.regional@bluewin.ch. Head: Laurence Vaucher
Local Museum - 1859
Local hist, arts and crafts, documents, horology, hist of the production of absinth - library 31023

Moudon

Musée du Vieux-Moudon, Château du Rochefort,le Bourg, 1510 Moudon, mail addr: c/o R. Bosshard, 9 Chemin de la Colline, 1510 Moudon - T: 0219052705. Head: Reymond Bosshard
Local Museum - 1910
Regional history, pre- and early history, interiors (16th-19th c), arms and military documents, tools and implements from ancient handicrafts, farm implements, wooden models for hand-printed textiles 31024

Musée Eugène Burnand, Rue du Château, 1510 Moudon, mail addr: CP 180, 1510 Moudon - T: 0219053318. Head: Olivier Duvoisin
Decorative Arts Museum - 1960
Works by Eugène Burnand (1850-1921) painting, drawing and engravings by local artist 31025

Moutier

Musée du Tour Automatique et d'Histoire de Moutier, 121 Rue Industrielle, 2740 Moutier - T: 0324936847, Fax: 0324936847, E-mail: intermout@moutier.ch, Internet: http://www.moutier.ch/utilpub.htm. Head: Roger Hayoz
Local Museum / Science&Tech Museum - 1996 31026

Musée Jurassien des Arts, 4 Rue Centrale, 2740 Moutier - T: 0324933677, Fax: 0324933665
Fine Arts Museum - 1958
Contemporary painting by Swiss and foreign artists, printing graphics 31027

Mühleberg

BKW-Museum, Wasserkraftwerk, 3203 Mühleberg - T: 0313305111, E-mail: infobern@bkw-fmb.ch, Internet: http://www.bkw.fmb.ch. Head: Richard Stauber
Science&Tech Museum - 1981
Water turbines, generators, regulators, electrical eng 31028

Mümliswil

Schweizer Kamm-Museum, Brüggliweg 724, 4717 Mümliswil - T: 0623912901
Special Museum - 1991 31029

Münchenstein

Elektrizitätsmuseum, Weidenstr 8, 4142 Münchenstein, mail addr: c/o Elektra Birseck, Weidenstr 27, 4142 Münchenstein - T: 0614154141, Fax: 0614154646, E-mail: elektra-birseck@ebm.ch, Internet: http://www.ebm.ch/museum/html. Head: Klaus Beerli
Science&Tech Museum - 1997 31030

Froschmuseum, Grabenackerstr 8, 4142 Münchenstein - T: 0614158118, 0614117741, Fax: 0614117703. Head: Elfi Hiss, Rolf Rindlisbacher
Natural History Museum - 1990
1990 31031

Mühlenmuseum Brüglingen, Merian Stiftung Basel, Brüglingen 6, 4142 Münchenstein - T: 0612263349, Fax: 0612263346, E-mail: a.stade@merianstiftung.ch, Internet: http://www.merianstiftung.ch
Science&Tech Museum - 1961
Functional mill, grinding wheels and equipment 31032

Münsingen

Öle-Museum, Mühletalstr 28, 3110 Münsingen - T: 0317212055
Special Museum - 1984 31033

Münster

Museum Münster, Im Pfarrhaus, 3985 Münster - T: 0279731162
Religious Arts Museum - 1969
Treasury of the church, sculptures, painting (12th-19th c), historical documents on the parish and on popular religious beliefs 31034

Mürren

Alpines Ballonsport-Museum, Sportzentrum, 3825 Mürren - T: 0338568686, 0338552276
Special Museum - 1991 31035

Müstair

Klostermuseum, Kloster Sankt Johann, 7537 Müstair - T: 0818516228, Fax: 0818516292, E-mail: goll@arch.ethz.ch, Internet: http://www.interreg-mrd.org. Head: Jürg Goll
Religious Arts Museum - 1938
Carolingian marble fragments, reproductions of Carolingian frescoes, sculptures, furnishings (16-17th c) 31036

Muhen

Strohhaus, Hardstr 4, 5037 Muhen - T: 0627233072
Agriculture Museum - 1963
Interior of an Aargau farm house with thatched roof, peasant life and agricultural implements, dairy, forestry, rural industries 31037

Muraz

Musée Valaisan de la Vigne et du Vin, Walliser Reb- und Weinmuseum, Château de Villa Sierre, 3964 Muraz - T: 0274564525, 0274563525, Fax: 0274563525, E-mail: mvvv@bluewin.ch. Head: Anne-D. Zufferey
Folklore Museum - 1991 31038

Muri (Aargau)

Klostermuseum, Klosterkirche, 5630 Muri (Aargau), mail addr: Postfach 313, 5630 Muri (Aargau) - T: 0566641385, E-mail: allemann.m@freiamt-online.ch. Head: Martin Allemann
Religious Arts Museum - 1972
Church treasury (17th-19th c), glass painting (16th c) 31039

Muriaux

Musée de l'Automobile, Centre du Village, 2338 Muriaux - T: 0329511040, Fax: 0329511321. Head: Claude Frésard
Science&Tech Museum - 1988 31040

Murten

Historisches Museum Murten, Ryf 4, 3280 Murten - T: 0266726200, 0266703100. Head: Heinz Kaufmann
Historical Museum - 1978
Prehistory, folk art, iconography, numismatics, arms, coats of arms, documents on the Burgundian wars 31041

Muttenz

Bauernhaus-Museum, Oberdorf 4, 4132 Muttenz - T: 0614666241, Fax: 0614666232, E-mail: jacques.gysin@muttenz.bl.ch, Internet: http://www.muttenz.ch. Head: Jacques Gysin
Agriculture Museum
Renovated farmhouse from 1444 31042

Kunsthaus Baselland, Sankt-Jakob-Str 170, 4132 Muttenz - T: 0613128388, Fax: 0613128389, E-mail: kunsthaus.bl@magnet.ch. Head: Sabine Schaschl
Association with Coll 31043

Ortsmuseum mit Karl-Jauslin-Sammlung, Schulstr 15, 4132 Muttenz - T: 0614666241, Fax: 0614666232, E-mail: jacques.gysin@mutenz.bl.ch, Internet: http://www.muttenz.ch. Head: Jacques Gysin
Local Museum - 1972
Estate of the painter Karl Jauslin (1842-1904), his oil paintings, drawings, graphic art, manuscripts, pre- and early history, archeological finds, geology, local history, tools and implements, agriculture, crafts - library 31044

Näfels

Museum des Landes Glarus, Freulerpalast, 8752 Näfels - T: 0556121378, Fax: 0556125232, E-mail: freulerpalast@bluewin.ch, Internet: http://www.freulerpalast.ch. Head: Dr. Jürg Davatz
Local Museum / Military Museum - 1946
Cultural history of canton Glarus, archaeological finds, uniforms and arms, banners, documents on colonel Caspar Freuler (17th c) and on local personalities in arts and science, antiquities, pictures, textile printing industry (18th-20th c) 31045

Naturwissenschaftliche Sammlungen des Kantons Glarus, Am Linthli 30, 8752 Näfels - T: 0556124949. Head: Roland Müller
Natural History Museum - 1839
Natural history, animal life of the canton Glarus, mammals, vertebrates and invertebrates, birds, butterflies, fish fossils, geology 31046

Neftenbach

Orts- und Weinbaumuseum, Stadt- und Dorftrotte, 8413 Neftenbach - T: 0523151868
Local Museum / Agriculture Museum - 1971
Local hist, interiors, domestic utensils, agricultural tools and implements, vestments, viticulture and wine press, flax processing 31047

Netstal

Kantonales Fischereimuseum Mettlen, Fischbrutanstalt, 8754 Netstal - T: 0556403301, 0556121060
Science&Tech Museum - 1996 31048

Kraftwerkmuseum Löntsch, 8754 Netstal - T: 0556402324. Head: Anton Zahner
Science&Tech Museum 31049

Neuchâtel

Bibliothèque Publique et Universitaire, Salle Rousseau, 3 Pl Numa-Droz, 2000 Neuchâtel, mail addr: CP 256, 2001 Neuchâtel - T: 0327177300, Fax: 0327177309, E-mail: Maryse.Schmidt-Surdez@bpu.unine.ch, Internet: http://bpun.unine.ch. Head: Michel Schlup
Library with Exhibitions - 1982 31050

Centre d'Art Neuchâtel, 37 Rue des Moulins, 2001 Neuchâtel - T: 0327240160, Fax: 0327240171, E-mail: info@can.ch, Internet: http://www.can.ch/can. Head: Jean-Pierre Huguet
Fine Arts Museum 31051

Musée d'Art et d'Histoire Neuchâtel, 1 Esplanade Léopold-Robert, 2001 Neuchâtel - T: 0327177920, Fax: 0327177929, E-mail: mahn@ne.ch, Internet: http://www.ne.ch/neuchatel/mahn. Head: Caroline Junier
Fine Arts Museum / Historical Museum - 1885
Art and hist of canton Neuchâtel, clock making and automats by Jaquet-Droz, coins and medals, ceramics, porcelain, glass, gold ornaments, arms from the Napoleonic period, documents and pictures concerning regional hist, painting, drawing, engravings and sculpture by Swiss artists, French impressionist painting - library 31052

Musée d'Ethnographie, 4 Rue Saint-Nicolas, 2000 Neuchâtel - T: 0327181960, Fax: 0327181969, E-mail: secretariat.men@ne.ch, Internet: http://www.men.ch. Head: Jacques Hainard
Ethnology Museum - 1795 31053

Muséum d'Histoire Naturelle, 14 Terreaux-Nord, 2000 Neuchâtel - T: 0327177960, Fax: 0327177969, E-mail: christophe.dufour@mhnn.unine.ch. Head: Christophe Dufour
Natural History Museum - 1835
Zoology, mammals, birds, geology, minerals 31054

L'Orangerie Galerie d'Art, 3a Rue de l'Orangerie, 2000 Neuchâtel - T: 0327241010. Head: Fernande Bovet
Public Gallery 31055

Neuhausen am Rheinfall

Fischereimuseum, Rosenbergstr 37, 8212 Neuhausen am Rheinfall - T: 013834030, Fax: 013839360. Head: Ruth Schneider
Special Museum - 1980 31056

Neunkirch

Ortsmuseum Neunkirch, Schloß Oberhof, 8213 Neunkirch - T: 0526811371
Local Museum - 1952 31057

La Neuveville

Musée d'Histoire, Ruelle de l'Hôtel de Ville, 2520 La Neuveville, mail addr: CP 260, 2520 La Neuveville - T: 032751148
Historical Museum - 1876
Local hist, Neolithic finds, 15th c cannons, firearms (16th-17th c), portraits of historical personalities, pictures and documents, pile dwellings 31058

Niederhelfenschwil

Stiftung Wilhelm Lehmann, Kobesenmühle, 9527 Niederhelfenschwil - T: 0719471115, 0719471716
Fine Arts Museum - 1987
Sculptures, drawings from Wilhelm Lehmann (1884-1974) 31059

Niederrohrdorf

Museum im Schulhaus, Oberdorfstr, 5443 Niederrohrdorf - T: 0564961126
Local Museum - 1991 31060

Nürensdorf

Ortsmuseum, Schloß, Neuhofstr 1, 8309 Nürensdorf - T: 018384050
Local Museum - 1976
Local history, agricultural implements, antiquities, pictures, relics from the former brewery at Nürensdorf 31061

Nyon

Musée du Léman, 8 Quai Louis Bonnard, 1260 Nyon 1 - T: 0223610949, Fax: 0223619220, E-mail: musee.leman@nyon.ch, Internet: http://www.museeduleman.ch
Natural History Museum - 1954
Nature and culture of the Lake Léman, navigation and fishing, local flora and fauna, aquariums scale models boats, arts 31062

Musée Historique et des Porcelaines, Château, 1260 Nyon, mail addr: CP 2655 Pl du Château, 1260 Nyon - T: 0223638282, 0223615888, Fax: 0223638286. Head: Monique Voélin-Dubey
Historical Museum / Decorative Arts Museum - 1869
Regional hist (16th-19th c), porcelain and faience manufactured in Nyon (18th-20th c), coll R. Reber of pharmaceutical objects and apothecary jars (16th-19th c) 31063

Musée Romain, Rue Maupertuis, 1260 Nyon - T: 0223617591, 0223638282, Fax: 0223638286, E-mail: musee.romain@nyon.ch, Internet: http://www.mrn.ch
Archaeological Museum - 1979
Roman finds from Colonia Julia Equestris, architecture, painting, ceramics, mosaic pictures, inscriptions, glass, coins, iron and bronze, relics of 1st c basilica, models 31064

Obergesteln

Kristall-Museum, Bei der Kirche, 3981 Obergesteln - T: 0279731836
Decorative Arts Museum - 1989 31065

Oberhasli

Nostalgisches Musikparadies, Rütisbergstr 12, 8156 Oberhasli - T: 018504971, Fax: 018334302, E-mail: kessler@cyberlink.ch, Internet: http://www.musikparadies.ch. Head: Adolf Kessler
Music Museum - 1992
100 mechanical and pneumatical music-instruments since 1770 31066

Oberhofen am Thunersee

Museum für Uhren und mechanische Musikinstrumente, Wichterheer-Gut, Staatsstr, 3653 Oberhofen am Thunersee, mail addr: Postfach, 3653 Oberhofen am Thunersee - T: 0332434377, 0332432958, Fax: 0332434377, Internet: http://www.uhrenmuseum.ch. Head: Dr. Hans Krähenbühl, Moritz Baumberger
Science&Tech Museum / Music Museum - 1995
Mechanical musical instruments, clocks 31067

Sammlung im Obersteg, Wichterheer-Gut, Staatsstr, 3653 Oberhofen am Thunersee - T: 0332433038, Fax: 0332433058, E-mail: museum.imobersteg@bluewin.ch. Head: Henriette Mentha
Fine Arts Museum - 1995
Modern painting and sculpture, french art (Cézanne, Picasso, Rouault, Chagall), russian art (Jawlensky, Soutine) 31068

Schloßmuseum, Schloß, 3653 Oberhofen am Thunersee - T: 0332431235, Fax: 0332433561, E-mail: vera.heuberger@bhm.unibe.ch. Head: Peter Jezler
Decorative Arts Museum - 1954
Interiors from the Middle Ages to the 19th c, arms, toy coll 31069

Oberrieden

Ortsgeschichtliche Sammlung, Schulhaus Pünt 8, 8942 Oberrieden - T: 017200872, 017203870, Fax: 017721878, E-mail: waldmeier.nobel@access.ch
Local Museum - 1970 31070

Oberriet

Gemeindemuseum Rothus, Staatsstr 176, 9463 Oberriet - T: 0717611712, 0717611643, Fax: 0717611712
Local Museum - 1975
Local history, agricultural implements, crafts, interiors, religious folk art, blacksmith's shop and models of buildings, shoemaker's workshop, peat-cutting, local customs - library, phototheque 31071

Oberuzwil

Ortsmuseum Oberuzwil, Statthalterhaus, 9242 Oberuzwil - T: 0719514613
Local Museum
Matthias Näf, Isaak Gröbli 31072

Oberweningen

Heimatmuseum, Zürcher Unterländer Museumsverein, Speicher, Chlupfwisstr 3, 8165 Oberweningen - T: 018561594
Local Museum - 1936
Regional history, costumes from Wehntal, peasant furnishings, religious antiquities, tools and implements for viticulture, agriculture and forestry, crafts, weights and measures 31073

Oetwil am See

Ortsmuseum Oetwil, Chilerain 10, 8618 Oetwil am See - T: 019292258
Local Museum - 1983
Silk weaver's accommodation 31074

Weinbaumuseum, Weiler Holzhausen, 8616 Oetwil am See - T: 019291147
Agriculture Museum - 1997 31075

Oftringen

Ortsmuseum, Alter Löwen, 4665 Oftringen
Local Museum - 1990 31076

Olten

Historisches Museum Olten, Konradstr 7, 4600 Olten - T: 0622128989, Fax: 0622128988
Historical Museum - 1901
Pre- and early history, ceramics, arms and uniforms, glass painting, tin, clocks, local industries, documents on town history 31077

Kunstmuseum Olten, Kirchgasse 8, 4600 Olten - T: 0622128676, Fax: 0622128676. Head:
Fine Arts Museum - 1846
Works by Martin Disteli (1802-1844) and his pupils, documents on Disteli's life, Swiss painting (19-20th c), sculpture, works by Albert Welti 31078

Naturmuseum Olten, Kirchgasse 10, 4600 Olten - T: 0622127919, Fax: 0622127927, E-mail: naturmuseum@stadt.olten.ch, Internet: http://www.naturmuseum-olten.ch. Head: Dr. Peter F. Flückiger
Natural History Museum - 1872
Swiss fauna, mineralogy, geology, paleontology 31079

Stadthaus Olten, Dornacherstr 1, 4600 Olten - T: 0622061111, Fax: 0622061203, E-mail: stadt@olten.ch, Internet: http://www.olten.ch
Local Museum 31080

Oltingen

Heimatmuseum Oltingen-Wenslingen-Anwil, Ehemalige Pfarrscheune, 4494 Oltingen - T: 0619910763, Fax: 0619910763
Local Museum - 1985 31081

Orbe

Musée d'Orbe, 23 Rue Centrale, 1350 Orbe - T: 0244411381, 0244410161. Head: Anette Combe, Vreni Segessenmann
Local Museum - 1950 31082

Pro Urba, Mosaiques Romaines, Boscéaz près d'Orbe, 1350 Orbe - T: 0244411381. Head: Annette Combe
Archaeological Museum 31083

Oron-le-Châtel

Château d'Oron, 1608 Oron-le-Châtel, mail addr: CP 6, 1608 Oron-le-Châtel - T: 0219077222, 0219079051, Fax: 0219079065, E-mail: a.locher@bluewin.ch, Internet: http://www.swisscastles.ch/Vaud/Oron/Oron.html. Head: Jean-Pierre Dresco
Decorative Arts Museum
Medieval castle with furnishings (17th-18th c), vessels, paintings and graphic art, arms - library 31084

Orselina

Museo Casa del Padre, Santuario Madonna del Sasso,Orselina,sopra Locarno, 6644 Orselina - T: 0917436265
Religious Arts Museum 31085

Ottikon (Gossau)

Dürstelerhaus, Wibergstr 2, 8626 Ottikon (Gossau) - T: 019354535, E-mail: hp.binder@bluewin.ch, Internet: http://www.gossau-zh.ch. Head: Hanspeter Binder
Local Museum 31086

Payerne

Musée de Payerne et Abbatiale, Pl du Tribunal, 1530 Payerne - T: 0266626704, E-mail: tourisme.payerne@mcnet.ch, Internet: http://www.payerne.ch. Head: Daniel Bosshard
Religious Arts Museum / Fine Arts Museum / Military Museum - 1869
Religious art, archeological finds, glasses, coins, capitals, paintings by Aimée Rapin (1868-1956), memorabilia of the general A.-H. Jomini (1779-1869) 31087

Perrefitte

Musée Au Filament Rouge, 17b Rte des Ecorcheresses, 2742 Perrefitte - T: 0324935728, Fax: 0324935728. Head: Bertrand Kissling
Science&Tech Museum - 1993 31088

Pfäffikon (Schwyz)

Seedamm Kulturzentrum, Stiftung Charles und Agnes Vögele, Gwattstr, 8808 Pfäffikon (Schwyz) - T: 0554161111, Fax: 0554161112, E-mail: info@seedamm-kultur.ch, Internet: http://www.seedamm-kultur.ch. Head: Norbert Lehmann
Fine Arts Museum - 1976
Coll "Moderne Kunst-unsere Gegenwart", Swiss Art since 1939 31089

Pfäffikon (Zürich)

Heimatmuseum am Pfäffikersee, Im Kehr am Seequai, 8330 Pfäffikon (Zürich) - T: 019504437, 019504280
Local Museum - 1876
Local history, archeological finds, agricultural implements - library 31090

Schreibmaschinen-Museum, Speckstr 3, 8330 Pfäffikon (Zürich) - T: 019503600, Fax: 019505592, E-mail: Stefan@Curta.CH, Internet: http://www.stefan.becks.ch. Head: Stefan Beck
Science&Tech Museum - 1992 31091

Pfyn

Pfahlbautenmuseum, Schulhaus, 8505 Pfyn - T: 0527651410
Open Air Museum 31092

Plan-les-Ouates

Musée de l'Automobile, 45 Ch Abérilu, 1228 Plan-les-Ouates
Science&Tech Museum 31093

Musée des Téléphones de Genève, 3 Rte du Camp, 1228 Plan-les-Ouates - T: 0223000053. Head: Marc Corbat
Science&Tech Museum - 1980 31094

Pontresina

Museum Alpin, Via Maistra, 7504 Pontresina - T: 0818427273, Fax: 0818388310, E-mail: info@pontresina.com, Internet: http://www.pontresina.com/museumalpin. Head: Annemarie Brülisauer
Local Museum - 1985 31095

Porrentruy

Fonds Ancien de la Bibliothèque Cantonale Jurassienne, 10 Rue des Annonciades, 2900 Porrentruy - T: 0324657410, Fax: 0324657499, E-mail: bibliotheque.cantonale@jura.ch, Internet: http://www.jura.ch. Head: Benoît Girard
Library with Exhibitions - 1984
Incunabula and manuscripts from 16-19th c 31096

Musée de l'Hôtel-Dieu, 5 Grand-Rue, 2900 Porrentruy - T: 0324667272, Fax: 0324667202, E-mail: mhd@museehoteldieu.ch. Head: Jeannine Jacquat
Local Museum - 1949
Regional history, pharmaceutics, posters, books and journals, manuscripts, engravings, works by local writers - engravings cabinet 31097

Musée Jurassien des Sciences Naturelles, 21-22 Rte de Fontenais, 2900 Porrentruy - T: 0324673712, 0324673750
Natural History Museum 31098

Poschiavo

Ente Museo Poschiavino, Palazzo Mengotti, 7742 Poschiavo - T: 0818443109. Head: Claudio Gisep
Local Museum 31099

Prangins

Musée National Suisse, Château de Prangins, 1197 Prangins - T: 0229948890, Fax: 0229948898, E-mail: info.prangins@slm.admin.ch, Internet: http://www.musee-suisse.ch. Head: Chantal de Schoulepnikoff
Historical Museum 31100

Pratteln

Jacquard-Stübli, Kirschgartenstr 4, 4133 Pratteln - T: 0618213728. Head: Elisabeth Löliger-Henggeler
Decorative Arts Museum - 1996 31101

Salzkammer, Rheinstr, Salinen Schweizerhalle, 4133 Pratteln 1 - E-mail: info@saline.ch
Science&Tech Museum - 1997 31102

Pregny-Chambésy

Musée des Suisses à l'Etranger, Château de Penthes, 18 Ch de l'Impératrice, 1292 Pregny-Chambésy - T: 0227349021, Fax: 0227344740, E-mail: musee@chateau-de-penthes.ch, Internet: http://www.chateau-de-penthes.ch. Head: Jean-René Bory
Historical Museum - 1961
Swiss military and political history in foreign countries (15-19th c), documents, medals, silver decorations, engravings, portraits, furniture, uniforms, arms, banners 31103

Pringy

Fromagerie de Démonstration de Gruyères, 1662 Pringy - T: 0279211410
Agriculture Museum 31104

Puidoux

Musée des Curiosités Horlogères, Ch de Tagnire, 1070 Puidoux - T: 0219463212, Fax: 0219462310. Head: Roger Donzé
Science&Tech Museum - 1992
3,000 watches, clocks and old watchmaking equipment 31105

Pully

Musée d'Art Contemporain - FAE, 85 Av du Général Guisan, 1009 Pully - T: 0217299146, Fax: 02172929149. Head: Asher B. Edelmam
Fine Arts Museum - 1991 31106

Musée de la Villa Romaine de Pully, Pl du Prieuré, 2 Av Samson-Reymondin, 1009 Pully - T: 0217295581, Fax: 0217295894, E-mail: musees.pully@bluewin.ch, Internet: http://www.lausanne.ch/musees/pully.htm. Head: Claire-Lise Bouaïche
Archaeological Museum - 1985 31107

Musée de Pully, 2 Chemin Davel, 1009 Pully - T: 0217295581, Fax: 0217295894, E-mail: musees.pully@bluewin.ch, Internet: http://www.lausanne.ch/musees/pully.htm. Head: Claire-Lise Bouaïche
Local Museum - 1946
Contemporary painting, memorabilia of local artists, writes and philosophers, local history and town views 31108

Rafz

Ortsmuseum, Oberdorf 2, 8197 Rafz - T: 018691031
Local Museum - 1966
Local history, agricultural implements, interiors, cooper's shop, wine press and distillery 31109

Rancate

Pinacoteca Cantonale Giovanni Züst, Via Pinacoteca Züst, 6862 Rancate - T: 0916464565, Fax: 0916464565, E-mail: pinacoteca.zuest@freesurf.ch. Head: Dr. Mariangela Agliati Ruggia
Fine Arts Museum - 1967
Painting, graphic arts, Tessin artists (19th-20th c): Serodine, Petrini, Orelli, Rinaldi, Rossi, Feragutti Visconti 31110

Rapperswil, Sankt Gallen

Circus Museum, Fischmarktpl 1, 8640 Rapperswil, Sankt Gallen - T: 0552205757, Fax: 0552205750. Head: Stefan Hantke
Performing Arts Museum - 1996 31111

Heimatmuseum Rapperswil, Am Herrenberg 40, 8640 Rapperswil, Sankt Gallen - T: 0552107164
Local Museum - 1942
Early history (pile worker, Roman, Allemannic), arts and crafts, religious art, paintings and portraits, arms, interiors, Gothic hall with mural paintings 31112

Polenmuseum Rapperswil, Schloß, 8640 Rapperswil, Sankt Gallen, mail addr: Postfach 1251, 8640 Rapperswil, Sankt Gallen - T: 0552101862, Fax: 0552100662, E-mail: muzeum.polskie@swissonline.ch, Internet: http://www.muzeum-polskie.org. Head: J. Morkowski
Historical Museum / Fine Arts Museum - 1870/1935/1975
Hist and cultural hist of Poland, folkore, Wincenty Lesseur coll of miniatures, Polish painting from the last 150 yrs - library 31113

Raron

Museum auf der Burg, Auf dem Burghügel,Im Pfarrhaus, 3942 Raron, mail addr: Postfach, 3942 Raron - T: 0279342969, 0279341620. Head: Helen Troger-Glenz
Local Museum - 1994 31114

Rebstein

Ortsgeschichtliche Sammlung Rebstein, Spritzenhaus,Bergstr, 9445 Rebstein - T: 0717773327
Local Museum - 1982 31115

Réclère

Préhisto-Parc et Grottes, Les Grottes, 2912 Réclère - T: 0324766155, Fax: 0324766233, E-mail: prehisto@bluewin.ch, Internet: http://www.swissgrottes.ch. Head: Eric Gigandet
Archaeological Museum - 1994 31116

Regensdorf

Gemeindemuseum, Mühlestr 22, 8105 Regensdorf - T: 018400061, Fax: 018400834
Local Museum - 1977
Regional cultural history, peasant life, village history 31117

Reiden

Kunstsammlung Robert Spreng, Johanniterschulhaus, 6260 Reiden. Head: Robert Käch
Fine Arts Museum - 1969 31118

Reigoldswil

Historische Ortssammlung, Bauernhaus Auf Feld, 4418 Reigoldswil, mail addr: c/o Dr. P. Suter, Stückben 27, 4424 Arboldswil - T: 0619312461
Local Museum - 1926
Pre- and early history, local and regional history 31119

Reinach (Aargau)

Tabak- und Zigarrenmuseum, 5734 Reinach (Aargau) - T: 0627712121, Fax: 0627717677
Special Museum - 1991 31120

Reinach (Basel-Land)

Heimatmuseum, Kirchgasse 9, 4153 Reinach (Basel-Land) - T: 0617114757, E-mail: hmmreinach@access.ch
Local Museum - 1961
Pre- and early history, local and regional history, porcelain and earthenware, religious traditions, handicrafts, agriculture, arms 31121

Reuenthal

Festungsmuseum Reuenthal, Auf dem Strick, 5324 Reuenthal, mail addr: Postfach 4293, 8052 Zürich - T: 0627723606, Fax: 0627723607, E-mail: -FestungReuenthal@cs.com, Internet: http://www.festungsmuseum.ch. Head: Willy Marques
Military Museum / Historical Museum / Science&Tech Museum - 1989 31122

Rheinfelden

Fricktaler Museum, Haus zur Sonne, Marktgasse 12, 4310 Rheinfelden - T: 0618311450, E-mail: -fricktaler.museum@bluewin.ch, Internet: http://www.rheinfelden.org/museum. Head: Kathrin Schöb
Local Museum - 1934
Pre- and early history, town history, crafts, industries, fishing, religious art, furniture, works of the painter Jakob Strasser - library, photo library 31123

Oldtimer Museum, Ehemaliges Hôtel des Salines, 4310 Rheinfelden, mail addr: c/o Fam. Grell, Quellenstr 51, 4310 Rheinfelden
Science&Tech Museum - 1978
European and American cars and racing cars, bicycles and motorcycles 31124

Richterswil

Heimatkundliche Sammlung, Haus zum Bären, Dorfbachstr 12, 8805 Richterswil - T: 017840685
Local Museum - 1939
Local history 31125

Sägereimuseum, Schönauweg 58, 8805 Richterswil - T: 017840970
Science&Tech Museum 31126

Rickenbach (Luzern)

Heimatmuseum Spycher, Beim Gasthaus Löwen, 6221 Rickenbach (Luzern) - T: 0419302550, 0419301213
Local Museum - 1980 31127

Riederalp

Alpmuseum Riederalp, Hütte Nagulschbalmu, 3987 Riederalp - T: 0279271365, Fax: 0279273313, E-mail: info@alpenmuseum.ch, Internet: http://www.alpenmuseum.ch. Head: Edelbert Kummer
Special Museum / Agriculture Museum / Folklore Museum - 1985
Local and regional hist, agriculture, dairy farming (cheese making) 31128

Riehen

Fondation Beyeler, Baselstr 101, 4125 Riehen - T: 0616459700, Fax: 0616459719, E-mail: fondation@beyeler.com, Internet: http://www.beyeler.com. Head: Ernst Beyeler
Fine Arts Museum - 1997
Works of classic modern art by the collectors Hildy and Ernst Beyeler, eg works by Picasso, Cézanne and others 31129

Sammlung Friedhof Hörnli, Altes Krematorium, Friedhof Hörnli, 4125 Riehen, mail addr: c/o Friedhofsamt, Hörnliallee 70, 4125 Riehen - T: 0616052100, Fax: 0616052200. Head: Dr. Ch. Schulz
Folklore Museum - 1987
Hair memorabilia, horse drawn hearses, ironworked grave-crosses 31130

Spielzeugmuseum, Dorf- und Rebbaumuseum, Baselstr 34, 4125 Riehen - T: 0616412829, 0616411982, Fax: 0616412635, E-mail: -spielzeugmuseum.riehen@gmx.ch, Internet: http://www.riehen.ch. Head: Bernhard Graf
Local Museum / Agriculture Museum / Folklore Museum / Special Museum - 1972
Toys from various countries, arts and crafts, peasants' life, doll's houses, Johann Rudolf Wettstein 31131

Riggisberg

Abegg-Stiftung, Werner-Abegg-Str 67, 3132 Riggisberg - T: 0318081201, Fax: 0318081200, E-mail: info@abegg-stiftung.ch, Internet: http://www.abegg-stiftung.ch. Head: Dr. Regula Schorta
Decorative Arts Museum / Special Museum - 1961
Applied art (6th millenium BC to 18th c AC), textiles - library, restoration workshop 31132

Ringgenberg

Dorfmuseum Schlossweid, Bei der Kirche, 3852 Ringgenberg - T: 0338223388, Fax: 0338233308, E-mail: mail@ringgenberg-goldswil.ch, Internet: http://www.ringgenberg-goldswil.ch
Local Museum - 1981 31133

Roche

Musée Suisse de l'Orgue, Schweizer Orgelmuseum, Av du Grand Saint-Bernard, 1852 Roche - T: 0219602200, Fax: 0219603685, E-mail: museeorgue@bluewin.ch, Internet: http://www.regart.ch/orgue. Head: Jacqueline Salchli
Music Museum - 1979 31134

Roggwil

Ortsmuseum, Sekundarschulstr, 4914 Roggwil - T: 0629293390
Local Museum - 1970 31135

Romanshorn

Kleines Museum am Hafen, Am SBB-Hafen, 8590 Romanshorn - T: 0714632704. Head: Johann Müller
Science&Tech Museum - 1988
Railway and shipping history 31136

Romont

Musée Suisse du Vitrail, Château de Romont, 1680 Romont, mail addr: CP 150, 1680 Romont - T: 0266521095, Fax: 0266524777, E-mail: -centre.recherche.vitrail@bluewin.ch, Internet: http://www.romont.ch/musee-vitrail. Head: Dr. Stefan Trümpler
Decorative Arts Museum / Fine Arts Museum - 1981
Projects and cartoons for stained glass windows 31137

Ropraz

Fondation L'Estrée, Espace Culturel, c/o Café de la Poste, Espace Culturel, 1088 Ropraz - T: 0219031173, 0219031812, Fax: 0219031173
Fine Arts Museum 31138

Rorschach

Automobil Museum Alte Garage, Beim Hafen, 9401 Rorschach - T: 0718416611, Fax: 0718417036, E-mail: info@alte-garage.ch, Internet: http://www.tourist-rorschach.ch
Science&Tech Museum - 1995
Rare oldtimer, nostalgic machines 31139

Museum im Kornhaus, Hafenpl, 9400 Rorschach, mail addr: Postfach 245, 9401 Rorschach - T: 0718414062, Fax: 0718414015. Head: Dr. Rudi Stambach
Local Museum - 1925
Early history, reconstructed cottages from Neolithic and Bronze Ages, interiors (15th-18th c), history of embroidery since 1830, history of the castle of Wartegg (Bourbon-Parma) 31140

Rothrist

Heimatmuseum, Rössliweg 1, 4852 Rothrist - T: 0627942950, 0627941616
Local Museum - 1967
Local hist, fossils, furniture, agricultural and craftmen's tools 31141

Rougemont

Musée des Minéraux et des Fossiles, Bâtiment Communal, 1659 Rougemont - T: 0269251166, Fax: 0269251167, E-mail: info@rougemont.ch, Internet: http://www.rougemont.ch. Head: Sonia Georges
Natural History Museum - 1975
Minerals and fossils from all over the world 31142

Rüeggisberg

Museum der Klosterruine mit Lapidarium, Kloster, 3088 Rüeggisberg - T: 0318090322, Fax: 0318094649, E-mail: akober@kirche-rueeggisberg.ch, Internet: http://www.kirche-rueeggisberg.ch
Religious Arts Museum / Historical Museum / Historic Site - 1947
Romanic sculpture (12th c) 31143

Rüschlikon

Ortsmuseum Rüschlikon, Nidelbadstr 58, 8803 Rüschlikon - T: 017247235, Fax: 017247236
Local Museum 31144

Rüti, Zürich

Ortsmuseum, Amtshaus, 8630 Rüti, Zürich - T: 0552407130, 0552408101
Local Museum - 1989 31145

Rupperswil

Dorfmuseum, Alter Schulweg, 5102 Rupperswil - T: 0628972627
Local Museum - 1984 31146

Saas Fee

Saaser Museum, Bei der Kirche, 3906 Saas Fee - T: 0279571475
Local Museum - 1983
Original study of Carl Zuckmayer, minerals 31147

Sachseln

Ausstellung Heinrich Federer, c/o Museum Bruder Klaus, Dorfstr 4, 6072 Sachseln - T: 0416605583, 0412107268, Fax: 0412107268. Head: Urs-Beat Frei
Special Museum - 1978
Memorabilia of the writer Heinrich Federer (1866-1928) 31148

Museum Bruder Klaus, Dorfstr 4, 6072 Sachseln - T: 0416605583, 0412107268, Fax: 0412107268, Internet: http://www.BruderKlaus.com. Head: Urs-Beat Frei
Religious Arts Museum - 1976
Documents on the hermit Nikolaus von der Flüe (1417-1487) 31149

Safien

Safier Heimatmuseum, Im Weiler Safien-Camana, 7107 Safien - T: 0816471161. Head: Mattli Hunger
Local Museum - 1981 31150

La Sagne

Musée La Sagne, Maison Communale, 103a Crêt, 2314 La Sagne - T: 0329315106. Head: Roger Vuille
Local Museum - 1876 31151

Saint-George

Musée de l'Ancienne Scierie, Les Moulins, 1261 Saint-George - T: 0223681527. Head: Paul Monney
Science&Tech Museum - 1989 31152

Saint-Gingolph

Musée des Traditions et des Barques du Léman, Le Château, 1898 Saint-Gingolph - T: 0244827022, Fax: 0244827023, E-mail: info@st-gingolph.ch, Internet: http://www.st-gingolph.ch/musee. Head: Dr. Michel Chansou
Historical Museum - 1982 31153

Saint-Imier

Musée Longines, Compagnie des Montres Longines, 2610 Saint-Imier - T: 0329425425, Fax: 0329425429, E-mail: longines@longines.com, Internet: http://www.longines.com. Head: Frédéric Donzé
Special Museum - 1992 31154

Saint-Maurice

Musée Cantonal d'Histoire Militaire, Musées Cantonaux du Valais, Château, 1890 Saint-Maurice, mail addr: 15 Pl de la Majorie, 1950 Sion - T: 0244852458, Fax: 0276064674. Head: Marie-Claude Morand
Military Museum - 1974
Uniforms, arms, various military items 31155

Saint-Prex

Musée du Verrier, Rue de la Verrerie, 1162 Saint-Prex - T: 0218231313, Fax: 0218231310
Decorative Arts Museum - 1982 31156

Saint-Sulpice, Neuchâtel

Ecomusée de la Haute-Areuse, Usine électrique, 2123 Saint-Sulpice, Neuchâtel - T: 0328613316, Fax: 0328613319, E-mail: info@ensa.ch, Internet: http://www.ensa.ch. Head: Francis Guye
Science&Tech Museum - 1994 31157

Sainte-Croix

Musée de Boîtes à Musique et Automates (Museum of Music Boxes and Automata), 2 Rue de l'Industrie, 1450 Sainte-Croix - T: 0244544477, Fax: 0244544479, E-mail: cima.ste-croix@bluewin.ch. Head: Stefan A. Müller, Liliane Gertsch
Decorative Arts Museum 31158

Musée des Arts et des Sciences, 10 Av des Alpes, 1450 Sainte-Croix - T: 0244542766. Head: Marc Hösli
Fine Arts Museum / Natural History Museum / Folklore Museum - 1872
Local industries from the 18th c to the present, mineralogy, paleontology, paintings 31159

Salenstein

Napoleon-Museum, Schloß Arenenberg, 8268 Salenstein - T: 0716633260, Fax: 0716633261, E-mail: napoleonmuseum@kttg.ch, Internet: http://www.napoleonmuseum.ch. Head: Dominik Gügel
Historical Museum / Historic Site - 1906
Napoleonic interiors, memorabilia of the Bonaparte family, music and graphic coll 31160

Salgesch

Walliser Reb- und Weinmuseum, Zumsfenhaus, 3970 Salgesch - T: 0274564525, Fax: 0274563525, E-mail: mvvv@bluewin.ch. Head: Anne-D. Zufferey
Decorative Arts Museum 31161

Samedan

Biblioteca Fundaziun Planta Samedan, Chesa Planta, 7503 Samedan, mail addr: Postfach 323Fundaziun Planta, 7503 Samedan - T: 0818500324, Fax: 0818500325. Head: Giovanni Netzer
Library with Exhibitions 31162

Plantahaus - Chesa Planta, Postfach 323, 7503 Samedan - T: 0818525268. Head: Silke Redolfi
Decorative Arts Museum - 1946
Patrician house (16th c) with Engadin interior, memorabilia of the Planta family, costumes, arms 31163

Samnaun Compatsch

Talmuseum Samnaun, Chasa Retica, Samnaun-Plan, 7562 Samnaun Compatsch, mail addr: Chasa Retica Plan, 7562 Samnaun Compatsch - T: 0818685858, Fax: 0818685652, E-mail: info@samnaun.ch, Internet: http://www.samnaun.ch. Head: Ludwig Jenal
Local Museum 31164

Samstagern

Genossenschaft Pro Sagi, Wasser-Sägerei Sagenbach, 8833 Samstagern - T: 017840970. Head: Hans Grämiger
Science&Tech Museum - 1991 31165

San Gottardo

Museo Nazionale del San Gottardo, Alte Sust, 6781 San Gottardo - T: 0918691525. Head: Carlo Peterposten
Local Museum - 1986 31166

San Vittore

Museo Moesano, Palazzo Viscardi, 6534 San Vittore - T: 0918272035. Head: Donato Salvi
Local Museum - 1949
Local history, peasants' implements, religious art 31167

Sankt Gallen

Ausstellungssaal Katharinen, c/o Kunstverein Sankt Gallen, Katharinengasse 11, 9000 Sankt Gallen - T: 0712235623, 0712420674, Fax: 0712420672, E-mail: kunstverein.sg@bluewin.ch
Public Gallery 31168

Historisches Museum Sankt Gallen, Stiftung Sankt Galler Museen, Museumstr 50, 9000 Sankt Gallen - T: 0712420642, Fax: 0712420644, E-mail: historisches_museum_sg@bluewin.ch. Head: Dr. Louis Specker
Historical Museum - 1877
Prehistory, history, bourgeois and rural style of living, folk art, costumes, fayence and porcelain, painted glass, toys, printed music - library 31169

Kunsthalle Sankt Gallen, Davidstr 40, 9000 Sankt Gallen - T: 0712221014, Fax: 0712221276. Head: Gianni Jetzer
Public Gallery 31170

Kunstmuseum, Museumstr 32, 9000 Sankt Gallen - T: 0712420671, Fax: 0712420672, E-mail: kunstmuseumsg@bluewin.ch. Head: Roland Wäspe
Fine Arts Museum - 1877
Painting (19th-20th c), graphic art (16th-20th c), sculpture 31171

Lapidarium, Stiftsbibliothek, Klosterhof 6d, 9004 Sankt Gallen - T: 0712273416, Fax: 0712273418, E-mail: Stibi@stibi.ch, Internet: http://www.stibi.ch. Head: Prof. Ernst Tremp
Fine Arts Museum - 1982 31172

Museum im Kirchhoferhaus, Stiftung Sankt Galler Museen, Museumstr 27, 9000 Sankt Gallen - T: 0712447521, 0712420642, Fax: 0712420644, E-mail: historisches_museum_sg@bluewin.ch. Head: Dr. Louis Specker
Local Museum
Prehistory coll, Giovanni Züst silver coll, coins, Eastern Swiss artists, rural painting 31173

Museum im Lagerhaus, Davidstr 44, 9000 Sankt Gallen - T: 0712235857, Fax: 0712235812, E-mail: p.s.schaufelberger@bluewin.ch. Head: Simone Schaufelberger-Breguet
Fine Arts Museum - 1988
Swiss naive art, art brut 31174

Naturmuseum, Museumstr 32, 9000 Sankt Gallen - T: 0712420670, Fax: 0712420672, E-mail: info@naturmuseumsg.ch, Internet: http://www.naturmuseumsg.ch. Head: Dr. Toni Bürgin
Natural History Museum - 1846 31175

Sammlung für Völkerkunde → Völkerkundemuseum Sankt Gallen

Sammlung Hauser und Wirth, Grünbergstr 7, 9001 Sankt Gallen - T: 0712285550, Fax: 0712285559, E-mail: info@lokremise.ch, Internet: http://www.lokremise.ch. Head: Dr. Michaela Unterdörfer
Fine Arts Museum 31176

Textilmuseum, Vadianstr 2, 9000 Sankt Gallen - T: 0712221744/45, Fax: 0712234239, E-mail: info@textilmuseum.ch, Internet: http://www.textilmuseum.ch
Special Museum - 1886
History of lace, whitework embroidery, Eastern Swiss embroidery, Textiles from egyptian tombs, ethnografic textiles 31177

Völkerkundemuseum Sankt Gallen, Stiftung Sankt Galler Museen, Museumstr 50, 9000 Sankt Gallen - T: 0712420643, Fax: 0712420644, E-mail: voelkerkundemuseum_sg@bluewin.ch. Head: Roland Steffan
Ethnology Museum - 1877
Ethnography of non-European countries 31178

Sankt Margrethen

Festungsmuseum Heldsberg, Heldsbergstr, 9430 Sankt Margrethen, mail addr: c/o A. Stähli, Sonnenstr 1, 9444 Diepoldsau - T: 0717448208, 0717334031, Fax: 0717379505, E-mail: alstaehli@dplanet.ch, Internet: http://www.festung.ch. Head: Alois Stähli
Military Museum - 1993 31179

Sankt Moritz

Engadiner Museum, Via dal Bagn 39, 7500 Sankt Moritz - T: 0818334333, Fax: 0818335007. Head: Ernst Fasser
Local Museum - 1905
Pre- and early history, Engadin interiors (16-19th c), domestic utensils, costumes, natural history, flora of the Alps 31180

Kunsthalle Sankt Moritz, Via dal Bagn 52, 7500 Sankt Moritz - T: 0818336775, Fax: 0818336775, Internet: http://www.kunsthallestmoritz.ch
Fine Arts Museum - 1982 31181

Mili Weber-Haus, Via Dimlej 35, 7500 Sankt Moritz - T: 0818333186
Fine Arts Museum - 1979 31182

Segantini-Museum, Via Somplaz 30, 7500 Sankt Moritz - T: 0818334454, Fax: 0818322454, E-mail: info@segantini-museum.ch, Internet: http://www.segantini-museum.ch. Head: Cornelia Pedretti
Fine Arts Museum - 1908
Oil paintings, sketches and drawings by Giovanni Segantini (1858-1899) 31183

Sankt Stephan

Ortsmuseum, Kuhnenhaus, 3772 Sankt Stephan - T: 0337221748, 0337222750
Local Museum - 1993 31184

Sargans

Gonzen-Museum, Sankt-Galler-Str 76, 7320 Sargans - T: 0817231217, Fax: 0817230492, E-mail: info@bergwerk-gonzen.ch, Internet: http://www.bergwerk-gonzen.ch. Head: Willi Eugster
Special Museum - 1983 31185

Historicum, Zürcherstr 5, 7320 Sargans - T: 0817231442, Fax: 0817237950. Head: Andy Hartmann, Felix Hartmann
Science&Tech Museum - 1940
Motorcars from 1910-1930, bicycles and motorcycles 31186

Museum Sarganserland, Schloß Sargans, 7320 Sargans - T: 0817236569, Fax: 0817236569, E-mail: museum.sarganserland@bluewin.de, Internet: http://www.pizol.ch/sargans. Head: Mathias Bugg
Local Museum - 1983
library, archive 31187

Schloß Sargans, 7320 Sargans. Head: Anton Stucky
Local Museum - 1966
Local and regional history, arms, hunting, furniture, paintings, history of mining 31188

Sarmenstorf

Badeanlage einer römischen Villa, Murimoosbau, 5614 Sarmenstorf - T: 0566672778. Head: Karl Baur
Archaeological Museum 31189

Jungsteinzeitliche Grabhügel, Zigiholz, 5614 Sarmenstorf - T: 0566672778. Head: Karl Baur
Archaeological Museum 31190

Sarnen

Altes Zeughaus Landenberg, 6060 Sarnen - T: 0416603233
Local Museum 31191

Heimatmuseum Sarnen, Brünigstr 127, 6061 Sarnen - T: 0416606522
Local Museum - 1877
Devotional pictures 31192

Sammlung Meinrad Burch-Korrodi, Brünigstr 178, 6060 Sarnen - T: 0416666243
Decorative Arts Museum - 1989
Works in gold and silver, Portait-coll, graphics, graphies of Innerschweiz 31193

La Sarraz

Château, Rue du Château, 1315 La Sarraz - T: 0218666423, Fax: 0218661180, Internet: http://www.swisscastles.ch./vaud/lasarraz. Head: Michel Dubois
Local Museum - 1911
Interiors (16th-19th c), painting (19th c), porcelain 31194

Musée du Cheval, Château, 1315 La Sarraz - T: 0218666423, Fax: 0218661180, E-mail: info@muche.ch, Internet: http://www.muche.ch. Head: Robert Chanson
Natural History Museum - 1982
Stirrups, spurs, saddles 31195

Savognin

Museum Regiunal, Sot Curt, 7460 Savognin - T: 0816841655
Local Museum 31196

Saxon

Glücksspielmuseum, Kasino, 1907 Saxon - T: 026441155
Special Museum
Myth of Fortuna, hist of gambling, Dostojewski (lost all his money and started writing his novel "The Gambler") 31197

Musée du Vieux-Saxon, Rue du Collège, 1907 Saxon - T: 0277441519
Local Museum - 1963
Local history, peasants' furniture, handicrafts, arms, local fauna 31198

Schänis

Ortsmuseum, Rathauspl, 8718 Schänis - T: 0556196161, Fax: 0556196169
Local Museum - 1992 31199

Schaffhausen

Hallen für neue Kunst, Baumgartenstr 23, 8200 Schaffhausen - T: 0526252515, Fax: 0526258474, E-mail: hfnk@modern-art.ch, Internet: http://www.modern-art.ch. Head: Urs Raussmüller, Christel Raussmüller-Sauer
Fine Arts Museum - 1984
International art of the 60s and 70s (Andre, Beuys, Flavin, Kounellis, LeWitt, Long, Mangold, Merz, Naumann, Ryman, Weiner) 31200

Museum Stemmler, Sporrengasse 7, 8200 Schaffhausen - T: 0526258846, Fax: 0526330788, E-mail: huberberghaus@swissonline.ch, Internet: http://www.allerheiligen.ch. Head: Markus Huber
Natural History Museum - 1962
Ornithology, mammals, snakes 31201

Museum zu Allerheiligen, Baumgartenstr 6, 8200 Schaffhausen - T: 0526330777, Fax: 0526330788, E-mail: admin.allerheiligen@stsh.ch, Internet: http://www.allerheiligen.ch. Head: Elisabeth Dalucas
Archaeological Museum / Fine Arts Museum / Historical Museum / Natural History Museum - 1921
Pre- and early hist, hist from the Roman period to the 19th c, art (15th-20th c), natural hist 31202

Waffenkammer im Munot-Turm, Munotverein, Munotstieg 17, 8200 Schaffhausen - T: 0526435607, Fax: 0526435660, E-mail: rolf.mueller@stsh.ch, Internet: http://www.munot.ch. Head: Martin Huber
Military Museum - 1906
Arms and weapons from the 15th to 17th c 31203

Schinznach Dorf

Heimatmuseum Schinznach-Dorf, Oberdorfstr 9, 5107 Schinznach Dorf - T: 0564636315, Fax: 0564636310, E-mail: gemeinde@schinznach-dorf.ch, Internet: http://www.schinznach-dorf.ch
Local Museum 31204

Schleitheim

Gipsmuseum Oberwiesen, Bachstr 18a, 8226 Schleitheim - T: 0526801805, 0526801129
Science&Tech Museum - 1937
Plaster production and manufacturing, pictures and documents, plaster mill (18th c) 31205

Ortsmuseum Schleitheim, Altes Schulhaus bei der Kirche, 8226 Schleitheim, mail addr: Postfach 79, 8226 Schleitheim - T: 0526801347, 0526801129
Local Museum 31206

Thermen-Museum Juliomagus, Salzbrunnenstr, 8226 Schleitheim - T: 0526801129. Head: Dr. Ruth E. Harder
Archaeological Museum - 1975
Roman archaeology 31207

Schlieren

Ortsmuseum Schlieren, Badenerstr 15, 8952 Schlieren - T: 017300502
Local Museum - 1956 31208

Schmiedrued

Weberei- und Heimatmuseum Ruedertal, Altes Schulhaus, Hauptstr, 5046 Schmiedrued, mail addr: Postfach 13, 5044 Schlossrued. Head: Kuno Matter
Local Museum - 1982 31209

Schmitten (Albula)

Ortsmuseum Schmitten, Im alten Schulhaus, 7493 Schmitten (Albula) - T: 0814041185, 0814164448
Local Museum - 1988 31210

Schönenwerd

Bally Schuhmuseum, Haus zum Felsgarten, Gösgerstr 15, 5012 Schönenwerd, mail addr: Via Industria 1, 6987 Caslano - T: 0628582641, Fax: 0916129167, E-mail: ugut@bally.ch. Head: Ursula Gut
Special Museum - 1942
Shoes form various countries and cultures, shoemaking 31211

Paul-Gugelmann-Museum, Schmiedengasse 37, 5012 Schönenwerd - T: 0628496540. Head: Esther Gassler
Fine Arts Museum - 1995
Sculptures 31212

Schweizerisches Meteoriten-und Mineralienmueum (closed) 31213

Schötz

Museum zur Ronmühle, Ronmühle, 6247 Schötz, mail addr: Postfach 113, 6247 Schötz - T: 0419802964, Fax: 0419803722. Head: Paul Würsch
Local Museum - 1950
Peasant furnishings and implements, folkore, arms and uniforms, furnished classroom (19th c), religious folk art 31214

Wiggertaler Museum, Dorfchärn, 6247 Schötz, mail addr: Postfach, 6247 Schätz - T: 0419702854. Head: Hansjörg Luterbach-Renggli
Local Museum - 1937
Pehistoric and Roman finds, arms (1780-1911), folklore - workshop 31215

Schüpfheim

Entlebucher Heimatmuseum, Kapuzinerweg 5, 6170 Schüpfheim - T: 0414841555. Head: Ernst Scherer, Manfred Scherer
Local Museum - 1969 31216

Schwanden (Glarus)

Dorfmuseum, Im Pulverturm, 8762 Schwanden (Glarus), mail addr: c/o Ernst Güttinger, Grundstr 13, 8762 Schwanden - T: 0556441729
Local Museum - 1952 31217

Schwarzenburg

Heimatmuseum der Region Schwarzwasser, Leimern 5, 3150 Schwarzenburg - T: 0317311677, 0317311391
Local Museum - 1990 31218

Schwyz

Bundesbriefmuseum, Bahnhofstr 20, 6430 Schwyz, mail addr: Postfach 357, 6431 Schwyz - T: 0418192064, Fax: 0418192089, E-mail: bbm@sz.ch, Internet: http://www.sz.ch/kultur. Head: Dr. Josef Wiget
Special Museum - 1936
Documents of the ancient confederacies, banners 31219

Forum der Schweizer Geschichte, Musée Suisse - Schweizerisches Landesmuseum, Hofmatt, 6431 Schwyz, mail addr: Postfach 140, 6430 Schwyz - T: 0418196011, Fax: 0418196010, E-mail: forumschwyz@slm.admin.ch, Internet: http://www.musee-suisse.ch/schwyz. Head: Stefan Aschwanden
Historical Museum - 1995 31220

Ital Reding-Hofstatt, Rickenbachstr 24, 6430 Schwyz, mail addr: Postfach 357, 6431 Schwyz - T: 0418114505. Head: Dr. Josef Wiget
Local Museum - 1982 31221

Schatzturm zu Schwyz, Archivgasse, 6430 Schwyz - T: 0418111724, E-mail: marcus.bamert@sz.ch. Head: Markus Bamert
Local Museum - 1948
Early history, local history, folklore, religious art 31222

Scuol

Museum Schmelzra, Val S-charl, 7550 Scuol - T: 0818612222, Fax: 0818612223, E-mail: Scuol@spin.ch, Internet: http://www.scuol.ch. Head: Ursina Ganzoni
Natural History Museum - 1997 31223

Unterengadiner Museum, Plaz 66, 7550 Scuol - T: 0818641963, 0818641801. Head: L. Rauch
Local Museum - 1954
Furnishings and domestic utensils, agricultural implements, folklore, prehistory, local history, local flora and fauna 31224

Sedrun

Museum La Truaisch, Via Bogn, 7188 Sedrun - T: 0819491227, Fax: 0819491065
Local Museum - 1986
Minerals 31225

Seedorf (Uri)

Mineralien Museum, Bauenstr, 6462 Seedorf (Uri), mail addr: Postfach 161, 6472 Erstfeld - T: 0418704206, 0418703492, E-mail: umf@bluewin.ch, Internet: http://www.museen-uri.ch. Head: Hannes Dollinger
Natural History Museum
Coll of minerals, fluorite room 31226

Schloss A Pro, Dorfstr, 6462 Seedorf (Uri) - T: 0418706532
Historical Museum - 1968 31227

Seengen

Schloß Hallwyl, 5707 Seengen - T: 0627676010, Fax: 0627676018, E-mail: schlosshallwyl@ag.ch, Internet: http://www.schlosshallwyl.ch. Head: Dr. Daniela Ball
Local Museum / Historic Site - 1925
12th c castle with moat, local history, documents on the castle and its inhabitants, 17th-18th c interiors, craft trades and local peasant culture and traditions 31228

Seewen

Museum für Musikautomaten, Sammlung Dr. hc H. Weiss-Stauffacher, Bollhübel 1, 4206 Seewen - T: 0619159880, Fax: 0619159890, E-mail: musikautomaten@slm.admin.ch, Internet: http://www.musee-suisse.ch/seewen. Head: Eduard Saluz
Music Museum / Science&Tech Museum - 1979
Swiss musical boxes, barrel-organs, all types of mechanical music instruments 31229

Seewis-Dorf

Alp-Museum Fasons, Fasons, Schesaplana Sennhütte, 7212 Seewis-Dorf - T: 0813251524, 0813251629
Agriculture Museum - 1989 31230

Semione

Collezione di Minerali e Fossili, Casa San Carlo, 6714 Semione - T: 0918701133. Head: Giulietta Gianora
Natural History Museum - 1972
Minerals and fossils from the region 31231

Sempach Stadt

Rathausmuseum, Rathaus, 6204 Sempach Stadt - T: 0412067070, Fax: 0414625005, E-mail: m.steger@sempach.ch, Internet: http://www.sempach.ch. Head: Marie-Therese Helfenstein
Local Museum - 1971
Pre- and early history, regional history, agricultural and craftmen's implements 31232

Sennwald

Textil- und Heimatmuseum, Stiftung Paul Aebi-Gaissmaier, Läui 90, 9466 Sennwald - T: 0817571106, Fax: 0817571403. Head: Richard E. Aebi
Local Museum / Special Museum - 1961 31233

Le Sentier

Espace Horloger de la Vallée de Joux, 2 Grand-Rue, 1347 Le Sentier - T: 0218457545, Fax: 0218457544, E-mail: espacehorloger@vtx.ch, Internet: http://www.espacehorloger.ch. Head: Muriel Golay
Science&Tech Museum - 1996 31234

Seon

Heimatmuseum Seon, Waltihaus, 5703 Seon - T: 0627751217
Local Museum - 1964 31235

Sierre

Collection d'Etains, Hôtel de Ville, 3960 Sierre, mail addr: Administration Communale, 3960 Sierre - T: 0274520111, Fax: 0274520250, E-mail: anne-marie.imhof@sierre.ch, Internet: http://www.sierre.ch. Head: Rachel Pralong-Salamin
Decorative Arts Museum - 1971
Tin coll (17th-19th c) 31236

Fondation Rainer Maria Rilke, 30 Rue du Bourg, 3960 Sierre, mail addr: CP 385, 3960 Sierre - T: 0274562646, Fax: 0274554908
Special Museum - 1987
Letters and manuscripts by Rainer Maria Rilke, Rudolf Kassner 31237

Sils in Engadin

Andrea Robbi-Stiftung, Chesa Fonio, 7514 Sils in Engadin - T: 0818266332. Head: Dr. Robert Barth
Fine Arts Museum - 1995 31238

Nietzsche-Haus, 7514 Sils in Engadin - T: 0818265369, Fax: 0818265334, E-mail: nietzschehaus@hotmail.com, Internet: http://www.nietzschehaus.ch. Head: Prof. Karl Pestalozzi
Special Museum - 1959
Memorabilia of Nietzsche (manuscripts, documents, his study) - research library 31239

Simplon Dorf

Ecomuseum Simplon, Dorfpl, 3907 Simplon Dorf - T: 0279791010, Fax: 0279791544. Head: Alfons Gerold
Local Museum - 1996 31240

Sion

Musée Cantonal d'Archéologie, Musées Cantonaux du Valais, 12 Rue des Châteaux, 1950 Sion, mail addr: 15 Pl de la Majorie - T: 0276064670, 0276064700/01, Fax: 0276064674. Head: Marie-Claude Morand
Archaeological Museum - 1976
Archaeological finds from Wallis, sculptures, glass and ceramics from the Mediterranean area 31241

Musée Cantonal des Beaux-Arts, Musées Cantonaux du Valais, 15 Pl des la Majorie, 1950 Sion - T: 0276064670, 0276064690, Fax: 0276064674. Head: Marie-Claude Morand
Fine Arts Museum - 1947
Painting and graphic arts - library 31242

Musée Cantonal d'Histoire, Musées Cantonaux du Valais, Château de Valère, 1950 Sion, mail addr: 15 Pl de la Majorie, 1950 Sion - T: 0276064670, Fax: 0276064674. Head: Marie-Claude Morand
Historical Museum / Historic Site - 1883
Textiles, ivory, religious art, ethnography 31243

Musée Cantonal d'Histoire Naturelle, Musées Cantonaux du Valais, 42 Av de la Gare, 1950 Sion, mail addr: CP 2244, 1950 Sion - T: 0276064730/31, Fax: 0276064674. Head: Marie-Claude Morand
Natural History Museum - 1830
Geology, mineralogy, zoology, botany - Natural History libraries 31244

Musée de l'Evéché, Pl de la Planta, 1950 Sion 2, mail addr: CP 2124, 1950 Sion 2 - T: 0273291818, Fax: 0273291836
Local Museum - 1994 31245

Trésor de la Cathédrale Notre-Dame-du-Glarier, Pl de la Cathédrale, 1950 Sion
Religious Arts Museum
Shrine with silver figures (11th c), casket (14th c), reliquary (12th c) 31246

Sissach

Heimat- und Posamentermuseum Sissach, Zunzgerstr 2, 4450 Sissach - T: 0619713212
Local Museum
Braid trimmings, tassles, silk ribbons, pattern books 31247

The Jukebox Collection, Alte Zunsgerstr 6a, 4450 Sissach - T: 0619716677, Fax: 0619711448
Music Museum 31248

Solothurn

Artilleriemuseum Solothurn, Krummer Turm, 4500 Solothurn - T: 0326221754, Fax: 0326221755, E-mail: m.reber@smile.ch. Head: Dr. Markus Reber
Military Museum 31249

Domschatz Sankt Ursen Kathedrale, Hauptgasse 75, 4500 Solothurn - T: 0326221991, Fax: 0326221915. Head: Dr. Max Banholzer
Religious Arts Museum - 1932
Religious arts and crafts, textiles (15th-19th c), Papal coins and medals 31250

Historisches Museum Blumenstein, Schloß Blumenstein, Blumensteinweg 12, 4500 Solothurn - T: 0326225470, Fax: 0326226771. Head: Regula Bielinski
Historical Museum - 1952
Crafts from Solothurn, historical musical instruments 31251

Kantonales Museum Altes Zeughaus, Wehrhistorisches Museum, Zeughauspl 1, 4500 Solothurn - T: 0326233528, 0326237062, Fax: 0326214387. Head: Dr. Marco Leutenegger
Military Museum - 19th c
Arms and armor, uniforms, cannons, flags, medals 31252

Kościuszko-Museum, Gurzelngasse 12, 4502 Solothurn, mail addr: Postfach 617, 4502 Solothurn - T: 0326228056/53, Fax: 0326226703. Head: Dr. Thomas Wallner
Special Museum - 1936
Memorial to the general Tadeusz Kościuszko (1746-1817) 31253

Kunstmuseum, Werkhofstr 30, 4500 Solothurn - T: 0326222307, Fax: 0326225001, E-mail: kunstmuseum@egs.so.ch, Internet: http://www.kunstmuseum-so.ch. Head: Dr. Christoph Vögele
Fine Arts Museum
Paintings by Holbein the Younger, Amiet, Hodler, Klimt, Braque, Matisse, Oppenheim, French Impressionists, Swiss painting (20th c) 31254

Naturmuseum Solothurn, Klosterpl 2, 4500 Solothurn - T: 0326227021, Fax: 0326227052, E-mail: naturmus@solnet.ch, Internet: http://www.naturmuseum-so.ch. Head: Walter Künzler
Natural History Museum - 1824
Regional animals, minerals and fossils 31255

Steinmuseum, Hauptgasse, 4500 Solothurn, mail addr: c/o Verein Solothurner Steinfreunde, Werkhofstr 19, 4500 Solothurn - T: 0326272695, Fax: 0326277693, E-mail: peter.jordan@bd.so.ch. Head: Peter Jordan
Natural History Museum
Stone crafts 31256

Sonogno

Museo di Val Verzasca, 6637 Sonogno - T: 0917461777. Head: Ferrini Giovanni
Local Museum
Regional history of the mountain dwellers, dairy farming, arms, folk costumes, religious folk art 31257

Sonvilier

Musée d'Armes et Objets Anciens, c/o A. Summermatter, 46 Rue Fritz-Marchand, 2615 Sonvilier - T: 0329415717
Military Museum - 1993 31258

Musée Sonvilier, c/o Collège, 2615 Sonvilier - T: 0329411120, 0323414084
Local Museum 31259

Spiez

Heimat- und Rebbaumuseum, Spiezbergstr 48, 3700 Spiez, mail addr: Postfach 120, 3700 Spiez - T: 0336547372
Local Museum / Agriculture Museum 31260

Schloß Spiez, Schloßstr 16, 3700 Spiez - T: 0336541506, Fax: 0336541506. Head: Gerhard Schafroth
Historic Site / Historical Museum - 1929
History of the castle since the 15th c, furnishings and interiors (13-18th c) 31261

Spiringen

Dörflihaus-Museum, 6464 Spiringen - T: 0418706460, Fax: 0418706485. Head: Josef Herger-Kaufmann
Local Museum - 1995 31262

Zielhaus am Klausenpass, 6464 Spiringen - T: 0418706460, Fax: 0418706485
Science&Tech Museum
Car and bycicle history, international race Klausenrennen 31263

Splügen

Heimatmuseum Rheinwald, Von-Schorsch-Haus, Oberdorfpl 65, 7435 Splügen - T: 0816641138
Local Museum 31264

Spreitenbach

Ortsmuseum Spreitenbach, Beim Sternenpl, 8957 Spreitenbach, mail addr: Postfach, 8957 Spreitenbach - T: 0564012869
Local Museum - 1979 31265

Stabio

Museo della Civiltà Contadina del Mendrisiotto, Via al Castello, 6855 Stabio - T: 0916416990, Fax: 0916416990, E-mail: mucico@bluewin.ch. Head: Sergio Pescia
Historical Museum 31266

Stadel (Winterthur)

Schloß Mörsburg, Mörsburgstr 30, 8404 Stadel (Winterthur) - T: 0523371396. Head: Renato Esseiva
Local Museum - 1902
Cultural history of Winterthur and the environs 31267

Stäfa

Ortsmuseum zur Farb, Dorfstr 15, 8712 Stäfa - T: 019261472, E-mail: wgliechti@goldnet.ch, Internet: http://www.goldnet.ch/farb/
Local Museum - 1945 31268

Stampa

Ciäsa Granda, 7605 Stampa - T: 0818221292. Head: Dr. R. Maurizio
Local Museum 31269

Museo Vallerano Bregagliotto, Cjäsa Granda, 7605 Stampa - T: 0818221716, E-mail: rkromer@pingnet.ch, Internet: http://www.reto.ch. Head: Dr. Remo Maurizio
Local Museum - 1953
Archaeology, mineralogy, regional history, domestic utensils, agricultural implements, works by Giovanni, Augusto, Alberto and Diego Giacometti 31270

Palazzo Castelmur, 7605 Stampa - T: 0818221554. Head: Cristina Crüzer
Decorative Arts Museum
Completely furnished patrician house (1732) and 1850 interior in the style of Louis Philippe's and Napoléon III's times local furniture and crafts 31271

Stans

Naturwissenschaftliche Sammlung, Kollegium Sankt Fidelis, 6370 Stans - T: 0416187466, Fax: 0416187489, E-mail: sekretariat@kollegistans.ch, Internet: http://www.kollegistans.ch. Head: Norbert Rohrer
Natural History Museum - 1980 31272

Nidwaldner Museum, Festung Füringen, Mürgstr 12, 6370 Stans - T: 0416187340, Fax: 0416187342, E-mail: museum@nw.ch, Internet: http://www.nidwaldner-museum.ch. Head: Marianne Baltensperger
Military Museum - 1985
Höfli 31273

Salzmagazin, Nidwaldner Museum, Stansstaderstr 23, 6370 Stans, mail addr: Mürgstr 12, 6370 Stans - T: 0416187340, Fax: 0416187342, E-mail: museum@nw.ch, Internet: http://www.nidwaldner-museum.ch. Head: Marianne Baltensperger
Fine Arts Museum 31274

Winkelriedhaus, Nidwaldner Museum, Engelbergstr, Stans-Oberdorf, 6370 Stans, mail addr: Mürgstr 12, 6370 Stans - T: 0416187340, Fax: 0416187342, E-mail: museum@nw.ch, Internet: http://www.nidwaldner-museum.ch. Head: Marianne Baltensperger
Folklore Museum 31275

Steckborn

Art ab dä Gass, Haus zum Heidenkreis 333, Seestr 160, 8266 Steckborn - T: 0527611758
Public Gallery 31276

Museum im Turmhof, Turmhof, 8266 Steckborn, mail addr: c/o H.P. Hausammann, Riedthaldenstr 10c, 8266 Steckborn - T: 0527612903, 0527613028. Head: Hans Peter Hausammann
Local Museum - 1934
Prehistory, Alemanic grave finds, Steckborn crafts esp. stove construction and tin vessels, religious objects, works of local artists 31277

Nähmaschinen-Museum, c/o Fritz Gegauf AG, Bernina-Nähmaschinenfabrik, Seestr, 8266 Steckborn - T: 0527621111, Fax: 0527621611, E-mail: Gertrud-Graemiger@bernina.com, Internet: http://www.bernina.com. Head: Hans-Peter Ueltschi
Science&Tech Museum - 1961
Historic sewing machines since 1800 31278

Steffisburg

Kunstsammlung Villa Schüpbach, Scheidgasse 11, 3612 Steffisburg - T: 0334394444, Fax: 0334394445, E-mail: praesidiales@steffisburg.ch. Head: Marcus Sartorius
Fine Arts Museum 31279

Sammlung Heinrich Brechbühl, Hombergstr 56, 3612 Steffisburg - T: 0334378000, Fax: 0334378000. Head: Christof Brechbühl
Music Museum - 1970
Mechanical musical instruments 31280

Stein am Rhein

Heimatmuseum Stein, Benediktinerkloster, 8260 Stein am Rhein - T: 0527414231
Local Museum 31281

Klostermuseum Sankt Georgen, Benediktinerkloster, 8260 Stein am Rhein - T: 0527412142, 0522692746, Fax: 0522692744. Head: Dr. Mariantonia Reinhard-Felice
Religious Arts Museum
Benedictine monastery (11th c) with interior (15th-16th c), wooden sculpture 31282

Museum Lindwurm, Understadt 18, 8260 Stein am Rhein - T: 0527412512, Fax: 0527414582. Head: August Scherrer
Local Museum - 1993 31283

Rathaussammlung, Rathaus, 8260 Stein am Rhein - T: 0527422040, Fax: 0527423040, E-mail: stadtarchiv@steinamrhein.ch, Internet: http://www.steinamrhein.ch. Head: Dr. M. Guisolan
Local Museum - 1894
Arms, stained glass windows (16th c), vessels, silver, porcelain, carved wooden chests, historic banners 31284

Stein, Appenzell-Ausserrhoden

Appenzeller Schaukäserei, Dorf 711, 9063 Stein, Appenzell-Ausserrhoden - T: 0713685070, Fax: 0713685075, E-mail: appenzeller-schaukaeserei@bluewin.ch, Internet: http://www.showcheese.ch. Head: Marco Maier
Special Museum 31285

Appenzeller Volkskunde-Museum, Bei der Schaukäserei, 9063 Stein, Appenzell-Ausserrhoden - T: 0713685056, Fax: 0713685055, E-mail: info@appenzeller-museum-stein.ch, Internet: http://www.appenzeller-museum-stein.ch. Head: Irene Schaller
Folklore Museum - 1987
Cheese dairy, agricultural tools, local industry, folk art 31286

Strengelbach

Dorfmuseum Graberhaus, Brittnauerstr, 4802 Strengelbach - T: 0627511573
Local Museum - 1991 31287

Studen

Fondation Saner, Stiftung für Schweizer Kunst, Autobahnausfahrt, 2557 Studen - T: 0323731317, Fax: 0323734009, E-mail: infoafondation-saner@ch, Internet: http://www.fondation-saner.ch. Head: Gerhard Saner
Fine Arts Museum - 1990
Swiss art of the 20th c (Amiet, Buri, Hodler, Vallet, Lohse, Graeser, Vallaton, G. Giacomettie, Bill, Glarner, Glattfelder, Loewensberg, Hinterreiter, Roth, Spoerri, Tingueli, Luginbühl, Linck) 31288

Sünikon

Ortsmuseum Steinmaur, Lindenstr 9, 8162 Sünikon - T: 018532226
Local Museum - 1991 31289

Suhr

Heimatmuseum Suhr, Tramstr 24, 5034 Suhr - T: 0628424235, 0628220489, Fax: 0628220489, E-mail: werner.meier@ziksuhr.ch
Local Museum - 1956
Dollhouses 31290

Sulz, Aargau

Nagelschmiede, Hauptstr 85, 5085 Sulz, Aargau - T: 0628751466, Fax: 0628672093, E-mail: - finanzverwaltung@sulz.ch, Internet: http://www.sulz.ch. Head: Erich Rüede
Science&Tech Museum - 1987
Forging of shoe-nails 31291

Sundlauenen

Höhlenmuseum, Waldhaus Beatushöhlen, 3800 Sundlauenen - T: 0338411643, Fax: 0338411064, E-mail: sundlauenen@beatushoehlen.ch, Internet: http://www.beatushoehlen.ch
Natural History Museum - 1984
Prehistoric cave dwellings, place of pilgrimage (St. Beatus) 31292

Sursee

Mechanisches Musikmuseum, Hotel Hirschen, 6210 Sursee - T: 0419211048, Fax: 0419212709, E-mail: info@hirschen.sursee.ch, Internet: http://www.hirschen-sursee.ch. Head: Léonard Wüst
Music Museum 31293

Museum im Kapuzinerkloster, SBB Station, 6210 Sursee - T: 0419212130
Religious Arts Museum
Life and history of the Kapuziner, paintings, sculpture 31294

Stiftung Stadtmuseum Sursee, c/o Stadtverwaltung, Chr.-Schyder-Str 2, 6210 Sursee - T: 0419263188, Fax: 0419201111, E-mail: museumsursee@bluewin.ch. Head: Bettina Staub
Local Museum
Local history and art, numismatics, manuscripts 31295

Tänikon

Agrotechnorama, Eidgenössische Forschungsanstalt, 8356 Tänikon - T: 0523683131, Fax: 0523651190, E-mail: info@fat.admin.ch, Internet: http://www.fat.ch. Head: Thomas Anken
Agriculture Museum - 1981 31296

Tafers

Sensler Museum, Kirchweg 2, 1712 Tafers - T: 0264942531, Fax: 0264942925
Local Museum - 1975
Regional art and hist 31297

Tarasp

Schloß Tarasp, Sparsels, 7553 Tarasp - T: 0818649368, Fax: 0818649373. Head: Jon Fanzun-Horber
Decorative Arts Museum - 1040
Furnishings and glass painting (esp. 16th-17th c), sculpture, Swiss arms 31298

Tegerfelden

Argauisch Kantonales Weinbaumuseum, 5306 Tegerfelden - T: 0562452700
Agriculture Museum / Special Museum - 1985 31299

Tenero

Museo d'Arte, Via Verbano, 6598 Tenero - T: 0917356034, Fax: 0917356019, E-mail: info@matasci-vini.ch, Internet: http://www.matasci.com. Head: Mario Matasci
Fine Arts Museum
Privat coll of wine and Paintings 31300

Territet-Veytaux

Musée Suisse de l'Audiovisuel - Audiorama, Anciennement Grand Hôtel et Hôtel des Alpes, 1820 Territet-Veytaux - T: 0219632233, Fax: 0219630294. Head: Bernard Nicod
Science&Tech Museum - 1992 31301

Les Muses, 16-20 Av de Naye, 1820 Territet-Veytaux - T: 0219635549, Fax: 0219635549
Fine Arts Museum 31302

Teufen

Alfred-Vogel-Museum, Hätschen, 9053 Teufen - T: 0713356611, Fax: 0713356612, E-mail: r.vetter@bioforce.ch, Internet: http://www.gesundheitsforum.ch. Head: Remo Vetter
Science&Tech Museum - 1991 31303

Grubenmann-Sammlung, Dorf 7, 9053 Teufen - T: 0713332443, 0713332066, Fax: 0713332066, E-mail: bibl.teufen@datacomm.ch, Internet: http://www.teufen.de. Head: Rosmarie Nüesch
Science&Tech Museum - 1979
18th c timber-frame construction (bridges, roof trusses, tools) 31304

Thalwil

Ortsmuseum, Alte Landstr 100, 8800 Thalwil - T: 017205084
Local Museum - 1992 31305

Thayngen

Reiat-Museum, Adler, Dorfstr, 8240 Thayngen, mail addr: c/o J. Stamm, Wistenstr 15, 8240 Thayngen - T: 0526493731. Head: Jörg Stamm
Local Museum - 1962 31306

Therwil

Dorfmuseum, Kirchrain 14, 4106 Therwil, mail addr: Postfach 148, 4106 Therwil - T: 0617220808
Local Museum - 1975
Comb production 1915-1984 31307

Thun

Kunstmuseum Thun, Hofstettenstr 14, 3600 Thun - T: 0332258420, Fax: 0332258906, E-mail: kunstmuseum@thun.ch, Internet: http://www.kunstmuseumthun.ch. Head: Madeleine Schuppli
Fine Arts Museum - 1948
Swiss and international 20th c art, ancient graphic arts, Swiss Pop Art and Photorealism 31308

Schloßmuseum Thun, Schloßberg 1, 3600 Thun - T: 0332232001, Fax: 0332232084, E-mail: info@schlossthun.ch, Internet: http://www.schlossthun.ch. Head: Gerhard Schmid
Local Museum - 1888
Tapestries (14th-15th c), rural ceramics from canton Bern, Swiss military arms and uniforms, toys, foklore, archaeology 31309

Schweizerisches Dampfmaschinenmuseum Vaporama, Fliederweg 11, 3600 Thun - T: 0332232324, Fax: 0332254060. Head: H.R. Dütschler
Science&Tech Museum
Steam machines and steam machinery 31310

Schweizerisches Gastronomie-Museum, Schloß Schadau, Seestr 45, 3600 Thun, mail addr: Postfach 184, 3602 Thun - T: 0332231432, Fax: 0332235432
Special Museum / Library with Exhibitions - 1988
Gastronomy, menues, Harry Schraemli - library, (museum temporarily closed for 1997) 31311

Wocher-Panorama der Stadt Thun um 1810, Pavillon im Schadaupark, 3600 Thun, mail addr: c/o Kunstmuseum Thun, Hofstettenstr 14, 3600 Thun - T: 0332232462, Fax: 0332285263, E-mail: kunstmuseum@thun.ch, Internet: http://www.kunstmuseumthun.ch. Head: Madeleine Schuppli
Fine Arts Museum - 1961
Panorama of Thun painted by Marquard Wocher 31312

Thunstetten

Schloß Thunstetten, 4922 Thunstetten - T: 0629631150
Local Museum 31313

Steinzeitmuseum, Oberfeld 78, 4922 Thunstetten - T: 0629631447, Fax: 0629631447. Head: Fritz Waldmann
Archaeological Museum 31314

Törbel

Rundgang Urchigs Terbil, 3923 Törbel - T: 0279521277, Fax: 0279521277, Internet: http://www.toerbel.ch. Head: Karlen Armin
Open Air Museum - 1991 31315

Tolochenaz

Pavillon Audrey Hepburn, Chemin des Plantées, 1131 Tolochenaz - T: 0218036464, Fax: 0218036464. Head: Georges Caille
Special Museum - 1996 31316

La Tour-de-Peilz

Musée Suisse du Jeu, Château, 1814 La Tour-de-Peilz - T: 0219444050, Fax: 0219444079, E-mail: info@msj.ch, Internet: http://www.msj.ch. Head: Christiane Racine
Special Museum - 1987
Strategic games 31317

Trachselwald

Schloß Trachselwald, 3456 Trachselwald - T: 0344312397
Local Museum 31318

Travers

Mines d'Asphalte de la Presta, La Presta, 2105 Travers - T: 0328633010, Fax: 0328631925, E-mail: hotelaigle@bluewin.ch. Head: Matthias von Wyss
Science&Tech Museum - 1986 31319

Musée de la Banderette, CP 19, 2105 Travers - T: 0328416453
Natural History Museum - 1901
Natural history, local flora, birds and insects, prehistoric finds, fossils, minerals, local history 31320

Trimmis

Heimatmuseum Trimmis, Primarschulhaus Saliet, 7203 Trimmis - T: 0813534110
Local Museum - 1963 31321

Trubschachen

Heimatmuseum Trubschachen, Hasenlehnmattestr 2, 3555 Trubschachen - T: 0344956029, 0344956038
Local Museum - 1978 31322

Trun

Museum Sursilvan, Cuort Ligia Grischa, 7166 Trun - T: 0819432309. Head: Dr. Pius Tomaschett
Local Museum - 1991
History, folklore, furnishings, contemporary paintings - galery Alois Carigiet 31323

Twann

Pfahlbausammlung Dr. h.c. Carl Irlet, Fraubunnenhaus, Hauptstr 120, 2513 Twann - T: 0323151159, Fax: 0323157183, E-mail: azwez@gmx.ch. Head: Annelise Zwez
Archaeological Museum - 1937
Finds from pile-work settlements 31324

Stiftung Rebhaus Wingreis, Wingreis, 2513 Twann - T: 0323151788, Fax: 0323152312. Head: Dr. Hans Hubacher
Local Museum - 1981 31325

Uetendorf

Schauglashütte, c/o SC Sarner Cristal AG, Glütschbachstr 2, 3661 Uetendorf
Science&Tech Museum 31326

Unterbözberg

Dorfmuseum Kirchbözberg, Bei der Kirche, 5224 Unterbözberg - T: 0564413257
Local Museum - 1994 31327

Unterengstringen

Ortsmuseum Unterengstringen, Weidstr 13, 8103 Unterengstringen - T: 017503234
Local Museum - 1970 31328

Unterentfelden

Staufferhaus - Sammlung Alt Unterentfelden, Hautptstr, 5035 Unterentfelden - T: 0627237771. Head: Trudi Richner
Local Museum - 1982 31329

Unterschächen

Bielen-Säge Museum, 6465 Unterschächen - T: 0418706460, Fax: 0418706485. Head: Josef Herger-Kaufmann
Science&Tech Museum - 1850 31330

Unterseen

Touristik-Museum, Obere Gasse 26, 3800 Unterseen - T: 0338229839, Fax: 0338266453, E-mail: info@schweitzer.org, Internet: http://www.unterseen.ch/museum
Special Museum - 1980 31331

Verein Kunstsammlung Unterseen, Stadthaus, 3800 Unterseen - T: 0338221609
Fine Arts Museum 31332

Untersiggenthal

Ortsmuseum, Dorfstr, 5417 Untersiggenthal - T: 0562882874
Local Museum - 1980 31333

Unterstammheim

Heimatmuseum Stammheimertal, Gemeindehaus, 8476 Unterstammheim - T: 0527451087, 0527451277, E-mail: primust@bluewin.ch
Local Museum - 1961
Rural furnishings and domestic utensils, local handicrafts, agriculture, viticulture, firefighting, toys - library 31334

Unterwasser

Sennerei-Museum, Haus Rotenbrunnen, Dorfstr, 9657 Unterwasser - T: 0719991273. Head: Hulda Bosshard-Frischknecht
Agriculture Museum - 1978
Alpine dairy 31335

Urdorf

Ortsmuseum Urdorf, Birmensdorferstr 102, 8902 Urdorf - T: 017341488, E-mail: hermannobrist@netscape.net
Local Museum - 1963 31336

Urnäsch

Museum für Appenzeller Brauchtum, Dorfpl, 9107 Urnäsch - T: 0713642322, 0713641487
Folklore Museum - 1976
Alpine dairy, folklore, crafts, furnishings, local history - library, archive, photo library 31337

Uster

Schweizer Jazzmuseum, Asylstr 10, 8610 Uster - T: 019401982, Fax: 019401980, E-mail: swiss@jazzorama.ch, Internet: http://www.jazzorama.ch. Head: Dr. Ch. Degen
Music Museum - 1992 31338

Villa am Aabach, Brauereistr 13, 8610 Uster - T: 019409991, Fax: 019421739, E-mail: villaamaabach@stadt-uster.ch, Internet: http://www.villaamaabach.ch. Head: Yvonne Höfliger
Fine Arts Museum
Design and crafts 31339

Utzenstorf

Schweizer Museum für Wild und Jagd, Schloß Landshut, Schlossstr 17, 3427 Utzenstorf - T: 0326654027, Fax: 0326654033, E-mail: info@schlosslandshut.ch, Internet: http://www.schloss-landshut.ch. Head: Dr. Peter Lüps
Natural History Museum - 1968
History of hunting, coll La Roche, coll of horn instuments, wildlife, coll of decoys 31340

Uznach

Heimatkundliche Sammlung, Zentrum Frohsinn, 8730 Uznach - T: 0552802245
Local Museum 31341

Valangin

Château et Musée de Valangin, 2042 Valangin - T: 0328572383, Fax: 0328572381. Head: Francoise Bonnet Borel
Fine Arts Museum / Decorative Arts Museum / Historic Site - 1894
Historic furniture, arms, vessels, arts and crafts, fashion clothing 19th-20th 31342

Valchava

Talmuseum Chasa Jaura, Casa Jaura, 7535 Valchava - T: 0818585317, Fax: 0818585317, E-mail: goll@arch.ethz.ch, Internet: http://www.interreg-mrd.org. Head: Dr. Jürg Goll
Local Museum 31343

Vallorbe

Fort de Vallorbe, 11 Les Grandes Forges, 1337 Vallorbe, mail addr: CP 90, 1337 Vallorbe - T: 0218432583, Fax: 0218432262, E-mail: conact@vallorbetourisme.ch, Internet: http://www.vallorbetourisme.ch. Head: G. Jaillet
Special Museum 31344

Grottes de Vallorbe, Source de l'Orbe, 1337 Vallorbe - T: 0218432274, 0218432583, Fax: 0218432262, E-mail: contact@vallorbetourism.ch, Internet: http://www.vallorbetourism.ch. Head: W. Zehnder
Special Museum 31345

Musée du Fer et du Chemin de Fer, 11 Rue des Grandes Forges, 1337 Vallorbe - T: 0218432583, Fax: 0218432262, E-mail: musee.du.fer@bluemail.ch, Internet: http://www.vallorbe-tourisme.ch. Head: Christian Schülé
Science&Tech Museum - 1980 31346

Musée Gyger, A la Gare CFF, 1337 Vallorbe - T: 0218431875. Head: R. Gyger
Archaeological Museum 31347

Vals

Gandahus, Mura, 7132 Vals - T: 0819351105, Fax: 0819207077, E-mail: valsinfo@bluewin.ch. Head: Jakob Schmid
Local Museum - 1946
Local history 31348

Vaz

Ortsmuseum, Bei der Kirche Zorten, 7082 Vaz - T: 0813846445, 0813841460
Local Museum 31349

Verbier

Musée Tradition et Modernité, Le Hameau, 1936 Verbier - T: 0277717560, Fax: 0277715250, E-mail: hameau@axiom.ch. Head: Pierre Dorsaz
Folklore Museum - 1994 31350

Veulden

Songt Hippolytus, Tgea da Plaz 9, 7404 Veulden - T: 0816551066. Head: Plasch Barandun
Local Museum / Agriculture Museum - 1971 31351

Vevey

Alimentarium, Musée de l'Alimentation-Une Fondation Nestlé, Quai Perdonnet, 1800 Vevey - T: 0219244111, Fax: 0219244563, E-mail: - alimentarium.vevey@nestle.com, Internet: http://www.alimentarium.ch. Head: Dr. Martin R. Schärer
Special Museum - 1985
Production, transformation, preservation, preparation, and consumption of food 31352

Château du Châtelard, 2 Pl du Marché, 1800 Vevey - T: 0219214214, Fax: 0219213493
Historic Site 31353

Musée de la Confrérie des Vignerons, 2 Rue du Château, 1800 Vevey - T: 0219238705, Fax: 0219238706, E-mail: confrerie@fetedesvignerons.ch, Internet: http://www.fetedes-vignerons.ch. Head: M.-H. Chaudet
Historical Museum / Folklore Museum - 1953
Viticulture since 1647, wine growers' festivals, costumes, films and inconography 31354

Musée de Sciences Naturelles, 2 Av de la Gare, 1800 Vevey. Head: Prof. Pierre-André Bugnon
Natural History Museum
Mineralogy, paleontology, zoology 31355

Musée Historique de Vevey, 2 Rue du Château, 1800 Vevey - T: 0219210722, Fax: 0219212504, E-mail: musee.historiq-e.vevey@bluewin.ch, Internet: http://www.swisscastles.ch/vaud/vevey. Head: Françoise Lambert
Historical Museum / Decorative Arts Museum - 1897
Pre- and early hist, local hist, furniture, arts and crafts, arms, wrought ironwork 31356

Musée Jenisch, Musée des Beaux-Arts de Vevey et Cabinet Cantonal des Estampes, 2 Av de la Gare, 1800 Vevey - T: 0219212950, Fax: 0219216292. Head: Bernard Blatter
Fine Arts Museum - 1897
European painting and sculpture (19th-20th c), graphic arts (16th-20th c) 31357

Musée Suisse de l'Appareil Photographique, 99 Grande Pl, 1800 Vevey - T: 0219252140, Fax: 0219216458, E-mail: cameramuseum@bluewin.ch, Internet: http://www.cameramuseum.ch. Head: Pascale Bonnard Yersin, Jean-Marc Bonnard Yersin
Science&Tech Museum - 1979
Photographic apparatuses and instruments 31358

Veyras

Musée C.C. Olsommer, Rue Ch.-Clos-Olsommer, 3968 Veyras - T: 0274552429, E-mail: info@musee-olsommer.ch, Internet: http://www.musee-olsommer.ch. Head: Séverine Favre
Fine Arts Museum - 1995 31359

Veytaux

Château de Chillon, 21 Av de Chillon, 1820 Veytaux - T: 0219668910, Fax: 0219668912, E-mail: chillon@worldcom.ch, Internet: http://www.chillon.ch. Head: Robert Herren
Historic Site
Decorated halls, vaults, coffered ceilings and pewter, weaponry, furniture 31360

Vicosoprano

Hexenturm, c/o Comme di Vicosoprano, 7603 Vicosoprano - T: 0818221716
Local Museum 31361

Visperterminen

Wohnmuseum Egga, Im Herrenviertel, 3932 Visperterminen - T: 0279468060, E-mail: archiplan@rhone.ch. Head: Gerold Vomsattel
Folklore Museum - 1997 31362

Vissoie

Musée Vissoie, c/o Anne-Lyse Melly, Rue du Musée, 3961 Vissoie - T: 0274751338
Local Museum - 1970 31363

Vnà

Ortsmuseum, Altes Schulhaus, 7557 Vnà - T: 0818663386
Local Museum - 1978 31364

Vorderthal

March-Museum, Kraftwerk Rempen, Wägitalstr 2, 8857 Vorderthal - T: 0554451770, Fax: 0554451491, E-mail: juerg.wyrsch@bluewin.ch, Internet: http://www.marchring.ch. Head: Dr. Jürg Wyrsch
Local Museum - 1977
Pre- and early history, regional history, religious art, domestic and agricultural implements, furniture, masks and carnival utensils - library, archives 31365

Wädenswil

Ortsmuseum zur Hohlen Eich, Schönenbergstr 22, 8820 Wädenswil - T: 017804629
Local Museum - 1941
Local history, peasant furnishings (18th-19th c), agricultural tools and implements, dairy, natural history - library, restoration workshop 31366

Wängi

Ortsmuseum, Adlerscheune, 9545 Wängi - T: 0523781608, Fax: 0523782908, E-mail: etrachsler.schub@bluewin.ch
Local Museum - 1960 31367

Wald, Zürich

Heimatmuseum, Rütistr 6, 8636 Wald, Zürich - T: 0552461203
Local Museum - 1937 31368

Walenstadt

Ortsmuseum, Altes Rathaus, 8880 Walenstadt - T: 0817352222, Fax: 0817352222
Local Museum - 1988 31369

Wallisellen

Ortsmuseum Wallisellen, Riedener Str 75, 8304 Wallisellen - T: 018335871, E-mail: albertgrimm@swissonline.ch
Local Museum - 1976 31370

Schreibmaschinenmuseum Baggenstos, Neugutstr 14, 8304 Wallisellen - T: 018326666, Fax: 018326660. Head: Thomas Baggenstos
Science&Tech Museum 31371

Waltensburg

Heimatmuseum, Arcun da Tradiziun, Casa Cadruvi, 7158 Waltensburg - T: 0819411088, 0819412553
Local Museum - 1975 31372

Wangen an der Aare

Ortsmuseum Bern, Gemeindehaus, 3380 Wangen an der Aare - T: 0326315070, Fax: 0326315090
Local Museum - 1952 31373

Warth

Ittinger Museum, Kartause Ittingen, 8532 Warth - T: 0527484120, Fax: 0527400110, E-mail: rene.schiffmann@kttg.ch. Head: Dr. René Schiffmann
Religious Arts Museum - 1977
Sacral art (16-18th c), religious sculpture 31374

Kunstmuseum des Kantons Thurgau, Kartause Ittingen, 8532 Warth - T: 0527484120, Fax: 0527400110, E-mail: kunstmuseum.thurgau@bluewin.ch, Internet: http://www.kunstmuseum.ch. Head: Markus Landert
Fine Arts Museum 31375

Weesen

Heimatmuseum Weesen, Paradiesli, 8872 Weesen, mail addr: Postfach, 8872 Weesen - T: 0556166016, 0556161302
Local Museum - 1983 31376

Weiach

Ortsmuseum Weiach, Lieberthaus, Oberdorf, 8187 Weiach, mail addr: Alte Poststr 4, 8187 Weiach - T: 018582518
Local Museum - 1968 31377

Weissenstein bei Solothurn

Weissenstein-Museum, Kurhaus, 4515 Weissenstein bei Solothurn - T: 0326226221, Fax: 0326237808. Head: Christoph Oetterli
Local Museum - 1992 31378

Werdenberg

Schloß Werdenberg, 9470 Werdenberg - T: 0817712950. Head: Karl Blaas
Decorative Arts Museum - 1957
13th c castle with furniture (17th-18th c), painting, graphic art, arms 31379

Wetzikon

Imkereimuseum Müli, c/o Rudolf Müller, Im Sandbühl 25, 8620 Wetzikon - T: 019325848, Fax: 019325848, E-mail: mullerrud@hotmail.com. Head: Rudolf Müller
Agriculture Museum - 1991 31380

Malermuseum Wetzikon, Stationsstr 4, 8620 Wetzikon - T: 019303486, Fax: 019303486, E-mail: Malermuseum@bluewin.ch
Special Museum - 1986 31381

Ortsmuseum Wetzikon, Farbstr 1, 8620 Wetzikon - T: 019325727, 019300205, E-mail: rebuesser@bluewin.ch, Internet: http://www.wetzikon.ch/Gemeinde. Head: Roger E. Büsser
Local Museum - 1887
Finds from pile-work settlement Robenhausen, peasant furniture, agricultural implements, assets of the composer H.G. Nägeli - library 31382

Wiedlisbach

Heimatmuseum Wiedlisbach, Hauptstr, 4537 Wiedlisbach - T: 0326362726
Local Museum 31383

Historisches Museum Wiedlisbach, Kornhaus, Städli 20, 4537 Wiedlisbach - T: 0326362726. Head: Arnold Heynen
Historical Museum - 1960 31384

Wiesen

Dorfmuseum, Haus zum Süesa Wichel, Obergass, 7494 Wiesen - T: 0814041523, 0814041413
Local Museum - 1978 31385

Wiesendangen

Ortsmuseum Wiesendangen, Burg, Dorfstr, 8542 Wiesendangen, mail addr: c/o J. Stutz, Frohbergstr 25, 8542 Wiesendangen - T: 0523209222
Local Museum - 1967
Local history, furniture (18th c), kitchen utensils, flax cultivation and treatment, including all phases of processing, tools and implements used in agriculture and crafts 31386

Wil

Kunsthalle Wil, Poststr 10, 9500 Wil - T: 0719117771, E-mail: frankn@khist.unizh.ch. Head: Frank Nievergelt
Fine Arts Museum 31387

Stadtmuseum Wil, Hofpl 88, 9500 Wil - T: 0719113855, 0719110457
Local Museum - 1909
Local history, furniture, religious art, tin, porcelain, seals, coins, arms, stoves, oil paintings 31388

Wila

Ortsmuseum Wila, Stationsstr, beim Bahnhof, 8492 Wila - T: 0523851712
Local Museum - 1983 31389

Wilchingen

Ortsmuseum Wilchingen, Dorfstr 138, 8217 Wilchingen - T: 0526870282, 0526812388, Fax: 0526870280, E-mail: bkuel.wilch@bluewin.ch, Internet: http://www.wilchingen.ch
Local Museum - 1983 31390

Wildegg

Schloß Wildegg, Schloß Wildegg, 5103 Wildegg - T: 0628931033, Fax: 0628931261, E-mail: -marianne.eichmann@slm.admin.ch, Internet: http://www.musee-suisse.ch/wildegg. Head: Erland Eichmann
Local Museum 31391

Wilderswil

Ortsmuseum Wilderswil, Alte Mühle am Saxetbach, 3812 Wilderswil - T: 0338229192
Local Museum - 1988
Alp garden 31392

Wildhaus

Zwingligeburtshaus, Beim Hotel Friedegg, 9658 Wildhaus - T: 0719992727, 0719992178, Fax: 0719992929
Historical Museum - 1910
Zwingli's birthplace, memorabilia of the reformer Hyldrych Zwingli 31393

Winkel

Römisches Freilichtmuseum, Römerwäldli, 8185 Winkel - T: 018602210
Archaeological Museum / Open Air Museum 31394

Winterthur

Fotomuseum Winterthur, Grüzenstr 44, 8400 Winterthur - T: 0522336086, Fax: 0522336097, E-mail: fotomuseum@fotomuseum.ch, Internet: http://www.fotomuseum.ch. Head: Urs Stahel
Fine Arts Museum - 1993 31395

Gewerbemuseum, Kirchpl 14, 8400 Winterthur - T: 0522675136, Fax: 0522676820, E-mail: gewerbemuseum@win.ch, Internet: http://www.gewerbemuseum.ch. Head: Claudia Cattaneo, Markus Rigert
Decorative Arts Museum - 1874
Art metalwork from five centuries, ceramics, stoves, tiles 31396

Historische Sammlung Schloß Hegi, Hegifeldstr 125, 8409 Winterthur
Historical Museum 31397

Kunsthalle Winterthur, Marktgasse 25, 8400 Winterthur - T: 0522675132. Head: Margrit Baumann-Huber
Public Gallery 31398

Kunstmuseum Winterthur, Museumstr 52, 8400 Winterthur, mail addr: Postfach 378, 8402 Winterthur - T: 0522675162, Fax: 0522675317, E-mail: info@kmw.ch, Internet: http://www.kmw.ch. Head: Dr. Dieter Schwarz
Fine Arts Museum - 1848
Swiss art (19-20th c), European art (since 1870), European sculpture, drawings and prints (19-20th c), American art (since 1960) - library, phototheque 31399

Münzkabinett und Antikensammlung der Stadt Winterthur, Lindstr 8, 8400 Winterthur, mail addr: Postfach 428, 8401 Winterthur - T: 0522675146, Fax: 0522676681, E-mail: muenzkabinett@win.ch, Internet: http://www.muenzkabinett.ch. Head: Benedikt Zäch
Special Museum / Museum of Classical Antiquities - 1661/1861
Swiss and antique coins and medals, papermoney - library 31400

Museum Briner und Kern, Stadthausstr 57, 8400 Winterthur - T: 0522675126, Fax: 0522676228, E-mail: museum.oskarreinhart@win.ch. Head: Dr. Peter Wegmann
Fine Arts Museum - 1970
European painters (16-19th c), esp Dutch 17th c Masters, European portrait miniatures (16-19th c) 31401

Museum der Winterthur-Versicherungen, General-Guisan-Str 40, 8400 Winterthur - T: 0522611111, Fax: 0522616111, E-mail: group.info@winterthur.ch, Internet: http://www.winterthur.com
Local Museum - 1987 31402

Museum Lindengut, Römerstr 8, 8400 Winterthur - T: 0522134777, 0522127489, Fax: 0522223915. Head: Renato Esseiva
Decorative Arts Museum - 1874
Local arts and crafts, interiors (18th c), clock making, tin, ceramics, glass painting 31403

Museum Oskar Reinhart am Stadtgarten, Stadthausstr 6, 8400 Winterthur - T: 0522675172, Fax: 0522676228, E-mail: museum.oskarreinhart@win.ch, Internet: http://www.museumoskar-reinhart.ch. Head: Dr. Peter Wegmann
Fine Arts Museum - 1951
18th, 19th and early 20th c German, Swiss and Austrian art esp German romanticism, realism, idealism and Swiss art, graphic arts - library 31404

Naturwissenschaftliche Sammlungen der Stadt Winterthur, Museumstr 52,im Kunstmuseum, 8400 Winterthur, mail addr: Postfach, 8402 Winterthur - T: 0522675166, Fax: 0522675319, E-mail: -hanskonrad.schmutz@win.ch
Natural History Museum - 1660
Paleontology, mineralogy, petrography, geology, botany, zoology, ethnography - library, workshop 31405

Sammlung Oskar Reinhart am Römerholz, Haldenstr 95, 8400 Winterthur - T: 0522692740/41, Fax: 0522692744, E-mail: sor@bak.admin.ch, Internet: http://www.kultur-schweiz.admin.ch/sor. Head: Dr. Mariantonia Reinhard-Felice
Fine Arts Museum - 1970
European Old Master painting and drawing, works by French 19th c painters and sculptors 31406

Schloss Hegi, Hegifeldstr 125, 8409 Winterthur - T: 0522423840, Fax: 0522425830. Head: Alfred Bütikofer
Historical Museum - 1947 31407

Technorama, Technoramastr 1, 8404 Winterthur - T: 0522430505, Fax: 0522422967, E-mail: info@technorama.ch, Internet: http://www.technorama.ch. Head: Remo Besio
Science&Tech Museum / Natural History Museum - 1982
Physics, mechanics, electricity, sound of wood, mechanical music, perception, mathe-magics, water/nature/ chaos, light and vision, about faces, spatial imaging, automation, toy trains, textiles - Youth laboratory 31408

Uhrensammlung Kellenberger, Gewerbemuseum, Kirchpl 14, 8400 Winterthur - T: 0522675136, Fax: 0522676820, E-mail: uhrensammlung@win.ch, Internet: http://www.gewerbemuseum.ch. Head: Brigitte Vinzens
Decorative Arts Museum - 1970 31409

Villa Flora Winterthur, Sammlung Hahnloser, Tösstalstr 44, 8400 Winterthur - T: 0522129966, Fax: 0522129965, E-mail: info@villaflora.ch, Internet: http://www.villaflora.ch. Head: Dr. Ursula Perucchi
Fine Arts Museum - 1995
French late impressionsm (Bonnard, Vallotton, Vuillard), Fauve (Matisse, Rouault) and precursors (Cézanne, Van Gogh, Redon) 31410

Völkerkundliche Sammlung, Museumstr 52, 8400 Winterthur - T: 0522675166, Fax: 0522675319, E-mail: hanskonrad.schmutz@win.ch
Ethnology Museum - 19th c 31411

Wittenbach

Museum Dorf, Sankt Ulrichsberg, 9303 Wittenbach - T: 0712982166. Head: Alfred Zwickl
Local Museum - 1964
Peasant musical instruments, furniture and implements, folklore, documents, tree-root carving by Wilhelm Lehmann 31412

Museum Oedenhof, Kronbühl, 9303 Wittenbach - T: 0712982166. Head: Alfred Zwickl
Agriculture Museum / Historical Museum - 1964
Agricultural devices, school items 31413

Schloss Dottenwil, c/o Museumsgesellschaft und IG-Dottenwil, Dottenwil, 9303 Wittenbach - T: 0712982662
Decorative Arts Museum / Public Gallery - 1998
Furniture and implements 31414

Wohlen (Aargau)

Freiämter Strohmuseum, Kirchenpl, 5610 Wohlen (Aargau) - T: 0566226026, Fax: 0566226026, E-mail: strohmuseum@wohlen.ch, Internet: http://www.wohlen.ch. Head: Dieter Kuhn, Jacques Isler
Science&Tech Museum / Local Museum - 1976
History of the Swiss Straw-braid Industry 31415

Wohlenschwil

Bauernmuseum Wohlenschwil, Alte Kirche, 5512 Wohlenschwil - T: 0564911487
Agriculture Museum - 1957
Peasant arts and crafts, models of Swiss farmhouse types 31416

Wolfhalden

Museum Wolfhalden, Haus zur alten Krone, 9427 Wolfhalden - T: 0718912142. Head: Ernst Züst
Local Museum - 1982 31417

Wolfhausen

Zweiradmuseum Bühler, Rütistr 1, 8633 Wolfhausen - T: 0552408452. Head: R.E. Bühler
Science&Tech Museum - 1958
Coll of bicycles (1817-1945) 31418

Worben

Heimatmuseum Worben, Neues Schulhaus, 3252 Worben - T: 0323842750
Local Museum 31419

Würenlos

Emma Kunz-Museum, Im Römersteinbruch, Steinbruchstr 5, 5436 Würenlos - T: 0564242060, Fax: 0564242062, E-mail: info@emma-kunz-zentrum.ch, Internet: http://www.emma-kunz-zentrum.ch. Head: Anton C. Meier
Fine Arts Museum - 1991 31420

Yverdon-les-Bains

Musée de la Science-Fiction, de l'Utopie et des Voyages Extraordinaires, Maison d'Ailleurs, 14 Pl Pestalozzi, 1400 Yverdon-les-Bains, mail addr: CP 945, 1400 Yverdon-les-Bains - T: 0244256438, Fax: 0244256575, E-mail: maison@ailleurs.ch, Internet: http://www.ailleurs.ch. Head: Patrick Gyger
Special Museum - 1976
Books, documents, pictures, toys relating to science fiction, utopia, and extraordinary journeys - exhibition hall, research library, lending library 31421

Musée d'Yverdon-les-Bains et sa Région, Château, 1401 Yverdon-les-Bains, mail addr: CP 968, 1401 Yverdon-les-Bains - T: 0244259310, Fax: 0244259312, E-mail: musee.yverdon@bluewin.ch. Head: Pierre Pache
Local Museum / Archaeological Museum - 1761
Pre- and early hist, regional hist, Roman boats, memorabilia of Johann H. Pestalozzi (1746-1827) 31422

Musée Suisse de la Mode, Château, 1400 Yverdon-les-Bains - T: 0244263164, 0244259310. Head: Sylvia Bracher
Special Museum 31423

Zeihen

Dorfmuseum, Im Gemeindehaus, 5079 Zeihen - T: 0628674040, Fax: 0628674049, E-mail: gemeindeverwaltung@zeihen.ch, Internet: http://www.zeihen.ch
Local Museum - 1975
Local history, geology, fossils 31424

Zermatt

Alpines Museum, Bei der Englischen Kirche, 3920 Zermatt - T: 0279674100, Fax: 0279675453. Head: Willy Hofstetter
Natural History Museum - 1958
Minerals and stones, relics from the Matterhorn catastrophe in 1865 and history of the first ascent, interior (19th c) from canton Wallis - library 31425

Radio Matterhorn Museum, Haus Glacier, Bahnhofstr, 3920 Zermatt - T: 0279674455. Head: Stephan Perren
Science&Tech Museum - 1995 31426

Zernez

Nationalparkhaus, Richtung Ofenpass, 7530 Zernez - T: 0818561378, 0818561282, Fax: 0818561740, E-mail: info@nationalpark.ch, Internet: http://www.nationalpark.ch. Head: Prof. Dr. Heinrich Haller
Natural History Museum - 1968 31427

Ziefen

Dorfmuseum, Im Rebacker 11, 4417 Ziefen - T: 0619312742
Local Museum 31428

Zillis

Ausstellung Kirche Zillis, Am Postpl, 7432 Zillis - T: 0816612255. Head: Toni Thaller
Religious Arts Museum - 1993 31429

Schamser Talmuseum, Tgea da Schons, Bei der Kirche, 7432 Zillis, mail addr: c/o C. Joos, Obere Plessurstr 47, 7000 Chur - T: 0812529766, 0816611419. Head: Cristian Joos
Local Museum - 1970 31430

Zimmerwald

Blasinstrumenten-Sammlung, Beim Dorfbrunnen, 3086 Zimmerwald, mail addr: c/o Burri, Morillonstr 11, 3007 Bern - T: 0313718378
Music Museum - 1970
Wind instruments 31431

Zinal

Maison du Vieux-Zinal, Au centre du Vieux-Village, 3961 Zinal - T: 0274751035. Head: Georges Vianin
Local Museum 31432

Zofingen

Kunst im Alten Schützenhaus, General-Guisan-Str 12, 4800 Zofingen, mail addr: Postfach, 4800 Zofingen - T: 062514829. Head: Jean-Pierre Dietschi, Marc F. Naville
Fine Arts Museum - 1982 31433

Museum, General-Guisan-Str 18, 4800 Zofingen - T: 0627516763. Head: René Wyss, Ulrich Lienhard
Local Museum - 1901
Pre- and early hist, geology, and mineralogy, zoology, coins, tin, arms coll 31434

Zollikon

Ortsmuseum Zollikon, Haus zum Felsengrund, Oberdorfstr 14, 8702 Zollikon - T: 013913565, 012594101, Fax: 013913565
Local Museum 31435

Stiftung für Eisenplastik, Sammlung Dr. Hans Koenig, Zollikerstr 86, 8702 Zollikon - T: 013913710, Fax: 013922397, E-mail: sammlung-koenig@smile.ch
Fine Arts Museum 31436

Zürich

Anthropologisches Institut und Museum der Universität Zürich, Bau 10, Winterthurer Str 190, 8057 Zürich - T: 016354954, Fax: 016356804, E-mail: smidi@aim.unizh.ch, Internet: http://www.anthro.unizh.ch. Head: Prof. V. Ziswiler
Natural History Museum / University Museum - 1984
Development of primates and hominides, coll of casts 31437

Archäologische Sammlung der Universität Zürich, Rämistr 73, 8006 Zürich - T: 016342811, 016342820, Fax: 016344902, E-mail: mangoe@archinst.unizh.ch, Internet: http://www.unizh.ch. Head: Prof. Dr. H.P. Isler
Archaeological Museum 31438

Architektur Forum Zürich, Neumarkt 15, 8004 Zürich - T: 012529295
Public Gallery 31439

Baugeschichtliches Archiv der Stadt Zürich, Neumarkt 4, 8001 Zürich - T: 012668686, Fax: 012668680, E-mail: thomas.meyer@hbd.stzh.ch, Internet: http://www.stadt-zuerich.ch. Head: Thomas Meyer
Library with Exhibitions
Historic city views and maps, house photographies 31440

Botanisches Museum der Universität Zürich, Zollikerstr 107, 8008 Zürich - T: 016348411, Fax: 016348403, E-mail: burlet@systbot.unizh.ch, Internet: http://www.sysbot.unizh.ch. Head: Prof. J. P. Linder
Natural History Museum / University Museum - 1834
Tropical Africa, New Caledonia 31441

Coninx Museum, Heuelstr 32, 8032 Zürich - T: 012520468, Fax: 012520422, E-mail: coninx-museum@freessurf.ch. Head: Cynthia Gavranić
Fine Arts Museum - 1990
Coll of Asiatic art, Swiss artists, Füssli, Goya, Hodler, Picasso, Kirchner, Kollwitz 31442

Geologisch-Mineralogische Ausstellung der Eidgenössischen Technischen Hochschule Zürich, Sonneggstr 5, 8092 Zürich - T: 016323679/787, Fax: 016321080/88, E-mail: brack@erdw.ethz.ch,, Internet: http://www.erdw.ethz.ch/geosamml. Head: Dr. P. Brack, Dr. M. Pika-Biolzi
Natural History Museum - 1925
Mineralogy, geology, precious stones, paleontology 31443

Graphische Sammlung der Eidgenössischen Technischen Hochschule, Rämistr 101, 8092 Zürich - T: 016324046, Fax: 016321168, E-mail: info@gs.gess.ethz.ch, Internet: http://www.museen-zuerich.ch. Head: Paul Tanner
Fine Arts Museum - 1867
European graphic arts (15th-20th c) 31444

Haus Konstruktiv, Selnaustr 25, 8001 Zürich - T: 012177080, Fax: 012177090, E-mail: info@hauskonstruktiv.ch, Internet: http://www.hauskon-struktiv.ch. Head: Dr. Ellen Ringier
Fine Arts Museum - 1987
Constructive art 31445

Haus zum Kiel, Museum Rietberg Zürich, Hirschengraben 20, 8001 Zürich - T: 012619652, Fax: 012025201, E-mail: museum@rietb.stzh.ch, Internet: http://www.rietberg.ch. Head: Dr. Albert Lutz
Fine Arts Museum 31446

Heidi Weber-Museum, Höschgasse 8, 8008 Zürich - T: 013836470, E-mail: bweber@lecorbusiermuseum.com, Internet: http://www.lecorbusiermuseum.com. Head: Heidi Weber
Fine Arts Museum
Paintings, sculpture, tapisseries by Le Corbusier, architecture - library 31447

Helmhaus, Limmatquai 31, 8001 Zürich - T: 012516177, Fax: 012615672, E-mail: info@helmhaus.org, Internet: http://www.helmhaus.org. Head: Simon Maurer
Fine Arts Museum 31448

Indianermuseum der Stadt Zürich, Feldstr 89, 8004 Zürich - T: 012410050, Fax: 012410038, E-mail: indianermuseum.zuerich@ssd.stzh.ch, Internet: http://www.indianermuseum.ch. Head: Denise Daenzer
Ethnology Museum - 1962
Ethnography of North-American Indian cultures 31449

Johann Jacobs Museum, Sammlung zur Kulturgeschichte des Kaffees, Seefeldquai 17, 8034 Zürich - T: 013886151, Fax: 013886137, E-mail: team@johann-jacobs-museum.ch, Internet: http://www.johann-jacobs-museum.ch. Head: Theo E. Brenner
Special Museum - 1984
Travel stories (16th-19th c), literature on coffee, graphics, paintings, porcelain, silver, cultural hist 31450

Kriminalmuseum der Kantonspolizei Zürich, Kasernenstr 29, 8004 Zürich, mail addr: Postfach, 8021 Zürich - T: 012472211, Fax: 012424193. Head: Peter Hauser
Special Museum 31451

Kunsthaus Zürich, Heimpl 1, 8001 Zürich - T: 012538484, Fax: 012538433, E-mail: info@kunsthaus.ch, Internet: http://www.kunsthaus.ch. Head: Dr. Christoph Becker
Fine Arts Museum - 1910
Swiss art (Nelkenmeister, Füssli, Böcklin, Segantini, Hodler, Vallotton, Giacometti), European Baroque painting, Monet, Cézanne, van Gogh, Nabis, Picasso, Chagall, Munch, Kokoschka, Baselitz, Twombly, Beuys - library 31452

Kunsthof Zürich, Hochschule für Gestaltung und Kunst, Limmatstr 44, 8005 Zürich - T: 014462312, Fax: 014462312, E-mail: kunsthof.zuerich@hgkz.ch, Internet: http://www.hgkz.ch. Head: Christoph Schenker
Fine Arts Museum / Open Air Museum 31453

Medizinhistorisches Museum der Universität Zürich, Rämistr 69, 8006 Zürich - T: 016342071, Fax: 016343690, E-mail: cmoergel@mhiz.unizh.ch, Internet: http://www.mhiz.unizh.ch/museum.html. Head: Dr. Christoph Mörgeli
Special Museum - 1915
Medical instruments and documents of two millennia, esp relating to ophthalmology, surgery, orthopedics, and medicine in Switzerland - library 31454

migros museum für gegenwartskunst, Limmatstr 270, 8005 Zürich - T: 012772050, Fax: 012776286, E-mail: info@migrosmuseum.ch, Internet: http://www.migrosmuseum.ch. Head: Heike Munder
Fine Arts Museum 31455

Mineralogisch-Petrografische Sammlungen der Eidgenössischen Technischen Hochschule, Sonneggstr 5, 8092 Zürich - T: 016323787, Fax: 016321088, E-mail: peter.brack@erdw.ethz.ch, Internet: http://www.erdw.ethz.ch/~geosamml
Natural History Museum / University Museum 31456

Moulagensammlung des Universitätsspitals und der Universität Zürich, Haldenbachstr 14, 8091 Zürich - T: 012555685, Fax: 012554403, E-mail: geiges@derm.unizh.ch, Internet: http://www.moulagen.ch. Head: Michael Geiges
Special Museum / University Museum - 1993
Wax models 31457

Mühlerama, Museum in der Mühle Tiefenbrunnen, Seefeldstr 231, 8008 Zürich - T: 014227660, Fax: 013807606, E-mail: info@muehlerama.ch, Internet: http://www.muehlerama.ch. Head: Charlotte Schütt
Science&Tech Museum - 1986
History of mills, nutritional hist, historic mill of 1913 in function 31458

Musee Suisse Keramiksammlung Zunfthaus zur Meisen, Zunfthaus zur Meisen, Münsterhof 20, 8001 Zürich, mail addr: Postfach 6789, 8023 Zürich - T: 012186511, Fax: 012112949, E-mail: kanzlei@slm.admin.ch, Internet: http://www.musee-suisse.ch. Head: Dr. Hanspeter Lanz
Decorative Arts Museum - 1956
Faience and porcelain (18th c) esp of Swiss manufacture 31459

Musee Suisse Schweizerisches Landesmuseum, Museumstr 2, 8001 Zürich, mail addr: Postfach 6789, 8023 Zürich - T: 012186511, Fax: 012112949, E-mail: kanzlei@slm.admin.ch, Internet: http://www.musee-suisse.ch. Head: Dr. Andres Furger
Historical Museum / Fine Arts Museum / Decorative Arts Museum - 1890
Military science, archaeology, early Middle Ages and Roman period, painting and sculpture, ceramics and glass, textiles and costumes, painted glass, toys, precious metals, clocks, scientific instruments, folklore, coins and medals - library, restoration workshop 31460

Museum Bärengasse, Bärengasse 20-22, 8001 Zürich - T: 012111716, Fax: 012112949, E-mail: Baerengasse@slm.admin.ch, Internet: http://www.musee-suisse.ch. Head: Dr. Andres Furger
Decorative Arts Museum - 1976
Interiors from ancient Zurich 31461

Museum Bärengasse, Schweizerisches Landesmuseum, Bärengasse 22, 8001 Zürich, mail addr: Postfach 6789, 8023 Zürich - T: 012186558, 012114705, Fax: 012112949, Internet: http://www.slmnet.ch. Head: Dr. A. Furger
Special Museum - 1976 31462

Museum Bellerive, Höschgasse 3, 8008 Zürich, mail addr: Postfach 831, 8034 Zürich - T: 013834376, Fax: 013834468, E-mail: roger.fayet@hgkz.ch, Internet: http://www.museum-gestaltung.ch. Head: Roger Fayet
Decorative Arts Museum - 1968
Ancient and modern textiles from various countries, tapestries, ceramics and glass (Art Nouveau to present), folk art, musical instrument and Marionettes (1981-1960) departments 31463

Museum für Gestaltung Zürich, Ausstellungsstr 60, 8005 Zürich, mail addr: Postfach, 8031 Zürich - T: 014462211, Fax: 014462233, E-mail: feedbach@hskz.ch, Internet: http://www.museum-gestaltung.ch. Head: Erika Keil
Decorative Arts Museum - 1875
Design, visual communication, poster art, arts and crafts, everyday culture - Graphic Coll, Design Coll, Poster Coll, library arts and crafts Coll 31464

Museum Rietberg Zürich, Villa Wesendonck, Gablerstr 15, 8002 Zürich - T: 012063131, Fax: 012063132, E-mail: museum@rietb.stzh.ch, Internet: http://www.rietberg.ch. Head: Dr. Albert Lutz
Fine Arts Museum - 1952
Classical arts of China, Japan, India, Africa and the Ancient Americas: sculptures from Southeast and Eastern Asia, Buddhist bronzes, ceramics and decorative art from the Far East, African and Oceanic sculptures, Swiss carnival masks 31465

Museum Schweizer Hotellerie und Tourismus, Trittligasse 8, 8001 Zürich - T: 012618083, 013918278, Fax: 013916158. Head: Beat Kleiner-Frick, Dorothee Kleiner-Frick
Special Museum - 1992 31466

Museum Strauhof, Augustinergasse 9, Zürich - T: 012163139
Fine Arts Museum 31467

Ortsmuseum Albisrieden, Triemlistr 2, 8047 Zürich, mail addr: Langgrütstr 143, 8047 Zürich - T: 014920331, Fax: 014920331, E-mail: hamstad@swissonline.ch. Head: Hans Amstad
Local Museum - 1950
Local history, farm implements and tools, ecclesiastical objects, old house (16th c) 31468

Ortsmuseum Höngg, Vogtsrain 2, 8049 Zürich - T: 013418361, Fax: 013414544. Head: Dr. Marianne Haffner
Local Museum - 1926
16th c wine growers' feudal tenure, viticulture, peasant interiors, craft trades 31469

Ortsmuseum Schwamendingen, Probsteistr 10, 8051 Zürich, mail addr: Postfach 86, 8051 Zürich - T: 013222518
Local Museum - 1974 31470

Ortsmuseum Wollishofen, Hornerhaus, Widmerstr 8, 8038 Zürich. Head: Elisabeth Schmid
Local Museum - 1985 31471

Paläontologisches Museum der Universität Zürich, Karl-Schmid-Str 4, 8006 Zürich - T: 016342339, Fax: 016344923, E-mail: hugo.bucher@pim.unizh.ch, Internet: http://www.palinst.unizh.ch. Head: Prof. Dr. H. Bucher
Natural History Museum - 1956
Middle Triassic marine fishes, reptiles and invertebrates, vertebrate from the Tertiary and Ice Age 31472

Park-Villa Rieter, Museum Rietberg Zürich, Gablerstr 15, 8002 Zürich - T: 012063131, Fax: 012063132, E-mail: museum@rietb.stzh.ch, Internet: http://www.rietberg.ch. Head: Dr. Albert Lutz
Fine Arts Museum
Indian, Chinese and Japanese painting, Japanese No-masks, Chinese cloisonné and snuff-bottles 31473

Puppenmuseum Sasha Morgenthaler, Museum Bärengasse, Bärengasse 22, 8001 Zürich - T: 012111716, Fax: 012112949, E-mail: webmaster@slm.admin.ch, Internet: http://www.musee-suisse.ch/D/museen/baerengasse/museum/html. Head: Dr. Andres Furger
Special Museum - 1977
Dolls by Sasha Morgenthaler (1893-1975) - closed until the end of 1998 31474

Shedhalle-Rote Fabrik, Seestr 395, 8038 Zürich - T: 014815950, Fax: 014815951, E-mail: info@shedhalle.ch, Internet: http://www.shedhalle.ch. Head: Sarah Mehler
Public Gallery / Fine Arts Museum 31475

Stiftung Sammlung E.G. Bührle, Zollikerstr 172, 8008 Zürich - T: 014220086, Fax: 014220347, E-mail: stiftung_egb@ihagholding.ch, Internet: http://www.buehrle.ch. Head: Hortense Anda-Bührle
Fine Arts Museum - 1960
Painting (19-20th c) esp impressionism, Old Masters, medieval sculpture 31476

Thomas-Mann-Archiv, c/o Eidgenössische Technische Hochschule, Schönberggasse 15, 8001 Zürich - T: 016324045, Fax: 016321254, E-mail: tma@tma.gess.ethz.ch, Internet: http://www.tma.ethz.ch/. Head: Dr. Thomas Sprecher
Library with Exhibitions 31477

Tibet Songtsen House, Albisriederstr 379, 8047 Zürich - T: 014005559, Fax: 014005558
Ethnology Museum 31478

Tram Museum Zürich, Limmattalstr 260, 8049 Zürich, mail addr: Postfach 6214, 8023 Zürich - T: 013415058, 013420762, Fax: 012715078, E-mail: mschnider@dplanet.ch, Internet: http://www.tram-museum.ch. Head: M. Schnider
Science&Tech Museum 31479

Uhrenmuseum Beyer, Bahnhofstr 31, 8001 Zürich - T: 012211080, Fax: 012113348, E-mail: museum@beyer-chronometrie.ch, Internet: http://www.beyer-ch.com. Head: René Beyer
Science&Tech Museum - 1970
Chronometers since the pre-Christian period such as non-mechanical clocks, iron clocks, Swiss wooden wheel clocks (1550-1750), French clocks (17th-19th c), pendulum clocks from Neuenburg (1700-1850), clocks from the Far East, navigation instruments 31480

Völkerkundemuseum der Universität Zürich, Pelikanstr 40, 8001 Zürich - T: 016349011, Fax: 016349050, E-mail: musethno@vmz.unizh.ch, Internet: http://www.unizh.ch/musethno. Head: Prof. Dr. Michael Oppitz
Ethnology Museum - 1888
Ethnography of America, Africa, Asia and polar regions - library, archives 31481

Zinnfiguren-Museum, Obere Zäune 19, 8001 Zürich - T: 012625720, 01(052)7612519. Head: Paul Krog
Decorative Arts Museum - 1985
Pewter figures, toys, depiction of battles, manufacture 31482

Zoologisches Museum der Universität Zürich, Karl-Schmid-Str 4, 8006 Zürich - T: 016343821, Fax: 016343839, E-mail: ausstell@zoolmus.unizh.ch, Internet: http://www.unizh.ch/zoolmus. Head: Prof. Vincent Ziswiler
Natural History Museum / University Museum - 1746
Vertebrates and invertebrates from Switzerland, birds and mammals from around the world, skeletons of extinct animals, molluscs 31483

Zürcher Abwassermuseum Kläranlage Werdhölzli, Bändlistr 108, 8010 Zürich - T: 014355111. Head: Hans Lüscher
Science&Tech Museum - 1988 31484

Zürcher Spielzeugmuseum, c/o Franz Carl Weber, Fortunagasse 15, 8001 Zürich - T: 012119305. Head: Ruth Holzer-Weber
Special Museum - 1956
Toys from the 18th c to the present 31485

Zug

Afrika-Museum, Sankt Oswaldsgasse 17, 6300 Zug - T: 0417110417, Fax: 0417115917, E-mail: P_Claver@swissonline.ch. Head: Elisabeth Burdak
Ethnology Museum - 1907 31486

Huberte Goote Gallery, Rigistr 2, 6300 Zug - T: 0417106570, Fax: 0417117102
Decorative Arts Museum / Fine Arts Museum 31487

Kantonales Museum für Urgeschichte → Museum für Urgeschichte(n)

Kunsthaus Zug, Dorfstr 27, 6300 Zug - T: 0417253344, Fax: 0417253345, E-mail: info@kunsthauszug.ch, Internet: http://www.museenzug.ch. Head: Dr. Matthias Haldemann
Fine Arts Museum 31488

Museum für Urgeschichte(n), Hofstr 15, 6300 Zug - T: 0417282880, Fax: 0417282881, E-mail: kmuz@zugernet.ch, Internet: http://www.museenzug.ch. Head: Irmgard Bauer
Archaeological Museum - 1930/1997
Regional finds from the Palaeolithic period to the Middle Ages 31489

Museum in der Burg Zug, Kirchenstr 11, 6300 Zug - T: 0417283297, Fax: 0417283298, E-mail: info@museum-burg.ch, Internet: http://www.museum-burg.ch. Head: Dr. Rolf Keller
Decorative Arts Museum / Local Museum - 1879/1982
Painting, sculpture, graphic arts, furniture, goldsmith work, tin, clocks, textiles, costumes, arms, uniforms, seals, coins - restoration workshop 31490

Zurzach

August Deusser-Museum, Schloß, Barzstr 2, 5330 Zurzach, mail addr: Postfach 21, 5330 Zurzach - T: 0562492050, Fax: 0562493026, E-mail: schloss-zurzach@swissonline.ch. Head: Hugo Ammann
Fine Arts Museum / Decorative Arts Museum - 1978
Paintings of August Deusser 31491

Bezirksmuseum Höfli, Quellenstr 1, 5330 Zurzach - T: 0562492592, 0562491267. Head: Alfred Hidber
Local Museum - 1947 31492

Johann Ulrich Steiger-Freilichtmuseum, Schloß, 5330 Zurzach - T: 0562492050, Fax: 0562493026
Open Air Museum - 1978 31493

Zweisimmen

Obersimmentaler Heimatmuseum, Heimathaus am Chilchstalden, 3770 Zweisimmen, mail addr: Postfach, 3770 Zweisimmen - T: 0337220201/02, Fax: 03322255. Head: Arnold Matti
Local Museum 31494

Syria

Aleppo

Aleppo National Museum, Aleppo - T: (021) 212400. Head: Shawqi M. Shaath
Archaeological Museum / Decorative Arts Museum / Historical Museum - 1931
Archeology, coins, jewelry, glass, sculpture, pottery - library 31495

Bosra

Museé d'Art Populaire du Hauran, Museé d'Antiquites de Bosra, Citadelle, Bosra - T: 105. Head: S. Moughdad
Archaeological Museum / Folklore Museum 31496

Damascus

Musée de Calligraphie et Epigraphie Arabe, Bab Brid, Damascus - T: (011) 2219746, Fax: 2247983
Fine Arts Museum 31497

Musée de l'Armée, Takkeya Souleymanya, Damascus
Military Museum 31498

National Museum of Damascus, Syrian University St, Damascus 4 - T: (011) 2214854, 2234331, Fax: 2247983, E-mail: antiquities@net.sy. Head: Dr. Abdal Razzaq Moaz
Fine Arts Museum / Museum of Classical Antiquities / Archaeological Museum / Historical Museum - 1919
Ancient Oriental art, Greek, Roman and Byzantine art, prehistoric and modern art 31499

Popular Traditions Museum Qasrelazem, Bzourieh St, Damascus - T: (011) 226160. Head: Hassan Kamal
Folklore Museum - 1954
Traditions and craft - library 31500

Deir ez-Zor

Deir ez-Zor Museum, Deir ez-Zor. Head: Assad Mahmoud
Archaeological Museum - 1974
Local archaeology - library 31501

Hama

Hama Museum, Rue Abul Fida, Hama - T: (033) 24550. Head: Abdul Razzaq Zaqzouq
Local Museum / Archaeological Museum - 1956
Local archeology, mosaics, sculpture, coins, glass 31502

Homs

Homs Museum, Cultural Centre, Tripoli St, Homs. Head: Majed El-Moussli
Archaeological Museum - 1978
Prehistoric exhibits 31503

Palmyra

Musée de Palmyra, Palmyra - T: (031) 910106, Fax: 913806. Head: Khaled Assaàd
Archaeological Museum
Local archeology, mosaics, sculpture 31504

Soueida

Musée de Soueida, Soueida - T: (016) 232035, 237859, Fax: (011) 2247983. Head: Hassan Hatoum
Museum of Classical Antiquities
Nabatean, Greek and Roman art and antiques 31505

Tartous

Tartous Museum, Mansheyyah St, Tartous - T: (043) 415. Head: Dr. Tawfiq Sulayman
Archaeological Museum
Local archeology, frescoes, mosaics, sculpture, glass, tools 31506

Tajikistan

Chorog

Chorožskij Istoriko-Kraevedčeskij Muzej (Horog Historical and Regional Museum), Ul Lenina 201, 736000 Chorog. Head: D. Palavonov
Historical Museum / Local Museum 31507

Chudžand

Chudžandskij Istoriko-Kraevedčeskij Muzej (Khodshents Historical and Regional Museum), Ul Lenina 67, 735700 Chudžand. Head: A.S. Kadyrov
Historical Museum / Local Museum 31508

Dušanbe

Respublikanskij Istoriko-Kraevedčeskij i Chudožestvennyj Muzej (Republican Regional History and Art Museum), ul Ajni 31, 734012 Dušanbe - T: (03772) 231544. Head: M. Makhmudov
Historical Museum / Fine Arts Museum
Culture, history and art of Tajikistan - library 31509

Isfara

Isfara Historical and Regional Museum, Jomi St 7, 735920 Isfara - T: 24005. Head: Abdugayyumi Asomaddin
Historical Museum / Decorative Arts Museum - 1970
Ceramics, ancient jewels, ancient skull caps and badges 31510

Kuljab

Kuljabskij Istoriko-Kraevedčeskij Muzej (Kuljab Historical and Regional Museum), Ul Lenina 33, 735360 Kuljab. Head: I. Dzhalilov
Historical Museum / Local Museum 31511

Nurek

Muzej po Istorii Stroitelstva Gidroelektričeskogo Zavoda v Nurke (Historical Museum of the Construction of the Nurek Hydroelectric Factory), 735300 Nurek
Science&Tech Museum 31512

Pendžikent

Respublikanskij Istoriko-Kraevedčeskij Muzej im. Rudaki Abuabdullo (Roudaki Abuabdullo Republican Historical and Regional Museum), Ul Lenina 13, 735500 Pendžikent. Head: N. Baymuradov
Historical Museum / Local Museum 31513

Ura-Tjube

Istoriko-Kraevedčeskij Muzej Ura Tjube (Ura-Tube Historical and Regional Museum), Ul Karla Marksa 10, 735610 Ura-Tjube. Head: N. Nasarov
Historical Museum / Local Museum 31514

Tanzania

Arusha

Arusha Declaration Museum, Kaloleni Rd, Arusha, mail addr: POB 7423, Arusha - T: (027) 2507800, E-mail: nnhm@habari.co.tz. Head: Constantinus M. Nyamabondo
Historical Museum - 1977
Traditional material to culture, contemporary art, handicraft, economy, Uhuru independence torch, photographs of furniture and utensils used at the Arusha Declaration Meeting (Jan. 1967) development after independence 31515

Arusha National History Museum, National Museums of Tanzania, POB 2160, Arusha
Natural History Museum 31516

Azimio la Arusha Museum, POB 7423, Arusha
Historical Museum
Political, social, economical history, archeology, furniture 31517

Ngurdoto Gate Museum, Arusha National Park, Arusha, mail addr: POB 3134, Arusha
Natural History Museum - 1960
Elephant teeth, rhinoceros horn and skulls, mounted mammals and birds, lepidopteran exhibits - library 31518

Bagamoyo

Bagamoyo Historical Museum, Bagamoyo Catholic Church, Bagamoyo, mail addr: POB 16, Bagamoyo - T: (052) 440063
Historical Museum - 1963
Natural hist, hist of slavery and of the German colonial period, hist of Bagamoyo as trade centre 31519

Chake Chake

Pemba Museum, Chake Hospital, Chake Chake - T: (024) 245, Fax: 2235241, E-mail: dama@zitec.org. Head: Hamad H. Omar
Historical Museum
Household articles, commerce, archaeology, ornaments, dresses 31520

Dar-es-Salaam

Dar-Es-Salaam National Museum, Shaban Robert St, Dar-es-Salaam, mail addr: POB 511, Dar-es-Salaam - T: (022) 222030, Fax: 2112752, E-mail: staff@twiga.com. Head: Dr. N.A. Kayombo
Ethnology Museum / Historical Museum - 1937
Anthropology, ethnography, hist, Zinjanthropus Boisei skull and paleo-faunal material from Olduvai and other early Stone Ages sites, marine biology - library 31521

Village Museum, National Museums of Tanzania, Bagamoyo Rd and Makaburi St, Dar-es-Salaam, mail addr: POB 511, Dar-es-Salaam - T: (022) 2700437, E-mail: village@natmus.or.tz. Head: Jackson Kihiyo
Open Air Museum / Ethnology Museum - 1967
Ethnography, folklore, traditional Tanzanian architecture, settlement and community layout, canoe 31522

Dodoma

Mineral Resources Divisional Museum, Kikuyu Av, Dodoma, mail addr: POB 903, Dodoma - T: (026) 20211, Fax: 24943, E-mail: mrd@twiga.com
Natural History Museum
Geology, rocks and minerals, fossils - research and laboratory services division 31523

Manyara

Manyara Museum, Manyara National Park, Entry Gate, Manyara, mail addr: POB 3134, Manyara
Natural History Museum
Wildlife and natural history 31524

Marangu

Kibo Art Gallery, Kilimanjaro, Marangu, mail addr: POB 98, Marangu
Fine Arts Museum - 1961
Paintings by Elimo Njau, sculptures by Kiasi Nikwitikie and Samwel Wanjau, stitch and dye pictures, African arts, anthropological exhibits from non-African cultures 31525

Mikumi

Mikumi Museum, Mikumi National Park, Entry Gate, Mikumi, mail addr: POB 642, Mikumi
Natural History Museum
Wildlife and natural history 31526

Mwanza

Sukuma Museum - Bujora, POB 76, Mwanza - T: (0742) 520114. Head: Andreas Msonge
Ethnology Museum - 1968
Sukuma traditions and culture, royal ethics, healing tools, traditional dances and art, Catholic liturgy in songs, dramas and dance - handicrafts centre, courses, archive 31527

Serengeti

Serengeti Museum, Headquarters of Serengeti National Park, Seronera, Serengeti, mail addr: POB 3134, Serengeti - T: (028) 2621515, 2620569, Fax: 2621515, E-mail: serengeti@africaonline.co.tz, Internet: http://www.dmms.de/serengeti. Head: Justin Hando
Natural History Museum
Wildlife, ornithology, illustrations of the migration of large mammals 31528

Tabora

Livingstone and Stanley Memorial, Tabora-Kwihara, Tabora, mail addr: POB 247, Tabora
Local Museum - 1957
Slavery chains, Nyamezi spears, Arabic weapons, memorabilia on David Livingstone 31529

Zanzibar

Beit al-Ajaib Museum with House of Wonders Museum, Old Fort, Zanzibar, mail addr: POB 116, Zanzibar - T: (024) 2230342, Fax: 2235241, E-mail: dama@zitec.org. Head: Hamad H. Omar
Historical Museum
Coll on Swahili civilization 31530

Palace Museum, Forodhani, Zanzibar, mail addr: POB 116, Zanzibar - T: (024) 2230342, Fax: 2235241, E-mail: dama@zitec.org. Head: Hamad H. Omar
Historical Museum
Coll related to Zanzibar Sultans 31531

Peace Memorial Museum, Mnazi Mmoja, Zanzibar, mail addr: POB 116, Zanzibar - T: (024) 32337, Fax: 2235241, E-mail: dama@zitec.org. Head: Hamad H. Omar
Local Museum
Early history of Zanzibar, local chiefdoms, Portuguese, colonization and revolution periods, natural history - library 31532

Thailand

Ayutthaya

Phipitapan Laeng chart Chantharakasem (Chantharakhasem National Museum), U-Thong Rd, Tambon Huaro, Ayutthaya - T: 50586
Historical Museum
Archeology, decorative arts 31533

Phipitapan Laeng chart Chao Sam Phraya (Chao Sam Phraya National Museum), Rochana Rd Tambon Pratuchai, Amphoe, Phra Nakhon St, Ayutthaya - T: 50587
Archaeological Museum
Archeology 31534

Bangkok

Armed Forces Survey Department Museum, Kalyanmaitri Rd, Bangkok - T: (02) 2230891
Military Museum - 1960
Military history 31535

Benchamabophit National Museum, Amphoe Dusit, Bangkok
Local Museum 31536

Bhirasri Museum of Modern Art, 90 Soi Attakarn Prasit, South Sathorn Rd, Bangkok - T: (02) 868965. Head: Acharn Damrong Wong-Uparaj
Fine Arts Museum
Modern art, Thai artists 31537

Chumbhot-Punthip Museum, Suan Phakkad Palace, 352 Sri Ayutthaya Rd, Phya Thai, Bangkok - T: (02) 2454934. Head: Vira Champanil
Local Museum - 1960 31538

Congdom Anatomical Museum, c/o Anatomical Science Department, Siriraj Hospital, Mahidol University, Bangkok. Head: Dr. Sanjai Sangvichien
Natural History Museum / University Museum
Human biology, anatomy 31539

Forensic Medicine Museum, Adulyadej Vikrom Bldg, Siriraj Hospital, Bangkok 10700 - T: (02) 4197000 ext 6578/79, Fax: 4113426
Special Museum
Forensic medicine and pathology 31540

Forest Entomology Museum, Lad Yao, Amphoe Bangkhen, Bangkok
Natural History Museum
Entomology, natural history 31541

Hill Tribes Museum, Commissioners Office of the Border Patrol Police, Phaholyothin Rd, Bangkok
Ethnology Museum
Ethnography of the Hill Tribes 31542

James H.W. Thompson House, Rama I Rd, Bangkok
Decorative Arts Museum
Traditional Thai furniture and interiors 31543

Kamthieng House, 131 Soi Asoke, Sukhumvit 21, Bangkok 10110 - T: (02) 66164707, Fax: 2583491, E-mail: info@siam-society.org, Internet: http://www.siam-society.org
Ethnology Museum - 1966
Traditional architecture, agricultural implements, Northern Thai architecture 31544

Mineralogy Museum, Rama VI Rd, Amphoe Phya Thai, Bangkok
Natural History Museum
Geology, mineralogy 31545

Museum of Medical Equipment, 315 Rajvithi Rd, Amphoe Phya Thai, Bangkok
Science&Tech Museum
Historical medical equipment 31546

Museum of the Royal Thai Air Force, Phaholyothin Rd, Bangkok - T: (02) 5796151
Military Museum - 1959
History of Royal Thai Air Force 31547

National Museum, Na Phra Thart Rd, Amphoe Phra Nakhon, Bangkok 10200 - T: (02) 2241396. Head: Chira Chongkol
Archaeological Museum / Decorative Arts Museum / Music Museum / Folklore Museum - 1926
Archaeology, textiles, weapons, ceramics, theatrical masks, books, musical intruments 31548

Parasite Museum, Faculty of Medicine, Mahidol University, Adulyadejvikrom Bldg, Siriraj Hospital, Bangkok 10700 - T: (02) 24197000 ext 6468, Fax: 24112084. Head: Prof. Darawan Wanachiwanawin
Natural History Museum 31549

Phra Chetuponwimonmangkhalaram National Museum, Amphoe Phra Nakhon, Bangkok - T: (02) 2220933
Local Museum - 1973 31550

Royal Barges National Museum, 80/1 Aroon-Amarin Rd, Bangkok - T: (02) 4240004
Special Museum
Barges used by Royal Thai family 31551

Science Centre for Education, 928 Sukhumvit Rd, Bangkok - T: (02) 3925960, Fax: 3910522, E-mail: salin01@sci-edu.nfe.go.th, Internet: http://www.sci-edu.nfe.go.th. Head: Urith Boonmark
Science&Tech Museum - 1964
History of science and technology in Thailand 31552

Silpakorn University Art Centre, Silpakorn U. Wang-Tha-Phra, Nah Pralan Rd, Bangkok, 10200 - T: (02) 2213841, Fax: 2213841, E-mail: vichoke.su.ac.th, Internet: http://www.art-centre.sv.ac.th
University Museum 31553

Sood Sangvichien Prehistoric Museum, c/o Mahidol University, Faculty of Medicine, Department of Anatomy, Siriraj Hospital, Bangkok 10700 - T: (02) 4197029, Fax: 4121371. Head: Prof. Sood M.D. Sangvichien
Archaeological Museum / University Museum
Palaeolithic archaeology and human evolution 31554

Suan Pakkad Palace, 352 Sri Ayudhya Rd, Bangkok
Historical Museum
Thai art, archeology, shells, minerals 31555

Battani

Thrai Kao, Amphoe Khok Pho, Battani
Local Museum 31556

Chiang Mai

Ob Luang, Amphoe Hod, Chiang Mai
Local Museum 31557

Phititapan Haeng Chart (National Museum Chiang Mai), Super Highway Rd, Tambol Chang Phuak, Chiang Mai 50300 - T: (053) 221308, Fax: 408568. Head: Tassanee Bhikul
Archaeological Museum / Historical Museum / Folklore Museum - 1971
Archaeology, history and ethnography of Thailand, popular art, handicrafts 31558

Chiang Rai

Chiang Saen National Museum, Tambon Wiang, Amphoe Chiangsan, Chiang Rai 57150
Local Museum / Ethnology Museum - 1957
Regional history and ethnography 31559

Kamphaeng Phet

Kamphaeng Phet National Museum, Pindamri Rd, Tambon Nai Muang, Amphoe Muang, Kamphaeng Phet - T: (055) 711570, Fax: 711921. Head: Patcharin Sukpramool
Archaeological Museum / Historical Museum - 1971
Local excavations, ethnography 31560

Kanchanaburi

Ban Kao Prehistoric Museum, Tambon Ban Kao, Amphoe Muang, Kanchanaburi
Archaeological Museum 31561

Khon Kaen

Phipittapan Tasatan Haengchart (Khon Kaen National Museum), Tambon Sala, Amphoe Muang, Khon Kaen 40000 - T: 36741. Head: Banteng Poonsil
Archaeological Museum - 1967
Archaeological coll 31562

Lampang

Lanna Museum, Amphoe Muang, Lampang
Local Museum 31563

Phathai Cave, Amphoe Ngao, Lampang
Local Museum 31564

Wat Phra Thart Lampang Luang Museum, Luang Amphoe Muang, Lampang
Local Museum - 1962
Local history, Buddhist art 31565

Lampun

Hariphunchai National Museum, 122 Indhrayongyot Rd, Muang District, Lampun - T: (053) 511186, Fax: 530536. Head: Saengchan Traikasem
Local Museum / Archaeological Museum / Ethnology Museum - 1979
Local history, archeology, ethnography 31566

Loei

Phukradung, Amphoe Phukradung, Loei
Local Museum 31567

Lopburi

Somdet Phra Narai National Museum, Tambon Tahin, Amphoe Muang, Lopburi - T: 411458
Archaeological Museum / Fine Arts Museum
Archaeological findings, paintings 31568

Nagara Pathama

National Museum, Nagara Pathama
Local Museum 31569

Nakhon Pathom

Phipitpan Haeng Chart Phra Pathom Chedi (Phra Pathom Chedi National Museum), Amphoe Muang, Nakhon Pathom 73000
Local Museum / Archaeological Museum - 1971
Regional archaeology, Buddhist artifacts 31570

Nakhon Ratchasima

Maha Wirawong National Museum, Wat Sutthichinda, Amphoe Muang, Nakhon Ratchasima
Local Museum - 1954 31571

Nakhon Si Thammarat

Kao Luang, Amphoe Muang, Nakhon Si Thammarat
Local Museum 31572

Phipitapantasatan Haeng Chart Nakhon Si Thammarat (Nakhon Si Thammarat National Museum), Ratchadamnern Rd, Tambon Mueang, Amphoe Mueang, Nakhon Si Thammarat 80000 - T: (075) 341075, Fax: 340419
Archaeological Museum / Ethnology Museum - 1971
Local archaeology, ethnography - library 31573

Phra Borommathat National Museum, Ratdemnern Rd, Tambon Nai Muang, Amphoe Muang, Nakhon Si Thammarat
Local Museum - 1927 31574

Nonthaburi

Nonthaburi Natural History Museum, Tambon Suan Yai, Nonthaburi - T: 5252168
Natural History Museum
Natural history of the region 31575

Petchabun

Nam Nao, Amphoe Lomkao, Petchabun
Local Museum 31576

Phachuab Khiri Khan

Army Museum of Infantry Center, Amphoe Pranburi, Phachuab Khiri Khan
Military Museum
Military history, weapons 31577

Sam Roi Yod, Amphoe Pranburi, Phachuab Khiri Khan
Local Museum 31578

Phetchaburi

Wachiraprasat Museum, Tambon Tarab, Amphoe Muang, Phetchaburi
Archaeological Museum / Ethnology Museum / Local Museum
Regional archaeology, history and ethnography 31579

Wat Ko Museum, Tambon Tarab, Amphoe Muang, Phetchaburi
Local Museum 31580

Phitsanulok

Phra Phuttachinnarat National Museum, Wat Phra Sri Ratana Mahathat, Amphoe Muang, Phitsanulok - T: (055) 241717
Archaeological Museum / Ethnology Museum / Local Museum
Regional archaeology, history and ethnography 31581

Tung Salaeng Luang, Amphoe Wang Theng, Phitsanulok
Local Museum 31582

Phuket

Ton Trai, Amphoe Thalang, Phuket
Local Museum - 1987 31583

Rayong

Phe, Amphoe Klaeng, Rayong
Local Museum 31584

Sakon Nakhon

Phupan, Amphoe Muang, Sakon Nakhon
Local Museum 31585

Samut Prakan

Ancient City, Sukhumvit Rd, Bang Pu, Samut Prakan - T: (02323) 9253, Fax: 9253, Internet: http://www.ancientcity.com. Head: Suvaporn Thongthew
Archaeological Museum / Open Air Museum 31586

Royal Thai Navy Museum, 126/1 Sukhumvit Rd, Tambon Bangmuang, Samut Prakan
Military Museum
History of the Royal Thai Navy 31587

Saraburi

Kao Yai, Amphoe Muak Lek, Saraburi
Local Museum 31588

Sing Buri

In Buri National Museum, Wat Bot, Amphoe In Buri, 76110 Sing Buri
Local Museum 31589

Songkhla

Matchimawas National Museum, Wat Matchimawas, Tambon Boyang, Songkhla
Archaeological Museum / Ethnology Museum / Local Museum
Regional archaeology, history and ethnography 31590

Sukhothai

Kao Ta Phet, Amphoe Muang, Sukhothai
Local Museum 31591

Phipitapan Laeng Chart Ram Khamhaeng (Ramkhamhaeng National Museum), Tambon Muang Kao, Amphoe Muang, Sukhothai - T: (055) 612167. Head: Pithaya Dam-den-Gnam
Local Museum / Archaeological Museum
Archaeological finds 31592

Sawanworanayok National Museum, Tambon Wang Pin Pat, Amphoe Sawankhalok, Sukhothai - T: (055) 641571
Local Museum 31593

Suphan Buri

Phipitapan Laeng Chart (U-Thong National Museum), Malaimaen, Amphoe U-Thong, Suphan Buri - T: (035) 551040, Fax: 551040. Head: Avudh Suwanasai
Archaeological Museum / Local Museum - 1961
Regional archeology and culture (5th-11th c) 31594

Surat Thani

Chaiya National Museum, Tambon Wiang, Amphoe Chaiya, Surat Thani 84110 - Fax: (077) 431066
Archaeological Museum / Ethnology Museum / Local Museum - 1931
Regional archaeology, history and ethnography 31595

Tak

Lan Sang, Amphoe Muang, Tak
Local Museum 31596

Trang

Kao Chong, Tambon Kachong, Trang
Local Museum 31597

Uttaradit

Ton Sak Yai, Amphoe Nam Pat, Uttaradit
Local Museum 31598

Togo

Aneho

Musée d'Histoire et d'Ethnographie, BP 108, Aneho - T: 216807
Historical Museum / Ethnology Museum 31599

Dapaong

Musée Régional des Savanes, BP 07, Dapaong - T: 708033
Local Museum 31600

Kara

Musée Régional de Kara, BP 29, Kara
Local Museum 31601

Lomé

Musée National du Togo, BP 12156, Lomé - T: 216807, Fax: 221839. Head: Nayondjoua Djanguenane
Ethnology Museum - 1974
Ethnography, art exhibits 31602

Sokadé

Musée Régional de Sokadé, BP 77, Sokadé - T: 501119
Local Museum 31603

Tonga

Nuku'alofa

Tupou College Museum, POB 25, Nuku'alofa
Historical Museum
Artifacts from Tonga's hist 31604

Trinidad and Tobago

Port-of-Spain

National Museum and Art Gallery of Trinidad and Tobago, 117 Frederick St, Port-of-Spain - T: (868) 623-5941, Fax: (868) 623-7116, E-mail: museum@tstt.net.tt. Head: Vel A. Lewis
Local Museum - 1892
Hist of Trinidad and Tobago, geology, archaeology, ethnography, art 31605

Tunisia

Carthage

Musée National de Carthage, Colline de Byrsa, 2016 Carthage - T: 71730036, Fax: 71730099. Head: Fethi Chelbi
Archaeological Museum / Museum of Classical Antiquities - 1964
Punic, Phoenician and Greek finds, Roman antiquities, Islamic items, near by: Tophet de Salambo, Parc Archéologique des Thermes d'Antonin, Parc Archéologique des Villas Romaines de l'Odéon - library, amphitheatre, theatre 31606

Djerba

Musée Sidi Zitouni, Houmt Souk, Rue Mohamed Badra, 4180 Djerba - T: 75650540
Local Museum
Local history and culture 31607

El-Jem

Musée d'Institut National de Archéologique d'El-Jem, 6 Rue Fadhe Ben Achour, 5160 El-Jem - T: 73630093
Archaeological Museum
Archaeology, finds from Roman town of Thysdrus 31608

Enfidaville

Musée d'Enfidaville, 4030 Enfidaville
Archaeological Museum
Archaeology, early Christian mosaics and inscriptions 31609

Gafsa

Musée Archéologique, Pl Piscine Romain, 2100 Gafsa - T: 76226992, 76221664
Archaeological Museum 31610

Hammamet

Musée Dar-Hammamet, Rue Sidi Abdallah, Ville Arabe, 8050 Hammamet - T: 72281206
Local Museum 31611

Jendouba

Musée Chemtou, Chemtou, 8100 Jendouba - T: 78602143
Local Museum 31612

Kairouan

Musée Raccada, Raccada, 3100 Kairouan - T: 77323337
Religious Arts Museum
Koran manuscripts, Islamic headstones, glass, ceramics 31613

Ksar Hellal

Musée Dar Ayed, 5070 Ksar Hellal
Local Museum
Local history coll 31614

Le Bardo

Musée National du Bardo, Palais du Bey M'Hammed, 2000 Le Bardo - T: 71513650, 71513842, Fax: 71514050. Head: Habib Ben Younes
Archaeological Museum / Fine Arts Museum - 1888
Relics of Punic, Greek and Roman art, ancient and modern Islamic art, coll of Roman mosaics - library 31615

Le Kef

Musée Régional des Arts et Traditions Populaires, 2 Pl A. Ben Aissa, 7100 Le Kef - T: 78204503
Folklore Museum
Ethnography, history, art 31616

Mahdia

Musée de Mahdia, 5100 Mahdia
Ethnology Museum / Historical Museum
Ethnography, history, art 31617

Makthar

Musée Archéologique de Makthar, 6140 Makthar
Archaeological Museum
Punic and Roman antiquities, sepulchral relics, pillars 31618

Manouba

Musée Militaire National, Palais de la Rose, 2010 Manouba - T: 71520220, 71520218
Military Museum 31619

Mareth

Musée Militaire Ligne Mareth, 1 Rte Médenine, 6080 Mareth - T: 75321033
Military Museum 31620

Moknine

Musée du Village, 5050 Moknine
Ethnology Museum / Historical Museum
Ethnography, history, art 31621

Monastir

Musée d'Art Islamique du Ribat, Monastir 5000 - T: 7361272
Fine Arts Museum / Historical Museum
Medieval hist, Islamic art 31622

Nabeul

Musée Archeologique du Cap Bon, 41 Av Habib Bourguiba, 8000 Nabeul - T: 72285509
Archaeological Museum 31623

Salacta

Musée de Salacta, Salacta
Local Museum 31624

Salammbô

Musée Océanographique Dar-El-Hout de Salammbô, 28 Av du 2 Mars 1934, 2025 Salammbô - T: 71730420, 71734044, 71730420, Fax: 71732622, E-mail: Amorelabed@instm.rnrt.tn, Internet: http://www.instm.rnrt.tn. Head: Amor El-Abed
Natural History Museum - 1924
Zoology, marine biology, oceanography, aquaric environment, fishing techniques - library, aquarium 31625

Sbeïtla

Musée Sbeïtla, El-Montazah, 1250 Sbeïtla, mail addr: BP 38, 1250 Sbeïtla - T: 77465785
Museum of Classical Antiquities / Local Museum
Roman antiquities 31626

Sfax

Musée Archéologique de Sfax, Av Habib Bourguiba, 3001 Sfax - T: 7429744
Archaeological Museum
Archaeology, mosaics 31627

Musée Dar Jellouli, 3001 Sfax
Ethnology Museum / Historical Museum
Ethnography, history, art 31628

Musée des Arts Populaires et Traditions, 5 Rue Sidi Ali Nouri, 3001 Sfax - T: 74221186, Fax: 74212161
Folklore Museum
Costumes, woodwork 31629

Sidi Bou Saïd

Musée Dar-El-Annabi, 18 Rue H. Thameur, 2026 Sidi Bou Saïd - T: 71727728, Fax: 71727728
Special Museum 31630

Musée Ennejma Ezzahra, 8 Rue du 2 Mars 1939, 2026 Sidi Bou Saïd - T: 71740102, 71746051, Fax: 71746490
Special Museum 31631

Sidi Boulbaba

Musée d'Art et Traditions Populaires, 6012 Sidi Boulbaba - T: 75281111
Folklore Museum 31632

Sousse

Musée de Sousse, Av A.K. Chebbi, 4000 Sousse - T: 73219011, Fax: 73219011
Archaeological Museum / Local Museum
Roman and Punic mosaics, sculptures, ceramics 31633

Tabarka

Musée de Tabarka, Rue de la Basilique, 8110 Tabarka - T: 78644281
Local Museum 31634

Téboursouk

Musée du 18 Novembre 1939, 9040 Téboursouk
Local Museum
Local history coll 31635

Tozeur

Musée Dar-Chraiet, Zone Industrielle, 2200 Tozeur, mail addr: BP 214, 2200 Tozeur - T: 76452100, Fax: 76452329, E-mail: darcherait@planet.tn
Local Museum 31636

Musée des Arts et Traditions, El-Haouadef, Vielle Ville, 2200 Tozeur - T: 76462034
Folklore Museum 31637

Tunis

Maison des Arts, Parc du Belvédère, 1002 Tunis - T: 71283749, Fax: 71795860. Head: Ali Louati
Fine Arts Museum - 1992
Modern art - library 31638

Musée Dar Bourguiba, Pl du Leader, Bab Menara, 1008 Tunis
Historical Museum
Tunesian history 31639

Musée des Arts et Traditions Populaires Dar Ben Abdallah, Imp Ben Abdallah, Bab Souika, 1006 Tunis - T: 71256195
Folklore Museum
Ethnography, history, art 31640

Musée du Mouvement National, Blvd du 9 Avril 1939, Bab Souika, 1006 Tunis - T: 71264941
Historical Museum
History of the National Movement 31641

Musée Postal, 3bis Rue Angleterre, 1000 Tunis - T: 71359327, 71329746
Special Museum
History of the postal service in Tunesia 31642

Utique

Musée d'Utique, 7060 Utique
Archaeological Museum
Punic and Roman antiquities 31643

Turkey

Adana

Adana Devlet Güzel Sanatlar Galerisi (Adana State Gallery), Sabancı Kültür Sitesi, Adana - T: (0322) 3524674, Fax: 3523290. Head: Mustafa Dulda
Public Gallery 31644

Adana Müzesi (Adana Museum), Seylan Cad, Adana - T: (0322) 4543855, Fax: 4543856
Local Museum / Archaeological Museum / Ethnology Museum - 1926
Archeology, ethnography - library, laboratory, conference hall 31645

Hacı Ömer Sabancı Kültür Merkezi (Hacı Ömer Sabancı Culture Center), Fuzuli Cad 2, 01330 Adana - T: (0332) 3523291. Head: Hacı Ahmet Yıldız
Public Gallery 31646

Adıyaman

Adıyaman Müzesi (Adıyaman Museum), Atatürk Cad, Adıyaman - T: (0416) 2162929, Fax: 2169898. Head: Mehmet Yetkin
Archaeological Museum 31647

Afyon

Afyon Arkeoloji Müzesi, Kurtuluş Cad, Afyon - T: (0272) 2151191
Archaeological Museum - 1933
Finds from the Neolithic, Hitite, Phrygian, Hellenistic, Roman and Byzantine periods - library, conference hall, laboratory 31648

Afyon Devlet Güzel Sanatlar Galerisi (Afyon State Gallery), Afyon, Afyon - T: (0272) 2142028, Fax: 2137601. Head: Abdülkadir Şaşmaz
Public Gallery 31649

Afyon

Afyon Etnografya Müzesi (Ethnographic Museum), Gedik Ahmed Pasha Medrese, Afyon
Ethnology Museum
Weapons, embroidery, tapestries, guilded books, copper dishes, in a 15th c medrese (Islamic university) 31650

Ahlat

Ahlat Açık Hava Müzesi (Open Air Museum), Ahlat
Open Air Museum / Archaeological Museum - 1971
Architectural works of the Seljuk period, tombs, Stone masonry, ethnography 31651

Akşehir

Atatürk ve Etnografya Müzesi (Atatürk and Ethnographic Museum), Akşehir
Historical Museum / Ethnology Museum - 1966
Memorabilia of the Turkish politician Atatürk (1880-1938), ethnography 31652

Medrese Müzesi (Museum of Stone Masonry), Sahir-Ata Medrese, Akşehir
Archaeological Museum - 1961
Inscriptions, tombstones and building blocks from the Roman, Byzantine, Seljuk and Ottoman periods, in a 13th c medrese (Islamic university) 31653

Alacahöyük

Alacahöyük Arkeoloji Müzesi (Archaeological Museum), Alacahöyük
Archaeological Museum - 1935
Findings from the Chalcolithic, Copper and Old Bronze Ages, Hitite, Phrygian and Late Phrygian periods 31654

Amasra

Amasra Müzesi (Amasra Museum), Amasra
Local Museum / Archaeological Museum / Ethnology Museum - 1945
Archeology, ethnography 31655

Amasya

Amasya Devlet Güzel Sanatlar Galerisi (Amasya State Gallery), Hazeranlar Konağı, Amasya - T: (0358) 2181869, Fax: 2187259. Head: Hürrem Özerdem
Public Gallery 31656

Amasya Müzesi (Amasya Museum), Atatürk Cad 123, 05100 Amasya - T: (0358) 2186957. Head: Mehmet Tektaş
Local Museum - 1926
Archeology, weapons, ethnographic objects from the Seljuk and Ottoman periods, mummies 31657

Anamur

Anamur Kültür Merkezi (Anamur Culture Center), Güzelyurt Mah. Şehir Stadyumu Yanı, Mersin, Anamur - T: (0324) 8142257, Fax: 8142257. Head: Nihat Yeler
Public Gallery 31658

Ankara

Anadolu Medeniyetleri Müzesi (Museum of Anatolian Civilisations), Kadife Sok, Hisar, 06240 Ankara - T: (0312) 3243160, Fax: 3112839, E-mail: anmedmuz@marketweb.net.tr. Head: Dr. Turhan Özkan
Archaeological Museum - 1921
Exhibits from the Paleolithic, Neolithic, Calcolithic, Old Bronze, Hitite, Phrygian, Urartu and Assyrian Trade Colonies periods, numismatics, classical periods (6th c BC up today and Ankara section) - laboratory, workshop, library, photography studio, documentation centre 31659

Anıtkabir Müzesi (Atatürks Mausoleum and Museum), Ankara - T: (0312) 2311861, Fax: 2315380
Special Museum - 1953
Memorial to the great Turkish politician Atatürk (1880-1938) - library 31660

Ankara Atatürk Kültür Merkezi (Ankara Atatürk Culture Center), Hipodrum Ulus, 06330 Ankara - T: (0312) 3845050, Fax: 3845060. Head: Serdar Gökten
Public Gallery 31661

Ankara Devlet Güzel Sanatlar Galerisi (Ankara State Gallery), Necati Bey Cad 55, Kızılay, 06700 Ankara - T: (0312) 2321945. Head: A. Seda Meral
Public Gallery 31662

Birinci Millet Meclisi Müzesi (First Turkish Grand National Assembly Museum), Ulus Meydanı, Ankara
Historical Museum - 1961
Documents and photographs concerning the First Assembly 31663

Etnografi Müzesi (Ethnographical Museum), Talat Paşa Bulvarı, Opera, 06100 Ankara - T: (0312) 3119556. Head: Sema Koçbaş
Ethnology Museum - 1930
Clothing room, embroidery room, tapestry room, hall of crafts, Ankara house, hall of objects from Tekkes, hall of Besim Atalay, hall of written works, hall of woodcarving - library, archives 31664

Gordion Müzesi (Gordion Museum), Polatlı, Ankara
Archaeological Museum 1969
Built near the Great Tumulus believed to be that of the Phrygian king Midas, archaeological items found during excavations at Gordion 31665

Kurtuluş Savaşı ve Cumhuriyet Müzeleri (Museums of the Turkish Independence War and Turkish Republic), Cumhuriyet Bulvarı 14-22, Ulus, Ankara - T: (0312) 31154 23. Head: Mustafa Süel
Historical Museum - 1961
library 31666

Turkuvaz Sanat Galerisi (Turkuvaz Art Gallery), Cinnah Cad, Kırkpınar Sok 5a, Cankaya, Ankara - T: (0312) 4391479, Fax: 4403759, E-mail: turkuvaz@turkuvazart.com, Internet: http://www.turkuvazart.com. Head: Taylan Tegin
Public Gallery
Works of a figurative nature and abstractly, paintings and plastic art 31667

Antakya/Hatay

Hatay Kültür Merkezi (Hatay Culture Center), Şehit Mustafa Sevgi Cad 8A, 24030 Antakya/Hatay - T: (0326) 2160652, Fax: 2133386. Head: Şükriye Aytuğ
Public Gallery 31668

Antalya

Antalya Devlet Güzel Sanatlar Galerisi (Antalya State Gallery), Yivli Minare Camii Külliyesi Atatürk Caddesi, Antalya - T: (0242) 2414687, Fax: 2476743. Head: Nuri Sezen
Public Gallery 31669

Antalya Müzesi (Antalya Museum), Konyaaltı Cad, Antalya 07050 - T: (0242) 2385688/89, Fax: 2385687. Head: Metin Pehlivaner
Local Museum - 1923
Natural hist, archaeology, hist, ethnography, prehist, scultpure 31670

Etnografi Müzesi (Ethnographic Museum), Yivli Minare Mosque, Antalya
Ethnology Museum - 1974
Clothing, domestic utensils, embroidery, tapestries, kilims, ornaments 31671

Yivli Minare Sanat Galerisi (Art Gallery), Mevlevi Dervish Tekke, Yivli Minare Mosque, Antalya
Public Gallery - 1973
Paintings and sculpture of modern, contemporary Turkish artists 31672

Aydın

Aydın Devlet Güzel Sanatlar Galerisi (Aydın State Gallery), Menderes Bulvarı Turistik Park 2, Aydın - T: (0256) 2252666, Fax: 2257514. Head: Hacı Çakmak
Public Gallery 31673

Aydın Müzesi, Aydın
Local Museum - 1959
Archeology, ethnography, ruins from the ancient city of Tralles 31674

Balıkesir

Balıkesir Devlet Güzel Sanatlar Galerisi (Balıkesir State Gallery), Eski Kuyumcular Mah. Çavuş Sok 30, Balıkesir - T: (0266) 2413045, Fax: 2453152. Head: F. Suzan Kutsioğlu
Public Gallery 31675

Bartın

Bartın Kültür Evi (Bartın Culture House), Bartın Kültür Evi Kırtepe Mah. Santral Sok, Bartın - T: (0378) 2282692, Fax: 2276639. Head:
Public Gallery 31676

Batman

Batman Kültür Merkezi (Batman Culture Center), Ziya Gökalp Mah. 1712 Sok 10, 72060 Batman - T: (0488) 2133021. Head: Abdulhalik Özdemir
Public Gallery 31677

Bebek

Aşiyan Müzesi (Asiyan Museum), Aşiyan Yokuşu 19, 80810 Bebek - T: (0222) 2636986. Head: Nebi Akgül
Special Museum
Home of the Turkish poet Tevfik Fikret, his paintings and drawings, poetry collections 31678

Istanbul Hisarlar Müzesi, Anadolu-Rumeli Hisarları, Yedikule Açıkhava Müzesi (Istanbul Fortress Museum), Yahya Kemal Cad 4ş2, 80810 Bebek
Historical Museum - 1968
15th c fortress on the Bosphorus, local hist - open air theatre 31679

Bergama

Bergama Arkeoloji Müzesi (Archeological Museum), Cumhuriyet Cad, Bergama - T: (0232) 6312883/84, Fax: 63310777. Head: M. Adnan Sarioglu
Archaeological Museum - 1936
Examples of architecture from the Hellenistic, Roman, Byzantine and Ottoman periods, findings from the Bergama Acropolis and Aesclepion 31680

Beşiktaş

Şehir Müzesi (City Museum), Barbaros Bulvarı, 80690 Beşiktaş. Head: Yasemin Masaracı
Local Museum - 1946
Local hist, applied art, ethnography, paintings on Istanbul city life 31681

Beyazıt

Türk Vakıf Hat Sanatları Müzesi (Museum of Manuscripts and Calligraphy), Beyazıt Meydanı, 34400 Beyazıt - T: (0212) 5275851. Head: Zübeyde Cihan Özsayıner
Decorative Arts Museum
Examples of fine Ottoman manuscripts and calligraphy, maps 31682

Beyoğlu

İstanbul Devlet Güzel Sanatlar Galerisi (İstanbul State Gallery), İstiklal Cad 209, 80050 Beyoğlu - T: (0212) 2433053, Fax: 5181279. Head: Ayla Yılmaz
Public Gallery 31683

Bilecik

Bilecik Devlet Güzel Sanatlar Galerisi (Bilecik State Gallery), Vilayet Binası, Bilecik - T: (0228) 2121006, Fax: 3613294. Head: Emine Özgen
Public Gallery 31684

Bingöl

Genç Kültür Merkezi (Genç Culture Center), Kültür Cad 83, Bingöl - T: (0426) 4113199, Fax: 4112822. Head: Burhanettin Anılır
Public Gallery 31685

Bodrum

Bodrum Sualtı Arkeolojisi Müzesi (Bodrum Museum of Underwater Archaeology), Bodrum Castle, 48400 Bodrum - T: (0252) 3161095, 3162516, Fax: 3137646, E-mail: sualtiarkmuz@superonline.com, Internet: http://www.bodrum-museum.com. Head: T. Oguzer Alpalptekin
Archaeological Museum - 1964
Exhibits from the Mycenaean civilisation (1500-1000 BC), underwater finds from the 6th to the 1st c BC, in a 15th c castle, amphora coll (14th c BC to 20th c AD), glass coll (11th c AD), shipwrecks (16th c BC to 16th c AD) - library, workshop, conservation laboratory 31686

Bolu

Bolu Devlet Güzel Sanatlar Galerisi (Bolu State Gallery), Kültür Merkezi, Bolu - T: (0374) 2151137, Fax: 2153632. Head: M. Sezai Aydın
Public Gallery 31687

Bolu Kültür Merkezi (Bolu Culture Center), Karamanlı Mah. Stadyum Cad 1, 14100 Bolu - T: (0374) 2150000. Head: Hüseyin Şahin
Public Gallery 31688

Burdur

Burdur Devlet Güzel Sanatlar Galerisi (Burdur State Gallery), Halı Sarayı 102, Burdur - T: (0248) 2335278, Fax: 2340014. Head: Zafer Özkütük
Public Gallery 31689

Burdur Müzesi (Burdur Museum), Özgür Mah Cevizli Sok 1, Burdur - T: (0248) 2331042, Fax: 2338763. Head: H. Ali Ekinci
Archaeological Museum - 1963
Finds from the Neolithic, Chalcolithic Ages, Phrygian, Hellenistic, Roman and Byzantine periods, in a medrese (Islamic university) from the Ottoman period 31690

Burgaz Adası

Sait Faik Müzesi (Sait Faik Museum), Çayır Sok15, 81350 Burgaz Adası. Head: Çetin Berkmen
Special Museum
House of the Turkish short story writer Sait Faik Abasıyanık 31691

Bursa

Atatürk Müzesi (Atatürk Museum), Çekirge, Bursa
Special Museum - 1973
Memorabilia of the great Turkish politician Atatürk (1880-1938), furnishing, photographs, documents 31692

Bursa Arkeoloji Müzesi (Bursa Archaeological Museum), Kültürpark, Bursa - T: (0224) 2344918, Fax: 2344919
Archaeological Museum - 1902
Coins and works of prehistoric times, works in stone and metal, ceramics, glass, art gallery - laboratory, library 31693

Bursa Devlet Güzel Sanatlar Galerisi (Bursa State Gallery), Heykel Karşısı, Bursa - T: (0224) 2219449, Fax: 2212377. Head: Satı Aykaş
Public Gallery 31694

Bursa Türk ve Islam Eserleri Müzesi (Bursa Turkish and Islamic Art Museum), Yeşildirek, Bursa - T: (0224) 277679
Fine Arts Museum - 1974
Works from the 14th c to the late Ottoman period 31695

Osmalı Evi (Ottoman House), Murad House, Muradiye, Bursa
Decorative Arts Museum
Typical Ottoman house, furniture, wooden ceiling and cupboards 31696

Çanakkale

Çanakkale Devlet Güzel Sanatlar Galerisi (Çanakkale State Gallery), Kayserili Ahmet Cad, Çanakkale - T: (0286) 2176161, Fax: 2124522. Head: Sevim Ateş
Public Gallery 31697

Çanakkale Müzesi (Museum Çanakkale), Izmir Cad, Çanakkale - T: (0286) 2173252, Fax: 2171105
Local Museum - 1961
Archeological finds from the excavations of Bozcaada Necropolis and Dardanos Tumulus, exhibits from the Phoenician, Greek, Roman, Byzantine and Ottoman periods, Calverton coll, ethnography, Turkish art works 31698

Çanakkale Şehitleri Heykeli ve Savaş Müzesi (Çanakkale Martyrs Monument and War Museum), Çanakkale
Military Museum - 1972
Memorial to the Turkish soldiers who fell in the Çanakkale War of 1914-1915, documents, photographs 31699

Truva Müzesi (Troy Museum), Çanakkale
Archaeological Museum
Pottery, figures, statues, glass objects 31700

Çankırı

Çankırı 100. Yıl Kültür Merkezi (Culture Center), Atatürk Bulvarı 2, 18100 Çankırı - T: (0376) 2136811, 2135965, Fax: 2131276. Head: Salih Delialioğlu
Public Gallery 31701

Çankırı Devlet Güzel Sanatlar Galerisi (Çankırı State Gallery), 100.Yıl Kültür Merkezi, Çankırı - T: (0376) 2130326, Fax: 2131276. Head: İsmail Çaylak
Public Gallery 31702

Çifteler

Yazılı Kaya Müzesi (Yazılıkaya Museum), 26736 Çifteler - T: (0222) 5847703. Head: Veysel Gündogdu
Archaeological Museum - 1936
Remains of Midas, a Phrygian city 31703

Çorum

Çorum Devlet Güzel Sanatlar Galerisi (Çorum State Gallery), Kültür Sitesi, Çorum - T: (0364) 2137038, Fax: 2120510. Head: Ömer Yabacıoğlu
Public Gallery 31704

Çorum Müzesi (Museum Çorum), Gülübey Mah Müze Sok, Çorum - T: (0364) 2131568, Fax: 2243025
Archaeological Museum - 1968
Archeological finds from the prehistoric, Hitite, Phrygian, Bzyantine, classical and Islamic periods, ethnography 31705

Denizli

Denizli Devlet Güzel Sanatlar Galerisi (Denizli State Gallery), İstiklal Cad İl Halk Kütüphanesi, Denizli - T: (0258) 2624323, Fax: 2650787. Head: Celal Günaydın
Public Gallery 31706

Hierapolis Arkeoloji Müzesi (Hierapolis Archeological Museum), Pamukkale, Denizli - T: (0258) 2722279, 2722034, Fax: 2636250. Head: H. Hüseyin Baysal
Archaeological Museum - 1984/2000
Finds from the excavations at Hierapolis, Roman bath, column capitals, grave Stelae, inscriptions, sarcophagi, Beycesultan findings - library 31707

Diyarbakır

Atatürk Müzesi (Atatürk's House), Semanoglu Evi, Diyarbakır
Special Museum
Memorabilia of the Turkish politician Atatürk (1880-1938) in the house in which he lived from 1916-1917 31708

Cahit Sıtkı Tarancı Müzesi (Cahit Sıtkı Tarancı Culture Museum), Diyarbakır
Special Museum - 1973
Memorabilia of the poet Cahit Sıtkı Tarancı in his birthplace, books, manuscripts, photographs 31709

Diyarbakır Arkeoloji ve Etnografi Müzesi (Archaeological and Ethnographic Museum), Ziya Gökalp Bulvarı, Diyarbakır - T: (0412) 2212753, Fax: 2230802
Archaeological Museum
Exhibits from the Assyrian, Hitite, Roman, Byzantine, Artuk and Ottoman periods, ethnography, in a 12th c medrese (Islamic university) - library 31710

Diyarbakır Devlet Güzel Sanatlar Galerisi (Diyarbakır State Gallery), Dağkapı Burcu, Diyarbakır - T: (0412) 2226469, Fax: 2244202. Head: Adem Yıldız
Public Gallery 31711

Ziya Gökalp Müzesi (Ziya Gökalp Museum), Diyarbakır
Special Museum - 1962
Memorabilia of the Turkish philosopher Ziya Gökalp in his birthplace, books, manuscripts, photographs 31712

Edirne

Edirne Arkoloji ve Etnografi Müzesi (Archaeological and Ethnographic Museum), Selimiye Camii Yanı, Edirne - T: (0284) 2251120
Archaeological Museum / Ethnology Museum - 1971
Carpets and kilims, ethnographic works, archeological examples from the civilisations of Anatolia and Thrace 31713

Edirne Devlet Güzel Sanatlar Galerisi (Edirne State Gallery), Eski Vali Konağı, Edirne - T: (0284) 2252039, Fax: 2230232. Head: Nadir Adlı
Public Gallery 31714

Türk ve Islam Eserleri Müzesi (Museum of Turkish and Islamic Art), Selimiye Mosque, Edirne
Fine Arts Museum / Religious Arts Museum - 1971
Stone inscriptions form the Ottoman period, embroidery, weapons, glass objects, carved wooden doors and cupboards 31715

Elazıg

Elazıg Arkeoloji ve Etnografi Müzesi (Elazıg Archaeological and Ethnological Museum), Fırat Üniversitesi Kampusü, Elazıg - T: (0424) 2122403
Archaeological Museum / Ethnology Museum - 1965
Archeological findings from prehistoric times to the Byzantine period, ethnographic works including embroidery, kilims and tapestries, domestic utensils, costumes 31716

Eregli

Eregli Arkeoloji ve Etnografi Müzesi (Archaeological and Ethnographic Museum), Bulvar Cad 16, Eregli
Archaeological Museum / Ethnology Museum
Archeological works from the Roman, Byzantine and Islamic periods, rock relief at Ivriz from the Neo-Hitite period (8th c BC), manuscripts, ethnographical objects, Enata coll, Canhasan coll 31717

Erzincan

Erzincan Kültür Merkezi (Erzincan Culture Center), Barış Manço Parkı İçi, 24030 Erzincan - T: (0446) 2235538, Fax: 2148022. Head: Cemal Polat
Public Gallery 31718

Erzurum

Çifte Minareli Medrese Müzesi (Çifte Minareli Medrese Museum), Erzurum
Archaeological Museum
Seljuk and Ottoman gravestones, in an 18th c medrese (Islamic university) from the Seljuk period 31719

Erzurum Arkeoloji ve Etnografi Müzesi (Erzurum Archeological and Ethnographical Museum), Yenişehir Cad No. 11, Erzurum - T: (0442) 2181406
Archaeological Museum
Findings from prehistoric times of the Byzantine period, ethnographic works, guilded books 31720

Erzurum Kültür Merkezi (Erzurum Culture Center), Paşalar Cad 1, 25100 Erzurum - T: (0442) 2188486. Head: Hasan Mazlumoğlu
Public Gallery 31721

Erzurum Resim ve Heykel Müzesi (Erzurum State Painting and Sculpture Museum), Kültür Merkezi, Erzurum - T: (0442) 2333158, Fax: 2230771. Head: Şahin Özbey
Fine Arts Museum
Modern and contemporary Turkish painting, sculpture and graphic arts 31722

Eskişehir

Eskişehir Arkeoloji Müzesi (Eskişehir Archaeological Museum), Akarbaşı Mah İrmak Sok, Eskişehir - T: (0222) 2301749, Fax: 2301749
Archaeological Museum - 1935
Archeological finds from the Chalcolithic, Hitite, Byzantine, Roman and Islamic periods - laboratory, workshop 31723

Eskişehir Atatürk ve Kültür Müzesi (Atatürk and Culture Museum), Eskişehir
Special Museum - 1970
Memorabilia of the Turkish politician Atatürk (1880-1938), ethnography 31724

Eskişehir Devlet Güzel Sanatlar Galerisi (Eskişehir State Gallery), Porsuk Bulvarı, Köprübaşı, Eskişehir - T: (0222) 2301378, Fax: 2306301. Head: Gülşen Akın
Public Gallery 31725

Etnografi Müzesi, Ottoman House (Ethnographic Museum), Yesil Efendi House, Dede, Eskişehir
Ethnology Museum
Ethnographic works from the region of Eskisehir, woodcarving 31726

Fatih

İstanbul Büyükşehir Belediyesi Karikatür ve Mizah Müzesi (İstanbul Museum of Caricature and Humour), Atatürk Bul Kovacılar Sok 12, 34230 Fatih - T: (0212) 5211264 703=5211264 710=1989. Head: Erdoğan Bozok
Fine Arts Museum
Coll on Ottoman and Turkish caricature 31727

İtfaiye Müzesi (Fire Brigade Museum), İtfaiye Cad 9, 34230 Fatih - T: (0212) 6350100
Special Museum - 1992
Examples of fire fighting and rescue tools 31728

Fethiye

Fethiye Kültür Merkezi (Fethiye Culture Center), Cumhuriyet Mah. Müze Sok, 48300 Fethiye - T: (0252) 6144946, Fax: 6144945. Head: Selahattin Güzel
Public Gallery 31729

Fethiye Müzesi (Museum Fethiye), Fethiye
Archaeological Museum - 1965
Exhibits from the Lycia, Roman and Byzantine periods, coins 31730

Gaziantep

Gaziantep Arkeoloji Müzesi (Gaziantep Archaeological Museum), Istasyon Cad, Gaziantep - T: (0342) 2311171, Fax: 2303017, E-mail: muze27@marketweb.net.tr
Archaeological Museum 31731

Gaziantep Devlet Güzel Sanatlar Galerisi (Gaziantep State Gallery), İl Halk Kütüphanesi, Gaziantep - T: (0342) 2318252, Fax: 2340604. Head: Şenel Tercan
Public Gallery 31732

Gaziantep Etnografi Müzesi (Museum Ethnography Gaziantep), Eyüboglu Mah Hanifioglu Sok No. 64, Gaziantep - T: (0342) 2304721
Ethnology Museum 31733

Geyre Köyü Karasu Aydın

Afrodisiyas Müzesi (Aphrodisias Museum), Geyre Köyü Karasu Aydın - T: (0256) 4488003, Fax: 4488262
Archaeological Museum - 1979
Finds from the archeological excavations of the ancient city of Aphrodisias, theatre, bath, sculpture, temples, Sebasteion 31734

Gülhane

Istanbul Arkeoloji Müzeleri (Archeological Museums of Istanbul), Osman Hamdi Bey Yokuşu, 34400 Gülhane - T: (0212) 5207741, Fax: 5274300. Head: Halil Özek
Archaeological Museum - 1869
Classical, Ancient Orient, exhibits from the Sumerian, Akkadian, Hittite, Assyrian, Egyptian, Urartu, Greek, Roman and Byzantine periods, Seljuk and Ottoman tiles and ceramics - library 31735

Gümüşsuyu

Ayşe ve Ercümend Kalmık Vakfı-Müzesi (Ayşe and Ercümend Kalmık Foundation- Museum), Sarayarkası Sok 35-37, 80060 Gümüşsuyu - T: (0212) 2450270, Fax: 2444661. Head: Zeynep Rona
Fine Arts Museum - 1995
Works of the Turkish painter Ercümend Kalmık, coll of paintings, works on paper, graphics 31736

Harput

Harput Müzesi (Harput Museum), Balak Gazi Sok, Harput
Archaeological Museum - 1960
Inscriptions from the Urartu Monarchy and Roman period, Islamic grave stones 31737

Hasköy

Aynalıkavak Kasrı (Aynalıkavak Pavillion), Aynalıkavak Cad, 80320 Hasköy - T: (0212) 1504094
Music Museum - 1792 31738

Hatay

Hatay Devlet Güzel Sanatlar Galerisi (Hatay State Gallery), Kültür Merkezi, Hatay - T: (0326) 2163397, Fax: 2133886. Head: Fethiye Yaldız
Public Gallery 31739

Hatay Müzesi (Hatay Museum), Gündüz Cad 1, Hatay - T: (0326) 2146167, Fax: 2133386. Head: Mehmet Erdem
Archaeological Museum - 1934
Mosaics from the 2nd to 5th c AD, column capitals, frescoes and statues from the Hitite to Roman periods, grave Stelae, Statue sarcophagi from the province of Hatay - conference hall, laboratory 31740

Hozat

Hozat Kültür Merkezi (Hozat Culture Center), Hamidiye Mah. Alpdoğan Sok 25, Hozat - T: (0428) 5612103. Head: Metin Bayram
Public Gallery 31741

İsparta

İsparta Devlet Güzel Sanatlar Galerisi (Isparta State Gallery), Çelebiler Mah. Kaymakkapı Meydanı Tuhafiyeciler Sitesi, İsparta - T: (0246) 2181804, Fax: 2236550. Head: Fehmi Taktak
Public Gallery 31742

Yalvaç Müzesi (Yalvaç Museum), Hükümet Cad, İsparta - T: (0246) 4415059, Fax: 4414937. Head: Dr. Mehmet Taslialan
Ethnology Museum 31743

İstanbul

Askeri Müze (Military Museum), Valikonağı Cad, Harbıye, 80200 İstanbul - T: (0212) 2332720, Fax: 2968618. Head: Baki Uslu
Military Museum - 1846
Weapons, military equipment, documents, uniforms, exhibits from the Liberation War and the Republic 31744

Ayasofya Müzesi (Hagia Sophia Museum), Sultanahmet Meydanı, Sultanahmet, 34400 İstanbul - T: (0212) 5229241, 5221750, Fax: 5125474, E-mail: ayasofyamuzesi@hotmail.com. Head: Mustafa Akkaya
Archaeological Museum - 1934
Byzantine and Turkish antiquities, located in Byzantine basilica built under the reign of imperator Justinian in the 6th c 31745

Basin Müzesi Sanat Galerisi (Press Museum), Divanyolu Cad 84, Cagaloglu, İstanbul - T: (0212) 5148458
Public Gallery - 1988
Documents on the hist of Turkish press, mass media 31746

Beyoglu Sanat Merkezi, Istklal Cad 437, Tünel, İstanbul - T: (0212) 2527755
Public Gallery 31747

Büyük Saray Mozaik Müzesi (The Great Palace Mosaic Museum), Arasta Çarşisi, Sultanahmet, 34400 İstanbul - T: (0212) 5181205, Fax: 5125474. Head: Mustafa Akkaya
Archaeological Museum
Mosaics from the 6th c AD of the Great Palace of Justinian I. 31748

Deniz Müzesi (Naval Museum), Iskele Cad, Beşiktaş, 80690 İstanbul - T: (0212) 2610040, Fax: 2606038. Head: Muhlis Ergin
Military Museum - 1897
Cannons, models, torpedos and mines, medals, paintings - library, archives 31749

Dolmabahçe Palace, Beşiktaş, 80680 İstanbul - T: (0212) 2369000, Fax: 2593292, Internet: http://www.dsarayeddoruk.net.tr. Head: İsmail Hakkı Celayır
Historic Site - 1984
19th c palace, built in a mixture of Renaissance and Baroque styles, original furnishings, historical documents, room where the Turkish politician Atatürk (1880-1938) died, clocks, textiles, carpets, chandeliers, paintings, porcelain 31750

Görüntü Sanatlari, Halaskargazi Cad 254, Osmanbey, İstanbul - T: (0212) 2316223
Fine Arts Museum 31751

İstanbul Divan Edebiyatı Müzesi (İstanbul Ottoman Poetry Museum), Galipdede Cad 15, Tünel, 30850 İstanbul - T: (0212) 245414, 2435045. Head: Kıvanç Arman
Special Museum / Music Museum - 1975
Examples of calligraphy, Mevlevî musical instruments, handwritten poetry coll 31752

KUSAV, 24-26 Köybaşı Cad., Yeniköy, 80870 İstanbul - T: (0212) 2623433, 2620986, Fax: 2627026, E-mail: kusav@kusav.org, Internet: http://www.kusav.org. Head: Çigdem Simavi
Association with Coll / Decorative Arts Museum 31753

Resim ve Heykel Müzesi (Museum of Painting and Sculpture), Dolmabahçe Cad, Beşiktaş, 80680 İstanbul - T: (0212) 2614298, 2594739, Fax: 2440398. Head: Prof. Kemal Iskender
Fine Arts Museum - 1937
Modern and contemporary Turkish art, paintings, sculptors, ceramics and graphic art 31754

Sadberk Hanım Müzesi, Vehbi Koç Vakfı (Sadbek Hanım Museum), Piyasa Cad 27-29, Büyükdere, 80890 İstanbul - T: (0212) 2420365. Head: Çetin Anlagan
Fine Arts Museum / Decorative Arts Museum - 1980
Archaeological objects, applied art, Turkish and Ottoman ethnography, calligraphy, Iznik tiles and ceramics 31755

Temel Sanat Kolleksiyon, Valikonagi Cad 165, Nisantasi, İstanbul - T: (0212) 2758242
Fine Arts Museum 31756

Topkapı Sarayı Müzesi (Topkapı Palace Museum), Sarayiçi, Sultanahmet, 34400 İstanbul - T: (0212) 5120480/84, 5224422, Fax: 5285991. Head: Dr. Filiz Çağman
Military Museum / Decorative Arts Museum
Turkish armour, cloth, embroidery, tiles, glass and porcelain, copper- and silverware, treasury objects, paintings, miniatures, illuminated manuscripts, royal coaches, Sevrés and Bohemian crystal and porcelain, selection of Islamic relics, clocks, Chinese and Japanese porcelain, Revan House, Baghdad House, Mecidiye House, Harem, all in a 15th c palace - library, archives 31757

Türk ve Islam Eserleri Müzesi (Museum of Turkish and Islamic Art), Ibrahim Pasa Sarayi, At Meydanı, Sultanahmet, 34400 İstanbul - T: (0212) 5181805/06, Fax: 5181807, E-mail: tiemist@superonline.com, Internet: http://www.tiem.org. Head: Dr. Nazan Ölçer
Folklore Museum / Religious Arts Museum - 1914
Coll of Turkish and Islamic rugs, illuminated manuscripts, sculpture in Stone and Stucco, woodcarvings, metalwork, ceramics, miniatures, in a 16th c building 31758

Vakıf Halı Müzesi (Carpet Museum), Sultanahmet Camii Avlusu, 34400 İstanbul - T: (0212) 5181330. Head: Serpil Özçelik
Decorative Arts Museum
Examples of old Seljuk and Ottoman carpets 31759

Vakıf Inşaat ve Sanat Eserleri Müzesi (Museum of Turkish tiles and wood-and-metal-work), Saraçhana Sok 1, 34260 Fatih İstanbul - T: (0212) 5251294. Head: Erdal Öztürk
Decorative Arts Museum
Examples of Turkish tiles and wood-and-metal work, tools 31760

Vakıf Kilim ve Düz Dokuma Yaygılar Müzesi (Museum of Kilims and Flatweaves), Sultanahmet Camii Avlusu, 34400 İstanbul - T: (0212) 5181330. Head: Serpil Özçelik
Decorative Arts Museum
Examples of old kilims and historical flatweaves, textiles from Anatolia 31761

Yedikule Fortress Museum, İstanbul
Historical Museum
Seven towers fortress, local history 31762

Yerebatan Sarnıcı (Yerebatan Cistern Museum), Yerebatan Cad 13, Sultanahmet, 34410 İstanbul - T: (0212) 5221259. Head: Salih Dogan
Archaeological Museum - 1987
Water cistern, built in the 6th c by the Byzantine emperor Justinian 31763

Yıldız Şale, Yıldız, 86080 İstanbul - T: (0212) 2594570, Fax: 2598826, Internet: http://www.dsarayeddoruk.net.tr. Head: İsmail Hakkı Celayır
Decorative Arts Museum - 1984
Ottoman civil architecture, visit of Wilhelm II, 400 square metres handweaved Hereke carpet, chandeliers, textiles 31764

İzmir

Atatürk Müzesi, Atatürk Cad 24, İzmir - T: (0232) 4848085, 4890796, Fax: 4830611
Special Museum
Memorabilia of the Turkish politician Atatürk (1881-1938), paintings, photographs 31765

İzmir Arkeoloji Müzesi (Izmir Archaeological Museum), Kültür Park, İzmir - T: (0232) 541010. Head: Mushin Yenim
Archaeological Museum - 1927
Works from the Chalcolithic age to the Byzantine period from the regions Izmir, Bergama, Sart and Ephesus 31766

İzmir Resim ve Heykel Müzesi (İzmir State Painting and Sculpture Museum), Mithatpaşa Cad 94, İzmir - T: (0232) 4848945, Fax: 4411398. Head: Cahit Koççoban
Fine Arts Museum - 1973
Modern and contemporary Turkish painting, sculpture and graphic arts 31767

Iznik

Iznik Müzesi (Iznik Museum), Nilufer Hatun Soup Kitchen, Iznik
Archaeological Museum / Ethnology Museum
Archeological and ethnographical works of the Hellenistic, Roman, Byzantine, Seljuk and Ottoman periods, marble sarcophagus in a 14 th c house, one of the earliest examples of Ottoman architecture - library 31768

Kadirli

Karatepe Açıkhava Müzesi (Karatepe Open Air Museum), Kadirli
Open Air Museum / Archaeological Museum
Finds from the excavations of a Late Hitite city dated 700-730 BC 31769

Kahramanmaraş

Kahramanmaraş Devlet Güzel Sanatlar Galerisi (Kahramanmaraş State Gallery), Sabancı Kültür Merkezi Atattürk Parkı İçi, Kahramanmaraş - T: (0344) 2234486, Fax: 2234481. Head: Ahmet Büyükçapar
Public Gallery 31770

Kahramanmaraş Kültür Merkezi (Kahramanmaraş Culture Center), Adana Yolu Üzeri Atatürk Parkı İçiCad, 46100 Kahramanmaraş - T: 0344) 2234485, Fax: 2234481. Head: Muzaffer Ramazanoğlu
Public Gallery 31771

Kahramanmaraş Müzesi (Kahramanmaraş Museum), Azarbeycan Bul Yenişehir Sok No. 43, Kahramanmaraş - T: (0344) 2234487
Archaeological Museum - 1947
Neo-Hitite reliefs, statues from the Roman and Byzantine periods, gravestones and masonry, ceramics, ethnography, coins - library 31772

Karaman

Karaman Müzesi (Karaman Museum), Hastahane Cad, Karaman - T: (0338) 113870
Archaeological Museum - 1962
Can Hasan excavation founds from the Chalcolithic period (5000-3000 BC), archeological finds from the Roman, Byzantine, Karamanogullari and Ottoman periods, ethnography - library 31773

Kars

Kars Devlet Güzel Sanatlar Galerisi (Kars State Gallery), Kültür Merkezi, Kars - T: (0474) 2235247, Fax: 2233311. Head: Settar Kaya
Public Gallery 31774

Kars Kültür Merkezi (Kars Culture Center), Cumhuriyet Mah. Lise Sok 15, 36100 Kars - T: (0474) 2238571, Fax: 2234411. Head: Mehmet Ablak
Public Gallery 31775

Kars Müzesi (Kars Museum), Istasyon Mah Cumhuriyet Cad No. 365, Kars - T: (0474) 2232433
Archaeological Museum - 1963
Archeology 31776

Kastamonu

Kastamonu Devlet Güzel Sanatlar Galerisi (Kastamonu State Gallery), Kültür Sitesi, Kastamonu - T: (0366) 2143233, Fax: 2124405. Head: Mustafa Yüksek
Public Gallery 31777

Rıfat Ilgaz Kültür Merkezi (Rıfat Ilgaz Culture Center), Cebrail Mah. 2, Hükümet Cad 3, 37200 Kastamonu - T: (0366) 2149795, Fax: 2124405. Head: Ünal Akgün
Public Gallery 31778

Kaymaklı

Yeraltı Müzesi (Underground City Museum), Kaymaklı
Archaeological Museum - 1965
Underground Christian dwellings from the Byzantine period (7th c) 31779

Kayseri

Kayseri Arkeoloji Müzesi (Kayseri Archaeological Museum), Gültepe Mah. Kışla Cad No. 2, Kayseri - T: (0352) 2222149
Archaeological Museum - 1969
Finds from the Kultepe excavations, Hitite works, ceramics from the Phrygian, Roman and Byzantine periods 31780

Kayseri Devlet Güzel Sanatlar Galerisi (Kayseri State Gallery), Cumhuriyet Mah. Tennuri Cad Atatürk Evi, Kayseri - T: (0352) 2220456, Fax: 2322581. Head: Hilmi Özcan
Public Gallery 31781

Kırıkkale

Kırıkkale Kültür Merkezi (Kırıkkale Culture Center), Fabrikalar Mah. Hükümet Konağı Yanı, 71100 Kırıkkale - T: (0318) 2242684, Fax: 2242555. Head: Emin Erdem
Public Gallery 31782

Kırşehir

Kırşehir Devlet Güzel Sanatlar Galerisi (Kırşehir State Gallery), Kültür Merkezi, Kırşehir - T: (0386) 2131340, Fax: 2123295. Head: Necdet Gencer
Public Gallery 31783

Kırşehir Kültür Merkezi (Kırşehir Culture Center), Ahi Evran Mah. Stadyum Cad, Kırşehir - T: (0386) 2130395, Fax: 2123295. Head: Metin Eren
Public Gallery 31784

Kocaeli

Kocaeli Devlet Güzel Sanatlar Galerisi (Kocaeli State Gallery), Eski Vali Konağı, Kocaeli - T: (02622) 3211960, Fax: 3245464. Head: Ahmet Özsağır
Public Gallery 31785

Kocaeli Sabancı Kültür Sitesi (Kocaeli Sabancı Culture House), Vilayet Karşısı E-5 Karayolu Altı, 0262 Kocaeli - T: (0262) 3228009, Fax: 3245463. Head: Saffet Yakar
Public Gallery 31786

Konya

Atatürk Müzesi, Konya Museums (Atatürk Museum), Konya. Head: Dr. Erdogan Erol
Special Museum - 1964
Memorabilia of the Turkish politician Atatürk (1880-1938) 31787

Konya Devlet Güzel Sanatlar Galerisi (Konya State Gallery), Babı Aksaray Mah. Mevlana Alanı 21, Konya - T: (0332) 3503925, Fax: 3534023. Head: Nilüfer Soylu
Public Gallery 31788

Konya Etnografi Müzesi (Konya Ethnographic Museum), Larende Cad, Konya - T: (0332) 3518958
Ethnology Museum - 1974
Costumes, handicrafts, jewelry, domestic utensils, weapons, coins 31789

Konya Müzesi (Konya Museum), Mevlana Mah, Konya - T: (0332) 3511215. Head: Dr. Erdogan Erol
Archaeological Museum - 1963
Gravestones, sarcophagus, inscriptions, exhibits from the Classic period 31790

Koyunoglu Müzesi (Koyunoglu Museum), Konya - T: (0332) 3511857, Fax: 2354630, 2378487, E-mail: bim@konya-bld.gov.tr, Internet: http://www.konya-bld.gov.tr. Head: Abdurrahman Korkmaz
Local Museum / Ethnology Museum - 1975
Koyunoglu coll including ethnographical objects, carpets, cloths, embroidery, guilded books, oil paintings 31791

Mevlâna Müzesi, Konya Museums (Mevlâna Rumi Museum), Konya - T: (0332) 3511215. Head: Dr. Erdogan Erol
Fine Arts Museum - 1927
Oriental art, manuscripts, crafts from the Seljuk period, tomb of the great Turkish-Persian philosopher-poet Rumi, mescid (small mosque), dervish cells, Mevlevî kitchen, examples of calligraphy, musical instruments, poetry collections - library 31792

Selçuk Müzesi, Konya Museums (Seljuk Museum), Inceminareli Medrese, Konya. Head: Dr. Erdogan Erol
Archaeological Museum - 1956
Examples of gravestones, inscriptions and buildings, stones from the Seljuk and Karamanogullari periods, figurative stone decorations from Konya castle 31793

Sırçalı Medrese Müzesi, Konya Museums (Sırçalı Medrese Museum), Konya. Head: Dr. Erdogan Erol
Archaeological Museum - 1960
Gravestones of historical and artistic value from the Seljuk, Beylik and Ottoman periods, in a 13th c medrese (Islamic university) 31794

Türk Seramik Müzesi, Konya Museums (Turkish Ceramics Museum), Karatay Medresi, Konya. Head: Dr. Erdogan Erol
Archaeological Museum
Wall tiles and porcelain dishes from the Seljuk, Beylik and Ottoman periods in a 13th c medrese (Islamic university) 31795

Kütahya

Kütahya Devlet Güzel Sanatlar Galerisi (Kütahya State Gallery), Belediye Arkası Kardeşler Apt. 16/1, Kütahya - T: (0274) 2236840, Fax: 2235535. Head: Yaşar Atasever
Public Gallery 31796

Kütahya Müzesi (Kütahya Museum), Cumhuriyet Mah Ulu Camii Yanı, Kütahya - T: (0274) 2236990
Archaeological Museum - 1965
Archeological finds from prehistoric times, the Hitite, Phrygian, Hellenistic, Roman and Byzantine periods, ethnographical coll from the region of Kütahya in a 14th c medrese (Islamic university) 31797

Malatya

Malatya Devlet Güzel Sanatlar Galerisi (Malatya State Gallery), Kültür Merkezi SSK Yanı, Malatya - T: (0422) 3239173, Fax: 3234928. Head: Batuhan Bozkurt
Public Gallery 31798

Malatya Müzesi (Malatya Museum), Dernek Mah Kanal Boyu, Malatya - T: (0422) 3213006
Archaeological Museum - 1969
Exhibits from the Chalcolithic, Early Bronze, Assyrian, Hitite Ages, Hellenistic, Roman, Byzantine, Seljuk and Ottoman periods 31799

Malatya Sabancı Kültür Merkezi (Malatya Sabancı Culture Center), İstasyon Virajı, 44080 Malatya - T: (0422) 3247612. Head: Yaşar Gündüz
Public Gallery 31800

Malazgirt

Malazgirt Kültür Merkezi (Malazgirt Culture Center), Danışment Gazi Mah. Yarbay Öner Cad 7, Malazgirt - T: (0436) 5112233
Public Gallery 31801

Manisa

Manisa Devlet Güzel Sanatlar Galerisi (Manisa State Gallery), Manisa - T: (0236) 2315568, Fax: 2310330. Head: Nazım Akbulut
Public Gallery 31802

Manisa Müzesi (Manisa Museum 600=Saruhan Bey Mah Murat Cad No. 107), Manisa - T: (0236) 2320062
Local Museum / Archaeological Museum / Ethnology Museum - 1935
Archeology, ethnography, Turkish art 31803

Mardin

Mardin Müzesi (Mardin Museum), Halk Kütüphanesi Binası Meydanbaşı, Mardin - T: (0482) 2121664
Local Museum - 1945
Coll of Islamic and pre-Islamic works, coins 31804

Mersin

75. Yıl Tarsus Kültür Merkezi (75. Yıl Tarsus Culture Center), İnceark Mahallesi Muaffak Uyar Cad, 33400 Mersin - T: (0324) 6141044, Fax: 6131352. Head: Sebahattin Deniz
Public Gallery 31805

Mersin Kültür Merkezi (Mersin Culture Center), Atatürk CadCumhuriyet Alanı, 33070 Mersin - T: (324) 2371903/04, Fax: 2371902. Head: Kerim Kıcıman
Public Gallery 31806

Milas

Milas Kültür Merkezi (Milas Culture Center), Hayıtlı Mah. İnönü Cad Ulucami Karşısı, Milas - T: (0252) 5124949, Fax: 5123333. Head: Osman Koca
Public Gallery 31807

Milas Müzesi (Milas Museum), Hayıtlı Mah. Köprülüler Cad No. 6, Milas - T: (0252) 5123970
Archaeological Museum - 1959
Archeology 31808

Mudanya

Mudanya Mutareke Evi Müzesi (Mudanya Armistice Museum), Mudanya - T: (0224) 5441068. Head: Öcal Özeren
Historical Museum - 1960
Historical house, where the Mudanya Armistice was signed, original furniture, bedrooms of Ismet Inonu and General Asim 31809

Muğla

Muğla Devlet Güzel Sanatlar Galerisi (Muğla State Gallery), Muğla - T: (0252) 2149015, Fax: 2148343. Head: Tuncay Pişiren
Public Gallery 31810

Muğla Kültür Merkezi (Muğla Culture Center), Müştakbey Mah. Eski Pastane Sok, Muğla - T: (0252) 2144933, Fax: 2146006. Head: Haydar Ökten
Public Gallery 31811

Narlıkuyu

Silifke Mozaik Müzesi (Silifke Mosaic Museum), Silifke-Anamur Cad, Narlıkuyu
Archaeological Museum - 1967
Roman period mosaics 31812

Nevşehir

Göreme Açıkhava Müzesi (Göreme Open Air Museum), Nevşehir
Open Air Museum
Byzantine period (7th-12th c) stone churches decorated with frescoes 31813

Haçıbektaş Müzesi (Museum Hacibektaş), Nevşehir Cad, Hacibektaş, Nevşehir - T: (0384) 4413022
Archaeological Museum
Exhibits from the Ottoman period, mescid (small mosque), tombs 31814

Nevşehir Arkeoloji ve Etnografya Müzesi (Nevşehir Archaeological and Ethnographic Museum), Imaret Bulvarı, Nevşehir
Archaeological Museum / Ethnology Museum
Archeological works from the Hitite, Phrygian, Byzantine periods, ethnography, in an 18th c building 31815

Nevşehir Devlet Güzel Sanatlar Galerisi (Nevşehir State Gallery), Kültür Merkezi, Nevşehir - T: (0384) 2131726, Fax: 2134260. Head: İsmail Başer
Public Gallery 31816

Nevşehir Kültür Merkezi (Nevşehir Culture Center), 350 Evler Sok Türbe Sok 1, Nevşehir - T: (0384) 2135050. Head: İsmail Başer
Public Gallery 31817

Nigde

Nigde Müzesi (Nigde Museum), Akmedrese, Nigde - T: (0388) 2323397
Archaeological Museum / Ethnology Museum - 1936
Archeology from the Roman, Byzantine, Hellenistic, Seljuk and Ottoman periods, ethnography 31818

Ordu

Ordu Devlet Güzel Sanatlar Galerisi (Ordu State Gallery), Şehir Otogarı Alt Katı, Ordu - T: (0452) 2232595, Fax: 2230064. Head: Ş. Nihal Durmaz
Public Gallery 31819

Rize

Rize Devlet Güzel Sanatlar Galerisi (Rize State Gallery), Özel İdare Tesisleri Müftü Mah., Rize - T: (0464) 2130634, Fax: 2130428. Head: İsmet Sivrikaya
Public Gallery 31820

Salihli/Manisa

Manisa Salihli Kültür Merkezi (Manisa Salihli Culture Center), Atatürk Cad 68A, 45300 Salihli/ Manisa - T: (0236) 7141990, Fax: 7132068. Head: Mehmet Bilgin
Public Gallery 31821

Samsun

19 Mayıs Müzesi (19 May Museum), Mintika Palace, Gazi Bulvari, Samsun
Historical Museum - 1930
History, archeology - library 31822

Atatürk Museum, Samsun Fair, Samsun
Special Museum - 1968
Memorabilia of the Turkish politician Atatürk (1880-1938) 31823

Samsun Devlet Güzel Sanatlar Galerisi (Samsun State Gallery), Fuar İçi, Samsun - T: (0362) 4322933, Fax: 4231158. Head: Ömer Pamuk
Public Gallery 31824

Şanlıurfa

Şanlıurfa Devlet Güzel Sanatlar Galerisi (Şanlıurfa State Gallery), Hacı Mahmut İzgördü Konağı, Şanlıurfa - T: (0414) 2155126, Fax: 3120118. Head: F. Nevin Güllüoğlu
Public Gallery 31825

Selçuk

Efes Müzesi (Ephesus Museum), 35920 Selçuk - T: (0232) 8926010, Fax: 8927002. Head: Selahattin Erdemgil
Archaeological Museum - 1964
Objects from the excavations of Ephesus since 1950's, finds from the Prehistoric, Mycenean, Greek, Roman, Byzantine and Turkish periods 31826

Seyitgazi

Museum Seyitgazi, Seyit Battalgazi Külliye, Seyitgazi
Archaeological Museum / Ethnology Museum - 1970
Archeology and ethnography in a house built in the Seljuk period 31827

Side

Side Müzesi (Side Museum), Selimiye Köyü, Side - T: (0242) 7531006, Fax: 7532749. Head: Orhan Atvur
Archaeological Museum - 1961
Roman period sculptures, reliefs, sarcophagi lodged in an ancient Roman bath 31828

Silifke - Içel

Silifke Müzesi (Silifke Museum), Taşucu Cad 111, Silifke - Içel - T: (0324) 7141919, Fax: 7142852
Archaeological Museum - 1940
Archeological finds from the Greek, Roman, Byzantine, Seljuk and Ottoman periods, Hellenistic ceramics, ethnography, numismatics, Ptolemys golden coin coll - conservation laboratory, library 31829

Sinop

Sinop Devlet Güzel Sanatlar Galerisi (Sinop State Gallery), İl Kültür Merkezi Binası Karantina Sok 12, Sinop - T: (0368) 2616762, Fax: 2614868. Head: Zerefşan Tatlıcan
Public Gallery 31830

Sinop Kültür Merkezi (Sinop Culture Center), Okulak Sok 54, 57000 Sinop - T: (0368) 2616154, Fax: 2614868. Head: Şaban Düğer
Public Gallery 31831

Sinop Müzesi (Sinop Museum), Okullar Cad, Sinop - T: (0362) 4350258
Archaeological Museum / Ethnology Museum - 1941
Archeology, ethnography, carpets, sarcophagi, inscriptions 31832

Sirkeci

Tanzimat Müzesi (Museum of the Turkish Revolution 1839), Gülhane Parkı, 34400 Sirkeci - T: (0212) 5126384. Head: Mehmet Özgerey
Historical Museum - 1952
Documents related to the Ottoman political reforms initiated in 1839 31833

Şişli

Ataürk Müzesi (Atatürk Revolution Museum), Halaskargazi Cad 250, 80260 Şişli
Historical Museum - 1943
Memorial to the Turkish politician Atatürk (1880-1938), documents, cloths, photographs 31834

Turkish Sports Museum, Buyukdere Cad., Tankanya, 80260 Şişli
Special Museum 31835

Sivas

4 Eylül Atatürk Müzesi (4 September Atatürk Museum), Taslı St, Sivas
Historical Museum
Historical hall where the Sivas Congress was held in 1919, Atatürk room, furniture, documents 31836

Museum of Antiquities, Buruciye Medrese, Sivas - T: (0346) 2212568
Archaeological Museum / Ethnology Museum - 1934
Silverware, ceramics, archeology, ethnography, sarcophagi, in a 13th c medrese (Islamic university) from the Seljuk period 31837

Sivas Atatürk Kültür Merkezi (Sivas Atatürk Culture Center), Halit Rıfat Paşa Cad Sigorta Hastanesi Yanı, 58030 Sivas - T: (0346) 2235908, Fax: 2234591. Head: Ahmet Opan
Public Gallery 31838

Sivas Devlet Güzel Sanatlar Galerisi (Sivas State Gallery), Atatürk Kültür Merkezi, Sivas - T: (0346) 2215128, Fax: 2239299. Head: R. Sefa İnce
Public Gallery 31839

Tarsus

Tarsus Müzesi (Tarsus Museum), Tarsus - T: (0324) 6130625
Archaeological Museum / Ethnology Museum - 1972
Archeology, ethnography 31840

Tekirdağ

Tekirdağ Devlet Güzel Sanatlar Galerisi (Tekirdağ State Gallery), Sarı Köşk, Tekirdağ - T: (0282) 2626012, Fax: 2628000. Head: Melahat Ayvaz
Public Gallery 31841

Tekirdag Müzesi (Tekirdag Museum), Vali Konagı Cad No. 21, Tekirdağ - T: (0282) 2612082
Local Museum 31842

Tire

Tire Müzesi (Tire Museum), Imaret Mosque, Tire
Archaeological Museum / Decorative Arts Museum - 1935
Roman period statues, clay sarcophagus, Roman, Byzantine and Islamic coins, embroidery, domestic utensils, hand-written Korans, Ottoman period glass objects, arms 31843

Tokat

Tokat Müzesi (Tokat Museum), Gaziosmanpaşa Bulvarı No. 143, Tokat - T: (0356) 2141509
Archaeological Museum / Ethnology Museum - 1926
Archeology, ethnography in a 13th c medrese (Islamic university) - archives 31844

Trabzon

Atatürk Evi (Atatürk House), Soguksu, Trabzon
Special Museum
Memorabilia of the Turkish politician Atatürk (1880-1938) 31845

Trabzon Devlet Güzel Sanatlar Galerisi (Trabzon State Gallery), Eski Valilik-Ortahisar, Trabzon - T: (0462) 3217081, Fax: 3260520. Head: Mustafa Sezgin
Public Gallery 31846

Trabzon Kültür Merkezi (Trabzon Culture Center), Ortahisar Mah. Eski Hükümet Konağı Binası, 61030 Trabzon - T: (0462) 3265157. Head: Denizay Altay
Public Gallery 31847

Ürgüp

Ürgüp Müzesi (Ürgüp Museum), Kayseri Cad No.39, Ürgüp - T: (0384) 3414082
Archaeological Museum / Ethnology Museum - 1971
Archeology from the Hitite, Phrygian, Roman and Byzantine periods, ethnography 31848

Urfa

Urfa Müzesi (Urfa Museum), Urfa
Archaeological Museum / Ethnology Museum - 1948
Exhibits from prehistoric times, the Greek, Roman and Byzantine periods, mosaics from Urfa Necropolis, Seljuk and Ottoman period inscriptions, ethnography 31849

Uşakş

Uşak Arkeoloji Müzesi (Uşak Archeological Museum), Kurtuluş Mah Dogan Sok No. 1, Uşakş - T: (0276) 2273930
Archaeological Museum / Ethnology Museum - 1970
Archeology 31850

Van

Van Devlet Güzel Sanatlar Galerisi (Van State Gallery), SSK Binası K. Karabekir Cad 51C, Van - T: (0432) 2162530, Fax: 2121734. Head: Maşuk Canbey
Public Gallery 31851

Van Kültür Merkezi (Van Culture Center), Fevzi Çakmak Cad Kültür Sok 24, 65100 Van - T: (0432) 2169692. Head: Salih Tatlı
Public Gallery 31852

Van Müzesi (Van Museum), Şerefiye Mah Hacı Osman Sok No. 9, Van - T: (0432) 2161139, Fax: 2142510
Archaeological Museum / Ethnology Museum - 1947
Archaeology, Urartu inscriptions, ethnography 31853

Viranşehir

Viranşehir Kültür Merkezi (Viranşehir Culture Center), Bahçelievler Mah. Stadyum Cad, Viranşehir - T: (0414) 5113901. Head: Sefer Aytar
Public Gallery 31854

Yalvaç

Yalvaç Müzesi, 32400 Yalvaç - T: (0246) 4415059, Fax: 4414937. Head: Dr. Mehmet Taşlialan
Archaeological Museum / Ethnology Museum - 1966
Archeology from 2500 B.C. to the 4th c A.D., works from the ruins of the ancient city of Antioch, ethnography, paintings by Turkish artists, Ottoman period manuscripts and inscriptions 31855

Yozgat

Yozgat Devlet Güzel Sanatlar Galerisi (Yozgat State Gallery), Kültür Merkezi, Yozgat - T: (0354) 2126822, Fax: 2126822. Head: Servet Dürüce
Public Gallery 31856

Yozgat Kültür Merkezi (Yozgat Culture Center), Medrese Mah. Kültür Sok 1, 66100 Yozgat - T: (0354) 2125158. Head: Mustafa Erdoğan
Public Gallery 31857

Yunus Emre

Yunus Emre Müzesi (Yunus Emre Museum), Yunus Emre
Special Museum - 1971
Memorabilia of the Turkish poet Yunus Emre 31858

Zonguldak

Zonguldak Devlet Güzel Sanatlar Galerisi (Zonguldak State Gallery), Gazipaşa Cad, Zonguldak - T: (0372) 2518289, Fax: 2536524. Head: Ali Bülent Göçmen
Public Gallery 31859

Turkmenistan

Ašhabad

Carpet Museum, Gorogly ul 5, Ašhabad - T: (012) 398887, 398879. Head: Tuvakbibi Kurbanovna Durdyeva
Special Museum
Antiques and world-renowned Turkmen carpets (hand-knotted) 31860

Muzej Izobrazitel'nych Iskusstv (State Museum of Fine Arts), ul Puškina 9, 744000 Ašhabad - T: (012) 256371. Head: Natalja Šabunts
Fine Arts Museum - 1938
European art, rugs from the Turkmenian region - library 31861

National Museum of Turkmenistan, Novofirjusinskoje Chaussee 30, Bersengi, 744000 Ašhabad - T: (012) 255138. Head: A. Atagarev
Historical Museum / Ethnology Museum - 1899
History, ethnography of the Turkmen people, archaeology and natural coll - library 31862

Čeleken

Čelekenskij Muzej (Celeken Museum), 4, District 35, Čeleken. Head: Bibi Klytcheva
Historical Museum / Local Museum 31863

Keneurgench

Kunja-Urgench Historical Site Museum, Moskovskaja ul 79, Keneurgench, Dašogus - T: (0360) 4721008. Head: Jagšimurad Aširov
Local Museum
Local history, mausoleums, architecture 31864

Kizyl-Arvat

Muzej Kizyl-Arvata (Kizyl-Arvat Museum), Kizyl-Arvat. Head: Anna Ustaeva
Historical Museum / Local Museum 31865

Mary

Ancien Merv Historical Site, Mary - T: (0522) 22217. Head: Redjep Djepbarov
Historical Museum
Old capital of Islam (11th c), high cultured city of the ancient time, the great Seljuks 31866

Historical and Ethnographical Museum, Komsomolskaja ul 1, Mary - T: (0522) 32722. Head: Maja Assadulina
Local Museum / Archaeological Museum
Archaeological finds of the Mary oasis 31867

Tačauz

Tačauz Muzej (Tacauz Museum), Vogzalnaja ul 23, Tačauz. Head: Oraz Muradov
Historical Museum / Local Museum 31868

Turkmenabat

Historical and Ethnographical Museum, Ul Šaidjanov 35, Turkmenabat - T: (0422) 48079. Head: Maja Akmamedova
Ethnology Museum / Local Museum
History and culture of Lebap area and the great silk road cities 31869

Turkmenbashi

Ethnographical Museum, Magtjmova ul 2, Turkmenbashi - T: (0222) 76213. Head: Akgul Kalpakova
Local Museum / Ethnology Museum
City history since 1717, Seljuk empire 31870

Uganda

Entebbe

Game and Fisheries Museum, Johnstone Rd, Entebbe, mail addr: POB 4, Entebbe - T: (042) 20073, 20520
Natural History Museum
Heads of game animals, bird skins, reptiles, fish, butterflies, hunting and fishing implements, weapons - library, aquarium, zoo 31871

Geological Survey Mines Museum, POB 9, Entebbe - T: (042) 20656, Fax: 20364. Head: S.A. Mboijana
Natural History Museum - 1919
Geology, rocks and minerals, meteorites - Mines, laboratory, library 31872

Wildlife Education Centre, POB 369, Entebbe - T: (042) 20520, Fax: 20073, E-mail: uweczoo@imul.com
Natural History Museum
Zoological coll of mammals, birds and reptiles 31873

Kampala

Department of Zoology Museum, Kampala, mail addr: c/o Makerere University, POB 7062, Kampala. Head: Robert Martin Kityo
Natural History Museum - 1963
Invertebrates, mollusks, insects, reptiles, mammals, fossils, ecology of the hippopotamus, clan animals of Bugunda, osteology, amphibians 31874

Forest Department Utilisation Division Museum, POB 1752, Kampala
Agriculture Museum - 1952
Uganda timber, preservation, seasoning and woodworking tests, logging and milling, entomology - library 31875

Geology Museum, c/o Makerere University, Kampala
Natural History Museum / University Museum 31876

Makerere Art Gallery, c/o Makerere School of Fine Art, POB 7062, Kampala
Fine Arts Museum - 1968
Paintings, sculpture, ceramics, graphics, works of East African artists 31877

Uganda Museum, Plot 15-7, Kira Rd, Kampala - T: (041) 244060, 233061, 25641, Fax: 245580. Head: Dr. E. Kamuhangire
Local Museum / Natural History Museum - 1908
Natural hist, paleontology, anthropology, ethnography, African musical instruments, science and industry - library, aquarium 31878

Lake Katwe

Queen Elizabeth National Park Museum, POB 22, Lake Katwe - T: (083) 44266, Fax: (041) 530159
Natural History Museum - 1952
Reptiles, mammals, hippopotamus skull, snakes, birds, fossils 31879

Mbarara

Folk Museum, Mbarara
Folklore Museum
Ethnography 31880

Murchison Falls

Murchison Falls National Park Museum, Via Majindi, Murchison Falls
Natural History Museum - 1952
Amphibia, reptiles, mammals 31881

Soroti

Folk Museum, Kennedy Sq, Soroti, mail addr: POB 58, Soroti
Folklore Museum
Ethnography, charms and bangles 31882

Ukraine

Alupka

Alupka State Palace and Park Preserve, Dvorcove šose 10, Alupka - T: (0654) 722951. Head: K.K. Kasperovič
Decorative Arts Museum - 1921
Russian noble culture, way of life in the 19th c, coll of 17th c maps of Europe and America - library 31883

Alušta

Aluštinskij Literaturno-Memorialnyj Muzej S.N. Sergeeva-Censkogo (Alushta S.N. Sergeev-Tsensky Literary Memorial Museum), vul Sergeeva-Censkogo 15, Alušta. Head: T.A. Fefjuca
Special Museum 31884

Bachčisaraj

Bachčisaraj State Historical and Cultural Preserve, vul Rična 133, 334410 Bachčisaraj - T: (06554) 42881, Fax: 42881, E-mail: hansaray@shine.krid.crimea.ua, Internet: http://www.hansaray.narod.ru. Head: Evgenij Petrov
Historical Museum / Archaeological Museum / Ethnology Museum / Fine Arts Museum - 1917
History and culture of the Crimean Tatars, fine art, prehistoric, antique, Byzantine archeology 31885

Čerkasy

Cherkasy Regional Museum, Ul Gogolja 265, 18000 Čerkasy
Local Museum - 1918
Natural history, history, economics, culture - library 31886

Černigiv

Chernigiv M.M. Kotsyubinski Literary Museum, ul Kocjubinskogo 3, 14000 Černigiv - T: (04622) 40459. Head: July Kocjubinski
Special Museum - 1934
Life and work of the Ukrainian writer M.M. Kotsyubinski - library 31887

Historical Museum by V. Tarnovsky, ul Gorkogo 4, 14000 Černigiv - T: (04622) 72650, Fax: 72650. Head: Anatoli Ivanovič Nedelja
Historical Museum - 1896
Coll of Cossack weaponry dating from 17-18th c, coll of old printed books dating from 16-18th c, coll of numismatics 19th-20th c, coll of precious metal and handicrafts from the 17th-20th c - library 31888

Černivci

Chernivtsi Local Museum, Kobyljanskoi 28, 58000 Černivci
Local Museum - 1944
Natural history, economics, culture - library 31889

Chernivtsi Yu.A. Fedkovich Memorial Museum, ul Pushkina 17, 58000 Černivci - T: (03722) 25678. Head: Dr. D. Fylypčuk
Special Museum - 1945
Memorial to the Ukrainian writer Yuri Fedkovich, portraits, photographs, book illustrations, books 31890

Charkiv

Charkivskij Istoričnij Muzej (Kharkiv Historical Museum), Vul Universitetska 5, 61003 Charkiv - T: (0572) 232094, 127694, Fax: 232094, Internet: http://goldpage.kharkov.com/him. Head: Anatolij A. Jankovskij
Historical Museum
Archeology, Hist of the region, World War II, labour movement, guns, ethnography, gold of Scythians, Ukrainian art - library 31891

Charkovskij Chudožestvennyj Muzej (Kharkiv Art Museum), Sovnarkomovskaja ul 11, 61002 Charkiv - T: (057) 433585, Fax: 433585. Head: V.V. Myzgina
Fine Arts Museum - 1935
Ukrainian, Russian and Westeuropean art, painting, graphics, sculpture, crafts - library 31892

Cherson

Chersonskij Kraevedčeskij Muzej (Kherson Local Museum), Pr Ušakova 16, 325000 Cherson, mail addr: Ul Lenina 9, 325000 Cherson - T: (0552) 41052, 41070, 41083. Head: Vladimir Alekseevič Kraev
Local Museum - 1890
Natural hist, hist, economics, culture - library 31893

Chmelnickij

Khmelnitski Regional Museum, Ul K. Libknechta 38, 280000 Chmelnickij
Natural History Museum - 1925
Natural history, history, economics, culture - library 31894

Dneprodzeržinsk

Dneprodzerzhinsk History Museum, 322600 Dneprodzeržinsk - T: (05692) 30224. Head: Nina Ciganok
Local Museum - 1931
Ukrainian hist, archeology, town hist - library 31895

Dnepropetrovsk

Diorama "Bitva za Dnepr", Dnepropetrovskij Gosudarstvennyj Istoričeskij Muzej im Javornickogo (Diorama "Battle at the Dnepr"), pr. K.Marksa 16, 49000 Dnepropetrovsk - T: (0562) 463426, E-mail: muzeum@a-teleport.com, Internet: http://www.museum.dp.ua. Head: Nadežda Ivanovna Kapustina
Special Museum / Historical Museum / Military Museum
The battle at the Dnepr in World War II 31896

Dnepropetrovsk State Art Museum, ul Ševčenko 21, 49000 Dnepropetrovsk
Fine Arts Museum - 1914
Russian and foreign art, hist of art, applied art, folk art - library 31897

Istoričeskij Muzej, Dnepropetrovskij gosudarstvennyj istoričeskij muzej im Javornickogo (Historical Museum), pr K. Marksa 186, 49000 Dnepropetrovsk - T: (0562) 463422, Fax: 460512, E-mail: muzeum@a-teleport.com, Internet: http://www.museum.dp.ua. Head: Nadežda Ivanovna Kapustina
Historical Museum / Local Museum
Memorabilia of the wrighter D.I. Javornickij 31898

Literaturnyj Muzej "Literaturnoe Pridneprovje", Dnepropetrovskij Gosudarstvennyj Istoričeskij Muzej im Javornickogo (Museum of Literature of the Dnepropetrovsk Region), pr K. Marksa 64, 49000 Dnepropetrovsk - T: (0562) 7780100, Fax: 460431, E-mail: muzeum@a-teleport.com, Internet: http://www.museum.dp.ua. Head: Nadežda Ivanovna Kapustina
Special Museum - 1849
Literature, esp. of the Dnepropetrovsk region - library 31899

Memorijalnyj Dom-muzej Javornickogo, Dnepropetrovskij Gosudarstvennyj Istoričeskij Muzej im Javornickogo (Memorial House of Javornickij), pl Ševčenko 5, 49000 Dnepropetrovsk - T: (0562) 472761, E-mail: muzeum@a-teleport.com, Internet: http://www.museum.dp.ua. Head: Nadežda Ivanovna Kapustina
Special Museum
Memorabilia of the wrighter D.I. Javornickij 31900

Doneck

Doneckij Oblastnoj Kraevedčeskij Muzej, ul Artema 84, 83000 Doneck
Local Museum - 1924
Local history, natural history, material showing how the former small mining settlement transformed into a major industrial area - library 31901

Donetsk Museum of Art, ul Artema 84, 83000 Doneck
Fine Arts Museum 31902

Feodosija

Aivazovsky Picture Gallery, Galerejnaja ul 2, 98100 Feodosija - T: (06562) 30929. Head: Taisia Sergeevna Trubnjakova
Public Gallery - 1880
Russian marine painting of hte 19th and 20th c, contemporary marine painting 31903

Ivano-Frankovsk

Ivano-Frankovsk Local Museum, Galickaja 4, 76000 Ivano-Frankovsk
Local Museum / Natural History Museum - 1939
Natural history, history, economics, culture - library 31904

Jalta

Muzej Kraevedenija (Local Museum), Puškinskaja ul 21, 98600 Jalta
Local Museum 31905

Usman Jusupov Memorial Museum, Ul Dačnaja 6, 98600 Jalta. Head: A. Abdurazakov
Local Museum 31906

Kamenec-Podolskij

State Historical Museum, Ul Ioanno-Predtečenska 2, Kamenec-Podolskij - T: (08049) 23784. Head: L.P. Stanislavska
Historical Museum - 1890
Ukrainian history 31907

Kamenka

Literaturno-memorialny Muzei A.S. Puškina i P.I. Čajkovskogo (Literary Memorial Museum of A.S. Pushkin and P.I. Chaikovski), ul Lenina 44, Kamenka
Special Museum / Music Museum - 1937
History of music, literary history, rare books, memorial to A.S. Pushkin and P.I. Chaikovski - library 31908

Kanev

Memorial Museum The Grave of T.G. Shevchenko, Kanev
Special Museum - 1939
Memorial to the Ukrainian writer Taras Grigorevich Shevchenko, literary history, grave of the poet - library 31909

Kerč

Kerčskij Gosudarstvennyj Istoriko-Kulturnyj Zapovednik (Kerch Culture-History Museum), ul Sverdlova 22, 334501 Kerč - T: 20475. Head: Pjotr Ivanovič Ivanenko
Local Museum - 1826
Archeology, Kurgan finds, regional hist - library 31910

Kirovograd

Kirovograd Regional Museum of Local History, Art and Nature, ul Lenina 40, 25050 Kirovograd - T: (052) 223597. Head: Pavel V. Bosiy
Local Museum / Fine Arts Museum / Natural History Museum - 1883/1944
library, archeological and monuments protection 31911

Kolodjažne

Literaturno-Memorialny Muzei Lesi Ukrayinky, Volynskyj Krajeznavčyj Muzej (Literary-Memorial Museum of Lesya Ukrayinka), 264441 Kolodjažne - T: 90224. Head: Vera Komzyuk
Special Museum - 1949
Documents, books, photographes, decorative objects, memorial pieces concerning Lesya Ukrayinka and her family 31912

Kolomja

Kolomya State Museum of Folk Art, vul Teatralna 25, Kolomja - T: 23912. Head: J. Tkačuk
Folklore Museum - 1926
Folk art, applied art - library 31913

Kortelisy

Kortelisy Historical Museum, 264431 Kortelisy - T: 264431. Head: Mariya Yaroshchuk
Historical Museum - 1980
Photographies 31914

Krivoj Rog

Local History Museum, Per Lenina 16, 50000 Krivoj Rog
Local Museum - 1960
Local history, history, economics, culture - library 31915

Kyïv

Bogdan and Varvara Khanenko Museum of Arts, ul Tereščentkivska 15, 05204 Kyïv - T: (044) 2250225. Head: V.I. Vinogradova
Fine Arts Museum - 1919
Paintings, sculptures, hist of Oriental (China, Japan etc) and European art - library 31916

Istoričeskij Muzej (Kiev State Historical Museum), ul Vladimirskaja 2, 05225 Kyïv - T: (044) 2286545. Head: I.E. Dudnik
Historical Museum - 1906
Exhibits tracing the history, economy and culture of the Ukrainian people from earliest times - library 31917

Kiev Lesya Ukrainka State Literature Museum, ul Saksaganskogo 97, 05232 Kyïv - T: (044) 2205752. Head: Irina L. Veremeeva
Special Museum - 1962
Exhibits on the life and work of the Ukrainian poets and artists of the 19th and early 20th c - library 31918

Kiev Museum of Russian Art, ul Tereščentkivska 9, 01000 Kyïv - T: (044) 2248288, Fax: 2246107. Head: T.M. Sodatova
Fine Arts Museum - 1922
Russian painting, sculpture, drawings, applied art - library 31919

Kiev Museum of Ukrainian Art, ul Kirova 6, 05204 Kyïv. Head: V.F. Jacenko
Fine Arts Museum - 1899
Icons, medieval and modern painting, portraits, wood carvings, fine art, archeology, art history - library 31920

Kiev Museum of Western and Oriental Art → Bogdan and Varvara Khanenko Museum of Arts

Kiev-Pechersky National Museum, ul Janvarskogo Vosstanija 21, 05215 Kyïv - T: (044) 2906646, Fax: 2904648
Fine Arts Museum
Ancient monastery, icons 31921

Kiev T.G. Shevchenko State Museum, bul Ševčenko 12, 05204 Kyïv - T: (044) 2242556. Head: E.P. Dorošenko
Special Museum - 1929
Life and work of the Ukrainian poet and revolutionary democrat Taras Grigorevich Shevchenko - library 31922

Saint Sophia of Kiev, ul Volodymyrska 24, 05225 Kyïv - T: (044) 2286706, Fax: 2297728, E-mail: info@sophia.kiev.ia. Head: Valentyna N. Ačkasova
Fine Arts Museum - 1934
11th c cathedral with early frescoes and mosaics 31923

State Museum of Theatrical, Musical and Cinematographic Art of Ukraine, Sičnevogo Povstanja 21-24, 05000 Kyïv - T: (044) 2905131, Fax: 2905131. Head: L.N. Matat
Performing Arts Museum / Music Museum - 1923
History of the performing arts in the Ukraine 31924

Ukrainian Museum of Folk and Decorative Art, ul Janvarskogo Vosstanija 21, 05215 Kyïv - T: (044) 2901343, Fax: 2939442. Head: V.G. Nagai
Decorative Arts Museum / Folklore Museum - 1954
Crafts, decorative arts in wood, folk art, embroidery, weaving, ceramics, glass, porcelain, costumes - library 31925

Luck

Kartynna Galereya, Volynskyj Krajeznavčyj Muzej (Fine Arts Gallery), Vul Kafedralna 1a, Luckyj Zamok, 263016 Luck - T: (03322) 23075. Head: Antonina Linnichenko
Fine Arts Museum - 1973
Ukrainian modern art, old Russian art, Polish art, pictures of Rybera, Manyasko, Burginion, Pussein 31926

Muzej Volynskoj Ikony, Volynskyj Krajeznavčyj Muzej (Museum of Volynian Orthodox Icons), Pr Peremogy 4, 263021 Luck - T: (03322) 43412. Head: Tatjana Jeliseeva
Religious Arts Museum - 1993
Orthodox icons, history of Orthodox art, Volynian school of icons 31927

Volynskyj Krajeznavčyj Muzej (Volynian Regional Museum), ul Šopena 20, 43021 Luck - T: (03322) 42591. Head: Anatoli Sylyuk
Local Museum - 1929
Local hist, ethnology, history, economics, culture, fine art (oil paintings of Burginion, Manjasko, Rybera), religious art (unique coll of Volynian school of icons, the Virgin of Holm, icon of Byzantine school 11th - 13th c.) - library, dept of restoration, photography dept 31928

Lugansk

Local Museum of History and Culture, K. Marksa 30, 91000 Lugansk - T: 522079. Head: Evgeny Nosovskoi
Local Museum - 1981
Local history, economics, culture, Marshal K. Voroshilov's fund, Russian Painting, Eastern Art - library, archives, funds 31929

Museum of Fine Art, Pochtovaya 3, 91000 Lugansk
Fine Arts Museum - 1955
library 31930

Lviv

Benedykt Dybowsky Zoological Museum, c/o Ivan Franko National University of Lviv, ul Chruževskij 4, 79005 Lviv - T: (0322) 964548, E-mail: zoomus@franco.lviv.ua, Internet: http://www.franko.lviv.ua/faculty/biologh/zoology.htm. Head: Igor Žydlovskij
Natural History Museum
Coll of animals 31931

Literaturno-memorialny Muzej Ivana Franko (Literary Memorial Museum of Ivan Franko), ul Ivana Franko 150-152, 79000 Lviv - T: (0322) 767760, Fax: 767760. Head: Roman Yozak
Special Museum - 1940
Memorabilia of the writer Ivan Franko (1856-1916), literary history - library 31932

Lviv Art Gallery, ul Stefanika 3, 79000 Lviv - T: (0322) 723948, Fax: 723009. Head: Boris G. Voznicky
Fine Arts Museum - 1907
West European and Ukrainian contemporary art - library, archive 31933

Lviv Historical Museum, pl Rynok 4-6, 79000 Lviv - T: (0322) 743304, Fax: 743304, E-mail: lhm@icmp.lviv.ua. Head: Bogdan N. Čajkovskij
Historical Museum - 1893
Hist of the western Ukraine from the earliest periods to the present - library 31934

Nacionalnij Muzej u Lvovi (National Museum in Lviv), pr Svobodi 20, 79008 Lviv - T: (0322) 728960, Fax: 759253. Head: Dr. Vasyl Otkovyč
Fine Arts Museum
Collections of Ukrainian art: icons, sacred art, fine art, folk art 31935

State Museum of Ethnography, Arts and Crafts, c/o Ukrainian Academy of Sciences, pr Lenina 15, 79000 Lviv
Ethnology Museum / Decorative Arts Museum - 1873
Folklore, costumes, applied arts, crafts 31936

State Museum of Natural History of NAS of Ukraine, National Academy of Sciences of Ukraine, Ul Teatralna 18, 79008 Lviv - T: (0322) 728917, Fax: 742307, E-mail: museum@lviv.net. Head: Prof. Dr. Juri Černobai
Natural History Museum - 1870
Natural history 19th-20th c with paleontology, geology, soils, plants, zoology, entomology - herbarium, library 31937

Nikolaev

Nikolaevsk Local Museum, ul Dekabristov 32, 54000 Nikolaev
Local Museum - 1950
Local history, history, economics, culture - library 31938

Novoselica

Muzej, Novoselica
Religious Arts Museum 31939

Odessa

Odessa Archaeological Museum, ul Langeronovskaja 4, 65026 Odessa - T: (0482) 220171, Fax: 220171, E-mail: archaeology@farlep.net, Internet: http://www.arhaeology.far-lep.odessa.ua. Head: V.P. Vančugov
Archaeological Museum - 1825
Archeology, history, numismatics - library 31940

Odessa Fine Arts Museum, ul Sofievskaja 5a, 65026 Odessa - T: (0482) 238272, Fax: 238393, E-mail: ofam@tm.odessa.ua, Internet: http://select.odessa.net/artmuseum. Head: Natalja Poliščuk
Fine Arts Museum - 1899
Fine Art 31941

Odessa Local History Museum, ul Cavannay 4, 65026 Odessa - T: (0482) 228490. Head: Nelly Zeskinskay
Local Museum - 1955
Local history, economics, culture, history - library 31942

Odessa State Museum of European and Oriental Art, ul Puškinskaja 9, 65026 Odessa - T: (0482) 224815, Fax: 246747, E-mail: odessa-museum@ukr.net, Internet: http://museum.in.net.ua. Head: Viktor S. Nykyforov
Fine Arts Museum - 1920
Art, contemporary art 31943

Poltava

Poltava Art Museum, Spaska 11, 36020 Poltava - T: (532) 72711. Head: Kim Salacki
Fine Arts Museum - 1919
library 31944

Poltava State Museum, pl Lenina 2, 36000 Poltava. Head: J.P. Belous
Local Museum - 1891
Life and work of the writers P. Mirny, I.P. Kotlyarevski, V.G. Korolenko, N.V. Gogol, local hist - library 31945

Rivne

Rivnenski Museum of Regional Studies, Dragomanov 19, 33028 Rivne - T: (0362) 267580,. Head: Volodimir Muširovski
Local Museum - 1940
Subjects of the Cossack era, medieval decorative art, icons - library 31946

Šepetovka

Literaturno-Memoralnyj Muzej N.A Ostrovskogo (Literary Memorial Museum of N.A. Ostrovski), Ostrovski 2, 30400 Šepetovka - T: 53620. Head: Vladimir Iljič Čikin
Special Museum - 1946
Memorabilia of the writer Nikolai Alekseevich Ostrovski, Russian and Soviet literature - library 31947

Sevastopol

Chudožestvennyj Muzei (Fine Arts Museum), Nachimovskiy pr 9, 99011 Sevastopol - T: (0692) 540367, 544636, Fax: 540367, E-mail: cxm@cheep.net.ua. Head: Natalia Bendyukova
Fine Arts Museum
Paintings, graphics, sculptures, crafts of the 19th and 20th from Russia, Ukraina, West Europe 31948

Khersones Museum of History and Archeology → National Preserve of Tauric Chersonesos

National Preserve of Tauric Chersonesos, Drevnaja ul 1, 99045 Sevastopol - T: (0692) 550278, Fax: 550278, E-mail: info@chersonesos.org, Internet: http://www.chersonesos.org. Head: Leonid V. Marchenko
Archaeological Museum / Historical Museum / Museum of Classical Antiquities / Open Air Museum - 1860
Finds from the excavation of the site of Khersones, an ancient Greek colony and Byzantine town - library, archives, monastary St.Clement 31949

Ševčenkovo

T.G. Shevchenko State Memorial Museum, Ševčenkovo. Head: T.V. Gulak
Special Museum - 1939
Exhibits illustrating Shevchenkos life, manuscripts, documentary material - library 31950

Simferopol

Etnografičeskij Muzej Tavrika, Krymski Kraevedčeskij Muzej (Ethnographical Museum Tavrika), ul Puškina 18, 95000 Simferopol, Krym. Head: Andrej Malgin
Special Museum - 1973
Archeology, ethnography 31951

Krymski Kraevedčeskij Muzej (Crimean Regional Museum), ul Gogolja 14, 95000 Simferopol, Krym - T: (0652) 252511, Fax: 252511. Head: Andrej Malgin
Local Museum - 1921
Regional history, cultural history, economics, archeology, ethnography - library, "Tavrika", dep. of ethnography 31952

Simferopolskij Chudožestvennyj Muzej (Simferopol Art Museum), ul Karla Libknechta 35, 95300 Simferopol - T: (0652) 275404. Head: N.D. Djačenko
Fine Arts Museum
Crimean art 31953

Sumy

Sumskij Oblastnoj Kraevedčeskij Muzej (Sumy Regional Museum), ul Lenina 45, 40000 Sumy
Local Museum - 1952
Regional history, economics, culture - library 31954

Sumy Art Gallery, Chervona Pl 1, 40030 Sumy - T: (0542) 220481. Head: G.V. Arefyeva
Public Gallery 31955

Sumy State Art Museum, ul Lenina 67, 40000 Sumy. Head: M.M. Komarov
Fine Arts Museum 31956

Ternopil

Ternopil Local Museum, Bugaychenko 3, 46000 Ternopil - T: (0352) 24477. Head: Benedikt Antonovich Lavrenyuk
Local Museum - 1907
Local history, economics, culture - library 31957

Ustyloog

Muzej Igora Stravinskogo (Music-Memeorial Museum of Igor Strawinsky), vul Stravsinskogo 3, 06441 Ustyloog - T: 93459. Head: Volodymyr Terezhchuk
Music Museum - 1990
History of Russian period of Igor Strawinsky's life 31958

Užgorod

Zakarpatskij Kraeznavčij Muzej (Zakarpatsk Regional Museum), vul Kapitulna 33, 294000 Užgorod - T: (0312) 36235, 34442
Local Museum - 1947
Regional hist, economics, culture - library 31959

Velikie Soročintsy

Velikosoročinskij literaturno-memorialnyj muzej im N.V. Gogolja (N.V. Gogol Literary Memorial Museum), ul Gogolja 32, Velikie Soročintsy
Special Museum - 1951
Memorabilia of the writer Nikolai Vasilevich Gogol, literary hist - library 31960

Vinnica

Vinnitsa Museum of Local Lore, Muzejskaya pl 1, 287100 Vinnica - T: (043) 322671. Head: Ludmila R. Caroeva
Local Museum - 1918
Local hist, nature, archeology, ethnography, ancient gold of the Ukraine (12th-9th c B.C.) - library 31961

Vladimir-Volynski

Vladimir-Volynski Local Museum, ul Mariyi Ulyanovoi 1, 264940 Vladimir-Volynski - T: 20793. Head: Vladimir Safonyuk
Local Museum
Local history 31962

Zaporože

Zaporoževskij Kraevedcheskij Muzej (Zaporozhe Local Museum), Pr Lenina 59, 69000 Zaporože
Local Museum - 1948
Local history, economics, culture - library 31963

Žytomyr

Regional Museum (Kraevedčeskij Muzej), Ul Komarova 8a, Žytomyr
Local Museum - 1900
Regional history, economics, natural history - library 31964

United Arab Emirates

Al-Ain

Al-Ain Museum, POB 15715, Al-Ain - T: (03) 641595, Fax: 658311. Head: Dr. Walid Yasin
Archaeological Museum - 1971
Archeological excavations at Al-Ain and Umm-Al-Nar Island - library 31965

Dubai

Dubai Museum, Old Al Fahidi Fort, Bur, Dubai - T: (04) 3531862, Fax: 3539445. Head: Ayesha Abdulla
Local Museum 31966

Sheikh Saeed's House, nr Shindaga Tunnel, Dubai - T: (04) 535928
Historical Museum 31967

Fujairah

Fujairah Museum, POB 1, Fujairah - T: (09) 229085, Fax: 229539
Local Museum 31968

Sharjah

Sharjah Archaeology Museum, Sheikh Rashid Bin Saqr Al-Qassimi St, Sharjah - T: (06) 5665466, Fax: 5660334, E-mail: ejasim@emirates.net.ae, Internet: http://www.archaeology.gov.ae. Head: Dr. Sabah Jasim
Archaeological Museum 31969

Sharjah Heritage Museum, POB 2258, Sharjah - T: (06) 512999, Fax: 368288, Internet: http://www.sharjahmuseums.com/heritage
Local Museum
Souq Al Arsah, Bait Al Naboodah, Al Midfaa house, Al Hisn Sharjah, Hisn Kalba 31970

Sharjah Islamic Museum, POB 5119, Sharjah - T: (06) 353334, Fax: 353746, Internet: http://www.sharjahmuseums.com/islamic
Religious Arts Museum 31971

Sharjah Natural History Museum, Sharjah-Dhaid Rd, Sharjah, mail addr: POB 25313, Sharjah - T: (06) 311411, Fax: 311000, Internet: http://www.sharjah-museums.com/natural/
Natural History Museum 31972

Sharjah Science Museum, nr Culture R/A, Sharjah, mail addr: POB 25700, Sharjah - T: (06) 514777, Fax: 514733, Internet: http://www.sharjah-museums.com/science
Science&Tech Museum 31973

United Kingdom

Abercrave

Dan-yr-Ogof Showcaves Museum, Glyntawe, Upper Swansea Valley, Abercrave - T: (01639) 730284, Fax: 730293. Head: Ian Gwilim
Natural History Museum - 1964 31974

Aberdare

Cynon Valley Museum, Depot Rd, Gadys, Aberdare CF44 8DL - T: (01685) 886729, Fax: 886730, E-mail: cvm@rhondda-cynon-raff.gov.uk. Head: Chris Wilson
Local Museum
Over 200 yrs history of Cynon valley 31975

Aberdeen

Aberdeen Art Gallery, Schoolhill, Aberdeen AB10 1FQ - T: (01224) 523700, Fax: 632133, E-mail: info@aagm.co.uk, Internet: http://www.aberdeencity.gov.uk. Head: Ciaran Monaghan
Fine Arts Museum - 1885
Fine and applied arts (18th-20th c), decorative art since 6th c - library 31976

Aberdeen Arts Centre, 33 King St, Aberdeen AB24 5AA - T: (01224) 635208, Fax: 626390, E-mail: enquiries@aberdeenartscentre.fsnet.uk, Internet: http://www.aberdeenartscentre.org.uk. Head: Arthur Deans
Public Gallery 31977

Aberdeen Maritime Museum, Shiprow, Aberdeen AB11 5BY - T: (01224) 337700, Fax: 213066, E-mail: info@aagm.co.uk, Internet: http://www.aagm.co.uk. Head: John Edwards
Historical Museum - 1984/97
North Sea oil and gas industry, shipping and fishing exhibitions, multi-media and hands-on exhibits 31978

Aberdeen University Natural History Museum, c/o Department of Zoology, Tillydrone Av, Aberdeen AB9 2TN - T: (01224) 272850, Fax: 272396, E-mail: m.gorman@abdn.ac.uk, Internet: http://www.abdn.ac.uk/zoology
University Museum / Natural History Museum
Ornithology, entomology, invertebrates/vertebrates coll 31979

Aberdeen University Natural Philosophy Museum, c/o School of Physics, Fraser Noble Bldg, Aberdeen AB24 3UE - T: (01224) 272507, Fax: 272497, E-mail: j.s.reid@abdn.ac.uk, Internet: http://www.abdn.ac.uk/~nph126. Head: Dr. John S. Reid
Science&Tech Museum / University Museum - 1971
Coll of apparatus used during the past 200 years for teaching and demonstrating the traditional branches of physics 31980

Anatomy Museum, c/o Marischal College, University of Aberdeen, Broad St, Aberdeen AB10 1YS - T: (01224) 274320, Fax: 274329, E-mail: i.stewart@abdu.ac.uk. Head: Dr. I. Stewart
University Museum / Natural History Museum
Human anatomical specimens and models 31981

The Blairs Museum, South Deeside Rd, Blairs, Aberdeen AB12 5YQ - T: (01224) 863767, Fax: 869424, E-mail: curator@blairs.net, Internet: http://www.blairs.net
Fine Arts Museum / Religious Arts Museum
Pictures of Mary Queen of Scots, Stuart portraits and memorabiia, 16th c Church robes, altarware 31982

Geology Department Museum, c/o University of Aberdeen, Meston Bldg, Aberdeen AB24 3UE - T: (01224) 273448, Fax: 272785
Natural History Museum 31983

Gordon Highlanders Museum, Saint Luke's, Viewfield Rd, Aberdeen AB15 7XH - T: (01224) 311200, Fax: 319323, E-mail: museum@gordonhighlanders.com, Internet: http://www.gordonhighlanders.com. Head: Sir Peter Graham
Military Museum - 1937
History of Gordon Highlanders regiment, uniforms, medals, pictures, trophies 31984

Grampian Police Museum, Grampian Police Headquarters, Queen St, Aberdeen AB9 1BA - T: (01224) 639111
Special Museum
Uniforms, truncheons, medals, photographs, books 31985

Grays School of Art Gallery and Museum, c/o Faculty of Design, The Robert Gordon University, Garthdee Rd, Aberdeen AB9 2QD - T: (01224) 263506/600
Public Gallery / University Museum 31986

Marischal Museum, Marischal College, University of Aberdeen, Broad St, Aberdeen AB10 1YS - T: (01224) 274301, Fax: 274302, E-mail: museum@abdn.ac.uk, Internet: http://www.abdn.ac.uk/marischal_museum. Head: Neil Curtis, Margot Wright
University Museum / Archaeological Museum / Museum of Classical Antiquities / Fine Arts Museum
Local archaeology, art, antiquities 31987

Peacock, 21 Castle St, Aberdeen AB11 5BQ - T: (01224) 639539, Fax: 627094, E-mail: -peacockprint.co.uk@virgin.net. Head: Lindsay Gordon
Public Gallery
Printmaking, photography, digital imaging, video 31988

Provost Skene's House, off Broad St, Guestrow, Aberdeen AB10 1AS - T: (01224) 641086, Fax: 632133, Internet: http://www.aagm.co.uk/psh.html. Head: Christine Rew
Decorative Arts Museum - 1953
Scottish furniture, costume archaeology, painted chapel ceiling (17th c) 31989

Robert Gordon University Museum, Heritage Unit, Clarke Bldg, Schoolhill, Aberdeen AB9 2FE - T: (01224) 262599
University Museum 31990

Satrosphere, 19 Justice Mill Ln, Aberdeen AB11 6EQ - T: (01224) 213232, Fax: 211685, E-mail: satrosphere@satrosphere.net, Internet: http://www.satrosphere.net. Head: Dr. Alistair M. Flett
Science&Tech Museum
Scientific instruments, computers 31991

Aberdovey

Outward Bound Museum, Outward Bound, Aberdovey LL35 0RA - T: (01654) 767464. Head: Nick Dawson
Local Museum 31992

Aberfeldy

Castle Menzies, Weem, Aberfeldy PH15 2JD - T: (01887) 820982, E-mail: menziesclan@tesco.net, Internet: http://www.menzies.org. Head: G.B. Menzies
Local Museum
Small Clan-Museum in a 16th c building 31993

Aberford

Lotherton Hall, Leeds Museums and Galleries, Aberford LS25 3EB - T: (0113) 2813259, Fax: 2812100, Internet: http://www.leeds.gov.uk. Head: Nick Winterbotham
Decorative Arts Museum / Fine Arts Museum - 1969
English and Continental paintings (17th-20th c), furniture, silver, British and oriental ceramics, costume, sculpture 31994

Abergavenny

Abergavenny Museum, Castle, Castle St, Abergavenny NP7 5EE - T: (01873) 854282, Fax: 858083, 736004, E-mail: -abergavennymuseum@monmouthshire.gov.uk. Head: Rachael Rogers
Local Museum - 1959
History and industries of the town and district, kitchen, rural craft, tools, Roman relics from Gobannium site, grocers shop 31995

Aberlady

Myreton Motor Museum, Aberlady EH32 0PZ - T: (01875) 870288
Science&Tech Museum - 1966
Cars from 1896, motor cycles from 1902, commercials from 1919, cycles from 1880, WWII military vehicles, enamel advertising 31996

Abernethy

Abernethy Museum, Cherrybank, Abernethy PH2 9LW - T: (0131) 3177300
Local Museum 31997

Abertillery

Abertillery Museum, Metropole Theater, Market St, Abertillery NP3 1TE - T: (01495) 213806, Internet: http://www.abertillery-net.co.uk/museum.html. Head: Don Bearcroft
Local Museum 31998

Aberystwyth

Aberystwyth Arts Centre, c/o University College of Wales, Penglais, Aberystwyth SY23 3DE - T: (01970) 622882, 622460, Fax: 622883, 622461, E-mail: etr@aber.ac.uk, Internet: http://www.aber.ac.uk/~arcwww. Head: Alan Hewson
University Museum / Fine Arts Museum
ceramics gallery 31999

Aberystwyth Yesterday, Little Chapel, New St, Aberystwyth - T: (01970) 617119
Local Museum 32000

The Ceramic Collection, c/o School of Art, University of Wales, Buarth Mawr, Aberystwyth SY23 1NG - T: (01970) 622460, Fax: 622461, E-mail: mov@aber.ac.uk, Internet: http://www.aber.ac.uk/ceramics. Head: Moira Vincentelli
Decorative Arts Museum - 1876
Studio Ceramics 32001

Ceredigion Museum, Coliseum, Terrace Rd, Aberystwyth SY23 2AQ - T: (01970) 633088, Fax: 633084, E-mail: museum@ceredigion.gov.uk, Internet: http://www.ceredigion.gov.uk/coliseum. Head: Michael Freeman
Local Museum - 1972
Alfred Worthington paintings, work of Hutchings, taxidermist 32002

School of Art Gallery and Museum, University of Wales, Buarth Mawr, Aberystwyth SY23 1NG - T: (01970) 622460, Fax: 622461, E-mail: neh@aber.ac.uk, Internet: http://www.aber.ac.uk/museum. Head: Robert Meyrick
Fine Arts Museum / Decorative Arts Museum / University Museum - 1876
Graphic art since 15th c, art in Wales since 1945, 20th c Italian and British photography, pottery (early 20th /contemporary British), slipware, Swansea and Nantgarw porcellain, Oriental ceramics 32003

Abingdon

Abingdon Museum, Old County Hall, Market Pl, Abingdon OX14 3HG - T: (01235) 523703, Fax: 536814, E-mail: enquiries@abingdonmuseum.free-online.co.uk. Head: Jill Draper
Local Museum - 1925
Local hist, archaeology, contemporary crafts, 17th c building 32004

Abinger Common

Mesolithic Museum, Abinger Manor, Abinger Common RH5 6JD - T: (01306) 730760. Head: Robert Clarke
Historical Museum - 1953
Hut build, flint coll 32005

Accrington

Haworth Art Gallery, Haworth Park, Manchester Rd, Accrington BB5 2JS - T: (01254) 233782, Fax: 301954, E-mail: haworth@hyndburnbc.gov.uk. Head: Jennifer A. Rennie
Public Gallery - 1921
19th-20th c paintings, watercolours, largest Tiffany glass coll in Europe 32006

Airdrie

Weavers Cottage Museum, 23-27 Wellwynd, Airdrie ML6 0BN - T: (0141) 3041975
Local Museum / Science&Tech Museum
Weaving loom, Monklands history 32007

Alcester

Coughton Court, Alcester B49 5JA - T: (01789) 400777, Fax: 765544, E-mail: carol@throckmortons.co.uk, Internet: http://www.coughton-court.co.uk
Decorative Arts Museum / Local Museum 32008

Ragley Hall, Alcester B49 5NJ - T: (01789) 762090, Fax: 764791, E-mail: info@ragleyhall.com, Internet: http://www.ragleyhall.com. Head: Marquess of Hertford
Fine Arts Museum / Decorative Arts Museum
Art 18th c, porcelain, furniture, baroque plasterwork 32009

Aldeburgh

Moot Hall Museum, Market Cross Pl, Aldeburgh IP15 5DS - T: (01728) 452158. Head: Clare Foss
Local Museum - 1911
1862 Anglo-Saxon Ship Burial finds, local history 32010

Alderney

Alderney Society Museum, The Old School, High St, Alderney GY9 3TG - T: (01481) 823222, Fax: 824979, E-mail: alderney.museum@virgin.net. Head: David Thornburrow
Local Museum - 1966
Local hist, arts and crafts, hist of the German occupation 1940-1945, Iron Age pottery finds, Elizabethan wreck 32011

Aldershot

Airborne Forces Museum, Browning Barracks, Aldershot GU11 2BU - T: (01252) 349619, Fax: 349203
Military Museum - 1969
World War II operational briefing models, aircraft models, equipment, vehicles, guns 32012

Aldershot Military Museum and Rushmoor Local History Gallery, Queens Av, Aldershot GU11 2LG - T: (01252) 314598, Fax: 342942, E-mail: musmim@hants.gov.uk, Internet: http://www.hants.gov.uk/museum/aldershot. Head: Ian Maine
Military Museum - 1984
Borough of Rushmoor local history coll, vehicle coll 32013

Army Medical Services Museum, Keogh Barracks, Ash Vale, Aldershot GU12 5RQ - T: (01252) 868612, Fax: 868832, E-mail: museum@keogh72.freeserve.co.uk
Military Museum - 1953
History of Army Medical Service since pre-Tudor times, Crimean relics, memorabilia on Napoleon I (1769-1821) and Wellington (1769-1852), Falklands and Gulfwar military uniforms 32014

Army Physical Training Corps Museum, Queens Av, Aldershot GU11 2LB - T: (01252) 347168, Fax: 340785, E-mail: regtsec@aptc.org.uk, Internet: http://www.aptc.org.uk. Head: A.A. Forbes
Military Museum
History of the Corps since 1860, achievements and personalities - library 32015

Royal Army Dental Corps Historical Museum, Evelyn Woods Rd, Aldershot GU11 2LS - T: (01252) 347976, Fax: 347726. Head: C.D. Parkinson
Military Museum / Science&Tech Museum - 1969
Hist of the Corps, developments in dental techniques, connection between dentistry and the Army from the origins of the British Army, following the restoration of the monarchy in 1660 to the present 32016

Royal Army Veterinary Corps Museum, Gallwey Rd, Aldershot GU11 2DQ - T: (01252) 24431 ext 2261
Military Museum 32017

Royal Corps of Transport Museum, Buller Barracks, Aldershot GU11 2BX - T: (01252) 3488374
Military Museum - 1946
Militaria on RCT and predecessors 32018

Alexandria

Tobias Smollett Museum, Castle Cameron, Alexandria G83 8QZ - T: (01389) 56226
Special Museum 32019

Alford, Aberdeenshire

Alford Heritage Centre, Mart Rd, Alford, Aberdeenshire AB33 8BZ - T: (019755) 62906
Local Museum 32020

Grampian Transport Museum, Alford, Aberdeenshire AB33 8AE - T: (01975) 562292, Fax: 562180, E-mail: info@g-t-m.freeserve.co.uk, Internet: http://www.gtm.org.uk
Science&Tech Museum 32021

Alford, Lincolnshire

Alford Manor House Museum, West St, Alford, Lincolnshire LN13 9DJ - T: (01507) 462143, 463073. Head: B. Read
Local Museum
Hist of Alford Manor House, Victorian Drawing Room, Shops from the past (Pharmaca, Veterinary Surgery, Bootmaker) Prison Cell, Victorian Schoolroom, coll of Roman finds, displays from the Salt Works and Sweetmakers, costumes and photographs from past local life, Alford's connection with America 32022

Alfriston

Clergy House, The Tye, Alfriston BN26 5TL - T: (01323) 870001, Fax: 871318, E-mail: ksdxxx@smtp.ntrust.org.uk, Internet: http://www.national-trust.org.uk. Head: Sarah Mann
Local Museum 32023

Allerford

West Somerset Rural Life Museum, Old School, Allerford TA24 8HN - T: (01643) 862529
Local Museum
Victorian kitchen, laundry, dairy, school desks, books, toys 32024

Allesley

Jaguar Daimler Heritage Trust, Jaguar Cars, Browns Ln, Allesley CV5 9DR - T: (024) 76402121, Fax: 76202777. Head: John Maries
Science&Tech Museum
Vehicles covering Jaguar, Daimler and Lanchester Cars 32025

Alloa

Aberdona Gallery, Aberdona Mains, Alloa FK10 3QP - T: (01259) 752721, Fax: 750276
Public Gallery 32026

Clackmannshire Council Museum, Speirs Centre, 29 Primrose St, Alloa FK10 1JJ - T: (01259) 216913, Fax: 721313, E-mail: smills@clacks.gov.uk, Internet: http://www.clacksweb.org.uk/dyna/musmain. Head: Susan Mills
Local Museum
Alloa pottery, textiles and woolen industry, social and indistrial history 32027

Alloway

Burns Cottage Museum, Alloway KA7 4PY - T: (01292) 441215, Fax: 441750. Head: John Manson
Special Museum - 1880
Cottage where poet Robert Burns (1759-1796) was born, memorabilia, manuscripts 32028

Tam O'Shanter Experience, Murdoch's Lone, Alloway - T: (01292) 443700, Fax: 441750, Internet: http://www.robertburns.org
Local Museum 32029

Alness

Clan Grant Museum, Grants of Dalvey, Alness IV17 0XT - T: (01349) 884111, Fax: 884100
Historical Museum 32030

Alnwick

Bondgate Gallery, 22 Narrowgate, Alnwick NE66 3JG - T: (01665) 576450
Public Gallery
Crafts, visual arts 32031

Fusiliers Museum of Northumberland, Abbots Tower, Alnwick Castle, Alnwick NE66 1NG - T: (01665) 602152, 510211, Fax: 603320, E-mail: fusnorthld@aol.com, Internet: http://www.northumberlandfusiliers.org.uk. Head: Peter H.D. Marr
Military Museum - 1970
Artefacts, uniforms, medals, weapons 32032

Museum of Antiquities, Alnwick Castle, Alnwick NE66 1NQ - T: (01665) 510777, Fax: 510876, E-mail: enquiries@alnwickcastle.com, Internet: http://www.alnwickcastle.com. Head: Clare Baxter
Historic Site / Archaeological Museum 32033

Museum of the Percy Tenantry Volunteers 1798-1814, Estate Office, Alnwick Castle, Alnwick NE66 1NQ - T: (01665) 510777, Fax: 510876. Head: Clare Baxter
Historical Museum
Arms and accountrements, Northern estate of the Duke of Northumberland 32034

Alresford

Mid Hampshire Railway Museum, Railway Station, Alresford SO24 9JG - T: (01962) 733810, Fax: 735448, Internet: http://www.watercressline.co.uk
Science&Tech Museum
Steam railway 32035

Alston

South Tynedale Museum Railway, Railway Station, Alston CA9 3JB - T: (01434) 381696, 382828
Science&Tech Museum
Steam and diesel narrow-gauge locomotives 32036

Althorp

Althorp Museum, The Stables, Althorp NN7 4HQ - T: (01604) 770107, Fax: 770042, E-mail: mail@althorp.com, Internet: http://www.althorp.com
Special Museum
Costume, memorabilia of Diana, Princess of Wales 32037

Alton

Allen Gallery, 10-12 Church St, Alton GU34 2BW - T: (01420) 82802, Fax: 84227, E-mail: musmtc@hants.gov.uk, Internet: http://www.hants.gov.uk/museums. Head: Tony Cross
Decorative Arts Museum
Works by W.H. Allen, ceramics from 1550 to the present day, silver - gallery, herb garden 32038

Curtis Museum, 3 High St, Alton GU34 1BA - T: (01420) 82802, Fax: 84227, E-mail: musmtc@hants.gov.uk, Internet: http://www.hants.gov.uk/museum/curtis. Head: Tony Cross
Local Museum - 1855
Local history, archaeology, geology, toys, hop growing, brewing - library 32039

Altrincham

Dunham Massey Hall, Altrincham WA14 4SJ - T: (0161) 9411025, Fax: 9297508. Head: Stephen Adams
Fine Arts Museum / Decorative Arts Museum
Fine coll of paintings, furniture and Huguenot silver - library 32040

Alva

Mill Trail Visitor Centre, West Stirling St, Alva FK12 5EN - T: (01259) 769696, Fax: 763100
Science&Tech Museum
History of weaving industry, spinning wheels and looms 32041

Alyth

Alyth Museum, Perth Museum and Art Gallery, Commercial St, Alyth PH11 8AF - T: (01738) 632488, Fax: 443505, E-mail: museum@pkc.gov.uk
Local Museum
Local histry 32042

Amberley

Amberley Working Museum, Houghton Bridge, Amberley BN18 9LT - T: (01798) 831370, Fax: 831831, E-mail: office@amberleymuseum.co.uk, Internet: http://www.amberleymuseum.co.uk. Head: Howard Stenning
Science&Tech Museum - 1979
Milne electrical coll, Southdown omnibus coll, narrow gauge railways, printing, radio, TV and telephones, concrete technology, roads and roadmaking, industrial buildings - archives 32043

Ambleside

Museum of Ambleside, Rydal Rd, Ambleside LA22 9BL - T: (015394) 31212, Fax: 31313, E-mail: almc@armitt.com. Head: Lynda Powell
Local Museum - 1958
Social and economic history, archaeology, geology, natural history 32044

Rydal Mount, Ambleside LA22 9LU - T: (015394) 33002, Fax: 31738, E-mail: Rydalmount@aol.com. Head: Peter Elkington, Marian Elkington
Local Museum - 1970
Portraits, furniture, personal possessions 32045

Amersham

Amersham Museum, 49 High St, Amersham HP7 0DP - T: (01494) 725754, Fax: 725754. Head: Monica Mullins
Local Museum
Local history, fossil and archeaological finds, wall paintings,lace making, strawplait work, brewing, postal services, agriculture 32046

Ancrum

Harestanes Countryside Visitor Centre, Harestanes, Ancrum TD8 6UQ - T: (01835) 830306, Fax: 830734, E-mail: mascott@scotborders.gov.uk
Natural History Museum
Environmental education, natural science, craft 32047

Andover

Andover Museum, 6 Church Close, Andover SP10 1DP - T: (01264) 366283, Fax: 339152, E-mail: andover.museum@virgin.net, Internet: http://www.hants.gov.uk/museum/andover. Head: David Allen
Local Museum
Local hist, archaeology, natural science 32048

Museum of the Iron Age, 6 Church Close, Andover SP10 1DP - T: (01264) 366283, Fax: 339152, E-mail: andover.museum@virgin.net, Internet: http://www.hants.gov.uk/museum/ironagem. Head: David Allen
Archaeological Museum
Finds from the excavations, hist of southern Britain in the Iron Age 32049

Annaghmore

Ardress Farm Museum, 64 Ardress Rd, Annaghmore BT62 1SQ - T: (028) 38851236. Head: Daniel Tennyson
Agriculture Museum - 1977 32050

Annan

Historic Resources Centre, c/o Annan Museum, Bank St, Annan DG12 6AA - T: (01461) 201384, Fax: 205876, E-mail: info@dumfriesmuseum.demon.co.uk, Internet: http://www.dumfriesmuseum.demon.co.uk/annhistrec.html
Local Museum
Ethnography, local history, relics, contemporary art, biographical essays 32051

Anstruther

Scottish Fisheries Museum, Saint Ayles, Habourhead, Anstruther KY10 3AB - T: (01333) 310628, Fax: 310628, E-mail: andrew@scottish-fisheries-museum.org, Internet: http://www.scottish-fisheries-museum.org. Head: Andrew Fox
Special Museum - 1969
History of Scotland's fishing industry and related trades, fishing gear, ship models and gear, fishermen's ethnography, whaling, aquarium, paintings and photographs with marine themes 32052

Antrim

Clotworthy Arts Centre, Castle Gardens, Randalstown Rd, Antrim BT41 4LH - T: (028) 94428000, Fax: 94460360, E-mail: clotworthy@antrim.gov.uk, Internet: http://www.antrim.gov.uk. Head: Kate Wimpress
Fine Arts Museum / Decorative Arts Museum
Art exhibits, scale model of Antrim castle, 17th c Anglo Dutch water garden 32053

Appin

Appin Wildlife Museum (closed) 32054

Castle Stalker, Appin - T: (01631) 76234, E-mail: info@castlestalker.com, Internet: http://www.castlestalker.com
Military Museum 32055

Appledore, Devon

North Devon Maritime Museum, Odun House, Odun Rd, Appledore, Devon EX39 1PT - T: (01237) 422064, Internet: http://www.php-net.com/ndmt. Head: A.E. Grant
Science&Tech Museum
Scale models of ships using North Devon ports from the 17th c onwards, paintings of ships and maritime scenes, and old photogr of the district and its people 32056

Arbigland

John Paul Jones Birthplace Museum, John Paul Jones Cottage, Arbigland DG2 8BQ - T: (01387) 880613, Fax: 260029, E-mail: postmaster@dumfriesmuseum.demon.co.uk, Internet: http://www.jpj.demon.co.uk. Head: Donald R. Usquhart
Special Museum
Navy history 32057

Arborfield

REME Museum of Technology, Isaac Newton Rd, Arborfield RG2 9N5 - T: (0118) 9763375, Fax: 9763375, E-mail: reme-museum@gtnet.gov.uk, Internet: http://www.reme-museum.org.uk. Head: I.W.J. Cleasby
Science&Tech Museum / Military Museum - 1958
Hist of the Corps of Royal Electrical and Mechanical Engineers, the British Army's equipment repair corps which was formed in 1942, documents, photos and equipment relating to REME 32058

Royal Electrical and Mechanical Engineers Museum → REME Museum of Technology

Arbroath

Abbot's House, Arbroath Abbey, Arbroath DD11 1EG - T: (01241) 2443101, Internet: http://home.clara.net/rabpert/a_house.htm
Archaeological Museum 32059

Arbroath Art Gallery, Library, Hill Terrace, Arbroath DD11 1PU - T: (01241) 875598, Fax: (01307) 462590, E-mail: the.meffan@angus.gov.uk
Fine Arts Museum - 1898
Local artists' works, 2 paintings by Breughel 32060

Arbroath Museum, Signal Tower, Ladyloan, Arbroath DD11 1PU - T: (01241) 875598, Fax: 439263, E-mail: signal.tower@angus.gov.uk, Internet: http://www.angus.gov.uk/history.htm. Head: Fiona Guest
Local Museum - 1843
Bell Rock lighthouse artifacts, fishing 32061

Saint Vigeans Museum, Saint Vigeans, Arbroath - T: (01241) 878756, 2443101
Religious Arts Museum - 1960
Picts, stone carvings of particular symbols 32062

Arlington

Arlington Court, Arlington EX31 4LP - T: (01271) 850296, Fax: 850711, E-mail: darsdm@smtp.ntrust.org.uk. Head: Susie Mercer
Special Museum
Napoleonic coll of horse draw carriages 32063

Armadale

Armadale Community Museum, West Main St, Armadale EH48 2JD - T: (01501) 678400, E-mail: armadale.library@westlothian.org.uk, Internet: http://www.wlonline.org. Head: Elizabeth Hunter
Local Museum 32064

Museum of the Isles, Clan Donald Visitor Centre, Armadale Castle, Armadale IV45 8RS - T: (01471) 844227, Fax: 844275
Historical Museum
Story of 1300 years of Clan Donald's hist and of the Lordship of the Isles 32065

Armagh

Armagh County Museum, The Mall East, Armagh BT61 9BE - T: (028) 37523070, Fax: 37522631, E-mail: acm.um@nics.gov.uk. Head: Catherine McCullough
Local Museum - 1935
Irish art, hist and natural hist of Armagh County since prehistoric times, local folklore, applied art incl some works and manuscripts by George Russell - library 32066

Hayloft Gallery, Palace Stable Heritage Centre, Palace Demesne, Armagh BT60 4EL - T: (028) 37529629, Fax: 37529630, E-mail: stables@armagh.gov.uk, Internet: http://www.armagh.gov.uk
Public Gallery 32067

Navan Centre, 81 Killylea Rd, Armagh BT60 4LD - T: (01861) 525550, Fax: 522323. Head: Danny Sutherland
Local Museum
History, archaeology and mythology of Navan Fort (Emain Macha) 32068

Royal Irish Fusiliers Museum, Sovereign's House, The Mall East, Armagh BT61 9DL - T: (028) 37522911, Fax: 37522911. Head: Amanda Moreno
Military Museum
Hist of the regiment, uniforms, photographs 32069

Saint Patrick's Trian, 40 English St, Armagh BT61 7BA - T: (028) 37521801, Fax: 37510180, E-mail: education@saintpatrickstrian.com, Internet: http://www.armaghvisit.com. Head: Debbie McCamphill
Local Museum
Local history from prehistory, Celts, Vikings, Brian Boru, Georgian times 32070

Arnol

Arnol Blackhouse Museum, Arnol PA86 9DB - T: (0131) 5568400
Archaeological Museum 32071

Arreton

Arreton Manor, Arreton PO30 3AA - T: (01983) 528134. Head: N.H. Schroeder
Decorative Arts Museum - 1961
Manor from period of Henry VIII to Charles I, Jacobean and Elizabethan furniture, dolls, toys, relics, National Wireless museum 32072

Arrington

Wimpole Hall and Home Farm, Arrington SG8 0BW - T: (01223) 207257, Fax: 207838, E-mail: aweusr@smtp.ntrust.org.uk, Internet: http://www.wimpole.org
Local Museum / Agriculture Museum 32073

Arundel

Arundel Museum and Heritage Centre, 61 High St, Arundel BN18 9AJ - T: (01903) 882456. Head: Alan Chapman
Local Museum - 1963 32074

Arundel Toy Museum Dolls House, 23 High St, Arundel BN18 9AD - T: (01903) 883101. Head: Diana Henderson
Special Museum - 1978
Britains model toy soldiers and animals/farms, small militaria, dolls houses and contents, games, tintoys, puppets, curiosities 32075

Ashburton

Ashburton Museum, 1 West St, Ashburton TQ13 7DT - T: (01364) 653278
Local Museum - 1954
Local history, American Indian antiques, costumes, arrows, tools 32076

Ashby-de-la-Zouch

Ashby-de-la-Zouch Museum, North St, Ashby-de-la-Zouch LE65 2HU - T: (01530) 560090. Head: Kenneth Hillier
Local Museum - 1982 32077

Ashford

Ashford Museum, Church Yard, Ashford - T: (01233) 631511, Fax: 502599, E-mail: a.d.terry@excite.co.uk. Head: Countess Mountbatten of Burma
Historical Museum
History of Ashford and the surrounding area, with exhibits reflecting the social and domestic life of the past 150 years, and the occupations carried on in the district 32078

Swanton Mill, Lower Mersham, Ashford TN25 7HS - T: (01233) 720223. Head: John Bickel
Science&Tech Museum 32079

Ashington

Woodhorn Colliery Museum, Queen Elizabeth II Park, Ashington NE63 9YF - T: (01670) 856968, Fax: 810958. Head: Barry Mead
Science&Tech Museum
Coal-mining and socila history of SE Northumberland 32080

Ashton, Oundle

National Dragonfly Biomuseum, Ashton Wold, Ashton, Oundle PE8 5LZ - T: (01832) 272427, E-mail: ndmashton@aol.com, Internet: http://www.natdragonflymuseum.org.uk
Natural History Museum / Science&Tech Museum
Larva-feeding sessions, dragonflies in art, live larvae in tanks, Victorian hydropower station, vintage farm machinery coll, blacksmith's forge, local crafts, fish coll 32081

Ashton-under-Lyne

Central Art Gallery, Old St, Ashton-under-Lyne OL6 - T: (0161) 3422650. Head: Elizabeth Marland
Public Gallery 32082

Museum of the Manchesters, Town Hall, Market Pl, Ashton-under-Lyne OL6 6DL - T: (0161) 3423078, Fax: 3431732. Head: Dr. Alan Wilson
Historical Museum - 1987
Social and regimental hist 32083

Portland Basin Museum, 1 Portland Pl, Ashton-under-Lyne OL7 0QA - T: (0161) 3432878, Fax: 3432869, E-mail: portland.basin@mail.gov.uk, Internet: http://www.tameside.gov.uk. Head: Dr. Alan Wilson
Local Museum 32084

Ashurst

National Dairy Museum, Longdown Dairy Farm, Deerleap Ln, Ashurst SO40 4UH - T: (023) 80293326. Head: Hannah Field
Agriculture Museum / Special Museum
Coll of horse-drawn and hand-pushed milk prams, history of dairy industry 32085

Ashwell

Ashwell Village Museum, Swan St, Ashwell SG7 5NY - T: (01462) 742956. Head: Peter Greener
Local Museum - 1930
Rural village life from the Stone Age to the present, a Tudor building, snuff and tinder boxes, straw-plaiting tools, lace-making tools, objects formerly used in farming and everyday life, leather eyeglasses 32086

Aston Munslow

White House Museum of Buildings and Country Life, NE Craven Arms, Aston Munslow SY7 9ER
Local Museum 32087

Auchinleck

Boswell Museum and Mausoleum, Church Hill, Auchinleck KA18 2AE - T: (01290) 421185, 420931
Historical Museum
Coll of Boswelliana 32088

Auckengill

Northland Viking Centre, Old School House, Auckengill KW1 4XP - T: (01955) 607771, Fax: 604524
Local Museum
Local history 32089

Augrès

Sir Francis Cook Gallery, Rte de la Trinité, Augrès JE3 5JN - T: (01534) 863333, Fax: 864437, E-mail: museum@jerseyheritagetrust.org
Public Gallery 32090

Avebury

Alexander Keiller Museum, High St, Avebury SN8 1RF - T: (01672) 539250, Fax: 539388, E-mail: wavgen@smtp.ntrust.org.uk. Head: Rosamund Cleal, Clare Conybeare
Archaeological Museum - 1938
Prehistoric artifacts from the world heritage site of Avebury, pottery, flint implements, animal bone, bone implements 32091

Great Barn Museum of Wiltshire Rural Life, Avebury SN8 1RF - T: (01672) 539555. Head: Susan Arnold
Local Museum - 1979
Rural and domestic life 32092

Aviemore

Strathspey Railway, Aviemore Station, Dalfaber Rd, Aviemore PH22 1PY - T: (01479) 810725, Fax: 811022, E-mail: laurence.grant@strathspey-railway.freeserve.co.uk, Internet: http://www.strathspeyrailway.co.uk. Head: Laurence Grant
Science&Tech Museum 32093

Axbridge

Axbridge Museum, King John's Hunting Lodge, The Square, Axbridge BS26 2AP - T: (01934) 732012, Fax: (01278) 444076, E-mail: museums@sedgemoor.gov.uk. Head: Sarah Harbige
Local Museum
Archaeology 32094

Axminster

Axminster Museum, Old Court House, Church St, Axminster EX13 5LL - T: (01297) 34137, Fax: 32929, E-mail: axminster-museum@ukf.net
Local Museum 32095

Aylesbury

Buckinghamshire County Museum, Church St, Aylesbury HP20 2QP - T: (01296) 331441, Fax: 334884, E-mail: museum@buckscc.gov.uk, Internet: http://www.buckscc.gov.uk/museum
Local Museum - 1847
Buckinghamshire artefacts, prints, watercolours, drawings and paintings, studio pottery 32096

Florence Nightingale Museum, Claydon House, Middle Claydon, Aylesbury MK18 2EY - T: (01296) 73349 ext 693
Historical Museum
Objects associated with Florence Nightingale and with the Crimean War during which she became a celebrated public figure 32097

Ayot-Saint-Lawrence

Shaw's Corner, Ayot-Saint-Lawrence AL6 9BX - T: (01438) 820307, Fax: 820307, E-mail: tscgen@smtp.ntrust.org.uk
Special Museum
Former home of George Bernard Shaw (1856-1950) from 1906 until his death, memorabilia including Nobel Prize related literature of 1925 and objects concerning the Oscar-winning work 'Pygmalion' 32098

Ayr

Ayrshire Yeomanry Museum, Rozelle House, Monument Rd, Ayr KA7 4NQ - T: (01292) 264091, Internet: http://www-saw.arts.ed.ac.uk/army/regiments/ayrshire.html
Military Museum 32099

Kyle and Carrick District Library and Museum, 12 Main St, Ayr KA8 8ED - T: (01292) 269141 ext 5227, Fax: 611593. Head: David T. Roy
Library with Exhibitions / Local Museum - 1934
Local history, rotating art coll 32100

Maclaurin Art Gallery, Rozelle Park, Monument Rd, Ayr KA7 4NQ - T: (01292) 443708, Fax: 442065. Head: Elizabeth I. Kwasnik
Fine Arts Museum - 1976
Maclaurin coll of contemporary art, fine and applied art, sculpture 32101

Rozelle House Galleries, Rozelle Park, Monument Rd, Ayr KA7 4NQ - T: (01292) 445447, 443708, Fax: 442065. Head: Elizabeth I. Kwasnik
Local Museum / Fine Arts Museum - 1982
Local history, military exhibition, fine and applied art, Tom O'Shanter paintings 32102

Bacup

Natural History Society and Folk Museum, 24 Yorkshire St, Bacup OL13 9AE - T: (01706) 873961. Head: Ben Ashworth
Natural History Museum / Local Museum - 1878
Geology, Neolothic objects, local nature, household objects 32103

Baginton

Coventry Steam Railway Museum, Rowley Rd, Baginton CV8 3AA - T: (01455) 634373, 635440, Fax: 610464
Science&Tech Museum
Locomotives, vans, coach, stean crane, rollers and tractors 32104

Lunt Roman Fort, Coventry Rd, Baginton CV8 3AA - T: (024) 76303567, Fax: 76832410, E-mail: ann.walker@coventry.gov.uk, Internet: http://www.coventrymuseums.org.uk
Historical Museum
Roman cavalry fort 32105

Midland Air Museum, Coventry Airport, Baginton CV8 3AA - T: (024) 76301033, Fax: 76301033
Science&Tech Museum
Sir Frank Whittle Jet Heritage Centre, Wings over Coventry 32106

Bagshot

Archaeology Centre, 4-10 London Rd, Bagshot GU19 5HN - T: (01276) 451181, E-mail: geoffreycole@shaat.netscapeonline.co.uk. Head: Geoffrey Cole
Archaeological Museum
Prehistoric, Roman, Saxon, medieval and post-medieval archaeological artefacts 32107

Baildon

Bracken Hall Countryside Centre, Glen Rd, Baildon BD17 5EA - T: (01274) 584140. Head: John Dallas
Natural History Museum - 1981
Wildlife, enviroment 32108

Bakewell

Chatsworth House, Bakewell DE45 1PP - T: (01246) 582204, Fax: 583536, E-mail: visit@chatsworth-house.co.uk, Internet: http://www.chatsworth-house.co.uk
Decorative Arts Museum 32109

Old House Museum, Cunningham Pl, Bakewell DE45 1DD - T: (01629) 813165, 815294
Local Museum - 1959
Costume, craftmen's tools, farming equipment, lacework, toys, cameras 32110

Bala

Bala Like Railway Museum, Station Llanuwchllyn, Bala LL23 7DD - T: (01678) 540666, Fax: 540535, Internet: http://www.bala-lake-railway.co.uk
Science&Tech Museum 32111

Canolfan Y Plase, Plassey St, Bala LL23 7SW - T: (01678) 520320. Head: I.B. Williams
Local Museum
Artwork and local heritage 32112

Ballallan

Museum Cheann A'Loch, School House, Ballallan PA87
Local Museum 32113

Ballasalla

Rushen Abbey, Manx National Heritage, Saint Mary's Abbey, Ballasalla IM1 3LY - T: (01624) 648000, Fax: 648001, E-mail: enquiries@nmh.gov.im, Internet: http://www.gov.im/mnh
Religious Arts Museum 32114

Ballindalloch

Glenfarclas Distillery Museum, Ballindalloch AB37 9BD - T: (01807) 500245, Fax: 500234, E-mail: j&ggrant@glenfarclas.demon.co.uk. Head: J. Grant
Science&Tech Museum - 1973 32115

Ballygrant

Finlaggan Centre, The Cottage, Ballygrant PA45 7QL - T: (01496) 810629, Fax: 810856, E-mail: LynMags@aol.com, Internet: http://www.islay.com
Local Museum 32116

Ballymena

Arthur Cottage, c/o Borough Council, 80 Galgorm Rd, Ballymena BT42 1AB - T: (028) 25880781, Fax: 25660400. Head: May Kirkpatrick, Sam Fleming
Historical Museum 32117

Ballymena Museum, Ballymena BT43 5EJ - T: (028) 25653663, Fax: 25638582. Head: William Blair
Local Museum / Folklore Museum
Mixed local history, folklife coll, farm machinery 32118

Royal Irish Regiment Museum, RIR Headquarter, Saint Patrick's Barracks, Ballymena BT43 7NX - T: (028) 25661383/355, Fax: 25661378. Head: J. Knox
Military Museum
Military history since 1689 32119

Ballymoney

Ballymoney Museum, 33 Charlotte St, Ballymoney BT53 6AY - T: (028) 27662280, Fax: 27667659, E-mail: kbeattie@curator.freeserve.co.uk
Local Museum
Local history since the earliest settlement in Ireland, motorcycle races, military history, popular culture, art, crafts 32120

Leslie Hill Open Farm, Ballymoney BT53 6QL - T: (028) 65663109, 65666803, Fax: 65666803
Agriculture Museum
Horse-drawn farm machines 32121

Bamburgh

Bamburgh Castle, Bamburgh NE69 7DF - T: (01668) 214515, Fax: 214060, E-mail: bamburghcastle@aol.com, Internet: http://www.bamburghcastle.com. Head: Francis Watson-Armstrong
Historical Museum 32122

Grace Darling Museum, Radcliffe Rd, Bamburgh NE69 7AE - T: (01668) 214465, Fax: 214465
Historical Museum - 1938 32123

Banbury

Banbury Museum, 8 Horsefair, Banbury OX16 0AA - T: (01295) 259855, Fax: 270556, E-mail: simontownsend@cherwell-dc.gov.uk, Internet: http://www.cherwell-dc.gov.uk/banburymuseum. Head: Simon Townsend
Local Museum - 1958
Banbury municipal coll containing weights and measures, banners, objects illustrating the material culture of Banbury and surrounding villages - archives, library 32124

Upton House, Banbury OX15 6HT - T: (01295) 670266, Fax: 670266, E-mail: vuplan@smtp.ntrust.org.uk, Internet: http://www.ntrusts-evern.org.uk. Head: Oliver Lane
Fine Arts Museum / Decorative Arts Museum / Historic Site - 1948
Brussels tapestries, porcelain from Sèvres, Chelsea figurines, furniture, coll of internationally important paintings 32125

Banchory

Banchory Museum, Bridge St, Banchory AB31 5SX - T: (01771) 622906, Fax: 622884, E-mail: heritage@aberdeenshire.gov.uk. Head: Dr. David M. Bertie
Local Museum - 1977
History of the Banchory area, social and domestic life, life and work of the local musician Scott Skinner, natural history, royal commemorative porcelain 32126

Crathes Castle, Crathes, Banchory AB31 5QJ - T: (01330) 844525, Fax: 844797, E-mail: crathes@nts.org.uk. Head: Arthur Martin
Decorative Arts Museum - 1951
Furnishings and decoration, painted ceiling from the end of the 16th c - garden 32127

Banff

Banff Museum, High St, Banff AB45 1AE - T: (01771) 622906, Fax: 622884, E-mail: heritage@aberdeenshire.gov.uk
Local Museum - 1828
Banff silver, arms and armour 32128

Bangor, Co. Down

North Down Heritage Centre, Town Hall, Bangor Castle, Bangor, Co. Down BT20 4BT - T: (028) 91270371, 91271200, Fax: 91271370, E-mail: -bangor_heritage_centre@yahoo.com, Internet: http://www.northdown.gov.uk/heritage/. Head: I.A. Wilson
Local Museum - 1984
Local hist 32129

Bangor, Gwynedd

Bangor Museum and Art Gallery, Ffordd Gwynedd, Bangor, Gwynedd LL57 1DT - T: (01248) 353368, Fax: 370426, E-mail: patwest@gwynedd.gov.uk. Head: Pat West
Local Museum - 1884
Archaeology, furniture, costume, textiles, prints 32130

Natural History Museum, c/o School of Biological Sciences, University of Wales, Brambell Bldg, Bangor, Gwynedd LL57 2UW - T: (01248) 351151 ext 2296, Fax: 371644, E-mail: w.wuster@bangor.ac.uk. Head: Dr. W. Wuster
Natural History Museum - 1900
Zoology, flowering of North Wales 32131

Penrhyn Castle, Bangor, Gwynedd LL57 4HN - T: (01248) 353084, Fax: 371281, E-mail: ppemsn@smtp.ntrust.org.uk. Head: Joan Bayliss
Fine Arts Museum / Decorative Arts Museum - 1952
19th c furnished castle, neo-Norman architecture, industrial railway, dolls, Dutch and Italian masters 32132

Barmouth

Barmouth Sailors' Institute Collection, The Quay, Barmouth LL42 1ET
Historical Museum
Maritime heritage 32133

Lifeboat Museum, RNLI Museum, Harbour, Pen-y-Cei, Barmouth LL42 1LZ
Science&Tech Museum
Old photographs of lifeboat and crews, rescue work at sea 32134

Ty Gwyn and Ty Crwn, The Quay, Barmouth LL42 1ET - T: (01341) 241333
Local Museum
History of Barmouth as a port 32135

Barnard Castle

The Bowes Museum, Barnard Castle DL12 8NP - T: (01833) 690606, Fax: 637163, E-mail: info@bowesmuseum.org.uk, Internet: http://www.bowesmuseum.org.uk. Head: Adrian Jenkins
Decorative Arts Museum / Fine Arts Museum / Local Museum - 1892
European painting, works by El Greco, Goya, Tiepolo, Boudin, Fragonard, pottery and porcelain, especially French, textiles, sculpture, furniture, other decorative arts 32136

Barnet

Museum of Domestic Design and Architecture MODA, Middlesex University, Cat Hill, Barnet EN4 8HT - T: (020) 84115244, Fax: 84115271, E-mail: moda@mdx.ac.uk, Internet: http://www.moda.mdx.ac.uk. Head: Ken Mannering
University Museum / Decorative Arts Museum
Silver studio coll, Sir Richards library, Peggy Anguz archive; Charles Hassler coll, British and American domestic design archive, crown wallpaper archive 32137

Barnoldswick

Bancroft Mill Engine Trust, Gillians Ln, Barnoldswick BB8 5QR - T: (01282) 865626
Science&Tech Museum
Corliss textile mill engine, weaving 32138

Barnsley, South Yorkshire

Cannon Hall Museum, Cawthorne, Barnsley, South Yorkshire S75 4AT - T: (01226) 790270, Fax: 792117, E-mail: cannonhall@barnsley.gov.uk
Fine Arts Museum 32139

Cooper Gallery, Church St, Barnsley, South Yorkshire S70 2AH - T: (01226) 242905, Fax: 297283, Internet: http://www.barnsley.gov.uk
Fine Arts Museum - 1980
17th, 18th and 19th c European paintings and English drawings and watercolours 32140

Worsbrough Mill Museum, Worsbrough Bridge, Barnsley, South Yorkshire S70 5LJ - T: (01226) 774527, Fax: 774527
Open Air Museum / Science&Tech Museum - 1976
Working 17th c water powered corn mill, working 19th c oil engine powered corn mill 32141

Barnstaple

Museum of Barnstaple and North Devon, The Square, Barnstaple EX32 8LN - T: (01271) 346747, Fax: 346407, E-mail: alison_mills@northdevon.gov.uk. Head: Jerry Lee
Local Museum - 1888
Local antiquities, North Devon pottery, geology, fossils, Roman pottery and coins from Martinhoe and old Barrow, natural history including butterflies, bird eggs, coins - incorporating the Royal Devon Yeomanry Museum 32142

Saint Anne's Chapel and Old Grammar School Museum (closed) 32143

Barrow-in-Furness

Dock Museum, North Rd, Barrow-in-Furness LA14 2PW - T: (01229) 894444, Fax: 811361, E-mail: dockmuseum@barrowbc.gov.uk, Internet: http://www.barrowtourism.co.uk. Head: Sue Jenkins
Local Museum - 1994
V.S.E.L. glass photographic negative archive, maritime, social hist, archaeology, geology, fine art 32144

Furness Abbey, Barrow-in-Furness LA13 0TJ - T: (01229) 823420
Fine Arts Museum
Architectural stonework, sculpture 32145

Barrowford

Pendle Heritage Centre, Park Hill, Barrowford BB9 6JQ - T: (01282) 661704, Fax: 611718. Head: E.M.J. Miller
Local Museum 32146

Barton-upon-Humber

Baysgarth House Museum, Baysgarth Leisure Park, Caistor Rd, Barton-upon-Humber DN18 6AH - T: (01652) 632318, Fax: 636659
Local Museum
18th cent mansion house, porcelain, local hist, archeology and geology 32147

Basildon

National Motorboat Museum, Wat Tyler Country Park, Pitsea Hall Ln, Basildon SS16 4UH - T: (01268) 550077, Fax: 581093, 584207. Head: Steven Prewer
Science&Tech Museum - 1986
Carstairs coll, Bert Savidge coll, motorboating (sports, leisure), in- and outboard motors, over 35 crafts - library 32148

Potland Museum, Langdon Conservation Centre, Third Av, Lower Dunton Rd, Basildon SS15 4DA - T: (01268) 419103, Fax: 546137
Local Museum - 1933 32149

Basing

Basing House, Redbridge Ln, Basing RG24 7HB - T: (01256) 467294, E-mail: musmat@hants.gov.uk, Internet: http://www.hants.gov.uk/museum/basingho
Archaeological Museum
Archaeological material 32150

Basingstoke

The Vyne, Sherborne Saint John, Basingstoke RG24 9ML - T: (01256) 881337, Fax: 881720, E-mail: svygen@smtp.ntrust.org.uk, Internet: http://www.nationaltrust.org.uk/southern. Head: J. Ingram
Decorative Arts Museum - 1958
Tudor house with renovations (1650-1760), Flemish glass, majolica tiles, panellig, furniture of Charles II, Queen Anne and Chippendale periods, rococo decoration 32151

Willis Museum, Old Town Hall, Market Pl, Basingstoke RG21 7QD - T: (01256) 465902, E-mail: musmst@hants.gov.uk, Internet: http://www.hants.gov.uk/museum/willis. Head: Sue Tapuss
Local Museum - 1930
Local hist, archaeology, natural sciences 32152

Bath

American Museum in Britain, Claverton Manor, Bath BA2 7BD - T: (01225) 460503, Fax: 480726, E-mail: amibbath@aol.com, Internet: http://www.americanmuseum.org. Head: William McNaught
Decorative Arts Museum - 1961
17th-19th c American decorative art and social hist, furnished period rooms, maritime hist, replica of Captain's cabin, Indian section, 18th c tavern, folk art gallery, New Gallery housing the Dallas Pratt Coll of maps - library 32153

Bath Abbey Heritage Vaults, 13 Kingston Bldgs, Bath BA1 1LT - T: (01225) 422462, Fax: 429990, E-mail: laj@heritagevaults.fsnet.co.uk
Religious Arts Museum 32154

Bath Industrial Heritage Centre → Museum of Bath at Work

Bath Police Museum, Manvers St, Bath BA1 1JN - T: (01225) 444343, 842482, Fax: 842523. Head: Bob Allard
Special Museum - 1966
Police helmets and headgear 32155

Bath Postal Museum, 8 Broad St, Bath BA1 5LJ - T: (01225) 460333, Fax: 460333, E-mail: info@bathpostalmuseum.org, Internet: http://www.bathpostalmuseum.org. Head: Elgar Jenkins
Special Museum - 1979
4,000 years of communication, fron Sumarian tablets 2,000 BC to email 32156

Bath Royal Literary and Scientific Institution, 16-18 Queen Sq, Bath BA1 2HP - T: (01225) 312084, Fax: 429452, E-mail: exxbrlsi@bath.ac.uk, Internet: http://www.bath.ac.uk/brlsi. Head: Brenda Vickery-Finch
Natural History Museum / Local Museum - 1824
Moore coll of fossils incl Type Specimens, Jewyns coll of natural hist, material-herbaria, Darwin letters and others from eminent naturalists, geology, ethnology, art, archaeology - library 32157

Beckford's Tower and Museum, Lansdown Rd, Bath BA1 9BH - T: (01225) 422212, 460705, Fax: 481850, E-mail: beckford@bptrust.demon.co.uk, Internet: http://www.bath-preservation-trust.org.uk/museums. Head: Arnold Wilson
Local Museum - 1977/2000 32158

Book Museum, Manvers St, Bath BA1 1JW - T: (01225) 446000, Fax: 482122, E-mail: ebayntun@aol.com
Special Museum
History of bookbinding, authors of Bath 32159

Building of Bath Museum, The Countess of Huntingdon's Chapel, The Vineyards, Bath BA1 5NA - T: (01225) 333895, Fax: 445473, E-mail: admin@bobm.freeserve.co.uk, Internet: http://www.bath-preservation-trust.org.uk. Head: Cathryn Spen
Special Museum 32160

Georgian Museum → Number 1 Royal Crescent Museum

Guildhall, High St, Bath BA1 5AW - T: (01225) 477724, Fax: 477442, E-mail: ian_burns@bathnes.gov.uk
Decorative Arts Museum
18th c Banqueting Room, chandeliers, coll of Royal portraits 32161

Holburne Museum of Art, Great Pulteney St, Bath BA2 4DB - T: (01225) 466669, Fax: 333121, Internet: http://www.bath.ac.uk/holburne. Head: Christopher Woodward
Decorative Arts Museum / Fine Arts Museum - 1893
Decorative and fine art, furniture, silver, miniatures, porcelain, majolica, bronzes, netsukes, paintings by Stubbs, Gainsborough, Guardi and 18th c Old Masters together with 20th c work by leading British artist-craftspeople embracing textiles, ceramics, furniture, calligraphy, sculpture - library 32162

Microworld, 4 Monmouth St, Bath BA1 2AJ - T: (01225) 333003, Fax: 333633, E-mail: info@theimpossiblemicroworld.com, Internet: http://www.theimpossiblemicroworld.com
Special Museum
Microscopic sculptures af animals, celebrities, buildings, works of art 32163

Museum of Bath at Work, Camden Works, Julian Rd, Bath BA1 2RH - T: (01225) 318348, Fax: 318348, E-mail: mobaw@hotmail.co.uk, Internet: http://www.bath-at-work.org.uk. Head: Stuart Burroughs
Science&Tech Museum - 1978
Coll of working machinery, hand-tools, brasswork, patterns, bottles and documents of all kinds, displayed as realistically as possible to convey an impression of the working life, local engineering, power generation - archive 32164

Museum of Costume, Bennett St, Bath BA1 2QH - T: (01225) 477789, Fax: 444793, E-mail: -costume_enquiries@bathnes.gov.uk, Internet: http://www.museumofcostume.co.uk. Head: P.C. Ruddock
Special Museum - 1963
Some pre-18th c costumes, mainly 18th c to present day dress for men, women and children, incl haute couture pcs - Fashion research centre 32165

Museum of East Asian Art, 12 Bennett St, Bath BA1 2QJ - T: (01225) 464640, Fax: 461718, E-mail: museum@east-asian-art.freeserve.co.uk, Internet: http://www.east-asian-art.co.uk. Head: Michelle Little
Fine Arts Museum
Over 1600 art treasures in pottery, stoneware, porcelain, bronze etc 32166

Number 1 Royal Crescent Museum, 1 Royal Crescent, Bath BA1 2LR - T: (01225) 428126, Fax: 481850, E-mail: admin@bptrust.demon.co.uk, Internet: http://www.bath-preservation-trust.org.uk/museums/no1. Head: Michael Briggs
Historical Museum - 1970
Georgian Town House, example of Palladian architecture redecorated and furnished, Beckfords Tower 32167

Roman Baths Museum, Pump Room, Stall St, Bath BA1 1LZ - T: (01225) 477774, Fax: 477243, E-mail: stephen_clews@bathnes.gov.uk, Internet: http://www.romanbaths.co.uk. Head: Stephen Clews
Archaeological Museum - 1895
Archaeological history of Bath in prehistoric, Roman, Saxon, medieval and later times 32168

The Royal Photographic Society Octagon Galleries, The Octagon, Milsom St, Bath BA1 1DN - T: (01225) 462841, Fax: 469880, E-mail: collection@collection.rps.org, Internet: http://www.rps.org. Head: Barry Lane
Special Museum - 1893/1980
Photography in all its aspects with special emphasis on British 19th and early 20th c photography, equipment and books, periodicals - library, archives 32169

Sally Lunn's Refreshment House and Kitchen Museum, 4 North Parade Passage, Bath BA1 1NX - T: (01225) 811311, 461634, Fax: 811800, E-mail: corsham@ad.com, Internet: http://www.sallylunns.co.uk. Head: Jonathan Overton, Julian Abraham
Historical Museum - 1680
Bakery and kitchen equipment 32170

Victoria Art Gallery, Bridge St, Bath BA2 4AT - T: (01225) 477772, Fax: 477231, E-mail: -victoria_enquiries@bathnes.gov.uk, Internet: http://www.victoriagal.org.uk. Head: Jon Benington
Fine Arts Museum / Decorative Arts Museum / Public Gallery - 1900
British paintings, sculptures, drawings and prints 18-20th c, ceramics and glass, European and British watches, British miniatures and silhouettes, craft, photography 32171

The William Herschel Museum, 19 New King St, Bath BA1 2BL - T: (01225) 311342, Fax: 446865, E-mail: whmb@hotmail.com, Internet: http://www.bath-preservation-trust.org.uk. Head: Prof. Francis Ring
Science&Tech Museum - 1978
Astronomy, 18th c music, thermology 32172

Bathgate

Bennie Museum, 9-11 Mansefield St, Bathgate EH48 4HU - T: (01506) 634944, E-mail: thornton@benniemuseum.freeserve.co.uk, Internet: http://www.benniemuseum.homestead.com. Head: William I. Millan
Local Museum
Local hist, early photographs, glass from Bathgate glassworks and Victoriana 32173

Batley

Bagshaw Museum, Wilton Park, Batley WF17 0AS - T: (01924) 326155, 472514, Fax: 326164, 420017, Internet: http://www.kirklees.gov.uk/services/cultural/museums/muspages/bagshaw.htm. Head: Kathryn White
Local Museum - 1911
Antiquities of Britain and other areas, relics, ethnography, local hist, industries, natural hist, geology, textile industry, Oriental ceramics and finds, egyptology, tropical rainforest 32174

Batley Art Gallery, Market Pl, Batley WF17 5DA - T: (01924) 326090, Fax: 326308. Head: Jenny Hall
Fine Arts Museum - 1948
Local arts and crafts, children's art, 19th-20th c art, works by Francis Bacon and Max Ernst - library 32175

Battle

Battle Abbey, Battle TN33 0AD - T: (014246) 773792, Fax: 775059
Historic Site 32176

Battle Museum of Local History, Memorial Hall, High St, Battle TN33 0AQ - T: (01424) 775955, Fax: 772827, E-mail: ann@battlehill.-freeserve.co.uk. Head: Anne Ainsley
Local Museum - 1956
Local history, Romano-British ironwork, gunpowder industry, battle artifacts, diorama of the Battle of Hastings and reproductions of the Bayeux Tapestry 32177

Buckleys Museum of Shops → Buckleys Yesterday's World

Buckleys Yesterday's World, 89-90 High St, Battle TN33 0AQ - T: (01424) 775378, Fax: 775174, E-mail: info@yesterdaysworld.co.uk, Internet: http://www.yesterdaysworld.co.uk. Head: Annette Buckley
Special Museum
Advertising material and the contents of old shops, Victorian and Edwardian social history 32178

Battlesbridge

Battlesbridge Motorcycle Museum, Maltings Rd, Battlesbridge SS11 7RF - T: (01268) 575000, Fax: 575001, E-mail: jimgallie@virgin.net
Science&Tech Museum 32179

Beaminster

Beaminster Museum, Whitcombe Rd, Beaminster DT8 3NB - T: (01308) 863623, 862773. Head: Marie Eedle
Local Museum 32180

Parnham House, Beaminster DT8 3NA - T: (01308) 862204, Fax: 863494
Local Museum 32181

Beamish

Beamish, North of England Open Air Museum, Beamish DH9 0RG - T: (0191) 3704000, Fax: 3704001, E-mail: museum@beamish.org.uk, Internet: http://www.beamish.org.uk. Head: Miriam Harte
Open Air Museum - 1971
Period areas (1820s and 1913), early railways, quilts - photographic archive, reference library, trade catalogues 32182

Beaumaris

Beaumaris Castle, Beaumaris LL58 8AB - T: (01248) 810361
Archaeological Museum 32183

Beaumaris Gaol and Courthouse, Steeple Ln, Beaumaris LL58 8ED - T: (01248) 810921, 724444, Fax: 750282. Head: Elspeth Micheson
Special Museum 32184

Museum of Childhood Memories, 1 Castle St, Beaumaris LL58 8AP - T: (01248) 712498, Fax: 716869, E-mail: bryn.brown@amserve.net, Internet: http://www.nwi.co.uk/museumofchildhood. Head: Robert Brown
Special Museum - 1973
Audio and visual entertainment, pottery and glass, trains, cars, clockwork toys, ships and aeroplanes, art, educational toys, dolls, games, money boxes 32185

Beccles

Beccles and District Museum, Leman House, Ballygate, Beccles NR34 9ND - T: (01502) 715722. Head: James Woodrow
Local Museum
Natural history, geology, archaeology 32186

Beckenham

Bethlem Royal Hospital Archives and Museum, Monks Orchard Rd, Beckenham BR3 3BX - T: (020) 87764307, 87764227, Fax: 87764045, E-mail: museum@bethlem.freeserve.co.uk. Head: Patricia Allderidge
Special Museum - 1970
Paintings and drawings by artists who have suffered from mental disorder, incl Richard Dadd, Louis Wain, Vaslav Nijinsky, William Kurelek, historical exhibits relating to Bethlem Hospital (the original 'Bedlam'), and to the history of psychiatry 32187

Bedale

Bedale Museum, Bedale Hall, Bedale DL8 1AA - T: (01677) 422037, Fax: 422037
Local Museum
Local history, clothing, toys, craft tools, hand-drawn fire engine from 1748 32188

Beddgelert

Sygun Copper Mine, Beddgelert LL55 4NE - T: (01766) 510100, Fax: 510102, E-mail: SnowdoniaMine@compuserve.com, Internet: http://ourworld.compuserve.com/homepages/SnowdoniaMine
Science&Tech Museum 32189

Beddington

Carew Manor and Dovecote, Church Rd, Beddington SM6 7NH - T: (020) 87704781, Fax: 87704777, E-mail: local.studies@sutton.gov.uk, Internet: http://www.sutton.gov.uk/lfl/heritage. Head: John Phillips
Historic Site 32190

Bedford

Bedford Central Library Gallery, Harpur St, Bedford MK40 1PG - T: (01234) 350931
Public Gallery 32191

Bedford Museum, Castle Ln, Bedford MK40 3XD - T: (01234) 353323, Fax: 273401, E-mail: bmuseum@bedford.gov.uk, Internet: http://www.bedfordmuseum.org. Head: R.A. Brind
Local Museum - 1959
Local archaeological finds, history, natural history, medieval tile pavement, iron age bronze mirror, lace gobelin 32192

Cecil Higgins Art Gallery, Castle Close, Castle Ln, Bedford MK40 3RP - T: (01234) 211222, Fax: 327149, E-mail: chag@bedford.gov.uk. Head: Caroline Bacon
Fine Arts Museum / Decorative Arts Museum - 1949
Fine and decorative arts, English watercolours, international prints, English and continental porcelain, glass, furniture, silver, sculptures, lace, costume, Handley-Read coll of Victorian and Edwardian decorative arts, William Burges room 32193

Elstow Moot Hall, Church End, Elstow, Bedford MK42 9XT - T: (01234) 266889, Fax: 228531, E-mail: wilemans@deed.bedfordshire.gov.uk. Head: M. Kenworthy
Historical Museum - 1951
17th c cultural history, local history, architecture 32194

John Bunyan Museum, Free Church, Mill St, Bedford MK40 3EU - T: (01234) 213722, Fax: 213722, E-mail: bmeeting@dialstart.net. Head: Doreen Watson
Special Museum - 1947
"The Pilgrim's Progress" in over 170 languages and dialects, artefacts relating to John Bunyan's life and times - library 32195

Beetham

Heron Corn Mill and Museum of Papermaking, Waterhouse Mills, Beetham LA7 7AR - T: (015395) 65027, Fax: 65033, E-mail: nt.stobbs@virgin.net. Head: Neil T. Stobbs
Science&Tech Museum - 1975/1988
18th c working water driven corn mill, machinery, displays tell the story of 900 yrs of milling, displays of papermaking separate from Corn Mill in restored carter's barn - Corn mill, Museum of Papermaking 32196

Belfast

Arts Council Gallery, 56 Dublin Rd, Belfast BT2 - T: (028) 90221402
Public Gallery 32197

Lagan Lookout Centre, 1 Donegall Quai, Belfast BT1 3EA - T: (028) 90315444, Fax: 90311955, E-mail: lookout@laganside.com, Internet: http://www.laganside.com
Science&Tech Museum
Engineeering, river development 32198

Natural History Museum, c/o School of Biology and Biochemistry, Queen's University, Medical and Biological Centre, 97 Lisburn Rd, Belfast BT9 7BL - T: (028) 90335786, Fax: 90236505, Internet: http://www.qub.ac.uk/bb/
Natural History Museum / University Museum
Educational zoology and geology collections 32199

Old Museum Arts Centre, 7 College Sq, Belfast BT1 6AR - T: (028) 90235053, Fax: 90322912, E-mail: info@oldmuseumartscentre.freeserve.co.uk, Internet: http://www.oldmuseumartscentre.org. Head: Anne McReynolds
Public Gallery 32200

Ormeau Baths Gallery, 18a Ormeau Av, Belfast BT2 8HQ - T: (028) 90321402, Fax: 90312232, E-mail: ormeaubathgallery@btinternet.com. Head: Hugh Mulholland
Fine Arts Museum
Contemporary Irish and international art 32201

The People's Museum, Fernhill House, Glencairn Park, Belfast BT13 3PT - T: (028) 90715599, Fax: 90715582. Head: Thomas G. Kirkham
Local Museum
Social and military coll 32202

Royal Ulster Rifles Regimental Museum, The Royal Irish Rangers, 5 Waring St, Belfast BT1 2EW - T: (028) 90232086, Fax: 90232086, E-mail: rurmuseum@yahoo.co.uk
Military Museum - 1935
Uniforms, medals, history of the regiment 32203

Ulster Museum, Museums and Galleries of Northern Ireland, Botanic Gardens, Belfast BT9 5AB - T: (028) 90383000, Fax: 90383003, E-mail: john.wilson.um@nics.gov.uk, Internet: http://www.ulstermuseum.org.uk. Head: John Wilson
Local Museum - 1892
International art, Irish painting, contemporary Irish art, silver ceramics, Williamite glass, Irish and European antiquities, treasure from Spanish Armada galleass Girona, Irish botany, zoology, geology, wildlife art, industrial technology and history, numismatics 32204

Whowhatwherewhenwhy W5, Odyssey, 2 Queen's Quay, Belfast BT3 9QQ - T: (028) 90467700, Internet: http://www.w5online.co.uk. Head: Dr. Sally Montgomery
Science&Tech Museum
Siences 32205

Belleek

Explorerne Museum, Erne Gateway Centre, Corry, Belleek PO35 5SB - T: (0028) 68658866, Fax: 68658833
Special Museum 32206

Bembridge

Bembridge Maritime Museum and Shipwreck Centre, Providence House, Sherbourne St, Bembridge PO35 5SB - T: (01983) 872223, Fax: 873125, E-mail: museum@isle-of-wight.uk.com, Internet: http://www.isle-of-wight.uk.com/shipwrecks. Head: Sue Macey
Historical Museum - 1978
Shipwrecks, maritime history, diving equipment, pirate gold and silver, steamship artefacts, salvage, lifeboats 32207

Benbecula

Museum Nan Eilean, Sgoil Lionacleit, Lionacleit, Benbecula HS7 5PJ - T: (01870) 602864, Fax: 602053, E-mail: danamacphee@cne-siar.gov.uk, Internet: http://www.cne-siar.gov.uk. Head: Richard Langhorne
Local Museum
History and culture of the islands 32208

Benburg

Blackwater Valley Museum, 89 Milltown Rd, Tullymore Etra, Benburg BT71 7LZ - T: (028) 37549885, 37549752, Fax: 90311264
Local Museum
Set of machinery, spinning, winding, warping, beaming, weaving, forge 32209

Benenden

Mervyn Quinlan Museum, Benenden Hospital, Goddards Green Rd, Benenden TN17 4AX - T: (01580) 240333, Fax: 241877, E-mail: wrichley@benenden.star.co.uk. Head: M. Quinlan
Historical Museum
History of the hospital 32210

Benson

Benson Veteran Cycle Museum, 61 Brook St, Benson OX10 6LH - T: (01491) 838414
Science&Tech Museum
600 veteran and vintage cycles (1818-1930) 32211

Berkeley

Berkeley Castle, Berkeley GL13 9BQ - T: (01453) 810332. Head: D. Attwood
Historical Museum
Paintings, furniture, tapestries, porcelain and silver 32212

Jenner Museum, The Chantry, Church Ln, Berkeley GL13 9BH - T: (01453) 810631, Fax: 811690, E-mail: manager@jennermuseum.com, Internet: http://www.jennermuseum.com. Head: D. Mullin
Special Museum - 1985
Illustration of the life and career of Edward Jenner, coll of memorabilia and personal possessions, computerized exhibition on immunology, medical science as founded by E. Jenner 32213

Berkhamsted

Dacorum Heritage, Museum Store, Clarence Rd, Berkhamsted HP4 3YL - T: (01442) 879525, Fax: 879525, E-mail: dacht@mattwheeler.-freeserve.co.uk, Internet: http://www.hertsmu-seums.org.uk/dacorum. Head: Matthew Wheeler
Local Museum
History of the borough of Dacorum 32214

Berkswell

Berkswell Village Museum, Lavender Hall Ln, Berkswell CV7 7BJ - T: (01676) 534981
Local Museum
Local artefacts (19th-20th c), Saxon Parish of Berkswell 32215

Bernera

Urras Eachdraibh Sgire Bhearnaraidh, 1 Croir, Bernera PA86 9LZ - T: (01851) 612285
Local Museum 32216

Berriew

Andrew Logan Museum of Sculpture, Berriew SY21 8PJ - T: (01686) 640689, Fax: 640764, E-mail: info@andrewlogan.com, Internet: http://www.andrewlogan.com. Head: Anne Collins
Fine Arts Museum 32217

Bersham

Bersham Heritage Centre and Ironworks, Bersham LL14 4HT - T: (01978) 261529, Fax: 361703. Head: Alan Watkin
Science&Tech Museum / Local Museum - 1983/1992 32218

Berwick-upon-Tweed

Berwick Barracks, The Parade, Ravensdowne, Berwick-upon-Tweed TD15 1DE - T: (01289) 304493, Fax: 601999. Head: Andrew Morrison
Military Museum
Exhibition on the history of the British infantry, 1660-1880, barrack-room of the 1780s, an Army schoolroom of the 1860s with period figures, and other tableaux 32219

Berwick Borough Museum and Art Gallery, Clock Block, Berwick Barracks, Ravensdowne, Berwick-upon-Tweed TD15 1DQ - T: (01289) 301869, Fax: 330540, E-mail: museum@berwick-upon-tweed.gov.uk. Head: Chris Green
Local Museum / Fine Arts Museum - 1867
Local hist, decorative objects in ceramics, bronze and brass, paintings, natural history, archaeology - library 32220

King's Own Scottish Borderers Regimental Museum, The Barracks, Ravensdowne, Berwick-upon-Tweed TD15 1DG - T: (01289) 307426, Fax: 331928. Head: C.G.O. Hogg
Military Museum - 1951
Uniforms, medals, trophies, hist of the regiment 32221

Lady Waterford Gallery, Ford Village, Berwick-upon-Tweed TD15 2QA - T: (01890) 820524, Fax: 820384
Local Museum 32222

Lindisfarne Wine and Spirit Museum, Palace Green, Berwick-upon-Tweed TD15 1HR - T: (01289) 305153, Fax: 302501. Head: Ronald Tait
Special Museum 32223

Paxton House, Berwick-upon-Tweed TD15 1SZ - T: (01289) 386291, Fax: 386660, E-mail: info@paxtonhouse.com, Internet: http://www.paxtonhouse.com. Head: Jacky Miller
Special Museum 32224

Bettyhill

Strathnaver Museum, Clachan, Bettyhill KW14 7SS - T: (01641) 521418, E-mail: strathnavermus@ukonline.co.uk
Local Museum - 1976
Highland clearances of Strathnaver, clan Mackay 32225

Betws-y-coed

Betws-y-coed Motor Museum, Betws-y-coed LL24 0AH - T: (01690) 710760
Science&Tech Museum
Vintage and classic vehicles 32226

Conwy Valley Railway Museum, Old Goods Yard, Betws-y-coed LL24 0AL - T: (01690) 710568, Fax: 710132
Science&Tech Museum / Local Museum - 1973
Historic maps of Conwy Valley, memorabilia from narrow, gauge railways, hist of L.N.W.R. Railway, signalling working models all gauges 32227

Beverley

Beverley Art Gallery, Champney Rd, Beverley HU17 9BQ - T: (01482) 883903, 884956, Fax: 883921. Head: Christine Brady
Public Gallery - 1906/1928
Regional art, contemporary art and craft, old paintings, prints, drawings and photographs 32228

Guildhall, Register Sq, Beverley HU17 9XX - T: (01482) 392776, Fax: 884747
Local Museum 32229

Museum of Army Transport, Flemingate, Beverley HU17 0NG - T: (01482) 860445, Fax: 872767. Head: Walter Dugan
Military Museum
Coll of Army road, rail, sea and air transport, exhibits of the Second World War, tank transporter train 32230

Bewdley

Bewdley Museum, The Shambles, Load St, Bewdley DY12 2AE - T: (01299) 403573, Fax: 404740, E-mail: museum_wfdc@online.rednet.co.uk. Head: Carol Bowsher
Historical Museum / Local Museum - 1972
Crafts and industries of the Wyne Forest, pewter brass 32231

Severn Valley Railway, Railway Station, Bewdley DY12 1BG - T: (01299) 403816, Fax: 400839, Internet: http://www.svr.co.uk
Science&Tech Museum
Steam locomotives and pre-nationalisation coaches 32232

Bexhill-on-Sea

Bexhill Museum, Egerton Rd, Bexhill-on-Sea TN39 3HL - T: (01424) 787950, Fax: 787950, E-mail: museum@rother.gov.uk, Internet: http://www.bexhillmuseum.co.uk
Local Museum - 1914
Regional, natural and social history, geology, antiquities, ethnography 32233

Bexhill Museum of Costume and Social History, Manor Gardens, Upper Sea Rd, Bexhill-on-Sea TN40 1RL - T: (01424) 210045
Special Museum 32234

Bibury

Arlington Mill Museum, Bibury GL7 5NL - T: (01285) 740368, Fax: 740368
Folklore Museum / Science&Tech Museum
Mill machinery, Victorian way of life 32235

Bickenhill

National Motorcycle Museum, Coventry Rd, Bickenhill B92 0EJ - T: (01675) 443311, Fax: 443310, E-mail: sales@nationalmotorcycle-museum.co.uk. Head: W.R. Richards
Science&Tech Museum - 1984
Coll of 700 British motorcycles dating from 1898 to the present day 32236

Bickleigh

Bickleigh Castle, Bickleigh EX16 8RP - T: (01884) 855363. Head: Michael Boxall
Historical Museum
Agricultural objects and toys, model ships, civil war arms and armour 32237

Bideford

The Burton Art Gallery and Museum, Kingsley Rd, Bideford EX39 2QQ - T: (01237) 471455, Fax: 473813, Internet: http://www.burtongallery.co.uk. Head: John Butler
Public Gallery - 1951/1994
Watercolour paintings Hubert Coop and Ackland Edwards, oils by Hunt, Opie, Fisher et al, ceramics, pewter, porcelain, Napoleonic ship models, local artefacts 32238

Hartland Quay Museum, Hartland Quay, Bideford EX39 6DU - T: (01288) 331353
Local Museum
History of the quay, coastal trades and industries, shipwreck, life-saving, Hartland Point Lighthouse, smuggling, geology and natural history 32239

Biggar

Biggar Gasworks Museum, c/o Biggar Museums Trust, Moat Park, Biggar ML12 6 DT - T: (0131) 6688000
Science&Tech Museum
Original 1914 equipment of gasworks, early history of the gas industry 32240

Brownsbank Cottage, Moat Park, Biggar ML12 6DT - T: (01899) 221050, Fax: 221050
Special Museum - 1992
Home of Hugh MacDiarmid, 1951-1978 32241

Crawfordjohn Heritage Venture, Crawfordjohn Church, Main St, Biggar ML12 6SS - T: (01864) 504206, Fax: 504206, E-mail: crawfordjohn-heritage@culturalprojects.co.uk. Head: Robert A. Clark
Local Museum
Traditional way of life, hill farms and community activity 32242

Gladstone Court Museum, North Back Rd, Biggar ML12 6DT - T: (01899) 221050, Fax: 221050, E-mail: margaret@bmtrust.freeserve.co.uk, Internet: http://www.biggar-net.co.uk. Head: Margaret Brown, Ann Matheson
Local Museum - 1968
Reconstructed street with various shops and trades 32243

Greenhill Covenanter's House, Burn Braes, Biggar ML12 6DT - T: (01899) 221050, Fax: 221050, E-mail: margaret@bmtrust.freeserve.co.uk. Head: Margaret Brown, Ann Matheson
Historical Museum - 1981
17th c furniture and artefacts 32244

John Buchan Centre, Moat Park, Biggar ML12 6HQ - T: (01899) 830223, 221050
Special Museum
Carrier and achievements of John Buchan as a novelist, lawyer, politician, soldier, historian, biographer and Governor-General of Canada, photographs, books, personal possessions of John Buchan and his family 32245

Moat Park Heritage Centre, Kirkstyle, Biggar ML12 6DT - T: (01899) 221050, Fax: 221050, E-mail: margaret@bmtrust.freeserve.co.uk, Internet: http://www.biggar-net.co.uk/museums. Head: Margaret Brown, Ann Matnesow
Local Museum - 1988
Embroidery, archaeology - local archives 32246

Bignor

Roman Villa Museum at Bignor, Bignor RH20 1PH - T: (01798) 869259, Fax: 869259, E-mail: - bingorromanvilla@care4free.net. Head: J. Tupper
Archaeological Museum - 1960
Samian pottery, tiles, finds from 1811 excavations, mosaics 32247

Billericay

Barleylands Farm Museum, Barleylands Rd, Billericay CM11 2UD - T: (01268) 532253, Fax: 290222, E-mail: barleyfarm@aol.com. Head: Chris Philpot
Agriculture Museum - 1984 32248

Cater Museum, 74 High St, Billericay CM12 9BS - T: (01277) 622023. Head: Christine Brewster
Local Museum - 1960
Local and regional history, prehistory, Victorian room settings, WWII exhibition, Zeppelin airship L32 which was destroyed near Billericay in 1916 32249

Billingham

Billingham Art Gallery, Queensway, Billingham TS23 2LN - T: (01642) 397590, Fax: 397594. Head: Kevin Allison
Public Gallery 32250

Birchington

Pembroke Lodge Family History Centre and Museum, 4 Station Approach, Birchington CT7 9RD - T: (01843) 841649. Head: J.J. Patterson-O'Regan
Historical Museum
Social history 32251

Powell-Cotton Museum and Quex House, Quex Park, Birchington CT7 0BH - T: (01843) 842168, Fax: 846661, E-mail: powell-cotton.museum@virgin.net, Internet: http://www.powell-cottonmuseum.co.uk. Head: C. Powell-Cotton
Ethnology Museum / Natural History Museum / Decorative Arts Museum - 1896
African and Asian natural hist and ethnography, primates, bovidae, dioramas of African and Asian animals, archaeology, firearms, oriental fine arts, European & English ceramics, Chinese imperial porcelain - library 32252

Birkenhead

Birkenhead Priory and Saint Mary's Tower, Priory St, Birkenhead CH41 5JH - T: (0151) 6661249, Fax: 6663965
Religious Arts Museum
History of the building and its development 32253

Birkenhead Tramways and Taylor Street Large Object Collections, 1 Taylor St, Birkenhead CH41 1BG - T: (0151) 6472128. Head: Kevin Johnson
Science&Tech Museum
Transport related objects incl. trams, buses, motorcycles and cars 32254

Shore Road Pumping Station, Hamilton St, Birkenhead CH41 6DN - T: (0151) 6501182, Fax: 6663965
Science&Tech Museum
Giant restored steam engine 32255

Williamson Art Gallery and Museum, Slatey Rd, Birkenhead CH43 4UE - T: (0151) 6524177, Fax: 6700253, E-mail: wag@museum-service.freeserve.co.uk. Head: Colin M. Simpson
Fine Arts Museum / Decorative Arts Museum - 1928
Paintings, sculpture, etchings, pottery, porcelain, glass, silver, furniture, local history, geology, numismatics, porcelain, shipping history, motor vehicle history - archive 32256

Wirral Museum, Town Hall, Hamilton St, Birkenhead CH41 5BR - T: (0151) 6664010, Fax: 6663965. Head: David Hillhouse
Local Museum - 2001
Social, industrial and commercial history 32257

Birmingham

Aston Hall, Birmingham Museums, Trinity Rd, Aston, Birmingham B6 6JD - T: (0121) 3270062, Fax: 3277162, Internet: http://www.birmingham.gov.uk/bmag. Head: Christopher Rice
Decorative Arts Museum - 1864
Jacobean house dating from 1616-1635, period furniture and rooms 32258

Aston Manor Transport Museum, Old Tram Depot, 208-216 Witton Ln, Birmingham B6 6QE - T: (0121) 3223398, Fax: 3080544
Science&Tech Museum
Over 100 vehicles, two unrestored tramcars, scale model tram, trolleybus layout 32259

Barber Institute of Fine Arts, c/o University of Birmingham, Edgbaston Park Rd, Birmingham B15 2TS - T: (0121) 4147333, Fax: 4143370, E-mail: info@barber.org.uk, Internet: http://www.barber.org.uk. Head: Prof. Richard Verdi
Fine Arts Museum - 1932
European art up to the 20th c, works by Bellini, Veronese, Rubens, Rembrandt, Frans Hals, Gainsborough, Reynolds, Degas, Gauguin 32260

Biological Sciences Collection, c/o School of Biological Sciences, University of Birmingham, Birmingham B15 2TT - T: (0121) 4145465, Fax: 4145925. Head: James Hamilton
Natural History Museum
herbarium 32261

Birmingham Institute of Art and Design, c/o University of Central England, Gosta Green, Birmingham B4 7DX - T: (0121) 3315860/61
Fine Arts Museum 32262

Birmingham Museum and Art Gallery, Chamberlain Sq, Birmingham B3 3DH - T: (0121) 3032834, Fax: 3031394, E-mail: bmag-enquiries@birmingham.gov.uk, Internet: http:www.bmag.org.uk. Head: Graham Allen
Fine Arts Museum / Decorative Arts Museum / Public Gallery - 1885
British and European painting and sculpture, Pre.Raphaelite paintings and drawings, contemporary art, drawings and watercolours, ceramics, metalwork, costume and textiles, jewellery and stained glass, coll from India, China, Japan and the Far East, archaeology and ethnography - picture library 32263

Birmingham Nature Centre, Pershore Rd, Edgbaston, Birmingham B5 7RL - T: (0121) 4727775, Fax: 4723040. Head: John Needle
Natural History Museum
Birdwatching, apiary culture, fishing, house pets, bird dioramas, African bush reconstruction 32264

Birmingham Railway Museum, 670 Warwick Rd, Tyseley, Birmingham B11 2HL - T: (0121) 7074696, Fax: 7644645, Internet: http://www.uel.ac.uk/pers/1278/rly-pres/birm.html. Head: C.M. Whitehouse
Science&Tech Museum / Open Air Museum - 1969
Steam locomotives, passenger trains driving exp. 32265

Bishop Asbury Cottage, Newton Rd, Great Barr, Birmingham B43 6HN - T: (0121) 5530759, Fax: 5255167, Internet: http://www.sandwell.gov.uk/heritage. Head: Catherine Nisbet
Religious Arts Museum 32266

Blakesley Hall, Blakesley Rd, Yardley, Birmingham B25 8RN - T: (0121) 7832193, Fax: 3032891, E-mail: irene.deboo@birmingham.gov.uk, Internet: http://www.bmag.org.uk. Head: Kristina Williamson
Historical Museum - 1935
Historic and archaeological objects, period rooms in Tudor house 32267

Chamberlain Museum of Pathology, c/o Medical School, University of Birmingham, Birmingham B15 2TT - T: (0121) 4144046, Fax: 4144036
Special Museum
History of medical education, human organs, anatomical coll 32268

Danford Collection of West African Art and Artefacts, c/o Centre of West African Studies, University of Birmingham, Edbaston, Birmingham B15 2TT - T: (0121) 4145128, Fax: 4143228, E-mail: cwas@bham.ac.uk. Head: Dr. S. Brown
Ethnology Museum / University Museum
Carvings, metalwork, textiles, paintings, domestic objects 32269

Ikon Gallery, 1 Oozells Sq, Brindleyplace, Birmingham B1 2HS - T: (0121) 2480708, Fax: 2480709, E-mail: art@ikon-gallery.co.uk, Internet: http://www.ikon-gallery.co.uk. Head: Jonathan Watkins
Public Gallery 32270

Jewellery Quarter Discovery Centre, 77-79 Vyse St, Hockley, Birmingham B18 6HA - T: (0121) 5543598, Fax: 5549700, Internet: http://www.bmag.org.uk. Head: Chris Rice
Decorative Arts Museum
Working jewellery factory, history of Birmingham jewellery industry 32271

Lapworth Museum of Geology, c/o School of Earth Sciences, University of Birmingham, Edgbaston Park Rd, Birmingham B15 2TT - T: (0121) 4147294, Fax: 4144942, E-mail: lapmus@bham.ac.uk, Internet: http://www.bham.ac.uk/EarthSciences/lapworth. Head: Dr. M.P. Smith
University Museum - 1880
Palaeozoic fossils of the West Midlands and Welsh Borders, UK, fossil fish, minerals, stone implements - archive 32272

Midlands Art Centre, Cannon Hill Park, Egbaston, Birmingham B12 9QH - T: (0121) 4404221, Fax: 4464372, E-mail: enquiries@mac-birmingham.org.uk, Internet: http://www.mac-birmingham.org.uk
Public Gallery 32273

Patrick Collection Motor Museum, 180 Lifford Ln, Birmingham B30 3NK - T: (0121) 4863399, Fax: 4863388. Head: J.A. Patrick
Science&Tech Museum - 1985
Motor vehicles since 1904 - reference library 32274

Sarehole Mill, Colebank Rd, Hall Green, Birmingham B13 0BD - T: (0121) 7776612, Fax: 3032891. Head: Kristina Sayle
Science&Tech Museum - 1969
Restored water mill (1760), hist of rural life, corn production, connections with Matthew Bovlton and J.R.R. Tolkien 32275

Selly Manor Museum, Cnr Maple and Sycamore Rds, Birmingham B30 2AE - T: (0121) 4720199, Fax: 4714101, E-mail: gillianellis@bvt.org.uk, Internet: http://www.bvt.org.uk. Head: Gillian Ellis
Decorative Arts Museum
Laurence Cadbury coll of Vernacular furniture (1500-1730) 32276

Soho House, Soho Av, off Soho Rd, Birmingham B18 5LB - T: (0121) 5549122, Fax: 5545929, Internet: http://www.birmingham.gov.uk/bmag. Head: Valerie Loggie
Science&Tech Museum
Industrial pioneer Matthew Boulton (1766-1809), Lunar Society, scientists, engineers and thinkers 32277

Thinktank, The Museum of Science and Discovery, Millennium Point, Curton St, Birmingham B4 7XG - T: (0121) 2022222/244, E-mail: faye.turner@thinktank.ac, Internet: http://www.thinktank.ac
Science&Tech Museum - 2001 32278

University Archaeology Museum, c/o Dept. Ancient History and Archaeology, University of Birmingham, Birmingham B15 2TT - T: (0121) 4145497, Fax: 4143595, E-mail: j.h.hamilton@bham.ac.uk. Head: James Hamilton
Archaeological Museum
Study coll, about 1,700 Greek, Mycenean, Roman and Egyptian artefacts 32279

Weoley Castle, Alwold Rd, Birmingham B29 5RX - T: (0121) 3031675
Historical Museum 32280

West Midlands Police Museum, 641 Stratford Rd, Sparkhill, Birmingham B11 6EA - T: (0121) 6267181, Fax: 6267066, E-mail: museumwmidpol@btinternet.com
Historical Museum
Police memorabilia 32281

Birsay

Orkney Farm and Folk Museum in Kirbuster, Kirbister Hill, Birsay KW17 2LR - T: (01856) 771268, Fax: 871560. Head: Katrina Mainland
Agriculture Museum / Folklore Museum 32282

Birstall

Oakwell Hall Country Park, Nutter Ln, Birstall WF17 9LG - T: (01924) 326240, Fax: 326249, E-mail: oakwell.hall@kirkleesmc.gov.uk. Head: Eric Brown
Historic Site - 1928
Elizabethan Manor House displayed as a family home of the 1690s, 17th c furniture, decorations - gardens 32283

Bishop Auckland

Binchester Roman Fort, Bishop Auckland DL13 - T: (01388) 663089, Fax: (0191) 3841336, E-mail: niall.hammond@durham.gov.uk, Internet: http://www.durham.gov.uk. Head: Niall Hammond
Archaeological Museum
Roman fort of Vinovia 32284

Bishopbriggs

Thomas Muir Museum, Huntershill Recreation Centre, Crowhill Rd, Bishopbriggs G66 1RW - T: (0141775) 1185
Historical Museum
Displays illustrating the life of the 18th c Scottish radical and reformer, Thomas Muir 32285

Thomas Muir of Huntersville Museum, Library, Bishopbriggs G66 1RW - T: (0141) 7751185
Local Museum 32286

Bishop's Castle

House on Crutches Museum, Tan House, Church St, Bishop's Castle SY9 5AA - T: (01588) 630007, E-mail: hocmuseum@tan-house.demon.co.uk
Local Museum
Agricultural tools, household objects, clothing, shop goods 32287

Bishop's Stortford

Bishop's Stortford Local History Museum, Cemetery Lodge, Apton Rd, Bishop's Stortford CM23 3SU. Head: W.J. Wright
Local Museum
Local trades, archaeology, architecture, local and family history 32288

Rhodes Memorial Museum and Commonwealth Centre, South Rd, Bishop's Stortford CM23 3JG - T: (01279) 651746, Fax: 467171, E-mail: rhodesmuseum@freeuk.com, Internet: http://www.hertsmuseums.org.uk. Head: Hannah Kay
Special Museum - 1938
Life and work of statesman Cecil John Rhodes, his birthplace, memorabilia, photos, documents, African ethnography and artwork 32289

Bishop's Waltham

Bishops Waltham Museum, Brook St, Bishop's Waltham SO32 1EB - T: (01489) 894970. Head: John Bosworth
Local Museum
Local history, Victorian pottery, brick making, brewing, local trades, shops 32290

Blackburn, Lancashire

Blackburn Museum and Art Gallery, Museum St, Blackburn, Lancashire BB1 7AJ - T: (01254) 667130, Fax: 680870, E-mail: stephen.whittle@blackburn.gov.uk, Internet: http://www.blackburn.gov.uk/museum. Head: E.H. Runswick
Fine Arts Museum / Historical Museum - 1874
Natural hist, geology, ethnography, applied and fine arts, Hart coll of coins, philatelics, medieval illuminated manuscripts, books, local hist, Lewis coll of Japanese prints, ornithology 32291

East Lancashire Regiment Museum, Museum St, Blackburn, Lancashire BB1 7AJ - T: (01254) 667130. Head: E.H. Runswick
Military Museum - 1934
Uniforms, medals, history of the Regiment, militaria 32292

Lewis Textile Museum, 3 Exchange St, Blackburn, Lancashire BB1 7AJ - T: (01254) 667130, Fax: 695370, E-mail: stephen.whittle@blackburn.gov.uk, Internet: http://www.blackburn.gov.uk/museum. Head: E.H. Runswick
Decorative Arts Museum / Science&Tech Museum - 1938
18th and 19th c cotton machinery, art gallery, hist of textile production 32293

Blackgang

Blackgang Sawmill and Saint Catherine's Quay, Blackgang PO38 2HN - T: (01983) 730330, Fax: 731267, E-mail: vectisventuresltd@btinternet.com, Internet: http://www.blackgangchine.com. Head: Simon Dabell
Historical Museum 32294

Blackpool

Grundy Art Gallery, Queen St, Blackpool FY1 1PX - T: (01253) 478170, Fax: 478172, Internet: http://www.blackpool.gov.uk. Head: Paul Flintoff
Fine Arts Museum - 1911
Contemporary paintings, watercolors, ivory, porcelain, Victorian and Edwardian oils, modern British painting 32295

Blackridge

Blackridge Community Museum, Library, Craig Inn Centre, Blackridge EH48 3RJ - T: (01506) 776347, Fax: 776190, E-mail: museums@westlothian.org.uk, Internet: http://www.wlonline.org
Local Museum 32296

Blaenau Ffestiniog

Gloddfa Ganol Slate Mine, Blaenau Ffestiniog LL41 3NB - T: (01766) 830664
Science&Tech Museum 32297

Llechwedd Slate Caverns, Blaenau Ffestiniog LL41 3NB - T: (01766) 830306, Fax: 831260, E-mail: llechwedd@aol.com. Head: R.H. Davies
Science&Tech Museum - 1972
The earliest slate extraction, sawing and dressing equipment, coll of narrow gauge railway stock 32298

Blaenavon

Big Pit National Mining Museum of Wales, Blaenavon NP4 9XP - T: (01495) 790311, Fax: 792618, E-mail: bigpit@nmgw.ac.uk, Internet: http://www.nmgw.ac.uk/bigpit. Head: Peter Walker
Science&Tech Museum - 1983
Preserved colliery shaft, winding engine and underground areas giving public guess & a former working colliery 32299

Pontypool and Blaenavon Railway, Council Office, High St, Blaenavon NP4 9XP - T: (01495) 792263
Science&Tech Museum
Locomotives, coaches 32300

Blair Atholl

Atholl Country Life Museum, Old School, Blair Atholl PH18 5SP - T: (01796) 481232, Fax: 481652, E-mail: janetcam@virgin.net, Internet: http://www.blairatholl.org.uk
Local Museum - 1982 32301

Blair Castle, Blair Atholl PH18 5TL - T: (01796) 481207, Fax: 481487, E-mail: office@blair-castle.co.uk, Internet: http://www.blair-castle.co.uk. Head: Geoff Crerar
Historical Museum
Furniture, paintings, arms and armour, china, lace and embroidery, masonic regalia and other treasures 32302

Blairgowrie

Errol Station Railway Heritage Centre, c/o Errol Station Trust, 48 Moyness Park Dr, Blairgowrie PH10 6LX - T: (015754) 222
Science&Tech Museum
Station from 1847 on the main Aberdeen-Glasgow line 32303

Blandford Forum

Blandford Forum Museum, Bere's Yard, Market Pl, Blandford Forum DT11 7HQ - T: (01258) 450388, E-mail: andrewsnhm@aol.com, Internet: http://www.blandford-town.co.uk. Head: Dr. Peter Andrews
Historical Museum
Illustration of the life and occupations of people in Blandford and its neighbourhood from prehistoric times to the present day, good coll of domestic equipment, local militaria and Victorian and Edwardian costumes 32304

Cavalcade of Costume, Lime Tree House, The Plocks, Blandford Forum DT11 7AA - T: (01258) 453006
Special Museum
Costumes and accessories from 18th c to 1960s 32305

Royal Signals Museum, Blandford Camp, Blandford Forum DT11 8RH - T: (01258) 482248, Fax: 482084, E-mail: royalsignalsmuseum@mail.army.mod.uk, Internet: http://www.royalsignals.army.org.uk/museum. Head: Cliff Walters
Military Museum - 1935
Communication equipment, uniforms, prints and photos relating to the corps 32306

Blantyre

David Livingstone Centre, 165 Station Rd, Blantyre G72 9BT - T: (01698) 823140, Fax: 821424, E-mail: kcarruthers@nts.org.uk. Head: Karen Carruthers
Special Museum - 1929
Memorabilia on explorer David Livingstone in the house of his birth 32307

Bletchley

Bletchley Park Exhibition, Wilton Av, Bletchley MK3 6EF - T: (01908) 640404, Fax: 274381, E-mail: info@bletchleypark.org.uk, Internet: http://www.bletchleypark.org.uk. Head: Christine Large
Science&Tech Museum / Historical Museum
Cryptography, WW 2 codebreaking computer, radar and electronics, WW 2 memorabilia 32308

Blickling

Blickling Hall, Blickling NR11 6NF - T: (01263) 738030, Fax: 731660, E-mail: abgusr@smtp.ntrust.org.uk. Head: Ian Wallis
Local Museum
Jacobian architecture, plaster ceilings, tapestries, furniture, pictures 32309

Blindley Heath

National Museum of Baking, Bannisters Bakery, Eastbourne Rd, Blindley Heath RH7 6LQ - T: (01342) 832086. Head: R. Bannister
Special Museum 32310

Bloxham

Bloxham Village Museum, Courthouse, Church St, Bloxham OX15 4ET - T: (01295) 721256, 720801, E-mail: peter.barwell@tesco.net. Head: John Phillips
Local Museum
Past life in this village 32311

Bodelwyddan

Bodelwyddan Castle Museum, Castle, Bodelwyddan LL18 5YA - T: (01745) 584060, Fax: 584563, E-mail: k.mason@btconnect.com. Head: Dr. Kevin Mason
Fine Arts Museum
Portraits, sculptures, furniture 32312

Bodiam

Bodiam Castle, Bodiam TN32 5UA - T: (01580) 830436, Fax: 830398, E-mail: kboxxx@smtp.ntrust.org.uk
Historical Museum - 1926
Relics connected with Bodiam castle 32313

Bodmin

Bodmin and Wenford Railway, General Station, Bodmin PL31 1AQ - T: (01208) 73666, Fax: 77963, Internet: http://www.members.aol.com/bodwenf
Science&Tech Museum
Various locomotives, carriages, wagons and steam crane 32314

Bodmin Town Museum, Mount Folly Sq, Bodmin PL31 2HQ - T: (01208) 77067, Fax: 79268, E-mail: bodmin.museum@ukonline.co.uk. Head: M. Tooze
Historical Museum / Natural History Museum
History and natural environment of Bodmin, coll illustrating the geology of the district and its plants and fauna 32315

Duke of Cornwall's Light Infantry Museum, The Keep, Bodmin PL31 1EG - T: (01208) 72810, Fax: 72810, E-mail: delimus@talk21.com, Internet: http://www.digiserve.com/msyoung/dcli.htm. Head: Richard Vyvyan-Robinson
Military Museum - 1923
Armaments, uniforms, military hist of the regiment, small arms, medals, badges, pictures 32316

Lanhydrock, Bodmin PL30 5AD - T: (01208) 73320, Fax: 74084, E-mail: clhlan@smtp.ntrust.org.uk, Internet: http://www.nationalkrusk.org.uk. Head: Andrea Marchington
Historical Museum
18th c and Brussels and Mortlake tapestries, family portraits painted by Kneller and Romney 32317

Pencarrow House, Washaway, Bodmin PL30 3AG - T: (01208) 841369, Fax: 841722, E-mail: pencarrow@aol.com, Internet: http://www.pencarrow.co.uk
Fine Arts Museum / Decorative Arts Museum
Family portraits, including works by Reynolds, Northcote and Devis, paintings by Samuel Scott, furnitures of the 18th and early 19th c 32318

Bognor Regis

Bognor Regis Museum, 69 High St, Bognor Regis PO21 1RY - T: (01243) 865636, Fax: (01903) 725254, E-mail: stephen_hill@arun.gov.uk. Head: Eve May
Local Museum
Social and local history (19th-20th c) 32319

Bolton

Bolton Museum and Art Gallery, Le Mans Crescent, Bolton BL1 1SE - T: (01204) 332211, Fax: 332241, E-mail: museums@bolton.gov.uk, Internet: http://www.boltonmuseums.org.uk. Head: Steve Garland
Natural History Museum / Fine Arts Museum / Local Museum - 1893
Natural hist, geology, fossils, archaeology, Egyptian coll, early English watercolors, British sculpture with works by Epstein, Moore, Hepworth, costumes, papers of inventor Samuel Crompton 32320

Bolton Museum and Art Gallery, Le Mans Crescent, Bolton BL1 1SE - T: (01204) 332211, Fax: 332241, E-mail: museums@bolton.gov.uk, Internet: http://www.boltonmuseums.org.uk. Head: Steve Garland
Natural History Museum / Fine Arts Museum / Local Museum - 1893
Natural hist, geology, fossils, archaeology, Egyptian coll, early English watercolors, British sculpture with works by Epstein, Moore, Hepworth, costumes, papers of inventor Samuel Crompton 32321

Bolton Steam Museum, Mornington Rd, Bolton BL1 4EU - T: (01257) 265003, E-mail: johnphillip@talk21.com, Internet: http://www.oldenginehouse.demon.co.uk/nmes.htm. Head: John Pillip
Science&Tech Museum
Stationary steam engines from textile industry, cotton mill 32322

Hall-I'Th'-Wood Museum, Green Way, off Crompton Way, Bolton BL1 8UA - T: (01204) 332370, E-mail: museum@bolton.gov.uk, Internet: http://www.boltonmuseums.co.uk. Head: Harold Farrell
Historical Museum - 1902
Manor dating from 1483-1648, furnishings, memorabilia of inventor Samuel Crompton 32323

Smithills Hall Museum, Smithills Dean Rd, Bolton BL1 7NP - T: (01204) 332377, E-mail: museum@bolton.gov.uk, Internet: http://www.boltonmuseums.co.uk. Head: Harold Farrell
Historical Museum - 1962
16th-19th c timbered manor, furnishings 32324

Bolventor

Potter's Museum of Curiosity, Old School, Jamaica Inn Courtyard, Bolventor PL15 7TS - T: (01566) 86838, Fax: 86838, E-mail: jamaicainn@eclipse.co.uk, Internet: http://www.jamaicainn.co.uk. Head: Rose Mullins
Special Museum - 1861
Museum founded by Walter Potter, Victorian naturalist and taxidermist, Daphne Du Maurie' novel 'Jamaica Inn', smuggling history 32325

Bo'ness

Bo'ness and Kinneil Railway, Bo'ness Station, off Union St, Bo'ness EH51 9AQ - T: (01506) 822298, Fax: 828766, E-mail: railway@srps.org.uk, Internet: http://www.srps.org.uk. Head: John Crompton
Science&Tech Museum
Scottish railways history 32326

Bo'ness Heritage Area, 17-19 North St, Bo'ness EH51 9AQ - T: (01506) 825855, Fax: 828766
Local Museum 32327

Kinneil Museum and Roman Fortlet, Duchess Anne Cottages, Kinneil Estate, Bo'ness EH51 0PR - T: (01506) 778530. Head: Maria Gillespie, Sheila Smith
Historical Museum / Archaeological Museum - 1976
Estate history, medieval village and church, excavations 32328

Museum of Communication, POB 12556, Bo'ness EH51 9YX - T: (01506) 823424. Head: Prof. C.W. Davidson
Science&Tech Museum
Coll of telephones, radio, telegraphy, computing, televion covering 20th c 32329

Boosbeck

Margrove - South Cleveland Heritage Centre, Margrove Park, Boosbeck TS12 3BZ - T: (01287) 610368, Fax: 610368
Local Museum / Natural History Museum
Moors, valley and coast of South Cleveland, historic maps 32330

Bootle

Art Gallery and Museum, Central Library, Stanley Rd, Bootle L20 6AG
Fine Arts Museum / Decorative Arts Museum
Pottery, ceramics, rotating exhibits, English porcelain 32331

Boroughbridge

Aldborough Roman Town Museum, Front St, Aldborough, Boroughbridge YO51 9ES - T: (01423) 322768
Archaeological Museum / Historic Site 32332

Boscombe

Museum of Childhood, 39 Ashley Rd, Boscombe BH5 - T: (01202) 33173
Special Museum
Dolls, comics, Meccano sets, Hornby trains, model ships and boats, jigsaws, games, toys and books 32333

Boston

Boston Guildhall Museum, South St, Boston PE21 6HT - T: (01205) 365954, E-mail: heritage@originalboston.freeserve.co.uk. Head: Andrew Crabtree
Local Museum - 1926
15th c building with medieval kitchen, cells used by Pilgrim Fathers pending trial in 1607, Council Chamber, Courtroom & Banqueting Hall Displays on archaeology, costume & textiles, ceramics, militaria, coins & tokens & Boston's maritime heritage 32334

Botley

Hampshire Farm Museum, Country Park, Brook Ln, Botley SO3 2ER - T: (01489) 787055. Head: Barbara Newbury
Agriculture Museum - 1984
Tools, implements machinery, domestic buildings 32335

Bourn

Wysing Arts, Fox Rd, Bourn CB3 7TX - T: (01954) 718881, Fax: 718500, E-mail: info@wysing.demon.co.uk, Internet: http://www.wysing.demon.co.uk. Head: Trystan Hawkins
Fine Arts Museum 32336

Bournemouth

Bournemouth Natural Science Society Museum, 39 Christchurch Rd, Bournemouth BH1 3NS - T: (01202) 553525, E-mail: administrator@bnss.org.uk, Internet: http://www.bnss.org.uk
Natural History Museum - 1903
Local natural hist, archaeology, zoology, herbarium (Dorset plants) entomology, geology, egyptology - botanical garden, library 32337

Bournemouth Transport Museum, Bldg 101, NW Industrial Estate, Bournemouth BH23 6NW
Science&Tech Museum
Coll of busses 32338

Russell-Cotes Art Gallery and Museum, East Cliff, Bournemouth BH1 3AA - T: (01202) 451800, Fax: 451851, E-mail: dedge@russell-cotes.demon.co.uk, Internet: http://www.russell-cotes.bournemouth.gov.uk. Head: Victoria Pirie
Fine Arts Museum / Ethnology Museum - 1922
Victorian painting, Japanese coll, ethnography from Oceania, New Zealand and Africa 32339

Shelley Rooms, Boscombe Manor, Beechwood Av, Bournemouth BH5 1NB - T: (01202) 303571, Fax: 451851, E-mail: dedge@russell-cotes.co.uk, Internet: http://www.russell.cotes.bournemouth.gov.uk. Head: Victoria Pirie
Special Museum - 1979
Memorabilia of P.B. Shelley, library of romantic works - library 32340

Bourton-on-the-Water

Cotswold Motoring Museum and Toy Collection, Old Mill, Bourton-on-the-Water GL5 2BY - T: (01451) 821255, E-mail: motormuseum@csma-netlink.co.uk. Head: Michael Tambini
Science&Tech Museum - 1978
Vintage enamel advertising signs, toys, cars 32341

Bovey Tracey

Devon Guild of Craftsmen Gallery, Riverside Mill, Bovey Tracey TQ13 9AF - T: (01626) 832223, Fax: 834220, E-mail: devonguild@crafts.org, Internet: http://www.crafts.org.uk. Head: Alexander Murdin
Historical Museum
Craftwork, changing exhibits invited contributors work in the gallery 32342

Bovington

Tank Museum, Bovington BH20 6JG - T: (01929) 405096, Fax: 405360, E-mail: info@tankmuseum.co.uk, Internet: http://www.tankmuseum.co.uk. Head: John Woodward
Military Museum - 1923
Hist of tank units, small arms and ammunition 32343

Bowness-on-Windermere

Blackwell - The Arts and Crafts House, Bowness-on-Windermere LA23 3JR - T: (015394) 46139, Fax: 88486, E-mail: info@blackwell.org.uk, Internet: http://www.blackwell.org.uk. Head: Edward King
Decorative Arts Museum - 2001
Rare surviving house from the arts and crafts movement, original interior, furniture, applied arts, crafts 32344

Steamboat Museum, Rayrigg Rd, Bowness-on-Windermere LA23 1BN - T: (015394) 45565, E-mail: steamboat@insites.co.uk
Science&Tech Museum 32345

Bracknell

Look Out Discovery Centre, Nine Mile Ride, Bracknell RG12 7QW - T: (01344) 354400, Fax: 354422, E-mail: thelookout@bracknell-forest.gov.uk, Internet: http://www.bracknell-forest.gov.uk/lookout
Science&Tech Museum 32346

South Hill Park Arts Centre, Bracknell RG12 7PA - T: (01344) 427272, Fax: 411427, E-mail: visual.art@southhillpark.org.uk
Public Gallery 32347

Bradford

Bowling Hall Museum, Bowling Hall Rd, Bradford BD4 7LP - T: (01274) 723057, Fax: 726220, Internet: http://www.bradford.gov.uk. Head: Paul Lawson
Local Museum - 1915
House with historic furniture, 17th and 18th c plaster ceilings, 17th-18th c furniture, watercolors, local history 32348

Bradford Industrial Museum and Horses at work, Moorside Rd, Eccleshill, Bradford BD2 3HP - T: (01274) 631756, Fax: 636362, E-mail: industrial.museum@bradford.gov.uk. Head: Paul W.G. Lawson
Science&Tech Museum / Historical Museum
History of local industry, industrial archaeology, wool, textiles, transport, horses, victorian mill 32349

Cartwright Hall Art Gallery, Lister Park, Bradford BD9 4NS - T: (01274) 751212, Fax: 481045, E-mail: cartwright.hall@bradford.gov.uk, Internet: http://www.bradford.gov.uk/tourism/museums. Head: Mark Suggitt
Fine Arts Museum - 1904
Old and modern British painting, drawings, watercolors, modern prints 32350

Colour Museum, 1 Providence St, Bradford BD1 2PW - T: (01274) 390955, Fax: 392888, E-mail: museum@sdc.org.uk, Internet: http://www.sdc.org.uk. Head: Sarah Burge
Special Museum - 1978
Textile industry 32351

Gallery II, c/o University of Bradford, Chesham Bldg, off Great Horton Rd, Bradford BD7 1DP - T: (01274) 383365, Fax: 305340
Fine Arts Museum / University Museum 32352

National Museum of Photography, Film and Television, Manchester Rd and Hallings, Bradford BD1 1NQ - T: (01274) 202030, Fax: 723155, E-mail: talk.nmpft@nmsi.ac.uk, Internet: http://www.nmpft.org.uk. Head: Amanda Nevill
Science&Tech Museum - 1983
Art, history and science of photography, film, television and digital imaging 32353

Peace Museum, 10 Peace Hall Yard, Bradford BD7 8UF - T: (01274) 780241, Fax: 780240, E-mail: peacemuseum@bradford.gov.uk, Internet: http://www.bradford.gov.uk/tourism/museums/peacemuseum.htm. Head: Craig Bowen
Historical Museum
Peace, non-violence and conflict resolution 32354

Bradford-on-Avon

Bradford-on-Avon Museum, Bridge St, Bradford-on-Avon BA15 1BY - T: (01225) 863280. Head: Roger Clark
Local Museum
Local history 32355

Bradford-on-Tone

Sheppy's Farm and Cider Museum, c/o R.J. Sheppy & Son, Three Bridges, Bradford-on-Tone TA4 1ER - T: (01823) 461233, Fax: 461712, E-mail: info@sheppyscider.com, Internet: http://www.sheppyscider.com. Head: Richard Sheppy
Science&Tech Museum
Old cidermaking equipment, agricultural implements and coopers' and other craftsmen's tools 32356

Brading

Aylmer Military Collection and Isle of Wight Home Guard Museum, Nunwell House, Brading PO36 0JQ - T: (01983) 407240. Head: John Alymer
Military Museum 32357

Isle of Wight Wax Works, 46 High St, Brading PO36 0DQ - T: (01983) 407286, Fax: 402112, E-mail: info@iwwaxworks.co.uk, Internet: http://www.iwwaxworks.co.uk
Special Museum - 1965
Wax tableaux of Island, national and international from Roman times to present day, includes the oldest house on the Island part dating 1066 AD instruments of torture from the Royal castle of Nuremberg, world of nature 32358

Lilliput Antique Doll and Toy Museum, High St, Brading PO36 0DJ - T: (01983) 407231, E-mail: lilliput.museum@btconnect.com, Internet: http://www.lilliputmuseum.com. Head: Graham K. Munday
Special Museum - 1974 32359

Roman Villa, Morton Old Rd, Brading PO36 0EN - T: (01983) 406223, Fax: 406223, Internet: http://www.brading.co.uk/romanvilla.html. Head: E.J. Guy
Archaeological Museum 32360

Braemar

Braemar Castle, Braemar AB35 5XQ - T: (013397) 41219, Fax: 41252, Internet: http://www.braemar-castle.co.uk
Historical Museum
Historic seat of the Farquharsons of Invercauld 32361

Braintree

Braintree District Museum, Manor St, Braintree CM7 3HW - T: (01376) 325266, Fax: 344345, Internet: http://www.braintree.gov.uk/museum. Head: Jean Grice
Local Museum
Textile and engineering industries, archaeology, social history, textiles, large photographic coll - Textile archive 32362

Working Silk Museum, New Mills, South St, Braintree CM7 3GB - T: (01376) 553393, Fax: 330642, Internet: http://www.humphries-weaving.co.uk. Head: Judy Monk
Fine Arts Museum
Textiles, 19th c machines, hand loom silk weavers 32363

Bramhall

Bramall Hall, Bramhall Park, Bramhall SK7 3NX - T: (0161) 4853708, Fax: 4866959
Historic Site
14th to 16th c half-timbered Hall 32364

Brandon

Brandon Heritage Museum, George St, Brandon IP27 0BX - T: (01225) 863280, Fax: (01204) 391352
Local Museum - 1991
Flint, fur and forestry industries, local history 32365

Braunton

Braunton and District Museum, Bakehouse Centre, Caen St, Braunton EX33 1AA - T: (01271) 816688, E-mail: braunton@devonmuseums.net, Internet: http://www.devonmuseums.net/braunton. Head: Kathy Lehan
Local Museum
Maritime, agriculture and village life 32366

Breamore

Breamore Countryside Museum, Breamore SP6 2DF - T: (01725) 512468, Fax: 512858, E-mail: breamore@estate.fsnet.co.uk. Head: Sir Edward Hulse
Local Museum - 1972
Hand tools, tractors, steam engines, blacksmith's and wheel-wright's shops, brewery, dairy, farmworkerscottage, harnessmakers, boot makers, village general store, village school, laundry, coopers', baker's and clockmaker's shop, village garage 32367

Breamore House, near Fordingbridge, Breamore SP6 2DF - T: (01725) 512233, Fax: 512858. Head: E. Hulse
Fine Arts Museum / Decorative Arts Museum / Folklore Museum - 1953
17th and 18th c furniture and paintings (mainly Dutch), tapestries, porcelain, 14 paintings of the intermingling of Indian races (c 1725), development of agricultural machinery, farm implements, aspects of a self-sufficient village 32368

Brechin

Brechin Museum, 10 Saint Ninian's Sq, Brechin DD9 7AD - T: (01356) 622687, Fax: 624271, E-mail: brechin.library@angus.gov.uk
Local Museum
Local history, antiquities 32369

Glenesk Folk Museum, The Retreat, Glenesk, Brechin DD9 7YT - T: (01356) 670254
Folklore Museum - 1955
Local rural life, period rooms, Victoriana 32370

Brecon

Brecknock Museum and Art Gallery, Captain's Walk, Brecon LD3 7DW - T: (01874) 624121, Fax: 611281, E-mail: brecknock.museum@powys.gov.uk. Head: David Moore
Local Museum - 1928
Natural and local hist, archaeology, ceramics, costumes, early Christian monuments, art - art gallery 32371

South Wales Borderers and Monmouthshire Regimental Museum of the Royal Regiment of Wales, The Barracks, Brecon LD3 7EB - T: (01874) 613310, Fax: 613275, E-mail: swb@rrw.org.uk, Internet: http://www.rrw.org.uk. Head: Martin Everett
Military Museum - 1934
Regimental hist, medals, armaments, Anglo-Zulu War 1879 - archive 32372

Brentwood

Brentwood Museum, Cementery Lodge, Lorne Rd, Brentwood CM14 5HH - T: (01277) 224012. Head: Pam Guiver, Audrey Puddy, Mary Humphreys
Local Museum
Social and domestic items, memorabilia from world wars, toys, games, furniture and costumes 32373

Brenzett

Brenzett Aeronautical Museum, Ivychurch Rd, Brenzett TN29 0EE - T: (01797) 344747, Internet: http://www.brenzettaeromuseum.co.uk. Head: Frank J. Beckley
Military Museum - 1972
Former Womens Land Army Hostel, coll incl engines and other relicts from British and American wartime aircraft, the 4 1/2 ton dam-buster bomb, designed by Sir Barnes Wallis in 1943, Vampire MKII, Dakota Nose, Canberra 32374

Brenzett Museum → Brenzett Aeronautical Museum

Bridgend

South Wales Police Museum, Cowbridge Rd, Bridgend CF31 3SU - T: (01656) 869315, Fax: 869477. Head: Jeremy Glenn
Special Museum - 1950
Policing in Glamorgan from the Celts to the present day, Edwardian police station, wartime tableau 32375

Bridgnorth

Bridgnorth Northgate Museum, Burgess Hall, High St, Bridgnorth WV16 4ER - T: (01746) 761859. Head: Alan Webb
Local Museum
Local history, firemarks, tokens, coins, agriculture 32376

Childhood and Costume Museum, Newmarket Bldg, Postern Gate, Bridgnorth WV16 4AA - T: (01746) 768550, 764636. Head: Jayne Griffiths
Folklore Museum - 1951
Clothes and accessories (1860-1960), toys, games, Victorian nursery, textiles, mineral coll 32377

Midland Motor Museum, Stanmore House, Stourbridge Rd, Bridgnorth WV15 6DT - T: (01746) 761761
Science&Tech Museum 32378

Bridgwater

Blake Museum, Blake St, Bridgwater TA6 3NB - T: (01278) 456127, Fax: 446412, E-mail: museums@sedgemoor.gov.uk, Internet: http://www.sedgemoor.gov.uk
Historical Museum - 1926
Local hist, archaeology, life and work of Admiral Blake (1598-1657) in the supposed place of his birth, relics on the Battle of Sedgemoor 32379

Somerset Brick and Tile Museum, East Quay, Bridgwater TA6 3NB - T: (01278) 426088, Fax: 320229, E-mail: county-museum@somerset.gov.uk, Internet: http://www.somerset.gov.uk/museums. Head: David Dawson
Historical Museum
Brick and tile industry 32380

Westonzoyland Pumping Station Museum, Hoopers Ln, Westonzoyland, Bridgwater, mail addr: c/o Mrs. B. Eaton, 38 Holway Hill, Taunton TA1 2HB - T: (01823) 275795, E-mail: wzlet@btinternet.com, Internet: http://www.btinternet.com/~wzlet
Science&Tech Museum - 1977
Land drainage, steam pumps and engines 32381

Bridlington

Bayle Museum, Baylegate, Bridlington YO16 5TW. Head: B.R. Langton
Local Museum - 1920
Victorian kitchen, Green Howard's Regemental room, courtroom of 1388, the monastic gatehouse of the Augustinian Priory 32382

Bridlington Harbour Museum, Harbour Rd, Bridlington YO15 2NR - T: (01262) 670148, Fax: 602041
Historical Museum 32383

Sewerby Hall Art Gallery and Museum, Museum of East Yorkshire, Church Ln, Sewerby, Bridlington YO1S 1EA - T: (01262) 677874, Fax: 674265, E-mail: sewerbyhall@yahoo.com, Internet: http://www.bridlington.net/sewerby. Head: J. Ginnever
Local Museum / Fine Arts Museum - 1936
19th c marine paintings by Henry Redmore of Hull, early 19th c local watercolours, local archaeology, farm implements, vintage motorcycles, horse-drawn vehicles, military uniforms with local associations, fossils from the nearby chalk cliffs, the various seabirds and waders found in the area, memorabilia on air-woman Amy Johnson 32384

Bridport

Bridport Museum, South St, Bridport DT6 3NR - T: (01308) 422116, Fax: 420659
Local Museum
Local hist, archaeology, natural hist, geology, trades, costumes, Victorian relics, net weaving 32385

Harbour Life Exhibition, Salt House, West Bay, Bridport DT6 4SA - T: (01308) 420997, Fax: 420659
Local Museum
Industry, history of Bridport Harbour 32386

Brierfield

Neville Blakey Museum of Locks, Keys and Safes, Burnley Rd, Brierfield BB9 5AD - T: (01282) 613593, Fax: 617550, E-mail: sales@blakeys.fsworld.co.uk. Head: W.H. Neville Blakey
Special Museum 32387

Brierley Hill

Brierley Hill Glass Museum, Moor St, Brierley Hill
Decorative Arts Museum - 1923
Local and foreign glass work, cameo glass by George Woodall 32388

Brighouse

Smith Art Gallery, Halifax Rd, Brighouse HD6 2AA - T: (01484) 719222, Fax: 719222
Public Gallery - 1907
Paintings, English watercolors, 19th c woodcarvings 32389

Brightlingsea

Brightlingsea Museum, 1 Duke St, Brightlingsea CO7 0EA. Head: Alfred Wakeling
Local Museum
Maritime and oyster industry, local history 32390

Brighton

Barlow Collection of Chinese Ceramics, Bronzes and Jades, c/o University of Sussex, Falmer, Brighton BN1 9QU - T: (01273) 606755 ext 3506, E-mail: k.mcloughlin@sussex.ac.uk, Internet: http://www.sussex.ac.uk/library/gen-info/barlow.html
Decorative Arts Museum
Chinese jades, bronzes, porcelain and ceramics 32391

Booth Museum of Natural History, 194 Dyke Rd, Brighton BN1 5AA - T: (01273) 292777, Fax: 292778, E-mail: boothmus@pavilion.co.uk. Head: J.A. Cooper, G. Legg
Natural History Museum - 1874
British birds, dioramas, butterflies, nymphalid butterflies, fossils - library 32392

Brighton Fishing Museum, 201 Kings Rd Arches, Brighton BN1 1NB - T: (01273) 723064. Head: Andy Durr
Special Museum - 1994
Boats, artifacts, pictures - film and historical archive 32393

Brighton Museum and Art Gallery, 4-5 Pavilion Bldgs, Church St, Brighton BN1 1EE - T: (01273) 290900, Fax: 292841, E-mail: visitor.services@brighton-hove.gov.uk, Internet: http://www.museum.brighton-hove.gov.uk. Head: Jessica Rutherford
Fine Arts Museum / Decorative Arts Museum / Local Museum - 1873
Fine coll of local and practical importance, Art Nouveau and Art Deco, fine art and non-Western art, costumes, Willett coll of pottery and porcelain - My Brighton - interactive local hist project 32394

Preston Manor, Preston Park, Brighton BN1 6SD - T: (01273) 292770, Fax: 292771, E-mail: david.beevers@brighton-hove.gov.uk, Internet: http://www.museums.brighton-hove.gov.uk. Head: David Beevers
Decorative Arts Museum - 1933
Macquoid bequest English and Continental period furniture, silver, pictures, panels of stained glass, 16th-19th c original 17th leather wall-hangings - archives 32395

Rottingdean Grange Art Gallery and National Toy Museum, The Rottingdean Green, Brighton BN2 7HA - T: (01273) 301004
Fine Arts Museum / Special Museum 32396

Royal Pavilion, Brighton Museum and Art Gallery, 4-5 Pavilion Bldgs, Church St, Brighton BN1 1EE - T: (01273) 290900, Fax: 292871, E-mail: visitor.services@brighton-hove.gov.uk, Internet: http://www.royalpavilion.brighton.co.uk. Head: Jessica Rutherford
Fine Arts Museum / Decorative Arts Museum - 1851
Seaside palace of George IV - designed by John Nash, exterior - Indian design - interiors in Chinese taste, items on loan from H.M. The Queen, 18th c gardens 32397

Stanmer Rural Museum, Stanmer Park, Brighton BN1 7HN - T: (01273) 509563. Head: R.A. Stopps
Folklore Museum - 1975
Rare horse trave, rural tools, local archaeological finds, agricultural implements 32398

University of Brighton Gallery, Grand Parade, Brighton - T: (01273) 643012, Fax: 643038, E-mail: c.l.matthews@bton.ac.uk, Internet: http://www.bton.ac.uk/gallery-theatre. Head: Sir David Watson
Public Gallery 32399

Bristol

Arnolfini, 16 Narrow Quai, Bristol BS1 4QA - T: (0117) 9299191, Fax: 9253876, E-mail: arnolfini@arnolfini.demon.co.uk, Internet: http://www.arnolfini.demon.co.uk. Head: Caroline Collier
Fine Arts Museum / Public Gallery
Contemporary and 20th c art 32400

Ashton Court Visitor Centre, Stable Block, Ashton Court Estate, Long Ashton, Bristol BS18 9JN - T: (0117) 9639174, Fax: 9532143. Head: Cellan Rhys-Michael
Local Museum
History of this landscape, temporary exhibits 32401

Blaise Castle House Museum, Henbury Rd, Bristol BS10 7QS - T: (0117) 9506789, Fax: 9593475, Internet: http://www.bristol-city.gov.uk/museums. Head: David J. Eveleigh
Local Museum - 1947
Regional social history, agricultural history, domestic life, costumes, toys, dairy 32402

Bristol City Museum and Art Gallery, Queens Rd, Bristol BS8 1RL - T: (0117) 9223571, Fax: 9222047, E-mail: general_museum@bristol-city.gov.uk, Internet: http://www.bristol-city.gov.uk/museums. Head: Stephen Price
Local Museum / Fine Arts Museum - 1905
Archaeology, geology, natural hist, transportation and technology of the area, ethnography, Classical and Egyptian finds, numismatics, local hist, fine art 32403

Bristol Industrial Museum, Princes Wharf, Wapping Rd, Bristol BS1 4RN - T: (0117) 9251470, Fax: 9297318, E-mail: andy_l_king@bristol-city.gov.uk, Internet: http://www.bristol-city.gov.uk/museums. Head: Andy King
Science&Tech Museum - 1978
Models of early ships, flight deck of Concorde, buses, cars and motorcycles, ships, cranes and railway stock, slave trade 32404

British Empire and Commonwealth Museum, Clock Tower Yard, Temple Meads, Bristol BS1 6QH - T: (0117) 9254980, 9292688, Fax: 9254983, E-mail: staff@empiremuseum.co.uk, Internet: http://www.empiremuseum.co.uk
Historical Museum
Social history, photographies - library, oral history archive 32405

Georgian House, 7 Great George St, Bristol BS1 5RR - T: (0117) 9211362, Fax: 9222047, E-mail: general_museum@bristol-city.gov.uk, Internet: http://www.bristol-city.gov.uk/museums. Head: Karin Walton
Decorative Arts Museum - 1937
Period furnishings 32406

Guild Gallery, 68 Park St, Bristol BS1 5JY - T: (0117) 9265548, Fax: 9255659, E-mail: bristolguild@70parkst.freeserve.co.uk. Head: John Stops
Public Gallery
Applied art, exhibits of paintings, prints, crafts 32407

Harvey's Wine Museum, 12 Denmark St, Bristol BS1 5DQ - T: (0117) 9275036, Fax: 9275001, Internet: http://www.j-harvey.co.uk. Head: Juliet Hawkes
Special Museum - 1965
18th c English drinking glass, antique delanters, bottles, corkscrews, bottle tickets and other wine-related artefacts and furniture 32408

Kings Weston Roman Villa, c/o City Museum and Art Gallery, Long Cross, Lawrence Weston, Bristol BS11 0LP - T: (0117) 9223571, Internet: http://www.bristol-city.gov.uk/museums
Archaeological Museum
Farmhouse with bathhouse 32409

Maritime Heritage Centre with SS Great Britain, Wapping Wharf, Gasferry Rd, Bristol BS1 6TY - T: (0117) 9260680, Fax: 9255788, E-mail: enquiries@ss-great-britain.com, Internet: http://www.ss-great-britain.com. Head: Matthew Tanner
Historical Museum
History of shipbuilding in Bristol 32410

Red Lodge, Park Row, Bristol BS1 5LJ - T: (0117) 9211360, Fax: 9222047, E-mail: general_museum@bristol-city.gov.uk, Internet: http://www.bristol-city.gov.uk/museums. Head: Karin Walton
Decorative Arts Museum
Elizabethan house, modified 18th c, furnishings 32411

University of Bristol Theatre Collection, c/o Department of Drama, Cantocks Close, Bristol BS8 1UP - T: (0117) 9287836, Fax: 9287832, E-mail: theatre-collection@bristol.ac.uk, Internet: http://www.bris.ac.uk/depts/drama. Head: Sarah Cuthill
Performing Arts Museum / University Museum
Written and graphic material, theatre history - archives 32412

Brixham

Brixham Museum, Bolton Cross, Brixham TQ5 8LZ - T: (01803) 856267, E-mail: mail@brixhamheritage.org.uk, Internet: http://www.brixhamheritage.org.uk. Head: Dr. Philip L. Armitage
Local Museum - 1958
Fishing, shipping, maritime and local history, archaeology 32413

Golden Hind Museum, The Quay, Habour, Brixham TQ5 8AW - T: (01803) 856223, E-mail: postmaster@goldenhind.co.uk, Internet: http://www.goldenhind.co.uk
Special Museum
Full sized replica of Sir Francis Drake's ship (16th c) 32414

Broadclyst

Paulise de Bush Costume Collection, Killerton House, Broadclyst EX5 3LE - T: (01392) 881345, Fax: 883112, E-mail: dklset@smtp.ntrust.org.uk. Head: Shelley Tobin
Decorative Arts Museum - 1978
Coll of costumes, which is displayed in a series of rooms furnished in different periods, from the 18th c to the present day 32415

Broadstairs

Bleak House, Fort Rd, Broadstairs CT10 1HD - T: (01843) 862224. Head: L.A. Longhi
Special Museum - 1958
Memorabilia on writer Charles Dickens (1811-1870) in the house where he wrote 'David Copperfield' and 'Bleak House' 32416

Crampton Tower Museum, Broadway, Broadstairs CT10 2AB - T: (01843) 864446. Head: Robert Tolhurst
Science&Tech Museum - 1978
Thomas Russell Crampton memorabilia, designer of locomotives, submarine telegraphic cable, gas and water works 32417

Dickens House Museum Broadstairs, 2 Victoria Parade, Broadstairs CT10 1QS - T: (01843) 863453, 861232, Fax: 863453, E-mail: aleeeault@aol.com. Head: Lee Ault
Special Museum - 1973
Dickens memorabila, costume and Victoriana 32418

Broadway

Broadway Magic Experience, 76 High St, Broadway WR12 7AJ - T: (01386) 858323, E-mail: bearsanddolls@hotmail.com, Internet: http://www.jks.org/broadwaybear-sanddolls.html
Special Museum
Automated childhood scenes 32419

Snowshill Manor, Snowshill, Broadway WR12 7JU - T: (01386) 852410, Fax: 852410, E-mail: snowshill@smtp.ntrust.org.uk, Internet: http://www.ntrustsevern.org.uk
Decorative Arts Museum - 1951
Wade Coll, Chinese and Japanese objects, nautical instruments, Japanese Samurai armour, musical instruments, costumes, toys, spinning and weaving tools, bicycles, farm wagon models 32420

Brockenhurst

Beaulieu Abbey Exhibition of Monastic Life, Beaulieu, Brockenhurst SO42 7ZN - T: (01590) 612345, Fax: 612624, E-mail: susan.tomkins@beaulieu.co.uk, Internet: http://www.beaulieu.co.uk. Head: Lord Montagu of Beaulieu, Kenneth G. Robinson
Religious Arts Museum - 1952
Story of daily life for the Cistercian Monks, who founded the Abbey in 1204 32421

National Motor Museum, John Montagu Bldg, Beaulieu, Brockenhurst SO42 7ZN - T: (01590) 612345, Fax: 612655, E-mail: info@beaulieu.co.uk. Head: Lord Montagu of Beaulieu
Science&Tech Museum - 1952
Cars, motorcycles, commercial vehicles, racing cars, photographs, books, film - archives 32422

Brodick

Arran Heritage Museum, Rosaburn, Brodick KA27 8DP - T: (01770) 302636. Head: A. Sillaks
Local Museum
Agricultural machinery, geology, archaeology, smiddy, naval photos 32423

Brodick Castle, Brodick KA27 8HY - T: (01770) 302202, Fax: 302312. Head: Ken Thorburn
Fine Arts Museum / Decorative Arts Museum
Beckford silver, porcelain, paintings, Duke of Hamilton and Earl of Rochford sport photos and trophies - garden 32424

Brokerswood

Phillips Countryside Museum, Woodland Park, Brokerswood BA13 4EH - T: (01373) 823880, Fax: 858474. Head: Barry Capon
Natural History Museum - 1971
Natural history and forestry, botany, ornithology 32425

Bromham

Bromham Mill and Art Gallery, Bridge End, Bromham MK43 8LP - T: (01234) 824330, Fax: 228531, E-mail: bromhmill@deed.bedfordshire.gov.uk, Internet: http://www.borneo.co.uk/bromham_mill. Head: M. Kenworthy
Public Gallery
Art, industrial heritage, natural environment 32426

Bromsgrove

Avoncroft Museum of Historic Buildings, Redditch Rd, Stoke Heath, Bromsgrove B60 4JR - T: (01527) 831886, Fax: 876934, E-mail: avoncroft1@compuserve.com, Internet: http://www.avoncroft.org.uk. Head: Simon Penn
Open Air Museum - 1969
16th c inn, 19th c post mill, granary and barn, 15th c merchant's house, hand-made nail and chain workshops, medieval guesten hall roof, 17th c cockpit, 18th c ice-house, perry mill, National Telephone Kiosk coll, 20th c pre-fab 32427

Bromsgrove Museum, 26 Birmingham Rd, Bromsgrove B61 0DD - T: (01527) 577983, Fax: 577983
Historical Museum - 1972
Social and industrial hist of the area, with exhibits covering glass, button, nail and salt-making, social hist of the 19th and early 20th c 32428

Bronwydd Arms

Gwili Steam Railway, Station, Bronwydd Arms SA33 6HT - T: (01267) 230666, Internet: http://www.gwili-railway.co.uk
Science&Tech Museum
Steam and diesel locomotives, carriages and wagons 32429

Brook

Agriculture Museum Brook, The Street, Brook TN25 5PF - T: (01304) 824969, Fax: 824969, E-mail: brian@bwimsett.freeserve.co.uk. Head: Brian Wimsett
Agriculture Museum 32430

Broseley

Clay Tobacco Pipe Museum, The Flat, Duke St, Broseley TF12 5LX - T: (01952) 882445. Head: Michael Vanns
Special Museum
Clay tobacco pipe factory 32431

Buckfastleigh

Buckfast Abbey, Buckfastleigh TQ11 0EE - T: (01364) 642519, Fax: 643891
Local Museum 32432

South Devon Railway, The Station, Buckfastleigh TQ11 0DZ - T: (01364) 642338, 643536, Fax: 642170, Internet: http://www.southdevon-railway.org. Head: Harold Eldridge
Science&Tech Museum
17 steam locomotives, 3 heritage diesels, 27 carriages, 35 freight wagons 32433

The Valiant Soldier, 79 Fore St, Buckfastleigh TQ11 0BS - T: (01364) 644522, E-mail: enquiries@valiantsoldier.org.uk. Head: Kate Johnson
Local Museum
Pub fittings, furniture, bar ephemera, promotional and domestic items, history coll 32434

Buckhaven

Buckhaven Museum, Library, College St, Buckhaven KY1 1LD - T: (01592) 412860, Fax: 412870
Historical Museum
History and techniques of the local fishing industry, life of families who earned a living from it, recreations of interiors of home of past generations of Buckhaven people 32435

Buckie

Buckie Drifter Maritime Museum, Freuchny Rd, Buckie AB56 1TT - T: (01542) 834646, Fax: 835995, Internet: http://www.moray.org/area/bdrifter/mbdrifter.html
Historical Museum
History of the town of Buckie, fishing industry, boats and techniques employed, navigation, achievements of the local lifeboat 32436

Peter Anson Gallery, Townhouse West, Cluny Pl, Buckie AB56 1HB - T: (01542) 832121, Fax: (01309) 675863, E-mail: alasdair.joyce@techleis.moray.gov.uk, Internet: http://www.moray.org/museums/ansongal
Fine Arts Museum
Watercolours by marine artist Peter Anson 32437

Buckingham

Buckingham Movie Museum, Printers Mews, Market Hill, Buckingham MK18 1JX - T: (01280) 816758
Special Museum
Coll of 200 projectors and 100 cine-cameras and accessories 32438

Old Gaol Museum, Market Hill, Buckingham MK18 1JX - T: (01280) 823020, Fax: 823020. Head: John Roberts
Local Museum
Story of Buckingham, military history 32439

Buckler's Hard

Buckler's Hard Village Maritime Museum, Beaulieu, Buckler's Hard SO42 7XB - T: (01590) 616203, Fax: 616283. Head: Mike Lucas
Science&Tech Museum - 1963
Shipping, 18th c naval vessels, model of Hard in 1803, memorabilia on Nelson, Sir Francis Chichester, display cottages 18th c, recreation of vinage life, with models 32440

Bude

Bude-Stratton Museum, The Wharf, Bude EX23 8LG - T: (01288) 353576, Fax: 353576, E-mail: theclerk@bstc.freeserve.co.uk. Head: Harvey Kendall
Historical Museum - 1976
Hist and working of the canal, by means of early photographs, models, drawings, plans and maps, development of Bude, shipwrecks and hist of the local lifeboat, railway, military and social hist 32441

Budleigh Salterton

Fairlynch Museum, 27 Fore St, Budleigh Salterton EX9 6NG - T: (01395) 442666. Head: Priscilla Hull
Local Museum
Prehistory, art, local history, ecology of Lower Otter Valley, geology 32442

Otterton Mill Centre and Working Museum, Fore Otterton St, Budleigh Salterton EX9 7HG - T: (01395) 568521, Fax: 568521, E-mail: ottertonmill@ukonline.co.uk, Internet: http://www.ottertonmill.co.uk. Head: Dr. Desna Greenhow
Science&Tech Museum - 1977
Use of water to drive mill machinery, production processes of flour, displays of crafts, fine arts and historical items - gallery, lace exhibition 32443

Bulwell

South Nottinghamshire Hussars Museum, TA Centre, Hucknall Ln, Bulwell NG6 8AQ - T: (0115) 9272251, Fax: 975420. Head: G.E. Aldridge
Military Museum
Regimental uniforms, models of vehicles and guns from WW II, paintings and trophies 32444

Bunbury

Bunbury Watermill, Mill Ln, off Bowes Gate Rd, Bunbury CW6 9PP
Science&Tech Museum 32445

Bungay

Bungay Museum, Council Office, Bungay NR35 1EE - T: (01986) 892176, 893155. Head: Christopher R.M. Theol
Local Museum
Local history, fossils, flint implements, coins, J.B. Scott memorabilia 32446

Burford

Tolsey Museum, 126 High St, Burford OX18 4QU - T: (01993) 823196. Head: Christopher Walker
Local Museum - 1960
Local governmental history, local crafts, social history 32447

Burghead

Burghead Museum, 16-18 Grant St, Burghead
Local Museum 32448

Burnham-on-Crouch

Burnham Museum, Coronation Rd, Burnham-on-Crouch CM0 8AA - T: (01621) 782670, E-mail: pfhammond@btinternet.com, Internet: http://www.burnham.gov.uk
Local Museum - 1981
archives 32449

Mangapps Farm Railway Museum, Mangapps Farm, Burnham-on-Crouch CM0 8QQ - T: (01621) 784898, Fax: 783833, Internet: http://www.mangapps.co.uk
Science&Tech Museum
Good wagons, carriages, steam and diesel locomotives, railway artefacts 32450

Burnley

Museum of Local Crafts and Industries, Towneley Holmes Rd, Burnley BB11 3RQ - T: (01282) 424213, Fax: 436138, E-mail: towneleyhall@burnley.gov.uk, Internet: http://www.burnley.gov.uk/towneley
Historical Museum
Social and industrial history, textiles, street scene, home life, a pub 32451

Natural History Centre, Towneley Hall, Burnley BB11 3 RQ - T: (01282) 424213, Fax: 436138, E-mail: nathist@gn.afc.org, Internet: http://www.burnley.gov.uk/towneley. Head: Michael T. Graham
Natural History Museum 32452

Queen Street Mill, Queen St, Harle Syke, Burnley BB10 2HX - T: (01282) 412555, Fax: 430220, Internet: http://www.lancashire.com/lcc/museums. Head: Robin Green
Science&Tech Museum
Steam powerd cotton weaving shed 32453

Towneley Hall Art Gallery and Museums, Towneley Holmes Rd, Burnley BB11 3RQ - T: (01282) 424213, Fax: 436138, E-mail: towneleyhall@burnley.gov.uk, Internet: http://www.towneleyhall.org
Fine Arts Museum / Decorative Arts Museum / Local Museum - 1902
Paintings, water colours, furnishings, period house, archaeology, local hist, natural hist, decorative arts 32454

Weavers' Triangle Visitor Centre, 85 Manchester Rd, Burnley BB11 1JZ - T: (01282) 452403. Head: Brian Hall
Historical Museum - 1980
Burnley's cotton industry and its workers, Victorian industrial area 32455

Burntisland

Burntisland Museum, 102 High St, Burntisland KY3 9AS - T: (01592) 412860, Fax: 412870. Head: Dallas Mechan
Local Museum 32456

Bursledon

Bursledon Windmill, Windmill Ln, Bursledon SO31 8BG - T: (023) 80404999, E-mail: musmgb@hants.gov.uk, Internet: http://hants.gov.uk/museums/windmill. Head: Dr. Gavin Bowie
Science&Tech Museum 32457

Manor Farm, Pylands Ln, Bursledon SO31 1BH - T: (01489) 787055. Head: Barbara Newbury
Agriculture Museum
Farm with machinery, woodworking, blacksmithing, farmhouse, living history displays 32458

Burston, Diss

Burston Strike School, The Firs, Burston, Diss IP22 5TP - T: (01379) 741565
Historical Museum
Events in 1914 which lead to the longest strike in history 32459

Burton Agnes

Burton Agnes Hall, Burton Agnes YO25 4NB - T: (01262) 490324, Fax: 490513, E-mail: burton.agnes@fannline.com, Internet: http://www.burton-agnes.com. Head: E.S. Cunliffe-Lister
Fine Arts Museum / Decorative Arts Museum - 1946
Elizabethan house with ceilings, overmantels, paintings by Reynolds, Gainsborough, Cotes, Marlow, Reinagle, also modern French paintings 32460

Burton-upon-Trent

Bass Museum of Brewing, Horninglow St, Burton-upon-Trent DE14 1YQ - T: (0845) 6000598, (01283) 511000, Fax: (01283) 513509, E-mail: enquiries@bass-museum.com, Internet: http://www.bass-museum.com. Head: Mike Maryon
Science&Tech Museum - 1977
Company records of Bass and Co. (Brewers) 32461

Burwash

Bateman's Kipling's House, Burwash TN19 7DS - T: (01435) 882302, Fax: 882811, E-mail: kbaxxx@smtp.ntrust.org.uk. Head: Jan Wallwork-Wright
Special Museum - 1939
Work and living rooms of writer Rudyard Kipling (1865-1936) in his former home, built 1634, manuscripts, Kiplings Rolls Royce, working water mill - Library 32462

Burwell

Burwell Museum, Mill Close, Burwell CB5 0HL - T: (01638) 605544, 741713
Local Museum
Local history 32463

Bury, Lancashire

Bury Art Gallery and Museum, Moss St, Bury, Lancashire BL9 0DG - T: (0161) 2535878, Fax: 2535915, E-mail: artgallery@bury.gov.uk, Internet: http://www.bury.gov.uk/culture.htm. Head: Richard Burns
Fine Arts Museum / Decorative Arts Museum / Local Museum
British paintings and drawings, local hist, natural hist, ornithology, archaeology, Wedgwood and local pottery, Bronze Age finds 32464

Bury Transport Museum, Castlecrof Rd, off Bolton St, Bury, Lancashire BL9 0LN - T: (01225) 333895, Fax: (01424) 775174
Science&Tech Museum
Road and rail transport, buses, lorries, traction engines 32465

Fusiliers' Museum Lancashire, Wellington Barracks, Bolton Rd, Bury, Lancashire BL8 2PL - T: (0161) 7642208, Fax: 7642208, E-mail: rrflhq@aol.com, Internet: http://www.thefusiliers.org. Head: John O'Grady
Military Museum - 1934
History of the regiment since 1688, uniforms, medals, militaria, Napoleonic relics 32466

Bury Saint Edmunds

Abbey Visitor Centre, Abbey Precinct, Bury Saint Edmunds IP33 - T: (01284) 763110, Fax: 757079, E-mail: maggie.goodger@stedsbc.gov.uk, Internet: http://www.stedmundsbury.gov.uk
Religious Arts Museum
Abbay history 32467

Bury Saint Edmunds Art Gallery, Market Cross, Bury Saint Edmunds IP28 7EF - T: (01284) 762081, Fax: 750774, E-mail: e.enquiries@burysted-artgall.org, Internet: http://www.burystedmundsart-gallery.org. Head: Barbara Taylor
Public Gallery 32468

John Gershom-Parkington Collection of Timekeeping Instruments, Manor House, Honey Hill, Bury Saint Edmunds IP33 1HF - T: (01284) 757076, Fax: 757079, E-mail: manor.house@burybo.stedsbc.gov.uk, Internet: http://www.stedmundsbury.gov.uk. Head: Viscount Midleton
Science&Tech Museum / Fine Arts Museum - 1953
Technological hist of timekeeping instruments, costume, fine art 32469

Moyse's Hall Museum, Cornhill, Bury Saint Edmunds IP33 1DX - T: (01284) 757488, Fax: 757079, E-mail: moyses@burybo.stedsbc.gov.uk, Internet: http://www.stedmundsbury.gov.uk. Head: Margaret Goodger
Local Museum - 1899
Prehistoric-medieval finds, regional natural history, local history, 12th c Norman building 32470

Suffolk Regiment Museum (temporary closed), Bury Saint Edmunds IP33 3RN - T: (01284) 752394. Head: A.G.B. Cobbold
Military Museum - 1935
Regimental history 32471

Buscot

Buscot House, Buscot SN7 8BU - T: (01367) 20786
Fine Arts Museum
Coll of paintings 32472

Bushey

Bushey Museum and Art Gallery, Rudolph Rd, Bushey WD23 3HW - T: (020) 84204057, 89503233, Fax: 84204923, E-mail: busmt@bushey.org.uk, Internet: http://www.busheymuseum.org. Head: Bryen Wood
Local Museum / Fine Arts Museum
Local history, Monro circle of artists and art schools 32473

Bushmead

John Dony Field Centre, Hancock Dr, Bushmead LU2 7SF - T: (01582) 486983, Fax: 422805, E-mail: tweent@luton.gov.uk, Internet: http://www.luton.gov.uk
Natural History Museum
Natural history, enviroment 32474

Bushmills

Causeway School Museum, 52 Causeway Rd, Bushmills BT57 8SU - T: (028) 20731777, Fax: 20732142. Head: P.G. French
Historical Museum 32475

Giant's Causeway and Bushmills Railway, Runkerry Rd, Bushmills BT57 8SZ - T: (028) 20732844, Fax: 20732844. Head: D.W. Laing
Science&Tech Museum 32476

Bute Town

Drenewydd Museum, 26-27 Lower Row, Bute Town NP2 5QH - T: (01443) 864224, Fax: 864228, E-mail: morgacl@caerphilly.gov.uk. Head: Chris Morgan
Local Museum
Ironworker's cottages, domestic and household objects 32477

Buxton

Buxton Museum and Art Gallery, Peak Bldgs, Terrace Rd, Buxton SK17 6DA - T: (01298) 24658, Fax: 79394, E-mail: buxton.museum@derbyshire.gov.uk, Internet: http://www.derbyshire.gov.uk/libraries&heritage. Head: Ros. Westwood
Fine Arts Museum / Natural History Museum / Local Museum - 1891
Prehistoric cave finds, geology, mineralogy, archaeology, art, craft, local hist 32478

Cadbury

Fursdon House, Cadbury EX5 5JS - T: (01392) 860860, Fax: 860126, E-mail: enquiries@fursdon.co.uk, Internet: http://www.fursdon.co.uk. Head: E.D. Fursdon
Special Museum
Coll of family possessions, furniture, portraits, everyday items, family costumes, coll of Iron Age and Roman material, old estate maps 32479

Cadeby

Cadeby Experience, Boston Collection and Brass Rubbing Centre, Old Rectory, Cadeby CV13 0AS - T: (01455) 290462. Head: J. Audrey Boston
Local Museum 32480

Cadeby Light Railway, Old Rectory, Cadeby CV13 0AS - T: (01455) 290462. Head: A. Boston
Science&Tech Museum - 1962
Railway relics, trains, locomotives, steam traction engine, steam rollers - library 32481

Caerleon

Roman Legionary Museum, High St, Caerleon NP18 1AE - T: (01633) 423134, Fax: 422869, E-mail: post@nmgw.ac.uk, Internet: http://www.nmgw.ac.uk/rlm. Head: P. Guest
Archaeological Museum - 1850
Finds from excavations at the fortress of the Second Augustan Legion 32482

Caernarfon

Caernarfon Maritime Museum, Victoria Dock, Caernarfon LL55 1SR - T: (01248) 752083. Head: F. Whitehead
Local Museum / Science&Tech Museum
History of Caernarfon as a harbour and port since Roman times, slate trade, maritime education, passenger traffic, particularly emigration, steam engine Seiont II, HMS Conway 32483

Royal Welch Fusiliers Regimental Museum, Queen's Tower, The Castle, Caernarfon LL55 2AY - T: (01286) 673362, Fax: 677042, E-mail: rwfusiliers@callnetuk.com. Head: P.A. Crocker
Military Museum - 1960
Hist of the regiment since 1689, documents, portraits, medals, weapons, uniforms, badges and pictures 32484

Segontium Roman Museum, Beddgelert Rd, Caernarfon LL55 2LN - T: (01286) 675625, Fax: 678416, E-mail: post@nmgw.ac.uk, Internet: http://www.nmgw.ac.uk/srm. Head: Anna Southall
Archaeological Museum - 1937
Finds from excavations at the former Roman fort Segontium, inscriptions, medals, urns, tools, armaments, pottery, household objects 32485

Caerphilly

Caerphilly Castle, Caerphilly CF2 1UF - T: (029) 20883143, Internet: http://www.castleswales.com/caerphil.html
Historical Museum
Full scale replica, working medieval siege engines 32486

Calbourne

Calbourne Water Mill and Rural Museum, Calbourne PO30 4JN - T: (01983) 531277
Historical Museum
War and country life 32487

Caldicot

Caldicot Castle, Church Rd, Caldicot NP26 4HU - T: (01291) 420241, Fax: 435094, E-mail: caldicotcastle@monmouthshire.gov.uk, Internet: http://www.caldicotcastle.co.uk. Head: Sarah Finch
Historic Site 32488

Callander

Rob Roy and Trossachs Victor Centre, Acaster Sq, Callander FK17 8ED - T: (01877) 330342, Fax: 330784. Head: Janet Michael
Historical Museum
Story of the highland folk hero Rob Roy MacGregor 32489

Calne

Atwell-Wilson Motor Museum, Stockley Ln, Calne SN11 0NF - T: (01249) 813119, Fax: 813119, E-mail: stoned@stonehenge.co.uk, Internet: http://www.stonehenge.co.uk
Science&Tech Museum
Coll of post vintage and classic vehicles, motorcycles 32490

Bowood House and Gardens, Calne SN11 0LZ - T: (01249) 812102, Fax: 821757, E-mail: houseandgardens@bowood.org.co.uk, Internet: http://www.bowood.org.co.uk. Head: Dr. Kate Fielden
Decorative Arts Museum / Fine Arts Museum / Historical Museum
Fine and decorative arts, paintings, watercolours, furniture, sculptures, architecture - library, archive 32491

Calverton

Calverton Folk Museum, Main St, Calverton NG14 6FB - T: (0115) 9654843, E-mail: cps@bay47.clara.net, Internet: http://www.welcome.to/calverton
Folklore Museum
Hosiery industry, framework knitting machine 32492

Camberley

National Army Museum, Sandhurst Outstation, Royal Military Academy Sandhurst, Camberley GU15 4PQ - T: (01276) 63344 ext 2457, Fax: 686316, E-mail: info@national-army-museum.ac.uk, Internet: http://www.national-army-museum.ac.uk
Military Museum
Indian army memorial room, study coll of uniforms and equipment 32493

Royal Military Academy Sandhurst Collection, Royal Military Academy, Camberley GU15 4PQ - T: (01276) 412489. Head: Peter Thwaites
Military Museum
History of the academy 32494

Staff College Museum, Camberley GU15 4NP - T: (01276) 412602, 412643, Fax: 412718. Head: Stephen Connelly
Historical Museum - 1958
History of college 1799-1990, staff uniforms 32495

Surrey Heath Museum, Surrey Heath House, Knoll Rd, Camberley GU15 3HD - T: (01276) 707284, Fax: 671158. Head: Sharon Cross
Local Museum - 1935
Local 19th and 20th c social hist, costume, natural hist, local photographs 32496

Cambo

Wallington Hall, Cambo NE61 4AR - T: (01670) 774283. Head: Bill Pashley
Decorative Arts Museum / Fine Arts Museum - 1688
House built in 1688 with 18th c furnishings, rococo plaster decorations, porcelain, needlework, 19th c hall decorated by W. Scott, Ruskin and others, Scott's pre-Raphaelite paintings 32497

Camborne

Camborne Museum, Cross St, Camborne TR14 8HA - T: (01209) 713544. Head: M. Matthews
Local Museum / Archaeological Museum
Stone Age finds, Iron an Bronze Age pottery, Roman Villa excavation finds, Mexican and Egyptian antiquities, old china and silver, numismatics, geology, mineralogy, local history, mining 32498

Trevithick Cottage, Penponds, Camborne TR14 0QG - T: (01209) 612154, Fax: 612142, E-mail: info@trevithicktrust.com, Internet: http://www.trevithicktrust.com. Head: L. Humphrey
Historical Museum / Fine Arts Museum
Oil paintings of himself, wife and family 32499

Cambridge

Cambridge and County Folk Museum, 2-3 Castle St, Cambridge CB3 0AQ - T: (01223) 355159, Fax: 576301, E-mail: info@folkmuseum.org.uk, Internet: http://www.folkmuseum.org.uk. Head: Cameron Hawke-Smith
Local Museum - 1936
Hist of Cambridge and Cambridgeshire county since the 17th c, looking at the everyday life of people in the area, wide-ranging colls, strengths, domestic items, toys, tools 32500

Cambridge Museum of Technology, Old Pumping Station, Cheddars Ln, Cambridge CB5 8LD - T: (01223) 368650. Head: Alan Denney
Science&Tech Museum
Local industry 32501

Cavendish Laboratory, c/o University of Cambridge, Dept. of Physics, Madingley Rd, Cambridge CB3 0HE - T: (01223) 337420, 337200, Fax: 766360, E-mail: spj20@phy.cam.ac.uk, Internet: http://www.phy.cam.ac.uk
Science&Tech Museum
Scientific instruments 32502

Fitzwilliam Museum, c/o University of Cambridge, Trumpington St, Cambridge CB2 1RB - T: (01223) 332900, Fax: 332923, E-mail: fitzmuseum-enquiries@lists.cam.ac.uk, Internet: http://www.fitzmuseum.cam.ac.uk. Head: Duncan Robinson
University Museum - 1816
Egyptian, Greek and Roman antiquities, numismatics, paintings, drawings, bronze objects - Hamilton Kerr Institute for the Conservation of Paintings 32503

Kettle's Yard, c/o University of Cambridge, Castle St, Cambridge CB3 0AQ - T: (01223) 352124, Fax: 324377, E-mail: mail@kettlesyard.cam.ac.uk, Internet: http://www.kettlesyard.co.uk. Head: Michael Harrison
Fine Arts Museum / University Museum - 1957
20th c art incl Ben Nicholson, Alfred Wallis, David Jones, Christopher Wood, Henri Gaudier-Brzeska 32504

Lewis Collection, Corpus Christi College, Cambridge CB2 1RH - T: (01223) 338000, Fax: 338061, E-mail: http://www.corpus.cam.nc.uk. Head: Dr. Christopher Kelly
Archaeological Museum / Decorative Arts Museum / University Museum
Classical and neo-classical gems, Greek and Roman coins, Greek and Roman figurines and pottery 32505

Museum of Classical Archaeology, c/o University of Cambridge, Sidgwick Av, Cambridge CB3 9DA - T: (01223) 335153, Fax: 335409, E-mail: jd125@cam.ac.uk, Internet: http://www.classics.cam.ac.uk/ark.html. Head: Dr. Mary Beard
Archaeological Museum - 1884 32506

New Hall Women's Art Collection, Huntingdon Rd, Cambridge CB3 0DF - T: (01223) 762100, E-mail: art@newhall.cam.ac.uk, Internet: http://www.newhall.cam.ac.uk
Fine Arts Museum 32507

Scott Polar Research Institute Museum, c/o University of Cambridge, Lensfield Rd, Cambridge CB2 1ER - T: (01223) 336540, 336555, Fax: 336549, E-mail: rkh10@cam.ac.uk, Internet: http://www.spri.cam.ac.uk. Head: R.K. Headland
Natural History Museum - 1920
Polar exploration and research, material from Antarctic expeditions of Captain Scott and from other historical British polar expeditions, exploration of the NW-Passage, relics, manuscripts, paintings, photographs, Eskimo art, ethnological coll - library, archives 32508

Sedgwick Museum of Geology, c/o University of Cambridge, Dept. of Earth Sciences, Downing St, Cambridge CB2 3EQ - T: (01223) 333456, Fax: 333450, E-mail: sedgmus@esc.cam.ac.uk, Internet: http://www.sedgwick.esc.cam.ac.uk. Head: Dr. D.B. Norman
Natural History Museum / University Museum - 1728/1904
Local, British, foreign rocks, fossils, minerals, memorabilia of scientist Adam Sedgwick, John Woodward coll (oldest intact geological coll), Darwin's Rocks - conservation laboratory, Sedgwick library 32509

University Museum of Archaeology and Anthropology, c/o University of Cambridge, Downing St, Cambridge CB2 3DZ - T: (01223) 333516, Fax: 333517, E-mail: cumaa@hermes.cam.ac.uk, Internet: http://cumaa.archanth.cam.ac.uk. Head: Prof. David W. Phillipson
Archaeological Museum / University Museum / Ethnology Museum - 1884
Prehistoric archaeology of all parts of the world, the archaeology of the Cambridge region from the paleolithic period to recent times, ethnographic material from all regions of the world with a particular emphasis on Oceania 32510

University Museum of Zoology, c/o University of Cambridge, Downing St, Cambridge CB2 3EJ - T: (01223) 336650, Fax: 336679, E-mail: umzc@zoo.cam.ac.uk, Internet: http://www.zoo.cam.ac.uk/museum. Head: Prof. Michael Akam
Natural History Museum / University Museum - 1814
Zoology: birds, fossil tetrapods, invertebrates, mammals, fish, reptiles and amphibians 32511

Whipple Museum of the History of Science, Free School Ln, Cambridge CB2 3RH - T: (01223) 330906, Fax: 334554, E-mail: hps-whipple-museum@lists.cam.ac.uk, Internet: http://www.hps.cam.ac.uk/whipple.html. Head: Liba Taub
Special Museum - 1951
Old scientific instruments, 16th-20th c books 32512

Camelford

British Cycling Museum, Old Station, Camelford PL32 9TZ - T: (01840) 212811, Fax: 212811, Internet: http://www.chycor.co.uk
Science&Tech Museum
Cycling history, 400 cycles, over 1,000 cycling medals, enamel signs and posters 32513

North Cornwall Museum and Gallery, The Clease, Camelford PL32 9PL - T: (01840) 212954, Fax: 212954, E-mail: camelfordfic@eurobell.co.uk. Head: Sally Holden
Local Museum / Folklore Museum 32514

Campbeltown

Campbeltown Museum, Public Library, Hall St, Campbeltown PA28 6BS - T: (01586) 552366 ext 2237, Fax: 552938, 705797, E-mail: mvhelmond@abc-museums.demon.co.uk, Internet: http://www.abc-museums.demon.co.uk. Head: Mary van Helmond
Local Museum - 1898 32515

Canterbury

Buffs Museum, National Art Museum, Royal East Kent Regiment, 18 High St, Canterbury CT1 2RA - T: (01227) 452747, Fax: 455047, Internet: http://www.canterburry-museum.co.uk. Head: Kenneth Reedie
Military Museum / Fine Arts Museum
Royal East Kent Regiment story, uniforms, weapons, medals, sporting and leisure pursuits 32516

Canterbury Cathedral Archives and Library, The Precincts, Canterbury CT1 2EH - T: (01227) 865330, 865287, Fax: 865222, E-mail: library@canterbury-cathedral.org, Internet: http://www.canterbury-cathedral.org. Head: Sheila Hingley
Library with Exhibitions 32517

Canterbury Heritage Museum, Poor Priests' Hospital, Stour St, Canterbury CT1 2RA - T: (01227) 452747, Fax: 455047, Internet: http://www.canterbury-museum.co.uk. Head: K.G.H. Reedie
Local Museum
History of Canterbury's 2000 years 32518

Canterbury Roman Museum, Longmarket, Butchery Ln, Canterbury CT1 2RA - T: (01227) 785575, Fax: 455047, Internet: http://www.canterbury-museum.co.uk. Head: K.G.H Reedie
Archaeological Museum / Historical Museum / Historic Site
Round a Roman site, excavated finds, mosaic floors, hands-on area 32519

Ethnic Doll and Toy Museum, Cogan House, 53 Saint Peter St, Canterbury CT1 2BE - T: (01227) 472986
Special Museum 32520

Royal Museum and Art Gallery, 18 High St, Canterbury CT1 2RA - T: (01227) 452747, Fax: 455047, Internet: http://www.canterbury-artgallery.co.uk. Head: K.G.H. Reedie
Fine Arts Museum / Decorative Arts Museum / Public Gallery - 1899
Decorative arts, picture coll, cattle paintings 32521

Saint Augustine's Abbey, Longport, Canterbury CT1 1TF - T: (01227) 767345, Fax: 767345. Head: Jan Summerfield
Religious Arts Museum
Religious art 32522

West Gate Towers, Saint Peters St, Canterbury - T: (01227) 452747, Fax: 455047, Internet: http://www.canterbury-museum.co.uk. Head: K.G.H. Reedie
Historical Museum - 1906
British and foreign armaments, relics in 14th c medieval gate 32523

Canvey Island

Castle Point Transport Museum, 105 Point Rd, Canvey Island SS8 7TP - T: (01268) 684272
Science&Tech Museum
Busses, coaches (1929-1972) 32524

Cardiff

Cardiff Castle, Castle St, Cardiff CF10 3RB - T: (029) 20878100, Fax: 20231417, E-mail: cardiffcastle@cardiff.gov.uk, Internet: http://www.cardiff-info.com/castle
Fine Arts Museum / Historical Museum
Architectural drawings, ceramics, painting, furniture, Burges coll, De Morgan coll 32525

Howard Gardens Gallery, University of Wales Institute, Howard Gardens, Cardiff CF24 0SP - T: (029) 20416678, Fax: 20416678, E-mail: wwarrilow@uwic.ac.uk. Head: Walt Warrilow
Public Gallery 32526

IBRA Collection, International Bee Research Association, 18 North Rd, Cardiff CF1 3DY - T: (029) 20372409, Fax: 20665522, E-mail: ibra@cardiff.ac.uk, Internet: http://www.cf.ac.uk/ibra
Special Museum
Bees and bee keeping 32527

National Museum and Gallery, Cathays Park, Cardiff CF10 3NP - T: (029) 20397951, Fax: 20373219, E-mail: post@nmgw.ac.uk, Internet: http://www.nmgw.ac.uk/nmgc. Head: Anna Southall
Archaeological Museum / Natural History Museum / Fine Arts Museum - 1907
Geology, mineralogy, fossils, botany, plant ecology, Welsh zoology, mollusks, entomology, Welsh archaeology up to the 16th c, numismatics, industrial history, European painting, sculpture, applied art, decorative objects, French art 32528

Oriel - Arts Council of Wales' Gallery, The Friary, Cardiff CF1 4AA - T: (029) 20399477, Fax: 20398500. Head: Jenni Spencer-Davies
Public Gallery 32529

Regimental Museum of 1st The Queen's Dragoon Guards, Cardiff Castle, Cardiff CF10 2RB - T: (029) 20781232, 20222253, Fax: 20781384, E-mail: morris602@netscapeonline.co.uk, Internet: http://www.qdg.org.uk. Head: Clive Morris
Military Museum 32530

Saint David's Hall, The Hayes, Cardiff CF1 2SH - T: (029) 20878500, Fax: 20878599
Public Gallery 32531

Techniquest, Stuart St, Cardiff CF10 5BW - T: (029) 20475475, Fax: 20482517, E-mail: info@techniquest.org, Internet: http://www.techniquest.org. Head: Colin Johnson
Science&Tech Museum
Science discovery centre - Planetarium planetarium 32532

The Welch Regiment Museum of The Royal Regiment of Wales (41st/ 69th Foot), Black and Barbican Towers, Cardiff Castle, Cardiff CF10 2RB - T: (029) 20229367, Internet: http://www.rrw.org.uk
Military Museum 32533

Welsh Industrial and Maritime Museum, Bute St, Cardiff CF1 6AN - T: (029) 20481919, Fax: 20487252. Head: Dr. E.S. Owen-Jones
Science&Tech Museum - 1977
Road and rail vehicles, ship models and paintings, power, machines, industrial progress, pumping, winding and driving engines, powered by steam, compressed air, gas oil and electricity, steel works, cement works, gas and electricity generation plants 32534

Cardigan

Cardigan Heritage Centre, Teifi Wharf, Castle St, Cardigan SA43 3AA - T: (01239) 614404, Fax: 614404
Local Museum
Town history 32535

Carlisle

Border Regiment and King's Own Royal Border Regiment Museum, Queen Mary's Tower, Castle, Carlisle CA3 8UR - T: (01228) 532774, Fax: 521275, E-mail: rhq@kingsownborder.demon.co.uk, Internet: http://www.army.mod.uk/army/press/museums/details/m.36bord.htm
Military Museum - 1932
Uniforms, badges, medals, pictures, silver, arms, dioramas, documents, trophies, militaria, photogr - archives 32536

Cathedral Treasury Museum, Carlisle Cathedral, 7 The Abbey, Carlisle CA3 8TZ - T: (01228) 548151, Fax: 547049, E-mail: office@carlislecathedral.org.uk, Internet: http://www.carlislecathedral.org.uk. Head: D.W.V. Weston
Religious Arts Museum / Archaeological Museum
Articles connected with the site from Roman times to the present day, portraits of Deans, 16th to 20th c Church plate, 15th c copes 32537

Guildhall Museum, Greenmarket, Carlisle CA2 4PW - T: (01228) 534781, 819925, Fax: 810249, E-mail: cheryle@carlisle-city.gov.uk. Head: Joanne Orr
Local Museum
History of the medieval Guilds and on the building itself, medieval iron-bound muniment chest and town bell, two 1599 silver bells, medieval measures and pottery, civic regalia, the pillory and stocks, wearing, local history 32538

Tullie House - City Museum and Art Gallery, Castle St, Carlisle CA3 8TP - T: (01228) 534781, Fax: 810249, E-mail: tullie-house@carlisle-city.gov.uk. Head: Joanne Orr
Local Museum - 1892
Regional antiquities, natural history, Lake District specimens, pre-Raphaelite, 19th c painting, modern paintings, English porcelain, Roman finds, ornithology, historic railways, local history 32539

Carlton Colville

East Anglia Transport Museum, Chapel Rd, Carlton Colville NR33 8BL - T: (01502) 518459
Science&Tech Museum
Trams, trolleybuses and a narrow gauge railway 32540

Carmarthen

Carmarthen Heritage Centre, The Quay, Carmarthen SA31 3AN
Local Museum
History of the River Tywi and the port of Carmarthen 32541

Carmarthen Museum → Carmarthenshire County Museum

Carmarthenshire County Museum, Abergwili, Carmarthen SA31 2JG - T: (01267) 231691, Fax: 223830, E-mail: chrisdelaney@carmarthenshire.gov.uk. Head: Chris Delaney
Archaeological Museum / Folklore Museum - 1905
Folklore, archaeology - library 32542

Carnforth

Leighton Hall, Carnforth LA5 9ST - T: (01524) 734474, Fax: 720357, E-mail: leightonhall@yahoo.co.uk, Internet: http://www.leightonhall.co.uk
Local Museum
Manor house dating from the 13th c with old and modern painting, antique furniture, Gillow family portraits 32543

Steamtown Railway Museum, Warton Rd, Carnforth LA5 9HX - T: (01524) 732100, Fax: 735518. Head: W.D. Smith
Science&Tech Museum 32544

Carrbridge

Landmark Forest Heritage Park, Main St, Carrbridge PH23 3AJ - T: (01479) 841613, Fax: 841384, E-mail: landmarkcentre@compuserve.com, Internet: http://www.landmark-centre.co.uk. Head: David Hayes
Natural History Museum - 1970
Hist, natural environment and wildlife of the Highlands, nature trails, microscopy, steampowered sawmill, working horse and woodcraft centre 32545

Carrickfergus

Carrickfergus Gasworks, Irish Quarter West, Carrickfergus BT38 7AB - T: (02890) 616480
Science&Tech Museum 32546

Castle Cary

Castle Cary and District Museum, Market House, High St, Castle Cary BA7 7AL - T: (01963) 350680, Internet: http://www.southsomerset.gov.uk
Local Museum 32547

Castle Combe

Castle Combe Museum, Combe Cottage, Castle Combe SN14 7HU - T: (01249) 782250, Fax: 782250, E-mail: abishop@northwilts.gov.uk. Head: Adrian Bishop
Local Museum
Artefacts and historical displays 32548

Castle Donington

Donington Grand Prix Collection, Donington Park, Castle Donington DE74 2RP - T: (01332) 811027, Fax: 812829, E-mail: donington@zoom.co.uk, Internet: http://www.doningtoncollection.com. Head: F.B. Wheatcroft
Special Museum - 1973
Coll of Grand Prix Racing cars, McLarren, BRM, Lotus, Ferrari, Vanwalls, Williams, amazing coll of helmets, Formula 1 racing 32549

Castle Douglas

Castle Douglas Art Gallery, King St, Castle Douglas DG7 1AE - T: (01556) 30291, Fax: 331643, E-mail: davidd@dumgal.gov.uk, Internet: http://www.dumfriesmuseum.demon.co.uk. Head: David Devereux
Public Gallery
Paintings by Ethel S.G. Bristowe, local artists 32550

Castleford

Castleford Museum Room, Library, Carlton St, Castleford WF10 2EW - T: (01924) 305351, Fax: 305353. Head: Gordon Watson
Archaeological Museum / Historical Museum - 1935
Finds from the old Roman town Legiolium, local pottery and glass, social history in 1800s 32551

Castleton

Castleton Village Museum, Methodist Schoolroom, Buxton Rd, Castleton S33 8WX - T: (01433) 620950. Head: Christine Thorpe
Local Museum
Local crafts, lead mining, rope-making, agriculture, Garland Ceremony and Blue John Caverns 32552

Castletown

Castle Rushen, Manx National Heritage, Castletown IM9 1AB - T: (01624) 648000, Fax: 648001, E-mail: enquiries@mnh.gov.im, Internet: http://www.gov.im/mnh. Head: Iain A. McKinlay
Historical Museum
Story of the Kings and Lords of Man 32553

Dunnet Pavilion, Dunnet Bay Caravan Site, Castletown KW14 8XD - T: (01847) 821531, Fax: 821531, E-mail: mary.legg@highland.gov.uk
Natural History Museum 32554

Nautical Museum - Peggy Story, Manx National Heritage, Castletown IM9 1AB - T: (01624) 648000, Fax: 648001, E-mail: enquiries@mnh.gov.im, Internet: http://www.mnh.gov.im. Head: Iain McKinley
Historical Museum 32555

Old Grammar School, Manx National Heritage, Castletown IM9 1AB - T: (01624) 648000, Fax: 648001, E-mail: enquiries@mnh.gov.im, Internet: http://www.mnh.gov.im. Head: Iain McKinley
Historical Museum
Hist oh Manx education 32556

Old House of Keys, Manx National Heritage, Castletown IM9 1AA - T: (01624) 648000, Fax: 648001, E-mail: enquiries@mnh.gov.im, Internet: http://www.mnh.gov.im
Historical Museum
Assambly and debating chamber for Manx parliament 32557

Câtel

Guernsey Folk Museum, Saumarez Park, Câtel GY5 7UJ - T: (01481) 255384, Fax: 255384, E-mail: folkmuseumntgsy@gtonline.gg, Internet: http://www.nationaltrust-gsy.org.gg. Head: Matt Harvey
Folklore Museum - 1968
Agriculture tools of the island, horse drawn machinery, farmhouse interior 32558

Caterham

East Surrey Museum, 1 Stafford Rd, Caterham CR3 6JG - T: (01883) 340275, E-mail: es@emuseums.freeserve.co.uk, Internet: http://www.tandridgedc.gov. Head: Anthea Hopkins
Local Museum
Local History 32559

Cavendish

Sue Ryder Foundation Museum, Sue Ryder Foundation Headquarters, Cavendish CO10 8AY - T: (01787) 280653, Fax: 280548
Local Museum - 1953
Life and work of Lady Ryder of Warsaw 32560

Cawdor

Cawdor Castle, Cawdor IV12 5RD - T: (01667) 404615, Fax: 404674, E-mail: info@cawdorcastle.com, Internet: http://www.cawdorcastle.com
Decorative Arts Museum 32561

Cawthorne

Regimental Museum of the 13th/18th Royal Hussars, Cannon Hall Museum, Cawthorne S75 4AT - T: (01226) 790270, Fax: 792117, E-mail: cannonhall@barnsley.gov.uk. Head: Dr. J. Whittaker
Military Museum 32562

Victoria Jubilee Museum, Taylor Hill, Cawthorne S75 4HQ - T: (01226) 790545. Head: G.B. Jackson
Local Museum - 1884
Local history, example of Cruck formation timbered building, Victoriana, domestic bygones 32563

Cenarth

National Coracle Centre, Cenarth Falls, Cenarth SA38 9JL - T: (01239) 710980, E-mail: martinfowler@btconnect.com, Internet: http://www.coraclecentre.co.uk. Head: Martin Fowler
Science&Tech Museum
Boat coll of coracles from Wales and other parts of the world 32564

Ceres

Fife Folk Museum, Weigh House, High St, Ceres KY15 5NF - T: (01334) 828180. Head: Dr. Paula Martin
Folklore Museum - 1968
Tools, scales, agricultural equipment, domestic items 32565

Chalfont Saint Giles

Chiltern Open Air Museum, Newland Park, Gorelands Ln, Chalfont Saint Giles HP8 4AD - T: (01494) 871117, 872163, Fax: 872163, Internet: http://homepages.tesco.net/~coam. Head: James Moir
Open Air Museum - 1976
Historic buildings, iron age house, Victorian farm 32566

Milton's Cottage, Deanway, Chalfont Saint Giles HP8 4JH - T: (01494) 872313, Fax: 873936, E-mail: miltonscottagepbirger@clara.net, Internet: http://www.clara.net/pbirger. Head: E.A. Dawson
Special Museum - 1887
Life and times of writer John Milton (1608-1674), editions of Milton's work, portraits and engravings of Milton, memorabilia 32567

Chapel Brampton

Northampton and Lamport Railway, Pitsford and Brampton Station, Pitsford Rd, Chapel Brampton NN6 8BA - T: (01604) 820327, E-mail: info@nlr.org.uk, Internet: http://www.nlr.org.uk
Science&Tech Museum
Steam trains 32568

Chard

Chard and District Museum, Godworthy House, 15 High St, Chard TA20 1QL - T: (01460) 65091, Internet: http://www.southsomerset.gov.uk. Head: P. Wood
Local Museum - 1970
John Stringfellow Pioneer of powered flight, James Gillingham maker of artificial limbs 32569

Forde Abbey, Chard TA20 4LU - T: (01460) 220231, Fax: 220296, E-mail: forde.abbay@virgin.net, Internet: http://www.fordeabbay.co.uk. Head: Mark Roper
Religious Arts Museum 32570

Hornsbury Mill, Hornsbury Hill, Chard TA20 3AQ - T: (01460) 63317, Fax: 63317, E-mail: hornsburymill@btclick.com, Internet: http://www.hornsburymill.co.uk. Head: S.J. Lewin
Science&Tech Museum - 1970
Milling machinery and equipment, agricultural implements, craftsmen's tools, domestic equipment and clothing 32571

Charlbury

Charlbury Museum, Corner House Community Centre, Market St, Charlbury OX7 3PN - T: (01608) 810060. Head: R. Prew
Local Museum
Traditional crafts and industry 32572

Chartwell

Chartwell House, Mapleton Rd, Chartwell TN16 1PS - T: (01732) 866368, Internet: http://www.bigginhill.co.uk/chartwell.htm. Head: Carole Kenwright
Historical Museum
Sir Winston Churchill's family house 32573

Chatham

Fort Amherst Heritage Museum, Dock Rd, Chatham ME4 4UB - T: (01634) 847747, Fax: 847747
Historical Museum
Napoleonic fortress, WWII, military artefacts 32574

Historic Dockyard Chatham, Dock Rd, Chatham ME4 4TZ - T: (01634) 823800, Fax: 823801, E-mail: info@chdt.org.uk, Internet: http://www.chdt.org.uk
Historical Museum
Georgian dockyard, ropes, flags, sails, warships incl HMS Cavalier, submarine Ocelot 32575

Kent Police Museum, Dock Rd, Chatham ME4 4TZ - T: (01634) 403260, Fax: 403260, E-mail: kentpolmus@aol.com, Internet: http://www.kent-police-museum.co.uk. Head: John Endicott
Historical Museum 32576

Medway Heritage Centre, Dock Rd, Chatham ME4 4SH - T: (01634) 408437. Head: R. Ingle
Local Museum
Artefacts and photographs to River Medway 32577

Royal Engineers Museum, Brompton Barracks, Chatham ME4 4UG - T: (01634) 406397, Fax: 822371, E-mail: remuseum.rhqre@gtnet.gov.uk, Internet: http://www.royalengineers.org.uk. Head: John Nowers
Science&Tech Museum / Military Museum - 1873
Hist of engineers' work, military engineering science, memorabilia on General 'Chinese' Gordon and Field Marshal Lord Kitchener of Khartoum 32578

World Naval Base → Historic Dockyard Chatham

Chawton

Jane Austen's House, Winchester Rd, Chawton GU34 1SD - T: (01420) 83262, Fax: 83262, Internet: http://www.janeaustenmuseum.org.uk. Head: T.F. Carpenter
Special Museum - 1949
Memorabilia of writer Jane Austen (1775-1817) 32579

Cheam

Whitehall, 1 Malden Rd, Cheam SM3 8QD - T: (020) 86431236, Fax: 87704777, E-mail: curators@whitehallcheam.fsnet.co.uk, Internet: http://www.sutton.gov.uk. Head: Laurel Joseph
Historical Museum - 1978
Arts, crafts and local history centre, displays of material from the excavations at Nonsuch Palace, Cheam Pottery and Cheam School, works by or featuring William Gilpin (caricatured by Rowlandson as Dr. Syntax) - archives, picture coll   32580

Cheddar

Cheddar Showcaves Museum, Cheddar BS27 3QF - T: (01934) 742343, Fax: 744637
Archaeological Museum / Natural History Museum - 1934
Archaeology and zoology of Cheddar Gorge area, paleolithic pleistocene finds, artefacts from local caves   32581

Cheddleton

Cheddleton Flint Mill, Leek Rd, Cheddleton ST13 7HL - T: (01782) 372561. Head: Ted Royle
Science&Tech Museum - 1967
Prime movers for the grinding of raw materials for the pottery industry, steam engines, transportation, grinding equipment   32582

Chelmsford

Chelmsford and Essex Museum → Chelmsford Museum

Chelmsford Museum, Oaklands Park, Moulsham St, Chelmsford CM2 9AQ - T: (01245) 615100, Fax: 611250, E-mail: oaklands@chelmsfordbc.gov.uk, Internet: http://www.chelmsfordbc.gov.uk/museums/index.shtml. Head: N.P. Wickenden
Local Museum - 1835
Natural hist, geology, archaeology, local hist, coins,decorative arts, paintings, glass, costume, military hist, developing science and technology museum   32583

Engine House Project, Chelmsford Museums, Sandford Mill, Chelmsford CM2 6NY - T: (01245) 475498, Fax: 475498, E-mail: engine.house@chelmsfordbc.gov.uk. Head: G. Bowles
Science&Tech Museum
Industrial coll   32584

Essex Police Museum, Headquarters Springfield, Chelmsford CM2 6DA - T: (01245) 491491 ext 50771, Fax: 452456, Internet: http://www.essex.police.uk. Head: Elizabeth Farnhill
Special Museum
Police history since 1836   32585

Essex Regiment Museum, Oaklands Park, Moulsham St, Chelmsford CM2 9AQ - T: (01245) 615100, Fax: 611250, E-mail: pompadour@chelmsfordbc.gov.uk, Internet: http://www.chelmsfordbc.gov.uk/museums/index.shtml. Head: I.D. Hook
Military Museum
Regimental hist   32586

Cheltenham

Axiom Centre for Arts, 57-59 Winchcombe St, Cheltenham GL52 2NE - T: (01242) 253183, Fax: 253183
Public Gallery   32587

Bugatti Trust Exhibition, Prescott Hill, Gotherington, Cheltenham GL52 4RD - T: (01242) 677201, Fax: 674191, E-mail: trust@bugatti.co.uk, Internet: http://www.bugatti.co.uk/trust. Head: Richard Day
Science&Tech Museum
Bugatti artefacts, technical drawings - photographic archive   32588

Chedworth Roman Villa Museum, Yanworthn Villa, Cheltenham GL54 3LJ - T: (01242) 890256
Archaeological Museum - 1865
Ruins of Roman villa, finds   32589

Cheltenham Art Gallery and Museum, Clarence St, Cheltenham GL50 3JT - T: (01242) 237431, Fax: 262334, E-mail: artgallery@cheltenham.gov.uk, Internet: http://www.cheltenhammuseum.org.uk. Head: George Breeze
Fine Arts Museum / Decorative Arts Museum - 1899
Dutch and other paintings, watercolours and local prints, English pottery and porcelain, geology, Cotswold area history, Chinese porcelain, memorabilia on Edward Wilson, internationally important coll of the Arts and Crafts Movement, furniture, metalwork, textiles   32590

Holst Birthplace Museum, 4 Clarence Rd, Pittville, Cheltenham GL52 2AY - T: (01242) 524846, Fax: 580182, E-mail: holstmuseum@btconnect.com, Internet: http://www.holstmuseum.org.uk. Head: Dr. Joanna Archibald
Music Museum
Musical instruments, Victorian history   32591

Chepstow

Chepstow Museum, Gwy House, Bridge St, Chepstow NP16 5EZ - T: (01291) 625981, Fax: 635005, E-mail: chepstowmuseum@monmouthshire.gov.uk. Head: Anne Rainsbury
Local Museum - 1949
Local and social history - education resource centre, paper conservation   32592

Tintern Abbey, Tintern Abbay Information Centre, Chepstow NP6 6SE - T: (01291) 689251
Religious Arts Museum
Ruins   32593

Chertsey

Chertsey Museum, The Cedars, 33 Windsor St, Chertsey KT16 8AT - T: (01932) 565764, Fax: 571118, E-mail: enquiries@chertseymuseum.org.uk, Internet: http://www.chertseymuseum.org.uk. Head: Stephen Nicholls
Local Museum / Decorative Arts Museum - 1965
Olive Matthews coll of English dress and accessories, local history, archaeology, ancient Greek pottery, horology   32594

Chesham

Chesham Town Museum, Library, Elgiva Ln, Chesham HP5 2JB - T: (01494) 783183. Head: Adrian Kerwood
Local Museum
Historical items   32595

Chester

Cheshire Military Museum, The Castle, Chester CH1 2DN - T: (01244) 327617, Fax: 401700, E-mail: david.blake@chester.ac.uk, Internet: http://www.chester.ac.uk/militarymuseum
Military Museum - 1924
Memorabilia on the 22nd Regiment, Cheshire Yeomanry, Battle of Meeanee 1843, memorabilia of Sir Charles Napier, Eaton Hall Officer Cadet School - archives   32596

Chester Toy and Doll Museum, 13a Lower Bridge St, Chester CH1 1RS - T: (01244) 346297, Fax: 340437. Head: K.W. McGimpsey
Special Museum
Matchbox toys, Dinky toys, dolls, teddies, toy soldiers, pedal cars and outdoor toys   32597

Dewa Roman Experience, Pierpoint Ln, Off Bridge St, Chester CH1 1NL - T: (01244) 343407, Fax: 347737. Head: Lesley Wilson
Archaeological Museum
Streets of Roman Chester   32598

Grosvenor Museum, 27 Grosvenor St, Chester CH1 2DD - T: (01244) 402008, Fax: 347587, E-mail: s.matthews@chestercc.gov.uk, Internet: http://www.chestercc.gov.uk/heritage/museum. Head: Sharn Matthews
Local Museum
Roman archaeology. local history, natural history, art, clocks, coins, silver, costume   32599

Chester-le-Street

Anker's House Museum, Church Chare, Chester-le-Street DH3 3QB - T: (0191) 3883295, Internet: http://www.ris.niaa.org.uk/museums/anker.htm
Archaeological Museum
Roman and Anglo-Saxon artefacts   32600

Chesterfield

Chesterfield Museum and Art Gallery, Saint Mary's Gate, Chesterfield S41 7TD - T: (01246) 345727, Fax: 345720, E-mail: museum@chesterfieldbc.gov.uk, Internet: http://www.chesterfieldbc.co.uk. Head: A.M. Knowles
Historical Museum - 1994
Locally produced salt glazed pottery (19th-20th c)   32601

Hardwick Hall, Doe Lea, Chesterfield S44 5QJ - T: (01246) 850430, Fax: 854200, E-mail: ehwxxx@smtp.ntrust.org.uk. Head: C. Corry-Thomas
Decorative Arts Museum - 1597
Furniture, tapestry, needlework, and portraits of the Cavendish family, late 16th c house, greatest of all Elizabethan houses and garden, corn mill and parkland   32602

Peacock Heritage Centre, Low Pavement, Chesterfield S40 1PB - T: (01246) 345777/78, Fax: 345770, E-mail: publicity@chesterfieldbc.gov.uk
Local Museum   32603

Revolution House, Hight St, Old Whittington, Chesterfield - T: (01246) 345727, Fax: 345720. Head: A.M. Knowles
Historical Museum - 1938
Restored 17th c building with 17th c furnishings, hist of the Revolution of 1688   32604

Chicheley

Beatty Museum, Chicheley Hall, Chicheley MK16 9JJ - T: (01234) 391252, Fax: 391388, E-mail: enquiries@chicheleyhall.co.uk, Internet: http://www.chicheleyhall.co.uk
Public Gallery   32605

Chichester

Cathedral Treasury, Royal Chantry, Cathedral Cloisters, Chichester PO19 1PX - T: (01243) 782595, Fax: 536190. Head: M.J. Moriarty
Religious Arts Museum
Historical ecclesiastical plate from diocese and cathedral   32606

Chichester District Museum, 29 Little London, Chichester PO19 1PB - T: (01243) 784683, Fax: 776766, E-mail: districtmuseum@chichester.gov.uk, Internet: http://www.chichester.gov.uk/museum
Local Museum - 1964
Local archaeology and social hist   32607

Fishbourne Roman Palace and Museum, The Sussex Archaeological Society, Salthill Rd, Fishbourne, Chichester PO19 2QR - T: (01243) 785859, Fax: 539266, E-mail: adminfish@sussexpast.co.uk, Internet: http://www.sussexpast.co.uk. Head: David J. Rudkin
Archaeological Museum - 1968
Roman ruins and finds, Britains largest coll of 'in-situ' Roman mosaic floors and other architectural and artefactual remains, formal Roman garden planted to its original plan   32608

Goodwood House, Goodwood, Chichester PO18 0PX - T: (01243) 755000, Fax: 755005, E-mail: housevisiting@goodwood.co.uk, Internet: http://www.goodwood.co.uk. Head: Duke of Richmond
Fine Arts Museum / Decorative Arts Museum - 1616
Family portraits, Sèvres porcelain, French furniture, 4 Gobelin tapestries, paintings by Van Dyck, Canaletto, English furniture   32609

Guildhall Museum, Priory Park, Chichester PO19 1PB, mail addr: 29 Little London, Chichester PO19 1PB - T: (01243) 784683, Fax: 776766, E-mail: districtmuseum@chichester.gov.uk, Internet: http://www.chichester.gov.uk/museum
Local Museum - 1930
Hist of the site/building   32610

Mechanical Music and Doll Collection, Church Rd, Portfield, Chichester PO19 4HN - T: (01243) 372646, Fax: 370299. Head: Lester Jones, Clive Jones
Music Museum / Special Museum - 1983
Disc musical boxes, mechanical musical instruments   32611

Pallant House Gallery, 9 North Pallant, Chichester PO19 1TJ - T: (01243) 774557, Fax: 536038, E-mail: pallant@pallant.co.uk, Internet: http://www.pallanthousegallery.com. Head: Stefan van Raay
Fine Arts Museum / Decorative Arts Museum - 1982
20th c British art, bow porcelain   32612

Royal Military Police Museum, Roussillon Barracks, Broyle Rd, Chichester PO19 4BN - T: (01243) 534225, Fax: 534288, E-mail: museum@rhqrmp.freeserve.co.uk, Internet: http://www.rhqrmp.freeserve.co.uk. Head: P.H.M. Squier
Military Museum - 1946
Military police, uniforms, medals, history, books, pictures, arms - archives   32613

Chicksands

Intelligence Corps Museum and Medmenham Collection, Defence Intelligence and Security Centre, Chicksands SG17 5PR - T: (01462) 752297, Fax: 752297, E-mail: dirikicacorpssec-e1@disc.mod.uk
Special Museum
Hist of Intelligence Corps, hist of air photography   32614

Chiddingstone

Chiddingstone Castle, Chiddingstone TN8 7AD - T: (01892) 870347
Historical Museum / Fine Arts Museum - 1956
Stuart royal letters and memorabilia, Jacobite coll, portraits, manuscripts, medals, Japanese boxes, swords, lacquer, armaments and metal objects, Buddhistic art, Egyptian objects 4000 BC-Roman times   32615

Chippenham

Chippenham Museum and Heritage Centre, 10 Market Pl, Chippenham SN15 3HF - T: (01249) 705020, Fax: 705025, E-mail: heritage@chippenham.gov.uk. Head: Mike Stone
Local Museum - 2000   32616

Yelde Hall Museum → Chippenham Museum and Heritage Centre

Chipping Campden

Woolstaplers Hall Museum, High St, Chipping Campden GL55 6HB - T: (01386) 840101, Fax: 840332. Head: Penny Woodley
Local Museum - 1970
Domestic equipment, 19th c woodworkers' tools, relics of a cinema of the 1920s, cameras and photographic equipment, photographs, cine cameras and projectors, typewriters, sewing

machines, man traps, apothecary and medical equipment, scientific instruments, baby carriages and clothes, Victorian flying balloon and stunt parachute 32617

Chipping Norton

Chipping Norton Museum of Local History, Westgate Centre, High St, Chipping Norton OX7 5AD - T: (01608) 658518, 641216, E-mail: museumcn@aol.com. Head: J.G. Howells
Local Museum
Agricultural tools and horse harnesses, local industries, tweed, brewing and agricultural engineering 32618

Chirk

Castell y Waun (Chirk Castle), Chirk LL14 5AF - T: (01691) 777701, Fax: 774706, E-mail: gcwmsn@smtp.ntrust.org.uk. Head: M.V. Wynne
Decorative Arts Museum / Fine Arts Museum
Paintings, decorative art, history, 16th, 17th, 18th and early 19th c decorations 32619

Chittlehampton

Cobbaton Combat Collection, Chittlehampton EX37 9RZ - T: (01769) 540740, 540414, Fax: 540141, E-mail: info@cobbatoncombat.co.uk, Internet: http://www.cobbatoncombat.co.uk. Head: Preston Isaac
Military Museum - 1980
60 Second World War British and Canadian tanks, trucks, guns and armoured cars, which have been restored to running order 32620

Chollerford

Clayton Collection Museum, Chesters Roman Fort, Chollerford NE46 4EP - T: (01434) 681379. Head: Georgina Plowright
Archaeological Museum - 1903
Roman coll from sites along central sector of hadrian's wall 32621

Chorley

Astley Hall Museum and Art Gallery, Astley Park, Chorley PR7 1NP - T: (01257) 515555, Fax: 515556, E-mail: astleyhall@lineone.net, Internet: http://www.astleyhall.co.uk. Head: Nigel Wright
Fine Arts Museum / Decorative Arts Museum - 1924
Jacobean furniture, paintings and etchings, Flemish tapestries, Leeds pottery, 18th c English glass, magnificent plaster ceilings 32622

Christchurch

Christchurch Tricyle Museum, Quay Rd, Christchurch BH23 1BY - T: (01202) 479849
Science&Tech Museum 32623

Red House Museum and Art Gallery, Quay Rd, Christchurch BH23 1BU - T: (01202) 482860, Fax: 481924, E-mail: musmjh@hants.gov.uk, Internet: http://www.hants.gov.uk/museums. Head: Jim Hunter
Local Museum - 1951
Paleolithic to medieval local archaeology, local hist, geology and natural hist, costumes, toys, dolls, domestic equipment, agricultural equipment, fashion plates, Victoriana, paintings, drawings, prints and photographs of local interest - library, herb garden 32624

Saint Michael's Loft Museum, Priory, Christchurch BH23 1BU - T: (01202) 485804
Decorative Arts Museum
Stonework and carving from Saxon to Tudor times 32625

Southern Electric Museum, Old Power Station, Bargates, Christchurch BH23 1QE - T: (01202) 480467, Fax: 480468. Head: Eric Jones
Science&Tech Museum
Working models of orginal experiments by Faraday, Richie and Barlow 32626

Chudleigh

Ugbrooke House, Chudleigh TQ13 0AD - T: (01626) 852179, Fax: 853322. Head: L.A. Martin
Military Museum
Private military coll, portraits 32627

Church Stretton

Acton Scott Historic Working Farm, Wenlock Lodge, Acton Scott, Church Stretton SY6 6QN - T: (01694) 781306, Fax: 781569, E-mail: - acton.scott.museum@shropshire-cc.gov.uk, Internet: http://www.shropshire-cc.gov.uk/museum.nsf. Head: Mike Barr
Open Air Museum / Agriculture Museum - 1975
Stock, crops and machinery (1870-1920), agriculture, rural crafts (wheelwright, farrier, blacksmith), dairy, period cottage - library, technical workshops, education 32628

Cirencester

Cirencester Lock-Up, Trinity Rd, Cirencester GL7 1BR - T: (01285) 655611, Fax: 643286, Internet: http://www.cotswold.gov.uk
Local Museum 32629

Corinium Museum, Park St, Cirencester GL7 2BX - T: (01285) 655611, Fax: 643286, E-mail: john.paddock@cotswold.gov.uk, Internet: http://www.cotswold.gov.uk. Head: Dr. J.M Paddock
Archaeological Museum / Local Museum - 1856
Romano-British antiquities from the site of Corinium Dobunnorum, archaeology, local history, military 32630

Clare

Ancient House Museum, High St, Clare CO10 8NY - T: (01787) 277520, E-mail: clareah@btinternet.com, Internet: http://www.clare-ancient-house-museum.co.uk. Head: David J. Ridley
Local Museum
Clare people and industries, exhibits from prehistoric to Victorian times 32631

Clatteringshaws

Galloway Deer Museum, Clatteringshaws DG7 3SQ - T: (01644) 2285
Natural History Museum
Red deer, roe deer, wild goats, local wildlife, geology of the district 32632

Claydon

Bygones Museum, Butlin Farm, Claydon OX17 1EP - T: (01295) 690258. Head: Catherine Fox
Agriculture Museum
Domestic equipment, agricultural implements, tools once used by rural craftsmen 32633

Cleethorpes

Humber Estuary Discovery Centre, The Lakeside, Kings Rd, Cleethorpes DN35 0AG - T: (01472) 323232, Fax: 323233, E-mail: discovery.centre@nelincs.gov.uk, Internet: http://www.time-discoverycentre.co.uk. Head: Lisa Edinborough
Historical Museum 32634

Clevedon

Clevedon Court, Tickenham Rd, Clevedon BS21 6QU - T: (01275) 872257
Decorative Arts Museum
Eltonware ceramics, Nailsea glass, prints of bridges 32635

Clitheroe

Castle Museum, Castle, Clitheroe BB7 1BA - T: (01200) 424635, Fax: 424568, E-mail: museum@ribblevalley.gov.uk, Internet: http://www.ribblevalley.gov.uk. Head: D. Mary Hornby
Local Museum
20 000 Geology specimens: International coll of rocks, minerals and fossils, local hist - earth science educational project 32636

Clun

Clun Local History Museum, Town Hall, The Square, Clun SY7 8JA - T: (01588) 640681, Fax: 640681, E-mail: jkenttomey@stapledon12.freeserve.uk. Head: J.K. Tomey
Archaeological Museum / Local Museum - 1934
Over 1000 flint artefacts Palaeolithic to Bronze Age 32637

Clydebank

Clydebank Museum, Old Town Hall, Dumbarton Rd, Clydebank G81 1UE - T: (01389) 738702, Fax: 738689, E-mail: curator@clydebankmuseum.sol.co.uk, Internet: http://www.west-dumbarton.gov.uk. Head: Mary Land
Local Museum
Local industry and social history, with special coll of ship models and sewing machines, shipbuilders history 32638

Coalbrookdale

Darby Houses, Rosehill and Dale House, Darby Rd, Coalbrookdale TF8 7EL - T: (01952) 432551. Head: John Challen
Historical Museum
Quaker ironmasters, Abraham Darby III, builder of the Iron Bridge 32639

Long Warehouse, Coalbrookdale TF8 7EL - T: (01952) 432141, Fax: 432751. Head: John Challen
Fine Arts Museum / Historical Museum
Elton coll of industrial art - library, archive 32640

Museum of Iron and Darby Furnace, Coalbrookdale TF8 7NR - T: (01952) 433418. Head: John Challen
Science&Tech Museum 32641

Coalport

Coalport China Museum, High St, Coalport TF8 7HT - T: (01952) 580650. Head: Ruth Denison
Decorative Arts Museum
History of China manufacturesince 1776, coll of Coalport and Caughley china 32642

Tar Tunnel, High St, Coalport TF8 7HS - T: (01952) 580627, Fax: 432204, E-mail: info@ironbridge.org.uk, Internet: http://www.ironbridge.org.uk. Head: Glen Lawes
Science&Tech Museum
18th c mining tunnel, natural bitumen 32643

Coalville

Snibston Discovery Park, Ashby Rd, Coalville LE16 3LN - T: (01530) 278444, Fax: 813301, E-mail: smastoris@leics.gov.uk. Head: Steph N. Mastoris
Science&Tech Museum
Transport, engineering, fashion, science, colliery 32644

Coatbridge

Summerlee Heritage Park, Heritage Way, Coatbridge ML5 1QD - T: (01236) 431261, Fax: 440429, Internet: http://www.summerlee.co.uk. Head: Carol Haddow
Local Museum / Historic Site - 1988
Social and industrial hist of Scotland's iron and steel and heavy engineering industries, coll of machinery and equipment, a steam winding engine, railway locomotives, two steam cranes, underground coalmine, recreated miner's cottages, Scotland's only electric tramway, art gallery 32645

Coate

Agricultural Museum, Water Country Park, Coate SN3 6AA
Agriculture Museum 32646

Cobham

Cobham Bus Museum, Redhill Rd, Cobham KT11 1EF - T: (01932) 868665, Fax: (01743) 358411, Internet: http://www.geocities.com/MotorCity/Downs/9026
Science&Tech Museum
London buses from 1925 to 1973 32647

Cockermouth

Cumberland Toy and Model Museum, Bank's Court, Market Pl, Cockermouth CA13 9NG - T: (01900) 827606, E-mail: rodmoore42@hotmail.com, Internet: http://www.toyandmodelmuseum.grb.cc. Head: Rod Moore
Special Museum - 1989
British toys from 1900 to present 32648

Printing House Museum, 102 Main St, Cockermouth CA13 9LX - T: (01900) 824984, Fax: 823124, E-mail: info@printinghouse.co.uk, Internet: http://www.printinghouse.co.uk. Head: David R. Winkworth
Science&Tech Museum - 1979
Hist of printing 15th c to 1970 (letterpress era), iron presses, platen presses, automatic presses, type founding machinery, stone and etching press 32649

Wordsworth House, Main St, Cockermouth CA13 9RX - T: (01900) 824805
Special Museum - 1937
First edition of William Wordworth's work, personal possessions, original paintings and watercolours by Turner, Morellese and Edward Dayes 32650

Cockley Cley

Iceni Village and Museums, Estate Office, Cockley Cley PE37 8AG - T: (01760) 721339, 24588, Fax: 721339. Head: Sir Samuel Roberts
Local Museum / Agriculture Museum - 1971
Carriage and farm implements, engines 32651

Colchester

Castle Museum, Colchester CO1 1TJ, mail addr: c/o Museum Resource Centre, 14 Ryegate Rd, Colchester CO1 1YG - T: (01206) 282931/2, 282939, Fax: 282925. Head: Philip Wise
Archaeological Museum - 1860
Material from Iron Age and Roman Colchester, Roman military tombstones, Roman pottery, bronze figure of Mercury - library 32652

East Anglian Railway Museum, Chappel and Wakes Colne Station, Colchester CO6 2DS - T: (01206) 242524, Fax: 242524, Internet: http://www.eastanglianrailwaymuseum.co.uk
Science&Tech Museum 32653

Hollytrees Museum, High St, Colchester CO1 1UG - T: (01206) 282931/2, 282940, Fax: 282925. Head: Tom Hodgson
Historical Museum - 1928
Georgian town house built in 1718 housing domestic displays of toys, costumes and decorative arts from the 18th, 19th and early 20th c - library 32654

Mansfield Costume Study Centre, 38 Churchfields, West Mersea, Colchester CO5 8QJ - T: (01206) 382513, E-mail: sarah@shehadeh1.freeserve.co.uk
Special Museum
Private costume coll, archive of books, slides, patterns - conservation workshop 32655

Minories Art Gallery, 74 High St, Firstsite, Colchester CO1 1UE - T: (01206) 577067, Fax: 577161
Public Gallery - 1956
Drawings and paintings by John Constable 32656

Natural History Museum, All Saints Church, High St, Colchester CO1 1YG - T: (01206) 282931/2, 282941, Fax: 282925. Head: Jeremy Bowdrey
Natural History Museum - 1958
Natural history of Essex 32657

Tymperleys Clock Museum, Trinity St, Colchester CO1 1JN - T: (01206) 282931/2, 282943, Fax: 282925
Science&Tech Museum - 1987
216 clocks and 12 watches 32658

University of Essex Exhibition Gallery, Wivenhoe Park, Colchester CO4 3SQ - T: (01206) 872074, 873333, Fax: 873598, E-mail: kennj@essex.ac.uk, Internet: http://www.essex.ac.uk. Head: Jessica Kenny
Fine Arts Museum / University Museum
150 works with regional focus, sited sculpture, contemporary Latin American art 32659

Coldstream

Coldstream Museum, 13 Market Sq, Coldstream TD12 4BD - T: (01890) 882630, Fax: 882631. Head: Ian Brown
Local Museum - 1971
Social and domestic hist of the Coldstream area, hist of the Coldstream guards regiment, raised in the town, 1659 32660

Hirsel Homestead Museum, The Hirsel, Coldstream TD12 4LP - T: (01890) 882834, Fax: 882834, E-mail: rogerdodd@btinternet.com. Head: Roger Dodd
Historical Museum
Archaeology, farming, forestry, the estate workshops, the laundry, the gardens, the dovecote, and natural history 32661

Colne

British in India Museum, Newtown St, Colne BB8 0JJ - T: (01282) 870215, 613129, Fax: 870215. Head: Henry Nelson
Historical Museum / Military Museum - 1972
Model soldiers, photographs, documents, paintings, postage stamps, letters, military uniforms - library 32662

Combe Martin

Combe Martin Museum, The Parade, Seaside, Combe Martin E34 0AP - T: (01271) 882441. Head: Jean Griffiths
Local Museum
Local industries, silver/lead mining, lime quarrying and burning, maritime, social history, photographs, documents - archives 32663

Compton, Devon

Compton Castle, Compton, Devon TQ3 1TA - T: (01803) 875740, Fax: 875740, E-mail: DPASET@smtp.ntrust.org.uk, Internet: http://www.national-trust.org.uk
Historic Site
Historic house and garden 32664

Compton, Surrey

Watts Gallery, Down Ln, Compton, Surrey GU3 1DQ - T: (01483) 810235. Head: Richard Jefferies
Fine Arts Museum - 1903
Paintings and sculptures by artist G.F. Watts 32665

Compton Verney

Compton Verney Collections (Reopens spring 2003), Compton Verney CV35 9HZ - T: (01926) 645500, Fax: 642224, E-mail: cvht@comptonverney.org.uk, Internet: http://www.comptonverney.org.uk. Head: Richard Gray
Fine Arts Museum
Old master paintings and British folk art 32666

Congleton

Little Moreton Hall, Congleton CW12 4SD - T: (01260) 272018, Fax: 292802, E-mail: mlmsca@smtp.ntrust.org.uk. Head: Dean V. Thomas
Decorative Arts Museum - 1937
Elizabethan house with woodwork, plaster decorations, oak furniture, pewter objects 32667

Coniston

Brantwood, Coniston LA21 8AD - T: (015394) 41396, Fax: 41263, E-mail: enquiries@brantwood.org.uk, Internet: http://www.brantwood.org.uk. Head: Howard Hull
Fine Arts Museum / Decorative Arts Museum
Former J. Ruskin's home, coll of Ruskin's watercolours and drawings, works by some of his friends, incl T.M. Rooke, Sir Edward Burne-Jones and William Holman Hunt, furniture, his personal possessions, books - library 32668

Ruskin Museum, Coniston Institute, Yewdale Rd, Coniston LA21 8DU - T: (015394) 41164, Fax: 41132, E-mail: curator@rusmus.free-online.co.uk, Internet: http://www.coniston.org.uk. Head: V.A.J. Slowe
Fine Arts Museum / Natural History Museum - 1900
Memorabilia of John Ruskin (1819-1900), incl watercolours, drawings, sketchbooks, geology, slate and coppermines 32669

Conwy

Aberconwy House, 2 Castle St, Conwy LL32 8AY - T: (01492) 592246, Fax: 860233. Head: Linda Thorpe
Local Museum
Medieval house that dates from the 14th c, now houses the Conwy Exhibition, depicting the life of the borough from Roman times to the present day 32670

Plas Mawr, High St, Conwy LL32 8DE - T: (01492) 593413. Head: L.H.S. Mercer
Historic Site
Plas Mawr is an Elizabethan mansion, built 1577-80, in virtually its original condition 32671

Royal Cambrian Academy of Art, Crown Ln, Conwy LL32 8AN - T: (01492) 593413, Fax: 593413, E-mail: rca@rcaconwy.org, Internet: http://www.rcaconwy.org. Head: Gwyneth Jones
Fine Arts Museum - 1881
Paintings, sculpture 32672

Cookham

Stanley Spencer Gallery, King's Hall, High St, Cookham SL6 9SJ - T: (01628) 523484, 471885, Internet: http://www.cookham.com. Head: Richard Hurley
Fine Arts Museum - 1962
Paintings and drawings by Stanley Spencer, reference works 32673

Cookstown

Wellbrook Beetling Mill, 20 Wellbrook Rd, Corkhill, Cookstown BT80 9RY - T: (028) 86748210, 86751735, E-mail: uspest@smtp.ntrust.org.uk
Science&Tech Museum 32674

Corbridge

Corbridge Roman Site Museum, Roman Site, Corbridge NE45 5NT - T: (01434) 632349, Fax: 633168, E-mail: georgiana.plowright@english-heritage.org.uk
Archaeological Museum - 1906
Roman inscriptions and other finds from the Roman town of Corstopitum 32675

Corfe Castle

Corfe Castle Museum, West St, Corfe Castle BH20 5HE. Head: W.J. Carter
Historical Museum
Early agricultural and clay working implements, clay and stone industries 32676

Cornhill-on-Tweed

Heatherslaw Mill, Ford and Etal Estates, Cornhill-on-Tweed TD12 4TJ - T: (01890) 820338, Fax: 820384, E-mail: tourism@ford-and-etal.co.uk. Head: Julia Nolan
Science&Tech Museum
Traditional milling of wheat 32677

Cornwall

Museum of Witchcraft, Boscastle, Cornwall PL35 0AE - T: (01840) 250111, E-mail: -museumofwitchcraft@compuserve.com, Internet: http://www.museumofwitchcraft.com. Head: Graham King
Special Museum
Displays on cursing, charms and spells, stone circles and ancient sacred sites, modern witchcraft, the persecution of witches 32678

Corpach

Treasures of the Earth, Rd fo the Isles A830, Corpach PH33 7JL - T: (01397) 772283, Fax: 772133
Natural History Museum
Coll of crystals, gemstones and fossils, simulation of cave, cavern and mining scene 32679

Corsham

Corsham Court, Corsham SN13 0BZ - T: (01249) 701610, Fax: 701610. Head: Pat Wallace
Fine Arts Museum / Decorative Arts Museum
Paintings by various old masters incl Filippo Lippi, Rubens, van Dyck, Reynolds, Guido Reni, furniture by Chippendale, Adam, Cobb, Johnson 32680

Hartham Park - Underground Quarry Museum, Park Ln, Corsham SN13 0QR - T: (01380) 828645. Head: David Pollard
Science&Tech Museum - 1989
Quarring, working and transport 32681

Cottesmore

Rutland Railway Museum, Ashwell Rd, Cottesmore LE15 7BX - T: (01572) 813203
Science&Tech Museum
Industrial railways, locomotives and wagons associated with local iron ore quarries 32682

Cotton

Mechanical Music Museum and Bygones, Blacksmith Rd, Cotton IP14 4QN - T: (01449) 613876, Internet: http://www.visitbritain.com. Head: Phyllis Keeble
Music Museum - 1982
Music boxes, polyphons, organettes, street pianos, barrel organs, pipe organs, fair organs, gigantic cafe organ, the Wurlitzer theatre pipe organ and many unusual items 32683

Cousland

Cousland Smiddy, 21 Hadfast Rd, Cousland EH22 2NZ - T: (0131) 6631058, Fax: 6632730, E-mail: smiddy@cousland99.freeserve.co.uk, Internet: http://www.propeller.net/cousland
Local Museum
Blacksmithing tools, farm machinery and tools 32684

Coventry

Coventry Toy Museum, Whitefriars Gate, Much Park St, Coventry CV1 2LT - T: (024) 76227560. Head: Ron Morgan
Special Museum
Coll of dolls, toys, games dating from 1750 to 1960, a display of amusement machines 32685

Coventry Watch Museum, POB 1714, Coventry CV3 6ZS - T: (024) 76402331, 76502916, E-mail: 100624.1127@compuserve.com, Internet: http://www.coventry.watches.org.uk
Science&Tech Museum
Coventry made clocks and watches, tools, watch industry, factories, and people at work 32686

Herbert Art Gallery and Museum, Jordan Well, Coventry CV1 5QP - T: (024) 76832381, 76832565, Fax: 76832410, E-mail: ann.walker@coventry.gov.uk, Internet: http://www.coventry-museum.org.uk. Head: Roger Vaughan, Margaret Rylatt
Fine Arts Museum / Local Museum - 1960
Sutherland sketches used in making Coventry Cathedral tapestry, local art, topography, local natural hist, silk ribbons, archaeology, social and industrial hist - Lunt Roman Fort 32687

Mead Gallery, c/o Warwick Arts Centre, University of Warwick, Coventry CV4 7AL - T: (024) 76524524, Fax: 76572664, E-mail: acaaf@csv.warwick.ac.uk. Head: Sarah Shalgosky
Fine Arts Museum
British post-war paintings, photographs, prints, sculpture 32688

Museum of British Road Transport, Saint Agnes Lane, Hales St, Coventry CV1 1PN - T: (024) 76832425, Fax: 76832465, E-mail: museum@mbrt.co.uk, Internet: http://www.mbrt.co.uk. Head: Barry Littlewood
Science&Tech Museum - 1980
230 bicycles, 75 motorcycles, more than 220 motor vehicles, a wide range of equipment and accessories - archives 32689

Whitefriars, London Rd, Coventry CV1 2JT - T: (024) 76832381, Fax: 76832410. Head: Roger Vaughan
Religious Arts Museum
14th c Carmelite friary 32690

Coverack

Poldowrian Museum of Prehistory, Coverack TR12 6RS - T: (01326) 280468
Archaeological Museum 32691

Cowbridge

Cowbridge and District Museum, Town Hall Cells, Cowbridge CF71 7AD - T: (01446) 775139. Head: D. Keith Jones
Local Museum
Local history, archaeology of Cowbridge 32692

Cowes

Cowes Maritime Museum, Beckford Rd, Cowes PO31 7SG - T: (01983) 293341/394, Fax: 293341, E-mail: tony.butler@iow.gov.uk. Head: Tony Butler
Science&Tech Museum - 1975
Items and archives from J. Samuel White & Co Ltd. shipbuilders, 5 small boats designed by Uffa Fox, yachting photos by Kirk of Cowes - library 32693

Sir Max Aitken Museum, 83 High St, Cowes PO31 7AJ - T: (01983) 295144, 293800, Fax: 200253
Special Museum
Paintings of maritime subjects, half models and full models of ships, including a number of Sir Max Aitken's own yachts, and souvenirs of former royal yachts 32694

Coxwold

Byland Abbey, Coxwold YO6 4BD - T: (01347) 868614. Head: Andrew Morrison
Religious Arts Museum 32695

Shandy Hall, Coxwold YO61 4AD - T: (01347) 868465, Fax: 868465, Internet: http://www.shandy-hall.org.uk. Head: Dr. Nicolas Barker
Special Museum
Place where Laurence Sterne wrote his 2 novels, relevant prints, paintings, books 32696

Cradley Heath

Haden Hall, Halesowen Rd, Cradley Heath B64 5LP - T: (01384) 569444, Fax: 412623
Historical Museum
Paintings, books etc 32697

Haden Hill House, Off Barrs Rd, Cradley Heath B64 7EX - T: (01384) 569444, Fax: 412623, Internet: http://www.sandwellmbc.broadnet.co.uk
Historical Museum 32698

Crail

Crail Museum, 62-64 Marketgate, Crail KY10 3TL - T: (01333) 450869
Local Museum - 1979
H.M.S. Jackdaw (world war II fleer air arm station) 32699

Crakehall

Crakehall Water Mill, Little Crakehall, Crakehall DL8 1HU - T: (01677) 423240, Internet: http://www.crakehall.org.uk
Science&Tech Museum 32700

Cranbrook

Cranbrook Museum, Carriers Rd, Cranbrook TN17 3JX - Internet: http://i.am/cranbrookmuseum. Head: Brian Brent
Local Museum
Local trades, social, domestic and community exhibits, Boyd Alexander Bird Coll - archives 32701

Crawley

Crawley Museum Centre, Goffs Park House, Old Horsham Rd, Southgate, Crawley RH11 8PE - T: (01293) 539088
Local Museum
Local history 32702

Ifield Watermill, Hydr Dr, Ifield, Crawley RH11 0PL - T: (01293) 539088
Science&Tech Museum
Milling machinery, rural crafts and local history 32703

Crayford

David Evans World of Silk, Bourne Industrial Park, Bourne Rd, Crayford DA1 4BP - T: (01322) 559401, Fax: 556420. Head: Liz Hulf
Special Museum
Hand blocks, craft tools and equipment used for silk screen printing, block printing 32704

Creetown

Creetown Exhibition Centre, 91 Saint John's St, Creetown DG8 7JE - T: (01671) 820343, 820251. Head: Andrew Ward
Local Museum 32705

Creetown Gem Rock Museum, Chain Rd, Creetown DG8 7HJ - T: (01671) 820357, Fax: 820554, E-mail: gem.rock@btinternet.com, Internet: http://www.gemrock.net. Head: Tim Stephenson
Natural History Museum - 1971
Scottish agate coll, British minerals, dinosaur egg fossil, cut gemstones, meteorite 32706

Cregneash

Cregneash Folk Village, Cregneash IM9 5PX - T: (01624) 648000, Fax: 648001, E-mail: enquiries@mnh.gov.im, Internet: http://www.gov.im/mnh. Head: Chris Page
Folklore Museum 32707

Cremyll

Mount Edgcumbe House, Cremyll PL10 1HZ - T: (01752) 822236, Fax: 822199. Head: Cynthia Gaskell
Decorative Arts Museum
Paintings, furniture, Plymouth porcelain 32708

Crewe

Museum of Primitive Methodism, Englesea Brook, Englesea Brook Methodist Chapel, Crewe CW2 5Q - T: (01270) 820836
Religious Arts Museum
Early pipe organ, printing press and chest of drawers pulpit, pottery, banners 32709

Railway Age, Vernon Wy, Crewe CW1 2DB - T: (01270) 212130
Science&Tech Museum
railway archives 32710

Crewkerne

Crewkerne and District Museum, Heritage Centre, Market Sq, Crewkerne TA18 7JU - T: (01460) 77079
Local Museum
Social and industrial history 32711

Criccieth

Criccieth Castle, off A497, Criccieth LL52 0AA - T: (01766) 522227
Archaeological Museum 32712

Cricklade

Cricklade Museum, 16 Calcutt St, Cricklade SN6 6BB - T: (01793) 750756. Head: T. Ramsden-Binks
Local Museum
Social history, Roman, Saxons, finds 32713

Cromarty

Cromarty Courthouse Museum, Church St, Cromarty IV11 8XA - T: (01381) 600418, Fax: 600408, E-mail: courthouse@mail.cali.co.uk, Internet: http://www.cali.co.uk/users/freeway/courthouse. Head: David Alston
Local Museum
Cromarty's rule in the history of Scottland 32714

Hugh Miller's Cottage, Church St, Cromarty IV11 8XA - T: (01381) 600245, Fax: 600391, E-mail: fgostwick@nts.org.uk. Head: Frieda Gostwick
Special Museum - 1890
Birthplace of Scottish geologist Hugh Miller (1802-1852), memorabilia, equipment, letters, fossil coll 32715

Cromer

Cromer Museum, East Cottages, Tucker St, Cromer NR27 9HB - T: (01263) 513543, Fax: 511651, E-mail: allstair.murphy.mus@norfolk.gov.uk, Internet: http://www.norfolk.gov.uk/Tourism/Museums. Head: Vanessa Trevelyan
Local Museum - 1978 32716

Henry Blogg Lifeboat Museum, The Gangway, Cromer NR27 9HE - T: (01263) 511294, Fax: 511294, E-mail: rfmuirhead@csma.netlink.co.uk. Head: Frank H. Muirhead
Historical Museum
Houses the lifeboat, H F Bailey 777, History of the lifeboat station from 1804, models 32717

Cromford

Cromford Mill, Mill Ln, Cromford DE4 3RQ - T: (01629) 824297, Fax: 823256, E-mail: info@arkwrightsociety.org.uk, Internet: http://www.arkwrightsociety.org.uk. Head: Dr. Christopher Charlton, Sir George Kenyon
Science&Tech Museum - 1979
Water powered cotton spinning mill 32718

Crosby-on-Eden

Solway Aviation Museum, Aviation House, Carlisle Airport, Crosby-on-Eden CA6 4NW - T: (01228) 573823, Fax: 573823, E-mail: info@solway-aviation-museum.org.uk, Internet: http://www.solway-aviation-museum.org.uk. Head: David Kirkpatrick
Science&Tech Museum
Local aviation heritage and the Blue Streak Project at Spadeadam 32719

Croydon

Croydon Museum, Croydon Clocktower, Katherine St, Croydon CR9 1ET - T: (020) 82531022, Fax: 82531003, E-mail: museum@croydon.gov.uk, Internet: http://www.croydon.gov.uk/museum. Head: Rachel Hasted
Local Museum / Decorative Arts Museum
Local people's lives, Riesco coll of Chinese porcelain 32720

Croydon Natural History and Scientific Society Museum, 96a Brighton Rd, Croydon CR2 6AD - T: (01883) 349206. Head: P. Sowan
Local Museum
Archaeology, geology, social history, ethnography 32721

Cuckfield

Cuckfield Museum, Queen's Hall, High St, Cuckfield RH17 5EL - T: (01444) 454276. Head: Marilyn McInnes
Local Museum
Local history 32722

Cullyhanna

Cardinal Ó Fiaich Heritage Centre, Áras an Chairdiméil Ó Fiaich, Slatequarry Rd, Cullyhanna BT35 0JH - T: (01693) 868757
Religious Arts Museum 32723

Culross

Culross Palace, Sandhaven, Culross KY12 8HT - T: (01383) 721814, Fax: 622049. Head: Grace C. Murray
Decorative Arts Museum - 1932
17th c wood panelling, painted ceilings and furniture 32724

Dunimarle Castle, Culross KY12 8JN - T: (01383) 229
Decorative Arts Museum
Palace (1597-1611) with wood-panelling, tempera ceiling 32725

Town House, Sandhaven, Culross KY12 8HT - T: (01383) 880359, Fax: 882675, E-mail: information@nts.org.uk, Internet: http://www.nts.org.uk
Local Museum 32726

Cumbernauld

Cumbernauld Museum, 8 Allander Walk, Cumbernauld G67 1EE - T: (01236) 725664, Fax: 458350
Local Museum 32727

Cumnock

Baird Institute Museum, 3 Lugar St, Cumnock KA18 1AD - T: (01290) 421701, Fax: 421701, Internet: http://www.east-ayrshire.gov.uk/tourism/4.1.2.a.tourism.html. Head: Charles J. Woodward
Decorative Arts Museum / Local Museum - 1891
Cumnock pottery, Mauchline boxware, Ayrshire embroidery and the "Lochnorris Collection" of artefacts mining equipment, photos, local and social history 32728

Cupar

Hill of Tarvit Mansion House, Cupar KY15 5PB - T: (01334) 653127, Fax: 653127, Internet: http://www.nts.org.uk. Head: K. Caldwell
Decorative Arts Museum / Fine Arts Museum
French, Chippendale and vernacular furniture, Dutch paintings and pictures by Scottish artists Raeburn and Ramsay, Flemish tapestries, Chinese porcelain and bronzes 32729

Cwmbran

Llanyrafon Farm, Llanfrecfa Way, Cwmbran NP44 6HT - T: (01633) 861810
Agriculture Museum
Story of farming in East Gwent 32730

Dagenham

Valence House Museum and Art Gallery, Becontree Av, Dagenham RM8 3HT - T: (020) 82275293, Fax: 82275293, E-mail: valencehousemuseum@hotmail.com, Internet: http://www.bardaglea.org.uk/4-valence. Head: Sue Curtis
Local Museum / Fine Arts Museum - 1938
Local hist, art gallery, herb garden - archives 32731

Dalbeattie

Dalbeattie Museum, Southwick Rd, Dalbeattie DG5 4HA - T: (01556) 610437
Local Museum
Local granite quarrying industy, shipping, the railway, mills history 32732

Dalkeith

Dalkeith Arts Centre, White Hart St, Dalkeith EH22 10AE - T: (0131) 6636986, 2713970, Fax: 4404635, E-mail: alan.reid@midlothian.gov.uk. Head: Alan Reid
Public Gallery 32733

Dalmellington

Cathcartston Visitor Centre, Dalmellington KA6 7QY - T: (01292) 550633, Fax: 550937
Local Museum
Hand-loom weaving, local coal, Iron and brockwork industries 32734

Scottish Industrial Railway Centre, Minnivey Colliery, Burnton, Dalmellington KA6 7PU - T: (01292) 531144. Head: Charles Robinson
Science&Tech Museum - 1980
Steam and diesel locomotives, rolling stock and cranes 32735

Darlington

Darlington Art Gallery, Crown St, Darlington DL1 1ND - T: (01325) 462034, Fax: 381556, E-mail: - crown.street.library@darlington.gov.uk. Head: Peter White
Public Gallery - 1933
Art 32736

Darlington Railway Centre and Museum, North Road Station, Darlington DL3 6ST - T: (01325) 460532
Science&Tech Museum - 1975
Material relating to the Stockton and Darlington Railway, Ken Hoole coll, North Eastern Railway Association Library - Ken Hoole Study Centre 32737

Raby Castle, Staindrop, Darlington - T: (01833) 660202, Fax: 660169, E-mail: admin@rabycastle.com, Internet: http://www.rabycastle.com
Fine Arts Museum
Dutch and Flemish paintings 32738

Dartford

Brooking Collection, c/o School of Land and Construction Management, University of Greenwich, Oakfield Ln, Dartford DA1 2SZ - T: (020) 83319897, Fax: 83319305. Head: Charles Brooking
Science&Tech Museum
Architectural detail and fittings, including doors, windows, staircase sections, timber mouldings, small ironmongery and fire grates 32739

Dartford Borough Museum, Market St, Dartford DA1 1EU - T: (01322) 343555, Fax: 343209
Local Museum - 1908
Natural hist, geology, prehistoric finds, Roman, Saxon and medieval finds, Saxon finds from Horton Kirby site 32740

Dartmouth

Dartmouth Castle, Dartmouth TQ6 0JN - T: (01803) 833588. Head: Tony Musty
Military Museum
Historic artillery and military items 32741

Dartmouth Museum, 6 The Butterwalk, Dartmouth TQ6 9PZ - T: (01803) 832923, E-mail: darmouth@devonmuseums.net, Internet: http://www.devonmuseums.net/dartmouth
Local Museum
Local and maritime hist, ship models, 17th c panelling 32742

Newcomen Engine House, Mayors Av, adj to The Butterwalk, Dartmouth TQ6 9YY - T: (01803) 834224, Fax: 835631, E-mail: enquire@dartmouth-tic.demon.co.uk, Internet: http://www.dartmouth-tic.demon.co.uk
Science&Tech Museum
Pressure/steam engine of 1725 32743

Darwen

Sunnyhurst Wood Visitor Centre, off Earnsdale Rd, Darwen BB3 - T: (01254) 701545, Fax: 701545, E-mail: countryside@blackburn.gov.uk
Public Gallery 32744

Daventry

Daventry Museum, Moot Hall, Market Sq, Daventry NN11 4BH - T: (01327) 302463, 71100, Fax: 706035. Head: Victoria Gabbitas
Local Museum - 1986 32745

Dawlish

Dawlish Museum, The Knowle, Barton Terrace, Dawlish EX7 9QH - T: (01626) 888557. Head: Brenda French
Local Museum - 1969
Local history, railway, industry, military, toys, clothes 32746

Deal

Deal Archaeological Collection, Library, Broad St, Deal - T: (01304) 374726
Archaeological Museum
Archaeological finds of the Deal area - library 32747

Deal Castle, Victoria Rd, Deal CT14 7BA - T: (01304) 372762. Head: Nick Moore
Historical Museum 32748

Maritime and Local History Museum, 22 Saint George's Rd, Deal CT14 6BA - T: (01304) 372679, E-mail: dealmuseum@lineone.net, Internet: http://home.freeuk.com/deal-museum. Head: Terry Williams
Historical Museum / Local Museum
Local history, people, boats 32749

Timeball Tower, Victoria Parade, Beach St, Deal CT14 7BP - T: (01304) 360897, 201200
Science&Tech Museum
Telegraphy and semaphores 32750

Dedham

Sir Alfred Munnings Art Museum, Castle House, Dedham CO7 6AZ - T: (01206) 322127, Fax: 322127. Head: Claire Woodage
Fine Arts Museum - 1970
Coll of paintings, sketches, studies of racehorses and of racing, equestrian portraits and hunting scenes, house, studios and grounds where Sir Alfred Munnings lived and painted for 40 yrs, large coll of his works 32751

Deepcut

Royal Logistic Corps Museum, Princess Royal Barracks, Deepcut GU16 6RW - T: (01252) 833371, Fax: 833484, E-mail: query@rlcmuseum.freeserve.co.uk. Head: D.F. Hazel
Military Museum
Military artefacts 32752

Denbigh

Denbigh Castle Museum, Denbigh - T: (0174571) 3979
Historical Museum
History of Denbigh, methods of castle warfare, the campaigns and castles of Edward I in North Wales, Richard Dudley, Earl of Leicester 32753

Denbigh Museum and Gallery, Hall Sq, Denbigh LL16 3NU - T: (01745) 816313, Fax: 816427, E-mail: manon.edwards@denbighshire.gov.uk. Head: Debbie Davis
Local Museum / Fine Arts Museum
Social, industrial and economical growth, cultural heritage 32754

Derby

Derby Industrial Museum, Silk Mill Ln, off Full St, Derby DE1 3AR - T: (01332) 255308, Fax: 716670, E-mail: David.Fraser@derby.gov.uk, Internet: http://www.derby.gov.uk/museums. Head: Roger Shelley
Science&Tech Museum - 1974
Rolls-Royce aero engine coll, items relating to the Midland Railway and especially to Railway Research carried out in Derby 32755

Derby Museum and Art Gallery, The Strand, Derby DE1 1BS - T: (01332) 716659, Fax: 716670, E-mail: David.Fraser@derby.gov.uk, Internet: http://www.derby.gov.uk/museums. Head: David Fraser
Fine Arts Museum / Local Museum - 1879
Paintings of Joseph Wright, history, geology, porcelain, paintings, drawings, engravings, numismatics 32756

The Eastern Museum, Kedleston Hall, Derby DE22 5JH - T: (01332) 842191, Fax: 841972, E-mail: ehdxxx@sntp.ntrust.org.uk
Ethnology Museum - 1927
Eastern silver, textiles, ceramics, metalworks, ivory, furniture 32757

Pickford's House Museum, 41 Friar Gate, Derby DE1 1DA - T: (01332) 255363, Fax: 255277, E-mail: David.Fraser@derby.gov.uk, Internet: http://www.derby.gov.uk/museums. Head: Ellen Malin, Elizabeth Spencer
Decorative Arts Museum - 1988
Georgian town house, historic costumes, toy theatres, decorative art, domestic life 32758

Regimental Museum of the 9th/12th Royal Lancers, The Strand, Derby DE1 1BS - T: (01332) 716656, Fax: 716670, E-mail: David.Fraser@derby.gov.uk, Internet: http://www.derby.gov.uk/museums. Head: A. Tarnowski
Military Museum 32759

Royal Crown Derby Museum, 194 Osmaston Rd, Derby DE23 8JZ - T: (01332) 712800, Fax: 72899, E-mail: enquiries@royal-crown-derby.co.uk, Internet: http://www.royal-crown-derby.co.uk
Decorative Arts Museum - 1969
Hist of ceramics production in Derby since 1748 32760

Dereham

Hobbies Museum of Fretwork, 34-36 Swaffham Rd, Dereham NR19 2QZ - T: (01362) 692985, Fax: 699145, E-mail: enquire@hobbies-dereham.co.uk, Internet: http://www.hobbies-dereham.co.uk
Special Museum
Machines and tools, fretwork articles 32761

Dervaig

The Old Byre Heritage Centre, Dervaig PA75 6QR - T: (01688) 400229, E-mail: theoldbyre@lineone.net. Head: J.M. Bradley
Natural History Museum / Local Museum
Natural history and history of Mull, geology, wildlife 32762

Devizes

Devizes Museum → Wiltshire Heritage Museum and Gallery

Kennet and Avon Canal Museum, Devizes Wharf, Couch Ln, Devizes SN10 1EB - T: (01380) 721279, 729489, Fax: 727870, E-mail: administrator@katrust.org. Head: Clive Hackford
Science&Tech Museum
History of the Kennet and Avon Canal from 1788 32763

Wiltshire Heritage Museum and Gallery, 41 Long St, Devizes SN10 1NS - T: (01380) 727369, Fax: 722150, E-mail: wanhs@wiltshireheritage.org.uk, Internet: http://www.wiltshireheritage.org.uk. Head: Dr. Paul Robinson
Archaeological Museum / Historical Museum / Fine Arts Museum / Local Museum - 1853
Archaeology, Stourhead and Bronze age coll, geological fossils, paintings by John Buckler, etchings by Robin Tanner - library, biological record centre 32764

Wiltshire Regiment Museum, Le Marchant Barracks, Devizes
Military Museum - 1933
Militaria on 62nd and 99th Regiment of Foot, Wiltshire Regiment and Militaria 32765

Dewsbury

Dewsbury Museum, Crow Nest Park, Heckmondwike Rd, Dewsbury WF13 0AS - T: (01924) 325100, E-mail: cultural-hq@geo2.poptel.org.uk, Internet: http://www.kirkleesmc.gov.uk. Head: Brian Haigh
Local Museum
Local history and childhood 32766

Dickleburgh

100th Bomb Group Memorial Museum, Common Rd, Dickleburgh IP21 4PH - T: (01379) 740708. Head: S.P. Hurry
Military Museum 32767

Didcot

Didcot Railway Centre, Didcot OX11 7NJ - T: (01235) 817200, Fax: 510621, E-mail: didrlyc@globalnet.co.uk, Internet: http://www.didcotrailway-centre.org.uk. Head: M. Dean
Science&Tech Museum - 1967
Great Western Railway locomotives and carriages 32768

Dingwall

Dingwall Museum, Town House, High St, Dingwall IV15 9RY - T: (01349) 865366. Head: Kate MacPherson
Local Museum - 1975
Local hist, military exhibits 32769

Disley

Lyme Hall, Lyme Park, Disley SK12 2NX - T: (01663) 762023, Fax: 765035, E-mail: mlyrec@smtp.ntrust.org.uk, Internet: http://www.national-trust.org.uk. Head: Kevin Reid
Decorative Arts Museum - 1946
16th c house, remodelled in 18th c in Palladian style interiors of many architectural fashions, Mortlake tapestries, limewood carvings, Heraldic glass, English clocks 32770

Diss

Bressingham Steam Museum, Thetford Rd, Bressingham, Diss IP22 2AB - T: (01379) 687386/82, Fax: 688085, E-mail: info@bressingham.co.uk, Internet: http://www.bressingham.co.uk. Head: Alan Bloom, David D. Ward, Mervyn Thompson
Science&Tech Museum - 1964/1973
Coll of steam engines, road and industrial engines, a steam-operated Victorian roundabout, steamhauled narrow gauge railways, locomotives, mechanical organ, fire fighting equipment dating from 1800's 32771

Diss Museum, The Shambles, Market Pl, Diss IP22 3AB - T: (01379) 650618, Fax: 643848. Head: Denise Beale
Local Museum
History and prehistory of the market town 32772

Ditchling

Ditchling Museum, Church Ln, Ditchling BN6 8TB - T: (01273) 844744, Fax: 844744, E-mail: ditchling.museum@mistral.co.uk, Internet: http://www.ditchling-museum.com. Head: Ann Phillips
Local Museum / Fine Arts Museum - 1985
Calligraphy, engraving, typography 32773

Dobwalls

The John Southern Gallery, Dobwalls Family Adventure Park, Dobwalls PL14 6HB - T: (01579) 320325, 321129, Fax: 321345. Head: John Southern
Fine Arts Museum
Steven Townsend (born 1955), Britain's dog painter, his limited prints, Carl Brenders (born 1937) nature paintings and his limited prints 32774

Thorburn Gallery → The John Southern Gallery

Doddington

Doddington Hall, Doddington LN6 4RU - T: (01522) 694308, Fax: 685259, E-mail: fionawatson@doddingtonhall.free-online.co.uk, Internet: http://www.doddingtonhall.free-online.co.uk. Head: Antony Jarvis
Association with Coll
China, glass, furniture, textiles, pictures 32775

Dollar

Dollar Museum, Castle Campbell Hall, 1 High St, Dollar FK14 7AY - T: (01259) 742895, 743239, Fax: 742895, E-mail: janet.carolan@btinternet.com. Head: Janet Carolan
Local Museum
Local hist, Dollar academy, Devon Valley railway, castle hist 32776

Dolwyddelan

Ty Mawr Wybrnant, Dolwyddelan LL25 0HJ
Special Museum
Birthplace of Bishop William Morgan who translated the Bible into Welsh which was the foundation of modern Welsh literature 32777

Doncaster

Brodsworth Hall, Brodsworth, Doncaster DN5 7XJ - T: (01302) 722598, Fax: 337165. Head: Peter Gordon-Smith
Historical Museum
Paintings, Italian sculpture, furnishings, kitchen equipment - gardens 32778

Doncaster Museum and Art Gallery, Chequer Rd, Doncaster DN1 2AE - T: (01302) 734293, Fax: 735409, E-mail: museum@doncaster.gov.uk, Internet: http://www.doncaster.gov.uk. Head: Goeff Preece
Local Museum / Fine Arts Museum - 1899
Regional hist, archaeology, natural hist, fine and decorative art, temporary exhibitions 32779

King's Own Yorkshire Light Infantry Regimental Museum, Chequer Rd, Doncaster DN1 2AE - T: (01302) 734293, Fax: 735409, E-mail: museum@doncaster.gov.uk, Internet: http://www.doncaster.gov.uk. Head: C.M.J. Deedes
Military Museum - 1950
History of King's Own Yorkshire Light Infantry, medals, armaments, uniforms 32780

Museum of South Yorkshire Life, Cusworth Hall, Cusworth Ln, Doncaster DN5 7TU - T: (01302) 782342, Fax: 782342, E-mail: museum@duncaster.gov.uk, Internet: http://www.doncaster.gov.uk. Head: Frank Carpenter
Historical Museum - 1967
Social history of South Yorkshire, coll illustrate life over last 200 years (domestic life, costume, childhood, transport) 32781

Sandtoft Transport Centre, Belton Rd, Sandtoft, Doncaster DN8 5SX - T: (01724) 711391, Internet: http://freespace.virgin.net/neil.worthington/sandtoft98.htm
Science&Tech Museum
Trolleybuses, motorbus, miniature railway, coll of small exhibits relating to trolleybus 32782

Donington-le-Heath

Manor House, Manor Rd, Donington-le-Heath LE67 2FW - T: (01530) 831259, Fax: 831259, E-mail: museums@leics.gov.uk, Internet: http://www.leics.gov.uk/lcc/tourism/attractions_-museums.html. Head: Peter Liddle
Decorative Arts Museum 32783

Dorchester

Athelhampton House, Dorchester - T: (01305) 848363, Fax: 848135, E-mail: pcooke@athelhampton, Internet: http://www.athelhampton.co.uk. Head: Patrick Cooke
Historic Site - 1957
House with 15th-16th c furniture 32784

Dinosaur Museum, Icen Way, Dorchester DT1 1EW - T: (01305) 269880, 269741, Fax: 268885, E-mail: info@dinosaur-museum.org.uk, Internet: http://www.dinosaur-museum.org.uk. Head: Jackie D. Ridley
Natural History Museum - 1984 32785

Dorset County Museum, High West St, Dorchester DT1 1XA - T: (01305) 262735, Fax: 257180, E-mail: dorsetcountymuseum@dor-mus.demon.co.uk, Internet: http://www.dorsetcountymuseum.co.uk
Local Museum - 1846
County archaeology, geology, biology, local and regional history, memorabilia, literature incl Thomas Hardy coll - library 32786

Dorset Teddy Bear Museum, Teddy Bear House, Antelope Walk, Dorchester DT1 1BE - T: (01305) 263200, 26974, Fax: 268885, E-mail: info@teddybearhouse.co.uk, Internet: http://www.teddybearhouse.co.uk. Head: Jackie Ridley
Special Museum 32787

Military Museum of Devon and Dorset, The Keep, Bridport Rd, Dorchester DT1 1RN - T: (01305) 264066, Fax: 250373, E-mail: keep.museum@talk21.com, Internet: http://www.keepmilitarymuseum.org. Head: R.A. Leonard
Military Museum - 1927
Uniforms, weapons, militaria, exhibits of Devon Regiment, Dorset Regiment, local militia and volunteers, Queens Own Dorset Yeomanry and Devonshire and Dorset Regiment - library, archives 32788

Old Crown Court and Shire Hall, 58-60 High West St, Dorchester DT1 1UZ - T: (01305) 252241, Fax: 257039, E-mail: tourism@westdorset.dc.gov.uk, Internet: http://www.westdorset.com
Historical Museum
Law and order (Rough Justice), Tolpuddle Martyrs 32789

Tutankhamun Exhibition, High West St, Dorchester DT1 1UW - T: (01305) 269571, 269741, Fax: 268885, E-mail: info@tutankhamun-exhibition.co.uk, Internet: http://www.tutankhamun-exhibition.co.uk. Head: Dr. Michael Ridley
Archaeological Museum - 1987 32790

Dorchester-on-Thames

Dorchester Abbey Museum, Abbey Guest House, Dorchester-on-Thames OX10 7HH - T: (01865) 340751, E-mail: richard.ridoll@freenet.co.uk, Internet: http://www.dorchester-abbey.org.uk. Head: Dr. Richard Riddell
Local Museum
Local history since prehistoric time 32791

Dorking

Dorking and District Museum, 62a West St, Dorking RH4 1BS - T: (01306) 876591. Head: J.G. Potter
Local Museum
Toys, domestic and agricultural displays, fossil coll 32792

Polesden Lacey, Dorking RH5 6BD - T: (01372) 453401, 452048, Fax: 452023, E-mail: spljxd@smtp.ntrust.org.uk. Head: Sue Forster
Decorative Arts Museum
Pictures, furniture, tapestries, art objects 32793

Dornie

Eilean Donan Castle Museum, Dornie IV40 8DX - T: (01599) 555202, Fax: 555262
Local Museum 32794

Dornoch

Dornoch Heritage Museum, Struie Rd, Ardoch, Dornoch - T: (01862) 810754
Local Museum 32795

Dorset

Museum of Net Manufacture, Bridgeacre, Uploders, Bridport, Dorset DT6 4PF - T: (01308) 485349, Fax: 485621. Head: Jacquie Summers
Historical Museum
Documents, ledgers, traditional tools, samples of natural fibres, historic trade 32796

Douglas, Isle of Man

Manx Museum, Manx National Heritage, Kingswood Grove, Douglas, Isle of Man IM1 3LY - T: (01624) 648000, Fax: 648001, E-mail: enquiries@mnh.gov.im, Internet: http://www.gov.im/mnh. Head: Stephen Harrison
Local Museum / Historical Museum / Fine Arts Museum
archive 32797

Douglas, Lanarkshire

Douglas Heritage Museum, Saint Sophia's Chapel, Bells Wynd, Douglas, Lanarkshire ML11 0QH - T: (01555) 851536
Local Museum
Village history, Douglas family 32798

Doune

Doune Motor Museum, Carse of Cambus, Doune FK16 6DF - T: (01786) 841203, Fax: 842070
Science&Tech Museum 32799

Dover

Agricultural Museum Brook, Old Post Office, Slip Ln, Alkham, Dover CT15 7DE - T: (01304) 824969, E-mail: brian@bwimsett.freeserve.co.uk
Agriculture Museum
Old farm equipment, medieval barn and oast house 32800

Crabble Corn Mill, Lower Rd, River, Dover CT17 0LW - T: (01304) 823292, 362569, Fax: 826040, E-mail: mill@invmed.demon.co.uk, Internet: http://www.invmed.demon.co.uk
Science&Tech Museum 32801

Dover Castle, Dover CT16 1HN - T: (01304) 201628, 211067, Fax: 214739. Head: Jan Summerfield
Historical Museum
Medieval fortress 32802

Dover Museum, Market Sq, Dover CT16 1PB - T: (01304) 201066, Fax: 241186, Internet: http://www.dover.gov.uk/museum. Head: Christine Waterman
Local Museum / Archaeological Museum / Public Gallery - 1836
Local history, ceramics, geology, transportation, embroidery, cameras, natural history, bronze age archaeology 32803

Dover Old Town Goal, Town Hall, Biggin St, Dover CT16 1DQ - T: (01304) 202723, 242766, Fax: 201200
Historical Museum
Courtroom, cells, Victorian prison 32804

Grand Shaft, Snargate St, Dover CT17 9BZ - T: (01304) 201200, Fax: 201200. Head: Trevor Jones
Military Museum
Vast military fortification 32805

Princess of Wales's Royal Regiment and Queen's Regiment Museum, 5 Keep Yard, Castle, Dover CT16 1HU - T: (01304) 240121, Fax: 240121, E-mail: pwrrqueensmuseum@tinyworld.co.uk
Military Museum 32806

Queen's Regiment Museum → Princess of Wales's Royal Regiment and Queen's Regiment Museum

Roman Tainted House, New St, Eythorne, Dover CT15 4DF - T: (01304) 203279
Archaeological Museum 32807

Wye College Museum of Agriculture → Agricultural Museum Brook

Downe

Darwin Museum → Down House

Down House, Luxted Rd, Downe BR6 7JT - T: (01689) 859119, Fax: 862755, Internet: http://www.english-heritage.org.uk. Head: Margaret Speller
Special Museum / Natural History Museum - 1929/1998
Memorabilia of biologist Charles Darwin, his study, portraits 32808

Downpatrick

Down County Museum, The Mall, Downpatrick BT30 6AH - T: (028) 44615218, Fax: 44615590, E-mail: museum@downdc.gov.uk, Internet: http://www.downdc.gov.uk. Head: Michael D. King
Local Museum - 1981 32809

Downpatrick Steam Railway, Railway Station, Market St, Downpatrick BT30 6LZ - T: (01396) 615779, E-mail: drm@downrail.freeserve.co.uk, Internet: http://www.uel.ac.uk/pers/1278/rly-pres/drm. Head: G. Cochrane
Science&Tech Museum
Steam and diesel locomotives, historic carriages and wagons, signal box, water tower, goods shed, travelling Post Office 32810

Draperstown

Plantation of Ulster Visitor Centre, 50 High St, Draperstown BT45 7AD - T: (028) 79627800, Fax: 79627732, E-mail: info@theflightoftheearlsexperience.com, Internet: http://www.theflightoftheearlsexperience.com. Head: Frank Larey
Agriculture Museum
Story of plantation of Ulster, Irish history from 1595 32811

Droitwich

Droitwich Spa Heritage Centre, Saint Richard's House, Victoria Sq, Droitwich WR9 8DS - T: (01905) 774312, Fax: 794226. Head: R.G. Pharo
Local Museum
Local artefacts from Roman times to the 17th c 32812

Hanbury Hall, School Rd, Droitwich WR9 7EA - T: (01527) 821214, Fax: 821251, E-mail: hanbury@smtp.ntrust.org.uk, Internet: http://www.ntrusts-evern.org.uk
Fine Arts Museum 32813

Drumnadrochit

Loch Ness 2000 Exhibition, Official Loch Ness Centre, Drumnadrochit IV63 6TU - T: (01456) 450573, Fax: 450770, E-mail: info@loch-ness-scotland.com, Internet: http://www.loch-ness-scotland.com. Head: R.W. Bremner
Special Museum 32814

Urquhart Castle, Drumnadrochit IV3 6TX - T: (01456) 450551. Head: Cameron McKenzie
Historical Museum 32815

Drumoak

Drum Castle, Drumoak AB3 5EY - T: (01330) 811204, Fax: 811962, E-mail: agordon@nts.org.uk, Internet: http://www.drum-castle.org.uk. Head: Alec Gordon
Historical Museum 32816

Dudley

Black Country Living Museum, Tipton Rd, Dudley DY1 4SQ - T: (0121) 5579643, Fax: 5574242, E-mail: info@bclm.co.uk, Internet: http://www.bclm.co.uk. Head: Ian N. Walden
Historical Museum - 1975
Social and industrial history of Black Country 32817

Dudley Museum and Art Gallery, Saint James's Rd, Dudley DY1 1HU - T: (01384) 815575, Fax: 815576, Internet: http://www.dudley.gov.uk. Head: Peter Barnes
Natural History Museum / Fine Arts Museum 32818

Royal Brierley Crystal Museum, Tipton Rd, Dudley DY1 4SH - T: (0121) 5305600, Fax: 5305590, E-mail: sales@royalbrierley.com, Internet: http://www.royalbrierley.com
Decorative Arts Museum 32819

Dufftown

Glenfiddich Distillery Museum, Glenfiddich Distillery, Dufftown AB5 4DH - T: (01340) 20373
Science&Tech Museum
19th-c furniture, many of the distillery ledgers, coopers' tools, and distillery equipment used in the past 32820

Dumbarton

Denny Ship Model Experiment Tank, Scottish Maritime Museum, Castle St, Dumbarton G82 1QS - T: (01389) 763444, Fax: 743093. Head: J.M. Tildesley
Science&Tech Museum
First ship model testing tank by William Froude (1883), drawing office, clay model moulding beds and shaping machinery 32821

Dumfries

Burns House, Burns St, Dumfries DG1 2PS - T: (01387) 255297, Fax: 265081, E-mail: info@dumfriesmuseum.demon.co.uk, Internet: http://www.dumfriesmuseum.demon.co.uk. Head: David Lockwood
Special Museum
House in which Robert Burns lived for three years prior to his death 32822

Crichton Royal Museum, Easterbrook Hall, Bankend Rd, Dumfries DG1 4TG - T: (01387) 244228, Fax: 269696, E-mail: Morag.Williams@btinternet.com, Internet: http://www.john.l.l.williams.btinternet.com. Head: Morag Williams
Historical Museum / Special Museum - 1989
Hist of Health Care, esp Mental Health Care in SW Scotland, Dumfries and Galloway, Art therapy creative work by patients 1839-1860 32823

Dumfries and Galloway Aviation Museum, Former Control Tower, Heathhall Industrial Estate, Dumfries DG2 3PH - T: (01387) 256680. Head: David Reid
Science&Tech Museum
Engines and aeronautica 32824

Dumfries Museum, Observatory, Corberry Hill, Dumfries DG2 7SW - T: (01387) 253374, Fax: 265081, E-mail: info@dumfriesmuseum.demon.co.uk, Internet: http://www.dumfriesmuseum.demon.co.uk. Head: David Lockwood
Local Museum - 1835
Geology, paleontology, mineralogy, botany, zoology, ethnography, costumes, photos, archaeology, social history 32825

Gracefield Arts Centre, 28 Edinburgh Rd, Dumfries DG1 1NW - T: (01387) 262084, Fax: 255173, Internet: http://www.dumgal.gov.uk. Head: D. Henderby
Fine Arts Museum
Coll of Scottish paintings (19th-20th c), art and craft exhibitions 32826

Old Bridge House Museum, Observatory, Mill Rd, Dumfries DG2 7BE - T: (01387) 256904, Fax: 265081, E-mail: info@dumfriesmuseum.demon.co.uk, Internet: http://www.dumfriesmuseum.demon.co.uk. Head: David Lockwood
Decorative Arts Museum - 1959/1960
Period furnishings, interiors, various rooms, ceramics, costumes, toys, books 32827

Robert Burns Centre, Mill Rd, Dumfries DG2 7BE - T: (01387) 264808, Fax: 264808, E-mail: info@dumfriesmuseum.demon.co.uk, Internet: http:www.dumfriesmuseum.demon.co.uk. Head: David Lockwood
Special Museum - 1986
Exhibitions, including an audio-visual presentation on Robert Burns and his life in Dumfries, and on the growth of interest in his life and poetry 32828

Dunbar

Dunbar Town House Museum, High St, Dunbar EH42 1ER - T: (01368) 863734, Fax: 828201, E-mail: elms@elothian-museums.demon.co.uk, Internet: http://www.dunbarmuseum.org
Local Museum
16th c house, archeology, photographs of old Dunbar 32829

John Muir Birthplace, 128 High St, Dunbar EH42 1ES - T: (01386) 862585, Fax: 828201, E-mail: elms@elothian-museums.demon.co.uk, Internet: http://www.elothian-museums.demon.co.uk/jmh-main.htm
Special Museum
Father of the conservation movement John Muir 32830

Dunbeath

Laidhay Croft Museum, Dunbeath KW6 6EH - T: (01593) 731244, Fax: 721548. Head: Elizabeth Cameron
Agriculture Museum / Local Museum - 1974
Examples of early agricultural machinery, household artefacts 32831

Dunblane

Dunblane Museum, 1 The Cross, Dunblane FK15 0AQ - T: (01786) 823440, 825691
Local Museum - 1943
Paintings, prints, medieval carvings, letters of Bishop Robert Leighton, Communion Tokens - library 32832

Dundee

Broughty Castle Museum, Broughty Ferry, Dundee DD5 2TF - T: (01382) 436916, Fax: 436951, E-mail: broughty@dundeecity.gov.uk, Internet: http://www.dundeecity.gov.uk/broughtycastle
Historical Museum - 1969
Local history, fishing, Dundee's former whaling industry tourism, the wildlife of the Tay estuary, weapons and armour, military history 32833

Duncan of Jordanstone College of Art and Design Exhibition, Perth Rd, Dundee DD1 4HT - T: (01382) 345330, Fax: 345192, E-mail: exhibitions@dundee.ac.uk, Internet: http://www.dundee.ac.uk
Public Gallery 32834

Frigate Unicorn, Victoria Dock, Dundee DD1 3JA - T: (01382) 200900, Fax: 200923, E-mail: frigateunicorn@hotmail.com, Internet: http://www.frigateunicorn.org.uk
Military Museum
Oldest British-built warship 'HMS Unicorn' 32835

McManus Galleries, Albert Sq, Dundee DD1 1DA - T: (01382) 432084, Fax: 432052, E-mail: arts.heritage@dundeecity.gov.uk, Internet: http://www.dundeecity.gov.uk. Head: S. Grinmond
Fine Arts Museum / Local Museum - 1873
19th c Scottish fine art, Dundee & Edinburgh silver, contemporary Scottish art & photography & crafts, local hist, civil, church & history material, archaeology, whaling material, etc. natural hist of the region incl taywhale skeleton, botany, geology, entomology, zoology 32836

Mills Observatory Museum, Balgay Park, Glamis Rd, Dundee DD2 2UB - T: (01382) 435846, Fax: 435962. Head: Jeff Lashley
Science&Tech Museum
Astronomy, space flight - planetarium 32837

Museum Collections, University of Dundee, Dundee DD1 4HN - T: (01382) 344310, Fax: 344107, E-mail: museum@dundee.ac.uk, Internet: http://www.dundee.ac.uk/museum/. Head: Matthew Jarron

Fine Arts Museum / University Museum / Natural History Museum / Science&Tech Museum
Scientific and medical instr, natural hist, historic and contemporary fine arts and design 32838

North Carr Lightship, Victoria Dock, Dundee DD1 3HW - T: (01382) 350353, Fax: 350353, E-mail: brian.callison@steamship.co.uk. Head: Brian Callison
Science&Tech Museum
Last manned light vessel North Carr (1933-1974) with contemporary furniture, fittings and machinery 32839

Old Steeple, Nethergate, Dundee DD1 1DG - T: (01382) 432322
Public Gallery 32840

Royal Research Ship Discovery, Discovery Point, Discovery Quay, Dundee DD1 4XA - T: (01382) 201245, Fax: 225891, E-mail: info@dundeeheritage.sol.co.uk, Internet: http://www.rrs-discovery.com. Head: Alan Rastin
Special Museum
Ship used by Robert Falcon Scott on the Antarctic Expedition of 1901-1904 32841

Seagate Gallery, 36-40 Seagate, Dundee DD1 2EJ - T: (01382) 26331
Public Gallery 32842

Verdant Works, 27 West Henderson's Wynd, Dundee DD1 5BT - T: (01382) 225282, Fax: 221612, E-mail: info@dundeeheritage.sol.co.uk, Internet: http://www.verdantworks.com. Head: Alan Rankin
Science&Tech Museum - 1996
Museum of Dundee's textile industries, 19th c flax and jute mill, historic textile machinery 32843

Dunfermline

Andrew Carnegie Birthplace Museum, Moodie St, Dunfermline KY12 7PL - T: (01383) 724302, Fax: 729002, E-mail: info@carnegiemuseum.co.uk, Internet: http://www.carnegiemuseum.co.uk. Head: Derrick Barclay
Special Museum - 1928
Birthplace of industrialist-philanthropist Andrew Carnegie with memorabilia, costumes, decorative arts 32844

Dunfermline Museum, Viewfield Terrace, Dunfermline KY12 7HY - T: (01383) 313838, Fax: 313837
Local Museum - 1961
Local industrial, social and natural history, significant local linen coll 32845

Pittencrieff House Museum, Pittencrieff Park, Dunfermline KY12 8QH - T: (01383) 722935, 313838
Local Museum
Costume 19th-20th c, local history, major arts, photographics 32846

Dungannon

United States Grant Ancestral Homestead, Dergenagh Rd, Dungannon BT70 1TW - T: (028) 87767259, Fax: 87767911, E-mail: killymaddy@nitic.net. Head: Libby McLean
Historical Museum
19th c agricultural implements, Ulysses Simpson Grant, 18th President of the USA 32847

Dunkeld

Dunkeld Cathedral Chapter House Museum, Cathedral St, Dunkeld PH8 0AW - T: (01350) 728732, Fax: 728732. Head: Eileen Cox
Local Museum
Ecclesiastical artefacts, an cross slab from the 9th-c, the Pictish Apostles Stone from the 9th c, temporary displays reflecting different aspect of social history - Archives 32848

Little Houses, High St, Dunkeld PH8 0AN - T: (013502) 727460. Head: Gillian Kelly
Local Museum 32849

Dunoon

Dunoon and Cowal Museum, Castle House, Dunoon PA23 7HH - T: (01369) 701422
Local Museum 32850

Dunrossnes

Shetland Croft House Museum, Voe, Boddam, Dunrossnes ZE2 9JG - T: (01595) 695057, Fax: 696729, E-mail: shetland.museum@zetnet.co.uk, Internet: http://www.shetland-museum.org.uk. Head: T. Watt
Agriculture Museum - 1972 32851

Duns

Biscuit Tin Museum, Manderston, Duns TD11 3PP - T: (01361) 883450, Fax: 882010, E-mail: palmer@manderston.co.uk, Internet: http://www.manderston.co.uk. Head: Lord Palmer
Decorative Arts Museum 32852

Duns Area Museum, 49 Newtown St, Duns TD11 3AU - T: (01361) 884114, Fax: 884104. Head: Ian Brown
Local Museum 32853

Jim Clark Room, 44 Newtown St, Duns TD11 3AU - T: (01361) 883960, 884114, Fax: 884104. Head: Ian Brown
Historical Museum - 1969
Trophies and other memorabilia, world champion of motor racing 32854

Dunster

Dunster Castle, Dunster TA24 6SL - T: (01643) 821314, Fax: 823000, E-mail: wdugen@smtp.ntrust.org.uk. Head: William Wake
Historical Museum 32855

Dunvegan

Dunvegan Castle, Dunvegan IV55 8WF - T: (01470) 521206, Fax: 521205, E-mail: info@dunvegancastle.com, Internet: http://www.dunvegancastle.com. Head: John Lambert
Historical Museum 32856

Dunwich

Dunwich Museum, Saint James' St, Dunwich IP17 3EA - T: (01728) 648796. Head: M. Caines
Historical Museum - 1972
Local history, natural history of the seashore, marshes, heathland and woodland 32857

Durham

Durham Cathedral Treasures of Saint Cuthbert, Cloisters, off the Cathedral, Durham DH1 3EH - T: (0191) 3864266, Fax: 3864267, E-mail: enquiries@durhamcathedral.co.uk, Internet: http://www.durhamcathedral.co.uk. Head: M. Kitchen
Religious Arts Museum - 1978
17th and 18th c altar plate, opus anglicanum embroidery, manuscripts, medieval bronze work, Saint Cuthbert relics 32858

Durham Heritage Centre and Museum, Saint Mary-le-Bow, North Bailey, Durham DH1 3ET - T: (0191) 3868719, 3845589. Head: J.M. Jones
Local Museum - 1975 32859

Durham Light Infantry Museum and Durham Art Gallery, Aykley Heads, Durham DH1 5TU - T: (0191) 3842214, Fax: 3861770, E-mail: dli@durham.gov.uk, Internet: http://www.durham.gov.uk/dli_website. Head: Steve Shannon
Military Museum / Fine Arts Museum - 1969/2000
Medals, uniforms, weapons, documents, arts 32860

Monks' Dormitory Museum, The Chapter Library, College, Durham DH1 3EH - T: (0191) 3862489, 3864266, Fax: 3864267, E-mail: r.c.norris@durham.ac.uk, Internet: http://www.durhamcatedral.co.uk
Religious Arts Museum 32861

Museum of Archaeology, c/o University of Durham, Old Fulling Mill, The Banks, Durham DH1 3EB - T: (0191) 3743623, Fax: 3743619, 3747911, E-mail: fulling.mill@durham.ac.uk, Internet: http://www.dur.ac.uk/fulling.mill. Head: Linda Brewster
Archaeological Museum - 1833
Oswald Plicque coll of Samian pottery, Roman stone inscriptions from Hadrian's Wall 32862

Oriental Museum, c/o University of Durham, Elvet Hill, Durham DH1 3TH - T: (0191) 3747911, Fax: 3747911, E-mail: oriental.museum@durham.ac.uk, Internet: http://www.dur.ac.uk/oriental.museum. Head: Linda Brewster
Fine Arts Museum / Decorative Arts Museum - 1960
Chinese ceramics, ancient Egyptian antiquities, Indian paintings and sculptures, Tibetan paintings and decorative art, hist of writing 32863

Duxford

Imperial War Museum Duxford, Airfield, Duxford CB2 4QR - T: (01223) 835000, Fax: 837267, Internet: http://www.iwm.org.uk. Head: Edward Inman
Military Museum - 1976
Largest coll of civil and military aircraft in GB also tanks, guns, naval exhibits, over 180 aircraft ranging from WWI biplanes, spitfires to concorde 32864

Royal Anglian Regiment Museum, Imperial War Museum, Airfield, Duxford CB2 4QR - T: (01223) 835000, Fax: 837267. Head: George Boss
Military Museum
Military coll of the East Anglian Regiments and the Royal Anglian Regiment, customs, uniforms, operations, weapons 32865

Dymchurch

New Hall, New Hall Close, Dymchurch TN29 0LF - T: (01303) 873897, Fax: 874788
Local Museum
Local artefacts, pottery, muskets, cannon balls, rifles and general miscellany 32866

Dysart

John McDouall Stuart Museum, Rectory Ln, Dysart KY1 2TP - T: (01592) 412860, Fax: 412870. Head: Dallas Machan
Historical Museum
Australian exploration by John McDouall, history of Dysart 32867

Earby

Museum of Yorkshire Dales Lead Mining, Old Grammar School, School Ln, Earby BB8 - T: (01282) 841422, Fax: 841422, E-mail: earby.leadmines@bun.com, Internet: http://www.ex.ac.uk/~rburt/minhistnet/emrg.html. Head: Peter R. Hart
Science&Tech Museum
Mining, miners' tools and equipment, photos 32868

Eardisland

Burton Court, Eardisland HR6 9DN - T: (01544) 388231, E-mail: helenjsimpson@hotmail.com. Head: Helen J. Simpson
Local Museum - 1967
Oriental and European costumes dating from the 16th c, natural history, ship and railway models, local history 32869

Earls Barton

Earls Barton Museum of Local Life, Barkers Factory Complex, Station Rd, Earls Barton NN6 0NT. Head: I.D. Flanagan
Local Museum
Local cottage industries, lace, boot and shoe making 32870

Easdale Island

Easdale Island Folk Museum, Easdale Island PA34 4TB - T: (01852) 300370, Fax: 300370, Internet: http://www.insomnia.demon.co.uk/eit/museumt. Head: Jean Adams
Folklore Museum - 1980
Industrial and domestic life of the Slate Islands during the 19th c 32871

East Budleigh

Countryside Museum, Bicton Park Botanical Gardens, East Budleigh EX9 7BJ - T: (01395) 568465, Fax: 568374, E-mail: museum@bictongardens.co.uk, Internet: http://www.bictongardens.co.uk. Head: Simon Listen
Local Museum - 1967
Agricultural and estate memorabilia 32872

East Carlton

East Carlton Steel Heritage Centre, Park, East Carlton LE16 8YF - T: (01536) 770977, Fax: 770661. Head: Chris Smith
Science&Tech Museum
Living room of 1930's steel worker, model of Corby Steel Works 32873

East Cowes

Osborne House, East Cowes PO32 6JY - T: (01983) 200022, Fax: 297281, 281380. Head: Alan Lock
Fine Arts Museum / Decorative Arts Museum - 1954
Queen Victoria's seaside home, build in 1845, mementoes of royal travel abroad, Indian plaster decoration, furniture, 400 works of art, pictures 32874

East Dereham

Bishop Bonner's Cottage Museum, Saint Withburga Ln, East Dereham NR19 1AA - T: (01362) 692736
Local Museum / Folklore Museum
Victorian clothing, pictures, toys, farm implements and local trades 32875

East Grinstead

Town Museum, East Court, College Ln, East Grinstead RH19 3LT - T: (01342) 712087
Local Museum
Coll of local handicrafts, 19th and 20th-c pottery 32876

East Hendred

Champs Chapel Museum, Chapel Sq, East Hendred OX12 8JN - T: (01235) 833312, Fax: 833312, E-mail: JSteveHendred@cs.com, Internet: http://www.hendred.org
Local Museum
Material of local interest 32877

East Kilbride

Hunter House, Maxwellton Rd, Calderwood, East Kilbride G74 3LU - T: (01355) 261261. Head: Andy Collins
Special Museum
Exhibition portraying the lives of John and William Hunter, 18th c scientists 32878

Museum of Scottish Country Life, National Museums of Scotland, Kittochside, East Kilbride G74 3LW - T: (0131) 3332674, Fax: 3332674. Head: John Shaw
Agriculture Museum - 2001
History of farming and rural life throughout Scotland 32879

East Linton

Preston Mill and Phantassie Doocot, East Linton - T: (01620) 860426
Science&Tech Museum 32880

East Molesey

Embroiderers' Guild Museum Collection, Apt 41, Hampton Court Palace, East Molesey KT8 9AU - T: (020) 89431229, Fax: 89779882, E-mail: administrator@embroiderersguild.org.uk, Internet: http://www.embroiderersguild.org.uk. Head: Michael Spender
Special Museum 32881

Hampton Court Palace, East Molesey KT8 9AU - T: (020) 87819500, Fax: 87819509, Internet: http://www.hrp.org.uk
Fine Arts Museum - 1514
Royal palace, original furnishings, Italian, Flemish, German, Dutch, Spanish paintings 32882

Mounted Branch Museum, Imber Court, East Molesey KT8 0BY - T: (020) 82475480
Special Museum
Uniforms and equipment, saddles, harness, paintings and photographs 32883

East Tilbury

Thameside Aviation Museum, Coalhouse Fort, East Tilbury, Essex - T: (01277) 655170, Fax: (0113) 2470219
Science&Tech Museum
Aviation archaeology 32884

East Winterslow

New Art Centre, Roche Court, Sculpture Park and Gallery, East Winterslow SP5 1BG - T: (01980) 862244, Fax: 862447, E-mail: nac@globalnet.co.uk, Internet: http://www.sculpture.uk.com. Head: Madeleine Bessborough
Fine Arts Museum 32885

Eastbourne

Eastbourne Heritage Centre, 2 Carlisle Rd, Eastbourne BN21 4JJ - T: (01323) 411189, 721825. Head: Owen Boydell
Local Museum 32886

Museum of Shops, 20 Cornfield Tce, Eastbourne BN21 4NS - T: (01323) 737143. Head: Graham Upton
Special Museum
Victorian-style shops 32887

Museum of the Royal National Lifeboat Institution, King Edward Parade, Eastbourne BN21 4BY - T: (01323) 730717. Head: I.M. Shearer
Special Museum - 1937
Hist of Eastbourne lifeboats from 1853 to present, lifeboat models, many photogr 32888

Queen's Royal Irish Hussars Museum, c/o Sussex Combined Services Museum, Redoubt Fortress, Royal Parade, Eastbourne BN22 7AQ - T: (01323) 410300, Fax: 732240, E-mail: - eastbourne_museums@breathmail.net. Head: Richard Callaghan
Military Museum
Medals, uniforms, prints and memorabilia 32889

Royal Sussex Regiment Museum, Redoubt Fortress, Royal Parade, Eastbourne BN21 4BP - T: (01323) 410300, Fax: 732240, E-mail: - eastbourne_museums@breathemail.net. Head: Richard Callaghan
Military Museum
Uniforms, medals, weapons, equipment and campaign medals illustrate the history of the former Royal Sussex Regiment from 1701 to 1966, photographs, books and documentary material 32890

Sussex Combined Services Museum, Redoubt Fortress, Royal Parade, Eastbourne BN22 7AQ - T: (01323) 410300, Fax: 732240, E-mail: - eastbourne_museums@breathemail.net. Head: Richard Callaghan
Military Museum
Uniforms, medals and other military artefacts 32891

Towner Art Gallery and Local Museum, High St, Old Town, Eastbourne BN20 8BB - T: (01323) 417961, 725112, Fax: 648182, E-mail: townergallery@eastbourne.gov.uk, Internet: http://www.eastbourne.gov.uk
Fine Arts Museum / Historical Museum - 1923
History of Eastbourne from prehistory onwords to the original station clock and an original Victorian kitchen British art of mainly 19th and 20th cc, coll of contemporary art 32892

Wishtower Puppet Museum, King Edward's Parade, Eastbourne BN21 4BY - T: (01323) 410400, Fax: 411620. Head: Mel Myland, Conny Myland
Special Museum - 1996
Victorian puppets of England, old TV and film puppets, shadow puppets of Asia, Judy & Punch 32893

Eastleigh

Eastleigh Museum, The Citadel, 25 High St, Eastleigh SO50 5LF - T: (023) 80643026, Fax: 80653582, E-mail: musmst@hants.gov.uk, Internet: http://www.hants.gov.uk/museum/eastlmus/. Head: Sue Tapliss
Local Museum
Local hist, railway, art gallery 32894

Royal Observer Corps Museum, 8 Roselands Close, Fair Oak, Eastleigh SO50 8GN - T: (023) 80693823, E-mail: xrocmunc@hants.gov.uk. Head: N.A. Cullingford
Military Museum 32895

Easton

Easton Farm Park, Easton IP13 0EQ - T: (01728) 746475, Fax: 747861, E-mail: easton@eastonfarmpark.co.uk, Internet: http://www.eastonfarmpark.co.uk. Head: John Kerr
Agriculture Museum
Farm buildings, dairy, farm machinery 32896

Easton-on-the-Hill

Priest's House, 40 West St, Easton-on-the-Hill PE9 3LS. Head: Paul Way
Local Museum
Local artefacts 32897

Eastwood

D.H. Lawrence Birthplace Museum, 8a Victoria St, Eastwood NG16 3AN - T: (01773) 717353, Fax: 713509. Head: Jane Lilleystone
Special Museum - 1975
Three original watercolours by D.H. Lawrence, original items of furniture owners by the Lawrence family, birthplace of D.H. Lawrence 32898

Durban House Heritage Centre, Mansfield Rd, Eastwood NG16 3DZ - T: (01773) 717353, Fax: 713509
Historical Museum
Local coal owners, D.H. Lawrence 32899

Ecclefechan

Thomas Carlyle's Birthplace, The Arches House, High St, Ecclefechan DG11 3DG - T: (01576) 300666. Head: Fiona Auchterlonie
Special Museum
Birthplace of writer Thomas Carlyle, coll of his belongings and copy manuscript letters, local artisan dwelling, 32900

Edenbridge

Eden Valley Museum, Church House, High St, Edenbridge TN8 5AR - T: (01732) 868102, E-mail: elizabethwright@yahoo.co.uk. Head: Elizabeth Wright
Local Museum
Changing fashions, social structures, economic history of the Eden Valley, coll photographs, paintings and engravings 32901

Hever Castle and Gardens, Edenbridge TN8 7NG - T: (01732) 865224, Fax: 866796, E-mail: mail@hevercastle.co.uk, Internet: http://www.hevercastle.co.uk. Head: Robert Pullin
Decorative Arts Museum
Furniture, paintings, tapestries, 16th c portraits 32902

Kent and Sharpshooters Yeomanry Museum, Hever Castle, Edenbridge TN8 7DB - T: (01732) 865224. Head: C.T.A. Hammond
Military Museum 32903

Edinburgh

Braidwood and Rushbrook Museum, Lauriston Pl, Edinburgh EH3 9DE - T: (0131) 2282401, Fax: 2298359, E-mail: csg@lothian.fire-uk.org, Internet: http://www.lothian.fire-uk.org. Head: I. McMurtie
Historical Museum
Engines, manual, horse drawn, steam and motorised pumps from 1806, fire related items since 1426 32904

Brass Rubbing Centre, Trinity Apse, Chalmers Close, High St, Edinburgh - T: (0131) 5564634, Fax: 5583103, Internet: http://www.cac.org.uk
Special Museum 32905

Camera Obscura, Outlook Tower, Castlehill, Edinburgh EH1 2LZ - T: (0131) 2263709, Fax: 2254239. Head: Andrew Johnson
Special Museum 32906

City Art Centre, 2 Market St, Edinburgh EH1 1DE - T: (0131) 5293993, Fax: 5293977, E-mail: enquiries@city-art-centre.demon.co.uk, Internet: http://www.cac.org.uk
Public Gallery - 1980
19th and 20th c artists, mostly Scottish 32907

Cockburn Museum, c/o Dept of Geology & Geophysics, University of Edinburgh, King's Bldg, West Mains Rd, Edinburgh EH9 3JF - T: (0131) 6508527, Fax: 6683184, E-mail: peder.aspen@ed.ac.uk. Head: Peder Aspen
Natural History Museum / University Museum
Rocks, fossils and minerals 32908

Dean Gallery, 73 Belford Rd, Edinburgh EH4 3DS - T: (0131) 6246200, Fax: 3432802, E-mail: enquiries@natgalscot.ac.uk, Internet: http://www.natgals.ac.uk. Head: Richard Calvocoressi
Fine Arts Museum 32909

Edinburgh Printmakers Workshop and Gallery, Wash-House, 23 Union St, Edinburgh EH1 3LR - T: (0131) 5572479, Fax: 5588418, E-mail: printmakers@ednet.co.uk, Internet: http://www.edinburgh-printmakers.co.uk. Head: David Watt
Public Gallery
Lithography, screenprinting, relief, etching fine art prints 32910

Edinburgh Scout Museum, 7 Valleyfield St, Edinburgh EH3 9LP - T: (0131) 2293756, Fax: 2219905
Special Museum
History of scout mouvement, memorabilia of movement in Edinburgh and worldwide 32911

Edinburgh University Anatomy Museum, c/o Department of Anatomy, University Medical School, Teviot Pl, Edinburgh EH8 9AG
Natural History Museum 32912

Edinburgh University Collection of Historic Musical Instruments, Reid Concert Hall, Bristo Sq, Edinburgh EH8 9AG - T: (0131) 6502422, Fax: 6502425, E-mail: euchmi@ed.ac.uk, Internet: http://www.music.ed.ac.uk/euchmi. Head: Dr. Arnold Myers
Music Museum / University Museum
Display of over 1,000 musical instruments showing 400 years of hist of folk and domestic music, bands and orchestras - Sound Laboratory 32913

Edinburgh University Natural History Collections, c/o ICAPB, Ashworth Laboratories, King' Bldgs, West Mains Rd, Edinburgh EH9 3JT - T: (0131) 6501000, Fax: 6673210, E-mail: pat.preston@ed.ac.uk, Internet: http://www.nhc.ed.ac.uk. Head: Dr. B.E. Matthews, Dr. P.M. Preston
Natural History Museum 32914

Exhibition at the Danish Cultural Institute, 3 Doune Terrace, Edinburgh EH3 6DY - T: (0131) 2257189, Fax: 2206162, E-mail: dci.dancult@dancult.demon.co.uk, Internet: http://www.dancult.demon.co.uk. Head: Mette Bligaard
Public Gallery
Danish paintings, prints, photography and craft 32915

Fruitmarket Gallery, 45 Market St, Edinburgh EH1 1DF - T: (0131) 2252383, Fax: 2203130, E-mail: info@fruitmarket.co.uk, Internet: http://www.fruitmarket.co.uk. Head: Graeme Murray
Public Gallery
Contemporary art 32916

Gallery of the Royal Scottish Academy, The Mound, Princes St, Edinburgh EH2 2EL - T: (0131) 2256671, Fax: 2252349. Head: An McKenzie Smith
Fine Arts Museum - 1826
Scottish painting & sculpture of the 19th & 20th c 32917

The Georgian House, 7 Charlotte Sq, Edinburgh EH2 4DR - T: (0131) 2252160, 2263318, Fax: 2263318, E-mail: thegeorgianhouse@nts.org.uk, Internet: http://www.nts.org.uk. Head: Jacqueline Wright
Decorative Arts Museum - 1975
Georgian house, furniture, life in Edinburgh (late 18th/ early 19th c) 32918

The Grand Lodge of Scotland Museum, 96 George St, Edinburgh EH2 3DH - T: (0131) 2255304, Fax: 2253953, E-mail: grandsecretary@sol.co.uk, Internet: http://www.grandlodgescotland.com. Head: Robert L.D. Cooper
Special Museum
Ceramics, glasware, artefacts relating to Freemasonry, manuscripts - library 32919

Granton Centre, National Museums of Scotland, 242 W Granton Rd, Edinburgh EH5 1JA - T: (0131) 2474470, Fax: 5514106, E-mail: info@nms.ac.uk, Internet: http://www.nms.ac.uk. Head: Dr. Gordon Rintoul
Local Museum 32920

Heriot-Watt University Archive Collections, Riccarton, Edinburgh EH14 4AS - T: (0131) 4513218, Fax: 4513164, Internet: http://www.hw.ac.uk/archive. Head: Ann Jones
University Museum / Historical Museum / Fine Arts Museum
History of the University, scientific and tachnical education in Scotland, art and artefacts, artists of the Edinburgh School 32921

Historic Scotland, Stenhouse Conservation Centre, 3 Stenhouse Mill Ln, Edinburgh EH11 3LR - T: (0131) 4435635, Fax: 4558260, E-mail: robert.wilmot@scotland.gov.uk, Internet: http://www.historic-scotland.gov.uk. Head: Robert Wilmot
Historical Museum 32922

Huntly House Museum, 142 Canongate, Edinburgh EH8 8DD - T: (0131) 5294143, Fax: 5573346, Internet: http://www.cac.org.uk
Local Museum / Decorative Arts Museum - 1932
Local history, Scottish pottery, local glass and silver, paintings, prints 32923

John Knox's House, 45 High St, Edinburgh EH1 1SR - T: (0131) 5569579, Fax: 5575224. Head: Dr. Donald Smith
Special Museum - 1849
Memorabilia on John Knox, memorabilia on James Mossman, goldsmith to Mary, Queen of Scots, memorabilia on Mary, information on 16th c Edinburgh 32924

Late Victorian Pharmacy, 36 York Pl, Edinburgh EH1 3HU - T: (0131) 5564386, Fax: 5560723
Special Museum 32925

Lauriston Castle, 2a Cramond Rd South, Edinburgh EH4 5QD - T: (0131) 3362060, Fax: 3127165, Internet: http://www.cac.org.uk. Head: David Scarratt
Decorative Arts Museum - 1926
"Blue John" Derbyshire Spar, wool mosaics, castle with period furnishings, tapestries, decorative arts 32926

Museum of Childhood, 42 High St, Royal Mile, Edinburgh EH1 1TG - T: (0131) 5294142, Fax: 5583103, E-mail: admin@musenmotchild-hood.fsnet.co.uk, Internet: http://www.cac.org.uk. Head: John Heyes
Special Museum - 1955
Social hist of childhood, hobbies, education, toys, dolls, games 32927

Museum of Fire, c/o Lothian and Borders Fire Brigade Headquarters, Lauriston Pl, Edinburgh EH3 9DE - T: (0131) 2282401, Fax: 2298359, E-mail: csg@lothian.fire-uk.org, Internet: http://www.lothian.fire-uk.org. Head: I. McMurtrie
Science&Tech Museum - 1966
Fire engines and fire-fighting equipment dating from the early 19th c to the present day, coll of badges, medals, photographs and records relating to fire-fighting 32928

Museum of Lighting, 59 Saint Stephen St, Edinburgh EH3 5AG - T: (0131) 5564503
Science&Tech Museum - 1972
All types of lighting equipment, hand-operated machines from the 19th-c lampmakers, Bocock - archive 32929

Museum of Scotland, National Museums of Scotland, Chambers St, Edinburgh EH1 1JF - T: (0131) 2474219, 2474422, Fax: 2204819, E-mail: info@nms.ac.uk, Internet: http://www.nms.ac.uk. Head: Dr. Gordon Rintoul
Historical Museum 32930

Museum of the Royal College of Surgeons of Edinburgh, 18 Nicholson St, Edinburgh EH8 9DW - T: (0131) 5271649, Fax: 5576406, E-mail: museum@rcsed.ac.uk, Internet: http://www.rcsed.ac.uk. Head: Prof. J. Temple
Special Museum - 1699
Surgery, pathology and medicine, dentistry 32931

Museum on the Mound, Bank of Scotland, The Mound, Edinburgh EH1 1YZ - T: (0131) 5291288, Fax: 5291307, E-mail: archives@bankofscotland.co.uk, Internet: http://www.bankofscotland.co.uk. Head: Helen Redmond-Cooper
Special Museum 32932

National Gallery of Scotland, The Mound, Edinburgh EH2 2EL - T: (0131) 6246200, Fax: 2200917, E-mail: enquiries@natgalscot.ac.uk, Internet: http://www.natgalscot.ac.uk. Head: Timothy Clifford
Fine Arts Museum - 1850
Paintings, drawings and prints by the greatest artists from the Renaissance to Post-Impressionism, incl Velazquez, El Greco, Rembrandt, Vermeer, Turner, Constable, Monet and Van Gogh 32933

National Museums of Scotland, Chambers St, Edinburgh EH1 1JF - T: (0131) 2257534, Fax: 2204819, E-mail: info@nms.ac.uk, Internet: http://www.nms.ac.uk. Head: Dr. Gordon Rintoul
Local Museum - 1781
Ancient and modern Scottish archaeology, hist, domestic life, applied art, numismatics, agriculture 32934

National War Museum of Scotland, National Museums of Scotland, The Castle, Edinburgh EH1 2NG - T: (0131) 2257534, Fax: 2253848, Internet: http://www.nms.ac.uk. Head: A.L. Carswell
Military Museum - 1930
Military history of Scotland and the experiance of war and military service, uniforms, weapons, paintings, sculpture, ptints 32935

Newhaven Heritage Museum, 24 Pier Pl, Edinburgh EH6 4LP - T: (0131) 5514165, Fax: 5573346, Internet: http://www.cac.org.uk
Historical Museum - 1994 32936

Palace of Holyroodhouse, The Royal Mile, Edinburgh EH8 8DX - T: (0131) 5561096, Fax: 5575256, E-mail: holyroodhouse@royalcollection.org.uk
Fine Arts Museum
Royal residence 32937

People's Story Museum, 163 Canongate, Royal Mile, Edinburgh EH8 8BN - T: (0131) 5294057, Fax: 5563439, E-mail: helen.peoplestory@virgin.net, Internet: http://www.cac.org.uk. Head: Helen Clark
Historical Museum - 1989
Social history material representing the life and work of Edinburgh's people over the past 200 years, coll of Trade Union banners, oral tape recordings, photos 32938

Pharmaceutical Society Museum, 36 York Pl, Edinburgh EH1 3HU - T: (0131) 5564386, Fax: 5588856, E-mail: 101561.2226@compuserve.com
Historical Museum 32939

Portfolio Gallery, 43 Candlemaker Row, Edinburgh EH1 2QB - T: (0131) 2201911, Fax: 2264287, E-mail: portfolio@ednet.co.uk, Internet: http://www.ednet.co.uk/~portfolio. Head: Gloria Chalmers
Public Gallery 32940

Regimental Museum of the Royal Scots Dragoon Guards, The Castle, Edinburgh EH1 2YT - T: (0131) 2204387
Military Museum 32941

Royal Incorporation of Architects in Scotland Gallery, 15 Rutland Sq, Edinburgh EH1 2BE - T: (0131) 2297545, Fax: 2282188, E-mail: acarolan@rias.org.uk, Internet: http://www.rias.org.uk. Head: Sebastian Tombs
Public Gallery
Architecture, design, visual arts 32942

Royal Museum, National Museums of Scotland, Chambers St, Edinburgh EH1 1JF - T: (0131) 2474219, Fax: 2204819, E-mail: info@nms.ac.uk, Internet: http://www.nms.ac.uk. Head: Dr. Gordon Rintoul
Archaeological Museum / Natural History Museum / Ethnology Museum / Science&Tech Museum - 1855
Archaeology, natural history, geology, technology, Oriental arts, ethnography of Plains Indians, Eastern Island and Maori cultures, Baule figures, minerals , fossils, mining and metallurgy, power industries, shipping, aeronautics, radiation, primitive arts, British birds - library 32943

Royal Scots Regimental Museum, Castle, Edinburgh EH1 2YT - T: (0131) 3105014, Fax: 3105019, E-mail: rhqroyalscots@edinburghcastle.fsnet.co.uk, Internet: http://www.theroyalscots.co.uk. Head: R.P. Mason
Military Museum - 1951
History, uniforms, medals, weapons, trophies of the regiment, militaria 32944

Royal Scottish Academy Collections, Dean Gallery, 73 Belford Rd, Edinburgh EH4 3DS - T: (0131) 6246277, Fax: 2252349, E-mail: joanna.soden@natgalscot.ac.uk. Head: Joanna Soden
Fine Arts Museum
Visual arts, fine art - library and archives 32945

Russell Collection of Early Keyboard Instruments, c/o Faculty of Music, University of Edinburgh, Saint Cecilia's Hall, Niddry St, Cowgate, Edinburgh EH1 1LJ - T: (0131) 6502805, Fax: 6502812, E-mail: - russell.collection@music.ed.ac.uk, Internet: http://www.music.ed.ac.uk/russell. Head: Dr. G.G. O'Brien
Music Museum - 1968
Harpsichords, virginals, spinets, clavichords, chamber organs and early pianos 32946

Scotch Whisky Heritage Centre, 354 Castlehill, The Royal Mile, Edinburgh EH1 2NE - T: (0131) 2200441, Fax: 2206288, E-mail: enquiries@whisky-heritage.co.uk, Internet: http://www.whisky-heritage.co.uk
Special Museum 32947

Scottish National Gallery of Modern Art and Dean Gallery, Belford Rd, Edinburgh EH4 3DR - T: (0131) 6246200, Fax: 3432802, E-mail: enquiries@natgalscot.ac.uk, Internet: http://www.natgalscot.ac.uk. Head: Timothy Clifford, Richard Calvocoressi
Public Gallery - 1960
20th c paintings, sculpture and graphic art incl works by Vuillard, Matisse, Kirchner, Picasso, Magritte, Miró, Dali and Ernst, coll of 20th c Scottish art - sculpture garden 32948

Scottish National Portrait Gallery, 1 Queen St, Edinburgh EH2 1JD - T: (0131) 6246200, Fax: 5583691, E-mail: pginfo@natgalscot.ac.uk, Internet: http://www.natgalscot.ac.uk. Head: James Holloway
Fine Arts Museum - 1882
Portraits in various media illustrating the hist of Scotland from the 16th c up to the present day, portraits of Scots but not all by Scots but by van Dyck, Gainsborough, Copley, Thorvaldsen, Rodin and Kokoschka 32949

Scottish Rugby Union Museum, Murrayfield Stadium, Edinburgh EH12 5PJ - T: (0131) 3465000, Fax: 3465001, E-mail: library@sru.org.uk, Internet: http://www.sru.org.uk. Head: William S. Watson
Special Museum
History and development of the game and the Scottish Rugby Union, jerseys, caps, balls, trophies, photos 32950

Scottish Traditions of Dance, 54 Blackfriars St, Edinburgh EH1 1NE - T: (0131) 5588737, Fax: 5588737
Performing Arts Museum 32951

Stills Gallery, 23 Cockburn St, Edinburgh - T: (0131) 6226200, Fax: 6226201, E-mail: info@stills.org, Internet: http://www.stills.org. Head: Kate Tregaskis
Public Gallery 32952

Talbot Rice Gallery, c/o University of Edinburgh, Old College, South Bridge, Edinburgh EH8 9YL - T: (0131) 6502211, Fax: 6502213, E-mail: valerie.fiddes@ed.ac.uk, Internet: http://www.trg.ed.ac.uk
Fine Arts Museum / University Museum
Coll of bronzes and paintings, esp Dutch and Italian contemporary Scottish art 32953

The Writers' Museum, Lady Stair's House, Lady Stair's Close, Lawnmarket, Edinburgh EH1 2PA - T: (0131) 5294901, Fax: 2205057, E-mail: enquiries@writersmuseum.demon.co.uk. Head: Herbert Coutts
Special Museum - 1907
Memorabilia of poets Robert Burns, Sir Walter Scott, Robert Louis Stevenson 32954

Egham

Egham Museum, Literary Institute, High St, Egham TW20 9EW - T: (01344) 843047. Head: John Mills
Historical Museum / Archaeological Museum
Archaeology and history of Egham, Thorpe and Virginia Water, displays relating to Magna Carta, which was sealed nearby at Runnymede 32955

Royal Holloway College Picture Gallery, Egham Hill, Egham - T: (01784) 34455, Fax: 473285, E-mail: m.cowline@rhul.ac.uk. Head: Dr. Mary Cowling
Fine Arts Museum / University Museum - 1887
Paintings by Frith, Filacs, Maclise, Landseer, Millais and others 32956

Egremont

Florence Mine Heritage Centre, Egremont CA22 2NR - T: (01946) 820683, Fax: 820683, E-mail: deilbeck@4unet.co.uk. Head: K. Nichol
Science&Tech Museum
Mining artefacts and geological displays 32957

Elgin

Elgin Museum, 1 High St, Moray, Elgin IV30 1EQ - T: (01343) 543675, Fax: 543675, E-mail: curator@elginmuseum.org.uk, Internet: http://www.elginmuseum.org.uk. Head: Richard Mabon
Local Museum - 1843
Local antiquities, Triassic and Permian reptile fossils, Devonian fish fossils, archaeology 32958

Ellesmere Port

Boat Museum, South Pier Rd, Ellesmere Port CH65 4FW - T: (0151) 3555017, Fax: 3554079, E-mail: bookings@boatmuseum.freeserve.co.uk. Head: Tracey McNaboe
Science&Tech Museum
60 canal and river craft, icebreakers, traditional boat-building techniques in progress, story of canal building, life of dock workers, working engines, canal hist 32959

Hooton Park Exhibition Centre, Hangars, West Rd, Hooton Park Airfield, Ellesmere Port CH65 1BQ - T: (0151) 3502598, Fax: 3502598. Head: D. Beckett, R. Frost, A. Terry, J. Graham
Science&Tech Museum
Classic vehicles (military and civil), aeronautical items, aircraft 32960

Ellisland

Ellisland Farm, Hollywood Rd, Ellisland DG2 0RP - T: (0138774) 426
Special Museum
Exhibits connected with the poet Robert Burns and his family, farming life 32961

Ellon

Museum of Farming Life, Pitmedden Garden, Ellon AB41 7PD - T: (01651) 842352, Fax: 843188, E-mail: sburgess@nts.org.uk. Head: Susan M. Burgess
Agriculture Museum - 1982
Coll of farm tools and domestic equipment, a furnished farmhouse and bothy, restored outbuildings, hist of Scottish farming 32962

Elsham

Clocktower Museum, Elsham Hall, Elsham DN20 0QZ - T: (01652) 688698, Fax: 688240, Internet: http://www.brigg.com/elsham.htm
Fine Arts Museum / Decorative Arts Museum
Resident artists and working craft 32963

Elvaston

Elvaston Castle Working Estate Museum, Borrowash Rd, Elvaston DE7 3EP - T: (01332) 573799, Fax: 758751. Head: Michael Tong
Local Museum / Open Air Museum
Crafts and activities (early 20th c), historical breeding of livestock 32964

Elvington

Yorkshire Air Museum, Halifax Way, Elvington YO41 4AU - T: (01904) 608595, Fax: 608246, E-mail: museum@yorksairmuseum.co.uk, Internet: http://www.yorksairmuseum.co.uk. Head: Ian Reed
Science&Tech Museum / Military Museum
Coll of WWII memorabilia, historical airframes and replica's (early days of aviation to modern military jets) - library 32965

Ely

Ely Museum, The Old Gaol, Market St, Ely CB7 4LS - T: (01353) 666655. Head: Zara Matthews
Local Museum
Social and natural history of the Isle of Ely, local archeology 32966

Oliver Cromwell's House, 29 Saint Mary's St, Ely CB7 4HF - T: (01353) 662062, Fax: 668518, E-mail: elytic@compuserve.com, Internet: http://www.elyeastcambs.co.uk
Special Museum
Rooms incl kitchen, palour, Civil War exhibition, Cromwell's study and a haunted room, fen drainage 32967

Stained Glass Museum, South Triforium, Ely Cathedral, Ely CB7 4DN - T: (01353) 660347, Fax: (01223) 327367, E-mail: stainedgm@lineone.net, Internet: http://www.stainedglas-smuseum.org. Head: Viscount Churchill
Decorative Arts Museum / Special Museum - 1972
100 windows from medieval to modern times, a photographic display of the styles and techniques of medieval glass, and models of a modern stained glass workshop, 19th-c glass, with examples of work from all the leading studios and designers 32968

Emsworth

Emsworth Museum, 10b North St, Emsworth PO10 7DD - T: (01243) 378091
Local Museum
Local history, sea-faring families, oyster fishermen and coastal trade in grain and coal 32969

Enfield

Forty Hall Museum, Forty Hill, Enfield EN2 9HA - T: (020) 83638196, Fax: 83639098
Decorative Arts Museum - 1955
Ceramics, history childhood, Middlesex maps, furniture, paintings, teaching 32970

Enniskillen

Fermanagh County Museum, Castle Barracks, Enniskillen - T: (02866) 325000, Fax: 327342, E-mail: castle@fermanagh.gov.uk, Internet: http://www.enniskillencastle.co.uk. Head: Helen Lanigan Woog
Local Museum 32971

Florence Court House, Florence Court, Enniskillen BT92 1DB - T: (028) 66348249, 66348788, Fax: 66348873, E-mail: UFCEST@smtp.ntrust.org.uk
Local Museum 32972

Royal Inniskilling Fusiliers Regimental Museum, The Castle, Enniskillen BT74 7HL - T: (028) 66323142, Fax: 66320359, E-mail: - rinnisfus_skins_museum@hotmail.com, Internet: http://www.advemet.ie/fermanagh/castle. Head: J.M. Dunlop
Military Museum - 1931
Hist of the Royal Inniskilling Fusiliers (1689-1968) and associated Fermanagh, Tyrone and Donegal militia regiments, displays on 6th Inniskilling Dragoons (cavalry regiment) - library 32973

Epping

North Weald Airfield Museum and Memorial, Astra House, Hurricane Way, North Weald, Epping CM16 6AA - T: (01922) 714162, Fax: 713193, E-mail: 106051.3271@compuserve.com, Internet: http://www.fly.to/northweald
Science&Tech Museum - 1989
Historic and vintage flying aircraft in a 1940 period setting 32974

Epsom

College Museum, Epsom College, Epsom KT17 4QJ - T: (01372) 728862
University Museum / Natural History Museum 32975

Epworth

Epworth Old Rectory, 1 Rectory St, Epworth DN9 1HX - T: (01427) 872268. Head: Andrew Milson
Historical Museum
Portraits, Prints, Furniture, Wesley family items - library 32976

Erith

Erith Museum, Erith Library, Walnut Tree Rd, Erith DA8 1RS - T: (01322) 336582
Local Museum - 1934
History of the town of Erith, archaeology and social history of Erith, with a reproduction of an Edwardian kitchen and a special section on local industries 32977

Errol

Megginch Castle, Errol PH1 - T: (01821) 2222
Historical Museum 32978

Etchingham

Haremere Hall, Etchingham TN19 7QJ - T: (01580) 81145, Internet: http://members.tripod.com/~harmer1/reunion78c.html
Decorative Arts Museum - 1978 32979

Eton

Eton College Natural History Museum, Eton College, Eton SL4 6EW - T: (01753) 671288, Fax: 671159. Head: Dr. David A.S. Smith
Natural History Museum / University Museum - 1875
Fossils, insects, molluscs, birds - Herbarium 32980

Museum of Eton Life, c/o Eton College, Eton SL4 6DB - T: (01753) 671177, Fax: 671265. Head: P. Hatfield
Historical Museum - 1985
Daily life and duties, food and living conditions, punishments, uniforms, and school books and equipment, history of rowing at the College and the Officer Training Corps 32981

Myers Museum, Brewhouse Gallery, Eton College, Eton SL4 6DW - T: (01753) 801538, Fax: 801538, E-mail: n.reeves@etoncollege.org.uk. Head: Dr. Nicholas Reeves
Archaeological Museum / University Museum
Egyptian archaeology collected by Major W.J. Myers between 1883 and his death in 1899, objects, dating from Predynastic times to the Coptic period, wooden models from tombs and a well-preserved panel portrait from a mummy of the 2nd c A.D. 32982

Ettrick

James Hogg Exhibition, Aikwood Tower, Ettrick TD7 5HJ - T: (01750) 752253
Special Museum
Life and work of the Scottish writer James Hogg 32983

Evesham

Almonry Heritage Centre, Abbey Gate, Evesham WR11 4BG - T: (01386) 446944, Fax: 442348, E-mail: tic@almonry.ndo.co.uk, Internet: http://www.evesham.uk.com
Local Museum / Archaeological Museum
History of the Vale of Evesham from prehistoric times to the present day, Romano-British, Anglo-Saxon and medieval items, together with material illustrating the history of the monastery, coll of agricultural implements 32984

Ewell

Bourne Hall Museum, Spring St, Ewell KT17 1UF - T: (020) 83941734, Fax: 87867265, Internet: http://www.epsom.townpage.co.uk. Head: Jeremy Harte
Decorative Arts Museum / Special Museum - 1969
Coll of some of the earliest wallpapers ever made (c 1690) and the Ann Hull Grundy coll of costume jewellery, prehistoric material found in the vicinity, Victorian and more modern costumes and accessories, and early cameras and radio sets, Roman archaeology, tools - library 32985

Exeter

Connections Discovery Centre, Rougemont House, Castle St, Exeter - T: (01392) 665360, Fax: 421252
Local Museum - 1911
Resources for schools: Egypt, Romans, World War II, Victorians, handling coll 32986

Guildhall, High St, Exeter - T: (01392) 265500, 77888, Fax: 201329
Local Museum 32987

Royal Albert Memorial Museum and Art Gallery, Queen St, Exeter EX4 3RX - T: (01392) 665858, Fax: 421252, E-mail: ramm-events@exeter.gov.uk, Internet: http://www.exeter.gov.uk. Head: Camilla Hampshire
Fine Arts Museum / Natural History Museum / Ethnology Museum / Historical Museum / Archaeological Museum - 1868
Natural hist, butterflies, birds, local geology, fine art, local artists, applied arts, Exeter silver, Devon pottery, Devon lace, ethnography, Polynesian, N. American Indian material, Yoruba sculptures, 18th and early 19th c Eskimo and N.W. Coast material, Benin head and Staff mount, 18th c Tahitian morning dress, flute glass 'Exeter flute' c 1660, harpsichord by Vincentius Sodi 32988

Saint Nicholas Priory, The Mint, off Fore St, Exeter EX4 3RX - T: (01392) 665858, Fax: 421252
Religious Arts Museum 32989

Exmouth

Exmouth Museum, Sheppards Row, Exeter Rd, Exmouth EX8 1PW. Head: Tom Haynes
Local Museum 32990

World of Country Life, Sandy Bay, Exmouth EX8 5BU - T: (01395) 274533, Fax: 273457, E-mail: - worldofcountrylife@hotmail.com, Internet: http://www.worldofcountrylife.co.uk
Folklore Museum / Science&Tech Museum
Vintage cars, classic motorbikes and steam traction engines, Fire engines, moving farm machinery, gypsy caravan 32991

Eyam

Eyam Museum, Hawkhill Rd, Eyam S32 5QP - T: (01433) 631371, Fax: 630777, Internet: http://www.cressbrook.co.uk/eyam/museum. Head: P. Hornann
Natural History Museum - 1994
Village heroism when in 1665 the had Bubonic Plague and quarantined themselved - C. Daniel Collection 32992

Eyemouth

Eyemouth Museum, Auld Kirk, Manse Rd, Eyemouth TD14 5JE - T: (01890) 750678. Head: Jean Bowle
Local Museum
History of the Eyemouth area and its people, with a special emphasis on the fishing industry, farming and the traditional trades and handicrafts 32993

Eynsford

Lullingstone Roman Villa, Eynsford DA4 0JA - T: (01322) 863467, Internet: http://www.english-heritage.org.uk. Head: Nick Moore
Archaeological Museum
Artefacts from the excavations of the 1960s 32994

Fair Isle

Auld Sköll, Utra, Fair Isle ZE2 9JU - T: (01595) 760209
Historical Museum 32995

Fakenham

Fakenham Museum of Gas and Local History, Hempton Rd, Fakenham NR21 9EP - T: (01328) 855579. Head: John G. Ashley
Science&Tech Museum / Local Museum 32996

Thursford Collection, Thursford Green, Fakenham NR21 0AS - T: (01328) 878477, Fax: 878415, E-mail: admin@thursfordcollection.co.uk. Head: J.R. Cusming
Science&Tech Museum / Music Museum - 1947
Steam and locomotives including showman's traction and ploughing engines, steam wagons, mechanical musical organs, Wurlitzer theater organ, concert organ, German organ Karl Frei 32997

Falkirk

Callendar House, Callendar Estate, Falkirk FK1 1YR - T: (01324) 503770, Fax: 503771, E-mail: callendarhouse@falkirkmuseum.demon.co.uk. Head: J.M. Sanderson
Historical Museum - 1991
Mansion, working kitchen of 1825 - History research centre 32998

Falkland

Falkland Palace and Garden, High St, Falkland KY7 7BU - T: (01337) 857397, Fax: (01324) 503771
Historical Museum - 1952
Chapel Royal, Royal Tennis Court (1539), Flemish tapestries 32999

Falmer

Gardner Arts Centre, University of Sussex, Falmer BN1 9RA - T: (01273) 685447, Fax: 678551, E-mail: marketing@gardnerarts.co.uk, Internet: http://www.gardnerarts.co.uk
Public Gallery 33000

Falmouth

Cornwall Maritime Museum → National Maritime Museum Cornwell

Falmouth Art Gallery, Municipal Buildings, The Moor, Falmouth TR11 2RT - T: (01326) 313863, Fax: 312662, E-mail: falag@uknetworks.co.uk, Internet: http://www.falmouthartgallery.com. Head: Brian Stewart
Fine Arts Museum / Public Gallery - 1978
Late 19th and early 20th c paintings (mainly British) donated by Alfred de Pass 33001

National Maritime Museum Cornwell (temporary closed), Discovery Quai, Falmouth TR11 3QY - T: (01326) 313388, Fax: 317878, E-mail: enquiries@nmmc.co.uk, Internet: http://www.nmmc.co.uk. Head: Peter Cowling
Historical Museum / Science&Tech Museum
Maritime history of Cornwall and the Falmouth Post Office Packet Service, models, photographs, navigational instruments, ship-building tools - Database of Cornish built vessels 1786-1914 33002

Pendennis Castle, Falmouth TR11 4LP - T: (01326) 316594, Fax: 319911. Head: Tony Musty
Historical Museum
Arms and uniforms, artillery, furnished interiors and discovery centre 33003

Fareham

Royal Armouries at Fort Nelson, Fort Nelson, Portsdown Hill, Down End Rd, Fareham PO17 6AN - T: (01329) 233734, Fax: 822092, E-mail: nelson@rmplc.co.uk, Internet: http://www.resort-guide/portsmouth/fort-nelson. Head: Christopher Henry
Historical Museum / Military Museum - 1988
19th c fortress home of the Royal armouries coll of artillery (worldwide 15th-20th c), regular exhibitions and firing days - Conservation education centre 33004

Westbury Manor Museum, 84 West St, Fareham PO16 0JJ - T: (01329) 824895, Fax: 825917, Internet: http://hants.gov.uk/museum/westbury. Head: Oonagh Palmer
Local Museum 33005

Faringdon

Buscot Park House, Faringdon SN7 8BU - T: (01367) 20786
Fine Arts Museum
Georgian house in park, containing Faringdon Coll of the English and Continental schools (Rembrandt, Murillo and Reynolds) 33006

Farleigh Hungerford

Farleigh Hungerford Castle, Farleigh Hungerford BA3 6RS - T: (01225) 754026, Internet: http://www.english-heritage.org.uk. Head: Tony Musty
Archaeological Museum
Ruins of a fortified manor house containing a furnished chapel and a small collection of architectural fragments 33007

Farndon

Stretton Water Mill, Stretton, Farndon CH3 6LN - E-mail: cheshiremuseums@cheshire.gov.uk
Science&Tech Museum 33008

Farnham

Farnhem Maltings Gallery, Farnham Maltings, Bridge Sq, Farnham GU9 7QR - T: (01252) 726234, Fax: 718177, E-mail: FarnMAlt@aol.com, Internet: http://www.farnhammaltings.com. Head: Tozzy Bridger
Public Gallery 33009

Foyer Gallery/James Hockey Gallery, Falkner Rd, Farnham GU9 7DS - T: (01252) 892668/46, Fax: 892667, E-mail: ckapteijn@surrart.ac.uk, Internet: http://www.surrart.ac.uk
Public Gallery 33010

Museum of Farnham, Willmer House, 38 West St, Farnham GU9 7DX - T: (01252) 715094, Fax: 715094, E-mail: fmuseum@waverley.gov.uk. Head: Anne Jones
Decorative Arts Museum - 1960
House (1718) with English decorative arts, local history, archaeology, 18th c furniture, costumes, William Cobbett memorabilia - Reference library 33011

Rural Life Centre, Reeds Rd, Tilford, Farnham GU10 2DL - T: (01252) 795571, Fax: 795571, E-mail: rural.life@argonet.co.uk, Internet: http://www.surreyweb.uk/rural-life. Head: Henry Jackson
Agriculture Museum - 1972
Waggons, farm implements, hand tools, dairy, kitchen, trades and crafts, rural life 1800-1950, arboretum, wheel whight 33012

Faversham

Fleur de Lis Heritage Centre, 10-13 Preston St, Faversham ME13 8NS - T: (01795) 534542, Fax: 533261, E-mail: faversham@btinternet.com, Internet: http://www.faversham.org/society/museum.html. Head: Arthur Percival
Local Museum - 1977
Telephones, explosives hist 33013

Maison Dieu, Water Lane, Ospringe, Faversham ME13 8TW - T: (01795) 533751, Fax: 533261, Internet: http://www.english-heritage.co.uk
Historical Museum - 1925
Medieval bldg, once part of complex which served as Royal lodge, pilgrims' hostel, hospital and almshouse for retired Royal retainers, now housing Roman finds and new displays illustrating Ospringe's eventful hist 33014

Ferniegair

Chatelherault, Ferniegair ML3 7UE - T: (01698) 426213, Fax: 421532
Historical Museum
Historic park, ruined Cadzow Castle, remains of coal mines 33015

Fetlar

Fetlar Interpretive Centre, Beach of Houbie, Fetlar ZE2 9DJ - T: (01957) 733206, Fax: 733219
Local Museum 33016

Filching

Motor Museum, Filching Manor, Filching BN26 5QA - T: (01323) 487838, Fax: 486331
Science&Tech Museum
Wealden Hall house, car coll, 1893-1997 karting circuit 33017

Filey

Filey Museum, 8-10 Queen St, Filey YO14 9HB - T: (01723) 515013. Head: Margaret Wilkins
Local Museum
Fishing, lifeboats, the seashore, rural and domestic objects 33018

Filkins

Swinford Museum, Filkins GL7 3JQ - T: (01367) 860209, 860334. Head: Mervyn Swinford
Agriculture Museum / Folklore Museum - 1931
Household and farm tools, stone craft 33019

Firle

Charleston Collection, Firle BN8 6LL - T: (01323) 811626, 811265, Fax: 811628, E-mail: charles@solutions-inc.co.uk, Internet: http://www.charleston.org. Head: Alastair Upton
Decorative Arts Museum - 1930
Domestic decorative art of Vanessa Bell and Duncan Grant 33020

Firle Place, Firle BN8 6LP - T: (01273) 858335, Fax: 858188, E-mail: gage@firleplace.co.uk
Decorative Arts Museum
Home of Viscount Gage, old masters, Sevres and English porcelain, fine French and English furniture 33021

Fishguard

West Wales Arts Centre, 16 West St, Fishguard SA65 9AE - T: (01348) 873867, E-mail: westwalesarts@btconnect.com, Internet: http://home.btconnect.com/west-wales-arts
Public Gallery
Paintings, sculpture, ceramics, jewllery and glass 33022

Fleetwood

Fleetwood Museum, Queen's Terrace, Fleetwood FY7 6BT - T: (01253) 876621, Fax: 878088, Internet: http://www.lancashire.com/lcc/museums. Head: Simon Hayhow
Natural History Museum - 1974
County Museum Service biology collections 33023

Flintham

Flintham Museum, Inholms Rd, Flintham NG23 5LF - T: (01636) 525111, E-mail: flintham.museum@lineone.net, Internet: http://www.flintham-museum.org.uk
Local Museum
Rural life, toys, postcards, pharmeceuticals, tobacco products, bike accessories, haberdashery and hardware - archive 33024

Flixton

Norfolk and Suffolk Aviation Museum, East Anglia's Aviation Heritage Centre, Buckeroo Way, The Street, Flixton NR35 1NZ - T: (01986) 896644, E-mail: nsam.flixton@virgin.net, Internet: http://www.aviationmuseum.net. Head: C.H.K. Wallis
Science&Tech Museum - 1972
Coll of over 26 aircraft and items from Pre-WW I to present day, civil and military 33025

Fochabers

Fochabers Folk Museum, Pringle Church, High St, Fochabers IV32 7PF - T: (01343) 820362, Fax: 821291. Head: Gordon Christie
Folklore Museum - 1984
Hist of the village of Fochabers since the late 18th c, coll of horse gigs and carts 33026

Folkestone

Elham Valley Line, Peene Yard, Peene, Newington, Folkestone CT18 8BA - T: (01303) 273690, Fax: 873939, E-mail: elvt.museum@virgin.net. Head: George Wright
Science&Tech Museum
Winston Churchill brought the Bochbuster railway gun during the war 33027

Folkestone Museum and Art Gallery, 2 Grace Hill, Folkestone CT20 1HD - T: (01303) 256710, Fax: 256710, E-mail: janet.adamson@kent.gov.uk. Head: J. Adamson
Local Museum - 1868
Natural hist, geology, local archaeology 33028

Metropole Galleries, The Leas, Folkestone CT20 2LS - T: (01303) 255070, Fax: 851353, E-mail: info@metropole.org.uk. Head: Nick Ewbank
Public Gallery 33029

Fordyce

Fordyce Joiner's Visitor Centre, Fordyce AB45 2SL - E-mail: heritage@aberdeenshire.gov.uk
Special Museum
Rural joiner's workshop, woodworking tools 33030

Forfar

Museum and Art Gallery, Meffan Institute, 20 West High St, Forfar DD8 1BB - T: (01307) 464123, 467017, Fax: 468451, E-mail: the.meffan@angus.gov.uk, Internet: http://www.angus.gov.uk/history. Head: Margaret H. King
Local Museum / Fine Arts Museum - 1898
Local hist, archaelogy, art esp. pictish stones 33031

Forncett Saint Mary

Forncett Industrial Steam Museum, Low Rd, Forncett Saint Mary NR16 1JJ - T: (01508) 488277, Internet: http://www.oldenginehouse.demon.co.uk/forncett.htm. Head: Dr. R. Francis
Science&Tech Museum
147 hp Cross Compound engine which was used to open Tower Bridge, 85t triple expansion water pump 33032

Forres

Brodie Castle, Brodie, Forres IV36 2TE - T: (01309) 641371, Fax: 641600, E-mail: brodiecastle@nts.org.uk. Head: Fionaanie Dingwall
Decorative Arts Museum / Fine Arts Museum - 1979
French furniture, English, Continental and Chinese porcelain and an important coll of 17th-c Dutch and 18th-c English paintings 33033

Falconer Museum, Tolbooth St, Forres IV36 1PH - T: (01309) 673701, Fax: 675863, E-mail: alasdair.joyce@museums.moray.gov.uk, Internet: http://www.moray.org/museums/falconer
Local Museum - 1871
Specialized herbaria, local history, natural history, Peter Anson - library 33034

Nelson Tower, Grant Park, Forres IV36 1FT - E-mail: alasdair.joyce@techleis.moray.gov.uk, Internet: http://www.moray.gov.uk/museums
Fine Arts Museum 33035

Fort William

Glenfinnan Station Museum, Glenfinnan Railway Station, Fort William PH37 4LT - T: (01397) 722295, Fax: 722291
Science&Tech Museum 33036

West Highland Museum, Cameron Sq, Fort William PH33 6AJ - T: (01397) 702169, Fax: 701927. Head: Fiona C. Marwick
Local Museum - 1922
Many aspects of the district and its hist, including geology, wildlife, tartans, maps and a coll of items connected with the 1745 Jacobite rising 33037

Foxton

Foxton Canal Museum, Middle Lock, Foxton LE16 7RA - T: (01858) 466185. Head: Mike Beech
Historical Museum
Canal items, 1793-1950, boat life and locks 33038

Framlingham

390th Bomb Group Memorial Air Museum, Parham Airfield, Framlingham - T: (01473) 711275. Head: Colin Durrant
Military Museum
Engines and other components of crashed U.S. and Allied aircraft, and many photographs and mementoes of the wartime life of both airmen and civilians, reconstructions of a radio hut and of a wartime office 33039

Lanman Museum, Castle, Framlingham IP13 9BP - T: (01728) 723330. Head: T.J. Gilder
Local Museum
Objects of historical, educational or artistic interest connected with the town of Framlingham and the surrounding villages 33040

Museum of the British Resistance Organisation, Parham Airfield, Framlingham - T: (01473) 711275. Head: Colin Durrant
Military Museum
Artifacts, photographs, Britain wartime, secret army 33041

Fraserburgh

Fraserburgh Museum, 37 Gralton Pl, Fraserburgh AB51 7LD
Local Museum 33042

Museum of Scottish Lighthouses, Kinnaird Head, Fraserburgh AB43 9DU - T: (01346) 511022, Fax: 511033, E-mail: enquiries@lighthousemuseum.demon.co.uk. Head: David Bett
Special Museum
Extensive collection of items relating to lighthouses in Scotland and the work of the Northern Lighthouse Board 33043

Freshwater

Dimbola Lodge, Terrace Ln, Freshwater PO40 9QE - T: (01983) 756814, Fax: 755578, E-mail: administrator@dimbola.co.uk, Internet: http://www.dimbola.co.uk. Head: Dr. Brian Hinton
Decorative Arts Museum
Glass plates, original Cameron images 33044

Medina Camera Museum, Golden Hill Fort, Freshwater - T: (01983) 753380. Head: Ken Robson
Science&Tech Museum
Coll of more than 60 cameras, taking both still and moving pictures, dating from the 1880s 33045

Frodsham

Castle Park Arts Centre, Fountain Ln, Frodsham WA6 6SE - T: (01928) 735832, Internet: http://www.castle-park-arts.co.uk
Fine Arts Museum 33046

Frome

Frome Museum, 1 North Parade, Frome BA11 1AT
Local Museum
History of local industries, including cloth-making, metal-casting, printing and quarrying, local geological section - library 33047

Fyvie

Fyvie Castle, Fyvie AB53 8JS - T: (01651) 891266, Fax: 891107
Local Museum
Coll of portraits including works by Batoni, Raeburn, Gainsborough, arms and armour, 16th c tapestries 33048

Gainsborough

Gainsborough Old Hall, Parnell St, Gainsborough DN21 2NB - T: (01427) 612669, Fax: 612779, E-mail: cumminsh@lincolnshire.gov.uk
Local Museum - 1974
In building dating from 1460, medieval room settings & kitchens, 17th c furniture 33049

Gairloch

Gairloch Heritage Museum, Achtercairn, Gairloch IV21 2BP - T: (01445) 712287, E-mail: info@GairlochHeritageMuseum.org.uk, Internet: http://www.GairlochHeritageMuseum.org.uk. Head: Roy Macintyre
Local Museum - 1977
Archaeology, wildlife, agriculture, dairying, wood processing and the domestic arts, family hist section - archive, library 33050

Galashiels

Galashiels Museum, Woollen Mill, Huddersfield St, Galashiels TD1 3BA - T: (01896) 2091
Local Museum
History of Galashiels, emphasising its close involvement with the woollen trade, all aspects of production, from spinning to the finished article 33051

Old Gala House, Scott Crescent, Galashiels TD1 3JS - T: (01750) 720096, Fax: 723282, E-mail: ssinclair@scotborckrs.gov.uk. Head: Ian Brown
Historical Museum
Home of Lairds of Gala, painted ceiling (1635) and wall (1988) 33052

Garlogie

Garlogie Mill Power House Museum, Garlogie AB32 6RX - T: (01224) 664228, E-mail: heritage@aberdeenshire.gov.uk
Science&Tech Museum
19th c beam engine, 20th c turbine 33053

Gateshead

Bowes Railway Heritage Museum, Springwell Village, Gateshead NE9 7QJ - T: (0191) 4161847, 4193349, E-mail: alison_gibson77@hotmail.com, Internet: http://www.bowesrailway.co.uk. Head: Phillip Dawe
Science&Tech Museum - 1976
Coll of historic colliery rolling stock, rope haulage equipment, coll of historic colliery buildings dating from 19th c 33054

The Gallery, Prince Consort Rd, Gateshead Central Library, Gateshead NE8 4LN - T: (0191) 4773478, Fax: 4771495
Public Gallery - 1917 33055

Shipley Art Gallery, Prince Consort Rd, Gateshead NE8 4JB - T: (0191) 4771495, Fax: 4787917, E-mail: shipley@tyne-wear-museums.org.uk
Fine Arts Museum / Decorative Arts Museum / Local Museum - 1917
17th-20th c British painting, also French, Flemish, German, Dutch and Italian painting, Schufelein Altar, contemporary craft, local glass, local industrial hist 33056

Gaydon

Heritage Motor Centre, Banbury Rd, Gaydon CV35 0BJ - T: (01926) 641188, Fax: 641555, E-mail: enquiries@heritagemotorcentre.org.uk, Internet: http://www.heritage.org.uk. Head: Julie Tew
Science&Tech Museum - 1993
Coll of over 200 historic cars, incl prototypes, concept vehicles, record breakers - archive, photographic library 33057

Gerston

Castletown Museum, Mingulay, Gerston KW12 6XQ
Local Museum 33058

Gillingham, Dorset

Gillingham Museum, Chantry Fields, Gillingham, Dorset SP8 4UA - T: (01747) 823176, E-mail: davidlloyd@btinternet.com, Internet: http://www.brwebsites.com/gillingham.museum/. Head: Lyn Light
Local Museum - 1958
Articles manufactured, used or found in Gillingham and documents from the 13th century to the present 33059

Gillingham, Kent

Gillingham Library Gallery, High St, Gillingham, Kent ME7 1BG - T: (01634) 281066, Fax: 855814
Public Gallery 33060

Royal Engineers Museum, Prince Arthur Rd, Gillingham, Kent ME4 4UG - T: (01634) 406397, Fax: 822371, E-mail: remuseum.rhqre@gtnet.gov.uk, Internet: http://www.royalengineers.org.uk. Head: John Nowers
Ethnology Museum
Lives and works, worldwide, of Britain's soldier-engineers from 1066, scientific and engineering equipment, medals, weapons and uniforms, ethnography, decorative arts, esp. Chinese and Sudanese material 33061

Sittingbourne and Kemsley Light Railway, 85 Balmoral Rd, Gillingham, Kent ME7 4QL - T: (01634) 852672, Fax: 852672
Science&Tech Museum
Narrow gauge locomotives and wagons, photographs 33062

Girvan

McKechnie Institute, Dalrymple St, Girvan KA26 9AE - T: (01465) 713643, Fax: 710208
Local Museum / Fine Arts Museum
Local history, community arts centre in a octagonal tower 33063

Penkill Castle, Girvan KA26 9TQ - T: (01465) 871219, Fax: 871215, E-mail: psbfd2@aol.com. Head: P.S.B.F. Dromgoole
Historic Site - 1978
Pre Raphaelite 33064

Glamis

Angus Folk Museum, Kirkwynd Cottages, Glamis DD8 1RT - T: (01307) 840288, Fax: 840233. Head: Kathleen Ager
Folklore Museum - 1957
Local 17th c stone-roofed cottages, agricultural implements, domestic artefacts 33065

Glamis Castle, Glamis DD8 1RJ - T: (01307) 840393, Fax: 840733, E-mail: admin@glamis-castle.co.uk, Internet: http://www.glamis-castle.co.uk. Head: Stuart Gill
Historical Museum
The castle was remodelled in the 17th century and contains rooms with historic pictures, furniture, porcelain and tapestries 33066

Glandford

Glandford Shell Museum, Glandford NR25 7JR - T: (01263) 740081, Fax: 740081, E-mail: sushell@dircon.co.uk. Head: S. Hullah
Special Museum - 1915
Sir Alfred Jodrell shell collection, jewelry, pottery, tapestry 33067

Glasgow

Arctic Penguin, 60 Tradeston St, Glasgow G5 8AG - T: (01433) 302213, Fax: 302213
Special Museum 33068

Burrell Collection, Pollok Country Park, 2060 Pollokshaws Rd, Glasgow G43 1AT - T: (0141) 2872550, Fax: 2872597. Head: Bridget McConnell, Mark O'Neill
Fine Arts Museum / Decorative Arts Museum / Museum of Classical Antiquities - 1983
Paintings, watercolors by Glasgow artists, ceramics, pottery, tapestries, antiquities, Islamic art, stained glass, sculpture, arms and armour, Oriental art, furniture, textiles 33069

Centre for Contemporary Arts, 346-354 Sauchiehall St, Glasgow G2 3JD - T: (0141) 3327521, Fax: 3323226, E-mail: gen@cca-glasgow.com, Internet: http://www.cca-glasgow.com. Head: Graham McKenzie
Public Gallery 33070

Clydebuilt, Scottish Maritime Museum, Kins Inch Rd, Glasgow G51 4BN - T: (0141) 8861013, Fax: 8861015, E-mail: clydebuilt@tinyworld.co.uk. Head: J.M. Tildesley
Science&Tech Museum
Story of the river Clyde, ships 33071

Collins Gallery, c/o University of Strathclyde, 22 Richmond St, Glasgow G1 1XQ - T: (0141) 5482558, Fax: 5524053, E-mail: collinsgallery@strath.ac.uk. Head: Laura Hamilton
Science&Tech Museum / Public Gallery / University Museum - 1973
Anderson coll of scientific instruments, contemporary Scottish art, prints 33072

Eastwood House, Eastwood Park, Giffnoclk, Glasgow G46 6UG - T: (0141) 6381101
Public Gallery 33073

Fossil Grove, Victoria Park, Glasgow G14 1BN - T: (0141) 9501448
Local Museum
330 million year old fossilised tree stumps 33074

Gallery of Modern Art, Queen St, Glasgow G1 3AZ - T: (0141) 2291996, Fax: 2045316
Fine Arts Museum - 1996
Paintings, sculptures and installations from around the world, artists represented include John Bellamy, Alan Davie, Peter Howson and Alison Watt 33075

Glasgow Art Gallery and Museum, Kelvingrove, Glasgow G3 8AG - T: (0141) 2872699, Fax: 2872690. Head: Mark O'Neill
Fine Arts Museum / Local Museum - 1902
British and European paintings including pictures by Rembrandt and Giorgione, 19th c French Impressionists, Scottish painting, sculpture, costume, silver, pottery and porcelain, arms and armour, wildlife and story of man in Scotland 33076

Glasgow Print Studio, 22-25 King St, Glasgow G1 5QP - T: (0141) 5520704, Fax: 5522919, E-mail: gallery@gpsart.co.uk, Internet: http://www.gpsart.co.uk. Head: John Mackechnie
Public Gallery
Work of Paolozzi, Bellany, Blackadder, Howson, Wiszniewski - workshops 33077

Glasgow School of Art - Mackintosh Collection, 167 Renfrew St, Glasgow G3 6RQ - T: (0141) 3534500, Fax: 3534746, E-mail: info@gsa.ac.uk, Internet: http://www.gsa.ac.uk. Head: Prof. Seona Reid
Fine Arts Museum / University Museum
Coll of furniture, watercolours and architectural designs and drawings by Charles Rennie Mackintosh and other GSA-artists 33078

Heatherbank Museum of Social Work, c/o Glasgow Caledonian University, City Campus, Cowcaddens Rd, Glasgow G4 0BA - T: (0141) 33138637, Fax: 3313005, E-mail: a.ramage@gcal.ac.uk, Internet: http://www.lib.gcal.ac.uk/heatherbank. Head: Alastair Ramage
Historical Museum - 1975
Photographic coll of historic pictures, some archive material and ephemera - library, picture library, social work archives 33079

Hunterian Art Gallery, c/o University of Glasgow, 82 Hillhead St, Glasgow G12 8QQ - T: (0141) 3305431, Fax: 3303618, E-mail: hunter@museum.gla.ac.uk, Internet: http://www.hunterian.gla.ac.uk
Fine Arts Museum / University Museum - 1980
Paintings, drawings, prints, furniture, sculpture, works by Charles Rennie Mackintosh, James McNeill Whistler 33080

Hunterian Museum, c/o University of Glasgow, University Av, Glasgow G12 8QQ - T: (0141) 3304221, Fax: 3303617, E-mail: hunter@museum.gla.ac.uk., Internet: http://www.hunterian.gla.ac.uk
Ethnology Museum / Natural History Museum / Archaeological Museum / University Museum - 1807
Coll of the celebrated physician and anatomist Dr. William Hunter, geology, rocks, minerals and fossils, incl 'Bearsden shark', archaeology - early civilizations in Scotland, ethnography, Greek, Roman and Scottish coins, scientific instruments 33081

Kelly Gallery, 118 Douglas St, Glasgow G2 4ET - T: (0141) 2486386, Fax: 2210417
Public Gallery 33082

McLellan Galleries, 270 Sauchiehall St, Glasgow G2 3EH - T: (0141) 3311854, Fax: 3329957. Head: Bridget McConnell
Public Gallery 33083

Museum of Anatomy, c/o IBLS, University of Glasgow, Laboratory of Human Anatomy, Glasgow G12 8QQ - T: (0141) 3305869, Fax: 3304299, E-mail: a.payne@bio.gla.ac.uk
Natural History Museum 33084

Museum of Piping, 30-34 McPhater St, Cowcadden, Glasgow G3 - T: (0141) 3530220, Fax: 3531570, E-mail: ysamson@thepipingcentre.co.uk, Internet: http://www.thepipingcentre.co.uk. Head: Roddy McLeod
Music Museum
Bagpipes, piping artefacts 33085

Museum of Transport, Kelvin Hall, 1 Bunhouse Rd, Glasgow G3 8DP - T: (0141) 2872720, Fax: 2872692
Science&Tech Museum - 1964
Railroad locomotives, bicycles, motorcycles, streetcars, automobiles, models, fire engines, baby carriages, steam road vehicles, horse-drawn carriages 33086

Pearce Institute, 840 Govan Rd, Glasgow G51 3UT - T: (0141) 4451941
Public Gallery 33087

People's Palace Museum, Glasgow Green, Glasgow G40 1AT - T: (0141) 5440223, Fax: 5500892. Head: Fiona Hayes
Historical Museum - 1898
Glaswegian social, economic and political hist since 1175, exhibits on popular culture, public art 33088

Pollok House, 2060 Pollokshaws Rd, Glasgow G43 1AT - T: (0141) 6166410, Fax: 6166521. Head: Robert S. Ferguson
Fine Arts Museum / Decorative Arts Museum - 1968
Stirling Maxwell coll incl Spanish school of painting El Greco, Goya, Murillo, British school, principally William Blake, decorative arts, furniture, pottery, porcelain, silver, bronzes 33089

Provan Hall House, Auchinlea Park, Auchinlea Rd, Glasgow G34 - T: (0141) 7711538
Decorative Arts Museum - 1983/2000 33090

Provand's Lordship, 3 Castle St, Glasgow G4 0RB - T: (0141) 5528819, Fax: 5524744. Head: Bridget McConnell
Historical Museum
Medieval building of 1471 33091

Royal Glasgow Institute of the Fine Arts, 5 Oswald St, Glasgow G1 4QR - T: (0141) 2487411, Fax: 2210417
Public Gallery 33092

Royal Highland Fusiliers Regimental Museum, 518 Sauchiehall St, Glasgow G2 3LW - T: (0141) 3320961, Fax: 3531493, E-mail: assregseg@rhr.org.uk, Internet: http://www.rhr.org.uk. Head: W. Shaw
Military Museum - 1969
History of the regiment since 1678, medals, uniforms, regimental silver, militaria 33093

Saint Mungo Museum of Religious Life and Art, 2 Castle St, Glasgow G4 0RH - T: (0141) 5532557, Fax: 5524744. Head: Bridget McConnell
Religious Arts Museum - 1993
Art objects associated with different religious faiths - Japanese Zen garden 33094

Scotland Street School Museum, 225 Scotland St, Glasgow G5 8QB - T: (0141) 2870500, Fax: 2870515. Head: Bridget McConnell
Historical Museum - 1990
Hist of education in Scotland from 1872, several historical classrooms, Edwardian cookery room, school hist, architectural hist (designed by Charles Rennie Mackintosh) 33095

Scottish Football Museum, c/o Museum of Transport, Kelvin Hall, 1 Bunhouse Rd, Glasgow G3 9DP - T: (0141) 2872697, Fax: 2872692, Internet: http://www.scottishfa.co.uk
Special Museum
Football memorabilia coll from SFA since 1873 33096

Scottish Jewish Museum, Garnethill Synagogue, 127 Hill St, Glasgow G3 6UB - T: (0141) 9562973
Historical Museum
archives 33097

Springburn Museum, Atlas Sq, Ayr St, Glasgow G21 4BW - T: (0141) 5571405, Fax: 5571405
Science&Tech Museum / Local Museum - 1986
Largest steam locomotive manufacture in Europe, community life 33098

Tenement House, 145 Buccleuch St, Glasgow G3 6QN - T: (0141) 3330183. Head: Lorna Hepburn
Local Museum
Typical lower middle class Glasgow tenement flat of the turn of the century with original furnishings and fittings. 33099

Zoology Museum, c/o IBLS, University of Glasgow, Graham Kerr Bldg, Glasgow G12 8QQ - T: (0141) 3304772, E-mail: m.reilly@museum.gla.ac.uk, Internet: http://www.hunterian.gla.ac.uk. Head: Margaret T. Reilly
Natural History Museum
Animal kingdom from microscopic creatures to elephants and whales 33100

Glastonbury

Glastonbury Abbey Museum, Abbey Gatehouse, Magdalene St, Glastonbury BA6 9EL - T: (01458) 832267, Fax: 832267, E-mail: glastonbury.abbey@dial.pipex.com, Internet: http://www.glastonburyabbey.com
Religious Arts Museum - 1908
Coll of tiles, carved stonework and miscellaneous artefacts from the site of the ruined Abbey, together with a model showing how the Abbey may have looked in 1539, before the Dissolution 33101

The Glastonbury Lake Village Museum, The Tribunal, 9 High St, Glastonbury BA6 9DP - T: (01458) 832954, Fax: 832949, E-mail: glastonbury.tic@ukonline.co.uk
Local Museum
Local history 33102

Lake Village Museum → The Glastonbury Lake Village Museum

Somerset Rural Life Museum, Abbey Farm, Chilkwell St, Glastonbury BA6 8DB - T: (01458) 831197, Fax: 834684, E-mail: mcgryspeerdt@somerset.gov.uk, Internet: http://somerset.gov.uk/museums. Head: Mary C. Gryspeerdt, David A. Walker
Local Museum - 1976
Agricultural machinery, tools, waggons and carts, baskets and basket making tools, cider making equipment, chedder cheese making presses and equipment, kitchen and general domestic colls, Somerset furniture, contrymen's smocks 33103

Glenavy

Ballance House, 118a Lisburn Rd, Glenavy BT29 4NY - T: (028) 92648492, Fax: 92648098, E-mail: ballancenz@aol.com, Internet: http://www.geocities.com/heartland/prairie/8890. Head: Keri Wilson
Historical Museum / Ethnology Museum
John Ballance (New Zealand premier 1891-93), ethnographical material, fine art, journals, books, furniture 33104

Glencoe

Glencoe and North Lorn Folk Museum, Glencoe PH49 4HP - T: (01855) 811664. Head: Rachel Grant
Local Museum
MacDonald and Jacobite relicts, domestic bygones, weapons, embroidery, costumes, agricultural items, Ballachulish slate industry, ethnology, military 33105

Glenesk

Glenesk Folk Museum, The Retreat, Glenesk DD9 7YT - T: (01356) 670254, Fax: 670321, E-mail: retreat@angusglens.co.uk, Internet: http://www.angusglens.co.uk. Head: Muriel McIntosh
Local Museum
Local history, costume coll 33106

Glenluce

Glenluce Motor Museum, Glenluce DG8 0NY - T: (01581) 300534, Fax: 300258
Science&Tech Museum
Vintage and classic cars, motor cycles memorabilia and old type garage 33107

Glenrothes

Corridor Gallery, Viewfield Rd, Glenrothes KY6 2RB - T: (01592) 415700
Public Gallery 33108

Glossop

Glossop Heritage Centre, Bank House, Henry St, Glossop SK13 8BW - T: (01457) 869176. Head: Peggy Davies
Local Museum
Local newspapers, local history 33109

Gloucester

Archaeology Unit and Transport Museum, Old Fire Station, Barbican Rd, Gloucester GL1 2JF - T: (01452) 526342, Fax: 503050. Head: Amanda Wadsley
Archaeological Museum / Science&Tech Museum
Horse-drawn manual fire-engine of c 1895,a horse-drawn tram of 1880, a Gloucestershire type of farm wagon, three Dursley-built Pedersen cycles, Morris Commercial of 1926, Cotton motorcycle of ca. 1923, various cycles from 18th and 19th c, J.E.S. motorcycle of 1912, Leyland Metz Fire Engine of ca. 1938, responsibility for the archaeology service and county-wide collections of Gloucester City Council 33110

City Museum and Art Gallery, Brunswick Rd, Gloucester GL1 1HP - T: (01452) 396131, Fax: 410898, E-mail: city.museum@gloucester.gov.uk, Internet: http://www.mylife.gloucester.gov.uk. Head: Linda Coode
Archaeological Museum - 1860
Archaeology, geology, botany, natural hist, English pottery, glass and silver objects, numismatics, art 33111

Gloucester Folk Museum, 99-103 Westgate St, Gloucester GL1 2PG - T: (01452) 396467, Fax: 330495, E-mail: folk.museum@gloucester.gov.uk, Internet: http://www.mylife.gloucester.gov.uk
Local Museum - 1935
Local hist since 1500, crafts, trades, farming tools, fishing, shops and workshops, toys and games, laundry and household equipment, steam engines, model aircraft, pewter, glass, pottery 33112

Gloucester Prison Museum, Barrack Sq, Gloucester GL1 2DN - T: (01452) 529551, Fax: 309320, E-mail: museum@breathmail.net, Internet: http://www.hmprisonservice.gov.uk. Head: Rita Goode
Historical Museum
History and development of Her Majesty Prison Gloucester 33113

National Waterways Museum, Llanthony Warehouse, Gloucester Docks, Gloucester GL1 2EH - T: (01452) 318054, Fax: 318066, E-mail: info@nwm.demon.co.uk, Internet: http://www.nwm.org.uk. Head: Tony Conder
Science&Tech Museum / Historical Museum - 1988
Inland waterways and its transport - archive 33114

Nature in Art, Wallsworth Hall, Tewkesbury Rd, Gloucester GL2 9PA - T: (01452) 731422, Fax: 730937, E-mail: ninart@globalnet.co.uk, Internet: http://www.nature-in-art.org.uk. Head: Simon H. Trapnell
Fine Arts Museum
Fine, decorative and applied art inspired by nature, any period, and country in all media 33115

Robert Opie Collection, Museum of Advertising and Packaging, Albert Warehouse, Gloucester Docks, Gloucester GL1 2EH - T: (01452) 302309, Fax: (01453) 731521, E-mail: edwardgarling@robertopiecollection.com, Internet: http://www.themuseum.co.uk. Head: Robert Opie
Special Museum - 1984
Hist of British consume product development 33116

Soldiers of Gloucestershire Museum, Custom House, Gloucester Docks, Gloucester GL1 2HE - T: (01452) 522682, Fax: 311116. Head: George C. Streatfield
Military Museum - 1989
Uniforms, medals, badges, paintings, arts and crafts - archives 33117

Glyn Ceiriog

Ceiriog Memorial Institute, High St, Glyn Ceiriog LL20 7EH - T: (01691) 718910, 718383
Special Museum 33118

Godalming

Charterhouse School Museum, Charterhouse, Godalming GU7 2DX - T: (01483) 421006, 291515, Fax: 291594, E-mail: dsh@charterhouse.org.uk
Local Museum
Local hist, ethnography, archaeology, natural hist 33119

Godalming Museum, 109a High St, Godalming GU7 1AQ - T: (01483) 426510, Fax: 523495, E-mail: museum@godalming.ndo.co.uk, Internet: http://www.godalming-museum.org.uk. Head: Alison Pattison
Local Museum - 1920
Local hist and industries, Gertrude Jekyll and Edwin Lutyens coll - local studies library 33120

Golcar

Colne Valley Museum, Cliffe Ash, Golcar HD7 4PY - T: (01484) 659762
Local Museum
Restored 19th century weavers' cottages. Demonstration of hand-loom weaving, working spinning jenny, spinning on saxony wheel and clog-making in gas-lit clogger's workshop 33121

Goldhanger

Maldon and District Agricultural and Domestic Museum, 47 Church St, Goldhanger CM9 8AR - T: (01621) 788647, Fax: 788647
Agriculture Museum / Folklore Museum
Coll of vintage farm machinery and tools, domestic bygones, printing machinery, photographs 33122

Golspie

Dunrobin Castle Museum, Dunrobin Castle, Golspie KW10 2SF - T: (01408) 633177, Fax: 634081, E-mail: dunrobin.est@btinternet.com. Head: Keith Jones
Decorative Arts Museum
Victorian castle, formerly a summerhouse, collections of game trophies and Pictish stones, local history, ornithology, geology, ethnography 33123

Gomersal

Red House Museum, Oxford Rd, Gomersal BD19 4JP - T: (01274) 335100, Fax: 335105, Internet: http://www.kirkleesmc.gov.uk/community/museums
Local Museum
Regency house with Brontë connections 33124

Gomshall

Gomshall Gallery, Station Rd, Gomshall GU5 9LB - T: (01483) 203795, Fax: 203282
Public Gallery 33125

Goole

Goole Museum and Art Gallery, Carlisle St, Goole DN14 5BG, mail addr: Eryc Offices, Church St, Goole DN14 5BG - T: (01405) 72225, Fax: 722256, E-mail: janet.tierney@eastriding.gov.uk
Local Museum / Fine Arts Museum - 1968
Local history, shipping, paintings 33126

Waterways Museum, Sobriety Project, Dutch River Side, Goole DN14 5TB - T: (01405) 768730, Fax: 769868, E-mail: waterwaysmuseum@btinternet.com
Historical Museum
Photographs, documents, industrial and waterways heritage 33127

Gordon

Mellerstain House, Mellerstain, Gordon TD3 6LG - T: (01573) 410225, Fax: 410636, E-mail: - mellerstain.house@virgin.net, Internet: http://www.muses.calligrafix.co.uk/mellerstain. Head: Earl of Haddington
Local Museum - 1952
Robert Adam architecture, old master paintings, antique dolls - Library 33128

Gorey

Mont Orgueil Castle, Rte de la Côte, Gorey JE3 6DN - T: (01534) 853292, Fax: 854303, E-mail: museum@jerseyheritagetrust.org, Internet: http://www.jerseyheritagetrust.org. Head: Michael Day
Historic Site / Archaeological Museum - 1907
Medieval castle, local archaeological finds 33129

Gosport

Fort Brockhurst, Gunner's Wy, Elson, Gosport PO12 4DS - T: (023) 92581059. Head: Nick Moore
Military Museum
Artillery coll 33130

Gosport Museum, Walpole Rd, Gosport PO12 1NS - T: (023) 92588035, Fax: 92501951, Internet: http://www.hants.gov.uk/museums/gosport. Head: I. Edelman
Local Museum - 1974
Local hist, geology - library 33131

Hovercraft Museum, 15 Saint Mark's Rd, Gosport PO12 2DA - T: (023) 92601310, Fax: 92601310, E-mail: chris@hovercraft-museum.org, Internet: http://www.hovercraft-museum.org. Head: Warwick Jacobs
Historical Museum / Science&Tech Museum
44 hovercraft and history 33132

Royal Navy Submarine Museum, Haslar Jetty Rd, Gosport PO12 2AS - T: (02392) 510354, Fax: 511349, E-mail: rnsubs@submus.co.uk, Internet: http://www.submus.co.uk. Head: J.J. Tall
Military Museum - 1963
Models of all British submarines from 1879 to the present day, H.M. Submarine Alliance, Holland I - library, photographic archive, diving museum 33133

Search Centre, 50 Clarence Rd, Gosport PO12 1BU - T: (023) 92501957, Fax: 92501921, E-mail: musmft@hants.gov.uk, Internet: http://www.hants.gov.uk/museum/search. Head: Janet Wildman
Science&Tech Museum
History and natural history 33134

Gott

Tingwall Agricultural Museum, 2 Veensgarth, Gott ZE2 9SB - T: (01595) 840344
Agriculture Museum
18th c farming 33135

Goudhurst

Finchcocks, Living Museum of Music, Goudhurst TN17 1HH - T: (01580) 211702, Fax: 211007, E-mail: katrina@finchcocks.co.uk, Internet: http://www.finchcocks.co.uk. Head: Richard Burnett
Music Museum - 1971
Coll of historical keyboard instruments, chamber organs, and a wide range of early pianos, musical furniture 33136

Gower

Gower Heritage Centre, Y Felin Ddwr, Parkmill, Gower SA3 2EM - T: (01792) 371206, Fax: 371471, E-mail: ghc@gmdawn.demon.co.uk, Internet: http://www.gmdawn.demon.co.uk/ghc
Local Museum / Agriculture Museum
Milling and wheelwrights equipment, agriculture and farming 33137

Grange-over-Sands

Lakeland Motor Museum, Holker Hall, Cark-in-Cartmel, Grange-over-Sands LA11 7PL - T: (015395) 58509, Fax: 58509. Head: Dr. D.J. Sidebottom
Science&Tech Museum - 1978
Classic and vintage cars, motor-cycles, cycles, tractors, engines and automobilia, 1920's garage re-creation, the Campbell Legend Bluebird exhibition, 33138

Grangemouth

Grangemouth Museum, Bo'ness Rd, Grangemouth FK3 8AG - T: (01324) 504699
Local Museum
Scotlands earliest planned industrial town, petroleum and chemical industries 33139

Workshop and Stores, 7-11 Abbotsinch Rd, Abbotsinch Industrial Estate, Grangemouth FK3 9UX - T: (01324) 504689, Fax: 504689
Local Museum
Extensive industrial collection, machines, hand tools, transport items 33140

Grantham

Belton House, Grantham NG32 2LS - T: (01476) 566116, Fax: 579071, E-mail: belton@smtp.ntrust.org.uk. Head: Duncan Bowen
Fine Arts Museum / Decorative Arts Museum
Plasterwork ceilings by Edward Goudge, wood carvings of the Grinling Gibbons School, portraits, furniture, tapestries, oriental porcelain 33141

Grantham Museum, Saint Peter's Hill, Grantham NG31 6PY - T: (01476) 568783, Fax: 592457, E-mail: grantham-museum@lineone.net. Head: A. Brearley
Local Museum - 1926
Local history from prehistoric to modern times, two special exhibitions are devoted to the town's famous personalities - Isaac Newton and Margaret Thatcher 33142

The Queen's Royal Lancers Museum, Belvoir Castle, Grantham NG32 1PD - T: (0115) 9573295, Fax: 9573195, E-mail: hhqandmuseumqrl@ukonline.co.uk, Internet: http://www.qrl.uk.com. Head: J.M. Holtby
Military Museum - 1963
Arms, uniforms, paintings, silver, medals - archives 33143

Grantown-on-Spey

Grantown Museum, Burnfield House, Burnfield Av, Grantown-on-Spey PH26 3HH - T: (01479) 872478, Fax: 872478, E-mail: molly.duckett@btinternet.com, Internet: http://grantown-on-spey.co.uk. Head: Gavin Cullen
Local Museum 33144

Grasmere

Dove Cottage and the Wordsworth Museum, Centre for British Romanticism, Town End, Grasmere LA22 9SH - T: (015394) 35544, Fax: 35748, E-mail: enquiries@wordsworth.org.uk, Internet: http://www.wordsworth.org.uk. Head: Dr. Robert Woof
Special Museum - 1890/1935
Former home of William Wordsworth (1770-1850) with memorabilia of the poet, books and manuscripts of major Romantic figures, lake district fine art and topography 33145

Grassington

Upper Wharfdale Folk Museum, 6 The Square, Grassington BD23 5HA - T: (01756) 753202
Folklore Museum
History of the Dales, with a special emphasis on farming, lead mining and domestic life 33146

Gravesend

Gravesham Museum, High St, Gravesend DA12 0BQ - T: (01474) 323159. Head: Georgina Hammond
Local Museum
Local archaeology and history, paintings 33147

Grays

Thurrock Museum, Thameside Complex, Orsett Rd, Grays RM17 5DX - T: (01375) 382555, Fax: 392666, E-mail: jcatton@thurrock.gov.uk, Internet: http://www.thurrock.gov.uk/museum. Head: Jonathan Catton
Local Museum - 1956
Local history and archaeology, maritime - Borough archives 33148

Great Ayton

Captain Cook's Schoolroom Museum, 101 High St, Great Ayton TS9 6NB - T: (01642) 724296
Historical Museum - 1928 33149

Great Bardfield

Great Bardfield Cage, Bridge St, Great Bardfield CM7 4ST - T: (01371) 810555. Head: Charles Holden
Local Museum 33150

Great Bardfield Cottage Museum, Dunmow Rd, Great Bardfield CM7 4ST - T: (01371) 810555. Head: Charles Holden
Local Museum
19th and 20th c domestic and agricultural artefacts, rural crafts 33151

Great Bookham

Polesden Lacey, Great Bookham RH5 6BD - T: (01372) 458203, 452048, Fax: 452023, E-mail: spljac@smtp.ntrust.org.uk. Head: J.A.C. McElwee
Decorative Arts Museum
Fine paintings, furniture, porcelain and silver 33152

Great Grimsby

Welholme Galleries, Welholme Rd, Great Grimsby DN32 9LP - T: (01472) 323576/78, Fax: 323577. Head: Richard Doughty
Local Museum / Fine Arts Museum 33153

Great Malvern

Malvern Museum, Abbey Gateway, Abbey Rd, Great Malvern WR14 3ES - T: (01684) 567811, E-mail: coraweaver@netscapeonline.co.uk. Head: M.J. Hebden
Local Museum - 1979
Geology, water-cure, radar 33154

Great Yarmouth

Elizabethan House Museum, 4 South Quay, Great Yarmouth NR30 2QH - T: (01493) 855746, Fax: 745459, E-mail: rachelkirk@mus.norfolk.gov.uk. Head: Dr. Sheila Watson
Historical Museum - 1975
Tudor merchant's house of 1596 with displays of social hist and domestic life, Victorian kitchen and scullery 33155

Great Yarmouth Museums, Tolhouse St, Great Yarmouth NR30 2SH - T: (01493) 745526, Fax: 745459. Head: Dr. Sheila Watson
Public Gallery - 1961 33156

Maritime Museum for East Anglia, 25 Marine Parade, Great Yarmouth NR30 2EN - T: (01493) 842267, Fax: 745459. Head: Dr. Sheila Watson
Historical Museum - 1967
Maritime hist of the district, fishing, historic racing lateener (1829), life saving 33157

Old Merchant's House and Row 111 Houses, South Quay, Great Yarmouth NR30 2RQ - T: (01493) 857900, Internet: http://www.english-heritage.org.uk. Head: Sara Lunt
Local Museum
Two 17th c town houses, original fixtures and displays of local architectural fittings salvaged from bombing in 1942/43 33158

Tolhouse Museum and Brass Rubbing Centre, Tolhouse St, Great Yarmouth NR30 2SH - T: (01493) 858900, Fax: 745459. Head: Dr. Sheila Watson
Historical Museum - 1976
Victorian prison cells 33159

Greenfield

Greenfield Valley Museum, Basingwerk House, Heritage Park, Greenfield CH8 7QB - T: (01352) 714172, Fax: 714791, Internet: http://www.marketsite.co.uk/greenfield/. Head: John Richards
Science&Tech Museum / Agriculture Museum
Farm machinery and industrial heritage 33160

Greenford

London Motorcycle Museum, Ravenor Farm, 29 Oldfield Ln, Greenford UB6 9LB - T: (020) 85756644, E-mail: thelmm@hotmail.com, Internet: http://www.motorcycle-uk.com/lmm.htm
Science&Tech Museum - 1999
60 motorcycles 33161

Greenhead

Roman Army Museum, Carvoran, Greenhead CA6 7JB - T: (016977) 47485, Fax: 47487, E-mail: vinolandatrust@btinternet.com, Internet: http://www.yell.co.uk/sites/vinolanda
Military Museum 33162

Greenock

McLean Museum and Art Gallery, 15 Kelly St, Greenock PA16 8JX - T: (01475) 715624, Fax: 715626, E-mail: museum@inverclyde.gov.uk, Internet: http://www.inverclyde.gov.uk. Head: Valerie N.S. Boa
Fine Arts Museum - 1876
Caird and McKellar coll of pictures, shipping, objects of J. Watt 33163

Gressenhall

Norfolk Rural Life Museum and Union Farm, Beech House, Gressenhall NR20 4DR - T: (01362) 860563, Fax: 860385, E-mail: andrew.mackay.mus@norfolk.gov.uk. Head: Andrew Mackay
Open Air Museum / Agriculture Museum - 1976
Agricultural hist of Norfolk county, Craftsman's Row with reconstructed village shop and other workshops 33164

Grimsby

National Fishing Heritage Centre, Alexandra Dock, Grimsby DN31 1UZ - T: (01472) 323345, Fax: 323555
Special Museum 33165

Guildford

Guildford Cathedral Treasury, Stag Hill, Guildford GU2 5UP - T: (01483) 565287, Fax: 303350. Head: Ann Wickham
Religious Arts Museum
Cathedral plate silver and other artefacts 33166

Guildford House Gallery, 155 High St, Guildford GU1 3AJ - T: (01483) 444740, Fax: 444742, E-mail: guildfordhouse@remote.guildford.gov.uk, Internet: http://www.guildfordhouse.co.uk. Head: Matthew Alexander
Fine Arts Museum - 1959
Topographical paintings, drawings and prints from the 18th to 20th centuries including pastel and oil portraits by local artist John Russell, 20th century craft collection, textiles, glass, ceramics - library 33167

Guildford Museum, Castle Arch, Guildford GU1 3SX - T: (01483) 444750, Fax: 532391, E-mail: museum@remote.guildford.gov.uk, Internet: http://www.surreyweb.org.uk/guildford-museum. Head: Matthew J. Alexander
Local Museum - 1898
County archaeology, history, needlework, ethnography, Saxon cemetery finds from Guildtown 33168

Lewis Elton Gallery, c/o University of Surrey, Guildford GU2 7XH - T: (01483) 300800, 879167, Fax: 300803, E-mail: s.wallach@surrey.ac.uk, Internet: http://www.surrey.ac.uk. Head: Patricia Grayburn
Public Gallery / University Museum 33169

Loseley House, Guildford GU3 1HS - T: (01483) 304440, Fax: 302036, E-mail: sally@loseley-park.com, Internet: http://www.loseley-park.com
Decorative Arts Museum
House (1562) with Elizabethan architecture, works of art, furniture, paintings, ceilings 33170

Queen's Royal Surrey Regiment Museum, Clandon Park, Guildford GU4 7RQ - T: (01483) 223419, Fax: 224636, E-mail: queenssurreys@care4free.net, Internet: http://www.surrey-online.co.uk/queenssurreys. Head: Penelope James
Military Museum
Militaria, medals, photographs and reference material relating to the Infantry Regiments of Surrey 33171

Haddington

Jane Welsh Carlyle's House, Lodge St, Haddington EH41 3DX - T: (01620) 823738, Fax: 825147. Head: Garth Morrison
Local Museum
House from the middle of the 18th century 33172

Lennoxlove House, Lennoxlove Estate, Haddington EH41 4NZ - T: (01620) 823720, Fax: 825112, E-mail: info@lennoxlove.org, Internet: http://www.lennoxlove.org
Fine Arts Museum 33173

Hagley

Hagley Hall, Hagley DY9 9LG - T: (01562) 882408, Fax: 882632
Fine Arts Museum
Pictures - library 33174

Hailes

Cistercian Museum, Hailes Abbey, Hailes GL54 5PB - T: (01242) 602398, Internet: http://www.englishheritage.org.uk. Head: Tony Musty
Religious Arts Museum
Medieval sculpture, coll of 13th c roof bosses, medieval tiles, manuscripts, pottery and iron work 33175

Hailsham

Hailsham Heritage Centre, Blackman's Yard, Market St, Hailsham BN27 2AE - T: (01323) 840947. Head: M. Alder
Local Museum - 1962 33176

Michelham Priory, Upper Dicker, Hailsham BN27 3QS - T: (01323) 844224, Fax: 844030, E-mail: adminmich@sussexpast.co.uk, Internet: http://www.sussexpast.co.uk. Head: Henry Warner
Fine Arts Museum / Decorative Arts Museum / Agriculture Museum - 1960
Medieval and Tudor-Jacobean furniture, 17th c tapestries, 16th-17th c ironwork, glass, 18th c paintings, agricultural and wheelwright tools and equipment, buildings date from 1229 and include 16th c Great Barn and working watermill 33177

Halesworth

Halesworth and District Museum, Railway Station, Station Rd, Halesworth IP19 8BZ - T: (01986) 873030. Head: Michael Fordham
Local Museum
Local geology and archaeology 33178

Halifax

Bankfield Museum, Akroyd Park, Boothtown Rd, Halifax HX3 6HG - T: (01422) 354823, 352334, Fax: 349020, E-mail: bankfield-museum@calderdale.gov.uk. Head: Rosemary Crook
Local Museum / Military Museum / Decorative Arts Museum - 1887
Textiles, crafts, militaria, toys, ethnography 33179

Calderdale Industrial Museum, Central Works, Square Rd, Halifax HX1 0QG - T: (01422) 358087, Fax: 349310
Science&Tech Museum - 1983
Textile machinery, wool and worsted, machine tools 33180

The Dean Clough Galleries, Halifax HX3 5AX - T: (01422) 250250, Fax: 341148, E-mail: linda@design-dimension.co.uk, Internet: http://www.DeanClough.com. Head: Roger Standen
Public Gallery 33181

Eureka! The Museum for Children, Discovery Rd, Halifax HX1 2NE - T: (01422) 330069, Fax: 330275, E-mail: info@eureka.org.uk, Internet: http://www.eureka.org.uk. Head: Leigh-Anne Stradeski
Special Museum - 1992 33182

Museum of The Duke of Wellington's Regiment, Boothtown Rd, Halifax HX3 6HG - T: (01422) 352334, Fax: 349020, E-mail: bankfield-museum@calderdale.gov.uk. Head: Philippa Mackenzie
Military Museum - 1959
History of the regiment, memorabilia on the first Duke of Wellington (1769-1852) 33183

Piece Hall Art Gallery, Piece Hall, Halifax HX1 1RE - T: (01422) 358087, Fax: 349310. Head: Barry Sheridan
Public Gallery
Temporary exhibition program, regular artists in residence, complementary workshops, educational programs 33184

Pre-Industrial Museum, Piece Hall, Halifax HX1 1PR - T: (01422) 359034, 358087
Historical Museum 33185

Shibden Hall Museum, West Yorkshire Folk Museum, Shibden Hall, Lister's Rd, Halifax HX3 6XG - T: (01422) 352246, Fax: 348440
Folklore Museum - 1937
15th c house with 17th-19th c furnishings, other old buildings, workshops, farm tools, vehicles, musical instruments, local pottery 33186

Hallaton

Hallaton Museum, Hog Ln, Hallaton LE16 8UE - T: (01858) 555416. Head: J. Morison
Local Museum
Local history, village life, agricultural artefacts 33187

Halstead

Brewery Chapel Museum, Adams Court, off Trinity St, Halstead CO9 1LF - T: (01787) 478463
Local Museum 33188

Hamilton

District Museum and Cameronians Regimental Museum → Low Parks Museums

Hamilton Museum, 129 Muir St, Hamilton ML3 6BJ - T: (01698) 283981, Fax: 283479. Head: Alison G. Reid
Local Museum - 1967
Costumes, weaving, natural hist, industrial hist, period kitchen, local hist, mining, engineering, in 17th c building, agriculture, restored 18th c assembly room with original plaster and musicians gallery, regimental museum, the cameronians (scottish rifles) 33189

Low Parks Museums, 129 Muir St, Hamilton ML3 6BJ - T: (01698) 328232, Fax: 328412
Military Museum / Local Museum - 1996
History of the regiment 33190

Harewood

Harewood House, c/o Harewood House Trust, Moor House, Harewood LS17 9LQ - T: (0113) 2181010, Fax: 2181002, E-mail: business@harewood.org, Internet: http://www.harewood.org. Head: Terence Suthers
Decorative Arts Museum 33191

Terrace Gallery → Harewood House

Harlech

Harlech Castle, Harlech LL46 2YH - T: (01766) 780552, Fax: 780552
Historic Site 33192

Harlow

Harlow Museum, Third Av, Harlow CM18 6YL - T: (01279) 446422, 454959, Fax: 626094, E-mail: richard.bartlett@harlow.gov.uk. Head: R.W. Bartlett
Local Museum - 1973
Roman, post-medieval pottery - library 33193

Mark Hall Cycle Museum, Muskham Rd, Harlow CM20 2LF - T: (01279) 439680. Head: Ken Kilvington
Science&Tech Museum - 1982
Over 75 cycles and accessories illustrating the history of the bicycle from 1818 to the present day 33194

Harray

Orkney Farm and Folk Museum, Corrigall, Harray KW17 2JR - T: (01856) 771411, Fax: 871560. Head: Harry Flett
Agriculture Museum / Folklore Museum 33195

Harrington

Carpetbagger Aviation Museum, Sunnyvale Farm, off Lamport Rd, Harrington NN6 9PF - T: (01604) 686608, E-mail: rtebbutt@aol.com. Head: J. Bernard Tebbutt
Science&Tech Museum / Military Museum
Memorabilia of 801st-492nd, Royal Observer Corps, Thor Rocket site 33196

Harrogate

Harlow Carr Museum of Gardening, Royal Horticultural Society, Crag Ln, Harrogate HG3 1QB - T: (01423) 565418, Fax: 530666, E-mail: education-harlowcarr@rhs.org.uk, Internet: http://www.harlowcarr.fsnet.co.uk. Head: Fred Dunning
Agriculture Museum - 1989
Old gardening equipment, gardening ephemera, large coll available to students 33197

Mercer Art Gallery, Swan Rd, Harrogate HG1 2SA - T: (01423) 566188, Fax: 566130, E-mail: lg12@harrogate.gov.uk, Internet: http://www.harrogate.gov.uk. Head: Mary J. Icershaw
Fine Arts Museum - 1991
Paintings, watercolors, lithographs, drawings, prints, reproductions 33198

Nidderdale Museum, Council Offices, King St, Pateley Bridge, Harrogate HG3 5LE - T: (01423) 711225
Local Museum - 1975
Domestic, farming and industrial material, costumes, a cobbler's shop, solicitor's office, general store, a Victorian parlour 33199

Royal Pump Room Museum, Royal Parade, Crescent Rd, Harrogate HG1 2RY - T: (01423) 566130, Fax: 840026, E-mail: LG12@harrogate.gov.uk, Internet: http://www.harrogate.gov.uk. Head: Mary J. Kershaw
Science&Tech Museum - 1953
History of sulphur and mineral wells, costumes, pottery, archaeology, local social life 33200

War Room and Motor House Collection, 30 Park Parade, Harrogate HG1 5AG - T: (01423) 500704. Head: Brian Jewell
Historical Museum / Science&Tech Museum
Exhibits from two WW's transport and architectural models 33201

Harrow

Harrow Museum, Headstone Manor, Pinner View, Harrow HA2 6PX - T: (020) 88612626, Fax: 88636407, E-mail: davidw@hacserve.tcom.co.uk, Internet: http://www.harrowarts.org.uk. Head: David Whorlow
Local Museum
History of Harrow 33202

Hartland

Hartland Quay Museum, Hartland Quay, Hartland EX39 6DU - T: (01288) 331353. Head: M.R. Myers, M. Nix
Local Museum - 1980
Geological and natural hist, a marine aquarium, maritime hist, shipwrecks, local hist, coastal industry 33203

Hartlepool

Hartlepool Art Gallery, Church Sq, Hartlepool TS24 8EQ - T: (01429) 869706, Fax: 523450
Fine Arts Museum
19th and 20th century paintings, oriental antiquities, displays of local history and the history of Christ Church - Japanese gallery 33204

HMS Trincomalee, Jackson Dock, Hartlepool TS24 0SQ - T: (01429) 223193, Fax: 864385
Science&Tech Museum
Historic ship 33205

Museum of Hartlepool, Jackson Dock, Hartlepool TS24 0SQ - T: (01429) 860077, Fax: 867332, E-mail: arts-museum@hartlepool.gov.uk, Internet: http://www.thisishartlepool.com
Local Museum - 1995
Local history stone age to present, natural history, fishing, shipbuilding, archaeology, local sailing craft 33206

Tees Archaeology, Sir William Gry House, Clarence Rd, Hartlepool TS24 8BT - T: (01429) 523455, Fax: 523477, E-mail: tees-archaeology@hartlepool.gov.uk. Head: R. Daniels
Archaeological Museum 33207

Harwich

Harwich Maritime Museum and Harwich Lifeboat Museum, Harwich Green, Harwich CO12 3NC - T: (01255) 503429, Fax: 503429, E-mail: theharwichsociety@quista.net, Internet: http://www.harwich-society.com. Head: T. Beirne, C. Farnell
Science&Tech Museum 33208

Harwich Redoubt Fort, Main Rd, Harwich CO12 3LT - T: (01255) 503429, Fax: 503429, E-mail: theharwichsociety@quista.net, Internet: http://www.harwich-society.com. Head: A. Rutter
Historical Museum
180ft diameter circular fort built 1808 against Napoleonic invasion, 11 guns/battlements 33209

Haslemere

Haslemere Educational Museum, 78 High St, Haslemere GU27 2LA - T: (01428) 642112, Fax: 645234, E-mail: HaslemereMuseum@compuserve.com. Head: Angela Gill
Historical Museum - 1888
Natural history, geology, ornithology, botany, prehistory, local history, peasant art 33210

Hastings

Fishermen's Museum, Rock-a-Nore Rd, Hastings TN34 3DW - T: (01424) 461446. Head: Brian Green
Historical Museum
Hastings fishing industry, maritime hist 33211

Hastings Museum and Art Gallery, Bohemia Rd, Hastings TN34 1ET - T: (01424) 781155, Fax: 781165, E-mail: curator@breathemail.net. Head: Victoria Williams
Fine Arts Museum / Ethnology Museum - 1890
Paintings, Oriental art, Pacific and American Indian ethnography, geology, zoology, archaeology, history, folklore, topography, Durbar Hall, Hawaiian feather cloak, majolica dish of 1594, Sussex pottery - library, archives, two North American Indian galleries 33212

Museum of Local History, Old Town Hall, High St, Hastings TN34 1EW - T: (01424) 781166, Fax: 781165, E-mail: curator@breathemail.net. Head: Victoria Williams
Historical Museum - 1949
Local archaeology and history, topography 33213

Shipwreck Heritage Centre, Rock-a-Nore Rd, Hastings TN34 3DW - T: (01424) 437452, Fax: 437452. Head: Peter Marsden
Archaeological Museum - 1986
Objects from historic and ancient shipwrecks around southern England, prehistoric, Roman, medieval and later 33214

Hatfield

Art and Design Gallery, c/o Faculty of Art & Design, University of Hertfordshire, College Ln, Hatfield AL10 9AB - T: (01707) 285376, Fax: 285310, E-mail: m.b.shaul@herts.ac.uk, Internet: http://www.herts.ac.uk/artdes. Head: Chris McIntyre
Public Gallery
Fine and applied arts, design and craft 33215

Mill Green Museum and Mill, Mill Green, Hatfield AL9 5PD - T: (01707) 271362, Fax: 272511, E-mail: mueum@welhar.gov.uk. Head: Carol Rigby
Local Museum / Science&Tech Museum - 1973
18th c brick-built, three-storey watermill, with early 19th c wood and iron machinery, 18th-c miller's house, the social hist of the Welwyn-Hatfield area, archaeology, domestic life, the railways, industry, farming and wartime, Belgic and Roman pottery from Welwyn, pottery from Hatfield - library 33216

Haughton

National Mining Museum, Lound Hall, Haughton DN22 8DF - T: (01623) 860728
Science&Tech Museum - 1970 33217

Havant

Havant Museum, East St, Havant PO9 1BS - T: (023) 92451155, Internet: http://www.hants.gov.uk/museums. Head: Dr. C.J. Palmer
Local Museum - 1977
Vokes Coll of sporting firearms, Havant local industries and local hist 33218

Havenstreet

Isle of Wight Steam Railway and Isle of Wight Railway Heritage Museum, Railway Station, Havenstreet PO33 4DS - T: (01983) 882204, Fax: 884515, Internet: http://www.iwsteam-railway.co.uk. Head: Hugh Boynton
Science&Tech Museum - 1971
Locomotives and rolling stock from early Isle of Wight-railways, oldest vehicle built in 1864, oldest locomotive built in 1876 - Documentary and photographic archive 33219

Haverfordwest

Scolton Manor Museum, Spittal, Haverfordwest SA62 5QL - T: (01437) 731457, Fax: 731743. Head: Mark Thomas
Local Museum - 1967
Social hist, costume, photographs, military hist, fine art, decorative art, natural hist, coins & numismatics, geology, archaeology 33220

Haverhill

Haverhill District Local History Centre, Town Hall Arts Centre, High St, Haverhill CB9 8AR - T: (01440) 714962
Local Museum
Photographs of local area, newspaper on microfilm 33221

Hawes

Dales Countryside Museum, Station Yard, Hawes DL8 3NT - T: (01969) 667494, Fax: 667165, E-mail: dcm@yorkshiredales.co.uk. Head: Fiona Rosher
Local Museum - 1979
History, agriculture, industry, local crafts transport, communications , telling the story of the people and landscape of the Dales 33222

Hawick

Drumlanrig's Tower, 1 Towerknowe, Hawick TD9 9EN - T: (01450) 377615, Fax: 378506. Head: Fiona Colton
Local Museum / Fine Arts Museum
Borders history, local traditions, Tom Scott Gallery of late Victorian watercolours 33223

Hawick Museum, Wilton Lodge Park, Hawick TD9 7JL - T: (01450) 373457, Fax: 378506. Head: Fiona Colton
Local Museum / Fine Arts Museum - 1856/1975
Scottish history, natural history, militaria, coins, knitwear industry, 19th-20th c paintings 33224

The Scott Gallery, Hawick Museum, Wilton Lodge Park, Hawick TD9 7JL - T: (01450) 373457, Fax: 378506, E-mail: hawickmuseum@hotmail.com.uk. Head: Ian Brown
Public Gallery 33225

Hawkinge

Kent Battle of Britain Museum, Aerodrome Rd, Hawkinge CT18 7AG - T: (01303) 893140, E-mail: - kentbattleofbritainmuseum@btinternet.com, Internet: http://www.kbobm.org. Head: Mike Llewellyn

Military Museum
Battle of Britain artefacts, aircraft, vehicles, weapons, flying equipment, prints and relics from over 600 crashed aircraft 33226

Hawkshead

Beatrix Potter Gallery, Main St, Hawkshead LA22 0NS - T: (015394) 36355, Fax: 36118, E-mail: ntrust@bpgallery.fsnet.co.uk. Head: Liz Hunter
Fine Arts Museum
Beatrix Potter's original drawings and illustrations of her children's storybooks 33227

Haworth

Brontë Parsonage Museum, Church St, Haworth BD22 8DR - T: (01535) 642323, Fax: 647131, E-mail: bronte@bronte.prestel.co.uk, Internet: http://www.bronte.org.uk. Head: Alan Bentley
Special Museum - 1895
Books, manuscripts, letters, paintings, drawings, furniture and personal treasures of the Brontë family 33228

Keighley and Worth Valley Railway Museum, Station, Haworth BD22 8NJ - T: (01535) 645214, 647777, Fax: 647317, Internet: http://www.kwvr.co.uk
Science&Tech Museum
Engines and rolling stock, Pullman train, vintage carriages and steam locomotives, station signs 33229

Haywards Heath

Lindfield Parvise Museum, All Saints Church Museum, High St, Lindfield, Haywards Heath - T: (01444) 482405
Religious Arts Museum - 1932 33230

Headcorn

Lashenden Air Warfare Museum, Aerodrome, Headcorn TN27 9HX - T: (01622) 890226, 206783, Fax: 206783, E-mail: lashairwar@aol.com. Head: D. Campbell
Science&Tech Museum
Aviation relics, uniforms, civilians at war, prisoners of war 33231

Heathfield

Sussex Farm Museum, Horam Manor, Heathfield TN21 0JB - T: (01435) 812597, Fax: 813716. Head: M.R.R. Goulden
Agriculture Museum 33232

Hebden Bridge

Automobilia, Billy Ln, Old Town, Wadsworth, Hebden Bridge HX7 8RY - T: (01422) 844775, Fax: 842884
Science&Tech Museum
Coll of cars, motorcycles, bicycles hr 33233

Heckington

Heckington Windmill, Hale Rd, Heckington NG34 9JJ - T: (01529) 461919
Science&Tech Museum
Ancillary machinery 33234

Hednesford

Museum of Cannock Chase, Valley Rd, Hednesford WS12 5TD - T: (01543) 877666, Fax: 428272, E-mail: museum@cannockchase.gov.uk. Head: Adrienne Whitehouse
Local Museum
Social history, industry, coal mining 33235

Hedon

Hedon Museum, Town Hall Complex, Saint Augustine's Gate, Hedon HU12 8EX - T: (01482) 890908
Local Museum 33236

Helensburgh

Hill House, Upper Colquhoun St, Helensburgh G84 9AJ - T: (01436) 673900, Fax: 674685, E-mail: aellis@nts.org.uk, Internet: http://www.nts.org.uk
Decorative Arts Museum
Domestic architecture of Charles Rennie Mackintosh, furniture, interior design, new domestic design (annual exhibition) 33237

Portico Gallery, 78 W Clyde St, Helensburgh G84 0AB - T: (01436) 671821, Fax: 677553
Fine Arts Museum 33238

Helmsdale

Timespan Museum and Art Gallery, Dunrobin St, Helmsdale KW8 6JX - T: (01431) 821327, Internet: http://www.timespan.org.uk
Local Museum / Public Gallery
Highland's people, natural hist, rare and medicinical plants - garden 33239

Helmshore

Helmshore Textile Museums, Holcombe Rd, Helmshore BB4 4NP - T: (01706) 226459, Fax: 218554, E-mail: helmshoremuseum@museumoflancs.org.uk, Internet: http://www.lancashire.com/lcc/museums. Head: Edmund Southworth
Science&Tech Museum - 1967
Platt coll of early textile machinery, Lancs textile industry 33240

Helston

Cornwall Aero Park, Clodgey Ln, Helston TR13 0QA - T: (01326) 573404, Fax: 573344, E-mail: flambards@connexions.co.uk, Internet: http://www.flambards.co.uk. Head: J.K. Hale
Science&Tech Museum - 1976
Flying machines, several aircraft, motorcycles motorcars and vehicles, historic streets, shops, houses, coaches, dresses, Victorian village, Britain in the Blitz historical aviation pioneers 33241

Flambards Victorian Village, Culdrose Manor, Helston TR13 0QA - T: (01326) 573404, Fax: 573344, E-mail: info@flambards.co.uk, Internet: http://www.flambards.co.uk. Head: James Kingsford Hale
Science&Tech Museum
Aeropark coll, aviation in peace and war, aviation pioneer Richard Pearse, chemist's shop, wedding fashions and wedding cakes 33242

Helston Folk Museum, The Old Butter Market, Market Pl, Helston TR13 8TH - T: (01326) 564027, Fax: 569714, E-mail: enquiries@helstonmuseum.org.uk, Internet: http://www.helstonmuseum.org.uk. Head: Martin Matthews
Local Museum - 1949
Local history 33243

National Museum of Gardening, Trevarno Estate and Gardens, Helston TR13 0RU - T: (01326) 574274, Fax: 574282, E-mail: enquiries@trevarnoestateandgardens.co.uk, Internet: http://www.trevarnoestateandgardens.co.uk. Head: Marye Porter
Special Museum
Garden tools, implements, requisites, memorabilia and ephemera 33244

Poldark Mine and Heritage Complex, Wendron, Helston TR13 0ER - T: (01326) 573173, 563166, Fax: 563166, E-mail: info@poldark-mine.co.uk, Internet: http://www.poldark-mine.co.uk. Head: Richard Williams
Science&Tech Museum - 1971
18th c tin mine heritage, Cornish beam engine, machinery 33245

Hemel Hempstead

Old Town Hall, High St, Hemel Hempstead HP1 3AE - T: (01442) 228095, Fax: 234072
Local Museum 33246

Henfield

Henfield Museum, Village Hall, Coopers Yard, Henfield BN5 9DB - T: (01273) 492546, Fax: 494898, E-mail: office@henfield.gov.uk, Internet: http://www.henfield.gov.uk. Head: Marjorie W. Carreck
Local Museum - 1948
Local hist, costume, agricultural and domestic bygones, local paintings and photographs, uniforms 33247

Henley-on-Thames

Fawley Court Historic House and Museum, Fawley Court, Henley-on-Thames RG9 3AE - T: (01491) 574917, Fax: 411587. Head: Henry Lipinski
Historical Museum / Military Museum
Books from 15th to 19th century in a few European languages, religious and secular paintings, early manuscripts, Polish documents, rare collections of European, Far and Middle Eastern militaria and arms 33248

River and Rowing Museum, Mill Meadows, Henley-on-Thames RG9 1BF - T: (01491) 415600, Fax: 415601, E-mail: museum@rrm.co.uk, Internet: http://www.rrm.co.uk. Head: Paul E. Mainds
Historical Museum
History, ecology and archaeology of the River Thames, development of the international sport of rowing and the town of Henley-on-Thames 33249

Stonor Park, Henley-on-Thames RG9 6HF - T: (01491) 638587, Fax: 638587, E-mail: jweaver@stonor.com, Internet: http://www.stonor.com. Head: Lord Camoys
Fine Arts Museum 33250

Heptonstall

Heptonstall Museum, Old Grammar School, Heptonstall HX7 7LY - T: (01422) 843738
Local Museum 33251

Hereford

Churchill House Museum and Hatton Gallery, Venns Ln, Aylestone Hill, Hereford HR1 1DE - T: (01432) 260693, Fax: 342492. Head: Judy Stevenson
Fine Arts Museum / Decorative Arts Museum - 1966
Costumes 1700-1980, furniture, early English watercolors, local art, glass, toys 33252

Cider Museum, Pomona Pl, Whitecross Rd, Hereford HR4 0LW, mail addr: 21 Ryelands St, Hereford HR4 0LW - T: (01432) 354207, Fax: 371641, Internet: http://www.cidermuseum.co.uk. Head: Brian Nelson
Agriculture Museum - 1981
Farm cider making, the evolution of the modern cider factory 33253

Hereford City Museum and Art Gallery, Broad St, Hereford HR4 9AU - T: (01432) 364691, 260692, Fax: 342492. Head: Jonathan Cooter
Local Museum / Fine Arts Museum - 1874
Roman remains, agricultural implements, natural hist, paintings and prints, glass and china, militaria, coins 33254

Herefordshire Light Infantry Regimental Museum, TA Centre, Harold St, Hereford - T: (01432) 272914
Military Museum
History and achievements of the Regiment, uniforms, weapons, medals, Colours and documents 33255

Mappa Mundi and Chained Library, 5 College Cloisters, Cathedral Close, Hereford HR1 2NG - T: (01432) 374202, Fax: 374220, E-mail: visits@herefordcathedral.co.uk
Library with Exhibitions - 1996
Medieval world map, chained medieval books, Anglo-Saxon gospels, Hereford breviary and the Wycliffe Cider Bible 33256

Old House, High Town, Hereford HR1 2AA - T: (01432) 260694, Fax: 342492. Head: David Llewellyn
Historical Museum - 1928
17th c furniture, model of the city (1640), civil war displays, Jacobean domestic architecture 33257

Piano Museum Collection, c/o Royal National College for the Blind, College Rd, Hereford HR1 1EB - T: (01432) 265725, Fax: 353478
Special Museum
Early keyboard instruments 33258

Saint John and Coningsby Medieval Museum, Coningsby Hospital, Widemarsh St, Hereford HR4 9HN - T: (01432) 272837. Head: Mary Statham
Historical Museum
History of the Order of St John and the wars during the 300 years of the Crusades, armour and emblazons, also models, in period dress and bandages, of the Coningsby pensioners who used the hospital 33259

Waterworks Museum - Hereford, Broomy Hill, Hereford - T: (01600) 890118, Fax: 890009, E-mail: hwm@marstow.demon.co.uk. Head: Dr. Noel Meeke
Science&Tech Museum
Hist of drinking water supplies, wide range of working pumping engines (steam, diesel, gas) incl a triple-expansion condensing steam engine by Worth, McKenzie & Co (1895) 33260

Herne Bay

Herne Bay Museum and Gallery, 12 William St, Herne Bay CT6 5EJ - T: (01227) 367368, Fax: 742560, Internet: http://www.hernebay-museum.co.uk
Local Museum / Fine Arts Museum
Displays about the town, about Reculver Roman Fort, archaeology and fossils 33261

Public Library and Museum, High St, Herne Bay CT6 5JY - T: (01227) 374896
Local Museum
Local history, natural history, Roman finds from Reculver 33262

Hertford

Hertford Museum, 18 Bull Plain, Hertford SG14 1DT - T: (01992) 582686, Fax: 534797
Local Museum - 1902
Geology, natural history, archaeology, history of East Hertfordshire, militaria, Saxon coins, ethnography 33263

Hessle

Hessle Whiting Mill, Hessle Foreshore, Hessle DN14 - T: (01405) 722251, Fax: 722256
Science&Tech Museum 33264

Hethersett

Fire Service Museum, Fire Service Headquarters, Norwich Rd, Hethersett HR9 3DM - T: (01603) 810351
Science&Tech Museum - 1985 33265

Hexham

Border History Museum, The Old Gaol, Hallgate, Hexham NE46 1XD - T: (01434) 652351, Fax: 652425, E-mail: lted@tynedale.gov.uk. Head: Janet Goodridge
Historical Museum - 1980
Weapons and armour 33266

Chesterholm Museum Roman Vindolanda, Bardon Mill, Hexham NE47 7JN - T: (01434) 344277, Fax: 344060, E-mail: info@vindolanda.com, Internet: http://www.vindolanda.com. Head: Robin Birley
Historical Museum / Archaeological Museum
Roman leather, textilles and wooden objects 33267

Housesteads Roman Fort and Museum, Haydon Bridge, Hexham NE47 6NN - T: (01434) 344363. Head: Georgina Plowright
Archaeological Museum - 1936
Inscriptions, sculptures, small finds, arm from Housesteads Roman Fort Arms 33268

Heywood

The Corgi Heritage Centre, 53 York St, Heywood OL10 4NR - T: (01706) 365812, Fax: 627811, E-mail: corgi@zen.co.uk, Internet: http://www.zen.co.uk/home/page/corgi
Special Museum
Model vehicle, history of Corgi toys 33269

High Wycombe

Hughenden Manor, High Wycombe HP14 4LA - T: (01494) 755573, 755565, Fax: 474284. Head: Roslyn Lee
Special Museum - 1948
Home of Prime Minister Benjamin Disraeli (1848-1881), containing much of his furniture, pictures, books 33270

Wycombe Museum, Castle Hill House, Priory Av, High Wycombe HP13 6PX - T: (01494) 421895, Fax: 421897, E-mail: enquiries@wycombemuseum.demon.co.uk, Internet: http://www.wycombe.gov.uk/museum. Head: Vicki Wood
Local Museum / Historical Museum - 1932
Windsor chair making industry, lace, local hist, domestic furniture - library 33271

Higher Bockhampton

Hardy's Cottage, Higher Bockhampton DT2 8QJ
Special Museum
Memorabilia of writer Thomas Hardy (1840-1928) 33272

Hillsborough

The Art Gallery Hillsborough, 12 Main St, Hillsborough BT26 6AE - T: (028) 92689896, Fax: 92688433, E-mail: bill@theartgallery.-freeserve.co.uk, Internet: http://www.theartgallery.-freeserve.co.uk
Fine Arts Museum
Irish art, contemporary pieces, watercolours, oils, etchings, stained glass 33273

Hillside

Sunnyside Museum, Sunnyside Royal Hospital, Hillside DD10 9JP - T: (01674) 830361, Fax: 830251. Head: Dr. K.M.G. Keddie
Special Museum
Administrative records from 1797, clinical records from 1815, photographs taken in Victorian and Edwardian times, medical instruments, a straitjacket, firefighting uniforms, replicas of nursing uniforms, examples of patients' craftwork 33274

Himley

Himley Hall, Himley Park, Himley DY3 4DF - T: (01902) 326665, Fax: 894163, E-mail: himley.pls@mbc-dudley.gov.uk, Internet: http://www.dudley.gov.uk. Head: Charles Hajdamach
Decorative Arts Museum - 1995
Temporary exhibitions programme 33275

Hinckley

Hinckley and District Museum, Framework Knitters' Cottage, Lower Bond St, Hinckley LE10 1QX - T: (01455) 251218. Head: H.A. Beavin
Local Museum
Hosiery and boot and shoe industries of Hinckley and district, machines, social history, WW I and II, pickering coll, local archaeological finds 33276

Hindley

Hindley Museum, Market St, Hindley WN2 3AU - T: (01942) 55287
Local Museum 33277

Hitchin

Hitchin Museum and Art Gallery, Paynes Park, Hitchin SG5 1EQ - T: (01462) 434476, Fax: 431316, E-mail: nhdc@hitchin.gov.uk, Internet: http://www.north.herts.gov.uk. Head: Gillian Riding
Local Museum - 1939
Local history, militaria, costumes, paintings by Samuel Lucas, Victorian chemist shop and physic garden 33278

Hoddesdon

Lowewood Museum, High St, Hoddesdon EN11 8BH - T: (01992) 445596, E-mail: lowewood@tesco.net, Internet: http://www.homepages.tesco.net/~hdp. Head: Neil Robbins
Local Museum - 1948
Archaeology, geology and social history 33279

Hollingbourne

Eyhorne Manor Laundry Museum, Hollingbourne ME17 1UU - T: (01627) 80514
Historical Museum - 1971
Laundry 33280

Holm

Norwood Museum, Graemshall, Holm KW17 2RX - T: (01856) 78217
Local Museum
Coll of Norris Wood 33281

Holmfirth

Postcard Museum, Huddersfield Rd, Holmfirth HD7 1JH - T: (01484) 682231
Special Museum - 1987
Slides, postcards, and films 33282

Holsworthy

Holsworthy Museum, Manor Office, Holsworthy EX22 6JG - T: (01409) 259337, E-mail: holsworthy@devonmuseum.net, Internet: http://www.devonmuseums.net/holsworthy. Head: Emma Bond
Local Museum
Local history, social, domestic and agricultural items 33283

Holy Island

Lindisfarne Priory, Holy Island TD15 2RX - T: (01289) 389200. Head: Andrew Morrison
Archaeological Museum
Anglo-Saxon sculpture and archaeological finds from the Priory 33284

Holyhead

Holyhead Maritime Museum, 8 Llainfain Estate, Llaingoch, Holyhead LL65 1NF - T: (01407) 769745, Fax: 769745, E-mail: jonncave4@aol.com, Internet: http://www.geocities.com/dickburnell. Head: William B. Carroll
Historical Museum
Photographs, plans, ship-models, marine tools 33285

Holywood

Ulster Folk and Transport Museum, Cultra, Holywood BT18 0EU - T: (028) 90428428, Fax: 90428728, E-mail: uftm@nidex.com, Internet: http://www.nidex.com/uftm. Head: Marshall McKee
Folklore Museum / Science&Tech Museum - 1958
History and social life of Northern Ireland, aviation, maritime, road and rail transport, reconstructed buildings, homes and shops, paintings, rural life, agriculture, fishing, crafts, music, textiles - archive, library 33286

Honiton

Allhallows Museum of Lace and Antiquities, High St, Honiton EX14 1PG - T: (01404) 44966, Fax: 46591, E-mail: dyateshoniton@msn.com, Internet: http://www.honitonlace.com
Local Museum - 1945
Honiton Pottery, antiquities, fossils, local history, industry, Doll's House 33287

Horndean

Goss and Crested China Centre, 62 Murray Rd, Horndean PO8 9JL - T: (023) 92597440, Fax: 92591975, E-mail: info@gosschinaclub.demon.co.uk, Internet: http://www.gosscrestedchina.co.uk. Head: Lynda Pine
Decorative Arts Museum
Souvenir china from Victorian and Edwardian times to WWI 33288

Hornsea

Hornsea Museum of Village Life, 11-13 Newbegin, Hornsea HU18 1AB - T: (01964) 533443, Internet: http://www.hornsea.com/museum. Head: Catherine Walker
Local Museum
Representations of the dairy, kitchen, parlour and bedroom of a c ago, tools of local craftsmen, photographs and postcards of local scenes, local industry, Hornsea Brick and Tile Works (c 1868-96), Hull and Hornsea Railway (1864-1964) 33289

Horringer

Ickworth House, The Rotunda, Horringer IP29 5QE - T: (01284) 735270, Fax: 735175. Head: Kate Carver
Decorative Arts Museum - 1957
House dating from 1795-1830 with 18th c French furniture, silver, paintings 33290

Horsham

Christ's Hospital Museum, Counting House, Christ's Hospital, Horsham RH13 7YP - T: (01403) 247444. Head: Nicholas Plumley
Historical Museum
Boys boarding school, manuscripts, models, statues, ephemera 33291

Horsham Arts Centre, North St, Horsham RH12 1RL - T: (01403) 259708, 268689, Fax: 211502
Public Gallery 33292

Horsham Museum, Causeway House, 9 Causeway, Horsham RH12 1HE - T: (01403) 254959, Fax: 217581, E-mail: museum@horsham.gov.uk. Head: Jeremy Knight
Local Museum - 1893
Costumes, toys, old bicycles, local crafts and industries, reconstructed shops, in 16th c house, Shelley, geology, saddlery, farming - archives 33293

Horsham Saint Faith

City of Norwich Aviation Museum, Old Norwich Rd, Horsham Saint Faith NR10 3JF - T: (01603) 893080, Internet: http://www.mth.vea.ac.uk/~h720/aviation/conam.html
Science&Tech Museum / Military Museum
Aviation history of Norfolk, Vulcan bomber and some military and civil aircraft 33294

Houghton

Houghton Hall Soldier Museum, Houghton Hall, Houghton PE31 6UE - T: (01485) 528569, Fax: 528167, E-mail: administrator@houghtenhall.comm, Internet: http://www.houghtenhall.com
Military Museum - 1978 33295

Hove

British Engineerium, Nevill Rd, Hove BN3 7QA - T: (01273) 559583, Fax: 566403, E-mail: info@britishengineerium.com, Internet: http://www.britishengineerium.com. Head: Dr. Jonathan E. Minns
Science&Tech Museum
Restored Victorian pumping station 33296

Hove Museum and Art Gallery, 19 New Church Rd, Hove BN3 4AB - T: (01273) 290200, Fax: 292827, E-mail: visitor.services@brighton-hove.gov.uk. Head: Abigail Thomas
Fine Arts Museum / Decorative Arts Museum - 1927
18th-19th and 20th c English art, English ceramics, toys, contemporary decorative arts (all media) 33297

West Blatchington Windmill, Holmes Av, Hove BN3 7LE - T: (01273) 776017. Head: Peter Hill
Science&Tech Museum - 1979
Artefacts of milling and agricultural hist 33298

Hoy

Scapa Flow Museum, Hoy KW16 3NT - T: (01856) 791300, E-mail: museum@orkneyheritage.com, Internet: http://www.orkneyheritage.com
Military Museum
Large military vehicles, boats, cranes, field artillery and railway rolling stock 33299

Huddersfield

Huddersfield Art Gallery, Princess Alexandra Walk, Huddersfield HD1 2SU - T: (01484) 221964, 221962, Fax: 221952, E-mail: robert.hall@kirkleesmc.gov.uk. Head: Robert Hall
Fine Arts Museum - 1898
British paintings, drawings, prints and sculpture since 1850 (Bacon, Hockney), changing exhibitions of contemporary art by regional and national artists in all media 33300

Tolson Memorial Museum, Ravensknowle Park, Wakefield Rd, Huddersfield HD5 8DJ - T: (01484) 223830, Fax: 223843. Head: Jenny Salton, J.H. Rumsby
Local Museum / Folklore Museum - 1920
Local history, natural history, mineralogy, geology, botany, zoology, local life in Stone Age, Bronze Age, Iron Age, Roman and medieval periods, dolls, English glass, woolens, old vehicles, money scales, Ronnie The Raven's puzzlepath 33301

Victoria Tower, Castle Hill, Lumb Ln, Almondbury, Huddersfield HD5 8DJ - T: (01484) 223830
Historical Museum
Prehistoric hill-fort and medieval earthworks 33302

Humshaugh

Clayton Collection Museum, Roman Fort Chollerford, Humshaugh NE49 4EP - T: (01434) 681379. Head: Georgina Plowright
Archaeological Museum
Roman inscriptions, sculpture, weapons, tools and ornaments from several forts 33303

Huntingdon

Cromwell Museum, Grammar School Walk, Huntingdon PE29 6LF - T: (01480) 375830, Fax: 459563, E-mail: john.goldsmith@cambridgeshire.gov.uk, Internet: http://www.cromwell.argonet.co.uk. Head: John Goldsmith
Historical Museum / Special Museum - 1962
Documents on Cromwell's time, portraits, memorabilia on Oliver Cromwell (1599-1658) 33304

Hinchingbrooke House, Brampton Rd, Huntingdon PE18 6BN - T: (01480) 451121. Head: J.J. Cronin
Historical Museum
Cromwell family and the Earls of Sandwich 33305

Huntly

Brander Museum, The Square, Huntly AB54 8AE - T: (01771) 622902, Fax: 622884, E-mail: heritage@aberdeenshire.gov.uk
Local Museum
Communion tokens, author George MacDonald memorabilia 33306

Leith Hall, Kennethmont, Huntly AB54 4NQ - T: (01464) 831216, Fax: 831594, E-mail: lpadgett@nts.org.uk, Internet: http://www.nts.org.uk/leith.html. Head: Robin Pellow
Historic Site / Military Museum 33307

Hutton-le-Hole

Ryedale Folk Museum, Hutton-le-Hole YO62 6UA - T: (01751) 417367. Head: Martin Watts
Open Air Museum / Folklore Museum - 1966
Tools, spinning, weaving, reconstructions of a 15th c Cruck house, 16th c manor house, 18th c cottage, 16th c glass furnace, agricultural coll of folk life 33308

Hynish

Skerryvore Museum, Upper Sq, Hynish PA77 6UQ - T: (01879) 2691, 220606, Fax: (01865) 311593. Head: C.D. Plant
Local Museum
Lighthouse story, pictures 33309

Hythe, Kent

Hythe Local History Room, 1 Stade St, Oaklands, Hythe, Kent CT21 6BG - T: (01303) 266152/53, Fax: 262912, E-mail: admin@hythe-kent.com, Internet: http://www.hythe-kent.com
Local Museum - 1933
Local history, archaeology, paintings, mititary history 33310

Ilchester

Ilchester Museum, Town Hall and Community Centre, High St, Ilchester BA22 8NQ - T: (01935) 841247. Head: Graham Mottram
Local Museum
Prehistory, Roman, Saxon, Medieval, Post Medieval history 33311

Ilfracombe

Ilfracombe Museum, Wilder Rd, Ilfracombe EX34 8AF - T: (01271) 863541, E-mail: ilfracombe@devonmuseums.net, Internet: http://www.devonmuseums.net. Head: Sue Pullen
Local Museum - 1932
Local history, archaeology, ethnography, natural history, fauna, Victorian relics, shipping, armaments, militaria 33312

Ilkeston

Erewash Museum, High St, Ilkeston DE7 5JA - T: (0115) 9071141, Fax: 9071121, E-mail: erewashmuseum@free4all.co.uk, Internet: http://www.erewash.gov.uk. Head: Julie Biddlecombe
Local Museum - 1981/82
Listed Georgian and Victorian town house with kitchen and scullery display and other rooms containing civic, local and social hist collections, Long Eaton Town Hall 33313

Ilkley

Manor House Museum and Art Gallery, Castle Yard, Ilkley LS29 9DT - T: (01943) 600066, Fax: 817079. Head: Paul Lawson
Local Museum - 1961
Local hist, Roman finds from Olicana Roman Fort, temporary art exhibitions in Elizabethan Manor House 33314

Ilminster

Perry's Cider Mills, Dowlish Wake, Ilminster TA19 0NY - T: (01460) 52681
Folklore Museum
Old farm tools, wagons, cider-making equipment, stone jars and related country living items 33315

Immingham

Immingham Museum, Margaret St, Immingham DN40 1LE - T: (01469) 577066, E-mail: immingham@bmummery.freeserve.co.uk. Head: Brian Mummery
Historical Museum
Coll of the Great Central Railway Society, creation of a port - archive 33316

Ingatestone

Ingatestone Hall, Ingatestone CM4 9NR
Historical Museum / Decorative Arts Museum - 1953
Essex history, furniture, china 33317

Innerleithen

Traquair House, Innerleithen EH44 6PW - T: (01896) 830323, Fax: 830639, E-mail: enquiries@traquair.co.uk, Internet: http://www.traquair.co.uk. Head: Catherine Maxwell Stuart
Decorative Arts Museum / Historical Museum - 1963
16th-17th c embroidery, Jacobite glass, silver, manuscripts, books, household objects, furniture, musical instruments, memorabilia of Mary, Queen of Scotland, 18th c Brew House 33318

Inveraray

Auchindrain Museum of Country Life, Auchindrain, Inveraray PA32 8XN - T: (01499) 500235. Head: John McDonald
Open Air Museum
West Highland farming township buildings, agricultural, domestic and social history 33319

Inveraray Bell Tower, All Saints' Episcopal Church, Inveraray PA32 8XJ - T: (01499) 302259
Religious Arts Museum 33320

Inveraray Castle, Cherry Park, Inveraray PA32 8XE - T: (01499) 302203, Fax: 302421, E-mail: enquiries@inveraray-castle.com, Internet: http://www.inveraray-castle.com
Decorative Arts Museum 33321

Inveraray Jail, Church Sq, Inveraray PA32 8TX - T: (01499) 302381, Fax: 302195, E-mail: inverarayjail@btclick.com. Head: Jim Linley
Special Museum
19th c Scottish prison 33322

Inveraray Maritime Museum, The Pier, Inveraray PA32 8UY - T: (01499) 302213
Historical Museum
Clyde maritime memorabilia, three masted schooner 33323

Inverkeithing

Inverkeithing Museum, The Friary, Queen St, Inverkeithing KY11 1LS - T: (01383) 313594
Local Museum
Social and local history 33324

Inverness

Culloden Visitor Centre, Culloden Moor, Inverness IV2 5EU - T: (01463) 790607, Fax: 794294, E-mail: rmackenzie@nts.org.uk. Head: Ross Mackenzie
Historical Museum - 1970
Historical display of the Battle of Culloden (1745/46), New Jacobite exhibition - Old Leanach Cottage 33325

Eden Court Art Gallery, Eden Court Theatre, Bishops Rd, Inverness IV3 5SA - T: (01463) 234234, E-mail: ecmail@cali.co.uk
Public Gallery 33326

Inverness Museum and Art Gallery, Castle Wynd, Inverness IV2 3EB - T: (01463) 237114, Fax: 225293, E-mail: inverness.museum@highland.gov.uk, Internet: http://www.highland.gov.uk/cl/publicservices/museumdetails/inverness.htm
Local Museum - 1825
Local hist, archaeology, paleontology, geology, bagpipes, local prints and paintings, old kitchen, silver, uniforms, costumes, weapons 33327

Regimental Museum of The Queen's Own Highlanders, Seaforth Highlanders and The Queen's Own Cameron Highlanders, Fort George, Inverness IV2 7TD - T: (01463) 224380, Internet: http://www-saw.arts.ed.ac.uk/army/regiments/queensownhighlanders.html
Military Museum
Chronological display of uniforms, pictures, equipment, medals, pipe banners 33328

Inverurie

Inverurie Carnegie Museum, The Square, Inverurie AB51 3SN - T: (01771) 622906, (01779) 477778, Fax: 622884, E-mail: heritage@aberdeenshire.gov.uk. Head: Dr. David M. Bertie
Local Museum - 1884
Local archaeology, geology, paleontology of Northern Scotland and England, coins, shells, natural history, North American Eskimo anthropological coll 33329

Ipswich

Christchurch Mansion, Soane St, Ipswich IP4 2BE - T: (01473) 433554, Fax: 433564, E-mail: -christchurch.mansion@ipswich.gov.uk, Internet: http://www.ipswich.gov.uk. Head: Tim Heyburn
Fine Arts Museum / Decorative Arts Museum / Public Gallery - 1896
English pottery, porcelain, glass, paintings (Gainsborough, Constable, Wilson Steer), prints, sculptures, furniture, in 16th c house 33330

Ipswich Museum, High St, Ipswich IP1 3QH - T: (01473) 433550/53, Fax: 433558, E-mail: museums@ipswich.gov.uk, Internet: http://www.ipswich.gov.uk/tourism/guide/museum.htm. Head: Tim Heyburn
Local Museum / Natural History Museum - 1881
Archaeology, geology, natural history, ethnology, wildlife 33331

Ipswich Transport Museum, Old Trolleybus Depot, Cobham Rd, Ipswich IP3 9JD - T: (01473) 715666, Fax: 832260, Internet: http://www.ipswichtransport-museum.co.uk. Head: Brian Dyes
Science&Tech Museum
Road transport, built or used in the Ipswich area, on air, water and rail transport - archive, library 33332

Ironbridge

Ironbridge Gorge Museum, The Wharfage, Ironbridge TF8 7AW - T: (01952) 433522, 432405, Fax: 432204, E-mail: info@ironbridge.org.uk, Internet: http://www.ironridge.org.uk. Head: Glen Lawes
Decorative Arts Museum / Open Air Museum - 1967/1997
Elton coll of industrial art (items representing the hist and growth of industry through paintings, engravings and books), decorative tiles, porcelain, iron - archives, library 33333

Ironbridge Tollhouse, Ironbridge TF8 7AQ - T: (01952) 884391. Head: David de Haan
Science&Tech Museum
First iron bridge, erected in 1779 33334

Teddy Bear Shop and Museum, Dale End, Ironbridge TF8 7AQ - T: (01952) 433029, Internet: http://www.vtel.co.uk/bears
Special Museum
Famous teddy bear factory, modern Merrythought products, historical coll of soft toys 33335

Irvine

Irvine Burns Club Museum, Fairburn, 5 Burns St, Irvine KA12 8RW - T: (01294) 274511
Special Museum
Flax dresser works, letters from Honorary Members Dickens, Garibaldi, Tennyson 33336

Scottish Maritime Museum, Laird Forge Bldgs, Gottries Rd, Irvine KA12 8QU - T: (01294) 278283, Fax: 313211. Head: J.M. Tildesley
Science&Tech Museum
Traditional maritime skills and handle, equipment, tools, boats, a Puffer 'Spartan', a tug 'Garnock' 33337

Vennel Gallery, 4-10 Glasgow Vennel, Irvine KA12 0BD - T: (01294) 275059, Fax: 275059, E-mail: vennel@globalnet.co.uk, Internet: http://www.northayrshiremuseums.org.ukl
Special Museum / Fine Arts Museum
Robert Burns' heckling shop and lodging house where he worked and lived, international art 33338

Isle-of-Barra

Dualchas-Museum Bharraigh Agus Bhatarsaidh, Castlebay, Isle-of-Barra HS9 5XD - T: (01871) 810413, Fax: 810413. Head: Malcolm MacNeil
Local Museum 33339

Isle-of-Iona

Infirmary Museum, Saint Ronan's Church Museum and Columba Centre, Iona Abbey, Isle-of-Iona PA76 6SN - T: (01828) 640411, Fax: 640217, E-mail: iona_abbay@compuserve.com, Internet: http://ourworld.compuserve.com/homepages/iona_abbay
Religious Arts Museum
Celtic gravestones and crosses, Celtic artefacts 33340

Iona Abbey Museum → Infirmary Museum, Saint Ronan's Church Museum and Columba Centre

Iona Heritage Centre, Isle-of-Iona PA76 6SJ - T: (01681) 700576, Fax: 700580, E-mail: heritage@ionagallery.com, Internet: http://www.isle-of-iona.com. Head: Mary Hay
Historical Museum
Social history 33341

Isle-of-Lewis

Dell Mill, North Dell, Ness, Isle-of-Lewis PA86 0SN
Science&Tech Museum
Equipment, machinery, local grain production 33342

Isle-of-Tiree

An Iodnlann, Am Bagh, Isle-of-Tiree PA77 6UN - T: (01879) 220323, Fax: 220893, E-mail: doc.holliday@dial.pipex.com. Head: Dr. John Holliday
Local Museum 33343

Isleworth

Osterley Park House, Jersey Rd, Isleworth TW7 4RB - T: (020) 82325050, Fax: 82325080, E-mail: tosgen@smtp.ntrust.org.uk
Decorative Arts Museum - 1949
18th c villa, neo-classical interior decoration and furnishings designed by Robert Adam, landscaped park 33344

Ivinghoe

Ford End Watermill, Ivinghoe LU7 9DY - T: (01582) 600391, Internet: http://www.pitstone.co.uk/around/watermill.htm
Science&Tech Museum
Milling machines and artefacts 33345

Jackfield

Jackfield Tile Museum, Jackfield TF8 7JX - T: (01952) 882030. Head: Michael Vanns
Decorative Arts Museum
Decorative wall and floor tiles 33346

Jarrow

Bede's World, Church Bank, Jarrow NE32 3DY - T: (0191) 4892106, Fax: 4282361, E-mail: visitor.info@bedesworld.co.uk, Internet: http://www.bedesworld.co.uk
Archaeological Museum - 1974
Finds from the Anglo-Saxon and medieval monastic site of St. Paul's, Anglo-Saxon demonstration farm - library 33347

Jedburgh

Jedburgh Castle Jail Museum, Castlegate, Jedburgh TD8 6BD - T: (01835) 863254, Fax: 864750. Head: Rosi Capper
Historical Museum - 1965
19th c prison life, local history coll 33348

Mary Queen of Scots' House, Queen St, Jedburgh TD8 6EN - T: (01835) 863331, Fax: 863331
Special Museum
Facility for the 400th anniversary of the death of Mary Stuart 33349

Kegworth

Kegworth Museum, 52 High St, Kegworth DE74 2DA - T: (01509) 672886, 214460
Local Museum
Village life and trades 33350

Keighley

Cliffe Castle Museum, Spring Gardens Ln, Keighley BD20 6LH - T: (01535) 618231, Fax: 610536, Internet: http://www.bradford.gov.uk/tourism/museums. Head: Jane Glaister
Local Museum / Natural History Museum - 1899
Paintings, sculpture, applied arts, household and farm tools, natural history, geology, archaeology, reconstructed craft shops, militaria, sports, toys, costumes 33351

East Riddlesden Hall, Bradford Rd, Keighley BD20 5EL - T: (01535) 607075, Fax: 691462, E-mail: yorker@smtp.ntrust.org.uk. Head: Anastasia Chylak
Decorative Arts Museum
Coll of furniture, textiles, embroidery, pweter 33352

Ingrow Loco Museum, Oxenhope Station, Keighley BD22 8NJ, mail addr: 296 Didsbury Rd, Heaton Mersey SK4 3JH - T: (01535) 645214
Science&Tech Museum - 1968
World War II steam locomotive built for the Allied forces, obtained from Poland, Sweden and the USA, British Rail and British industrial railway systems, 35 steam and 7 diesel locomotives and two German railbusses, steam engines dated between 1874 and 1957 from Britain, Sweden, Poland and the USA 33353

Keighley and Worth Valley Light Railway Museum → Ingrow Loco Museum

Museum of Rail Travel, Ingrow, Keighley BD22 8NJ - T: (01535) 680425, Fax: 610796, E-mail: admin@vintagecarriagestrust.org, Internet: http://www.vintagecarriagestrust.org
Science&Tech Museum
Coll of historic railway coaches 33354

Kelmscott

Kelmscott Manor, Kelmscott GL7 3HJ - T: (01367) 252486, Fax: 253754, E-mail: admin@kelmscottmanor.co.uk, Internet: http://www.kelmscottmanor.co.uk. Head: Sue Ashworth
Decorative Arts Museum
Home of William Morris, coll of textiles, furniture and drawings 33355

Kelso

Floors Castle, Roxburghe Estate's Office, Kelso TD5 7SF - T: (01573) 223333, Fax: 226056, E-mail: marketing@floorscastle.com, Internet: http://www.floorscastle.com. Head: Duke of Roxburghe
Fine Arts Museum 33356

Kelso Museum and Turret Gallery, Turret House, Abbey Court, Kelso TD5 7JA - T: (01573) 223464, Fax: 373993. Head: Ian Brown
Local Museum - 1983
Growth of Kelso and its importance as a market town, hist of the local skinning industry - temporarily closed till the beginning of 1998, for further info please call (01750) 20096 33357

Kelvedon Hatch

Kelvedon Hatch Secret Nuclear Bunker, Kelvedon Hall Ln, Kelvedon Hatch CM14 5TL - T: (01217) 364883, Fax: 372562, E-mail: bunker@japar.demon.co.uk, Internet: http://www.japar.demon.co.uk. Head: M. Parrish
Historical Museum
Cold war artefacts 33358

Kendal

Abbot Hall Art Gallery, Kendal LA9 5AL - T: (01539) 722464, Fax: 722494, E-mail: info@abbothall.org.uk, Internet: http://www.abbothall.org.uk. Head: Edward King
Fine Arts Museum - 1962
18th c furnished rooms, paintings, sculpture, pottery, portraits by Kendal painters, Romney, works by Schwitters, Ruskin, Riley, Turner and Nicholson, watercolours of the English Lake District 33359

Kendal Museum, Station Rd, Kendal LA9 6BT - T: (01539) 721374, Fax: 737976, E-mail: info@kendalmuseum.org.uk, Internet: http://www.kendalmuseum.org.uk. Head: Edward King
Local Museum - 1796
Local history, archaeology, geology, natural history, British birds and mounted mammals 33360

Museum of Lakeland Life, Abbot Hall, Kendal LA9 5AL - T: (01539) 722464, Fax: 722494, E-mail: info@lakelandmuseum.org.uk, Internet: http://www.lakelandmuseum.org.uk. Head: Edward King
Local Museum - 1970
Local cultural hist of Lake District area, industry, period rooms, costumes, trades, farming, printing presses, weaving equipment, photogr coll, Simpson furniture, Arthur Ransome Society 33361

Sizergh Castle, Kendal LA8 8AE - T: (015395) 60070, Fax: 61621, E-mail: rsizer@smtp.ntrust.org.uk
Local Museum 33362

Kenton

Powderham Castle, Kenton EX6 8JQ - T: (01626) 890243, Fax: 890729, E-mail: castle@powderham.co.uk, Internet: http://www.powderham.co.uk. Head: Tim Faulkner
Fine Arts Museum 33363

Keswick

Cars of the Stars Motor Museum, Standish St, Keswick CA12 5LS - T: (017687) 73757, Fax: 72090, E-mail: cotsmm@aol.com, Internet: http://www.carsofthestars.com. Head: John Nelson, Philip Nelson
Science&Tech Museum
Celebrity TV and film vehicles 33364

Cumberland Pencil Museum, Southey Works, Greta Bridge, Keswick CA12 5NG - T: (017687) 73626, Fax: 74679, E-mail: museum@acco-uk.co.uk, Internet: http://www.pencils.co.uk. Head: D.J. Sharrock
Special Museum - 1981
Process of pencil manufacture, history of pencils using 33365

Keswick Museum and Art Gallery, Fitz Park, Station Rd, Keswick CA12 4NF - T: (017687) 73263, Fax: 80390, E-mail: hazel.davison@allerdale.gov.uk
Local Museum / Fine Arts Museum - 1873
Keswick's social hist, natural hist, archeology, lit coll, geology 33366

Mirehouse, Underskiddaw, Keswick CA12 4QE - T: (017687) 72287, Fax: 72287, E-mail: info@mireho.freeserve.co.uk. Head: J.H.F. Spedding
Fine Arts Museum
Pictures, furniture, works by Constable, Turner, De Wint, Hearne, Girtin, Romney, Morland, coll of papers and books of Francis Bacon 33367

Kettering

Alfred East Art Gallery, Sheep St, Kettering NN16 0AN - T: (01536) 534274, Fax: 534370, E-mail: kettering.museum@exite.co.uk, Internet: http://www.kettering.gov.uk. Head: Su Davies
Public Gallery - 1913
English paintings, watercolors, drawings and prints since 1800 33368

Boughton House, Kettering NN14 1BJ - T: (01536) 515731, Fax: 417255, E-mail: llt@boughtonhouse.org.uk, Internet: http://www.boughtonhouse.org.uk. Head: Gareth Fitzpatrick
Fine Arts Museum
Paintings of Van Dyck, English and Flemish tapestries, Armoury 33369

Manor House Museum, Sheep St, Kettering NN16 0AN - T: (01536) 534219, Fax: 534370. Head: Su Davies
Local Museum
History of Kettering Borough, geology, archaeology, social and industrial history 33370

Kew

Kew Bridge Steam Museum, Green Dragon Ln, Brentford, Kew TW8 0EN - T: (020) 85684757, Fax: 85699978, E-mail: info@kbsm.org, Internet: http://www.kbsm.org. Head: Tony Cundick, Lesley Bossine
Science&Tech Museum - 1975
Cornish beam engines dating from 1820 plus other stationary steam engines, all housed in a Victorian waterworks, 'Water for Life' exhibition on London's water supply 33371

Kew Palace Museum of the Royal Botanic Gardens (temporary closed), Royal Botanic Gardens, Kew TW9 3AB - T: (020) 87819500, Fax: 89481197, Internet: http://www.hrp.org.uk. Head: Prof. Peter Crane
Natural History Museum - 1759
Tropical Plant Species, economic botany coll 33372

Public Record Office Museum, Ruskin Av, Kew TW9 4DU - T: (020) 83925279, Fax: 83925345, E-mail: events@pro.gov.uk, Internet: http://www.pro.gov.uk. Head: Claire Bertrand
Special Museum - 1902
Millenium treasure 33373

Kidderminster

Kidderminster Railway Museum, Station Approach, Comberton Hill, Kidderminster DY10 1QX - T: (01562) 825316
Science&Tech Museum
Railways of the British Isles, signalling equipment 33374

Worcestershire County Museum, Hartlebury Castle, Kidderminster DY11 7XZ - T: (01299) 250416, Fax: 251890, E-mail: Museum@worcestershire.gov.uk, Internet: http://www.worcestershire.gov.uk/museum. Head: Robin Hill
Local Museum - 1966
Horse-drawn vehicles including gypsy caravans, glass, crafts, toys, costumes, folk life, archaeology coll from the Victorian period, including costume, transport, domestic life, agriculture and crafts and trades - library 33375

Kidwelly

Kidwelly Industrial Museum, Broadford, Kidwelly SA17 4LW - T: (01554) 891078
Science&Tech Museum
Local history, tinplate industry, local coal industry, gear and steam winding engine from Morlais colliery, geology, 33376

Kilbarchan

Weaver's Cottage, The Cross, Kilbarchan PA10 2JG - T: (01505) 705588. Head: Michael Hunter
Historical Museum - 1954
18th c cottage, handloom weaver, looms, weaving equipment, domestic utensils, local history 33377

Kildonan

Museum Chill Donnan, Old School, Kildonan PA81 5R2
Local Museum 33378

Killiecrankie

Pass of Killiecrankie Visitor Centre, Killiecrankie PH16 5LG - T: (01796) 473233, Fax: 473233
Historical Museum / Natural History Museum
Historic battle of 1689, natural history 33379

Killingworth

John Sinclair Railway Collection, Dial Cottage, Great Lime Rd, West Moor, Killingworth NE12 5BA - T: (01670) 355899, E-mail: peterdonnelly@iname.com. Head: Peter Donnelly
Science&Tech Museum
Signalling, booking office, lamps, signs, the permanent way, posters 33380

Kilmarnock

Dean Castle, Dean Rd, off Glasgow Rd, Kilmarnock KA3 1XB - T: (01563) 554702, Fax: 554720, E-mail: donna.chisholm@east-ayrshire.gov.uk. Head: Donna Chrisholm
Historical Museum - 1976
Medieval arms and armour, musical instruments, tapestries 33381

Dick Institute Museum and Art Gallery, 14 Elmbank Av, Kilmarnock KA1 3BU - T: (01563) 554343, Fax: 554344, E-mail: jason.sutcliffe@east-ayrshire.gov.uk, Internet: http://www.east-ayrshire.gov.uk. Head: Donna Chisholm
Natural History Museum / Fine Arts Museum - 1901
Geology, ethnography, archaeology, conchology, armaments, numismatics, church and trade relics, paintings, etchings, sculptures, old bibles, incunabula, fine art, local and social history 33382

Kilmartin

Museum of Ancient Culture, Kilmartin House, Kilmartin PA31 8RQ - T: (01546) 510278, Fax: 510330, E-mail: museum@kilmartin.org, Internet: http://www.kilmartin.org. Head: Colin Schafer
Historical Museum / Archaeological Museum
Archaeology, landscape interpretation, prehistory, early Schotish history, neolithic, bronze age, Dalriada, rock art, ancient monuments 33383

Kilmaurs

Kilmaurs Historical Society Museum, 13 Irvine Rd, Kilmaurs KA3 2RJ
Historical Museum 33384

Kilsyth

Colzuim Museum, Colzium House, Colzium-Lennox Estate, Kilsyth G65 0PY - T: (01236) 735077, Fax: 781407
Local Museum
Local hist, battle of Kilsyth - garden, woodland walk, chilren's zoo 33385

Kilsyth's Heritage, Library, Burngreen, Kilsyth G65 0HT - T: (01236) 735077, Fax: 781407
Local Museum
History of Kilsyth from the 18th c 33386

Kilwinning

Dalgarven Mill, Museum of Ayrshire Country Life and Costume, Dalry Rd, Kilwinning KA13 6PL - T: (01294) 552448. Head: Moyra Ferguson
Science&Tech Museum / Folklore Museum
Water-driven flour mill, agricultural and domestic implements, costume 33387

Kilwinning Abbey Tower, Main St, Kilwinning KA13 6AN - T: (01294) 464174, Fax: 464174, Internet: http://www.users.globalnet.co.uk/~vennel
Local Museum
Local and social history 33388

King's Lynn

King's Lynn Arts Centre, 27-29 King St, King's Lynn - T: (01553) 779095, Fax: 766834, E-mail: - entertainment_admin@west-norfolk.gov.uk, Internet: http://www.kingslynnarts.org.uk. Head: Liz Falconbridge
Public Gallery 33389

King's Lynn Museum, Market St, King's Lynn PE30 1NL - T: (01553) 775001, Fax: 775001. Head: Robin Hanley
Local Museum - 1904
Natural hist, archaeology, local hist, geology, temporary exhibition gallery 33390

Tales of the Old Gaol House, Saturday Market Pl, King's Lynn PE30 5DQ - T: (01553) 774297, Fax: 772361, E-mail: gaolhouse@west-norfolk.gov.uk, Internet: http://www.west-norfolk.gov.uk
Historical Museum
History of crime and punishment in Lynn, King John Cup (1340), King John Sword 33391

Town House Museum of Lynn Life, 46 Queen St, King's Lynn PE30 5DQ - T: (01553) 773450, Fax: 775001. Head: Robin Hanley
Folklore Museum - 1992
Ceramic and glass, furniture, Victoriana 33392

True's Yard Fishing Heritage Centre, North St, King's Lynn PE30 1QW - T: (01553) 770479, Fax: 765100, E-mail: trues.yard@virgin.net, Internet: http://welcome.to/truesyard. Head: Dr. Andrew Lane
Historical Museum 33393

Kingsbridge

Cookworthy Museum of Rural Life in South Devon, 108 Fore St, Kingsbridge TQ7 1AW - T: (01548) 853235, E-mail: wcookworthy@talk21.com. Head: Jane Marley
Local Museum - 1971
Cookworthy's porcelain and work as a chemist, costumes, craft tools, photos, agricultural machinery, Edwardian pharmacy, Victorian kitchen - library 33394

Kingston-upon-Hull

Burton Constable Hall, Kingston-upon-Hull HU11 4LN - T: (01964) 562400, Fax: 563229, E-mail: enquires@burtonconstable.com, Internet: http://www.burtonconstable.com. Head: Dr. D.P. Connell
Decorative Arts Museum
Paintings, furniture 33395

Ferens Art Gallery, Hull City Museum & Art Gallery, Queen Victoria Sq, Kingston-upon-Hull HU1 3RA - T: (01482) 613902, Fax: 613710, E-mail: museums@hullcc.gov.uk, Internet: http://www.hullcc.gov.uk/museums. Head: Ann Bukantas
Fine Arts Museum - 1927
Coll of old masters (British, Dutch, Flemish, French, Italian), portraits (16th c to present), marine painting, 19th & 20th c British art, contemporary British painting, sculpture and photography 33396

Hands on History, Old Grammar School Museum, South Church Side, Kingston-upon-Hull HU1 1RR - T: (01482) 613902, Fax: 613710, E-mail: museums@hullcc.gov.uk, Internet: http://www.hullcc.gov.uk/museums. Head: Simon R. Green
Historical Museum
Hull and its people, Victorian Britain, ancient Egypt 33397

Hull and East Riding Museum, 36 High St, Kingston-upon-Hull HU1 1NQ - T: (01482) 613902, Fax: 613913, E-mail: museum@hullcc.demon.co.uk, Internet: http://www.hullcc.gov.uk/museums. Head: Gail Foreman
Archaeological Museum - 1904
Prehistoric and early hist of Humberside, mosaics found at the Roman villa at Horkstow, material from Iron Age chariot burials on the Worlds 33398

Hull Maritime Museum, Queen Victoria Sq, Kingston-upon-Hull HU1 3DX - T: (01482) 613902, Fax: 613710, E-mail: arthur.credland@hullcc.gov.uk, Internet: http://www.hullcc.gov.uk/museums. Head: Arthur G. Credland
Special Museum - 1975
Whaling, shipbuilding, weapons, gear, maritime history, marine paintings, shipmodels, scrimshaw work - library 33399

Hull University Art Collection, Middleton Hall, Cottingham Rd, Kingston-upon-Hull HU6 7RX - T: (01482) 465035, Fax: 465192, E-mail: j.g.bernasconi@hist.hull.ac.uk, Internet: http://www.hull.ac.uk/hull/pub_web/art.html. Head: John G. Bernasconi
Public Gallery / Decorative Arts Museum - 1963
Art in Britain 1890-1940, the Thompson Collections of Chinese porcelain 33400

M.V. Arctic Corsair, River Hull, High St, Kingston-upon-Hull HU1 3DX - T: (01482) 613902, Fax: 613710. Head: Arthur G. Credland
Science&Tech Museum
Deep sea trawler (1960) 33401

Spurn Lightship, Castle St - Hull Marina, Kingston-upon-Hull HU1 3DX - T: (01482) 613902, Fax: 613710, E-mail: museum@hullcc.gov.uk, Internet: http://www.hullcc.gov.uk/museums. Head: Arthur G. Credland
Science&Tech Museum 33402

Streetlife, Hull Museum of Transport, 26 High St, Old Town, Kingston-upon-Hull HU1 1NQ - T: (01482) 613902, Fax: 613710, E-mail: museum@hullcc.gov.uk, Internet: http://www.hullcc.gov.uk/museums. Head: Stephen Goodhand
Science&Tech Museum 33403

Wilberforce House Museum, 25 High St, Kingston-upon-Hull HU1 1NE - T: (01482) 613902, Fax: 613710, E-mail: museums@hullcc.gov.uk, Internet: http://www.hullcc.gov.uk/museums. Head: Brian Hayton
Historical Museum - 1906
Silver, costume, dolls, slavery, slave trade and abolition, items relating to William Wilberforce, born here in 1759 - library 33404

Yorkshire Water's Museum, Springhead Av and Willerby Rd, Kingston-upon-Hull HU5 5HZ - T: (01482) 652283. Head: Douglas W. Atkinson, Peter D. Cranswick
Science&Tech Museum
Victorian 90" beam engine, local history of water supply since 1923 33405

Kingston-upon-Thames

Kingston Museum, Wheatfield Way, Kingston-upon-Thames KT1 2PS - T: (020) 85476465, Fax: 85476747, Internet: http://www.kingston.gov.uk/museum. Head: Tracey Mardles
Local Museum - 1904
Archaeology, oral hist, social hist, borougn archives, Eadweard Muybridge colls, Martin Brothers (art pottery) 33406

The Stanley Picker Gallery, Middle Mill Island, Knights Park, Kingston-upon-Thames KT1 2QJ - T: (020) 85478074, Fax: 85478068, E-mail: picker@kingston.ac.uk, Internet: http://www.kingston.ac.uk/picker. Head: Prof. Bruce Russell
Public Gallery 33407

Kingswinford

Broadfield House Glass Museum, Compton Dr, Kingswinford DY6 9NS - T: (01384) 812745, Fax: 812746, E-mail: glass.pls@mbc@dudley.gov.uk, Internet: http://www.dudley.gov.uk. Head: Emma Warren
Decorative Arts Museum
Coll of British glass from the 17th c to the present 33408

Kingussie

Highland Folk Museum, Am Fasgadh, Duke St, Kingussie PH21 1JG - T: (01540) 661307, Fax: 661631, E-mail: highland.folk@highland.gov.uk, Internet: http://www.highlandfolk.com
Folklore Museum - 1934
Agriculture, costume, furniture, tartans, folklore, social history, vehicles 33409

Kinnesswood

Michael Bruce Cottage Museum, The Cobbles, Kinnesswood KY13 9HL - T: (01592) 840203. Head: Dr. David M. Munro
Special Museum - 1906
Manuscripts by poet Michale Bruce, local articles 33410

Kinross

Kinross Museum, temporary closed, 108-110 High St, Kinross KY13 7DA - T: (01738) 632488, Fax: 443505, E-mail: kinross-museum@tulbol.demon.co.uk, Internet: http://www.tulbol.demon.co.uk
Local Museum 33411

Kirkcaldy

Kirkcaldy Museum and Art Gallery, War Memorial Gardens, Kirkcaldy KY1 1YG - T: (01592) 412860, Fax: 412870, Internet: http://home.clara.net/standrewsmuseum
Local Museum - 1926
Local ceramics (Wanyss ware), paintings by W.M. McTaggart and S.J. Peploe, Adam Smith items, archaeology, history, natural sciences 33412

Kirkcudbright

Broughton House and Garden, 12 High St, Kirkcudbright DG6 4JX - T: (01557) 330437, Fax: 330437, E-mail: fscott@nts.org.uk, Internet: http://www.nts.org.uk. Head: F.E. Scott
Special Museum - 1950
18th c town house, photographs, paintings by Hornel, Dumfries and Galloway history and literature - library 33413

The Stewartry Museum, 6 Saint Mary St, Kirkcudbright DG6 4AQ - T: (01557) 331643, Fax: 331643, E-mail: davidd@dumgal.gov.uk. Head: David Devereux
Local Museum - 1881
Items concerning the Stewartry of Kirkcudbright, natural history, geology, archaeology, fine art 33414

Tolbooth Art Centre, High St, Kirkcudbright DG6 4JL - T: (01557) 331556, Fax: 331643, E-mail: davidd@dumgal.gov.uk. Head: David Devereux
Public Gallery
Paintings from the art colony, contemporary art 33415

Kirkintilloch

Auld Kirk Museum, Auld Kirk and Barony Chambers, Cowgate, The Cross, Kirkintilloch G66 1AB - T: (0141) 7751185, 5780144, Fax: 7777649, 5780140. Head: Susan Jeffrey
Local Museum
Local history, art and craft living conditions of working-class families (early 20th c), weaving, mining, boatbuilding and ironfounding industries, displays of tools, equipment and photographs 33416

Kirkoswald

Souter Johnnie's House, Main St, Kirkoswald KA19 8HY - T: (01655) 760603
Special Museum
Home of John Daidson, village cobbler and original Souter 33417

Kirkwall

Orkney Museum, Tankerness House, Broad St, Kirkwall KW15 1DH - T: (01856) 873191, Fax: 871560, E-mail: museum@orkney.gov.uk. Head: Bruce S. Wilson
Folklore Museum - 1980/86
Orkney craft and trade items, archaeological coll, social history 33418

Orkney Wireless Museum, Kiln Corner, Junction Rd, Kirkwall KW15 1LB - T: (01856) 871400, 874272, Internet: http://www.owm.org.uk. Head: Peter MacDonald
Science&Tech Museum - 1983
Coll of wartime radio and defences used at Scapa Flow, also hist of domestic wireless in Orkney 33419

Kirriemuir

Barrie's Birthplace, 9 Brechin Rd, Kirriemuir DD8 4BX - T: (01575) 572646. Head: K. Gilmour, S. Philp
Special Museum - 1963
Life and work of writer Sir James M. Barrie (1860-1937), memorabilia, manuscripts 33420

Klevedon

Feering and Kelvedon Local History Museum, Aylett's School, Maldon Rd, Klevedon CO5 9AH - T: (01376) 571206, Fax: 573163, E-mail: alipes@dial.pipex.com
Local Museum
Local history, Roman remains, manorial history, agricultural and domestic, schools, transport, post 33421

Knaresborough

Knaresborough Castle and Old Courthouse Museum, Castle Grounds, Knaresborough HG5 8AS - T: (01423) 556188, Fax: 556130, E-mail: lg12@harrogate.gov.uk, Internet: http://www.harrogate.gov.uk
Local Museum / Fine Arts Museum
Medieval castle with King's Tower, underground sallyport, tudor courthouse, civil war gallery, local history, site archaeology, art 33422

Saint Robert's Cave, Abbay Rd, Knaresborough HG5 8AS - T: (01423) 556188, Fax: 556130, E-mail: lg12@harrogate.gov.uk
Religious Arts Museum 33423

Knebworth

Knebworth House, Park, Knebworth SG3 6PY - T: (01438) 812661, Fax: 811908, E-mail: info@knebworthhouse.com, Internet: http://www.knebworthhouse.com. Head: Martha Lytton Cobbold
Decorative Arts Museum
Tudor to Victorian, Gothic and 20th c interior, wallpapers, rustic wall paintings, literary coll 33424

Knutsford

First Penny Farthing Musum, 92 King St, Knutsford WA16 6ED - T: (01565) 653974
Science&Tech Museum
Largest coll of penny farthing bicycle in the UK 33425

Knutsford Heritage Centre, 90a King St, Knutsford WA16 6ED - T: (01565) 650506
Local Museum 33426

Tabley House Collection, Tabley House, Knutsford WA16 0HB - T: (01565) 750151, Fax: 653230. Head: Peter Cannon-Brookes
Fine Arts Museum / Historic Site
Coll of British paintings (1790's to 1826) formed by Sir John-Flemming Leicester Bart 33427

Tatton Park, Knutsford WA16 6QN - T: (01625) 534400, Fax: 534403, E-mail: tatton@cheshire.gov.co.uk, Internet: http://www.tattonpark.org.uk
Decorative Arts Museum
Coll Gillow furniture, pictures by Canaletto, Carracci, De Heem, Poussin, Nazzari, Van Dyck, silver by Paul Storr, porcelain, European, English and Chinese, carpet 33428

Kyle

Raasay Museum, 6 Osgaig Park, Raasay, Kyle
Local Museum 33429

Lacock

Fox Talbot Museum, Lacock SN15 2LG - T: (01249) 730459, Fax: 730501, E-mail: m.w.gray@bath.ac.uk, Internet: http://www.r-cube.co.uk/fox-talbot. Head: Michael Gray
Science&Tech Museum - 1975
Coll of manuscripts, documents, correspondence and photographs relating to the invention and discovery of the positive/negative photographic process by William Henry Fox Talbot (1800-1877) - research and documentation facilities 33430

Lackham Museum of Agriculture and Rural Life, Wiltshire College Lackham, Lacock SN15 2NY - T: (01249) 466847, Fax: 444474, E-mail: daviaj@wiltshire.ac.uk, Internet: http://www.lackham.co.uk. Head: Andrew Davies
Agriculture Museum - 1946
Agricultural tools, machinery, rural life displays, historic farm buildings 33431

Lanark

Lanark Museum, 8 Westport, Lanark ML11 9HD - T: (01555) 666681, Internet: http://www.biggar-net.co.uk/lanarkmuseum
Local Museum
Lanark history, 19th c costume, photographs, maps and plans 33432

Lancaster

Cottage Museum, 15 Castle Hill, Lancaster LA1 1YS - T: (01524) 388716, Fax: 841692, E-mail: awhite@lancaster.gov.uk, Internet: http://www.lancaster.gov.uk/council/museums. Head: Dr. Andrew White
Decorative Arts Museum - 1978
Artisan cottage, furnished in the style of the 1820s 33433

Judges' Lodgings, Church St, Lancaster LA1 1YS - T: (01524) 32808, 846315, Fax: 846315, Internet: http://www.lancashire.com/lcc/museums. Head: Edmund Southworth
Decorative Arts Museum / Special Museum
Local hist, toys, dolls, games, costumes, coll of Gillow furniture (18th-20th c) 33434

King's Own Royal Regiment Museum, Market Sq, Lancaster LA1 1HT - T: (01524) 64637, Fax: 841692, E-mail: kingsownmuseum@iname.com, Internet: http://www.lancaster.gov.uk/council/museums. Head: Dr. Andrew White
Military Museum - 1929
Archives, medals, photographs, uniforms, memorabilia 33435

Lancaster City Museum, Old Town Hall, Market Sq, Lancaster LA1 1HT - T: (01524) 64637, Fax: 841692, E-mail: awhite@lancaster.gov.uk, Internet: http://www.lancaster.gov.uk/council/museums. Head: Dr. Andrew White
Local Museum / Decorative Arts Museum / Military Museum / Archaeological Museum - 1923
Local hist, decorative arts, Roman finds, weights and measures, Gillow furniture, drawings, local paintings 33436

Lancaster Maritime Museum, Custom House, Saint George's Quay, Lancaster LA1 1RB - T: (01524) 382264, Fax: 841692, E-mail: ndalziel@lancaster.gov.uk, Internet: http://www.lancaster.gov.uk/council/museums. Head: Dr. Andrew White
Science&Tech Museum - 1985
Ship models, ship fittings, navigational aids, customs equipment, charts 33437

Peter Scott Gallery, c/o University of Lancaster, Lancaster LA1 4YW - T: (01524) 593057, Fax: 592603, E-mail: m.p.gavagan@lancaster.ac.uk, Internet: http://www.lancs.ac.uk/users/peterscott. Head: Mary Gavagan
Fine Arts Museum / Decorative Arts Museum / University Museum
Art, pottery, ceramics, sculptures 33438

Roman Bath House, Vicarage Field, Lancaster LA1 1HN - T: (01524) 64637, Internet: http://www.lancaster.gov.uk/council/museums
Archaeological Museum 33439

Ruskin Library, c/o Lancaster University, Lancaster LA1 4YH - T: (01524) 593587, Fax: 593580, E-mail: ruskin.library@lancaster.ac.uk, Internet: http://www.lancs.ac.uk/users/ruskinlib. Head: S.G. Wildman
Library with Exhibitions / Fine Arts Museum / University Museum - 1997
Memorabilia of the writer John Ruskin, paintings, drawings by artists associated with him, photographs, letters - library 33440

Lancing

College Museum, Lancing College, Lancing BN15 0RW - T: (01791) 72213
University Museum / Natural History Museum
Sciences 33441

Langbank

The Dolly Mixture, Finlaystone Country Estate, Langbank PA14 6TJ - T: (01475) 540505, Fax: 540285, E-mail: info@finlaystone.co.uk, Internet: http://www.finlaystone.co.uk. Head: C.J. MacMillan
Special Museum - 1996
Finlaystone Doll Collection - The Dolly Mixture - All sorts of dolls from around the world 33442

Langholm

Clan Armstrong Museum, Lodge Walk, Castleholm, Langholm DG13 0NY - T: (013873) 75702, 81610, Fax: 71760, E-mail: info@clanarmstrong.org, Internet: http://www.clanarmstrong.org
Historical Museum
Armstrong artefacts, maps, documents, portraits, weapons, armour, ancient Reiver clan of the Scottish border - library 33443

Langton Matravers

Coach House Museum → Langton Matravers Museum

Langton Matravers Museum, Saint George's Close, Langton Matravers BH19 3HZ - T: (01929) 423168, Fax: 427534, E-mail: langtonia@cwcom.net, Internet: http://www.langton.mcmail.com. Head: R.J. Saville
Science&Tech Museum - 1974
History of the local stone industry from Roman times to the present day, quarrying equipment, stone-masons' tools, a full-scale model of a section of underground working, examples of the test pieces produced by apprentices, photographs illustrating the quarrymen's work 33444

Lanreath

Farm and Folk Museum, Churchtown, Lanreath PL13 2NX - T: (01503) 220321. Head: John Facey
Agriculture Museum / Folklore Museum - 1973
Wagons, tractors, stationary engines, binder, winnowing machine, potato riddler, carding machine, chaff cutter, turnip slicer, barn thresher, household-clocks, telephones, typewriters 33445

Lapworth

Packwood House, Lapworth B94 6AT - T: (01564) 782024, Fax: 782912
Decorative Arts Museum - 1941
17th c country house with tapestries, needlework, English antique furniture, topiary 33446

Largs

Largs Museum, Kirkgate House, Manse Court, Largs KA30 8AW - T: (01475) 687081, E-mail: mike.mackenzie2@virgin.net, Internet: http://freespace.virgin.net/mike.mackenzie2/LDHSoc.htm
Local Museum - 1973
Local hist 33447

Larne

Larne Museum, Carnegie Arts Centre, 2 Victoria Rd, Larne BT40 1RN - T: (028) 28279482. Head: Joan Morris
Local Museum
Country kitchen, smithy, agricultural implements, old photographs, old newspapers, maps 33448

Latheron

Clan Gunn Museum, Old Parish Church, Latheron KW1 4DD - T: (01593) 721325, Fax: 721325
Local Museum
Hist of Orkney and the North 33449

Lauder

Thirlestane Castle, Lauder TD2 6RU - T: (01578) 722430, Fax: 722761, E-mail: admin@thirlestane-castle.co.uk, Internet: http://www.thirlestane-castle.co.uk. Head: P.D. Jarvis
Local Museum 33450

Laugharne

Dylan Thomas Boathouse, Dylan's Walk, Laugharne SA33 4SD - T: (01994) 427420
Special Museum
Dylan Thomas' writing hut, memorabilia 33451

Launceston

Launceston Steam Railway, Saint Thomas Rd, Launceston PL15 8DA - T: (01566) 775665
Science&Tech Museum
Locomotives, vintage cars and motorcycles, stationary steam engines, machine tools 33452

Lawrence House Museum, 9 Castle St, Launceston PL15 8BA - T: (01566) 773277. Head: Jean Brown
Local Museum
Local history, WWII and home front, coins, feudal dues, rural and domestic Victorian life, costume 33453

Laxey

Great Laxey Wheel and Mines Trail, Manx National Heritage, Laxey IM4 7AH - T: (01624) 648000, Fax: 648001, E-mail: enquiries@mnh.gov.im, Internet: http://www.mnh.gov.im. Head: Phil Hollis
Science&Tech Museum 33454

Murray's Motorcycle Museum, The Bungalow, Snaefell, Laxey IM4 - T: (01624) 861719
Science&Tech Museum
Over 120 motorcycles (1902-1961), motoring memorabilia 33455

Vintage Motor Cycle Museum → Murray's Motorcycle Museum

Laxfield

Laxfield and District Museum, The Guildhall, Laxfield IP13 8DU - T: (01986) 798421
Local Museum
Rural domestic and working life, local archaeology, costumes and natural history 33456

Leadhills

Leadhills Miners' Library Museum, 13 Main St, Leadhills ML12 8SU - T: (01864) 504206, Fax: 504206, E-mail: leadhills-library@culturalprojects.co.uk. Head: Harry Shaw
Library with Exhibitions
Original book stock, library holds objects, photos 33457

Leamington Spa

Leamington Spa Art Gallery and Museum, Royal Pump Rooms, The Parade, Leamington Spa CV32 4AA - T: (01926) 742700, Fax: 742705, E-mail: prooms@warwickdc.gov.uk, Internet: http://www.royal-pump-rooms.co.uk. Head: Jeffrey Watkin
Fine Arts Museum / Local Museum / Historical Museum - 1928
British, Dutch, Flemish paintings (16th-20th c), ceramics from Delft, Wedgwood-Whieldon, Worchester, 18th c drinking glasses, costumes, photography, ethnography, social hist 33458

Leatherhead

Leatherhead Museum of Local History, 64 Church St, Leatherhead KT22 8DP - T: (01372) 386348. Head: Peter Tarplee
Local Museum
Local history, coll of Art Deco Ashtead pottery 33459

Ledaig

Lorn Museum, An Sailean, Ledaig PA37 1QS - T: (01631) 720282. Head: Catherine MacDonald
Local Museum 33460

Ledbury

Eastnor Castle, Ledbury HR8 1RN - T: (01531) 633160, Fax: 631776, E-mail: EastnorCastle@btinternet.com. Head: James & Sarah Hervey Bathurst
Decorative Arts Museum / Fine Arts Museum - 1850
Armour, Italian furniture, pictures, tapestries - library 33461

Leeds

Abbey House Museum, Leeds Museums and Galleries, Kirkstall Rd, Leeds LS5 3EH - T: (0113) 2755821, Fax: 2749439. Head: Dr. Evelyn Silber
Decorative Arts Museum / Local Museum - 1926
18th to 20th-c costumes, toys and dolls, a large coll of domestic appliances and tableware, reconstructions of three street scenes of late 18th and 19th-c cottages, workshops and shops 33462

Art Library, Municipal Bldgs, Leeds LS1 3AB - T: (0113) 2478247
Library with Exhibitions 33463

City Art Gallery, Leeds Museums and Galleries, The Headrow, Leeds LS1 3AA - T: (0113) 2478248, Fax: 2449689
Fine Arts Museum - 1888
Victorian paintings, early English watercolours, British 20th c paintings and sculpture 33464

City Museum, Leeds Museums and Galleries, The Headrow, Calverley St, Leeds LS1 3AA - T: (0113) 2478275, Fax: 2342300, E-mail: evelyn.silber@leeds.gov.uk. Head: Dr. Evelyn Silber
Local Museum - 1820
Natural science, archaeology, anthropology, local history 33465

Department of Semitic Studies Collection, c/o University of Leeds, Leeds LS2 9JT
Archaeological Museum - 1960
Biblical history, Palestina archaeology, Near Eastern ethnology, manuscripts 33466

Henry Moore Institute, 74 The Headrow, Leeds LS1 3AH - T: (0113) 2343158, 2467467, Fax: 2461481, E-mail: hmi@henry-moore.ac.uk, Internet: http://www.henry-moore-fdn.co.uk. Head: Penelope Curtis
Fine Arts Museum
Sculpture production and reception, drawings, letters - research facilities 33467

Horsforth Village Museum, 3-5 The Green, Horsforth, Leeds LS18 5JB - T: (0113) 2819877, E-mail: horsforthmuseum@hotmail.com, Internet: http://www.yourhorseforth.co.uk/history.htm
Local Museum
Local history 33468

Industrial Museum, Leeds Museums and Galleries, Armley Mills, Canal Rd, Leeds LS12 2QF - T: (0113) 2637861, Fax: 2637861, E-mail: - armleymills.indmuseum@virgin.net, Internet: http://www.leeds.gov.uk/tourinfo/attract/museum/armley. Head: Dr. Evelyn Silber
Science&Tech Museum
Large woollen mill, textiles, printing 33469

Leeds Metropolitan University Gallery, Woodhouse Ln, Leeds LS1 3HE - T: (0113) 2833130, Fax: 2835999, Internet: http://www.lmu.ac.uk/arts. Head: Moira Innes
Public Gallery 33470

Museum of the History of Education, c/o University of Leeds, Parkinson Court, Leeds LS2 9JT - T: (0113) 2431751 ext 4665, Fax: 2431751 ext 4541, E-mail: museum@education.leeds.ac.uk, Internet: http://education.leeds.ac.uk/~edu/inted/museum.htm. Head: Dr. E.J. Foster
Historical Museum / Special Museum - 1951
Hist of education in England, old school books, samplers, equipment, portraits, foundation charters, local school hist, text books, photographs 33471

Royal Armouries Museum, Armouries Dr, Leeds LS10 1LT - T: (0113) 2201999, Fax: 2201934, E-mail: enquiries@armouries.org.uk, Internet: http://www.armouries.org.uk. Head: G.M. Wilson
Military Museum - 1996
Arms and armour coll, five galleries describe the evolution of arms and armour in war, tournament, oriental, self-defence and hunting, computer programmes and films on this topic - Conservation, library, education centre 33472

Second World War Experience Centre, 6-8 York Pl, Leeds LS1 2DS - T: (0113) 2450475, Fax: 2349265, E-mail: enquiries@war-experience.org, Internet: http://www.war-experience.org. Head: Dr. Peter Liddle
Historical Museum
Soldiers, sailors and airmen, daily civilian and military experience, women and children in every community during wartime 33473

Temple Newsam House, Leeds Museums and Galleries (closed until 2003), Temple Newsham Rd, off Selby Rd, Leeds LS15 0AE - T: (0113) 2647321, Fax: 2602285, E-mail: evelyn.silber@leeds.gov, Internet: http://www.leeds.gov.uk. Head: Dr. Evelyn Silber
Fine Arts Museum / Decorative Arts Museum - 1922
English and Continental paintings (16th-20th c), furniture, silver, ceramics, country house from 1490 33474

Tetley's Brewery Wharf, The Waterfront, Leeds LS1 1QG - T: (0113) 2420666, Fax: 2594125. Head: Ian Glenholme
Science&Tech Museum
History of Joshua Tetley & Son Brewery, brewing and allied trades 33475

Thackray Museum, Beckett St, Leeds LS9 7LN - T: (0113) 2444343, Fax: 2470219, E-mail: info@thackraymuseum.org, Internet: http://www.thackraymuseum.org. Head: Fiona Elliot
Historical Museum
History of surgery, medicine and health care 33476

Thwaite Mills Watermill, Thwaite Ln, Stourton, Leeds LS10 1RP - T: (0113) 2496453, Fax: 2776737. Head: Nick Winrerborham
Science&Tech Museum
Working water-powered mill 33477

University Gallery Leeds, Parkinson Bldg, Woodhouse Ln, Leeds LS2 9JT - T: (0113) 2332777, Fax: 2335561, E-mail: h.m.diaper@leeds.ac.uk, Internet: http://www.leeds.ac.uk/library/gall. Head: Hilary Diaper
Public Gallery / University Museum
British paintings, drawings and prints (19th-20th c) 33478

Leek

Brindley Mill and James Brindley Museum, Mill St, Leek ST13 5PG - T: (01538) 381446
Science&Tech Museum
Centre of information on the life and work of James Brindley (1716-72), water powered corn mill 33479

Leek Art Gallery, Nicholson Institute, Stockwell St, Leek ST13 6DW - T: (01538) 483732, Fax: 483733, E-mail: alison.strauss@staffsmoorlands.gov.uk, Internet: http://www.staffmoorlands.gov.uk
Public Gallery - 1884 33480

Leicester

Abbey Pumping Station Museum, Corporation Rd, off Abbey Ln, Leicester LE4 5PX - T: (0116) 2995111, Fax: 2995125, Internet: http://www.leicestermuseums.ac.uk. Head: Stuart Warburton
Science&Tech Museum
Horse drawn vehicles, bicycles, motorcycles, motor vehicles, 1891 Beam pumping engines 33481

Belgrave Hall and Gardens, Church Rd, off Thurcaston Rd, Leicester LE4 5PE - T: (0116) 2666590, Fax: 2613063, E-mail: marte001@leicester.gov.uk, Internet: http://www.leicester-museums.ac.uk. Head: Sarah Leritt
Decorative Arts Museum
Queen Anne House with 18th-19th c furniture, botanical/ historical gardens 33482

City Gallery, 90 Granby St, Leicester LE1 1DJ - T: (0116) 2540595, Fax: 2540593
Public Gallery 33483

Guildhall, Guildhall Ln, Leicester LE1 5FQ - T: (0116) 2532569, Fax: 2539626, Internet: http://www.leicestermuseums.ac.uk. Head: Nick Ladlow
Historical Museum
Medieval timber construction 33484

Holly Hayes Environmental Resources Centre, 216 Birstall Rd, Leicester LE4 4DG - T: (0116) 2671950, Fax: 2677112, E-mail: dlott@leics.gov.uk, Internet: http://www.leics.gov.uk. Head: D.A. Lott
Natural History Museum
Wildlife of Leicestershire and Rutland, coll of lichens, fungi, mosses and liverworts 33485

Jewry Wall Museum, Saint Nicholas Circle, Leicester LE1 4LB - T: (0116) 2473021, Fax: 2512257, E-mail: lucaj001@leicester.gov.uk, Internet: http://www.leicestermuseums.ac.uk. Head: S. Levitt
Archaeological Museum - 1966
Roman wall dating from the 2nd c, local archaeology, Roman milestone, mosaics and painted wallplaster 33486

Leicestershire CCC Museum, County Ground, Grace Rd, Leicester LE2 8AD - T: (0116) 2832128, Fax: 2440363, E-mail: james.whitaker.leics@ecb.co.uk, Internet: http://www.leicesters-hireccc.co.uk. Head: J.J. Whitaker
Special Museum
Coll of cricket memorabilia to the Leicestershire County Cricket Club 33487

Museum and Art Gallery Leicester, 53 New Walk, Leicester LE1 7EA - T: (0116) 2554100, Fax: 2473057, E-mail: hidemool@leicester.gov.uk, Internet: http://www.leicestermuseums.ac.uk. Head: J.G. Martin
Fine Arts Museum / Decorative Arts Museum / Natural History Museum - 1849
Geology, natural hist, mammalogy, ornithology, ichthyology, biology, English painting, German expressionists, French painting (19th-20th c), old masters, English ceramics, silver, egyptology - library 33488

Museum of the Royal Leicestershire Regiment, Magazine Gateway, Oxford St, Leicester LE2 7BY - T: (0116) 2473222, Fax: 2470403. Head: S. Levitt
Military Museum - 1969
Hist of the Royal Leicestershire Regiment, in building from 1400, medieval gateway - closed till 1998 for refurbishment 33489

Newarke Houses Museum, The Newarke, Leicester LE2 7BY - T: (0116) 2473222, Fax: 2470403, Internet: http://www.leicestermuseums.ac.uk. Head: Nick Ladlow
Music Museum / Science&Tech Museum - 1940
Clock making, mechanical musical instruments, reconstructed 19th c street, reconstructed workshop of 18th c clockmaker Samuel Deacon, sewing accessories, tokens, toys, Gimson furniture 33490

The National Gas Museum Trust, c/o British Gas, Aylestone Rd, Leicester LE2 7QH - T: (0116) 2503190, Fax: 2503190, E-mail: information@gasmuseum.co.uk, Internet: http://www.gasmuseum.co.uk. Head: T.D. Pickford
Science&Tech Museum - 1977
Gas production (tools and equipment), gas lighting, meters, gas appliances (heating, cooking etc.) 33491

William Carey Museum, Central Baptist Church, Charles St, Leicester LE1 1LA - T: (0116) 2766862, Internet: http://www.central-baptist.org.uk
Religious Arts Museum
Life of William Carey (1762-1834), modern Overseas missions 33492

Leigh, Lancashire

Turnpike Gallery, Civic Sq, Leigh, Lancashire WN7 1EB - T: (01942) 404469, Fax: 404447, E-mail: turnpikegallery@wiganmbc.gov.uk, Internet: http://www.wiganmbc.gov.uk. Head: Kerri Moogen
Public Gallery
20th c prints, contemporary art 33493

Leighton Buzzard

Ascott House, Ascott Estate, Office Wing, Leighton Buzzard LU7 0PS - T: (01296) 688242, Fax: 681904, E-mail: info@ascottestate.co.uk, Internet: http://www.ascottestate.co.uk
Decorative Arts Museum
French and Chippendale furniture, original needlework, paintings by Rubens, Hogarth, Gainsborough, Hobbema, Oriental porcelain, former possession of Anthony de Rothschild 33494

Leighton Buzzard Railway Collection, Page's Park Station, Billington Rd, Leighton Buzzard LU7 8TN - T: (01525) 373888, Fax: 377814, E-mail: info@buzzrail.co.uk, Internet: http://www.buzzrail.co.uk. Head: Alfred Fisher
Science&Tech Museum
Over 50 unique and historic locomotives 33495

Leiston

Long Shop Museum, Main St, Leiston IP16 4ES - T: (01728) 832189, Fax: 832189, E-mail: longshop@care4free.net, Internet: http://www.longshop.care4free.net. Head: Stephen Mael
Science&Tech Museum - 1980
History of Richard Garrett eng works for over 200 years 1778-1980, display of Leiston air base occupied by 357th fighter group USAAF World War II 33496

Leominster

Croft Castle, Leominster HR6 9PW - T: (01568) 780246
Fine Arts Museum 33497

Leominster Folk Museum, Etnam St, Leominster HR6 8AL - T: (01568) 615186. Head: Lynne Moult
Folklore Museum / Local Museum
Local trades and industry, cider house, dairy, costume, social history 33498

Lerwick

Böd of Gremista Museum, Gremista, Lerwick ZE1 0PX - T: (01595) 694386, Fax: 696729, E-mail: shetland.museum@zetnet.co.uk, Internet: http://www.shetland-museum.org.uk. Head: T. Watt
Historical Museum
Birthplace of Arthur Anderson 33499

Shetland Museum, Lower Hillhead, Lerwick ZE1 0EL - T: (01595) 695057, Fax: 696729, E-mail: shetland.museum@zetnet.co.uk, Internet: http://www.shetland-museum.org.uk. Head: T. Watt
Local Museum - 1970 33500

Letchworth

First Garden City Heritage Museum, 296 Norton Way S, Letchworth SG6 1SU - T: (01462) 482710, Fax: 486056, E-mail: fgchm@letchworth.com, Internet: http://www.letchworth.com
Local Museum - 1977 33501

Museum and Art Gallery, Broadway, Letchworth SG6 3PF - T: (01462) 685647, Fax: 481879, E-mail: letchworth.museum@nhdc.gov.uk, Internet: http://www.nhdc.gov.uk. Head: Rosamond Allwood
Local Museum / Fine Arts Museum - 1914
Archaeology, natural hist, local hist, fine and decorative art, costume 33502

Lewes

Anne of Cleves House Museum, 52 Southover High St, Lewes BN7 1JA - T: (01273) 474610, Fax: 486990, E-mail: molewes@sussexpast.co.uk
Decorative Arts Museum / Folklore Museum
Furniture, domestic equipment and a wide range of material illustrating the everyday life of local people during the 19th and early 20th c 33503

Military Heritage Museum, 7-9 West St, Lewes BN7 2NJ - T: (01273) 480208, Fax: 476562, E-mail: WallisandWallis@inatos.co.uk
Military Museum - 1977
Roy Butler Coll - Hist of the British army 1650-1914 33504

Museum of Sussex Archaeology, Barbican House, 169 High St, Lewes BN7 1YE - T: (01273) 486290, Fax: 486990, E-mail: castle@sussexpast.co.uk, Internet: http://www.sussexpast.co.uk. Head: Emma Young
Archaeological Museum
Prehistoric, Roman and Saxon archaeology, watercolors 33505

Leyland

British Commercial Vehicle Museum, King St, Leyland PR5 1LE - T: (01772) 451011, Fax: 623404. Head: Andrew Buchan
Science&Tech Museum - 1983
Historic commercial vehicles and buses, truck and bus building 33506

South Ribble Museum and Exhibition Centre, Old Grammar School, Church Rd, Leyland PR5 1EJ - T: (01772) 422041, Fax: 625363. Head: Dr. D.A. Hunt
Local Museum
Archaeological material from excavations at the Roman site at Walton-le-Dale, and a wide range of smaller items relating to the history of the town and the area 33507

Lichfield

Friary Art Gallery, The Friary, Lichfield WS13 6QG - T: (01543) 510700, Fax: 510716, E-mail: lichfield.library@staffordshire.gov.uk. Head: Elizabeth Rees-Jones, Fiona Bailey
Library with Exhibitions - 1859
Crafts, textiles 33508

Hanch Hall, Lichfield WS13 8HH - T: (01543) 490308. Head: Colin Lee, Linda Lee
Local Museum 33509

Lichfield Heritage Centre, Market Sq, Lichfield WS13 6LG - T: (01543) 256611, Fax: 414749, E-mail: heritage@lichfield.gov.uk, Internet: http://www.lichfield.gov.uk/heritage. Head: J.E. Rackham
Local Museum 33510

Samuel Johnson Birthplace Museum, Breadmarket St, Lichfield WS13 6LG - T: (01543) 264972, Fax: 414779, E-mail: sjmuseum@lichfield.gov.uk, Internet: http://www.lichfield.gov.uk
Special Museum - 1901
Memorabilia of Dr. Samuel Johnson (1709-1784), paintings, association books, documents, letters of Johnson, Boswell, Anna Seward - library 33511

Staffordshire Regiment Museum, Whittington Barracks, Lichfield WS14 9PY - T: (0121) 3113240, Fax: 3113205, E-mail: museum@rhqstaffords.fsnet.co.uk, Internet: http://www.armymuseums.org.uk. Head: E. Green
Military Museum - 1963
Hist of the regiment, medals, armaments, uniforms, exterior WWI trench, Anderson shelters 33512

Wall Roman Site and Museum - Letocetum, Watling St, Lichfield WS14 0AW - T: (01543) 480768. Head: Sara Lunt
Archaeological Museum - 1912
Roman finds, pottery, coins, tools, glass 33513

Lifton

Dingles Steam Village, Lifton PL16 0AT - T: (01566) 783425, Fax: 783584, E-mail: richard@dinglesteam.co.uk, Internet: http://www.dinglesteam.co.uk
Science&Tech Museum
Steam and other early road rollers, lorries, fairground engines and industrial engines, old road signs, fairground art, belt driven machinery 33514

Lincoln

City and County Museum, 12 Friars Ln, Lincoln LN2 5AL - T: (01522) 530401, Fax: 530724, E-mail: librarian@lincolncathedral.com. Head: Dr. Nicholas Bennett
Historical Museum
Perhistoric, Roman and medievial Lincolnshire, armoury 33515

Lawn, Union Rd, Lincoln LN1 3BL - T: (01522) 560330
Science&Tech Museum
Sir Joseph Banks Conservatory and aquarium 33516

Lincoln Cathedral Treasury, Cathedral, Lincoln - T: (01522) 552222 ext 2805, 811308. Head: O.T. Griffin
Religious Arts Museum 33517

Lincolnshire Road Transport Museum, Whisby Rd, off Doddington Rd, Lincoln LN6 3QT - T: (01522) 689497
Science&Tech Museum - 1959/93
Vehicles dating from 1920s to 1960s, mostly restored and with local connections 33518

Museum of Lincolnshire Life, Old Barracks, Burton Rd, Lincoln LN1 3LY - T: (01522) 528448, Fax: 521264, E-mail: finchj@lincolnshire.gov.uk. Head: Jon Finch
Local Museum - 1969
Agricultural and industrial machinery, horse-drawn vehicles, displays devoted to domestic, community and commercial life within the county, crafts and trades, Royal Lincolnshire Regiment - windmill archive 33519

Old Toy Show, 26 Westgate, Lincoln LN1 3BD - T: (01522) 520534
Special Museum
Toys from the 1790's to the 1970's 33520

Royal Lincolnshire Regiment Museum, Burton Rd, Lincoln LN1 3LY - T: (01522) 528448, Fax: 521264, E-mail: finchj@lincolnshire.gov.uk. Head: Jon Finch
Military Museum - 1986
Hist of the regiment, uniforms, medals, war trophies, armaments, social history coll relating to Lincolnshire 33521

Usher Gallery, Lindum Rd, Lincoln LN2 1NN - T: (01522) 527980, Fax: 560165, E-mail: woodr@lincolnshire.gov.uk
Fine Arts Museum / Decorative Arts Museum - 1927
Paintings, watercolours, watches, miniatures, silver, porcelain, manuscripts and memorabilia of Alfred Lord Tennyson (1809-1892) 33522

Linford

Walton Hall Museum, Walton Hall Rd, Linford SS17 0RH - T: (01375) 671874, Fax: 641268
Science&Tech Museum
Historic farm machinery, gypsy caravan, motor rollers 33523

Linlithgow

Canal Museum, Canal Basin, Manse Rd, Linlithgow EH49 6AJ - T: (01506) 671215, E-mail: info@lucs.org.uk, Internet: http://www.lucs.org.uk
Science&Tech Museum / Historic Site 33524

House of the Binns, Linlithgow EH49 7NA - T: (01506) 834255. Head: Kathleen Dalyell
Historical Museum / Decorative Arts Museum - 1944
Historic home of the Dalyells, 17th c moulded plaster ceilings, paintings, porcelain, furniture 33525

Linlithgow Palace, Edinburgh Rd, Linlithgow EH49 6QS - T: (01506) 842896
Decorative Arts Museum 33526

Linlithgow Story, Annet House, 143 High St, Linlithgow EH49 7JH - T: (01506) 670677
Local Museum 33527

Liphook

Hollycombe Steam Collection, Iron Hill, Liphook GU30 7UP - T: (01428) 724900, Fax: 723682, E-mail: hollycombe@btinternet.com, Internet: http://www.hollycombe.co.uk. Head: Chris Hooker
Science&Tech Museum 33528

Lisburn

Irish Linen Centre and Lisburn Museum, Market Sq, Lisburn BT28 1AG - T: (028) 92663377, Fax: 92672624. Head: Brian Mackey
Local Museum
Archaeology, social history, art and industry of the Lagan valley 33529

Lisnaskea

Folklife Display, Library, Lisnaskea BT92 0AD - T: (028) 67721222
Local Museum 33530

Litcham

Litcham Village Museum, Fourways, Mileham Rd, Litcham PE32 2NZ - T: (01328) 701383. Head: R.W. Shaw
Local Museum
Local artefacts 33531

Little Walsingham

Shirehall Museum, Common Pl, Little Walsingham NR22 6BP - T: (01328) 820510, Fax: 820098, E-mail: walsingham.museum@farmline.com, Internet: http://www.walsingham.uk.com
Historical Museum
Local and village history, pilgrimages to Walsingham, court 33532

Littlehampton

Littlehampton Museum, Manor House, Church St, Littlehampton BN17 5EP - T: (01903) 738100, Fax: 731690, E-mail: rebecca.fardelli@arun.co.uk
Local Museum - 1928
Nautical and maritime exhibits, photography 33533

Liverpool

Croxteth Hall, Croxteth Hall Ln, Liverpool L12 0HB - T: (0151) 2285311, Fax: 2282817, Internet: http://www.croxteth.co.uk. Head: Irene Vickers
Decorative Arts Museum
Edwardian furnishings 33534

Her Majesty Customs and Excise National Museum, Merseyside Maritime Museum, Albert Dock, Liverpool L3 4AQ - T: (0151) 2070001, Fax: 4784590. Head: Karen Bradbury
Special Museum 33535

Lark Lane Motor Museum, 1 Hesketh St, Liverpool
Science&Tech Museum
Cars, motorcycles and a wide range of mechanical devices 33536

Liverpool Museum, William Brown St, Liverpool L3 8EN - T: (0151) 2070001, 4784399, Fax: 4784390, Internet: http://www.nmgm.org.uk. Head: R.A. Foster
Local Museum - 1851
Archaeology, astronomy, botany, ethnology, geology, ceramics, decorative arts, zoology, musical instruments, vivarium and aquarium, natural history 33537

Liverpool Scottish Regimental Museum, Forbes House, Score Ln, Childwall, Liverpool L16 2NG - T: (0151) 7727711
Military Museum
Uniforms, weapons, equipment, photographs and documents, history of the Regiment from 1900 to the present day 33538

Merseyside Maritime Museum, Albert Dock, Liverpool L3 4AQ - T: (0151) 4784499, 2070001, Fax: 4784590, Internet: http://www.nmgm.org.uk. Head: Michael Stammmers
Science&Tech Museum - 1980
Coll of full-size craft, including the pilot boat, Edmund Gardner (1953), coll of models, paintings, marine equipment, the history of cargo-handling in the Port of Liverpool, the development and operation of the enclosed dock system 33539

Museum of Archaeology, Classics and Oriental Studies, c/o University of Liverpool, 14 Abercromby Sq, Liverpool L69 3BX - T: (0151) 7942467, Fax: 7942226, E-mail: winkerpa@liverpool.ac.uk, Internet: http://www.liv.ac.uk/archaeology_classics. Head: Elizabeth A. Slater
Archaeological Museum
Objects from the excavations in Egypt and the Near East, classical Aegean and prehistoric antiquities, coins 33540

Museum of Dentistry, c/o School of Dental Surgery, University of Liverpool, Pembroke Pl, Liverpool L69 3BX - T: (0151) 7065279, 7062000, Fax: 7065809. Head: John Cooper
Special Museum - 1880
History of dentistry, dentistal education, equipment 33541

Museum of Liverpool Life, Pier Head, Liverpool L3 1PZ - T: (0151) 4784060, 2070001, Fax: 4784090. Head: Graham Boxer
Historical Museum - 1993
Displays on Making a Living, Demanding a Voice and Mersey Culture, forthcoming developments: Phase 2 - Homes and Communities, Phase 3 - The King's Regiment 33542

Open Eye Photography Gallery, 28-32 Wood St, Liverpool L1 4AQ - T: (0151) 7099460, Fax: 7093059, E-mail: info@openeye.u-net.com. Head: Paul Mellor
Public Gallery 33543

Speke Hall, The Walk, Liverpool L24 1XD - T: (0151) 4277231, Fax: 4279860. Head: S. Osborne
Decorative Arts Museum - 1970
Decorative art, social history, interior design (16th-19th c), furniture (17th-19th c), Victorian furnishings (19th c) 33544

Sudley House, Mossley Hill Rd, Liverpool L18 8BX - T: (0151) 7243245, Fax: 7290531, Internet: http://www.nmgm.org.uk. Head: Julian Treuherz
Fine Arts Museum - 1986
British paintings 33545

Tate Liverpool, Albert Dock, Liverpool L3 4BB - T: (0151) 7027400, Fax: 7027401, E-mail: liverpoolinfo@tate.org.uk, Internet: http://www.tate.org.uk/liverpool. Head: Christoph Grunenberg
Public Gallery - 1988
National coll of 20th c art 33546

University of Liverpool Art Gallery, 3 Abercromby Sq, Liverpool L69 7WY - T: (0151) 7942348, Fax: 7942343, E-mail: acompton@liverpool.ac.uk. Head: Ann Compton
Fine Arts Museum / University Museum - 1977
Watercolours by Turner, Girtin, Cozens, Cotman, early English porcelain, oil paintings by Turner, Audubon, Joseph Wright of Derby, Augustus John, sculpture by Epstein 33547

Walker Art Gallery, William Brown St, Liverpool L3 8EL - T: (0151) 4784199, 4784612, Fax: 4784190, Internet: http://www.nmgm.org.uk. Head: Julian Treuherz
Fine Arts Museum - 1877
European painting, sculpture, drawings, watercolors and prints since 1300, Italian, Dutch and Flemish paintings (13th-17th c), British paintings (17th-19th c), 19th c Liverpool art, contemporary painting 33548

Livingston

Almond Valley Heritage Centre, Millfield, Kirkton North, Livingston EH54 7AR - T: (01506) 414957, Fax: 497771, E-mail: info@almondvalley.co.uk, Internet: http://www.almondvalley.co.uk
Local Museum - 1990
Agriculture, Scottish shale oil industry, local & social history. 33549

Llanberis

Electric Mountain - Museum of North Wales, Amgueddfa'r Gogledd, Llanberis LL55 4UR - T: (01286) 870636, Fax: 873001. Head: Eluned Davies
Local Museum
Art, temporary exhibitions, underground trips to Dinorwig pumped storage power station 33550

Llanberis Lake Railway, Gilfach Ddu, Llanberis LL55 4TY - T: (01286) 870549, Fax: 870549, E-mail: llr@lake-railway.freeserve.co.uk, Internet: http://www.lake-railway.freeserve.co.uk
Science&Tech Museum 33551

Welsh Slate Museum, Pardarn Country Park, Llanberis LL55 4TY - T: (01286) 870630, Fax: 871906, E-mail: slate@nmgw.ac.uk, Internet: http://www.nmgw.ac.uk/wsm. Head: Dr. Dafydd Roberts
Natural History Museum - 1971
Geology, industry, slate, engineering, victorian technology, social history, mining, quarrying 33552

Llandrindod Wells

Museum of Local History and Industry, Temple St, Llandrindod Wells LD1 5DL - T: (01686) 412605. Head: Chris Wilson
Local Museum / Archaeological Museum
Castell Collen Roman Fort, archaeology, local history and industry, dolls, life in Llanidloes 19th-20th c 33553

National Cycle Collection, Automobile Palace, Temple St, Llandrindod Wells - T: (01597) 825531, Fax: 825531. Head: David Higman
Science&Tech Museum
Bicycle since 1818, photographs, early lighting art, racing stars 33554

Radnorshire Museum, Temple St, Llandrindod Wells LD1 5DL - T: (01597) 824513, Fax: 825781, E-mail: radnorshire.museum@powys.gov.uk. Head: Chris Wilson
Local Museum 33555

Llandudno

Llandudno Museum and Art Gallery, Chardon House, 17-19 Gloddaeth St, Llandudno LL30 2DD - T: (01492) 876517, Fax: 876517, E-mail: llandudno.museum@lineone.net
Local Museum / Fine Arts Museum
Archaeology, history and early industry of the area, with a special section on early 20th-c tourism and entertainment 33556

Oriel Mostyn, 12 Vaughan St, Llandudno LL30 1AB - T: (01492) 879201, 870875, Fax: 878869, E-mail: post@mostyn.org, Internet: http://www.mostyn.org. Head: Martin Barlow
Public Gallery 33557

Llandysul

Museum of the Welsh Woollen Industry, Dre-fach Felindre, Llandysul SA44 5UP - T: (01559) 370929, Fax: 371592, E-mail: post@nmgw.ac.uk, Internet: http://www.nmgw.ac.uk/mwwi
Science&Tech Museum
Manufacture of woollen cloth from fleece to fabric, development of Wales' most important rural industry from its domestic beginnings to the 19th and early 20th-c factory units, coll of textile machinery and tools, a working waterwheel 33558

Teifi Valley Railway, Henllan Station Yard, Henllan, Llandysul SA44 5TD - T: (01559) 371077, Fax: 371077, E-mail: teifivr@f9.co.uk
Science&Tech Museum
Steam locomotive, Motorail diesel units 33559

Llanelli

Bwlch Farm Stable Museum, Bwlch Farm, Bynea, Llanelli SA14 9ST - T: (01554) 772036
Agriculture Museum
Roman archaeological material found in the area, farm implements and tools, and relics of the Second World War 33560

Parc Howard Museum and Art Gallery, Parc Howard, Felinfoel Rd, Llanelli SA15 3AS - T: (01554) 772029, Fax: (01267) 223830, E-mail: ChrisDelaney@carmarthenshire.gov.uk, Internet: http://www.carmarthenshire.gov.uk
Decorative Arts Museum / Fine Arts Museum / Local Museum - 1912
Pottery, art 33561

Public Library Gallery, Vaughan St, Llanelli SA15 3AS - T: (01554) 773538, Fax: 750125. Head: D.F. Griffiths
Public Gallery 33562

Llanfair Caereinion

Welshpool and Llanfair Light Railway, The Station, Llanfair Caereinion SY21 0SF - T: (01938) 810441, Fax: 810861, E-mail: info@wllr.org.uk, Internet: http://www.wllr.org.uk
Science&Tech Museum
Narrow gauge steam railway 33563

Llanfairpwll

Plas Newydd, Llanfairpwll LL61 6DQ - T: (01248) 714795, Fax: 713673, E-mail: ppnmsn@smtp.ntrust.org.uk. Head: Paul Carr-Griffin
Historical Museum
Wall paintings, relics of the 1st Marquess of Anglesey and the Battle of Waterloo, and the Ryan coll of military uniforms and headdresses 33564

Llangefni

Oriel Ynys Mon (Anglesey Heritage Gallery), Rhosmeirch, Llangefni LL77 7TQ - T: (01248) 724444, Fax: 750282, E-mail: agxlh@anglesey.gov.uk. Head: Alun Gruffydd
Local Museum
Tunnivliffe wildlife art coll, Welsh art, archaeology, geology, social history 33565

Llangernyw

Sir Henry Jones Museum, Y Cwm, Llangernyw LL22 8PR - T: (01492) 575371, Fax: 513664. Head: John Hughes
Local Museum
Furniture and domestic items, craft tools, books, photographs and costume relating to Sir Henry Jones and village life 33566

Llangollen

Canal Museum, The Wharf, Llangollen LL20 8TA - T: (01978) 860702, Fax: 860702, E-mail: sue@horsedrawnboats.co.uk, Internet: http://www.horsedrawnboats.co.uk. Head: D.R. Knapp, S. Knapp
Historical Museum - 1974 33567

Llangollen Motor Museum, Pentrefelin, Llangollen LL20 8EE - T: (01978) 860324. Head: Ann Owen
Science&Tech Museum
Cars, motorcycles, memorabilia from 1910-1970's, history of Britain's canals 33568

Plas Newydd, Hill St, Llangollen LL20 8AW - T: (01978) 861314, Fax: 861906, E-mail: mcmahon_rose@hotmail.com. Head: Rose MacMahon
Special Museum
Home of the Ladies of Llangollen 33569

Llanidloes

Llanidloes Museum, Town Hall, Great Oak St, Llanidloes SY18 6BU, mail addr: c/o Powysland Museum, Canal Wharf, Welshpool SY21 7AQ - T: (01938) 554656, Fax: 554656, E-mail: powysland@powys.gov.uk. Head: Eva B. Bredsdorff
Local Museum - 1933 33570

Llantrisant

Model House Gallery, Bull Ring, Llantrisant CF72 8EB - T: (01443) 237758, Fax: 224718
Public Gallery 33571

Llanystumdwy

Lloyd George Museum and Highgate, Cyfarwyddwr, Llanystumdwy LL52 0SH - T: (01766) 522071, Fax: 522071, E-mail: nestthomas@gwynedd.gov.uk. Head: Dafydd Whittall
Historical Museum - 1948
Caskets, original punch cartoons, original archives concerning Versailles Peace Treaty 33572

Llwynypia

Rhondda Museum, Glyncornel Environmental Study Centre, Llwynypia CF40 2HT - T: (01443) 431727
Local Museum 33573

Lochwinnoch

Lochwinnoch Community Museum, High St, Lochwinnoch PA12 4AB - T: (01505) 842615, Fax: 8899240. Head: Martine Morletta
Local Museum - 1984
Local agriculture, industry and village life 33574

Lockerbie

Rammerscales, Lockerbie DG11 1LD - T: (01387) 811988
Fine Arts Museum
20th c paintings, tapestries, sculpture 33575

London

198 Gallery, 194-198 Railton Rd, Herne Hill, London SE24 0LU - T: (020) 79788309, Fax: 76521418, E-mail: gallery@198gallery.co.uk, Internet: http://www.198gallery.co.uk. Head: Lucy Davies
Public Gallery
Contemporary art by artists from diverse cultural backgrounds - education centre 33576

Alexander Fleming Laboratory Museum, Saint Mary's Hospital, Praed St, London W2 1NY - T: (020) 78866528, Fax: 78866739, E-mail: kevin.brown@st-marys.nhs.uk. Head: Kevin Brown
Science&Tech Museum - 1993
Reconstruction of the laboratory in which Fleming discovered Penicillin in 1928 33577

Alfred Dunhill Museum, 48 Jermyn st, London SW1Y 6DL - T: (020) 78388233, Fax: 78388556. Head: Peter Tilley
Museum of Classical Antiquities
Alfred Dunhill Antique products, incl. motoring accessories, lightes, watchens, pens, compendiums - archive 33578

All Hallows Undercroft Museum, Byward St, London EC3R 5BJ - T: (020) 74812928, Fax: 74883333
Religious Arts Museum
Roman pavement in situ, classical tombstones, a model of the Roman city, ancient registers, a Crusader Altar 33579

Anaesthetic Museum, c/o Dept. of Anaesthesia, Saint Bartholomew's Hospital, London EC1A 7BE - T: (020) 76017518. Head: D.J. Wilkinson
Historical Museum
Encompasses apparatus general, local anaesthetics since 1800's 33580

Architecture Foundation, 30 Bury St, London SW1Y - T: (020) 78399389
Public Gallery 33581

Baden-Powell House, 65-67 Queen's Gate, London SW7 5JS - T: (020) 75847031, Fax: 75906902, E-mail: bph.hostel@scout.org.uk, Internet: http://www.scoutbase.org.uk
Special Museum - 1961
Life and work of Lord Robert Baden-Powell (1857-1941), founder of the Boy Scouts 33582

Bank of England Museum, Threadneedle St, London EC2R 8AH - T: (020) 76015545, Fax: 76015808, E-mail: museum@bankofengland.co.uk, Internet: http://www.bankofengland.co.uk/mus_arch.htm. Head: John Keyworth
Special Museum - 1988
Banknotes, coins and medals, photographs, pictures, prints and drawings, statuary, artefacts, Roman and medieval 33583

Bankside Gallery, 48 Hopton St, Blackfriars, London SE1 9JH - T: (020) 79287521, Fax: 79282820, E-mail: info@banksidegallery.com, Internet: http://www.banksidegallery.com. Head: Judy Dixey
Public Gallery 33584

Banqueting House, Whitehall, London SW1 2ER - T: (020) 79304179, Fax: 79308268. Head: Irma Hay
Fine Arts Museum
Historic building, completed in 1622 to a design by Inigo Jones, ceiling paintings by Rubens installed in 1635 33585

Barbican Art, Barbican Centre, Silk St, London EC2Y 8DS - T: (020) 76388891, Fax: 73822308, Internet: http://www.barbican.org.uk. Head: John Hoole
Public Gallery 33586

Barnet Museum, 31 Wood St, Barnet, London EN5 4BE - T: (020) 84408066. Head: Dr. Gilian Gear
Local Museum - 1935
Barnet district history, costume photogr - library 33587

BBC Experience, Broadcasting House, Portland Pl, London W1A 1AA - T: (020) 77651686, Fax: 77655731, E-mail: bbcexperience@bbc.co.uk, Internet: http://www.bbc.co.uk/experience. Head: Helen Mackintosh
Science&Tech Museum
Film, radio archives and artefacts, history of the BBC and British broadcasting 33588

Ben Uri Art Society and Gallery, 21 Dean St, London W1V 6NE - T: (020) 74372852, Fax: 74821414, E-mail: benuri@ort.org, Internet: http://www.benuri.ort.org. Head: Jo Velleman
Public Gallery
Contemporary art by Jewish artists, paintings, drawings, sculptures 33589

Benjamin Franklin House, 36 Craven St, London WC2N 5NF - T: (020) 79309121, Fax: 79309124, E-mail: BenjaminFranklinHouse@msn.com, Internet: http://www.BenjaminFranklinHouse.org.uk
Historical Museum 33590

Bexley Museum, Hall Pl, Bourne Rd, Bexley, London DA5 1PQ - T: (01322) 526574, Fax: 522921, E-mail: janice@bexleymuseum.freeserv.co.uk, Internet: http://www.hallplaceandgardens.com. Head: Martin Purslow
Historical Museum - 1934
Local geology, archaeology, fauna and flora, minerals, Roman finds, local history and industries 33591

BOC Museum, The Charles King Collection, 9 Bedford Sq, London WC1B 3RE - T: (020) 76318806, Fax: 76314352, E-mail: heritage@aagbi.org, Internet: http://www.aagbi.org. Head: Patricia Willis
Historical Museum
Historic anaesthetic equipment 33592

Bramah Tea and Coffee Museum, 1 Maguire St, Butlers Wharf, London SE1 2NQ - T: (020) 73780222, Fax: 73780219, Internet: http://www.bramahmuseum.co.uk. Head: Edward Bramah
Special Museum - 1992
Large coll of teapots and coffee making machinery 33593

British Dental Association Museum, 64 Wimpole St, London W1M 8AL - T: (020) 75634563, Fax: 74875232, Internet: http://www.bda.dentistry.org.uk
Historical Museum
History, art and science of dental surgery 33594

British Film Institute Collections, 21 Stephen St, London W1T 1LN - T: (020) 72551444, Fax: 75807503, E-mail: gail.nolan@bfi.org.uk, Internet: http://www.bfi.org.uk. Head: Jon Teckman
Special Museum 33595

British Library, Exhibition Galleries, 96 Euston Rd, London NW1 2DB - T: (020) 74127000, 74127332, Fax: 74127340, E-mail: visitor-services@bl.uk, Internet: http://www.bl.uk. Head: Lynne Brindley
Library with Exhibitions
Permanent display: Magna Carta, first folio of Shakespeare's works, Gutenberg Bible 33596

British Museum, Great Russell St, London WC1B 3DG - T: (020) 73238000, Fax: 73238616, E-mail: information@thebritishmuseum.ac.uk, Internet: http://www.thebritishmuseum.ac.uk. Head: Dr. Robert G.W. Anderson
Museum of Classical Antiquities - 1753
Coins and medals, Egyptian antiquities, ethnography, Greek and Roman antiquities, Japanese antiquities, medieval and latge antiquities, oriental antiquities, prehistoric and Romano-British antiquities, prints & drawings, western Asiatic antiquities 33597

British Optical Association Museum, c/o College of Optometrists, 42 Craven St, London WC2N 5NG - T: (020) 78396000, Fax: 78396800, E-mail: museum@college-optometrists.org, Internet: http://www.collegeoptometrists.org/college/museum
Historical Museum
Optical and ophthalmic items, incl. spectacles, pince- nez, lorgnettes, spyglasses, lenses and artificial eyes, diagnostic instruments, fine art, ceramics, oil paintings - library 33598

British Red Cross Museum and Archives, 9 Grosvenor Crescent, London SW1X 7EJ - T: (020) 72015153, Fax: 72356456, E-mail: enquiry@redcross.org.uk, Internet: http://www.redcross.org.uk/museum&archives
Special Museum
Uniforms, medals, badges and other items of equipment, textiles, medical equipment, humanitarian aid - archive 33599

Bruce Castle Museum, Lordship Ln, Tottenham, London N17 8NU - T: (020) 88088772, Fax: 88084118
Historical Museum - 1906
Local history, British postal history, Middlesex Regimental history - library 33600

Brunei Gallery, c/o SOAS, Thornhaugh St, Russell Sq, London WC1H OXG - T: (020) 73236036, Fax: 73236010, E-mail: gallery@soas.ac.uk, Internet: http://www.soas.ac.uk/gallery. Head: Jacqueline Arrol-Barker
Ethnology Museum / Fine Arts Museum
Work of and from Asia and Africa, non-western culture and art 33601

Brunel Engine House, Railway Av, Rotherhithe, London SE16 4LF - T: (020) 72313840, E-mail: robert.hulse@brunelenginehouse.org.uk, Internet: http://www.brunelenginehouse.org.uk. Head: Robert Hulse
Historic Site - 1974
Unique compound horizontal V steam engine, model and watercolours of Sir Marc Brunel's tunnel (1st underwater thoroughfare) 33602

Cabaret Mechanical Theatre, 33-34 The Market, Covent Garden, London WC2E 8RE - T: (020) 73797961, Fax: 74975445, E-mail: Barecat@Cabaret.co.uk, Internet: http://www.cabaret.co.uk. Head: Susan Jackson
Science&Tech Museum - 1984
Coll of contemporary automata and mechanical sculpture, Paul Spooner, Keith Newstead, Ron Fuller, Peter Markey, Tim Hunkin 33603

Cabinet War Rooms, Clive Steps, King Charles St, London SW1A 2AQ - T: (020) 79306961, Fax: 78395897, E-mail: cwr@imw.org.uk, Internet: http://www.iwm.org.uk. Head: Phil Reed
Historical Museum - 1984
Churchill's underground Headquarter, 21 rooms for Churchill and his staff, including the Cabinet Room, the Map Room, Churchill's bedroom and the Transatlantic Telephone Room 33604

Camden Arts Centre, Arkwright Rd, London NW3 6DG - T: (020) 74352643, 74355224, Fax: 77943371, E-mail: info@camdenartscentre.org, Internet: http://www.cemdenartscentre.org. Head: Jenni Lomax
Public Gallery
Contemporary art, painting and pottery 33605

Canada House Gallery, Trafalgar Sq, London SW1Y 5BJ - T: (020) 72586537, Fax: 72586434, Internet: http://www.dfait-maeci.gc.ca. Head: Michael Regan
Public Gallery 33606

Carlyle's House, 24 Cheyne Row, London SW3 5HL - T: (020) 73527087
Special Museum - 1895
Home of Thomas and Jane Carlyle with furniture, books, letters, personal effects and portraits - library 33607

Carshalton Water Tower, West St, Carshalton, London SM5 3PN - T: (020) 786470984. Head: Jean Knight
Science&Tech Museum
18th c water tower, bathroom, pump chamber, saloon, prints 33608

A Celebration of Immigration, 19 Princelet St, London E1 6QH - T: (020) 72475352, Fax: 73751490, E-mail: information@19princeletstreet.org.uk, Internet: http://www.19princeletstreet.org.uk

Historical Museum
Various waves of immigration through the East End of London, religious textiles of the Jewish life - archive 33609

Chapter House, East Cloister, Westminster Abbey, London SW1P 3PE - T: (020) 72225897, Fax: 72220960, Internet: http://www.english-heritage.org.uk
Local Museum 33610

Chartered Insurance Institute's Museum, The Hall, 20 Aldermanbury, London EC2V 7HY - T: (020) 74174412, Fax: 77260131. Head: K. Clayden
Special Museum - 1934
History of insurance, insurance company fire brigades, fire marks, early firefighting equipment - library 33611

Chisenhale Gallery, 64 Chisenhale Rd, London E3 5QZ - T: (020) 89814518, Fax: 89807169, E-mail: mail@chisenhale.org.uk, Internet: http://www.chisenhale.org.uk. Head: Anna Harding
Public Gallery 33612

Chiswick House, Burlington Ln, Chiswick, London W4 2RP - T: (020) 87421978, Fax: 87423104, Internet: http://www.english-heritage.org.uk
Local Museum
18th century furniture and interiors, paintings collection from 17th-19th century 33613

Church Farmhouse Museum, Greyhound Hill, Hendon, London NW4 4JR - T: (020) 82030130, Fax: 83592666, Internet: http://www.earl.org.uk/partners/barnet/churchf.htm. Head: Gerrard Roots
Local Museum - 1955
Period furniture, local hist 33614

Cinema Museum, 2 Dugard Way, Kennington, London SE11 4TH - T: (020) 78402200, Fax: 78402299, E-mail: martin@cinemamuseum.org.uk. Head: Martin Humphries
Performing Arts Museum
History of cinemas since 1896 33615

City of London Police Museum, 37 Wood St, London EC2P 2NQ - T: (020) 76012747. Head: Roger Appleby
Historical Museum
Police and the policing of the city, insignia truncheons, tipstaves, uniforms and photographs 33616

Clipper Ship "Cutty Sark", King William Walk, London SE10 9HT - T: (020) 88583445, Fax: 88533589, E-mail: info@cuttysark.org.uk, Internet: http://www.cuttysark.org.uk. Head: S.T. Waite
Science&Tech Museum - 1957
Restored ship, launched 1869, with figureheads, ship hist 33617

Collection of Portraits and Performance History, Royal College of Music, Prince Consort Rd, South Kensington, London SW7 2BS - T: (020) 75914340, Fax: 75897740, E-mail: museum@rcm.ac.uk, Internet: http://www.rcm.ac.uk
Performing Arts Museum / Fine Arts Museum
Printed music, portraits 33618

Collection of the Worshipful Company of Clockmakers, Clock Room, Guildhall Library, Aldermanbury, London EC2P 2EJ - T: (020) 7606303 ext 1865/66. Head: Sir George White
Science&Tech Museum
Clocks, watches and marine timekeepers, the majority dating between late 16th c and the mid of 19th c - library 33619

Commonwealth Institute, Kensington High St, London W8 6NQ - T: (020) 76034535, Fax: 76027374, E-mail: information@commonwealth.org.uk, Internet: http://www.commonwealth.org.uk. Head: David French
Public Gallery - 1962
Exhibitions of commonwealth countries, commonwealth artists, culture, literature, books, artefacts from commonwealth countries - library, educational programmes 33620

Courtauld Institute Gallery, Somerset House, Strand, London WC2R 0RN - T: (020) 78482526, Fax: 78482589, E-mail: galleryinfo@courtauld.ac.uk, Internet: http://www.courtauld.ac.uk. Head: John Murdoch
Fine Arts Museum - 1958
French Impressionists, Post-Impressionists and European Old Masters (14th-15th c) 33621

Crafts Council Collection, 44a Pentonville Rd, Islington, London N1 9BY - T: (020) 72787700, Fax: 78334479, E-mail: reference@craftscouncil.org.uk, Internet: http://www.craftscouncil.org.uk. Head: Janet Barnes
Decorative Arts Museum - 1971
Crafts - gallery, education workshop, picture and reference libraries 33622

Crossness Engines Display, Old Works, Belvedere Rd, Abbey Wood, London SE2 9AQ - T: (020) 83113711, Fax: 83036723, E-mail: xn.martin.wilson@care4free.net, Internet: http://www.interlink.co.uk/crossness. Head: Margaret Wilken
Science&Tech Museum
Four 1865 James Watt rotative beam engines 33623

Crystal Palace Museum, Anerley Hill, London SE19 2BA - T: (020) 86760700, Fax: 86760700. Head: K. Kiss
Historical Museum
Oil paintings, ceramics, medals, papers, 3-dimensional objects, history of the Crystal Palace 33624

Cuming Museum, 155-157 Walworth Rd, London SE17 1RS - T: (020) 77011342, E-mail: cumming@museum/freeserve.co.uk. Head: Sophie Perkins
Archaeological Museum / Decorative Arts Museum - 1902
Roman and medieval remains from archaeological excavations, coll of London superstitions, worldwide coll of the Cuming family 33625

De Morgan Centre, 38 West Hill, Wandsworth, London SW18 1RZ - T: (020) 88711144, E-mail: info@demorgancentre.org.uk, Internet: http://www.demorgan.org.uk. Head: Caroline Reed
Fine Arts Museum
Paintings and drawings by Evelyn De Morgan, ceramics by William De Morgan 33626

Delfina, 50 Bermondsey St, London SE1 3UD - T: (020) 73576600, Fax: 73570250
Public Gallery
Modern and contemporary art 33627

Department of Geological Sciences Collection, c/o University College London, Gower St, London WC1E 6BT - T: (020) 76797900, Fax: 73871612, E-mail: w.kirk@ucl.ac.uk. Head: Wendy Kirk
Natural History Museum
Geological specimens, rocks, minerals and fossils 33628

Design Museum, Butlers Wharf, 28 Shad Thames, London SE1 2YD - T: (020) 74036933, Fax: 73786540, Internet: http://www.designmuseum.org. Head: Alice Rawsthorn
Fine Arts Museum - 1989 33629

The Dickens House Museum, 48 Doughty St, London WC1N 2LX - T: (020) 74052127, Fax: 78315175, E-mail: dhmuseum@rmplc.co.uk, Internet: http://www.dickensmuseum.com. Head: Andrew Xavier
Special Museum / Library with Exhibitions / Historic Site - 1925
Former home of the writer Charles Dickens (1812-1870), memorabilia, manuscripts, letters, first editions, furniture - library 33630

Dr. Johnson's House, 17 Gough Sq, London EC4A 3DE - T: (020) 73533745, E-mail: curator@drjh.dircon.co.uk, Internet: http://www.drjh.dircon.uk
Special Museum - 1912
Memorabilia on Samuel Johnson (1709-1784) 33631

Drawings Collection, Royal Institute of British Architects, 21 Portman Sq, London W1H 6LP - T: (020) 73073698, Fax: 74863797, E-mail: drawings@inst.riba.org, Internet: http://www.architecture.com. Head: Charles Hind
Fine Arts Museum 33632

Dulwich Picture Gallery, Gallery Rd, Dulwich Village, London SE21 7AD - T: (020) 86935254, Fax: 82998700, E-mail: info@dulwichpicture-gallery.org.uk, Internet: http://www.dulwichpicture-gallery.org.uk. Head: Desmond Shawe-Taylor
Fine Arts Museum - 1811
Paintings by Poussin, Gainsborough, Canaletto Rembrandt, Rubens, building by Sir John Soane 33633

Ealing College Gallery, 83 The Avenue, London W3 8UX - T: (020) 82316303, Internet: http://www.etc.ac.uk
University Museum 33634

Eltham Palace, Court Yard, Eltham, London SE9 5QE - T: (020) 82482577, Fax: 82942621
Decorative Arts Museum / Historical Museum - 1999
Rare 1935 Art Deco style house 33635

Estorick Collection of Modern Italian Art, 39a Canonbury Sq, Islington, London N1 2AN - T: (020) 77049522, Fax: 77049531, E-mail: curator@estorickcollection.com, Internet: http://www.estorickcollection.com. Head: Alexandra Noble
Fine Arts Museum 33636

Fan Museum, 12 Crooms Hill, Greenwich, London SE10 8ER - T: (020) 88587879, 83051441, Fax: 82931889. Head: H.E. Alexander
Decorative Arts Museum - 1985
European 17th and 18th c fans, fan leaves, important oriental export fans 33637

Fenton House, Hampstead Grove, Hampstead, London NW3 6RT - T: (020) 74353471, Fax: 74353471, E-mail: fenton@smtp.ntrust.org.uk
Music Museum / Decorative Arts Museum - 1953
Benton-Fletcher coll of early musical instruments, Binning coll of porcelain, Georgian furniture, needlework 33638

Firepower - The Royal Artillery Museum, Royal Arsenal, Warren Ln, Woolwich, London SE18 6ST - T: (020) 88557755, Fax: 88557100, E-mail: info@firepower.gov.uk, Internet: http://www.firepower.gov.uk. Head: John Vimpary
Military Museum - 2001
Guns, scientific instruments, artefacts, uniforms and medals 33639

Florence Nightingale Museum, Saint Thomas's Hospital, 2 Lambeth Palace Rd, London SE1 7EW - T: (020) 76200374, Fax: 79281760, E-mail: juwa@florence-nightingale.co.uk, Internet: http://www.florence-nightingale.co.uk. Head: Alex Attewell
Historical Museum - 1989
Nightingale memorabilia 33640

Foundation for Women's Art, 11 Northburgh St, London EC1V 0AH - T: (020) 72514881, Fax: 72514882. Head: Belinda Harding
Fine Arts Museum
archives 33641

Foundling Museum, 40 Brunswick Sq, London WC1N 1AU - T: (020) 78413600, Fax: 78378084, E-mail: rhian@foundlingmuseum.org.uk. Head: Rhian Harris
Fine Arts Museum
London's first art gallery, works by Hogarth, Gainsborough and Reynolds, social history 33642

Freud Museum, 20 Maresfield Gardens, Hampstead, London NW3 5SX - T: (020) 74352002, Fax: 74311401, E-mail: freud@gn.apc.org, Internet: http://www.freud.org.uk. Head: Erica Davies
Special Museum - 1986
Sigmund Freud's complete working environment, including the famous couch, his library and coll of 2000 Greek, Roman and Egyptian antiquities 33643

Fusiliers London Volunteers' Museum, 213 Balham High Rd, London SW17 7BQ - T: (020) 86721168. Head: A.H. Mayle
Military Museum 33644

Geffrye Museum, Kingsland Rd, Shoreditch, London E2 8EA - T: (020) 77399893, Fax: 77295647, E-mail: info@geffrye-museum.org.uk, Internet: http://www.geffrye-museum.org.uk. Head: David Dewing
Decorative Arts Museum - 1914
English domestic interiors from 1600-2000, walled herb garden and period garden rooms fom 17th to 20th c - library 33645

Geological Museum, Exhibition Rd, South Kensington, London SW7 2DE - T: (020) 79388765
Natural History Museum - 1837
Fossils and rocks of Great Britain, minerals, gemstones in their parent rock associations, in their natural crystal form and in their final cut state, national coll of photographs of British scenery and geology - library 33646

Gilbert Collection, Somerset House, Strand, London WC2R 1LN - T: (020) 74209400, Fax: 72404060, E-mail: info@gilbert-collection.org.uk, Internet: http://www.gilbert-collection.org.uk. Head: Tom L. Freudenheim
Fine Arts Museum / Decorative Arts Museum - 2000
Decorative art, European silver, gold snuff boxes, Italian mosaics 33647

Goldsmiths' Hall, Foster Lane, London EC2V 6BN - T: (020) 76067010, Fax: 76061511, E-mail: the.clerk@thegoldsmiths.co.uk, Internet: http://www.thegoldsmiths.co.uk. Head: R. Buchanan-Dunlop
Decorative Arts Museum
English silver, modern jewelry since 1960 - library 33648

Gordon Museum, Saint Thomas St, London SE1 9RT - T: (020) 79554358, E-mail: william.edwards@kcl.ac.uk. Head: William Edwards
Special Museum
Specimens of human disease, wax models of anatomical dissection and skin diseases 33649

Government Art Collection, Queen's Yard, 179 Tottenham Court Rd, London W1T 7PA - T: (020) 72116041, Fax: 72116032, E-mail: enquiries@culture.gov.uk, Internet: http://www.culture.gov.uk/gac.htm. Head: Penny Johnson
Fine Arts Museum - 1898
British art since the 16th c from Hogarth to Hockney, Gainsborough to Hepworth and Edward Lear to Gillian Wearing 33650

Grange Museum of Community History, Neasden Ln, Neasden, London NW10 1QB - T: (020) 84528311, Fax: 82084233, E-mail: stephen@grangemus.freeserve.co.uk, Internet: http://www.brent.gov.uk. Head: Stephen Allen
Historical Museum - 1977
Archive of the British Empire exhibition held at Wembley 1924, historical displays relating to Brent people 33651

Grant Museum of Zoology and Comparative Anatomy, c/o Biology Department, University College London, Darwin Bldg, Gower St, London WC1E 6BT - T: (020) 76792647, Fax: 76767096, E-mail: zoology.museum@ucl.ac.uk, Internet: http://www.collections.ucl.ac.uk/zoology. Head: Dr. H.J. Chatterjee
Natural History Museum / University Museum - 1828
Robert Edmund Grant, T.H. Huxley, E. Ray Lankester, DMS Watson, J. Cloudsly Thompson colls, Quagga skeleton and many rare, endangered and extinct animals, extensive skeletal and fossil coll 33652

Greenwich Borough Museum, 232 Plumstead High St, London SE18 1JT - T: (020) 88553240, Fax: 83165754, E-mail: beverley.burford@greenwich.gov.uk
Local Museum - 1919
Local history, natural history 33653

Greenwich Local History Centre, 90 Mycenae Rd, Blackheath, London SE3 7SE - T: (020) 88584631, Fax: 82934721, E-mail: local.history@greenwich.gov.uk. Head: Julian Watson
Local Museum - 1972
A.R. Martin coll of documents relating to Greenwich, Blackheath and Charlton 33654

Greenwich Theatre Art Gallery, Crooms Hill, London SE10 8ES - T: (020) 88584447, Fax: 88588042
Performing Arts Museum 33655

The Guards Museum, Wellington Barracks, Birdcage Walk, London SW1E 6HQ - T: (020) 74143271, Fax: 74143429. Head: David Horn
Military Museum
Uniforms, weapons, memorabilia illustratings 33656

Guide Heritage Centre, 17-19 Buckingham Palace Rd, London SW1W 0PT - T: (020) 75921818, Fax: 78288317, E-mail: heritage@guides.org.uk
Historical Museum
archive 33657

Guildhall Art Gallery, 2 Guildhall Yard, London EC2P 2EJ - T: (020) 73323700, Fax: 73323342, E-mail: - guildhall.artgallery@corpoflondon.gov.uk, Internet: http://www.guildhall-art-gallery.org.uk. Head: Melvyn Barnes
Fine Arts Museum - 1886
London paintings, 19th c works of art, portraits, sculpture, Sir Matthew Smith Studio coll 33658

Guinness Archives, c/o Guinness, Park Royal Brewery, London NW10 7RR - T: (020) 89635278, Fax: 89635173, E-mail: sue.garland@guinness.com
Special Museum
Advertising, packaging and business records relating to Guinness in Britain and abroad 33659

Gunnersbury Park Museum, Gunnersbury Park, Popes Ln, London W3 8LQ - T: (020) 89921612, Fax: 87520686, E-mail: gp-museum@cip.org.uk
Local Museum / Archaeological Museum / Historic Site - 1929
Local archaeology, Sadler coll of flints, Middlesex maps and topography, costumes, toys and dolls, transportation, local crafts and industries - library 33660

Hackney Museum, Parkside Library, Victoria Park Rd, London E9 7JL - T: (020) 89866914, Fax: 89857600, E-mail: hmuseum@hackney.gov.uk, Internet: http://www.hackney.gov.uk/hackneymuseum. Head: Alex Sydney
Local Museum
History of Hackney, Chalmers Bequest coll of artworks 33661

Hamilton's Gallery, 13 Carlos Pl, London W1Y 5AG - T: (020) 74999493/94, Fax: 76299919, Internet: http://www.art-on-line.com/hamiltons
Fine Arts Museum 33662

Hampstead Museum, Burgh House, New End Sq, London NW3 1LT - T: (020) 74310144, Fax: 74358817, E-mail: hamsteadmuseum@talk21.com
Local Museum - 1979
Local history, Helen Allingham coll, Isokon furniture 33663

Haringey Museum, Bruce Castle, Lordship Ln, Tottenham, London N17 8NU - T: (020) 88088772, Fax: 88084118, E-mail: museum.services@haringey.gov.uk, Internet: http://www.haringey.gov.uk. Head: Sian Harrington
Local Museum 33664

Hayward Gallery, Belvedere Rd, London SE1 8XZ - T: (020) 79604242, E-mail: visual_arts@hayward.org.uk, Internet: http://www.haywardgallery.org.uk. Head: Susan Ferleger Brades
Fine Arts Museum - 1968
Arts council coll, national touring exhibitions 33665

Her Majesty Tower of London, Tower Hill, London EC3N 4AB - T: (020) 77090765, Internet: http://www.hrp.org.uk. Head: Dr. Edward Impey
Historical Museum / Decorative Arts Museum
Royal palace and fortress, White Tower, towers and remparts, royal lodgings, Chapel Royal of Saint Peter at Vincula, crown jewels 33666

Heritage Services Consignia, Freeling House, Phoenix Pl, London WC1X 0DL - T: (020) 72392570, Fax: 72392576, E-mail: heritage@consignia.com, Internet: http://www.consignia.com/heritage. Head: Martin Rush
Special Museum - 1965
Philatelics, British stamps since 1840, world coll since 1878, special display on the creation of the One Penny Black 1840, Postal services and artefacts 33667

HMS Belfast, Morgans Ln, off Tooley St, London SE1 2JH - T: (020) 79406300, Fax: 74030719, E-mail: hmsbelfast@iwm.org.uk, Internet: http://www.iwm.org.uk. Head: J. Wenzel
Military Museum - 1971
Armoured warship of WWII, Royal Navy 33668

Hogarth's House, Hogarth Ln, Great West Rd, Chiswick, London W4 2QN - T: (020) 89946757, Fax: 85834595
Fine Arts Museum - 1904
Prints, engravings 33669

Honeywood Heritage Centre, Honeywood Walk, Carshalton, London SM5 3NX - T: (020) 87704297, Fax: 87704777, Internet: http://www.sutton.gov.uk
Local Museum
Hist of London borough Sutton 33670

Horniman Museum, 100 London Rd, Forest Hill, London SE23 3PQ - T: (020) 86991872, Fax: 82915506, E-mail: enquiry@horniman.ac.uk, Internet: http://www.horniman.ac.uk. Head: Janet Vitmayer
Local Museum / Ethnology Museum / Music Museum - 1890
Ethnography, natural history, musical instruments - library, gardens, Living Waters aquarium, conservation 33671

Hunterian Museum, 35-43 Lincoln's Inn Fields, London WC2A 3PN - T: (020) 78696560, E-mail: museum@rcseng.ac.uk, Internet: http://www.rcseng.ac.uk/museums
Special Museum - 1813
Anatomy, physiology and pathology from the coll of John Hunter (1728-1793) historical surgical instruments 33672

Imperial War Museum, Lambeth Rd, London SE1 6HZ - T: (020) 74165000, Fax: 74165374, E-mail: mail@iwm.org.uk, Internet: http://www.iwm.org.uk. Head: R.W.K. Crawford
Historical Museum - 1917
Wars since 1914, armaments, documents, books involving Britain and the Commonwealth, films, records, photographs, drawings, paintings, sculpture - library, reference dept, archives 33673

Inns of Court and City Yeomanry Museum, 10 Stone Bldgs, Lincoln's Inn, London WC2A 3TG - T: (020) 74058112, Fax: 74143496. Head: M.J. O'Beirne
Military Museum
Hist of 2 regiments, the Inns of Court Regiment and City of London Yeomanry from 1780 to date 33674

Institute of Contemporary Arts, The Mall, London SW1Y 5AH - T: (020) 79303647, Fax: 78730051, E-mail: info@ica.org.uk, Internet: http://www.ica.org.uk. Head: Philip Dodd
Public Gallery 33675

Islington Education Artefact Library, Barnsbury Complex, Barnsbury Park, London N1 1QG - T: (020) 75275524, Fax: 75275564, E-mail: library@iels.demon.co.uk
Historical Museum
History, science, natural history, religion and multiculture 33676

Islington Museum, Foyer Gallery, Islington Town Hall, Upper St, London N1 2UD - T: (020) 73549442, Fax: 75273049, Internet: http://www.islington.gov.uk/localinfo/leisure/museum. Head: Alison Lister
Local Museum
Local and social history of Islington borough, popular culture 33677

Jewel Tower, Abingdon Rd, Westminster, London SW1P 3JY - T: (020) 72222219, Fax: 72222219, Internet: http://www.english-heritage.org.uk
Local Museum 33678

Jewish Museum, Raymond Burton House, 129-131 Albert St, London NW1 7NB - T: (020) 72841997, Fax: 72679008, E-mail: admin@jmus.org.uk, Internet: http://www.jewmusm.ort.org. Head: Rickie Burman
Religious Arts Museum / Historical Museum - 1932
Jewish ceremonial art and hist 33679

Jewish Museum Finchley, 80 East End Rd, London N3 2SY - T: (020) 83491143, Fax: 83432162, E-mail: jml.finchley@lineone.net, Internet: http://www.jewmusm.ort.net. Head: Rickie Burman
Religious Arts Museum / Historical Museum
History of Jewish immigration and settlement in London 33680

Keats House, Keats Grove, Wentworth Pl, London NW3 2RR - T: (020) 74352062, Fax: 74319293, E-mail: keatshouse@corpoflondon.org.uk, Internet: http://www.keatshouse.org.uk. Head: Christina M. Gee
Special Museum - 1925
Life and work of the poet John Keats (1795-1821), manuscripts, relics, furniture - library 33681

Kenwood House, The Iveagh Bequest, Hampstead Ln, London NW3 7JR - T: (020) 83481286, Fax: 79733891, Internet: http://www.english-heritage.org.uk. Head: Julie Ehlen, Susan Coventry
Local Museum - 1927
Paintings by Rembrandt, Vermeer, Gainsborough, Reynolds and others, 18th c furniture and sculpture 33682

Kingsgate Gallery, 114 Kingsgate Rd, London NW6 2JG - T: (020) 73287878, Fax: 73287878. Head: Stephen Williams
Public Gallery
Contemporary art 33683

Kirkaldy Testing Museum, 99 Southwark St, Southwark, London SE1 0JF - T: (020) 76201580
Science&Tech Museum
David Kirkaldy's original all-purpose testing machine 33684

Kodak Museum, Headstone Rd, Harrow, London HA1 1PD
Science&Tech Museum - 1927
History of photography, camera design, cinematography, magic lanterns, stereoscopy, radiography 33685

Kufa Gallery, 26 Westbourne Grove, London W2 5RH - T: (020) 72291928, Fax: 72438513, E-mail: kufa@dircon.co.uk, Internet: http://www.kufa.dircon.co.uk
Public Gallery
Islamic and Middle Eastern Art and architecture 33686

Lauderdale House, Waterlow Park, Highgate Hill, London N6 5HG - T: (020) 83488716, Fax: 84429099, Internet: http://www.lauderdale.org.uk. Head: Carolyn Naish
Local Museum
Fine art, photography, local hist 33687

Leighton House Art Gallery and Museum, 12 Holland Park Rd, Kensington, London W14 8LZ - T: (020) 76023316, Fax: 73712467, Internet: http://www.rbkc.gov.uk/LeightonHouseMuseum. Head: Daniel Robbins
Special Museum - 1896
Leighton drawings coll, Leighton letters and archive 33688

Library and Collection of the Worshipful Company of Clockmakers, Clock Room, Guildhall Library, Aldermanbury, London EC2P 2EJ - T: (020) 73321865, E-mail: keeper@clockmakers.org, Internet: http://www.clockmakers.org. Head: Sir George White
Special Museum - 1813
Old clocks, marine chronometers, watch keys 33689

Linley Sambourne House, 18 Stafford Terrace, Kensington, London W8 7BH - T: (020) 79370663, 76023316, Fax: 73712467. Head: Sheila Ayres
Decorative Arts Museum
Edward Linley Sambourne, political cartoonist at punch magazine, funishings 33690

Little Holland House, 40 Beeches Av, Carshalton, London SM5 3LW - T: (020) 87704781, Fax: 87704777, E-mail: valary.murphy@sutten.gov.uk, Internet: http://www.sutton.gov.uk/lfl/heritage/lhh. Head: Valary Murphy
Decorative Arts Museum - 1974
Furniture, paintings and craft by Frank R. Dickinson 33691

Livesey Museum for Children, 682 Old Kent Rd, London SE15 1JF - T: (020) 76395604, Fax: 72775384, E-mail: livesey.museum@southwark.gov.uk, Internet: http://www.livesey-museum.org.uk. Head: Theresa Dhaliwal
Special Museum - 1974
Interactive childrens museum 33692

Lloyd's Nelson Collection, c/o Lloyd's, Lime St, London EC3M 7HA - T: (020) 76237100, Fax: 73276400
Special Museum
Silver, documents, letters, objects of art associated with Admiral Lord Nelson and his contemporaries 33693

London Brass Rubbing Centre, The Crypt, Saint Martin-in-the-Fields Church, Trafalgar Sq, London WC2N 4JJ - T: (020) 79309306, Fax: 79309306. Head: A. Dodwell, P. Dodwell
Decorative Arts Museum
Coll of facsimile monumental church brasses from the medieval and Tudor periods portraying kings, knights, merchants and families, designs from Celtic sources 33694

London Canal Museum, 12-13 New Wharf Rd, King's Cross, London N1 9RT - T: (020) 77130836, Fax: 77130836, E-mail: enq@canalmuseum.org.uk, Internet: http://www.canalmuseum.org.uk. Head: Alex Nunes
Historical Museum
Inland waterways of the London region 33695

London Fire Brigade Museum, 94a Southwark Bridge Rd, Southwark, London SE1 0EG - T: (020) 75872894, Fax: 75872878, E-mail: museum@lfcda.org.uk. Head: Esther Mann
Historical Museum
Fire appliances, equipment, clothing, medals and miscellanea (17th-20th c), fire-related art 33696

London Institute Gallery, 65 Davies St, London W1K 5DA - T: (020) 75148083, Fax: 75146131, E-mail: gallery@linst.ac.uk
Public Gallery
Art and design 33697

London Irish Rifles Regimental Museum, Duke of York Headquarters, Kings Rd, Chelsea, London SW3 4RX
Military Museum 33698

London Scottish Regimental Museum, 95 Horseferry Rd, London SW1P 2DX - T: (020) 76301639, Fax: 72337909
Military Museum
History of the regiment 33699

London Sewing Machine Museum, 292-312 Balham High Rd, Tooting Bec, London SW17 7AA - T: (020) 86827916, Fax: 87674726, E-mail: wimbledonsewingmachinecoltd@btinternet.com, Internet: http://www.sewantique.com. Head: Ray Rushton
Science&Tech Museum
Industrial and domestic sewing machines from 1850-1950 33700

London Toy and Model Museum, 21-23 Craven Hill, London W2 3EN - T: (020) 77068000, Fax: 77068823, E-mail: gba67@dial.pipex.com, Internet: http://www.londontoy.com. Head: Glen Sharman
Special Museum - 1982
Including dolls, bears, tinplate toys, model, tains, antique coalmine model, garden railway 33701

London's Transport Museum, Covent Garden Piazza, London WC2E 7BB - T: (020) 73796344, Fax: 75657254, E-mail: contact@ltmuseum.co.uk, Internet: http://www.ltmuseum.co.uk. Head: Sam Mullins
Science&Tech Museum - 1980
London transport history, coll of historic vehicles and artefacts - photographic library, reference library 33702

Madame Tussaud's, Marylebone Rd, London NW1 5LR - T: (020) 79356861, Fax: 74650862. Head: M. Jolly, D. Robertson
Special Museum - 1770
Wax figures, planetarium 33703

Mall Galleries, The Mall, London SW1Y 5BD - T: (020) 79306844, Fax: 78397830, E-mail: - kmartinmallgalleries@dial.pipex.com, Internet: http://www.mallgalleries.org.uk
Public Gallery 33704

Mander and Mitchenson Theatre Collection, c/o Salvation Army Headquarters, 101 Queen Victoria St, London EC4P 4EP - T: (020) 72360182, Fax: 72360184, E-mail: richard@mander-and-mitchenson.co.uk, Internet: http://www.mander-and-mitchenson.co.uk
Performing Arts Museum
Theatre, music hall, pantomime, circus, opera, ballet, incl. posters, playbills, programmes, engravings, photo- graphs, paintings, manuscripts, china and unique ephemera 33705

Markfield Beam Engine and Museum, Markfield Rd, South Tottenham, London N15 4RB - T: (020) 88007061, Fax: 88020680. Head: A.J. Spackman
Science&Tech Museum
Beam pumping engine, public health engineering 33706

Martinware Pottery Collection, Library, Osterley Park Rd, London UB2 4BL - T: (020) 85743412
Decorative Arts Museum 33707

MCC Museum, Lord's Cricket Ground, Saint John's Wood, London NW8 8QN - T: (020) 72891611, Fax: 74321062, E-mail: glenys.williams@mcc.org.uk, Internet: http://www-uk.cricket.org.uk/link_to_database/national/eng/clubs/mcc/mccmuseum.html. Head: Stephen Green
Historical Museum - 1953
History of cricket, pictures, relics, trophies, art objects - library 33708

Metropolitan Police Hospital Museum, New Scotland Yard Broadway, London SW1H 0BG - T: (020) 83052824, Fax: 82936692. Head: Paul Dew
Historical Museum
Beat duty equipment, uniforms, books, documents, photos, medals, paintings, police station furnishings 33709

Michael Faraday's Laboratory and Museum, The Royal Institution of Great Britain, 21 Albemarle St, London W1S 4BS - T: (020) 74092992, Fax: 76293569, E-mail: ri@ri.ac.uk, Internet: http://www.ri.ac.uk. Head: Prof. Susan Greenfield
Science&Tech Museum - 1972
Unique coll of Faraday's original apparatus, diaries 33710

Millwall FC Museum, Millwall Football Club, Zampa Rd, London SE16 3LN - T: (020) 86980793, Fax: 86980793. Head: Chris Bethell
Special Museum
Football and social history from 1885 to date 33711

MoCHA, 61 Malmesbury Terrace, London E3 2EB - T: (020) 89830820, Fax: 89830820, E-mail: develoopment@mocha.co.uk, Internet: http://www.mocha.co.uk
Special Museum
Embryonic coll of culinary history and recipe books, ephemera and journals, Susan Campbell coll 33712

Morley Gallery, Art Centre, Morley College, 61 Westminster Bridge Rd, London SE1 7HT - T: (020) 74509226, Fax: 79284074, E-mail: janet.browne@morleycollege.ac.uk
Public Gallery / University Museum 33713

Museum of Artillery in the Rotunda, Repository Rd, Woolwich, London SE18 4DN - T: (020) 87813127, Fax: 83165402, Internet: http://www.firepower.org.uk
Military Museum
Fuses, ammunition, artillery instruments, rockets, edge weapons, display of artillery from the 14th c to present day 33714

Museum of Childhood at Bethnal Green, Cambridge Heath Rd, London E2 9PA - T: (020) 89802415, Fax: 89835225, E-mail: k.bines@vam.ac.uk, Internet: http://www.museumofchildhood.org.uk. Head: Diane Lees
Special Museum - 1872
Toys, dolls, games, puppets, children's books, doll's houses, teddy bears, toy soldiers, trains, nursery coll incl children's costume and furniture, baby equipment 33715

Museum of Freemasonery, Freemasons Hall, Great Queen St, London WC2B 5AZ - T: (020) 73959251, Fax: 74047418. Head: D.E. Clements
Special Museum - 1837
Coll of class, porcelain, silver, furniture, paintings - Library 33716

Museum of Fulham Palace, Bishop's Av, London SW6 6EA - T: (020) 77363233, Fax: 77363233
Historical Museum
Archaeology, paintings, stained glass, history of the Palace 33717

Museum of Garden History, Saint Mary at Lambeth, Lambeth Palace Rd, London SE1 7LB - T: (020) 74018865, Fax: 74018869, E-mail: info@museumgardenhistory.org, Internet: http://www.museumgardenhistory.org. Head: Rosemary Nicholson
Historical Museum - 1977
Historic garden tools 33718

Museum of Installation, 175 Deptford High St, London SE8 3NU - T: (020) 86928778, Fax: 86928122, E-mail: moi@dircon.co.uk, Internet: http://www.moi.org.uk. Head: Nicolas de Oliveira, Nicola Oxley, Michael Petry, Jeremy Wood
Fine Arts Museum
Installations - archive 33719

Museum of Instruments, Royal College of Music, Prince Consort Rd, South Kensington, London SW7 2BS - T: (020) 75914346, Fax: 75897740, E-mail: museum@rcm.ac.uk, Internet: http://www.rcm.ac.uk
Music Museum - 1883
Old stringed, wind and keyboard instruments 33720

Museum of London, London Wall, London EC2Y 5HN - T: (020) 76003699, Fax: 76001058, E-mail: info@museumoflondon.org.uk, Internet: http://www.museumoflondon.org.uk. Head: Dr. Simon Thurley
Historical Museum - 1912
Prehistoric, Roman and medieval antiquities, costumes, decorative art objects, topography, history and social life of London, royal relics, Parliament and legal history, Cromwellian period relics, objects relating to the Great Fire of London, toys, fire engines, glass, suffragettes 33721

Museum of Mankind, British Museum, Burlington Gardens, London W1 - T: (020) 74372224
Historical Museum / Archaeological Museum 33722

Museum of Methodism, 49 City Rd, London EC1Y 1AU - T: (0207) 2532262, Fax: 6083825. Head: Noorah Al-Gailani
Religious Arts Museum - 1984
Wesleyana, paintings, manuscript letters, social history 33723

Museum of the Moving Images, South Bank, Waterloo, London SE1 8XT - T: (020) 74012636, 79283535, Fax: 79287938, E-mail: oliver.eynon@bfi.org.uk, Internet: http://www.bfi.org.uk. Head: Caroline Ellis
Historical Museum - 1988
Early optical toys, costumes from modern science fiction films, Charlie Chaplin's hat and cane, Fred Astaire's tail coat, the IBA coll of period television sets, the world's first fourscreen unit 33724

Museum of the Order of Saint John, Saint John's Gate, Saint John's Ln, Clerkenwell, London EC1M 4DA - T: (020) 72536644, Fax: 73360587, E-mail: museum@nhq.sja.org.uk, Internet: http://www.sja.org.uk/history. Head: Pamela Willis
Religious Arts Museum / Historical Museum - 1915
Silver, coins, armaments, medals, furniture, documents on the order of Saint John, manuscripts, uniforms, glass, ceramics, paintings, prints, cartography, textiles, Saint John Ambulance, hist of religious military order - library 33725

Museum of the Royal College of Surgeons → Hunterian Museum

Museum of the Royal Pharmaceutical Society of Great Britain, 1 Lambeth High St, London SE1 7JN - T: (0207) 7359141 ext 354, Fax: 7930232, E-mail: museum@rpsgb.org.uk, Internet: http://www.rpsgb.org.uk. Head: Caroline M. Reed
Special Museum - 1841
History of pharmacy, 17th-18th c drugs, English Delft drug jars, mortars, retail and dispensing equipment 33726

Museum of Women's Art, 55-63 Goswell Rd, London EC1V 7EN - T: (020) 77300717, Fax: 78236573
Fine Arts Museum 33727

Musical Museum, 368 High St, Brentford, London TW8 0BD - T: (020) 85608108, Internet: http://www.musicalmuseum.co.uk. Head: Michael J. Ryder
Music Museum - 1963
Automatic musical instruments in working order, pianos, music rolls, Welte Philharmonic Reprocuding Pipe Organ Model, Wurlitzer Theater Organ, Double Mills Violano Virtuoso, Hupfeld Phonoliszt Violina, Hupfeld Animatic Clavitist Sinfonie-Jazz and orchestra, Edison Phonograph, Hupfeld Piano, Street Barrel Pianos and Organs, Broadwood Grand Piano 33728

Narwhal Inuit Art Gallery, 55 Linden Gardens, Chiswick, London W4 2EH - T: (020) 87471575, Fax: 87421268, E-mail: narwhalman@aol.com
Ethnology Museum
Canadian, Russian and Greenlandic Inuit art 33729

National Army Museum, Royal Hospital Rd, London SW3 4HT - T: (020) 77300717, Fax: 78236573, E-mail: info@national-army-museum.ac.uk, Internet: http://www.national-army-museum.ac.uk. Head: I. Robertson
Military Museum - 1960

Hist of the British Army 1415-2000, Indian Army until 1947, colonial forces, uniforms, weapons, medals, British military painting, early photographs - library 33730

National Gallery, Trafalgar Sq, London WC2N 5DN - T: (020) 77472885, Fax: 77472423, E-mail: information@ng-london.org.uk, Internet: http://www.nationalgallery.org.uk. Head: Neil MacGregor
Fine Arts Museum - 1824
Western European paintings from 1250-1900 incl works by Leonardo, Rembrandt, and others, British painters from Hogarth to Turner, 19th c French painting such as Cézanne, Van Gogh 33731

National Hearing Aid Museum, Royal Throat, Nose and Ear Hospital, Grays Inn Rd, London WC1X 1DA - T: (020) 79151390, Fax: 79151646, E-mail: p.turner@ucl.ac.uk
Science&Tech Museum
Hearing aids and test equipment, the first cochlea implant device to be fitted in the United Kingdom 33732

National Maritime Museum, Romney Rd, London SE10 9NF - T: (020) 78584422, Fax: 73126632, Internet: http://www.nmm.ac.uk. Head: Richard Ormond
Science&Tech Museum - 1934
Maritime hist of Britain, Navy, Merchant Service, yachting, ship models and plans 1700-1990, oil paintings, Nelson memorabilia, astronomical instruments (17th-20th c), globes since 1530, rare books from 1474, manuscripts - library 33733

National Portrait Gallery, 2 Saint Martin's Pl, London WC2H 0HE - T: (020) 73060055, Fax: 73060056, Internet: http://www.npg.org.uk. Head: Dr. Charles Saumarez Smith
Fine Arts Museum - 1856
National coll of portraits (15th-21st c), incl paintings, sculptures, miniatures, engravings and photographs - archive, library; Montacute House, Beningbrough Hall, Bodelwyddan Castle 33734

Natural History Museum, Cromwell Rd, London SW7 5BD - T: (020) 79425000, Fax: 79389290, E-mail: information@nhm.ac.uk, Internet: http://www.nhm.ac.uk. Head: Sir Neil Chalmers
Natural History Museum - 1881
Botany, entomology, mineralogy, palaeontology, zoology, ornithology 33735

Newham Museum, Cnr Romford and Rabbits Rd, London E12 5JY - T: (020) 85140274, Fax: 85148221, E-mail: tom.mcallister@newham.gov.uk, Internet: http://www.newham.gov.uk/leisure/museums/mmp.htm. Head: Sean Sherman
Local Museum - 1900
Archaeology, local history, Bow porcelain, work of Madge Gill (local outsider artist) - museum education 33736

North Woolwich Old Station Museum, Pier Rd, North Woolwich, London E16 2JJ - T: (020) 74747244, Internet: http://www.newham.gov.uk/leisure/museums/
Local Museum 33737

Old Operating Theatre, Museum and Herb Garret, Londons Museums of Health and Medicine, 9a Saint Thomas St, London SE1 9RY - T: (020) 79554791, Fax: 73788383, E-mail: curator@thegarret.org.uk, Internet: http://www.thegarret.org.uk. Head: Kevin Flude
Special Museum - 1957
Medicine, surgery, hospitals, Florence Nightingale, herbal medicine 33738

Old Speech Room Gallery, Harrow School, High St, Harrow, London - T: (020) 88128205, 88728000, Fax: 84233112, E-mail: crl@harrowschool.org.uk. Head: Carolyn R. Leder
Historical Museum
School's coll (Egyptian and Greek antiquities, watercolours, printed books) 33739

Painters's Hall, Little Trinity Ln, London EC4V 2AD - T: (020) 72367070, Fax: 72367074. Head: R.E.J. Clarke
Decorative Arts Museum / Fine Arts Museum
Miscellaneous portraits, coll of silver 33740

Palace of Westminster, Houses of Parliament, London SW1A 0AA - T: (020) 72196218, 72195503, Fax: 72194250. Head: Malcolm Hay
Decorative Arts Museum
Coll of Victorian wall paintings depicting scenes from British history, coll of political portraits, and works of art, coll of Gothic Revival furniture 33741

Pathological Museum, Saint Bartholomew's, Royal London School of medicine Smithfield, London EC1A 7BE - T: (020) 76018537, Fax: 76018530, E-mail: d.g.lowe@mds.qmw.ac.uk, Internet: http://www.mds.qmw.ac.uk/
Special Museum 33742

The Paul Mellon Centre for Studies in British Art, 16 Bedford Sq, London WC1B 3JA - T: (020) 75800311, Fax: 76366730, E-mail: info@paul-mellon-centre.ac.uk, Internet: http://www.paul-mellon-centre.ac.uk. Head: Brian Allen
Fine Arts Museum - 1970
British painting, sculpture and architecture - library,, archive 33743

Percival David Foundation of Chinese Art, School of Oriental and African Studies, University of London, 53 Gordon Sq, London WC1H 0PD - T: (020) 73873909, Fax: 73835163, E-mail: sp17@soas.ac.uk, Internet: http://www.pdfmuseum.org.uk. Head: Stacey Pierson
Decorative Arts Museum - 1950
Finest coll of Chinese ceramics outside China, dating mainly to the period 10th-18th c - subscription reference library 33744

Petrie Museum of Egyptian Archaeology, University College London, Malet Pl, London WC1E 6BT - T: (020) 76792884, Fax: 76792886, E-mail: petrie.museum@ucl.ac.uk, Internet: http://petrie.ucl.ac.uk. Head: S. MacDonald
Archaeological Museum / University Museum - 1913
Archaeology, hieroglyphic texts, Sir William M. Flinders Petrie (1853-1942) 33745

Photographers Gallery, 5 Great Newport St, London WC2H 7HY - T: (020) 78311772, Fax: 78369704. Head: Pam Wompjell
Public Gallery 33746

Pitshanger Manor and Gallery, Walpole Park, Matlock Ln, Ealing, London W5 5EQ - T: (020) 85671227, Fax: 85670595, E-mail: pitshanger@ealing.gov.uk, Internet: http://www.ealing.gov.uk/pitshanger. Head: Neena Sohal
Decorative Arts Museum / Local Museum
Martinware pottery, contemporary art exhibitions 33747

Polish Cultural Institution Gallery, 34 Portland Pl, London W1N 4HQ - T: (020) 76366032, Fax: 76372190. Head: Aleksandra Czapiewska
Public Gallery
Polish paintings, graphics, photography, posters, tapestry, folk art 33748

Pollock's Toy Museum, 1 Scala St, London W1T HTL - T: (020) 76363452, E-mail: toymuseum@hotmail.com. Head: Veronica Sheppard
Special Museum / Historical Museum - 1956
Old toys and games, toytheatres 33749

POSK Gallery, 238-246 King St, London W6 0RF - T: (020) 87411940, Fax: 87463798. Head: Janina Baranowska
Public Gallery - 1980
Posk coll of 80 paintings by Polish Artists working in Great Britain, Motz coll: engravings, maps, tin plate, armour, Polish paintings (19th-20th c) 33750

Pump House Gallery, Battersea Park, London SW11 4NJ - T: (020) 88717572, Fax: 82289062
Public Gallery
Contemporary art 33751

Pumphouse Educational Museum, Lavender Pond and Nature Park, Lavender Rd, Rotherhithe, London SE16 5DZ - T: (020) 72312976, Fax: 72312976, E-mail: cmarais@ukonline.co.uk. Head: Caroline Marais
Local Museum
Dockers tools, life in Rotherhithe, replica 6ft Queen Elizabeth II wedding cake 33752

Queen Elizabeth's Hunting Lodge, Rangers Rd, Chingford, London E4 7QH - T: (020) 85296681, Fax: 85298209. Head: J.L. Wisenfeld
Historical Museum - 1895
Local history, archaeology, forestry, zoology, botany 33753

The Queen's Gallery, Buckingham Palace, London SW1A 1AA - T: (020) 73212233, Fax: 79309625, E-mail: information@royalcollection.org.uk, Internet: http://www.royal.gov.uk. Head: Sir Hugh Roberts
Fine Arts Museum - 1962
Paintings, drawings, artworks from Royal coll, furniture, clocks, porcelain, silver, scientific instruments, books, miniatures, gems 33754

Ragged School Museum, 46-50 Copperfield Rd, London E3 4RR - T: (020) 89806405, Fax: 89833481, E-mail: enquiries@raggedschool-museum.org.uk, Internet: http://www.raggedschool-museum.org.uk. Head: Dr. Claire Seymour
Special Museum - 1990
Tools from local trades 33755

Ranger's House, Chesterfield Walk, Blackheath, London SE10 8QX - T: (020) 88530035, Fax: 88530090, Internet: http://www.english-heritage.org.uk. Head: John Jacob
Historical Museum - 1688
The Suffolk Coll 33756

Royal Academy of Arts Gallery, Burlington House, Piccadilly, London W1V 0DS - T: (020) 73008000, Fax: 73008001, Internet: http://www.RoyalAcademy.org.uk. Head: Philip Dowson
Public Gallery - 1768
Temporary exhibitions of painting, sculpture, architecture and engraving 33757

Royal Air Force Museum, Grahame Park Way, London NW9 5LL - T: (020) 82052266, Fax: 82001751, E-mail: info@rafmuseum.com, Internet: http://www.rafmuseum.com. Head: Dr. Michael A. Fopp
Military Museum - 1972
Sister Museum at Cosford, reserve coll at Stafford, one of the best WWII fighter coll in the world, 70 aircraft on permanent display 33758

Royal Armouries, Tower of London, London EC3N 4AB - T: (020) 74806358, Fax: 74812922, E-mail: enquiries@armouries.org.uk, Internet: http://www.armouries.org.uk. Head: G.M. Wilson
Historical Museum / Military Museum / Decorative Arts Museum
Eight galleries tell the story of the evolution of the Tower and the Armouries itself over the centuries, incl weapons of the historic Tower arsenal, Royal Tudor and Stuart armours, coll 16th-19th c - Education centre, archives 33759

Royal Bank of Scotland Art Collection, Drapers Garden, 12 Throgmorton St, London EC2N 2DL - T: (020) 79205493, Fax: 74546613. Head: Rosemary Harris
Fine Arts Museum / Public Gallery
Works from the 17th c to the present day with focus on the 20th c post-war British art 33760

Royal Ceremonial Dress Collection, Kensington Palace, London W8 4PX - T: (020) 79379561, Fax: 73760198, Internet: http://www.hrp.org.uk. Head: Nigel Arch
Special Museum
Royal and ceremonial dress 33761

Royal College of Art, Kensington Gore, London SW7 2EU - T: (020) 75904444, Fax: 75904124, E-mail: info@rca.ac.uk, Internet: http://www.rca.ac.uk. Head: Prof. Christopher Frayling
Public Gallery 33762

Royal College of Obstetricians and Gynaecologists Collection, 27 Sussex Pl, Regent's Park, London NW1 4RG - T: (020) 77726309, Fax: 72628331, E-mail: library@rcog.org.uk. Head: Ian L.C. Fergusson
Historical Museum
Obstetrical and gynaecological instruments, incl. original Chamberlen instruments 33763

Royal College of Physicians Museums, 11 Saint Andrews Pl, Regent's Park, London NW1 4LE - T: (020) 79351174 ext 312, Fax: 74863729, E-mail: info@rcplondon.ac.uk, Internet: http://www.rcplondon.ac.uk
Fine Arts Museum
Portraits, sculptures and miniatures, mainly of past presidents of the college 33764

Royal Fusiliers Regimental Museum, Tower of London, London EC3 4AB - T: (020) 74885612, Fax: 74811093. Head: C.P. Bowes-Crick
Military Museum - 1949
History of regiment 1685-1968, silver, documents, armaments, uniforms 33765

Royal Hospital Chelsea Museum, Royal Hospital Rd, Chelsea, London SW3 4SR - T: (020) 78815203, Fax: 78815463, E-mail: roylhospch@aol.com
Military Museum / Historical Museum
Royal hospital artefacts, medals and uniforms, veteran soldiers 33766

Royal London Hospital Archives and Museum, Turner St, Whitechapel, London E1 1BB - T: (020) 73777608, Fax: 73777413, E-mail: r.j.evans@mds.qmw.ac.uk
Historical Museum - 1897
Medical science history 33767

Royal Mews, Buckingham Palace, London SW1A 1AA - T: (020) 78391377, Fax: 79309625, E-mail: information@royalcollection.org.uk, Internet: http://www.the-royal-collection.org.uk. Head: Hugh Roberts
Historical Museum - 1825
The Monarch's magnificent gilded State carriages and coaches, incl the unique Gold State Coach are housed here together with their horses and State liveries 33768

Royal Mint Sovereign Gallery, 7 Grosvenor Gardens, London SW1W 0BH - T: (020) 75928601, E-mail: charmaine.boga@salves.royalmint.gov.uk, Internet: http://www.royalmint.com
Special Museum 33769

Royal Observatory Greenwich, Romney Rd, Greenwich, London SE10 9NF - T: (020) 88584422, Fax: 83126771, E-mail: enquiries@nmm.ac.uk, Internet: http://www.rog.nmm.ac.uk. Head: Roy Clare
Science&Tech Museum 33770

Royal Society of British Sculptors, 108 Old Brompton Rd, London SW7 3RA - T: (020) 73738615, Fax: 73703721, E-mail: info@rbs.org.uk, Internet: http://www.rbs.org.uk
Public Gallery 33771

RSA Library, c/o Royal Society for the Encouragement of Arts, Manufactures and Commerce, 8 John Adam St, London WC2N 6EZ - T: (020) 74516874, Fax: 78395805, E-mail: library@rsa.org.uk, Internet: http://www.rsa.org.uk. Head: Paul Crake
Library with Exhibitions 33772

Saatchi Gallery, 98a Boundary Rd, London NW8 0RH - T: (020) 76248299, Fax: 76243798. Head:
Public Gallery 33773

Saint Bartholomew's Hospital Museum, West Smithfield, London EC1A 7BE - T: (020) 76018152, E-mail: marion.rea@bartsandthelondon.nhs.uk, Internet: http://www.bartsandthelondon.org.uk
Historical Museum
Archives 33774

Saint Bride's Crypt Museum, Saint Bride's Church, Fleet St, London EC4Y 8AU - T: (020) 74270133, Fax: 75834867, E-mail: info@stbrides.com. Head: James Irving
Religious Arts Museum - 1957
History of Fleet Street, Roman ruins, former church ruins 33775

Salvation Army International Heritage Centre, 101 Queen Victoria St, London EC4P 4EP - T: (020) 73320101 ext 8704, Fax: 73328099, E-mail: heritage@salvationarmy.org, Internet: http://www.salvationarmy.org/history.htm. Head: James Boyden
Historical Museum 33776

Science Museum, The National Museum of Science & Industry, Exhibition Rd, South Kensington, London SW7 2DD - T: (020) 79388000, 79424455, Fax: 79388118, Internet: http://www.nmsi.ac.uk. Head: Neil Cossons
Science&Tech Museum - 1857
Hist of science and industry, agriculture, astronomy, air, sea and land transport, civil, electrical, marine and mechanical engineering, jet engines, geophysics, telcommunications, domestic appliances, spacetechnology, chemistry, medicine, interactive galleries 33777

Serpentine Gallery, Kensington Gardens, London W2 3XA - T: (020) 72981515, Fax: 74024103, Internet: http://www.serpentinegallery.org. Head: Julia Peyton-Jones
Public Gallery - 1970 33778

Shakespeare's Globe Exhibition, Bankside, London SE1 - T: (020) 79021500, Fax: 79021515, E-mail: davidm@shakespearesglobe.com. Head: Michael Holden, Mark Rylance, Sandra Moretto
Special Museum 33779

Sherlock Holmes Museum, 221b Baker St, London NW1 6XE - T: (020) 79358866, Fax: 77381269, E-mail: info@sherlock-holmes.co.uk, Internet: http://www.sherlock-holmes.co.uk. Head: Grace Riley
Special Museum - 1990
Victorian memorabilia 33780

Sir John Soane's Museum, 13 Lincoln's Inn Fields, London WC2A 3BP - T: (020) 74052107, Fax: 78313957, E-mail: will.palin.soane3@ukgateway.net, Internet: http://www.soane.org
Fine Arts Museum / Decorative Arts Museum - 1833
Sir John Soane's private art and antiquities coll, paintings (Hogarth, Turner), architectural and other drawings - library 33781

The Sladmore Gallery of Sculpture, 32 Bruton Pl, Berkeley Sq, London W1X 7AA - T: (020) 74990365, Fax: 74091381, E-mail: sculpture@sladmore.com, Internet: http://www.sladmore.com
Fine Arts Museum
19th and 20th c bronze sculptures 33782

Small Mansions Arts Centre, Gunnersbury Park, Popes Ln, London W3 8IQ - T: (020) 89938312
Fine Arts Museum 33783

South London Gallery, 65 Peckham Rd, London SE5 8UH - T: (020) 77036120, Fax: 72524730, E-mail: mail@southlondonart.com, Internet: http://www.southlondongallery.org. Head: Margot Heller
Fine Arts Museum - 1891
Victorian paintings and drawings, small coll of contemporary British art, coll of 20th c original prints, topographical paintings and drawings 33784

Southside House, Wimbledon Common, London SW19 4R - T: (020) 89467643
Decorative Arts Museum 33785

Spencer House, 27 Saint James's Pl, London SW1A 1NR - T: (020) 74998620, Fax: 74092952, Internet: http://www.spencerhouse.co.uk. Head: Jane Rick
Fine Arts Museum / Decorative Arts Museum
Built in 1756-66, London's finest surviving private palace, 18th c furniture and paintings 33786

Stephens Collection, Avenue House, East End Rd, Finchley, London N3 3QE - T: (020) 83467812
Historical Museum
History of the Stephens Ink Company 33787

Strang Print Room, University College London, Gower St, London WC1E 6BT - T: (020) 738737050 ext 2540, Fax: 78132803, E-mail: college.art@ucl, Internet: http://www.collections.ucl.ac.uk
Fine Arts Museum
Coll of fine german drawings,old master prints, plaster models, drawings by Flaxman, early english watercolours and english prints, japanese ukiyo-e prints, history of the slade school 33788

Studio Glass Gallery, 63 Connaught St, London W2 2AE - T: (020) 77063013/69
Public Gallery 33789

Syon House, Syon Park, Brentford, London TW8 8JF - T: (020) 85600881, Fax: 85680936, E-mail: info@@syonpark.co.uk, Internet: http://www.syonpark.co.uk
Historic Site - 1415
Robert Adam furniture and decoration, famous picture coll, home of the Dukes of Northumberland 33790

Tate Gallery of British Art, Millbank, London SW1P 4RG - T: (020) 78878000, Fax: 78878007, E-mail: information@tate.org.uk, Internet: http://www.tate.org.uk. Head: Nicholas Serota, Stephen Deuchar, Sandy Nairne
Fine Arts Museum - 1897
National art coll of British painting from 16th c to the present, modern foreign painting from the Impressionists, modern British and foreign sculpture, Turner bequest, Pre-Raphaelites - library and archive of 20th c art 33791

Tate Modern, Tate Gallery of Modern Art, Bankside, London SE1 9TG - T: (020) 78878000, Fax: 74015052, E-mail: information@tate.org.uk, Internet: http://www.tate.org.uk/modern. Head: Nicholas Serota, Sandy Nairne
Fine Arts Museum - 2000
International 20th c art incl major works by some of the most influential artists of this century such as Picasso, Matisse, Dalí, Duchamp, Moore, Bacon, Gabo, Giacometti and Warhol 33792

Thames Police Museum, Wapping Police Station, 98 Wapping High St, London E1 9NE - T: (020) 72754421, Fax: 72754490, E-mail: thames.metpol@gtnet.gov.uk
Special Museum
Uniforms and items 33793

Theatre Museum, National Museum of the Performing Arts, Russel St, London WC2E 7PR - T: (020) 79434700, Fax: 79434777, Internet: http://www.theatermuseum.org. Head: Margaret Bentron
Performing Arts Museum - 1984
Stage models, costumes, prints, drawings, puppets, props and memorabilia 33794

Tower Bridge Experience, Tower Bridge, London SE1 2UP - T: (020) 74033761, Fax: 73577935, E-mail: enquiries@towerbridge.org.uk, Internet: http://www.towerbridge.org.uk. Head: Keith Patterson
Science&Tech Museum - 1982
Original Victorian steam machinery 33795

TWO 10 Gallery, 210 Euston Rd, London NW1 2BE - T: (020) 76118888, Fax: 76118562, E-mail: k.arnold@wellcome.ac.uk, Internet: http://www.wellcome.ac.uk. Head: Dr. Ken Arnold
Natural History Museum / Fine Arts Museum
Exhibitions on the interaction between medical scienes and art 33796

United Grand Lodge of England Library and Museum → Museum of Freemasonery

Vestry House Museum, Vestry Rd, Walthamstow, London E17 9NH - T: (020) 85091917, E-mail: vestry.house@al.lbwf.gov.uk, Internet: http://www.lbwf.gov.uk/_arts/whatson/museums/vhm/vhm.htm. Head: Charles Small,
Local Museum - 1931
Bremer car, built between 1892-94 - local studies library and archives 33797

Veterinary Museum, c/o Library, Royal Veterinary College, Royal College St, London NW1 0TU - T: (020) 74685162, Fax: 74685162, Internet: http://www.rvc.ac.uk
Historical Museum - 1992
Development of veterinary education and science, veterinary instruments, print and manuscript items, pictures, history of veterinary medicine in the UK 33798

Victoria and Albert Museum, Cromwell Rd, South Kensington, London SW7 2RL - T: (020) 79422000, Fax: 79422266, E-mail: postmaster@vam.ac.uk, Internet: http://www.vam.ac.uk/collections/theatre. Head: Mark Jones
Decorative Arts Museum - 1852
European and early medieval art, Gothic art and tapestries, Italian Renaissance art, Raphael cartoons, continental art from 1500-1800, British art (1500-1900) and watercolors, Far Eastern and Islamic art, Indian art, applied arts, jewellery, costumes, musical instruments, textiles, embroidery, metalwork, armour, stained glass, pottery and porcelain, Limoges enamels, earthenware, alabasters, casts, furniture, bookart, miniatures - library 33799

Vintage Museum of Photography, Kirkdale Corner, London SE26 4NL - T: (020) 87785416, Fax: 87785841, E-mail: sales@vintagecameras.co.uk, Internet: http://www.vintage-cameras.co.uk/lkd
Special Museum 33800

Vintage Wireless Museum, 23 Rosendale Rd, West Dulwich, London SE21 8DS - T: (020) 86703667. Head: Gerald Wells
Science&Tech Museum / Historical Museum
Broadcast receiving history, TV and radio 33801

Wallace Collection, Hertford House, Manchester Sq, London W1U 3BN - T: (020) 75639500, Fax: 72242155, E-mail: admin@the-wallace-collection.org.uk, Internet: http://www.the-wallace-collection.org.uk. Head: Rosalind J. Savill
Fine Arts Museum - 1900
Paintings of all European schools, 17th c Dutch painting, incl works by Titian, Rubens, Van Dyck, Rembrandt, 18th c French art, sculpture, goldsmith art, porcelain, majolica, European and Oriental armaments, French furniture 33802

Wandsworth Museum, Courthouse, 11 Garratt Ln, London SW18 4AQ - T: (020) 88717074, Fax: 88714602, E-mail: wandsworthmuseum@wandsworth.gov.uk. Head: Patricia Astley Cooper
Local Museum - 1986 33803

Wellcome Museum of Medical Science, 183 Euston Rd, London NW1 2BE - T: (020) 76117211, Fax: 76118545, E-mail: k.arnold@wellcome.ac.uk, Internet: http://www.wellcome.ac.uk
Historical Museum - 1914
Tropical medicine, molecular biology, contagious diseases 33804

Wellington Museum, Apsley House, Hyde Park Cnr, London W1J 7NT - T: (020) 74995676, Fax: 74936576, Internet: http://www.apsteyhouse.org.uk. Head: Alicia Robinson
Decorative Arts Museum / Fine Arts Museum - 1952
Art coll, decorative objects, paintings, silver, sculpture, porcelain 33805

Wesley's House and Museum, 47 City Rd, London EC1Y 1AU - T: (0207) 2532262, Fax: 6083825. Head: Noorah Al-Gailani
Special Museum - 1898
John Wesley's library, personal memorabilia, largest coll of Wesleyana in the world 33806

Westminster Abbey Museum, Westminster Abbey, London SW1P 3PA - T: (020) 72225152, Fax: 72332072
Religious Arts Museum - 1987 33807

Westminster Dragoons Museum, Cavalry House, Duke of York's Headquarter, Chelsea, London SW3 4SC - T: (020) 88567995. Head: John Annett
Military Museum
Uniforms and artefacts of the Westminster Dragoons 33808

Whitechapel Art Gallery, 80-82 Whitechapel High St, London E1 7QX - T: (020) 75227878, Fax: 73771685, E-mail: info@whitechapel.org, Internet: http://www.whitechapel.org. Head: Iwona Blazwick
Public Gallery - 1901 33809

William Morris Gallery and Brangwyn Gift, Lloyd Park, Forest Rd, London E17 4PP - T: (020) 85273782, Fax: 85277070, Internet: http://www.lbwf.gov.uk/wmg. Head: Norah Gillow
Decorative Arts Museum - 1950
19th/early 20th c English arts & crafts, decorative arts, life & work of socialist poet William Morris 1834-1896, incl work by Morris & Co. and the Pre-Raphaelites - library, archive 33810

The William Morris Society, Kelmscott House, 26 Upper Mall, London W6 9TA - T: (020) 87413735, Fax: 87485207, E-mail: william.morris@care4free.net, Internet: http://www.morrissociety.org
Association with Coll 33811

Wimbledon Lawn Tennis Museum, All England Lawn Tennis Club, Church Rd, Wimbledon, London SW19 5AE - T: (020) 89466131, Fax: 89446497, E-mail: museum@aeltc.com, Internet: http://www.wimbledon.org/museum. Head: Honor Godfrey
Special Museum - 1977
Prints, photos, pictures on Wimbledon, objects, pictures etc. relating to the history of tennis - Kenneth Ritchie Wimbledon Library 33812

Wimbledon Society Museum, 22 Ridgway, Wimbledon, London SW19 4NQ - T: (020) 83957147, Fax: 89446497, E-mail: cyril.maidment@clara.net. Head: Cyril Maidment
Local Museum - 1916
Flints, artefacts, prints, watercolours, maps, photographs, manuscripts, natural hist, ephemera 33813

Wimbledon Windmill Museum, Windmill Rd, Wimbledon Common, London SW19 5NR - T: (020) 89472825. Head: N. Plastow
Science&Tech Museum - 1976 33814

Woodlands Art Gallery, 90 Mycenae Rd, Blackheath, London SE3 7SE - T: (020) 88585847, Fax: 88585847, Internet: http://www.wag.co.uk. Head: Pat Bowring
Public Gallery 33815

Londonderry

Foyle Valley Railway Museum, Foyle Rd, Londonderry BT48 6SQ - T: (028) 71265234, Fax: 71370080
Science&Tech Museum
Local railway memorabilia and rolling stock 33816

Harbour Museum, Harbour Sq, Londonderry BT48 6AF - T: (028) 71377331, Fax: 71377633
Local Museum
History of the city, maritimes 33817

Orchard Gallery, Orchard St, Londonderry - T: (028) 71269675, Fax: 71267273. Head: L. Kelly
Fine Arts Museum 33818

Tower Museum, Union Hall Pl, Londonderry BT48 6LU - T: (028) 71372411, Fax: 71377633, E-mail: tower.museum@derrycity.gov.uk. Head: Dermot Francis
Local Museum - 1992
Local history 33819

Workhouse Museum, Glendermott Rd, Waterside, Londonderry BT47 6BG - T: (028) 71318328, Fax: 71377633. Head: Dermot Francis
Historical Museum
Protection of North Atlantic convoys during WW II, Workhouse Guardians, comparisons between Irish and African famines 33820

Long Eaton

Long Eaton Tower Hall, Derby Rd, Long Eaton NG10 1LU - T: (0115) 9071141, E-mail: erewashmuseum@free4all.co.uk, Internet: http://www.erewash.gov.uk
Local Museum / Fine Arts Museum
Paintings, mostly 18th and 19th c oils, local history 33821

Long Hanborough

Combe Mill Beam Engine and Working Museum, Long Hanborough OX8 8ET - T: (01608) 643377. Head: Bob Staunton
Science&Tech Museum
19th c sawmill, working forge, 19th c artifacts 33822

Oxford Bus Museum Trust, Old Station Yard, Main Rd, Long Hanborough OX8 8LA - T: (01993) 883617, Internet: http://www.geocities/motorcity/lane/5050
Science&Tech Museum
Public transport from Oxford and Oxfordshire, local buses, horse trams 33823

Long Melford

Melford Hall, Long Melford CO10 9AA - T: (01787) 880286
Decorative Arts Museum
Coll of furniture and porcelain 33824

Long Wittenham

Pendon Museum of Miniature Landscape and Transport, Long Wittenham OX14 4QD - T: (01865) 407365, 408143, Internet: http://ds.dial.pipex.com/sfb/pendon.htm
Historical Museum - 1952
The Vale Scene, based on the Vale of White Horse, with model buildings illustrating a cross-section of local building styles and materials over the years 33825

Looe

Old Guildhall Museum, Higher Market St, Looe PL13 1BP - T: (01503) 263709, Fax: 265674
Local Museum
Looe history, fishing, smuggling, stocks, courthouse, ceramics, model boats 33826

Lossiemouth

Lossiemouth Fisheries and Community Museum, Pitgaveny St, Lossiemouth IV31 6AA - T: (01343) 543221
Local Museum 33827

Lostwithiel

Lostwithiel Museum, 16 Fore St, Lostwithiel PL22 0BW - T: (01208) 872513. Head: Jeanne Jones
Local Museum
Former town jail, houses local domestic and agricultural exhibits 33828

Loughborough

Bellfoundry Museum, Freehold St, Loughborough LE11 1AR - T: (01509) 233414, 212241, Fax: 263305, E-mail: museum@taylorbells.co.uk, Internet: http://www.taylorbells.co.uk. Head: Robert Bracegirdle
Special Museum
Bells and bellfounding 33829

Charnwood Museum, Granby St, Loughborough LE11 3DU - T: (01509) 233754, 233737, Fax: 268140. Head: Susan Cooke
Local Museum
Natural history of Charnwood borough, social and cultural history 33830

Great Central Railway Museum, Great Central Station, Loughborough LE11 1RW - T: (01509) 230726, Fax: 239791, E-mail: booking-office@gcrailway.co.uk, Internet: http://www.gcrailway.co.uk. Head: Graham Oliver
Special Museum
Station signs, loco's name and number plates, cast iron notices, silverware, signalling equipment, maps and diagrams, models, photos 33831

Old Rectory Museum, Rectory Pl, Loughborough LE11 1UW - T: (01509) 634704, Fax: 634839
Archaeological Museum
Local archaeological finds 33832

War Memorial Carillon Tower and Military Museum, Queen's Park, Loughborough LE11 2TT - T: (01509) 263370, 634704, Fax: 262370
Military Museum 33833

Loughgall

Dan Winters House - Ancestral Home, 9 The Diamond, Derryloughan Rd, Loughgall BT61 8PH - T: (028) 38851344, E-mail: winter@orangenet.org, Internet: http://www.orangenet.org/winter. Head: Hilda Winter
Historical Museum
17th c family chair, Rushlamp, thatching needle, 1903 pram, guns and lead shot, sword from The Battle of the Diamond 1795, churn, milk separator 33834

Louth

Louth Museum, 4 Broadbank, Louth LN11 6EQ - T: (01507) 601211, Internet: http://www.louth.org.uk
Local Museum - 1910
Impressions of seals collected by G.W. Gordon, architect James Fowler (1828-92), woodcarver Thomas Wilkinson Wallis (1821-1903) 33835

Lower Broadheath

The Elgar Birthplace Museum, Crown East Ln, Lower Broadheath WR2 6RH - T: (01905) 333224, Fax: 333426, Internet: http://www.elgar.org. Head: Catherine Sloan
Music Museum - 1938
Memorabilia of composer Edward Elgar (1857-1934), manuscripts, clippings, photos 33836

Lower Methil

Lower Methil Heritage Centre, 272 High St, Lower Methil KY8 3EQ - T: (01333) 422100, Fax: 422101, Internet: http://www.virtual-pc.com/museum/methil
Local Museum 33837

Lower Stondon

Stondon Museum, Station Rd, Lower Stondon SG16 6JN - T: (01462) 850339, Fax: 850824
Science&Tech Museum
Coll of transport, replica of Captain Cooks ship HM Bark Endeavour 33838

Lowestoft

Lowestoft and East Suffolk Maritime Museum, Fisherman's Cottage, Sparrows Nest Park, Whapload Rd, Lowestoft NR32 1XG - T: (01502) 561963. Head: P. Parker
Historical Museum - 1968
Hist of local fishing (1900-1995), evolution of R.N. Lifeboats, Marine Art Gallery 33839

Lowestoft Museum, Broad House, Nicholas Everitt Park, Oulton Broad, Lowestoft NR33 9JR - T: (01502) 511457, 5133795. Head: J. Reed
Local Museum - 1972
Lowestoft porcelain, archaeology, history 33840

Royal Naval Patrol Service Association Museum, Europa Room, Sparrows Nest, Lowestoft NR32 1XG - T: (01502) 586250
Historical Museum / Military Museum
Naval uniforms, memorabilia, records, log books, photos, working models 33841

Ludham

Toad Hole Cottage Museum, How Hill, Ludham NR29 5PG - T: (01692) 678763, Fax: 678763
Local Museum
Home and working life on the Broads marshes 33842

Ludlow

Ludlow Museum, Shropshire County Museum, Castle St, Ludlow SY8 1AS - T: (01584) 875384, 873857, Fax: 872019, E-mail: ludlow.museum@skropshire-cc.gov.uk, Internet: http://www.shropshire-cc.gov.uk/museum.nsf. Head: Katherine J. Andrew
Local Museum 33843

Luton

Bedfordshire and Hertfordshire Regiment Association Museum Collection, Wardown Park, Luton LU2 7HA - T: (01582) 746723, Fax: 746763
Military Museum
Medals, memorabilia, uniforms, equipment - library 33844

The Gallery, c/o Luton Cental Library, Saint George's Sq, Luton LU1 2NG - T: (01582) 419584, Fax: 459401
Public Gallery 33845

Luton Museum and Art Gallery, Wardown Park, Old Bedford Rd, Luton LU2 7HA - T: (01582) 746722, Fax: 746763, E-mail: hampson@luton.gov.uk, Internet: http://www.museums.co.uk/luton. Head: Leslie Hampson
Local Museum / Fine Arts Museum - 1928
Regional social hist, archaeology, industrial hist, local art, lace, textiles, costumes, toys, rural trades, crafts, porcelain, glass, furniture, household objects 33846

Stockwood Craft Museum and Mossman Gallery, Stockwood Park, Farley Hill, Luton LU1 4BH - T: (01582) 738714, Fax: 746763, E-mail: p.stevenson@virgin.net, Internet: http://www.luton.gov.uk. Head: Marian Nicols
Local Museum
Horse-drawn vehicles, rural life, crafts and trades 33847

Lutterworth

Percy Pilcher Museum, Stanford Hall, Lutterworth LE17 6DH - T: (01788) 860250, Fax: 0860870, E-mail: stanford.hall@virginnet.co.uk, Internet: http://www.stanfordhall.co.uk
Science&Tech Museum
First man in England to fly using unpowered flight 33848

Sherrier Resources Centre, Church St, Lutterworth LE17 4AG - T: (0116) 2656783, Fax: (01455) 552845, E-mail: museums@leics.gov.uk. Head: Eleanor Thomas
Local Museum
Natural, life, working, archaeology, domestic life, artworks 33849

Stanford Hall Motorcycle Museum, Stanford Hall, Lutterworth LE17 6DH - T: (01788) 860250, Fax: 860870, E-mail: enquiries@stanfordhall.co.uk, Internet: http://www.stanfordhall.co.uk. Head: Robert G. Thomas
Science&Tech Museum - 1962
Old motorcycles, machines, flying, bicycles machine 33850

Lydd

Lydd Town Museum, Old Fire Station, Queens Rd, Lydd TN29 9DF - T: (01797) 366566
Local Museum
Old fire engine, horse bus and unique beach cart, the army, agriculture, fishing and the fire service 33851

Lydney

Norchard Railway Centre, Dean Forest Railway Museum, Forest Rd, New Mill, Lydney GL15 4ET - T: (01594) 843423, 845840, Fax: 845840, Internet: http://www.dfrweb.fg.co.uk. Head: Fergus Scoon
Science&Tech Museum
Last remaining part of original Severn and Wye railway, railway artefacts since 1809 33852

Lyme Regis

Dinosaurland, Coombe St, Lyme Regis DT7 3PY - T: (01297) 443541. Head: Steve Davies, Jenny Davies
Natural History Museum - 1995
Fossils, models and live animals, coll of Jurassic fossils 33853

Lyme Regis Philpot Museum, Bridge St, Lyme Regis DT7 3QA - T: (01297) 443370, E-mail: info@lymeregismuseum.co.uk, Internet: http://www.lymeregismuseum.co.uk
Local Museum
Geology, local history, literary 33854

Lymington

Saint Barbe Museum and Art Gallery, New St, Lymington SO41 9BH - T: (01590) 676969, Fax: 679997, E-mail: office@stbarbe-museum.org.uk, Internet: http://www.stbarbe-museum.org.uk. Head: Steven Marshall
Local Museum / Fine Arts Museum
Local history, boat building, fishing, engineering, social history and archaeology 33855

Lyndhurst

New Forest Museum and Visitor Centre, High St, Lyndhurst SO43 7NY - T: (023) 80283914, Fax: 80284236, E-mail: nfmuseum@lineone.net, Internet: http://www.hants.gov.uk/leisure/museums/new. Head: Louise Bessant
Natural History Museum
History, traditions, character and wildlife of New Forest 33856

Lynton

Lyn and Exmoor Museum, Saint Vincent's Cottage, Market St, Lynton EX35 6AF - T: (01598) 752219, Internet: http://www.devonmuseum.net/lynton. Head: John Pedder
Local Museum
Arts, crafts, implements depicting history and life, railway, lifeboat, flood features, Victorian doll's house 33857

Lytham Saint Anne's

Lytham Hall, Ballam Rd, Lytham Saint Anne's FY8 4LE - T: (01253) 736652, Fax: 737656. Head: E.M.J. Miller
Decorative Arts Museum
Portraits of the Clifton family, landscape pictures, Gillow furniture 33858

Lytham Heritage Centre, 2 Henry St, Lytham Saint Anne's FY8 5LE - T: (01253) 730787, Fax: 730767. Head: Alan Ashton
Local Museum
Lytham history, local artists and art societies 33859

Lytham Lifeboat Museum, East Beach, Lytham Saint Anne's FY8 5EQ - T: (01253) 730155, Internet: http://www.legendol.freeserve.co.uk/lythrnli.html. Head: Frank Kilroy
Historical Museum 33860

Lytham Windmill Museum, East Beach, Lytham Saint Anne's FY8 5EQ - T: (01253) 794879
Science&Tech Museum
History of mills and milling 33861

Toy and Teddy Bear Museum, 373 Clifton Drive N, Lytham Saint Anne's FY8 2PA - T: (01253) 713705. Head: Irena Thompson
Special Museum
Teddy bears, toys, games 33862

Macclesfield

Gawsworth Hall, Church Ln, Macclesfield SK11 9RN - T: (01260) 223456, Fax: 223469, E-mail: gawsworth@lineone.net, Internet: http://www.gawsworth.com
Decorative Arts Museum 33863

Jodrell Bank Science Centre and Arboretum, Lower Withington, Macclesfield SK11 9DL - T: (01477) 571339, Fax: 571695, E-mail: visitorcentre@jb.man.ac.uk, Internet: http://www.jb.man.ac.uk/scicen. Head: Sylvia Chaplin
Science&Tech Museum - 1880
Lovell radio telescope, displays on astronomy, space, energy and satellites, planetarium, arboretum 33864

Macclesfield Silk Museum, Heritage Centre, Roe St, Macclesfield SK11 6XD - T: (01625) 613210, Fax: 617880, E-mail: postmaster@silk-macc.u-net.com, Internet: http://www.silk-macclesfield.org. Head: Lauranne Collins
Historical Museum / Local Museum - 1987
Hist of the building and of the Macclesfield Sunday School, religious, educational and social life of the town, silk industry, social and industrial change 33865

Paradise Mill Silk Museum, Paradise Mill, Old Park Ln, Macclesfield SK11 6TJ - T: (01625) 618228, Fax: 617880, E-mail: postmaster@silk-macc.u-net.com, Internet: http://www.silk-maaclesfield.org. Head: L.M. Collins
Science&Tech Museum - 1984
A typical Victorian silk mill, working conditions, story of the firm Cartwright & Sheldon, yarn preparation machinery, a design and card-cutting room, 26 silk jacquard handlooms, weaving demonstration 33866

West Park Museum and Art Gallery, Prestbury Rd, Macclesfield SK10 3BJ - T: (01625) 619831, Fax: 617880, E-mail: postmaster@silk-macc.u-net.com, Internet: http://www.silk-macclesfield.org. Head: Louanne Collins
Local Museum / Decorative Arts Museum / Fine Arts Museum - 1898
Art, Egyptian antiquities, local coll 33867

Machynlleth

Corris Railway Museum, Station Yard, Corris, Machynlleth SY20 9SH - T: (01654) 761624, E-mail: alfo@corris.co.uk, Internet: http://www.corris.co.uk
Science&Tech Museum - 1970
Locomotives, brake van, coaches, a number of wagons, hist and photogr of the railway 33868

The Museum of Modern Art, Y Tabernacl, Heol Penrallt, Machynlleth SY20 8AJ - T: (01654) 703355, Fax: 702160, E-mail: momawales@tabernac.dircon.co.uk, Internet: http://www.tabernac.dircon.co.uk. Head: Ruth Lambert
Fine Arts Museum
British/Welsh paintings 20th c 33869

Madeley

Blists Hill Victorian Town Open Air Museum, Legges Way, Madeley - T: (01952) 586063, 583003, Fax: 588016. Head: Michael Ward
Open Air Museum
Working Victorian town: foundry, candle factory, saw mill, printing shop 33870

Magherafelt

Bellaghy Bawn, Castle St, Bellaghy, Magherafelt BT45 8LA - T: (028) 79386812, Fax: 79386556
Local Museum
Plantation coll, local artefacts, literature 33871

Maidenhead

Courage Shire Horse Centre, Cherry Garden Ln, Maidenhead SL6 3QD - T: (01628) 824848, Fax: 8472. Head: I.B. Fisher
Special Museum 33872

Royal Borough Collection, Town Hall, Saint Ives Rd, Maidenhead SL6 1QS - T: (01628) 798888
Fine Arts Museum 33873

Maidstone

Dog Collar Museum, Leeds Castle, Maidstone ME17 1PL - T: (01622) 765400, Fax: 767838, E-mail: enquiries@leeds-castle.co.uk, Internet: http://www.leeds-castle.co.uk. Head: W.A.A. Wells
Special Museum
Coll of dog collars, of iron, brass, silver and leather from 16th c 33874

Maidstone Library Gallery, Saint Faith's St, Maidstone ME14 1LH - T: (01622) 752344, Fax: 754980
Public Gallery 33875

Maidstone Museum and Bentlif Art Gallery, Saint Faith's St, Maidstone ME14 1LH - T: (01622) 754497, 756405, Fax: 685022, Internet: http://www.museum.maidstone.gov.uk. Head: Claire Mason
Local Museum / Archaeological Museum / Fine Arts Museum / Natural History Museum - 1858
17 c & 18 c furniture in Elizabethan setting, costume, musical instruments, military coll, 17th c Dutch and Italian paintings, watercolors, archaeology, ethnography (SW Pacific), esp. china and glass, natural history, local history & industry, numismatics, carriages 33876

Queen's Own Royal West Kent Regimental Museum, Saint Faith's St, Maidstone ME14 1LH - T: (01622) 754497, Fax: 685022. Head: H.B.H. Waring
Military Museum - 1961
History of the unit 33877

Tyrwhitt-Drake Museum of Carriages, Archbishop's Stables, Mill St, Maidstone ME15 6YE - T: (01622) 754497, Fax: 685022. Head: Richard Powell
Science&Tech Museum - 1946
Horse-drawn coaches and carriages (17th to 19th c) 33878

Maldon

Maldon District Museum, 47 Mill Rd, Maldon CM9 5HX - T: (01621) 842688
Local Museum
Social history 33879

Mallaig

Mallaig Heritage Centre, Station Rd, Mallaig PH41 4PY - T: (01687) 462085, Fax: 462085, E-mail: info@mallaigheritage.org.uk, Internet: http://www.mallaigheritage.org.uk. Head: Trish Macintyre
Local Museum
Local history, social history of West Lochaber, railway, steamers, fishing, agriculture 33880

Malmesbury

Athelstan Museum, Town Hall, Cross Hayes, Malmesbury SN16 9BZ - T: (01666) 829258, Fax: 829258, E-mail: athelstanmuseum@northwilts.gov.uk. Head: J.R. Prince
Local Museum - 1979
Malmesbury lacemaking industry, Malmesbury branch railway, costume, local engineering company, bicycles, coins 33881

Malton

Eden Camp, Modern History Theme Museum, Eden Camp, Malton YO17 6RT - T: (01653) 697777, Fax: 698243, E-mail: admin@edencamp.co.uk, Internet: http://www.edencamp.co.uk. Head: S.A. Jaques
Historical Museum - 1987
History of the British wartime, series of reconstructed scenes, story of civilian life during World War II 33882

Malton Museum, Old Town Hall, Market Pl, Malton YO17 7LP - T: (01653) 695136, 692610
Archaeological Museum
Roman finds, coins, Samian ceramics, iron, bronze and stone objects 33883

Manchester

Chethams's Hospital and Library, Long Millgate, Manchester M3 1SB - T: (0161) 8347961, Fax: 8395797, E-mail: librarian@chethams.org.uk, Internet: http://www.chethams.org.uk
Historical Museum
Printed books, manuscripts, ephemera, newspapers, photographs, prints, maps, drawings, paintings, furniture 33884

Gallery of Costume, Manchester City Art Gallery, Platt Hall, Rusholme, Manchester M14 5LL - T: (0161) 2245217, Fax: 2563278, Internet: http://www.cityartgalleries.org.uk. Head: Anthea Jarvis
Special Museum - 1947
History of costumes since 1700, housed in a 1760s building - library 33885

Greater Manchester Police Museum, Newton St, Manchester M1 1ES - T: (0161) 8563287, Fax: 8563286
Historical Museum - 1981 33886

Heaton Hall, Manchester City Art Gallery, Heaton Park, Prestwich, Manchester M25 5SW - T: (0161) 2341456, Fax: 2367369, E-mail: c.storey@notes.manchester.gov.uk, Internet: http://www.cityartgalleries.org.uk. Head: Virginia Tandy
Fine Arts Museum / Decorative Arts Museum - 1906
Neo-classical interiors, furniture, ceramics, paintings, plasterwork, musical instruments 33887

Holden Gallery, c/o Faculty of Art and Design, Manchester Metropolitan University, Cavendish St, Manchester M15 6BR - T: (0161) 2476225, Fax: 2476870
Fine Arts Museum 33888

Manchester City Art Gallery, Mosley St, Manchester M2 3JL - T: (0161) 2341465, Fax: 2367369, E-mail: k.gowland@notes.manchester.gov.uk, Internet: http://www.cityartgalleries.org.uk. Head: Virginia Tandy
Fine Arts Museum / Decorative Arts Museum - 1882
British art, painting, drawing, sculptures, decorative arts 33889

Manchester Jewish Museum, 190 Cheetham Hill Rd, Manchester M8 8LW - T: (0161) 8349879, Fax: 8349801, E-mail: info@manchesterjewishmuseum.com, Internet: http://www.manchesterjewishmuseum.com
Historical Museum / Religious Arts Museum
Hist of Manchester's Jewish community over the past 250 years 33890

Manchester Museum, c/o University of Manchester, Oxford Rd, Manchester M13 9PL - T: (0161) 2752634, Fax: 2752676, Internet: http://www.museum.man.ac.uk. Head: Tristram Besterman
Archaeological Museum / Natural History Museum / University Museum / Ethnology Museum
Egyptian coll, geology, zoology, entomology, botany, ethnology, numismatics, archaeology 33891

Manchester Museum of Transport, Boyle St, Cheetham, Manchester M8 8UW - T: (0161) 2052122, Fax: 2052122, E-mail: gmtsenquire@btinternet.com, Internet: http://www.gmts.co.uk. Head: Dennis Talbot
Science&Tech Museum - 1979
Transports, busses, trams 33892

Manchester Transport Museum, Heaton Park, Manchester M9 0GH - T: (0161) 7401919. Head: Robert Hill
Science&Tech Museum
Tramway, tramcars, artefacts 33893

Manchester United Museum and Tour Centre, Sir Matt Busby Way, Old Trafford, Manchester M16 0RA - T: (0161) 8688631, Fax: 8688861, E-mail: tours@manutd.co.uk. Head: Mike Maxfield
Special Museum - 1986
British Football - education dept 33894

Manchester University Medical School Museum, Medical Admin., Stopford Bldg, Oxford Rd, Manchester M13 9PT - T: (0161) 2755027, Fax: 2755584. Head: William A. Jackson
Historical Museum / University Museum
Medical, surgical and pharmaceutical equipment, instruments, trade catalogues, photographs 33895

Museum of Science and Industry in Manchester, Liverpool Rd, Castlefield, Manchester M3 4FP - T: (0161) 8322244, Fax: 6060104, E-mail: marketing@msim.org.uk, Internet: http://www.msim.org.uk. Head: Dr. J. Patrick Greene
Science&Tech Museum - 1983
World's oldest passenger railway station, steam engines, electricity, gas, air and space, textiles - library, restoration workshop 33896

National Museum of Labour History, 103 Princess St, Manchester M1 6DD - T: (0161) 2287212, Fax: 2375965, E-mail: admin@nmlhweb.org, Internet: http://www.nmlhweb.org. Head: Nicholas Mansfield
Historical Museum
Working class life and institutions, labour and women's movements, banners, photographs, badges, tools, regalia, paintings 33897

Pankhurst Centre, 60-62 Nelson St, Chorlton-on-Medlock, Manchester M13 9WP - T: (0161) 2735673, Fax: 2743525, E-mail: pankhurst@zetnet.co.uk. Head: Yvonne Edge
Historical Museum
Women's suffrage movement 33898

People's History Museum, Pump House, Left Bank, Bridge St, Manchester M3 3ER - T: (0161) 8396061, Fax: 8396027, E-mail: info@peopleshistory-museum.org.uk, Internet: http://www.peopleshistorymuseum.org.uk. Head: Nicholas Mansfield
Historical Museum - 1994
Banners 33899

Portico Library and Gallery, 57 Mosley St, Manchester M2 3HY - T: (0161) 2366785, Fax: 2366803, E-mail: librarian@theportico.org.uk, Internet: http://www.theportico.org.uk
Public Gallery 33900

Whitworth Art Gallery, c/o University of Manchester, Oxford Rd, Manchester M15 6ER - T: (0161) 2757450, Fax: 2757451, E-mail: whitworth@man.ac.uk, Internet: http://www.whitworth.man.ac.uk. Head: Alistair Smith
Fine Arts Museum / University Museum - 1889
British water colors and drawings, Old Master prints and drawings, Japanese prints, textiles, contemporary British art, wallpapers - library 33901

Wythenshawe Hall, Manchester City Art Gallery, Wythenshawe Park, Northenden, Manchester M23 0AB - T: (0161) 2341456, Fax: 2367369, E-mail: r.shrigley@notes.manchester.gov.uk, Internet: http://www.cityartgalleries.org.uk. Head: Virginia Tandy
Decorative Arts Museum / Fine Arts Museum - 1930
17th-19th c furniture and pictures housed in country manor 33902

Mansfield

Mansfield Museum and Art Gallery, Leeming St, Mansfield NG18 1NG - T: (01623) 463088, Fax: 412922, E-mail: mansfield_museum@hotmail.com, Internet: http://www.mansfield-dc.gov.uk
Local Museum / Fine Arts Museum - 1904
Natural hist, local hist, art works, ceramics, archaeology, Buxton watercolors, Wedgwood and Pinxton China 33903

Marazion

Giant's Castle, Saint Michael's Mount, Treryn, Marazion TR17 0HT - T: (01736) 710507
Special Museum 33904

March

March and District Museum, High St, March PE15 9JJ - T: (01354) 655300, Fax: 653714
Local Museum
Coll of domestic and agricultural artefacts 33905

Margam

Abbey and Stones Museum, Port Talbot, Margam - T: (01639) 891548, Fax: 891548
Religious Arts Museum 33906

Margate

Lifeboat House, The Rendezvous, Margate Harbour, Margate CT9 1AA - T: (01843) 221613
Special Museum 33907

Margate Caves, 1 Northdown Rd, Margate CT9 2RN - T: (01843) 220139, Fax: 834428. Head: Iris Harvey
Historical Museum 33908

Old Town Hall Museum, Market Pl, Margate CT9 1ER - T: (01843) 231213, E-mail: margatemuseum@bonkers16.freeserve.co.uk
Local Museum 33909

Tudor House, Hosking Memorial Museum (temporary closed), King St, Margate CT9 1DA - T: (01843) 225511 ext 2520
Local Museum 33910

Market Bosworth

Bosworth Battlefield Visitor Centre and Country Park, Sutton Cheney, Market Bosworth CV13 0AD - T: (01455) 290429, Fax: 292841, Internet: http://www.leics.gov.uk
Historical Museum 33911

Market Harborough

Harborough Museum, Council Offices, Adam and Eve St, Market Harborough LE16 7AG - T: (01858) 821085, Fax: 821086, E-mail: - harboroughmuseum@uklink.net. Head: H.E. Broughton
Local Museum 33912

Rockingham Castle, Market Harborough LE16 8TH - T: (01858) 770240, Fax: (01536) 771692, E-mail: michaeltebbutt@btconnect.com, Internet: http://www.northants-uk.com/roc-cas
Fine Arts Museum
Fine pictures, furniture 33913

Market Lavington

Market Lavington Village Museum, Church St, Market Lavington SN10 4DT - T: (01380) 818736, Fax: 816222. Head: Peggy Gye
Local Museum
Life in the village 33914

Maryport

The Battery - Senhouse Roman Museum, Sea Brows, Maryport CA15 6JD - T: (01900) 816168, Fax: 816168
Archaeological Museum 33915

Maryport Maritime Museum, 1 Senhouse St, Maryport CA15 6AB - T: (01900) 813738, Fax: 819496
Historical Museum / Science&Tech Museum - 1976
Maryport local hist, maritime hist 33916

Matlock

Caudwell's Mill & Craft Centre, Rowsley, Matlock DE4 2EB - T: (01629) 734374, Fax: 734374, E-mail: raymarjoran@compuserve.com. Head: Ray Marjoram
Science&Tech Museum - 1982
Flour mill machinery 33917

Model Railway Museum, Royal Bank Bldg, Temple Rd, Matlock DE4 3PG - T: (01629) 580797. Head: Bill Hudson
Special Museum 33918

National Tramway Museum, Crich, Matlock DE4 5DP - T: (01773) 852565, Fax: 852326, E-mail: info@tramway.co.uk, Internet: http://www.tramway.co.uk. Head: David Senior
Science&Tech Museum - 1959
Coll of tramcars, built between 1873 and 1969, from Britain and abroad - library, restoration workshop 33919

Peak District Mining Museum, The Pavilion, Matlock DE4 3NR - T: (01629) 583834. Head: Alan Mutter
Science&Tech Museum - 1978
Artifacts relating to the history of lead mining from the Roman period to present day, mining tools, water pressure engine built in 1819 33920

Peak Rail Museum, Station, Matlock DE4 3NA - T: (01629) 580381, Fax: 760645, E-mail: peakrail@peakrail.co.uk, Internet: http://www.peakrail.co.uk
Science&Tech Museum 33921

Mauchline

Burns House Museum, Castle St, Mauchline KA5 5BS - T: (01290) 550045. Head: D.I. Lyell
Special Museum - 1969
Memorabilia on Poet Robert Burns, Mauchline Boxware, curling stones 33922

Maud

Maud Railway Museum, Station, Maud AB42 5LY - T: (01224) 664228, E-mail: heritage@aberdeenshire.gov.uk
Science&Tech Museum 33923

Maybole

Culzean Castle and Country Park, Culzean Castle, Maybole KA19 8LE - T: (01655) 884455, Fax: 884503, E-mail: culzean@nts.org.uk, Internet: http://www.nts.org.uk. Head: Michael L. Tebbutt
Decorative Arts Museum - 1945
Interiors, fittings designed by Robert Adam, staircase, plaster ceilings, 18th c castle built by Robert Adam 33924

Measham

Measham Museum, High St, Measham DE12 7HZ - T: (01530) 273956, Fax: 273986. Head: Denise Barnsley
Local Museum
Local history, Measham ware pottery, mining artefacts, Hart coll, pictures 33925

Meigle

Meigle Museum of Sculptured Stones, Dundee Rd, Meigle PH12 8SB - T: (01828) 640612, Fax: 640612, Internet: http://www.historic-scotland.gov.uk
Archaeological Museum - ca 1890
Pictish and early Christian stone objects 33926

Melbourne

Melbourne Hall, Church Sq, Melbourne DE73 1EN - T: (01332) 862502, Fax: 862263
Fine Arts Museum 33927

Melrose

Abbotsford House, Melrose TD6 9BQ - T: (01896) 752043, Fax: 752916, E-mail: abbotsford@melrose.border.et.co.uk
Special Museum / Historical Museum
Relics of Sir Walter Scott - library 33928

Melrose Abbey Museum, Melrose - T: (01896) 822562
Religious Arts Museum
Abbey pottery, floor, tiles, stone sculpture 33929

Melton Mowbray

Melton Carnegie Museum, Thorpe End, Melton Mowbray LE13 1RB - T: (01664) 569946, Fax: 569946, E-mail: museums@leics.gov.uk, Internet: htpp://www.leics.gov.uk. Head: H. Broughton
Local Museum - 1977
Local history, hunting pictures 33930

Meopham

Meopham Windmill, Wrotham Rd, Meopham DA13 0QA - T: (01474) 813779, Fax: 813779
Science&Tech Museum 33931

Mere

Mere Museum, Barton Ln, Mere BA12 6JA - T: (01747) 860546, E-mail: curator@meremuseum.fsnet.co.uk. Head: Dr. D., Longbourne
Local Museum 33932

Merthyr Tydfil

Cyfarthfa Castle Museum and Art Gallery, Brecon Rd, Merthyr Tydfil CF47 8RE - T: (01685) 723112, Fax: 723146, E-mail: museum@cyfarthfapark.-freeserve.co.uk
Decorative Arts Museum / Fine Arts Museum - 1910
Paintings, ceramics, silver, natural history, geology, ethnology, local history, industrial history 33933

Joseph Parry's Cottage, 4 Chapel Row, Merthyr Tydfil CF48 1BN - T: (01685) 721858, 723112, Fax: 723112. Head: Scott Reid
Music Museum - 1979
Story of the Welsh composer Joseph Parry 33934

Ygnysfach Iron Heritage Centre, Ynysfach Rd, Merthyr Tydfil CF48 1AG - T: (01685) 723112, Fax: 723112
Historical Museum
Museum of the iron industry, ironworker's cottage 33935

Merton

Barometer World Museum, Quicksilver Barn, Merton EX20 3DS - T: (01805) 603443, Fax: 603344, E-mail: barometerworld@barometerworld.co.uk, Internet: http://www.barometerworld.co.uk. Head: Philip Collins
Special Museum
Barometers 33936

Methil

Methil Heritage Centre, 272 High St, Methil KY8 3EQ - T: (01333) 422100, Fax: 422101. Head: Kevan Brown
Local Museum
Local history 33937

Methlick

Haddo House, Methlick AB41 7EQ - T: (01651) 851440, Fax: 851888, E-mail: haddo@nts.gov.uk. Head: Lorraine Hesketh-Campbell
Decorative Arts Museum
Earls of Aberdeen mansion 33938

Mevagissey

Folk Museum, Frazier House, East Quay, Mevagissey PL26 6PP - T: (01726) 843568. Head: Ron Forder
Folklore Museum 33939

Mickley

Thomas Bewick's Birthplace, Station Bank, nr Stocksfield, Mickley NE43 7DD - T: (01661) 843276. Head: Hugh Dixon
Special Museum / Fine Arts Museum - 1990
Engravings and prints from Bewick's wood blocks 33940

Middle Claydon

Claydon House, Middle Claydon MK18 2EY - T: (01296) 730349, Fax: 738511, E-mail: tcdgen@smtp.ntrust.org.uk
Decorative Arts Museum
Rococo State rooms with carving and decoration by Luke Lightfoot and plasterwork by Joseph Rose the younger 33941

Middle Wallop

Museum of Army Flying, Middle Wallop SO20 8DY - T: (01980) 674421, Fax: (01264) 781694, E-mail: enquiries@flying-museum.org.uk, Internet: http://www.flying-museum.org.uk. Head: Dr. Edward Tait
Military Museum
British Army's flying history, balloons in Bechuanaland, helicopters in the Falklands campaign of 1982, Army helicopters and fixed-wing aircraft, a captured Huey helicopter, British WWII assault gliders 33942

Middlesbrough

Captain Cook Birthplace Museum, Stewart Park, Marton, Middlesbrough TS7 6AS - T: (01642) 515658, Fax: 813781. Head: Jeanette Grainger
Special Museum - 1978
The life of Cook, a reconstruction of the below-deck accomodation in his famous ship, the Endeavour, galleries illustrating countries he visited until his death in Hawaii in 1779, ethnographical material 33943

Cleveland Crafts Centre, 57 Gilkes St, Middlesbrough TS1 5EL - T: (01642) 262376, Fax: 226351. Head: Tracey Taylor
Decorative Arts Museum
Decorative arts (16th-20th c), contemporary drawings, glass, ceramics, textiles, works of wood, pottery, non-precious contemporary jewellery 33944

Dorman Memorial Museum, Linthorpe Rd, Middlesbrough TS5 6LA - T: (01642) 813781, Fax: 358100
Local Museum - 1904
Natural hist, industrial and social hist, pottery, conchology, archaeology 33945

Middlesbrough Art Gallery, 320 Linthorpe Rd, Middlesbrough TS1 3QY - T: (01642) 358139, Fax: 358138. Head: Julia Bell
Public Gallery - 1958
20th c British works, contemporary international art 33946

Newham Grange Leisure Farm Museum, Coulby Newham, Middlesbrough - T: (01642) 300261, Fax: 300276
Agriculture Museum
History of farming in Cleveland, reconstructions of a farmhouse kitchen, a veterinary surgeon's room, a saddler's shop, coll of farm tools, implements and equipment 33947

Middleton-by-Wirksworth

Middleton Top Engine House, Middleton-by-Wirksworth DE4 4LS - T: (01629) 823204, Fax: 825336
Science&Tech Museum - 1974
Restored Beam Winding Engine of 1830 33948

Mildenhall, Suffolk

Mildenhall and District Museum, 6 King St, Mildenhall, Suffolk IP28 7EX - T: (01638) 716970
Local Museum
Local history, history of RAF Mildenhall, archaeology 33949

Milford Haven

Milford Haven Museum, Old Customs House, Sybil Way, The Docks, Milford Haven SA73 3AF - T: (01646) 694496
Local Museum
History of the town and waterway, fishing port 33950

Milford, Staffordshire

Shugborough Estate Museum, Milford, Staffordshire ST17 0XB - T: (01889) 881388, Fax: 881323, Internet: http://www.staffordshire.gov.uk/shugboro/shugpark.htm. Head: Geoff Elkin
Local Museum - 1966
The social and agricultural history of rural Staffordshire, stables, laundry, ironing room, brewhouse, coachhouse, coll of horse-drawn vehicles ranges from family coaches and carriages to farm carts 33951

Millom

Folk Museum, Saint Georges Rd, Millom LA18 4DD - T: (01229) 772555, Internet: http://www.visitcumbria.com/wc/milmmus.htm
Folklore Museum 33952

Millport

Museum of the Cumbraes, Garrison House, Garrison Grounds, Millport KA28 0DG - T: (01475) 531191, Fax: 531191, E-mail: namuseum@globalnet.co.uk, Internet: http://www.users.globalnet.co.uk/~vennel. Head: Michael P. Gallagher
Local Museum
Local history in a reconstructed wash house 33953

Robertson Museum and Aquarium, c/o University Marine Biological Station, Millport KA28 0EG - T: (01475) 530581/82, Fax: 530601, E-mail: donna.murphy@millport.gla.ac.uk, Internet: http://www.gla.ac.uk/acad/marine. Head: Dr. Rupert Ormond
Natural History Museum - 1900
Local marine life 33954

Milngavie

Lillie Art Gallery, Station Rd, Milngavie G62 8BZ - T: (0141) 5788847, Fax: 5700244, E-mail: - hildegarde.berwick@eastdunbarton.gov.uk. Head: Hildegarde Berwick
Fine Arts Museum - 1962
Paintings 20th c, water colors and etchings by Robert Lillie, drawings by Joan Eardley 33955

Milnrow

Ellenroad Engine House, Elizabethan Way, Milnrow OL16 4LG - T: (01706) 881952, E-mail: ellenroad@aol.com
Science&Tech Museum 33956

Milton Abbas

Park Farm Museum, Park Farm, Blanford, Milton Abbas DT11 0AX - T: (01258) 880216
Agriculture Museum 33957

Milton Keynes

Milton Keynes Gallery, 900 Midsummer Blvd, Central, Milton Keynes MK9 3QA - T: (01908) 676900, Fax: 558308, E-mail: mkgallery@mktgc.co.uk, Internet: http://www.mkweb.co.uk/mkg. Head: Stephen Snoddy
Public Gallery 33958

Milton Keynes Museum of Industry, McConnell Dr, Wolverton, Milton Keynes MK12 5EJ - T: (01908) 316222, Fax: 319148. Head: Bill Griffiths
Science&Tech Museum 33959

Warner Archive, c/o TDL, Bradbourne Dr, Tilbrook, Milton Keynes MK7 8BE - T: (01908) 658021, Fax: 658020, E-mail: sue-kerry@zoffany.uk.com
Historical Museum / Decorative Arts Museum
Textiles, designs, Warner Fabrics, Wilson, Keith, Norris, Walters, Scott Richmond and Helios 33960

Minehead

West Somerset Railway, Station, Minehead TA24 5BG - T: (01643) 704996, 707650, Fax: 706349, E-mail: info@west-somerset-railway.co.uk, Internet: http://www.west-somerset-railway.co.uk. Head: Mark Smith
Science&Tech Museum
Colls of Great Western Railway artefacts, Somerset and Dorset Railway artefacts 33961

Minera

Minera Lead Mines, Wern Rd, Minera LL11 3DU - T: (01978) 753400
Science&Tech Museum
19th c lead mine, beam engine house, geology 33962

Minster

Minster Abbey, Church St, Minster CT12 4HF - T: (01843) 821254
Religious Arts Museum 33963

Mintlaw

Aberdeenshire Farming Museum, Aden Country Park, Mintlaw AB42 5FQ - T: (01771) 622906, Fax: 622884, E-mail: heritage@aberdeenshire.gov.uk. Head: William K. Milne
Open Air Museum / Agriculture Museum
Agricultural colls, history of farming in NE Scotland 33964

Mistley

Essex Secret Bunker Museum, Crown Bldg, Shrublands Rd, Mistley CO11 1HS - T: (01206) 392271, Fax: 393847, E-mail: info@essexsecretbunker.com, Internet: http://www.essexsecretbunker.com. Head: Murray F. Stewart
Historical Museum
Cold war equipment - archives 33965

Mitcham

Wandle Industrial Museum, Vestry Hall Annexe, London Rd, Mitcham CR4 3UD - T: (020) 86480127, Fax: 86850249, E-mail: curator@wandleindustrial-museum.freeserve.co.uk
Science&Tech Museum
Life and industries of the River Wandle 33966

Moffat

Moffat Museum, The Neuk, Church Gate, Moffat DG10 9EG - T: (01683) 220868
Local Museum 33967

Moira

Moira Furnace, Furnace Ln, Moira DE12 6AT - T: (01283) 224667, Fax: 224667
Science&Tech Museum
Cast iron goods produced at the furnace foundary, foundryman's tools, social history 33968

Mold

Daniel Owen Museum, Earl Rd, Mold CH7 1AP - T: (01352) 754791
Library with Exhibitions / Public Gallery 33969

Oriel Gallery, Clwyd Theatr Cymru, Mold CH7 1YA - T: (01352) 756331, Fax: 758323, E-mail: theatr@globalnet.co.uk. Head: Jonathan Le Vay
Public Gallery 33970

Moneymore

Springhill Costume Museum, Magherafelt, Springhill, Moneymore BT45 7NQ - T: (028) 86747927, Fax: 86747927, E-mail: UPSET@smpt.ntrust.org.uk
Special Museum 33971

Moniaive

James Paterson Museum, Meadowcroft, North St, Moniaive DG3 4HR - T: (01848) 200583, Internet: http://www.lepad.demon.co.uk/pater-j.html. Head: Anne Paterson
Special Museum 33972

Maxwelton House Museum, Maxwelton, Moniaive DG3 4DX - T: (01848) 200385
Local Museum - 1973 33973

Monmouth

Castle and Regimental Museum, The Castle, Monmouth NP25 3BS - T: (01600) 772175, Fax: 716930, E-mail: curator@monmouthcastle-museum.org.uk, Internet: http://www.monmouth-castlemuseum.org.uk. Head: P. Lynesmith
Military Museum 33974

Nelson Museum and Local History Centre, Priory St, Monmouth NP25 3XA - T: (01600) 713519, Fax: 775001, E-mail: nelsonmuseum@monmouthshite.gov.uk. Head: Andrew Helme
Historical Museum - 1924
Documents and material concerning Nelson, local coll including the Hon. Charles Stuart Rolls (of Rolls Royce Fame) - commercial conservation service 33975

Montacute

National Portrait Gallery, Montacute House, Montacute TA15 6XP - T: (01935) 823289, Fax: 826921
Decorative Arts Museum
Furniture, tapestries, wood panelling, amorial glass, portraits of Tudor and Jacobean courts 33976

Montgomery

Old Bell Museum, Arthur St, Montgomery SY15 6RH - T: (01686) 668313
Local Museum
Local history, railway, industry 33977

Montrose

House of Dun, Montrose DD10 9LQ - T: (01674) 810264, Fax: 810722
Historic Site
Georgian house built in 1730, exhibition on the architecture of house and garden 33978

Montrose Air Station Museum, Waldron Rd, Broomfield, Montrose DD10 9BB - T: (01674) 673107, 674210, Fax: 674210, E-mail: 106212.152@compuserve.com, Internet: http://www.airspeed.freeservers.com
Military Museum
Aircrafts, wartime artefacts 33979

Montrose Museum and Art Gallery, Panmure Pl, Montrose DO10 8HE - T: (01674) 673232, Fax: (01307) 462590, E-mail: montrose.museum@angus.gov.uk, Internet: http://www.angus.gov.uk. Head: Rachel Benvie
Local Museum / Fine Arts Museum - 1837
Social history, ethnography, natural science, fossils, watercolours, sculpture and etchings, geology, molluscs 33980

William Lamb Memorial Studio, 24 Market St, Montrose DD10 8NB - T: (01674) 673232, Fax: (01307) 462590, E-mail: montrose.museum@angus.gov.uk, Internet: http://www.angus.gov.uk. Head: R. Benvie
Fine Arts Museum
Sculptures, wood carvings, etchings, drawings, watercolours 33981

Moreton-in-Marsh

Wellington Aviation Museum, British School House, Broadway Rd, Moreton-in-Marsh GL56 0BG - T: (01608) 650323, Fax: 650323. Head: Gerry V. Tyack
Local Museum / Military Museum
Royal Air Force treasures, local history 33982

Moreton Morrell

Warwickshire Museum of Rural Life, Warwickshire College of Agriculture, Moreton Morrell - T: (01926) 493431 ext 2021
Agriculture Museum
Implements, equipment, important farming activities such as ploughing, sowing, harvesting and dairying, locally made ploughs 33983

Morpeth

Chantry Bagpipe Museum, Bridge St, Morpeth NE61 1PJ - T: (01670) 519466, Fax: 511326. Head: Anne Moore
Music Museum - 1987
W.A. Cocks Coll of bagpipes and manuscripts 33984

Motherwell

Motherwell Heritage Centre, High St, Motherwell ML1 3HU - T: (01698) 251000, Fax: 268867, E-mail: heritage@mhc158.freeserve.co.uk, Internet: http://www.motherwell.museum.com. Head: Carol Haddow
Local Museum - 1996
Heritage from the Roman period, the rise and fall of heavy industry, present days - study room, exhibition gallery 33985

Mottistone

Bembridge Windmill Museum, Strawberry Ln, Mottistone PO30 4EA - T: (01983) 873945
Science&Tech Museum 33986

Mouldsworth

Mouldsworth Motor Museum, Smithy Ln, Mouldsworth CH3 8AR - T: (01928) 731781
Science&Tech Museum
Automobilia, motoring, art, enamel signs 33987

Much Hadham

Forge Museum, The Forge, High St, Much Hadham SG10 6BS - T: (01279) 843301, Fax: 843301, E-mail: christinaharrison@hotmail.com, Internet: http://www.hertsmuseum.org.uk. Head: Christina Harrison
Science&Tech Museum
Tools, blacksmith's shop and works, beekeeping equipment 33988

Much Marcle

Hellen's House, off A449, Much Marcle HR8 2LY - T: (01531) 660668
Decorative Arts Museum 33989

Much Wenlock

Much Wenlock Museum, The Square, High St, Much Wenlock TF13 6HR - T: (01952) 727773. Head: Nigel Nixon
Local Museum
Modern Olympics 33990

Mullach Ban

Mullach Ban Folk Museum, Tullymacrieve, Mullach Ban BT35 9XA - T: (028) 30888278, Fax: 30888100, E-mail: micealsdsa@dial.pipex.com
Folklore Museum / Agriculture Museum
Past agricultural way of life 33991

Mytchett

Basingstoke Canal Exhibition, Mytchett Place Rd, Mytchett GU16 6DD - T: (01252) 370073, Fax: 371758, E-mail: bas.canal@talk21.com, Internet: http://www.basingstoke-canal.co.uk
Historical Museum
200 year history of the Basingstoke Canal 33992

Nairn

Nairn Fishertown Museum, Laing Hall, King St, Nairn IV12 4SA - T: (01667) 456278
Local Museum
Domestic life of the fishertown, fishing industry around Moray Firth 33993

Nairn Museum, Viewfield House, Viewfield Dr, Nairn IV12 4EE - T: (01667) 456798
Local Museum - 1985
Literary Institute's coll, folk life, Rocks minerals, fossiles, natural history 33994

Nantgarw

Nantgarw China Works Museum, Tyla Gwyn, Nantgarw CF15 7TB - T: (01443) 841703, Fax: 841826. Head: Gerry Towell
Decorative Arts Museum
William Billingsley, 19th-c porcelain maker and decorator 33995

Nantwich

Nantwich Museum, Pillory St, Nantwich CW5 5BQ - T: (01270) 627104
Local Museum 33996

Narberth

Blackpool Mill, Canaston Bridge, Narberth SA67 8BL - T: (01437) 541233
Science&Tech Museum 33997

Wilson Museum of Narberth, 13 Market Sq, Narberth SA67 7AU - T: (01834) 861719. Head: Pauline Griffiths
Local Museum
Local history, brewery items, local shops and businesses, costume, toys, postcards and domestic items 33998

Naseby

Battle and Farm Museum, Purlieu Farm, Naseby NN6 7DD - T: (01604) 740241, Internet: http://www.hillyer.demon.co.uk/museum.htm
Military Museum / Agriculture Museum - 1975
Battle of 1645, agriculture 33999

Neath

Cefn Coed Colliery Museum, Neath Rd, Crynant, Neath SA10 8SN - T: (01639) 750556, Fax: 750556. Head: Robert Merrill
Historical Museum - 1980
Mining of coal, story of men and machines 34000

Neath Museum, Gwyn Hall, Orchard St, Neath SA11 1DT - T: (01639) 645741, 645726, Fax: 645726
Local Museum
Local history, archaeology, natural history, art gallery 34001

Nelson

Llancaiach Fawr Living History Museum, Llancaiach Fawr Manor, Nelson CF46 6ER - T: (01443) 412248, Fax: 412688. Head: Kevin C. Joss
Local Museum
Social history, decorative arts, archaeology 34002

Nenthead

Nenthead Mines Museum, Nenthead CA9 3PD - T: (01434) 382037, Fax: 382294, E-mail: -administration.office@virgin.net, Internet: http://www.npht.com
Science&Tech Museum
History and geology of this lead mining area 34003

Ness

Ionad Dualchais Nis, Lionel Old School, Ness PA86
Historical Museum
Crofting, past domestic life - archives 34004

Nether Stowey

Coleridge Cottage, 35 Lime St, Nether Stowey TA5 1NQ - T: (01278) 732662. Head: Derrick Woolf
Special Museum - 1908
Memorablia of poet Samuel Taylor Coleridge (1772-1834) 34005

New Abbey

Museum of Costume, National Museums of Scotland, Shambellie House, New Abbey DG2 8HQ - T: (01387) 850375, Fax: 850461, Internet: http://www.nms.ac.uk/costume. Head: Dale Idiens
Special Museum - 1977
Costumes from 1850 to 1950, European fashionable dress 34006

New Lanark

New Lanark World Heritage Village, New Lanark Mills, New Lanark ML11 9DB - T: (01555) 661345, Fax: 665738, E-mail: visit@newlanark.org, Internet: http://www.newlanark.org. Head: J. Arnold
Historical Museum - 1785
New Millennium experience, 19th c textile machinery, period housing and shop 34007

New Milton

Sammy Miller Motorcycle Museum, Bashley Cross Road, New Milton BH25 5SZ - T: (01425) 620777, Fax: 619696, E-mail: info@sammymiller.co.uk, Internet: http://www.sammymiller.co.uk
Science&Tech Museum
Motorcycles of the world 34008

New Pitsligo

Northfield Farm Museum, New Pitsligo AB43 6PX - T: (01771) 653504
Agriculture Museum
Coll of historic farm machinery and household impl 34009

New Romney

Romney Toy and Model Museum, Romney Hythe and Dymchurch Railway, New Romney Station, New Romney TN28 8PL - T: (01797) 362353, Fax: 363591, E-mail: rhdr@dels.demon.co.uk, Internet: http://rhdr.demon.co.uk
Special Museum
World's smallest public railway, traditional toys 34010

New Tredegar

Elliot Colliery Winding House, White Rose Way, New Tredegar NP2 6DF - T: (01443) 864224, Fax: 864228, E-mail: morgacl@caerphilly.gov.uk. Head: Chris Morgan
Science&Tech Museum
Thornwill and Warham steam engine, history of mining in Caerphilly county borough 34011

Newark-on-Trent

Castle Story, Gilstrap Heritage Centre, Castlegate, Newark-on-Trent NG24 1BG - T: (01636) 611908, Fax: 612274, E-mail: gilstrap@newark-sherwooddc.gov.uk, Internet: http://www.newark-sherwooddc.gov.uk
Local Museum 34012

Gilstrap Heritage Centre, Castlegate, Newark-on-Trent NG24 1BG - T: (01636) 611908, Fax: 612274, E-mail: gilstrap@newark-sherwooddc.gov.uk, Internet: http://www.newark-sherwooddc.gov.uk
Historical Museum 34013

Millgate Museum, 48 Millgate, Newark-on-Trent NG24 4TS - T: (01636) 655730, Fax: 655735, E-mail: museums@newark-sherwooddc.gov.uk, Internet: http://www.newark-sherwooddc.gov.uk. Head: Melissa Hall
Folklore Museum - 1978
Items mid-19th c-1950's relating to everyday life 34014

Newark Air Museum, Airfield Winthorpe, Newark-on-Trent NG24 2NY - T: (01636) 707170, Fax: 707170, E-mail: newarkair@lineone.net, Internet: http://www.newarkairmuseum.co.uk. Head: H.F. Heey
Science&Tech Museum
Aircraft, instruments, avionics, memorabilia, uniforms 34015

Newark Museum, Appleton Gate, Newark-on-Trent NG24 1JY - T: (01636) 655740, Fax: 655745, E-mail: museums@newark-sherwooddc.gov.uk, Internet: http://www.newark-sherwooddc.gov.uk. Head: M.J. Hall
Local Museum - 1912
Archaeology, social hist, art, natural science, photogr, coins, documents 34016

Newark Town Treasures and Art Gallery, Market Pl, Newark-on-Trent NG24 1DU - T: (01636) 680333, Fax: 680350, E-mail: post@newark.gov.uk, Internet: http://www.newark.gov.uk. Head: Patty Temple
Decorative Arts Museum / Fine Arts Museum
Civic plate, insignia, regalia and fine art 34017

Saint Mary Magdalene Treasury, Parish Church, Newark-on-Trent - T: (01636) 706473
Religious Arts Museum 34018

The Time Museum, Upton Hall, Upton, Newark-on-Trent NG23 5TE - T: (01636) 813795/96, Fax: 812258, E-mail: clocks@bhi.co.uk, Internet: http://www.bhi.co.uk. Head: M. Taylor
Special Museum - 1858 34019

Vina Cooke Museum of Dolls and Bygone Childhood, Old Rectory, Cromwell, Newark-on-Trent NG23 6JE - T: (01636) 821364. Head: Vina Cooke
Special Museum - 1984
Dolls, costume, general items associated with childhood 34020

Newburgh

Laing Museum, High St, Newburgh KY14 6DX - T: (01337) 840223, Fax: 412710
Local Museum 34021

Newburn

Newburn Hall Motor Museum, 35 Townfield Gardens, Newburn NE15 8PY - T: (0191) 2642977. Head: D.M. Porrelli
Science&Tech Museum
Cars and motorcycles, model cars 34022

Newbury

British Balloon Museum, c/o West Berkshire Museum, The Wharf, Newbury RG14 5AS - T: (01635) 30511, E-mail: tjthafb@aol.com, Internet: http://www.britishballoonmuseum.or.uk. Head: John Baker
Special Museum / Science&Tech Museum
Cloud-hopper balloon, two baskets, model of hot air burner built 1904, balloon envelopes, baskets and related items - library 34023

West Berkshire Museum, The Wharf, Newbury RG14 5AS - T: (01635) 30511, Fax: 38535, E-mail: heritage@westberks.gov.uk, Internet: http://www.westberks.gov.uk
Local Museum - 1904
Archaeology, medieval hist, natural hist, Bronze Age objects, local pottery, costume, pewter, local and social hist 34024

Newcastle-under-Lyme

Borough Museum and Art Gallery, Brampton Park, Newcastle-under-Lyme ST5 0QP - T: (01782) 619705, Fax: 626857. Head: Delyth Enticott
Local Museum / Decorative Arts Museum / Fine Arts Museum / Public Gallery - 1943
Staffordshire pottery, weapons, clocks, toys, local and civic hist, English paintings from 18th c to present 34025

Newcastle-upon-Tyne

A Soldier's Life, Regimental Museum of the 15th/19th The King's Royal Hussars and Northumberland Hussars and Light Dragoons, Blandford Sq, Newcastle-upon-Tyne NE1 4JA - T: (0191) 2326789, Fax: 2302614, E-mail: ralph.thompson@tyne-wear-museums.org.uk
Military Museum 34026

Castle Keep Museum, Castle Garth, Newcastle-upon-Tyne NE1 1RQ - T: (0191) 2327938
Local Museum 34027

Discovery Museum, Blandford House, Blandford Sq, Newcastle-upon-Tyne NE1 4JA - T: (0191) 2326789, Fax: 2302614. Head: Dr. David Fleming
Special Museum 34028

Hancock Museum, Barras Bridge, Newcastle-upon-Tyne NE2 4PT - T: (0191) 2226765, Fax: 2226753, E-mail: hancock.museum@newcastle.ac.uk, Internet: http://www.ncl.ac.uk/hancock. Head: Iain Watson
Natural History Museum / University Museum - 1829
Natural hist, mounted birds, Hutton fossilised plants, Hancock and Atthey fossilised vertebrates, N.J. Winch Herbarium, Hancock correspondence 34029

Hatton Gallery, c/o University of Newcastle, The Quadrangle, Newcastle-upon-Tyne NE1 7RU - T: (0191) 2226057, Fax: 2226057, E-mail: hatton-gallery@ncl.ac.uk, Internet: http://www.ncl.ac.uk/hatton. Head: Lucy Whetstone
Fine Arts Museum / University Museum - 1926
14th-18th c European paintings, 16th-18th c Italian art, contemporary English drawings, Uhlman coll of African sculpture, Kurt Schwitters' Elterwater 'Merzbau' 34030

Laing Art Gallery, New Bridge St, Newcastle-upon-Tyne NE1 8AG - T: (0191) 2327734, Fax: 2220952, E-mail: julie.milne@tyne-wear-museums.org.uk
Fine Arts Museum - 1904
British paintings and water colors, Egyptian, Greek and Roman finds, pottery, porcelain, silver, glass, pewter, armaments, costumes, textiles 34031

Military Vehicle Museum, Exhibition Park Pavilion, Newcastle-upon-Tyne NE2 4PZ - T: (0191) 2817222, Fax: (01962) 73544, E-mail: miltmuseum@aol.com, Internet: http:www://military-museum.org.uk
Military Museum
Military vehicles and artefakt since 1900, soldiers life 34032

Museum of Antiquities of the University, c/o University of Newcastle-upon-Tyne, The Quadrangle, Newcastle-upon-Tyne NE1 7RU - T: (0191) 2227846/9, Fax: 2228561, E-mail: m.o.antiquities@ncl.ac.uk, Internet: http://www.ncl.ac.uk/antiquities. Head: L. Allason Jones
Archaeological Museum / University Museum - 1813
Roman inscriptions, sculptures, small finds, prehistoric and Anglo Saxon, antiquities from north Britain (from Paleolithic period to Tudors and Stuarts) - library 34033

Shefton Museum of Greek Art and Archaeology, c/o University of Newcastle, Dept. of Classics, Armstrong Bldg, Newcastle-upon-Tyne NE1 7RU - T: (0191) 2228996, Fax: 2228561, E-mail: m.o.antiquities@ncl.ac.uk, Internet: http://www.ncl.ac.uk/shefton-museum. Head: L. Allason-Jones
Fine Arts Museum / Archaeological Museum / University Museum - 1956
Classical art and archaeology, Corinthian bronze helmet, Apulian helmet, 6th c Laconian handles, Greek bronze hand mirrors, 7th c B.C. Etruscan bucchero, Pelike by Pan Painter, Italic late archaic carved amber, Tarantine and Sicilian terra cotta 34034

Trinity House, 29 Broad Chare, Quayside, Newcastle-upon-Tyne NE1 3DQ - T: (0191) 2328226, Fax: 2328448, E-mail: ncl_trinityhouse@hotmail.com
Science&Tech Museum 34035

The University Gallery, c/o University of Northumbria, Sandyford Rd, Newcastle-upon-Tyne NE1 8ST - T: (0191) 2274424, Fax: 2274718, E-mail: mara-helen.wood@unn.ac.uk. Head: Mara-Helen Wood
Public Gallery
1977 34036

Newent

Shambles Museum, 16-24 Church St, Newent GL18 1PP - T: (01531) 822144, Fax: 821120. Head: H. Chapman
Historical Museum
Complete Victorian town layout with shops, houses, gardens 34037

Newhaven

Local and Maritime Museum, Paradise Leisure Park, Avis Rd, Newhaven BN9 9EE - T: (01273) 612530. Head: Lord Greenway, Robert Bailey
Local Museum / Science&Tech Museum 34038

Newhaven Fort, Fort Rd, Newhaven BN9 9DL - T: (01273) 517622, Fax: 512059, E-mail: ian.everest@newhavenfort.org.uk, Internet: http://www.newhavenfort.org.uk
Military Museum 34039

Planet Earth Museum, Paradise Park, Avis Rd, Newhaven BN9 0DH - T: (01273) 512123, Fax: 616005, E-mail: enquiries@paradisepark.co.uk, Internet: http://www.paradisepark.co.uk
Natural History Museum
Fossils, minerals and crystals from around the world 34040

Newlyn

Pilchard Works, Tolcarne, Newlyn TR18 5QH - T: (01736) 332112, Fax: 332442, E-mail: pilchardco@aol.com, Internet: http://www.pilchards.com
Science&Tech Museum 34041

Newmarket

BSAT Gallery, British Sporting Art Trust, 99 High St, Newmarket CB8 8LU - T: (01264) 710344, Fax: 710114, 332442, E-mail: pilchardco@aol.com
Fine Arts Museum 34042

National Horseracing Museum, 99 High St, Newmarket CB8 8JL - T: (01638) 667333, Fax: 665600, Internet: http://www.nhrm.co.uk. Head: H. Bracegirdle
Special Museum - 1983
Archive, Hands on gallery 34043

Newport, Gwent

Museum and Art Gallery, John Frost Sq, Newport, Gwent NP20 1PA - T: (01633) 840064, Fax: 222615, E-mail: museum@newport.gov.uk
Local Museum / Decorative Arts Museum / Fine Arts Museum - 1888
Local archaeology, Roman caerwent, natural sciences, geology, zoology, local history, social & industrial, art, 18th & 19th British watercolours, 20th c British oil paintings, ceramics including teapots 34044

Tredegar House and Park, Coedkernew, Newport, Gwent NP10 8YW - T: (01633) 815880, Fax: 815895
Archaeological Museum 34045

Newport, Isle of Wight

Carisbrooke Castle Museum, Carisbrooke Castle, Newport, Isle of Wight PO30 1XY - T: (01983) 523112, Fax: 532126, E-mail: carismus@lineone.net, Internet: http://www.carisbrookecastle-museum.org.uk. Head: Rosemary Cooper
Historical Museum - 1898
Isle of Wight hist, material associated with Charles I and the Civil War, objects owned by Alfred Lord Tennyson 34046

Cothey Bottom Heritage Centre, Guildhall, High St, Newport, Isle of Wight PO30 1TY - T: (01983) 823822, Fax: 823841, E-mail: mbishop@iwight.gov.uk. Head: Dr. Michael Bishop
Local Museum 34047

Museum of Island History, The Guildhall, High St, Newport, Isle of Wight PO30 1TY - T: (01983) 823366, Fax: 823841. Head: Michael Bishop
Local Museum
Archaeology, geology, palaeontology, social history and fine art 34048

Roman Villa, Cypress Rd, Newport, Isle of Wight PO30 1HE - T: (01983) 529720, Fax: 823841, E-mail: tonybutler@low.gov.uk. Head: Dr. Mike Bishop
Archaeological Museum / Historic Site - 1963
Roman finds, villa ruins, mosaics 34049

Newport Pagnell

Beatty Museum, Chicheley Hall, Newport Pagnell MK16 9JJ - T: (01234) 391252, Fax: 391388, E-mail: enquiries@chicheleyhall.co.uk, Internet: http://www.chicheleyhall.co.uk
Military Museum
Memorabilia and photographs of Admiral Beatty 34050

Newport Pagnell Historical Society Museum, Chandos Hall, Silver St, Newport Pagnell MK16 0EG - T: (01908) 610852/53
Local Museum
Archaeological, domestic and trade artefacts 34051

Newquay

Lappa Valley Steam Railway, Saint Newlyn East, Newquay TR8 5HZ - T: (01872) 510317, E-mail: steam@lappa.freeserve.co.uk, Internet: http://www.lappa-railway.co.uk. Head: Amanda Booth
Science&Tech Museum 34052

Trerice, Kestle Mill, Newquay TR8 4PG - T: (01637) 875404
Local Museum 34053

Newry

Newry and Mourne Arts Centre and Museum, 1a Bank Parade, Newry BT35 6HP - T: (028) 3066232, Fax: 30266839. Head: Mark Hughes, Noreen Cunningham
Public Gallery / Local Museum 34054

Newry Museum, 1a Bank Parade, Newry BT35 6HP - T: (01693) 66232, Fax: 66839
Local Museum 34055

Newton Abbot

Newton Abbot Town and Great Western Railway Museum, 2a Saint Paul's Rd, Newton Abbot TQ12 2HP - T: (01626) 201121, Fax: 201119, E-mail: museum@newtonabbot-tc.gov.uk, Internet: http://www.newtonabbot-tc.gov.uk. Head: Felicity Cole
Local Museum / Science&Tech Museum
Local social history, Aller Vale Art pottery coll, Mapleton Butterfly Coll, signal box, railway memorabilia 34056

Newton Aycliffe

Aycliffe and District Bus Preservation Society, 110 Fewston Close, Newton Aycliffe DL5 7HF. Head: John Gibson
Science&Tech Museum
Vintage united automobile services vehicles, Darlington Corporation busses 34057

Newton Stewart

The Museum, York Rd, Newton Stewart DG8 6HH - T: (01671) 402472, E-mail: jmclay@argonet.co.uk. Head: D. Ferries
Local Museum - 1978 34058

Newtongrange

Scottish Mining Museum, Lady Victoria Colliery, Newtongrange EH22 4QN - T: (0131) 6637519, Fax: 6541618. Head: F. Waters
Science&Tech Museum
Machinery and artefacts relating to 900 yrs of Scottish coal mining, historic 'A-listed' Victorian colliery - Library 34059

Newtonmore

Clan Macpherson House and Museum, Main St, Newtonmore PH20 1DE - T: (015403) 673332
Special Museum
Family hist, relicts associated with Prince Charles Edward Stuart (Bonnie Prince Charlie) 34060

Newtown, Powys

Newtown Textile Museum, 5-7 Commercial St, Newtown, Powys SY16 2BL, mail addr: c/o Powysland Museum, Canal Wharf, Welshpool SY21 7AQ - T: (01938) 554656, Fax: 554656, E-mail: powysland@powys.gov.uk. Head: Eva B. Bredsdorff
Special Museum - 1964
Crafts, Newtown woollen industry 1790-1910 34061

Oriel 31, Davies Memorial Gallery, Oriel Goffa Davies, Y Drenewydd, Newtown, Powys SY16 2NZ - T: (01686) 625041, Fax: 623633, E-mail: enquiries@oriel31.org, Internet: http://www.oriel31.org. Head: Amanda Farr
Public Gallery - 1985 34062

Robert Owen Memorial Museum, Broad St, Newtown, Powys SY16 2BB - T: (01686) 626345, E-mail: johnd@robert-owen.midwales.com, Internet: http://www.robert-owen.midwales.com. Head: John H. Davidson
Special Museum - 1929
Life of socialist Robert Owen (1771-1858) 34063

W.H. Smith Museum, c/o W.H. Smith & Son Ltd., 24 High St, Newtown, Powys SY16 2NP - T: (01686) 626280. Head: H. Hyde
Historical Museum
Original oak shop front, tiling and mirrors, plaster relief decoration, models, photographs and a variety of historical momentoes, history of W.H. Smith from its beginning in 1792 until the present day 34064

Newtownards

Ards Art Centre, Town Hall, Conway Sq, Newtownards BT23 4DB - T: (028) 91810803, Fax: 91823131, E-mail: arts@ards-council.gov.uk. Head: Eilis O'Baoill
Public Gallery 34065

Somme Heritage Centre, 233 Bangor Rd, Newtownards BT23 7PH - T: (028) 91823202, Fax: 91823214, E-mail: sommeassociation@dnet.co.uk, Internet: http://www.irishsoldier.org
Military Museum
WW I through 10th and 16th (Irish) Divisions and 36th (Ulster) Division, Battle of the Somme, uniforms and artefacts 34066

North Berwick

Museum of Flight, National Museums of Scotland, East Fortune Airfield, North Berwick EH39 5LF - T: (01620) 880308, Fax: 880355, E-mail: museum_of_flight@sol.co.uk, Internet: http://www.scotwings.com. Head: Dann Kemp
Science&Tech Museum - 1971
Aircrafts on a WW II airfield 34067

North Berwick Museum, School Rd, North Berwick EH39 4JU - T: (01620) 895457, Fax: 828201, E-mail: elms@elothian-museums.demon.co.uk, Internet: http://www.elothian-museums.demon.co.uk. Head: Peter Gray
Local Museum - 1957
Local and domestic hist, natural hist, archaeology, hist of the Royal Burgh of North Berwick 34068

North Leverton

North Leverton Windmill, West View, Sturton Rd, North Leverton DN22 0AB - T: (01427) 880662, 880573
Science&Tech Museum
Coll of stationary barn engines 34069

North Shields

Stephenson Railway Museum, Middle Engine Lane, West Chirton, North Shields NE29 8DX - T: (0191) 2007145. Head: Sharon Granville
Science&Tech Museum 34070

Northampton

Abington Museum, Abington Park, Northampton NN1 5LW - T: (01604) 631454, Fax: 238720, E-mail: museums@northampton.gov.uk, Internet: http://www.northampton.gov.uk/museums. Head: Sheila M. Stone
Local Museum 34071

Museum of the Northamptonshire Regiment, Abington Park, Northampton NN1 5LW - T: (01604) 631454, Fax: 238720, E-mail: museums@northamton.gov.uk, Internet: http://www.northampton.gov.uk/museums. Head: Sheila Stone
Military Museum 34072

National Fairground Museum, Riverside Park, Northampton NN1 5NX, mail addr: Ch. English, Fairground Heritage Trust, 10 Park Pl, London SW1A 1LP
Special Museum
Photographs, works drawings and social history of fair- ground operators, makers and decorators 34073

Northampton Central Museum and Art Gallery, Guildhall Rd, Northampton NN1 1DP - T: (01604) 238548, Fax: 238720, E-mail: museums@northampton.gov.uk, Internet: http://www.northamton.gov.uk/museums. Head: Sheila M. Stone
Local Museum / Fine Arts Museum - 1865
Northampton archaeology, geology, natural history, ethnography, Italian and modern English paintings, decorative arts, boots and shoes, leathercraft 34074

Northleach

Cotswold Heritage Centre, Fosseway, Northleach GL54 3JH - T: (01451) 860715, Fax: 860091, E-mail: john.poddock@cotswold.gov.uk, Internet: http://www.cotswold.co.uk. Head: Dr. John Paddock
Agriculture Museum - 1981
Agricultural hist, horse-drawn, implements and tools, Lloyd Baker coll of farm waggons 34075

Keith Harding's World of Mechanical Music, Oak House, High St, Northleach GL54 3ET - T: (01451) 860181, Fax: 861133, E-mail: keith@mechanicalmusic.co.uk, Internet: http://www.mechanicalmusic.co.uk. Head: Keith Harding
Music Museum - 1977
Self-playing musical instruments, clocks - restoration workshops 34076

Northwich

Lion Salt Works, Ollershaw Ln, Marston, Northwich CW9 6ES - T: (01606) 41823, Fax: 41823, E-mail: afielding@lionsalt.demon.co.uk, Internet: http://www.lionsaltworkstrust.co.uk. Head: Andrew Fielding
Science&Tech Museum 34077

Salt Museum, 162 London Rd, Northwich CW9 8AB - T: (01606) 41331, Fax: 350420, E-mail: cheshiremuseums@cheshire.gov.uk, Internet: http://www.cheshire.gov.uk/saltmuseum. Head: Stephen Penney
Special Museum
Salt making in Cheshire 34078

Norwich

Bridewell Museum, Bridewell Alley, Norwich NR2 1AQ - T: (01603) 629127. Head: John Renton
Local Museum - 1925
Textiles, shoes, timepieces, printing, brewing and iron founding, pharmacy, manufacturing industries 34079

Castle Museum, Castle, Norwich NR1 3JU - T: (01603) 493625, Fax: 765651, Internet: http://www.ecn.co.uk/norfolkcc/tourism/museums. Head: Vanessa Travelyan
Decorative Arts Museum / Fine Arts Museum - 1894
Fine and applied arts, archaeology, geology, natural hist, social hist, Norwich paintings, porcelain, silver, coins 34080

Felbrigg Hall, Roughton, Norwich NR11 8PR - T: (01263) 837444, Fax: 837032, E-mail: afgusr@smtp.ntrust.org.uk
Decorative Arts Museum
Historic country house with complete furnishings and fittings 34081

Inspire - Hands-on Science Centre, Saint Michael's Church, Coslany St, Norwich NR3 3DT - T: (01603) 612612, Fax: 616721, E-mail: inspire@science-project.org, Internet: http://www.science-project.org. Head: Ian Simmons
Science&Tech Museum 34082

John Jarrold Printing Museum, Whitefriars, Norwich NR3 1SH - T: (01603) 660211, Fax: 630162
Science&Tech Museum - 1982 34083

Mustard Shop Museum, 15 Royal Arcade, Norwich NR2 1NQ - T: (01603) 627889, Fax: 762142, Internet: http://www.mustardshop.com. Head: Avril Houseago
Special Museum - 1973
Colman's mustard manufaturing history 34084

Norwich Gallery, c/o Norwich School of Art and Design, Saint George St, Norwich NR3 1BB - T: (01603) 610561, Fax: 615728, E-mail: info@norwichgallery.co.uk, Internet: http://www.norwich-gallery.co.uk. Head: Lynda Morris
University Museum / Public Gallery 34085

Royal Air Force Air Defence Radar Museum, RAF Neatishead, Norwich NR12 8YB - T: (01692) 633309, Fax: 633214, Internet: http://www.neatishead.raf.mod.uk. Head: Doug Robb
Science&Tech Museum / Military Museum
History of radar and air defence since 1935, radar engineering, military communications systems, Cold War operations room, Royal Observer Corps rooms, ballistic missile and space defence, Bloodhound missile systems, radar vehicles 34086

Royal Norfolk Regimental Museum, Shirehall, Market Av, Norwich NR1 3JQ - T: (01603) 493649, Fax: 765651
Military Museum - 1933
Hist of regiment, medals, uniforms, hist of British Army 34087

Sainsbury Centre for Visual Arts, c/o University of East Anglia, Norwich NR4 7TJ - T: (01603) 593199, Fax: 259401, E-mail: scva@uea.ac.uk, Internet: http://www.uea.ac.uk/scva. Head: Nichola Johnson
Fine Arts Museum / Association with Coll / University Museum - 1978
Robert and Lisa Sainsbury coll, Anderson coll of Art Nouveau, coll of abstract/constructivist art and Design 34088

Saint Peter Hungate Church Museum, Princes St, Norwich NR3 1AE - T: (01603) 667231, Fax: 493623
Religious Arts Museum - 1936
In 15th c church, hist of parish life, illuminated manuscripts, church musical instruments 34089

Strangers Hall Museum of Domestic Life, Charing Cross, Norwich NR2 4AL - T: (01603) 667229, Fax: 765651. Head: Vanessa Trevelyan
Decorative Arts Museum - 1922
House with parts dating from 14th c, period rooms, toys, transportation, tapestries 34090

Nottingham

Brewhouse Yard Museum, Castle Blvd, Nottingham NG7 1FB - T: (0115) 9153600, Fax: 9153601, E-mail: suellap@notmusghy.demon.co.uk, Internet: http://www.nottinghamcity.gov.uk. Head: Michael Williams
Local Museum - 1977
Daily life material in Nottingham, local working, domestic, community, personal life from 1750 to present 34091

Castle Museum and Art Gallery, Castle, off Friar Ln, Nottingham NG1 6EL - T: (0115) 9153700, Fax: 9153653, E-mail: marketing@notmusghy.demon.co.uk. Head: Dr. Michael Williams
Decorative Arts Museum / Fine Arts Museum - 1878
Fine and applied arts, archaeology, militaria, medieval alabaster, English glass and silver, ceramics 34092

Djanogly Art Gallery, c/o Arts Centre, University of Nottingham, University Park, Nottingham NG7 2RD - T: (0115) 9513192, Fax: 9513194, E-mail: neil.bennison@nottingham.ac.uk, Internet: http://www.nottingham.ac.uk/artscentre. Head: Joanne Wright
Fine Arts Museum / University Museum - 1956
Duke of Newcastle coll: a bequest of family portraits from the 17th to 19th c, Glen Bott Bequest: a coll of watercolours and drawings of the British School (19th-20th c) 34093

Galleries of Justice, Shire Hall, High Pavement, Lace Market, Nottingham NG1 1HN - T: (0115) 9520555, Fax: 9939828, E-mail: info@galleriesofjustice.org.uk, Internet: http://www.galleriesofjustice.org.uk. Head: Louise Connell
Historical Museum
Gaol, court rooms and 1905 police station, crime and punishment 34094

Green's Mill and Science Centre, Windmill Ln, Sneinton, Nottingham NG2 4QB - T: (0115) 9156878, Fax: 9156875, E-mail: enquiries@greenmill.org.uk, Internet: http://www.greensmill.org.uk. Head: Jo Kemp
Science&Tech Museum - 1985
Mathematics, physics, mills and milling, science 34095

Industrial Museum, Courtyard Bldgs, Wollaton Hall, Nottingham NG8 2AE - T: (0115) 9153910, Fax: 9153941. Head: Dr. Michael Williams
Science&Tech Museum - 1971
Lace machinery, bicycles, telecommunications, steam engines 34096

Museum of Costume and Textiles, 51 Castle Gate, Nottingham NG1 6AF - T: (0115) 9153500, Fax: 9153599
Special Museum
Dresses, laces, textiles 34097

Museum of Nottingham Lace, 3-5 High Pavement, Nottingham NG1 1HF - T: (0115) 9897300, Fax: 9897301, E-mail: val@nottinghamlace.org, Internet: http://www.nottinghamlace.org. Head: Joan King
Special Museum - 1980
Complete history of Nottingham lace 34098

Natural History Museum, Wollaton Hall, Nottingham NG8 2AE - T: (0115) 9153900, Fax: 9153932
Natural History Museum - 1867
Mounted British and foreign birds, birds eggs, herbaria, European Diptera, lepidoptera, British aculeates, British beetles, mounted African big game heads, paleontology, fossils, Nottinghamshire plant and animal coll - library, Nottinghamshire Enironmental Archive, City Wildlife Database 34099

Nottingham University Museum, University Park, Nottingham NG7 2RD - T: (0115) 9514820, 9514813, Fax: 9514812, E-mail: roger.wilson@nottingham.ac.uk. Head: Prof. R.J.A. Wilson
University Museum / Archaeological Museum
Prehistoric, Roman and medieval artefacts from Eastern England, Bronze Age and Greek Mediterranean ceramics 34100

Regimental Museum of the Sherwood Foresters, Castle, Nottingham NG1 6EL - T: (0115) 9465415, Fax: 9469853, E-mail: rhqwfr-nottm@lineone.net
Military Museum - 1964
History of Nottinghamshire and Derbyshire Infantry Regiments since 1741, armaments, medals, uniforms 34101

Sherwood Foresters Regimental Museum, The Castle, Nottingham NG1 6EL - T: (0115) 9153700, Fax: 9792934. Head: J.O.M. Hackett
Military Museum
Worcestershire and Sherwood Foresters Regiment, uniforms, weapons, badges and models 34102

William Booth Birthplace Museum, 14 Notintone Pl, Sneiton, Nottingham NG2 4QG - T: (0115) 9503927, Fax: 9598604, E-mail: djepson@salvationarmy.ndo.co.uk
Special Museum 34103

Yard Gallery, Wollaton Park, Nottingham NG8 2AE - T: (0115) 9153920, Fax: 9153932
Public Gallery 34104

Nuneaton

Museum and Art Gallery, Riversley Park, Nuneaton CV11 5TU - T: (024) 76350720, Fax: 76343559, E-mail: museum@nuneaton-bedworthbc.gov.uk
Local Museum - 1917
Roman to late-medieval archaeology, ethnography, George Eliot Coll, Baffin Land Inuit material, miniatures, oil painting and watercolours 34105

Nunnington

Carlisle Collection of Miniature Rooms, Nunnington Hall, Attic Rm, Nunnington YO62 5UY - T: (01439) 748283, Fax: 748283, E-mail: yorknu@smtp.ntrust.org.uk
Special Museum - 1981 34106

Oakham

Normanton Church Museum, Rutland Water, Oakham LE15 8PX - T: (01572) 653026/27, Fax: 653027
Local Museum - 1985
Fossils, Anglo Saxon artefacts 34107

Oakham Castle, Rutland County Museum, Market Pl, Oakham LE15 6HW - T: (01572) 758440, Fax: 758445, E-mail: museum@rutland.gov.uk, Internet: http://www.rutnet.co.uk/rcc/rutlandmuseums
Historical Museum
12th c Great Hall of Norman Castle, coll of horseshoes 34108

Rutland County Museum, Catmose St, Oakham LE15 6HW - T: (01572) 758440, Fax: 758445, E-mail: museum@rutland.gov.uk, Internet: http://www.rutnet.co.uk/rcc/rutlandmuseums
Local Museum - 1967
Local history and archaeology, Anglo-Saxon and other finds, farm tools, rural trades 34109

Oban

McCaig Museum (temporary closed), Corran Halls, Oban PA34 5AB - T: (01631) 564211 ext 221, 564046
Local Museum 34110

War and Peace Exhibition, North Pier, Oban PA34 - T: (01631) 563977, 563452. Head: Ronald MacIntyre
Historical Museum / Military Museum 34111

Okehampton

Finch Foundry Working Museum, Sticklepath, Okehampton EX20 2NW - T: (01837) 840046, Fax: 840046. Head: Matthew Applegate
Science&Tech Museum - 1966
Working water powered tilt hammers 34112

Museum of Dartmoor Life, 3 West St, Okehampton EX20 1HQ - T: (01837) 52295, Fax: 52295, E-mail: dartmoormuseum@eclipse.co.uk, Internet: http://www.museumofdartmoorlife.eclipse.co.uk
Folklore Museum 34113

Museum of Waterpower → Finch Foundry Working Museum

Old Warden

Shuttleworth Collection, Aerodrome, Old Warden SG18 9EP - T: (01767) 627288, Fax: 626229, E-mail: enquiries@shuttleworth.org, Internet: http://www.shuttleworth.org
Science&Tech Museum
Classic grass aerodrome, historic aeroplanes, aviation from a 1909 Bleriot XI to a 1942 Spitfire, veteran and vintage cars, motorcycles and horse-drawn carriages 34114

Oldham

Gallery Oldham, Greaves St, Oldham OL1 1AL - T: (0161) 9114657, Fax: 9114669, E-mail: ecs.galleryoldham@oldham.gov.uk, Internet: http://www.oldham.gov.uk. Head: Sheena MacFarlane
Fine Arts Museum / Local Museum - 1883/2002
Social, industrial and natural history of the region, 19th-20th c British paintings and sculpture, English watercolors, glass, Oriental art objects 34115

Oldham Art Gallery → Gallery Oldham

Oldland

Artemis Archery Collection, 29 Batley Court, Oldland BS30 8YZ - T: (0117) 9323276, Fax: 9323276
Special Museum
Victorian and Edwardian longbows, archery artefacts 34116

Olney

Cowper and Newton Museum, Orchardside, Market Pl, Olney MK46 4AJ - T: (01234) 711516, Fax: (0870) 1640662, E-mail: cnm@mkheritage.co.uk, Internet: http://www.cowperand-newtonmuseum.org
Special Museum - 1900
Memorabilia of writer William Cowper (1731-1800), memorabilia of the hymn writer and antislave campaigner Reverent John Newton (1725-1807), lace industry 34117

Omagh

Ulster-American Folk Park, Museums and Galleries of Northern Irland, 2 Mellon Rd, Castle Town, Omagh BT78 5QY - T: (028) 82243292, Fax: 82242241, E-mail: uafp@iol.ie, Internet: http://www.folkpark.com. Head: J.A. Gilmour
Open Air Museum / Folklore Museum / Historical Museum - 1976
Series of buildings representing life in Ulster and North America in the 18th and 19th c, exhibitions on emigration and the Atlantic crossing, ship and dockside gallery, a reconstuction of an early 19th c sailing brig - library 34118

Ulster History Park, Cullion, Omagh BT79 7SU - T: (028) 81648188, Fax: 81648011, E-mail: uhp@omagh.gov.uk, Internet: http://www.omagh.gov.uk/historypark.htm. Head: Anthony Candon
Historical Museum
Models of homes and monuments (17th c) 34119

Onchan

Groudle Glen Railway, Groudle Glen, Onchan IM3 2EE - T: (01624) 670453
Science&Tech Museum
Narrow gauge steam railway, steam loco Sea Lion, built in 1896 34120

Orpington

Crofton Roman Villa, Crofton Rd, Orpington BR6 8AD - T: (01689) 873826, E-mail: bromley.museum@bromley.gov.uk, Internet: http://www.bromley.gov.uk
Archaeological Museum 34121

London Borough of Bromley Museum, The Priory, Church Hill, Orpington BR6 0HH - T: (01689) 873826, E-mail: bromley.museum@bromley.gov.uk, Internet: http://www.bromley.gov.uk/museums. Head: Dr. Alan Tyler
Local Museum - 1965
Avebury coll 34122

Otley

Otley Museum, Civic Centre, Cross Green, Otley LS21 1HP - T: (01943) 461052
Local Museum - 1962
Archives relating to the printing machine industry in Otley, large coll of flints from the region 34123

Oulton Broad

ISCA Maritime Museum (temporary closed for re-location), Caldecott Rd, Oulton Broad NR32 3PH - T: (01502) 585606, Fax: 589014, E-mail: -isca.maritimemuseum@btinternet.com, Internet: http://www.btinternet.com/~isca.maritimemuseum. Head: Andrew Thornhill
Science&Tech Museum - 1969
The Boats on display are drawn from every continent and include British, American, Arab, Chinese and Indian craft, the world's oldest working steamboat, the dredger designed by Isambard Kingdom Brunel for use in Bridgwater docks 34124

Oundle

Oundle Museum, The Courthouse, Mill Rd, Oundle PE8 4BW - T: (01832) 273422, 273871
Local Museum 34125

Owermoigne

Mill House Cider Museum and Dorset Collection of Clocks, Owermoigne DT2 8HZ - T: (01305) 852220, Fax: 854760. Head: D.J. Whatmoor
Special Museum
Horology, cider mills and presses, long case and Turret clocks 34126

Oxford

Ashmolean Museum of Art and Archaeology, Oxford University, Beaumont St, Oxford OX1 2PH - T: (01865) 278000, Fax: 278018, Internet: http://www.ashmol.ox.ac.uk. Head: Dr. Christopher Brown
Archaeological Museum / Fine Arts Museum / University Museum - 1683
Archaeology of Britain, Europe, the Mediterranean, Egypt, the Near East, Italian, French, Dutch, Flemish and English paintings, Old Master drawings, modern drawings, watercolours, prints, miniatures, European ceramics, sculpture, bronze and silver, engraved portraits, numismatics, Oriental art, Indian and Islamic arts and crafts 34127

Bate Collection of Historical Instruments, Faculty of Music, Saint Aldatés, Oxford OX1 1DB - T: (01865) 276139, Fax: 76128, E-mail: bate.collection@music.ox.ac.uk, Internet: http://www.ashmol.ox.ac.uk/bcmipage.html
Music Museum / University Museum 34128

British Telecom Museum, 35 Speedwell St, Oxford OX1 1RH - T: (01865) 246601, Fax: 790428
Science&Tech Museum
Telephone and telegraph equipment illustrating the history and evolution of telecommunications, 150 telephones from Alexander Graham Bell's 'Gallows' telephone of 1875 to modern instruments 34129

Christ Church Cathedral Treasury, Christ Church, Oxford OX1 1DP - T: (01865) 201971, Fax: 276277, E-mail: edward.evans@christ-church.ox.ac.uk. Head: Edward Evans
Religious Arts Museum
Church plate 34130

Christ Church Picture Gallery, Christ Church, Canterbury Quadrangle, Oxford OX1 1DP - T: (01865) 276172, Fax: 202429, E-mail: -dennis.harrington@chch.ox.ac.uk, Internet: http://www.chch.ox.ac.uk. Head: Christopher Baker
Public Gallery - 1968
Old Master paintings and drawings 1300-1750 34131

The Crypt - Town Hall Plate Room, Town Hall, Saint Aldate's, Oxford OX1 1BX - T: (01865) 249811, Fax: 252388
Decorative Arts Museum
Historic civic plate, large silver gilt mace, two Sear-geant's maces, gold porringer, cups and covers 34132

Museum of Modern Art, 30 Pembroke St, Oxford OX1 1BP - T: (01865) 722733, 813830, Fax: 722573, E-mail: info@moma.org.uk, Internet: http://www.moma.org.uk. Head: Andrew Nairne
Fine Arts Museum - 1966
Temporary exhibitions 34133

Museum of Oxford, Saint Aldates, Oxford OX1 1DZ - T: (01865) 252761, 815539, Fax: 202447, E-mail: VC@Oxfordmuseum.freeserve.co.uk. Head: V. Collett
Local Museum - 1975
Objects relating to the hist of the city and University of Oxford 34134

Museum of the History of Science, c/o University of Oxford, Broad St, Oxford OX1 3AZ - T: (01865) 277280, Fax: 277288, E-mail: museum@mhs.ox.ac.uk, Internet: http://www.mhs.ox.ac.uk. Head: James A. Bennett
Science&Tech Museum - 1924
Historic scientific instruments (astrolabes, armillary spheres, sundials, clocks and watches, microscopes and telescopes, various apparatus) - library 34135

The Oxford Story, Broad St, Oxford OX1 3AJ - T: (01865) 728822, Fax: 791716, E-mail: oxfordstory@uk2.net, Internet: http://www.oxfordstory.co.uk
Historical Museum
Review of Oxford's past 34136

Oxford University Museum of Natural History, Park Rd, Oxford OX1 3PW - T: (01865) 272950, 272966, Fax: 272970, E-mail: info@oum.ac.uk, Internet: http://www.oum.ox.ac.uk. Head: Prof. K.S. Thomson
University Museum / Natural History Museum - 1860
Entomology, geology, mineralogy, zoology 34137

Oxford University Press Museum, Walton St, Oxford OX2 6DP - T: (01865) 267527, Fax: 267908, E-mail: mawma@oup.co.uk. Head: Dr. Martin Maw
Special Museum
OUP's history from the middle ages to the age of techno- logy, historical printing and typographical artefacts - archives 34138

Pitt Rivers Museum, c/o University of Oxford, South Parks Rd, Oxford OX1 3PP - T: (01865) 270927, Fax: 270943, E-mail: prm@pitt-rivers-museum.oxford.ac.uk, Internet: http://www.prm.ox.ac.uk. Head: Dr. Michael O'Hanlon
Ethnology Museum / University Museum - 1884
Prehistoric archaeology, musical instruments, Captain Cook's material collected 1773-1774, African art, North American, Arctic, Pacific material, masks, textiles, arms and armour, amulets, charms, costumes, pottery, lamps and jewellery - archives, Balfour Library 34139

Regimental Museum of the Oxfordshire and Buckinghamshire Light Infantry, T.A. Centre, Slade Park, Headington, Oxford OX3 7JJ - T: (01865) 780128
Military Museum 34140

Rotunda Museum of Antique Dolls Houses, 44 Iffley Turn, Oxford OX4 4DU
Decorative Arts Museum - 1963
Antique doll houses and their contents (glass, china, silver) showing social history 1700-1900 34141

Paddock Wood

Hop Farm, Beltring, Paddock Wood TN12 6PY - T: (01622) 872068, Fax: 872630. Head: Brent Pollard
Agriculture Museum
Exhibits of rural crafts, hop-growing and processing, agricultural tools and implements, and horse harness and equipment 34142

Padiham

Rachel Kay Shuttleworth Textile Collections, Gawthorpe Hall, Padiham BB12 8UA - T: (01282) 773963
Decorative Arts Museum
Embroideries from 17th c including goldwork, whitework, canvas work, quilts, lacework, costumes from 1750 - library 34143

Padstow

Padstow Museum, The Institute, Market Pl, Padstow PL28 8AD - T: (01841) 532470. Head: John Buckingham
Local Museum 34144

Paignton

Kirkham House, Kirkham St, Paignton TQ3 3AX - T: (0117) 9750700, Fax: 9750701. Head: Tony Musty
Decorative Arts Museum
Coll of reproduction furniture 34145

Paignton and Dartmouth Steam Railway, Queen's Park Station, Torbay Rd, Paignton TQ4 6AF - T: (01803) 555872, Fax: 664313, E-mail: pdsr@talk21.com
Science&Tech Museum 34146

Paisley

Paisley Museum and Art Gallery, High St, Paisley PA1 2BA - T: (0141) 8893151, Fax: 8899240, Internet: http://www.cqm.co.uk/www/rdc/leisurestart. Head: Andrea J. Kerr
Local Museum / Fine Arts Museum - 1870
Art, local history, natural history, local weaving art, Paisley Shawl Coll - observatory 34147

Palacerigg

Palacerigg House, Country Park, Palacerigg, G67 3HU - T: (01236) 735077, Fax: 781407
Local Museum 34148

Patna

Dunaskin Open Air Museum, Waterside, Dalmellington Rd, Patna KA6 7JF - T: (01292) 531144, Fax: 532314, E-mail: dunaskin@btconnect.com, Internet: http://www.yell.co.uk/sites/dunaskin
Open Air Museum / Science&Tech Museum
Ironworks, coal mining, brickworks, social and industrial history 34149

Paulerspury

Sir Henry Royce Memorial Foundation, The Hunt House, Paulerspury NN12 7NA - T: (01327) 811048, Fax: 811797, E-mail: shrmf@rrec.co.uk, Internet: http://www.henry-royce.org. Head: Philip Hall
Science&Tech Museum
Life and work of Henry Royce, Rolls-Royce cars 34150

Peebles

Cornice Museum of Ornamental Plasterwork, Innerleithen Rd, Peebles EH45 8BA - T: (01721) 720212, Fax: 720212
Special Museum 34151

Tweeddale Museum, c/o Chambers Institute, High St, Peebles EH45 8AQ - T: (01721) 724820, Fax: 729924, E-mail: rhannay@scotborders.gov.uk. Head: Rosemary Hannay
Natural History Museum / Archaeological Museum / Local Museum - 1859
Geology coll and local prehistoric material 34152

Peel

House of Manannan, Manx National Heritage, Peel IM5 1AA - T: (01624) 648000, Fax: 648001, E-mail: enquiries@mnh.gov.im, Internet: http://www.mnh.gov.im. Head: Dave Parsons
Historical Museum
Celtic, Viking and maritime traditions 34153

Peel Castle, Manx National Heritage, Peel IM5 1AB - T: (01624) 648000, Fax: 648001, E-mail: enquiries@mnh.gov.im, Internet: http://www.gov.im/mnh
Religious Arts Museum / Historic Site 34154

Pembroke

Castle Hill Museum → The Museum of the Home

The Museum of the Home, 7 Westgate Hill, Pembroke SA71 4LB - T: (01646) 681200. Head: Judy Stimson
Historical Museum - 1986
Domestic equipment, games and toys 34155

Penarth

Turner House Gallery, Plymouth Rd, Penarth CF64 3DM - T: (029) 20708870, E-mail: post@nmgw.ac.uk, Internet: http://www.nmgw.ac.uk/thg. Head: A. Southall
Fine Arts Museum / Decorative Arts Museum / Public Gallery
Fine and applied arts 34156

Pendeen

Geevor Tin Mining Museum, Geevor Tin Mines, Pendeen TR19 7EW - T: (01736) 788662, Fax: 786059, E-mail: pch@geevor.com, Internet: http://www.greevor.com. Head: W.G. Lakin
Science&Tech Museum
History of tin mining in Cornwall, geology, Cornish minerals, mining artefacts 34157

Pendeen Lighthouse, Pendeen TR19 7ED - T: (01736) 788418, Fax: 786059, E-mail: info@trevithicktrust.com, Internet: http://www.trevithicktrust.com
Science&Tech Museum
Engine room with sounder 34158

Penicuik

Scottish Infantry Divisional Museum, The Scottish Division Depot, Glencorse Barracks, Milton Bridge, Penicuik EH26 0NP - T: (01968) 72651 ext 239
Military Museum
History of infantry weapons 34159

Penrith

Brougham Castle, Penrith CA10 2AA - T: (01768) 862488. Head: Andrew Morrison
Archaeological Museum
Finds from the castle and nearby Roman site 34160

Dalemain Historic House, Penrith CA11 0HB - T: (017684) 86450, E-mail: admin@dalemain.com, Internet: http://www.dalemain.com
Historical Museum 34161

Penrith Museum, Robinson's School, Middlegate, Penrith CA11 7PT - T: (01768) 212228, Fax: 891754, E-mail: museum@eden.gov.uk. Head: Judith Clarke
Local Museum - 1990 34162

Steam Museum, 24 Castlegate, Penrith CA11 7JB - T: (01768) 62154
Science&Tech Museum 34163

Penshurst

Penshurst Place and Toy Museum, Penshurst TN11 8DG - T: (01892) 870307, Fax: 870866, E-mail: enquiries@penshurstplace.com, Internet: http://www.penshurstplace.com. Head: Viscount de L'Isle
Special Museum 34164

Penzance

Cornwall Geological Museum, Saint John's Hall, Alverton St, Penzance TR18 2QR - T: (01736) 332400, Fax: 332400, E-mail: honsec@geological.org.uk, Internet: http://www.geological.-nildram.co.uk. Head: David Freegman
Natural History Museum - 1914
Mineralogy, petrography, paleontology, Cornwall geology 34165

Natural History and Antiquarian Museum → Penlee House Gallery and Museum

Newlyn Art Gallery, New Rd, Newlyn, Penzance TR18 5PZ - T: (01736) 363715, Fax: 331578. Head: Elizabeth Knowles
Public Gallery - 1895 34166

Penlee House Gallery and Museum, Morrab Rd, Penzance TR18 4HE - T: (01736) 363625, Fax: 361312, E-mail: info@penlee-house.demon.co.uk, Internet: http://www.penleehouse.org.uk. Head: Alison LLoyd
Fine Arts Museum / Local Museum / Archaeological Museum
Archaeology, local history, natural history, Bronze Age pottery 34167

Trinity House National Lighthouse Centre, Wharf Rd, Penzance TR18 4BN - T: (01736) 360077
Science&Tech Museum - 1990
Coll of lighthouse equipment 34168

Perranporth

Perranzabuloe Folk Museum, Oddfellows Hall, Ponsmere Rd, Perranporth TR6 0BW
Local Museum
History of mining, fishing, farming 34169

Perth

Fergusson Gallery, Marshall Pl, Perth PH2 8NU - T: (01738) 441944, Fax: 621152, E-mail: museum@PKC.gov.uk, Internet: http://www.pkc.gov.uk/ah/fergussongallery.htm. Head: Michael Taylor
Fine Arts Museum 34170

Perth Museum and Art Gallery, 78 George St, Perth PH1 5LB - T: (01738) 632488, Fax: 443505, E-mail: museum@pkc.gov.uk, Internet: http://www.pkc.gov.uk. Head: M.A. Taylor
Local Museum / Fine Arts Museum / Natural History Museum / Public Gallery - 1935
Scottish and other paintings, applied art (Perth silver and glass), regional natural history, ethnography, archaeology, geology, antiquities 34171

Regimental Museum of the Black Watch, Balhousie Castle, Hay St, Perth PH1 5HR - T: (0131) 3108530, Fax: (01738) 643245, E-mail: museum@theblackwatch.co.uk. Head: S.J. Lindsay
Military Museum - 1924
History of Black Watch, related regiments, paintings, royal relics, uniforms, trophies from 1740 to the present 34172

Scone Palace, Perth PH2 6BD - T: (01738) 552300, Fax: 552588, E-mail: visit@scone-palace.co.uk, Internet: http://www.scone-palace.co.uk. Head: Elspeth Bruce
Decorative Arts Museum
Finest French furniture, china, clocks, ivories, needlework, vases, several historic rooms, halls and galleries 34173

Peterborough

Peterborough Museum and Art Gallery, Priestgate, Peterborough PE1 1LF - T: (01733) 343329, Fax: 341928, E-mail: museum@petersborough.gov.uk
Local Museum - 1880
Archaeology, history, geology, marine reptils, natural history, ceramics, glass, portraits, paintings, finds from Castor, Napoleonic P.O.W. coll from Norman cross, bone carving, straw marquetry 34174

Railworld, Oundle Rd, Peterborough PE2 9NR - T: (01733) 344240, Fax: 344240, Internet: http://www.railworld.net. Head: Richard Paten
Science&Tech Museum - 1993
Exhibits on future and worldwide railway developments, incl Maglev trains, steam age exhibits 34175

Peterhead

Arbuthnot Museum, Saint Peter St, Peterhead AB42 1QD - T: (01771) 622906, Fax: 622884, E-mail: heritage@aberdeenshire.gov.uk. Head: Dr. David M. Bertie
Local Museum - 1850
Local hist, fishing, shipping and whaling, coin and medal coll, 19th c Inuit ethnography 34176

Petersfield

Bear Museum, 38 Dragon St, Petersfield GU31 4JJ - T: (01730) 265108, E-mail: bears@dial.pipex.com, Internet: http://www.bearmuseum.co.uk. Head: Judy Sparrow, John Sparrow
Special Museum - 1984
The world's first museum of teddy bears 34177

Flora Twort Gallery, Church Path, 21 The Square, Petersfield GU32 1HS - T: (01730) 260756, E-mail: musmtc@hants.gov.uk, Internet: http://www.hants.gov.museums
Public Gallery 34178

Petersfield Museum, The Old Courthouse, Saint Peters Rd, Petersfield GU32 3HX - T: (01730) 262601
Local Museum 34179

Uppark Exhibition, South Harting, Petersfield GU31 5QR - T: (01730) 825415, Fax: 825873
Special Museum
The fire of 1989 and subsequent restoration 34180

Petworth

Coultershaw Water Pump, Coultershaw Mill, Station Rd, Petworth GU28 0JE - T: (01903) 505626
Science&Tech Museum
Waterwheel-driven pump, other pumps 34181

The Petworth Cottage Museum, 346 High St, Petworth GU28 0AU - T: (01798) 342100. Head: Jacqueline Golden
Historical Museum
Petworth House as a seamstress, lighting is by gas, heating by coal-fired range 34182

Petworth House, Petworth GU28 0AE - T: (01798) 342207, Fax: 342963, E-mail: spesht@smtp.ntrust.org.uk, Internet: http://www.national-trust.org.uk/regions/southern
Fine Arts Museum
Old Masters, sculpture (Turner, Van Dyck, Laguerre) 34183

Pevensey

Court House and Museum, High St, Pevensey BN24 5LF - T: (01323) 762309
Local Museum 34184

Pewsey

Pewsey Heritage Centre, Whatleys Old Foundry, Avonside Works, High St, Pewsey SN9 5AF - T: (01672) 56240, 562617. Head: Michael J. Asbury
Local Museum
Farming, commerce, the home, engineering 34185

Pickering

Beck Isle Museum of Rural Life, Beck Isle, Pickering YO18 8DU - T: (01751) 473653. Head: G. Clitheroe
Open Air Museum / Local Museum - 1967
Reconstructed rooms and shops, photographic work of the late "Sidney Smith", works of James McNeill Whistler 34186

North Yorkshire Moors Railway, Station, Pickering YO18 7AJ - T: (01751) 472508, Fax: 476970, E-mail: admin@nymrpickering.fsnet.co.uk, Internet: http://www.northyorkshiremoors-railway.com
Science&Tech Museum 34187

Pinxton

John King Workshop Museum, Victoria Rd, Pinxton NG16 6LR - T: (01773) 860137
Science&Tech Museum
Mining, engineering, railway artifacts 34188

Pitlochry

Clan Donnachaidh Museum, Bruar, Pitlochry PH18 5TW - T: (01796) 483264, Fax: 483338. Head: Ann McBay
Historical Museum
Items related to the Jacobite rising of 1745 34189

Pitlochry Festival Theatre Art Gallery, Port-na-Craig, Pitlochry PH16 5DR - T: (01796) 484600, Fax: 484616, E-mail: boxoffice@pitlochry.org.uk. Head: Roy Wilson
Performing Arts Museum - 1951 34190

Pitstone

Pitstone Green Farm Museum, Vicarage Rd, Pitstone LU7 9EY - T: (01296) 668223
Agriculture Museum 34191

Pittenweem

Kellie Castle, Pittenweem KY10 2RF - T: (01333) 720271. Head: M. Pirnie
Decorative Arts Museum 34192

Plumridge

Sperrin Heritage Centre, 274 Glenelly Rd, Plumridge BT79 8LS - T: (028) 81648142, Fax: 81648143
Local Museum
Treasure, ghosts, gold and poteen 34193

Plymouth

City Museum and Art Gallery, Drake Circus, Plymouth PL4 8AJ - T: (01752) 304774, Fax: 304775, E-mail: Plymouth.Museum@plymouth.gov.uk
Local Museum - 1897
Porcelain, cotton coll, paintings, drawings, prints, early printed books, 17th c portraits, American birds, ceramics, personalia of Sir Francis Drake, archaeology, ethnography, model ships, Oceanic coll, tokens, photography, minerals herbarium 34194

Elizabethan House, 32 New St, Plymouth PL1 2NA - T: (01752) 304774, Fax: 304775
Decorative Arts Museum 34195

Merchant's House Museum, 33 Saint Andrew's St, Plymouth - T: (01752) 304774, Fax: 304775, E-mail: plymouth.museum@plymouth.gov.uk. Head: N. Moyle
Historical Museum - 1977
Social, economic and maritime history of Plymouth 34196

Plymouth Arts Centre, 38 Looe St, Plymouth PL4 8AJ - T: (01752) 221450
Public Gallery 34197

Saltram House, Plympton, Plymouth PL7 1UH - T: (01752) 333500, Fax: 336474, E-mail: dsaltr@smtp.ntrust.org.uk, Internet: http://www.national-trust.org.uk. Head: Susan M. Baumbach
Fine Arts Museum 34198

Smeaton's Tower, The Hoe, Plymouth PL1 2NZ - T: (01752) 600608, 603300, Fax: 256361, E-mail: di.gillard@plymouth.gov.uk
Science&Tech Museum
Historic lighthouse 34199

Pocklington

Stewart Collection, Burnby Hall Gardens, Pocklington YO4 2QF - T: (01759) 302068
Local Museum 34200

Point Clear Bay

Museum of the 40's, Martello Tower, Point Clear Bay CO16 8NG
Military Museum / Science&Tech Museum
Navy in WW II 34201

Polegate

Windmill and Milling Museum, Park Croft, Polegate BN26 5LB - T: (01323) 734496. Head: Lawrence Stevens
Science&Tech Museum 34202

Pontefract

Pontefract Castle Museum, Castle Chain, Pontefract WF8 1QH - T: (01977) 723440. Head: W. Dugdale
Historical Museum 34203

Pontefract Museum, 5 Salter Row, Pontefract WF8 1BA - T: (01977) 722740, Fax: 722742
Local Museum
Archaeology, local history 34204

Ponterwyd

Llywernog Silver-Lead Mine Museum, Ponterwyd SY23 3AB - T: (01970) 890620, Fax: (01545) 570823, E-mail: silverrivermine@cs.com. Head: Peter Lloyd Harvey
Science&Tech Museum
Coll of mining artefacts 34205

Pontypool

Junction Cottage, Lower Mill, off Fontain Rd, Pontymoile, Pontypool NP4 0RF - T: (0800) 5422663, Fax: (01495) 755877, E-mail: junctioncottage@messages.co.uk, Internet: http://www.junctioncottage.co.uk
Special Museum 34206

Pontypool Museums, Park Bldgs, Pontypool NP4 6JH - T: (01495) 752036, Fax: 752043, E-mail: pontypoolmuseum@hotmail.com. Head: D. Wildgust
Local Museum - 1978 34207

Torfaen Museum, Park Bldgs, Pontypool NP4 6JH - T: (01495) 752036, Fax: 752043. Head: Martin Buckridge
Local Museum
Social and industrial history of Torfaen 34208

Pontypridd

Pontypridd Historical and Cultural Centre, Bridge St, Pontypridd CF37 4PE - T: (01443) 409512, Fax: 485565. Head: Brian Davies
Local Museum
Social history, industry, agriculture, culture and recreation 34209

Pool

Camborne School of Mines Geological Museum and Art Gallery, c/o University of Exeter, Pool TR15 3SE - T: (01209) 714866, Fax: 716977, E-mail: l.atkinson@csm.ex.ac.uk, Internet: http://www.ex.ac.uk/csm/museum2.htm. Head: Lesley Atkinson
Natural History Museum / Public Gallery
Rocks and minerals, incl. fluorescent, radioactive, gem and ore minerals, art exhibitions 34210

Cornish Mines, Engines and Cornwall Industrial Discovery Centre, Pool TR15 3NP - T: (01209) 315027, Fax: 315027, E-mail: info@trevithicktrust.com, Internet: http://www.trevithicktrust.com
Science&Tech Museum
Cornish beam-engines used for mine winding and pumping 34211

Poole

Old Lifeboat Museum, East Quay, Poole
Science&Tech Museum
1938 lifeboat Thomas Kirk Wright 34212

Poole Arts Centre, Seldown Gallery, Kingland Rd, Poole BH15 1UG - T: (01202) 665334. Head: Alistair Wilkinson
Public Gallery 34213

Royal National Lifeboat Institution Headquarters Museum, West Quay Rd, Poole BH15 1HZ - T: (01202) 663000, Fax: 663167, Internet: http://www.rnli.org.uk. Head: Andrew Freemantle
Science&Tech Museum
Lifeboat rescues, models, paintings, artefacts, fundraising 34214

Scaplen's Court Museum, High St, Poole BH15 1BW - T: (01202) 262600, Fax: 262622, E-mail: museums@poole.gov.uk, Internet: http://www.poole.gov.uk/culturalservices/museums. Head: Clive Fisher
Special Museum / Historical Museum - 1932 34215

Waterfront Museum, 4 High St, Poole BH15 1BW - T: (01202) 262600, Fax: 262622, E-mail: museums@poole.gov.uk, Internet: http://www.poole.gov.uk/culturalservices/museums. Head: Clive Fisher
Historical Museum - 1989
Boats and shipping, local hist, archaeology 34216

Port Charlotte

Museum of Islay Life, Port Charlotte PA48 7UN - T: (01496) 850358, Fax: 850358, E-mail: imt@islaymuseum.freeserve.co.uk, Internet: http://www.islaymuseum.freeserve.co.uk
Local Museum - 1977
Victorian domestic items, industry, carved stone coll 6th to 16th c - lapidarium, library 34217

Port-of-Ness

Ness Historical Society Museum, Old School, Lionel, Port-of-Ness PA86 0TG - T: (01851) 81576
Local Museum
History and occupations of the Ness area of Lewis, coll of photographic, printed and written material, fishing equipment, domestic utensils, implements used in crofting 34218

Port Saint Mary

Cregneash Village Folk Museum, Manx National Heritage, Port Saint Mary IM9 5AE - T: (01624) 648000, Fax: 648001, E-mail: enquiries@mnh.gov.im, Internet: http://www.mnh.gov.im
Folklore Museum 34219

Port Sunlight

Lady Lever Art Gallery, Port Sunlight L62 5EQ - T: (0151) 207001, Fax: 4784140, Internet: http://www.nmgm.org.uk. Head: Richard Foster
Fine Arts Museum - 1922
British and other paintings, watercolors, sculpture, porcelain, furniture 34220

Port Sunlight Heritage Centre, 95 Greendale Rd, Port Sunlight L62 4XE - T: (0151) 6446466, Fax: 6448973
Historical Museum / Special Museum
Story of William Hesketh Lever, his soap factory, period soap packaging 34221

Port Talbot

South Wales Miner's Museum, Afan Argoed Country Park, Cynonville, Port Talbot - T: (01639) 850564, Fax: 850446. Head: Glyn Thomas
Science&Tech Museum 34222

Portchester

Portchester Castle, Castle St, Portchester PO16 9QW - T: (023) 92378291, Internet: http://www.englisj-heritage.org.uk. Head: Nick Moore
Local Museum 34223

Porthcawl

Porthcawl Museum, Old Police Station, John St, Porthcawl CF36 3DT - T: (01656) 782111
Local Museum
Local and maritime hist, military hist of 49th Recce Regiment, costume, photographs - archives 34224

Porthcurno

Museum of Submarine Telegraphy, Porthcurno TR19 6JX - T: (01736) 810966, Fax: 810966, E-mail: tunnels@tunnels.demon.co.uk, Internet: http://www.porthcurno.org.uk
Science&Tech Museum
Coll of working submarine telegraphy equipment, under- ground WW II tunnels 34225

Porthmadog

Festiniog Railway Museum, Harbour Station, Porthmadog LL49 9NF - T: (01766) 513402, Fax: 514024, Internet: http://www.whr.co.uk/whr
Science&Tech Museum - 1955
History of Festiniog and allied railway systems 34226

Maritime Museum, Oakley, Nr. 1 Wharf, The Harbour, Porthmadog LL49 9LU - T: (01766) 513736
Historical Museum 34227

Portland

Portland Castle, Castletown, Portland - T: (01305) 820539, Fax: 860853, Internet: http://www.english-heritage.org.uk. Head: Tony Musty
Local Museum 34228

Portland Museum, 217 Wakeham, Portland DT5 1HS - T: (01305) 821804, Fax: 761654, E-mail: tourism@weymouth.gov.uk, Internet: http://www.weymouth.gov.uk
Natural History Museum - 1930
Cunnington, fossil coll (c 1925) of national importance being the best coll of faunal fossils from the Portlandian rocks 34229

Portslade-by-Sea

Foredown Tower, Foredown Rd, Portslade-by-Sea BN41 2EW - T: (01273) 292092, Fax: 292092, E-mail: visitor.services@brighton-hove.gov.uk
Natural History Museum
Camera obscura, astronomy, gallery of surrounding countryside 34230

Portsmouth

Charles Dickens Birthplace Museum, 393 Old Commercial Rd, Portsmouth PO1 4QL - T: (023) 92827261, Fax: 92875276, E-mail: devans@portsmouthcc.gov.uk, Internet: http://www.portsmouthmuseums.co.uk. Head: Sarah Quail
Special Museum - 1904
Birthplace of writer Charles Dickens (1812-1870), furniture, memorabilia, prints 34231

City Museum and Records Office, Museum Rd, Portsmouth PO1 2LJ - T: (023) 92827261, Fax: 92875276, E-mail: devans@portsmouthcc.gov.uk, Internet: http://www.portsmouthmuseums.co.uk. Head: Sarah Quail
Local Museum / Decorative Arts Museum / Fine Arts Museum / Historical Museum - 1972
Local history, ceramics, sculpture, paintings, wood engravings, prints, furniture, glass 34232

City of Portsmouth Preserved Transport Depot, 48-54 Broad St, Portsmouth PO1 2JE - T: (023) 92818223, E-mail: friends@cpptd.freeserve.co.uk, Internet: http://www.cpptd.freeserve.co.uk
Science&Tech Museum
Veteran and vintage buses, trams and a trolleybus 34233

D-Day Museum and Overlord Embroidery, Clarence Esplanade, Southsea, Portsmouth PO5 3NT - T: (023) 92827261, Fax: 92875276, E-mail: devans@portsmouthcc.gov.uk, Internet: http://www.portsmouthmuseums.co.uk. Head: Sarah Quail
Military Museum - 1984
"The Overlord embroidery" D-day military hist 34234

Eastney Beam Engine House, Henderson Rd, Eastney, Portsmouth PO4 9JF - T: (023) 92827261, Fax: 92875276, E-mail: devans@portsmouthcc.gov.uk. Head: Sarah Quail
Science&Tech Museum 34235

Fort Widley, A333, Portsdown Hill, Portsmouth PO6 3LS - T: (023) 92324553
Military Museum
Bunker, tunnels, the Great Ditch 34236

HMS Victory, HM Naval Base, Portsmouth PO1 3PZ - T: (023) 92819604, Internet: http://www.flagship.org.uk
Military Museum
Flagship of Lord Nelson at the Battle of Trafalgar 34237

HMS Warrior 1860, Victory Gate, HM Naval Base, Portsmouth PO1 3QX - T: (023) 92778600, Fax: 92778601, E-mail: info@hmswarrior.org, Internet: http://www.hmswarrior.org. Head: David Newbery
Military Museum - 1987
Historic warship 34238

Mary Rose Museum, HM Naval Base, College Rd, Portsmouth PO1 3LX - T: (023) 92750521, Fax: 92870588, E-mail: maryrose@cix.co.uk, Internet: http://www.maryrose.org. Head: Charles Payton
Military Museum
Objects recovered from the wreck of Henry VIII's warship, the 'Mary Rose', surviving portion of the ship's hull 34239

Museum of the Dockyard Apprentice, Unicorn Training Centre, Market Way, Portsmouth PO1 4AU - T: (023) 92822571
Historical Museum
History of the Unicorn Training Centre 34240

Natural History Museum, Cumberland House, Eastern Parade, Southsea, Portsmouth PO4 9RF - T: (023) 92827261, Fax: 92875276, E-mail: devans@portsmouthcc.gov.uk
Natural History Museum 34241

Royal Marines Museum, Eastney, Southsea, Portsmouth PO4 9PX - T: (023) 92819385, Fax: 92838420, E-mail: info@royalmarines-museum.co.uk, Internet: http://www.royalmarines-museum.co.uk. Head: C. Newbery
Military Museum - 1958/1975
Documents, paintings, weapons, uniforms, campaign relics since 1664, band and music paraphernalia 34242

Royal Naval Museum Portsmouth, HM Naval Base, PP66, Portsmouth PO1 3NH - T: (023) 92727562, Fax: 92727575, E-mail: information@royalnavalmuseum.org, Internet: http://www.royalnavalmuseum.org. Head: H. Campbell McMurray, C.S. White
Military Museum - 1911
Figureheads, ship models, ship furniture, memorabilia of Lord Nelson, panorama of the Battle of Trafalgar, history of the Royal Navy from earliest times to present - library, full research facilities 34243

Southsea Castle, Clarence Esplanade, Southsea, Portsmouth PO5 3PA - T: (023) 92827261, Fax: 92875276, E-mail: devans@portsmouthcc.gov.uk, Internet: http://www.portsmouthmuseums.co.uk. Head: Sarah Quail
Military Museum - 1967
History of Portsmouth fortress, tudor, civilwar, Victorian military hist 34244

Treadgolds Museum, 1 Bishop St, Portsmouth PO1 3DA - T: (023) 92824745, Fax: 92837310, Internet: http://www.hants.gov.uk/museums. Head: Peter Lawton
Special Museum
Machine and hand tools, materials, business archives, Treadgolds, ironmongers and engineers 34245

Potterne

Wiltshire Fire Defence Collection, Fire Brigade Headquarters, Manor House, Potterne SN10 5PP - T: (01380) 723601
Science&Tech Museum 34246

Potters Bar

Wyllotts Museum and Local History Centre, Wyllotts Pl, Darkes Ln, Potters Bar EN6 4HN - T: (01707) 645005 ext 20
Local Museum
History and archaeology of Potters Bar, telephones, Potters Bar Zeppelin 34247

Prescot

Museum of Clock and Watch Making, 34 Church St, Prescot L34 3LA - T: (0151) 4307787, Fax: 4307219
Science&Tech Museum 34248

Prescot Museum, 34 Church St, Prescot L34 3LA - T: (0151) 4307787, Fax: 4307219. Head: R. John Griffiths
Science&Tech Museum - 1982
Horology, earthenware 34249

Presteigne

The Judge's Lodging, Broad St, Presteigne LD8 2AD - T: (01544) 260650/51, Fax: 260652, Internet: http://www.judgeslodging.org.uk. Head: Gabrielle Rivers
Local Museum - 1980
Victorian domestic life, law and order, local/regional hist 34250

Preston

Harris Museum and Art Gallery, Market Sq, Preston PR1 2PP - T: (01772) 258248, Fax: 886764, E-mail: harris.museum@preston.gov.uk, Internet: http://www.visitpreston.com. Head: Alexandra Walker
Fine Arts Museum / Decorative Arts Museum / Local Museum - 1893
Fine art, Devis Coll of 18th c paintings, Newsham Bequest of 19th c British paintings, Haslam Bequest of 19th c watercolors, decorative art, costumes, ceramics, porcelain, social hist, archaeology, skeleton of Mesolithic elk, photogr 34251

Museum of Lancashire, Stanley St, Preston PR1 4YP - T: (01772) 264075, Fax: 264079, E-mail: museum.enquiries@mus.lancscc.co.uk. Head: Edmund Southworth
Local Museum / Natural History Museum 34252

Queen's Lancashire Regiment Museum, Fulwood Barracks, Watling St Rd, Preston PR2 8AA - T: (01772) 260362, Fax: 260583. Head: Mike Glover
Military Museum - 1926
Regimental history, uniforms, silver, trophies, weapons - library, archive 34253

Prestongrange

Prestongrange Industrial Heritage Museum, Preston Rd, Prestongrange EH32 9RX - T: (0131) 6532904, Fax: (01620) 828201, E-mail: elms@elothian-museums.demon.co.uk, Internet: http://www.elothian-museums.demon.co.uk. Head: Peter Gray
Science&Tech Museum
History of Prestongrange colliery and brickworks, colliery locomotives, 800 years mining history 34254

Prickwillow

Prickwillow Drainage Engine Museum, Main St, Prickwillow CB7 4UN - T: (01353) 688360, Fax: 723456. Head: Les Walton
Science&Tech Museum 34255

Pudsey

Moravian Museum, 55-57 Fulneck, Pudsey LS28 8NT - T: (0113) 564862, 2564147
Special Museum
Moravian lace and emboidery, ethnography 34256

Pulborough

Parham Elizabethan House & Gardens, Parham Park, Pulborough RH20 4HS - T: (01903) 744888, Fax: 746557, E-mail: parham@dial.pipex.com, Internet: http://www.parhaminsussex.co.uk
Fine Arts Museum - 1577
Historical portraits, needlework, Equestrian portrait of Henry Frederick, Prince of Wales, Kangaroo by Stubbs 34257

Purton

Purton Museum, Library, High St, Purton SN5 4AA - T: (01793) 770648, E-mail: dixon_quarry@msn.com. Head: Rick Dixon
Local Museum
Local history, archaeological material, agricultural hand tools 34258

Quainton

Buckinghamshire Railway Centre, Quainton Road Station, Quainton HP22 4BY - T: (01296) 655720, Fax: 655720, Internet: http://www.bucksrail-centre.org.uk. Head: D. Bratton
Science&Tech Museum
Steam/Diesel locomotives, carriages, wagons, railway artefacts 34259

Quatt

Dudmaston House, Quatt WV15 6QN - T: (01746) 780866, Fax: 780744, E-mail: mduefe@smtp.ntrust.org.uk
Decorative Arts Museum
Dutch flower paintings, fine furniture 34260

Radstock

Midsomer Norton and District Museum, Market Hall, Wateroo Rd, Radstock BA3 3ER - T: (01761) 437722, Fax: 420470, E-mail: radstockmuseum@ukonline.co.uk, Internet: http://www.radstock-museum.co.uk
Local Museum
Local history, industrial archaeology, mining 34261

Rainham

Rainham Hall, The Broadway, Rainham RM13 9YN - T: (01494) 528051, Fax: 463310
Decorative Arts Museum
Plasterworks, carved porch and interor 34262

Ramsey, Cambridgeshire

Ramsey Rural Museum, Wood Lane, Ramsey, Cambridgeshire PE26 2TY - T: (01487) 815715
Local Museum 34263

Ramsey, Isle of Man

Grove Rural Life Museum, Manx National Heritage, Andreas Rd, Ramsey, Isle of Man IM8 3UA - T: (01624) 648000, Fax: 648001, E-mail: enquiries@mnh.gov.im, Internet: http://www.gov.im/mnh
Historical Museum 34264

Ramsgate

Maritime Museum, Pier Yard, Royal Harbour, Ramsgate CT11 8LS - T: (01843) 587765, Fax: 582359. Head: Michael Cates
Science&Tech Museum - 1984
Artifacts from H.M.S. Stirling Castle wrecked on the Goodwin sands in the great storm of 1703, historic ship coll includes steam tug Cervia and Dunkirk little ship motor yacht Sundowner 34265

Motor Museum, Westcliff Hall, Ramsgate CT11 9JX - T: (01843) 581948. Head: D. Sharpe
Science&Tech Museum 34266

Ramsgate Library Gallery, Guildford Lawn, Ramsgate CT11 9AY - T: (01843) 593532, Fax: 293015
Public Gallery 34267

Ramsgate Museum, Guildford Lawn, Ramsgate CT11 9AY - T: (01843) 593532, Fax: 852692. Head: Beth Thomson
Local Museum - 1912 34268

Spitfire and Hurricane Memorial Building, Airfield, Manston Rd, Ramsgate CT12 5DF - T: (01843) 821940, Fax: 821940, Internet: http://www.spitfire-museum.com
Historical Museum
Spitfire and hurricane fighter, aviation-related artefacts 34269

Ravenglass

Muncaster Castle, Ravenglass CA18 1RQ - T: (01229) 717614, Fax: 717010, E-mail: info@muncastercastle.co.uk, Internet: http://www.muncastercastle.co.uk. Head: Peter Frost-Pennington
Fine Arts Museum 34270

Muncaster Watermill, Ravenglass CA18 1ST - T: (01229) 717232, Internet: http://www.muncaster.co.uk/mill
Science&Tech Museum 34271

Railway Museum, c/o Ravenglass and Eskdale Railway Co. Ltd., Ravenglass CA18 1SW - T: (01229) 717171, Fax: 717011, E-mail: rer@netcomuk.co.uk, Internet: http://www.ravenglass.railway.co.uk
Science&Tech Museum - 1978
History of the Ravenglass and Eskdale Railway since 1875 and its effect on the area 34272

Raveningham

History of Advertising Trust Archive, 12 Raveningham Centre, Raveningham N14 6NU - T: (01508) 548623, Fax: 548478, E-mail: hatadvert@email.msn.com, Internet: http://www.hatads.org.uk
Special Museum
Advertising, prints, film, posters, commercials, art-work, guard books, research company records and memoranda of historical interest 34273

Ravenshead

Gordon Brown Collection, Longdale Craft Centre, Longdale Ln, Ravenshead NG15 9AH - T: (01623) 794858, 796952. Head: Gordon Brown
Decorative Arts Museum 34274

Longdale Craft Centre and Museum, Longdale Ln, Ravenshead NG15 9AH - T: (01623) 794858, Fax: 794858, Internet: http://www.longdale.co.uk. Head: Gordon Brown
Science&Tech Museum 34275

Newstead Abbey, Abbay Park, Ravenshead NG15 8GE - T: (01623) 455900/03, Fax: 455904, Internet: http://www.newsteadabbay.org.uk
Special Museum - 1170
Roe-Byron Coll: Poet's possessions and furniture, manuscripts, letters and first editions, 18th and 19th c furniture - library 34276

Papplewick Pumping Station, Longdale Ln, Ravenshead NG15 9AJ - T: (0115) 9632938, Fax: 9557172, E-mail: gerrybarnes@tvalley48.freeserve.co.uk, Internet: http://www.papplewickpumpingstation.co.uk
Science&Tech Museum
Boilers, beam engines, working forge, colliery winding engine, 7.25" gauge passenger carrying steam railway 34277

Rawtenstall

Rossendale Footware Heritage Museum, Greenbridge Works, Fallbarn Rd, Rawtenstall BB4 7NY - T: (01706) 235155, Fax: 229643
Special Museum 34278

Rossendale Museum, Whitaker Park, Haslingden Rd, Rawtenstall BB4 6RE - T: (01706) 217777, 244682, Fax: 250037. Head: Sandra Cruise
Local Museum - 1902
Local history, fine and decorative arts, natural history 34279

Reading

Blake's Lock Museum, Gas Works Rd, off Kenavon Dr, Reading RG1 3DH - T: (0118) 9015145, Fax: 9399881. Head: Karen Hull
Historical Museum - 1985
Waterways (rivers Thames and Kennet), traders and industries of Reading 34280

Cole Museum of Zoology, c/o School of Animal and Microbial Science, University of Reading, Whiteknights, Reading RG6 2AJ - T: (0118) 9318466, Fax: 9316644, Internet: http://www.ams.rdg.ac.uk/info/colemuseum.html. Head: Prof. Peter Holland
Natural History Museum - 1906
Form and function in the animal kingdom 34281

Museum of English Rural Life, Whiteknights, Reading RG6 6AG, mail addr: c/o Rural History Centre, University of Reading, POB 229, Reading RG6 6AG - T: (0118) 9318660, Fax: 9751264, E-mail: rhc@reading.ac.uk, Internet: http://www.ruralhistory.org. Head: Prof. R.W. Hoyle
Agriculture Museum - 1951
Farming development, history of local rural life - library 34282

Museum of Reading, Town Hall, Blagrave St, Reading RG1 1QH - T: (0118) 9399800, Fax: 9399881, E-mail: mail@readingmuseum.org, Internet: http://www.readingmuseum.org. Head: Karen Hull
Decorative Arts Museum / Archaeological Museum / Local Museum - 1993
Britain's only full-size replica of the Bayeux Tapestry, the Silchester coll (Roman artefacts from Callera Atrebatum, now Silchester) 34283

Reading Abbay Gateway, The Forbury, Reading RG1 1QH - T: (0118) 9399809/05, Fax: 9566719
Religious Arts Museum 34284

Ure Museum of Greek Archaeology, c/o Dept. of Classics, Faculty of Letters, University of Reading, Whiteknights, Reading RG6 6AA - T: (0118) 9316599, Fax: 9316661, E-mail: iks01ah@reading.ac.uk, Internet: http://www.rdg.ac.uk/ure. Head: Dr. Amy C. Smith
Archaeological Museum / Museum of Classical Antiquities / University Museum - 1922
Greek, Egyptian antiquities, Boeotian and South Italian vases 34285

Redcar

Kirkleatham Museum, Kirkleatham, Redcar TS10 5NW - T: (01642) 479500, Fax: 474199, E-mail: museum_services@redcar-cleveland.gov.uk. Head: P. Philo
Local Museum - 1981
Local 19th c artists (the staithes group incl Dame Laura Knight), commondale pottery, poster coll (some international from Poland and Germany), photographic coll, maritime hist incl lifeboats of the north east coast, iron stone mining, iron making, fishing 34286

Zetland Lifeboat Museum, 5 King St, Redcar TS10 3PF - T: (01642) 486952
Science&Tech Museum - 1969
Shipping and fishing, industrial development, sea rescue, oldest lifeboat, ship models, marine paintings, scientific instruments 34287

Redditch

Forge Mill Needle Museum and Bordesley Abbey Visitor Centre, Needle Mill Ln, Riverside, Redditch B98 8HY - T: (01527) 62509, Fax: 66721, E-mail: museum@redditchbc.gov.uk, Internet: http://www.redditchbc.gov.uk. Head: Gillian Wilson
Science&Tech Museum / Archaeological Museum - 1983
Needles and fishing tackle from the Redditch needle-making district - Bordesley Abbey archaeological archive 34288

Redruth

Geological Museum and Art Gallery, University of Exeter, Camborne School of Mines, Redruth TR15 3SE - T: (01209) 714866, Fax: 716977, E-mail: scamm@csm.ex.ac.uk, Internet: http://geo-server.ex.ac.uk. Head: Simon Camm
Natural History Museum - 1888
Robert Hunt Coll of minerals, flurorescent minerals, ore specimens, Cornish minerals, fossils, worldwide coll of rocks and minerals, shows by local artists - library 34289

Tolgos Tin, c/o Cornish Gold Site, Portreath Rd, Redruth TR15 3SE - T: (01209) 215185, Fax: 219786, E-mail: info@trevithicktrust.com, Internet: http://www.trevithicktrust.com
Science&Tech Museum - 1921
Tin-streaming machinery in operation, Holmans Museum of aviation equipment - library 34290

Reeth

Swaledale Folk Museum, Village Green, Reeth DL11 6QT - T: (01748) 884373. Head: Erica Law
Folklore Museum - 1975
Folk exhibits, social hist and traditions of the Dale, sheep farming, lead mining 34291

Reigate

Museum of the Holmesdale Natural History Club, 14 Croydon Rd, Reigate RH2 0PG - Internet: http://www.hnhc.co.uk
Natural History Museum / Local Museum - 1857
Fossils, local archaeological finds, coll of British birds, herbarium, coll of photographs and postcards, local history, geology 34292

Renishaw

Renishaw Hall Museum, Renishaw S21 3WB - T: (01246) 432310, Fax: 430760, E-mail: info@renishawhall.free-online.co.uk, Internet: http://www.sitwell.co.uk. Head: Stephen David Fidler
Fine Arts Museum
Art, John Piper music and theatre exhibits, Sitwell memorabilia 34293

Retford

Bassetlaw Museum and Percy Laws Memorial Gallery, Amcott House, 40 Grove St, Retford DN22 6JU - T: (01777) 713749, Fax: 713749. Head: Malcolm J. Dolby
Local Museum / Fine Arts Museum - 1986
Local archaeology, civic, social and agricultural history, fine and applied art 34294

Rhayader

Rhayader and District Museum, Bank House, East St, Rhayader LD6 5DL - T: (01597) 810052. Head: T.G.B. Lawrence
Local Museum
History and archaeology of the area 34295

Rhuddlan

Rhuddlan Castle, Rhuddlan LL18 5AE - T: (01745) 590777
Archaeological Museum 34296

Rhyl

Rhyl Library, Museum and Arts Centre, Church St, Rhyl LL18 3AA - T: (01745) 353814, Fax: 331438. Head: Rose Mahon
Local Museum
Town's role, firstly as a fishing village and later as a seaside resort, maritime and social history 34297

Ribchester

Ribchester Roman Museum, Riverside, Bremetennacum, Ribchester PR3 3XS - T: (01254) 878261. Head: Patrick Tostevin
Archaeological Museum - 1914
Roman finds from old Roman fort and civilian settlement, interpretive models 34298

Richmond, North Yorkshire

Georgian Theatre Royal Museum, Victoria Rd, Richmond, North Yorkshire DL10 4DW - T: (01748) 823710, 823021, Fax: 823710. Head: Bill Sellars
Performing Arts Museum
Coll of original playbills from 1792 to the 1840s, the oldest and largest complete set of painted scenery in Britain, dating from 1836, displays of model theatres, photographs 34299

Green Howards Museum, Trinity Church Sq, Richmond, North Yorkshire DL10 4QN - T: (01748) 822133, Fax: 826561, E-mail: green.howards@virgin.net, Internet: http://www.greenhowards.org.uk. Head: N.D. McIntosh
Military Museum - 1973
History of the regiment since 1688, uniforms, medals, equipment, paintings, photographs & memorabilia 34300

Richmondshire Museum, Ryder's Wynd, Richmond, North Yorkshire DL10 4JA - T: (01748) 825611
Local Museum
Development of the Richmond area since 1071, earlier archaeological material, Anglo-Saxon carved stones, farming and craftsmen's tools and equipment, leadmining relics, costumes, needlework, reconstructions of a carpenter's and a blacksmith's shop, model of Richmond railway station, old photographs and prints 34301

Richmond, Surrey

Ham House, Ham St, Petersham, Richmond, Surrey TW10 7RS - T: (020) 89401950, Fax: 83326903, E-mail: shhgen@smtp.ntrust.org.uk, Internet: nationaltrust.org.uk/southern
Local Museum
19th-c kitchen, textiles, paintings and tapestries 34302

Museum No 1, Royal Botanic Gardens, Kew, Richmond, Surrey TW9 3AE - T: (020) 83325706, Fax: 83325768, E-mail: h.prendergast@rbgkew.org.uk, Internet: http://www.rbgkew.org.uk/c&6. Head: H.D.V. Prendergast
Natural History Museum
Economic botany coll, useful plants and their products worldwide, wood coll 34303

Museum of Richmond, Old Town Hall, Whittaker Av, Richmond, Surrey KT9 1TP - T: (020) 83321141, Fax: 89487570, E-mail: musrich@globalnet.co.uk, Internet: http://www.museumofrichmond.com
Local Museum
Local history 34304

Queen Charlotte's Cottage, Kew Gardens, Kew Rd, Richmond, Surrey TW9 3AB - T: (020) 77819500, Internet: http://ww.hrp.org.uk
Historical Museum
Royal picnic house 34305

Rickmansworth

Three Rivers Museum and Local History, Basing House, Rickmansworth WD3 8QH - T: (01923) 710365
Local Museum 34306

Rievaulx

Rievaulx Abbay, Rievaulx YO6 5LB - T: (01439) 798340, Fax: 798480, E-mail: yorknu@smtp.ntrust.org.uk. Head: Andrew Morrison
Decorative Arts Museum / Religious Arts Museum
English landscape design in the 18th c, medieval tiles, everyday items 34307

Ripley, Derbyshire

Midland Railway Centre, Butterley Station, Ripley, Derbyshire DE5 3QZ - T: (01773) 747674, Fax: 570721, E-mail: info@midlandrailway-centre.co.uk. Head: Dudley Fowkes
Science&Tech Museum 34308

Ripley, North Yorkshire

Ripley Castle, Ripley, North Yorkshire HG3 3AY - T: (01423) 770152, Fax: 771745, E-mail: enquiries@ripleycastle.co.uk, Internet: http://www.ripleycastle.co.uk. Head: Sir Thomas C.W. Ingilby
Historical Museum - 1418
Civil War armour, Elizabethan panelling 34309

Ripon

Newby Hall, Ripon HG4 5AE - T: (01765) 322583, Fax: (01423) 324452, E-mail: info@newbyhall.com, Internet: http://www.newbyhall.com. Head: Richard Compton
Fine Arts Museum / Decorative Arts Museum
Classical statuary, Chippendale furniture, chamber pots, Gobelin tapestries 34310

Norton Conyers, Ripon HG4 5EQ - T: (01765) 640333, Fax: 640333, E-mail: norton.conyers@ripon.org. Head: Sir James Graham, Lady Graham
Local Museum / Fine Arts Museum / Decorative Arts Museum 34311

Ripon Prison and Police Museum, 27 Saint Marygate, Ripon HG4 1LX - T: (01765) 690799. Head: J.K. Whitehead
Historical Museum
Police mementoes and equipment from the 17th c to the present day, illustration of the 17th to 19th-c methods of confinement and punishment 34312

Ripon Workhouse Museum, Sharow View, Allhallowgate, Ripon HG4 1LE. Head: Ralph Lindley
Historical Museum
Victorian poor law artefacts 34313

Robin Hood's Bay

Robin Hood's Bay and Fylingdale Museum, Fisherhead, Robin Hood's Bay YO22 4ST - T: (01947) 880097
Local Museum
Local social history, geology 34314

Rochdale

Rochdale Art and Heritage Centre, Esplanade, Rochdale OL16 1AQ - T: (01706) 342154, Fax: 712723, E-mail: artgallery@rochdale.gov.uk. Head: Andrew Pearce
Fine Arts Museum / Local Museum - 1903
British paintings and watercolours, contemporary paintings, local social history 34315

Rochdale Pioneers Museum, 31 Toad Ln, Rochdale OL12 0NU - T: (01706) 524920, Fax: 2462946, E-mail: museum@co-op.ac.uk, Internet: http://www.co-op.ac.uk/toad_lane.htm. Head: Gillian Lonergan
Historical Museum - 1931
Formation of the Rochdale Equitable Pioneers Society, which marked the beginning of the worldwide co-operative movement, Co-operative Wholesale Society, celebrations (1944 and 1994) celebrations, international social reformer and co-operator Robert Owen 34316

Rochester

Charles Dickens Centre, Eastgate House, High St, Rochester ME1 1EW - T: (01634) 844176, Fax: 844676
Special Museum - 1903
Victorian furniture, memorabilia of Charles Dickens 34317

Guildhall Museum, High St, Rochester ME1 1PY - T: (01634) 848717, Fax: 832919, E-mail: guildhall.museum@medway.gov.uk. Head: Peter Boreham
Historical Museum
18th-19th c prison hulks, prisoner-of-war ship models 34318

Medway Towns Gallery, Civic Centre, Strood, Rochester ME20 4AW - T: (01634) 727777
Public Gallery 34319

Strood Library Gallery, 32 Bryant Rd, Strood, Rochester ME2 3EP - T: (01634) 718161, Fax: 718161
Public Gallery 34320

Rockbourne

Rockbourne Roman Villa, Rockbourne SP6 3PG - T: (01725) 518541, E-mail: musuijh@hants.gov.uk, Internet: http://www.hants.gov.uk/museum/rockbourne. Head: Jim Hunter
Archaeological Museum
Mosaics and hypocaust exposed 34321

Rolvenden

C.M. Booth Collection of Historic Vehicles, c/o Falstaff Antiques, 63-67 High St, Rolvenden TN17 4LP - T: (01580) 241234. Head: C.M. Booth
Science&Tech Museum - 1972
Morgan 3-wheel cars 34322

Romsey

Mountbatten Exhibition, Broadlands, Romsey SO51 9ZD - T: (01794) 505010, Fax: 505040, E-mail: admin@broadlands.net, Internet: http://www.broadlands.net
Historical Museum
Lives and careers of Lord and Lady Mountbatten 34323

Rosemarkie

Groam House Museum, High St, Rosemarkie IV10 8UF - T: (01381) 620961, Fax: 621730, E-mail: groamhouse@ecosse.net
Archaeological Museum - 1989
13 Pictish sculptured stones & Rosemarkie Pictish cross-slab, artistic impressions of Ross and Cromarty Pictish stones, photographs of all the Pictish carved stones in Scotland, celtic art by George Bain 34324

Roslin

Rosslyn Chapel, Roslin EH25 9PU - T: (0131) 4402159, Fax: 4401979, E-mail: rosslych@aol.com, Internet: http://www.rosslynchapel.org.uk. Head: Stuart Beattie
Historic Site 34325

Rothbury

Cragside House, Rothbury NE65 7PX - T: (01669) 620150, Fax: 620066, E-mail: ncrvmx@smtp.ntrust.org.uk
Decorative Arts Museum
Original furniture and fittings, stained glass, earliest wallpaper, Lord Armstrong's first hydro-electric lighting 34326

Rotherham

Clifton Park Museum, Clifton Ln, Rotherham S65 2AA - T: (01709) 823635, Fax: 823631, E-mail: steve.blackbourn@rotherham.gov.uk, Internet: http://www.rotherham.gov.uk. Head: Di Billups
Local Museum - 1893
Rockingham porcelain, Roman archaeology 34327

Rotherham Art Gallery, Walker Pl, Rotherham S65 1JH - T: (01709) 823621, Fax: 823653, E-mail: david.gilbert@rotherham.gov.uk. Head: David Gilbert
Public Gallery - 1893
Fine and decorative art 34328

York and Lancaster Regimental Museum, Arts Centre, Walker Pl, Rotherham S65 1JH - T: (01709) 382121 ext 3633, Fax: 823631, E-mail: steve.blackbourn@rotherham.gov.uk, Internet: http://www.rotherham.gov.uk. Head: Di Billupsr
Military Museum - 1930
Uniform, orders, medals and effects of field marshal Viscount H.C.O. Plumer of Messines 34329

Rothesay

Bute Museum, Stuart St, Rothesay PA20 0BR - T: (01700) 502248, E-mail: tdclegg@cs.com. Head: Alexandra Montgomery
Local Museum - 1905
Local archaeology, geology, mineralogy, natural history, social history 34330

Royston

Royston and District Museum, Lower King St, Royston SG8 5AL - T: (01763) 242587. Head: Jane Vincent
Local Museum
Local archaeology, social history, local art 34331

Ruddington

Nottingham Transport Heritage Centre, Mere Way, Ruddington NG11 6NX - T: (0115) 9405705, Fax: 9405909, Internet: http://www.nthc.org.uk. Head: Alan Kemp
Science&Tech Museum
Steam railway and bus, signal boxes and sundry railwayana 34332

Ruddington Framework Knitters' Museum, Chapel St, Ruddington NG11 6HE - T: (0115) 9846914, Fax: 9841174, E-mail: jack@smirfitt.demon.co.uk, Internet: http://www.rfkm.org. Head: Prof. Stanley Chapman
Special Museum - 1971 34333

Ruddington Village Museum, Saint Peters Rooms, Church St, Ruddington NG11 6HA - T: (0115) 9146645. Head: Gavin Walker
Local Museum - 1968
Village history, fish and chips shop, pharmacy 34334

Rufford

Rufford Old Hall, nr Ormskirk, Rufford L40 1SG - T: (01704) 821254, Fax: 821254, E-mail: rrufoh@smtp.ntrust.org.uk. Head: Carol Chalmers
Folklore Museum - 1936
Antique furniture, tapestries, armaments 34335

Rugby

HM Prison Service Museum, Newbold Revel, Rugby CV23 0TH - T: (01788) 834167/68, Fax: 834186, E-mail: museum@breathemail.net, Internet: http://www.hmprisonservice.gov.uk. Head: Elizabeth Cheetham
Special Museum - 1982
Irons, fetters, gyves, a door from cells visited by the Wesley brothers at Oxford Prison, original tools, uniforms, photographs, objects - archives 34336

James Gilbert Rugby Football Museum, 5 Saint Matthews St, Rugby CV21 3BY - T: (01788) 333889, Fax: 540795, E-mail: sales@james-gilbert.com. Head: Pat Kidd
Special Museum - 1985
History of the development of Rugby football 34337

Rugby Art Gallery and Museum, Saint Matthews St, Rugby CV21 3BZ - T: (01788) 533201, Fax: 533204, E-mail: rugbyartgallery&museum@rugby.gov.uk. Head: Wendy Parry
Public Gallery / Local Museum - 2000
Rugby coll, British art (20th c) 34338

Rugby School Museum, 10 Little Church St, Rugby CV21 3AW - T: (01788) 556109, Fax: 556228, E-mail: museum@rugby-school.warwks.sch.uk. Head: Rusty MacLean
Historical Museum / Special Museum
School history and artefacts, early Rugby Football memorabilia, art colls 34339

Rugeley

Brindley Bank Pumping Station and Museum, Wolseley Rd, Rugeley WS15 2EU - T: (01922) 38282
Science&Tech Museum
Flowmeters, pumps, maps, documents and other items illustrating the history of the Waterworks and the public water supply in the area 34340

Runcorn

Norton Priory Museum, Manor Park, Tudor Rd, Runcorn WA7 1SX - T: (01928) 569895, Fax: 589743, E-mail: info@nortonpriory.org, Internet: http://www.nortonpriory.org. Head: Steven Miller
Religious Arts Museum - 1975
Medieval decorated floor tiles, medieval carved stonework, remains of medieval priory, medieval mosaic tile floor (70 sq.m.), statue of St. Christopher, 12th c undercroft, contemporary sculpture - priory remains, gardens 34341

Rustington

Rustington Heritage Exhibition Centre, 34 Woodlands Av, Rustington BN16 3HB - T: (01903) 784792
Local Museum
Social history 34342

Ruthin

Ruthin Craft Centre, Park Rd, Ruthin LL15 1BB - T: (01824) 704774, Fax: 702060. Head: Philip Hughes, Jane Gerrard
Decorative Arts Museum 34343

Ruthwell

Savings Banks Museum, Ruthwell DG1 4NN - T: (01387) 870640, E-mail: tsbmuseum@btinternet.com, Internet: http://www.lloydstsb.com/savingsbanksmuseum
Special Museum - 1974
History of saving bank movement, coll of money boxes, bank memorabilia, familiy history - archive 34344

Rye

Rye Art Gallery, Ockman Ln and East St, Rye TN31 7JY - T: (01797) 223218, 222433, Fax: 225376. Head: Eric Money
Fine Arts Museum / Decorative Arts Museum
Contemporary fine art and craft 34345

Rye Castle Museum, 3 East St, Rye TN31 7JY - T: (01797) 226728. Head: A.V Downend
Local Museum - 1928
Medieval Rye pottery, modern Rye pottery, prints and drawings local scenes, local militaria, costumes, cinque ports regalia, 18th c fire engine, toys 34346

Rye Heritage Centre Town Model, Son et Lumière, Strand Quay, Rye TN31 7AY - T: (01797) 226696, Fax: 223460, E-mail: ryetic@rother.gov.uk, Internet: http://www.rye.org.uk/heritage. Head: J. Arkley
Local Museum 34347

Saffron Walden

Audley End House, Saffron Walden CB11 4JF - T: (01799) 522842, Fax: 521276. Head: Gareth Hughes
Decorative Arts Museum
House history, Howard, Neville and Cornwallis coll, early neo-classical furniture, British Portraits, natural history, silver coll 34348

Fry Public Art Gallery, Bridge End Gardens, Castle St, Saffron Walden CB10 1BD - T: (01799) 513779, E-mail: gcummings@totalise.co.uk, Internet: http://www.fryartgallery.org. Head: Nigel Weaver
Fine Arts Museum - 1985
Works by 20th c artists from the area of North West Essex, like Ravilious, Bawden, Rothenstein, Aldridge 34349

Saffron Walden Museum, Museum St, Saffron Walden CB10 1JL - T: (01799) 510333, Fax: 510334, E-mail: museum@uttlesford.gov.uk. Head: Carolyn Wingfield
Local Museum - 1832
Local archaeology, hilt of a 6th c ring sword, unique viking pendant necklace from saxon walden cemetery, social and natural hist, geology, ethnography, ceramics, glass, costumes, furniture, dolls 34350

Saint Albans

De Havilland Aircraft Heritage Centre, Mosquito Aircraft Museum, Salisbury Hall, London Colney, Saint Albans AL2 1EX - T: (01727) 822051, 826400, Fax: 826400, Internet: http://www.hertsmuseums.org.uk. Head: Ralph Steiner
Science&Tech Museum - 1959
Displays of de Havilland aircraft, Mosquito prototype - Library 34351

Kingsbury Watermill Museum, Saint Michaels Village, Saint Albans AL3 4SJ - T: (01727) 853502, Fax: 832662
Science&Tech Museum / Agriculture Museum
Old farm implements 34352

Margaret Harvey Gallery, c/o Faculty of Art & Design, University of Herfordshire, 7 Hatfield Rd, Saint Albans AL1 3RS - T: (01707) 285376, Fax: 285310, E-mail: s.moore@herts.ac.uk. Head: Chris McIntyre
Public Gallery 34353

Museum of Saint Albans, Hatfield Rd, Saint Albans AL1 3RR - T: (01727) 819340, Fax: 837472, E-mail: museum@stalbans.gov.uk, Internet: http://www.stalbansmuseums.org.uk. Head: Mark Suggitt
Local Museum - 1898
Salaman coll of trade and craft tools, social and local history, natural sciences 34354

Saint Albans Organ Museum, 320 Camp Rd, Saint Albans AL1 5PB - T: (01727) 851557, 869693, Fax: 851557. Head: Bill Walker
Music Museum - 1959
Two theatre pipe organs, four Belgian cafe organs, music boxes, mills violino vertuoso, player pianos, player reed organs 34355

Verulamium Museum, Saint Michael's, Saint Albans AL3 4SW - T: (01727) 751810, Fax: 859919, E-mail: museum@stalbans.gov.uk, Internet: http://www.stalbansmuseums.org.uk. Head: Mark Suggitt
Archaeological Museum - 1939
Iron Age & Roman, excavated at Verulamium, c. 100 BC-AD 450, Roman hypocaust 34356

Saint Andrews

Bell Pettigrew Museum, c/o University of Saint Andrews, Bute Medical Bldg, Saint Andrews KY16 9TS - T: (01334) 463498, Fax: 462401, E-mail: dse1@st-and.ac.uk, Internet: http://medialab.st-and.ac.uk/bellpet. Head: Prof. P.G. Willmer
Natural History Museum / University Museum 34357

British Golf Museum, Bruce Embankment, Saint Andrews KY16 9AB - T: (01334) 460046, Fax: 460064, E-mail: hilrywebster@randagc.org, Internet: http://www.britishgolfmuseum.co.uk. Head: Kathryn Baker
Special Museum
Golf history in Britain since the middle ages, clubs, balls, trophies, costume, paintings 34358

Crawford Arts Centre, 93 North St, Saint Andrews KY16 9AD - T: (01334) 474610, Fax: 479880, E-mail: crawfordarts@crawfordarts.free-online.co.uk, Internet: http://www.crawfordarts.free-online.co.uk. Head: Diana A. Sykes
Public Gallery 34359

Saint Andrews Cathedral Museum, Saint Andrews - T: (0131) 2443101
Religious Arts Museum - 1950
Early Christian crosses, medieval cathedral relics, pre-Reformation tomb stones, 9th-10th c sarcophagus 34360

Saint Andrews Museum, Doubledykes Rd, Saint Andrews KY16 9DP - T: (01334) 412934, 412690, Fax: 413214, E-mail: museums.east@fife.gov.uk, Internet: http://home.clara.net/standrewsmuseum
Local Museum
Social history, archaeology 34361

Saint Andrews Preservation Museum, 12 North St, Saint Andrews - T: (01334) 477629, Internet: http://www.activitypoint.co.uk. Head: Susan Keracher
Local Museum 34362

Saint Andrews University Museum Collection, University of Saint Andrews, Saint Andrews KY16 9AL - T: (01334) 462417, Fax: 462401, E-mail: hr1c@st-andrews.ac.uk, Internet: http://www.st-and.ac.uk/services/muscoll. Head: Prof. Ian A. Carradice
Natural History Museum / Ethnology Museum / Fine Arts Museum / University Museum
Fine and applied art, silver, furniture, anatomy, pathology, chemistry, ethnography, geology, psychology, zoology, natural history, Amerindians, scientific apparatus and instruments 34363

Scotland's Secret Bunker, Troywood, Saint Andrews KY16 8QH - T: (01333) 310301, Fax: 312040, E-mail: mod@secretbunker.co.uk, Internet: http://www.secretbunker.co.uk
Historical Museum
Underground secret nuclear command bunker 34364

Saint Asaph

Saint Asaph Cathedral Treasury, The Cathedral, Saint Asaph LL19 0RD - T: (01745) 583429, Internet: http://www.stasaphcathedral.org.uk
Religious Arts Museum
Relics relating to the Clwyd area 34365

Saint Austell

Charlestown Shipwreck and Heritage Centre, Charlestown Harbour, Saint Austell PL25 3NJ - T: (01726) 69897, Fax: 68025. Head: John Brian Kneale
Historical Museum - 1976
Town and port hist, largest coll of shipwreck artefacts in UK, Richard Larn (diver) 34366

Wheal Martyn China Clay Museum, Carthew, Saint Austell PL26 8XG - T: (01726) 850362, Fax: 850362, E-mail: info@wheal-martyn.com, Internet: http://www.wheal-martyn.com
Historical Museum 34367

Saint Brelade

Noirmont Command Bunker, Noirmont Point, Saint Brelade JE3 8JA - T: (01534) 482089
Historical Museum
German artillery command bunker 34368

Saint Dominick

Shamrock and Cotehele Quay Museum, National Maritime Museum Outstation, Cotehele Quay, Saint Dominick PL12 6TA - T: (020) 88584422, (01579) 350830, Fax: (020) 83126632. Head: Peter Allington
Science&Tech Museum - 1979
Historic sailing barge Shamrock 34369

Saint Fagans

Museum of Welsh Life, Saint Fagans CF5 6XB - T: (029) 20573500, Fax: 20573490, E-mail: post@nmgw.ac.uk, Internet: http://www.nmgw.ac.uk/mwl
Open Air Museum / Folklore Museum - 1948
Farmhouses, cottages, Victorian shop complex, tollhouse, tannery, smithy, corn mill, woollen mill, bakehouse, pottery 34370

Saint Helens

Saint Helens Museum, Library, Victoria Sq, Saint Helens WA10 1DY - T: (01744) 456960, Fax: 456961. Head: Joanne Howdle
Local Museum
Local history and industry, oils and watercolours, decorative art, archaeology, Egyptology, antiquities 34371

World of Glass, Chalon Way, Saint Helens WA10 1BX - T: (01744) 22766, Fax: 616966, E-mail: info@worldofglass.com, Internet: http://www.worldofglass.com. Head: Gordon Kirk
Decorative Arts Museum / Local Museum
Industrial archaeology, local history, coll of antique vessel glass 34372

Saint Helier

Barreau Le Maistre Art Gallery, Jersey Museum, The Weighbridge, Saint Helier JE2 3NF - T: (01534) 633300, Fax: 633301, E-mail: museum@jerseyheritagetrust.org, Internet: http://www.jerseyheritagetrust.org. Head: Michael Day
Fine Arts Museum 34373

Elizabeth Castle, Saint Aubins Bay, Saint Helier JE2 6QN - T: (01534) 723971, Fax: 610338, E-mail: museum@jerseyheritagetrust.org, Internet: http://www.jerseyheritagetrust.org. Head: Michael Day
Fine Arts Museum / Local Museum / Military Museum / Historic Site - 1923
Jersey militia, numismatic coll, silver, German occupation, regional hist, hist. tableaux, paintings by Jersey Artists 34374

Jersey Museum, The Weighbridge, Saint Helier JE2 3NF - T: (01534) 633300, Fax: 633301, E-mail: museum@jerseyheritagetrust.org.uk, Internet: http://www.jerseyheritagetrust.org. Head: Michael Day
Local Museum - 1992
Archaeology, German occupation, prison hist, rural life, finance, art 34375

Jersey Photographic Museum, Hôtel de France, Saint Saviour Rd, Saint Helier JE1 7PX - T: (01543) 614700, Fax: 887342, E-mail: ian.parker@jerseymail.co.uk, Internet: http://www.style2000.com/rollei_museum.html
Science&Tech Museum
Cameras, images, processing, history of photography since 1840 34376

Occupation Tapestry Gallery and Maritime Museum, New North Quay, Saint Helier JE2 3ND - T: (01534) 811043, Fax: 874099, E-mail: museum@jerseyheritagetrust.org, Internet: http://www.jerseyheritagetrust.org. Head: Michael Day
Decorative Arts Museum / Special Museum - 1996
Twelve-panel tapestry depicting the occupation of Jersey during WWII by Germany 34377

Saint Ives, Cambridgeshire

Norris Museum, 41 The Broadway, Saint Ives, Cambridgeshire PE17 5BX - T: (01480) 497314, E-mail: norris.st-ives-tc@co-net.com. Head: R.I. Burn-Murdoch
Local Museum - 1931
Archaeology of all periods, French prisoner-of-war material from Norman Cross, ice-skates, 18th c fire engine, local prints, paintings, newspapers, paleolithic finds, lace production - library 34378

Saint Ives, Cornwall

Barbara Hepworth Museum and Sculpture Garden, Barnoon Hill, Saint Ives, Cornwall TR26 1TG - T: (01736) 796226, Fax: 794480, Internet: http://www.tate.org.uk. Head: Susan Daniel McElroy
Fine Arts Museum - 1976
A selection of sculptures devoted to the work of Barbara Hepworth (1903-75) 34379

Barnes Museum of Cinematography, 44 Fore St, Saint Ives, Cornwall TR26 1HE
Special Museum - 1963
Puppets used in the ancient Chinese and Japanese shadowplays, peepshows, thaumatrope, phenakistiscope, zoetrope, praxinoscope, examples of the camera obscura, early photographic techniques incl. daguerreotype and abrotype, 3-D photography, stereoscopes, early film cameras and projectors, history of the magic lantern slides 34380

Penwith Galleries, Back Rd W, Saint Ives, Cornwall TR26 1NL - T: (01736) 795579. Head: Kathleen Watkins
Fine Arts Museum - 1949
Paintings, sculpture, pottery 34381

Saint Ives Museum, Wheal Dream, Saint Ives, Cornwall TR26 1PR - T: (01736) 796005. Head: Stanley Cock
Local Museum - 1951
Local industries, arts, crafts, fishing, mining, paintings, folklore 34382

Saint Ives Society of Artists Members Gallery (Norway Gallery) and Mariners Gallery, Old Mariners Church, Norway Sq, Saint Ives, Cornwall TR26 1NA - T: (01736) 795582, Fax: 731823, E-mail: gallery@stivessocietyofartists.com, Internet: http://www.stivessocietyofartists.com. Head: Brian Mitchell
Public Gallery - 1926
Paintings, sculpture 34383

Tate Saint Ives, Porthmeor Beach, Saint Ives, Cornwall TR26 1TG - T: (01736) 796226, Fax: 794480, Internet: http://www.tate.org.uk. Head: Susan Daniel McElroy
Public Gallery - 1993
Changing displays of 20th c art in the context of Cornwall focusing on the modern tradition for which St Ives has become famous, works by contemporary artists 34384

Saint Lawrence

German Underground Hospital, Les Charrières Malorey, Meadowbank, Saint Lawrence JE3 1FU - T: (01534) 863442, Fax: 865970. Head: James McScowan
Military Museum
Wartime occupation, arms 34385

Hamptonne Country Life Museum, Rue de la Patente, Saint Lawrence JE3 1HG - T: (01534) 863955, Fax: 863935, E-mail: museum@jerseyheritagetrust.org, Internet: http://jerseyheritagetrust.org
Agriculture Museum - 1993
Restored farm complex tracing its hist through centuries of development 34386

Saint Margaret's Bay

Saint Margaret's Museum, Beach Rd, Saint Margaret's Bay CT15 6DZ - T: (01304) 852764, Fax: 853626
Local Museum
Marine and local history, ships' badges 34387

Saint Margaret's Hope

W. Hourston Smithy Museum, Cromarty Sq, Saint Margaret's Hope KW17 2RH - T: (01856) 831558
Historical Museum
Blacksmiths equipment, machinery, tools, horse-drawn implements and smith-made articles 34388

Saint Mary's

Isles of Scilly Museum, Church St, Saint Mary's TR21 0JT - T: (01720) 422337, Fax: 422337, E-mail: ios.museum@talk21.com, Internet: http://www.aboutbritain.com/islesofscillymuseum.htm. Head: Steve Ottery
Local Museum
Scilly archaeology, history, shipwrecks, birds, flowers and lichens 34389

Saint Neots

Saint Neots Museum, 8 New St, Saint Neots PE19 1AE - T: (01480) 388921, Fax: 388791, Internet: http://www.stneotsmuseum.freeserve.co.uk. Head: Anna Mercer
Local Museum
Local history, local archaeology, crafts and trades, home and community life 34390

Saint Ouen

Channel Islands Military Museum, The Five Mile Rd, Saint Ouen JE3 - T: (01534) 723136, Fax: 485647, E-mail: damienhorn@cinergy.co.uk
Historical Museum / Military Museum
Civilian and military items (June 1940-May 1945) 34391

Jersey Battle of Flowers Museum, La Robeline, Mont des Corvees, Saint Ouen JE3 2ES - T: (01534) 482408. Head: Florence Bechelet
Special Museum
Animals and birds, made with dried wildflowers 34392

Saint Peter

Jersey Motor Museum, La Rue de l'Eglise, Saint Peter JE3 7AG - T: (01534) 482966. Head: F.M. Wilcock
Science&Tech Museum - 1973
Veteran and Vintage cars, motorcycles, Allied and German military vehicles of World War II, aero engines, railway carriage, early motor car lamps, early car radios and accessories 34393

Saint Peter's Bunker, German Occupation Museum, Saint Peter JE3 7AF - T: (01534) 481048
Military Museum - 1965
Military items of the German Army in WWII, seven rooms in an original underground bunker, German 'Enigma' decoding machine 34394

Saint Peter Port

Castle Cornet Military and Maritime Museums, Castle Emplacement, Saint Peter Port GY1 - T: (01481) 721657, Fax: 714021, E-mail: admin@museum.guernsey.net, Internet: http://www.museum.guernsey.net. Head: P.M. Sarl
Military Museum - 1950
Royal militia coll 34395

Guernsey Museum and Art Gallery, Candie Gardens, Saint Peter Port GY1 1UG - T: (01481) 726518, Fax: 715177, E-mail: admin@museum.guernsey.net, Internet: http://www.museum.guernsey.net. Head: P.M. Sarl
Archaeological Museum / Local Museum / Fine Arts Museum
Natural hist, local watercolours, Frederick Corbin Lukis, Joshua Gosselin 34396

Hauteville House, Maison de Victor Hugo Paris, 38 Hauteville, Saint Peter Port GY1 1DG - T: (01481) 721911, Fax: 715913, E-mail: hugohouse@gtonline.net. Head: Véronique Bascoul
Special Museum
Exile House of Victor Hugo, in which he lived from 1856 to 1870, decorated in his very own unique style, using tapestries, Delft tiles carvings, chinoiseries etc - garden 34397

Royal Air Force Museum 201 Squadron, Castle Cornet, Saint Peter Port GY1 1AU - T: (01481) 721657, Fax: 714021, E-mail: admin@museum.guernsey.net, Internet: http://www.museum.guernsey.net. Head: P.M. Sarl
Military Museum - 2001
Hist of Guernset's own Squadron 34398

Shipwreck Museum, Fort Grey, Rocquaine Bay, Saint Peter Port GY1 9BY - T: (01481) 265036, Fax: 715177, E-mail: admin@museum.guernsey.net, Internet: http://www.museum.guernsey.net. Head: P.M. Sarl
Historical Museum
Shipworks 34399

Story of Castle Cornet, Castle Cornet, Saint Peter Port GY1 1AU - T: (01481) 721657, Fax: 714021, E-mail: admin@museum.guernsey.net, Internet: http://www.museum.guernsey.net. Head: P.M. Sarl
Fine Arts Museum - 1997
Objects and paintings depicting the hist of the Castle 34400

Salcombe

Overbeck's Museum → Salcombe Maritime Museum

Salcombe Maritime Museum, Council Hall, Market St, Salcombe TQ8 8LW - T: (01548) 842893
Historical Museum - 1938
Secret childrens room, doll coll, Britain's lead soldier coll, paper conservation/illustration 34401

Salford

Chapman Gallery, University of Salford, Crescent, Salford M5 4WT - T: (0161) 7455000 ext 3219
Public Gallery 34402

The Lowry Gallery, Pier 8, Salford M5 2AZ - T: (0161) 8762020, Fax: 8762021, Internet: http://www.thelowry.com. Head: David Alston
Fine Arts Museum
Coll of paintings and drawings by L.S. Lowry 34403

Ordsall Hall Museum, Ordsall Ln, Salford M5 3AN - T: (0161) 8720251, Fax: 8724951, E-mail: admin@ordsallhall.org.uk, Internet: http://www.ordsallhall.org.uk. Head: Cindy Shaw
Folklore Museum - 1972
Folk life, leather figures, sword made in Solingen 34404

Salford Art Gallery and Museum, Crescent Peel Park, Salford M5 4WU - T: (0161) 7362649, Fax: 7459490, E-mail: salford.museum@salford.gov.uk, Internet: http://www.salford.gov.uk. Head: Sheena Macfarlane
Local Museum / Fine Arts Museum - 1850
Fine and applied arts, social and local history 34405

Viewpoint Photographic Gallery, Old Fire Station, Crescent, Salford M5 4NZ - T: (0161) 7371040, 7369448, Fax: 7371091. Head: Simon Grennan
Public Gallery 34406

Salisbury

Edwin Young Collection, c/o Salisbury Library and Galleries, Market Pl, Salisbury SP1 1BL - T: (01722) 410614, Fax: 413214. Head: Peter Mason
Fine Arts Museum
Victorian and Edwardian oils and watercolours, contemporary paintings 34407

John Creasey Museum, c/o Salisbury Library and Galleries, Market Pl, Salisbury SP1 1BL - T: (01722) 324145, Fax: 413214. Head: Peter Mason
Special Museum / Fine Arts Museum
John Creasey's work, a local author - all editions, all languages, all pseudonyms (23 in all), contemporary art 34408

Mompesson House, The Close, Salisbury SP1 2EL - T: (01722) 335659, Fax: 321559
Fine Arts Museum / Decorative Arts Museum
18th c drinking glasses, furniture, ceramics 34409

Royal Gloucestershire, Berkshire and Wiltshire Regiment Museum, 58 The Close, Salisbury SP1 2EX - T: (01722) 414536, Fax: 421626, E-mail: curator@thewardrobe.org.uk, Internet: http://www.thewardrobe.org.uk. Head: D.G. Chilton
Military Museum - 1982
History of the Regiment over a period of more than 200 years, include uniforms, weapons, equipment, campaign relics, medals and Regimental silver 34410

Salisbury and South Wiltshire Museum, Kings House, 65 The Close, Salisbury SP1 2EN - T: (01722) 332151, Fax: 325611, E-mail: museum@salisburymuseum.freeserve.co.uk, Internet: http://www.salisburymuseum.org.uk. Head: P.R. Saunders
Local Museum / Archaeological Museum / Decorative Arts Museum - 1860
Archaeology, ceramics, English china, glass, Pitt Rivers coll, Brixie Jarvis coll of Wedgwood, Lace, Salisbury Giant - library 34411

Saltash

Saltash Heritage Centre, 17 Lower Fore St, Saltash PL12 6JQ - T: (01752) 848466. Head: David Coles
Local Museum
Local history 34412

Saltcoats

North Ayrshire Museum, Manse St, Kirkgate, Saltcoats KA21 5AA - T: (01294) 464174, Fax: 464234, E-mail: namuseum@globalnet.co.uk, Internet: http://www.northayrshiremuseums.org.uk. Head: Dr. Martin Bellamy
Local Museum - 1957
Local history, stone carvings, old kitchen 34413

Sandal

Sandal Castle, Manygates Ln, Sandal WF1 5PD - T: (01924) 305352
Historical Museum 34414

Sandford Orcas

Manor House, Sandford Orcas DT9 4SB - T: (01963) 220206. Head: Sir Mervyn Medlycott
Fine Arts Museum / Decorative Arts Museum
Queen Anne and Chippendale furniture, 17th c Dutch and 18th c English pictures, coll medieval stained glass 34415

Sandhaven

Sandhaven Meal Mill, Sandhaven AB43 4EP - E-mail: heritage@aberdeenshire.gov.uk
Science&Tech Museum
Scottish meal mill used for grinding oats 34416

Sandhurst, Berkshire

National Army Museum Sandhurst Departments, Royal Military Academy, Sandhurst, Berkshire GU15 4PQ - T: (01276) 63344 ext 2457. Head: I.G. Robertson
Military Museum 34417

Sandling

Museum of Kent Life, Lock Ln, Sandling ME14 3AU - T: (01622) 763936, Fax: 662024, E-mail: enquiries@museum-kentlife.co.uk, Internet: http://www.museum-kentlife.co.uk. Head:

Nigel Chew
Open Air Museum / Local Museum - 1983
Agricultural rural coll mainly from Kent: hopping industry darling buds of May exhibit, life in Kent exhibit, hop, herb and kitchen gardens, oast, granary, barn, farmhouse, farmyard, village hall 34418

Sandown

Dinosaur Isle, Culver Parade, Sandown PO36 8QA - T: (01983) 404344, Fax: 407502, E-mail: dinosaur@iow.gov.uk. Head: Martin Munt
Natural History Museum - 1913
Fossils, dinosaurs, local rocks 34419

Museum of Isle of Wight Geology → Dinosaur Isle

Sandringham

Sandringham House Museum, Sandringham PE35 6EN - T: (01553) 772675, Fax: (01485) 541571, Internet: http://www.sandringhamestate.co.uk. Head: G. Pattinson
Local Museum / Science&Tech Museum
Photogr, commemorative china, Royal Daimler cars, fire engine 34420

Sandwich

Guildhall Museum, Cattle Market, Sandwich CT13 9AN - T: (01304) 617197, Fax: 620170, Internet: http://www.sandwich-kent-uk.net. Head: C.A. Wanostrocht
Historical Museum - 1930
Victorian photogr by a Sandwich photographer 1869 to 1897, 50 Nazi propaganda photogr of the German Army in the field, as distributed to their Embassies worldwide in the 1939-45 War 34421

Richborough Castle - Roman Fort, Richborough Rd, Sandwich CT13 9JW - T: (01304) 612013, Fax: 612013. Head: Tracey Wahdan
Archaeological Museum - 1930
Roman finds, pottery, tools, coins, ornaments 34422

White Mill Folk Museum, Ash Rd, Sandwich CT13 9JB - T: (01304) 612076, Internet: http://www.kent.museums.org.uk/whitemill
Local Museum
Agricultural implements, artefacts and craft workers' tools, domestic artefacts, blacksmith forge 34423

Sanquhar

Sanquhar Tolbooth Museum, High St, Sanquhar DG4 6BN - T: (01659) 50186, E-mail: info@dumfriesmuseum.demon.co.uk. Head: Robert Martin
Local Museum
1735 town house, local history, geology knitting 34424

Sauchen

Castle Fraser, Sauchen AB51 7LD - T: (01330) 833463. Head: Eric Wilkinson
Historical Museum 34425

Sawrey

Hill Top, Sawrey LA22 0LF - T: (015394) 36269, Fax: 36118, E-mail: rpmht@smtp.ntrust.org.uk. Head: Caroline Binder
Special Museum
Beatrix Potter wrote many "Peter Rabbit" books here, furniture, china and other possessions 34426

Saxtead

Saxtead Green Post Mill, Saxtead Green, Saxtead IP13 9QQ - T: (01728) 685789. Head: Tom Johnston
Science&Tech Museum
Milling equipment, tools 34427

Scalloway

Scalloway Museum, Main St, Scalloway
Local Museum
Coll of objects relating to Scalloway and the nearby islands, dating from Neolithic times to the present day, a large photographic archive, Scalloway's role in the WWII 34428

Scarborough

Crescent Arts, The Crescent, Scarborough YO11 2PW - T: (01723) 371461, Fax: 506674, E-mail: info@crescentarts.co.uk, Internet: http://www.crescentarts.co.uk. Head: Mary Butter
Public Gallery 34429

Rotunda Museum od Archaeology and Local History, Museum Terrace, Vernon Rd, Scarborough YO11 2NN - T: (01723) 232323, Fax: 376941. Head: Karen Snowden
Archaeological Museum / Local Museum - 1829
Regional archaeological coll, esp mesolithic, Bronze Age and medieval, fine surviving example of early purpose-built museums 34430

Scarborough Art Gallery, The Crescent, Scarborough YO11 2PW - T: (01723) 232323, Fax: 376941. Head: Helen Watson
Fine Arts Museum - 1947
Paintings (17th-20th c), local paintings (19th c), contemporary prints 34431

Wood End Museum, Londesborough Lodge, The Crescent, Scarborough YO11 2PW - T: (01723) 367326, Fax: 376941. Head: Karen Snowden
Natural History Museum - 1951
Regional fauna, flora and geology, entomology, conchology, vertebrates 34432

Scunthorpe

Normanby Hall, Normanby Hall Country Park, Scunthorpe DN15 9HU - T: (01724) 720588, Fax: 720337, Internet: http://www.northlincs.gov.uk/museums. Head: Susan Hopkinson
Decorative Arts Museum - 1964
Period furniture, decorations, costume galleries - Normanby park farming museum 34433

Normanby Park Farming Museum, Normanby Hall, Country Park, Scunthorpe DN15 9HU - T: (01724) 720588, Fax: 720337, Internet: http://www.northlincs.gov.uk/museums. Head: Susan Hopkinson
Agriculture Museum - 1989
Rural crafts and industry, transport, agriculture - Normanby Hall 34434

North Lincolnshire Museum, Oswald Rd, Scunthorpe DN15 7BD - T: (01724) 843533, Fax: 270474, E-mail: steve.thompson@northlincs.gov.uk, Internet: http://www.northlincs.gov.uk/museums
Local Museum - 1909
Geology, history and natural hist, archaeology, agriculture 34435

Seaford

Seaford Museum of Local History, 74 Martello Tower, Esplanade, Seaford BN25 1JH - T: (01323) 898222, E-mail: museumseaford@tinyonline.co.uk, Internet: http://www1.cnl.net/~seaford/history/seaford/museum.htm
Local Museum - 1970
Housing register, huge photographic coll, Connie Brewer coll, television and radio 34436

Seaton

Seaton Delaval Hall, Estate Office, Seaton NE26 4QR - T: (0191) 2371493. Head: Lord Hastings
Decorative Arts Museum
Pictures and documents 34437

Seaview

National Wireless Museum, Puckpool Park, Seaview PO34 5AR - T: (01983) 567665
Science&Tech Museum
History of wireless communications 34438

Seething

448th Bomb Group Memorial Museum, Airfield, Seething NR15 1AL - T: (01603) 614041
Military Museum 34439

Selborne

Gilbert White's House and the Oates Museum, The Wakes, Selborne GU34 3JH - T: (01420) 511275, Fax: 511040, E-mail: gilbertwhite@btinternet.com. Head: Maria Newbery
Special Museum - 1955
Restored 18th c home of Gilbert White, travels of Frank Oates in Africa, Cpt. L. Oates Antarctic fame - library 34440

Oates Memorial Museum and Gilbert White Museum → Gilbert White's House and the Oates Museum

Romany Folklore Museum and Workshop, Selborne GU34 3JW - T: (01420) 50486
Folklore Museum
Coll of living vans, other vehicles undergoing restoration in the workshop, the early history, language, music, dress and crafts of the gypsies 34441

Selkirk

Bowhill Collection, Selkirk TD7 5ET - T: (01750) 722204, Fax: 722204, E-mail: bht@buccleuch.com, Internet: http://www.heritageontheweb.co.uk. Head: Duke of Buccleuch
Decorative Arts Museum / Fine Arts Museum
Art coll, French furniture, silver, porcelain, relicts of Duke of Monmouth, Queen Victoria ans Sir Walter Scott 34442

Halliwell's House Museum, Halliwell's Close, Market Pl, Selkirk TD7 4BL - T: (01750) 720096, 720054, Fax: 723282, E-mail: museums@scotborders.gov.uk. Head: Ian Brown
Local Museum - 1984
Late 19th/early 20thc domestic ironmongery 34443

Robson Gallery, Halliwells House Museum, Market Pl, Selkirk TD7 4BL - T: (01750) 720096, Fax: 723282, E-mail: museums@scotborders.gov.uk. Head: Ian Brown
Public Gallery 34444

Sir Walter Scott's Courtroom, Town Hall, Market Pl, Selkirk TD7 4BT - T: (01750) 720096, Fax: 723282, E-mail: museums@scotborders.gov.uk. Head: Ian Brown
Local Museum - 1994 34445

Selsey

Selsey Lifeboat Museum, Kingsway, Selsey PO20 0DL - T: (01243) 602387, Fax: 607790, E-mail: terry@kaytel.fsnet.co.uk
Historical Museum 34446

Settle

Museum of North Craven Life, The Folly, Settle BD24 9RN
Local Museum
Local history 34447

Sevenoaks

Knole, Sevenoaks TN15 0RP - T: (01732) 462100, 450608, Fax: 465528, E-mail: kknxxx@smtp.ntrust.org.uk. Head: Jane Sedge
Decorative Arts Museum
State rooms, paintings, furniture, tapestries, silver 34448

Sevenoaks Museum and Gallery, Library, Buckhurst Ln, Sevenoaks TN13 1LQ - T: (01732) 453118, 452384, Fax: 742682
Local Museum
Local geology, history, archaeology, local fossils, paintings 34449

Shackerstone

Shackerstone Railway Museum, Shackerstone Station, Shackerstone CV13 6NW - T: (01827) 880754
Science&Tech Museum
Coll of railway items, signalbox equipment, station signs, timetables from 1857 and dining-car crockery, eighteen paraffin lamps, a coll of WWII-railway posters 34450

Shaftesbury

Shaftesbury Abbey and Museum, Park Walk, Shaftesbury SP7 8JR - T: (01747) 852910, Fax: 852910, E-mail: user@shaftesburyabbey.fsnet.co.uk. Head: Anna McDowell
Archaeological Museum - 1951
Tiles, stone finds, Saxon relics, reconstruction of old church 34451

Shaftesbury Town Museum, Gold Hill, Shaftesbury SP7 8JW - T: (01747) 852157. Head: Pat Gates
Local Museum 34452

Shallowford

Izaak Walton's Cottage, Worston Ln, Shallowford ST15 0PA - T: (01785) 760278, Fax: 760278. Head: Richard Halliwell
Local Museum / Special Museum
Local history, fishing, material on Izaak Walton (1593-1683) author of 'The Compleat Angler' 34453

Sheerness

Minster Abbey Gatehouse Museum, Minster, Union Rd, Sheerness ME12 2HW - T: (01795) 872303, 661119
Local Museum
Local memorabilia, fossils, tools, costume, telephones, radios, photographs, toys 34454

Sheffield

Abbeydale Industrial Hamlet, Abbeydale Rd S, Sheffield S7 2QW - T: (0114) 2367731, Fax: 2353196, E-mail: postmaster@simt.co.uk, Internet: http://www.simt.co.uk. Head: John Hamshere
Science&Tech Museum - 1970
A fully restored 18th c water-powered skythe and steel works, four working water wheels, craftsmen on site, science, production of steel tools, development of steel manufacturing 34455

Bishops' House Museum, Norton Lees Ln, Sheffield S8 9BE - T: (0114) 2782600, Fax: 2782604, E-mail: info@sheffieldgalleries.org.uk, Internet: http://www.sheffieldgalleries.org.uk. Head: Dr. Gordon Rintoul
Special Museum - 1976
16th and 17th c oak furniture 34456

Fire Police Museum, 101-109 West Bar, Sheffield S3 8PT - T: (0114) 2491999, Fax: 2491999, Internet: http://www.hedgepig.freeserve.co.uk
Historical Museum
Fire fighting, police coll, Charlie Peace exhibition 34457

Graves Art Gallery, Surrey St, Sheffield S1 1XZ - T: (0114) 2782600, Fax: 2782604, E-mail: info@sheffieldgalleries.org.uk, Internet: http://www.sheffieldgalleries.org.uk. Head: Dr. Gordon Rintoul
Fine Arts Museum 34458

Handsworth Saint Mary's Museum, Handsworth Parish Centre, Rectory Grounds, Sheffield S13 9BZ - T: (0114) 2692537
Local Museum
Coll of photographs, artefacts and documents of the local community 34459

Kelham Island Museum, Alma St, off Corporation St, Sheffield S3 8RY - T: (0114) 2722106, Fax: 2757847, E-mail: postmaster@simt.co.uk, Internet: http://www.simt.co.uk. Head: John Hamshere
Historical Museum / Science&Tech Museum - 1982
Story of Sheffield, industry and life, working steam engine, workshops, working cutlers and craftspeople - library; lecture room 34460

Millennium Galleries, Arundel Gate, Sheffield S1 2PP - T: (0114) 2782600, Fax: 2782604, E-mail: info@sheffieldgalleries.org.uk, Internet: http://www.sheffieldgalleries.org.uk. Head: Dr. Gordon Rintoul
Fine Arts Museum / Decorative Arts Museum - 2001
Metalworks, Ruskin coll, craft, design, visal art 34461

Ruskin Gallery → Millennium Galleries

Sheffield Bus Museum, Tinsley Tram Sheds, Sheffield Rd, Tinsley, Sheffield S9 2FY - T: (0114) 2553010, E-mail: webmaster@sheffieldbusmuseum.com, Internet: http://www.sheffieldbusmuseum.com. Head: David Roberts, Eric Wilson, Mike Greenwood, Keith Beeden
Science&Tech Museum
Buses from Sheffield area, tramcars 34462

Sheffield City Museum and Mappin Art Gallery, Weston Park, Sheffield S10 2TP - T: (0114) 2782600, Fax: 2782604, E-mail: info@sheffieldgalleries.org.uk, Internet: http://www.sheffieldgalleries.org.uk. Head: Dr. Gordon Rintoul
Local Museum / Fine Arts Museum - 1875
Archaeology, antiquities, armaments, applied arts, natural hist, relics, ethnography, geology, glass, entomology, numismatics, porcelain, paintings (16th- 19th c) 34463

Shepherd Wheel, Whiteley Woods, off Hangingwater Rd, Sheffield S11 - T: (0114) 2367731, Fax: 2353196, Internet: http://www.smit.co.uk
Science&Tech Museum - 1973
Old water-driven cutlery-grinding shop 34464

Traditional Heritage Museum, 605 Ecclesall Rd, Sheffield S11 8PT - T: (0114) 2226296, E-mail: j.widdowson@sheffield.ac.uk, Internet: http://www.shef.ac.uk/uni/projects/cectal. Head: Prof. J.D.A. Widdowson
Local Museum / University Museum
Life and work in Sheffield area 34465

Shepton Mallet

Shepton Mallet Museum, Council Offices, Great Ostry, Shepton Mallet
Local Museum / Natural History Museum / Archaeological Museum - 1900
Geology, fossils, Roman kiln and jewelry 34466

Sherborne

Sherborne Castle, New Rd, Sherborne DT9 5NR - T: (01935) 813182, Fax: 816727, E-mail: enquiries@sherbornecastle.com, Internet: http://www.sherbornecastle.com
Fine Arts Museum / Decorative Arts Museum - 1594
Oriental porcelain, painting 'Procession of Elizabethl' attributed to Peake the Elder - library 34467

Sherborne Museum, Abbeygate House, Church Ln, Sherborne DT9 3BP - T: (01935) 812252. Head: E. Webber
Local Museum - 1968
Local history, prehistoric finds, geology, Roman and medieval relics, silk production, 20th c fiberglass, local architecture and 14th c wall painting 34468

Worldwide Butterflies and Lullingstone Silk Farm, Compton House, Sherborne DT9 4QN - T: (01935) 74608, Fax: 29937
Natural History Museum - 1960 34469

Sheringham

North Norfolk Railway Museum, Station, Sheringham NR26 8RA - T: (01263) 822045, Fax: 823794
Science&Tech Museum 34470

Sheringham Museum, Station Rd, Sheringham NR26 8RE - T: (01263) 821871, Fax: 825741
Local Museum
Local history, customs and development, local families, boat building, lifeboats, fishing industry, geology, art gallery 34471

Shifnal

Royal Air Force Museum, Cosford, Shifnal TF11 8UP - T: (01902) 376200, Fax: 376211, E-mail: cosford@rafmuseum.com, Internet: http://www.cosfordairshow.co.uk. Head: John Francis
Historical Museum
Military and civil aircraft, including the Victor and Vulcan bombers, the Hastings, the York, the Bristol 188, the last airworthy Britannia and other airliners used by British Airways, Missiles and aero engines also on display 34472

Shildon

Timothy Hackworth Victorian Railway Museum, Soho Cottages, Hackworth Close, Shildon DL4 1PQ - T: (01388) 777999, Fax: 777999, Internet: http://www.hackworthmuseum.co.uk. Head: Alan Pearce
Science&Tech Museum - 1975
Sans Pareil locomotive, family memorabilia, Stockton and Darlington railway, Soho works beam engine, Braddyll Locomotive C 1836 34473

Shipley

Museum of Victorian Reed Organs and Harmoniums, Victoria Hall, Victoria Rd, Saltaire, Shipley BD18 3JS - T: (01274) 585601, E-mail: phil@harmoniumservice.demon.co.uk. Head: Phil Fluke, Pam Fluke
Music Museum - 1986
Coll of around 100 instruments, Harmoniums of all types and styles 34474

Shoreham

Shoreham Aircraft Museum, Shoreham TN14 7TB - T: (01959) 524416, Fax: 524416, Internet: http://www.s-a-m.freeserve.co.uk
Science&Tech Museum
Aviation relics from crashed British and German aircraft (summer of 1940), flying equipment 34475

Shoreham-by-Sea

Marlipins Museum (closed until June 2003), 36 High St, Shoreham-by-Sea BN43 5DA - T: (01273) 462994, Fax: (01323) 844030, E-mail: smomich@sussexpast.co.uk, Internet: http://www.sussexpast.co.uk. Head: Helen E. Poole
Local Museum - 1922/1928
Local history, paintings of ships, ship models, in a 12th-14th c building 34476

Shotts

Shotts Heritage Centre, Benhar Rd, Shotts ML27 5EN - T: (01501) 821556
Local Museum
Iron and coal industries and social history, local studies 34477

Shrewsbury

Attingham Park Exhibition, Shrewsbury SY4 4TP - T: (01743) 708162, 708123, Fax: 708175
Decorative Arts Museum
Italian furniture (c 1810), silver and pictures, printed pottery 34478

Clive House Museum, College Hill, Shrewsbury SY1 1LT - T: (01743) 354811, Fax: 358411, E-mail: museums@shrewsbury-atcham.gov.uk, Internet: http://www.shrewsburymuseums.com
Local Museum
Archaeology, geology of Shropshire, paintings and prints, prehistory, local and regional social history, natural history 34479

Coleham Pumping Station, Longden Coleham, Shrewsbury SY3 7DB - T: (01743) 362947, Fax: 358411, E-mail: museums@shrewsbury-atcham.gov.uk, Internet: http://www.shrewsbury-museums.com
Science&Tech Museum 34480

Radbrook Culinary Museum, Centre for Catering and Management Studies, Radbrook Rd, Shrewsbury SY3 9BL - T: (01743) 232686, Fax: 271563
Special Museum - 1985
Food, nutrition, housecraft, education 34481

Rowley's House Museum → Shrewsbury Museum and Art Gallery

Shrewsbury Castle, Castle St, Shrewsbury SY1 2AT - T: (01743) 358516, Fax: 358411, E-mail: museums@shrewsbury-atcham.gov.uk, Internet: http://www.shrewsburymuseums.com. Head: Steve Martin
Decorative Arts Museum 34482

Shrewsbury Museum and Art Gallery, Rowley's House, Barker St, Shrewsbury SY1 1QH - T: (01743) 361196, Fax: 358411, E-mail: museums@shrewsbury-atcham.gov.uk, Internet: http://www.shrewsburymuseums.com. Head: Peter Boyd, Mary White
Local Museum / Archaeological Museum / Decorative Arts Museum - 1935
Main repository of excavated material from Viroconium, Shropshire geology and prehist, natural hist incl Shropshire herbarium, costume, decorative arts incl Shropshire manufacturers 34483

Shropshire Regimental Museum, Castle, Shrewsbury SY1 2AT - T: (01743) 262292, 358516, Fax: 358411, E-mail: shropsrm@zoom.co.uk, Internet: http://www.shropshireregimental.co.uk. Head: Peter Duckers
Military Museum 34484

Shropshire

Boscobel House, Brewood, Bishop's Wood, Shropshire ST19 9AR - T: (01902) 850244. Head: Peter Trickett
Local Museum
Furniture, textiles, agricultural machinery, forge, dairy and salting room 34485

Sibsey

Trader Windmill, Sibsey PE22 0UT - T: (01205) 460647, E-mail: traderwindmill@sibsey.fsnet.co.uk, Internet: http://www.sibsey.fsnet.co.uk/trager_windmill_sibsey.htm
Science&Tech Museum
Flour milling related machinery and bygones 34486

Sidmouth

Sidmouth Museum, Hope Cottage, Church St, Sidmouth EX10 8LY - T: (01395) 516139
Local Museum
Local history 34487

Vintage Toy and Train Museum, Field's Department Store, Market Pl, Sidmouth EX10 8LU - T: (01395) 515124 ext 208. Head: R.D.N. Salisbury
Special Museum - 1982
Coll of metal and mechanical toys made between 1925 and 1975, coll of French Hornby trains, made at the Meccano factory in Paris between 1930 and 1950, sets of GWR wooden jigsaw puzzles 34488

Silchester

Calleva Museum, The Rectory, Bramley Rd, Silchester RG7 2LU, mail addr: 11 Romans Gate, Pamber Heath RG26 3EH - T: (0118) 9700825. Head: Prof. M.G. Fulford
Archaeological Museum - 1951
Roman period 34489

Singleton

Weald and Downland Open Air Museum, Singleton PO18 0EU - T: (01243) 811348, Fax: 811475, E-mail: wealddown@mistral.co.uk, Internet: http://www.wealddown.co.uk. Head: Richard Harris
Open Air Museum / Agriculture Museum - 1967
40 historic buildings, plumbing, carpentry, wheelwrighting, blacksmithing and shepherding equipment, working watermill, medieval farmstead 34490

Sittingbourne

Dolphin Yard Sailing Barge Museum, Crown Quay Ln, Sittingbourne ME10 3SN - T: (01795) 423215, 470598, Internet: http://www.kentacces.org.uk/artmuse/dolphin. Head: Peter J. Morgan
Science&Tech Museum - 1969
Sailing barge artefacts, photographs, maps, documents, brickmaking tools, sample bricks, moored in our basin is the Thames Sailingbarge Cambria 34491

Sittingbourne Heritage Museum, 67 East St, Sittingbourne ME10 4BQ - T: (01795) 423215
Local Museum
Archaeological finds, local history 34492

Skegness

Church Farm Museum, Church Rd S, Skegness PE25 2ET - T: (01754) 766658, Fax: 766658. Head: Heather Cummins
Open Air Museum / Agriculture Museum - 1976 34493

Skidby

Skidby Windmill and Museum of East Riding Rural Life, Beverley Rd, Skidby HU16 5TF - T: (01482) 848405, Fax: 848432, E-mail: janet.tierney@eastriding.gov.uk. Head: Janet Tierney, Jane Bielby
Historical Museum / Agriculture Museum - 1974
Alex West (agricultural exhibits) 34494

Skinningrove

Tom Leonard Mining Museum, Deepdale, Skinningrove TS13 4AP - T: (01287) 642877, Fax: 642970, E-mail: visits@ironstonemuseum.co.uk, Internet: http://www.ironstonemuseum.co.uk
Science&Tech Museum
Social history, tools, minestone face 34495

Skipton

Craven Museum, Town Hall, High St, Skipton BD23 1AH - T: (01756) 706407, Fax: 706412, E-mail: museum@cravendc.gov.uk, Internet: http://www.cravendc.gov.uk. Head: Andrew Mackay
Local Museum - 1928 34496

Embsay Bolton Abbey Steam Railway, Bolton Abbey Station, Skipton BD23 6AF - T: (01756) 710614, Fax: 710720, E-mail: embsay.steam@btinternet.com, Internet: http://www.yorkshirenet.co.uk/embsaybasteamrailway. Head: Stephen Walker
Science&Tech Museum - 1968
Coll of industrial steam locomotives in Britain, items of passenger and freight rolling stock, photogr and documents illustrates the hist of the line and of the Trust which operates it 34497

Sledmere

Sledmere House, Sledmere YO25 3XG - T: (01377) 236637, Fax: 236500
Fine Arts Museum 34498

Slough

Slough Museum, 278-286 High St, Slough SL1 1NB - T: (01753) 526422, Fax: 526422, E-mail: sloughmuseum@slosm.freeserve.co.uk. Head: Joanna Follett
Local Museum 34499

Smethwick

Avery Historical Museum, c/o Avery-Berkel, Foundry Ln, Smethwick B66 2LP - T: (0870) 9034343, Fax: (0121) 5652677, E-mail: info@avery-berkel.com, Internet: http://www.avery-berkel.com. Head: H.J. Green
Historical Museum - 1928
Coll of scales, weights and records relating to the hist of weighing 34500

Soudley

Dean Heritage Museum, Camp Mill, Soudley GL14 2UB - T: (01594) 822170, E-mail: deanmuse@btinternet.com. Head: Kate Biggs
Local Museum - 1982
Forest of dean, foresty, royal hunting, clocks, mining, geology, archaeology, social/industrial history - reference library 34501

South Molton

South Molton and District Museum, Guildhall, South Molton EX36 3AB - T: (01769) 572951, Fax: 574008, E-mail: curatorsouthmolton@lineone.net, Internet: http://www.devonmuseums.net/southmolton. Head: Ruth Spires
Local Museum - 1951
Local hist, farming and mining, pewter, fire engines, cider presses, local painting, pottery, original royal charters 34502

South Queensferry

Dalmeny House, South Queensferry EH30 9TQ - T: (0131) 3311888, Fax: 3311788, E-mail: events@dalmeny.co.uk, Internet: http://www.dalmeny.co.uk
Decorative Arts Museum
French furniture, tapestries, porcelain from Mentmore, Napleonic coll, British portraits 34503

Hopetoun House, South Queensferry EH30 9SL - T: (0131) 3312451, Fax: 3191885. Head: P. Normand
Decorative Arts Museum / Fine Arts Museum - 1700
Paintings, mid-18th c furniture, sculpture, manuscripts, costumes, tapestries, architecture 34504

Queensferry Museum, 53 High St, South Queensferry EH30 9HP - T: (0131) 3315545, Fax: 5573346. Head: Denise Brace
Local Museum - 1951
History of the Royal Burgh 34505

South Shields

Arbeia Roman Fort and Museum, Baring St, South Shields NE33 2BB - T: (0191) 4561369, Fax: 4276862, E-mail: liz.elliott@tyne-wear-museums.org.uk. Head: David Fleming
Archaeological Museum - 1953
Roman finds from the fort 34506

South Shields Museum and Art Gallery, Ocean Rd, South Shields NE33 2TA - T: (0191) 4568740, Fax: 4567850, E-mail: alisdair.wilson@tyne-wear-museums.org.uk
Local Museum / Fine Arts Museum - 1876
Glass, natural hist, local hist 34507

South Witham

Geeson Brothers Motor Cycle Museum, 4-6 Water Ln, South Witham NG33 5PH - T: (01572) 767280, 768195
Science&Tech Museum
85 British bikes, automobilia 34508

Southall

Collection of Martinware Pottery, Southall Library, Osterley Park Rd, Southall UB2 4BL - T: (020) 85743412, Fax: 85717629. Head: Neena Sohal
Decorative Arts Museum 34509

Saint Bernard's Hospital Museum and Chapel, c/o Hammersmith and Fulham Mental Health Trust, Saint Bernard's Hospital, Uxbridge Rd, Southall UB1 3EU - T: (020) 83548183/8109, Fax: 83548035. Head: Pauline May
Historical Museum
Hospital records, incl. leather restraints and padded cell 34510

Southampton

Ancient Order of Foresters, College Pl, Southampton SO15 2FE - T: (023) 80229655, Fax: 80229657
Religious Arts Museum
Regalia, certificates, photographs, badges, banners, memorabilia and court room furniture 34511

Bitterne Local History Centre, 225 Peartree Av, Bitterne, Southampton SO19 7RD - T: (023) 80490948, E-mail: jimbrown@byterne.screaming.net, Internet: http://www.bittern-e2.freeserve.co.uk
Local Museum
Lives of the people, gentry and traders of Bitterne 34512

Hawthorns Urban Wildlife Centre, Hawthorns Centre, Southampton Common, Southampton SO15 7NN - T: (023) 80671921, Fax: 80676859, E-mail: l.hand@southampton.gov.uk, Internet: http://www.southampton.gov.uk/leisure
Natural History Museum - 1980
Biological records 34513

John Hansard Gallery, University of Southampton, Highfield, Southampton SO17 1BJ - T: (023) 80592158, Fax: 80594192, E-mail: hansard@soton.ac.uk. Head: Stephen Foster
Public Gallery 34514

Museum of Archaeology, God's House Tower, Winkle St, Southampton SO14 7NY - T: (023) 80635904, Fax: 80339601, E-mail: historic.sites@southampton.gov.uk, Internet: http://www.southampton.gov.uk/leisure/heritage. Head: Dr. Andy Russel
Archaeological Museum - 1960
Local archaeology (prehist, Roman, Saxon and Medieval), medieval and post-medieval ceramics from excavations in Southampton, in early 15th c tower - archeological archive 34515

Southampton City Art Gallery, Civic Centre, Southampton SO14 7LP - T: (023) 80832277, 80632601, Fax: 80832153, E-mail: art.gallery@southampton.gov.uk, Internet: http://www.southampton.gov.uk/leisure/arts. Head: Godfrey Worsdale
Public Gallery - 1939
18th-20th c English paintings, Continental Old Masters 14th-18th c, modern French paintings, incl the Impressionist, also sculpture and ceramics, paintings and drawings, contemporary British art 34516

Southampton Hall of Aviation, Albert Rd S, Southampton SO1 3FR - T: (023) 80635830, Fax: 80223383, E-mail: spitfirehome@compuserve.com. Head: Alan Jones
Science&Tech Museum - 1982
History of Solent aviation, story of 26 aircraft companies 34517

Southampton Maritime Museum, Wool House, Town Quay, Bugle St, Southampton SO14 2AR - T: (023) 80223941, 80635904, Fax: 80339601, E-mail: historic.sites@southampton.gov.uk, Internet: http://www.southamton.gov.uk/leisure/heritage. Head: Sian Jones
Science&Tech Museum - 1962
Models of the great liners and shipping ephemera, Titanic to Queen Mary, docks model showing the port c 1938 and associated displays, in 14th c warehouse 34518

Town Wall Walk, High St, Southampton SO14 7LP - T: (023) 80625904, Fax: 80339601, Internet: http://www.southampton.gov.uk/leisure/heritage. Head: Sian Jones
Historic Site
Fully interpreted medieval walls and other monuments 34519

Tudor House Museum, Bugle St, Southampton SO14 2AD - T: (023) 80635904, 80332513, Fax: 80339601, E-mail: historic.sites@southampton.gov.uk, Internet: http://www.southampton.gov.uk/leisure/heritage. Head: Sian Jones
Local Museum - 1912
Furniture, domestic artefacts, paintings and drawings of Southampton, costumes and decorative arts, in a late medieval town house 34520

Southborough

Salomons Memento Rooms, David Salomons House, Broomhill Rd, Southborough TN3 0TG - T: (01892) 515152, Fax: 539102, E-mail: enquiries@salomons.org.uk, Internet: http://www.salomons.org.uk
Religious Arts Museum
Mementoes of three David Salomons 34521

Southend-on-Sea

Beecroft Art Gallery, Station Rd, Westcliff-on-Sea, Southend-on-Sea SS0 7RA - T: (01702) 347418, Fax: 215631. Head: Clare Hunt
Fine Arts Museum - 1953
Permanent coll by artists as Constable, Molenaer, Bright, Epstein, Weight, Lear and Seago, Thorpe-Smith coll of local works, Todman coll, drawings of Nubia by Alan Sorrell 34522

Central Museum, Victoria Av, Southend-on-Sea SS2 6EW - T: (01702) 215131, 434449, Fax: 349806, E-mail: southendmuseum@hotmail.com, Internet: http://www.southendmuseums.co.uk. Head: J.F. Skinner
Local Museum
Natural and human history of south-east Essex, Planetarium 34523

Focal Point Gallery, Southend Central Library, Victoria Av, Southend-on-Sea SS2 6EX - T: (01702) 612621 ext 207, Fax: 469241, E-mail: admin@focalpoint.org.uk, Internet: http://www.focalpoint.org.uk. Head: Lesley Farrell
Public Gallery 34524

Prittlewell Priory Museum, Priory Park, Victoria Av, Southend-on-Sea SS1 2TF - T: (01702) 342878, Fax: 349806, E-mail: southendmuseum@hotmail.com, Internet: http://www.southend-

museums.co.uk. Head: J.F. Skinner
Local Museum - 1922
National history of South East Essex, medieval life, printing, radio and television 34525

Southchurch Hall Museum, Southchurch Hall Close, Southend-on-Sea - T: (01702) 467671, Fax: 349806. Head: Richard Pace
Historical Museum - 1974
Medieval manor house with 17th c furnishings, built in 1340 34526

Southend Pier Museum, Southend Pier, Western Esplanade, Southend-on-Sea SS1 2EQ - T: (01702) 611214, 614553. Head: Peggy Dowie
Historical Museum
History of the pier, buildings, staff, illuminations, pleasure boats, war years, lifeboats, disasters, pier transport and railway 34527

Southport

Atkinson Art Gallery, Lord St, Southport PR8 1DH - T: (01704) 533133 ext 2110, Fax: (0151) 9342109
Public Gallery - 1878
Paintings, drawings, watercolours, prints, sculptures 34528

Botanic Gardens Museum, Churchtown, Southport PR8 7NB - T: (01704) 227547, Fax: 224112
Natural History Museum - 1938
Toys, Liverpool porcelain, natural hist, Victorian artefacts 34529

British Lawnmower Museum, 106-114 Shakespeare St, Southport PR8 5AJ - T: (01704) 501336, Fax: 500564, E-mail: info@lawnmowerworld.co.uk, Internet: http://www.lawnmowerworld.co.uk. Head: B. Radam
Special Museum
Garden machinery, 200 lawnmowers 34530

Southwick

Manor Cottage Heritage Centre, Southwick St, Southwick BN42 4TE - T: (01273) 465164, E-mail: nigel.divers@unisonfree.net
Historical Museum / Decorative Arts Museum
Coll of modern, specially worked needlework panels depicting the history of Southwick 34531

Southwold

Southwold Museum, 9-11 Victoria St, Southwold IP18 6HZ - T: (01502) 722437, 724180. Head: M. Child
Local Museum - 1933
Local hist, Southwold railway relics, natural hist, battle of Sole Bay, tokens, coins, watercolours 34532

Spalding

Ayscoughfee Hall Museum, Churchgate, Spalding PE11 2RA - T: (01775) 725468, Fax: 762715, Internet: http://www.sholland.gov.uk. Head: S. Sladen
Local Museum
Medieval manor house, local and social history, bird coll 34533

Pinchbeck Marsh Engine and Land Drainage Museum, Pinchbeck Marsh of West Marsh Rd, Spalding PE11 3UW - T: (01775) 725861, 725468, Fax: 767689
Science&Tech Museum
Drain pipes, pumps, gas and oil engines, a dragline excavator, hand tools, digging tools, turf cutters, weed cutters, fishing spears, plank road equipment, lamps, steam engine, punt 34534

Spalding Gentlemen's Society Museum, Broad St, Spalding PE11 1TB - T: (01775) 724658. Head: N. Leveritt
Local Museum - 1710
Local history, ceramics, glass, coins, medals, trade tokens 34535

Sparkford

Haynes Motor Museum, Castle Cary Rd, Sparkford BA22 7LH - T: (01963) 440804, Fax: 441004, E-mail: mike@haynesmotormuseum.co.uk, Internet: http://www.haynesmotormuseum.co.uk. Head: John H. Haynes
Science&Tech Museum - 1985
1905 Daimler detachable top limousine, the 1965 AC Cobra, motoring and motorcycling items of historical and cultural interest, American coll, Red coll of sports cars, William Morris Garages, 1929 model J. Deusenberg, Derham bodied tourster, V16 Cadillac, speedway motorcycles 34536

Spean Bridge

Clan Cameron Museum, Achnacarry, Spean Bridge PH34 4EJ - T: (01397) 712090, E-mail: museum@achnacarry.fsnet.co.uk, Internet: http://www.clan-cameron.org. Head: Sir Donald Cameron of Lochiel
Historical Museum
Hist of Cameron Clan and their involvement in the Bonnie Prince Charlie rising 34537

Spey Bay

Tugnet Ice House, Tugnet, Spey Bay IV32 7DU - T: (01309) 673701, Fax: 675863, E-mail: alasdair.joyce@techleis.moray.gov.uk, Internet: http://www.moray.org/museums/tugnetic
Special Museum
Salmon fishing and boat building on the River Spey 34538

Staffin

Staffin Museum, 6 Ellishadder, Staffin IV51 9JE - T: (01470) 562321. Head: Dugald Alexander Ross
Historical Museum - 1977
The only fossilized dinosaur bone from Scotland, it was found in Skye in 1994, neolithic arrowheads and axeheads 34539

Stafford

Ancient High House, Greengate St, Stafford ST16 2JA - T: (01785) 619131, Fax: 619132, E-mail: ahh@staffordbc.gov.uk, Internet: http://staffordbc.gov.uk. Head: Jill Fox
Historic Site
England's largest timber-framed town house built in 1595, period room settings 34540

Royal Air Force Museum Reserve Collection, RAF Stafford, Beaconside, Stafford ST18 0AQ - T: (01785) 258200, Fax: 220080, Internet: http://www.rafmuseum.com. Head: Ken Hunter
Military Museum / Science&Tech Museum 34541

Shire Hall Gallery, Market Sq, Stafford ST16 2LD - T: (01785) 278345, Fax: 278327, E-mail: -shirehallgallery@staffordshire.gov.uk, Internet: http://www.staffordshire.gov.uk/shirehallgallery. Head: Kim Tudor
Fine Arts Museum / Decorative Arts Museum - 1927
Works by Staffordshire artists and of subjects in the county, contemporary jewellery coll by British makers 34542

Stafford Castle and Visitor Centre, Newport Rd, Stafford ST16 1DJ - T: (01785) 257698, Fax: 257698, E-mail: castlebc@btconnect.com. Head: Nicholas Thomas
Historical Museum / Archaeological Museum
Archaeological display 34543

Staines

Spelthorne Museum, Old Fire Station, Market Sq, Staines TW18 4RH - T: (01784) 461804, E-mail: staff@spelthorne.free-online.co.uk. Head: Ralph Parsons
Local Museum
Archaeology, local history and social history, Roman town model, Victorian kitchen, 1738 fire engine 34544

Stalybridge

Astley-Cheetham Art Gallery, Trinity St, Stalybridge SK15 2BN - T: (0161) 3382708, 3383831, Fax: 3431732
Public Gallery
Art, craft, photograpgy 34545

Stamford

Burghley House, Stamford PE9 3JY - T: (01780) 752451, Fax: 480125, E-mail: burghley@dial.pipex.com, Internet: http://www.stamford.co.uk. Head: D.M. Parratt
Fine Arts Museum / Decorative Arts Museum
Italian paintings 17th c, fine oriental ceramics, European furniture, works of art 34546

Stamford Brewery Museum, All Saints St, Stamford PE9 2PA - T: (01780) 52186
Science&Tech Museum
Victorian steam brewery 34547

Stamford Museum, Broad St, Stamford PE9 1PJ - T: (01780) 766317, Fax: 480363, E-mail: crawleyt@lincolnshire.gov.uk. Head: Tracey Crawley
Local Museum - 1961
Archaeology, medieval pottery, social history relating to town of Stamford 34548

Stansted Mountfitchet

House on the Hill Museums Adventure, Stansted Mountfitchet CM24 8SP - T: (01279) 813567, Fax: 816391, E-mail: gold@enta.net, Internet: http://www.gold.enta.net. Head: Jeremy Goldsmith
Special Museum - 1991
Action man coll, star wars coll, toys, books, games since late Victorian times 34549

Mountfitchet Castle and Norman Village, Mountfitchet Castle, Stansted Mountfitchet CM24 8SP - T: (01279) 813237, Fax: 816391. Head: A. Goldsmith
Historic Site - 1986 34550

Stansted Mountfitchet Windmill, Millside, Stansted Mountfitchet CM24 8BL - T: (01279) 813214
Science&Tech Museum
Tower mill, machinery 34551

Staplehurst

Brattle Farm Museum, Staplehurst TN12 0HE - T: (01580) 891222, Fax: 891222. Head: Brian Thompson
Agriculture Museum / Historical Museum
Vintage cars, motorcycles, bicycles, tractors, wagons, horse-drawn machinery, hand tools and crafts, war items, laundry and dairy 34552

Stevenage

Boxfield Gallery, Stevenage Arts and Leisure Centre, Stevenage SG1 1LZ - T: (01438) 766644, Fax: 766675
Public Gallery 34553

Stevenage Museum, Saint George's Way, Stevenage SG1 1XX - T: (01438) 218881, Fax: 218882, E-mail: museum@stevenage.gov.uk, Internet: http://www.stevenage.gov.uk. Head: Maggie Appleton
Local Museum - 1954
Local hist, archaeology, natural hist, geology 34554

Stevington

Stevington Windmill, Stevington MK43 7QB - T: (01234) 824330, Fax: 228531
Science&Tech Museum 34555

Stewarton

Stewarton and District Museum, Council Chambers, Avenue Sq, Stewarton KA3 5AB, mail addr: 17 Grange Terrace, Kilmarnock KA1 2JR - T: (01563) 524748, E-mail: ianhmac@aol.com. Head: I.H. Macdonald
Local Museum - 1980
Local industry, bonnet-making 34556

Steyning

Steyning Museum, Church St, Steyning BN44 3YB - T: (01903) 813333. Head: Jack Campbell
Local Museum
Hist of Steyning from Saxon times to the present day, photographs, documents and objects 34557

Stibbington

Nene Valley Railway, Wansford Station, Stibbington PE8 6LR - T: (01780) 784444, Fax: 784440
Science&Tech Museum
Steam and diesel locomotives and rolling stock, railwayana 34558

Sticklepath

Museum of Rural Industry, Oakhampton, Sticklepath EX20 2NW - T: (01837) 840286
Science&Tech Museum
Agriculture 34559

Stirling

Argyll and Sutherland Highlanders Regimental Museum, Castle, Stirling FK8 1EH - T: (01786) 475165, Fax: 446038, E-mail: museum@argylls.co.uk, Internet: http://www.argylls.co.uk. Head: C.A. Campbell
Military Museum - 1961
History of regiment since 1794, medals, pictures, silver armours, uniforms 34560

Art Collection, c/o University of Stirling, Stirling FK9 4LA - T: (01786) 466050, Fax: 466866, E-mail: v.a.m.fairweather@stir.ac.uk, Internet: http://www.stir.ac.uk/artcol. Head: Valerie A. Fairweather
Fine Arts Museum
Paintings, prints, sculptures, tapestries, J.D. Fergusson 34561

Bannockburn Heritage Centre, Glasgow Rd, Stirling FK7 0LJ - T: (01786) 812664, Fax: 810892, E-mail: bannockburn@nts.org.uk, Internet: http://www.nts.org.uk
Historical Museum - 1987
Scottish history 34562

MacRobert Gallery, c/o University of Stirling, MacRobert Arts Centre, Stirling FK9 4LA - T: (01786) 467155, Fax: 451369, E-mail: macrobert-arts@stirling.ac.uk, Internet: http://www.stir.ac.uk/macrobert. Head: Liz Moran
Public Gallery 34563

National Wallace Monument, Abbey Craig, Hillfoots Rd, Stirling FK9 5LF - T: (01786) 472140, Fax: 461332. Head: Eleanor Muir
Historical Museum
Scotlands National hero Sir William Wallace, famous Scots, countryside, history 34564

Smith Art Gallery and Museum, 40 Albert Pl, Dumbarton Rd, Stirling FK8 2RQ - T: (01786) 471917, Fax: 449523, E-mail: museum@smithartgallery.demon.co.uk, Internet: http://www.smithartgallery.demon.co.uk. Head: Elspeth King
Local Museum / Fine Arts Museum - 1874
Local hist, archaeology, ethnology, geology, paintings, watercolors, pistols 34565

Stirling Old Town Jail, Saint John St, Stirling FK8 1EA - T: (01786) 450050, Fax: 471301, E-mail: info@scottish-heritage.heartlands.org, Internet: http://www.scottish.heartlands.org. Head: Neil Craig
Historical Museum 34566

Stockport

Hat Works, Museum of Hatting, Wellington Mill, Wellington Rd S, Stockport SK3 0EU - T: (0161) 8557773, Fax: 4808735, E-mail: heritage@dial.pipex.com, Internet: http://www.hatworks.org.uk. Head: John Baker
Special Museum - 2000
Hatting coll, machinery, historical and contemporary hats 34567

Stockport Art Gallery, Wellington Rd S, Stockport SK3 8AB - T: (0161) 4744453/54, Fax: 4804960. Head: John Sculley
Fine Arts Museum - 1924
Paintings, sculptures, bronze of Yehudi Menuhin by Epstein 34568

Stockport Museum, Vernon Park, Turncroft Ln, Stockport SK1 4AR - T: (0161) 4744460, Fax: 4744449. Head: John Baker
Local Museum - 1860
Local history, natural history, applied arts, example of a window made from 'Blue John' fluorspar 34569

Stockton-on-Tees

Green Dragon Museum, Theatre Yard, off Silver St, Stockton-on-Tees TS18 1AT - T: (01642) 393938, Fax: 391433. Head: Alan Cracket
Local Museum - 1973
Social, industrial and administrative development, ship models, coll of local pottery 34570

Preston Hall Museum, Preston Park, Yarm Rd, Stockton-on-Tees TS18 3RH - T: (01642) 781184, Fax: 391433. Head: Mark Rowland Jones
Local Museum - 1953
Arms, working crafts, Victorian life, toys 34571

Stoke Bruerne

Canal Museum, Stoke Bruerne NN12 7SE - T: (01604) 862229, Fax: 864199, E-mail: -british.waterways@sosb.globalnet.co.uk
Historical Museum - 1963
Canal history, 200 years of inland waterways 34572

Stoke-on-Trent

Chatterley Whitfield Mining Museum, Tunstall, Stoke-on-Trent ST6 8UN - T: (01782) 813337. Head: P. Gifford
Science&Tech Museum
2.000-foot deep Hesketh shaft, different methods of extraction used over the past 150 years 34573

Etruria Industrial Museum, Lower Bedford St, Etruria, Stoke-on-Trent ST4 7AF - T: (01782) 287557, Fax: 260192. Head: Hadley Perry
Science&Tech Museum - 1991
Ceramic processing, steam beam engine (1820), grinding machinery (1856), blacksmithing coll 34574

Flaxman Gallery, c/o Staffordshire Polytechnic, College Rd, Stoke-on-Trent ST4 2DE - T: (01782) 744531
Fine Arts Museum / Decorative Arts Museum 34575

Ford Green Hall, Ford Green Rd, Smallthorne, Stoke-on-Trent ST6 1NG - T: (01782) 233195, Fax: 233194, Internet: http://www.stoke.gov.uk/fordgreenhall. Head: Angela Graham
Decorative Arts Museum - 1952
In 17th c framed house, period furniture, household objects 34576

Gladstone Pottery Museum, Uttoxeter Rd, Longton, Stoke-on-Trent ST3 1PQ - T: (01782) 319232, 311378, Fax: 598640, E-mail: gladstone@stoke.gov.uk, Internet: http://www.stoke.gov.uk/gladstone. Head: H. Wood
Special Museum
Story of the British pottery industry, the history of the industry in Staffordshire, social history, tiles and tilemaking, sanitary ware, colour and decoration 34577

Minton Museum, London Rd, Stoke-on-Trent ST4 7QD - T: (01782) 292095, 292292, Fax: 292099, E-mail: heritage@royal-doulton.com
Local Museum 34578

The Potteries Museum and Art Gallery, Bethesda St, Hanley, Stoke-on-Trent ST1 3DW - T: (01782) 232323, Fax: 232500, E-mail: museums@stoke.gov.uk, Internet: http://www.stoke.gov.uk/museums. Head: I. Lawley
Archaeological Museum / Fine Arts Museum / Decorative Arts Museum / Natural History Museum - 1956
Staffordshire pottery and porcelain, Continental and Oriental pottery, sculpture, natural history, local history, 18th c watercolors, English paintings, contemporary art 34579

Sir Henry Doulton Gallery, c/o Royal Doulton Ltd., Visitor Centre, Nile St, Burslem, Stoke-on-Trent ST6 2AJ - T: (01782) 292433/34, Fax: 292499, 292424,

E-mail: heritage@royal-doulton.com, Internet: http://www.royal-doulton.com. Head: Joan Jones
Fine Arts Museum / Decorative Arts Museum - 1984
Hist and development of Royal Doulton, Royal Doulton figures 34580

Spode Museum, Church St, Stoke-on-Trent ST4 1BX - T: (01782) 744011, Fax: 572526, E-mail: spodemuseum@spode.co.uk, Internet: http://www.spode.co.uk. Head: Pam Woolliscroft
Decorative Arts Museum - 1938
Spode & Copeland ceramics since 1780, bone china and transfer printed wares 34581

Wedgwood Museum, Barlaston, Stoke-on-Trent ST12 9ES - T: (01782) 282818, Fax: 223315, E-mail: info@wedgwoodmuseum.org.uk, Internet: http://www.wedgwoodmuseum.com. Head: Gaye Blake Roberts
Decorative Arts Museum - 1906
Wedgwood family hist, ceramics, paintings and manuscripts, mason's ironstone, historical pottery, comprehensive coll of the works of Wedgwood - library, archives 34582

Stonehaven

Tolbooth Museum, Old Pier, Stonehaven AB39 2JU - T: (01771) 622906, Fax: 622884, E-mail: heritage@aberdeenshire.gov.uk. Head: Dr. David M. Bertie
Local Museum - 1963 34583

Stornoway

An Lanntair, Town Hall, South Beach, Stornoway HSI 2BX - T: (01851) 703307, Fax: 703307, E-mail: lanntair@sol.co.uk, Internet: http://www.lanntair.com. Head: Roddy Murray
Public Gallery 34584

Museum Nan Eilean, Steornabhagh, Francis St, Stornoway HS1 2NF - T: (01851) 703773 ext 266, Fax: 706318, E-mail: rlanghorne@cne-siar.gov.uk, Internet: http://www.cne-siar.gov.uk. Head: Richard Langhorne
Archaeological Museum / Historical Museum
Archeology of Lewis and Harris, history of the islands, maritime, fishing, crofting coll 34585

Stourton

Stourhead House, Stourton BA12 6QH - T: (01747) 842020. Head: Maggie McKean
Fine Arts Museum / Decorative Arts Museum - 1720
Furniture, paintings, porcelain, furniture designed by Thomas Chippendale, the Younger 34586

Stowmarket

Museum of East Anglian Life, Abbot's Hall, Stowmarket IP14 1DL - T: (01449) 612229, Fax: 672307, E-mail: meal@meal.fsnet.co.uk, Internet: http://www.suffolkcc.gov.uk/central/meal. Head: Miriam Stead
Historical Museum - 1965
Rural life in East Anglia, household equipment, farm and craft tools, re-erected watermill, wind pump, smithy 34587

Strachur

Strachur Smiddy Museum, The Clachan, Strachur PA27 8DG - T: (01369) 860565. Head: Cathie Montgomery
Science&Tech Museum 34588

Stranraer

Castle of Saint John, Castle St, Stranraer DG9 7RT - T: (01776) 705088, Fax: 705835, E-mail: JohnPic@dumgal.gov.uk, Internet: http://www.dumfriesmuseums.demon.co.uk. Head: John Pickin
Historical Museum
Castle hist, town jail in the 18th and 19th c 34589

Stranraer Museum, 55 George St, Stranraer DG9 7JP - T: (01776) 705088, Fax: 705835, E-mail: JohnPic@dumgal.gov.uk, Internet: http://www.dumfriesmuseum.demon.co.uk. Head: John Pickin
Local Museum - 1939
Social and local history, archaeology, art, numismatics, costume, photos - archive 34590

Stratfield Saye

Stratfield Saye House and Wellington Exhibition, Stratfield Saye RG27 0AS - T: (01256) 882882, Fax: 882882, Internet: http://www.stratfield-saye.co.uk
Historical Museum
Bonaparte coll, paintings 34591

Stratford-upon-Avon

Anne Hathaway's Cottage, Shakespeare Birthplace Trust, Shottery, Stratford-upon-Avon CV37 9HH - T: (01789) 292100, Fax: 296083, E-mail: info@shakespeare.org.uk, Internet: http://www.shakespeare.org.uk. Head: Roger Pringle
Special Museum
Thatched farmhouse, home of Anne Hathaway before her marriage to Shakespeare in 1582, period furniture since 16th c with traditional English cottage garden and orchard 34592

Hall's Croft, Shakespeare Birthplace Trust, Old Town, Stratford-upon-Avon CV37 6BG - T: (01789) 292107, Fax: 296083, E-mail: info@shakespeare.org.uk, Internet: http://www.shakespeare.org.uk. Head: Roger Pringle
Special Museum - 1847
Home of Shakespeare's daughter Susanna and her husband Dr. John Hall, Tudor and Jacobean furniture, period medical Exhibition 34593

Harvard House, Shakespeare Birthplace Trust, High St, Stratford-upon-Avon CV37 - T: (01789) 204507, Fax: 296083, E-mail: info@sheakespeare.org.uk, Internet: http://www.sheakespeare.org.uk. Head: Roger Pringle
Special Museum
Neish Pewter Coll 34594

Mary Arden's House and the Countryside Museum, Shakespeare Birthplace Trust, Wilmcote, Stratford-upon-Avon CV37 9UN - T: (01789) 293455, Fax: 296083, E-mail: info@shakespeare.org.uk, Internet: http://www.shakespeare.org.uk. Head: Roger Pringle
Special Museum
Tudor farmhouse, home of Mary Arden (Shakespeare's mother) before her marriage to John Shakespeare, exhibitions and displays of life and work on the land over the centuries 34595

Nash's House and New Place, Shakespeare Birthplace Trust, Chapel St, Stratford-upon-Avon CV37 6EP - T: (01789) 292325, 204016, Fax: 296083, E-mail: info@shakespeare.org.uk, Internet: http://www.shakespeare.org.uk. Head: Roger Pringle
Special Museum
Nash's House, former home of Thomas Nash, husband of Elizabeth Hall (Shakespeare's grand-daughter), adjacent to stunning Elizabethan-style Knott garden set in foundations of New Place, Shakespeare's home from 1597 until he died in 1616 34596

Royal Shakespeare Company Collection, Royal Shakespeare Theatre, Waterside, Stratford-upon-Avon CV37 6BB - T: (01789) 296655, Fax: 294810, E-mail: david.howells@RSC.org.uk. Head: David Howells
Performing Arts Museum - 1881
Relics of famous actors and actresses, portraits of actors, paintings of scenes from Shakespeare's plays, sculptures, scenery and costume designs, costume coll plus props, production photographs, programmes, posters, stage equipment - archive 34597

Shakespeare Birthplace Trust, Shakespeare Centre, Henley St, Stratford-upon-Avon CV37 6QW - T: (01789) 204016, Fax: 296083, E-mail: info@shakespeare.org.uk, Internet: http://www.shakespeare.org.uk. Head: Roger Pringle
Special Museum - 1847
16th c timbered house, Shakespeare's birthplace, memorabilia, ceramics, books, documents, pictures - specialist Shakespeare library, records office, education department 34598

The Teddy Bear Museum, 19 Greenhill St, Stratford-upon-Avon CV37 6LF - T: (01789) 293160, Fax: 87413454, E-mail: info@theteddybearmuseum.com, Internet: http://www.theteddybearmuseum.com. Head: Sylvia Coote
Special Museum - 1988 34599

Strathaven

John Hastie Museum, 8 Threestanes Rd, Strathaven ML10 6DX - T: (01357) 521257
Historical Museum / Decorative Arts Museum
History of Strathaven, with special displays on the weaving industry, Covenanting and the Radical Uprising, coll of porcelain 34600

Strathpeffer

Highland Museum of Childhood, The Old Station, Strathpeffer IV14 9DH - T: (01997) 421031, Fax: 421031, E-mail: info@hmoc.freeserve.co.uk, Internet: http://www.hmoc.freeserve.co.uk. Head: Jennifer Maxwell
Special Museum - 1992
Childhood in the Highlands, doll & toy coll 34601

Strathpeffer Spa Pumping Room Exhibition, Park House Studio, The Square, Strathpeffer IV14 9DL - T: (01997) 420124
Science&Tech Museum 34602

Street

Shoe Museum, c/o C. & J. Clark Ltd., High St, Street BA16 0YA - T: (01458) 842169, Fax: 443196, E-mail: janet.targett@clarks.com. Head: John Kerry
Special Museum - 1974 34603

Stretham

Stretham Old Engine, Green End Ln, Stretham CB6 3LE - T: (01353) 649210, 648106. Head: E. Langford
Science&Tech Museum
Pumping station (1831) 34604

Stromness

Pier Arts Centre, 28-30 Victoria St, Stromness KW16 3AA - T: (01856) 850209, Fax: 851462, E-mail: info@pierartscentre.com
Public Gallery - 1979
20th c art, paintings, Barbara Hepworth, Naum Gabo, Ben Nicholson, Alfred Wallis 34605

Stromness Museum, 52 Alfred St, Stromness KW16 3DF - T: (01856) 850025, Internet: http://www.orknet.co.uk/stromness-museum. Head: B. Wilson
Local Museum - 1837
Orkney maritime and local history, natural history, birds and fossils, Stone Age finds, ship models, Invit carvings, fishing 34606

Stroud

The Museum in the Park, Stratford Park, Stratford Rd, Stroud GL5 4AF - T: (01453) 763394, Fax: 752400, E-mail: museum@stroud.gov.uk. Head: Susan P. Hayward
Local Museum - 1899
Geology, archaeology, fine and decorative arts, social hist 34607

Stroud Museum → The Museum in the Park

Styal

Quarry Bank Mill, Styal SK9 4LA - T: (01625) 527468, Fax: 539267, E-mail: msyrec@smtp.ntrust.org.uk, Internet: http://www.quarrybankmill.org.uk. Head: Andrew Backhouse
Science&Tech Museum - 1976
Working textile museum, hist of cotton, skilled machine demonstrators and costumed interpreters 34608

Sudbury, Derbyshire

Museum of Childhood, Sudbury Hall, Sudbury, Derbyshire DE6 5HT - T: (01283) 585305, Fax: 585139. Head: Carolyn Aldridge
Special Museum - 1974
Betty Cadbury coll of playthings past - education dept. 34609

Sudbury, Suffolk

Gainsborough's House, 46 Gainsborough St, Sudbury, Suffolk CO10 2EU - T: (01787) 372958, Fax: 376991, E-mail: mail@gainsborough.org, Internet: http://www.gainsborough.org. Head: Hugh Belsey
Fine Arts Museum - 1958
Paintings, drawings and prints by Thomas Gainsborough 34610

Sulgrave

Sulgrave Manor, Manor Rd, Sulgrave OX17 2SD - T: (01295) 760205, Fax: 768056, E-mail: sulgrave-manor@talk21.com, Internet: http://www.sulgrave-manor.org.uk. Head: Martin Sirot Smith
Historic Site
Tudor furniture and artefacts, Queen Anne furniture and artefacts, Washington memorabilia 34611

Sunderland

Monkwearmouth Station Museum, North Bridge St, Sunderland SR5 1AP - T: (0191) 5677075, Fax: 5109415, E-mail: juliet.horsley@tyne-wear-museums.org.uk. Head: Juliet Horsley
Science&Tech Museum - 1973
Land transport in North East England, rail exhibits and other land transport items 34612

National Glass Centre, Liberty Way, Sunderland SR6 0GL - T: (0191) 5155555, Fax: 5155556, E-mail: info@ngctr.demon.co.uk
Decorative Arts Museum 34613

North East Aircraft Museum, Old Washington Rd, Sunderland SR5 3HZ - T: (0191) 5190662, Internet: http://www.neam.co.uk. Head: William Fulton
Science&Tech Museum 34614

Northern Gallery for Contemporary Art, Fawcett St, Sunderland SR1 1RE - T: (0191) 5141235, Fax: 5148444, Internet: http://www.ngca.co.uk. Head: Ele Carpenter
Public Gallery 34615

Ryhope Engines Museum, Pumping Station, Ryhope, Sunderland SR2 0ND - T: (0191) 5210235, E-mail: webmaster@g3wte.demon.co.uk, Internet: http://www.g3wte.demon.co.uk
Science&Tech Museum - 1973
Mechanical engineering design and construction, beam engines and pumps, history of water supply, pair of beam engines (1868) complete with boilers, chimneys etc. 34616

Saint Peter's Church, Vicarage, Saint Peter's Way, Sunderland SR6 0DY - T: (0191) 5673726
Religious Arts Museum / Historic Site 34617

Sunderland Museum and Art Gallery, Borough Rd, Sunderland SR1 1PP - T: (0191) 5650723, Fax: 5650713, E-mail: neil.sinclair@tyne-wear-museums.org.uk
Decorative Arts Museum / Fine Arts Museum / Natural History Museum - 1846
Pottery and glass, Wearside paintings, prints, etchings and photographs, Wearside maritime history, British silver, zoology, botany, geology, industries, archaeology 34618

Sutton, Norwich

Sutton Windmill and Broads Museum, Mill Rd, Sutton, Norwich NR12 9RZ - T: (01692) 581195. Head: Chris Nunn
Local Museum
Social history, tricycles, engines, pharmacy, tobacco 34619

Sutton-on-the-Forest

Sutton Park, Sutton-on-the-Forest YO61 1DP - T: (01347) 810249, Fax: 811251, E-mail: suttonpark@fsbdial.co.uk, Internet: http://www.statelyhome.co.uk
Fine Arts Museum / Decorative Arts Museum
Furniture, paintings, porcelain, plasterwork by Cortese 34620

Sutton Poyntz

Water Supply Museum, Pumping Station, Sutton Poyntz DT3 6LT - T: (01225) 526327, Fax: 834287
Science&Tech Museum
Water turbine pump from 1857, pumping plant and artefacts 34621

Swaffham

Swaffham Museum, 4 London St, Swaffham PE37 7DQ - T: (01760) 721230, Fax: 720469. Head: Patricia Finch
Local Museum
Local and social history, hand crafted figures from English literature 34622

Swalcliffe

Swalcliffe Barn, Shipston Rd, Swalcliffe OX15 5ET - T: (01295) 788278
Local Museum
Agricultural and trade vehicles, local history 34623

Swanage

Tithe Barn Museum and Art Centre, Church Hill, Swanage BH19 1HU - T: (01929) 427174. Head: David Haysom
Local Museum / Fine Arts Museum / Archaeological Museum - 1976
Fossils of the area, examples of the various beds of Purbeck stone, exhibitions of archaeological, architectural and social history material relating to the district, paintings and sculpture 34624

Swansea

Egypt Centre, c/o University of Wales Swansea, Singleton Park, Swansea SA2 8PP - T: (01792) 295960, Fax: 295739, E-mail: c.a.graves-Brown@swansea.ac.uk, Internet: http://www.egyptcentre.org.uk. Head: Carolyn Graves-Brown
University Museum / Historical Museum / Archaeological Museum - 1998 34625

Glynn Vivian Art Gallery, Alexandra Rd, Swansea SA1 5DZ - T: (01792) 655006, 651738, Fax: 651713, E-mail: glynn.vivian.gallery@swansea.gov.uk, Internet: http://www.swansea.gov.uk. Head: Jenni Spencer-Davies
Fine Arts Museum - 1911
Swansea and Nantgarw pottery and porcelain, glass, 20th c Welsh art 34626

Maritime and Industrial Museum, Maritime Quarter, Museum Sq, Swansea SA1 1SN - T: (01792) 470371, 650351, Fax: 654200, E-mail: -swansea.maritime.museum@business.ntl.com. Head: Michael Lewis
Science&Tech Museum 34627

Mission Gallery, Gloucester Pl, Maritime Quarter, Swansea SA1 1TY - T: (01792) 652016, Fax: 652016. Head: Jane Phillips
Public Gallery 34628

Swansea Museum, Victoria Rd, Maritime Quarter, Swansea SA1 1SN - T: (01792) 653763, Fax: 652585, E-mail: swansea.museum@swansea.gov.uk, Internet: http://www.swansea.gov.uk. Head: Rosalyn P. Gee
Local Museum - 1835
Social history, archaeology, ceramics, natural history, Welsh ethnography, numismatics, maps, topography, photography, manuscripts - library 34629

Swindon

Great Western Railway Museum → STEAM Museum of the Great Western Railway

Lydiard House, Lydiard Tregoze, Swindon SN5 3PA - T: (01793) 770401, Fax: 877909. Head: Sarah Finch-Crisp
Fine Arts Museum / Decorative Arts Museum - 1955
Palladian mansion, ancestral home of the Viscount of Bolingbroke, furniture, family portrait coll - 17th c parish church 34630

Railway Village Museum, 34 Faringdon Rd, Swindon SN1 5BJ - T: (01793) 466556, Fax: 466615, Internet: http://www.steam-museum.org.uk
Science&Tech Museum - 1980
The Railway Village built in the 1840s 34631

Richard Jefferies Museum, Marlborough Rd, Swindon SN3 6AA - T: (01793) 466556, Fax: 484141. Head: Robert Dickinson
Special Museum - 1962
Memorabilia on Richard Jefferies, manuscripts, memorabilia on local poet Alfred Williams 34632

Royal Wiltshire Yeomanry Museum, Yeomanry House, Church Pl, Swindon SN1 5EH - T: (01793) 523865, Fax: 529350
Military Museum
Military uniforms, militaria 34633

STEAM Museum of the Great Western Railway, Kemble Dr, Swindon SN2 2TA - T: (01793) 466646, Fax: 466615, E-mail: lsmith@swindon.gov.uk, Internet: http://www.steam-museum.org.uk. Head: Tim Bryan
Science&Tech Museum - 1962/2000
Hist of railway, hist locomotives, models, illustrations 34634

Swindon Museum and Art Gallery, Bath Rd, Swindon SN1 4BA - T: (01793) 466556, Fax: 484141. Head: Robert Dickinson
Local Museum / Fine Arts Museum - 1919
Numismatics, natural hist, ethnography, 20th c British paintings, local arcaeology and social history 34635

Symbister

Hanseatic Booth or The Pier House, Symbister ZE2 9AA - T: (01806) 566240. Head: J.L. Simpson
Local Museum 34636

Tain

Tain and District Museum, Castle Brae, Tower St, Tain IV19 1DY - T: (01862) 894089, Fax: 894089, E-mail: info@tainmuseum.demon.co.uk, Internet: http://www.tainmuseum.demon.co.uk. Head: Estelle Quick
Historical Museum - 1966 34637

Tamworth

Tamworth Castle Museum, The Holloway, Tamworth B79 7NA - T: (01827) 709626, Fax: 709630, E-mail: heritage@tamworth.gov.uk, Internet: http://www.tamworthcastle.co.uk
Local Museum - 1899
Local hist, archaeology, Saxon and Norman coins, costumes, heraldry, arms - archives 34638

Tangmere

Military Aviation Museum, Tangmere Airfield, Tangmere PO20 6ES - T: (01243) 775223, Fax: 789490, E-mail: admin@tangmere-museum.org.uk, Internet: http://www.tangmere-museum.org.uk. Head: Alan Bower
Military Museum
British world speed record aircraft-meteorand hunter - Library 34639

Tarbert

An Tairbeart Museum, Campbeltown Rd, Tarbert - T: (01880) 820190
Local Museum 34640

Tarbolton

Bachelor's Club, Sandgate St, Tarbolton KA5 5RB - T: (01292) 541940
Special Museum - 1938
Memorabilia of Robert Burns and his friends, period furnishings, free masonery 34641

Tarporley

Beeston Castle, Tarporley CW6 9TX - T: (01829) 260464. Head: Andrew Morrison
Archaeological Museum
Archeological finds 34642

Tattershall

Guardhouse Museum, Tattershall Castle, Tattershall LN4 4LR - T: (01526) 342543, Fax: 342543, E-mail: etcxxx@smtp.ntrust.org.uk
Archaeological Museum
Model of the Castle (17th c), Lord Curzon artefacts, fossils, axe-heads, archaeological material, pottery, glass and metal objects 34643

Taunton

Somerset County Museum, The Castle, Castle Green, Taunton TA1 4AA - T: (01823) 320200, Fax: 320229, E-mail: county-museums@somerset.gov.uk, Internet: http://www.somerset.gov.uk/museums. Head: David Dawson
Local Museum
Archaeology, geology, biology, pottery, costume and textiles and other applied crafts 34644

Somerset Cricket Museum, 7 Priory Av, Taunton TA1 1XX - T: (01823) 275893
Special Museum
Cricket memorabilia - library 34645

Somerset Military Museum, Castle, Taunton TA1 4AA - T: (01823) 320201, Fax: 320229. Head: D. Eliot
Military Museum - 1921
Militaria 34646

Tavistock

Morwellham Quay Historic Port & Copper Mine, Morwellham, Tavistock PL19 8JL - T: (01822) 832766, Fax: 833808, E-mail: enquiries@morwellham-quay.co.uk, Internet: http://www.mrwellham-quay.co.uk. Head: Peter Kenwright
Open Air Museum - 1970
George and Charlotte Copper Mine, industry, archaeology, local hist, River Port 34647

Teignmouth

Teignmouth Museum, 29 French St, Teignmouth TQ14 8ST - T: (016267) 777041, 862265, Internet: http://website.lineone.net/~teignmuseum. Head: B.R. King
Local Museum - 1978
Spanish Armada Patache/Zabra, bronze swivel guns, pottery, copper cooking and caulking pots, other items of iron, Church Rocks Wreck, Church Rocks Teignmouth Devon, local/maritime history, lace, lifeboats, Haldon aerodrome, Bruneli athmospheric railway 34648

Tenbury Wells

Tenbury and District Museum, Goff's School, Cross St, Tenbury Wells WR15 8EG - T: (01299) 832143. Head: John Greenhill
Local Museum
Local history, bath and fountain from spa, farming, Victorian kitchen 34649

Tenby

Tenby Museum and Art Gallery, Castle Hill, Tenby SA70 7BP - T: (01834) 842809, Fax: 842809, E-mail: tenbymuseum@hotmail.com, Internet: http://www.tenbymuseum.free-online.co.uk. Head: Jon Beynon
Fine Arts Museum / Local Museum / Natural History Museum - 1878
Geology, archaeology, natural an social hist of Pembrokeshire, local hist of Tenby 34650

Tenterden

Colonel Stephens Railway Museum, Station, Station Rd, Tenterden TN30 6HE - T: (01580) 765350, Fax: 763468. Head: John Miller
Special Museum
Paperwork from the 16 light railways associated with Lt Colonel Holman F. Stephens, railway promoter, engineer and manager, his railway and military career 34651

Ellen Terry Memorial Museum, Smallhythe Pl, Tenterden TN30 7NG - T: (01580) 762334, Fax: 762334, E-mail: ksm@smtp.ntrust.org.uk. Head: M.A. Weare
Performing Arts Museum - 1929
Memorabilia on actress Dame Ellen Terry, costumes, Edith Craig archive 34652

Kent and East Sussex Railway, Tenterden Town Station, Station Rd, Tenterden TN30 6HE - T: (01580) 765155, Fax: 765654, E-mail: kesroffice@aol.com, Internet: http://www.kesr.org.uk
Science&Tech Museum
Engines, carriages, goods vehicles 34653

Tenterden and District Museum, Station Rd, Tenterden TN30 6HN - T: (01580) 764310, Fax: 766648. Head: Debbie Greaves
Local Museum - 1976
Hist of Tenterden, weights and measures of the former Borough, scale model of the town as it was in the mid 19th c, domestic and business life of Tenterden in the 18th and 19th c 34654

Tetbury

Tetbury Police Museum, 63 Long St, Tetbury GL8 8AA - T: (01666) 504670, Fax: 504670, E-mail: brian@tetburypolicemuseum.fsnet.co.uk. Head: Brian E. Toney
Historical Museum
Cells, artefacts, uniforms, history of the force 34655

Tewkesbury

John Moore Countryside Museum, 41 Church St, Tewkesbury GL20 5SN - T: (01684) 297174, E-mail: myecrofte@aol.com, Internet: http://www.gloster.demon.co.uk/jmcm. Head: Simon R. Lawton
Special Museum
Row of medieval cottages, furnishings, domestic environment, British woodland and wetland wildlife, writer and naturalist John Moore 34656

Little Museum, 45 Church St, Tewkesbury GL20 5SN - T: (01684) 297174. Head: S.R. Lawton
Local Museum 34657

Tewkesbury Museum, 64 Barton St, Tewkesbury GL20 5PX - T: (01684) 292185, 295027. Head: Bruce Mitchell
Local Museum - 1962
Hist, trades and industries of Tewkesbury, a diorama of the Battle of Tewkesbury in 1471, models of fairground machines, coll of woodworking tools 34658

Thetford

Ancient House Museum, White Hart St, Thetford IP24 1AA - T: (01842) 752599, Fax: 752599, E-mail: oliver.bone.mus@norfolk.gov.uk. Head: Oliver Bone
Local Museum - 1924
Early tudor house, local history and industries 34659

Duleep Singh Picture Collection, c/o Ancient House Museum, White Hart St, Thetford IP24 IAA - T: (01842) 752599
Fine Arts Museum - 1924
Timber framed house from 1480, displays of Thetford and Breckland life, Roman treasure hoard, herb garden 34660

Euston Hall, Thetford IP24 2QP - T: (01842) 766366. Head: Duke of Grafton
Fine Arts Museum 34661

Thirsk

Sion Hill Hall, Kirby Wiske, Thirsk YO7 4EU - T: (01845) 587206, Fax: 587486, E-mail: -enquiries.sionhall@virgin.net, Internet: http://www.sionhillhall.co.uk
Fine Arts Museum / Decorative Arts Museum 34662

Thirsk Museum, 14-16 Kirkgate, Thirsk YO7 1PQ - T: (01845) 527707, 524510, E-mail: thirskmuseum@supanet.com, Internet: http://thirskmuseum.org. Head: J.C. Harding
Local Museum - 1975
Local life, hist and industry, exhibits of cobblers' and blacksmith's tools, veterinary and medical equipment, Victorian clothing, esp underwear, children's games, archaeological finds, medieval pottery, cameras and cricket mementoes, agricultural implements, pharmaceutical products and equipment, photographs 34663

Thornbury

Thornbury and District Museum, 4 Chapel St, Thornbury BS35 2BJ - T: (01454) 857774, Fax: 281638. Head: Vic Hallett
Local Museum
Local social history, landscape history, local crafts and industry, farming - archive 34664

Thorney

Thorney Heritage Centre, The Tankyard, Station Rd, Thorney PE6 0QE - T: (01733) 270908, E-mail: dot.thorney@tesco.net
Local Museum
History of the village 34665

Thornhaugh

Sacrewell Farm and Country Centre, Sacrewell, Thornhaugh PE8 6HJ - T: (01780) 782254, Fax: 782254, E-mail: wsatrust@supanet.com, Internet: http://www.sacrewell.org.uk. Head: Michael Armitage
Agriculture Museum - 1987 34666

Thornhill, Central

Farmlife Centre, Dunaverig, Ruskie, Thornhill, Central FK8 3QW - T: (01786) 850277, Fax: 850404. Head: Sarah Stewart
Agriculture Museum
A small mixed farm, the story of the parish of Ruskie from ancient times to the present day, models, photographs, charts, implements 34667

Thornhill, Dumfriesshire

Alex Brown Museum of Scottish Cycling, Drumlanrig Castle, Thornhill, Dumfriesshire DG3 4AQ - T: (01848) 31555
Science&Tech Museum 34668

Drumlanrig Castle, Thornhill, Dumfriesshire DG3 4AQ - T: (01848) 330248, Fax: 331682, E-mail: bre@drumlanrigcastle.org.uk, Internet: http://www.drumlanrigcastle.org.uk. Head: Claire Fisher
Decorative Arts Museum 34669

Threlkeld

Threlkeld Quarry and Mining Museum, Quarry, Threlkeld CA12 4TT - T: (017687) 79747. Head: Ian Hartland
Science&Tech Museum
Minerals, steam cranes, geological and industrial history 34670

Throwley

Belmont Collection, Belmont Park, Throwley ME13 0HH - T: (01795) 890202. Head: Jonathan Betts
Science&Tech Museum
Clocks and watches coll 34671

Thurgoland

Wortley Top Forge, Thurgoland S30 7DN - T: (0114) 2887576
Science&Tech Museum
Iron works, water wheels, hammers, cranes, stationary steam engine coll 34672

Thurso

Thurso Heritage Museum, Town Hall, High St, Thurso KW14 8AG - T: (01847) 62459. Head: E. Angus
Local Museum - 1970
Pictish stones 34673

Tilbury

Tilbury Fort, 2 Office Block, The Fort, Tilbury RM18 7NR - T: (01375) 858489. Head: Sara Lunt
Military Museum
WW I and II memorabilia 34674

Tiptree

Tiptree Museum, Tiptree CO5 0RF - T: (01621) 814524, Fax: 814555, E-mail: tiptree@tiptree.com, Internet: http://www.tiptree.com
Local Museum
Jam making equipment, story of village life 34675

Tiverton

Tiverton Museum of Mid Devon Life, Beck's Sq, Tiverton EX16 6PJ - T: (01884) 256295, E-mail: tivertonmus@eclipse.co.uk, Internet: http://www.tivertonmuseum.org.uk. Head: Patrick Brooke
Science&Tech Museum / Local Museum / Agriculture Museum - 1960
Wagons, agricultural implements, railway, clocks, industries, crafts - library 34676

Tobermory

Mull Museum, Columbia Bldg, Main St, Tobermory PA75 6NY - T: (01688) 302493. Head: Dr. W.H. Clegg
Local Museum
Isle of Mull history - library, archives 34677

Toddington

Gloucestershire Warwickshire Railway, Railway Station, Toddington GL54 5DT - T: (01242) 621405, Internet: http://www.gwsr.plc.uk
Science&Tech Museum
Stand and gauge steam and diesel locomotives, carriages, wagons 34678

Tolpuddle

Tolpuddle Martyrs Museum, TUC Memorial Cottages, Tolpuddle DT2 7EH - T: (01305) 848237, Fax: 848237, Internet: http://www.tolpuddle-martyrs.org.uk. Head: Janet Pickering
Historical Museum
Story of the six agricultural workers transported to Australia in 1834 34679

Tomintoul

Tomintoul Museum, The Square, Tomintoul AB3 9ET - T: (01807) 580440, Fax: 675863, E-mail: alasdair.joyce@techleis.moray.gov.uk, Internet: http://www.moray.org/museums/tomintou. Head: R. Inglis
Local Museum
Local and natural hist, geology 34680

Topsham

Topsham Museum, Holman House, 25 The Strand, Topsham EX3 0AX - T: (01392) 873244, E-mail: museum@topsham.org, Internet: http://www.devonmuseums.net/topsham
Local Museum - 1967
Local history, crafts, shipbuilding, lacemaking, fishing 34681

Torquay

Torquay Museum, 529 Babbacombe Rd, Torquay TQ1 1HG - T: (01803) 293975, Fax: 294186. Head: Ros Palmer
Local Museum - 1844
Geology, entomology, botany, folk life, social history - local studies, library 34682

Torre Abbey Gallery, The King's Dr, Torquay TQ2 5JX - T: (01803) 293593, Fax: 215948, E-mail: torre-abbey@torbay.gov.uk, Internet: http://www.torre-abbey.org.uk. Head: Dr. Michael Rhodes
Fine Arts Museum / Decorative Arts Museum - 1930
Paintings, furniture, glass, archaeology, historic building, the most complete medieval monastery in Devon and Cornwall 34683

Torrington

Dartington Glass Museum, Groot Ammers, Torrington EX38 7AN - T: (01805) 626262, Fax: 626263, E-mail: enquiries@dartington.co.uk, Internet: http://www.dartington.co.uk. Head: Richard Barnes
Decorative Arts Museum - 1987
Dartington Crystal production from 1967 to present, non Dartington Crystal, historical glass from 1650 to today 34684

Torrington Museum, Town Hall, High St, Torrington EX38 8HN - T: (01805) 624324. Head: Emma Bond
Local Museum
Local and social history, trade - archive 34685

Totnes

British Photographic Museum, Bowden House, Totnes TQ9 7PW - T: (01803) 863664
Science&Tech Museum - 1974
Moving-picture photographic equipment of the period 1875 to 1960 34686

Totnes Costume Museum, Bogan House, 43 High St, Totnes TQ9 5NP - T: (01803) 862857. Head: Peter Clapham, Julie Fox
Special Museum
Coll of period costume since mid 18th c 34687

Totnes Elizabethan Museum, 70 Fore St, Totnes TQ9 5RU - T: (01803) 863821. Head: Louis Irwin
Local Museum - 1961
Period furniture, costumes, farm and household objects, archaeology, toys, computers - library, archive 34688

Trefeca

Howell Harris Museum, Trefeca LD3 0PP - T: (01874) 711423, Fax: 712212, E-mail: trefeca@surfaid.org, Internet: http://www.ebcpcw.org.uk. Head: G. Rhys
Local Museum - 1957
Local and religious hist, Howell Harris (1714-1773) 34689

Trehafod

Rhondda Heritage Park, Lewis Merthyr Colliery, Coed Cae Rd, Trehafod CF37 7NP - T: (01443) 682036, Fax: 687420, E-mail: rhonpark@netwales.co.uk, Internet: http://www.netwales.co.uk/rhondda-heritage. Head: Mick Payne
Local Museum
Social, cultural and industrial history of the Rhondda and South Wales Valleys 34690

Tresco

Valhalla Museum, Abbey Gardens, Tresco TR24 0QH - T: (01720) 422849, Fax: 422106
Special Museum
Figureheads and ships' carvings from wrecks 34691

Tring

Natural History Museum, Akeman St, Tring HP23 6AP - T: (020) 79426158, Fax: 79426150, E-mail: r.prys-jones@nhm.ac.uk. Head: Dr. R. Prys-Jones
Natural History Museum
Coll of birds 34692

Walter Rothschild Zoological Museum, Akeman St, Tring HP23 6AP - T: (020) 79426171, Fax: 79426150, E-mail: t.wild@nhm.ac.uk, Internet: http://www.nhm.ac.uk. Head: Dr. Neil R. Chalmers
Natural History Museum - 1892
Ornithological coll of the Natural History Museum, London SW (research coll, not open to the public), zoological specimens, most of which were collected by Walter Rothschild (open to the public) 34693

Trowbridge

Trowbridge Museum, The Shires, Court St, Trowbridge BA14 8AT - T: (01225) 751339, Fax: 754608, E-mail: clyall@trowbridge-museum.co.uk, Internet: http://www.trowbridge-museum.co.uk. Head: Clare Lyall
Science&Tech Museum - 1976
Textile machinery, West of England woollen industry 34694

Truro

Royal Cornwall Museum, River St, Truro TR1 2SJ - T: (01872) 272205, Fax: 240514, E-mail: royal-cornwall-museum@freeserve.co.uk, Internet: http://www.royalcornwallmuseum.org.uk. Head: Caroline Dudley
Natural History Museum / Fine Arts Museum - 1818
Philip Rashleigh coll of minerals, John Opie, artist, Newlyn School paintings, old master drawings - Courtney library and archives 34695

Tunbridge Wells

Tunbridge Wells Museum and Art Gallery, Civic Centre, Mount Pleasant, Tunbridge Wells TN1 1JN - T: (01892) 554171, Fax: 534227, Internet: http://www.tunbridgewells.gov.uk/museum
Local Museum / Public Gallery - 1885
Victorian paintings, local hist, natural hist, prints, drawings, dolls, toys, Tunbridge ware, archaeology, historic costume 34696

Turriff

Delgatie Castle, Turriff AB53 5TD - T: (01888) 563479, Fax: 563479. Head: Joan Johnson
Historical Museum / Fine Arts Museum / Decorative Arts Museum
Arts, arms and armour, paintings, furniture, history 34697

Old Post Office Museum, 24 High St, Turriff AB53 4DS - T: (01888) 563451. Head: Anna E. Cormack
Local Museum - 1999
Local goverment and history 34698

Session Cottage Museum, Session Close, Castle St, Turriff AB53 4AS - T: (01888) 563451. Head: Anna E. Cormack
Historical Museum - 1982
Lighting, domestic irons 34699

Turton Bottoms

Turton Tower, Chapeltown Rd, Turton Bottoms BL7 0HG - T: (01204) 852203, Fax: 853759, Internet: http://www.lancashire.com/lcc/museums. Head: Martin Robinson-Dowland
Decorative Arts Museum - 1952
National coll, furniture, 16th, 17th and 19th c, arms and armour, metalwork, paintings 34700

Twickenham

Marble Hill House, Richmond Rd, Twickenham TW1 2NL - T: (020) 88925115, Fax: 86079976, Internet: http://www.english-heritage.org.uk
Fine Arts Museum - 1966
Overdoor and overmantel paintings by G.P. Painini 34701

Museum of Rugby, Rugby Football Union, Rugby Rd, Twickenham TW1 1DZ - T: (020) 88928877, Fax: 88922817, E-mail: museum@rfu.com, Internet: http://www.rfu.com. Head: J. Smith
Special Museum
Rugby memorabilia, photographs and books 34702

Museum of the Royal Military School of Music, Kneller Hall, Twickenham TW2 7DU - T: (020) 88985533, Fax: 88987906. Head: R.G. Swift
Music Museum - 1935
Old music instruments 34703

Orleans House Gallery, Riverside, Twickenham TW1 3DJ - T: (020) 88920221, Fax: 87440501, E-mail: m.denovellis@richmond.gov.uk, Internet: http://www.richmond.gov.uk/depts/opps/leisure/arts/orleanshouse. Head: Rachel Tranter
Local Museum / Fine Arts Museum - 1972
Nearly 800 topographical paintings, prints and photographs of Richmond, Twickenham Hampton court area, Sir Richard Burton coll (paintings, portraits, photos, letters, personal objects, 1821-1890) 34704

Tywyn

Narrow Gauge Railway Museum, Wharf Station, Tywyn LL36 9EY - T: (01654) 710472, E-mail: chris.white@messages.co.uk, Internet: http://www.talyllyn.co.uk/ngrm. Head: A.C. White
Science&Tech Museum - 1956
Locomotives and wagons of Narrow Gauge Railways of Britain and Ireland 34705

Uckfield

Bluebell Railway, Sheffield Park Station, Uckfield TN22 3QL - T: (01825) 723777, Fax: 724139, Internet: http://www.bluebell-railway.co.uk. Head: J.E. Potter
Science&Tech Museum - 1960
Train tickets, badges, timetables 34706

Uffculme

Coldharbour Mill, Working Wool Museum, Uffculme EX15 3EE - T: (01884) 840960, Fax: 840858, E-mail: info@coldharbourmill.org.uk, Internet: http://www.coldharbourmill.org.uk
Science&Tech Museum - 1982
Turn-of-the-c worsted spinning machinery, spinning mule and looms, steam engine, new world tapestry 34707

Uffington

Tom Brown School Museum, Broad St, Uffington SN7 7RA - T: (01367) 820259, E-mail: museum@uffington.net, Internet: http://www.uffington.net/museum. Head: Sharon Smith
Historical Museum - 1984
150 editions of Tom Brown's schoolday by Thomas Hughes 34708

Ullapool

Ullapool Museum, 7-8 West Argyle St, Ullapool IV26 2TY - T: (01854) 612987, Fax: 612987, E-mail: ulmuseum@waverider.co.uk. Head: Alex Eaton
Local Museum - 1988/96
Village tapestry and quilt, natural hist, education, genealogy, archaeology, social hist, fishing, religion, emigration - archive 34709

Ulverston

Laurel and Hardy Museum, 4c Upperbrook St, Ulverston LA12 7BH - T: (01229) 582292, Fax: 580870. Head: Marion Grave
Special Museum
Memorabilia of Stan Laurel and Lucille Hardy, waxwork models 34710

Stott Park Bobbin Mill, Low Stott Park, Ulverston LA12 8AX - T: (015395) 31087, Fax: (015394) 43742. Head: M.J. Nield
Science&Tech Museum - 1983
Bobbin turning with Victorian machinery, working Victorian static steam engine 34711

Upminster

Upminster Tithe Barn, Agricultural and Folk Museum, Hall Ln, Upminster RM14 1AU - T: (01708) 447535, Fax: 447535
Agriculture Museum / Folklore Museum - 1978 34712

Uppermill

Saddleworth Museum and Art Gallery, High St, Uppermill OL3 6HS - T: (01457) 874093, Fax: 870336, E-mail: museum-curator@saddleworth.net, Internet: http://www.saddleworth.net. Head: Kirsty Mairsrdson
Science&Tech Museum / Fine Arts Museum - 1962
Textile machinery, transport, art - archive 34713

Usk

Usk Rural Life Museum, Malt Barn, New Market St, Usk NP5 1AU - T: (01291) 673777, E-mail: uskrurallife.museum@virgin.net, Internet: http://www.uskmuseum.member.easyspace.com. Head: A. Davies
Agriculture Museum - 1966
Agricultural and rural artefacts, vintage machinery 34714

Uttoxeter

Uttoxeter Heritage Centre, 34-36 Carter St, Uttoxeter ST14 8EU - T: (01889) 567176, Fax: 568426
Local Museum
Local history 34715

Ventnor

Museum of Smuggling History, Botanic Garden, Ventnor PO38 1UL - T: (01983) 853677. Head: J.R. Dowling
Special Museum - 1972
The only museum in the world depicting methods of smuggling in England over 700 years to the present 34716

Ventnor Heritage Museum, 11 Spring Hill, Ventnor PO38 1PE - T: (01983) 855407. Head: Graham Bennett
Local Museum
Local history, old photographs, prints 34717

Waddesdon

Waddesdon Manor, The Rothschild Collection, Waddesdon HP18 0JH - T: (01296) 653203, Fax: 653212, Internet: http://www.waddesdon.org.uk. Head: Philippa Glanville
Decorative Arts Museum / Fine Arts Museum - 1959
18th c French decorative arts, 18th c English portraits, 17th c Dutch and Flemish painting, majolica, glass, 16th c Renaissance jewellery, 16th-17th c European arms, 14th-16th c French, Italian and Flemish illuminated manuscripts, 18th c French books and bindings 34718

Wainfleet

Magdalen Museum, Saint John St, Wainfleet PE24 4DL - T: (01754) 880343
Historical Museum 34719

Wakefield

Clarke Hall, Aberford Rd, Wakefield WF1 4AL - T: (01924) 302700, Fax: 302700, E-mail: info@clarke-hall.co.uk, Internet: http://www.clarke-hall.co.uk. Head: Susan Morton
Decorative Arts Museum
17th c gentleman farmer's house 34720

National Coal Mining Museum for England, Caphouse Colliery, New Rd, Overton, Wakefield WF4 4RH - T: (01924) 848806, Fax: 840694, E-mail: info@ncm.org.uk, Internet: http://www.ncm.org.uk. Head: Dr. Margaret Faull
Science&Tech Museum - 1988
Colliery site buildings incl original twin-cylinder steam winding engine, mining in the English coalfields, mining literature, photos, mine safety lamps, mining related coll - research library, photographic coll 34721

Nostell Priory, Doncaster Rd, Wakefield WF4 1QE - T: (01924) 863892, Fax: 865282
Special Museum
Chippendale coll, Robert Adam's finest interiors 34722

Stephen G. Beaumont Museum, Fieldhead Hospital, Ouchthorpe Ln, Wakefield WF1 3SP - T: (01924) 328654, Fax: 327340, E-mail: sarahgarner@wpchtr.northy.nhs.uk, Internet: http://www.wpch.tr.northy.nhs.uk. Head: A. Lawrence Ashworth
Historical Museum
Originally West Riding Pauper Lunatic Asylum, plans, records, documents, scale model of 1818, surgical and medical equipment, tradesmen's tools 34723

Wakefield Art Gallery, Wentworth Terrace, Wakefield WF1 3QW - T: (01924) 305796, 305900, Fax: 305770. Head: Antonino Vella
Public Gallery - 1934
20th c British and other paintings, sculpture 34724

Wakefield Museum, Wood St, Wakefield WF1 2EW - T: (01924) 305351, Fax: 305353, Internet: http://www.wakefield.gov.uk/community/museums&arts. Head: Gordon Watson
Local Museum - 1920
Local history, natural history, costumes, photogr - Resource Centre 34725

Walkerburn

Scottish Museum of Woollen Textiles, Tweedvale Mill, Walkerburn EH43 6AH - T: (0189687) 281/83
Special Museum
Weaver's cottage and weaver's shed, appropriate furnishings and equipment, examples of 18th to 20th-c wool and cloth patterns 34726

Wallingford

Wallingford Museum, Flint House, High St, Wallingford OX10 0DB - T: (01491) 835065. Head: S. Dewey
Local Museum
History of the town, items date from the 19th and 20th c, Civil War relics, a model of Wallingford Castle 34727

Wallsend

Buddle Arts Centre, 258b Station Rd, Wallsend NE28 8RH - T: (0191) 2007132, Fax: 2007142, E-mail: buddle@ntynearts.demon.co.uk
Public Gallery
Prints 34728

Segedunum Roman Fort, Bath and Museum, Buddle St, Wallsend NE28 6HR - T: (0191) 2955757, Fax: 2955858, E-mail: segedunum@tyne-wear-museums.org.uk. Head: Bill Griffiths
Archaeological Museum 34729

Wallsend Heritage Centre → Segedunum Roman Fort, Bath and Museum

Walmer

Walmer Castle, Kingsdown Rd, Walmer CT14 7LJ - T: (01304) 364288, Fax: 364826. Head: Jan Summerfield
Decorative Arts Museum
Wellington memorabilia 34730

Walsall

Birchills Canal Museum, Old Birchills, Walsall WS3 8QD - T: (01922) 645778, Fax: 632824, E-mail: museum@walsall.gov.uk, Internet: http://www.walsall.org.uk/museum
Historical Museum
Life and like working on the Walsall Canal 34731

Jerome K. Jerome Birthplace Museum, Belsize House, Bradford St, Walsall WS1 1PN - T: (01922) 627686, 629000, Fax: 721065, 720885, E-mail: fwmp@gogough.demon.co.uk, Internet: http://www.barleyfen.demon.co.uk/jkj
Special Museum
Story of the life and work of the famous author 34732

The New Art Gallery Walsall, Gallery Sq, Walsall WS2 8LG - T: (01922) 654400, Fax: 654401, E-mail: mclaughlinr@walsall.gov.uk, Internet: http://www.artatwarsall.org.uk. Head: Peter Jenkinson
Public Gallery - 1887/2000
Garman Ryan Coll: works by Matisse, Modigliani, Pissarro, Manet, Constable, Van Gogh, prints and sculpture; non-Western artefacts, social and local hist of Walsall 34733

Walsall Leather Museum, Littleton St W, Walsall WS2 8EQ - T: (01922) 721153, Fax: 725827, E-mail: leathermuseum@walsall.gov.uk, Internet: http://www.walsalldirect.co.uk/whatson/leathermuseum.htm. Head: Michael Glasson
Special Museum - 1988
Designer leatherwork, lethergoods, saddlery, harness trades - library, photo archive 34734

Walsall Local History Centre, Essex St, Walsall WS2 7AS - T: (01922) 721305, Fax: 634954, E-mail: -localhistorycentre@walsall.gov.uk, Internet: http://www.earl.org.uk/partners/walsall
Local Museum 34735

Walsall Museum, Lichfield St, Walsall WS1 1TR - T: (01922) 653116, Fax: 632824, E-mail: museum@walsall.gov.uk, Internet: http://www.walsall.org.uk/museum. Head: Peter Jenkinson
Local Museum
Locally made goods, social history, changing costume, contemporary colls 34736

Walsall Museum and Art Gallery → The New Art Gallery Walsall

Waltham Abbey

Epping Forest District Museum, 39-41 Sun St, Waltham Abbey EN9 1EL - T: (01992) 716882, Fax: 700427, E-mail: museum@efdc.fsnet.co.uk, Internet: http://www.eppingforestdistrict-museum.org.uk. Head: Tony O'Connor
Local Museum

Objects, documents, photographs and pictures relating to the social history of the area, an bi-annual 'Art in Essex' exhibition of work by county artists 34737

Walton-on-the-Naze

Walton Maritime Museum, Old Lifeboat House, East Tce, Walton-on-the-Naze CO14 8AA - T: (01255) 678259
Historical Museum / Local Museum
Geology, fossils, flints, military history, local lifeboats, piers, old mills 34738

Wanlockhead

Museum of Lead Mining, Wanlockhead ML12 6UT - T: (01659) 74387, Fax: 74481, E-mail: ggodfrey@goldpan.co.uk, Internet: http://www.leadmining-museum.co.uk. Head: Gerard Godfrey
Science&Tech Museum / Natural History Museum - 1974
Rare mineral coll, unique mining engines - library 34739

Wantage

Charney Basset Mill, Charney Basset, Wantage OX12 0EN - T: (01235) 868677, 763752
Science&Tech Museum
Watermill, machinery and millwrighting coll, dressing machine 34740

Vale and Downland Museum, Church St, Wantage OX12 8BL - T: (01235) 771447, Fax: 764316, E-mail: museum@wantage.com, Internet: http://www.wantage.com/museum. Head: Richard Halliwell
Local Museum - 1983 34741

Ware

Ware Museum, The Priory Lodge, Ware SG12 9AL - T: (01920) 487848. Head: David Perman
Local Museum
Local and historical objects, archaeology, malting industry, railcar manufacturers 34742

Warminster

Dewey Museum, Library, Three Horseshoes Mall, Warminster BA12 9BT - T: (01985) 216022, Fax: 846332, E-mail: deweywar@ukonline.co.uk. Head: G.A. Hardy
Local Museum - 1972
History of Warminster and the surrounding area, the geology of the area 34743

Infantry and Small Arms School Corps Weapons Collection, Warminster Training Centre, Warminster BA12 0DJ - T: (01985) 222487, Fax: 222211
Military Museum - 1853
Coll of infantry firearms, dating from the 16th c to the present day, and ranging from small pocket pistols to heavy anti-tank weapons - documentation 34744

Longleat House, Warminster BA12 7NW - T: (01985) 844400, Fax: 844885, E-mail: enquiries@longleat.co.uk, Internet: http://www.longleat.co.uk. Head: Marquess of Bath
Historical Museum / Fine Arts Museum - 1541
6th Marquess of Bath's coll of Churchilliana and Hitleriana and children's books; incunabula, medieval manuscripts, porcelain, Italian/Dutch paintings, English portraits, French/Italian/English furniture - library, archives 34745

Warrington

Walton Hall Heritage Centre, Walton Hall Gardens, Walton Lea Rd, Warrington WA4 6SN - T: (01925) 601617, Fax: 861868, E-mail: waltonhall@warrington.gov.uk. Head: Keith Webb
Local Museum - 1995 34746

Warrington Museum and Art Gallery, Bold St, Warrington WA1 1JG - T: (01925) 442392, Fax: 442399, E-mail: museum@warrington.gov.uk, Internet: http://www.warrington.gov.uk/museum. Head: Sally Coleman
Local Museum / Public Gallery - 1848
Local hist, Romano-British finds from Wilderspool, prehistory, ethnology, natural hist, local industries, early English watercolours, ceramics, local longcase clocks 34747

Warwick

Midland Warplane Museum (temporary closed), Warwick, mail addr: 46 Arthur St, Kenilworth CV8 2HE
Historical Museum 34748

Queen's Own Hussars Museum, Lord Leycester Hospital, High St, Warwick CV34 4BH - T: (01926) 492035, Fax: 492035, E-mail: qohmuseum@netscapeonline.co.uk, Internet: http://www.army.mod.uk. Head: P.J. Timmons
Military Museum - 1966
History of regiments, uniforms, medals, silver goblets - library 34749

Royal Regiment of Fusiliers Museum, Saint John's House, Warwick CV34 4NF - T: (01926) 491653, Fax: (01869) 257633. Head: R.G. Mills
Military Museum
County Infantry Regiment 34750

Saint John's House, Saint John's, Warwick CV34 4NF - T: (01926) 412021, E-mail: museum@warwickshire.gov.uk, Internet: http://www.warwickshire.gov.uk. Head: Dr. Helen Maclagan
Historical Museum - 1961
Social hist, costume, domestic artefacts 34751

Warwick Castle, Castle Hill, Warwick CV34 4QU - T: (01926) 495421, Fax: 401692, E-mail: -custumer.information@warwick-castle.com, Internet: http://www.warwick-castle.co.uk. Head: S.E. Montgomery
Historic Site
Over 1000 items of amour & weaponry, "A Royal Weekend Party 1898", award-winning wax exhibit by Madame Tussauds depicting a weekend party 34752

Warwick Doll Museum, Oken's House, Castle St, Warwick CV34 4BP - T: (01926) 495546, 412500, Fax: 419840, E-mail: museum@warwickshire.gov.uk, Internet: http://www.warwickshire.gov.uk/museum. Head: Helen Maclagan
Special Museum - 1955
Old dolls and toys, Teddy Bears 34753

Warwickshire Museum, Market Pl, Warwick CV34 4SA - T: (01926) 412500, Fax: 419840, E-mail: museum@warwickshire.gov.uk, Internet: http://www.warwickshire.gov.uk. Head: Helen Maclagan
Local Museum - 1836
Archaeology, geology, natural history, musical instruments, tapestry map 34754

Warwickshire Yeomanry Museum, Court House, Jury St, Warwick CV34 4EW - T: (01926) 492212, Fax: 411694, E-mail: wtc.admin@btclick.com. Head: Michael Burman
Military Museum
History of the Yeomanry from 1794 to 1968, uniforms, the swords, firearms, pictures and paintings relating to the Regiment, campaign relics 34755

Washford

Somerset and Dorset Railway Trust Museum, Railway Station, Washford TA23 0PP - T: (01984) 640869, E-mail: info@sdrt.org, Internet: http://www.sdrt.org. Head: Michael Gates
Science&Tech Museum
Locomotives, rolling stock, railway buildings, signs, small artefacts, plans, railway signal box 34756

Washington, Tyne and Wear

Arts Centre, Biddick Ln, Fatfield, Washington, Tyne and Wear NE38 8AB - T: (0191) 2193455, Fax: 2193466
Public Gallery 34757

Washington Old Hall, The Avenue, District 4, Washington, Tyne and Wear NE38 7LE - T: (0191) 4166879, Fax: 4192065, Internet: http://www.washington.co.uk
Special Museum
Ancestral home of the first President of the United States from which the family took its name 34758

Watchet

Watchet Market House Museum, Market St, Watchet TA23 0AN, mail addr: 7 Periton Court, Parkhouse Rd, Minehead TA24 8AE - T: (01984) 631345. Head: W.H. Norman
Local Museum - 1979
Maritime history of the port of Watchet, archaeology, Saxon Mint, industry, railways, mining 34759

Waterbeach

Farmland Museum and Denny Abbey, Ely Road, Waterbeach CB5 9PQ - T: (01223) 860988, Fax: 860988, E-mail: f.m.denny@tesco.net, Internet: http://www.dennyfarmlandmuseum.org.uk
Agriculture Museum - 1997
Interactive displays on farming, esp village life in the 1940/50s, Denny Abbey 34760

Watford

Watford Museum, 194 High St, Watford WD1 2HG - T: (01923) 232297, Fax: 244772, E-mail: museum@artsteam-watford.co.uk, Internet: http://www.watford.gov.uk/leisure. Head: Victoria Barlow
Fine Arts Museum / Local Museum - 1981
Fine art coll (17th-18th c), North European genre painting, 19th c English landscape, sculpture by Sir Jacob Epstein, African art coll, local hist, archaeology 34761

Weardale

Weardale Museum, Ireshopeburn, Weardale DL14 - T: (01388) 537417. Head: Peter Bowes
Local Museum
Typical Weardale cottage room, geology, farming, railways, water resources and early settlement 34762

Wearhead

Killhope, the North of England Lead Mining Museum, Cowshill, Wearhead DL13 1AR - T: (01388) 537505, Fax: 537617, Internet: http://www.durham.gov.uk
Science&Tech Museum
Lead mining, waterwheels 34763

Wednesbury

Wednesbury Museum and Art Gallery, Holyhead Rd, Wednesbury WS10 7DF - T: (0121) 5560683, Fax: 5051625, Internet: http://www.sandwell.gov.uk/heritage. Head: Raj Pal
Local Museum / Fine Arts Museum - 1891
William Howson-Taylor-Ruskin pottery, Helen Caddick ethnography coll, George Robbins geological coll, English 19th c oil paintings and watercolours, ethnography, local hist, geology, decorative arts 34764

Welbeck

Creswell Crags Museum, off Crags Rd, Welbeck S80 3LH - T: (01909) 720378, E-mail: info@creswell-crags.org.uk, Internet: http://www.creswell-crags.org.uk. Head: Brian Chambers
Archaeological Museum
Animal skeletons, ecofacts and artefacts of Pleistocene research 34765

Harley Gallery, Welbeck S80 3LW - T: (01909) 501700, Fax: 488747, E-mail: igee@thg.globalnet.co.uk. Head: Gill Wilson
Fine Arts Museum
Contemporary visual arts 34766

Wellesbourne

Wellesbourne Wartime Museum, Airfield, Control Tower Entrance, Wellesbourne CV35 9EU - T: (01926) 855031
Historical Museum
Underground bunker, roll of honour 316 airmen killed while serving at Wellesbourne 1941-45 34767

Wellingborough

Irchester Narrow Gauge Railway Museum, Irchester Country Park, Wellingborough MK43, mail addr: c/o RUC Office, 71 Bedford Rd, Cranfield MK43 0EX - T: (01234) 750469, E-mail: itchester@kingstonray.freeserve.co.uk, Internet: http://www.ikingston.demon.co.uk/ingrt
Science&Tech Museum
8 steam and diesel locomotives 34768

Wellingborough Heritage Centre, Croyland Hall, Burstead Pl, Wellingborough NN8 1AH - T: (01933) 276838
Local Museum 34769

Wells

Wells Museum, 8 Cathedral Green, Wells BA5 2UE - T: (01749) 673477, Fax: 675337, E-mail: wellsmuseum@ukonline.co.uk, Internet: http://www.yell.co.uk/sites/wellsmuseum. Head: Estelle Jakeman
Local Museum / Archaeological Museum - 1893
Archaeology, natural history, geology, speleology, social history, needlework samplers 34770

Wells-next-the-Sea

Bygones at Holkham, Holkham Park, Wells-next-the-Sea NR23 1AB - T: (01328) 711383, Fax: 711707, E-mail: m.monk@holkham.co.uk, Internet: http://www.holkham.co.uk. Head: Michael Daley
Agriculture Museum
Agricultural Bygones, craft, domestic items, steam and motor vehicles, farming 34771

Wells Walsingham Light Railway, Stiffkey Rd, Wells-next-the-Sea NR23 1QB - T: (01328) 710631
Science&Tech Museum
Garrat steam locomotive, carriages 34772

Welshpool

Powis Castle, Welshpool SY21 8RF - T: (01938) 551920, 551944, Fax: 554336, E-mail: ppcmsn@smtp.ntrust.org.uk. Head: Caroline Sier
Decorative Arts Museum - 1987
Plasterwork and panelling, paintings, tapestries, early Georgian furniture and relics of Clive of India 34773

Powysland Museum and Montgomery Canal Centre, Canal Wharf, Welshpool SY21 7AQ - T: (01938) 554656, Fax: 554656, E-mail: powysland@powys.gov.uk. Head: Eva B. Bredsdorff
Local Museum - 1874
Archiological finds, social history 34774

Welwyn

Welwyn Roman Baths, By Pass, Welwyn AL6 9HT - T: (01707) 271362, Fax: 272511, E-mail: museum@welhar.gov.uk. Head: Carol Rigby
Archaeological Museum - 1975
Remains of a 3rd c AD bath house 34775

Wensleydale

Yorkshire Museum of Carriages and Horse Drawn Vehicles, Yore Bridge, Aysgarth Falls, Wensleydale DL8 3SR - T: (01969) 663399, Fax: 663399. Head: David Kiely, Ann Kiely
Science&Tech Museum
Coll of both everyday and more lavish horse-drawn vehicles in Britain today 34776

West Bretton

Yorkshire Sculpture Park, Bretton Hall, West Bretton WF4 4LG - T: (01924) 830302, 830579, Fax: 830044, E-mail: office@ysp.co.uk, Internet: http://www.ysp.co.uk. Head: Peter Murray
Fine Arts Museum 34777

West Bromwich

Oak House Museum, Oak Rd, West Bromwich B70 8HJ - T: (0121) 5530759, Fax: 5255167, Internet: http://www.sandwell.gov.uk/heritage. Head: Raj Pal
Decorative Arts Museum - 1898
Fine coll of oak furniture of 16th c and 17th c, 17th c interiors 34778

West Clandon

Queen's Royal Surrey Regiment Museum, Clandon Park, West Clandon GU4 7RQ - T: (01483) 223419, Fax: 224636, E-mail: queenssurrey@care4free.net, Internet: http://www.surrey-online.co.uk/queenssurreys
Military Museum 34779

West Hoathly

Priest House, North Ln, West Hoathly RH19 4PP - T: (01342) 810479, E-mail: priest@sussexpast.co.uk, Internet: http://www.sussexpast.co.uk. Head: Antony Smith
Local Museum - 1908
Vernacular furniture, domestic implements, embroidery 34780

West Kilbride

West Kilbride Museum, Public Hall, Arthur St, West Kilbride KA23 9EN - T: (01294) 882987
Local Museum 34781

West Malling

Outreach Collection, KCC, Gibson Dr, Kings Hill, West Malling ME19 4AL - T: (01622) 671411 ext 5226, 605226, Fax: 605221, E-mail: peter.divall@kent.gov.uk, Internet: http://www.kent.gov.uk/arts/libserv/loan1.html
Historical Museum
Models and replicas which illustrate the history, natural history and development of Kent and of the wider world 34782

West Mersea

Mersea Island Museum, High St, West Mersea CO5 8QD - T: (01206) 385191. Head: David W. Gallifant
Local Museum 34783

West Walton

Fenland and West Norfolk Aviation Museum, Old Lynn Rd, West Walton PE14 7DA - T: (01945) 584440, Fax: 581984, E-mail: petewinning@compuserve.com. Head: Richard Mason
Science&Tech Museum
Aircraft crash sites, Boeing 747 flight deck, general aviation memorabilia 34784

West Wycombe

West Wycombe Motor Museum, Chorley Rd, West Wycombe
Science&Tech Museum 34785

West Wycombe Park House, West Wycombe HP14 3AJ - T: (01494) 52441
Fine Arts Museum
Contemporary frescos, painted ceilings 34786

Westbury

Woodland Heritage Museum, Woodland Park, Brokerswood, Westbury BA13 4EH - T: (01373) 823880, Fax: 858474. Head: S.H. Capon
Natural History Museum
Wildlife diorama, a bird wall and exhibits on forestry, bird eggs, natural history 34787

Westerham

Quebec House, Quebec Sq, Westerham TN16 1TD - T: (01959) 562206. Head: David Boston
Historical Museum
General Wolfe's early years, battle of Quebec 34788

Sqerryes Court, Goodley Stock Rd, Westerham TN16 1SJ - T: (01959) 562345, Fax: 565949, E-mail: squerryes.court@squerryes.co.uk, Internet: http://www.squerryes.co.uk
Fine Arts Museum
Paintings (Dutch 17th c, English 18th) tapestries, furniture, porcelain, General James Wolfe 34789

Weston-super-Mare

The Helicopter Museum, Heliport, Locking Moor Rd, Weston-super-Mare BS24 8PP - T: (01934) 635227, Fax: 645230, E-mail: office@helimuseum.fsnet.co.uk, Internet: http://www.helicoptermuseum.freeserve.co.uk. Head: Elfan Rees
Science&Tech Museum - 1979
Bristol Belvedere, Cierva C-30A, Fairey Rotodyne, Mil Mi-1, PZL Swidnik SM-2, Westland Lynx 3, Sud Super Frelon, MBB Bo-102, Mil M.24D, Queens Flight Wessex XV 733 34790

North Somerset Museum, Burlington St, Weston-super-Mare BS23 1PR - T: (01934) 621028, Fax: 612526, E-mail: museum.service@n-somerset.gov.uk, Internet: http://www.n-somerset.gov.uk/museum. Head: Nick Goff
Local Museum 34791

Weston-under-Lizard

Weston Park, Weston-under-Lizard TF11 8LE - T: (01952) 850207, Fax: 850430, E-mail: enquiries@weston-park.com, Internet: http://www.weston-park.com. Head: Colin Sweeney
Decorative Arts Museum / Fine Arts Museum - 1671
House built 1671 with English, Flemish and Italian paintings, furniture, books, tapestries, art objects 34792

Wetheringsett

Museum of the Mid-Suffolk Light Railway, Brockford Station, Wetheringsett IP14 5PW - T: (01449) 766899
Science&Tech Museum 34793

Weybourne

Muckleburgh Collection, Weybourne NR25 7EG - T: (01263) 588210, Fax: 588425, E-mail: info@muckleburgh.fsnet.co.uk, Internet: http://www.fsnet.co.uk/muckleburgh. Head: Christine Swettenham
Military Museum
Military, Suffolk and Norforlk Yeomanry 34794

Weybridge

Brooklands Museum, Brooklands Rd, Weybridge KT13 0QN - T: (01932) 857381, Fax: 855465, E-mail: brooklands@dial.pipex.com, Internet: http://www.motor-software.co.uk/brooklands. Head: J. Michael Phillips
Science&Tech Museum
British motorsport and aviation, Brooklands cars, aircraft, motorcycles, cycles, John Cobb's 24-litre Napier-Railton, Wellington bomber of Loch Ness 34795

Elmbridge Museum, Church St, Weybridge KT13 8DE - T: (01932) 843573, Fax: 846552, E-mail: info@elm-mus.datanet.co.uk, Internet: http://www.surrey-online.co.uk/elm-mus. Head: Michael Rowe
Local Museum - 1909/1996
Local history, archaeology, excavated material from Oatlands palace, costume, natural history 34796

Weymouth

Deep Sea Adventure and Diving Museum, Custom House Quay, Weymouth - T: (01305) 760690, Fax: 760690
Special Museum 34797

Nothe Fort Museum of Coastal Defence, Barrack Rd, Weymouth DT4 8UF - T: (01305) 766626, Fax: 766465, E-mail: fortressweymouth@btconnect.com, Internet: http://www.weymouth.gov.uk/nothe.htm. Head: Alisdair Murray
Military Museum - 1979
Coastal fortress, coll of guns, weapons and equipment, military badges, torpedos, uniforms 34798

Tudor House, 3 Trinity St, Weymouth DT4 8TW - T: (01305) 812341
Historical Museum
17th c life 34799

Weymouth Museum, Timewalk and Brewery Museum, Brewer's Quay, Hope Sq, Weymouth DT4 8TR - T: (01305) 777622, Fax: 761680. Head: Rodney Alcock
Historical Museum
Local and social history, costume, prints, paintings, Bussell coll - archives 34800

Whaley Thorns

Whaley Thorns Heritage Centre and Museum, Cock Shut Ln, Whaley Thorns NG20 9HA - T: (01623) 742525, Fax: (01246) 813200. Head: John Hyatt
Agriculture Museum
Old farming, sheep shearing and many more implements 34801

Whaplode

Museum of Entertainment, Rutland Cottage, Millgate, Whaplode PE12 6SF - T: (01406) 540379. Head: Iris Tunnicliff
Performing Arts Museum
History of entertainment, mechanical music, the fairground, radio, TV, cinema, theatre 34802

Whitburn

Whitburn Community Museum, Union Rd, Whitburn EH47 0AR - T: (01501) 678050, E-mail: whitburn.library@westlothian.org.uk, Internet: http://www.wlonline.org. Head: Hilda Gibson
Local Museum 34803

Whitburn Community Museum, Library, Union Rd, Whitburn EH47 0AR - T: (01506) 776347, Fax: 776190, E-mail: museums@westlothian.org.uk, Internet: http://www.wlonline.org
Local Museum
Whitburn and its mining past 34804

Whitby

Captain Cook Memorial Museum, John Walker's House, Grape Ln, Whitby YO22 4BA - T: (01947) 601900, Fax: 601900, E-mail: -captcookmuseumwhitby@ukgateway.net, Internet: http://www.cookmuseumwhitby.co.uk
Historical Museum
House where Captain Cook lived 34805

Museum of Victorian Whitby, 4 Sandgate, Whitby YO22 4DB - T: (01947) 601221
Local Museum
Life in Victorian Whitby, whaling, jet mining and jewellery manufacturing 34806

Sutcliffe Gallery, 1 Flowergate, Whitby YO21 3BA - T: (01947) 602239, Fax: 820287, E-mail: photographs@sutcliffe-gallery.fsnet.co.uk, Internet: http://www.sutcliffe-gallery.co.uk
Fine Arts Museum
Prints, photofraphy, negative coll of works by Frank Meadow (19th c) 34807

Whitby Abbey Museum, Whitby YO22 4JT - T: (01947) 603568. Head: Andrew Morrison
Archaeological Museum - 2001
Architectural material from the abbey 34808

Whitby Heritage Centre, 17-18 Grape Ln, Whitby YO22 4BA - T: (01947) 600170, Internet: http://www.whitbyarchives.freeserve.co.uk
Local Museum
Local history - archives 34809

Whitby Museum, Pannett Park, Whitby YO21 1RE - T: (01947) 602908, Fax: 897638, E-mail: graham@durain.demon.co.uk, Internet: http://www.whitby-museum.org.uk. Head: Lady Normanby
Local Museum - 1823
Local history, archaeology, geology, natural history, shipping, fossils, paintings, ceramics, costumes, Scoresby, Captain Cook, toys and dolls, militaria - library, archives 34810

Whitchurch, Hampshire

Whitchurch Silk Mill, 28 Winchester St, Whitchurch, Hampshire RG28 7AL - T: (01256) 892065, Fax: 893882. Head: Christine Beresford
Science&Tech Museum
Textile watermill, 19th-c machinery 34811

Whitehaven

The Beacon Whitehaven, West Strand, Whitehaven CA28 7LY - T: (01946) 592302, Fax: 599025, E-mail: thebeacon@copelandbc.gov.uk, Internet: http://www.copelandbc.gov.uk. Head: Kate Christie
Local Museum / Fine Arts Museum - 1996
Maritime hist, coal mining, pottery, social hist - library 34812

Haig Colliery Mining Museum, Solway Rd, Kells, Whitehaven CA28 9BG - T: (01946) 599949, Fax: 61896, E-mail: museum@haig1.freeserve.co.uk, Internet: http://www.haig1.freeserve.co.uk
Science&Tech Museum
Standard gauge Huslet locomotive and coal waggons, mining history 34813

Whitehaven Museum and Art Gallery → The Beacon Whitehaven

Whitfield

Dover Transport Museum, White Cliffs Business Park, Port Zone, Whitfield CT16 2HJ - T: (01304) 822409, 204612. Head: Colin Smith
Science&Tech Museum
Local transport history by land, sea and air 34814

Whithorn

Whithorn - Cradle of Christianity, 45-47 George St, Whithorn DG8 8NS - T: (01988) 500508, Fax: 500508
Religious Arts Museum 34815

Whithorn Priory and Museum, Bruce St, Whithorn DG8 8P4 - T: (0131) 24431010. Head: Michael Lyons
Archaeological Museum - 1908
Early Christian medieval stonework, Latins Stone 450 AD to mid 5th c, St Peters Cross, 7th c, 10th c Monrieith Cross, fine coll of other crosses 34816

Whitstable

Whitstable Museum and Gallery, Oxford St, Whitstable CT5 1DB - T: (01227) 276998, Fax: 772379, Internet: http://www.whitstable-museum.co.uk. Head: Kenneth Reedie
Historical Museum / Fine Arts Museum
Seafaring tradition (oyster industry, divers), fine coll of maritime art 34817

Whitstable Oyser and Fishery Exhibition, Harbour, East Quay, Whitstable CT5 1AB - T: (01227) 280753, Fax: 264829, E-mail: bayes@seasalter.evnet.co.uk. Head: Norman Goodman
Special Museum
Traditional oyster and fishing industry, oyster farming, science and technology 34818

Whittlesey

Whittlesey Museum, Town Hall, Market St, Whittlesey PE7 1BD - T: (01733) 840968. Head: Maureen Watson
Local Museum
Local trades and industry 34819

Whittlesford

Peppin Brown Art Gallery, Old School, High St, Whittlesford CB2 4LT - T: (01223) 836394
Fine Arts Museum 34820

Whitworth

Whitworth Historical Society Museum, North St, Whitworth OL12 8RE - T: (01706) 853655
Local Museum
Coll of quarry tools, photographs, books, local council records 34821

Wick

Caithness District Museum, Bruce Bldg, Sinclaire Terrace, Wick KW1 5AB - T: (01955) 603761, Fax: 605744
Local Museum 34822

Wick Heritage Centre, 20 Bank Row, Wick KW1 5EY - T: (01955) 605393, Fax: 605393
Local Museum / Fine Arts Museum
Coll of photographs of 115 years history, art gallery 34823

Widnes

Catalyst, Science Discovery Centre, Gossage Bldg, Mersey Rd, Widnes WA8 0DF - T: (0151) 4201121, Fax: 4952030, E-mail: info@catalyst.org.uk, Internet: http://www.catalyst.org.uk. Head: C. Allison
Science&Tech Museum - 1989 34824

Wigan

History Shop, Library St, Wigan WN1 1NU - T: (01942) 828128, Fax: 827645, E-mail: heritage@wiganmbc.gov.uk. Head: P. Butler
Local Museum - 1992
Local and family hist, archaeology, numismatics, local art, industries 34825

Wigan Pier, Trencherfield Mill, Wigan WN3 4EU - T: (01942) 323666, Fax: 701927, Internet: http://www.wigangov.co.uk. Head: Carole Tydesley, Paul David
Local Museum
Social and industrial life in Wigan in 1900 34826

Willenhall

Willenhall Lock Museum, 54-56 New Rd, Willenhall WV13 2DA - T: (01902) 634542, Fax: 634542, Internet: http://members.tripod.co.uk/lock_museum/. Head: John Whistance
Science&Tech Museum - 1987
17th-20th c locks and keys, early 20th c womens childrens's clothing 34827

Willenhall Museum, Library, Walsall St, Willenhall WV13 2EX - T: (01922) 653116, 653196, Fax: 38224, E-mail: museum@walsall.gov.uk
Local Museum
History of this Midland town 34828

Williton

Bakelite Museum, Orchard Mill, Williton TA4 4NS - T: (01984) 632133, 632322, E-mail: info@bakelitemuseum.com, Internet: http://www.balelitemuseum..com
Decorative Arts Museum
Design 34829

Wilmington

Wilmington Priory, Polegate, Wilmington BN26 5SW - T: (01323) 870537
Agriculture Museum - 1925
Old agricultural implements 34830

Wilton

Wilton House, Wilton SP2 0BJ - T: (01722) 746729, Fax: 744447, E-mail: tourism@wiltonhouse.com, Internet: http://www.wiltonhouse.com. Head: S. Salmon
Historic Site / Fine Arts Museum
Paintings, interior, art coll 34831

Wimborne Minster

Priest's House Museum, 23-27 High St, Wimborne Minster BH21 1HR - T: (01202) 882533, Fax: 882533
Local Museum - 1962
Local hist, archaeology, Bronze Age and Romano-British finds, toys 34832

Wincanton

Wincanton Museum, 32 High St, Wincanton BA9 9JF - T: (01963) 34063
Local Museum 34833

Winchcombe

Sudeley Castle, Winchcombe GL54 5JD - T: (01242) 602308, Fax: 602959, E-mail: marketing@sudeley.org.uk, Internet: http://www.sudeley-castle.co.uk. Head: Timothy Baylis
Historical Museum
Relics and art, paintings by Turner, Van Dijk, Rubens 34834

Winchcombe Folk and Police Museum, Old Town Hall, High St, Winchcombe GL54 5LJ - T: (01242) 609151. Head: Barbara Edward
Local Museum / Historical Museum
Local hist, police uniforms and equipment 34835

Winchcombe Railway Museum, 23 Gloucester St, Winchcombe GL54 - T: (01242) 620641. Head: Tim Petchey
Science&Tech Museum - 1968
Tickets, labels, horsedrawn railway road vehicles, mechanical signalling, lineside notices 34836

Winchelsea

Winchelsea Museum, Court Hall, Winchelsea TN36 4EN - T: (01797) 226382. Head: G. Alexander
Local Museum - 1945
Cinque Ports, town history, maps, seals, coins, pictures, pottery, clay pipes, model of the town in 1292 34837

Winchester

Adjutant General's Corps Museum, Worthy Down, Winchester SO21 2RG - T: (01962) 887435, 887919, Fax: 887690, E-mail: agc.regtsec@virgin.net. Head: J. Mills
Military Museum
Uniforms, badges and medals, old office machines, documents related to Royal Army Pay Corps, Educational Corps, Military Provost Corps, Army Legal Corps, Women' Royal Army Corps 34838

Balfour Museum of Hampshire Red Cross History, Red Cross House, Stockbridge Rd, Winchester SO22 5JD - T: (01962) 865174, Fax: 869721
Historical Museum
History of the British Red Cross, Hampshire branch - archives 34839

City Museum, The Square, Winchester SO23 7DW - T: (01962) 848269, Fax: 848299, E-mail: museum@winchester.gov.uk, Internet: http://www.winchester.gov.uk/heritage. Head: Kenneth Qualmann
Archaeological Museum / Local Museum - 1847
Archeology and history of Winchester 34840

Guildhall Gallery, Broadway, Winchester SO23 9LJ - T: (01962) 848289, Fax: 848299, E-mail: museums@winchester.gov.uk, Internet: http://www.winchester.gov.uk/heritage. Head: Geoffrey Denford
Public Gallery - 1969 34841

Gurkha Museum, Peninsula Barracks, Romsey Rd, Winchester SO23 8TS - T: (01962) 842832, 843657, Fax: 877597. Head: Christopher Bullock
Military Museum / Ethnology Museum
Story of Gurkha since 1815, ethnographic objects from Nepal, India, Tibet and Afghanistan 34842

The King's Royal Hussars Museum, Peninsula Barracks, Romsey Rd, Winchester SO23 8TS - T: (01962) 828539, Fax: 828538, E-mail: beresford@krhmuseum.freeserve.co.uk, Internet: http://www.hans.gov.uk/leisure/museums/royalhus. Head: P. Beresford
Military Museum - 1980
Story of the Regiment from the raising of the 10th and 11th Hussars (originally Light Dragoons) in 1715, armoured vehicles, uniforms, equipment, medals, photographs and campaign relics 34843

Light Infantry Museum, Peninsula Barracks, Romsey Rd, Winchester SO23 8TS - T: (01962) 828550, 828530, Fax: 828534, Internet: http://www.army.doc.uk/army/press/museums/details/m158light.html
Military Museum
Modern military museum, elite regiment, Berlin wall, Gulf war, Bosnia exhibition 34844

Royal Green Jackets Museum, Peninsula Barracks, Romsey Rd, Winchester SO23 8TS - T: (01962) 828549, Fax: 828500, E-mail: museum@royalgreenjackets.co.uk. Head: K. Grai
Military Museum - 1926
Regimental history, pictures, silver, medals 34845

Royal Hampshire Regiment Museum, Serle's House, Southgate St, Winchester SO23 9EG - T: (01962) 863658, Fax: 888302. Head: H.D.H. Keatinge
Military Museum - 1933
History of the regiment - archive 34846

Textile Conservation Centre, University of Southampton, Winchester Campus, Park Av, Winchester SO23 8DL - T: (023) 80597100, Fax: 80597101, E-mail: tccuk@soton.ac.uk, Internet: http://www.soton.ac.uk/~wsart/tcc.htm. Head: Nell Hoare
Special Museum
Karen Finch Library 34847

Westgate Museum, High St, Winchester - T: (01962) 848269, Fax: 848299, E-mail: museums@winchester.gov.uk, Internet: http://www.winchester.gov.uk/heritage. Head: Dr. G.T. Denford
Local Museum - 1898
Medieval building: coll of weights and standards 34848

Winchester Cathedral Triforium Gallery, Cathedral, South Transept, Winchester SO23 9LS - T: (01962) 853137, Fax: 841519, E-mail: john.hardacre@dial.pipex.com, Internet: http://www.win.diocese.org.uk/cath_explore.html. Head: John Hardacre
Religious Arts Museum
Artistic and archeological material from the Cathedral, stone and wooden sculpture 34849

Winchester College Treasury, College St, Winchester - T: (01962) 866079, Fax: 843005. Head: Victoria Hebron
Fine Arts Museum
Historic documents, antique silver, ceramics, Egyptian and Central American objects, antique scientific instruments, modern crafts 34850

Windermere

Windermere Steamboat Museum, Rayrigg Rd, Windermere LA23 1BN - T: (015394) 45565, Fax: 48769, E-mail: steamboat@insites.co.uk, Internet: http://www.steamboat.co.uk
Science&Tech Museum - 1977
Coll of 35 steam, sail and motorboats undercover in a purpose built wet dock made on Lake Windermere - art gallery, library 34851

Windsor

Dorney Court, Dorney, Windsor SL4 6QP - T: (01628) 604638, Fax: 665772, E-mail: palmer@dorneycourt.co.uk, Internet: http://www.dorneycourt.co.uk. Head: Pereerine Palmer
Historical Museum - 1440 34852

Household Cavalry Museum, Combermere Barracks, Windsor SL4 3DN - T: (01753) 868222
Military Museum - 1952
Regimental history, uniforms, armaments, pictures 34853

Royal Berkshire Yeomanry Cavalry Museum, Territorial Army Centre, Bolton Rd, Windsor SL4 3JG - T: (01753) 860600, Fax: 854946
Military Museum 34854

Royal Borough Museum Collection, Tinkers Ln, Windsor SL4 4LR - T: (01628) 796829, Fax: 796859, E-mail: olivia.goodend@rbwm.gov.uk. Head: Olivia Goodend
Local Museum
Royal borough of Windsor and Maidenhead history 34855

Town and Crown Exhibition, Royal Windsor Information Centre, 24 High St, Windsor SL4 1LH - T: (01753) 743918, Fax: 743917, E-mail: windsor.tic@rbwm.gov.uk. Head: Judith Hunter
Local Museum / Special Museum
History of the town of Windsor 34856

Windsor Castle, Royal Collections, Windsor SL4 1NJ - T: (01753) 868286, E-mail: windsorcastle@Royalcollection.org.uk, Internet: http://www.royalresidences.com
Fine Arts Museum / Decorative Arts Museum
State apartments - library 34857

Wisbech

Peckover House, North Brink, Wisbech PE13 1JR - T: (01945) 583463, Fax: 583463, E-mail: aprigx@smtp.ntrust.org.uk
Decorative Arts Museum 34858

Wisbech and Fenland Museum, 5 Museum Sq, Wisbech PE13 1ES - T: (01945) 583817, Fax: 589050. Head: Dr. Jane Hubbard
Local Museum / Decorative Arts Museum - 1835
Pottery and porcelain, figures, local photographs, manuscripts by Dickens and Lewis, calotypes by Samuel Smith, early Madagascar photos, parish records, african ethnography, geology, Fenland hist and folklife, coins, applied art, fossils - library, archives 34859

Withernsea

Withernsea Lighthouse Museum, Hull Rd, Withernsea HU19 2DY - T: (01964) 614834, Internet: http://www.yell.co.uk/sites/wsealighthousemuseum
Science&Tech Museum 34860

Witney

Bishop of Winchester's Palace Site, Mount House, The Green, Witney - T: (01993) 772602, Fax: 813239, E-mail: oxonmuseum@oxfordshire.gov.uk, Internet: http://www.oxfordshire.gov.uk
Historic Site
12th c palace 34861

Cogges Manor Farm Museum, Church Ln, Cogges, Witney OX28 3LA - T: (01993) 772602, Fax: 703056. Head: Clare Pope
Agriculture Museum - 1976
Historic Manor House with Victorian period room displays, 17th c study with original painted panelling, agricultural history, tools, wagon coll 34862

Witney and District Museum and Art Gallery, Gloucester Court Mews, High St, Witney OX8 6LX - T: (01993) 775915
Local Museum
Social history, fine art, military history, photographic coll 34863

Woburn

Woburn Abbey, South Courtyard, Woburn MK17 9WA - T: (01525) 290666, Fax: 290271, E-mail: enquiries@woburnabbay.co.uk, Internet: http://www.woburnabbay.co.uk
Decorative Arts Museum
Coll of English and French furniture (18th c), paintings by Canaletto, Reynolds, Van Dijk 34864

Woking

The Galleries, Chobham Rd, Woking GU21 1JK - T: (01483) 725517, Fax: 725501, E-mail: info@thegalleries.org.uk. Head: Amana Devonshire
Local Museum
Life in Woking past and present, arts and crafts 34865

Wollaston

Wollaston Heritage Museum, 102-104 High St, Wollaston NN29 7RJ - T: (01933) 664468. Head: D. Hall
Local Museum
Farming implements, archaeological finds from the area, village life, paintings by local artists, footware manufacture, lace making 34866

Wolverhampton

Bantock House, Bantock Park, Finchfield Rd, Wolverhampton WV3 9LQ - T: (01902) 552195, Fax: 552196. Head: Nicholas Dodd
Decorative Arts Museum / Local Museum
Enamels, steel jewellery, japanned ware 34867

Bilston Craft Gallery, Mount Pleasant, Bilston, Wolverhampton WV14 7LU - T: (01902) 552507, Fax: 552504, E-mail: info.wag@dial.pipex.com, Internet: http://www.wolverhamptonart.org.uk
Local Museum - 1937
Local hist, enamels, contemporary crafts exhibitions 34868

Wightwick Manor, Wightwick Bank, Wolverhampton WV6 8EE - T: (01902) 761400, Fax: 764663, E-mail: mwtman@smtp.ntrust.org.uk
Local Museum 34869

Wolverhampton Art Gallery, Lichfield St, Wolverhampton WV1 1DU - T: (01902) 552055, Fax: 552053, E-mail: info.wag@dial.pipex.com, Internet: http://www.wolverhamptonart.org.uk. Head: Nicholas Dodd
Fine Arts Museum - 1884
British 18th-20th c paintings and sculpture, British and American Pop Art and contemporary paintings, geology, interactive display "ways of seeing" 34870

Wolverton

Stacey Hill Museum, Stacey Hill Farm, Southern Way, Wolverton MK12 5EJ - T: (01908) 316222, 319148, Internet: http://www.mkheritage.co.uk/shs
Agriculture Museum 34871

Woodbridge

Suffolk Punch Heary Horse Museum, Market Hill, Woodbridge IP12 4LU - T: (01394) 380643, Fax: sec@suffolkhousesociety.org.uk
Special Museum 34872

Woodbridge Museum, 5a Market Hill, Woodbridge IP12 4LP - T: (01394) 380502. Head: P. Hayworth
Local Museum - 1981 34873

Woodchurch

Woodchurch Village Life Museum, Susans Hill, Woodchurch TN26 3RE - T: (01233) 860240, Internet: http://www.woodchurchmuseum.fsnet.com. Head: G. Loynes
Local Museum
Social history of the village, vehicles, agricultural equipment, ceramics, coins, household items, books, papers and photographs 34874

Woodhall Spa

Woodhall Spa Cottage Museum, Bungalow, Iddesleigh Rd, Woodhall Spa LN10 6SH - T: (01526) 353775
Local Museum
History of Woodhall Spa, geology 34875

Woodstock

Blenheim Palace, Woodstock OX20 1PX - T: (01993) 811091, Fax: 813527. Head: Nick Day
Fine Arts Museum / Decorative Arts Museum
Tapestries, paintings, sculpture, porcelain, fine furniture 34876

The Oxfordshire Museum, Fletcher's House, Park St, Woodstock OX20 1SN - T: (01993) 811456, Fax: 813239, E-mail: oxon.museum@oxfordshire.gov.uk, Internet: http://www.oxfordshire.gov.uk. Head: Carol Anderson
Local Museum - 1965
Archaeology, history and natural environment of Oxfordshire, county's innovative industry 34877

Wookey Hole

Wookey Hole Cave Diving and Archaeological Museum, Wookey Hole BA5 1BB - T: (01749) 672243, Fax: 677749, E-mail: witch@wookey.co.uk, Internet: http://www.wookey.co.uk. Head: Peter Haylings
Natural History Museum / Archaeological Museum - 1980
Archaeological finds, cave exploration, geology, cave diving, myth and legends 34878

Woolpit

Woolpit and District Museum, The Institute, Woolpit IP30 9QH - T: (01359) 240822. Head: John Wiley
Local Museum - 1983
Coll of items from the village and its immediate surroundings 34879

Worcester

Commandery Museum, Sidbury, Worcester WR1 2HU - T: (01905) 361821, Fax: 361822, E-mail: thecommandery@cityofworcester.gov.uk, Internet: http://www.cityofworcester.gov.uk. Head: Amanda Lunt
Local Museum - 1977
Local hist, english Civil War, 15th c wall paintings 34880

Museum of Local Life, Friar St, Worcester WR1 2NA - T: (01905) 722349, Fax: 722350, E-mail: nburnett@cityofworcester.gov.uk, Internet: http://www.cityofworcester.gov.uk. Head: N.A. Burnett
Local Museum - 1971
Local social hist, domestic items 34881

Museum of the Worcestershire Regiment, Foregate St, Worcester WR1 1DT - T: (01905) 25371, Fax: 722350. Head: D.W. Reevees
Military Museum
History of the regiment, medals, uniforms, equipment 34882

Museum of Worcester Porcelain, Severn St, Worcester WR1 2NE - T: (01905) 23221, Fax: 617807, E-mail: museum@royal-worcester.co.uk, Internet: http://www.royal-worchester.co.uk. Head: Amanda Savidge, T.G. Westbrook
Decorative Arts Museum - 1946
Worcester porcelain since 1751 34883

Worcester City Museum and Art Gallery, Foregate St, Worcester WR1 1DT - T: (01905) 25371, Fax: 616979. Head: Anthony J. Audas
Local Museum / Fine Arts Museum - 1833
Area hist, geology, natural hist, archaeology, glass, ceramics, local prints, watercolors 34884

Worcestershire Yeomanry Cavalry Museum, Foregate St, Worcester WR1 1DT - T: (01905) 25371, Fax: 616979. Head: Tim Bridges
Military Museum - 1929
Hist of regiment, medals, uniforms, decorations, documents and prints 34885

Workington

Helena Thompson Museum, Park End Rd, Workington CA14 4DE - T: (01900) 326255, Fax: 326256, E-mail: helena.thompson@allerdale.gov.uk, Internet: http://www.allerdale.dov.uk. Head: Philip Crouch
Local Museum - 1940
Workington's social and industrial hist, costume, ceramics, other decorative art 34886

Worksop

IBTE Museum of Telecommunication, Queen St, Worksop S80 2AN - T: (01909) 483680. Head: Tim Toulson
Science&Tech Museum
Telephones, telex, overhead wires, underground cables 34887

Mr. Straw's House, 7 Blyth Grove, Worksop S81 0JG - T: (01909) 482380. Head: Susie Barnett
Historical Museum
Family ephemera, costume, furniture and household objects 34888

Worksop Museum, Memorial Av, Worksop S80 2BP - T: (01777) 713749, Fax: 713749. Head: Malcolm J. Dolby
Local Museum
Local history, archaeology, natural history, Stone Age finds 34889

Worthing

Worthing Museum and Art Gallery, Chapel Rd, Worthing BN11 1HP - T: (01903) 239999 ext 1150, Fax: 236277, E-mail: museum@worthing.gov.uk, Internet: http://www.worthing.gov.uk
Local Museum / Decorative Arts Museum / Fine Arts Museum - 1908
Archaeology, geology, local history, costumes, paintings, decorative arts, toys 34890

Wotton-under-Edge

Wotton Heritage Centre, The Chipping, Wotton-under-Edge GL12 7AD - T: (01453) 521541, Fax: wootonhs@freeuk.com. Head: Beryl A. Kingan
Local Museum
Local and family history - library 34891

Wrexham

Erddig Agricultural Museum, Felin Puleston, Wrexham LL13 0YT - T: (01978) 355314, Fax: 313333, E-mail: erddig@ntrust.org.uk. Head: Gavin Hogg
Decorative Arts Museum
Furniture, domestic outbuildings, vehicles 34892

Geological Museum of North Wales, Bwlchgwyn Quarry, Wrexham LL11 5UY - T: (01978) 757573
Natural History Museum 34893

King's Mill Visitor Centre, King's Mill Rd, Wrexham LL13 0NT - T: (01978) 358916
Science&Tech Museum
Restored mill featuring life and work in an 18th c mill, waterwheel, by appointment 34894

Wrexham Arts Centre, Rhosddu Rd, Wrexham LL11 1AU - T: (01978) 292093, Fax: 292611, E-mail: arts.centre@wrexham.gov.uk, Internet: http://www.wrexham.gov.uk. Head: Tracy Simpson
Public Gallery 34895

Wrexham County Borough Museum, County Bldgs, Regent St, Wrexham LL11 1RB - T: (01978) 358916, Fax: 353882. Head: Alan Watkin
Local Museum
Local hist, iron and coal industry (18th-19th c), bronze age skeleton of Brymbo man, archeology 34896

Wroughton

Science Museum Wroughton, The National Museum of Science & Industry, Wroughton Airfield, Wroughton SN4 9NS - T: (01793) 814466, Fax: 813569, E-mail: m.atkinson@nmsi.ac.uk, Internet: http://www.sciencemuseum.org.uk/wroughton. Head: Lindsay Sharp
Science&Tech Museum 34897

Wroxeter

Viroconium Museum, Wroxeter Roman City, Roman Site, Wroxeter SY5 6PH - T: (01743) 761330. Head: Sara Lunt
Archaeological Museum
Archeological finds, pottery, coins, metalwork 34898

Wylam

Wylam Railway Museum, Falcon Centre, Falcon Terrace, Wylam NE41 8EE - T: (01661) 852174. Head: Philip R.B. Brooks
Science&Tech Museum - 1981 34899

Wymondham

Wymondham Heritage Museum, 10 The Bridewell, Norwich Rd, Wymondham NR18 0NS - T: (01953) 600205, Internet: http://www.wymondham-norfolk.co.uk
Local Museum
Local history 34900

Yanworth

Chedworth Roman Villa, Yanworth GL54 3LJ - T: (01242) 890256, Fax: 890544. Head: Philip Bethell
Archaeological Museum - 1865
Roman walls, mosaic floors, bath suites, wooden buildings, heating in Roman houses, Roman gardens, religion in Roman times, archaeology, classical history 34901

Yarmouth

Maritime Heritage Exhibition, Fort Victoria Museum, Fort Victoria Country Park, off Westhill Ln, Yarmouth PO41 0RW - T: (01983) 761214, Fax: (023) 80593052, E-mail: hwtma@mail.soc.soton.ac.uk, Internet: http://www.soc.coton.ac.uk/hwtma. Head: Paul Blake
Historical Museum 34902

Yell

Old Haa, Burravoe, Yell ZE2 9AY - T: (019577) 22339. Head: A. Nisbet
Local Museum
Arts and crafts, local history, tapes of Shetland music and folklore, Bobby Tulloch collection, genealogy 34903

Yelverton

Buckland Abbey, Yelverton PL20 6EY - T: (01822) 853607, Fax: 855448. Head: Michael Coxson
Historic Site - 1952
Drakes drum, standards, portraits and family pictures, furniture and ship navigation equipment 34904

Yelverton Paperweight Centre, 4 Buckland Tce, Leg O'Mutton Cnr, Yelverton PL20 6AD - T: (01822) 854250, Fax: 854250, E-mail: paperweightcentre@btinternet.com, Internet: http://www.paperweight-centre.co.uk
Fine Arts Museum
Work of glass artists and others 34905

Yeovil

Country Life Museum, Priest House, Brympton d'Evercy, Yeovil BA22 8TD - T: (01935) 862528
Folklore Museum
Coll of old domestic appliances 34906

Museum of South Somerset, Hendford, Yeovil BA20 1UN - T: (01935) 424774, Fax: 475281, E-mail: marion.barnes@southsomerset.gov.uk, Internet: http://www.zynet.co.uk/somerset/altrac/sout_mus.html. Head: Marion Barnes
Local Museum - 1928
Archaeology, industries, household and farm tools, topography, armaments, glass, costumes 34907

Yeovilton

Fleet Air Arm Museum - Concorde, The National Museum of Science & Industry, D6, Royal Naval Air Station, Yeovilton BA22 8HT - T: (01935) 840565, Fax: 842630, E-mail: enquires@fleetairarm.com, Internet: http://www.fleetairarm.com. Head: Graham Mottram
Military Museum - 1964
Paintings, photographs, weapons, medals and uniforms, coll of model aircraft and model ships, the ultimate "carrier" experience a flight deck on land with eleven carrier-borne aircraft 34908

York

Archaeological Resource Centre, Saint Saviourgate, York - T: (01904) 654324, Fax: 627097, E-mail: enquiries.arc.yat@yorkarch.demon.co.uk, Internet: http://www.jorvik-viking-centre.co.uk/arc
Archaeological Museum 34909

Beningbrough Hall, Beningbrough, York YO30 1DD - T: (01904) 470666, Fax: 470002, E-mail: yorkbn@smtp.ntrust.org.uk
Fine Arts Museum - 1979
Restored early Georgian country house, National portrait gallery 34910

Castle Museum, Eye of York, nr Clifford's Tower, Coppergate, York YO1 1RY - T: (01904) 653611, Fax: 671078, E-mail: castle.museum@york.gov.uk, Internet: http://www.york.gov.uk. Head: Keith Matthews
Ethnology Museum / Historical Museum - 1938
Yorkshire ethnology, period rooms, household and farm tools, militaria, costumes, crafts 34911

Divisional Kohima Museum, Imphal Barracks, Fulford Rd, York YO1 4AU - T: (01904) 662381, Fax: 662744. Head: Robin McDermott
Military Museum 34912

Fairfax House Museum, Castlegate, York YO1 9RN - T: (01904) 655543, Fax: 652262, E-mail: peterbrown@fairfaxhouse.co.uk, Internet: http://www.fairfaxhouse.co.uk. Head: Peter B. Brown
Decorative Arts Museum / Fine Arts Museum - 1984
18th c English furniture, clocks, dining room, silver, paintings and glass, elaborate stucco ceilings 34913

Impressions Gallery of Photography, 29 Castlegate, York YO1 9RN - T: (01904) 654724, Fax: 651509, E-mail: info@impressions-gallery.com, Internet: http://www.impressions-gallery.com
Fine Arts Museum
Contemporary photography 34914

Merchant Adventurers' Hall, Fossgate, York YO1 9XD - T: (01904) 654818, Fax: 654818, E-mail: the.clerk@mahall-york.demon.co.uk, Internet: http://www.theyorkcompany.sagenet.co.uk
Decorative Arts Museum
Early furniture, silver and portraits, pottery and other objects 34915

National Railway Museum, The National Museum of Science and Industry, Leeman Rd, York YO26 4XJ - T: (01904) 621261, Fax: 611112, E-mail: nrm@nmsi.ac.uk, Internet: http://www.nrm.org.uk. Head: Andrew Scott, Chris Allender
Science&Tech Museum - 1975
Mallard - the world's fastest steam locomotive, Queen Victoria's Royal Carriages, Working Replica of Stephenson's Rocket, Japanese Bullet train - library, archives and picture archives 34916

Regimental Museum of the Royal Dragoon Guards and the Prince of Wales's Own Regiment of Yorkshire, 3a Tower St, York YO1 9SB - T: (01904) 642036, Fax: 642036, Internet: http://www.army.mod.uk. Head: W.A. Henshall
Military Museum
Uniforms, paintings, pictures, medals, horse furniture, weapons, soldiers' personal memorabilia, regiments history 34917

Treasurer's House, Minster Yard, York YO1 2JL - T: (01904) 624247, Fax: 647372, E-mail: yorkth@smtp.ntrust.org.uk. Head: Norma Sutherland
Decorative Arts Museum - 1930
Furniture 17th-18th c, pictures, glass, ceramics 34918

Viking City of Jorvik, Coppergate, York YO1 9WT - T: (01904) 643211, Fax: 627097, E-mail: marketing.jorvik@lineone.net, Internet: http://www.jorvik-viking-centre.co.uk. Head: Nicola Bexon
Archaeological Museum / Historical Museum
Viking life and trade 34919

York City Art Gallery, Exhibition Sq, York YO1 7EW - T: (01904) 551861, Fax: 551866, E-mail: art.gallery@york.gov.uk, Internet: http://www.york.gov.uk/heritage/museums/art. Head: Richard Green
Fine Arts Museum - 1879
European painting 1350-1930, topographical prints and drawings, Italian paintings, English stoneware pottery - library 34920

York Racing Museum (closed until 2004), Racecourse, The Knavesmire, York YO23 1EX - T: (01904) 620911, Fax: 611071, E-mail: info@yorkracecourse.co.uk, Internet: http://www.yorkracecourse.co.uk. Head: Scott Brown
Special Museum - 1965
Horce racing 34921

York Story, Saint Mary Castlegate, York YO1 9RN - T: (01904) 628632
Local Museum
Social and architectural history of York 34922

Yorkshire Museum, Museum Gardens, York YO1 7FR - T: (01904) 551800, Fax: 551802, E-mail: yorkshire.museum@york.gov.uk, Internet: http://www.york.gov.uk
Local Museum - 1822
Archaeology, decorative art, pottery, biology, mammals, entomology, herbarium, geology, fossils, minerals, numismatics, figures - library 34923

Yorkshire Museum of Farming, Murton Park, York YO19 5UF - T: (01904) 489966, Fax: 489159
Agriculture Museum - 1982
Viking village, Roman fort, Celtic houses, 200 years farm machinery and equipment 34924

Zennor

Wayside Folk Museum, Old Mill House, Zennor TR26 3DA - T: (01736) 796945
Folklore Museum - 1935
Mining, household objects, milling, fishing, archaeology, wheelwrights and carpenters shop, blacksmiths, agriculture, millers cottage kitchen and parlour, childhood memories, the sea, village dairy, cobblers shop working water wheels, photographies 34925

Uruguay

Mercedes

Museo de Mercedes, 75000 Mercedes
Natural History Museum / Ethnology Museum
Natural history, palaeontology, geology, ethnography of Venezuela 34926

Montevideo

Centro de Artistas Plásticos, Calle Charrúa 2009, 11200 Montevideo
Fine Arts Museum 34927

Centro Municipal de Exposiciones, Pl Fabini, 11400 Montevideo
Public Gallery 34928

Galería de Cinemateca, Calle Dr. Lorenzo Carnelli 1311, 11200 Montevideo
Special Museum 34929

Galería Pocitos, Calle Alejandro Chucarro 1036, 11300 Montevideo - T: (02) 7082957
Public Gallery 34930

Museo Aeronáutico, Calle Dámaso Antonio Larrañaga 4045, 12000 Montevideo - T: (02) 2152039
Science&Tech Museum 34931

Museo de Armas, Fortaleza del Cerro de Montevideo, 11000 Montevideo
Military Museum
Military, armaments 34932

Museo de Arte Contemporáneo, Calle 18 de Julio 965, 11000 Montevideo
Fine Arts Museum 34933

Museo de Arte Industrial, Calle San Salvador 1674, 12000 Montevideo
Decorative Arts Museum
Applied arts, crafts 34934

Museo de Descubrimiento, Calle Zabala y Calle Piedras, 11000 Montevideo
Historical Museum
Evokes the journeys of Cristobal Colón, the meeting of the two worlds, maps, dioramas and photographs 34935

Museo de Historia del Arte y Arte Precolombino y Colonial, Calle Ejido 1326, 11200 Montevideo - T: (02) 989252
Fine Arts Museum 34936

Museo de la Dirección Nacional de Minería y Geología, Calle Hervidero 2861, 11800 Montevideo - T: (02) 201951, Fax: 201951. Head: Dr. Gonzalo llarramendi
Science&Tech Museum / Natural History Museum - 1934
Geology, mining, Fernando A. Tabó 34937

Museo del Azulejo, Calle Cavia 3080, 10000 Montevideo - T: (02) 7096352
Special Museum 34938

Museo del Gaucho, Calle 18 de Julio 998, 11000 Montevideo
Ethnology Museum 34939

Museo Ernesto Laroche, Calle General Gregorio Suárez 2716, Punta Carretas, 11000 Montevideo - T: (02) 700637, 704166. Head: Walter Ernesto Laroche
Local Museum
Local history 34940

Museo Histórico Nacional, Casa de Lavalleja (National Historical Museum), Calle Zabala 1469, 11000 Montevideo - T: (02) 951028
Historical Museum 34941

Museo Histórico Nacional, Casa Rivera (National Historical Museum), Calle Rincón 437, 11000 Montevideo - T: (02) 9151051, Fax: 9156863, E-mail: mhistoricnac@mixmail.com. Head: Prof. Enrique Mena Segarra
Historical Museum - 1900
Prehistoric and colonial Indian cultural hist, Uruguay political hist, military, armaments, music 34942

Museo Juan Manuel Blanes, Av Millán 4015, 11700 Montevideo - T: (02) 362248. Head: María del Carmen Heguerte de Soria, Jorge Satut
Fine Arts Museum
Sculpture, paintings, drawings, graphic arts, woodcarvings 34943

Museo Juan Zorrilla, Calle J.L. Zorrilla de San Martín 96, 11300 Montevideo - T: (02) 701818
Special Museum
Life and work of Juan Zorilla de San Martín 34944

Museo Municipal de Bellas Artes, Av Millán 4015, 11700 Montevideo - T: (02) 385420. Head: Mario C. Tempone
Fine Arts Museum - 1928
Paintings, graphic arts, sculpture, woodcarvings 34945

Museo Municipal de la Construcción, Calle Piedras 528, 11000 Montevideo - T: (02) 954087
Science&Tech Museum 34946

Museo Nacional de Antropología, Av de las Instrucciones 948, 12900 Montevideo - T: (02) 393353
Ethnology Museum 34947

Museo Nacional de Artes Visuales, C Julio Herrera y Reissig, esq Av Tomás Giribaldi s/n, Parque Rodó, 11300 Montevideo - T: (02) 7116124/27, Fax: 7116054, Internet: http://www.zfm.com/mnav
Fine Arts Museum
library 34948

Museo Nacional de Bellas Artes, Av Tomás E. Giribaldi 2283, Parque Rodó, 11300 Montevideo - T: (02) 43800. Head: Angel Kalenberg
Fine Arts Museum
Paintings, sculptures, graphic arts of Uruguay and America, works by Joaquín Torres García - library 34949

Museo Nacional de Historia Natural, Calle Buenos Aires 652, 11000 Montevideo, mail addr: Apdo 399, 11000 Montevideo - T: (02) 9160908, Fax: 9170213, E-mail: amones@adinet.com.uy, Internet: http://www.chana.mec.gub/frame2.htm
Natural History Museum - 1837
Botany, zoology, anthropology, geology, paleontology - library 34950

Museo Pedagógico José Pedro Varela, Plaza de Cagancha 1175, 11100 Montevideo - T: (02) 9004744, Fax: 9084131, E-mail: lemamc@adinet.com.uy, Internet: http://www.crnti.edu.uy/museo. Head: María del Carmen Lema Pensado
Special Museum - 1889
Educational hist 34951

Museo Severino Pose, Calle Eduardo Acevedo Díaz 1229, 11200 Montevideo - T: (02) 483563
Local Museum 34952

Museo Torres García, Calle Sarandi 683, 11000 Montevideo - T: (02) 9162663, Fax: 9152635, E-mail: torresgarcia@montevideo.com.uy, Internet: http://www.torresgarcia.org.uy. Head: Jipiena Perera Díaz
Local Museum 34953

Museo y Archivo Histórico Municipal, Cabildo de Montevideo, Calle Juan Carlos Gómez 1362, 11000 Montevideo - T: (02) 982826. Head: Jorge Rodriguez Delucchi
Local Museum - 1915
Paintings, jewelry, icons, furniture, documents, maps - library 34954

Museo y Biblioteca Blanco Acevedo, Calle Zabala 1469, 11000 Montevideo
Local Museum 34955

Museo y Jardin Botánico Profesor Atilio Lombardo, Av 19 de Abril 1181, 11700 Montevideo - T: (02) 3364005, Fax: 3366488. Head: Pablo B. Ross
Natural History Museum / Local Museum - 1902
Botany 34956

Museo Zoológico Dámaso A. Larrañaga, Rambla República de Chile 4215, 11400 Montevideo - T: (02) 620258. Head: Juan Pablo Cuello
Natural History Museum - 1956
Zoology - library 34957

Museos del Gaucho y de la Moneda, Banco de la República Oriental del Uruguay, Calle 18 de Julio No 998, 11100 Montevideo - T: (02) 908764. Head: Frederico Slinger
Special Museum
Banknotes, coins, history of banking 34958

Palacio Taranco, Calle 25 de Mayo 376, Montevideo
Public Gallery 34959

Montvideo

Sala de Arte Carlos F. Sáez, Calle Rincón 575, 11000 Montvideo
Fine Arts Museum 34960

Rivera

Museo Municipal de Artes Plásticas, Calle Artigas 1019, Rivera - Internet: http://www.turismo.gub.uy/plasti.htm
Fine Arts Museum - 1995 34961

Museo Municipal de Historia y Arqueología, Calle Artigas 1019, Rivera
Local Museum / Archaeological Museum - 1946 34962

Salto

Museo Histórico Municipal, Calle Amorín 55, 50000 Salto
Local Museum
Local history 34963

San José de Mayo

Museo de Bellas Artes Departamental de San José, Calle Dr Julián Beccerro de Bengoa 493, 80000 San José de Mayo - T: 3642. Head: César Bernesconi
Fine Arts Museum - 1947
Paintings, sculptures, graphic art, ceramics - library 34964

Tacuarembó

Museo del Indio y del Gaucho, Calle 25 de Mayo 315, 45000 Tacuarembó. Head: Washington Escobar
Ethnology Museum
Indian and Gaucho arts and crafts, armaments, implements 34965

Treinta y Tres

Museo de Bellas Artes Agustin Araujo, Pablo Zufriategui 1272, Treinta y Tres - Internet: http://www.turismo.gub.uy/araujo.htm
Fine Arts Museum 34966

U.S.A.

Abercrombie ND

Fort Abercrombie Historic Site, 816 Broadway St, Abercrombie, ND 58001 - T: (701) 553-8513. Head: Samuel Wegner
Historical Museum - 1961 34967

Aberdeen SD

Dacotah Prairie Museum and Lamont Art Gallery, 21 S Main St, Aberdeen, SD 57402-0395 - T: (605) 626-7117, Fax: (605) 626-4026, E-mail: bcmuseum@midco.net, Internet: http://www.brown.sd.us/museum. Head: Sue Gates
Local Museum - 1964
Local hist, Anerican Indian art - Ruth Bunker Memorial library 34968

Northern Galleries, Northern State University, 1200 S Jay St, Aberdeen, SD 57401 - T: (605) 626-2596, Fax: (605) 626-2263, E-mail: mulvaner@wolf.northern.edu. Head: Rebecca Mulvaney
Fine Arts Museum - 1902
Drawings, paintings, prints, photography, sculpture 34969

Aberdeen Proving Ground MD

United States Army Ordnance Museum, c/o U.S. Army Ordnance Center and School, Aberdeen Proving Ground, MD 21005 - T: (410) 278-3602, 278-2396, Fax: (410) 278-7473, E-mail: museum@ocs2.apg.army.mil. Head: William F. Atwater
Military Museum - 1919
Military history 34970

Abilene KS

Dickinson County Heritage Center, 412 S Campbell St, Abilene, KS 67410 - T: (785) 263-2681, Fax: (785) 263-0380, E-mail: dchs@ikansas.com. Head: Jeff Sheets
Local Museum - 1928
Local history - telephone hist 34971

Dwight D. Eisenhower Library-Museum, SE 4th St, Abilene, KS 67410 - T: (913) 263-4751, Fax: (913) 263-4218, E-mail: library@eisenhower.nara.gov, Internet: http://www.eisenhower.utexas.edu/. Head: Daniel D. Holt
Library with Exhibitions - 1962
Presidential library 34972

Greyhound Hall of Fame, 407 S Buckeye, Abilene, KS 67410 - T: (913) 263-3000, Fax: (785) 263-1704, E-mail: ghf@classicnet.net. Head: Charles Marriot, Edward Scheele
Special Museum - 1963
Greyhound sports 34973

Museum of Independent Telephony, 412 S Campbell, Abilene, KS 67410 - T: (785) 263-2681, Fax: (785) 263-0380, E-mail: dchs@ikansas.com, Internet: http://www.geocities.com/museumofindependenttelephony. Head: Robin Sherck
Science&Tech Museum - 1973
Telephonic history 34974

Western Museum, 201 SE 6th, Abilene, KS 67410 - T: (913) 263-4612. Head: B.G. French
Local Museum
Local history, housed in Rock Island Railroad Stn 34975

Abingdon VA

William King Regional Arts Center, 415 Academy Dr, Abingdon, VA 24212 - T: (540) 628-5005, Fax: (540) 628-3922, E-mail: willking@naxs.com, Internet: http://www.wkrac.org. Head: Betsy K. White
Fine Arts Museum - 1979 34976

Abington MA

Dyer Memorial Library, 28 Centre Av, Abington, MA 02351 - T: (781) 878-8480. Head: Joice Himawan
Library with Exhibitions - 1932
Civil war monographs 34977

Abiquiu NM

Florence Hawley Ellis Museum of Anthropology, Ghost Ranch Conference Center, Abiquiu, NM 87510-9601 - T: (505) 685-4333 ext 118, Fax: (505) 685-4519, Internet: http://www.newmexico-ghostranch.org. Head: Cheryl Muceus
Ethnology Museum - 1980
Anthropology 34978

Ruth Hall Museum of Paleontology, Ghost Ranch Conference Center, Abiquiu, NM 87510-9601 - T: (505) 685-4333 ext 118, Fax: (505) 685-4519, Internet: http://www.newmexico-ghostranch.org. Head: Cheryl Muceus
Natural History Museum - 1980
Paleontology, geology 34979

Accokeek MD

The Accokeek Foundation, 3400 Bryan Point Rd, Accokeek, MD 20607 - T: (301) 283-2113, Fax: (301) 283-2049, E-mail: accofound@accokeek.org, Internet: http://www.accokeek.org. Head: Wilton C. Corkern
Agriculture Museum - 1958
Agriculture 34980

Acme MI

The Music House, 7377 U.S. 31 N, Acme, MI 49610 - T: (616) 938-9300, Fax: (616) 938-3650, E-mail: musichouse@coslink.net, Internet: http://www.musichouse.org. Head: Robert L. Jackson, David L. Stiffler
Music Museum - 1983
Music, musical instrument 34981

Acton MA

The Discovery Museums, 177 Main St, Acton, MA 01720 - T: (978) 264-4200, Fax: (978) 264-0210, E-mail: discover@ultranet.com, Internet: http://www.ultranet.com/~discover. Head: Deborah J. Gilpin, Geoff Nelson, Denise LeBlanc, Lauren Kotkin
Ethnology Museum - 1981
Children's museums, Sea of Clouds 34982

Ada MN

Memorial Museum, 2nd St and 2nd Av E, Ada, MN 56510-1604 - T: (218) 784-4989, 784-4141, Fax: (218) 784-3475. Head: R. De Floren
Local Museum - 1957
Village museum 34983

Addison VT

Chimmey Point Tavern, 7305 VT Rte 125, Addison, VT 05491 - T: (802) 759-2412, Fax: (802) 759-2547, E-mail: chimneypoint@dca.state.vt.us, Internet: http://www.historicvermont.org. Head: Elsa Gilbertson
Local Museum - 1968
Historic building 34984

John Strong Mansion, Rte 17, Addison, VT 05491 - T: (802) 545-2153, E-mail: sbutton@together.net
Local Museum - 1934
Historic house 34985

Adrian MI

Klemm Gallery, Siena Heights College, 1247 Siena Heights Dr, Adrian, MI 49221 - T: (517) 264-7863, Fax: (517) 264-7704, E-mail: pbarr@sienahts.edu, Internet: http://www.sienahts.edu/~arts. Head: Dr. Peter J. Barr
Fine Arts Museum - 1919
National artists 34986

Aiken SC

Aiken County Historical Museum, 433 New Berry St SW, Aiken, SC 29801 - T: (803) 642-2015, Fax: (803) 642-2016, E-mail: acmuseum@duesouth.net, Internet: http://www.duesouth.net. Head: Carolyn W. Miles, Owen Clary
Local Museum - 1970
Regional hist 34987

Aiken Thoroughbred Racing Hall of Fame and Museum, Whiskey Rd and Dupree Pl, Aiken, SC 29801 - T: (803) 642-7758, 642-7648, Fax: (803) 642-7639, E-mail: lhall@aiken.net. Head: Joan B. Tower
Special Museum - 1979
Horse races 34988

Akron CO

Washington County Museum, 34445 Hwy 63, Akron, CO 80720 - T: (970) 345-6446
Local Museum - 1958
Local history, Burlington northern school house 34989

Akron OH

Akron Art Museum, 70 E Market St, Akron, OH 44308-2084 - T: (330) 376-9185, Fax: (330) 376-1180, E-mail: mail@akronartmuseum.org, Internet: http://www.akronartmuseum.org. Head: Mitchell Kahan, Joan Lauck
Fine Arts Museum - 1922 34990

National Inventors Hall of Fame, 221 S Broadway, Akron, OH 44308 - T: (800) 968-4332, (330) 762-6565, Fax: (330) 762-6313, Internet: http://www.invent.org. Head: David G. Fink, Cornelia Eichorn
Science&Tech Museum - 1973
Science 34991

Stan Hywet Hall and Gardens, 714 N Portage Path, Akron, OH 44303-1399 - T: (330) 836-5533, Fax: (330) 836-2680, Internet: http://www.stanhywet.org. Head: Harry P. Lynch
Decorative Arts Museum / Historical Museum - 1957 34992

Summit County Historical Society Museum, 550 Copley Rd, Akron, OH 44320 - T: (330) 535-1120, Fax: (330) 376-6868, E-mail: schs@akronschs.org, Internet: http://www.akronschs.org. Head: Charles Pierson, Paula G. Moran
Historical Museum - 1924 34993

Alamogordo NM

Space Center, Top of New Mexico, Hwy 2001, Alamogordo, NM 88310 - T: (505) 437-2840, Fax: (505) 434-2245, E-mail: djstarkey@zianet.com, Internet: http://abcc.nmsu.edu/~bwood. Head: Don J. Starkey
Science&Tech Museum - 1973 34994

Tularosa Basin Historical Society Museum, 1301 White Sands Blvd, Alamogordo, NM 88310 - T: (505) 434-4438, E-mail: tbhs@rocketmail.com, Internet: http://www.alamogordo.com/tbhs. Head: Mildred Evaskovich
Historical Museum - 1971 34995

Alamosa CO

Adams State College Luther Bean Museum, Richardson Hall, Alamosa, CO 81102 - T: (719) 587-7011, Fax: (719) 587-7522. Head: Shelly Andrews
Historical Museum / Ethnology Museum / Archaeological Museum / Museum of Classical Antiquities / Open Air Museum - 1968
Anthropology, ethnology, Indian, history 34996

Albany GA

Albany Museum of Art, 311 Meadowlark Dr, Albany, GA 31707 - T: (912) 439-8400, Fax: (912) 439-1332, E-mail: curator@albanymuseum.com, Internet: http://www.albanymuseum.com. Head: Timothy Close
Fine Arts Museum - 1964
Archaeology, ethnography, costumes and textiles, decorative arts, paintings, photographs, prints, drawings, graphic arts, sculpture 34997

Thronateeska Heritage Foundation, 100 Roosevelt Av, Albany, GA 31701 - T: (912) 435-1572, 432-6955, Fax: (912) 435-1572, Internet: http://www.heritagecenter.org. Head: Mary Ligon, Joseph H. Kitchens, Tom Finicyle
Local Museum - 1974
Local history 34998

Albany NY

Albany Institute of History and Art, 125 Washington Av, Albany, NY 12210-2296 - T: (518) 463-4478, Fax: (518) 462-1522, Internet: http://www.albanyinstitute.org. Head: Christine M. Miles
Fine Arts Museum / Historical Museum - 1791 34999

Historic Cherry Hill, 523 1/2 S Pearl St, Albany, NY 12202 - T: (518) 434-4791, Fax: (518) 434-4806. Head: John Abbuhl, Liselle LaFrance
Decorative Arts Museum / Historical Museum - 1964 35000

New York State Museum, 3099 Cultural Education Center, Empire State Plaza, Albany, NY 12230 - T: (518) 474-5812, Fax: (518) 473-8496, Internet: http://www.nysm.nysed.gov. Head: Clifford A. Siegfried
Local Museum - 1870 35001

Schuyler Mansion State Historic Site, 32 Catherine St, Albany, NY 12202 - T: (518) 434-0834, Fax: (518) 434-3821, Internet: http://www.nysparks.com. Head: Marcy Shaffer
Historical Museum - 1911 35002

Shaker Heritage Society Museum, 1848 Shaker Meeting House, Albany Shaker Rd, Albany, NY 12211 - T: (518) 456-7890, Fax: (518) 452-7348, E-mail: shakerwv@crisny.org, Internet: http://crisny.org/notforprofit-shakerwv. Head: Edward Pratt
Local Museum - 1977
Local hist 35003

Ten Broeck Mansion, 9 Ten Broeck Pl, Albany, NY 12210 - T: (518) 436-9826, Fax: (518) 436-1489, E-mail: history@tenbroeck.org, Internet: http://www.tenbroeck.org. Head: Kerry A. Delaney
Decorative Arts Museum / Historical Museum - 1947 35004

University Art Museum, c/o State University of New York at Albany, 1400 Washington Av, Albany, NY 12222 - T: (518) 442-4035, Fax: (518) 442-5075, Internet: http://www.albany.edu/museum. Head: Marijo Dougherty
Fine Arts Museum / University Museum - 1967 35005

Albany TX

The Old Jail Art Center, 201 S Second St, Albany, TX 76430 - T: (915) 762-2269, Fax: (915) 762-2260, E-mail: ojac@camalott.com. Head: Margaret Blagg
Fine Arts Museum - 1977
Art 35006

Albemarle NC

Morrow Mountain State Park Museum, 49104 Morrow Mountain Rd, Albemarle, NC 28001 - T: (704) 982-4402. Head: Timothy McCree
Natural History Museum - 1962 35007

Stanly County Historic Museum, 245 E Main St, Albemarle, NC 28001 - T: (704) 986-3777, Fax: (704) 986-3778, E-mail: cdwyer@co.stanly.nc.us, Internet: http://www.co.stanly.nc.us/departments/museum. Head: Christine M. Dwyer
Historical Museum - 1972 35008

Albert Lea MN

Freeborn County Historical Museum, 1031 Bridge Av, Albert Lea, MN 56007 - T: (507) 373-8003. Head: Bob Entorf, Bev Jackson
Local Museum / Open Air Museum - 1948
Regional history, pioneer village - library 35009

Albion MI

Bobbitt Visual Arts Center, 805 Cass St, Albion, MI 49224 - T: (517) 629-0246, Fax: (517) 629-0752, E-mail: rkreger@albion.edu, Internet: http://www.albion.edu. Head: Prof. Lynne Chytilo
Fine Arts Museum / University Museum - 1835
Contempotary artists 35010

Brueckner Museum, 13725 Starr Commonwealth Rd, Albion, MI 49224-9580 - T: (517) 629-5593 ext 431, Fax: (517) 629-2317, Internet: http://www.starr.org. Head: Arlin E. Ness
Fine Arts Museum - 1956 35011

Gardner House Museum, 509 S Superior St, Albion, MI 49224 - T: (517) 629-5100. Head: Marorie Ulbrich
Local Museum - 1958
Local history 35012

Albuquerque NM

Albuquerque Museum, 2000 Mountain Rd NW, Albuquerque, NM 87104 - T: (505) 243-7255, Fax: (505) 764-6546, E-mail: mnason@cabq.gov, Internet: http://w3.cabq.gov/museum. Head: James C. Moore
Fine Arts Museum / Historical Museum - 1967 35013

Explora Science Center and Children's Museum, 800 Rio Grande, Albuquerque, NM 87104 - T: (505) 842-6188, Fax: (505) 842-0607. Head: Jack McVinny
Science&Tech Museum - 1996
Science 35014

Indian Pueblo Cultural Center, 2401 12th St NW, Albuquerque, NM 87104 - T: (505) 843-7270, Fax: (505) 842-6959, Internet: http://www.indianpueblo.org. Head: Ron Solimon
Ethnology Museum / Historical Museum - 1976
Indian hist 35015

Institute of Meteoritics Meteorite Museum, c/o University of New Mexico, Albuquerque, NM 87131 - T: (505) 277-2747, Fax: (505) 277-3577, Internet: http://epswww.unm.edu/iom. Head: Dr. James J. Papike
University Museum / Natural History Museum - 1944 35016

Jonson Gallery, University of New Mexico Art Museum, 1909 Las Lomas NE, Albuquerque, NM 87131 - T: (505) 277-4967, Fax: (505) 277-3188, E-mail: jonsong@unm.edu, Internet: http://www.unm.edu/~jonsong
Fine Arts Museum / University Museum - 1950 35017

Maxwell Museum of Anthropology, c/o University of New Mexico, Albuquerque, NM 87131-1201 - T: (505) 277-4405, Fax: (505) 277-1547, E-mail: gbawden@unm.edu, Internet: http://www.unm.edu/~maxwell. Head: Dr. Garth L. Bawden, Ian Wagoner, Patricia Cyman
University Museum / Ethnology Museum / Archaeological Museum / Science&Tech Museum / Folklore Museum - 1932 35018

Museum of Southwestern Biology, c/o Biology Department, University of New Mexico, Albuquerque, NM 87131 - T: (505) 277-3781, Fax: (505) 277-0304, E-mail: tlowrey@unm.edu. Head: Timothy K. Lowrey
University Museum / Natural History Museum - 1930
Birds, mammals, plants, arthropods, fishes, reptiles, amphibians - frozen tissues coll 35019

National Atomic Museum, S Wyoming Blvd, Bldg 20358, Kirtland Air Force Base East, Albuquerque, NM 87185-1490 - T: (505) 284-3243, Fax: (505) 284-3244, E-mail: info@atomicmuseum.com, Internet: http://www.atomicmuseum.com. Head: Jim Walther
Science&Tech Museum - 1969
Energy, science, weapons, history, aircraft, robotics, medicine 35020

New Mexico Museum of Natural History and Science, 1801 Mountain Rd NW, Albuquerque, NM 87104-1375 - T: (505) 841-2800, Fax: (505) 841-2866, E-mail: mtanner@nmmnh.state.nm.us, Internet: http://www.nmmnh.state.nm.us. Head: Richard A. Smartt
Natural History Museum / Science&Tech Museum - 1986 35021

Rattlesnake Museum, 202 San Felipe, Albuquerque, NM 87104-1426 - T: (505) 242-6569, Fax: (505) 242-6569, E-mail: zoomuseum@aol.com, Internet: http://www.rattlesnakes.com. Head: Bob Myers
Natural History Museum - 1990
Herpetology 35022

Telephone Pioneer Museum of New Mexico, 110 Fourth St NW, Albuquerque, NM 87103 - T: (505) 842-2937. Head: Neal Roch
Science&Tech Museum - 1961 35023

University Art Museum, University of New Mexico Center for the Arts, Rm 1017, Albuquerque, NM 87131-1416 - T: (505) 277-4001, Fax: (505) 277-7315, E-mail: lbahm@unm.edu, Internet: http://www.unm.edu. Head: Peter Walch
Fine Arts Museum / University Museum - 1963 35024

Very Special Arts Gallery, 4904 Fourth St NW, Albuquerque, NM 87107 - T: (505) 345-2872, Fax: (505) 345-2896, E-mail: info@vfranm.org. Head: Beth Rudolph
Fine Arts Museum - 1994
Drawings, paintings, ceramics, crafts, folk art 35025

Alden KS

Atchinson, Topeka and Santa Fe Depot, POB 158, Alden, KS 67512 - T: (316) 534-2425, E-mail: prflrcraft@aol.com. Head: Sara Fair Sleeper
Science&Tech Museum - 1970
Transportation 35026

Alden NY

Alden Historical Society Museum, 13213 Broadway, Alden, NY 14004 - T: (716) 937-7606. Head: Ronald Savage
Historical Museum - 1965 35027

Aledo IL

Essley-Noble Museum, Mercer County Historical Society, 1406 SE 2nd Av, Aledo, IL 61231 - T: (309) 584-4820
Local Museum - 1959
Local history 35028

Alexandria LA

Alexandria Museum of Art, 933 Main St, Alexandria, LA 71301 - T: (318) 443-3458, Fax: (318) 443-0545, E-mail: amoaart.com@aol, Internet: http://www.themuseum.org. Head: Mark A. Tullos
Fine Arts Museum - 1977
Art, housed in a old Bank Bldg 35029

Alexandria MN

Runestone Museum, 206 N Broadway, Alexandria, MN 56308 - T: (320) 763-3160, Fax: (320) 763-9705, E-mail: bigole@rea-alp.com. Head: LuAnn W. Patton
Archaeological Museum - 1958
History, youth 35030

Alexandria VA

Alexandria Archaeology Museum, 105 N Union St, Alexandria, VA 22314 - T: (703) 838-4399, Fax: (703) 838-6491, E-mail: archaeology@ci.alexandria.va.us, Internet: http://ci.alexandria.va.us/oha/archaeology. Head: Dr. Pamela J. Cressey
Archaeological Museum - 1977
Archaeology 35031

Alexandria Black History Resource Center, 638 N Alfred St, Alexandria, VA 22314 - T: (703) 838-4356, Fax: (703) 706-3999. Head: Louis Hicks
Local Museum - 1983
African American hist 35032

The Athenaeum, 201 Prince St, Alexandria, VA 22314 - T: (703) 548-0035, Fax: (703) 768-7471. Head: Mary Gaissert Jackson
Fine Arts Museum - 1964
Art 35033

Carlyle House Historic Park, 121 N Fairfax St, Alexandria, VA 22314 - T: (703) 549-2997, Fax: (703) 549-5738, E-mail: mrcoleman@juno.com, Internet: http://www.carlylehouse.org. Head: Mary Ruth Coleman
Local Museum - 1976
Historic house 35034

Collingwood Museum on Americanism, 8301 E Boulevard Dr, Alexandria, VA 22308 - T: (703) 765-1652, Fax: (703) 765-8390, E-mail: clmal@arols.com
Historical Museum - 1977
American hist 35035

Fort Ward Museum and Historic Site, 4301 W Braddock Rd, Alexandria, VA 22304 - T: (703) 838-4848, Fax: (703) 671-7350, E-mail: fort.ward@ci.alexandria.va.us, Internet: http://ci.alexandria.va.us/oha/fortward/html. Head: Wanda S. Dowell
Military Museum - 1964
Military hist, Civil War coll and Union Fort 35036

Friendship Firehouse, 107 S Alfred St, Alexandria, VA 22314 - T: (703) 838-3891, Fax: (703) 838-6451, Internet: http://ci.alexandria.va.us/oha/. Head: Jean Federico
Science&Tech Museum - 1993 35037

Gadsby's Tavern Museum, 134 N Royal St, Alexandria, VA 22314 - T: (703) 838-4242, Fax: (703) 838-4270, E-mail: gadsbys.tavern@ci.alexandria.va.us, Internet: http://ci.alexandria.va.us/oha/gadsbystavern.html. Head: Gretchen M. Bulova
Local Museum - 1976
Historic buildings 35038

George Washington Masonic National Memorial, 101 Callahan Dr, Alexandria, VA 22301 - T: (703) 683-2007, Fax: (703) 519-9270, E-mail: gseghers@gwmemorial.org, Internet: http://www.gwmemorial.org. Head: George D. Seghers
Historical Museum - 1910
History 35039

The John Q. Adams Center for the History of Otolaryngology - Head and Neck Surgery, 1 Prince St, Alexandria, VA 22314 - T: (703) 836-4444, Fax: (703) 683-5100, E-mail: jrozen@entnet.org, Internet: http://www.entnet.org/museum. Head: Jenny Rozen
Special Museum - 1990
Medical hist 35040

Lee-Fendall House, 614 Oronoco St, Alexandria, VA 22314 - T: (703) 548-1789, Fax: (703) 548-0931, Internet: http://www.funside.com. Head: Kathleen Schroeder
Local Museum - 1974
Historic house 35041

The Lyceum - Alexandria's History Museum, 201 S Washington St, Alexandria, VA 22314 - T: (703) 838-4994, Fax: (703) 838-4997, E-mail: lyceum@ci.alexandria.va.us, Internet: http://ci.alexandria.va.us/oha/lyceum. Head: Jim Mackay
Historical Museum - 1974
History 35042

Ramsay House, 221 King St, Alexandria, VA 22314 - T: (703) 838-4200 ext 212, Fax: (703) 838-4683, E-mail: jmitchell@funside.com, Internet: http://www.funside.com. Head: Joanne Mitchell
Local Museum - 1962
Historic house 35043

Stabler-Leadbeater Apothecary Museum, 105-107 S Fairfax St, Alexandria, VA 22314 - T: (703) 836-3713, Fax: (703) 836-3713. Head: Sara Becker
Special Museum - 1792
Pharmacy 35044

Torpedo Factory Art Center, 105 N Union St, Alexandria, VA 22314 - T: (703) 838-4199, 838-4565, Internet: http://ci.alexandria.va.us/OHA/torpedofactory
Fine Arts Museum / Folklore Museum - 1974
Art 35045

Alfred NY

The Scein-Joseph International Museum of Ceramic Art, New York State College of Ceramics at Alfred University, Alfred, NY 14802 - T: (607) 871-2421, Fax: (607) 871-2615, E-mail: carneym@bigvax.alfred.edu, Internet: http://www.ceramics-museum.alfred.edu. Head: Dr. Margaret Carney
Decorative Arts Museum - 1900 35046

Alice TX

South Texas Museum, 66 S Wright St, Alice, TX 78332 - T: (512) 668-8891, Fax: (512) 664-3327, E-mail: awells@vsta.com. Head: Mary Dru Burns
Local Museum - 1975
Local hist 35047

Aline OK

Sod House Museum, Rte 1, Aline, OK 73716 - T: (405) 463-2441. Head: Blake Wade
Historical Museum - 1968 35048

Allaire NJ

Historic Allaire Village, Allaire State Park, Rte 524, Allaire, NJ 07727-3715 - T: (732) 919-3500, Fax: (732) 938-3302, E-mail: allairevillage@bytheshore.com, Internet: http://www.allaire-village.org. Head: John Curtis
Open Air Museum / Local Museum - 1957 35049

Allegan MI

Allegan County Historical and Old Jail Museum, 113 Walnut St, Allegan, MI 49010 - T: (616) 673-8292, 673-4853. Head: Robert Hoyt, Marguerite Miller
Local Museum - 1952
Regional history, former county jail and sheriff's home 35050

Allentown PA

Allentown Art Museum, Fifth and Court Sts, Allentown, PA 18105 - T: (610) 432-4333 ext 10, Fax: (610) 434-7409, E-mail: marketing@allentownartmuseum.org, Internet: http://www.allentownartmuseum.org. Head: Peter F. Blume
Fine Arts Museum - 1934 35051

Allied Air Force Museum, Queen City Airport, 1730 Vultee St, Allentown, PA 18103 - T: (610) 791-5122, Fax: (610) 791-5453. Head: Joseph B. Fillman
Military Museum / Science&Tech Museum - 1984
Aeronautics 35052

Lehigh County Historical Society Museum, Hamilton at Fifth St, Allentown, PA 18101 - T: (610) 435-1074, Fax: (610) 435-9812. Head: Bernard P. Fishman
Historical Museum - 1904 35053

Alliance NE

Knight Museum of High Plains Heritage, 908 Yellowstone, Alliance, NE 69301 - T: (308) 762-2384, 762-5400 ext 261, Fax: (308) 762-7848, E-mail: museum@panhandle.net, Internet: http://www.alliance-ets.com. Head: Richard Cayer
Local Museum - 1965
Local hist 35054

Allison IA

Butler County Historical Museum, Little Yellow Schoolhouse, Butler County Fair Grounds, Allison, IA 50602 - T: (319) 267-2255. Head: Deb Bochmann
Local Museum - 1956
Local history 35055

Alma CO

Alma Firehouse and Mining Museum, 1 W Buckskin Rd, Alma, CO 80420-0336 - T: (719) 836-3413, 836-3117. Head: Don Gostisha
Historical Museum - 1976
Fire fighting 35056

Alma KS

Wabaunsee County Historical Museum, Missouri and Third Sts, Alma, KS 66401 - T: (785) 765-2200
Local Museum - 1968
Regional history 35057

Almond NY

Hagadorn House Museum, 7 N Main St, Almond, NY 14804 - T: (607) 276-6781, E-mail: bakerd@infoblvd.net, Internet: http://www.rootsweb.com/~nyahs/AlmondHS.html. Head: Charlotte Baker
Historical Museum - 1965 35058

Alpena MI

Jesse Besser Museum, 491 Johnson St, Alpena, MI 49707-1496 - T: (517) 356-2202, Fax: (517) 356-3133, E-mail: jbmuseum@northland.lib.mi.us, Internet: http://www.oweb.com/upnorth/museum/. Head: Dr. Janice V. McLean
Local Museum - 1962
Art, history and science of Northeast Michigan, anthropology, natural history 35059

Alpine TX

Museum of the Big Bend, Sul Ross State University, Alpine, TX 79832 - T: (915) 837-8143, Fax: (915) 837-8381, E-mail: maryb@sulross.edu, Internet: http://www.sulross.edu/~museum/. Head: Larry Francell
Local Museum - 1926
Regional hist 35060

Altenburg MO

Perry County Lutheran Historical Society Museum, 866 Hwy C, Altenburg, MO 63732 - T: (573) 824-5542. Head: Leonard A. Kuehnert
Historical Museum / Religious Arts Museum - 1910 35061

Alton IL

Alton Museum of History and Art, 2809 College Av, Alton, IL 62002 - T: (618) 462-2763, Fax: (618) 462-6390, E-mail: altonmuseum@yahoo.com, Internet: http://www.altonweb.com/museum/index.html. Head: Lois Lobbig
Fine Arts Museum / Historical Museum - 1971
History, art 35062

Altoona PA

Altoona Railroader's Memorial Museum, 1300 Ninth Av, Altoona, PA 16602 - T: (814) 946-0834, Fax: (814) 946-9457, E-mail: info@railroadcity.com, Internet: http://www.railroadcity.com. Head: R. Cummins McNitt
Science&Tech Museum - 1980 35063

Alturas CA

Modoc County Historical Museum, 600 S Main St, Alturas, CA 96101 - T: (916) 233-6328. Head: Paula Murphy
Local Museum - 1967
Regional history 35064

Altus OK

Museum of the Western Prairie, 1100 Memorial Dr, Altus, OK 73521 - T: (580) 482-1044, Fax: (580) 482-0128, E-mail: muswestpr@ok-history.mus.ok.us, Internet: http://www.ok-history.mus.ok.us/mus-sites/masnum18.htm. Head: Burna Cole
Historical Museum - 1970 35065

Alva OK

Cherokee Strip Museum, 901 14 St, Alva, OK 73717 - T: (580) 327-2030. Head: Phyllis Fisher
Local Museum - 1961 35066

Northwestern Oklahoma State University Museum, Jesse Dunn Hall, 709 Oklahoma Blvd, Alva, OK 73717 - T: (580) 327-1700 ext 8513, Fax: (580) 327-1881, E-mail: vnpowders@nwosu.edu, Internet: http://www.nwosu.edu. Head: Dr. Vernon Powders
University Museum - 1902 35067

Amana IA

Museum of Amana History, 4310 220th Trail, Amana, IA 52203 - T: (319) 622-3567, Fax: (319) 622-6481, E-mail: amherit@juno.com. Head: Lanny Haldy
Local Museum / Folklore Museum - 1969
Local hist 35068

Amarillo TX

Amarillo Museum of Art, 2200 S Van Buren, Amarillo, TX 79109 - T: (806) 371-5050, Fax: (806) 373-9235, E-mail: amoa@arn.net, Internet: http://www.amarilloart.org. Head: Patrick McCracken
Fine Arts Museum - 1972
Art 35069

American Quarter Horse Heritage Center and Museum, 2601 I-40, E, Amarillo, TX 79104 - T: (806) 376-5181, Fax: (806) 376-1005, E-mail: museum@aqha.org, Internet: http://www.aqha.org. Head: Jerry Windham, James Moy
Special Museum - 1991
Equine, Hall of Fame 35070

Don Harrington Discovery Center, 1200 Streit Dr, Amarillo, TX 79106 - T: (806) 355-9547 ext 20, Fax: (806) 355-5703, E-mail: dhdc.org, Internet: http://www.dhdc.org. Head: Tom Haliday, Greg Shuman
Science&Tech Museum - 1968
Science and technology 35071

Ambridge PA

Harmonie Associates Museum, Old Economy Village Museum, 14 and Church Sts, Ambridge, PA 15003 - T: (724) 266-1803, Fax: (724) 266-5101. Head: Linda Swaney
Historical Museum - 1956
Historical Society 35072

Old Economy Village, 14 and Church Sts, Ambridge, PA 15003 - T: (724) 266-4500, Fax: (724) 266-7506, E-mail: mlandis@phmc.state.pa.us, Internet: http://www.oldeconomyvillage.org. Head: Mary Ann Landis
Open Air Museum - 1919
18 buildings of the original town of Economy (now Ambridge), PA, built between 1824 and 1831 35073

American Falls ID

Massacre Rocks State Park Museum, 3592 Park Lane, American Falls, ID 83211-5555 - T: (208) 548-2672, E-mail: mas@idpr.state.id.us
Natural History Museum - 1967 35074

Ames IA

Brunnier Art Museum, Iowa State University, 290 Scheman Bldg, Ames, IA 50011 - T: (515) 294-3342, Fax: (515) 294-7070, E-mail: museums@muse.adp.iastate.edu, Internet: http://www.museums.iastate.edu. Head: Lynette Pohlman
Decorative Arts Museum / Fine Arts Museum / University Museum - 1975
Decorative and fine arts 35075

Farm House Museum, Knoll Rd, Iowa State University Campus, Ames, IA 50011 - T: (515) 294-3342, 294-7426, Fax: (515) 294-7070, Internet: http://www.museums.iastate.edu. Head: Lynette Pohlman
University Museum / Agriculture Museum - 1976 35076

Gallery 181, 134 Design, College of Design, Iowa State University, Ames, IA 50011 - T: (515) 294-0728, Fax: (515) 294-9755. Head: Prof. Barbara J. Bruene
Fine Arts Museum / University Museum - 1978
Art 35077

The Octagon Center for the Arts, 427 Douglas Av, Ames, IA 50010-6281 - T: (515) 232-5331, Fax: (515) 232-5088, E-mail: octagoncen@aol.com. Head: Teresa Albertson
Fine Arts Museum - 1966
Art 35078

Amesbury MA

The Bartlett Museum, 270 Main St, Amesbury, MA 01913 - T: (978) 388-4528, 388-7950
Local Museum - 1968
History, housed in a Old Victorian School house 35079

John Greenleaf Whittier Home, 86 Friend St, Amesbury, MA 01913 - T: (508) 388-0689
Special Museum - 1898
Home of poet and abolitionist John Greenleaf Whittier 35080

Amherst MA

Amherst History Museum, Strong House, 67 Amity St, Amherst, MA 01002 - T: (413) 256-0678. Head: Melinda LeLacheur
Local Museum - 1899
Local hist 35081

Dickinson Homestead, 280 Main St, Amherst, MA 01002 - T: (413) 542-8161, Internet: http://www.amherst.edu/~edhouse. Head: Cindy Dickinson
Special Museum - 1965
Literature, local hist 35082

Mead Art Museum, Amherst College, Amherst, MA 01002-5000 - T: (413) 542-2335, 542-2295, Fax: (413) 542-2117, E-mail: mead@unix.amherst.edu, Internet: http://www.amherst.edu/~mead. Head: Jill Meredith
Fine Arts Museum / University Museum - 1821
American art 35083

Museum of Zoology, University of Massachusetts, Dept. of Biology, Amherst, MA 01003 - T: (413) 545-2902, Fax: (413) 545-3243, E-mail: mmnh@bio.umass.edu, Internet: http://snapper.bio.umass.edu/vmmnh. Head: William Bemis
University Museum / Natural History Museum - 1863
Zoology, fishes, amphibians and reptiles, invertebrates, mammals, birds 35084

National Yiddish Book Center, Harry and Jeanette Weinberg Bldg, 1021 West St, Amherst, MA 01002-3375 - T: (413) 256-4900 ext 103, Fax: (413) 256-4700, E-mail: yiddish@bikher.org, Internet: http://www.yiddishbookcenter.org. Head: Aaron Lanaky
Historical Museum / Religious Arts Museum - 1980
Yiddish culture 35085

The Pratt Museum of Natural History, Amherst College, Amherst, MA 01002 - T: (413) 542-2165, Fax: (413) 542-2713, E-mail: llthomas@amherst.edu, Internet: http://www.amherst.edu/~pratt/. Head: Dr. Edward S. Belt
University Museum / Natural History Museum - 1848
Natural history, paleontology, mineralogy, petrology 35086

University Gallery, University of Massachusetts at Amherst, Fine Arts Center, 151 Presidents Dr, Amherst, MA 01003-9331 - T: (413) 545-3670, Fax: (413) 545-2018, E-mail: ugallery@acad.umass.edu, Internet: http://www.umass.edu/fac/universitygallery. Head: Betsy Siersma
Fine Arts Museum / University Museum - 1975
Art gallery 35087

Amherst NY

Amherst Museum, 3755 Tonawanda Creek Rd, Amherst, NY 14228 - T: (716) 689-1440, Fax: (716) 689-1409, E-mail: amhmuseum@adelphia.net, Internet: http://www.amherstmuseum.org. Head: Lynn S. Beman
Local Museum - 1970
Local history and culture, historic buildings 35088

Amherst VA

Amherst County Museum, 154 S Main St, Amherst, VA 24521 - T: (804) 946-9068, E-mail: achmuseum@aol.com, Internet: http://members.aol.com/achmuseum/achmhis.htm. Head: Michael N. Morell
Local Museum / Folklore Museum - 1973
Local hist 35089

Amory MS

Amory Regional Museum, 715 Third St, Amory, MS 38821 - T: (601) 256-2761. Head: Gene Pierce
Local Museum - 1976 35090

Amsterdam NY

Walter Elwood Museum, 300 Guy Park Av, Amsterdam, NY 12010-2228 - T: (518) 843-5151, Fax: (518) 843-6098. Head: Mary Margaret Gage
Local Museum - 1940 35091

Anaconda MT

Copper Village Museum and Arts Center, 401 E Commercial, Anaconda, MT 59711 - T: (406) 563-2422. Head: Carol Jette
Fine Arts Museum / Historical Museum - 1971
library 35092

Anacortes WA

Anacortes Museum, 1305 8th, Anacortes, WA 98221 - T: (360) 293-1915, Fax: (360) 293-1929, E-mail: museum@cityofanacortes.org, Internet: http://www.anacorteshistorymuseum.org. Head: Garry Cline
Local Museum - 1957
Local hist 35093

Anadarko OK

Anadarko Philomathic Museum, 311 E Main St, Anadarko, OK 73005 - T: (405) 247-3240
Local Museum - 1936 35094

Indian City U.S.A., Hwy 8, 2 1/2 miles SE of Anakarko, Anadarko, OK 73005 - T: (405) 247-5661, Fax: (405) 247-2467, E-mail: indiancity@aol.com, Internet: http://www.indiancityusa.com. Head: Wayne E. Venable
Historical Museum / Natural History Museum / Ethnology Museum - 1955 35095

National Hall of Fame for Famous American Indians, Hwy 62 E, Anadarko, OK 73005 - T: (405) 247-5555, Fax: (405) 247-5571, E-mail: dailynews@tanet.net. Head: Joe McBride
Historical Museum - 1952 35096

Southern Plains Indian Museum, 715 E Central Blvd, Anadarko, OK 73005, mail addr: POB 749, Anadarko, OK 73005 - T: (405) 247-6221, Fax: (405) 247-7593. Head: Rosemary Ellison
Ethnology Museum / Folklore Museum - 1947 35097

Anaheim CA

Anaheim Museum, 241 S Anaheim Blvd, Anaheim, CA 92805 - T: (714) 778-3301, Fax: (714) 778-6740, E-mail: joycemuse@aol.com. Head: Joyce Franklin
Local Museum / Historical Museum - 1982
Local history 35098

Anaktuvuk Pass AK

Simon Paneak Memorial Museum, 341 Mekiana Rd, Anaktuvuk Pass, AK 99721 - T: (907) 661-3413, Fax: (907) 661-3414, E-mail: vweber@co.north-slope.ak.us, Internet: http://199.165.80.10/villages/akp/museum/paneak.htm. Head: Benjiman Nageak
Local Museum - 1986
Local history, ethnography 35099

Anchorage AK

Alaska Aviation Heritage Museum, 4721 Aircraft Dr, Anchorage, AK 99502 - T: (907) 248-5325, Fax: (907) 248-6391. Head: Ted Spencer
Science&Tech Museum - 1988 35100

Anchorage Museum of History and Art, 121 W Seventh Av, Anchorage, AK 99501 - T: (907) 343-6172, Fax: (907) 343-6149, E-mail: museum@ci.anchorage.ak.us, Internet: http://www.anchoragemuseum.org. Head: Patricia B. Wolf
Fine Arts Museum / Historical Museum / Ethnology Museum - 1968
History, art 35101

Cook Inlet Historical Society Museum, 121 W 7th Av, Anchorage, AK 99501-3696 - T: (907) 343-4326, Fax: (907) 343-6149. Head: James K. Barnett
Local Museum - 1955
Local history 35102

Heritage Library and Museum, 301 W Northern Lights Blvd, Anchorage, AK 99503 - T: (907) 265-2834, Fax: (907) 265-2002. Head: Gail Hollinger
Fine Arts Museum / Ethnology Museum - 1968 35103

The Imaginarium, 737 W Fifth Av, Ste G, Anchorage, AK 99501 - T: (907) 276-3179-1, Fax: (907) 258-4306, E-mail: info@imaginarium.org, Internet: http://www.imaginarium.org. Head: Christopher B. Cable
Science&Tech Museum - 1987
Science, technology 35104

Oscar Anderson House Museum, 420 M St, Anchorage, AK 99501 - T: (907) 274-2336, 333-6563, Fax: (907) 274-3610, Internet: http://www.customcpu.com/np/ahpi. Head: Mary A. Flaherty
Historical Museum - 1982 35105

Anderson IN

Alford House-Anderson Fine Arts Center, 32 W Tenth St, Anderson, IN 46016-1406 - T: (765) 649-1248, Fax: (765) 649-0199, E-mail: andersnart@netdirect.net, Internet: http://www.andersonart.org/index.html. Head: Dave Harbert, Deborah McBratney-Stapleton
Fine Arts Museum - 1966 35106

Gustav Jeeninga Museum of Bible and Near Eastern Studies, Theology Bldg, 1123 Anderson University Blvd, Anderson, IN 46012-3495 - T: (765) 649-9071, Fax: (765) 641-3851, E-mail: dneidert@anderson.edu, Internet: http://www.anderson.edu. Head: David Neidert
University Museum / Archaeological Museum / Religious Arts Museum - 1963
Archaeology, religion 35107

Anderson SC

Anderson County Arts Center, 405 N Main St, Anderson, SC 29621 - T: (864) 224-8811, Fax: (864) 224-8864, E-mail: artscenter@carol.net, Internet: http://members.carol.net/~artscenter. Head: Judy Swain
Public Gallery - 1972 35108

Anderson County Museum, 101 S Main St, Anderson, SC 29624 - T: (864) 260-4737, Fax: (803) 260-4044, E-mail: acm@andersoncountysc.org, Internet: http://www.andersoncountysc.org/museum.htm. Head: Paula Reel
Military Museum - 1983
Local hist 35109

Andover MA

Addison Gallery of American Art, Phillips Academy, Andover, MA 01810 - T: (978) 749-4015, Fax: (978) 749-4025, E-mail: addison@andover.edu, Internet: http://www.addisongallery.org. Head: Adam D. Weinberg
Fine Arts Museum - 1931
American art 35110

Andover Historical Society Museum, 97 Main St, Andover, MA 01810 - T: (978) 475-2236, Fax: (978) 470-2741, E-mail: andhists@ma.ultranet.com, Internet: http://www.ultranet.com/~andhists. Head: Christine Paradis Stelzer
Local Museum - 1911
Local history 35111

Robert S. Peabody Museum of Archaeology, 175 Main St, Andover, MA 01810 - T: (978) 749-4490, Fax: (978) 749-4495, Internet: http://www.andover.edu/rspeabody. Head: James W. Bradley
Archaeological Museum - 1901
Archaeology 35112

Angleton TX

Brazoria County Historical Museum, 100 E Cedar, Angleton, TX 77515 - T: (919) 864-1208, Fax: (919) 864-1217, E-mail: director@bchm.org, Internet: http://www.bchm.org. Head: Jackie Haynes
Historical Museum - 1983
Local hist 35113

Angola IN

General Lewis B. Hershey Museum, Tri-State University, Ford Memorial Library, 1 University Av, Angola, IN 46703 - T: (219) 665-4162, 665-4100, Fax: (219) 665-4777, E-mail: zimmermani@tristate.edu, Internet: http://www.tristate.edu. Head: Dr. Earl Brooks
University Museum / Military Museum - 1970
Military 35114

Ann Arbor MI

Ann Arbor Art Center, 117 W Liberty, Ann Arbor, MI 48104 - T: (734) 994-8004 ext 110, Fax: (734) 994-3610, E-mail: info@annaarborartscenter.org, Internet: http://www.annaarborartscenter.org. Head: Deborah Campbell
Fine Arts Museum - 1909
Art 35115

Ann Arbor Hands-On Museum, 220 E Ann St, Ann Arbor, MI 48104 - T: (313) 995-5439, Fax: (313) 995-1188, Internet: http://www.aahom.org. Head: James P. Frenza
Science&Tech Museum - 1982
Science, technology, central firehouse 35116

Artrain, 1100 N Main St, Ste 106, Ann Arbor, MI 48104 - T: (734) 747-8300, Fax: (734) 742-8530, Internet: http://www.artrainusa.org. Head: Debra Polich
Fine Arts Museum - 1971
Traveling art, housed in five railroad cars 35117

Exhibit Museum of Natural History, University of Michigan, 1109 Geddes Av, Ann Arbor, MI 48109-1079 - T: (734) 763-4190, Fax: (734) 647-2767, E-mail: dmadaj@umich.edu, Internet: http://www.exhibits.lsa.umich.edu. Head: Dr. William R. Farrand, Matthew P. Linke
University Museum / Natural History Museum - 1881
Natural history - planetarium 35118

Jean Paul Slusser Gallery, University of Michigan, School of Art and Design, Arts/Architecture Bldg, N Campus, 2000 Bonisteel Blvd, Ann Arbor, MI 48109-2069 - T: (734) 936-2082, Fax: (734) 615-6761, E-mail: slussergallery@umich.edu, Internet: http://www.umich.edu/~webteam/soad. Head: Todd Cashbaugh
University Museum / Fine Arts Museum
Art, design, architecture 35119

Kelsey Museum of Ancient Archaeology, 434 S State St, Ann Arbor, MI 48109 - T: (734) 764-9304, Fax: (734) 763-8976, Internet: http://www.umich.edu/~kelseydb. Head: Sharon C. Herbert
University Museum / Archaeological Museum / Museum of Classical Antiquities - 1928
Archaeology, Hellenic, Roman and Egypt antiques, photos 35120

Museum of Anthropology, University of Michigan, 4009 Ruthven Museums Bldg, Ann Arbor, MI 48109 - T: (734) 764- 0485, Fax: (734) 763-7783, E-mail: anthro-museum@umich.edu, Internet: http://www.umma.lsa.umich.edu. Head: Robert Whallon
University Museum / Ethnology Museum / Archaeological Museum - 1922
Anthropology, archaeology, old world civilization 35121

Museum of Art, University of Michigan, 525 S State St, Ann Arbor, MI 48109-1354 - T: (734) 764-0395, Fax: (734) 764-3731, E-mail: umma.info@umich.edu, Internet: http://www.umich.edu/~umma/. Head: James Steward
Fine Arts Museum / University Museum - 1946
Western paintings and sculptures 12th c to the present, Old Master prints and contemporary prints and drawings, photography, Asian, African, Oceanic art, Islamic ceramics 35122

Museum of Zoology, University of Michigan, 1109 Geddes, Ann Arbor, MI 48109-1079 - T: (734) 764-0476, Fax: (734) 763-4080. Head: Prof. Gerald R. Smith
University Museum / Natural History Museum - 1838
Zoology 35123

Stearns Collection of Musical Instruments, University of Michigan, School of Music, Ann Arbor, MI 48109-2085 - T: (734) 763-4389, 764-2539, Fax: (734) 763-5097. Head: Margo Halsted
Music Museum - 1899 35124

Annandale-on-Hudson NY

Center for Curatorial Studies, Bard College, Annandale-on-Hudson, NY 12504-5000 - T: (845) 758-7598, Fax: (845) 758-2442, E-mail: ccs@bard.edu, Internet: http://www.bard.edu/ccs. Head: Mamada Crus
Fine Arts Museum - 1990
Contemporary art 35125

Annapolis MD

Charles Carroll House of Annapolis, 107 Duke of Gloucester St, Annapolis, MD 21401 - T: (410) 269-1737, Fax: (410) 269-1746, E-mail: ccarroll@toad.net. Head: Sandria B. Ross
Historic Site - 1987 35126

Elizabeth Myers Mitchell Art Gallery, Saint John's College, 60 College Av, Annapolis, MD 21401 - T: (410) 626-2556, Fax: (410) 626-2886, E-mail: h-schaller@sjea.edu, Internet: http://www.sjca.edu. Head: Hydee Schaller
Fine Arts Museum / University Museum - 1989
Art gallery 35127

Hammond-Harwood House Museum, 19 Maryland Av, Annapolis, MD 21401 - T: (410) 269-1714, Fax: (410) 267-6891, E-mail: hammondharwood@annapolis.net. Head: Carol L. Hutchinson, Carter C. Lively
Historical Museum / Folklore Museum - 1938 35128

Historic Annapolis Foundation, 18 Pinkney St, Annapolis, MD 21401 - T: (410) 267-7619, Fax: (410) 267-6189, Internet: http://www.annapolis.org. Head: Ann M. Fligsten, William Sherman, Dan Sams
Local Museum - 1952
Local history, 1715 Shiplap House 35129

United States Naval Academy Museum, 118 Maryland Av, Annapolis, MD 21402-5034 - T: (410) 293-2108, Fax: (410) 293-2108, Internet: http://www.usna.edu/museum
Fine Arts Museum / Historical Museum - 1845
Naval hist 35130

Anniston AL

Anniston Museum of Natural History, 800 Museum Dr, Anniston, AL 36202 - T: (256) 237-6766, Fax: (256) 237-6776, E-mail: info@annistonmuseum.org, Internet: http://www.annistonmuseum.org. Head: Cheryl H. Bragg, Renee Morrison
Natural History Museum - 1930 35131

Anoka MN

Anoka County Historical and Genealogical Museum, 1900 Third Av S, Anoka, MN 55303 - T: (612) 421-0600. Head: John Weaver, Jean Smith, Vickie Wendel
Local Museum - 1934
Regional history 35132

Ansted WV

Hawks Nest State Park, Rte 60, Ansted, WV 25812 - T: (304) 658-5212, 658-5196, Fax: (304) 658-4549. Head: Thomas L. Shriver
Local Museum - 1935
Local hist 35133

Antigo WI

Langlade County Historical Society Museum, 404 Superior St, Antigo, WI 54409 - T: (715) 627-4464
Local Museum - 1929
Local hist 35134

Antwerp OH

Ehrhart Museum, 118 N Main St, Antwerp, OH 45813 - T: (419) 258-2665, Fax: (419) 258-1875. Head: Randy Shaffer
Natural History Museum - 1963 35135

Apalachicola FL

John Gorrie Museum, 46 6th St and Avenue D, Apalachicola, FL 32329, mail addr: POB 267, Apalachicola, FL 32329-0267 - T: (850) 653-9347, Internet: http://www.baynavigator.com. Head: Fran P. Mainella
Science&Tech Museum - 1955
Inventor of machine tomate ice, fore-runner of refrigerator and air conditioning 35136

Apple Valley CA

Victor Valley Museum and Art Gallery, 11873 Apple Valley Rd, Apple Valley, CA 92308 - T: (760) 240-2111, Fax: (760) 240-5290. Head: Calvin Camara, Carl Mason
Fine Arts Museum / Natural History Museum - 1976
Natural hist, art 35137

Appleton WI

Appleton Art Center, 130 N Morrison St, Appleton, WI 54911 - T: (920) 733-4089, Fax: (920) 733-4149, E-mail: appleart@execpc.com. Head: Jerry Iverson, Tracey Jenks
Fine Arts Museum - 1960
Art 35138

Hearthstone Historic House Museum, 625 W Prospect Av, Appleton, WI 54911 - T: (920) 730-8204, Fax: (920) 730-8266, E-mail: fr.hearthstone@juno.com, Internet: http://www.focol.org/~hearthst. Head: Beverly Harrington
Historical Museum / Science&Tech Museum - 1986
First residence in the world to be lighted from a central hydroelectric powerplant using the Edison system in 1882 35139

Outagamie Museum and Houdini Historical Center, 330 E College Av, Appleton, WI 54911 - T: (920) 733-8445, Fax: (920) 733-8636, E-mail: ochs@foxvalleyhistory.org, Internet: http://www.foxvalley-history.org. Head: Jo Ellen Wolangk
Local Museum - 1872
Hist of technology, regional hist 35140

Wriston Art Center Galleries, Lawrence University, 613 E College Av, Appleton, WI 54912-0599 - T: (414) 832-6621, Fax: (414) 832-7362, E-mail: nadine.wassman@lawrence.edu, Internet: http://cwis.lawrence.edu/www/campus/wriston/
University Museum / Fine Arts Museum - 1989 35141

Arapahoe NE

Furnas-Gosper Historical Society Museum, 401 Nebraska Av, Arapahoe, NE 68922. Head: Larry Williams
Local Museum - 1966 35142

Arcata CA

Humboldt State University Natural History Museum, 1315 G St, Arcata, CA 95521 - T: (707) 826-4479, Fax: (707) 826-4477, E-mail: mlz1@axe.humboldt.edu, Internet: http://www.humboldt.edu/~natmus/. Head: Melissa L. Zielinski
University Museum / Natural History Museum - 1989
Natural hist 35143

Reese Bullen Gallery, Humboldt State University, Arcata, CA 95521 - T: (707) 826-5802, Fax: (707) 826-3628, E-mail: mm1@humboldt.edu, Internet: http://www.humboldt.edu/~rbg/. Head: Martin Morgan
University Museum - 1970
Art 35144

Ardmore OK

Charles B. Goddard Center for Visual and Performing Arts, First Av and D St SW, Ardmore, OK 73401 - T: (580) 226-0909, Fax: (580) 226-8891, E-mail: godart@brightok.net. Head: Mort Hamilton
Fine Arts Museum / Performing Arts Museum - 1969 35145

Eliza Cruce Hall Doll Museum, 320 E Northwest, Ardmore, OK 73401 - T: (405) 223-8290. Head: Carolyn J. Franks
Special Museum - 1971 35146

Argonia KS

Salter Museum, 220 W Garfield, Argonia, KS 67004 - T: (316) 435-6990
Historical Museum - 1961
Home of America's first woman mayor Susanna M. Salter 35147

Arkadelphia AR

Henderson State University Museum, The Stone House, Henderson and 10th, Arkadelphia, AR 71923 - T: (870) 246-7311, Fax: (870) 246-3199
University Museum / Local Museum - 1953 35148

Arlington MA

Arlington Historical Society, 7 Jason St, Arlington, MA 02476 - T: (781) 648-4300, Internet: http://www.arlhs.org. Head: James Gibbons
Historical Museum - 1897
Local history 35149

Old Schwamb Mill, 17 Mill Ln, Arlington, MA 02476-4189 - T: (781) 643-0554, Fax: (781) 648-8809, E-mail: schwambmil@aol.com, Internet: http://www.oldschwambill.org. Head: Patricia C. Fitzmaurice
Science&Tech Museum - 1969
Industrial history, waterpowered mill 35150

Arlington TX

Arlington Museum of Art, 201 W Main St, Arlington, TX 76010 - T: (817) 275-4600, Fax: (817) 860-4800, Internet: http://www.txart.org. Head: Jeff Hansen, Anne Allen
Fine Arts Museum - 1987 35151

The Gallery at UTA, c/o Univeersity of Texas at Arlington, 700 W Second St, Arlington, TX 76019 - T: (817) 272-2790, 272-3143, Fax: (817) 272-2805, E-mail: bhuerta@uta.edu, Internet: www.uta.edu/art. Head: Benito Huerta
Fine Arts Museum / University Museum - 1975
Contemporary art 35152

Arlington VA

Arlington Arts Center, 3550 Wilson Blvd, Arlington, VA 22201 - T: (703) 524-1494, Fax: (703) 527-4050, E-mail: artcenter@erols.com. Head: Carole Sullivan
Fine Arts Museum - 1976
Art 35153

Arlington Historical Museum, 1805 S Arlington Ridge Rd, Arlington, VA 22202 - T: (703) 892-4204, 812-9479, E-mail: arlhistory@aol.com, Internet: http://members.aol.com/arlhistory. Head: Frank Impala, Dr. Harold Handerson
Local Museum - 1963
Local hist 35154

Arlington House - The Robert E. Lee Memorial, Arlington National Cemetery, Arlington, VA 22211 - T: (703) 557-0613, Fax: (703) 557-0613, E-mail: gwmp-arlingtonhouse@nps.gov, Internet: http://www.arho.nps.gov. Head: Terry Carustrom
Local Museum - 1925
Historic house, residence of Gen. Robert E. Lee 35155

The Newseum, The Freedom Forum Newseum, 1101 Wilson Blvd, Arlington, VA 22209 - T: (703) 284-3700, 8-639-7386, Fax: (703) 284-3770, Internet: http://www.newseum.org. Head: Joe Urschel
Historical Museum - 1997
History and present time 35156

Arlington Heights IL

Arlington Heights Historical Museum, 110 W Fremont St, Arlington Heights, IL 60004 - T: (847) 255-1225, Fax: (847) 255-1570, E-mail: susan@ahpd.org, Internet: http://www.ahpd.org
Local Museum - 1957
Local history 35157

Armonk NY

North Castle Historical Society Museum, 440 Bedford Rd, Armonk, NY 10504 - T: (914) 273-4510. Head: Joan Krantz
Local Museum - 1971 35158

Armour SD

Douglas County Museum Complex, Courthouse Grounds, Armour, SD 57313 - T: (605) 724-2129. Head: Laverne Vanderwerff
Local Museum - 1958
Local hist 35159

Arrow Rock MO

Arrow Rock State Historic Site, Fourth and Van Buren, Arrow Rock, MO 65320 - T: (660) 837-3330, Fax: (660) 837-3300, E-mail: dsparro@mail.dnr.state.mo.us, Internet: http://www.mostateparks.com/arrowrock.htm. Head: Michael Dickey
Historical Museum / Open Air Museum - 1923 35160

Artesia NM

Artesia Historical Museum and Art Center, 505 Richardson Av, Artesia, NM 88210 - T: (505) 748-2390, Fax: (505) 746-3886, E-mail: ahmac@pvtnetworks.net. Head: Nancy Dunn
Historical Museum - 1970 35161

Arthurdale WV

Arthurdale Heritage Museum, Q and A Rds, Arthurdale, WV 26520 - T: (304) 864-3959, Fax: (304) 864-4602, E-mail: ahi1934@aol.com, Internet: http://www.arthurdaleheritage.org. Head: Rae Delgado, Deanna Hornyak
Local Museum - 1987
Local hist 35162

Arvada CO

Arvada Center for the Arts and Humanities, 6901 Wadsworth Blvd, Arvada, CO 80003 - T: (303) 431-3080, Fax: (303) 431-3083, E-mail: kathy-a@arvadacenter.org, Internet: http://www.arvadacenter.org. Head: Deborah F. Jordy, Kathy Andrews
Fine Arts Museum / Historical Museum - 1976
Art, history 35163

Asheville NC

Asheville Art Museum, 2 S Pack Sq, Asheville, NC 28801 - T: (828) 253-3227, Fax: (828) 257-4503, E-mail: mailbox@ashevilleart.org, Internet: http://www.ashevilleart.org. Head: Pamela L. Myers
Fine Arts Museum - 1948 35164

Biltmore Estate, 1 N Pack Sq, Asheville, NC 28801 - T: (828) 255-1776, Fax: (828) 255-1111, E-mail: smiller@biltmore.com, Internet: http://www.biltmore.com. Head: William A.V. Cecil
Local Museum - 1930 35165

Colburn Gem and Mineral Museum, 2 S Pack Sq, Asheville, NC 28801 - T: (704) 254-7162, Fax: (704) 251-5652, Internet: http://main.nc.colburn. Head: Hal Mahan, Rebecca B. Lamb
Natural History Museum - 1960 35166

Estes-Winn Antique Automobile Museum, 111 Grovewood Rd, Asheville, NC 28804 - T: (828) 253-7651, Fax: (704) 254-2489, E-mail: automuseum@grovewood.com, Internet: http://www.grovewood.com. Head: S.M. Patton
Science&Tech Museum - 1970 35167

Folk Art Center, Milepost 382, Blue Ridge Pkwy, Asheville, NC 28815 - T: (828) 298-7928, Fax: (828) 298-7962, E-mail: shcg@buncombe.main.nc.us, Internet: http://www.southernhighlandguild.org. Head: Rudy Tell, Ruth Summers
Folklore Museum - 1930
Robert W. Gray library and archives 35168

Grovewood Gallery, 111 Grovewood Rd, Asheville, NC 28804 - T: (828) 253-7651, Fax: (828) 254-2489, E-mail: homespun@grovewood.com, Internet: http://grovewood@grovewood.com. Head: S.M. Patton
Special Museum - 1901 35169

Health Adventure, 2 S Pack Sq, Asheville, NC 28802-0180 - T: (828) 254-6373, Fax: (828) 257-4521, E-mail: info@health-adventure.com, Internet: http://health-adventure.com. Head: Diana Bilbrey, Maralee Gollberg
Special Museum - 1968 35170

Smith-McDowell House Museum, 283 Victoria Rd, Asheville, NC 28801 - T: (828) 253-9231, Fax: (828) 253-5518, E-mail: smithmcdowellhouse@msn.com, Internet: http://www.wnchistory.org. Head: JoAnn Grimes, Rebecca B. Lamb, Ellen Shaylor
Historic Site - 1981 35171

Thomas Wolfe Memorial, 52 N Market St, Asheville, NC 28801 - T: (828) 253-8304, Fax: (828) 252-8171, E-mail: wolfememorial@worldnet.att.net, Internet: http://home.att.net/~wolfe.html. Head: Steve Hill
Historical Museum - 1949 35172

Ashland MA

Ashland Historical Museum, 2 Myrtle St, Ashland, MA 01721 - T: (508) 881-8183, 881-3319
Local Museum - 1905
Local history 35173

Ashland ME

Ashland Logging Museum, Box 866, Ashland, ME 04732 - T: (207) 435-6039, Fax: (207) 435-6579
Ethnology Museum - 1964
Reproduction of an early logging camp 35174

Ashland NE

Strategic Air Command Museum, 28210 W Park Hwy, Ashland, NE 68003 - T: (800) 358-5029, Fax: (402) 944-3160, E-mail: staff@sacmuseum.org, Internet: http://www.sacmuseum.org. Head: Scott Hazelrigg, Dennis Haun
Military Museum - 1959
Aerospace 35175

Ashland NH

Pauline E. Glidden Toy Museum, Pleasant St, Ashland, NH 03217-9401 - T: (603) 968-7289. Head: Shirley Splaine
Special Museum - 1990
Toys 35176

Whipple House Museum, 14 Pleasant St, Ashland, NH 03217-0175 - T: (603) 968-7716, Fax: (603) 968-7716
Local Museum / Historical Museum - 1970
Local history, home of George Hoyt Whipple, Nobel Prize for medicine 35177

Ashland OH

The Coburn Gallery, Ashland College Arts & Humanities Gallery, 401 College Ave, Ashland, OH 44805 - T: (419) 289-4142. Head: Larry Schiemann
Fine Arts Museum / Public Gallery
Contemporary works 35178

Ashland OR

Schneider Museum of Art, Southern Oregon University, 1250 Siskiyou Blvd, Ashland, OR 97520 - T: (541) 552-6245, Fax: (541) 552-8241, E-mail: hofer@sou.edu, Internet: http://www.sou.edu. Head: Nan Trout, Mary Gardiner
University Museum / Fine Arts Museum - 1986 35179

Southern Oregon University Museum of Vertebrate Natural History, 1250 Siskiyou Blvd, Ashland, OR 97520 - T: (541) 552-6341, Fax: (541) 552-6415, E-mail: low@sou.edu
University Museum / Natural History Museum - 1969 35180

Ashland PA

Museum of Anthracite Mining, Pine and 17 Sts, Ashland, PA 17921 - T: (570) 875-4708, Fax: (570) 875-3732, Internet: http://www.phmc.state.pa.us. Head: Steven Ling
Science&Tech Museum / Historical Museum - 1970 35181

Ashley ND

McIntosh County Historical Society Museum, 117 3rd Av, Ashley, ND 58413 - T: (701) 288-3388. Head: Marvin A. Vossler
Local Museum - 1977
Local hist 35182

Ashley Falls MA

Colonel Ashley House, Cooper Hill Rd, Ashley Falls, MA 01222 - T: (413) 229-8600, E-mail: donrRid@ttor.org. Head: Frederick Winthrop
Historical Museum - 1972
Oldest house in Berkshire County 35183

Ashtabula OH

Ashtabula Arts Center, 2928 W 13 St, Ashtabula, OH 44004 - T: (440) 964-3396, Fax: (440) 964-3396, E-mail: aac@suite224.net, Internet: http://www.ashartscenter.org. Head: Judy Robson, Elizabeth Koski
Fine Arts Museum - 1953 35184

Ashville OH

Slate Run Living Historical Farm, Metro Parks, 9130 Marcy Rd, Ashville, OH 43103 - T: (614) 833-1880, Fax: (614) 837-3809. Head: John O'Meara
Local Museum / Agriculture Museum - 1976
Local hist 35185

Aspen CO

Aspen Art Museum, 590 N Mill St, Aspen, CO 81611 - T: (970) 925-8050, Fax: (970) 925-8054, E-mail: info@aspenartmuseum.org, Internet: http://www.aspenartmuseum.org. Head: Dean Sobel
Fine Arts Museum - 1979 35186

Aspen Historical Museum, 620 W Bleeker St, Aspen, CO 81611 - T: (970) 925-3721, Fax: (970) 925-5347, E-mail: ahistory@rof.net. Head: Sam Shogren
Local Museum - 1969
Local history, Wheeler-Stallard house 35187

Astoria NY

American Museum of the Moving Image, 35 Av at 36 St, Astoria, NY 11106 - T: (718) 784-4520, Fax: (718) 784-4681, E-mail: info@ammi.org, Internet: http://www.ammi.org. Head: Rochelle Slovin
Special Museum - 1977 35188

Astoria OR

Columbia River Maritime Museum, 1792 Marine Dr, Astoria, OR 97103 - T: (503) 325-2323, Fax: (503) 325-2331, E-mail: information@crmm.org, Internet: http://www.crmm.org. Head: Jerry Ostermiller
Historical Museum / Science&Tech Museum - 1962 35189

Fort Clatsop National Memorial, Rte 3, Astoria, OR 97103 - T: (503) 861-2471, Fax: (503) 861-2585, E-mail: focl_administration@nps.gov. Head: Cynthia Orlando
Open Air Museum / Military Museum - 1958 35190

The Heritage Museum, Clatsop Historical Society, 1618 Exchange St, Astoria, OR 97103 - T: (503) 325-2203, Fax: (503) 338-6265, E-mail: cchs@seasurf.net, Internet: http://www.clatsophistorical-society.org. Head: Michelle Schmitter
Local Museum - 1985
Local history 35191

Uppertown Firefighters Museum, Clatsop Historical Society, 30th and Marine Dr, Astoria, OR 97103 - T: (503) 325-2203, Fax: (503) 338-6265, E-mail: cchs@seasurf.net, Internet: http://www.clatsophistoricalsociety.org. Head: Michelle Schmitter
Historical Museum - 1990
Firefighting 35192

Atascadero CA

Atascadero Historical Society Museum, 6500 Palma Av, Atascadero, CA 93422 - T: (805) 466-8341, Fax: (805) 461-0606. Head: Mike Lindsay
Local Museum - 1965
Local history 35193

Atchison KS

Atchison County Historical Society Museum, 200 S 10th St, Santa Fe Depot, Atchison, KS 66002 - T: (913) 367-6238, E-mail: atohhistory@journey.com. Head: Chris Taylor
Local Museum - 1966
Local history, westward expansion, Lewis O'Clark, Amelia Barhart 35194

The Muchnic Gallery, 704 N 4th, Atchison, KS 66002 - T: (913) 367-4278, Fax: (913) 367-2939, E-mail: atchart@ponyexpress.net, Internet: http://www.atchisonart.org. Head: Gloria Conkle Davis
Public Gallery - 1970
Art gallery 35195

Athens GA

Church-Waddel-Brumby House Museum, 280 E Dougherty St, Athens, GA 30601 - T: (706) 353-1820, Fax: (706) 353-1770, Internet: http://www.visitathensga.com. Head: Sharon Logan
Historical Museum - 1968 35196

Georgia Museum of Art, University of Georgia, 90 Carlton St, Athens, GA 30602-679 - T: (706) 542-4662, Fax: (706) 542-1051, E-mail: buramsey@arches.uga.edu, Internet: http://www.uga.edu/gamuseum/. Head: William U. Eiland
Fine Arts Museum / University Museum - 1945
Prints, drawings, paintings, photographs, graphics 35197

Lyndon House Art Center, 293 Hoyt St, Athens, GA 30601 - T: (706) 613-3623, 613-3800, Fax: (706) 613-3627. Head: Nancy Lukasiewicz
Fine Arts Museum / Decorative Arts Museum - 1973
Art 35198

Taylor-Grady House, 634 Prince Av, Athens, GA 30601 - T: (706) 549-8688, Fax: (706) 613-0860, E-mail: jlathens@aol.com. Head: Jill Bateman
Historical Museum - 1968
1844 Henry W. Grady home 35199

United States Navy Supply Corps Museum, 1425 Prince Av, Athens, GA 30606-2205 - T: (706) 354-7349, Fax: (706) 354-7239, Internet: http://www.nscs.com. Head: Dan Roth
Military Museum - 1974
Naval Museum housed in 1910 Carnegie Library 35200

University of Georgia Museum of Natural History, Natural History Bldg, University of Georgia, Athens, GA 30602-1882 - T: (706) 542-1663, Fax: (706) 542-3920, E-mail: ereitz@museum.nhm.uga.edu, Internet: http://museum.nhm.uga.edu/. Head: Dr. E. Reitz
University Museum / Natural History Museum - 1977
Zooarchaeology, botany, paleontology, geology, mycology, palynology, entomology 35201

Athens OH

Kennedy Museum of Art, Lin Hall, Ohio University, Athens, OH 45701-2979 - T: (740) 593-1304, Fax: (740) 593-1305, E-mail: kenmus@www.cats.ohiou.edu, Internet: http://www.ohiou.edu/museum. Head: Raymond Tymas-Jones
Fine Arts Museum / University Museum - 1993 35202

Seigfred Gallery, Ohio University, School of Art, Seigfred Hall 528, Athens, OH 45701 - T: (740) 593-4290, Fax: (740) 593-0457. Head: Jenita Landrum-Bittle
Fine Arts Museum - 1993 35203

Athens PA

Tioga Point Museum, 724 S Main St, Athens, PA 18810 - T: (717) 888-7225, E-mail: tiogapoint@exotrope.net. Head: Dr. Arthur B. King, Bonnie Stacy
Local Museum - 1895
Native american art, archaeology 35204

Athens TN

McMinn County Living Heritage Museum, 522 W Madison Av, Athens, TN 37303 - T: (423) 745-0329, Fax: (423) 745-0329, E-mail: livher@usit.net, Internet: http://www.usit.com/livher/. Head: Ann Davis
Decorative Arts Museum / Local Museum - 1982
Local hist 35205

Atlanta GA

Apex Museum, 135 Auburn Av NE, Atlanta, GA 30303 - T: (404) 521-2739, Fax: (404) 523-3248 (call first), E-mail: blackhis@bellsouth.net, Internet: http://www.apexmuseum.org. Head: Dan Moore, Bethany J. Campbell
Fine Arts Museum / Historical Museum - 1978 35206

The Atlanta College of Art, 1280 Peachtree St, NE, Atlanta, GA 30309 - T: (404) 733-5001, Fax: (404) 733-5201. Head: Ellen L. Meyer
Fine Arts Museum / Public Gallery - 1928
Art Gallery 35207

Atlanta Contemporary Art Center and Nexus Press, 535 Means St NW, Atlanta, GA 30318 - T: (404) 688-1970, Fax: (404) 577-5856, E-mail: gallery@thecontemporary.org, Internet: http://www.thecontemporary.org. Head: Sam Gappmayer, Teresa Bramlette
Fine Arts Museum - 1973 35208

The Atlanta Cyclorama, 800-C Cherokee Dr SE, Atlanta, GA 30315 - T: (404) 658-7625, Fax: (404) 658-7045, E-mail: atlcyclorama@mindspring.com, Internet: http://www.BCAAtlanta.org. Head: Pauline M. Smith
Fine Arts Museum / Historical Museum - 1898
Art, Civil War, c.1886 Cyclorama that depicts the July 22, 1864 Battle of Atlanta 35209

Atlanta History Museum, Atlanta History Center, 130 W Paces Ferry Rd, NW, Atlanta, GA 30305-1366 - T: (404) 814-4000, Fax: (404) 814-4186, Internet: http://www.atlantahistorycenter.com. Head: Rick Beard
Historical Museum / Military Museum / Open Air Museum - 1926
Local history, historic houses, gardens - library 35210

Atlanta International Museum of Art and Design, 285 Peachtree Center Av, Atlanta, GA 30303 - T: (404) 688-2467, Fax: (404) 521-9311, Internet: http://www.atlantainternationalmuseum.org. Head: John Johnes, Angelyn S. Chandler
Fine Arts Museum - 1989 35211

Atlanta Museum, 537-39 Peachtree St, NE, Atlanta, GA 30308 - T: (404) 872-8233. Head: J.H. Elliott
Local Museum - 1938
General Museum 35212

Callanwolde Fine Arts Center, 980 Briarcliff Rd, NE, Atlanta, GA 30306 - T: (404) 872-5338, Fax: (404) 872-5175, E-mail: callanwolde@mindspring.com, Internet: http://www.mindspring.com/~callanwolde. Head: Samuel Goldman, Laurie Allan
Fine Arts Museum - 1973 35213

Center for Puppetry Arts, 1404 Spring St, Atlanta, GA 30309 - T: (404) 873-3089 ext 110, Fax: (404) 873-9907, E-mail: puppet@mindspring.com, Internet: http://www.puppet.org. Head: Vincent Anthony
Special Museum - 1978
Puppetry 35214

Fernbank Science Center, 156 Heaton Park Dr, NE, Atlanta, GA 30307-1398 - T: (404) 378-4311, Fax: (404) 370-1336, E-mail: fernbank@fernbank.edu, Internet: http://fsc.fernbank.edu. Head: Mary A. Hiers
Natural History Museum - 1967 35215

Georgia Capitol Museum, Rm 431, Georgia State Capitol, Atlanta, GA 30334 - T: (404) 651-6996, Fax: (404) 657-3801, E-mail: dolson@sos.state.ga.us, Internet: http://www.sos.ga.us. Head: Dorothy Olson
Historical Museum - 1895 35216

Georgia State University Art Gallery, University Plaza, Atlanta, GA 30303 - T: (404) 651-2257, 651-3424, Fax: (404) 651-1779. Head: Teri Williams
Public Gallery / Fine Arts Museum / University Museum - 1970 35217

High Museum of Art, 1280 Peachtree St, NE, Atlanta, GA 30309 - T: (404) 733-4200, Fax: (404) 733-4502, Internet: http://www.high.org. Head: Michael Shapiro
Fine Arts Museum - 1926
Audiovisual and film, decorative arts, paintings, photographs, prints, drawings, graphic arts, sculpture 35218

High Museum of Art, Folk Art and Photography Galleries, 30 John Wesley Dobbs Av, Atlanta, GA 30303 - T: (404) 577-6940, Fax: (404) 653-0916, Internet: http://www.high.org. Head: Dr. Ned Rifkin
Fine Arts Museum - 1986
Art 35219

The Margaret Mitchell House & Museum, 999 Peachtree St, Atlanta, GA 30309 - T: (404) 249-7015, Fax: (404) 249-9388, E-mail: mary_rosetaylor@gwtw.org, Internet: http://www.gwtw.org. Head: Mary Rose Taylor
Historical Museum - 1990 35220

Martin Luther King, Jr. Center for Nonviolent Social Change, 449 Auburn Av, NE, Atlanta, GA 30312 - T: (404) 526-8900, Fax: (404) 526-8984, E-mail: mlktr@aol.com, Internet: http://www.thekingctr.com. Head: Dexter Scott King
Historical Museum - 1968
History at the Martin Luther King, Jr. National Historic Site - educational center, archives 35221

Martin Luther King Jr. National Historic Site and Preservation District, 450 Auburn Av NE, Atlanta, GA 30312 - T: (404) 331-5190, Fax: (404) 730-3112. Head: Frank Catroppa
Historical Museum / Historic Site - 1980
Neighborhood in which Dr. Martin Luther King, Jr. grew up, incl birthplace, boyhood home, church and gravesite 35222

Michael C. Carlos Museum, Emory University, 571 S Kilgo St, Atlanta, GA 30322 - T: (404) 727-4282, Fax: (404) 727-4292, E-mail: aghirsc@emory.edu, Internet: http://www.emory.edu/carlos. Head: Anthony Hirschel
Fine Arts Museum / University Museum / Archaeological Museum - 1920
Arts, archaeology 35223

Museum of the Jimmy Carter Library, 441 Freedom Pkwy, Atlanta, GA 30307 - T: (404) 331-3942, Fax: (404) 730-2215, E-mail: library@carter.nara.gov, Internet: http://jimmycarterlibrary.org. Head: Jay E. Hakes
Library with Exhibitions - 1986
Presidential library 35224

Nexus Contemporary Art Center → Atlanta Contemporary Art Center and Nexus Press

Oglethorpe University Museum, 4484 Peachtree Rd, Atlanta, GA 30319 - T: (404) 364-8558, Fax: (404) 364-8556, E-mail: museum@oglethorpe.edu, Internet: http://museum.oglethorpe.edu. Head: Lloyd Nick
Fine Arts Museum / University Museum - 1993
Art 35225

Photographic Investments Gallery, 3977 Briarcliff Rd, Atlanta, GA 30345 - T: (404) 320-1012, Fax: (404) 320-3465, E-mail: ecsymmes@aol.com. Head: Edwin C. Symmes
Fine Arts Museum - 1979
Photography Art 35226

Robert C. Williams American Museum of Papermaking, Institute of Paper Science and Technology, 500 10th St, Atlanta, GA 30318 - T: (404) 894-7840, Fax: (404) 894-4778, E-mail: cindy.bowden@ipst.edu, Internet: http://www.ipst.edu/amp/. Head: Cindy Bowden
Science&Tech Museum - 1936
Technology 35227

Salvation Army Southern Historical Museum, 1032 Metropolitan Pkwy SW, Atlanta, GA 30310-3488 - T: (404) 752-7578, Fax: (404) 753-1932, E-mail: salmerritt@aol.com, Internet: http://www.salvationarmysouth.org/history.htm. Head: John G. Merritt
Religious Arts Museum - 1986
Religion 35228

Science and Technology Museum of Atlanta, 395 Piedmont Av NE, Atlanta, GA 30308 - T: (404) 522-5500 ext 202, Fax: (404) 525-6906, Internet: http://www.scitek.org. Head: Gwen Crider, Angelle Cooper, Mary K. Roarabaugh
Natural History Museum / Science&Tech Museum - 1988 35229

Wren's Nest House Museum, 1050 R.D. Abernathy Blvd SW, Atlanta, GA 30310-1812 - T: (404) 753-7735 ext1, Fax: (404) 753-8535, E-mail: wrensnest@mindspring.com, Internet: http://www.accessatlanta.com/community/groups/wrensnest/. Head: Sharon Crutchfield
Special Museum - 1909
Home of Joel Chandler Harris, creator of Uncle Remus and chronicler of stories 35230

Atlantic Beach NC

Fort Macon, E Fort Macon Rd, Atlantic Beach, NC 28512 - T: (919) 726-3775, Fax: (919) 726-2497, E-mail: ftmacon@starfishnet.com. Head: Jody A. Merritt
Historical Museum - 1924 35231

Atlantic City NJ

Atlantic City Historical Museum, New Jersey Av and The Boardwalk, Garden Pier, Atlantic City, NJ 08401 - T: (609) 347-5839, 344-1943, Fax: (609) 347-5284, E-mail: ac08401@aol.com, Internet: http://www.acmuseum.org. Head: Vicki Gold Levi
Local Museum - 1982
Local hist 35232

Historic Gardner's Basin, 800 N New Hampshire Av, Atlantic City, NJ 08401 - T: (609) 348-2880, Fax: (609) 345-4238, Internet: http://www.oceanlifecenter.com. Head: Jack Keith
Local Museum - 1976 35233

Attleboro MA

Attleboro Museum, 86 Park St, Attleboro, MA 02703 - T: (508) 222-2644, Fax: (508) 226-4401, Internet: http://www.attleboromuseum.org. Head: Gerry Hickman, Dore Van Dyke
Fine Arts Museum / Public Gallery - 1929
Regional American prints, paintings, civil war coll 35234

Atwater CA

Castle Air Museum, 5050 Santa Fe Rd, Atwater, CA 95301 - T: (209) 723-2178, Fax: (209) 723-0323, E-mail: cam@elite.net, Internet: http://www.elite.net/castle-air. Head: Jack Gotchey
Military Museum - 1981 35235

Auburn IN

Auburn-Cord-Duesenberg Museum, 1600 S Wayne St, Auburn, IN 46706 - T: (219) 925-1444, Fax: (219) 925-6266, Internet: http://www.acdmuseum.org
Science&Tech Museum - 1973
Transportation 35236

National Automotive and Truck Museum of the United States, 1000 Gordon M. Buehrig Pl, Auburn, IN 46706-0686 - T: (219) 925-9100, Fax: (219) 925-8695, E-mail: natmus@ctlnet.com, Internet: http://www.natmus.com
Science&Tech Museum - 1989 35237

Auburn ME

Androscoggin Historical Society Museum, County Bldg, 2 Turner St, Auburn, ME 04210-5978 - T: (207) 784-0586, E-mail: ltigapa@aol.com, Internet: http://www.rootsweb.com/~meandrhs. Head: A.B. Palmer
Local Museum / Historical Museum - 1923
County history 35238

Auburn NY

Cayuga Museum and Case Research Lab Museum, 203 Genesee St, Auburn, NY 13021 - T: (315) 253-8051, Fax: (315) 253-9829, E-mail: cayugamuseum@cayuganet.org, Internet: http://www.cayuganet.org/cayugamuseum. Head: Jim Richerson
Local Museum - 1936
Indian artefacts, history 35239

Owasco Teyetasta → Cayuga Museum and Case Research Lab Museum

Schweinfurth Memorial Art Center, 205 Genesee St, Auburn, NY 13021 - T: (315) 255-1553, Fax: (315) 255-0871, E-mail: smac@relex.com. Head: Donna Lamb
Fine Arts Museum - 1975 35240

Seward House, 33 South St, Auburn, NY 13021 - T: (315) 252-1283
Local Museum - 1951 35241

Ward O'Hara Agricultural Museum of Cayuga County, E Lake Rd, Auburn, NY 13021 - T: (315) 252-7644, Internet: http://www.cayuganet.org. Head: Norman Riley
Agriculture Museum - 1975 35242

Audubon PA

Mill Grove Audubon Wildlife Sanctuary, 1201 Audubon and Pawlings Rds, Audubon, PA 19407-7125 - T: (610) 666-5593, Fax: (610) 666-1490, E-mail: millgrove@mail.montcopa.org, Internet: http://www.montcopa.org/historicsites. Head: Linda S. Boice
Fine Arts Museum / Natural History Museum / Historical Museum - 1951 35243

Augusta GA

Augusta Richmond County Museum, 560 Reynolds St, Augusta, GA 30901 - T: (706) 722-8454, Fax: (706) 724-5192. Head: Scott W. Loehr, Gordon A. Blaker, Paul Bright, Katie B. Brown
Historical Museum - 1937
The past of Augusta, Georgia and its environs 35244

Ezekiel Harris House, 1822 Broad St, Augusta, GA 30904, mail addr: POB 37, Augusta, GA 30903-0037 - T: (706) 724-0436, Fax: (706) 724-3083. Head: Erick D. Montgomery
Local Museum - 1965 35245

Gertrude Herbert Institute of Art, 506 Telfair St, Augusta, GA 30901 - T: (706) 722-5495, Fax: (706) 722-3670, E-mail: ghia@ghia.org, Internet: http://www.ghia.org. Head: Cheryl W. O'Keeffe, Amy E. Meybohm
Fine Arts Museum - 1937
Paintings, sculptures, graphics 35246

Meadow Garden, 1320 Independence Dr, Augusta, GA 30901-1038 - T: (706) 724-4174
Historical Museum
1791-1804 residence of George Walton, signer of the Declaration of Independence 35247

Morris Museum of Art, 1 Tenth St, Augusta, GA 30901-1134 - T: (706) 724-7501, Fax: (706) 724-7612, E-mail: mormuse@themorris.org, Internet: http://www.themorris.org. Head: Louise Keith Claussen
Fine Arts Museum - 1985 35248

Augusta KS

Augusta Historical Museum, 303 State, Augusta, KS 67010 - T: (316) 775-5655. Head: Diana Herrman
Local Museum - 1938
Local history, genealogy 35249

Augusta ME

Blaine House, 192 State St, Augusta, ME 04330 - T: (207) 287-2121
Local Museum
Blaine House, governer's mansion of Maine 35250

Maine State Museum, 83 State House Station, State House Complex, Augusta, ME 04333-0083 - T: (207) 287-2301, Fax: (207) 287-6633, E-mail: museum@state.me.us, Internet: http://www.state.me.us/museum/. Head: Joseph R. Phillips
Local Museum - 1837
History, natural history, archaeology, fine arts, graphics 35251

Old Fort Western, 16 Cony St, Augusta, ME 04330 - T: (207) 626-2385, Fax: (207) 626-2304, E-mail: oldfort@oldfortwestern.org, Internet: http://www.oldfortwestern.org. Head: Jay Adams
Historical Museum - 1922
Historic house 35252

Auriesville NY

Kateri Galleries, National Shrine of the North American Martyrs, off Rte 5S, Auriesville, NY 12016 - T: (518) 853-3033, Fax: (518) 853-3051. Head: John G. Marzolf
Religious Arts Museum - 1950 35253

Aurora CO

Aurora History Museum, 15001 E Alameda Dr, Aurora, CO 80012-1547 - T: (303) 739-6660, Fax: (303) 739-6657, E-mail: auroramuseum@ci.aurora.co.us, Internet: http://www.auroragov.org
Local Museum - 1979
History 35254

Aurora IL

Aurora Historical Museum, Cedar and Oak Sts, Aurora, IL 60506 - T: (630) 897-9029, Fax: (630) 906-0657. Head: John R. Jaros
Local Museum - 1906
Local history 35255

Aurora Public Art Commission, 20 E Downer Pl, Aurora, IL 60507 - T: (630) 844-3623, 906-0654, Fax: (630) 892-0741. Head: Rena J. Church
Fine Arts Museum - 1996
Art 35256

Blackberry Farm-Pioneer Village, 100 S Barnes Rd, Aurora, IL 60506 - T: (630) 264-7405, Fax: (630) 892-1661, E-mail: bfpvfupd@aol.com, Internet: http://www.foxvalleyparkdistrict.org. Head: Lorraine Beasley
Historical Museum / Agriculture Museum - 1969
Village, agriculture 35257

Grand Army of the Republic Memorial and Veteran's Military Museum, 23 E Downer Pl, Aurora, IL 60505 - T: (630) 897-7221. Head: Charles Gates
Military Museum - 1875
Military 35258

Schingoethe Center for Native American Cultures, Aurora University, Dunham Hall, 347 S Gladstone, Aurora, IL 60506-4892 - T: (630) 844-5402, Fax: (630) 844-8884, E-mail: dbachman@admin.aurora.edu, Internet: http://www.aurora.edu/museum. Head: Dona Bachman
University Museum / Ethnology Museum / Folklore Museum - 1989
Native American cultures 35259

SciTech Museum, 18 W Benton, Aurora, IL 60506 - T: (630) 859-3434, Fax: (630) 859-8692, E-mail: mir@scitech.com, Internet: http://scitech.mus.il.us/. Head: Dr. Ronen Mir
Science&Tech Museum - 1988
Science, technology 35260

Aurora IN

Hillforest House Museum, 213 Fifth St, Aurora, IN 47001 - T: (812) 926-0087, Fax: (812) 926-1075, E-mail: hillforest@seidata.com, Internet: http://www.dearborncounty.org/history/hillfor.html. Head: Christopher Baltz
Historical Museum - 1956
Victorian Ohio River Valley mansion 35261

Aurora NE

Plainsman Museum, 210 16 St, Aurora, NE 68818 - T: (402) 694-6531, E-mail: smpolak@hamilton.net, Internet: http://www.plainsmanmuseum.org. Head: Wesley C. Huenefeld, Sarah Polak
Local Museum - 1935 35262

Aurora OH

Aurora Historical Society Museum, 115 E Pioneer Trail, Aurora, OH 44202 - T: (330) 562-6502. Head: John Rumbold
Local Museum - 1968 35263

Austin TX

Austin Children's Museum, 201 Colorado St, Austin, TX 78701-3922 - T: (512) 472-2494; 2499, Fax: (512) 472-2495, Internet: www.austinkids.org. Head: Gwen Crider
Special Museum - 1983 35264

Austin History Center, 810 Guadalupe St, Austin, TX 78701 - T: (512) 499-7480, Fax: (512) 499-7483, E-mail: ahc@coa1.ci.austin.tx.us, Internet: http://www.ci.austin.tx.us. Head: Amalia Rodriguez-Mendoza
Local Museum - 1955
Local history - library 35265

Austin Museum of Art, 823 Congress Av, Austin, TX 78701 - T: (512) 495-9224, Fax: (512) 495-9029, E-mail: info@amoa.org, Internet: http://www.amoa.org. Head: Elizabeth Ferrer
Fine Arts Museum - 1961
Art 35266

Center for American History, Sid Richardson Hall, Unit 2, University of Texas, Austin, TX 78712 - T: (512) 495-4515, Fax: (512) 495-4542, E-mail: cahref@uts.cc.utexas.edu, Internet: http://www.cah.utexas.edu. Head: Dr. Don Carleton, H.G. Dulaney
Historical Museum
History 35267

Elisabet Ney Museum, 304 E 44th St, Austin, TX 78751 - T: (512) 458-2255, Fax: (512) 453-0638, E-mail: enm@ci.anstin.tx.us, Internet: http://www.austin360.com/community/neys. Head: Mary Collins Blackmon
Fine Arts Museum - 1911
Sculptures 35268

The French Legation Museum, 802 San Marcos St, Austin, TX 78702 - T: (512) 472-8180, Fax: (512) 472-9457, E-mail: dubois@french-legation.mus.tx.us, Internet: http://www.french-legation.mus.tx.us. Head: Pete Wehmeyer
Historical Museum - 1956
History 35269

Jack S. Blanton Museum of Art, University of Texas at Austin, Austin, TX 78712-1205 - T: (512) 471-7324, Fax: (512) 471-7023, E-mail: blantonmuseum@utexas.edu, Internet: http://www.blantonmuseum.org. Head: Jessie Otto Hite
Fine Arts Museum / University Museum - 1963
Art 35270

Jourdan-Bachman Pioneer Farm, 11418 Sprinkle Cut Off Rd, Austin, TX 78754 - T: (512) 837-1215, Fax: (512) 837-4503, E-mail: jbfarmer@eden.com, Internet: http://www.pioneerfarm.org. Head: John Hirsch
Agriculture Museum - 1975
Historical agriculture 35271

Lyndon Baines Johnson Museum, 2313 Red River St, Austin, TX 78705-5702 - T: (512) 916-5137 ext 0, Fax: (512) 478-9104, E-mail: library@johnson.nara.gov, Internet: http://www.lbjlib.utexas.edu. Head: Harry J. Middleton
Library with Exhibitions - 1971
Presidential library 35272

Mexic-Arte Museum, 419 Congress St, Austin, TX 78701 - T: (512) 480-9373, Fax: (512) 480-8626, E-mail: mexicarte@inetmail.att.net, Internet: http://www.main.org/mexic-arte. Head: Sylvia Orozco
Fine Arts Museum - 1984
Art, focus on Mexican and Latin American culture 35273

Neill-Cochran Museum House, 2310 San Gabriel St, Austin, TX 78705 - T: (512) 478-2335. Head: Kathleen Peterson-Moussaid
Local Museum - 1956
Historic house 35274

O. Henry Home and Museum, 409 E. 5th St, Austin, TX 78701 - T: (512) 472-1903, Fax: (512) 472-7102, E-mail: valerie.bennett@ci.austin.tx.us, Internet: http://www.ci.austin.tx.us/parks/ohenry.htm. Head: Valerie Bennett
Local Museum - 1934
Historic house 35275

Texas Governor's Mansion, 1010 Colorado, Austin, TX 78701 - T: (512) 463-5518, 463-5516, Internet: http://www.txfgm.org
Local Museum
Historic house 35276

Texas Memorial Museum, 2400 Trinity, Austin, TX 78705 - T: (512) 471-1604, Fax: (512) 471-4794, E-mail: tmmweb@uts.cc.utexas.edu, Internet: http://www.utexas.edu/depts/tmm/. Head: Edward C. Theriot, Timothy Rowe
Historical Museum / Ethnology Museum / Natural History Museum - 1936
Natural Science, cultural hist 35277

Umlauf Sculpture Garden and Museum, 605 Robert E. Lee Rd, Austin, TX 78704 - T: (512) 445-5582, Fax: (512) 445-5583, Internet: http://www.umlaufsculpture.org. Head: Nelie Plourde
Fine Arts Museum - 1991
Sculpture 35278

Women and Their Work, 1710 Lavaca St, Austin, TX 78701 - T: (512) 477-1064, Fax: (512) 477-1090, E-mail: wtw@eden.com, Internet: www.womenand-theirwork.org. Head: Chris Cowden
Fine Arts Museum - 1978 35279

Avalon CA

Catalina Island Museum, Casino Bldg, Avalon, CA 90704 - T: (310) 510-2414, Fax: (310) 510-2780, E-mail: museum@catalinas.net, Internet: http://www.catalina.com/museum/. Head: Stacey A. Otte
Historical Museum / Archaeological Museum - 1953
Regional history 35280

Avon CT

The Avon Historical Society Museum, 8 E Main St, Avon, CT 06001 - T: (860) 678-7621, 673-3580
Local Museum
Local hist 35281

Aztec NM

Aztec Museum and Pioneer Village, 125 N Main Av, Aztec, NM 87410-1923 - T: (505) 334-9829, Fax: (505) 334-7648, E-mail: azmus@juno.com, Internet: http://www.cyberport.com/aztec. Head: Barry Coopen
Historical Museum - 1963 35282

Bailey NC

The Country Doctor Museum, 6629 Vance St, Bailey, NC 27807 - T: (252) 235-4165. Head: Isabel H. Gover, Carolyn B. Bissette
Historical Museum - 1967
Practice of medicine 18th-19th c 35283

Bainbridge OH

Dr. John Harris Dental Museum, 208 W Main St, Bainbridge, OH 45612 - T: (513) 561-7009. Head: Dr. Jack W. Gottschalk
Special Museum - 1939 35284

Baird TX

Callahan County Pioneer Museum, 100 W 4th, B-1, Baird, TX 79504-5305 - T: (915) 854-1718, Fax: (915) 854-1227. Head: Inez Wylie
Local Museum - 1940
Local hist 35285

Baker MT

O'Fallon Historical Museum, 723 S Main St, Baker, MT 59313 - T: (406) 778-3265. Head: Harold Jensen, Lora Heyen
Historical Museum - 1968 35286

Baker City OR

National Historic Oregon Trail Interpretive Center, Oregon Hwy 86, Baker City, OR 97814 - T: (541) 523-1845, Fax: (541) 523-1834, E-mail: nhotic@or.blm.gov, Internet: http://www.or.blm.gov/nhotic. Head: Dave Hunsaker
Local Museum - 1992 35287

Bakersfield CA

Bakersfield Museum of Art, 1930 R St, Bakersfield, CA 93301 - T: (661) 323-7219, Fax: (661) 323-7266, Internet: http://www.bmao.org. Head: Charles G. Meyer
Fine Arts Museum - 1987
Art 35288

Kern County Museum, 3801 Chester Av, Bakersfield, CA 93301 - T: (661) 852-5000, Fax: (661) 322-6415, E-mail: caenriquez@kem.org, Internet: http://www.kcmuseum.org. Head: Carola Rupert Enriquez
Local Museum - 1945
Local history, culture - children's museum 35289

Baldwin NY

Baldwin Historical Society Museum, 1980 Grand Av, Baldwin, NY 11510 - T: (516) 223-6900. Head: Jack Bryck
Local Museum - 1971 35290

Baldwin City KS

Old Castle Museum, Baker University, 515 Fifth St, Baldwin City, KS 66006-0065 - T: (913) 594-6809, Fax: (913) 594-2522. Head: Brenda Day
Historical Museum - 1953
Original Santa Fe Trail Post Office, replica of Kibbee cabin 35291

William A. Quayle Bible Collection, Baker University, Collins Library, Spencer Quayle Wing, 8th and Grove Sts, Baldwin City, KS 66006 - T: (913) 594-8414, Fax: (913) 594-6721. Head: Dr. John M. Forbes
University Museum / Religious Arts Museum / Library with Exhibitions - 1925
Rare Bibles 35292

Ballston Spa NY

Brookside Saratoga County Historical Society, 6 Charlton St, Ballston Spa, NY 12020 - T: (518) 885-4000, Fax: (518) 885-7085, E-mail: info@brooksidemuseum.org, Internet: http://www.brooksidemuseum.org. Head: Susie Kilpatrick
Local Museum - 1962 35293

Balsam Lake WI

Polk County Museum, Main St, Balsam Lake, WI 54810 - T: (715) 485-3292, Internet: http://www.co.polk.wi.us/museum.
Local Museum - 1960
Local hist 35294

Baltimore MD

The Albin O. Kuhn Gallery, University of Maryland-Baltimore County, 1000 Hilltop Circle, Baltimore, MD 21250 - T: (410) 455-2270, Fax: (410) 455-1153, Internet: http://www.umbc.edu/library. Head: Cynthia Wayne
University Museum / Fine Arts Museum - 1975
Art 35295

American Visionary Art Museum, 800 Key Hwy, Baltimore, MD 21230 - T: (410) 244-1900, Fax: (410) 244-5858, E-mail: AVAM.org, Internet: http://www.doubleclickd.com/avamhome.html. Head: Rebecca Hoffberger, Mark Ward
Fine Arts Museum - 1995
Art 35296

The B & O Railroad Museum, Smithsonian Institution, 901 W Pratt St, Baltimore, MD 21223 - T: (410) 752-2490, Fax: (410) 752-2499, E-mail: info@borail.org, Internet: http://www.borail.org. Head: Courtney B. Wilson
Historical Museum / Science&Tech Museum - 1953
Transport, site of c.1830 B & O Railroad's Mt Clare shops, site of first common carrier rail service in the US, which received SFB Morse's first long distance telegraph message in 1844 35297

Babe Ruth Birthplace and Baseball Center, 216 Emory St, Baltimore, MD 21230 - T: (410) 727-1539, Fax: (410) 727-1652, Internet: http://www.baberuthmuseum.com. Head: Michael L. Gibbons
Special Museum / Fine Arts Museum - 1974
Sports 35298

Baltimore Maritime Museum, Pier 3, Pratt St, Baltimore, MD 21202 - T: (410) 396-3453, Fax: (410) 396-3393, E-mail: admin@baltomarinemuseum.org, Internet: http://www.baltomarinemuseum.org. Head: John Kellett
Historical Museum - 1982
Coast Guard cutter, WW II submarine, lightship, lighthouse 35299

The Baltimore Museum of Art, Art Museum Dr, Baltimore, MD 21218-3898 - T: (410) 396-7100, Fax: (410) 396-7153, Internet: http://www.artbma.org. Head: Doreen Bolger
Fine Arts Museum - 1914
Arts of America, Africa, Asia, Oceania, decorative arts, drawings, prints, photography - sculpture gardens 35300

Baltimore Museum of Industry, 1415 Key Hwy, Baltimore, MD 21230 - T: (410) 727-4808, Fax: (410) 727-4869, E-mail: bmi@charm.net, Internet: http://www.charm.net/~bmi. Head: William H. Cole
Historical Museum / Science&Tech Museum - 1981
History, industry, housed in a water front oyster cannery 35301

Baltimore Public Works Museum, 751 Eastern Av, Baltimore, MD 21202 - T: (410) 396-1509, 396-5565, Fax: (410) 545-6781, E-mail: bpwm@erols.com. Head: Mari B. Ross, Vince Pompa
Historical Museum / Science&Tech Museum - 1982
Urban environmental history, sewage pumping stn 35302

Baltimore Streetcar Museum, 1901 Falls Rd, Baltimore, MD 21211 - T: (410) 547-0264, Fax: (410) 547-0264, Internet: http://www.baltimoremd.com/streetcar. Head: John J. O'Neill
Special Museum / Science&Tech Museum - 1966
Transport, RR Terminal 35303

Baltimores Black American Museum, 1767 Carswell St, Baltimore, MD 21218 - T: (410) 243-9600
Ethnology Museum / Historical Museum 35304

Contemporary Museum, 100 W Centre St, Baltimore, MD 21201 - T: (410) 783-5720, Fax: (410) 783-5722, E-mail: info@contemporary.org, Internet: http://www.contemporary.org. Head: Gary Sangster
Fine Arts Museum - 1989 35305

Cylburn Nature Museum, 4915 Greenspring Av, Baltimore, MD 21209 - T: (410) 396-0180, Fax: (410) 367-8039. Head: Jane Baldwin, Patsy Perlman
Natural History Museum - 1954
Natural history, horticulture 35306

Dr. Samuel D. Harris National Museum of Dentistry, 31 S Greene St, Baltimore, MD 21201 - T: (410) 706-8314, Fax: (410) 706-8313, E-mail: rkwoo1@dental.umaryland.edu, Internet: http://www.dental.umaryland.edu/dental/museum. Head: Dr. Ben Z. Swanson
Special Museum - 1840
Dentistry 35307

Edgar Allan Poe House and Museum, 203 N Amity St, Baltimore, MD 21223 - T: (410) 396-4866, Fax: (410) 396-5662
Special Museum - 1923
Home of Edgar Allan Poe 35308

Eubie Blake Jazz Museum and Gallery, 847 N Howard St, Baltimore, MD 21201 - T: (410) 225-3110, Fax: (410) 225-3139, E-mail: eubieblake@erols.com, Internet: http://www.eubieblake.org. Head: Camay Murphy, Leslie C. Howard
Music Museum - 1983 35309

Evergreen House, Johns Hopkins University, 4545 N Charles St, Baltimore, MD 21210 - T: (410) 516-0341, Fax: (410) 516-0864, E-mail: ckelly@jhu.edu, Internet: http://www.jhu.edu/~evrgreen/. Head: Cindy Kelly
Historical Museum - 1952
Historic House, purchased for the Garrett family in 1878 35310

Fort McHenry, End of E Fort Av, Baltimore, MD 21230-5393 - T: (410) 962-4290, Fax: (410) 962-2500, Internet: http://www.nps.gov/fomc
Historic Site / Historical Museum / Military Museum - 1933
Site of bombardment which inspired Francis Scott Key to write "The Star-Spangled Banner", 1861-65 site of Union Prison Camp, 1917-25 U.S. Army General Hospital 2 35311

Great Blacks in Wax Museum, 1601-03 E North Av, Baltimore, MD 21213-1409 - T: (410) 563-3404, Fax: (410) 675-5040, Internet: http://www.gbiw.org. Head: Dr. Joanne M. Martin
Historical Museum / Decorative Arts Museum - 1983
History, wax figures 35312

Homewood House Museum, Johns Hopkins University, 3400 N Charles St, Baltimore, MD 21218 - T: (410) 516-5589, Fax: (410) 516-7859, E-mail: homewood@jhunix.hcf.jhu.edu, Internet: http://www.jhu.edu/historichouses. Head: Cindy. Kelly
University Museum / Historical Museum / Museum of Classical Antiquities - 1987 35313

James E. Lewis Museum of Art, Morgan State University, Carl Murphy Fine Arts Center, Coldspring Ln and Hillen Rd, Baltimore, MD 21251 - T: (410) 319-3030, Fax: (410) 319-4024, E-mail: gtenabe@moac.morgan.edu, Internet: http://www.morgan.edu. Head: Gabriel S. Tenabe
Fine Arts Museum / University Museum - 1955
Arts 35314

Jewish Museum of Maryland, 15 Lloyd St, Baltimore, MD 21202 - T: (410) 732-6400, Fax: (410) 732-6451, E-mail: info@jewishmuseummd.org, Internet: http://

www.jewishmuseummd.org. Head: Avi Y. Decter, Linda Skolnik, Deborah Cardin
Historical Museum - 1960
Two restored synagogues - research archives, library 35315

The Johns Hopkins University Archaeological Collection, 129 Gilman Hall, 34th and Charles, Baltimore, MD 21218 - T: (410) 516-8402, Fax: (410) 516-5218
Museum of Classical Antiquities / University Museum / Archaeological Museum - 1884
Classical art, archaeology 35316

The Lacrosse Museum and National Hull of Fame, 113 W University Pkwy, Baltimore, MD 21210 - T: (410) 235-6882 ext 122, Fax: (410) 366-6735, E-mail: info@lacrosse.org, Internet: http://www.lacrosse.org. Head: Joshua W. Christian
Folklore Museum / Special Museum - 1959
National Hall of Fame 35317

Lovely Lane Museum, 2200 Saint Paul St, Baltimore, MD 21218 - T: (410) 889-4458, E-mail: lovinmus@bcpl.net. Head: Dennis Whitmore, Edwin Sohell
Religious Arts Museum - 1855
Religion, methodist history, Strawbridge shrine 35318

Maryland Art Place, 34 Market Pl, Baltimore, MD 21202 - T: (410) 962-8565, Fax: (410) 244-8017, E-mail: map@charm.net, Internet: http://www.mdartplace.org. Head: Jack Rasmussen
Fine Arts Museum - 1981 35319

Maryland Institute Museum, College of Art Exhibitions, 1300 Mount Royal Av, Baltimore, MD 21217 - T: (410) 225-2280, Fax: (410) 225-2396, E-mail: whipps@mica.edu, Internet: http://www.mica.edu. Head: Fred Lazarus, Will Hipps
Fine Arts Museum / University Museum - 1826
Art 35320

Maryland Science Center, 601 Light St, Baltimore, MD 21230 - T: (410) 685-2370, Fax: (410) 545-5974, Internet: http://www.mdsci.org. Head: Gregory Paul Andorfer
Science&Tech Museum - 1797
Science, technology - planetarium 35321

Meredith Gallery, 805 N Charles St, Baltimore, MD 21201 - T: (410) 837-3575, Fax: (410) 837-3577, Internet: http://www.meredithgallery.com. Head: Judith Lippman
Decorative Arts Museum - 1977 35322

Mount Clare Museum House, 1500 Washington Blvd, Baltimore, MD 21230 - T: (410) 837-3262, Fax: (410) 837-0251, E-mail: mtclare@msn.com, Internet: http://www.erols.com/mountclare-museumhouse. Head: Alan E. Gephardt
Historical Museum / Decorative Arts Museum - 1917
Mansion 35323

Mount Vernon Museum of Incandescent Lighting, 717 Washington Pl, Baltimore, MD 21201 - T: (410) 752-8586. Head: Hugh Francis Hicks
Science&Tech Museum - 1963
Science, technology, development of the electronic light bulb (1878-now) 35324

Museum for Contemporary Arts → Contemporary Museum

Museum Hall, 1767 Carswell St, Baltimore, MD 21218 - T: (410) 243-9600
Local Museum 35325

Museum of Maryland History, Maryland Historical Society, 201 W Monument St, Baltimore, MD 21201 - T: (410) 685-3750, Fax: (410) 385-2105, E-mail: mray@mdhs.org, Internet: http://www.mdhs.org. Head: Dennis A. Fiori
Local Museum - 1844
Regional history - library 35326

National Museum of Ceramic Art and Glass, 2406 Shelleydale Dr, Baltimore, MD 21209 - T: (410) 764-1042, Fax: (410) 764-1042. Head: Richard Taylor
Decorative Arts Museum - 1994
Ceramic art, glass 35327

Port Discovery - Children's Museum in Baltimore, 34 Market Pl, Ste 905, Baltimore, MD 21202 - T: (410) 727-8120, Fax: (410) 727-3042, E-mail: portdiscovery@compuserve.com. Head: Kathy Dwyer Southern, Dr. Beatrice Taylor
Ethnology Museum - 1977 35328

Rosenberg Gallery, Goucher College, 1021 Dulaney Valley Rd, Baltimore, MD 21204 - T: (410) 337-6333, Fax: (410) 337-6405, E-mail: lburns@goucher.edu, Internet: http://www.goucher.edu/rosenberg. Head: Laura Burns
University Museum / Fine Arts Museum - 1964 35329

Star-Spangled Banner Flag House and 1812 Museum, 844 E Pratt St, Baltimore, MD 21202 - T: (410) 837-1793, Fax: (410) 837-1812, E-mail: info@flaghouse, Internet: http://www.flaghouse.org. Head: Sally Johnston
Historical Museum - 1927
Home of Mary Pickersgill, maker of the 30'x42' banner which flew over Fort McHenry during the War of 1812 35330

Steamship Collection, University of Baltimore, Library, 1420 Maryland Av, Baltimore, MD 21201-5779 - T: (410) 837-4334, Fax: (410) 837-4330, E-mail: ahouse@ubmail.ubalt.edu, Internet: http://www.ubalt.edu/archives/ship/ship.htm. Head: Tim Dacey
University Museum / Library with Exhibitions - 1940 35331

Walters Art Gallery, 600 N Charles St, Baltimore, MD 21201 - T: (410) 547-9000, Fax: (410) 783-7969, 752-4797, E-mail: gvikan@thewalters.org, Internet: http://www.thewalters.org. Head: Dr. Gary Vikan, Terry Drayman-Weisser, Diane Stillman
Fine Arts Museum - 1931
Art, rare books 35332

The Walters Art Museum, 600 N Charles St, Baltimore, MD 21201-5185 - T: (410) 547-9000, Fax: (410) 783-7969, Internet: http://www.thewalters.org. Head: Dr. Gary Vikan
Local Museum / Historical Museum - 1931 35333

Bancroft NE

John G. Neihardt Center, Nebraska State Historical Society, Elm and Washington, Bancroft, NE 68004 - T: (402) 648-3388, Fax: (402) 648-3388, E-mail: neihardt@gpcom.net, Internet: http://www.neihardt.com. Head: Nancy S. Gillis
Historic Site / Library with Exhibitions / Historical Museum - 1976 35334

Bangor ME

Bangor Historical Society Museum, 159 Union St, Bangor, ME 04401 - T: (207) 942-5766, Fax: (207) 941-0266, E-mail: bangorhistorical@hotmail.com, Internet: http://www.bairnet.org. Head: Margaret Puckett
Local Museum - 1864
Local history 35335

Cole Land Transportation Museum, 405 Perry Rd, Bangor, ME 04401 - T: (207) 990-3600, Fax: (207) 990-2653, E-mail: maii@colemuseum.com, Internet: http://www.colemuseum.org. Head: Garrett Cole
Science&Tech Museum - 1990 35336

Isaac Farrar Mansion, 17 Second St, Bangor, ME 04401 - T: (207) 941-2808, Fax: (207) 941-2812. Head: Lynda Clyve, Carol Colson
Local Museum - 1972
Historic house 35337

Banning CA

Malki Museum, 11-795 Fields Rd, Banning, CA 92220 - T: (909) 849-7289, 849-8304. Head: Katherine Siva Saubel
Historical Museum / Ethnology Museum / Folklore Museum - 1964
Indians 35338

Bar Harbor ME

Abbe Museum, Sieur de Monts Spring, Acadia National Park, Bar Harbor, ME 04609 - T: (207) 288-3519, 288-2179, Fax: (207) 288-8979, E-mail: abbe@midmaine.com, Internet: http://www.acadia.net/abbemuseum. Head: Diane Kopec
Ethnology Museum / Archaeological Museum - 1928
Archaeology, anthropology, ethnology 35339

Bar Harbor Historical Society Museum, 33 Ledgelawn Av, Bar Harbor, ME 04609 - T: (207) 288-3807, 288-0000. Head: Deborah Dyer
Local Museum - 1946
Local history 35340

George B. Dorr Museum of Natural History, College of the Atlantic, 105 Eden St, Bar Harbor, ME 04609 - T: (207) 288-5015, Fax: (207) 288-2917, E-mail: museum@ecology.coa.edu, Internet: http://www.coamuseum.org. Head: Dr. Stephen Ressel
Natural History Museum - 1982
Natural history 35341

Baraboo WI

Circus World Museum, 550 Water St, Baraboo, WI 53913 - T: (608) 356-8341, Fax: (608) 356-1800, E-mail: circusworld@baraboo.com, Internet: http://www.circusworldmuseum.com. Head: Greg Parkinson
Performing Arts Museum / Historic Site / Special Museum - 1959
Circus hist 35342

International Crane Foundation Museum, E 11376 Shady Lane Rd, Baraboo, WI 53913-0447 - T: (608) 356-9462, Fax: (608) 356-9465, E-mail: cranes@savingcranes.org, Internet: http://www.baraboo.com/bus/icf/whowhat.htm. Head: James T. Harris
Natural History Museum - 1973
Ornithology 35343

Sauk County Historical Museum, 531 4th Av, Baraboo, WI 53913 - T: (608) 356-1001. Head: Peter Shrake
Local Museum - 1906
Local hist 35344

Bardstown KY

My Old Kentucky Home, 501 E Stephen Foster Av, Bardstown, KY 40004 - T: (502) 348-3502, 323-7803, Fax: (502) 349-0054. Head: Alice Heaton
Special Museum - 1922
Home of Judge John Rowan, where Stephen Foster wrote My Old Kentucky Home 35345

Oscar Getz Museum of Whiskey History, 114 N Fifth St, Bardstown, KY 40004-1402 - T: (502) 348-2999, Fax: (502) 348-9325. Head: Mary Hite
Local Museum / Special Museum - 1984
Local history, Whiskey history 35346

Barkers Island WI

S.S. Meteor Maritime Museum, Hwy 2 and 53, Barkers Island, WI 54880 - T: (715) 392-5742, 394-5712, Fax: (715) 394-3810, Internet: http://www.superiorwi.com
Science&Tech Museum - 1973
Historic ships 35347

Barnesville OH

Gay 90's Mansion Museum, 532 N Chestnut St, Barnesville, OH 43713 - T: (614) 425-2926. Head: Marietta Martin, Howard Lemasters
Historical Museum - 1966 35348

Barnet VT

Barnet Historical Society Museum, Goodwille House, Barnet, VT 05821 - T: (802) 633-2611. Head: Lorna Grady
Local Museum - 1967
Local hist 35349

Barnstable MA

Donald G. Trayser Memorial Museum, 3353 Main St, Barnstable, MA 02630, mail addr: 230 South St Town Hall, Hyannis, MA 02601 - T: (617) 362-2092, 790-6270. Head: Patricia Jones Anderson
Local Museum - 1960
History, Old Customs House 35350

Olde Colonial Courthouse, Main St, Rte 6A, Barnstable, MA 02630 - T: (508) 362-8927, 362-6889, Internet: http://www.capehistory.com. Head: Carol Clarke Di Vico
Historical Museum - 1949
Sachem Iyanough's gravesite dedicated to early Indians who befriended Pilgrims 35351

Barnwell SC

Barnwell County Museum, Hagood and Marlboro Aves, Barnwell, SC 29812 - T: (803) 259-1916, 259-3277
Local Museum - 1978
Local hist 35352

Barre MA

Barre Historical Museum, 18 Common St, Barre, MA 01005 - T: (978) 355-4067
Local Museum - 1955
Local history 35353

Barrington IL

Barrington Area Historical Museum, 212 W Main St, Barrington, IL 60010 - T: (708) 381-1730, Fax: (708) 381-1766. Head: Dean Maiben, Michael J. Harkins
Local Museum - 1969
Local history, housed in two Folk Victorian Houses 35354

Bartlesville OK

Frank Phillips Home, 1107 S Cherokee, Bartlesville, OK 74003 - T: (918) 336-2491, Fax: (918) 336-3529. Head: J. Blake Wade
Local Museum - 1973 35355

Woolaroc Museum, State Hwy 123, Bartlesville, OK 74003 - T: (918) 336-0307 ext 10, Fax: (918) 336-0084, E-mail: woolaroc1@aol.com, Internet: http://www.woolaroc.org. Head: Robert R. Lansdown
Fine Arts Museum / Historical Museum - 1929 35356

Barton VT

Crystal Lake Falls Historical Museum, 97 Water St, Barton, VT 05822 - T: (802) 525-3583, 525-6251, Fax: (802) 525-3583. Head: Avis Harper
Local Museum / Science&Tech Museum - 1984
Local hist and industry 35357

Basking Ridge NJ

Environmental Education Center, 190 Lord Stirling Rd, Basking Ridge, NJ 07920 - T: (908) 766-2489, Fax: (908) 766-2687, Internet: http/www.park.co.somerset.nj.us. Head: Catherine Schrein
Natural History Museum - 1970 35358

Bastrop LA

Snyder Museum and Creative Arts Center, 1620 E Madison Av, Bastrop, LA 71220 - T: (318) 281-8760. Head: Madeline Herring, Joni H. Noble
Fine Arts Museum / Local Museum - 1974
Local history, art 35359

Batavia IL

Batavia Depot Museum, 155 Houston, Batavia, IL 60510 - T: (630) 406-5274, Fax: (630) 879-9537. Head: Carla Hill
Local Museum - 1960
Local history, housed in 1854 Batavia Depot, one of the oldest railroad station on the Burlington Line 35360

Batavia NY

Holland Land Office Museum, 131 W Main St, Batavia, NY 14020 - T: (716) 343-4727
Local Museum - 1894 35361

Bath ME

Maine Maritime Museum, 243 Washington St, Bath, ME 04530 - T: (207) 443-1316, Fax: (207) 443-1665, Internet: http://www.bathmaine.com/. Head: Thomas R. Wilcox
Historical Museum - 1964
Maritime, historic shipyard 35362

Bath NC

Historic Bath State Historic Site, NC Hwy 92, Bath, NC 27808 - T: (252) 923-3971, Fax: (252) 923-0174, E-mail: historicbath@tri-countynet.net, Internet: http://www.ah.dcr.state.nc.us/sections/hs/bath/bath.htm. Head: Gerald Butler
Historic Site - 1963 35363

Bath OH

Hale Farm and Village, 2686 Oak Hill Rd, Bath, OH 44210 - T: (330) 666-3711, Fax: (330) 666-9497, E-mail: ihuber@wrhs.org, Internet: http://www.wrhs.org
Open Air Museum / Agriculture Museum - 1957 35364

Baton Rouge LA

Louisiana Arts and Science Center, 100 S River Rd, Baton Rouge, LA 70802 - T: (225) 344-5272, 344-9478, Fax: (225) 344-9477, E-mail: lasc@lascmuseum.org, Internet: http://www.lascmuseum.org. Head: Carol Sommerfeldt Gikas
Fine Arts Museum / Science&Tech Museum - 1960
Art, science, former Illinois Central Railroad Station 35365

Louisiana Naval War Memorial U.S.S. Kidd, 305 S River Rd, Baton Rouge, LA 70802 - T: (225) 342-1942, Fax: (225) 342-2039, E-mail: kidd661@aol.com, Internet: http://www.usskidd.com. Head: H. Maury Drummond
Military Museum - 1981
Maritime, historic ship 35366

Louisiana Old State Capitol, Center for Political and Governmental History, 100 North Blvd, Baton Rouge, LA 70801 - T: (504) 342-0500, Fax: (504) 342-0316, E-mail: osc@sec.state.la.us, Internet: http://www.sec.state.la.us. Head: Mary Louise Prudhomme
Historical Museum - 1990
Louisiana State history 35367

Louisiana State University Museum of Art, Memorial Tower, Baton Rouge, LA 70803 - T: (504) 388-4003, Fax: (504) 334-4016, E-mail: indiana@lsu.edu. Head: Steven W. Rosen
Fine Arts Museum / University Museum - 1959
Art 35368

Magnolia Mound Plantation, 2161 Nicholson Dr, Baton Rouge, LA 70802 - T: (504) 343-4955, Fax: (504) 343-6739, Internet: http://lhn.lsu.edu/lhin/habs/magnolia/poemm/. Head: Suzette Tannehill, Gwen A. Edwards
Open Air Museum / Local Museum - 1968
Plantation house and outbuildings 35369

Museum of Natural Science, 119 Foster Hall, LSU, Baton Rouge, LA 70803 - T: (225) 388-2855, Fax: (225) 388-3075, E-mail: namark@unix1sncc.lsu.edu, Internet: http://www.museum.lsu.edu. Head: Dr. Mark S. Hafner
University Museum / Natural History Museum - 1936
Paleontology, anthropology, mammals, birds, fishes, reptiles 35370

Old Bogan Central Firefighters Museum, 427 Laurel St, Baton Rouge, LA 70801 - T: (504) 344-8558, Fax: (504) 344-7777. Head: Jo Ellen Kearny, Amy Weaver Hollister
Historical Museum - 1973
Fire fighting 35371

Rural Life Museum and Windrush Gardens, 4600 Essen Ln, Baton Rouge, LA 70809 - T: (504) 765-2437, Fax: (504) 765-2639. Head: David Floyd
Local Museum - 1970
Local hist 35372

Battle Creek MI

Art Center of Battle Creek, 265 E Emmett St, Battle Creek, MI 49017 - T: (616) 962-9511, Fax: (616) 969-3838. Head: Cathy Callala
Fine Arts Museum - 1948
Art gallery of Michigan artists 35373

Kimball House Museum, 196 Capital Av NE, Battle Creek, MI 49017 - T: (616) 965-2613, Fax: (616) 966-2495, E-mail: bch1st@net.link.net. Head: Michael Evans
Local Museum - 1966 35374

Kingman Museum of Natural History, W Michigan Av at 20th St, Battle Creek, MI 49017 - T: (616) 965-5117, Fax: (616) 962-5610
Natural History Museum - 1869
Natural history 35375

Battle Ground IN

Tippecanoe Battlefield, 200 Battle Ground Av, Battle Ground, IN 47920 - T: (765) 567-2147, Fax: (765) 567-2149, E-mail: cindy@tcha@mus.in.us, Internet: http://www.tcha.mus.in.us. Head: Kevin O'Brian
Historic Site - 1972
Keththppecanuk, a lonf forgotten settlement, Tippecanoe and Tyler, Two 35376

Baudette MN

Lake of the Woods County Museum, 8th Av SE, Baudette, MN 56623 - T: (218) 634-1200
Local Museum - 1978
County history 35377

Bay City MI

Historical Museum of Bay County, 321 Washington Av, Bay City, MI 48708 - T: (517) 893-5733, Fax: (517) 893-5741, Internet: http://www.bchsmuseum.org. Head: Gay McInerney
Historical Museum - 1919
County history 35378

Bay City TX

Matagorda County Museum, 2100 Av F, Bay City, TX 77414-0851 - T: (409) 245-7502, Fax: (409) 245-1233. Head: Jack Hollister
Local Museum - 1965
Regional history 35379

Bay View MI

Bay View Historical Museum, Bay View Association Encampment, Bay View, MI 49770 - T: (616) 347-6225. Head: Robert J. Blok
Local Museum - 1970
Local hist 35380

Bay Village OH

Rose Hill Museum, 27715 Lake Rd, Bay Village, OH 44140 - T: (440) 871-7338, Internet: http://www.victoriana.com/bvhs. Head: Eric Eakin
Historical Museum - 1960 35381

Bayside NY

QCC Art Gallery, 222-05 56th Av, Bayside, NY 11364-1497 - T: (718) 631-6396, Fax: (718) 631-6620, E-mail: f.quintanilla@qcc.cuny.edu, Internet: http://qcc.cuni.edu. Head: Faustino Quintanilla
University Museum / Fine Arts Museum - 1966 35382

Beacon NY

Madam Brett Homestead, 50 Van Nydeck Av, Beacon, NY 12508 - T: (914) 831-6533. Head: Denise Doring Van Buren
Local Museum - 1954 35383

Bear Mountain NY

Bear Mountain Trailside Museums Wildlife Center, Bear Mountain State Park, Bear Mountain, NY 10911 - T: (914) 786-2701 ext 263, Internet: http://www.trailsidenewyork.com. Head: John Focht
Natural History Museum - 1927 35384

Beatrice NE

Gage County Historical Museum, 101 N Second, Beatrice, NE 68310 - T: (402) 228-1679, Internet: http://www.infoanalytic.com/gage/beatrice.html. Head: Kent Wilson
Historical Museum - 1971 35385

Homestead National Monument of America, RR 3, Beatrice, NE 68310 - T: (402) 223-3514, Fax: (402) 228-4231, Internet: http://www.nps.gov
Agriculture Museum - 1936 35386

Beaufort NC

Beaufort Historic Site, 138 Turner St, Beaufort, NC 28516 - T: (252) 728-5225, Fax: (252) 728-4966, E-mail: bha@bmd.clis.com, Internet: http://www.historicbeaufort.com. Head: Patricia Suggs
Local Museum - 1960 35387

North Carolina Maritime Museum, 315 Front St, Beaufort, NC 28516 - T: (252) 728-7317, Fax: (252) 728-2108, E-mail: maritime@ncsl.dcr.state.nc.us, Internet: http://www.ah.dcr.state.nc.us/sections/maritime. Head: Dr. George Ward Shannon
Natural History Museum / Science&Tech Museum - 1975 35388

Beaufort SC

Beaufort Museum, 713 Craven St, Beaufort, SC 29902 - T: (843) 525-7077, 525-7005, 525-7017, Fax: (843) 525-7013, E-mail: bftmuseum@islc.net, Internet: http://www.cityofbeaufort.crglmuseum.htm
Fine Arts Museum / Local Museum - 1939
Local hist 35389

The Verdier House, 801 Bay St, Beaufort, SC 29902 - T: (843) 524-6335, Fax: (843) 524-6240, E-mail: histbft@hargray.com. Head: Jefferson Mansell
Local Museum - 1977
Historic house 35390

Beaumont TX

Art Museum of Southeast Texas, 500 Main St, Beaumont, TX 77701 - T: (409) 832-3432, Fax: (409) 832-8508, E-mail: info@amset.org, Internet: http://www.amset.org. Head: Lynn P. Castle
Fine Arts Museum - 1950
Art 35391

The Art Studio, 720 Franklin St, Beaumont, TX 77701 - T: (409) 838-5393, E-mail: artstudio@artstudio.org, Internet: http://www.artstudio.org. Head: Greg Busceme
Fine Arts Museum - 1983
Art 35392

Beaumont Art League, 2675 Gulf St, Fairgrounds, Beaumont, TX 77703 - T: (409) 833-4179, Fax: (409) 833-4179, E-mail: abarr91511@aol.com. Head: Frank Gerrietts
Fine Arts Museum - 1943
Art 35393

Dishman Art Gallery, 1030 Lavaca, Beaumont, TX 77705 - T: (409) 880-8959, Fax: (409) 880-1799, E-mail: lokensgall@hal.lamar.edu. Head: Dr. Lynne Lokensgard
Fine Arts Museum / Public Gallery - 1983
Art 35394

Edison Plaza Museum, 350 Pine St, Beaumont, TX 77701 - T: (409) 839-3089, Fax: (409) 839-3077. Head: Michael Barnhill
Local Museum - 1980
Local hist 35395

Fire Museum of Texas, 400 Walnut, Beaumont, TX 77701 - T: (409) 880-3927, Fax: (409) 833-5166, E-mail: bmtfire@sat.net
Science&Tech Museum - 1986 35396

John Jay French House, 3025 French Rd, Beaumont, TX 77706 - T: (409) 898-0348, Fax: (409) 898-8487. Head: Nell Truman
Local Museum - 1968
Historic house 35397

McFaddin-Ward House, 1906 McFaddin Av, Beaumont, TX 77701 - T: (409) 832-1906, 832-1906, Fax: (409) 832-3483, E-mail: info@mcfaddin-ward.org, Internet: http://www.mcfaddin-ward.org. Head: Metthew White
Local Museum - 1982
Historic house 35398

Texas Energy Museum, 600 Main St, Beaumont, TX 77701 - T: (409) 833-5100, Fax: (409) 833-4282, E-mail: smithtem@msn.com, Internet: http://www.texasenergymuseum.orgum/. Head: D. Ryan Smith
Science&Tech Museum - 1987
Industry history 35399

Beaver Dam WI

Dodge County Historical Society Museum, 105 Park Av, Beaver Dam, WI 53916 - T: (920) 887-1266. Head: Joanne L. Wells
Local Museum - 1938
Local hist 35400

Beaver Island MI

Beaver Island Historical Museum, 26275 Main St, Beaver Island, MI 49782 - T: (616) 448-2254, Fax: (616) 448-2106, E-mail: news@beaverisland.net, Internet: http://beaverisland.net. Head: James Willis, William Cashman
Local Museum - 1957
Local history 35401

Becker MN

Sherburne County Historical Museum, 13122 First St, Becker, MN 55308 - T: (612) 261-4433, Fax: (612) 261-4437. Head: Craig Schwarzkopf, Kurt K. Kragness
Local Museum - 1972
Regional history 35402

Beckley WV

Youth Museum of Southern West Virginia, New River Park, Beckley, WV 25802 - T: (304) 252-3730, Fax: (304) 252-3764, E-mail: ymswv@citynet.net. Head: David Beeman, Sandi Parker
Special Museum - 1977 35403

Bedford IN

Lawrence County Historical Museum, Rm 12, Court House, Bedford, IN 47421 - T: (812) 275-4141
Local Museum - 1928
Local history 35404

Bedford NY

Museum of the Bedford Historical Society, 38 Village Green, Bedford, NY 10586 - T: (914) 234-9751, Fax: (914) 234-6195, E-mail: bedhist@bestweb.net. Head: Linda DeMenocal, Lynne Ryan
Local Museum - 1916 35405

Bedford PA

Fort Bedford Museum, Fort Bedford Dr, Bedford, PA 15522 - T: (814) 623-8891, Fax: (814) 623-2011, E-mail: FBM@nb.net, Internet: http://www.NB.net/~fbm/index.htm. Head: William H. Clark
Local Museum - 1958 35406

Bedford VA

Bedford City/County Museum, 201 E Main St, Bedford, VA 24523 - T: (540) 586-4520. Head: Ellen A. Wandrei
Local Museum - 1932
Local hist 35407

Bedford Corners NY

Westmoreland Sanctuary, 260 Chestnut Ridge Rd, Bedford Corners, NY 10549 - T: (914) 666-8448, Fax: (914) 242-1175, E-mail: mail@westmorelandsanctuary.org, Internet: http://www.westmorelandsanctuary.org. Head: Stephen A. Ricker
Natural History Museum - 1957 35408

Belchertown MA

The Stone House Museum, 20 Maple St, Belchertown, MA 01007 - T: (413) 323-6573
Historical Museum - 1904 35409

Belcourt ND

Turtle Mountain Chippewa Heritage Center, Turtle Mountain Chippewa Historical Society, Hwy 5, Belcourt, ND 58316 - T: (701) 477-6140, Fax: (701) 477-6836, Internet: http://chippewa.etma.com. Head: Wannetta Benett
Fine Arts Museum / Historical Museum - 1985
History, art 35410

Belhaven NC

Belhaven Memorial Museum, POB 220, Belhaven, NC 27810 - T: (252) 943-3055, Fax: (252) 943-2357, Internet: http://www.beaufort-county.com/Belhaven/museum. Head: Peg McKnight
Historical Museum - 1965 35411

Bellefonte PA

Centre County Library Historical Museum, 203 N Allegheny St, Bellefonte, PA 16823 - T: (814) 355-1516, Fax: (814) 355-2700, E-mail: paroom@naccess.net, Internet: http://www.ccfpl.org. Head: Lydianne Bulazo, Charlene K. Brungard
Local Museum - 1939 35412

Belleville IL

Saint Clair County Historical Museum, 701 E Washington St, Belleville, IL 62220 - T: (618) 234-0600. Head: Robert Fietsam
Local Museum - 1905
Regional history 35413

Belleville MI

Belleville Area Museum, 405 Main St, Belleville, MI 48111 - T: (734) 697-1944, Fax: (734) 697-1944. Head: Fred Hudson, Diane Wilson
Historical Museum - 1989
Local history 35414

Bellevue NE

Fontenelle Forest Association Museum, 1111 Bellevue Blvd N, Bellevue, NE 68005 - T: (402) 731-3140, Fax: (402) 731-2403. Head: Kenneth H. Finch, Gary Garabrandt
Natural History Museum - 1913 35415

Sarpy County Historical Museum, 2402 SAC Pl, Bellevue, NE 68005-3932 - T: (402) 292-1880. Head: Gary Iske
Local Museum - 1970 35416

Bellevue WA

Bellevue Art Museum, 510 Bellevue Wayne, Bellevue, WA 98004 - T: (425) 519-0270, Fax: (425) 637-1799, E-mail: bam@bellevueart.org, Internet: http://www.bellevueart.org. Head: Diane M. Douglas
Fine Arts Museum - 1975
Art 35417

Rosalie Whyel Museum of Doll Art, 1116 108th Av, NE, Bellevue, WA 98004 - T: (425) 455-1116, Fax: (425) 455-4793, E-mail: dollart@dollart.com, Internet: http://www.dollart.com/dollart. Head: Rosalie Whyel
Special Museum / Decorative Arts Museum - 1989 35418

Bellflower IL

Bellflower Genealogical and Historical Society Museum, Latcha St, Bellflower, IL 61724 - T: (309) 722-3757, 722-3467. Head: Dorothy Woliung, Phyllis Kumler
Local Museum - 1976
Early 1900 Illinois Central Railroad Depot 35419

Bellingham WA

Viking Union Gallery, Western Washington University, 516 High St, Bellingham, WA 98225 - T: (360) 650-6534, Fax: (360) 650-6507. Head: Susan Musi
Fine Arts Museum / University Museum - 1899
Art 35420

Western Gallery, Western Washington University, Bellingham, WA 98225-9068 - T: (360) 650-3963, Fax: (360) 650-6878, E-mail: clarklan@cms.wwu.edu, Internet: http://www.ac.wwu.edu/~sculptur/. Head: Sarah Clark-Langager
University Museum / Fine Arts Museum - 1950
Fine and performing art 35421

Whatcom Museum of History and Art, 121 Prospect St, Bellingham, WA 98225 - T: (360) 676-6981, Fax: (360) 738-7409, E-mail: tlivesay@cob.org, Internet: http://www.whatcommuseum.org. Head: Mary Pettus
Local Museum - 1940
Art, history 35422

Bellows Falls VT

Adams Old Stone Grist Mill, Mill St, Bellows Falls, VT 05101 - T: (802) 463-3706
Local Museum / Open Air Museum - 1965
Local hist 35423

Rockingham Free Museum, 65 Westminster St, Bellows Falls, VT 05101 - T: (802) 463-4270, E-mail: rockingham@dol.state.vt.us. Head: Devik Wyman
Historical Museum - 1909
Local hist 35424

Bellport NY

Bellport-Brookhaven Historical Society Museum, 31 Bellport Ln, Bellport, NY 11713 - T: (516) 286-0888. Head: Francis G. Fosmine
Historical Museum - 1963 35425

Belmont CA

The San Mateo County Arts Council, 1219 Ralston Av, Belmont, CA 94002 - T: (650) 593-1816, Fax: (650) 593-4716, E-mail: smcoarts@aol.com, Internet: http://www.smcoarts.org. Head: Peter Weiglin, Matias Varela
Fine Arts Museum - 1972
Contemporary gallery 35426

The Wiegand Gallery, College of Notre Dame, 1500 Ralston Av, Belmont, CA 94002 - T: (650) 508-3595, 593-1601, Fax: (650) 508-3488, E-mail: elainek@cnd.edu. Head: Charles Strong
Fine Arts Museum / University Museum - 1970 35427

Belmont NY

Allegany County Museum, 11 Wells St, Belmont, NY 14813 - T: (716) 268-9293, Fax: (716) 268-9446. Head: Craig R. Braack
Local Museum - 1970 35428

Americana Manse, Whitney-Halsey Home, Cnr of Whitney Pl, Belmont, NY 14813 - T: (716) 268-5130. Head: Ruth Czankus
Local Museum - 1964 35429

Belmont VT

Community Historical Museum of Mount Holly, Tarbelville Rd, Belmont, VT 05730 - T: (802) 259-2460
Local Museum - 1968
Local hist 35430

Beloit KS

Little Red Schoolhouse-Living Library, Roadside Park, N Walnut and Hwy 24, Beloit, KS 67420 - T: (913) 738-5301. Head: Mildred Peterson
Historical Museum - 1907
Education, one-room school 35431

Beloit WI

Logan Museum of Anthropology, 700 College St, Beloit, WI 53511 - T: (608) 363-2677, Fax: (608) 363-2248, Internet: http://www.beloit.edu/~museum/logan. Head: Dr. William Green
University Museum / Ethnology Museum / Archaeological Museum - 1892
Anthropology 35432

Wright Museum of Art, 700 College St, Beloit, WI 53511 - T: (608) 363-2677, Fax: (608) 363-2718, E-mail: wilsont@beloit.edu, Internet: http://www.beloit.edu/libmuseum.html. Head: Henry Moy
Fine Arts Museum / University Museum - 1892
Art 35433

Belton SC

South Carolina Tennis Hall of Fame, Belton, SC 29627 - T: (864) 338-7751, Fax: (864) 338-4034. Head: Rex Maynard
Special Museum - 1984
Tennis 35434

Belton TX

Bell County Museum, 201 N Main St, Belton, TX 76513 - T: (254) 933-5243, Fax: (254) 933-5756, E-mail: museum@vvm.com, Internet: http://www.vvm.com/~museum. Head: Stephanie Turnham
Local Museum - 1975
Local hist 35435

Belvidere IL

Boone County Historical Society Museum, 311 Whitney Blvd, Belvidere, IL 61008 - T: (815) 544-8391, Fax: (815) 544-8391. Head: Bernard Allen, George Gibson
Local Museum - 1968
Local history - library 35436

Bement IL

Bryant Cottage, 146 E Wilson Av, Bement, IL 61813 - T: (217) 678-8184. Head: Marilyn L. Ayers
Historical Museum - 1925
1856 Bryant Cottage where the Lincoln-Douglas Debates were verbally agreed to be part of the 1858 Senate campaigns 35437

Bemidji MN

Beltrami County Historical Museum, 7301 Frontage Rd NW, Bemidji, MN 56619 - T: (218) 751-7824, Fax: (218) 751-2234, E-mail: bchsm@bji.net. Head: Dick Florhaug, Wanda Hoyum
Local Museum - 1949
Regional history 35438

Bend OR

High Desert Museum, 59800 S Hwy 97, Bend, OR 97702-7963 - T: (541) 382-4754, Fax: (541) 382-5256, E-mail: info@highdesert.org, Internet: http://www.highdesert.org
Ethnology Museum / Natural History Museum / Historical Museum - 1974 35439

Benicia CA

Benicia Historical Museum, 2024 Camel Rd, Benicia, CA 94510 - T: (707) 745-5435, 745-5869, Fax: (707) 745-2135, E-mail: cbarn@flash.net, Internet: http://www.flash.net/~cbarn. Head: Beverly Phelan
Historical Museum - 1985
Local history 35440

Benjamin TX

Knox County Museum, Courthouse, Benjamin, TX 79505 - T: (940) 454-2241. Head: Mary Jane Young
Local Museum - 1966
Local hist 35441

Benkelman NE

Dundy County Historical Society Museum, 522 Araphahoe, Benkelman, NE 69021 - T: (308) 423-2750. Head: Betty Deyle, Dee Fries
Local Museum - 1970 35442

Bennettsville SC

Jennings-Brown House Female Academy, 119 S Marlboro St, Bennettsville, SC 29512 - T: (843) 479-5624, E-mail: marlborough@mecsc.net. Head: Ron J. Munnerlyn
Local Museum - 1967
Historic house 35443

Marlboro County Historical Museum, 123 S Marlboro St, Bennettsville, SC 29512 - T: (843) 479-5624, E-mail: marlborough@mecse.net. Head: Ron J. Munnerlyn
Local Museum - 1970
Local hist 35444

Bennington VT

The Bennington Museum, W Main St, Bennington, VT 05201 - T: (802) 447-1571, Fax: (802) 442-8305, E-mail: bennmuse@sover.net, Internet: http://www.benningtonmuseum.com. Head: Steven Miller
Fine Arts Museum / Decorative Arts Museum / Local Museum - 1875
Art, decorative arts, local hist 35445

Southern Vermont College Art Gallery, Monument Av, Bennington, VT 05201 - T: (802) 442-5427, Fax: (802) 447-4695. Head: Greg Winterhalter
Fine Arts Museum / University Museum - 1979
Art 35446

Benson MN

Swift County Historical Museum, Swift County Historical Society, 2135 Minnesota Av, Bldg 2, Benson, MN 56215 - T: (320) 843-4467. Head: George Clemens, Marlys Gallagher
Historical Museum - 1929
Regional history 35447

Benton WI

Swindler's Ridge Museum, 25 W Main St, Benton, WI 53803 - T: (608) 759-5182. Head: Peg Roberts
Historical Museum - 1993 35448

Benton Harbor MI

Morton House Museum, 501 Territorial, Benton Harbor, MI 49022 - T: (616) 925-7011, Internet: http://www.parrett.net/~morton. Head: Miriam Pede
Local Museum - 1966
Local hist 35449

Benzonia MI

Benzie Area Historical Museum, 6941 Traverse Av, Benzonia, MI 49616 - T: (616) 882-5539, Fax: (231) 882-5539. Head: Debbra Eckhout
Local Museum - 1969
Local hist 35450

Berea KY

Berea College Burroughs Geological Museum, Main St, Berea, KY 40404 - T: (859) 985-3351 ext 6290, Fax: (859) 985-3303, E-mail: larry_lipchinsky@berea.edu, Internet: http://www.berea.edu/. Head: Zelek L. Lipchinsky
University Museum / Natural History Museum - 1920
Geology 35451

Berea College Doris Ulmann Galleries, Corner of Chestnut and Elipse St, Berea, KY 40404 - T: (606) 986-9341 ext 5530, Fax: (859) 985-3541, E-mail: robert_boyce@berea.edu, Internet: http://www.berea.edu/. Head: John Zhang
Fine Arts Museum / University Museum - 1975
Art 35452

Berea OH

Fawick Art Gallery, Baldwin-Wallace College, 275 Eastland Rd, Berea, OH 44017 - T: (440) 826-2152, Fax: (440) 826-3380, Internet: http://www.baldwin-wallacecollege.com. Head: Prof. Paul Jacklitch
Fine Arts Museum
Drawings and prints from 16th - 20th c, paintings, sculptures by American Midwest artists 35453

Bergen NY

Bergen Museum of Local History, 7547 Lake Rd, Bergen, NY 14416 - T: (716) 494-1121. Head: Henry Hastings
Local Museum - 1964 35454

Berkeley CA

Badè Institute of Biblical Archaeology and Howell Bible Collection, 1798 Scenic Av, Berkeley, CA 94709 - T: (510) 849-1272, Fax: (510) 845-8948, E-mail: bade@psr.edu, Internet: http://www.psr.edu/bade. Head: Ruth Ohm
Religious Arts Museum / Archaeological Museum - 1926
Archaeology, religion, rare bibles 35455

Ben Keley Art Museum and Pacific Film Archive, University of California, 2626 Bancroft Way, Berkeley, CA 94704 - T: (510) 642-0808, Fax: (510) 642-4889, E-mail: sgong@uclink2.berkeley.edu, Internet: http://www.bampfa.berkeley.edu. Head: Kevin Consey
Fine Arts Museum / University Museum - 1965
Art, film, video 35456

Berkeley Art Center, 1275 Walnut St, Berkeley, CA 94709 - T: (510) 644-6893, Fax: (510) 540-0343, Internet: http://www.berkeyartcenter.org. Head: Katherine Aoki, Robbin Henderson
Fine Arts Museum - 1967
Art 35457

Essig Museum of Entomology, University of California, Berkeley, 211 and 311 Wellman Hall, Berkeley, CA 94720 - T: (510) 643-0804, Fax: (510) 642-7428, E-mail: cbarr@nature.berkeley.edu, Internet: http://www.mip.berkeley.edu/essig/. Head: Rosemarie G. Gillespie
University Museum / Natural History Museum - 1939
Entomology, esp arachnids and other terreestrial arthropods 35458

Judah L. Magnes Museum, 2911 Russell St, Berkeley, CA 94705 - T: (510) 549-6950, Fax: (510) 849-3673, E-mail: pfpr@magnesmuseum.org, Internet: http://www.magnesmuseum.org. Head: Susan Morris
Fine Arts Museum / Religious Arts Museum - 1962
Judaica, historic Berkeley mansion, prints, drawings, paintings, sculptures, Western US Jewish history 35459

Lawrence Hall of Science, University of California, 1 Centennial Dr, Berkeley, CA 94720-5200 - T: (510) 642-5132, Fax: (510) 642-1055, E-mail: lhsinfo@uclink.berkeley.edu, Internet: http://www.laurence-hallofscience.edu. Head: Dr. Ian Carmichael
Natural History Museum / Science&Tech Museum
Science, technology 35460

Museum of Paleontology, University of California at Berkeley, 1101 Valley Life Sciences Bldg, Berkeley, CA 94720-4780 - T: (510) 642-1821, Fax: (510) 642-1822, Internet: http://www.ucmp.berkeley.edu. Head: David R. Lindberg
Natural History Museum - 1921
Vertebrates, plants, invertebrates, microfossils 35461

Museum of Vertebrate Zoology, University of California, 3101 Valley Life Sciences Bldg, Berkeley, CA 94720-3160 - T: (510) 642-3567, Fax: (510) 643-8238, Internet: http://www.mip.berkeley.edu/mvz/. Head: James L. Patton
University Museum / Natural History Museum - 1908
Zoology, herpetology, mammology 35462

Phoebe Apperson Hearst Museum of Anthropology, University of California, 103 Kroeber Hall, Berkeley, CA 94720-3712 - T: (510) 642-3682, Fax: (510) 642-6271, E-mail: pahma@uclink.berkeley.edu, Internet: http://www.qal.berkeley/~hearst. Head: Rosemary Joyce
University Museum / Ethnology Museum / Archaeological Museum - 1901
Anthropology 35463

Berkeley Springs WV

Museum of the Berkeley Springs, POB 99, Berkeley Springs, WV 25411 - T: (304) 258-3743. Head: Hettie G. Hawvermale
Local Museum - 1984 35464

Berlin MA

Berlin Art and Historical Collections, Woodward Av, Berlin, MA 01503 - T: (978) 838-2502. Head: Barry W. Eager
Local Museum / Fine Arts Museum - 1950
Art, history 35465

Berlin WI

Berlin Historical Society Museum of Local History, 111 S Adams Av, Berlin, WI 54923 - T: (920) 361-4343
Local Museum - 1962
Local hist 35466

Bermuda LA

Beau Fort Plantation Home, 4078 Hwy 494 and Hwy 119, Bermuda, LA 71456 - T: (318) 352-9580, 352-5340, Fax: (318) 352-7280, E-mail: beaufort@worldnetla.net. Head: Jack O. Brittain
Folklore Museum - 1790
1790 Creole one and one-half cottage type building 35467

Berrien Springs MI

Siegfried H. Horn Archaeological Museum, Andrews University, Berrien Springs, MI 49104-0990 - T: (616) 471-3273, Fax: (616) 471-3619, E-mail: hornmusm@andrews.edu, Internet: http://www.andrews.edu/ARCHAEOLOGY
Archaeological Museum - 1970
Archaeology 35468

Berryville AR

Saunders Memorial Museum, 113-15 E Madison St, Berryville, AR 72616 - T: (870) 423-2563. Head: Hazel Prentice Burkett
Museum of Classical Antiquities / Special Museum - 1955
Gun, period furnishings 35469

Berryville VA

Clarke County Historical Museum, 104 N Church St, North Wing, Berryville, VA 22611 - T: (540) 955-2600, Fax: (540) 955-0285, E-mail: ccha@visuallink.com, Internet: http://www.visuallink.net/ccha. Head: Sarah P. Trumbower
Local Museum - 1983
Regional history 35470

Bessemer AL

Bessemer Hall of History, 1905 Alabama Av, Bessemer, AL 35020 - T: (205) 426-1633. Head: Dominga N. Toner
Local Museum - 1970 35471

Bethany WV

Historic Bethany, Bethany College, Bethany, WV 26032 - T: (304) 829-7285, Fax: (304) 829-7287, E-mail: historic@mail.bethanywv.edu, Internet: http://www.bethanywv.edu. Head: Dr. D. Duane Cummins
University Museum / Historical Museum - 1840 35472

Bethel ME

Bethel Historical Society's Regional History Center, 10-14 Broad St, Bethel, ME 04217-0012 - T: (207) 824-2908, Fax: (207) 824-0882, E-mail: history@bdc.bethel.me.us, Internet: http://orion.bdc.bethel.me.us/~history. Head: Dr. Stanley Russell Howe
Historical Museum - 1974
Regional history of Northern New England, federal style house - Research library, period house museum, 35473

Bethesda MD

DeWitt Stetten Jr. Museum of Medical Research, National Institutes of Health, Bldg 31, Bethesda, MD 20892-2092 - T: (301) 496-6610, Fax: (301) 402-1434, E-mail: vharden@helix.nih.gov, Internet: http://www.nih.gov/od/museum. Head: Victoria A. Harden
Historical Museum - 1987
Medicine, Warren Grant Magnuson Clinical Center 35474

Bethlehem NH

Crossroads of America, 6 Trudeau Rd, Bethlehem, NH 03574 - T: (603) 869-3919, E-mail: Roger.Hinds@fothBBS. Head: Roger Hinds
Special Museum - 1981
Model railroad, toy 35475

Bethlehem PA

Historic Bethlehem, 459 Old York Rd, Bethlehem, PA 18018 - T: (610) 882-0450, Fax: (610) 882-0460, Internet: http://www.historicbethlehem.org. Head: Charlene Donchez Mowers
Historical Museum - 1957 35476

Kemerer Museum of Decorative Arts, 427 N New St, Bethlehem, PA 18018 - T: (610) 868-6868, Fax: (610) 882-0460, Internet: http://www.historic-bethlehem.org. Head: Charlene Donchez Mowers
Decorative Arts Museum - 1954 35477

Lehigh University Art Galleries/Museum, Zoellner Arts Center, 420 E Packer Av, Bethlehem, PA 18015 - T: (610) 758-3615, Fax: (610) 758-4580, E-mail: rv02@lehigh.edu, Internet: http://www.lehigh.edu. Head: Ricardo Viera
Fine Arts Museum / University Museum - 1864 35478

Moravian Museum of Bethlehem, 66 W Church St, Bethlehem, PA 18018 - T: (610) 867-0173, Fax: (610) 694-0960, Internet: http://www.historic-bethlehem.org. Head: Charlene Donchez Mowers
Local Museum / Religious Arts Museum - 1938 35479

Bettendorf IA

Family Museum of Arts and Science, 2900 Learning Campus Dr, Bettendorf, IA 52722 - T: (319) 344-4106, Fax: (319) 344-4164, Internet: http://www.familymuseum.org. Head: Tracey K. Kuehl
Fine Arts Museum / Natural History Museum - 1974
Children's museum 35480

Beverly MA

Beverly Historical Museum, 117 Cabot St, Beverly, MA 01915 - T: (508) 922-1186, Fax: (508) 922-7387, E-mail: beverlyhistoricalsociety@nii.net, Internet: http://www.beverlyhistory.org. Head: Stephen P. Hall
Local Museum - 1891
Local history, John Cabot mansion, John Balch house, Hale farm - genealogical research 35481

Beverly OH

Oliver Tucker Historic Museum, State Rte 60, Beverly, OH 45715 - T: (614) 984-2489
Local Museum - 1971 35482

Beverly WA

Wanapum Dam Heritage Center, Hwy 243, Beverly, WA 98823 - T: (509) 754-3541 ext 2571, Fax: (509) 754-5074. Head: Leon Hoepner
Local Museum / Folklore Museum - 1966
Local hist 35483

Beverly WV

Randolph County Museum, Main St, Beverly, WV 26253 - T: (304) 636-1959. Head: Phyllis Baxter
Local Museum - 1924 35484

Beverly Hills CA

California Museum of Ancient Art, POB 10515, Beverly Hills, CA 90213 - T: (818) 762-5500, E-mail: cmaa@earthlink.net. Head: John D. Hofbauer, Jerôme Berman
Archaeological Museum - 1983
Near Eastern art and archaeology (Egypt, Mesopotamia, the Holy Land) 35485

The Museum of Television and Radio, 465 N Beverly Dr, Beverly Hills, CA 90210 - T: (310) 786-1000, Fax: (310) 786-1086, E-mail: lramos@mtr.org, Internet: http://www.mtr.org. Head: Steve Bell
Science&Tech Museum - 1996
Communication 35486

Bexley OH

Bexley Historical Society Museum, 2242 E Main St, Bexley, OH 43209-2319 - T: (614) 235-8694, Fax: (614) 235-3420
Local Museum - 1974 35487

Big Horn WY

Bradford Brinton Memorial, 239 Brinton Rd, Big Horn, WY 82833 - T: (307) 672-3173, Fax: (307) 672-3258, E-mail: kls_bbm@vcn.com, Internet: http://www.bradfordbrintonmemorial.com. Head: Kenneth L. Schuster
Fine Arts Museum - 1961
Art 35488

Big Pool MD

Fort Frederick, 11100 Fort Frederick Rd, Big Pool, MD 21711 - T: (301) 842-2155, Fax: (301) 842-0028, Internet: http://www.dwr.state.md.us. Head: Scott Allen
Fine Arts Museum / Military Museum - 1922
Historic building and site 35489

Big Spring TX

Heritage Museum and Potton House, 510 Scurry, Big Spring, TX 79720 - T: (915) 267-8255, Fax: (915) 267-8255, E-mail: angela@xroadstx.com
Local Museum - 1971
Local hist 35490

Biglerville PA

National Apple Museum, 154 W Hanover St, Biglerville, PA 17307-0656 - T: (717) 677-4556, Internet: http://www.uads.k12.pa.us/upperadams. Head: Dick Mountfort
Agriculture Museum - 1990
Agriculture 35491

Billings MT

Northcutt Steele Gallery, Montana State University Billings, 1500 N 30th St, Billings, MT 59101-0298 - T: (406) 657-2324, Fax: (406) 657-2187, E-mail: njussila@msu-b.edu. Head: Neil Jussila
Fine Arts Museum
Visual art 35492

Peter Yegen Jr. Yellowstone County Museum, 1950 Terminal Circle, Logan Field, Billings, MT 59105 - T: (406) 256-6811, Fax: (406) 256-6811, E-mail: ycm@pyjrycm.org, Internet: http://www.pyjrycm.org. Head: Suzanne Warner
Local Museum - 1953
Indian artifacts, Western memorabilia, military items, dinosaur bones, Leory Greene paintings 35493

Western Heritage Center, 2822 Montana Av, Billings, MT 59101 - T: (406) 256-6809 ext 21, Fax: (406) 256-6850, E-mail: heritage@ywhc.org, Internet: http://www.ywhc.org. Head: Lynda Bourque Moss
Historical Museum - 1971 35494

Yellowstone Art Museum, 401 N 27 St, Billings, MT 59101 - T: (406) 256-6804, Fax: (406) 256-6817, E-mail: artinfo@artmuseum.org, Internet: http://yellowstone.artmuseum.org. Head: Robert Knight
Fine Arts Museum - 1964
Contemporary art and prints, abstract expresionists art 35495

Biloxi MS

Beauvoir, Jefferson Davis Home and Presidential Library, 2244 Beach Blvd, Biloxi, MS 39531 - T: (228) 388-9074, Fax: (228) 388-7082, E-mail: majedwards@aol.com, Internet: http://www.beauvoir.org. Head: Robert L. Hawkins
Historical Museum / Military Museum / Historic Site - 1941 35496

George E. Ohr Arts and Cultural Center → The Ohr-O'Keefe Museum of Art

Mardi Gras Museum, 119 Rue Magnolia, Biloxi, MS 39530 - T: (601) 435-6245, Fax: (601) 435-6246, E-mail: bilosimuseum@ms.us. Head: Lolly Barnes
Historical Museum
History Museum, housed in the restored antebellum 1847 Magnolia Hotel 35497

Maritime and Seafood Industry Museum, 115 First St, Biloxi, MS 39530 - T: (228) 435-6320, Fax: (228) 435-6309, E-mail: schoonen@maritimemuseum.org, Internet: http://maritimemuseum.net. Head: Gavin Schmidt, Robin Krohn
Historical Museum / Science&Tech Museum - 1986
Maritime and seafood industry 35498

Museum of Biloxi, 119 Rue Magnolia, Biloxi, MS 39530 - T: (601) 435-6308, Fax: (601) 435-6246, E-mail: biloximuseum@ms.us. Head: Lolly Barnes
Natural History Museum 35499

The Ohr-O'Keefe Museum of Art, 136 George E. Ohr St, Biloxi, MS 39530 - T: (228) 374-5547, Fax: (228) 436-3641, E-mail: info@georgeohr.org, Internet: http://www.georgeohr.com. Head: Marjorie E. Gowdy
Fine Arts Museum - 1989
Art, ceramics 35500

Binghamton NY

Broome County Historical Society Museum, 30 Front St, Binghamton, NY 13905 - T: (607) 772-0660, Fax: (607) 771-8905, E-mail: broomehistory@tier.net, Internet: http://www.sites.tier.net/broomehistory/. Head: David J. Dixon
Local Museum - 1919 35501

Discovery Center of the Southern Tier, 60 Morgan Rd, Binghamton, NY 13903 - T: (607) 773-8750, Fax: (607) 773-8019, E-mail: discovery@tier.net, Internet: http://www.tier.net/discovery. Head: Elaine Kelly, Trisha Chastaine-Sage
Special Museum - 1983 35502

Roberson Museum and Science Center, 30 Front St, Binghamton, NY 13905 - T: (607) 772-0660, Fax: (607) 771-8905, Internet: http://www.kopernik.org. Head: David E. Chesebrough
Fine Arts Museum / Historical Museum / Science&Tech Museum - 1954 35503

University Art Museum, State University of New York at Binghamton, Binghamton, NY 13902-6000 - T: (607) 777-2634, Fax: (607) 777-2836, E-mail: hogan@binghamton.edu. Head: Lynn Gamwell
Fine Arts Museum / University Museum - 1967 35504

Birdsboro PA

Daniel Boone Homestead, 400 Daniel Boone Rd, Birdsboro, PA 19508 - T: (610) 582-4900, Fax: (610) 582-1744. Head: Gerald Vermeesch
Local Museum / Folklore Museum / Open Air Museum - 1937 35505

Birmingham AL

Agnes Gallery, 1919 15th Av, S, Birmingham, AL 35205 - T: (205) 939-3393, Fax: (205) 393-0063, E-mail: agnesgalle@aol.com, Internet: http://www.agnesgallery.com. Head: Jon Coffelt, Shawn Boley
Fine Arts Museum - 1993 35506

Arlington Museum, 331 Cotton Av SW, Birmingham, AL 35211 - T: (205) 780-5656, Fax: (205) 788-0585. Head: Daniel F. Brooks
Local Museum - 1953 35507

Birmingham Civil Rights Institute Museum, 520 16 St, Birmingham, AL 35203 - T: (205) 328-9696, Fax: (205) 323-5219, E-mail: bcri.info@bcri.bham.al.us, Internet: http://www.bcri.bham.al.us. Head: Dr. Ethel Hall, Dr. Lawrence Pijeaux
Historical Museum - 1991 35508

Birmingham Museum of Art, 2000 8th Av N, Birmingham, AL 35203 - T: (205) 254-2566, Fax: (205) 254-2714, E-mail: jhatchett@artsBMA.org, Internet: http://www.artsBMA.org. Head: Gail Andrews Trechsel
Fine Arts Museum - 1951
American, European and Asian art, decorative art, renaissance art - Hanson library 35509

McWane Center, 200 19th St N, Birmingham, AL 35203 - T: (205) 714-8300, Fax: (205) 714-8400, Internet: http://www.mcwane.org
Science&Tech Museum - 1997
Science, technology 35510

Red Mountain Museum → McWane Center

Sloss Furnaces National Historic Landmark, First Av N and 32nd St, Birmingham, AL 35222 - T: (205) 324-1911, Fax: (205) 324-6758. Head: Robert R. Rathburn
Science&Tech Museum - 1983
Industry, ironmaking plant incl blast furnaces, blowing engines, power house, boilers 35511

Southern Museum of Flight, 4343 N 73rd St, Birmingham, AL 35206-3642 - T: (205) 833-8226, Fax: (205) 836-2439, E-mail: -southernmuseumofflight@compuserve.com, Internet: http://www.bham.net/flight/museum.html. Head: Dr. J. Dudley Pewitt
Science&Tech Museum - 1965
Aviation, transportation 35512

Visual Arts Gallery, University of Alabama at Birmingham, Birmingham, AL 35294-1260 - T: (205) 934-4941, Fax: (205) 975-2836, Internet: http://www.uab.edu. Head: Antoinette Spanos Nordan
Fine Arts Museum / University Museum - 1972
Art 35513

Birmingham MI

Birmingham-Bloomfield Art Center, 1516 S Cranbrook Rd, Birmingham, MI 48009 - T: (248) 644-0866, Fax: (248) 644-7904, Internet: http://www.bbartcenter.org. Head: Janet E. Torno
Fine Arts Museum - 1956
Art 35514

Bisbee AZ

Bisbee Mining and Historical Museum, 5 Copper Queen Plaza, Bisbee, AZ 85603 - T: (520) 432-7071, 432-7848, Fax: (520) 432-7800, E-mail: bisbeemuseum@theriver.com, Internet: http://www.azstarnet.com/nonprofit/bisbeemuseum. Head: Carrie Gustavson
Historical Museum / Science&Tech Museum - 1971
Local hist, mining 35515

Bishop CA

Laws Railroad Museum, Silver Canyon Rd, Bishop, CA 93515 - T: (760) 873-5950, Internet: http://mammothweb.com/sierraweb/bishop/laws. Head: Denton Sonke
Local Museum / Historical Museum / Historic Site - 1966
Laws Railroad Depot and 22 other buildings 35516

Bishop Hill IL

Bishop Hill Heritage Museum, 103 N Bishop Hill St, Bishop Hill, IL 61419 - T: (309) 927-3899, Fax: (309) 927-3010, E-mail: bhha@winco.net. Head: Morris Nelson, Michael G. Wendel
Local Museum - 1962
Local history, Swedish communal settlement founded in 1846 by religious dissenters 35517

Bismarck ND

De Mores State Historic Site, North Dakota Heritage Center, Bismarck, ND 58505-0830 - T: (701) 328-2666, Fax: (701) 328-3710, Internet: http://www.state.nd.us/hist/. Head: Merl Paaverud
Local Museum - 1936 35518

Former Governors' Mansion, 320 Av B East, Bismarck, ND 58501 - T: (701) 255-3819, 328-2666, Fax: (701) 328-3710, Internet: http://www.state.nd.us/hist/. Head: Merl Paaverud
Local Museum - 1895
Historic house 35519

State Historical Society of North Dakota Museum, North Dakota Heritage Center, 612 East Blvd, Bismarck, ND 58505 - T: (701) 328-2666, Fax: (701) 328-3710, E-mail: histsoc@state.nd.us, Internet: http://www.state.nd.us/hist. Head: Merl Paaverud
Local Museum - 1895 35520

Black Hawk CO

Lace House Museum, 161 Main St, Black Hawk, CO 80422 - T: (303) 582-5221, Fax: (303) 582-0429
Historical Museum - 1976 35521

Blacksburg SC

Kings Mountain National Military Park, 2625 Park Rd, Blacksburg, SC 29702 - T: (864) 936-7921, Fax: (864) 936-9897, Internet: http://www.nps.gov/kimo.htm. Head: D. Broadbert
Military Museum - 1931
Military hist 35522

Blacksburg VA

Historic Smithfield, 1000 Smithfield Plantation Rd, Blacksburg, VA 24060 - T: (540) 231-3947, Fax: (540) 231-3006, E-mail: -smithfield.plantation@vt.edu, Internet: http://www.civic.bev.net/smithfield. Head: Bill Rogers
Local Museum - 1964
Historic house 35523

Museum of the Geological Sciences, Virginia Polytechnic Institute and State University, Derring Hall, Blacksburg, VA 24061 - T: (540) 231-6029, Fax: (540) 231-3386, E-mail: seriksn@vt.edu. Head: Susan C. Eriksson
University Museum / Natural History Museum - 1969
Geology, mineralogy 35524

Smithfield Plantation → Historic Smithfield

Blackwell OK

Top of Oklahoma Historical Museum, 303 S Main St, Blackwell, OK 74631 - T: (405) 363-0209, Fax: (580) 363-0209. Head: George Glaze
Local Museum - 1972 35525

Blairsville GA

Union County Historical Society Museum, Town Square, Blairsville, GA 30512 - T: (706) 745-5493. Head: Ann Farabee
Local Museum - 1988
Local hist 35526

Blakely GA

Kolomoki Mounds State Park Museum, Indian Mounds Rd, off U.S. Hwy 27 and Kolomoki Rds, Blakely, GA 31723 - T: (229) 724-2150/51, Fax: (229) 724-2152, E-mail: kolomoki@alltel.net, Internet: http://www.gastateparks.org
Archaeological Museum - 1951
13th-century Indian burial mound and village 35527

Blanding UT

Edge of the Cedars State Park, 660 West, 400 N, Blanding, UT 84511 - T: (435) 678-2238, Fax: (435) 678-3348, E-mail: nrdpr@edgeofthecedars. Head: Michael Nelson
Ethnology Museum - 1976
Remains of 700 AD to 1220 AD structures, ancient dwellings of the Anasazi Indian culture 35528

Bloomfield NJ

Historical Society of Bloomfield Museum, 90 Broad St, Bloomfield, NJ 07003 - T: (973) 566-6220, Fax: (201) 429-0170. Head: Ina Campbell
Local Museum - 1966 35529

Bloomfield NY

A.W.A. Electronic-Communication Museum, Village Green, Rtes 5 and 20, Bloomfield, NY 14469 - T: (716) 392-3088, Fax: (716) 392-3088, E-mail: k2mp@etnet.net, Internet: http://www.antiquewireless.org
Science&Tech Museum - 1953 35530

Bloomfield Academy Museum, 8 South Av, Bloomfield, NY 14443 - T: (716) 657-7244, Fax: (716) 657-7244, E-mail: celsb@frontiernet.net. Head: Charles Thomas, Carl J. Elsbree
Historical Museum - 1967 35531

Bloomfield Hills MI

Cranbrook Art Museum, 39221 Woodward Av, Bloomfield Hills, MI 48303-0801 - T: (248) 645-3323, Fax: (248) 645-3324, E-mail: artmuseum@cranbrook.edu, Internet: http://www.cranbrook.edu/museum. Head: Gregory M. Wittkopp
Fine Arts Museum - 1927
Contemporary art, architecture and design - library 35532

Cranbrook House and Gardens Auxiliary, 380 Lone Pine Rd, Bloomfield Hills, MI 48303-0801 - T: (248) 645-3141, Fax: (248) 645-3085
Local Museum - 1971
Home of George Gough and Ellen Scripps Booth 35533

Cranbrook Institute of Science, 39221 Woodward, Bloomfield Hills, MI 48303-0801 - T: (248) 645-3200, Fax: (248) 645-3050, Internet: http://www.cranbrook.edu. Head: Talbert B. Spence
Natural History Museum / Science&Tech Museum - 1932
Science 35534

Bloomington IL

The David Davis Mansion, 1000 E Monroe Dr, Bloomington, IL 61701 - T: (309) 828-1084, Fax: (309) 828-3493, E-mail: davismansion@yahoo.com, Internet: http://www.davismansion.org. Head: Dr. Marcia Young
Historical Museum - 1960
David Davis' Second Empire Italianate brick mansion (Abraham Lincoln's campaign manager) 35535

McLean County Arts Center, 601 N East St, Bloomington, IL 61701 - T: (309) 829-0011, Fax: (309) 829-4928, E-mail: mcac@dave-world.net, Internet: http://www.mcac.org. Head: Catherine Sutloff
Fine Arts Museum / Association with Coll - 1922 35536

Mclean County Museum of History, Mclean County Historical Society, 200 N Main, Bloomington, IL 61701 - T: (309) 827-0428, Fax: (309) 827-0100, E-mail: gregkoos@gte.net, Internet: http://www.mettistory.org. Head: Greg Koos
Local Museum - 1892
Library and Archives 35537

Bloomington IN

Elizabeth Sage Historic Costume Collection, Memorial Hall E 232, Indiana University, Bloomington, IN 47405 - T: (812) 855-4627, 855-5223, Fax: (812) 855-4869, E-mail: rowold@indiana.edu. Head: Nelda M. Christ
Special Museum - 1935
Textiles, costume 35538

Fine Arts Gallery, Indiana University, 123 Fine Arts Bldg, Bloomington, IN 47405 - T: (812) 855-8490, Fax: (812) 855-7498, E-mail: sofa@indiana.edu, Internet: http://www.fa.indiana.edu/~sofa/. Head: Betsy Stirratt
Fine Arts Museum / University Museum - 1987 35539

Indiana University Art Museum, E 7th St, Bloomington, IN 47405 - T: (812) 855-5445, Fax: (812) 855-1023, E-mail: iuartmus@indiana.edu, Internet: http://www.indiana.edu/~iuam. Head: Adelheid M. Gealt
Fine Arts Museum - 1941 35540

Monroe County Historical Society, 202 E Sixth St, Bloomington, IN 47408 - T: (812) 332-2517, Fax: (812) 355-5593, E-mail: mchm@kiva.net, Internet: http://www.kiva.net/~mchm/museum.htm. Head: Samuel D. Bohl
Local Museum - 1980
County history 35541

William Hammond Mathers Museum, 416 N Indiana Av, Bloomington, IN 47405 - T: (812) 855-6873, Fax: (812) 855-0205, E-mail: mathers@indiana.edu, Internet: http://www.indiana.edu/~mathers/. Head: Geoffrey Conrad
Folklore Museum / Historical Museum / Ethnology Museum / University Museum - 1963
Anthropology, history, folklore 35542

Bloomington MN

Bloomington Art Center, 10206 Penn Av S, Bloomington, MN 55431 - T: (952) 563-4777, Fax: (952) 563-8744, E-mail: bac@bloomingtonartcenter.com, Internet: http://www.bloomingtonartcenter.com. Head: Susan M. Anderson, Mark J. Miller, Michael Hoyt
Fine Arts Museum / Performing Arts Museum - 1976
Multi-Disciplinary art, performing and visual, Rachel Flentje (exhibitions) 35543

Bloomington Historical Museum, 10200 Penn Av, S, Bloomington, MN 55431 - T: (612) 948-8881. Head: Vonda Kelly
Local Museum - 1964
Regional history 35544

Bloomsburg PA

Columbia County Museum, 225 Market St, Bloomsburg, PA 17815-0360 - T: (570) 784-1600, Internet: http://www.colcohist-gensoc.org. Head: Bonnie Farver, Julia Driskell
Local Museum - 1914
Local hist 35545

Blue Earth MN

Wakefield House Museum, 405 E Sixth St, Blue Earth, MN 56013 - T: (507) 526-5421
Local Museum - 1948 35546

Blue Hill ME

Parson Fisher House, Jonathan Fisher Memorial, Mines Rd, Blue Hill, ME 04614 - T: (207) 374-2159, E-mail: sandra8962@aol.com. Head: Eric Linnel
Folklore Museum / Local Museum - 1965 35547

Blue Mountain Lake NY

Adirondack Museum, Rts 28N and 30, Blue Mountain Lake, NY 12812-0099 - T: (518) 352-7311 ext 101, Fax: (518) 352-7653, E-mail: Acaroll@adkmuseum.org, Internet: http://www.adkmuseum.org. Head: Jackie Day
Local Museum - 1952 35548

Bluefield WV

Science Center of West Virginia, 500 Bland St, Bluefield, WV 24701 - T: (304) 325-8855, Fax: (304) 324-0513. Head: Patty Wilkinson, Thomas R. Willmitch
Natural History Museum / Science&Tech Museum - 1994 35549

Bluffton IN

Wells County Historical Museum, 420 W Market St, Bluffton, IN 46714 - T: (219) 824-9956, E-mail: belliott@parlorcity.com, Internet: http://www.parlorcity.com
Local Museum - 1935
Local history 35550

Blunt SD

Mentor Graham Museum, 103 N Commercial Av, Blunt, SD 57522
Local Museum - 1950
Local hist 35551

Boalsburg PA

Boal Mansion Museum, Business Rte 322, Boalsburg, PA 16827 - T: (814) 466-6210, E-mail: boalmus@vicon.net, Internet: http://www.vicon.net/~boalmus. Head: Christopher Lee, Mathilde Boal Lee
Fine Arts Museum / Historical Museum - 1952 35552

Pennsylvania Military Museum and 28th Division Shrine, Rtes 322 and 45, Boalsburg, PA 16827 - T: (814) 466-6263, Fax: (814) 466-6618. Head: Vickie Ziegler, William J. Leech
Military Museum - 1969 35553

Boca Raton FL

Boca Raton Historical Society Museum, 71 N Federal Hwy, Boca Raton, FL 33432 - T: (561) 395-6766, Fax: (561) 395-4049, E-mail: bocahist@aol.com, Internet: http://www.bocahistory.org. Head: Mary Csar
Historical Museum - 1972 35554

Boca Raton Museum of Art, 501 Plaza Real, Boca Raton, FL 33432 - T: (516) 392-2500, Fax: (516) 391-6410, E-mail: bocart@gate.net, Internet: http://www.bocamuseum.org. Head: George S. Bolge
Fine Arts Museum - 1951 35555

Children's Museum of Boca Raton, 498 Crawford Blvd, Boca Raton, FL 33432 - T: (407) 368-6875, Fax: (407) 395-7764. Head: Tom Neuman, Poppi Mercier
Special Museum - 1979 35556

International Museum of Cartoon Art, 201 Plaza Real, Boca Raton, FL 33432 - T: (561) 391-2200, Fax: (561) 391-2721, E-mail: imca@worldnet.att.netn.org, Internet: http://www.cartoon.org. Head: Jerry Robinson, Abigail Roeloffs
Fine Arts Museum - 1974
Art, cartoons, comic strips and books, magazine illustration - Library 35557

Boise ID

Boise Art Museum, 670 S Julia Davis Dr, Boise, ID 83702 - T: (208) 345-8330, Fax: (208) 345-2247, E-mail: comments@boiseartmuseum.org, Internet: http://www.boiseartmuseum.org. Head: Lucinda Barnes
Fine Arts Museum - 1931
General Arts 35558

Discovery Center of Idaho, 131 Myrtle St, Boise, ID 83702 - T: (208) 343-9895, Fax: (208) 343-0105, E-mail: discover@scidaho.org, Internet: http://www.scidaho.org. Head: Rika Clement
Science&Tech Museum - 1986 35559

Idaho Museum of Mining and Geology, 2455 Old Penitentiary Rd, Boise, ID 83712 - T: (208) 368-9876. Head: Edward D. Fields
Natural History Museum / Science&Tech Museum - 1989
Mining, mineralogy 35560

Idaho State Historical Museum, 610 N Julia Davis Dr, Boise, ID 83702 - T: (208) 334-2120, Fax: (208) 334-4059, E-mail: jochoa@shs.state.id.us, Internet: http://www.state.id.us/ishs/. Head: Steve Guerber
Historical Museum - 1881
History 35561

Bolinas CA

Bolinas Museum, 48 Wharf Rd, Bolinas, CA 94924 - T: (415) 868-0330, Fax: (415) 868-0607. Head: Sue Wright, Dolores Richards
Fine Arts Museum / Local Museum - 1982
Art, local history 35562

Bolivar OH

Fort Laurens State Memorial, 11067 Fort Laurens Rd NW, Bolivar, OH 44612 - T: (330) 874-2059, Fax: (330) 874-2936, E-mail: kmfzoar@compuserve.com, Internet: http://ohiohistory.org. Head: Kathleen M. Fernández
Military Museum - 1972 35563

Bolton MA

Bolton Historical Museum, Sawyer House, 676 Main St, Bolton, MA 01740 - T: (508) 779-6392. Head: Tim Feihler
Local Museum - 1962
Local history, farm/barn blacksmith shop 35564

Bolton Landing NY

Marcella Sembrich Opera Museum, 4800 Lake Shore Dr, Bolton Landing, NY 12814-0417 - T: (518) 644-2492, Fax: (518) 644-2191, E-mail: sembrich@webtv.net, Internet: htpp://www.operamuseum.com. Head: Anita Behr Richards
Music Museum - 1937
Golden age of Opera 35565

Bonham TX

Fort Inglish, Hwy 56 and Chinner St, Bonham, TX 75418 - T: (903) 583-3943, 640-2228. Head: Nick Long
Military Museum - 1976
Military hist 35566

The Sam Rayburn Museum, 800 W Sam Rayburn Dr, Bonham, TX 75418 - T: (903) 583-2455, Fax: (903) 583-7394. Head: H.G. Dulaney
Local Museum - 1957
Local hist 35567

Bonner Springs KS

The National Agricultural Center and Hall of Fame, 630 Hall of Fame Dr, Bonner Springs, KS 66012 - T: (913) 721-1075, Fax: (913) 721-1202, Internet: http://www.aghalloffame.com. Head: Tim Nimz
Agriculture Museum / Science&Tech Museum / Historical Museum - 1958
Agriculture 35568

Wyandotte County Museum, 631 N 126th St, Bonner Springs, KS 66012 - T: (913) 721-1078, Fax: (913) 721-1394, E-mail: wycomus@toto.net. Head: Rebecca L. Barber
Local Museum - 1889
Regional history 35569

Boone IA

Boone County Historical Center, 602 Story St, Boone, IA 50036 - T: (515) 432-1907, E-mail: bchs@opencominc.com. Head: Jerry Ober, Charles W. Irwin
Folklore Museum / Historical Museum / Natural History Museum - 1965 35570

Mamie Doud Eisenhower Birthplace, 709 Carroll St, Boone, IA 50036 - T: (515) 432-1896, Fax: (515) 432-2571, Internet: http://www.booneiowa.com/mamie. Head: Larry Adams
Historic Site - 1970 35571

Boonsboro MD

Boonsborough Museum of History, 113 N Main St, Boonsboro, MD 21713-1007 - T: (301) 432-6969, Fax: (301) 416-2222. Head: Douglas G. Bast
Historical Museum - 1975 35572

Boonville IN

Warrick County Museum, 217 S First St, Boonville, IN 47601 - T: (812) 897-3100, Fax: (812) 897-6104. Head: Jo Ann Baum, Virginia S. Allen
Local Museum - 1976
Local hist 35573

Boothbay ME

Boothbay Railway Village, Rte 27, Boothbay, ME 04537 - T: (207) 633-4727, Fax: (207) 633-4733, E-mail: railvill@lincoln.midcoast.com, Internet: http://www.railwayvillage.org. Head: Robert Ryan
Science&Tech Museum / Open Air Museum / Historical Museum - 1962
Transportation 35574

Boothbay Harbor ME

Boothbay Region Art Foundation, 7 Townsend Av, Boothbay Harbor, ME 04538 - T: (207) 633-2703. Head: Cheryl Blaydon
Fine Arts Museum - 1964 35575

Boothwyn PA

Real World Computer Museum, c/o US Ikon Naaman Creek Center, 7 Creek Pkwy, Boothwyn, PA 19061 - T: (610) 494-9000, Fax: (610) 494-2090, E-mail: museum@phila.usconnect.com, Internet: http://uscphl.com/museum. Head: Craig Collins
Science&Tech Museum - 1990
Computer 35576

Bordentown NJ

Bordentown Historical Society Museum, 211 Crosswicks St, Bordentown, NJ 08505 - T: (609) 298-1740
Local Museum - 1930 35577

Borger TX

Hutchinson County Museum, 618 N Main, Borger, TX 79007 - T: (806) 273-0130, Fax: (806) 273-0128. Head: Edward Benz
Local Museum - 1977
Local hist 35578

Borrego Springs CA

Anza-Borrego Desert Museum, 200 Palm Cyn Dr, Borrego Springs, CA 92004 - T: (760) 767-5311, Fax: (760) 767-3427, Internet: http://www.anzaborrego.statepark.org. Head: David VanCleve
Ethnology Museum / Archaeological Museum - 1979
Archaeology, paleontology 35579

Boston MA

Ancient and Honorable Artillery Company Museum, Armory, Faneuil Hall, Boston, MA 02109 - T: (617) 227-1638, Fax: (617) 227-7221
Military Museum - 1638
Military hist 35580

The Art Institute of Boston Main Gallery, 700 Beacon St, Boston, MA 02215 - T: (617) 262-1223, Fax: (617) 437-1226, Internet: http://www.aiboston.edu. Head: Bonnell Robinson
Fine Arts Museum / Public Gallery / University Museum
Art gallery 35581

Boston Athenaeum, 10 1/2 Beacon St, Boston, MA 02108 - T: (617) 227-0270, Fax: (617) 227-5266, E-mail: starzyk@bostonathenaeum.org, Internet: http://www.bostonathenaeum.org. Head: Richard Wendorf
Fine Arts Museum / Library with Exhibitions - 1807
Library with art coll 35582

Boston Fire Museum, 344 Congress St, Boston, MA 02210 - T: (617) 482-1344, 776-1288, Fax: (617) 666-1431
Historical Museum - 1977
Fire fighting history, Congress Street Fire Station 35583

Boston National Historical Park, Charlestown Navy Yard, Boston, MA 02129 - T: (617) 242-5648, Fax: (617) 241-8650, E-mail: marty_blatt@nps.gov, Internet: http://www.nps.gov/bost/. Head: Terry Savage
Historic Site / Archaeological Museum - 1974 35584

Boston Public Library Art Collections, 700 Boylston St, Boston, MA 02116 - T: (617) 536-5400, Fax: (617) 236-4306, Internet: http://www.bpl.org
Fine Arts Museum / Library with Exhibitions - 1852
Library with art colls 35585

Boston University Art Gallery, 855 Commonwealth Av, Boston, MA 02215 - T: (617) 353-4672, Fax: (617) 353-4509, E-mail: gallery@bu.edu, Internet: http://www.bu.edu/art. Head: John R. Stomberg
Fine Arts Museum / University Museum - 1960
Art gallery 35586

Bromfield Art Gallery, 560 Harrison Av, Boston, MA 02118-2436 - T: (617) 451-3605, E-mail: - www.bromfieldartgallery.com. Head: Florence Montgomery
Public Gallery - 1974 35587

The Children's Museum, Museum Wharf, 300 Congress St, Boston, MA 02210-1034 - T: (617) 426-6500, Fax: (617) 426-1944, E-mail: bostonkids@hotmail.com, Internet: http://www.bostonkids.org. Head: Louis B. Casagrande
Ethnology Museum - 1913 35588

Commonwealth Museum, 220 William T. Morrissey Blvd, Boston, MA 02125 - T: (617) 727-9268, Fax: (617) 825-3613, Internet: http://www.state.ma.us/sec/mus. Head: Maxine Trost
Historical Museum - 1986
State history 35589

Gibson House, 137 Beacon St, Boston, MA 02116 - T: (617) 267-6338, Fax: (617) 267-5121, E-mail: gibsonmuseum@aol.com. Head: Barbara Thibault, Edward W. Gordon
Historical Museum - 1957
Historic house, decorative art, paintings, sculptures, Victorian furniture 35590

Harrison Gray Otis House, 141 Cambridge St, Boston, MA 02114 - T: (617) 227-3956, Fax: (617) 227-9204, Internet: http://www.spnea.org
Decorative Arts Museum / Historic Site - 1910
New England antiquities 35591

Institute of Contemporary Art, 955 Boylston St, Boston, MA 02115-3194 - T: (617) 927-6620, Fax: (617) 266-4021, E-mail: jmedvedow@icaboston.org, Internet: www.icaboston.org. Head: Jill Medvedow
Fine Arts Museum - 1936 35592

Isabella Stewart Gardner Museum, 280 The Fenway, Boston, MA 02115 - T: (617) 566-1401, Fax: (617) 566-7653, E-mail: aquinn@isgm.org, Internet: www.gardnermuseum.org. Head: Anne Hawley
Fine Arts Museum - 1903
Art, housed in 15th-century Venetian style bldg 35593

John F. Kennedy Presidential Library-Museum, Columbia Point, Boston, MA 02125 - T: (617) 929-4500, Fax: (617) 929-4538, E-mail: library@kennedy.nara.gov, Internet: http://www.jfklibrary.org. Head: Maria Curosa Stanwich
Special Museum - 1979
History, presidential library, documents, film, photos 35594

Massachusetts Historical Society Museum, 1154 Boylston St, Boston, MA 02215 - Fax: (617) 859-0074, E-mail: library@masshist.org, Internet: http://www.masshist.org. Head: Henry Lee, William M. Fowler
Historical Museum - 1791
State history - library 35595

Mobius Gallery, 354 Congress St, Boston, MA 02210 - T: (617) 542-7416, Fax: (617) 451-2910, E-mail: mobius@mobius.org, Internet: www.mobius.org. Head: Jed Speare
Fine Arts Museum - 1977 35596

Museum of Fine Arts, 465 Huntington Av, Boston, MA 02115-5519 - T: (617) 267-9300, E-mail: webmaster@mfa.org, Internet: http://www.mfa.org. Head: Malcolm Rogers, Frances H. Colburn
Fine Arts Museum - 1870
Ancient Egyptian, Nubian and Near Eastern art, decorative art, Asiatic art, drawings, photography, European and American paintings, contemporary art 35597

Museum of Science, Science Park, Boston, MA 02114-1099 - T: (617) 589-0100, 723-2500, Fax: (617) 589-0454, E-mail: webteam@www.mos.org, Internet: http://www.mos.org. Head: David W. Ellis
Natural History Museum / Science&Tech Museum - 1830
Science technology 35598

Museum of the National Center of Afro-American Artists, 300 Walnut Av, Boston, MA 02119 - T: (617) 442-8614, 442-8014, Fax: (617) 445-5525. Head: Edmund B. Gaither
Fine Arts Museum - 1969
Afro-American art 35599

Nichols House Museum, 55 Mount Vernon St, Boston, MA 02108 - T: (617) 227-6993, Fax: (617) 723-8026, E-mail: nhm@cannel1.com. Head: Flavia Ciglianond
Decorative Arts Museum - 1961
Decorative arts, former Beacon Hill home of Rose Standish Nichols 35600

Old South Meeting House, 310 Washington St, Boston, MA 02108 - T: (617) 482-6439, Fax: (617) 482-9621. Head: Lowell A. Warren, Emily Curran
Historical Museum / Historic Site - 1877 35601

Old State House, 206 Washington St, Boston, MA 02109 - T: (617) 720-1713, Fax: (617) 720-3289, E-mail: bostoniansociety@bostonhistory.org, Internet: http://www.bostonhistory.org. Head: Anne D. Emerson
Historical Museum - 1881
History - library 35602

Paul Revere House, 19 North Sq, Boston, MA 02113 - T: (617) 523-2338, Fax: (617) 523-1775, E-mail: staff@paulreverehouse.org, Internet: http://www.paulreverehouse.org. Head: Nina Zannieri
Historical Museum - 1907
History, c.1680 Paul Revere house (Boston's oldest) 35603

Photographic Resource Center, 602 Commonwealth Av, Boston, MA 02215 - T: (617) 353-0700, Fax: (617) 353-1662, E-mail: prc@bu.edu, Internet: http://web.bu.edu/PRC. Head: Pamela Allara, Terrence Morash
Public Gallery / Fine Arts Museum - 1976 35604

Shirley-Eustis House, 33 Shirley St, Boston, MA 02119 - T: (617) 442-2275, Fax: (617) 442-2270, Internet: http://www.shirleyeustushouse.org. Head: Phebe Goodman, Tamsen E. George
Historical Museum - 1913
1747 Georgian country house, furnished according to Gov. William Eustis inventory 1825, 1806 Gardner Carriage House 35605

The Sports Museum of New England, 1175 Soldiers Field Rd, Boston, MA 02134 - T: (617) 787-7678, Fax: (617) 787-8152, E-mail: sm1175@aol.com, Internet: http://www.sportsmuseum.org. Head: Brian Dowling
Special Museum - 1977 35606

Urbanarts, 140 Clarendon St, Boston, MA 02116 - T: (617) 536-2880. Head: Pamela Worden
Fine Arts Museum 35607

USS Constitution Museum, Boston National Historical Park, Charlestown Navy Yard, Boston, MA 02129-1797 - T: (617) 426-1812, Fax: (617) 242-0496, Internet: http://www.ussconstitutionmuseum.org. Head: Burt Logan
Military Museum - 1972
Historic ship, old ironsides, launched 1797, world's oldest commissioned warship afloat 35608

Boubonnais IL

Exploration Station, A Children's Museum, 1095 W Perry St, Boubonnais, IL 60914 - T: (815) 933-9905, Fax: (815) 933-5468. Head: Bruce Baum
Special Museum - 1987 35609

Boulder CO

Boulder Museum of History, 1206 Euclid Av, Boulder, CO 80302 - T: (303) 449-3464, Fax: (303) 938-8322, E-mail: wgordon444@aol.com, Internet: http://www.ben.boulder.cu.us/arts/bmh. Head: Wendy Gordon
Local Museum - 1944
Local history 35610

CU Art Galleries, University of Colorado, Boulder, CO 80309 - T: (303) 492-8300, Fax: (303) 735-4197, Internet: http://www.colorado.edu/cuartgalleries. Head: Susan Krane
Fine Arts Museum - 1939
Colorado coll 35611

Heritage Center, University of Colorado, Boulder Campus, Old Main St, Boulder, CO 80309 - T: (303) 492-6329, Fax: (303) 492-6799, E-mail: oltmans_k@cufund.colorado.edu. Head: Kay Oltmans
University Museum / Local Museum - 1985
Local hist 35612

Leanin' Tree Museum of Western Art, 6055 Longbow Dr, Boulder, CO 80301 - T: (303) 530-1442 ext 299, Fax: (303) 530-7283, E-mail: artmuseum@leanintree.com, Internet: http://www.leanintree.com. Head: Edward P. Trumble
Fine Arts Museum - 1974
Art of the American West 35613

University of Colorado Museum, Broadway, between 15th and 16th St, Boulder, CO 80309 - T: (303) 492-6892, Fax: (303) 492-4195, E-mail: susan.reinke@colorado.edu, Internet: http://stripe.colorado.edu/~ucm/. Head: Prof. Linda S. Cordell
Natural History Museum - 1902
Natural history, anthropology, botany, zoology, geology, entomology, osteology 35614

Boulder UT

Anasazi State Park, 460 North Hwy 12, Boulder, UT 84716 - T: (435) 335-7308, Fax: (435) 335-7352. Head: C. Nelson
Archaeological Museum - 1970
1050-1200 AD, excavated Anasazi Indian Village 35615

Boulder City NV

Boulder City Museum-Hoover Dam Museum, 1305 Arizona St, Boulder City, NV 89005 - T: (702) 294-1988, Fax: (702) 294-4380, E-mail: bcmuseum@aol.com, Internet: http://www.accessnv.com/bcmha/index.htm. Head: Robert Ferraro, Charles Haraway
Science&Tech Museum - 1981 35616

Bourne MA

Aptucxet Trading Post Museum, 24 Aptucxet Rd, Bourne, MA 02532-0795 - T: (508) 759-9487
Historical Museum - 1921
Trading post, reconstructed on original 1627 site 35617

Bowie AZ

Fort Bowie, 13 mi S of Bowie, on Apache Pass Rd, Bowie, AZ 85605 - T: (520) 847-2500, Fax: (520) 847-2221, Internet: http://www.nps.gov
Historical Museum / Military Museum - 1964
Ruins of military structures, Apache Pass Overland Mail Station 35618

Bowie MD

City of Bowie Museums, 12207 Tulip Grove Dr, Bowie, MD 20715 - T: (301) 809-3088, Fax: (301) 809-2308, E-mail: bowiemuseums@juno.com, Internet: http://www.cityofbowie.org/comserv/museum.htm. Head: Stephen E. Patrick
Local Museum - 1968
Local hist 35619

Bowling Green FL

Paynes Creek Historic State Park, 888 Lake Branch Rd, Bowling Green, FL 33834 - T: (863) 375-4717, Fax: (863) 375-4510, E-mail: pcshs@strato.net, Internet: http://www.dep.state.fl.us
Historical Museum / Folklore Museum - 1981
Fort Chokonikla, Seminole Indian War Fort 35620

Bowling Green KY

The Kentucky Museum, Western Kentucky University, 1 Big Red Way, Bowling Green, KY 42101 - T: (502) 745-2592, Fax: (502) 745-4878, E-mail: Riley.Handy@wku.edu, Internet: http://www2.wku/edu/www/library/museum/
University Museum / Local Museum - 1931
Regional history 35621

National Corvette Museum, 350 Corvette Dr, Bowling Green, KY 42101 - T: (270) 781-7973, Fax: (270) 781-5286, E-mail: strode@corvettemuseum.com, Internet: http://www.corvettemuseum.com. Head: Wendell Strode
Science&Tech Museum - 1989 35622

Riverview at Hobson Grove, 1100 W Main Av, Bowling Green, KY 42102-4859 - T: (270) 843-5565, Fax: (270) 843-5557, E-mail: rivervw@bowlinggreen.net, Internet: http://www.bgky.org/riverview.htm. Head: Levi Word, Kenneth Webb
Decorative Arts Museum / Historical Museum / Historic Site - 1972 35623

Western Kentucky University Gallery, Rm 441, Ivan Wilson Center for Fine Arts, Bowling Green, KY 42101 - T: (270) 745-3944, Fax: (270) 745-5932, E-mail: art@wku.edu, Internet: http://www.wku.edu/dept/academic/ahss/art. Head: Kim Chalmers
Fine Arts Museum / Public Gallery / University Museum - 1973
Art 35624

Bowling Green OH

Bowling Green State University Fine Arts Center Galleries, Fine Arts Center, Bowling Green State University, Bowling Green, OH 43403-0211 - T: (419) 372-8525, Fax: (419) 372-2544, E-mail: jnathan@bgnet.bgsu.edu, Internet: http://www.bgsu.edu/departments/art/main/2galler.html. Head: Jaqueline S Nathan
Fine Arts Museum / University Museum - 1960 35625

Wood County Historical Center, 13660 County Home Rd, Bowling Green, OH 43402 - T: (419) 352-0967, Fax: (419) 352-6220, E-mail: wchisctr@wcnet.org, Internet: http://www.wcnet.org/~wchisctr. Head: Stacey Hann-Ruff
Local Museum - 1955 35626

Boyertown PA

Boyertown Museum of Historic Vehicles, 85 S Walnut St, Boyertown, PA 19512-1415 - T: (610) 367-2090, Fax: (610) 367-9712, E-mail: museum@enter.net. Head: Dennis E. Leh, Kenneth D. Wells
Science&Tech Museum - 1968
Vehicle building in Southeastern Pennsylvania 35627

Boys Town NE

Boys Town Hall of History, 14057 Flanagan Blvd, Boys Town, NE 68010 - T: (402) 498-1185, Fax: (402) 498-1159, E-mail: lyncht@baystacon.org, Internet: http://www.boystown.org. Head: Thomas J. Lynch
Historic Site - 1986
History 35628

Bozeman MT

Helen E. Copeland Gallery, Montana State University, MSU School of Art, Haynes Hall, Bozeman, MT 59717 - T: (406) 994-2562, Fax: (406) 994-3680, E-mail: dungan@montana.edu, Internet: http://www.montana.edu/wwwart. Head: Erica Howe Dungan
Fine Arts Museum / University Museum - 1974
Japanese patterns, native American ceramics, prints 35629

Museum of the Rockies, 600 W Kagy, Bozeman, MT 59717 - T: (406) 994-2251, Fax: (406) 994-2682, E-mail: sfischer@montana.edu, Internet: http://www.museumoftherockies.org. Head: Marilyn F. Wessel
Local Museum - 1956
American Western and Indian art, drawings, anthropology, archaeology, ethnology, decorative arts 35630

Bradenton FL

Art League of Manatee County, 209 9th St W, Bradenton, FL 34205 - T: (941) 746-2862, Fax: (941) 746-2319, E-mail: artleague@almc.org, Internet: http://www.almc.org. Head: John Langford, Patricia Richmond
Fine Arts Museum - 1937 35631

Manatee Village Historical Park Museum, 604 15th St E, Bradenton, FL 34208 - T: (941) 749-7165, Internet: http://www.clerkofcourts.com
Historic Site - 1974
Local history 35632

South Florida Museum, 201 10th St, W, Bradenton, FL 34205 - T: (941) 746-4132, Fax: (941) 746-2556, Internet: http://www.sfmbp.org. Head: Dan Blalock, Dr. Peter Bennett
Local Museum / Natural History Museum - 1946 35633

Bradford VT

Bradford Historical Society Museum, Town Hall, Main St, Bradford, VT 05033 - T: (802) 222-4727, 222-9026
Local Museum - 1959
Local hist 35634

Brainerd MN

Crow Wing County Historical Museum, 320 W Laurel St, Brainerd, MN 56401 - T: (218) 829-3268, Fax: (218) 828-4434, E-mail: cwchistsoc@brainerdonline.com. Head: Mary Lou Moudry
Local Museum - 1927
Local history 35635

Braintree MA

Braintree Historical Society Museum, 31 Tenney Rd, Braintree, MA 02184-6512 - T: (781) 848-1640, Fax: (781) 380-0731, E-mail: generalthyer@bhs.org, Internet: http://www.bs.org. Head: Brian A. Kolnero
Local Museum - 1930
History, decorative arts, antique furniture, American and Japanese fans 35636

Branchville SC

Branchville Railroad Shrine and Museum, 7505 Freedom Rd, Branchville, SC 29432 - T: (803) 274-8821. Head: Luther Folk
Science&Tech Museum - 1969
Transportation 35637

Branford CT

Harrison House, 124 Main St, Branford, CT 06405 - T: (203) 488-4828. Head: William B. Davis
Historical Museum - 1960 35638

Brattleboro VT

Brattleboro Museum and Art Center, 10 Vernon St, Brattleboro, VT 05301-3390 - T: (802) 257-0124, Fax: (802) 258-9182, E-mail: bmac@sover.net, Internet: http://www.brattlebowmuseum.org. Head: Christine Holderness
Fine Arts Museum / Local Museum - 1972
Visual art, local hist 35639

Brazosport TX

Brazosport Museum of Natural Science, 400 College Dr., Brazosport, TX 77566 - T: (409) 265-7831. Head: J.H. McIver
Natural History Museum / Science&Tech Museum - 1962
Natural science 35640

Brea CA

City of Brea Gallery, 1 Civic Center Circle, Brea, CA 92821 - T: (714) 990-7730, Fax: (714) 990-2258, Internet: http://www.ci.brea.ca.us. Head: Tim O'Donnell
Fine Arts Museum / Public Gallery - 1980 35641

Breckenridge MN

Wilkin County Historical Museum, 704 Nebraska Av, Breckenridge, MN 56520 - T: (218) 643-1303. Head: Gordon Martinson
Local Museum - 1965
Regional history 35642

Breckenridge TX

Swenson Memorial Museum of Stephens County, 116 W Walker, Breckenridge, TX 76424 - T: (254) 559-8471. Head: Freda Mitchell
Local Museum - 1970
Local hist 35643

Bremerton WA

Bremerton Naval Museum, 130 Washington Av, Bremerton, WA 98337 - T: (360) 479-7447, Fax: (360) 377-4186, E-mail: bremnavmuseum@silverlink.net. Head: Helen DeVine
Military Museum - 1954
Naval hist 35644

Kitsap Museum, 280 4th St, Bremerton, WA 98337 - T: (360) 479-6226, Fax: (360) 415-9294, E-mail: kchsmuseum@telebyte.net, Internet: http://www.waynes.net/kchsm/
Historical Museum - 1949
Local hist 35645

Brenham TX

Texas Baptist Historical Center Museum, 10405 FM 50, Brenham, TX 77833 - T: (409) 836-5117, Fax: (409) 836-2929. Head: Paul Sevar
Religious Arts Museum - 1965
Religion 35646

Brevard NC

Spiers Gallery, Sims Art Center, Brevard, NC 28712 - T: (828) 883-8292 ext 2245, Fax: (828) 884-3790, E-mail: tmurray@brevard.edu, Internet: http://www.brevard.edu.. Head: Timm Murray
Fine Arts Museum / University Museum 35647

Brewster MA

Cape Cod Museum of Natural History, 869 Rte 6A, Brewster, MA 02631 - T: (508) 896-3867, Fax: (508) 896-8844, Internet: http://www.ccmnh.com/. Head: George Stevens
Natural History Museum - 1954
Natural history 35648

New England Fire and History Museum, 1439 Main St, Rte 6A, Brewster, MA 02631 - T: (508) 896-5711, 432-2450, Internet: http://www.cape.cod.us. Head: Eugene I. Morris
Local Museum - 1972
Fire fighting, local history 35649

Brewton AL

Thomas E. McMillan Museum, Jefferson Davis College, 220 Alco Dr, Brewton, AL 36426 - T: (334) 809-1607, Fax: (334) 867-7399. Head: John T. Powell
Decorative Arts Museum / University Museum / Archaeological Museum - 1978 35650

Bridgehampton NY

Bridgehampton Historical Society Museum, 2368 Main St, Bridgehampton, NY 11932-0977 - T: (631) 537-1088, Fax: (631) 537-4225, E-mail: bhhs@hamptons.com, Internet: http://www.hamptons.com/bhhs. Head: Paul Brennan
Historical Museum - 1956 35651

Bridgeport AL

Russell Cave National Monument Museum, 3729 County Rd 98, Bridgeport, AL 35740 - T: (256) 495-2672, Fax: (256) 495-9220, E-mail: cave@trailler.com, Internet: http://nps.gov/ruca. Head: Bill Springer
Archaeological Museum - 1961
Archaeology 35652

Bridgeport CA

Bodie State Historic Park, Hwy 270, Bridgeport, CA 93517, mail addr: POB 515, Bridgeport, CA 93517 - T: (760) 647-6445, Fax: (760) 647-6486, E-mail: bodie@qnet.com, Internet: http://www.ceres.ca.gov/sierradsp/bodie.html
Historic Site / Open Air Museum - 1962
1859-1942 Gold Rush Mining Boom Town 35653

Bridgeport CT

Barnum Museum, 820 Main St, Bridgeport, CT 06604 - T: (203) 331-1104, Fax: (203) 339-4341, Internet: http://www.barnum-museum.org. Head: Collin Baron, Barbara Kram
Performing Arts Museum - 1893
Circus history 35654

The Discovery Museum, 4450 Park Av, Bridgeport, CT 06604 - T: (203) 372-3521, Fax: (203) 374-1929, E-mail: audley@discoverymuseum.org, Internet: http://www.discovery.museum.org. Head: Paul Audley, Lynn Hamilton
Fine Arts Museum / Science&Tech Museum - 1958
Art, science - planetarium 35655

Housatonic Museum of Art, 900 Lafayette Blvd, Bridgeport, CT 06604-4704 - T: (203) 332-5203, 332-5052, Fax: (203) 332-5123, E-mail: ho_zella@commnet.edu, Internet: http://www.hctc.commnet.edu. Head: Robbin Zella
Fine Arts Museum / University Museum - 1967 35656

University Art Gallery, Bernhard Arts and Humanities Center, 84 Iranistan Av, Bridgeport, CT 06601-2449 - T: (203) 576-4402, 576-4419, Fax: (203) 576-4051, E-mail: tjuliusb@cr2.nai.net. Head: Thomas Juliusburger
Fine Arts Museum / University Museum - 1972
Art gallery 35657

Bridgeton NJ

New Sweden Farmstead Museum, City Park, Bridgeton, NJ 08302 - T: (609) 455-3230, Fax: (609) 455-7491, Internet: http://marcons@cccnj.net. Head: J. Stephen Carnahan
Historical Museum / Agriculture Museum - 1983
Reproduction of 17th-century farmstead 35658

Bridgewater VA

Reuel B. Pritchett Museum, Bridgewater College, E College St, Bridgewater, VA 22812 - T: (540) 828-5462, 828-5414, Fax: (540) 828-5482, E-mail: tbarkley@bridgewater.edu, Internet: http://www.bridgewater.edu
Decorative Arts Museum / University Museum / Ethnology Museum - 1954 35659

Bridgton ME

Bridgton Historical Museum, Gibbs Av, Bridgton, ME 04009 - T: (207) 647-3699, E-mail: bhs@megalink.net, Internet: http://www.megalink.net/~bhs. Head: David Freeman
Local Museum / Folklore Museum - 1953
Local history 35660

Brigham City UT

Brigham City Museum-Gallery, 24 N 300 W, Brigham City, UT 84302 - T: (435) 723-6769, Fax: (435) 723-6769. Head: Colleen Bradford, Larry Douglass
Local Museum - 1970
Art, historical coll focussing the Mormon Communitarian Society in Brigham City 1865-1881 35661

Golden Spike National Historic Site, POB 897, Brigham City, UT 84302 - T: (435) 471-2209, Fax: (435) 471-2341, E-mail: gosp_interpretation@nps.gov, Internet: http://www.nps.gov/gosp. Head: Bruce Powell
Local Museum - 1965
Local hist 35662

Brighton CO

Adams County Museum, 9601 Henderson Rd, Brighton, CO 80601-8100 - T: (303) 659-7103. Head: David Rose
Local Museum / Agriculture Museum - 1987 35663

Bristol CT

American Clock and Watch Museum, 100 Maple St, Bristol, CT 06010 - T: (860) 583-6070, Fax: (860) 583-1862. Head: Elaine A. Reynolds Connelly
Special Museum - 1952
Horology 35664

New England Carousel Museum, 95 Riverside Av, Bristol, CT 06010 - T: (860) 585-5411, Fax: (860) 585-5411, E-mail: caramuse@aol.com, Internet: http://www.thecarouselmuseum.com. Head: Edward Krawiecki, Louise L. DeMars
Special Museum - 1989 35665

Bristol RI

Bristol Historical and Preservation Society Museum, 48 Court St, Bristol, RI 02809 - T: (401) 253-7223, Fax: (401) 253-7223. Head: Reinhard Battcher
Local Museum - 1936
Local hist 35666

Coggeshall Farm Museum, Rte 114, Poppasquash Rd, Bristol, RI 02809 - T: (401) 253-9062. Head: Walter Katkevich
Historical Museum - 1968
Rural life on a RI coastal farm 35667

Haffenreffer Museum of Anthropology, Brown University, Mount Hope Grant, 300 Tower St, Bristol, RI 02809-4050 - T: (401) 253-8388, 253-1287, Fax: (401) 253-1198, E-mail: kathleen_luke@Brown.edu, Internet: http://www.brown.edu/facilities/haffenreffer. Head: Shepard Krech III.
University Museum / Ethnology Museum - 1956
Anthropology 35668

Herreshoff Marine Museum/America's Cup Hall of Fame, 1 Burnside St, Bristol, RI 02809 - T: (401) 253-5000, Fax: (401) 253-6222, E-mail: herreshoff@ids.net, Internet: http://www.herreshoff.org
Historical Museum - 1971
Maritime hist 35669

Brockport NY

Tower Fine Arts Gallery, SUNY Brockport, Tower Fine Arts Bldg, Brockport, NY 14420 - T: (716) 395-2209, Fax: (716) 395-2588, E-mail: llonnen@po.brockport.edu. Head: Elizabeth McDade
University Museum / Fine Arts Museum - 1964 35670

Brockton MA

Fuller Museum of Art, 455 Oak St, Brockton, MA 02301-1395 - T: (508) 588-6000, Fax: (508) 587-6191, Internet: http://www.fullermuseum.org. Head: Jennifer Atkinson
Fine Arts Museum - 1969
Art 35671

Bronx NY

Bartow-Pell Mansion Museum, 895 Shore Rd, Pelham Bay Park, Bronx, NY 10464 - T: (718) 885-1461, Fax: (718) 885-9164, E-mail: bhmew@aol.com. Head: Mary Ellen Williamson
Local Museum - 1914 35672

Bronx County Historical Society Museum, 3309 Bainbridge Av, Bronx, NY 10467 - T: (718) 881-8900, Fax: (718) 881-4827, Internet: http://www.bronxhistoricalsociety.org. Head: Dr. Gary D. Hermalyn
Local Museum - 1897 35673

Bronx Museum of the Arts, 1040 Grand Concourse, Bronx, NY 10456 - T: (718) 681-6000 ext 154, Fax: (718) 681-6181
Fine Arts Museum - 1971 35674

Brooklyn Arts Council Gallery, 195 Cadman Plaza W, Bronx, NY 11201 - T: (718) 625-0080. Head: Pamela Billig
Association with Coll
Junior Children's Museum of Art 35675

City Island Nautical Museum, 190 Fordham St, Bronx, NY 10464 - T: (718) 885-0008
Historical Museum - 1964 35676

Edgar Allan Poe Cottage, Poe Park, Grand Concourse, E Kingsbridge Rd, Bronx, NY 10458 - T: (718) 881-8900, Fax: (718) 881-4827, Internet: http://www.bronxhistoricalsociety.org. Head: Dr. Gary D. Hermalyn
Local Museum - 1955
Historic house 35677

Hall of Fame for Great Americans, Bronx Community College, University Av and W 181 St, Bronx, NY 10453 - T: (718) 220-5162, Fax: (718) 220-6287, Internet: http://www.bcc.cuny.edu. Head: Ralph Rourke
Historical Museum - 1900
American hist, beaux arts archtitecture and sculpture 35678

Judaica Museum of the Hebrew Home for the Aged at Riverdale, 5961 Palisade Av, Bronx, NY 10471 - T: (718) 518-1787, Fax: (718) 581-1009, E-mail: khsmus@aol.com, Internet: http://www.hebrewhome.org/museum. Head: Karen S. Franklin
Folklore Museum / Religious Arts Museum - 1982
Judaica 35679

Lehman College Art Gallery, 250 Bedford Park Blvd W, Bronx, NY 10468-1589 - T: (718) 960-8731, Fax: (718) 960-8212, E-mail: susan@alpha.lehman.cuny.edu, Internet: http://math240.lehman.cuny.edu/art/galleryinfo.html. Head: Susan Hoeltzel
Fine Arts Museum / University Museum - 1985
Art 35680

Museum of Bronx History, Varian Park, 3266 Bainbridge Av at E 208th St, Bronx, NY 10467 - T: (718) 881-8900, Fax: (718) 881-4827, E-mail: DocHermalyn@bronxhistoricalsociety.org, Internet: http://www.bronxhistoricalsociety.org. Head: Dr. Gary D. Hermalyn
Local Museum - 1955
Local hist 35681

Museum of Migrating People, Harry S. Truman High School, 750 Baychester Av, Bronx, NY 10475 - T: (718) 904-5400
Local Museum - 1974 35682

North Wind Undersea Institute, 610 City Island Av, Bronx, NY 10464 - T: (718) 885-0701, Fax: (718) 885-1008, Internet: http://www.northwind.org. Head: Michael Sandlofer, Irene Sullivan
Natural History Museum - 1976
Marine hist 35683

Van Cortlandt House Museum, Van Cortlandt Park, Bronx, NY 10471 - T: (718) 543-3344, Fax: (718) 543-3315, E-mail: vancortlandthouse@juno.com. Head: Thomas B. Hynson Brown, Laura Carpenter Correa
Historical Museum - 1896
House built by Frederick Van Cortlandt 35684

Brookfield CT

Brookfield Craft Center, Rte 25, Brookfield, CT 06804 - T: (203) 775-4526, Fax: (203) 740-7815, E-mail: brkfldcrft@aol.com, Internet: http://www.craftweb.com/org/brookfld/. Head: John I. Russell
Decorative Arts Museum - 1954
Craft, old grist mill 35685

Brookfield VT

Historical Society of Brookfield Museum, Ridge Rd, Brookfield, VT 05036 - T: (802) 276-3959
Local Museum - 1933
Local hist 35686

Marvin Newton House, Ridge Rd, Brookfield, VT 05036 - T: (802) 276-3959
Local Museum - 1935
Historic house 35687

Brookings SD

Brookings Arts Council, 524 Fourth St, Brookings, SD 57006 - T: (605) 692-4177, Fax: (605) 692-8298, E-mail: arts@brookings.net, Internet: http://www.mjts.com/bac. Head: Nancy Hartenhoff
Fine Arts Museum / Folklore Museum - 1977
Cultural arts 35688

South Dakota Art Museum, Harvey Dunn St and Medary Av, Brookings, SD 57007-0999 - T: (605) 688-5423, Fax: (605) 688-4445, E-mail: sdsu_sdam@sdstate.edu, Internet: http://www.sdartmuseum.sdstate.edu. Head: M. Lynn Verschoor
Fine Arts Museum - 1969
Art 35689

State Agricultural Heritage Museum, South Dakota State University, 925 11th St, Brookings, SD 57007 - T: (605) 688-6226, Fax: (605) 688-6303, E-mail: sdsu_agmuseum@sdstate.edu, Internet: http://www.agmuseum.com. Head: John C. Awald
Agriculture Museum / University Museum - 1967
Agricultural hist 35690

Brookline MA

Brookline Historical Society Museum, 347 Harvard St, Brookline, MA 02146 - T: (617) 566-5747
Local Museum - 1901
Local history 35691

Frederick Law Olmsted Historic Site, 99 Warren St, Brookline, MA 02445 - T: (617) 566-1689, Fax: (617) 232-3964, E-mail: olmsted_archives@nps.gov, Internet: http://www.nps.gov/frla. Head: Myra Harrison
Historic Site - 1979
Home and office of Frederick Law Olmsted, landscape plans and drawings 35692

John Fitzgerald Kennedy House, 83 Beals St, Brookline, MA 02146 - T: (617) 566-7937, Fax: (617) 232-3964, E-mail: frla_kennedy_nhs@nps.gov, Internet: http://www.nps.gov/jofi. Head: Rolf Diamant
Historical Museum - 1969
Birthplace of John F. Kennedy 35693

Museum of Afro-American History, 138 Mountfork St, Brookline, MA 02446 - T: (617) 739-1200, Fax: (617) 739-1285, E-mail: tmckin1751@.aol.com, Internet: http://www.afroammuseum.org. Head: Sylvia Watts McKinney
Historical Museum - 1966
African American hist 35694

Museum of Transportation, 15 Newton St, Brookline, MA 02445 - T: (617) 522-6547, Fax: (617) 524-0170, Internet: http://www.mot.org. Head: Glenn S. Pare
Science&Tech Museum - 1952
Transport 35695

Brooklyn CT

New England Center for Contemporary Art, Rte 169, Brooklyn, CT 06234 - T: (860) 774-8899, Fax: (860) 779-9291, E-mail: museum@museum-necca.org, Internet: http://www.museum-necca.org. Head: Henry Riseman
Fine Arts Museum - 1975
Contemporary art 35696

Brooklyn NY

Brooklyn Children's Museum, 145 Brooklyn Av, Brooklyn, NY 11213 - T: (718) 735-4402, Fax: (718) 604-7442, E-mail: acanty@bchildmus.org, Internet: http://www.bchildmus.org. Head: Peggi Einhorn, Carol Enseki, Cheryl Bartholow, Beth Alberty, Paul Pearson
Special Museum - 1899 35697

Brooklyn Museum of Art, 200 Eastern Pkwy, Brooklyn, NY 11238-6052 - T: (718) 638-5000, Fax: (718) 638-3731, E-mail: bklynmus@echonyc.com, Internet: http://www.brooklynart.org. Head: Robert S. Rubin
Fine Arts Museum - 1823 35698

Harbor Defense Museum of New York City, Bldg 230, Fort Hamilton, Brooklyn, NY 11252-5701 - T: (718) 630-4349, Fax: (718) 630-4709
Military Museum - 1966 35699

The Kurdish Museum, 144 Underhill Av, Brooklyn, NY 11238 - T: (718) 783-7930, Fax: (718) 398-4365, E-mail: kurdishlib@aol.com. Head: Dr. Vera Beaudin Saeedpour
Ethnology Museum / Folklore Museum - 1988
Ethnology 35700

Lefferts Homestead, 95 Prospect Park W, Brooklyn, NY 11215 - T: (718) 965-8953, Fax: (718) 965-8972. Head: Vivienne Shaffer
Local Museum - 1918 35701

Marian and Religious Museum, 545 74th St, Brooklyn, NY 11209 - T: (718) 238-4113, Fax: (718) 238-4113. Head: Armand J. Williamson
Folklore Museum / Religious Arts Museum - 1978
Religious art and folk art 35702

New York Transit Museum, Boerum Pl and Schermerhorn St, Brooklyn, NY 11201, mail addr: 130 Livingston St, Brooklyn, NY 11201 - T: (718) 243-8601, Fax: (718) 522-2339, Internet: http://www.mta.nyc.us. Head: Gabrielle Shubert
Science&Tech Museum - 1976
Urban transportation 35703

Rotunda Gallery, 33 Clinton St, Brooklyn, NY 11201 - T: (718) 875-4047, Fax: (718) 488-0609, E-mail: rotunda@brooklynx.org, Internet: http://www.brooklynx.org/rotunda. Head: Janet Riker
Public Gallery - 1981 35704

Rubelle and Norman Schafler Gallery, 200 Willoughby Av, Brooklyn, NY 11205 - T: (718) 636-3517, Fax: (718) 636-3785, Internet: http://www.pratt.edu/exhibitions. Head: Eleanor Moretta
Fine Arts Museum / University Museum - 1967
Art 35705

Brooklyn OH

Brooklyn Historical Society Museum, 4442 Ridge Rd, Brooklyn, OH 44144-3353 - T: (216) 749-2804. Head: Barbara Stepic
Local Museum - 1970 35706

Brooklyn Park MN

Art Gallery, North Hennepin Community College, 7411 85th Ave N, Brooklyn Park, MN 55445 - T: (612) 424-0702, Fax: (612) 424-0929, Internet: http://www.nh.cc.mn.us. Head: Susan McDonald
Fine Arts Museum
Student works and local artists 35707

Brookneal VA

Red Hill-Patrick Henry National Memorial, 1250 Red Hill Rd, Brookneal, VA 24528 - T: (804) 376-2044, Fax: (804) 376-2647, E-mail: RedHill@lynchburg.net, Internet: http://www.redhill.org. Head: Dr. Jon Kukla
Historical Museum - 1944
Local hist 35708

Brooks Air Force Base TX

Edward H. White II Memorial Museum, 70 ABG/MU HSC AFMC, Brooks Air Force Base, TX 78235-5329 - T: (210) 536-2204, Fax: (210) 240-3224, E-mail: museum@brooks.af.mil. Head: Ulysses S. Rhodes
Science&Tech Museum / Historical Museum - 1966
Aeronautics 35709

Brookville IN

Franklin County Museum, 5th and Mill St, Brookville, IN 47012 - T: (317) 647-5182. Head: Mick Wilz
Local Museum - 1969
Local history, housed in a original Franklin County Seminary bldg 35710

Brookville NY

Hillwood Art Museum, C.W. Post Campus, Long Island University, Brookville, NY 11548 - T: (516) 299-4073, Fax: (516) 299-4180, E-mail: museum@raptor.liu.edu, Internet: http://www.liu.edu/hillwood.html. Head: Dr. David Steinberg, Barry Stern
Fine Arts Museum / University Museum - 1973
Precolumbian and African art, contemporary photography, prints 35711

Browning MT

Museum of the Plains Indian, Junction of Hwys 2 and 89 W, Browning, MT 59417 - T: (406) 338-2230, Fax: (406) 338-7404, E-mail: mpi@3rivers.net, Internet: http://www.iacb.doi.gov. Head: Meridith Z. Stanton
Folklore Museum - 1941
American Indian artefacts and crafts 35712

Scriver Museum of Montana Wildlife and Hall of Bronze, POB 172, Browning, MT 59417 - T: (406) 338-5425, Fax: (406) 338-5425
Natural History Museum - 1953 35713

Brownington VT

The Old Stone House Museum, 28 Old Stone House Rd, Brownington, VT 05860 - T: (802) 754-2022, E-mail: osh@together.net, Internet: http://homepages.together.net/. Head: Alfred W. Fuller, Tracy N. Martin
Local Museum - 1916
Local hist 35714

Browns Valley MN

Sam Brown Memorial Park, West Broadway, Browns Valley, MN 56219 - T: (320) 695-2110. Head: Shirley J. Ecker
Historical Museum - 1932
Log cabin of 1863, one room country school house 35715

Brownsville OR

Linn County Historical Museum and Moyer House, 101 Park Av, Brownsville, OR 97327 - T: (503) 466-3390, 446-3070, Fax: (541) 466-5312, E-mail: jmoyer@peak.org, Internet: http://lchm-friends.peak.org. Head: Brian Carrol
Local Museum / Folklore Museum - 1962
Local hist 35716

Brownsville TX

Brownsville Museum of Fine Art, 230 Neale Dr, Brownsville, TX 78520 - T: (956) 542-0941, Fax: (956) 542-7094. Head: Tina Garbo Bailey
Fine Arts Museum - 1935
Art 35717

Brownville NE

Brownville Historical Society Museum, Main St, Brownville, NE 68321 - T: (402) 825-6001
Local Museum - 1956 35718

Meriwether Lewis Dredge Museum, RR 1, Brownville State Recreation Area, Brownville, NE 68321 - T: (402) 825-3341
Local Museum - 1977 35719

Brownville NY

General Jacob Brown Mansion, 216 Brown Blvd, Brownville, NY 13615 - T: (315) 782-7650, Fax: (315) 786-1178. Head: Constance G. Hoard
Military Museum - 1978 35720

Brunswick GA

Hofwyl-Broadfield Plantation, 5556 US Hwy 17N, Brunswick, GA 31525 - T: (912) 264-7333, E-mail: hofwyl@darientel.net. Head: Bill Rivers
Agriculture Museum - 1974
Historic plantation 35721

Brunswick MD

Brunswick Railroad Museum, 40 W Potomac St, Brunswick, MD 21716 - T: (301) 834-7100, Internet: http://www.bhs.edu.rrmus.rrmus.html. Head: Lee B. Smith
Science&Tech Museum - 1974
Transportation 35722

Brunswick ME

Bowdoin College Museum of Art, Walker Art Bldg, 9400 College Station, Brunswick, ME 04011-8494 - T: (207) 725-3275, Fax: (207) 725-3762, E-mail: artmuseum@bowdoin.edu, Internet: http://www.bowdoin.edu/artmuseum. Head: Katy Kline
Fine Arts Museum / University Museum - 1811
Art 35723

The Peary-MacMillan Arctic Museum, Bowdoin College, 9500 College Stn, Brunswick, ME 04011-8495 - T: (207) 725-3416, 725-3062, Fax: (207) 725-3499, Internet: http://www.bowdoin.edu/dept/arctic. Head: Dr. Susan A. Kaplan
Ethnology Museum / University Museum - 1967
Ethnology, archaeology, natural history 35724

Pejepscot Historical Society Museum, 159 Park Row, Brunswick, ME 04011 - T: (207) 729-6606, Fax: (207) 729-6012, E-mail: pejepscot@curtislibrary.com, Internet: http://www.curtislibrary.com/pejepscot.htm. Head: Deborah A. Smith
Local Museum - 1888
Regional history 35725

Bryan TX

Brazos Valley Museum of Natural History, 3232 Briarcrest Dr, Bryan, TX 77802 - T: (409) 776-2195, Fax: (409) 774-0252, E-mail: bvmnh@myriad.net, Internet: http://bvmuseum.myriad.net. Head: Thomas F. Lynch
Natural History Museum - 1961
Natural hist 35726

Bryant Pond ME

Woodstock Historical Society Museum, 70 S Main St, Bryant Pond, ME 04219 - T: (207) 665-2450
Historical Museum - 1979
Local hist 35727

Bryn Athyn PA

Glencairn Museum, 1001 Cathedral Rd, Bryn Athyn, PA 19009-0757 - T: (215) 938-2600, Fax: (215) 914-2986, E-mail: dfcarey@newchurch.edu, Internet: http://www.glencairnmuseum.org. Head: Stephen H. Morley
Religious Arts Museum - 1878
History, religious art 35728

Bucksport ME

Bucksport Historical Museum, Main St, Bucksport, ME 04416 - T: (207) 567-3623. Head: Frances D. Beamis
Local Museum - 1964
Local history, Old Maine Central Railroad Station 35729

Bucyrus OH

Bucyrus Historical Society Museum, 202 S Walnut St, Bucyrus, OH 44820 - T: (419) 562-6386. Head: Dr. John K. Kurtz
Local Museum - 1969 35730

Buena Park CA

Buena Park Historical Society Museum, 6631 Beach Blvd, Buena Park, CA 90621 - T: (714) 562-3570
Local Museum - 1967 35731

The Printing Museum, POB 644a, Buena Park, CA 90622 - T: (714) 523-2070. Head: Mark Barbour
Science&Tech Museum - 1988
Typography 35732

Buffalo MN

Wright County Historical Museum, 2001 Hwy 25 N, Buffalo, MN 55313 - T: (763) 682-7323, Fax: (612) 682-6178
Local Museum - 1967
Regional history 35733

Buffalo NY

Albright-Knox Art Gallery, 1285 Elmwood Av, Buffalo, NY 14222 - T: (716) 882-8700, Fax: (716) 882-1958, E-mail: corlick@albrightknox.org, Internet: http://www.albrightknox.org. Head: Douglas G. Schultz
Fine Arts Museum - 1862
Painting, sculpture, photography, works on paper 35734

Benjamin and Dr. Edgar R. Cofeld Judaic Museum of Temple Beth Zion, 805 Delaware Av, Buffalo, NY 14209 - T: (716) 836-6565, Fax: (716) 831-1126, E-mail: tbz@webt.com, Internet: http://www.tbz.org. Head: Mortimer Spiller
Special Museum / Religious Arts Museum - 1981 35735

Buffalo and Erie County Historical Society Museum, 25 Nottingham Ct, Buffalo, NY 14216 - T: (716) 873-9644, Fax: (716) 873-8754, E-mail: bechs@buffnet.net, Internet: http://www.bechs.org. Head: Carl L. Bucki, William Siener, Walter Mayer
Local Museum - 1862 35736

Buffalo and Erie County Naval and Military Park, One Naval Park Cove, Buffalo, NY 14202 - T: (716) 847-1773, Fax: (716) 847-6405, E-mail: navalpark@ch.ci.buffalo.ny.us, Internet: http://www.buffalonavalpark.org. Head: Patrick J. Cunningham
Military Museum - 1979
Military hist 35737

Buffalo Museum of Science, 1020 Humboldt Pkwy, Buffalo, NY 14211 - T: (716) 896-5200 ext 308, Fax: (716) 897-6723, E-mail: dchesebrough@sciencebuff.org, Internet: http://www.buffalomuseumofscience.org
Natural History Museum - 1861 35738

Burchfield-Penney Art Center, Buffalo State College, 1300 Elmwood Av, Buffalo, NY 14222 - T: (716) 878-6011, Fax: (716) 878-6003, E-mail: burchfld@buffalostate.edu, Internet: http://www.burchfield-penney.org. Head: Ted Pietrzak, Nancy Weekly
Fine Arts Museum - 1966
Western New York art and craft, watercolors by Charles E. Burchfield 35739

Center for Exploratory and Perceptual Art, 617 Main St, Buffalo, NY 14203 - T: (716) 856-2717, Fax: (716) 270-0184, E-mail: cepa@aol.com, Internet: http://cepa.buffnet.com. Head: Lawrence F. Brose
Fine Arts Museum - 1974 35740

El Museo Francisco Oller y Diego Rivera, 91 Allen St, Buffalo, NY 14202 - T: (716) 884-9362
Fine Arts Museum 35741

Theodore Roosevelt Inaugural National Historic Site, 641 Delaware Av, Buffalo, NY 14202 - T: (716) 884-0095, Fax: (716) 884-0330, Internet: http://www.nps.gov/thri/. Head: Molly Quackenbush
Historical Museum - 1971
Buffalo Barracks, the site of the inauguration of Pres. Theodore Roosevelt in 1901 35742

University at Buffalo Art Gallery, 201A Center for the Arts, Buffalo, NY 14260-6000 - T: (716) 645-6912, Fax: (716) 645-6753, E-mail: ub-ag@acsu.buffalo.edu, Internet: http://www.artgallery.-buffalo.edu. Head: Al Harris
Fine Arts Museum / University Museum - 1994
Art 35743

Buford GA

Lanier Museum of Natural History, 2601 Buford Dam Rd, Buford, GA 30518 - T: (770) 932-4460, Fax: (770) 932-3055, E-mail: rappca@co.gwinnett.ga.us, Internet: http://member.grpa.org/gwinnett/
Natural History Museum - 1978
Botany, zoology, geology, paleontology 35744

Burfordville MO

Bollinger Mill State Historic Site, 113 Bollinger Mill Rd, Burfordville, MO 63739 - T: (573) 243-4591, Fax: (573) 243-5385
Open Air Museum / Local Museum - 1967 35745

Burlington IA

The Apple Trees Museum, 1616 Dill St, Burlington, IA 52601 - T: (319) 753-2449, E-mail: dmcohist@interl.net. Head: Marjorie Fitzsimmons
Historical Museum / Agriculture Museum - 1972
Charles E. Perkins mansion 35746

Art Guild of Burlington Gallery, Seventh and Washington, Burlington, IA 52601 - T: (319) 754-8069, Fax: (319) 754-4731, E-mail: arts4living@aol.com. Head: Burton Prugh, Lois Rigdon
Fine Arts Museum / Public Gallery - 1966 35747

Phelps House, 521 Columbia, Burlington, IA 52601 - T: (319) 753-5880, E-mail: dmcohist@interl.net. Head: Marjorie Fitzsimmons
Decorative Arts Museum - 1974
1851 Victorian mansion 35748

Burlington MA

Burlington Historical Museum, 106 Bedford St, Burlington, MA 01803 - T: (781) 270-1600, Fax: (781) 270-1608, E-mail: archives@burlmass.org, Internet: http://www.burlington.org/archives. Head: Joyce Fay
Local Museum / Historic Site - 1970
Historical and todays artifacts 35749

Burlington ME

Stewart M. Lord Memorial Museum, Burlington, ME 04448 - T: (207) 732-4121
Historical Museum / Folklore Museum - 1968
History , restored tavern, housing wagons, surry boat 35750

Burlington NC

Alamance Battleground, 5803 S NC Rte 62, Burlington, NC 27215 - T: (336) 227-4785, Fax: (336) 227-4787, E-mail: alamance@ncsl.dcr.state.nc.us, Internet: http://www.ah.dcr.state.nc.us/sections/hs/alamance. Head: Bryan Dalton
Open Air Museum / Military Museum - 1955 35751

Burlington NJ

Burlington County Historical Society Museum, 451 High St, Burlington, NJ 08016 - T: (609) 386-4773, Fax: (609) 386-4828, E-mail: bchsnj@earthlink.net. Head: Douglas E. Winterick
Historical Museum - 1915
Decorative arts, clocks, quilts, Delaware River Decoys 35752

Colonial Burlington Foundation, 213 Wood St, Burlington, NJ 08016 - T: (609) 239-2266, Fax: (609) 386-3415, E-mail: jacques@colorite-resins.com. Head: Gary E. Jacques
Local Museum - 1939 35753

Hoskins House, 202 High St, Burlington, NJ 08016 - T: (609) 386-3993, Fax: (609) 386-0214. Head: Rita Kloss
Local Museum / Folklore Museum - 1975
Local history 35754

Burlington VT

The Children's Discovery Museum of Vermont, 1 College St, Burlington, VT 05401 - T: (802) 864-1848, Fax: (802) 864-6832, E-mail: lcbsc@together.net, Internet: http://www.uvm.edu/~lcbsc/. Head: Betsy Rosenbluth
Special Museum - 1995
Children's museum 35755

Francis Colburn Gallery, University of Vermont, Art Department, Williams Hall, Burlington, VT 05405 - T: (802) 656-2014, Fax: (802) 656-2064
Fine Arts Museum / University Museum - 1975
Art 35756

Robert Hull Fleming Museum, University of Vermont, Colchester Av, Burlington, VT 05405-0064 - T: (802) 656-0750, Fax: (802) 656-8059, Internet: http://www.uvm.edu/~fleming. Head: Ann Porter
Fine Arts Museum / University Museum / Ethnology Museum - 1931
Art, anthropology 35757

Burnet TX

Fort Croghan Museum, 703 Buchanan Dr, Burnet, TX 78611 - T: (512) 756-8281, Fax: (512) 756-2548, E-mail: piejoy@tstar.net. Head: Neva Clark
Local Museum / Historic Site - 1957
Local hist 35758

Burns OR

Harney County Historical Museum, 18 W D St, Burns, OR 97720 - T: (503) 573-5618, Fax: (541) 573-5618
Local Museum - 1960 35759

Burr Oak IA

Laura Ingalls Wilder Museum, 3603 236th Av, Burr Oak, IA 52101 - T: (319) 735-5916, Fax: (319) 735-5916, Internet: http://bluffcountry.com/liwbo.htm. Head: Heidi Hotvedt
Natural History Museum / Special Museum - 1976 35760

Burton OH

Century Village, 14653 E Park St, Burton, OH 44021 - T: (216) 834-4012, Fax: (216) 834-4012. Head: George A. Chittle
Open Air Museum / Historical Museum - 1938 35761

Burwell NE

Fort Hartsuff, RR 1, Burwell, NE 68823 - T: (308) 346-4715, Fax: (308) 346-4715
Military Museum - 1874 35762

Bushnell FL

Dade Battlefield Historic State Park, 7200 County Rd 603, Bushnell, FL 33513 - T: (352) 793-4781, Fax: (352) 793-4230, E-mail: dbshs@sum.net, Internet: http://www.dep.state.fl.us/parks. Head: Barbara Roberts-Webster
Historic Site / Historical Museum - 1921
Site of a battle between Seminole and US soldiers on Dec. 28, 1835 35763

Butte MT

Butte Silver Bow Arts Chateau, 321 W Broadway, Butte, MT 59701 - T: (406) 723-7600, Fax: (406) 723-5083, E-mail: glenv@in-tch.com, Internet: http://www.artschateau.org. Head: Glenn Vodish
Fine Arts Museum - 1977
Contemporary regional art 35764

Copper King Mansion, 219 W Granite, Butte, MT 59701 - T: (406) 782-7580. Head: John Thompson
Fine Arts Museum / Decorative Arts Museum - 1966 35765

Mineral Museum, Montana Tech. of the University of Montana, 1300 W Park St, Butte, MT 59701-8997 - T: (406) 496-4414, Fax: (406) 496-4451, E-mail: dberg@mtech.edu, Internet: http://mbmgsun.mtech.edu. Head: Dr. Richard B. Berg
University Museum / Natural History Museum / Science&Tech Museum - 1900 35766

World Museum of Mining, West End of Park St, Butte, MT 59702 - T: (406) 723-7211, E-mail: gwalter@miningmuseum.org, Internet: http://www.miningmuseum.org. Head: Geraldine Walter
Science&Tech Museum - 1964 35767

Buzzards Bay MA

Captain Charles H. Hurley Library Museum, 101 Academy Dr, Buzzards Bay, MA 02532 - T: (508) 830-5000, 830-5035, Fax: (508) 830-5074, E-mail: mbosse@bridge.mma.mass.edu, Internet: http://www.mma.mass.edu/mma.html. Head: Maurice Bosse
Historical Museum - 1980
Maritime naval museum - library 35768

Byron NY

Byron Historical Museum, E Main St, Byron, NY 14422 - T: (716) 548-2252
Local Museum - 1967 35769

Cable WI

Cable Natural History Museum, County Hwy M and Randysek Rd, Cable, WI 54821 - T: (715) 798-3890, Fax: (715) 798-3828, E-mail: cnhm@win.bright.net. Head: Allison D. Slavick
Natural History Museum - 1968
Natural hist 35770

Cabot VT

Cabot Historical Society Museum, 193 McKinistry St, Cabot, VT 05647 - T: (802) 563-2558, 563-2547
Local Museum - 1966
Local hist 35771

Cadillac MI

Wexford County Historical Museum, 127 Beech St, Cadillac, MI 49601 - T: (231) 775-1717, Fax: (231) 775-0888
Local Museum - 1978
Local hist 35772

Cahokia IL

Cahokia Courthouse State Historic Site, 107 Elm St, Cahokia, IL 62206 - T: (618) 332-1782. Head: Molly McKenzie
Historical Museum - 1940
Residence build 1737 35773

Cairo IL

Magnolia Manor Museum, 2700 Washington Av, Cairo, IL 62914 - T: (618) 734-0201
Local Museum - 1952 35774

Caldwell ID

Kiwanis Van Slyke Museum Foundation, Caldwell Municipal Park, Grant and Kimball Sts, Caldwell, ID 83605 - T: (208) 459-2229. Head: Milton Roelofs
Local Museum / Agriculture Museum - 1958 35775

Rosenthal Gallery of Art, Albertson College of Idaho, 2112 Cleveland Blvd, Caldwell, ID 83605 - T: (208) 459-5321, Fax: (208) 454-2077, E-mail: gclassen@albertson.edu, Internet: http://www.acofi.edu/art/galleries/rosenthal.htm. Head: Garth Claassen
Fine Arts Museum / University Museum - 1891
Art 35776

Caldwell NJ

Grover Cleveland Birthplace, 207 Bloomfield Av, Caldwell, NJ 07006 - T: (973) 226-1810
Local Museum - 1913 35777

Visceglia Art Gallery, Caldwell College, 9 Ryerson Av, Caldwell, NJ 07006 - T: (973) 618-3457, Internet: http://www.caldwell.edu/news/art_index. Head: Kendall Baker
Fine Arts Museum - 1970 35778

Caldwell TX

Burleson County Historical Museum, Burleson County Courthouse, Caldwell, TX 77836 - T: (409) 567-4128, 567-3218
Local Museum - 1968
Local hist 35779

Caledonia NY

Big Springs Museum, Main St, Caledonia, NY 14423 - T: (716) 538-6996
Local Museum - 1936 35780

Calhoun GA

New Echota, 1211 Chatsworth Hwy NE, Calhoun, GA 30701 - T: (706) 624-1321, Fax: (706) 624-1323, E-mail: n_echoda@innerx.net. Head: David Gomez
Historic Site / Open Air Museum
1825 capital town of Cherokee Nation 35781

Calistoga CA

Sharpsteen Museum, 1311 Washington St, Calistoga, CA 94515 - T: (707) 942-5911, Fax: (707) 942-6325, E-mail: sdblomq@aol.com, Internet: http://www.sharpsteen-museum.org. Head: Shirley Blomquist
Local Museum - 1978 35782

Calumet MI

Coppertown U.S.A., 109 Red Jacket Rd, Calumet, MI 49913 - T: (906) 337-4354, Internet: http://www.uppermichigan.com/coppertown. Head: Richard Dana
Science&Tech Museum - 1973
Restored Mining Co. Complex, former Calumet and Hecla Mining Co 35783

Cambridge MA

Arthur M. Sackler Museum, 485 Broadway, Cambridge, MA 02138 - T: (617) 495-2397
Fine Arts Museum 35784

Botanical Museum of Harvard University, 26 Oxford St, Cambridge, MA 02138 - T: (617) 495-2326, Fax: (617) 495-5667
University Museum / Natural History Museum - 1858
Botany 35785

Cambridge Historical Museum, 159 Brattle St, Cambridge, MA 02138 - T: (617) 547-4252, Fax: (617) 661-1623. Head: W. Wyllis Bibbins, Aurore Eaton
Local Museum - 1905
Local history 35786

Harvard Museum of Natural History, 24-26 Oxford St, Cambridge, MA 02138 - T: (617) 496-8204, Fax: (617) 496-8206, E-mail: hmnh@oeb.harvard.edu, Internet: http://www.hmnh.harvard.edu. Head: Joshua Basseches
University Museum / Natural History Museum - 1995
University's three natural history institutions: Botanical Museum, Museum of Comparative Zoology, Mineralogical Museum 35787

Harvard University Art Museums, Fogg Art Museum, Arthur M. Sackler Museum, Busch-Reisinger Museum, 32 Quincy St, Cambridge, MA 02138 - T: (617) 495-9400, Internet: http://www.artmuseums.harvard.edu. Head: James Cuno, Elizabeth Moors Cabot, John Moors Cabot
Fine Arts Museum / University Museum - 1895
Art 35788

Harvard University Semitic Museum, 6 Divinity Av, Cambridge, MA 02138 - T: (617) 495-4631, Fax: (617) 496-8904, E-mail: davis4@fas.harvard.edu, Internet: http://www.fas.harvard.edu/~semitic/. Head: Prof. Lawrence Stager
University Museum / Archaeological Museum - 1889
Ancient and medieval Near East archaeology 35789

Longfellow National Historic Site, 105 Brattle St, Cambridge, MA 02138 - T: (617) 876-4491, Fax: (617) 876-6014, E-mail: FRLA_longfellow@nps.gov, Internet: http://www.nps.gov/long
Historical Museum - 1972
Home of Henry Wadsworth Longfellow, headqaurters of George Washington 1775-1776 - library 35790

Margaret Hutchinson Compton Gallery, 77 Massachusetts Av, Bldg 10, Cambridge, MA 02139-4307 - T: (617) 253-4444, Fax: (617) 253-8994, Internet: http://web.mit.edu/museum. Head: Jane Pickering
Fine Arts Museum / Science&Tech Museum - 1978
Technology 35791

Mineralogical Museum of Harvard University, 24 Oxford St, Cambridge, MA 02138 - T: (617) 495-4758, Fax: (617) 495-8839. Head: Prof. Michael B. McElroy
Natural History Museum - 1784
Mineralogy 35792

MIT-List Visual Arts Center, 20 Ames St, Wiesner Bldg E15-109, Cambridge, MA 02139 - T: (617) 253-4680, 253-4400, Fax: (617) 258-7265, E-mail: freilach@mit.edu, Internet: http://web.mit.edu/lvac/www. Head: Jane Farver
Fine Arts Museum / University Museum - 1963
Art gallery, visual arts 35793

The MIT Museum, 265 Massachusetts Av, Cambridge, MA 02139-4307 - T: (617) 253-4444, Fax: (617) 253-8994, E-mail: museum@mit.edu, Internet: http://web.mit.edu/museum. Head: Jane Pickering
University Museum / Science&Tech Museum - 1971
Science, technology, architecture 35794

Peabody Museum of Archaeology and Ethnology, 11 Divinity Av, Cambridge, MA 02138 - T: (617) 496-1027, Fax: (617) 495-7535, Internet: http://www.peabody.harvard.edu. Head: Dr. Rubie Watson
University Museum / Ethnology Museum / Archaeological Museum - 1866
Anthropology, archaeology, ethnology 35795

Cambridge MD

Dorchester County Historical Society Museum, 902 LaGrange Av, Cambridge, MD 21613 - T: (410) 228-7953, Fax: (410) 221-0603, E-mail: merchant@shore.intercom.net. Head: Albert F. Schuchardt
Local Museum - 1953 35796

Cambridge NE

Cambridge Museum, 612 Penn St, Cambridge, NE 69022 - T: (308) 697-4385
Fine Arts Museum / Local Museum - 1938
Local history 35797

Cambridge OH

Cambridge Glass Museum, 812 Jefferson Av, Cambridge, OH 43725 - T: (614) 432-3045. Head: Harold D. Bennett, Dorthy E. Bennett
Decorative Arts Museum - 1973 35798

Guernsey County Museum, 218 N Eighth St, Cambridge, OH 43725 - T: (740) 439-5884
Local Museum - 1964
Regional hist, county hall of fame, military 35799

Cambridge City IN

Huddleston Farmhouse Inn Museum, 838 National Rd, Mt Auburn, Cambridge City, IN 47327 - T: (765) 478-3172, Fax: (765) 478-3410, E-mail: cdeiber@infocom.com, Internet: http:www.historiclandmarks.org. Head: J. Reid Williamson, Fred M. Holycross
Historical Museum / Agriculture Museum - 1977
Federal style brick, 3-story farmhouse 35800

Camden AR

McCollum-Chidester House Museum, 926 Washington St, NW, Camden, AR 71701 - T: (870) 836-9243, 836-4580
Historical Museum - 1847
Stage Coach House, Union general quartered here during Battle at Poison Springs, furniture and personal effects of family (1863-1963) - Leake-Ingham library 35801

Camden NJ

Camden County Historical Society Museum, Park Blvd and Euclid Av, Camden, NJ 08103 - T: (856) 964-3333, Fax: (856) 964-0378, Internet: http://www.cchsnj.org. Head: John R. Seitten
Local Museum - 1899 35802

Stedman Art Gallery, Rutgers State University of New Jersey, Camden, NJ 08102 - T: (856) 225-6245, Fax: (609) 225-6597, E-mail: arts@camdenrutgers.edu, Internet: http://seca.camden-rutgers.edu. Head: Virginia Oberlin Steel
Fine Arts Museum - 1975
Modern and Contemporary art 35803

Walt Whitman House, 328 Mickle Blvd, Camden, NJ 08103 - T: (856) 964-5383, E-mail: whitmanshs@snip.net. Head: Leo Blake
Historical Museum - 1946 35804

Camden NY

Carriage House Museum, 2 N Park St, Camden, NY 13316 - T: (315) 245-4652. Head: Elaine Norton
Historical Museum - 1975 35805

Camden SC

Camden Archives and Museum, 1314 Broad St, Camden, SC 29020-3535 - T: (803) 425-6050, Fax: (803) 424-4053, Internet: http://www.mindspring.com/~camdenarchives/index.html. Head: Agnes Corbett
Local Museum - 1973
Local hist 35806

Fine Arts Center of Kershaw County, 810 Lyttleton St, Camden, SC 29020 - T: (803) 425-7676, Fax: (803) 425-7679, E-mail: fackc@infoave.net. Head: Susan F. Harper
Fine Arts Museum - 1976
Art 35807

Historic Camden Revolutionary War Site, 222 Broad St, Camden, SC 29020 - T: (803) 432-9841, Fax: (803) 432-3815. Head: Joanna Craig
Local Museum - 1967
Local hist 35808

Kershaw County Historical Society Museum, 811 Fair St, Camden, SC 29020 - T: (803) 425-1123, E-mail: kchistory@mindspring.com, Internet: http://go.to/~kchistory. Head: Kathleen P. Stahl
Local Museum - 1954
Local hist 35809

Cameron TX

Milam County Historical Museum, Main and Fannin Sts, Cameron, TX 76520 - T: (254) 697-4770, 697-8963, Fax: (254) 697-4433, E-mail: milamco@hot1.net. Head: Charles King
Local Museum - 1977
Local hist 35810

Cameron WI

Barron County Historical Society's Pioneer Village Museum, 1 1/2 mile west of Cameron on Museum Rd, Cameron, WI 54822 - T: (715) 458-2841. Head: Maxine Wiesner
Local Museum - 1960
State and local hist 35811

Camp Douglas WI

Wisconsin National Guard Memorial Library and Museum, 101 Independence Dr, Camp Douglas, WI 54618 - T: (608) 427-1280, Fax: (608) 427-1399. Head: Eric Lent
Military Museum - 1984 35812

Campbell CA

Ainsley House, 300 Grant St, Campbell, CA 95008 - T: (408) 866-2118, Fax: (408) 866-2795, Internet: http://www.ci.campbell.ca.us. Head: Robert Pedretti
Historical Museum - 1964 35813

Campbell Historical Museum, 300 Grant St, Campbell, CA 95008 - T: (408) 866-2119, Fax: (408) 866-2795, Internet: http://www.ci.campbell.ca.us. Head: Robert Pedretti
Historical Museum - 1964 35814

Canaan NY

Canaan Historical Society Museum, Warner's Crossing Rd, Canaan, NY 12029 - T: (518) 781-4801
Local Museum - 1963 35815

Canajoharie NY

Canajoharie Library and Art Gallery, 2 Erie Blvd, Canajoharie, NY 13317 - T: (518) 673-2314, Fax: (518) 673-5243, E-mail: can_traha@sals.edu, Internet: http://www.clag.org. Head: Eric Trahan
Fine Arts Museum / Library with Exhibitions - 1929 35816

Canal Fulton OH

Canal Fulton Heritage Society Museum, 103 Tuscarawas St, Canal Fulton, OH 44614. Head: Edward Shuman
Local Museum - 1968 35817

Canandaigua NY

Granger Homestead Society Museum, 295 N Main St, Canandaigua, NY 14424 - T: (716) 394-1472, Fax: (716) 394-6958, E-mail: ghomestead@aol, Internet: http://www.ggw.org/freenet/s/granger/granger.htm. Head: Saralinda Hooker
Local Museum - 1946 35818

Ontario County Historical Society Museum, 55 N Main St, Canandaigua, NY 14424 - T: (716) 394-4975, Fax: (716) 394-9351, E-mail: ochs@eznet.net, Internet: http://www.ochs.org. Head: Edward Varno
Historical Museum - 1902 35819

Cannon Falls MN

Cannon Falls Area Historical Museum, 208 W Mill St, Cannon Falls, MN 55009 - T: (507) 263-4080. Head: John Otto, Heidi Holmes Helgren
Local Museum - 1979
Regional history, town fire hall 35820

Canon City CO

Canon City Municipal Museum, 612 Royal Gorge Blvd, Canon City, CO 81212 - T: (719) 269-9018, Fax: (719) 249-9017. Head: Pol Saint-Paul
Local Museum - 1928
Local history 35821

Canterbury CT

Prudence Crandall Museum, Rts 14 and 169, Canterbury Green, Canterbury, CT 06331-0058 - T: (860) 546-9916, Fax: (860) 546-7803
Historical Museum - 1984
New England life in 19th c, abolitionism, education 35822

Canterbury NH

Canterbury Shaker Village, 288 Shaker Rd, Canterbury, NH 03224 - T: (603) 783-9511, Fax: (603) 783-9152, E-mail: shakers@totalnetnh.net, Internet: http://www.shakers.org
Open Air Museum / Local Museum - 1969 35823

Canton MA

Canton Historical Museum, 1400 Washington St, Canton, MA 02021 - T: (781) 828-8537. Head: James Roche
Local Museum - 1893
Local history 35824

Canton NY

Pierrepont Museum, 868 State Hwy 68, Canton, NY 13617 - T: (315) 386-8311, Fax: (315) 379-0415
Decorative Arts Museum - 1977 35825

Richard F. Brush Art Gallery and Permanent Collection, Saint Lawrence University, Romoda Dr, Canton, NY 13617 - T: (315) 229-5174, Fax: (315) 229-7445, E-mail: ctedford@stlawu.edu, Internet: http://www.stlawu.edu/gallery. Head: Catherine L. Tedford
Fine Arts Museum / University Museum - 1967 35826

Silas Wright Jr. Historic House, 3 E Main St, Canton, NY 13617 - T: (315) 386-8133, Fax: (315) 386-8134, E-mail: slcha@northnet.org, Internet: http://www.slcha.org. Head: Trent Trulock
Local Museum - 1947
archive 35827

Canton OH

Canton Museum of Art, 1001 Market Av N, Canton, OH 44702 - T: (330) 453-7666, Fax: (330) 453-1032, E-mail: staff@cantonart.orgom, Internet: http:/www.cantonart.org. Head: Jack Hank, M.J. Albacete
Fine Arts Museum - 1935 35828

McKinley Museum and McKinley National Memorial, 800 McKinley Monument Dr NW, Canton, OH 44708 - T: (330) 455-7043, Fax: (330) 455-1137, E-mail: mmuseum@neo.rr.com, Internet: http://www.mckinleymuseum.org. Head: Joyce Yut, Jane Mahoney, Rosemary Anderson, Jane Mahoney
Historical Museum / Science&Tech Museum / Natural History Museum - 1946 35829

National Football Museum, 2121 George Halas Dr NW, Canton, OH 44708 - T: (330) 456-8207, Fax: (330) 456-8175, Internet: http://www.profootballhof.com. Head: John Bankert
Special Museum - 1963 35830

Canyon TX

Panhandle-Plains Historical Museum, 2401 Fourth Av, Canyon, TX 79015 - T: (806) 651-2244, Fax: (806) 651-2250, E-mail: museum@wtamu.edu, Internet: http://www.wtamu.edu/museum/home. Head: Walter R. Davis
Local Museum - 1921
Local hist 35831

Cape Coral FL

The Children's Science Center, 2915 NE Pine Island Rd, Cape Coral, FL 33909 - T: (941) 997-0012, Fax: (941) 997-7215, E-mail: scicentr@juno.com, Internet: http://www.cyberstreet.com/csc. Head: Nancy Glickman
Science&Tech Museum - 1989 35832

Cape Girardeau MO

Southeast Missouri State University Museum, 1 University Pl, Cape Girardeau, MO 63701 - T: (573) 651-2260, Fax: (573) 651-2200, E-mail: museum@semovm.semo.edu. Head: Jennifer L. Strayer
University Museum - 1976 35833

Cape May NJ

Mid-Atlantic Center for the Arts, 1048 Washington St, Cape May, NJ 08204-0340 - T: (609) 884-5404, Fax: (609) 884-2006, E-mail: mac4arts@capemaymac.org, Internet: http://www.capemaymac.org. Head: B. Michael Zuckerman
Fine Arts Museum - 1970 35834

Cape May Court House NJ

Cape May County Historical Museum, 504 Rte 9 N, Cape May Court House, NJ 08210 - T: (609) 465-3535, Fax: (609) 465-4274, E-mail: CELang@aol.com, Internet: http://www.beachcomber.com. Head: James Waltz
Local Museum - 1927 35835

Leaming's Run Garden and Colonial Farm, 1845 Rte 9 N, Cape May Court House, NJ 08210 - T: (609) 465-5871, Internet: http://njsouth.com/index-leamingsrun.htm. Head: Gregg Aprill
Agriculture Museum - 1978
Agriculture 35836

Cape Vincent NY

Cape Vincent Historical Museum, James St, Cape Vincent, NY 13618 - T: (315) 654-4400. Head: J. Thompson, Mary Hamilton, Peter Margrey
Local Museum - 1968 35837

Capitola Village CA

Capitola Historical Museum, 410 Capitola Av, Capitola Village, CA 95010 - T: (408) 464-0322, Fax: (408) 479-8879. Head: Carolyn Swift
Historical Museum - 1967 35838

Carbondale IL

University Museum, Southern Illinois University, 2469 Faner Hall N, Carbondale, IL 62901-4508 - T: (618) 453-5388, Fax: (618) 453-7409, E-mail: museum@siu.edu, Internet: http://www.museum.siu.edu/. Head: Lorilee C. Huffman
University Museum / Local Museum - 1869
University history 35839

Caribou ME

Nylander Museum, 657Main St, Caribou, ME 04736 - T: (207) 493-4209. Head: Jeremiah Leary
Natural History Museum - 1938
Natural history 35840

Carlisle PA

Hamilton Library and Two Mile House, 21 N Pitt St, Carlisle, PA 17013 - T: (717) 249-7610, Fax: (717) 258-9332, E-mail: info@historicalsociety.com, Internet: http://www.historicalsociety.com. Head: Linda F. Witmer
Historical Museum / Library with Exhibitions - 1874 35841

United States Army Military History Institute Museum, 22 Ashburn Dr, Carlisle, PA 17013-5008 - T: (717) 245-3971, Fax: (717) 245-3711, E-mail: usamhi@carlisle.army.mil, Internet: http://carlisle-www.army.mil/usamhi. Head: Edwin M. Perry
Military Museum - 1967 35842

Carlsbad CA

Carlsbad Children's Museum → Children's Discovery Museum of North County

Children's Discovery Museum of North County, 300 Carlsbad Village Dr, Carlsbad, CA 92008 - T: (760) 720-0737, Fax: (760) 720-0336, E-mail: vaavoom@aol.com, Internet: http://www.museumfor-children.org. Head: Catherine Boyle
Special Museum - 1992 35843

Carlsbad NM

Carlsbad Museum and Art Center, 418 W Fox St, Carlsbad, NM 88220 - T: (505) 887-0276, Fax: (505) 885-8809. Head: Verginia Dodier
Fine Arts Museum / Archaeological Museum / Historical Museum / Science&Tech Museum - 1931 35844

Carmel CA

Mission San Carlos Borromeo Del Rio Carmelo, 3080 Rio Rd, Carmel, CA 93923 - T: (831) 624-3600, Fax: (831) 624-0658, Internet: http://www.carmelmission.org
Historical Museum / Religious Arts Museum - 1770 35845

Carmi IL

White County Historical Museums, Ratcliff Inn, L.Haas Store, Matsel Cabin, Robinson-Stewart House, 203 N Church St, Carmi, IL 62821 - T: (618) 382-8425, E-mail: cbconly@midwest.net, Internet: http://www.rootsweb.com/~ilwcohs. Head: Jim Pumphrey
Local Museum - 1957
Local history 35846

Carpinteria CA

Carpinteria Valley Historical Society Museum, 956 Maple Av, Carpinteria, CA 93013 - T: (805) 684-3112, Fax: (805) 684-4721. Head: Bradley R. Miles, David W. Griggs
Historical Museum - 1959 35847

Carrollton MS

Merrill Museum, Rte 1, Carrollton, MS 38917 - T: (601) 237-9254. Head: Kay Slocum
Local Museum - 1961
Local history 35848

Carrollton OH

McCook House, Civil War Museum, Public Sq, Carrollton, OH 44615 - T: (330) 627-3345, E-mail: ohswww@winslo.ohio.gov, Internet: http://www.ohiohistory.org/places/mcookhse/. Head: John Wadsworth
Historical Museum - 1963 35849

Carson CA

University Art Gallery, CSU Dominguez Hills, 1000 E Victoria St, Carson, CA 90747 - T: (310) 243-3334, Fax: (310) 217-6967, E-mail: kzimmerer@csudh.edu. Head: Kathy Zimmerer
University Museum / Fine Arts Museum - 1978 35850

Carson City NV

Bowers Mansion, 4005 US 395 N, Carson City, NV 89704 - T: (775) 849-0201, Fax: (775) 849-9568
Historical Museum - 1946 35851

Nevada State Museum, 600 N Carson St, Carson City, NV 89701 - T: (702) 687-4811, Fax: (702) 687-4168, Internet: http://www.clan.lib.nv.us/docs/museums/st/stmus.htm. Head: Douglas Sutherland
Historical Museum / Natural History Museum - 1939 35852

Stewart Indian Cultural Center, 1329 Stanford Dr, Carson City, NV 89701 - T: (702) 882-1808
Folklore Museum / Ethnology Museum 35853

Cartersville GA

Etowah Indian Mounds Historical Site, 813 Indian Mounds Rd, SW, Cartersville, GA 30120 - T: (770) 387-3747, Fax: (770) 387-3972, E-mail: etowahl@innerx.net. Head: Elizabeth Bell
Ethnology Museum / Archaeological Museum - 1953
Indian, archaeology 35854

The History Center, 13 N Wall St, Cartersville, GA 30120 - T: (770) 382-3818, Fax: (770) 382-0288, Internet: http://www.etowah.org. Head: Michele Rodgers
Historical Museum - 1987
Local hist 35855

Roselawn Museum, 224 W Cherokee Av, Cartersville, GA 30120 - T: (770) 387-5162. Head: Steven Ellis
Religious Arts Museum - 1973
Victorian mansion, former home of evangelist Samuel Porter Jones 35856

Carthage IL

Hancock County Historical Museum, Courthouse, Carthage, IL 62321. Head: Don Parker
Local Museum - 1968
1906-8 Stone Courthouse, on historical site in Carthage 35857

Carthage MO

Powers Museum, 1617 Oak St, Carthage, MO 64836 - T: (417) 358-2667, E-mail: pmuseum@ecarthage.com, Internet: http://www.powersmuseum.com. Head: Michele Hansford
Local Museum - 1982
Local hist 35858

Casa Grande AZ

Casa Grande History Museum, 110 W Florence Blvd, Casa Grande, AZ 85222 - T: (520) 836-2223, Fax: (520) 836-5065, E-mail: cgvhs@hotmail.com. Head: Gloria A. Smith
Local Museum - 1964
Local history - library 35859

Cashmere WA

Chelan County Historical Museum, 600 Cotlets Way, Cashmere, WA 98815 - T: (509) 782-3230, Fax: (509) 782-8905, E-mail: cchspvm@aol.com. Head: Bill Rietveldt
Local Museum - 1956
Local hist 35860

Casper WY

Fort Caspar Museum, 4001 Fort Caspar Rd, Casper, WY 82604 - T: (307) 235-8462, Fax: (307) 235-8464, E-mail: ftcaspr@trib.com, Internet: http://www.fortcasparwyoming.com. Head: Richard L. Young
Military Museum - 1936
Military hist 35861

Nicolaysen Art Museum, 400 East Collins Dr, Casper, WY 82601 - T: (307) 235-5247, Fax: (307) 235-0923, E-mail: nic_art@trib.com, Internet: http://www.thenic.org. Head: Joe Ellis
Fine Arts Museum - 1967
Art 35862

Cassville WI

Stonefield Historic Site, 12195 County Rd V V, Cassville, WI 53806 - T: (608) 725-5210, Fax: (608) 725-5919, E-mail: stonefld@pcll.net. Head: James Temmer
Agriculture Museum / Open Air Museum - 1952
Agriculture 35863

Castalian Springs TN

Historic Cragfont, 200 Cragfront Rd, Castalian Springs, TN 37031 - T: (615) 452-7070, Internet: http://www.srlab.net/cragfort/
Local Museum - 1958
Historic house, home of General James Winchester 35864

Castile NY

William Pryor Letchworth Museum, 1 Letchworth State Park, Castile, NY 14427 - T: (716) 493-3617, Fax: (716) 493-5272. Head: Brian Scriven
Natural History Museum - 1913 35865

Castine ME

Castine Scientific Society Museum, Perkins St, Castine, ME 04421 - T: (207) 326-8545, Fax: (207) 326-8545. Head: Norman Doudiet
Natural History Museum - 1921
Science 35866

Castleton VT

Castleton Historical Society Museum, The Higley Homestead, Main St, Castleton, VT 05735-0219 - T: (802) 468-5523. Head: John Rehlen
Local Museum - 1973
Local hist 35867

Catasaugua PA

George Taylor House, Lehigh and Poplar Sts, Catasaugua, PA 18032 - T: (610) 435-4664, Fax: (610) 435-9812. Head: Robert M. McGovern, Andree M. Mey
Local Museum - 1904 35868

Cathlamet WA

Wahkiakum County Historical Museum, 65 River St, Cathlamet, WA 98612 - T: (360) 795-3954. Head: Ralph Keyser
Local Museum - 1956
Local hist 35869

Cattaraugus NY

Cattaraugus Area Historical Center, 23 Main St, Cattaraugus, NY 14719 - T: (716) 257-3312
Local Museum - 1955 35870

Cavalier ND

Pioneer Heritage Center, 13571 Hwy 5, Cavalier, ND 58220 - T: (701) 265-4561, Fax: (701) 265-4443, E-mail: isp@state.nd.us. Head: Alice Olson
Local Museum - 1989
Local hist, settlement story (1870-1920) 35871

Cazenovia NY

Cazenovia College Chapman Art Center Gallery, Cazenovia College, Cazenovia, NY 13035 - T: (315) 655-7273, Fax: (315) 655-2190, E-mail: jaistars@cazcollege.edu, Internet: http://www.cazcollege.edu. Head: John Aistars
Fine Arts Museum / University Museum - 1978 35872

Lorenzo State Historic Site, 17 Rippleton Rd, Cazenovia, NY 13035 - T: (315) 655-3200, Fax: (315) 655-4304, E-mail: lincklaen@juno.com. Head: Russell A. Grills
Historic Site - 1968 35873

Cedar City UT

Braithwaite Fine Arts Gallery, Southern Utah University, Cedar City, UT 84720 - T: (435) 586-5432, Fax: (435) 865-8012, E-mail: museums@suu.edu, Internet: http://www.suu.edu/pva/artgallery. Head: Lydia Johnson
Fine Arts Museum / University Museum - 1976
Art 35874

Iron Mission Museum, 635 N Main St, Cedar City, UT 84720 - T: (435) 586-9290, Fax: (435) 8665-6830, E-mail: nrdpr.ironmiss@state.ut.us. Head: Todd Prince
Historical Museum - 1973
Pioneer hist 35875

Cedar Falls IA

Cedar Falls Historical Museum, 303 Franklin St, Cedar Falls, IA 50613 - T: (319) 266-5149, 277-8817, Fax: (319) 268-1812, E-mail: cfhistsoc@cfu.cybernet.net. Head: Floyd Winter, Brian C. Collins
Local Museum - 1968
Local history 35876

Gallery of Art, University of Northern Iowa, Kamerick Art Bldg, Cedar Falls, IA 50614-0362 - T: (319) 273-2077, Fax: (319) 273-2731. Head: Rachel Flint
Fine Arts Museum / University Museum - 1978
Art gallery 35877

James and Meryl Hearst Center for the Arts, 304 W Seerley Blvd, Cedar Falls, IA 50613 - T: (319) 273-8641, Fax: (319) 273-8659, E-mail: huberm@ci.cedar-falls.ia.us, Internet: http://www.hearstcenter.com. Head: Mary Huber
Fine Arts Museum / Open Air Museum - 1989
Arts - sculpture garden 35878

University of Northern Iowa Museum, 3219 Hudson Rd, Cedar Falls, IA 50614-0199 - T: (319) 273-2188, Fax: (319) 273-6924, E-mail: doris.mitchell@uni.edu, Internet: http://www.uni.edu/museum. Head: Sue Grosboll
University Museum - 1892 35879

Cedar Key FL

Cedar Key State Museum, 12231 SW 166 Court, Cedar Key, FL 32625 - T: (352) 543-5350, 543-5567, Fax: (352) 543-6315, E-mail: cksma@svic.net. Head: Virginia R. Wetherell
Local Museum / Natural History Museum - 1962 35880

Cedar Lake IN

Lake of the Red Cedars Museum, 7808 W 138th St, Constitution Av, Cedar Lake, IN 46303 - T: (219) 374-6157. Head: Therese Gasparo, Anne Zimmerman
Local Museum - 1977
Local history 35881

Cedar Rapids IA

Brucemore, 2160 Linden Dr SE, Cedar Rapids, IA 52403 - T: (319) 362-7375, Fax: (319) 362-9481, E-mail: mail@brucemore.org, Internet: http://www.brucemore.org. Head: Peggy Whitworth
Historical Museum / Historic Site - 1981
Historic Site, culture, housed in 21-room Queen Anne-style mansion 35882

Cedar Rapids Museum of Art, 410 Third Av, SE, Cedar Rapids, IA 52401 - T: (319) 366-7503, Fax: (319) 366-4111, E-mail: crma@earthlink.net, Internet: http://www.crma.org. Head: Terence Pitts
Fine Arts Museum - 1905
Art 35883

Iowa Masonic Library and Museum, 813 1st Av, SE, Cedar Rapids, IA 52402 - T: (319) 365-1438, Fax: (319) 365-1439, E-mail: Grand-Lodge-IA@msn.com, Internet: http://www.freemasonry.org/IA
Local Museum - 1845
Local history - library 35884

Linn County Historical Society Museum, 615 First Av, Cedar Rapids, IA 52401-2022 - T: (319) 362-1501, Fax: (319) 362-6790, Internet: http://www.historycenter.org. Head: Linda Langston
Local Museum - 1969 35885

National Czech and Slovak Museum, 30 16th Av SW, Cedar Rapids, IA 52404 - T: (319) 362-8500, Fax: (319) 363-2209, Internet: http://www.ncsml.org
Special Museum - 1974
Ethnic museum, 1880-1900 restored Czech immigrant home 35886

Science Station Museum, 427 First St, SE, Cedar Rapids, IA 52401 - T: (319) 366-0968, Fax: (319) 366-4590, E-mail: scistat@netins.net, Internet: http://www.netins.net/showcase/scistat. Head: Teel Salaun, Ganesh Ganpat
Science&Tech Museum - 1986
Science, housed in a fire station bldg 35887

Cedarburg WI

Ozaukee Art Center, W 62 N 718 Riveredge Dr, Cedarburg, WI 53012 - T: (414) 377-8230. Head: Lon Horton, Paul Yank
Fine Arts Museum - 1971
Art 35888

Cedartown GA

Polk County Historical Museum, 311 N College St, Cedartown, GA 30125 - T: (404) 748-0073. Head: Nancy Alford
Local Museum - 1974
Regional history 35889

Celina OH

Mercer County Historical Museum, 130 E Market, Celina, OH 45822-0512 - T: (419) 586-6065, E-mail: histalig@bright.net. Head: Joyce L. Alig
Historical Museum - 1959 35890

Centennial WY

Nici Self Museum, Hwy 130, 28 miles west of Laramie, Centennial, WY 82055 - T: (307) 742-7158, Fax: (307) 634-4955. Head: Jim Chase
Local Museum - 1974
Local hist 35891

Center Sandwich NH

Sandwich Historical Society Museum, 4 Maple St, Center Sandwich, NH 03227 - T: (603) 284-6269, Fax: (603) 284-6269, E-mail: shistory@worldpath.net, Internet: http://sandwichnh.com/history. Head: D. Bruce Montgomery, Rick Fabian
Local Museum / Fine Arts Museum - 1917
Paintings, furniture 35892

Centerport NY

Suffolk County Vanderbilt Museum, 180 Little Neck Rd, Centerport, NY 11721 - T: (516) 854-5562, Fax: (516) 854-5527 and 5591, E-mail: vanderbilt@webscope.com, Internet: http://www.webscope.com/vanderbilt. Head: J. Lance Mallamo, Edward Quaranta
Natural History Museum - 1950 35893

Central City CO

Central City Opera House Museum, 200 Eureka St, Central City, CO 80293 - T: (303) 292-6500, Fax: (303) 292-4958, E-mail: ccopera@mho.net, Internet: http://www.artstozoo.org/ccopera. Head: P.G. Pearce
Performing Arts Museum - 1932
Theater museum, housed in Teller House Hotel Museum 35894

Gilpin History Museum, 228 E High St, Central City, CO 80427-0247 - T: (303) 582-5283, Fax: (303) 582-5283, E-mail: gchs@ecentral.com, Internet: http://www.coloradomuseums.org/gilpin.htm. Head: Linda Jones, James J. Prochaska
Local Museum - 1971
Regional history 35895

Chadds Ford PA

Brandywine Battlefield, US Rte 1, Chadds Ford, PA 19317 - T: (610) 459-3342, Fax: (610) 459-9586, Internet: http://www.ushistory.org/brandywine. Head: Toni E. Collins
Military Museum / Historic Site / Open Air Museum - 1947 35896

Brandywine River Museum, US Rte 1 at PA Rte 100, Chadds Ford, PA 19317 - T: (610) 388-2700, Fax: (610) 388-1197, E-mail: inquiries@brandwyne.org, Internet: http://www.brandywinemuseum.org.. Head: James H. Duff
Fine Arts Museum - 1971 35897

Christian C. Sanderson Museum, Rte 100 N, Chadds Ford, PA 19317 - T: (610) 388-6545. Head: Thomas R. Thompson
Local Museum - 1967 35898

Chadron NE

Chadron State College Main Gallery, 1000 Main St, Chadron, NE 69337 - T: (308) 432-6326, Fax: (308) 432-3561, E-mail: rbird@csc.edu. Head: Richard Bird
Fine Arts Museum - 1967 35899

Dawes County Historical Society Museum, 341 Country Club Rd, Chadron, NE 69337 - T: (308) 432-4999, 432-2309. Head: Dean Carpenter, Belvadine Lecher
Local Museum - 1964
Local history 35900

Eleanor Barbour Cook Museum of Geology, Chadron State College, 1000 Main St, Chadron, NE 69337 - T: (308) 432-6293, Fax: (308) 432-6434, E-mail: mleite@csc1.csc.edu, Internet: http://www.csc.edu. Head: Prof. Michael Leite
University Museum / Natural History Museum - 1939 35901

Museum of the Fur Trade, 6321 E Hwy 20, Chadron, NE 69337 - T: (308) 432-3843, Fax: (308) 432-5943, E-mail: museum@furtrade.org, Internet: http://www.furtrade.org. Head: William R. Hanson, Gail DeBuse Potter
Historical Museum - 1955 35902

Chagrin Falls OH

Chagrin Falls Historical Society Museum, 21 Walnut St, Chagrin Falls, OH 44022 - T: (440) 247-4695
Local Museum - 1949 35903

Chamberlain SD

Akta Lakota Museum, Saint Joseph's Indian School, Chamberlain, SD 57325 - T: (605) 734-3452, Fax: (605) 734-3388. Head: Dixie Thompson
Historical Museum / Folklore Museum - 1991 35904

Chambersburg PA

Old Brown's Mill School, 1051 S Coldbrook Av, Chambersburg, PA 17201 - T: (717) 787-3602, Fax: (717) 783-1073
Local Museum - 1956 35905

Champaign IL

Champaign County Historical Museum, 102 E University Av, Champaign, IL 61820 - T: (217) 356-1010, E-mail: director@champaignmuseum.org, Internet: http://www.champaignmuseum.org. Head: Paul Idlem
Historical Museum - 1972
Local history 35906

Krannert Art Museum, University of Illinois, 500 E Peabody Dr, Champaign, IL 61820 - T: (217) 333-1860, Fax: (217) 333-0883, E-mail: schumach@uiuc.edu, Internet: http://www.art.uiuc.edu/kam/. Head: Dr. Josef Helfenstein
Fine Arts Museum - 1961
Art 35907

Parkland College Art Gallery, 2400 W Bradley, Champaign, IL 61821-1899 - T: (217) 351-2485, Fax: (217) 373-3899, Internet: http://www.parkland.cc.il.us/gallery. Head: Denise Seif
Fine Arts Museum - 1980 35908

Chandler AZ

Chandler Museum, 178 E Commonwealth Av, Chandler, AZ 85225 - T: (602) 786-2842
Local Museum - 1969
Local history 35909

Chandler OK

Lincoln County Historical Society Museum of Pioneer History, 717 Manvel Av, Chandler, OK 74834 - T: (405) 258-2425
Local Museum - 1954 35910

Chanute KS

Martin and Osa Johnson Safari Museum, 111 N Lincoln Av, Chanute, KS 66720 - T: (316) 431-2730, Fax: (316) 431-3848, E-mail: osajohns@safarimuseum.com, Internet: http://www.safarimuseum.com. Head: Conrad G. Froehlich
Special Museum - 1961
Biography, ethnography, film/photo, Santa Fe Train Depot 35911

Chapel Hill NC

Ackland Art Museum, University of North Carolina, Columbia and Franklin Sts, Chapel Hill, NC 27599 - T: (919) 966-5736, Fax: (919) 966-1400, E-mail: ackland@email.unc.edu, Internet: http://www.ackland.org. Head: Gerald D. Bolas
Fine Arts Museum - 1958 35912

Chappaqua NY

Horace Greeley House, 100 King St, Chappaqua, NY 10514 - T: (914) 238-4666, Fax: (914) 238-1296. Head: Albert Hutin, Betsy Towl
Local Museum - 1966 35913

Chappell Hill TX

Chappell Hill Historical Society Museum, 9220 Poplar St, Chappell Hill, TX 77426 - T: (979) 836-6033, Fax: (979) 836-7438, E-mail: chmuseum@alpha1.net, Internet: http://www.chappell-hillmuseum.org. Head: Ladonna Vest
Local Museum / Historical Museum - 1964
Local hist 35914

Charles City IA

Floyd County Historical Museum, 500 Gilbert St, Charles City, IA 50616-2738 - T: (641) 228-1099, Fax: (641) 228-1157, E-mail: fchs@fiai.net, Internet: http://www.floydcountymuseum.org. Head: Robert Baron, Frank B. McKinney
Local Museum / Historical Museum - 1961
Local history 35915

Charles City VA

Berkeley Plantation, 12602 Harrison Landing Rd, Charles City, VA 23030 - T: (804) 829-6018, Fax: (804) 829-6757, Internet: http://www.berkeley-plantation.com. Head: Grace Eggleston Jamieson
Local Museum - 1619
Historic house 35916

Sherwood Forest Plantation, 14501 John Tyler Memorial Hwy, Charles City, VA 23030 - T: (804) 829-5377, Fax: (804) 829-2947, E-mail: ktylerl@sherwoodforest.org, Internet: http://www.sherwoodforest.org. Head: Frances P.B. Tyler, Kay Montgomery Tyler
Historic Site - 1975
Historic house, home of President John Tyler 35917

Shirley Plantation, 501 Shirley Plantation Rd, Charles City, VA 23030 - T: (804) 829-5121, Fax: (804) 829-6322, E-mail: information@shirleyplantation.com, Internet: http://www.shirleyplantation.com. Head: Charles Hill Carter
Local Museum - 1613
Historic house 35918

Charleston IL

Tarble Arts Center, Eastern Illinois University, S 9th St at Cleveland Av, Charleston, IL 61920-3099 - T: (217) 581-2787, Fax: (217) 581-7138, E-mail: cfmw@eiu.edu, Internet: http://www.eiu.edu/~tarble. Head: Michael Watts
Fine Arts Museum / University Museum - 1982
Art 35919

Charleston MO

Mississippi County Historical Society Museum, 403 N Main, Charleston, MO 63834 - T: (314) 683-4348. Head: Patrick Rolwing
Historical Museum - 1966 35920

Charleston SC

American Military Museum, 44 John St, Charleston, SC 29403 - T: (803) 723-9620, E-mail: ammilmus@aol.com. Head: George E. Meagher
Military Museum - 1987
Military hist 35921

Avery Research Center for African American History and Culture, 125 Bull St, College of Charleston, Charleston, SC 29424 - T: (843) 953-7609, Fax: (843) 953-7607, Internet: http://www.cofc.edu/~avery.rsc. Head: W. Marvin Dulaney, Curtis J. Franks
Historical Museum - 1985
History 35922

Best Friend of Charleston Museum, 456 King St, Charleston, SC 29403 - T: (843) 973-7269
Science&Tech Museum - 1968
Railroad 35923

Charles Towne Landing 1670, 1500 Old Town Rd, Charleston, SC 29407 - T: (843) 852-4200, Fax: (803) 852-4205, E-mail: - charles_towne_landing_sp@prt.state.sc.us, Internet: http://www.southcarolinaparks.com. Head: Ron Fischer
Historic Site / Historical Museum - 1970
1670 site of the first permanent English settlement in South Carolina 35924

The Charleston Museum, 360 Meeting St, Charleston, SC 29403-6297 - T: (803) 722-2996, Fax: (843) 722-1784, Internet: http://www.charlestonmuseum.com. Head: Dr. John R. Brumgardt
Local Museum - 1773
Local hist, ceramics, decorative art, furniture, glass - library 35925

The Citadel Archives and Museum, The Military College of South Carolina, 171 Moultrie St, Charleston, SC 29409 - T: (843) 953-6846, Fax: (843) 953-6956, E-mail: yatesj@citadel.edu, Internet: http://www.citadel.edu/archivesandmuseum. Head: Jane M. Yates
Historical Museum - 1842
History 35926

City Hall Council Chamber Gallery, 80 Broad St, Charleston, SC 29401 - T: (843) 724-3799, 577-6970, Fax: (843) 720-3827. Head: Joseph P. Riley
Fine Arts Museum / Historical Museum - 1818
Art, history 35927

Drayton Hall, 3380 Ashley River Rd, Hwy 61, Charleston, SC 29414 - T: (843) 769-2600, Fax: (803) 766-0878, E-mail: dhmail@draytonhall.org, Internet: http://www.draytonhall.org. Head: George W. McDaniel
Historic Site - 1974
Historic house 35928

Elizabeth O'Neill Verner Studio Museum, 38 Tradd St, Charleston, SC 29401 - T: (843) 722-4246, Fax: (843) 722-1763, E-mail: info@vernergallery.com, Internet: http://www.vernergallery.com. Head: Lese Corrigan
Fine Arts Museum - 1970
Works by E. O'Neill Verner 35929

Gibbes Museum of Art, 135 Meeting St, Charleston, SC 29401 - T: (843) 722-2706, Fax: (843) 720-1682, E-mail: gibbes@charleston.net, Internet: http://www.gibbes.com. Head: Paul C. Figueroa
Fine Arts Museum - 1858
Portraits, Japanese woodblock prints, contemporary American art - library 35930

Halsey Gallery, College of Charleston, School of the Arts, 66 George St, Charleston, SC 29424-0001 - T: (843) 953-5680, Fax: (843) 953-7890, E-mail: sloanm@cofc.edu. Head: Mark Sloan
Fine Arts Museum / University Museum - 1978 35931

Historic Charleston Foundation, 40 E Bay, Charleston, SC 29401 - T: (843) 723-1623, Fax: (843) 577-2067, Internet: http://historiccharleston.org. Head: Jon H. Poston, Judy Middleton, Cornelia H. Pelzer
Local Museum - 1947
Local hist 35932

John Rivers Communications Museum, 58 George St, College of Charleston, Charleston, SC 29424 - T: (843) 953-5810, E-mail: evansc@cofc.edu. Head: Cathy Evans
Science&Tech Museum / University Museum - 1989
Communications 35933

Macaulay Museum of Dental History, Medical University of South Carolina, 175 Ashley Av, Charleston, SC 29425 - T: (843) 792-2288, Fax: (843) 792-8619
Special Museum - 1975
Dental hist 35934

Magnolia Plantation, 3550 Ashley River Rd, Charleston, SC 29414 - T: (843) 571-1266, Fax: (843) 571-5346, E-mail: tours@magnoliaplantation.com, Internet: http://www.magnoliaplantation.com. Head: J. Drayton Hastie
Fine Arts Museum / Local Museum / Natural History Museum / Historic Site - 1676
Historic house 35935

Middleton Place Foundation, 4300 Ashley River Rd, Charleston, SC 29414 - T: (843) 556-6020, Fax: (843) 766-4460, Internet: http://www.middletonplace.org. Head: Charles H.P. Duell
Decorative Arts Museum / Historical Museum - 1974
Historic House: restored 1755 structure 35936

Old Exchange and Provost Dungeon, 122 East Bay St, Charleston, SC 29401 - T: (843) 727-2165, Fax: (843) 727-2163, E-mail: oldexchange@infoave.net, Internet: http://www.oldexchange.com. Head: Frances McCarthy
Historic Site - 1976
Local hist 35937

Powder Magazine, 79 Cumberland St, Charleston, SC 29401 - T: (843) 723-1623, Fax: (843) 577-2067, Internet: http://www.historiccharleston.org. Head: Jane Hanahan, Carter Hudgins
Local Museum - 1713
Local hist 35938

South Carolina Historical Society Museum, 100 Meeting St, Charleston, SC 29401 - T: (843) 723-3225, Fax: (843) 723-8584, E-mail: info@schistory.org, Internet: http://www.schistory.org. Head: David O. Percy
Historical Museum - 1855
Regional history, Robert Mills Bldg 35939

Charleston WV

Sunrise Museum, 746 Myrtle Rd, Charleston, WV 25314 - T: (304) 344-8035, Fax: (304) 344-8038, E-mail: sunrise@citynet.net, Internet: http://www.sunrisemuseum.org
Fine Arts Museum - 1961
Art 35940

West Virginia State Museum, Capitol Complex, Charleston, WV 25305 - T: (304) 558-0220, Fax: (304) 558-2779. Head: Lakin Ray Cook, Fredrick Armstrong, Sharon Mullins, S. Lilly, Susan Pierce, Nancy Herholdt, Gerry Reilly, Susan Yoho
Local Museum - 1905
Local hist 35941

Charlestown MA

Bunker Hill Museum, 43 Monument Sq, Charlestown, MA 02129 - T: (617) 242-1843. Head: Kathleen Whelan
Historical Museum - 1975
Bunker Hill Monument grounds 35942

Charlestown NH

Old Fort Number 4 Associates, Springfield Rd, Rte 11, Charlestown, NH 03603 - T: (603) 826-5700, Fax: (603) 826-3368, E-mail: fortat4@cyberportal.net, Internet: http://www.fort.at.4.com. Head: James D. Parillo
Local Museum - 1948 35943

Charlotte NC

Afro-American Cultural Center, 401 N Myers St, Charlotte, NC 28202 - T: (704) 374-1565, Fax: (704) 374-9273. Head: Cynthia Lewis Schaal
Folklore Museum - 1974
African American culture 35944

Carolinas Historic Aviation Museum, 4108 Airport Dr, Charlotte, NC 28208 - T: (704) 359-8442, Fax: (704) 359-8442, E-mail: chacboss@aol.com. Head: Floyd S. Wilson
Science&Tech Museum - 1991
Aviation 35945

Charlotte Museum of History and Hezekiah Alexander Homesite, 3500 Shamrock Dr, Charlotte, NC 28215 - T: (704) 568-1774, Fax: (704) 566-1817, E-mail: info@charlottemuseum.org, Internet: http://www.charlottemuseum.org. Head: William P. Massey
Local Museum - 1976 35946

Discovery Place, 301 N Tryon St, Charlotte, NC 28202 - T: (704) 372-6261, Fax: (704) 337-2670, Internet: http://www.discoveryplace.org. Head: Freda H. Nicholson
Natural History Museum / Science&Tech Museum - 1981 35947

Mint Museum of Art, 2730 Randolph Rd, Charlotte, NC 28207 - T: (704) 337-2000, Fax: (704) 337-2101, E-mail: pbusher@mintmuseum.org, Internet: http://www.mintmuseum.org. Head: Charles Mo, Harry Creemers, Carolyn Mints, Cheryl Palmer
Fine Arts Museum - 1933 35948

Mint Museum of Craft and Design, 220 N Tryon St, Charlotte, NC 28202 - T: (704) 337-2000, Fax: (704) 337-2101, E-mail: pbusher@mintmuseum.org, Internet: http://www.mintmuseum.org. Head: Mark Leach
Decorative Arts Museum - 1998 35949

Museum of the New South, 324 North College St, Charlotte, NC 28202 - T: (704) 333-1887, Fax: (704) 333-1896. Head: Emily F. Zimmern
Historical Museum - 1991 35950

Nature Museum, 1658 Sterling Rd, Charlotte, NC 28209 - T: (704) 372-6261, Fax: (704) 372-8540, Internet: http://www.discoveryplace.org. Head: Freda H. Nicholson
Natural History Museum - 1947 35951

Charlottesville VA

Ash Lawn-Highland, College of William and Mary, 1000 James Monroe Pkwy, Charlottesville, VA 22902 - T: (804) 293-9539, Fax: (804) 293-8000, E-mail: ashlawnjm@aol.com, Internet: http://avenue.org/ashlawn. Head: Carolyn C. Holmes
Decorative Arts Museum / Historic Site - 1930
Historic house 35952

Bayly Art Museum of the University of Virginia, Rugby Rd, Charlottesville, VA 22904-4119 - T: (804) 924-3592, Fax: (804) 924-6321, E-mail: cjh6r@virginia.edu, Internet: http://www.virginia.edu/~bayly/. Head: Jill Hartz
Fine Arts Museum / University Museum - 1935
Art 35953

Children's Health Museum, Primary Care Center, Lee St and Park Pl, Charlottesville, VA 22908 - T: (804) 924-1593, Fax: (804) 982-4379, E-mail: epv4p@virginia.edu, Internet: http://nsc.virginia.edu/medcntr/health-museum. Head: Ellen Vaughan
Historical Museum - 1982
Children's health 35954

Historic Michie Tavern, 683 Thomas Jefferson Pkwy, Rte 53, Charlottesville, VA 22902 - T: (804) 977-1234, Fax: (804) 296-7203, E-mail: info@michietavern.com, Internet: http://www.michietavern.com
Local Museum - 1928
Historic house 35955

The Rotunda, University of Virginia, Charlottesville, VA 22903 - T: (804) 924-7969, 924-1019, Fax: (804) 924-1364, Internet: http://www.virginia.edu/~urelat/Tours/rotunda. Head: Carolyn Laquatra
University Museum / Local Museum - 1819
Historic buildings, site of Thomas Jefferson's original academical village 35956

Second Street Gallery, 201 Second St, Charlottesville, VA 22902 - T: (804) 977-7284, Fax: (804) 979-9793, E-mail: ssg@cstone.net, Internet: http://www.avenue.org/ssg. Head: Leah Stoddard
Fine Arts Museum - 1973
Contemporary art 35957

The Virginia Discovery Museum, 524 E Main St, Charlottesville, VA 22902 - T: (804) 977-1025, Fax: (804) 977-9681, E-mail: vdm@cstone.net, Internet: http://www.vadm.org. Head: Peppy G. Linden
Special Museum - 1981
Childrens' Museum 35958

Chase City VA

MacCallum More Museum, 603 Hudgins St, Chase City, VA 23924 - T: (804) 372-0502, 372-3120, Fax: (804) 372-3483. Head: Gay Butler, Brenda Arriaga
Ethnology Museum - 1991
Anthropology 35959

Chatsworth GA

Vann House, 82 Hwy 225N, Spring Place, Chatsworth, GA 30705 - T: (706) 695-2598, Fax: (706) 517-4255, E-mail: vannhouse@alltel.net. Head: Marcia Kendrick
Historical Museum - 1952 35960

Chattanooga TN

Chattanooga African-American Museum, 200 E Martin Luther King Blvd, Chattanooga, TN 37403 - T: (423) 267-8658, Fax: (423) 267-1076, E-mail: caami@bellsouth.net, Internet: http://www.caamhistory.com. Head: Vilma S. Fields
Historical Museum - 1983 35961

Chattanooga Regional History Museum, 400 Chestnut St, Chattanooga, TN 37402 - T: (423) 265-3247, Fax: (423) 266-9280. Head: Norman O. Burns
Local Museum - 1978
Regional hist 35962

Cress Gallery of Art, c/o University of Tennessee at Chattanooga, Dept. of Art, Fine Arts Center, 615 McCallie Av, Chattanooga, TN 37403 - T: (423) 755-4178, Fax: (423) 755-5249, E-mail: kim-renz@utc.edu, Internet: http://www.utc.edu/finearts. Head: Ruth Grover
Fine Arts Museum / University Museum - 1952
Graphics, paintings, student's works 35963

Houston Museum of Decorative Arts, 201 High St, Chattanooga, TN 37403 - T: (423) 267-7176. Head: Amy H. Frierson
Decorative Arts Museum - 1949
American decorative arts 1750-1930 35964

Hunter Museum of American Art, 10 Bluff View, Chattanooga, TN 37403-1197 - T: (423) 267-0968, Fax: (423) 267-9844, Internet: http://www.huntermuseum.org. Head: Robert A. Kret
Fine Arts Museum - 1952
American paintings, photography, prints, sculpture, glass 35965

Siskin Museum of Religious and Ceremonial Art, 1 Siskin Plaza, Chattanooga, TN 37403 - T: (423) 634-1700, Fax: (423) 634-1717
Religious Arts Museum - 1950
Religious art 35966

Tennessee Valley Railroad Museum, 4119 Cromwell Rd, Chattanooga, TN 37421 - T: (423) 894-8028, Fax: (423) 894-8029, E-mail: info@tvrail.com, Internet: http://www.tvrail.com. Head: Robert M. Soule
Science&Tech Museum - 1961
Railroad 35967

Chazy NY

Alice T. Miner Colonial Collection, 9618 Main St, Chazy, NY 12921 - T: (518) 846-7336, Fax: (518) 846-8771, E-mail: minermuseum@westelcom.com. Head: Joan T. Burke, Frederick G. Smith
Local Museum - 1924 35968

Chehalis WA

Lewis County Historical Museum, 599 NW Front Way, Chehalis, WA 98532 - T: (360) 748-0831, Fax: (360) 740-5646, E-mail: lchm@myhome.net, Internet: http://www.lewiscountymuseum.org. Head: Barbara Laughton
Local Museum - 1979
Local hist 35969

Chelmsford MA

Chelmsford Historical Museum, 40 Byam Rd, Chelmsford, MA 01824 - T: (978) 256-2311
Local Museum - 1930
Local history, housed in Barrett-Byam homestead 35970

Chelsea MI

Gerald E. Eddy Geology Center, 17030 Bush Rd, Chelsea, MI 48118 - T: (734) 475-3170, Fax: (734) 475-6421, E-mail: eddy.geoctr@juno.com, Internet: http://www.dnr.state.mi.us
Natural History Museum - 1976
Geology 35971

Cheraw SC

Cheraw Lyceum Museum, 200 Market St, Cheraw, SC 29520 - T: (843) 537-8425, Fax: (843) 537-8407, E-mail: townofcherawtour@mindspring.com, Internet: http://www.cheraw.com. Head: J. William Taylor
Local Museum - 1962
Local hist 35972

Cherokee IA

Joseph A. Tallman Museum, Mental Health Institute, 1205 W Cedar Loop, Cherokee, IA 51012 - T: (712) 225-2594, Fax: (712) 225-6969, E-mail: larmstrl@dhs.state.IA.us. Head: Dr. Tom Deiker
Historical Museum - 1961
Psychiatry 35973

Sanford Museum, 117 E Willow St, Cherokee, IA 51012 - T: (712) 225-3922, E-mail: sanford@cherokee.k12.ia.us, Internet: http://www.whs.cherokee.K12.ia.us/mainfolder/sanford/sanhome.htm. Head: Linda Burkhart
Local Museum - 1941
General museum - planetarium 35974

Cherokee NC

Mountain Farm Museum, 1194 Newfound Gap Rd, Cherokee, NC 28719 - T: (828) 497-1900
Agriculture Museum - 1945 35975

Museum of the Cherokee Indian, Hwy 441, N Drama Rd, Cherokee, NC 28719 - T: (828) 497-3481, Fax: (828) 497-4985. Head: Ken Blankenship
Historical Museum / Ethnology Museum - 1948 35976

Cherry Valley CA

Edward Dean Museum of Decorative Arts, 9401 Oak Glen Rd, Cherry Valley, CA 92223 - T: (909) 845-2626, Fax: (909) 845-2628. Head: Belinda McLaughlin
Decorative Arts Museum - 1958 35977

Cherry Valley NY

Cherry Valley Museum, 49 Main St, Cherry Valley, NY 13320 - T: (607) 264-3303. Head: James Johnson
Local Museum - 1958 35978

Cherryville NC

C. Grier Beam Truck Museum, 117 N Mountain St, Cherryville, NC 28021 - T: (704) 445-9010
Science&Tech Museum - 1982 35979

Chesnee SC

Cowpens National Battlefield, POB 308, Chesnee, SC 29323 - T: (864) 461-2828, Fax: (864) 461-7077, E-mail: cowp-information@nps.gov, Internet: http://www.nps.gov/cowp/
Historic Site / Military Museum - 1933
Military hist, site of the 1781 Battle of Cowpens 35980

Chester MT

Liberty County Museum, Second St E and Madison, Chester, MT 59522 - T: (406) 759-5256. Head: Shirley Lybeck
Local Museum - 1969 35981

Liberty Village Arts Center and Gallery, 410 Main St, Chester, MT 59522 - T: (406) 759-5652, Fax: (406) 759-5652. Head: Christi Lakey
Folklore Museum - 1976
Paintings, quilts by local artists 35982

Chester PA

Widener University Art Collection and Gallery, 14 and Chestnut Sts, Chester, PA 19013 - T: (610) 499-1189, Fax: (610) 499-4425, E-mail: rebecca.m.warda@widener.edu, Internet: http://www.widener.edu/campuslife.edu. Head: Rebecca M. Warda
Fine Arts Museum / University Museum - 1970 35983

Chester SC

Chester County Museum, 107 McAliley St, Chester, SC 29706 - T: (803) 385-2330, 581-4354. Head: Gary Roberts
Historical Museum - 1959
Local hist 35984

Chester VT

Chester Art Guild, The Green, Main St, Chester, VT 05143 - T: (802) 875-3767. Head: Doris Ingram
Fine Arts Museum - 1960
Art 35985

Chesterfield MA

Edwards Memorial Museum, 3 North Rd, Chesterfield, MA 01012 - T: (413) 296-4054
Folklore Museum - 1950 35986

Chesterfield MO

River Hills Park Museum, 800 Guy Park Dr, Chesterfield, MO 63005 - T: (314) 458-3813, Fax: (314) 458-9105. Head: George Hosack
Natural History Museum - 1972 35987

Thornhill Historic Site and 19th Century Village, 15185 Olive Blvd, Chesterfield, MO 63017-1805 - T: (314) 532-7298, Fax: (314) 532-0604, Internet: http://www.st-louiscountyparks.com. Head: Jim Foley
Local Museum - 1968
Local hist 35988

Chesterfield VA

Chesterfield County Museum, Chesterfield Courthouse Sq, Chesterfield, VA 23832 - T: (804) 777-9663, Fax: (804) 777-9643, E-mail: farmerdp@co.chesterfield.va.us. Head: Dennis Farmer
Local Museum - 1961
Local hist 35989

Chestnut Hill MA

Longyear Museum, 1125 Boylston St, Chestnut Hill, MA 02467 - T: (617) 278-9000, Fax: (617) 218-9003, E-mail: letters@longyear.org, Internet: http://www.longyear.org. Head: John Baehrend, Stephen R. Howard
Historical Museum / Religious Arts Museum - 1923
History 35990

McMullen Museum of Art, Boston Collage, Devlin Hall 108, Chestnut Hill, MA 02467 - T: (617) 552-8587, Fax: (617) 552-8577, E-mail: netzer@bc.edu, Internet: http://www.bc.edu/artmuseum. Head: Dr. Nancy Netzer
Fine Arts Museum / Public Gallery / University Museum - 1986
Art 35991

Chetopa KS

Chetopa Historical Museum, 419 Maple St, Chetopa, KS 67336 - T: (316) 236-7121. Head: Fannie Bassett
Local Museum - 1881
Local history 35992

Cheyenne OK

Black Kettle Museum, Intersection of US 283 and State Hwy 47, Cheyenne, OK 73628 - T: (580) 497-3929, E-mail: bkmus@ok-hstory.mus.ok.us
Local Museum - 1958 35993

Cheyenne WY

Cheyenne Frontier Days Old West Museum, 4610 N Carey Av, Cheyenne, WY 82001 - T: (307) 778-7290, Fax: (307) 778-7288, Internet: http://www.oldwestmuseum.org. Head: Wayne Hansent
Local Museum - 1978 35994

Historic Governors' Mansion, 300 E 21st St, Cheyenne, WY 82001 - T: (307) 777-7878, Fax: (307) 635-7077, E-mail: sphs@state.wy.us, Internet: http://commerce.state.wy.us/sphs. Head: Bill Gentle
Local Museum - 1904
Historic building 35995

Wyoming Arts Council Gallery, 2320 Capitol Av, Cheyenne, WY 82002 - T: (307) 777-7742, Fax: (307) 777-5499, E-mail: lfranc@missc.state.wy.us, Internet: http://www.commerce.state.wy.us/cr/arts. Head: John G. Coe
Fine Arts Museum - 1976
Art 35996

Wyoming State Museum, Barrett Bldg, 2301 Central Av, Cheyenne, WY 82002 - T: (307) 777-7022, Fax: (307) 777-5375, E-mail: wsm@missc.state.wy.us, Internet: http://commerce.state.wy.us/cr/wsm/index.htm. Head: Marie Wilson-McKee
Historical Museum - 1895
State hist 35997

Chicago IL

A.R.C. Gallery, 1040 W Huron, Chicago, IL 60622 - T: (312) 733-2787, Fax: (312) 733-2787, Internet: http://www.icsp.net/arc. Head: Aviva Kramer
Public Gallery - 1973 35998

Art Gallery in Chicago, Northern Illinois University Art Gallery in Chicago, 215 W Superior, Chicago, IL 60610 - T: (312) 642-6010, Fax: (312) 642-9635, E-mail: julie@xsite.net, Internet: http://www.vpa.niv.edu/museum. Head: Julie Charmelo
Fine Arts Museum / University Museum - 1984 35999

The Art Institute of Chicago, 111 S Michigan Av, Chicago, IL 60603-6110 - T: (312) 443-3600, Fax: (312) 443-0849, Internet: http://www.artic.edu. Head: James N. Wood
Fine Arts Museum - 1879
Architecture, paintings, drawings, prints, photos, decorative art, art from America, Asia, Europe - Ryerson and Burnham libraries, art school 36000

Artemisia Gallery, 700 N Carpenter, Chicago, IL 60622 - T: (312) 226-7323, Fax: (312) 226-7756, E-mail: artemisi@enteract.com, Internet: http://www.artemisia.org. Head: Marji Vecchio
Public Gallery - 1973 36001

Balzekas Museum of Lithuanian Culture, 6500 S Pulaski Rd, Chicago, IL 60629 - T: (773) 582-6500, Fax: (773) 582-5133, E-mail: editor@lithuanian-museum.org. Head: Stanley Balzekas, Robert Balzekas, Edward Mankus, Val Martis, Karile Vaitkute
Historical Museum / Folklore Museum / Fine Arts Museum - 1966
Ethnology, folklore, numismatics, folk art - library, archive 36002

Charnley-Persky House Museum, 1365 N Astor St, Chicago, IL 60610-2144 - T: (312) 573-1365, Fax: (312) 573-1141, E-mail: psaliga@sah.org, Internet: http://www.sah.org. Head: Christopher Mead, Pauline Saliga
Local Museum - 1998
Local hist 36003

Chicago Architecture Foundation, 224 S Michigan Av, Ste 368, Chicago, IL 60604-2501 - T: (312) 922-3432 ext 224, Fax: (312) 922-2607, E-mail: losmond@architecture.org, Internet: http://www.architecture.org. Head: Lynn Osmond
Fine Arts Museum - 1966
Architecture 36004

The Chicago Athenaeum - Museum of Architecture and Design, 307 N Michigan Av, Chicago, IL 60601 - T: (312) 372-1083, Fax: (312) 372-1085, Internet: http://www.chi-athenaeum.org/. Head: Christian K. Narkiewicz Laine
Fine Arts Museum - 1988
Architecture and design 36005

Chicago Children's Museum, 700 E Grand Av, Navy Pier, Chicago, IL 60611 - T: (312) 527-1000, Fax: (312) 527-9082, Internet: http://www.chichildrensmuseum.org
Special Museum - 1982 36006

Chicago Cultural Center, 78 E Washington St, Chicago, IL 60602 - T: (312) 744-6630, Fax: (312) 744-2089, E-mail: culture@cityofchicago.org, Internet: http://www.cityofchicago.org/CulturalAffairs/. Head: Gregory Knight
Public Gallery - 1897
Paintings, sculptures photographs, ceramics, graphics, design, mixed media, installations 36007

Chicago Historical Society, Clark St at North Av, Chicago, IL 60614-6071 - T: (312) 642-4600, Fax: (312) 266-2077, Internet: http://www.chicago-history.org. Head: Connie G. Bunch
Historical Museum - 1856
History of Chicago 36008

Clarke House Museum, 1821 S Indiana Av, Chicago, IL 60616-1333 - T: (312) 745-0040, Fax: (312) 745-0077, E-mail: clarkehouse@interaccess.com, Internet: http://www.cityofchicago.org/culturalaffairs
Local Museum - 1984
Greek Revival building, oldest home in Chicago 36009

Columbia College Art Gallery, 72 E Eleventh St, Chicago, IL 60605-2312 - T: (312) 663-1600 ext 7104, Fax: (312) 344-8067. Head: Denise Miller, Dr. John Mulvany
Fine Arts Museum / University Museum - 1984 36010

Contemporary Art Workshop, 542 W Grant Pl, Chicago, IL 60614 - T: (773) 472-4004, Fax: (773) 472-4505. Head: John Kearney, Lynn Kearney
Public Gallery 36011

The David and Alfred Smart Museum of Art, 5550 S Greenwood Av, Chicago, IL 60637 - T: (773) 702-0200, 834-1778, Fax: (773) 702-3121, E-mail: smartmuseum@uchicago.edu, Internet: http://smartmuseum.uchicago.edu. Head: Kimberly Rorschach
Fine Arts Museum / University Museum - 1974 36012

DePaul University Art Gallery, 2350 N Kenmore, Chicago, IL 60614 - T: (773) 325-7506, Fax: (773) 325-4506, E-mail: llincoln@wppost.depaul.edu, Internet: http://www.depaul.edu/~gallery. Head: Louise Lincoln
Fine Arts Museum / University Museum - 1987 36013

Dusable Museum of African-American History, 740 E 56th Pl, Chicago, IL 60637 - T: (773) 947-0600, Fax: (773) 947-0677, Internet: http://www.dusable.org
Historical Museum / Ethnology Museum - 1961
Ethnography 36014

Feet First: The Scholl Story, 1001 N Dearborn Rd, Chicago, IL 60610 - T: (312) 280-2904, Fax: (312) 280-2997. Head: Terrence Albright
Historical Museum - 1993
Podiatry 36015

Field Museum of Natural History, Roosevelt Rd at Lake Shore Dr, Chicago, IL 60605 - T: (312) 922-9410, Fax: (312) 922-0741, E-mail: jmcarter@fmnh.org. Head: John W. McCarter
Natural History Museum - 1893
Natural history, zoology, geology, botany 36016

Frederick C. Robie House, 5757 S Woodlawn Av, Chicago, IL 60637 - T: (773) 834-1847, Fax: (773) 834-1538, E-mail: mercuri@wrightplus.org, Internet: http://www.wrightplus.org. Head: Joan B. Mercuri
Historical Museum - 1974
Residence of Frederick C. Robie 36017

Gallery 2, School of the Art Institute of Chicago, 847 W Jackson Blvd, Chicago, IL 60607 - T: (312) 563-5162, Fax: (312) 563-0510, E-mail: saicg2@artic.edu, Internet: http://www.artic.edu. Head: Anthony Wight
Fine Arts Museum / University Museum - 1988 36018

Glessner House Museum, 1800 S Prairie Av, Chicago, IL 60616-1333 - T: (312) 326-1480, Fax: (312) 326-1397, Internet: http://www.glessnerhouse.org. Head: Donna Magnani, Monica Ann Leventhal
Historical Museum - 1994
Home designed by H.H. Richardson 36019

Hellenic Museum and Cultural Center, 168 N Michigan Av, Chicago, IL 60610 - T: (312) 726-1234, Fax: (312) 726-8539. Head: Konstantinos Armiros, Jeanne Costopoulos Weeks
Folklore Museum / Historical Museum / Museum of Classical Antiquities / Archaeological Museum - 1987 36020

Historic Pullman Foundation, Pullman Museum, 11141 S Cottage Grove Av, Chicago, IL 60628 - T: (773) 785-8901, Fax: (773) 785-8182, E-mail: PullmanHPF@aol.com, Internet: http://www.pullmanil.org. Head: Cynthia McMahon, Deborah Bellamy-Jawor
Historical Museum - 1973
Historic District, first planned model industrial community in 1880 36021

Hyde Park Art Center, 5307 S Hyde Park Blvd, Chicago, IL 60615 - T: (773) 324-5520, Fax: (773) 324-6641, E-mail: info@hydeparkart.org, Internet: http://www.hydeparkart.org. Head: Chuck Thurow
Fine Arts Museum 36022

Hyde Park Art Center, 5307 S Hyde Park Blvd, Chicago, IL 60615 - T: (312) 324-5520, Fax: (312) 324-6641, E-mail: info@hydeparkart.org, Internet: http://www.hydeparkart.org. Head: Chuck Thurow
Fine Arts Museum - 1939
Art gallery 36023

Illinois Art Gallery, 100 W Randolph, Ste 2-100, Chicago, IL 60601 - T: (312) 814-5322, Fax: (312) 814-3471, E-mail: ksmith@museum-state.il.us, Internet: http://www.museum.@state.il.us. Head: Kent Smith
Fine Arts Museum / Public Gallery - 1985 36024

International Museum of Surgical Science, 1524 N Lake Shore Dr, Chicago, IL 60610 - T: (312) 642-6502, Fax: (312) 642-9516, E-mail: info@imss.org, Internet: http://www.imss.org. Head: Raymond Dieter
Special Museum - 1953
Medicine 36025

Jane Addams' Hull-House Museum, University of Illinois Chicago, 800 S Halsted St, Chicago, IL 60607-7017 - T: (312) 413-5353, Fax: (312) 413-2092, E-mail: jahh@uic.edu, Internet: http://www.uic.edu/jaddams/hull/hull_house. Head: Margaret Strobel
Historical Museum - 1967
Hull Mansion occupied by Jane Addams in 1889, serving as the first settlement building of Hull House complex 36026

The Lithuanian Museum, 5620 S Claremont Av, Chicago, IL 60636-1039 - T: (773) 434-4545, Fax: (773) 434-9363, E-mail: lithuanianresearch@ameritech.net. Head: Skirmante Miglinas, Milda Budrys
Fine Arts Museum / Historical Museum - 1989
Lithuanian history 36027

The Martin D'Arcy Museum of Art, Loyola University Museum of Medieval, Renaissance and Baroque Art, 6525 N Sheridan Rd, Chicago, IL 60626 - T: (773) 508-2679, Fax: (773) 508-2993, Internet: http://www.darcy.luc.edu. Head: Dr. Sally Metzler
Fine Arts Museum / University Museum - 1969
European art 36028

Mexican Fine Arts Center Museum, 1852 W 19th St, Chicago, IL 60608 - T: (312) 738-1503, Fax: (312) 738-9740, E-mail: carlost@mfacmchicago.org, Internet: http://www.mfacmchicago.org. Head: Carlos Tortolero, Cesareo Moreno
Fine Arts Museum / Folklore Museum - 1982
Art 36029

The Museum of Broadcast Communications, 78 E Washington St, Chicago, IL 60602-9837 - T: (312) 629-6000, Fax: (312) 629-6009, E-mail: programs@museum.tv, Internet: http://www.museum.tv
Science&Tech Museum / Special Museum - 1987
Historic and contemporary radio and TV memorabilia - archives 36030

Museum of Contemporary Art, 220 E Chicago Av, Chicago, IL 60611-2604 - T: (312) 280-2660, Fax: (312) 397-4095, E-mail: pr@machicago.org, Internet: http://www.mcachicago.org. Head: Robert Fitzpatrick
Fine Arts Museum - 1967
Contemporary art 36031

The Museum of Contemporary Photography, Columbia College Chicago, 600 S Michigan Av, Chicago, IL 60605-1901 - T: (312) 663-5554, Fax: (312) 344-8067, Internet: http://www.mocp.org. Head: Sara McNear
University Museum - 1976
Photography 36032

Museum of Decorative Art, 4611 N Lincoln Av, Chicago, IL 60625 - T: (773) 989-4310
Decorative Arts Museum 36033

Museum of Holography, 1134 W Washington Blvd, Chicago, IL 60607 - T: (312) 226-1007, Fax: (312) 829-9636, E-mail: hologram@flash.net, Internet: http://holographiccenter.com. Head: Loren Billings, John Hoffmann
Special Museum
Holography 36034

Museum of Science and Industry, 5700 S Lake Shore Dr, Chicago, IL 60637 - T: (773) 684-9844, Fax: (773) 684-7141, Internet: http://www.msichicago.org. Head: David R. Mosena, Dr. Barry Aprison
Natural History Museum / Science&Tech Museum - 1926
Science, technology, housed in classic Greek structure constructed as the Palace of Fine Arts for the World's Fair Columbian Exposition of 1893 in Chicago 36035

The National Time Museum, 57th St and Lake Shore Dr, Chicago, IL 60637-2093 - T: (312) 742-1412. Head: Michael Lash
Science&Tech Museum - 2001
Horology 36036

National Vietnam Veterans Art Museum, 1801 S Indiana Av, Chicago, IL 60616 - T: (312) 326-0270, Fax: (312) 326-9767
Fine Arts Museum 36037

The Nature Museum of the Chicago Academy of Sciences, 2060 N Clark St, Chicago, IL 60614 - T: (773) 549-0606, Fax: (773) 549-5199, E-mail: cas@chias.org, Internet: http://www.chias.org. Head: Kevin Coffee
Natural History Museum - 1857
Natural science 36038

Northern Illinois University Art Gallery in Chicago → Art Gallery in Chicago

Oriental Institute Museum, University of Chicago, 1155 E 58th St, Chicago, IL 60637 - T: (773) 702-9520, Fax: (773) 702-9853, E-mail: oi-museum@uchicago.edu, Internet: http://www-oi.uchicago.edu/oi/. Head: Karen L. Wilson
Fine Arts Museum / Archaeological Museum / University Museum - 1894
Archaeology, ancient history, art 36039

The Palette and Chisel, 1012 N Dearborn St, Chicago, IL 60610 - T: (312) 642-4149, Fax: (312) 642-4317, E-mail: finearts@wwa.com, Internet: http://www.paletteandchisel.org. Head: Frank Holt, Michael Smith
Fine Arts Museum / Public Gallery - 1895
Art Academy, paintings, sculptures 36040

The Peace Museum, 100 N Central Park Av, Chicago, IL 60610 - T: (773) 638-6450, Fax: (312) 440-1267, E-mail: virginia@peacemuseum.org, Internet: http://www.peacemuseum.org. Head: Virginia Albaneso
Fine Arts Museum / Special Museum - 1981 36041

Polish Museum of America, 984 N Milwaukee Av, Chicago, IL 60622-4104 - T: (773) 384-3352 and 3731, Fax: (773) 384-3799, E-mail: pma@prcua.org, Internet: http://www.prcua.org/pma. Head: Jan McLorys, Joan Kosinski
Folklore Museum / Ethnology Museum - 1937
Polonica, Paderewski memorabilia, world fair 1939, art 36042

The Renaissance Society at the University of Chicago, 5811 S Ellis Av, Chicago, IL 60637 - T: (773) 702-8670, Fax: (773) 702-9669, Internet: http://www.renaissancesociety.org. Head: Timothy Flood, Susanne Ghez
Fine Arts Museum - 1915 36043

Roy Boyd Gallery, 739 N Wells St, Chicago, IL 60610 - T: (312) 642-1606, Fax: (312) 642-2143. Head: Roy Bod
Fine Arts Museum
Contemporary American paintings, Russian and Baltic photography, sculpture and works on paper 36044

Spertus Museum, 618 S Michigan Av, Chicago, IL 60605 - T: (312) 322-1747, Fax: (312) 922-3934, E-mail: musm@spertus.edu, Internet: http://www.spertus.edu. Head: Mark Akgulian
Archaeological Museum / Religious Arts Museum - 1968
Culture, art, archaeology 36045

Stephen A. Douglas Tomb, 636 E 35th St, Chicago, IL 60616 - T: (312) 225-2620, Fax: (312) 225-7855. Head: Michael Carson
Historic Site - 1865
1866-1881 Stephen A. Douglas Tomb 36046

Swedish American Museum Association of Chicago Museum, 5211 N Clark St, Chicago, IL 60640 - T: (312) 728-8111, Fax: (312) 728-8870, E-mail: museum@samac.org, Internet: http://www.samac.org. Head: Margareta Alexander, Kerstin Lane
Folklore Museum - 1976
Swedish history 36047

Terra Museum of American Art, 666 N Michigan Av, Chicago, IL 60611, mail addr: 664 N Michigan Av, Chicago, IL 60611 - T: (312) 664-3939 ext 1233, Fax: (312) 664-2052, E-mail: terra@terramuseum.org, Internet: http://www.terramuseum.org. Head: Stuart Popowcer, John Hallmark Neff
Fine Arts Museum - 1979 36048

The Time Museum → The National Time Museum

Ukrainian National Museum, 721 N Oakley Blvd, Chicago, IL 60612 - T: (312) 421-8020, Fax: (773) 693-7479, E-mail: hankewych@msn.com, Internet: http://www.ukrntlmuseum.org. Head: Jaroslaw J. Hankewych
Folklore Museum - 1952
Folk art 36049

Chico CA

Bidwell Mansion State Historic Park, 525 Esplanade, Chico, CA 95926 - T: (530) 895-6144, Fax: (530) 895-6699. Head: Paul Holman
Historical Museum - 1964 36050

Chico Museum, 141 Salem St, Chico, CA 95928 - T: (530) 891-4336, Fax: (530) 891-4336
Local Museum - 1980
Local history 36051

Janet Turner Print Collection and Gallery, California State University, Chico, Chico, CA 95929-0820 - T: (530) 898-4476, Fax: (530) 898-5581, E-mail: csullivan@exchange.csuchico.edu, Internet: http://www.csuchico.edu/hfa. Head: Catherine Sullivan Sturgeon
University Museum / Fine Arts Museum - 1981
Fine art prints 36052

Museum of Anthropology, California State University-Chico, Chico, CA 95929-0400 - T: (530) 898-5397, Fax: (530) 898-6143, E-mail: anthromuseum@csuchico.edu. Head: Keith L. Johnson, Dr. Stacy Schaefer
University Museum / Ethnology Museum - 1969 36053

Childress TX

Childress County Heritage Museum, 210 3rd St, Childress, TX 79201 - T: (940) 937-2261. Head: Wiliam Blackburn, Jenny Lou Taylor
Local Museum - 1976
Local hist 36054

Chillicothe MO

George W. Somerville Historical Library, Livingston County Library, 450 Locust, Chillicothe, MO 64601 - T: (660) 646-0547, Fax: (660) 646-5504, E-mail: ugy001@mail.connect.more.net, Internet: http://www.livcolibrary.org. Head: Patricia Henry, Karen Hicklin
Library with Exhibitions - 1966 36055

Grand River Historical Society Museum, 1401 Forest Dr, Chillicothe, MO 64601 - T: (816) 646-3430
Historical Museum - 1959 36056

Chillicothe OH

Adena State Memorial, Adena Rd, Chillicothe, OH 45601 - T: (740) 772-1500, Fax: (740) 775-2746, Internet: http://www.ohiohistory.org/places/adena/
Local Museum - 1946 36057

Hopewell Culture National Historic Park, 16062 State Rte 104, Chillicothe, OH 45601-8694 - T: (740) 774-1125, Fax: (740) 774-1140, Internet: http://www.nps.gov/hocu
Ethnology Museum - 1923
200 B.C.-500 A.D. Hopewell Indian mound enclosure 36058

Ross County Historical Society Museum, 45 W Fifth St, Chillicothe, OH 45601 - T: (740) 772-1936, E-mail: info@rosscountyhistorical.org, Internet: http://www.rosscountyhistorical.org. Head: Patricia Medert, Thomas G. Kuhn
Local Museum - 1896 36059

Chiloquin OR

Collier Memorial State Park and Logging Museum, 46000 Hwy 97 N, 30 miles north of Klamath Falls, Chiloquin, OR 97624 - T: (541) 783-2471, Fax: (541) 783-2707, Internet: http://www.pdr.state.or.us
Historical Museum - 1945 36060

Chincoteague VA

The Oyster and Maritime Museum of Chincoteague, POB 352, Chincoteague, VA 23336 - T: (804) 336-6117. Head: James Bott
Natural History Museum / Science&Tech Museum / Historical Museum - 1966
Natural science, maritime hist, Fresnel lens 36061

Chino CA

Yorba-Slaughter Adobe Museum, 17127 Pomona Rincon Rd, Chino, CA 91710 - T: (909) 597-8570, Fax: (909)307-0539704= http://www.co.san-bernardino.ca.us/ccr/museum/museum.html, E-mail: adeegan@co.san-bernardino.ca.us. Head: Paul J. Oles
Historical Museum - 1976 36062

Chinook MT

Blaine County Museum, 501 Indiana, Chinook, MT 59523 - T: (406) 357-2590. Head: Stuart C. MacKenzie
Local Museum - 1977 36063

Chiriaco Summit CA

General Patton Memorial Museum, 62-510 Chiriaco Rd, Chiriaco Summit, CA 92201 - T: (760) 227-3483, Fax: (760) 227-3483. Head: Jan Holmlund
Military Museum - 1988
Military, headquarters of WW II Desert Training Areas 36064

Chisholm MN

Ironworld Discovery Center, Hwy 169 W, Chisholm, MN 55719 - T: (218) 254-7959, Fax: (218) 254-7972, E-mail: reception@ironworld.com, Internet: http://www.ironworld.com. Head: Marianne Bouska
Local Museum / Science&Tech Museum - 1977
Mining, regional history 36065

Chittenango NY

Chittenango Landing Canal Boat Museum, 7010 Lakeport Rd, Chittenango, NY 13037 - T: (315) 687-3801, Fax: (315) 687-3801. Head: Dr. Robert E. Hager
Science&Tech Museum - 1986 36066

Choteau MT

Old Trail Museum, 823 Main St, Choteau, MT 59422 - T: (406) 466-5332, E-mail: otm@3rivers.net, Internet: http://www.oldtrailmuseum.org. Head: Corlene Martin
Agriculture Museum - 1985 36067

Christiansburg VA

Montgomery Museum and Lewis Miller Regional Art Center, 300 S Pepper St, Christiansburg, VA 24073 - T: (540) 382-5644, Fax: (540) 382-9127. Head: Linda L Martin
Local Museum / Fine Arts Museum - 1983
Local hist, art 36068

Church Rock NM

Red Rock Museum, Red Rock State Park, Church Rock, NM 87311 - T: (505) 863-1337, Fax: (505) 863-1297, E-mail: rrsp@ci.gallup.nm.us, Internet: http://www.ci.gallup.nm.us/rrsp. Head: Joe Athens
Ethnology Museum / Natural History Museum / Public Gallery - 1951 36069

Cimarron NM

Old Mill Museum, Rte 1, Cimarron, NM 87714 - T: (505) 376-2913
Local Museum - 1967 36070

The Philmont Museum and Seton Memorial Library, Philmont Scout Ranch, Cimarron, NM 87714 - T: (505) 376-2281 ext 46, Fax: (505) 376-2602, E-mail: philmuse@cimarrov.sprin-gercoop.com. Head: Stephen Zimmer
Fine Arts Museum / Local Museum - 1967 36071

Cincinnati OH

Betts House Research Center, 416 Clark St, Betts-Longworth Historic District, Cincinnati, OH 45203-1420 - T: (513) 651-0734, Fax: (513) 651-2143, E-mail: BettsHouse@Juno.com. Head: Susan Vesio-Steinkamp
Local Museum - 1995
Local hist 36072

Cary Cottage, 7000 Hamilton Av, Cincinnati, OH 45231 - T: (513) 522-3860, Fax: (513) 728-3946, E-mail: clovernook@clovernook.org, Internet: http://www.clovernook.org. Head: Marvin Kramer
Historical Museum - 1973 36073

Cincinnati Art Museum, 953 Eden Park Dr, Cincinnati, OH 45202-1596 - T: (513) 639-2995, Fax: (513) 639-2888, E-mail: information@cincyart.org, Internet: http://www.cincinna-tiartmuseum.org. Head: Timothy Rub
Fine Arts Museum / Decorative Arts Museum - 1881 36074

Cincinnati Fire Museum, 315 W Court St, Cincinnati, OH 45202 - T: (513) 621-5571. Head: Ray Toelke, Nancy S. Kohnen
Special Museum - 1979 36075

Cincinnati Museum Center, 1301 Western Av, Cincinnati, OH 45203 - T: (513) 287-7000, Fax: (513) 287-7029, Internet: http://www.cincymuseum.org. Head: Douglass W. McDonald, Sandra Shipley, Elisabeth Jones
Ethnology Museum / Local Museum / Natural History Museum / Science&Tech Museum - 1835 36076

Contemporary Arts Center, 115 E Fifth St, Cincinnati, OH 45202-3998 - T: (513) 345-8400, Fax: (513) 721-7418, E-mail: admin@spiral.org, Internet: http://www.spiral.org. Head: Charles Desmarais
Fine Arts Museum - 1939 36077

DAAP Galleries, University of Cincinnati, Cincinnati, OH 45221-0016 - T: (513) 556-3210, Fax: (513) 556-3288, E-mail: anne.timpano@uc.edu, Internet: http://www.uc.edu/arch. Head: Anne Timpano
Fine Arts Museum / University Museum - 1993
Art 36078

Hebrew Union College-Jewish Institute of Religion Skirball Museum, 3101 Clifton Av, Cincinnati, OH 45220 - T: (513) 221-1875, Fax: (513) 221-1842, E-mail: jlucas@cnhuc.edu, Internet: http://www.huc.edu
Fine Arts Museum / University Museum / Historical Museum / Folklore Museum / Archaeological Museum / Religious Arts Museum - 1913 36079

Indian Hill Historical Society Museum, 8100 Given Rd, Cincinnati, OH 45243 - T: (513) 891-1873, Fax: (513) 248-0176, E-mail: ihhist@one.net, Internet: http://www.indianhill.org. Head: Margaret Gillespie
Local Museum - 1973 36080

Studio San Giuseppe Art Gallery, College of Mount Saint Joseph, 5701 Delhi Rd, Cincinnati, OH 45233-1670 - T: (513) 244-4314, Fax: (513) 244-4222, E-mail: Jerry-Bellas@mail.msj.edu, Internet: http://www.msj.edu. Head: Gerald M. Bellas
Fine Arts Museum / University Museum / Public Gallery - 1962 36081

Taft Museum of Art, 316 Pike St, Cincinnati, OH 45202-4293 - T: (513) 241-0343, Fax: (513) 241-7762, E-mail: taftmuseum@taftmuseum.org, Internet: http://www.taftmuseum.org. Head: Phillip C. Long
Fine Arts Museum - 1932
Furnishings, coll of Duncan Phyfe furniture, paintings, old masters 36082

Trailside Nature Center and Museum, Brookline Dr, Burnet Woods Park, Cincinnati, OH 45220 - T: (513) 321-6070, Fax: (513) 751-3679, E-mail: vivian.wagner@cinparks.rcc.org. Head: Jack Wilson, Vivian Wagner
Natural History Museum - 1930 36083

William Howard Taft National Historic Site, 2038 Auburn Av, Cincinnati, OH 45219 - T: (513) 684-3262, Fax: (513) 684-3627, E-mail: wiho_superintendent@nps.gov, Internet: http://www.nps.gov/wiho/index.html. Head: Kurt C. Topham
Historical Museum - 1969 36084

Xavier University Art Gallery, 3800 Victory Pkwy, Cincinnati, OH 45207-7311 - T: (513) 745-3811, Fax: (513) 745-1098. Head: Katherine Vetz
University Museum / Fine Arts Museum - 1831 36085

Circle MT

McCone County Museum, 801 First Av S, Circle, MT 59215 - T: (406) 485-2414
Local Museum - 1953 36086

City of Industry CA

Workman and Temple Family Homestead Museum, 15415 E Don Julian Rd, City of Industry, CA 91745 - T: (626) 968-8492, Fax: (626) 968-2048, E-mail: info@homesteadmuseum.org, Internet: http://www.homesteadmuseum.org. Head: Karen Graham Wade
Historical Museum - 1981 36087

Claremont CA

Clark Humanities Museum, Humanities Bldg, Scripps College, Claremont, CA 91711 - T: (909) 607-3606, Fax: (909) 607-7143. Head: Dr. Eric T. Haskell
Local Museum / University Museum - 1970 36088

Montgomery Gallery, Pomona College Museum of Art, 330 N College Av, Claremont, CA 91711 - T: (909) 621-8283, Fax: (909) 621-8989, E-mail: mharth@pomona.edu, Internet: http://www.pomona.edu/montgomery. Head: Marjorie L. Harth
Fine Arts Museum / University Museum - 1958 36089

Petterson Museum of Intercultural Art, 730 Plymouth Rd, Claremont, CA 91711 - T: (909) 399-5544, 621-9581, Fax: (909) 399-5508
Fine Arts Museum / Decorative Arts Museum - 1968
International folk and fine art 36090

Raymond M. Alf Museum of Paleontology, 1175 W Base Line Rd, Claremont, CA 91711 - T: (909) 624-3587, Fax: (909) 621-4582, E-mail: dlofgren@webb.org, Internet: http://www.alfmuseum.org. Head: Donald Lofgren
Natural History Museum - 1937 36091

Claremont NH

Claremont Museum, 26 Mulberry St, Claremont, NH 03743 - T: (603) 543-1400
Local Museum - 1966 36092

Claremore OK

J.M. Davis Arms and Historical Museum, 333 N Lynn Riggs Blvd, Claremore, OK 74017 - T: (918) 341-5707, Fax: (918) 341-5771, E-mail: american@onenet.net, Internet: http://www.state.ok.us/~jmdavis/. Head: Shirley Johnson
Local Museum - 1965 36093

Will Rogers Memorial, 1720 W Will Rogers Blvd, Claremore, OK 74018 - T: (918) 341-0719, Fax: (918) 343-8119, E-mail: wrinfo@willrogers.org, Internet: http://www.willrogers.org. Head: Joseph H. Carter
Historical Museum - 1938 36094

Clarence NY

Historical Society of the Town of Clarence Museum, 10465 Main St, Clarence, NY 14031 - T: (781) 741-3780
Local Museum - 1954 36095

Clarion PA

Hazel Sandford Gallery, Clarion University of Pennsylvania, Merick-Boyd Bldg, Clarion, PA 16214 - T: (814) 226-2412, 226-2523, Fax: (814) 226-2723. Head: Dianne Malley
Fine Arts Museum / University Museum - 1982
Art gallery 36096

Sutton-Ditz House Museum, 18 Grant St, Clarion, PA 16214 - T: (814) 226-4450, Fax: (814) 226-7106, E-mail: cchs@csonline.net, Internet: http://www.csonline.net/cchs/. Head: Lindsley A. Dunn
Local Museum - 1955 36097

Clark CO

Hahns Peak Area Historical Museum, Hahns Peak Village, Clark, CO 80428 - T: (970) 879-6781. Head: Rilla Wiggins
Local Museum - 1972
Regional history, Old Horse Barn, one room school house 36098

Clark NJ

Dr. William Robinson Plantation, 593 Madison Hill Rd, Clark, NJ 07066 - T: (732) 381-3081. Head: Eleanor Warren, Constance Brewer
Local Museum - 1974 36099

Clark SD

Beauvais Heritage Center, Hwy 212, Clark, SD 57225 - T: (605) 532-3722, 532-5216. Head: Ailene Luckhurst
Local Museum - 1978
Cultural hist, pioneer home, depot, store, military, religion, machine, tool 36100

Clarksdale MS

Delta Blues Museum, 114 Delta Av, Clarksdale, MS 38614 - T: (662) 627-6820, Fax: (662) 627-7263, E-mail: dbmuseum@clarksdale.com, Internet: http://www.deltabluesmuseum.org. Head: Missie Craig
Music Museum - 1979 36101

Clarkson NE

Clarkson Historical Museum, 221 Pine St, Clarkson, NE 68629 - T: (402) 892-3854. Head: Evelyn D. Podany
Local Museum - 1967 36102

Clarkston WA

Valley Art Center, 842 6th St, Clarkston, WA 99403 - T: (509) 758-8331, Internet: http://www.valleyarts.qpg.com. Head: Pat Rosenberger
Fine Arts Museum - 1968
Art 36103

Clarksville TN

Clarksville-Montgomery County Museum, 200 S Second St, Clarksville, TN 37040 - T: (931) 648-5780, Fax: (931) 553-5179. Head: Ned Crouch
Local Museum - 1984
Local hist 36104

Mabel Larson Fine Arts Gallery, Austin Peay State University, POB 4677, Clarksville, TN 37044 - T: (615) 648-7333
Fine Arts Museum - 1994
Drawings 36105

Margaret Fort Trahern Gallery, College and Eighth Sts, Clarksville, TN 37044 - T: (931) 221-7333, Fax: (931) 221-5997, 221-7219, E-mail: holteb@apsu02.apsu.edu. Head: Bettye Holte
Fine Arts Museum / University Museum - 1974
Art 36106

Clarksville VA

Prestwould Foundation, U.S. 15, 2 miles N of Clarksville, Clarksville, VA 23927 - T: (804) 374-8672. Head: Dr. Julian D. Hudson
Local Museum - 1963
Local hist 36107

Clawson MI

Clawson Historical Museum, 41 Fisher Ct, Clawson, MI 48017 - T: (248) 588-9169
Local Museum - 1973
Local history 36108

Clay City KY

Red River Historical Society Museum, 4541 Main St, Clay City, KY 40312 - T: (606) 663-2555. Head: Larry G. Meadows
Local Museum - 1966
Local history, archaeology, photography, genealogy 36109

Clayton ID

Custer Museum, Yankee Fork Ranger District Museum, Clayton, ID 83227 - T: (208) 838-2201, Fax: (208) 838-3329. Head: Craig Wolford
Historical Museum - 1961
Located on site of 1870 Gold Rush 36110

Clayton NY

American Handweaving Museum → Handweaving Museum and Arts Center

Antique Boat Museum, 750 Mary St, Clayton, NY 13624 - T: (315) 686-4104, Fax: (315) 686-2775, E-mail: abm@gisco.net, Internet: http://www.abm.org. Head: William G. Danforth
Historical Museum - 1964 36111

Handweaving Museum and Arts Center, 314 John St, Clayton, NY 13624 - T: (315) 686-4123, Fax: (315) 686-3459, E-mail: hmac@gisco.net, Internet: http://www.thousandislands.com/ahmtics. Head: Beth Conlon
Special Museum - 1966 36112

Thousand Islands Museum of Clayton, 403 Riverside Dr, Town Hall Opera House, Clayton, NY 13624 - T: (315) 686-5794, Fax: (315) 686-4867, E-mail: timuseum@gisco.net, Internet: http://www.thousandislands.com/timuseum. Head: Linda Schleher
Historical Museum - 1964 36113

Cle Elum WA

Carpenter Home Museum, 302 W 3rd St, Cle Elum, WA 98922 - T: (509) 674-5702. Head: Sarah Engdahl
Historical Museum / Special Museum - 1990
Home, with ballroom and a special maid's room 36114

Cle Elum Telephone Museum, 221 E 1st St, Cle Elum, WA 98922 - T: (509) 674-5702. Head: Sarah Engdahl
Science&Tech Museum - 1967
Communications 36115

Clear Lake WI

Clear Lake Area Historical Museum, 450 Fifth Av, Clear Lake, WI 54005 - T: (715) 263-3050, 263-2042. Head: Charles T. Clark
Local Museum - 1977
Local hist 36116

Clearfield PA

Clearfield County Historical Society Museum, 104 E Pine St, Clearfield, PA 16830 - T: (814) 765-6125
Local Museum - 1955 36117

Clearwater FL

Napoleonic Society of America, 1115 Ponce de Leon Blvd, Clearwater, FL 33756 - T: (727) 586-1779, Fax: (727) 581-2578, E-mail: napoleonic1@juno.com, Internet: http://www.napoleonic-society.org. Head: Robert M. Snibbe
Historical Museum / Military Museum - 1983
History - library 36118

Cleburne TX

Layland Museum, 201 N Caddo, Cleburne, TX 76031 - T: (817) 645-0940, Fax: (817) 645-0926. Head: Julie P. Backer
Historical Museum - 1964
History of domestic life, photographs, archives 36119

Clemson SC

Fort Hill - The John C. Calhoun House, Fort Hill St, Clemson University, Clemson, SC 29634 - T: (864) 656-2475, 656-4789, Fax: (864) 656-1026. Head: William D. Hiott
Local Museum - 1889
Historic house, home of John C. Calhoun 36120

Hanover House, c/o South Carolina Botanical Garden,, Perimeter Rd, Clemson University, Clemson, SC 29634 - T: (864) 656-2241, 656-2475, Fax: (803) 656-1026. Head: William D. Hiott
Local Museum - 1941
Historic house 36121

Rudolph E. Lee Gallery, College of Architecture, Arts and Humanities Lee Hall, Clemson University, Clemson, SC 29634 - T: (864) 656-3883, Fax: (864) 656-7523. Head: David Houston
Fine Arts Museum / University Museum - 1956
Architecture, graphics, paintings 36122

Clermont IA

Montauk, POB 372, Clermont, IA 52135 - T: (319) 423-7173, Fax: (319) 423-7378, E-mail: nwest@max.state.ia.us
Historical Museum - 1968
Home of William Larrabee, Iowa's 12th Governor 36123

Clermont NY

Clermont State Historic Site, 1 Clermont Av, Clermont, NY 12526 - T: (518) 537-4240, Fax: (518) 537-6240, E-mail: friendsofclermont@epix.com, Internet: http://www.friendsofclermont.org. Head: Bruce E. Naramore
Local Museum - 1962 36124

Cleveland MS

Fielding L. Wright Art Center, Delta State University, Cleveland, MS 38733 - T: (662) 846-4720, Fax: (662) 846-4726, E-mail: bherisn@dsu.deltast.edu. Head: Patricia Brown
Fine Arts Museum / University Museum - 1924 36125

Cleveland OH

The Children's Museum of Cleveland, 10730 Euclid Av, Cleveland, OH 44106-2200 - T: (216) 791-7114, Fax: (216) 791-8838, Internet: http://www.museum4kids.com. Head: Karen L. Prasser
Special Museum - 1986 36126

Cleveland Center for Contemporary Art, 8501 Carnegie Av, Cleveland, OH 44106 - T: (216) 421-8671, Fax: (216) 421-0737, E-mail: jwilhelm@contemporaryart.org, Internet: http://www.contemporaryart.org. Head: Jill Snyder
Fine Arts Museum - 1968 36127

Cleveland Museum of Art, 11150 East Blvd, Cleveland, OH 44106 - T: (216) 421-7350, (888) 242-0033, Fax: (216) 421-0411, E-mail: info@CMA-oh.org, Internet: http://www.clevelandart.org. Head: Katharine Lee Reid
Fine Arts Museum - 1913 36128

Cleveland Museum of Natural History, 1 Wade Oval Dr, Cleveland, OH 44106-1767 - T: (216) 231-4600 ext 235, Fax: (216) 231-5919, E-mail: info@cmnh.org, Internet: http://www.cmnh.org. Head: Dr. Bruce Latimer
Natural History Museum - 1920 36129

Cleveland Police Museum, 1300 Ontario St, Cleveland, OH 44113-1600 - T: (216) 623-5055, Fax: (216) 623-5145, E-mail: museum@stratos.net, Internet: http://www.clevelandpolicemuseum.org
Special Museum - 1983
Police hist 36130

Cleveland State University Art Gallery, 2307 Chester Av, Cleveland, OH 44114-3607 - T: (216) 687-2103, Fax: (216) 687-2275, E-mail: artgallery@csuohio.edu, Internet: http://www.csuohio.edu/art/gallery. Head: Robert Thurmer, Dr. Clair Van Ummerson
Fine Arts Museum / University Museum - 1973 36131

Dittrick Museum of Medical History, Case Western Reserve University, 11000 Euclid Av, Cleveland, OH 44106-1714 - T: (216) 368-3648, Fax: (216) 368-6421, E-mail: jme3@po.cwru.edu, Internet: http://www.cwru.edu/artsci/dittrick/home.htm. Head: Dr. James M. Edmonson
Historical Museum - 1926
Library 36132

Dunham Tavern Museum, 6709 Euclid Av, Cleveland, OH 44103 - T: (216) 431-1060. Head: Barbara Peterson, Raymond L. Cushing
Local Museum - 1939 36133

Health Museum of Cleveland, 8911 Euclid Av, Cleveland, OH 44106 - T: (216) 231-5010, Fax: (216) 231-5129, E-mail: marks@healthmuseum.org, Internet: http://healthmuseum.org. Head: Michael J. Marks
Special Museum - 1936 36134

International Women's Air and Space Museum, 1501 N Marginal Rd, Cleveland, OH 44114 - T: (216) 623-1111, Fax: (216) 623-1113, E-mail: jhrubec@iwasm.org, Internet: http://www.iwasm.org. Head: Joan Hrubec
Science&Tech Museum - 1976
History of Women in Air and space 36135

NASA Lewis Research Center's Visitor Center, 21000 Brookpark Rd, MS 8-1, Cleveland, OH 44135 - T: (216) 433-6689, Fax: (216) 433-3344, E-mail: sam.r.pingatore@lere.nasa.gov, Internet: http://www.lerc.nasa.gov/internal
Science&Tech Museum - 1976 36136

Reinberger Galleries, Cleveland Institute of Art, 11141 East Blvd, Cleveland, OH 44106 - T: (216) 421-7407, Fax: (216) 421-7438, Internet: http://www.cia.edu. Head: Bruce Checefsky
Public Gallery 36137

The Rock and Roll Hall of Fame and Museum, 1 Key Plaza, Cleveland, OH 44114-1022 - T: (216) 781-7625, Fax: (216) 781-1832, E-mail: director@rockhall.org, Internet: http://www.rockhall.com
Music Museum - 1985
Rock and Roll music 36138

Romanian Ethnic Art Museum, 3256 Warren Rd, Cleveland, OH 44111 - T: (216) 941-5550, Fax: (216) 941-3368, Internet: http://www.smroc.org. Head: George Dobrea
Ethnology Museum - 1960
Folk art, Romanian art, costumes, ceramics, painters, rugs, silver & woodwork 36139

Spaces, 2220 Superior Viaduct, Cleveland, OH 44113 - T: (216) 621-2314, Fax: (216) 621-2314, E-mail: spaces@apk.net, Internet: http://www.spacesgallery.org. Head: Susan R Channing
Public Gallery
Special exhibitions of contemporary artists 36140

Temple Museum of Religious Art, 1855 Ansel Rd, Cleveland, OH 44106 - T: (216) 831-3233, Fax: (216) 831-4216. Head: Jeremy Handler
Religious Arts Museum - 1950 36141

Ukrainian Museum, 1202 Kenilworth Av, Cleveland, OH 44113 - T: (216) 781-4329, Fax: (216) 522-0552, E-mail: staff@umacleveland.org, Internet: http://www.umacleveland.org. Head: Andrew Fedynsky
Fine Arts Museum / Folklore Museum / Historical Museum - 1952 36142

Western Reserve Historical Society Museum, 10825 East Blvd, Cleveland, OH 44106-1788 - T: (216) 721-5722, Fax: (216) 721-8934, Internet: http://www.wrhs.org. Head: Patrick H. Reymann, Richard L. Ehrlich
Historical Museum - 1867 36143

Cleveland TN

Red Clay State Historical Park, 1140 Red Clay Park Rd, SW, Cleveland, TN 37311 - T: (423) 478-0339. Head: Lois I. Osborne
Historic Site - 1979
Historic site, seat of the former Cherokee government and site of eleven general councils national affairs 36144

Clewiston FL

Clewiston Museum, 112 S Commercio St, Clewiston, FL 33440-3706 - T: (941) 983-2870. Head: Miller Couse, Joe McCrary
Local Museum - 1984 36145

Clifton NJ

Hamilton House Museum, 971 Valley Rd, Clifton, NJ 07013 - T: (973) 744-5707
Local Museum - 1974 36146

Clifton Forge VA

Alleghany Highlands Arts and Crafts Center, 439 E Ridgeway St, Clifton Forge, VA 24422 - T: (540) 862-4447. Head: Martha Hall, Nancy Newhard-Farrar
Decorative Arts Museum - 1984
Arts, crafts 36147

Clinton IL

C.H. Moore Homestead, 219 E Woodlawn St, Clinton, IL 61727 - T: (217) 935-6066, Fax: (217) 935-0553, E-mail: chmoure@davesword.net. Head: Karen Steward
Local Museum - 1967
General museum housed in C.H. Moore home 36148

Clinton MD

Surratt House Museum, 9118 Brandywine Rd, Clinton, MD 20735 - T: (301) 868-1121, Fax: (301) 868-8177, Internet: http://www.surrat.org. Head: Laurie Verge
Historical Museum - 1976
Historic house, Civil Warand Lincoln assassination 36149

Clinton MO

Henry County Museum and Cultural Arts Center, 203 W Franklin St, Clinton, MO 64735 - T: (660) 885-8414, Fax: (660) 890-2228, E-mail: hcmus@mid-america.net. Head: Chris Gordon
Decorative Arts Museum / Local Museum - 1974
Architecture, drawings, archaeology, ethnology, costumes, decorative art, Eskimo art, dolls, Oriental, Persian and Greek antiquities 36150

Clinton MS

Mississippi Baptist Historical Commission Museum, Mississippi College Library, College St, Clinton, MS 39058 - T: (601) 925-3434, Fax: (601) 925-3435, E-mail: mbhc@mc.edu, Internet: http://www.mc.edu
Religious Arts Museum / University Museum - 1887 36151

Clinton NJ

Hunterdon Historical Museum, 56 Main St, Clinton, NJ 08809-0005 - T: (908) 735-4101, Fax: (908) 735-0914, E-mail: hhmredmill@yahoo.com. Head: Dr. Charles Spibierl
Local Museum - 1960 36152

Hunterdon Museum of Art, 7 Lower Center St, Clinton, NJ 08809 - T: (908) 735-8415, Fax: (908) 735-8416, Internet: http://www.hunterdonmuseumofart.org. Head: Marjorie Frankel Nathanson, Kristen Accola
Fine Arts Museum - 1952
Print coll 36153

Clinton NY

Emerson Gallery, Hamilton College, 198 College Hill Rd, Clinton, NY 13323 - T: (315) 859-4396, Fax: (315) 859-4687. Head: Lise Holst
Fine Arts Museum / University Museum - 1982 36154

Clinton OK

Oklahoma Route 66 Museum, 2229 Gary Blvd, Clinton, OK 73601 - T: (580) 323-7866. Head: Pat A. Smith
Local Museum - 1967 36155

Cloquet MN

Carlton County Historical Museum and Heritage Center, 406 Cloquet Av, Cloquet, MN 55720-1750 - T: (218) 879-1938, Fax: (218) 879-1938, E-mail: cchs@cpinternet.com. Head: Milo Rasmusen, Marlene Wisuri
Historical Museum - 1949
Regional history 36156

Cloudcroft NM

Sacramento Mountains Historical Museum, Hwy 82, Cloudcroft, NM 88317 - T: (505) 682-2932. Head: Patrick Rand
Local Museum - 1977 36157

Cloutierville LA

The Kate Chopin House and Bayou Folk Museum, 243 Hwy 495, Cloutierville, LA 71416 - T: (318) 379-2233, Fax: (318) 379-0055. Head: Saidee W. Newell, Amanda Chenault
Special Museum - 1965
Home of Creole writer Kate Chopin from 1880-1884 36158

Cockeysville MD

Baltimore County Historical Museum, 9811 Van Buren Ln, Cockeysville, MD 21030 - T: (410) 666-1876 and 1878, Internet: http://www.bcplonline.org/branchpgs/bchs/bchshome.html. Head: Ann Rutledge
Local Museum - 1959
Regional history 36159

Cocoa FL

Brevard Museum, 2201 Michigan Av, Cocoa, FL 32926-5618 - T: (321) 632-1830, Fax: (321) 631-7551, E-mail: brevardmuseum@palmnet.net, Internet: http://www5.palmnet.net/~brevardmuseum. Head: Ann L. Lawton
Local Museum / Natural History Museum - 1969
History, natural history 36160

Cody WY

Buffalo Bill Historical Center, 720 Sheridan Av, Cody, WY 82414 - T: (307) 587-4771 ext 0, Fax: (307) 587-5714, E-mail: bbhc@wavecom.net, Internet: http://www.bbhc.park.wy.us. Head: B. Byron Price
Historical Museum / Fine Arts Museum - 1917
American history coll, art 36161

Coffeyville KS

Dalton Defenders Museum, 113 E 8th, Coffeyville, KS 67337 - T: (316) 251-5944, Fax: (316) 251-5448, E-mail: chamber@coffeyville.com, Internet: http://www.terraworld.net/lbarndollar/dalton.htm. Head: Lue Barndollar
Historical Museum - 1954
History 36162

Cohasset MA

Caleb Lothrop House, 14 Summer St, Cohasset, MA 02025 - T: (781) 383-1434, E-mail: tlg@dreamcom.net
Historical Museum - 1974
Federal house 36163

Cohasset Maritime Museum, 4 Elm St, Cohasset, MA 02025 - T: (781) 383-1434, E-mail: tlg@dreamcom.net
Historical Museum / Folklore Museum - 1957
Maritime hist 36164

David Nichols-Captain John Wilson House, 4 Elm St, Cohasset, MA 02025 - T: (781) 383-1434, E-mail: tlg@dreamcom.net
Historical Museum - 1936 36165

Colby KS

The Prairie Museum of Art and History, 1905 S Franklin, Colby, KS 67701, mail addr: POB 465, Colby, KS 67701 - T: (913) 462-4590, Fax: (785) 462-4592, E-mail: prairiem@colby.ixks.com, Internet: http://www.prairiemuseum.org. Head: Sue Ellen Taylor
Local Museum - 1959
Local history, art - archives 36166

Cold Spring NY

Putnam County Historical Society and Foundry School Museum, 63 Chestnut St, Cold Spring, NY 10516 - T: (914) 265-4010, Fax: (914) 265-2884, E-mail: pchs@highlands.com. Head: Doris Shaw
Local Museum - 1906 36167

Cold Spring Harbor NY

Cold Spring Harbor Whaling Museum, Main St, Cold Spring Harbor, NY 11724 - T: (516) 367-3418, Fax: (516) 692-7037, Internet: http://www.cshl.org/cshm/whale.htm. Head: Ann M. Gill
Special Museum - 1936 36168

Colfax IA

Trainland U.S.A., 3135 Hwy 117 N, Colfax, IA 50054 - T: (515) 674-3813. Head: Leland Atwood
Decorative Arts Museum - 1981
Toys 36169

College Park MD

The Art Gallery, University of Meryland, 1202 Art-Sociology Bldg, College Park, MD 20742 - T: (301) 405-2763, Fax: (301) 314-7774, E-mail: artgal@umail.umd.edu, Internet: http://www.inform.umd.edu/ArtGal. Head: Scott Habes
Fine Arts Museum / University Museum - 1966
Art 36170

College Park Aviation Museum, 1985 Cpl. Frank Scott Dr, College Park, MD 20740 - T: (301) 864-6029, Fax: (301) 927-6472, Internet: http://www.pgparks.com. Head: Catherine Allen
Science&Tech Museum / Historical Museum - 1982
Aviation, oldest continually operating airport in the world 36171

College Station TX

J. Wayne Stark University Center Galleries, Mem. Student Center, College Station, TX 77844 - T: (979) 845-6081, Fax: (979) 862-3381, E-mail: uart@stark.tamu.edu, Internet: http://stark.tamu.edu
Fine Arts Museum / University Museum - 1973
Art 36172

MSC Forsyth Center Galleries, Texas A & M University, Memorial Student Center, Joe Routt Blvd, College Station, TX 77844-9081 - T: (409) 845-9251, Fax: (409) 845-5117, E-mail: fcg@msc.tamu.edu, Internet: http://forsyth.tamu.edu. Head: Timothy Novak
Fine Arts Museum / Decorative Arts Museum / University Museum - 1989
Art 36173

Collegeville PA

Philip and Muriel Berman Museum of Art, Ursinus College, 601 East Main St, Collegeville, PA 19426-1000 - T: (610) 409-3500, Fax: (610) 409-3664, E-mail: lhanover@ursinus.edu, Internet: http://www.ursinus.edu. Head: Lisa Tremper Hanover
Fine Arts Museum / University Museum - 1987
Art 36174

Collingswood NJ

Film Forum - Film Archives, 579A Haddon Av, Collingswood, NJ 08108-1445 - T: (856) 854-3221. Head: David J. Grossman
Performing Arts Museum / Special Museum - 1989
Color design, social issues on film 36175

Collinsville IL

Cahokia Mounds State Historic Site, 30 Ramey St, Collinsville, IL 62234 - T: (618) 346-5160, Fax: (618) 346-5162, E-mail: cahokiamounds@ezl.com, Internet: http://www.cahokiamounds.com. Head: Christina Pallozola
Ethnology Museum / Archaeological Museum - 1930
Archaeology, 800-1500 A.D., site of largest prehistoric Indian city in North America 36176

Collinsville OK

Collinsville Depot Museum, 115 S 10, Collinsville, OK 74021 - T: (918) 371-3540. Head: Bill Thomas
Historical Museum - 1975 36177

Colonial Beach VA

George Washington Birthplace National Monument, 1732 Popes Creek Rd, Colonial Beach, VA 22443 - T: (804) 224-1732, Fax: (804) 224-2142, E-mail: gewa_park_information@nps.gov, Internet: http://www.nps.gov/gewa. Head: John J. Donahue
Local Museum - 1932
Birthplace of George Washington 36178

Colorado City TX

Heart of West Texas Museum, 340 E 3rd St, Colorado City, TX 79512 - T: (915) 728-8285, Fax: (915) 728-2597, E-mail: museum@bitstreet.com. Head: A.W. Rowe, Shirley Bradley
Local Museum - 1960
Local hist 36179

Colorado Springs CO

Carriage House Museum, 16 Lake Circle, Colorado Springs, CO 80906 - T: (719) 634-7711 ext 5704
Science&Tech Museum - 1941
Transportation 36180

Colorado Springs Fine Arts Center, 30 W Dale St, Colorado Springs, CO 80903 - T: (719) 634-5581, Fax: (719) 634-0570, Internet: http://www.csfineartscenter.org. Head: David Turner
Fine Arts Museum - 1936
Art 36181

Colorado Springs Museum, 215 S Tejon, Colorado Springs, CO 80903 - T: (719) 385-5990, Fax: (719) 385-5645, E-mail: cosmuseum@ci.colospgs.co.us, Internet: http://www.cspm.org. Head: William C. Holmes
Local Museum - 1937
Local history 36182

Gallery of Contemporary Art, University of Colorado, 1420 Austin Bluffs Pkwy, Colorado Springs, CO 80933-7150 - T: (719) 262-3567, 262-3504, Fax: (719) 262-3183, E-mail: griggs@mail.uccs.edu, Internet: http://harpy.uccs.edu/gallery/framesgallery.html. Head: Gerry Riggs
Fine Arts Museum / University Museum - 1981
Contemporary art 36183

McAllister House Museum, 423 N Cascade Av, Colorado Springs, CO 80903 - T: (719) 635-7925, Fax: (719) 528-5869, E-mail: patric@oldcolo.com, Internet: http://oldcolo.com/hist/mcallister
Historical Museum - 1961
Major Henry McAllister home 36184

May Natural History Museum and Museum of Space Exploration, John May Museum Ctr, 710 Rock Creek Canyon Rd, Colorado Springs, CO 80926-9799 - T: (719) 576-0450, Fax: (719) 576-3644, Internet: http://www.maymuseum-camp-rvpark.com. Head: John M. May
Science&Tech Museum / Natural History Museum - 1941
Natural history, entomology, space exploration 36185

Museum of the American Numismatic Association, 818 N Cascade, Colorado Springs, CO 80903 - T: (719) 632-2646, Fax: (719) 634-4085, E-mail: anamus@money.org, Internet: http://www.money.org. Head: Edward C. Rochette
Special Museum - 1967
Numismatics 36186

Pro Rodeo Hall of Fame and Museum of the American Cowboy, 101 Pro Rodeo Dr, Colorado Springs, CO 80919 - T: (719) 528-4761, Fax: (719) 548-4874, E-mail: phildebrand@prorodeo.com, Internet: http://www.prorodeo.com. Head: Steven J. Hatchell
Special Museum - 1979
Rodeo and Cowboy history 36187

Western Museum of Mining and Industry, 1025 N Gate Rd, Colorado Springs, CO 80921 - T: (719) 488-0880, Fax: (719) 488-9261, E-mail: westernmuseum@aol.com, Internet: http://www.wmmi.org. Head: Linda D. LeMieux
Science&Tech Museum - 1970
Mining, technology history 36188

World Figure Skating Museum and Hall of Fame, 20 First St, Colorado Springs, CO 80906 - T: (719) 635-5200, Fax: (719) 635-9548, E-mail: museum@usfsa.org, Internet: http://www.worldskatingmuseum.org
Special Museum - 1964
Sports 36189

Colter Bay Village WY

Colter Bay Indian Arts Museum, Visitor Center, Colter Bay Village, WY 83012 - T: (307) 739-3591, Fax: (307) 739-3504, E-mail: danna_kinsey@nps.gov, Internet: http://www.nps.gov/grte/
Fine Arts Museum / Ethnology Museum - 1972
Indian arts 36190

Colton CA

Colton Area Museum, 380 N La Cadena Dr, Colton, CA 92324 - T: (909) 824-8814. Head: Paula Olson
Local Museum / Historic Site - 1984
Indian artifacts 36191

Colton Point MD

Saint Clements Island-Potomac River Museum, 38370 Pointbreeze Rd, Colton Point, MD 20626 - T: (301) 769-2222, Fax: (301) 769-2225, E-mail: pineypoint@erols. Head: Michael E. Humphries
Historic Site / Historical Museum / Archaeological Museum - 1975
Archaeology, history, 1634 landing site of Maryland colonists, first Roman Catholic mass in English colonies 36192

Columbia CA

Columbia State Historic Park, 22708 Broadway, Columbia, CA 95310 - T: (209) 532-4301, Fax: (209) 532-5064, E-mail: calavera@goldrush.com, Internet: http://www.sierra.park-s.state.ca.us
Historical Museum / Special Museum - 1945 36193

Columbia MD

African Art Museum of Maryland, 5430 Vantage Point Rd, Columbia, MD 21044-0105 - T: (410) 730-7105, Fax: (410) 715-3047, E-mail: -africanartmuseum@erols.com, Internet: http://www.africanartmuseum.org. Head: Doris H. Ligon
Fine Arts Museum / Ethnology Museum - 1980
African art 36194

Columbia MO

Davis Art Gallery, Stephens College, Columbia, MO 65215 - T: (573) 876-4267, Fax: (573) 876-7248, Internet: http://www.stephens.edu. Head: Robert Friedman
Fine Arts Museum / University Museum - 1962 36195

Lewis, James and Nellie Stratton Gallery, Stephens College, 1200 Biway, Columbia, MO 65215 - T: (573) 876-7627 ext 173, Fax: (573) 876-7248. Head: Rosalind Kimball-Moulton
Fine Arts Museum
Modern graphics and paintings, primitive sculpture 36196

Museum of Anthropology, University of Missouri, 104 Swallow Hall, Columbia, MO 65211 - T: (573) 882-3573, Fax: (573) 884-1435, E-mail: FrenchME@missouri.edu, Internet: http://coas.missouri.edu/anthromu. Head: Michael J. O'Brien
University Museum / Ethnology Museum - 1949 36197

Museum of Art and Archaeology, University of Missouri, Pickard Hall, University Av and S Ninth St, Columbia, MO 65211 - T: (573) 882-3591, Fax: (573) 884-4039, Internet: http://www.research.missouri.edu/museum. Head: Marlene Perchinske
Fine Arts Museum / University Museum / Archaeological Museum - 1957 36198

State Historical Society of Missouri Museum, 1020 Lowry St, Columbia, MO 65201-7298 - T: (573) 882-7083, Fax: (573) 884-4950, E-mail: shsofmo@umsystem.edu, Internet: http://www.system.missouri.edu/shs. Head: Dr. James W. Goodrich
Historical Museum - 1898 36199

Columbia PA

National Watch and Clock Museum, 514 Poplar St, Columbia, PA 17512-2130 - T: (717) 684-8261, Fax: (717) 684-0878, E-mail: nconnelly@nawcc.org, Internet: http://www.nawcc.org. Head: Nancy Connelly
Science&Tech Museum - 1971 36200

Wright's Ferry Mansion, Second and Cherry Sts, Columbia, PA 17512 - T: (717) 684-4325. Head: Thomas Cook
Local Museum - 1974 36201

Columbia SC

Columbia Museum of Art, Main and Hampton Sts, Columbia, SC 29201, mail addr: POB 2068, Columbia, SC 29202 - T: (803) 799-2810, Fax: (803) 343-2150, E-mail: ellen@colmusart.org, Internet: http://www.columbiamuseum.org. Head: Salvatore G. Cilella
Fine Arts Museum - 1950
Art 36202

Governor's Mansion, 800 Richland St, Columbia, SC 29201 - T: (803) 737-1710, Fax: (803) 737-3860. Head: James H. Hodges
Historic Site - 1855
Historic house 36203

Hampton-Preston Mansion, 1615 Blanding St, Columbia, SC 29201 - T: (803) 252-1770, Fax: (803) 929-7695. Head: Dr. John G. Sproat, Arrington Cox
Historical Museum - 1961
Historic house 36204

Historic Columbia Foundation, 1601 Richland St, Columbia, SC 29201 - T: (803) 252-7742, Fax: (803) 929-7695. Head: Dr. John G. Sproat, Arrington Cox, John Sherrer
Local Museum - 1961
Local hist 36205

McKissick Museum, University of South Carolina, Pendleton and Bull Sts, Columbia, SC 29208 - T: (803) 777-7251, Fax: (803) 777-2829, E-mail: lynn.robertson@sc.edu, Internet: http://www.cla.sc.edu/mcks. Head: Lynn Robertson
Folklore Museum / Natural History Museum / University Museum - 1976
Folk art, natural sciences, material culture 36206

Mann-Simons Cottage, 1403 Richland St, Columbia, SC 29201 - T: (803) 252-1770, Fax: (803) 252-5001. Head: Dr. John G. Sproat, Arrington Cox
Historical Museum - 1961
House dedicated to free African American Celia Mann and her family who lived here until 1970 36207

Robert Mills Historic House and Park, Historic Columbia Foundation, 1601 Richland St, Columbia, SC 29201 - T: (803) 252-1770, Fax: (803) 929-7695. Head: Roger D. Poston, Cynthia Moses Nesmith
Local Museum - 1961
Local hist 36208

South Carolina Confederate Relic Room and Museum, 301 Gervais St, Columbia, SC 29201 - T: (803) 737-8095, Fax: (803) 737-8099, Internet: http://www.state.sc.us/crr. Head: W. Allen Roberson
Historical Museum - 1896
History 36209

South Carolina Law Enforcement Officers Hall of Fame, 5400 Broad River Rd, Columbia, SC 29212 - T: (803) 896-8199, Fax: (803) 896-8067
Special Museum / Historical Museum - 1979
Law enforcement artifacts 36210

South Carolina State Museum, 301 Gervais St, Columbia, SC 29201 - T: (803) 898-4921, Fax: (803) 898-4917, E-mail: artcurator@museum.state.sc.us, Internet: http://www.museum.state.sc.us. Head: Dr. Overton G. Ganong
Local Museum - 1973
Local hist, culture, art, natural history, science, technology 36211

Columbia TN

James K. Polk Ancestral Home, 301 W 7th St, Columbia, TN 38401 - T: (931) 388-2354, Fax: (931) 388-5971, E-mail: jkpolk@usit.net, Internet: http://www.jameskpolk.com. Head: John C. Holtzapple
Historic Site - 1924
Historic house 36212

Columbia City IN

Whitley County Historical Museum, 108 W Jefferson, Columbia City, IN 46725 - T: (219) 244-6372, Fax: (219) 244-6384, Internet: http://www.whitleynet.org/historical/. Head: Ruth Kirk
Local Museum - 1963
County history 36213

Columbia Falls ME

Ruggles House, off U.S. Rte 1, Columbia Falls, ME 04623 - T: (207) 483-4637, 546-7429, E-mail: ruggles@midmaine.com. Head: Richard Grant
Historical Museum - 1949 36214

Columbiana OH

Historical Society of Columbiana-Fairfield Township Museum, 10 E Park Av, Columbiana, OH 44408 - T: (330) 482-2983
Local Museum - 1953 36215

Columbus GA

The Columbus Museum, 1251 Wynnton Rd, Columbus, GA 31906 - T: (706) 649-0713, Fax: (706) 649-1070, E-mail: colmuseum@mcsd.ga.net, Internet: http://www.columbusmuseum.com. Head: Charles Thomas Butler
Fine Arts Museum / Historical Museum - 1952
Archaeology, costumes and textiles, decorative arts, paintings, photos, prints, drawings, graphics, sculpture, furnishings, personal artifacts 36216

Historic Columbus Foundation, 700 Broadway, Columbus, GA 31901 - T: (706) 322-0756, Fax: (706) 576-4760, E-mail: hcf.inc@minspring.com, Internet: http://www.historic-columbus.com. Head: Stephen G. Gunby, Virginia T. Peebles
Historical Museum - 1966
Five house museums incl c.1870 first brick house in original residential part of city 36217

Woodruff Museum of Civil War Naval History, South Commons at Victory Dr, Columbus, GA 31902, mail addr: Box 1022, Columbus, GA 31902 - T: (706) 324-7334, Fax: (706) 324-2070, E-mail: cwnavy@portcolumbus.org, Internet: http://www.portcolumbus.org. Head: Bruce Smith
Military Museum - 1962
Naval Museum 36218

Columbus IN

Bartholomew County Historical Museum, 524 Third St, Columbus, IN 47201 - T: (812) 372-3541. Head: Laura J. Moses
Local Museum - 1921
Local History 36219

Indianapolis Museum of Art - Columbus Gallery, 390 The Commons, Columbus, IN 47201-6764 - T: (812) 376-2597, Fax: (812) 375-2724, E-mail: imacg@hsonline.net, Internet: http://www.ima-art.org. Head: Andrew B. Simms, Jerry Handley
Fine Arts Museum - 1974
Art 36220

Columbus KY

Columbus-Belmont Civil War Museum, 350 Park Rd, Columbus, KY 42032 - T: (502) 677-2327, Fax: (502) 677-4013, E-mail: cindy.lynch@state.us.mail, Internet: http://www.kystateparks.com/angencies/parks/columbus.htm. Head: Cindy Lynch
Historical Museum / Military Museum - 1934
History, civil war, military 36221

Columbus MS

Blewitt-Harrison-Lee Museum, 316 Seventh St N, Columbus, MS 39701 - T: (662) 329-3533. Head: Caroline Neault
Local Museum - 1960
Local artifacts, furniture, jewelry, pictures, portraits 36222

Florence McLeod Hazard Museum, 316 Seventh St N, Columbus, MS 39701 - T: (662) 327-8888. Head: John Davis, Caroline Neault
Historical Museum - 1959 36223

Mississippi University for Women Museum, Fant Library, Columbus, MS 39701 - T: (601) 329-7334, Fax: (601) 329-7348, E-mail: fdavison@muw.edu, Internet: http://www.muw.edu. Head: Dr. Clyda S. Rent
University Museum - 1978 36224

Columbus OH

ACME Art Gallery, 1129 N High St, Columbus, OH 43201 - T: (614) 299-4003, Internet: http://www.acmeart.com. Head: Margaret Evans
Fine Arts Museum 36225

Columbus Cultural Arts Center, 139 W Main St, Columbus, OH 43215 - T: (614) 645-7047, Fax: (614) 645-5862, E-mail: jljohnson@cmhmetro.net, Internet: http://www.culturalartscen-teronline.com. Head: Richard Wissler, Jennifer L. Johnson
Fine Arts Museum / Folklore Museum / Historical Museum - 1978 36226

Columbus Museum of Art, 480 E Broad St, Columbus, OH 43215 - T: (614) 221-6801, Fax: (614) 221-0226, Internet: http://www.columbusart.mus.oh.us. Head: Irvin M. Lippman
Fine Arts Museum - 1878 36227

COSI Columbus, 333 W Broad St, Columbus, OH 43215-3773 - T: (614) 228-2674, Fax: (614) 228-6363, E-mail: cosi@cosi.org, Internet: http://www.cosi.org. Head: Kathryn D. Sullivan
Science&Tech Museum - 1964 36228

Kelton House Museum & Garden, 586 E Town St, Columbus, OH 43215-4888 - T: (614) 464-2022, Fax: (614) 464-3346, E-mail: Keltonhouse@cs.com
Special Museum / Folklore Museum - 1976
Historic house 36229

Ohio Historical Center, 1982 Velma Av, Columbus, OH 43211-2497 - T: (614) 297-2300, Fax: (614) 297-2318, E-mail: ohsref.ohiohistory.org, Internet: http://www.ohiohistory.org
Historical Museum - 1885 36230

Orton Geological Museum, Ohio State University, 155 S Oval Mall, Columbus, OH 43210 - T: (614) 292-6896, Fax: (614) 292-1496. Head: Prof. Stig M. Bergstrom
University Museum / Natural History Museum - 1892 36231

Schumacher Gallery, Capital University, 2199 E Main St, Columbus, OH 43209 - T: (614) 236-6319, Fax: (614) 236-6490. Head: Dr. Cassandra Tellier
Fine Arts Museum / University Museum - 1964 36232

Wexner Center for the Arts, Ohio State University, 1871 N High St, Columbus, OH 43210-1393 - T: (614) 292-0330, Fax: (614) 292-3369, E-mail: wexner@cgrg.ohio-state.edu, Internet: http://www.wexarts.org. Head: Sherri Geldin, Sarah J. Rogers, Charles Helm, Patricia Trumps
Fine Arts Museum / University Museum / Performing Arts Museum - 1989 36233

Commack NY

Long Island Culture History Museum, Hoyt Farm Park, New Hwy, Commack, NY 11725, mail addr: POB 1542, Stony Brook, NY 11790 - T: (516) 929-8725, Fax: (516) 929-6967. Head: Gaynell Stone
Historical Museum / Archaeological Museum / Open Air Museum - 1986
History, archaeology 36234

Commerce

University Gallery, Texas A & M University, POB 3011, TX 75429 Commerce - T: (903) 886-5208, Fax: (214) 886-5415, E-mail: BarbaraFrey@tamu-commerce.edu. Head: Barbara Frey
Fine Arts Museum - 1979 36235

Comstock TX

Seminole Canyon State Historical Park, U.S. Hwy 90 West, Comstock, TX 78837 - T: (915) 292-4464, Fax: (915) 292-4596
Archaeological Museum - 1980
Archaeology site, containing 4,000-year old pictographs 36236

Concord MA

Concord Art Association Museum, 37 Lexington Rd, Concord, MA 01742 - T: (508) 369-2578, Fax: (508) 371-2496
Fine Arts Museum - 1922
Art gallery 36237

Concord Museum, 200 Lexington Rd, Concord, MA 01742 - T: (978) 369-9763, Fax: (978) 369-9660, E-mail: cm1@concordmuseum.org, Internet: http://www.concordmuseum.org. Head: Desiree Caldwell
Decorative Arts Museum / Local Museum / Historical Museum - 1886
Local history, decorative arts 36238

Minute Man National Historical Park, 174 Liberty St, Concord, MA 01742 - T: (978) 369-6993, Fax: (978) 371-2483, Internet: http://www.nps.gov/mima. Head: Nancy Nelson
Historical Museum / Archaeological Museum - 1959
Along 1775 battle road, 19th c wayside, Nathaniel Hawthorne, Alcott and Lothrop family home 36239

The Old Manse, 269 Monument St, Concord, MA 01742, mail addr: POB 572, Concord, MA 01742 - T: (978) 369-3909, Fax: (978) 287-6154, E-mail: oldmanse@ttor.org, Internet: http://www.thetrustees.org
Historical Museum - 1939
Site of the 1st major skirmish of the Revolutionary War 1775, home to Ralph Waldo Emerson and Nathaniel Hawthorne 36240

Orchard House - Home of the Alcotts, 399 Lexington Rd, Concord, MA 01742 - T: (978) 369-4118, Fax: (978) 369-1367, E-mail: info@louisamayalcott.org, Internet: http://www.louisamayalcott.org. Head: Jan Turnquist
Special Museum - 1911
House where Louisa May Alcott wrote Little Women, Bronson Alcott's School of Philosophy, American history, art 36241

Ralph Waldo Emerson House, 28 Cambridge Turnpike at Lexington Rd, Concord, MA 01742 - T: (978) 369-2236. Head: William Bancroft, Barbara Mongan
Historical Museum - 1930 36242

Concord MI

Historic Mann House, 205 Hanover St, Concord, MI 49237 - T: (517) 524-8943
Historical Museum - 1970 36243

Concord NH

Art Center In Hargate, Saint Paul's School, 325 Pleasant St, Concord, NH 03301 - T: (603) 229-4644, Fax: (603) 229-4649, E-mail: ksmith@sps.edu, Internet: http://www.sps.edu/arts/hargate/index.shtml. Head: Colin J. Callahan
Fine Arts Museum - 1967
Drawings, graphics, paintings, sculpture, school gifts - Ohrstrom library 36244

Museum of New Hampshire History, 6 Eagle Sq, Concord, NH 03301 - T: (603) 226-3189, Fax: (603) 226-3198, E-mail: jvachon@nhhistory.org, Internet: http://www.nhhistory.org. Head: John L. Frisbee
Decorative Arts Museum / Historical Museum - 1823 36245

Pierce Manse, 14 Penacook St, Concord, NH 03301 - T: (603) 224-5954. Head: Florence Holden
Historical Museum - 1966
1842-1848 home of President Franklin Pierce 36246

Concordia KS

Cloud County Historical Museum, 635 Broadway, Concordia, KS 66901 - T: (913) 243-2866
Local Museum - 1959
Local history 36247

Connersville IN

Henry H. Blommel Historic Automotive Data Collection, 427 E County Rd, 215 S, Connersville, IN 47331 - T: (317) 825-9259
Science&Tech Museum - 1928
Automotive industry 36248

Constantine MI

John S. Barry Historical Society Museum, 300 N Washington, Constantine, MI 49042 - T: (616) 435-5825. Head: Dr. Vercler
Local Museum - 1945
Local history, 1835-1847 Governor Barry House 36249

Conway AR

Faulkner County Museum, Courthouse Square, 805 Locust St, Conway, AR 72032 - T: (501) 329-5918. Head: Dr. George H. Thompson
Local Museum - 1959
Local history 36250

Conway SC

Horry County Museum, 428 Main St, Conway, SC 29526 - T: (803) 248-1542, Fax: (843) 248-1854, E-mail: hcmuseum@sccoast.net
Historical Museum / Ethnology Museum / Archaeological Museum - 1979
Anthropology, history, archaeology 36251

Cookeville TN

Cookeville Art Gallery, 186 S Walnut, Cookeville, TN 38501 - T: (615) 526-2424. Head: Linda McGraw
Public Gallery - 1961 36252

Cookeville Depot Museum, 116 W Broad St, Cookeville, TN 38503 - T: (931) 528-8570, Fax: (931) 526-1167, E-mail: depot@ci.cookeville.tn.us. Head: Judy Duke
Science&Tech Museum - 1984
Transportation, railroads 36253

Coolidge AZ

Casa Grande Ruins, 1100 Ruins Dr, Coolidge, AZ 85228 - T: (520) 723-3172, Fax: (520) 723-7209, Internet: http://www.cagr.mps.gov
Historic Site / Archaeological Museum - 1892
Archaeology, located on Hohokam village, approx. A.D. 500-1450 36254

Coolspring PA

Coolspring Power Museum, Main St, Coolspring, PA 15730 - T: (814) 849-6883, Fax: (814) 849-5495, E-mail: coolspring@penn.com, Internet: http://www.coopspringpowermuseum.org. Head: John Wilcox, Whitey Forman, Preston Foster, Edward Kuntz, Vance Packard, John Kline, Paul Harvey
Science&Tech Museum - 1985
Internal combustion engine technology, electric generators, oil field technology 36255

Cooperstown NY

The Farmers' Museum, Lake Rd, Cooperstown, NY 13326 - T: (607) 547-1450, Fax: (607) 547-1499, E-mail: nysha1@aol.com, Internet: http://www.farmersmuseum.org
Open Air Museum / Agriculture Museum - 1943
Early 19th-century Village, agricultural tools and implements 36256

Fenimore Art Museum, Lake Rd, Cooperstown, NY 13326 - T: (607) 547-1400, Fax: (607) 547-1404, E-mail: nysha1@aol.com, Internet: http://www.nysha.org. Head: Dr. Gilbert T. Vincent
Fine Arts Museum - 1899 36257

National Baseball Hall of Fame and Museum, 25 Main St, Cooperstown, NY 13326 - T: (607) 547-7200, Fax: (607) 547-2044, E-mail: info@baseballhalloffame.org., Internet: http://www.baseballhalloffame.org
Special Museum - 1936 36258

Coos Bay OR

Coos Art Museum, 235 Anderson, Coos Bay, OR 97420 - T: (541) 267-3901, Fax: (541) 267-4877, Internet: http://www.coosart.org. Head: Kathy Rosencrantz
Fine Arts Museum - 1950 36259

Copper Center AK

George I. Ashby Memorial Museum, Mile 101 Old Richardson Hwy, Copper Center Loop Rd, Copper Center, AK 99573 - T: (907) 822-5285. Head: Fred Williams
Local Museum 36260

Copper Harbor MI

Fort Wilkins Historic Complex, Fort Wilkins, Copper Harbor, MI 49918 - T: (906) 289-4215, Fax: (906) 289-4939. Head: Dan Plesher
Local Museum - 1923
Outdoor museum incl Fort Wilkins, Pittsburgh and Boston Co. Mine, lighthouse 36261

Coral Gables FL

Coral Gables Merrick House, 907 Coral Way, Coral Gables, Coral Gables, FL 33134 - T: (305) 460-5361, Fax: (305) 460-5371, E-mail: cmcgeehan@citybeautiful.net, Internet: http://www.citybeautiful.net
Decorative Arts Museum - 1976
Plantation house belonging to family of founder of Coral Gables 36262

Creatabilitoys! - Museum of Advertising Icons, 1550 Madruga Av, Coral Gables, FL 33146 - T: (305) 663-7374, Fax: (305) 669-0092, E-mail: info@creatability.com, Internet: http://www.toymuseum.com. Head: Ritchie Lucas
Decorative Arts Museum - 1995
Toys and dolls 36263

The Florida Museum of Hispanic and Latin American Art, 4006 Aurora St, Coral Gables, FL 33126-1414 - T: (305) 444-7060, Fax: (305) 261-6996, E-mail: Hispmuseum@aol.com, Internet: http://www.latinoweb.com/museo/. Head: Raul M. Oyuela
Fine Arts Museum - 1991
Art 36264

Lowe Art Museum, University of Miami, 1301 Stanford Dr, Coral Gables, FL 33124-6310 - T: (305) 284-3603, Fax: (305) 284-2024, E-mail: bdursum@miami.edu, Internet: http://www.lowemuseum.org. Head: Brian A. Dursum
Fine Arts Museum / University Museum - 1950 36265

Coralville IA

Johnson County Heritage Museum, 310 Fifth St, Coralville, IA 52241 - T: (319) 351-5738, Fax: (319) 351-5310. Head: John Chadima, Laurie Robinson
Local Museum - 1973
Local history 36266

Cordele GA

Georgia Veterans Memorial Museum, 2459-A Hwy 280 W, Cordele, GA 31015 - T: (912) 276-2371, Fax: (912) 276-2372, E-mail: gavets@sowega.net. Head: Charles Luther
Military Museum - 1962
Military hist 36267

Cordova AK

Cordova Historical Museum, 622 1st St, Cordova, AK 99574 - T: (907) 424-6665, Fax: (907) 424-6666, E-mail: cdvmsm@ptialaska.net. Head: Gayle Beckett, Cathy R. Sherman
Local Museum - 1966
General museum 36268

Corning NY

Benjamin Patterson Inn Museum Complex, 59 W Pulteney St, Corning, NY 14830-2212 - T: (607) 937-5281, Fax: (607) 937-5281, E-mail: BenPATT@juno.com. Head: Norma Bird, Roger Grigsby
Historical Museum - 1976 36269

Corning Glass Center, 151 Centerway, Corning, NY 14831 - T: (607) 974-8173, Fax: (607) 974-8310, Internet: http://www.corning.com/cgc/cgchome.html. Head: Romaine L. Crawford-Mulley
Decorative Arts Museum - 1951 36270

Corning Museum of Glass, 1 Corning Glass Center, Corning, NY 14830-2253 - T: (607) 937-5371, Fax: (607) 974-8470, E-mail: cmg@cmog.org, Internet: http://www.cmog.org. Head: David B. Whitehouse
Decorative Arts Museum - 1951 36271

Rockwell Museum of Western Art, 111 Cedar St, Corning, NY 14830-2694 - T: (607) 937-5386, Fax: (607) 974-4536, E-mail: info@rockwellmuseum.org, Internet: http://www.rockwellmuseum.org. Head: Stuart A. Chase
Fine Arts Museum / Decorative Arts Museum - 1976 36272

Cornish NH

Saint Gaudens National Historic Site, Saint Gaudens Rd, Cornish, NH 03745 - T: (603) 675-2175, Fax: (603) 675-2701, E-mail: saga@nps.gov, Internet: http://www.nps.gov/saga. Head: John Dryfhout
Fine Arts Museum - 1926 36273

Cornwall CT

Cornwall Historical Museum, 7 Pine St, Cornwall, CT 06753. Head: Michael R. Gannett
Local Museum - 1964
Local history 36274

Cornwall PA

Cornwall Iron Furnace, Rexmont Rd at Boyd St, Cornwall, PA 17016 - T: (717) 272-9711, Fax: (717) 272-0450. Head: Stephen G. Somers
Science&Tech Museum - 1931 36275

Cornwall-on-Hudson NY

Museum of the Hudson Highlands, The Boulevard, Cornwall-on-Hudson, NY 12520 - T: (845) 534-5506, Fax: (845) 534-4581, E-mail: rzito@museumhudsonhighlands.org, Internet: http://www.museumhudsonhighlands.org. Head: Ross Zito
Fine Arts Museum / Natural History Museum - 1962 36276

Corpus Christi TX

Art Museum of South Texas, 1902 N Shoreline, Corpus Christi, TX 78401 - T: (361) 825-3500, Fax: (361) 825-3520, E-mail: stiawel@mail.tamucc.edu, Internet: http://www.stia.org. Head: Dr. William G. Otton
Fine Arts Museum - 1960
Art 36277

Asian Cultures Museum, 1809 N Champarral St, Corpus Christi, TX 78401 - T: (361) 882-2641, Fax: (361) 882-5718, E-mail: asiancm@yahoo.com, Internet: www.geocities.com/asiancm. Head: Catherine LaCroix
Decorative Arts Museum - 1973 36278

Corpus Christi Museum of Science and History, 1900 N Chaparral, Corpus Christi, TX 78401 - T: (512) 883-2862, Fax: (512) 884-7392. Head: Richard R. Stryker
Local Museum - 1957
Local hist 36279

USS Lexington Museum on the Bay, 2914 N Shoreline Blvd, Corpus Christi, TX 78402 - T: (800) ladylex, Fax: (512) 883-8361, Internet: http://www.usslexington.com. Head: Frank Montesano, M. Charles Reustle
Military Museum - 1991
Naval military hist 36280

Corrales NM

Dia Center for the Arts, POB 2993, Corrales, NM 87048 - T: (505) 898-3335, Fax: (505) 898-3336, Internet: http://www.diacenter.org
Fine Arts Museum 36281

Corry PA

Corry Area Historical Society Museum, 937 Mead Av, Corry, PA 16407 - T: (814) 664-4749, Internet: http://www.tbscc.com. Head: James R. Nelson
Local Museum - 1965
locomotive, generalogy research 36282

Corsicana TX

Navarro County Historical Society Museum, 912 W Park Av, Corsicana, TX 75110 - T: (903) 654-4846
Local Museum - 1956
8 log buildings contructed in Navarro County during 1838-1865 36283

Cortez CO

Crow Canyon Archaeological Center, 23390 County Rd K, Cortez, CO 81321 - T: (970) 565-8975, Fax: (970) 565-4859, E-mail: ltbaca@crowcanyon.org, Internet: http://www.crowcanyon.org. Head: Ricky Lightfoot
Archaeological Museum - 1983
Archaeology 36284

Cortland NY

1890 House-Museum and Center for Victorian Arts, 37 Tompkins St, Cortland, NY 13045-2555 - T: (607) 756-7551. Head: John Finn, John H. Nozynski
Decorative Arts Museum / Fine Arts Museum - 1975 36285

Bowers Science Museum, Bowers Hall, State University of New York at Cortland, Cortland, NY 13045 - T: (607) 753-2715, Fax: (607) 753-2927. Head: Dr. Peter K. Ducey
University Museum / Natural History Museum / Science&Tech Museum - 1964 36286

Cortland County Historical Society Museum, 25 Homer Av, Cortland, NY 13045 - T: (607) 756-6071. Head: Mary Ann Kane
Local Museum - 1925
library 36287

Dowd Fine Arts Gallery, State University of New York, Suny Cortland, Cortland, NY 13045 - T: (607) 753-4216, Fax: (607) 753-5728, E-mail: graffa@cortland.edu, Internet: http://www.cortland.edu/art/dowd.html. Head: Allison Graff
Fine Arts Museum / University Museum - 1967
Art gallery 36288

Corydon IA

Prairie Trails Museum of Wayne County, Hwy 2 E, Corydon, IA 50060 - T: (515) 872-2211, Fax: (515) 872-2664. Head: Hal Greenlee
Local Museum - 1942
General museum 36289

Coshocton OH

Johnson-Humrickhouse Museum, Roscoe Village, 300 N Whitewoman St, Coshocton, OH 43812 - T: (740) 622-8710, Fax: (740) 622-8710, E-mail: jhmuseum@clover.net, Internet: http://jhm.lib.oh.us. Head: Patti Malenke
Local Museum - 1931
American Indian, Japanese, Chinese, American and European decorative arts, weapon, Ohio history 36290

Roscoe Village Foundation, 381 Hill St, Coshocton, OH 43812 - T: (740) 622-9310, Fax: (614) 623-6555, E-mail: rvmarketing@coshocton.com, Internet: http://www.roscoevillage.com. Head: John Rodriguez, Thomas Mackie
Historic Site / Open Air Museum - 1968 36291

Cottage Grove OR

Cottage Grove Museum, 147 High St and Birch Av, Cottage Grove, OR 97424 - T: (541) 942-3963, 942-5334. Head: Isabelle S. Woolcott
Local Museum - 1961
Local hist 36292

Cottonwood ID

The Historical Museum at Saint Gertrude, Keuterville Rd, Cottonwood, ID 83522-9408 - T: (208) 962-7123, Fax: (208) 962-8647, E-mail: museum@micron.net, Internet: http://www.webpark.net/~museum. Head: Lyle Wirtanen
Local Museum - 1931 36293

Cottonwood Falls KS

Roniger Memorial Museum, 315 Union, Cottonwood Falls, KS 66845 - T: (316) 273-6310, 273-6412, Fax: (316) 273-6671, E-mail: dcroy@valu-live.net. Head: David E. Croy
Historical Museum / Special Museum - 1959
History, old courthouse 36294

Cotuit MA

Cahoon Museum of American Art, 4676 Falmouth Rd, Cotuit, MA 02635 - T: (508) 428-7581, Fax: (508) 420-3709, E-mail: cmaa@cahoonmuseum.org, Internet: http://www.cahoonmuseum.org. Head: Cindy Nickerson
Fine Arts Museum - 1984 36295

Historical Society of Santuit and Cotuit, 1148 Main St, Cotuit, MA 02635 - T: (508) 428-2199. Head: Jessica Grassetti
Local Museum - 1954
Restored home of village carpenter, local history 36296

Coudersport PA

Potter County Historical Society Museum, 308 N Main St, Coudersport, PA 16915 - T: (814) 274-8124. Head: Robert K. Currin
Local Museum - 1919 36297

Council Bluffs IA

Historic General Dodge House, 605 3rd St, Council Bluffs, IA 51503 - T: (712) 322-2406. Head: Cheryl L. Nelson-Stover
Local Museum / Decorative Arts Museum - 1961
Historic house 36298

Council Grove KS

Kaw Mission, 500 N Mission, Council Grove, KS 66846 - T: (316) 767-5410
Ethnology Museum - 1951 36299

Courtland VA

Rawls Museum Arts, 22376 Linden St, Courtland, VA 23837 - T: (757) 653-0754, Fax: (757) 653-0341, E-mail: rma@bcldar.com. Head: Barbara Easton-Moore
Fine Arts Museum - 1958
Art, visual arts 36300

Coventry RI

Western Rhode Island Civic Museum, 7 Station St, Coventry, RI 02816 - T: (401) 821-4095. Head: Lynda Hawkins
Local Museum - 1945
Local hist 36301

Covington KY

Behringer-Crawford Museum, 1600 Montague Rd, Devou Park, Covington, KY 41012 - T: (859) 491-4003, Fax: (859) 491-4006. Head: Laurie Risch
Local Museum - 1950
Local hist 36302

The Railway Exposition, 315 W Southern Av, Covington, KY 41015 - T: (513) 761-3500
Science&Tech Museum - 1975
Railway 36303

Coweta OK

Mission Bell Museum, W Cypress and South Av B, Coweta, OK 74429 - T: (918) 486-2513
Local Museum - 1977 36304

Coxsackie NY

Bronck Museum, 90 County Rte 42, Coxsackie, NY 12051 - T: (518) 731-6490, Fax: (518) 731-7672, Internet: http://www.gchistory.org. Head: Shelby Mattice
Local Museum - 1929
Vedder library 36305

Cozad NE

The 100th Meridian Museum, 206 E Eighth St, Cozad, NE 69130 - T: (308) 784-1100, 784-2704. Head: Judy Andres, Glenda France
Local Museum - 1994 36306

Craig CO

Museum of Northwest Colorado, 590 Yampa Av, Craig, CO 81625 - T: (970) 824-6360, Fax: (970) 824-7175, E-mail: musnwco.cmn.net, Internet: http://www.museumnwco.org. Head: Dan Davidson
Local Museum - 1964
Regional history 36307

Cranbury NJ

Cranbury Historical and Preservation Society Museum, 4 Park Pl E, Cranbury, NJ 08512 - T: (609) 395-0420, E-mail: WDW158@aol.com
Historical Museum / Local Museum - 1967
History center, library 36308

Crawford NE

Fort Robinson Museum, US Hwy 20, Crawford, NE 69339 - T: (308) 665-2919, Fax: (308) 665-2917, E-mail: fortrob@bbc.net. Head: Thomas R. Buecker
Military Museum - 1956 36309

Crawfordsville IN

Ben-Hur Museum, Pike St at Wallace Av, Crawfordsville, IN 47933 - T: (765) 362-5769, 364-5175, Fax: (765) 364-5179, E-mail: study@wico.net, Internet: http://www.ben-hur.com. Head: Cheryl Keim
Historical Museum / Library with Exhibitions - 1896
1896 General Lew Wallace Study, author of 'Ben-Hur' - library 36310

The Lane Place, 212 S Water St, Crawfordsville, IN 47933 - T: (317) 362-3416. Head: Conrad Harvey, Michael D. Hall
Historical Museum / Decorative Arts Museum - 1911
Home of Henry S. Lane, governor and senator of Indiana 36311

The Old Jail Museum, c/o Montgomery County Cultural Foundation, 225 N Washington, Crawfordsville, IN 47933 - T: (765) 362-5222, Fax: (765) 362-5222, E-mail: oldjail@tctc.com, Internet: http://crawfordsville.org/jail.html. Head: Ron Bodine
Historical Museum - 1975
1882 Old Jail only remaining rotating circular jail still in working condition 36312

Crawfordville GA

Confederate Museum, Alexander St, Crawfordville, GA 30631 - T: (706) 456-2221, 456-2602, Fax: (706) 456-2396, E-mail: ahssp@g-net.net, Internet: http://www.g-net.net/~ahssp/. Head: Randy Trammell
Historical Museum - 1952
History Museum 36313

Crazy Horse SD

Indian Museum of North America, Av of the Chiefs, Crazy Horse, SD 57730-9506 - T: (605) 673-4681, Fax: (605) 673-2185, E-mail: memorial@crazyhorse.com, Internet: http://www.crazyhorse.org. Head: Anne Ziolkowski
Ethnology Museum - 1972
Indian culture 36314

Crescent City CA

Del Norte County Historical Society Museum, 577 H St, Crescent City, CA 95531 - T: (707) 464-3922. Head: Sean Smith
Local Museum - 1951 36315

Crestline OH

Crestline Shunk Museum, 211 Thoman St, Crestline, OH 44827 - T: (419) 683-3410. Head: Nancy Everly
Local Museum - 1947 36316

Creston IA

Union County Historical Complex, McKinley Park, Creston, IA 50801 - T: (515) 782-4247. Head: Paul Roeder
Local Museum / Open Air Museum - 1966
General and village museum, 10 pioneer bldgs 36317

Crestwood MO

Thomas Sappington House Museum, 1015 S Sappington Rd, Crestwood, MO 63126 - T: (314) 822-8171, Fax: (314) 129-4794, E-mail: lblumer@ci.crestwood.mo.us, Internet: http://www.ci.crestwood.mo.us. Head: Doris Moeller
Historical Museum - 1965 36318

Creswell NC

Somerset Place State Historic Site, 2572 Lake Shore Rd, Creswell, NC 27928 - T: (919) 797-4560, Fax: (919) 797-4171, E-mail: somerset@coastalnet.com, Internet: http://www.ah.dcr.state.nc.us/hs/somerset/somerset.htm. Head: Dorothy Spruill Redford
Local Museum - 1969 36319

Cripple Creek CO

Cripple Creek District Museum, 500 E Bennett Av, Cripple Creek, CO 80813 - T: (719) 689-9540, Fax: (719) 689-0512, Internet: http://www.cripplecreek.com. Head: Richard W. Johnson, Erik Swanson
Fine Arts Museum / Local Museum - 1953
Local history, historic camp where gold was discovered in 1890 36320

Critz VA

Reynolds Homestead, 463 Homestead Ln, Critz, VA 24082 - T: (703) 694-7181, Fax: (703) 694-7183, E-mail: registrar.reynolds.homestead@vt.edu, Internet: http://www.cis.vt.edu/reynolds_homestead/defualt.html. Head: David D. Britt
Fine Arts Museum / Local Museum - 1970
Historic house 36321

Crockett TX

Discover Houston County Visitors Center-Museum, 303 S First St, Crockett, TX 75835 - T: (409) 544-9520
Local Museum - 1983
Local hist 36322

Croghan NY

American Maple Museum, POB 81, Croghan, NY 13327 - T: (315) 346-1107
Agriculture Museum - 1977 36323

Crookston MN

Polk County Historical Museum, 719 E Robert, Crookston, MN 56716 - T: (218) 281-1038. Head: Allen Brolsma
Local Museum - 1930
Regional history 36324

Crosby ND

Divide County Historical Society Museum, Pioneer Village, Crosby, ND 58730 - T: (701) 965-6297. Head: Perry E. Rosenquist
Local Museum - 1969
Regional history 36325

Crosbyton TX

Crosby County Pioneer Memorial Museum, 101 W Main intersection U.S. 82 and F.M. 651, Crosbyton, TX 79322 - T: (806) 675-2331, 675-2906, Fax: (804) 649-0878, E-mail: ccpmm@door.net, Internet: http://www.door.net//ccmuseum/. Head: Gary Mitchel, Verna Anne Wheeler
Local Museum - 1958
Local hist 36326

Cross Creek FL

Marjorie Kinnan Rawlings State Historic Site, S. R. 325 at Cross Creek, Hawthorne Cross Creek, FL 32640 - T: (352) 466-9273, Fax: (352) 466-4743, E-mail: mkrshs@bellsouth.net
Historical Museum / Agriculture Museum - 1970
1930's citrus farm and home of Marjorie Kinnan Rawlings, a rambling Cracker farmhouse 36327

Cross River NY

Trailside Nature Museum, Ward Pound Ridge Reservation, Cross River, NY 10518 - T: (914) 763-3993, Fax: (914) 763-2429
Natural History Museum - 1937 36328

Crowley LA

Crowley Art Association and Gallery, 220 N Parkerson, Crowley, LA 70527-2003 - T: (337) 783-3747
Fine Arts Museum / Decorative Arts Museum - 1980
Art gallery, crafts 36329

The Rice Museum, W Hwy 90, Crowley, LA 70527-1176 - T: (318) 783-6842, Fax: (318) 788-0459. Head: Diane Hoffpauer
Special Museum - 1970 36330

Crown Point NY

Crown Point State Historic Site, Bridge Rd, Crown Point, NY 12928 - T: (518) 597-3666, Fax: (518) 597-4668. Head: Bill Farar
Military Museum - 1910
1734 remains of French fort, 1759 British Fort Crown Point and Outwork fortifications controlling Lake Champlain 36331

Crystal River FL

Crystal River State Archaeological Site, 3400 N Museum Pt, Crystal River, FL 34428 - T: (352) 795-3817, Fax: (352) 795-6061, E-mail: crsas@sunco.com
Archaeological Museum - 1965 36332

Cuddebackville NY

Neversink Valley Area Museum, D and H Canal Park, Hoag Rd, Cuddebackville, NY 12729 - T: (845) 754-8870, E-mail: nvam@magiccarpet.com, Internet: http://www.neversinkmuseum.org. Head: Donna E. Steffens
Local Museum / Natural History Museum - 1964 36333

Cuero TX

DeWitt County Historical Museum, 312 E Broadway, Cuero, TX 77954 - T: (361) 275-6322. Head: Jean Ann Sheppard
Local Museum - 1973
Local hist 36334

Culbertson MT

Northeastern Montana Threshers and Antique Association Museum, POB 12, Culbertson, MT 59218 - T: (406) 787-5265, E-mail: elk1@nemontel.net. Head: David Krogedal
Agriculture Museum - 1964 36335

Cullman AL

Cullman County Museum, 211 Second Av, NE, Cullman, AL 35055 - T: (205) 739-1258, Fax: (205) 737-8782, E-mail: efuller@hiwaay.net, Internet: http://www.cullman.com/museum. Head: Elaine L. Fuller
Local Museum - 1975
Local history, housed in replica of 1873 home of Col. John G. Cullman, founder of Cullman 36336

Cullowhee NC

Mountain Heritage Center, Western Carolina University, Cullowhee, NC 28723 - T: (828) 227-7129, Internet: http://www.wcu.edu/mhc. Head: H. Tyler Blethen
Historical Museum / University Museum - 1975 36337

Cumberland MD

Allegany County Historical Museum, 218 Washington St, Cumberland, MD 21502 - T: (301) 777-8678, Fax: (301) 777-8678 ext 51, E-mail: hhouse@allconct.org, Internet: http://historichouse.allconct.org. Head: Sharon Nealis
Local Museum - 1937
Historic house, regional history 36338

George Washington's Headquarters, Greene St, Cumberland, MD 21502 - T: (301) 759-6636, Fax: (301) 759-3223, Internet: http://www.ci.cumberland.md.us. Head: Diane Johnson
Historical Museum - 1925
1755 log cabin built during the French and Indian war 36339

Cummington MA

Kingman Tavern Historical Museum, 41 Main St, Cummington, MA 01026 - T: (413) 634-5527, 634-5335. Head: Stephen Howese
Local Museum - 1968
Local history, frame bldg used as a post office, Masonic Lodge meeting hall and tavern 36340

William Cullen Bryant Homestead, 207 Bryant Rd, Cummington, MA 01026 - T: (413) 634-2244, Fax: (413) 296-5239, E-mail: bryanthomestead@hor.org, Internet: http://www.therrustees.org. Head: Andrew Kendall
Special Museum - 1928
Boyhood home and stuff summer residence of literary figure William Cullen Bryant 36341

Cupertino CA

Cupertino Historical Museum, 10185 N Stelling Rd, Cupertino, CA 95014 - T: (408) 973-1495, Fax: (408) 973-1495. Head: Sharon Blaine, Ethel Worn
Local Museum - 1990
Local history 36342

Euphrat Museum of Art, De Anza College, 21250 Stevens Creek Blvd, Cupertino, CA 95014 - T: (408) 864-8836, Fax: (408) 864-8738. Head: Nancy Newman, Jan Rindfleisch
University Museum / Fine Arts Museum - 1971 36343

Currie MN

End-O-Line Railroad Museum, 440 N Mill St, Currie, MN 56123-1004 - T: (507) 763-3708, 763-3113, Fax: (507) 763-3708, E-mail: louise@endoline.com, Internet: http://www.endoline.com. Head: Louise Gervais
Science&Tech Museum - 1972
Railroads 36344

Currie NC

Moores Creek National Battlefield, 40 Patriots Hall Dr, Currie, NC 28435 - T: (910) 283-5591, Fax: (910) 283-5351, Internet: http://www.nps.gov/mocr. Head: Ann Childress
Open Air Museum / Military Museum - 1926 36345

Custer SD

Custer County 1881 Courthouse Museum, 411 Mount Rushmore Rd, Custer, SD 57730 - T: (605) 673-2443. Head: Dan McPherson
Local Museum - 1974
Local hist 36346

National Museum of Woodcarving, Hwy 16 W, Custer, SD 57730 - T: (605) 673-4404, Fax: (605) 673-3843, E-mail: woodcarv@gwtc.net. Head: Dale Schaffer
Fine Arts Museum - 1966
Woodcarvings 36347

Dade City FL

Pioneer Florida Museum, 15602 Pioneer Museum Rd, Dade City, FL 33526 - T: (352) 567-0262, Fax: (352) 567-1262, E-mail: pioneer@innet.com, Internet: http://www.dadecity.com/museum
Historical Museum / Agriculture Museum - 1961 36348

Dahlonega GA

Dahlonega Courthouse Gold Museum, 1 Public Sq, Dahlonega, GA 30533 - T: (706) 864-2257, Fax: (706) 864-8370, E-mail: dgmgold@alltel.net, Internet: http://www.dgmgold@alltel.net. Head: Sharon Johnson
Historical Museum / Science&Tech Museum - 1966
Tools and equipment, personal artefacts, furnishings 36349

Dalhart TX

Dallam-Hartley XIT Museum, POB 710, Dalhart, TX 79022 - T: (806) 249-5390, Fax: (806) 244-3031, E-mail: xitmusm@xit.net. Head: Nicky Olson
Local Museum - 1975
Local history and ranching 36350

Dallas NC

Gaston County Museum of Art and History, 131 W Main St, Dallas, NC 28034 - T: (704) 922-7681, Fax: (704) 922-7683, E-mail: museum@co-gaston.nc.us, Internet: http//www.museumstogether.com. Head: Barbara H. Brose
Fine Arts Museum / Historical Museum - 1975 36351

Dallas TX

The Age of Steam Railroad Museum, 1105 Washington St, Fair Park, Dallas, TX 75315-3259 - T: (214) 428-0101, Fax: (214) 426-1937, E-mail: info@dallasrailwaymuseum.com, Internet: http://www.dallasrailwaymuseum.com. Head: Robert Willis, Robert LaPrelle
Science&Tech Museum - 1963
Railroad 36352

Biblical Arts Center, 7500 Park Ln, Dallas, TX 75225 - T: (214) 691-4661, Fax: (214) 691-4752, E-mail: rrazy@ix.netcom.com, Internet: http://www.biblicalarts.org. Head: Ronnie L Roese
Religious Arts Museum - 1966
Religious art 36353

Cultural Heritage Center, Davy Crockett School, 401 N Carroll, Dallas, TX 75246 - T: (214) 841-5355. Head: Dr. Doris Freeling
Decorative Arts Museum - 1976
Decorative arts 36354

Dallas Historical Society Museum, Hall of State, Fair Park, 3939 Grand Av, Dallas, TX 75315 - T: (214) 421-4500, Fax: (214) 42l-7500, E-mail: dhs@dallashistory.org, Internet: http://www.dallashistory.org. Head: Lisa Hemby
Local Museum - 1922
Local hist 36355

Dallas Memorial Center for Holocaust Studies, 7900 Northaven, Dallas, TX 75230 - T: (214) 750-4654, Fax: (214) 750-4672, E-mail: dmchs@postoffice.swbell.net. Head: David Bell, Frieda Soble
Historical Museum - 1984
Holocaust memorial - library 36356

Dallas Museum of Art, 1717 N Harwood St, Dallas, TX 75201 - T: (214) 922-1200, Fax: (214) 922-1350, Internet: www.dm-art.org. Head: Dr. John R. Lane
Fine Arts Museum - 1903 36357

Dallas Museum of Natural History, Fair Park, 3535 Grand Av, Dallas, TX 75210 - T: (214) 421-3466 ext 200, Fax: (214) 428-4356, Internet: http://www.dallasdino.org. Head: Robert H. Townsend
Natural History Museum - 1935
Natural hist 36358

Dallas Visual Art Center, 2801 Swiss Av, Dallas, TX 75204-5987 - T: (214) 821-2522, Fax: (214) 821-9103, Internet: www.dallasvisualart.org. Head: Joan Davidow
Fine Arts Museum / Public Gallery - 1981 36359

Frontiers of Flight Museum, 8008 Cedar Springs Blvd, Dallas, TX 75235 - T: (214) 350-3600, 350-1651, Fax: (214) 351-0101, E-mail: gwlodge@airmail.net, Internet: http://www.flightmuseum.com. Head: George W. Lodge
Science&Tech Museum - 1988
Aeronautical history 36360

International Museum of Cultures, 7500 W Camp Wisdom Rd, Dallas, TX 75236 - T: (972) 708-7406, Fax: (972) 708-7341, E-mail: imc_museum@sil.org, Internet: http://www.sil.org/imc/. Head: Marie FaeKamm
Ethnology Museum - 1974
Anthropology 36361

Meadows Museum, c/o Southern Methodist University, 5900 Bishop Blvd, Dallas, TX 75205 - T: (214) 768-2516, Fax: (214) 768-1688, E-mail: slunsfor@mail.smu.edu, Internet: http://www2.smu.edu/meadowsmuseum. Head: John Lunsford
Fine Arts Museum / University Museum - 1965
Spanish art 36362

Old City Park - The Historical Village of Dallas, 1717 Gano St, Dallas, TX 75215 - T: (214) 421-5141, Fax: (214) 428-6351, E-mail: dagns@airmail.net, Internet: http://www.oldcitypark.org. Head: Gary N. Smith, Jennifer Bransom
Local Museum - 1966
Historic village 36363

Sixth Floor Museum at Dealey Plaza, 411 Elm St, Ste 120, Dallas, TX 75202-3301 - T: (214) 747-6660, Fax: (214) 747-6662, E-mail: jfk@jfk.org, Internet: http://www.jfk.org. Head: Jeff West
Historical Museum - 1989
John F. Kennedy and the memory of a nation 36364

Southwest Museum of Science and Technology, 1318 Second Av in Fair Park, Dallas, TX 75210 - T: (214) 428-7200 ext 301, Fax: (214) 428-2033, E-mail: mac@scienceplace.org, Internet: http://www.scienceplace.org. Head: Dr. William M. Sudduth
Science&Tech Museum - 1946
Science and technology 36365

Dalton GA

Creative Arts Guild, 520 W Waugh St, Dalton, GA 30722-1485 - T: (706) 278-0168, Fax: (706) 278-6996. Head: David Renz, Ann Treadwell
Fine Arts Museum - 1963
Paintings, prints, drawings, photos, sculptures 36366

Crown Gardens Museum, 715 Chattanooga Av, Dalton, GA 30720 - T: (706) 278-0217. Head: Marvin Sowder, Marcelle White
Local Museum - 1977
1848 Blunt House, 1908 Wright Hotel-Chatsworth, 1840 John Hamilton House-Chatsworth Depot 36367

Dalton MA

Crane Museum, Rtes 8 and 9, Dalton, MA 01226 - T: (413) 684-6481, Fax: (413) 684-0817, E-mail: info@crane.com, Internet: http://www.crane.com
Historical Museum / Science&Tech Museum - 1930
Industry, 1844 old stone mill 36368

Dana IN

Ernie Pyle House, 107 Maple, Dana, IN 47847-0338 - T: (765) 665-3633, Fax: (765) 665-9312, E-mail: erniepyleshs@sobax.net
Historical Museum - 1976
Birthplace of Ernie Pyle, noted WW II journalist 36369

Danbury CT

Danbury Museum, 43 Main St, Danbury, CT 06810 - T: (203) 743-5200, Fax: (203) 743-1131, E-mail: dmhs@danburyhistorical.org, Internet: http://www.danburyhistorical.org. Head: James Arconti, Levi Newsome
Local Museum - 1942
Local history, Charles Ives birthplace 36370

Military Museum of Southern New England, 125 Park Av, Danbury, CT 06810 - T: (203) 790-9277, Fax: (203) 790-0420, E-mail: mmsne@juno.com, Internet: http://www.danbury.org/org/military. Head: John V. Valluzzo, Philip A. Cocchiola
Military Museum - 1985
Military hist 36371

Danbury WI

Forts Folle Avoine Historic Park, 8500 County Rd U, Danbury, WI 54830 - T: (715) 866-8890, E-mail: fahp@centuryinter.net, Internet: http://www.mwd.com/burnett/. Head: Peggy Tolbert
Local Museum - 1945
Fur trade 36372

Dania FL

Graves Museum of Archaeology and Natural History, 481 S Federal Hwy, Dania, FL 33004 - T: (954) 925-7770 ext 14, Fax: (954) 925-7064, E-mail: digit@gravesmuseum.org, Internet: http://www.gravesmuseum.org. Head: Robert P. Kelley
Archaeological Museum / Natural History Museum - 1980
Archaeology, paleontology, natural history 36373

Danvers MA

Danvers Historical Society Exhibition, 9 Page St, Danvers, MA 01923 - T: (978) 777-1666, Fax: (978) 777-5028, E-mail: dhs@danvershistory.org. Head: Glenn Uminowicz
Historical Museum - 1889
Local history 36374

Rebecca Nurse Homestead, 149 Pine St, Danvers, MA 01923 - T: (978) 774-8799, Internet: http://www.rebeccanurse.org/
Historical Museum - 1974
1678 home of Rebecca Nurse, hanged as a witch in 1692 36375

Danville CA

Eugene O'Neill National Historic Site, POB 280, Danville, CA 94526 - T: (925) 838-0249, Fax: (925) 838-9471, Internet: http://www.nps.gov
Historical Museum - 1976 36376

Danville IL

Vermilion County Museum, 116 N Gilbert St, Danville, IL 61832-8506 - T: (217) 442-2922, 442-2001. Head: Donald Richter
Local Museum - 1964
History, housed in 1855 Dr. Fithian Home, doctor's residence, often visited by Abraham Lincoln 36377

Danville KY

Constitution Square, 134 S Second St, Danville, KY 40422 - T: (606) 239-7089, Fax: (606) 239-7894, E-mail: brenda.willoughby@mail.state.ky.us, Internet: http://www.kystateparks.com/agencies/parks/constsq2.htm. Head: Brenda Willoughby
Historic Site - 1937
Historic site 36378

McDowell House and Apothecary Shop, 125 S Second St, Danville, KY 40422 - T: (859) 236-2804, Fax: (859) 236-2804, E-mail: mcdhse@kih.net, Internet: http://www.mcdowellhouse.org. Head: Carol J. Senn
Historical Museum / Historic Site - 1939
McDowell House 1800, 1795 Apothecary shop 36379

Danville VA

Danville Museum of Fine Arts and History, 975 Main St, Danville, VA 24541 - T: (804) 793-5644, Fax: (804) 799-6145, E-mail: dmfah@gamewood.net, Internet: http://www.danvillemuseum.org. Head: John Hunnicut, Nancy Perry
Fine Arts Museum / Historical Museum - 1974
Art, history 36380

Daphne AL

American Sport Art Museum and Archives, 1 Academy Dr, Daphne, AL 36526-7055 - T: (334) 626-3303, Fax: (334) 621-2527, E-mail: asama@ussa-sport.ussa.edu, Internet: http://www.asama.org
Fine Arts Museum / University Museum / Special Museum - 1985 36381

Darien CT

Bates-Scofield Homestead, 45 Old King's Hwy, N, Darien, CT 06820 - T: (203) 655-9233. Head: Madeline Hart
Historical Museum - 1954 36382

Darien GA

Fort King George Historic Site, Fort King George Dr, Darien, GA 31305 - T: (912) 437-4770, Fax: (912) 437-5419, E-mail: ftkgeo@darientel.net, Internet: http://www.darientel.net~ftkgeo. Head: Ken Akins
Historic Site / Historical Museum / Military Museum - 1961
Archaeology, photos, ethnography 36383

Darlington SC

Joe Weatherly Museum, 1301 Harry Byrd Hwy, Darlington, SC 29532 - T: (803) 395-8821, Fax: (803) 393-3911, Internet: http://www.darlingtonraceway.com
Science&Tech Museum - 1965
Stock cars 36384

Davenport IA

Davenport Museum of Art, 1737 W 12th St, Davenport, IA 52804 - T: (319) 326-7805, Fax: (319) 326-7876, E-mail: swb@ci.davenport.ia.us, Internet: http://www.art-dma.org. Head: Dr. William Steven Bradley
Fine Arts Museum - 1925
Art 36385

Putnam Museum of History and Natural Science, 1717 W 12th St, Davenport, IA 52804 - T: (319) 324-1054, Fax: (319) 324-6638, E-mail: museum@putnam.org, Internet: http://www.putnam.org. Head: Christopher J. Reich
Historical Museum / Ethnology Museum / Natural History Museum - 1867
History, natural science, anthropology 36386

Davenport WA

Fort Spokane Visitor Center and Museum, HCR 11, POB 51, Davenport, WA 99122 - T: (509) 725-2715, 633-3836, Fax: (509) 633-3834
Military Museum - 1965
Military hist 36387

Davie FL

Young at Art Children's Museum, 11584 W State Rd 84, Davie, FL 33325 - T: (954) 424-0085 ext 21, Fax: (954) 370-5057, Internet: http://www.youngatartmuseum.org. Head: Mindy Shrago
Special Museum - 1985
Hands-On Children's museum 36388

Davis CA

Davis Art Center, 1919 F St, Davis, CA 95616 - T: (530) 756-4100, Fax: (530) 756-3041, E-mail: davisart@dcn.davis.ca.us. Head: Jackie Steven
Folklore Museum - 1959
Art 36389

Memorial Union Art Gallery, Memorial Union Bldg, University of California, Davis, CA 95616 - T: (530) 752-2885, Fax: (530) 754-4387, E-mail: mebrudin@ucdavis.edu, Internet: http://campusrecreation.ucdavis.edu. Head: Roger Hankins
Fine Arts Museum / University Museum - 1965 36390

Pence Gallery, 212 D St, Davis, CA 95616 - T: (530) 758-3370, Fax: (530) 758-4670, E-mail: pencegallery@davis.com. Head: Nancy M. Servis
Fine Arts Museum / Public Gallery - 1975 36391

Richard L. Nelson Gallery and the Fine Arts Collection, University of California, Department of Art, Davis, CA 95616 - T: (530) 752-8500, Fax: (530) 754-9122, E-mail: 1pamerson@ucdavis.edu. Head: Anne P. Gray, Price Amerson
Fine Arts Museum / University Museum - 1976
Art 36392

R.M. Bohart Museum of Entomology, Dept of Entomology, University of California, 1 Shields Av, Davis, CA 95616-8584 - T: (530) 752-0493, Fax: (530) 752-9464, E-mail: bohart@ucdavis.edu, Internet: http://cbshome.ucdavis.edu/bohart/. Head: Dr. Lynn S. Kimsey
University Museum / Natural History Museum - 1946 36393

Daviston AL

Horseshoe Bend National Military Park, 11288 Horseshoe Bend Rd, Daviston, AL 36256 - T: (256) 234-7111, Fax: (256) 329-9905, E-mail: - HOBEAdministration@nps.gov, Internet: http://www.nps.gov/hobe/. Head: Willie C. Madison
Historic Site / Historical Museum - 1959
Horseshoe Bend Battlefield, location of final battle of the Creek Indian War of 1813-1814 36394

Davisville MO

Dillard Mill State Historic Site, Dept of Nature Resources, Div of State Parks, Davisville, MO 65456 - T: (573) 244-3120, Fax: (573) 244-5672, E-mail: dillmill@misn.com, Internet: http://www.dnr.state.mo.us/dsp
Historical Museum - 1975 36395

Dawson Springs KY

Dawson Springs Museum and Art Center, 127 S Main St, Dawson Springs, KY 42408 - T: (270) 797-3503, 797-3891. Head: Claude A. Holeman
Fine Arts Museum / Decorative Arts Museum / Historical Museum - 1986
Art, hist 36396

Dayton OH

Boonshoft Museum of Discovery, 2600 DeWeese Pkwy, Dayton, OH 45414 - T: (937) 275-7431, Fax: (937) 275-5811, E-mail: damuseum@gte.net, Internet: http://www.boonshoftmuseum.org. Head: Mark Meister
Archaeological Museum / Natural History Museum / Science&Tech Museum - 1893 36397

Carillon Historical Park, 1000 Carillon Blvd, Dayton, OH 45409 - T: (937) 293-2841 ext 100, Fax: (937) 293-5798, E-mail: chpdayton@aol.com, Internet: http://www.carillonpark.org. Head: Mary Mathews, Jeanne Palermo
Historical Museum - 1950 36398

Dayton Art Institute, 456 Belmonte Park N, Dayton, OH 45405 - T: (937) 223-5277, Fax: (937) 223-3140, E-mail: info@daytonartinstitue.org, Internet: http://www.daytonartinstitute.org. Head: Alexander Lee Nyerges
Fine Arts Museum - 1919 36399

Dayton Museum of Discovery → Boonshoft Museum of Discovery

Montgomery County Historical Society Research Center, 224 North St.Clair St, Dayton, OH 45402 - T: (937) 228-6271, Fax: (937) 331-7160, E-mail: mchsdayton@aol.com, Internet: http://www.daytonhistory.org. Head: Brian Hackett
Historical Museum - 1896
archive 36400

Patterson Homestead, 1815 Brown St, Dayton, OH 45409 - T: (937) 222-9724, Fax: (937) 222-0345, Internet: http://www.daytonhistory.org
Decorative Arts Museum / Historical Museum - 1953 36401

Paul Laurence Dunbar State Memorial, 219 N Paul Laurence Dunbar St, Dayton, OH 45407 - T: (937) 224-7061, Fax: (937) 224-5625, 224-7051, E-mail: pldunbar@coax.net, Internet: http://www.ohiohistory.org. Head: Laverne Sci
Historical Museum / Historic Site - 1936 36402

Sunwatch Indian Village - Archaeological Park, 2301 W River Rd, Dayton, OH 45418 - T: (937) 268-8199, Fax: (937) 268-1760, Internet: http://www.sunwatch.org. Head: Mark Meister
Historical Museum / Archaeological Museum - 1988
Prehistory 36403

Wright State University Art Galleries, 3640 Colonel Glenn Hwy, Dayton, OH 45435 - T: (937) 775-2978, Fax: (937) 775-4082, E-mail: cmartin@desire.wright.edu, Internet: http://www.wright.edu/artgalleries/. Head: Craig Martin
Fine Arts Museum / University Museum - 1974 36404

Dayton VA

Shenandoah Valley Folk Art and Heritage Center, 382 High St, Dayton, VA 22821 - T: (540) 879-2616, Fax: (540) 879-2616, E-mail: heritag1@shentel.net, Internet: http://www.heritagecenter.com. Head: Larry Bowers
Local Museum / Folklore Museum - 1895
Local hist, folk art, civil war 36405

Dayton WA

Dayton Historical Depot Society Museum, 222 E Commercial St, Dayton, WA 99328 - T: (509) 382-2026, Fax: (509) 382-4726. Head: Russell P. Markus
Local Museum - 1974 36406

Daytona Beach FL

Halifax Historical Museum, 252 S Beach St, Daytona Beach, FL 32114 - T: (904) 255-6976, Fax: (904) 255-7605, E-mail: mail@halifaxhistorical.org, Internet: http://www.halifaxhistorical.org. Head: Roy Midkiff
Local Museum - 1949
Local history 36407

The Museum of Arts and Sciences, 1040 Museum Blvd, Daytona Beach, FL 32114 - T: (904) 255-0285 ext 14, Fax: (904) 255-5040, E-mail: moas@n-jcenter, Internet: http://www.moas.org. Head: Gary Russell Libby
Fine Arts Museum / Local Museum / Natural History Museum - 1971
American, European, African and Cuban fine, folk and decorative art 36408

Southeast Museum of Photography, Daytona Beach Community College, 1200 W International Speedway Blvd, Daytona Beach, FL 32114 - T: (904) 947-3165, Fax: (904) 254-4487, E-mail: nordsta@dbcc.cc.fl.us, Internet: http://www.dbcc.cc.fl.us. Head: Alison Devine Nordstrom
Fine Arts Museum / Science&Tech Museum - 1979
Photography 36409

De Land FL

De Land Museum of Art, 600 N Woodland Blvd, De Land, FL 32720-3447 - T: (904) 734-4371, Fax: (904) 734-7697. Head: Mark Alexander
Fine Arts Museum - 1951 36410

The Duncan Gallery of Art, Sampson Hall, Stetson University, De Land, FL 32720-3756 - T: (904) 822-7266, Fax: (904) 822-7268, E-mail: gbolding@stetson.edu, Internet: http://www.stetson.edu/departments/art. Head: Dan Gunderson
Fine Arts Museum / University Museum - 1965 36411

Gillespie Museum of Minerals, Stetson University, 234 E Michigan Av, De Land, FL 32720 - T: (904) 822-7330, Fax: (904) 822-7328, E-mail: hvanter@stetson.edu. Head: Dr. Robert S. Chauvin
University Museum / Natural History Museum - 1958
Mineralogy 36412

De Pere WI

White Pillars Museum, 403 N Broadway, De Pere, WI 54115 - T: (920) 336-3877. Head: Laurel Towns
Local Museum - 1970
Local hist 36413

De Smet SD

De Smet Depot Museum, 104 Calumet Ave NE, De Smet, SD 57231 - T: (605) 854-3991. Head: Mark Hoek
Local Museum - 1965
Local hist 36414

Deadwood SD

Adams Museum and House, 54 Sherman St, Deadwood, SD 57732 - T: (605) 578-1714, 578-1928, Fax: (605) 578-1194, E-mail: director@adamsmuseumandhouse.org, Internet: http://www.adamsmuseumandhouse.org. Head: Mary A. Kopco
Local Museum - 1930
Local hist 36415

House of Roses, Senator Wilson Home, 15 Forest Av, Deadwood, SD 57732 - T: (605) 722-1879. Head: Michael Bockwoldt
Historical Museum - 1976
Historic house, antique Victorian furniture, paintings, old prints 36416

Dearborn MI

Automotive Hall of Fame, 21400 Oakwood Blvd, Dearborn, MI 48124 - T: (313) 240-4000, Fax: (313) 240-8641. Head: Gene McKinney
Science&Tech Museum - 1939 36417

Dearborn Historical Museum, 915 Brady St, Dearborn, MI 48124 - T: (313) 565-3000, Fax: (313) 565-4848
Historical Museum - 1950
Local history, ex powder magazine 36418

Henry Ford Estate, Universty of Michigan-Dearborn, Evergreen Rd, Dearborn, MI 48128 - T: (313) 593-5590, 593-5128, 593-5593, Fax: (313) 593-5243, Internet: http://www.umd.umich.edu/fairlane. Head: Dr. D. Werling
Local Museum - 1957
Historic house, former home of Henry Ford 36419

Henry Ford Museum and Greenfield Village, 20900 Oakwood Blvd, Dearborn, MI 48124 - T: (313) 271-1620, Fax: (313) 982-6250, E-mail: barbh@hfmgv.org, Internet: http://www.hfmgv.org. Head: Steven K. Hamp, Denise Thal
Historical Museum - 1929
History 36420

Death Valley CA

Death Valley National Park Visitor Center and Museum, Death Valley National Park, Death Valley, CA 92328 - T: (760) 786-2331, Fax: (760) 786-3283, E-mail: blair-davenport@nps.gov, Internet: http://www.nps.gov/deva
Local Museum / Ethnology Museum / Archaeological Museum / Historical Museum - 1933 36421

Decatur AL

The Art Gallery, John C. Calhoun State Community College, Hwy 31 N, Fine Arts Bldg, Decatur, AL 35609-2216 - T: (205) 306-2500, 306-2699, Fax: (205) 306-2889, Internet: http://www.calhoun.cc.al.us. Head: Dr. Richard Carpenter
Fine Arts Museum / University Museum - 1965 36422

Decatur GA

Dalton Gallery, Agnes Scott College, E College Av, Decatur, GA 30030 - T: (404) 471-6000, Fax: (404) 471-5369, E-mail: aparry@agnesscott.edu, Internet: http://www.agnesscott.edu
Fine Arts Museum / University Museum - 1957
Decorative art, paintings, sculpturs 36423

DeKalb Historical Society Museum, 101 E Court Square, Decatur, GA 30030 - T: (404) 373-1088, Fax: (404) 373-8287, E-mail: dhs@dekalbhistory.org, Internet: http://www.dekalbhistory.us. Head: Betty Willis, Sue Ellen Owens
Local Museum - 1947
Local history, Old Courthouse, personal artefacts, costumes, photos 36424

Decatur IL

Birks Museum, Millikin University, 1184 W Main, Decatur, IL 62522 - T: (217) 424-6337, Fax: (217) 424-3993, E-mail: ewalker@mail.millikin.edu, Internet: http://www.millikin.edu. Head: Edwin G. Walker
Decorative Arts Museum / University Museum - 1981
China, glass, paper weights 36425

Kirkland Fine Arts Center-Perkinson Gallery, Millikin University, 1184 W Main St, Decatur, IL 62522 - T: (217) 424-6227, Fax: (217) 424-3993, E-mail: jschietinger@mail.millikin.edu. Head: James Schietinger
Fine Arts Museum / University Museum - 1969 36426

Macon County Museum, 5580 N Fork Rd, Decatur, IL 62521 - T: (217) 422-4919, Fax: (217) 422-4773, E-mail: mchs@fgi.net, Internet: http://www.fgi.net/~mchs. Head: Ary Anderson, Christopher D. Gordy
Local Museum - 1973
Local history 36427

Decatur IN

Adams County Historical Museum, 420 W Monroe St, Decatur, IN 46733 - T: (219) 724-2341. Head: Gordon Gregg
Local Museum - 1965
Local history, in Charles Dugan Home 36428

Decatur MI

Historical Newton Home, 20689 Marcellus Hwy, Decatur, MI 49045 - T: (616) 445-9016. Head: Abigail Schten
Historical Museum 36429

Decatur TX

Wise County Heritage Museum, 1602 S Trinity, Decatur, TX 76234 - T: (940) 627-5586. Head: George Beeson, Rosalie Gregg
Local Museum - 1967
Local hist 36430

Decorah IA

Fine Arts Collection, 700 College Dr, Luther College Library, Decorah, IA 52101-1042 - T: (319) 387-1195, Fax: (319) 387-1657, E-mail: kempjane@luther.edu, Internet: http://www.luther.edu/~library/. Head: Jane Kemp
Fine Arts Museum / University Museum
Art 36431

Vesterheim Norwegian-American Museum, 523 W Water St, Decorah, IA 52101-0379 - T: (319) 382-9681, Fax: (319) 382-8828, E-mail: vesterheim@vesterheim.org, Internet: http://vesterheim.org. Head: Janet Blohm Pultz
Ethnology Museum / Folklore Museum - 1877
Ethnology, genealogy 36432

Dedham MA

Dedham Historical Museum, 612 High St, Dedham, MA 02027-0215 - T: (781) 326-1385, Fax: (781) 326-5762, E-mail: society@dedhamhistorical.org, Internet: http://www.dedhamhistorical.org. Head: Ronald F. Frazier
Fine Arts Museum / Decorative Arts Museum / Local Museum - 1859
Local history, pottery, Katharine Pratt silver, fine arts, furniture 36433

Fairbanks House, 511 East St, Dedham, MA 02026 - T: (781) 326-1170, Fax: (781) 326-2147, E-mail: fairbankshouse@aol.com, Internet: http://www.fairbankshouse.org
Historical Museum / Museum of Classical Antiquities - 1903
Oldest surviving timber frame house in North America, built for Fairbanks family, furnishings 36434

Deer Isle ME

Deer Isle-Stonington Historical Society Museum, Rte 15A, Deer Isle, ME 04627 - T: (207) 348-2897. Head: Paul Stubing
Historical Museum - 1959
Local history 36435

Deer Lodge MT

Grant-Kohrs Ranch National Historic Site, 210 Missouri Av, Deer Lodge, MT 59722 - T: (406) 846-2070, Fax: (406) 846-3962, E-mail: Chris-ford@nps.gov, Internet: http://www.nps.gov/grko. Head: Darlene Koontz
Historic Site - 1972 36436

Old Prison Museum, 1106 Main St, Deer Lodge, MT 59722 - T: (406) 846-3111, Fax: (406) 846-3156. Head: Andrew C. Towe
Historical Museum - 1952 36437

Powell County Museum, 1193 Main St, Deer Lodge, MT 59722 - T: (406) 846-1694, Fax: (406) 846-3156. Head: Andrew C. Towe
Local Museum - 1964 36438

Deerfield MA

Historic Deerfield, The Street, Deerfield, MA 01342 - T: (413) 774-5581, Fax: (413) 773-7415, E-mail: tours@historic-deerfield.org, Internet: http://www.historic-deerfield.org. Head: Donald R. Friary
Decorative Arts Museum / Folklore Museum / Local Museum - 1952
Local history 36439

Memorial Hall Museum, 8 Memorial St, Deerfield, MA 01342 - T: (413) 774-7476, Fax: (413) 774-5400, E-mail: pvma@shaysnet.com, Internet: http://www.old-deerfield.org. Head: Timothy C. Neumann
Decorative Arts Museum / Local Museum - 1870
Local history, decorative arts, Deerfield Academy Building 36440

Defiance MO

Historic Daniel Boone Home and Boonesfield Village, 1868 Hwy F, Defiance, MO 63341 - T: (314) 798-2005, Fax: (314) 798-2914, Internet: http://www.geocities.com/Athens/Parthenon/7109/. Head: Randall Andrae
Open Air Museum / Local Museum - 1803 36441

DeKalb IL

Anthropology Museum, Northern Illinois University, DeKalb, IL 60115 - T: (815) 753-0230, Fax: (815) 753-7027, E-mail: mdeemer@niu.edu, Internet: http://www.niu.edu/anthro_museum. Head: Winifred Creamer, Milton Deemer
University Museum / Ethnology Museum / Archaeological Museum - 1964
Anthropology, archaeology 36442

Art Museum, Northern Illinois University, Altgeld Hall, DeKalb, IL 60115 - T: (815) 753-1936, Fax: (815) 753-7897, E-mail: pdoherty@niu.edu. Head: Peggy Doherty
Fine Arts Museum / University Museum - 1970
Art 36443

Ellwood House Museum, 509 N First St, DeKalb, IL 60115 - T: (815) 756-4609, Fax: (815) 756-4645, Internet: http://www.bios.niu.edu/ellwood. Head: Gerald J. Brauer
Historical Museum - 1965 36444

Del Rio TX

Whitehead Memorial Museum, 1308 S Main St, Del Rio, TX 78840 - T: (210) 774-7568, Fax: (830) 768-0223, E-mail: director@whitehead-museum.com, Internet: http://www.whitehead.museum.com. Head: Charles Chandler, Lee Lincoln
Local Museum - 1962
Local hist 36445

Delafield WI

Hawks Inn, 426 Wells St, Delafield, WI 53018 - T: (414) 646-4794. Head: Otto Heinze
Local Museum - 1960
Historic building 36446

Saint John's Northwestern Military Academy Museum, 1101 N Genesee St, Delafield, WI 53018 - T: (414) 646-3311, 646-7164, Fax: (414) 646-7155, E-mail: cmoore@execpc.com, Internet: http://www.sjnma.org. Head: Charles Moore
Military Museum - 1984
Military hist 36447

Delano CA

Delano Heritage Park, 330 Lexington, Delano, CA 93215 - T: (661) 725-6730, Fax: (559) 757-2402, E-mail: dmuseum@lightspeed.net, Internet: http://www.delano/historicalsociety.usrc.net/pa. Head: Peter Finocchiaro
Local Museum / Natural History Museum - 1961 36448

Delaware City DE

Fort Delaware Society Museum, 108 Old Reedy Point Bridge Rd, Delaware City, DE 19706 - T: (302) 834-1630, E-mail: FTDsociety@del.net, Internet: http://www.del.net/org/fort. Head: William G. Robelen
Military Museum - 1950
Military hist 36449

Delray Beach FL

Cornell Museum, 51 N Swinton Av, Delray Beach, FL 33444 - T: (561) 243-7922, Fax: (561) 243-7022, E-mail: museum@oldschool.org, Internet: http://www.oldschool.org/oldschool. Head: Gloria Rejune Adams
Fine Arts Museum - 1990
Fine art, sculpture 36450

The Morikami Museum and Japanese Gardens, 4000 Morikami Park Rd, Delray Beach, FL 33446 - T: (561) 495-0233, Fax: (561) 499-2557, E-mail: morikami@co.palm-beach.fl.us, Internet: http://www.morikami.org. Head: Larry Rosensweig
Ethnology Museum / Folklore Museum - 1977
Ethnology, Japanese culture 36451

Delta CO

Delta County Museum, 251 Meeker St, Delta, CO 81416 - T: (970) 874-8721, E-mail: deltamuseum@aol.com. Head: James Wetzel
Local Museum - 1964
Regional history 36452

Delta UT

Great Basin Museum, 328 W 100 N, Delta, UT 84624 - T: (801) 864-5013, Fax: (801) 864-2446. Head: Charlotte K. Morrison
Local Museum - 1988 36453

Delton MI

Bernard Historical Museum, 7135 W Delton Rd, Delton, MI 49046 - T: (616) 623-5451. Head: Richard Martin
Local Museum - 1962
Local history 36454

Deming NM

Deming-Luna Mimbres Museum, 301 S Silver St, Deming, NM 88030 - T: (505) 546-2382, E-mail: dim-museum@zinet.com. Head: Sharon Lein
Local Museum / Decorative Arts Museum - 1955
Local hist, vintage clothing, Mimbres Indian artifacts, American Indian art, anthropology, folk art, decorative art 36455

Demopolis AL

Gaineswood, 805 S Cedar Av, Demopolis, AL 36732 - T: (334) 289-4846, Fax: (334) 289-1027, E-mail: gaineswood@demopolis.com, Internet: http://www.demopolis.com/gaineswood/. Head: Matthew D. Hartzell
Historical Museum / Historic Site - 1975
History 36456

Denison TX

Eisenhower Birthplace, 609 S Lamar, Denison, TX 75020 - T: (903) 465-8908, Fax: (903) 465-8988, E-mail: eisenhower@texoma.net, Internet: http://www.eisenhowerbirthplace.org. Head: Kurt Kemp
Local Museum - 1946
Historic house where Dwight D. Eisenhower was born 36457

Dennis MA

Cape Museum of Fine Arts, 60 Hope Lane Rt 6A, Dennis, MA 02638 - T: (508) 385-4477, Fax: (508) 385-7933, E-mail: cmfa@capecod.net. Head: Joseph E. Signore, Gregory Harper
Fine Arts Museum / Public Gallery - 1981
Art 36458

Denton TX

Denton County Historical Museum, 5800 North I-35, Denton, TX 76207 - T: (940) 380-0877, Fax: (940) 380-1699, E-mail: DCHMINC@aol.com. Head: Judy Selph
Local Museum - 1977
Local hist 36459

First Ladies of Texas Historic Costumes Collection, Texas Woman's University, Denton, TX 76204 - T: (940) 898-3350, Fax: (940) 898-3306. Head: Dr. Carol Surles
Special Museum - 1940
Costumes 36460

Texas Woman's University Art Galleries, 1 Circle Dr, Denton, TX 76204 - T: (940) 898-2530, Fax: (940) 898-2496, E-mail: visualarts@twu.edu, Internet: http://www.twu.edu. Head: Corky Stuckenbruck
Fine Arts Museum / University Museum - 1901
Art 36461

University of North Texas Art Gallery, School of Visual Arts, Mulberry at Welch, Denton, TX 76203 - T: (940) 565-4005, Fax: (940) 565-4717, E-mail: block@art.unt.edu, Internet: http://www.art.unt.edu. Head: Diana Block
University Museum / Fine Arts Museum - 1972 36462

Denver CO

Black American West Museum and Heritage Center, 3091 California St, Denver, CO 80205 - T: (303) 292-2566, Fax: (303) 382-1981, E-mail: BAWMHC@aol.com, Internet: http://www.coax.net/people/lwf/bawmus.htm
Historical Museum - 1971
African American hist 36463

Byers-Evans House Museum, 1310 Bannock St, Denver, CO 80204 - T: (303) 620-4933, Fax: (303) 620-4795, E-mail: byer@rmi.net. Head: Kevin Gramer
Historical Museum - 1990 36464

Center for the Visual Arts, Metropolitan State College of Denver, 1734 Wazee St, Denver, CO 80202 - T: (303) 294-5207, Fax: (303) 294-5210, E-mail: perishos@mscd.edu, Internet: http://www.mscd.edu/news/cva. Head: Sally L. Perisho
Fine Arts Museum / University Museum - 1991
Art 36465

Children's Museum of Denver, 2121 Children's Museum Dr, Denver, CO 80211 - T: (303) 433-7444, Fax: (303) 433-9520, E-mail: lindaf@cmdenver.org, Internet: http://www.cmdenver.org. Head: Dr. Linda E. Farley
Special Museum - 1973 36466

Colorado Historical Society Museum, 1300 Broadway, Denver, CO 80203 - T: (303) 866-3682, Fax: (303) 866-5739, Internet: http://www.coloradohistory.org. Head: Georgianna Contiguglia
Historical Museum - 1879
State history 36467

Colorado Photographic Arts Center, 1513 Boulder St, Denver, CO 80211 - T: (303) 433-9591, Fax: (303) 278-3693. Head: R. Skip
Public Gallery 36468

Core, 2045 Larimer St, Denver, CO 80205 - T: (303) 297-8428, E-mail: rgarriott@electricstores.com, Internet: http://www.corenwartspace.com. Head: Dave Griffin
Public Gallery 36469

Denver Art Museum, 100 W 14th Av Pkwy, Denver, CO 80204 - T: (720) 865-5001, Fax: (720) 865-5028, 913-0001, E-mail: web-mail@denverartmuseum.org, Internet: http://www.denverartmuseum.org. Head: Lewis I. Sharp
Fine Arts Museum - 1893
Native art, contemporary and modern art, architecture, paintings, graphics, sculptures 36470

Denver Museum of Miniatures, Dolls and Toys, 1880 Gaylord St, Denver, CO 80206 - T: (303) 322-1053, Fax: (303) 322-3704, E-mail: ldsbc@aol.com, Internet: http://www.westresearch.com/dmmdt/start. Head: Jim Harrington, Laura Douglas
Special Museum - 1981 36471

Denver Museum of Natural History, City Park, Denver, CO 80205 - T: (303) 370-6387, Fax: (303) 331-6492, Internet: http://www.dmnh.org. Head: Dr. D.D. Hilke
Natural History Museum - 1900
Natural history, archaeology, paleontology, mammals, entomology, earth and space sciences 36472

Forney Transportation Museum, 4303 Brighton Blvd, Denver, CO 80216 - T: (303) 297-1113, E-mail: forney@info2000.net, Internet: http://www.forneymuseum.com. Head: Jack D. Forney
Science&Tech Museum - 1961
Transport 36473

Grant-Humphreys Mansion, 770 Pennsylvania St, Denver, CO 80203 - T: (303) 894-2505, Fax: (303) 894-2508, E-mail: gran@rmi.net. Head: Kevin Gramer
Historical Museum - 1976
Historic Beaux-Arts style home 36474

Mizel Museum of Judaica, 560 S Monaco Pkwy, Denver, CO 80224 - T: (303) 333-4156, Fax: (303) 331-8477, E-mail: museum@mizelmuseum.org, Internet: http://www.mizelmuseum.org. Head: Ellen Premacks
Religious Arts Museum - 1982
Religious art and culture 36475

Molly Brown House Museum, 1340 Pennsylvania St, Denver, CO 80203 - T: (303) 832-4092, Fax: (303) 832-2340, Internet: http://www.mollybrown.org. Head: Leigh A. Grinstead
Historical Museum - 1970 36476

Museo de Las Americas, 861 Santa Fe Dr, Denver, CO 80204 - T: (303) 571-4401, Fax: (303) 607-9761, E-mail: jose@museo.org, Internet: http://www.museo.com. Head: Jose Aguayo
Fine Arts Museum / Historical Museum - 1991
Art and history 36477

Museum of Anthropology, University of Denver, 2199 S University Blvd, Denver, CO 80208 - T: (303) 871-2406, Fax: (303) 871-2437, E-mail: dsaitta@du.edu, Internet: http://www.du.edu/duma/duma.html. Head: Dr. Dean J. Saitta
University Museum / Ethnology Museum - 1932
Anthropology 36478

Pearce-McAllister Cottage, 1880 Gaylord St, Denver, CO 80206 - T: (303) 322-1053
Historical Museum - 1972
1899 Dutch Colonial Revival home 36479

Pirate Contemporary Art Oasis, 1370 Verbana, Denver, CO 80220 - T: (303) 458-6058. Head: Phil Bender
Public Gallery 36480

Rocky Mountain College of Art and Design Galleries, 6875 E Evans Av, Denver, CO 80224 - T: (303) 753-6046, Fax: (303) 759-4970, Internet: http://www.rmcad.edu. Head: Steven Steele
Fine Arts Museum / University Museum - 1963 36481

Rocky Mountain Conservation Center, University of Denver, 2420 S University Blvd, Denver, CO 80208 - T: (303) 733-2508, Fax: (303) 733-2508, E-mail: lmellon@du.edu, Internet: http://www.du.edu/rmcc. Head: Mellon
Special Museum
Photography, textiles, archaeologie, ethnology, maps 36482

School of Art and Art History Gallery, University of Denver, 2121 E Asbury Av, Denver, CO 80210 - T: (303) 871-2846, Fax: (303) 871-4112. Head: Bethany Kriegsman
Fine Arts Museum / University Museum - 1940
Art 36483

Spark Gallery, 1535 Platte St, Denver, CO 80202 - T: (303) 455-4435
Public Gallery
Drawings, photography, prints, sculptures 36484

Trianon Museum and Art Gallery, 335 14th St, Denver, CO 80202 - T: (303) 623-0739
Fine Arts Museum / Public Gallery 36485

Vance Kirkland Museum, 1311 Pearl St, Denver, CO 80203 - T: (303) 832-8576, Fax: (303) 832-8404, E-mail: info@vancekirkland.org, Internet: http://www.vancekirkland.org. Head: Hugh Grant
Fine Arts Museum / Decorative Arts Museum - 1932
Paintings by Colorado artists, Vance Kirkland, works by Frank Lloyd Wright, Russel and Mary Wright, Eva Zeisel 36486

Des Arc AR

Prairie County Museum, Hwy 38 and Hwy 11, Des Arc, AR 72040 - T: (501) 256-3711. Head: Judy Burrow
Local Museum - 1971
County history 36487

Des Moines IA

Des Moines Art Center, 4700 Grand Av, Des Moines, IA 50312 - T: (515) 277-4405, Fax: (515) 271-0357, E-mail: marketing@desmoinesartcenter.org, Internet: http://www.desmoinsartcenter.org. Head: Susan Lubowsky Talbott
Fine Arts Museum - 1933
19th-20th c art 36488

Hoyt Sherman Place, 1501 Woodland Av, Des Moines, IA 50309 - T: (515) 244-0507, Fax: (515) 237-3582. Head: Dave Schladetzky
Fine Arts Museum - 1907
Art 36489

Polk County Heritage Gallery, 3 Court Av, Des Moines, IA 50309 - T: (515) 286-3215, Fax: (515) 286-3082, Internet: http://www.co.polk.ia.us. Head: Mel Shivvers, Gene Phillips
Public Gallery - 1980
Art 36490

Polk County Historical Society, 317 SW 42nd St, Des Moines, IA 50312 - T: (515) 255-6657. Head: Betty Putnam
Local Museum - 1938
Local history, Fort Des Moines II 36491

Salisbury House, 4025 Tonawanda Dr, Des Moines, IA 50312 - T: (515) 274-1777, Fax: (515) 279-2659, E-mail: salhouse@dwx.com, Internet: http://www.salisburyhouse.org. Head: Scott Brunscheen
Historical Museum / Special Museum - 1993 36492

Science Center of Iowa, 4500 Grand Av, Greenwood-Ashworth Park, Des Moines, IA 50312-2499 - T: (515) 274-4138, Fax: (515) 274-3404, E-mail: info@sciowa.org, Internet: http://www.sciowa.org. Head: Mary B. Sellers
Science&Tech Museum - 1965
Science, technology 36493

State Historical Society of Iowa Museum, 600 E Locust St, Des Moines, IA 50319 - T: (515) 281-6412, Fax: (515) 282-0502, Internet: http://www.uiowa.edu/~shsi/. Head: Tom Morain
Local Museum - 1892
Regional history, natural history 36494

Terrace Hill Historic Site and Governor's Mansion, 2300 Grand Av, Des Moines, IA 50312 - T: (515) 281-3604, Fax: (515) 281-7267, E-mail: bfiler@max.state.ia.us. Head: Don Byers, Barbara Filer
Local Museum - 1971 36495

Des Plaines IL

Des Plaines Historical Museum, 789 Pearson St, Des Plaines, IL 60016-4506 - T: (847) 391-5399, Fax: (847) 297-1710, E-mail: dphslibrary@juno.com, Internet: http://nsn.nslsilus.org/dpkhome/dphs. Head: Joy A. Matthiessen
Local Museum - 1967
Local history 36496

Detroit MI

Black Legends of Professional Basketball Museum, POB 02384, Detroit, MI 48214 - T: (313) 822-8208, Fax: (313) 822-8227, Internet: http://www.projectbait.com/legends. Head: Dr. John Kline
Special Museum - 1997 36497

Center Galleries, c/o Center for Creative Studies, College of Art and Design, 301 Frederick Douglas Av, Detroit, MI 48202 - T: (313) 664-7800, Fax: (313) 664-7880, Internet: http://www.ccscad.edu. Head: Michelle M. Spivak
Fine Arts Museum / University Museum - 1989 36498

Charles H. Wright Museum of African American History, 315 E Warren Av, Detroit, MI 48201 - T: (313) 494-5800, Fax: (313) 494-5855, Internet: http://www.maah-detroit.org
Folklore Museum / Historical Museum - 1965
History, ethnography, folk art 36499

Children's Museum, 67 E Kirby St, Detroit, MI 48202 - T: (313) 873-8100, Fax: (313) 873-3384, Internet: http://dpsnet.detpub.k12.mi.us/museum/docs/. Head: Dwight R. Levens
Ethnology Museum - 1917 36500

Community Arts Gallery, c/o Dept. of Arts, Wayne State University, 150 Community Arts Bldg, Dept of Art, Detroit, MI 48202 - T: (313) 577-2423, 577-2203, Fax: (313) 577-8935, E-mail: s.dupret@wayne.edu, Internet: http://www.art.wayne.edu
Fine Arts Museum / University Museum - 1958
American and European graphics, paintings, sculpture 36501

Detroit Artists Market, 4719 Woodward Av, Detroit, MI 48201 - T: (313) 832-8540, Fax: (313) 832-8543, E-mail: detroitartists@juno.com, Internet: http://www.detroitartistsmarket.org. Head: Marialuisa Belmonte
Fine Arts Museum - 1932
Paintings, photographs, prints, drawings, sculpture, ceramics, glass 36502

Detroit Focus Gallery, 33 E Grand River, Detroit, MI 48232-0823 - T: (313) 533-2900. Head: Robert Crise jr.
Fine Arts Museum
Michigan visual artists 36503

Detroit Historical Museum, 5401 Woodward Av, Detroit, MI 48202 - T: (313) 833-1805, Fax: (313) 833-5342, Internet: http://www.detroithistorical.org. Head: Dennis Zenbala
Historical Museum / Local Museum - 1928
History, social and marine history 36504

The Detroit Institute of Arts, 5200 Woodward Av, Detroit, MI 48202 - T: (313) 833-7900, Fax: (313) 833-2357, Internet: http://www.dia.org. Head: Graham W.J. Beal
Fine Arts Museum - 1885
Ancient American, African, Near Eastern and Asien art, modern and contemporary art and design, New World culture, graphics, European sculpture, painting and decorative art, photgraphy 36505

Detroit Science Center, 5020 John R. St, Detroit, MI 48202 - T: (313) 577-8400 ext 440, Fax: (313) 832-1623, E-mail: info@sciencedetroit.org, Internet: http://www.sciencedetroit.org. Head: Mel J. Drumm, Sofia Villanueva
Science&Tech Museum - 1970
Science 36506

Dossin Great Lakes Museum, 100 Strand Dr, Belle Isle, Detroit, MI 48207 - T: (313) 852-4051
Local Museum - 1948
Great Lakes history 36507

Gospel Music Hall of Fame and Museum, 18301 W McNichols St, Detroit, MI 48219 - T: (313) 592-0017, Fax: (313) 592-8762, Internet: http://www.gmhf.org. Head: Sherry Dupree
Music Museum - 1995 36508

International Institute of Metropolitan Detroit, 111 E Kirby St, Detroit, MI 48202 - T: (313) 871-8600, Fax: (313) 871-1651. Head: Stanley Goleg, Richard G. Thipodean
Fine Arts Museum / Folklore Museum - 1919
International and ethnic folk art 36509

Michigan Chapter Gallery, National Conference of Artists, 216 Fisher Bldg, 3011 W Grand Blvd, Detroit, MI 48202 - T: (313) 875-0923, Fax: (313) 875-7537, E-mail: gallery@ncamich.org, Internet: http://www.ncamich.org. Head: Esther Vivian Brewer
Fine Arts Museum
African Americam artists 36510

Michigan Sports Hall of Fame, Cobo Conference Center, 1 N Washington Blvd, Detroit, MI 48226, mail addr: 32985 Hamilton Court, Ste 218, Farmington Hill, MI 48334 - T: (248) 848-0252, (313) 259-4333, Fax: (248) 848-1060. Head: William F. McLaughlin
Special Museum - 1955
Sports 36511

Motown Historical Museum, 2648 W Grand Blvd, Detroit, MI 48208-1237 - T: (313) 875-2264, Fax: (313) 875-2267, E-mail: motownmus@aol.com. Head: Esther Gordy Edwards
Music Museum - 1988
Hist of Motown Records, recording artists 36512

Pewabic Pottery Museum, 10125 E Jefferson St, Detroit, MI 48214 - T: (313) 822-0954, Fax: (313) 822-6266, E-mail: pewabic@pewabic.com, Internet: http://www.pewabic.com. Head: Terese Ireland
Decorative Arts Museum - 1903
Arts, crafts, pottery factory 36513

Wayne State University Museum of Anthropology, 4841 Cass Av, Detroit, MI 48202 - T: (313) 577-2598, Fax: (313) 577-9759, E-mail: tamara.bray@wayne.edu. Head: Tamara Bray
University Museum / Ethnology Museum / Archaeological Museum - 1958
Anthropology, ethnography, archaeology 36514

Wayne State University Museum of Natural History, Biological Sciences Bldg, 5047 Gullen Mall, Detroit, MI 48202 - T: (313) 577-2921, 577-2873, Fax: (313) 577-6891, E-mail: rhough@lifesci.wayne.edu
University Museum / Natural History Museum - 1972
Natural History - herbarium 36515

Your Heritage House, Fine Arts Center for Youth, 110 E Ferry Av, Detroit, MI 48202 - T: (313) 871-1667. Head: Josephine Harreld Love
Decorative Arts Museum / Fine Arts Museum - 1969
Fine arts for Youth, toys, games, puppets, children's music - library 36516

Detroit Lakes MN

Becker County Historical Museum, Summit and W Front St, Detroit Lakes, MN 56501 - T: (218) 847-2938, Fax: (218) 847-5048, E-mail: bolerud@tekstar.com. Head: Becky Olerud
Local Museum - 1883
Local history 36517

Dewey OK

Dewey Hotel, 801 N Delaware, Dewey, OK 74029 - T: (918) 532-4416
Local Museum - 1967 36518

Tom Mix Museum, 721 N Delaware, Dewey, OK 74029 - T: (918) 534-1555. Head: Edgar Weston
Local Museum - 1973 36519

Dexter ME

Dexter Historical Society Museums, Main St, Dexter, ME 04930 - T: (207) 924-3043, 924-5721, E-mail: dexhist@ctel.net, Internet: http://www.dextermaine.org. Head: Richard Whitney
Local Museum - 1966
Local history, Grist mill, Millers house, Carr school 36520

Dexter MI

Dexter Area Museum, 3443 Inverness, Dexter, MI 48130 - T: (734) 426-2519, E-mail: dexmuseum@aol.com, Internet: http://www.hvcn.org/info/dextermuseum. Head: Nina Doletsky-Rackham
Local Museum - 1976
Local hist 36521

Dickinson ND

Dakota Dinosaur Museum, 200 Museum Dr, Dickinson, ND 58601 - T: (701) 225-3466, Fax: (701) 227-0534, E-mail: info@dakotadino.com, Internet: http://www.dakotadino.com. Head: Alice League
Science&Tech Museum - 1991
Paleontology, geology 36522

Gallery of Art, Dickinson State University, Dickinson, ND 58601-4896 - T: (701) 483-2312, Fax: (701) 483-2006, E-mail: sharon_linnehan@dsu.nodak.edu. Head: Sharon Linnehan
Fine Arts Museum
Contemporary graphics, Zoe Bailer paintings, American art 36523

Dighton KS

Lane County Historical Museum, 333 N Main St, Dighton, KS 67839 - T: (316) 397-5652
Local Museum - 1976
Regional history 36524

Dillingham AK

Samuel K. Fox Museum, Seward and D Sts, Dillingham, AK 99576 - T: (907) 842-5610, Fax: (907) 842-5691. Head: Rebecca Porter
Ethnology Museum - 1974
Alaskan Native and Indian museum 36525

Dillon MT

Beaverhead County Museum, 15 S Montana, Dillon, MT 59725-2433 - T: (406) 683-5027. Head: Stan Smith
Historical Museum - 1947 36526

Western Montana College Art Gallery, 710 S Atlantic St, Dillon, MT 59725-3598 - T: (406) 683-7232, Fax: (406) 683-7493. Head: Randy Horst
Fine Arts Museum / University Museum - 1986
Seidensticker wildlife trophy coll - Lucy Carson Library 36527

Dillon SC

James W. Dillon House Museum, POB 1288, Dillon, SC 29536 - T: (843) 774-9051, Fax: (843) 774-5521. Head: Monroe McIntyre
Local Museum
Local hist 36528

Dixon IL

John Deere House, 8393 S Main, Grand Detour, Dixon, IL 61021-9406 - T: (815) 652-4551, Fax: (815) 652-3835. Head: Don Margenthaler
Local Museum - 1953 36529

Ronald Reagan Boyhood Home, 816 S Hennepin Av, Dixon, IL 61021 - T: (815) 288-3830, Fax: (815) 288-6757. Head: Norm Wymbs
Local Museum - 1980
Historic house 36530

Dodge City KS

Boot Hill Museum, Front St, Dodge City, KS 67801 - T: (316) 227-8188, Fax: (316) 227-7673, E-mail: frontst@pld.com, Internet: http://www.boothill.org. Head: Lori Reetz, Tammy Moody
Historical Museum - 1947
Western history, located on Boot Hill 36531

Dolores CO

Anasazi Heritage Center, 27501 Hwy 184, Dolores, CO 81323 - T: (970) 882-4811, Fax: (970) 882-7035, E-mail: meastin@co.blm.gov, Internet: http://www.co.blm.gov/ahc/hmepge.htm. Head: LouAnn Jacobson
Ethnology Museum / Archaeological Museum - 1988
Archaeology 36532

Dora AL

Alabama Mining Museum, 120 East St, Dora, AL 35062 - T: (205) 648-2442. Head: Bonnie Sue Groves
Historical Museum / Science&Tech Museum - 1982
Mining, 1905 steam locomotive, ore car and caboose; c.1900 Oakman, Alabama railroad depot bldg, c.1930 U.S. post office 36533

Dorchester NE

Saline County Historical Society Museum, Hwy 33, S of Main St, Dorchester, NE 68343 - T: (402) 947-2911, Fax: (402) 947-2911. Head: Norma Knoche
Local Museum - 1956 36534

Dothan AL

Landmark Park, Hwy. 431 N, Dothan, AL 36302 - T: (334) 794-3452, Fax: (334) 677-7229. Head: William M. Holman
Agriculture Museum - 1976
Official Museum of Agriculture for the State of Alabama 36535

Wiregrass Museum of Art, 126 Museum Av, Dothan, AL 36303-1624 - T: (334) 794-3871, Fax: (334) 615-2217, E-mail: wmuseum@snowhill.com. Head: Sam W. Kates
Fine Arts Museum - 1988
Art 36536

Douglas AZ

Slaughter Ranch Museum, 6153 Geronimo Trail, Douglas, AZ 85608 - T: (520) 558-2474, Fax: (602) 933-3777. Head: Harvey Finks
Local Museum - 1982
Local hist 36537

Douglas MI

Steamship Keewatin, Harbour Village, Douglas, MI 49406 - T: (616) 857-2107, Fax: (616) 857-2107. Head: R.J. Peterson
Historical Museum / Science&Tech Museum - 1965
Historic Ship, former 1907 Great Lakes passenger steamship of the Canadian Pacific Railroad 36538

Douglas WY

Fort Fetterman State Museum, 752 Hwy 93, Douglas, WY 82633 - T: (307) 358-2864, 684-7629, Fax: (307) 358-2864, E-mail: rwilso@missc.state.wy.us. Head: Bill Gentle
Military Museum - 1963
Military hist, life of the native Americans (Dakota, Cheyenne, Shoshone) 36539

Wyoming Pioneer Memorial Museum, Wyoming State Fairgrounds, 400 W Center St, Douglas, WY 82633 - T: (307) 358-9288, Fax: (307) 358-9293. Head: Arlene E. Earnst
Local Museum - 1956
Local hist 36540

Douglass KS

Douglass Historical Museum, 318 S Forest, Douglass, KS 67039 - T: (316) 746-2319, 746-2122. Head: Francis Renfro, Jean Valentine
Historical Museum - 1949
Pioneer museum 36541

Dover DE

Biggs Museum of American Art, 406 Federal St, Dover, DE 19901, mail addr: POB 711, Dover, DE 19903 - T: (302) 674-2111, Fax: (302) 674-5133, E-mail: biggs@delaware.net, Internet: http://www.biggsmuseum.org. Head: Karol A. Schmiegel
Fine Arts Museum - 1989
Art Museum housed in 1858 County Office Building 36542

Delaware Agricultural Museum and Village, 866 N Dupont Hwy, Dover, DE 19901 - T: (302) 734-1618, Fax: (302) 734-0457, E-mail: DAMV@dol.net, Internet: http://www.agriculturalmuseum.org. Head: Elizabeth A. Brewer
Local Museum / Agriculture Museum - 1974
Rural life, agricultural hist and technology 36543

Delaware State Museums, Rose Cottage, 102 S State St, Dover, DE 19901 - T: (302) 739-5316, Fax: (302) 739-6712, E-mail: jistewart.de.us, Internet: http://www.destatemuseums.org
Local Museum - 1931
Local hist 36544

Dover MA

Caryl House, 107 Dedham St, Dover, MA 02030 - T: (508) 785-1832, Fax: (508) 785-0789
Local Museum - 1920
Historic house 36545

Sawin Memorial Building, 80 Dedham St, Dover, MA 02030 - T: (508) 785-1832, Fax: (508) 785-0789
Local Museum - 1907
Regional history 36546

Dover NH

Annie E. Woodman Institute, 182 Central Av, Dover, NH 03821-0146 - T: (603) 742-1038
Local Museum - 1916 36547

Dover OH

J.E. Reeves Home and Museum, 325 E Iron Av, Dover, OH 44622 - T: (330) 343-7040, (800) 815-2794, Fax: (330) 343-6290, E-mail: reeves@tusco.net, Internet: http://web.tusco.net/tourism/reeves. Head: James D. Nixon, Chris Nixon
Local Museum - 1958 36548

Warther Museum, 331 Karl Av, Dover, OH 44622 - T: (330) 343-7513, E-mail: wartherknives@wilkshire.net, Internet: http://www.warthers.com. Head: David R. Warther
Decorative Arts Museum / Agriculture Museum - 1936 36549

Dover-Foxcroft ME

Blacksmith Shop Museum, 100 Dawes Rd, Dover-Foxcroft, ME 04426 - T: (207) 564-8618
Historical Museum - 1963 36550

Dowagiac MI

Southwestern Michigan College Museum, 58900 Cherry Grove Rd, Dowagiac, MI 49047 - T: (616) 782-1374, Fax: (616) 782-1460, Internet: http://smc.cc.mi.us. Head: Jill P. Dixon
University Museum / Historical Museum / Science&Tech Museum - 1982
History Museum and Science Center 36551

Downers Grove IL

The Downers Grove Museum, 831 Maple Av, Downers Grove, IL 60515 - T: (630) 963-1309, Fax: (630) 963-0496, E-mail: mharmon@xnet.com, Internet: http://www.dgparks.org/museum/mumain.html
Local Museum - 1968
Local history 36552

Downey CA

Downey Museum of Art, 10419 S Rives Av, Downey, CA 90241 - T: (562) 861-0419. Head: Kate Davies
Fine Arts Museum - 1957 36553

Downieville CA

Downieville Museum, 330 Main St, Downieville, CA 95936 - T: (530) 289-3423, Fax: (530) 289-1501, E-mail: arniekej@sccn.net. Head: Kevel Jane Gutman
Local Museum - 1932 36554

Doylestown PA

Fonthill Museum, E Court St, Doylestown, PA 18901 - T: (215) 348-9461, Fax: (215) 348-9462, E-mail: info@fonthillmuseum.org, Internet: http://www.fonthillmuseum.org. Head: Douglas C. Dolan
Decorative Arts Museum / Historical Museum - 1930
Home of Henry C. Mercer (1856-1930), noted archeologist, arts and crafts 36555

James A. Michener Art Museum, 138 S Pine St, Doylestown, PA 18901 - T: (215) 340-9800, Fax: (215) 340-9807, Internet: http://www.michenerartmuseum.org. Head: Bruce Katsiff
Fine Arts Museum - 1987
Pennsylvania impressionism 20th c 36556

Mercer Museum, 84 S Pine St, Doylestown, PA 18901-4999 - T: (215) 345-0210, Fax: (215) 230-0823, E-mail: info@mercermuseum.org, Internet: http://www.mercermuseum.org. Head: Douglas C. Dolan
Folklore Museum / Historical Museum / Science&Tech Museum - 1916 36557

Dragoon AZ

The Amerind Foundation, 2100 N Amerind Rd, Dragoon, AZ 85609, mail addr: POB 400, Dragoon, AZ 85609 - T: (520) 586-3666, Fax: (520) 586-4679, E-mail: amerind@amerind.org, Internet: http://www.amerind.org. Head: William Duncan Fulton, Dr. Anne I. Woosley
Local Museum - 1937
Archaeology, ethnology, art 36558

Drummond Island MI

Drummond Island Historical Museum, Water St, Drummond Island, MI 49726 - T: (906) 493-5746. Head: Harry Ropp, John Lowe, Judge Michael McDonald, Rosalie Sasso, Catherine Ashley
Local Museum - 1961
Local history 36559

Dublin GA

Dublin-Laurens Museum, 311 Academy Av, Dublin, GA 31040-1461 - T: (478) 272-9242, E-mail: history@nlamerica.com. Head: John Bogle, Scott Thompson
Special Museum - 1979
Archaeology, geology, paintings, photos, artefacts, housed in 1904 restored Carnegie Library 36560

Dubois WY

Wind River Historical Center Dubois Museum, 909 West Ramshorn, Dubois, WY 82513 - T: (307) 455-2284, Fax: (307) 455-3852, E-mail: jbendel@wyoming.com, Internet: http://www.windriverhistory.org. Head: Dr. Sharon Kahin
Local Museum - 1976
Local hist, natural hist - Lucius Burch Center for Western Traditions 36561

Dubuque IA

Dubuque Museum of Art, 701 Locust St, Dubuque, IA 52001 - T: (319) 557-1851, Fax: (319) 557-7826, E-mail: dbqartmuseum@mcleodusa.net, Internet: http://www.dbqartmuseum.com. Head: Nelson Britt, Tim Conlon
Fine Arts Museum / Folklore Museum - 1874
Art 36562

Mississippi River Museum, 400 E 3rd St, Dubuque, IA 52001 - T: (319) 557-9545, Fax: (319) 583-1241, E-mail: rivermuseum@mwci.net. Head: Jerome A. Enzler
Historical Museum - 1950
Maritime and naval history, Mississippi Riverboats - archives 36563

Duluth GA

Gwinettt Fine Arts Center → Jacqueline Casey Hudgens Center for the Arts

Jacqueline Casey Hudgens Center for the Arts, 6400 Sugarloaf Pkwy, Bldg 300, Duluth, GA 30097 - T: (770) 623-6002, Fax: (770) 623-3555, E-mail: elliott@hudgenscenter.org, Internet: http://www.hudgenscenter.org. Head: Nancy Gullickson
Fine Arts Museum - 1981 36564

Southeastern Railway Museum, 3595 Peachtree Rd, Duluth, GA 30096 - T: (770) 476-2013, Fax: (770) 908-8322, E-mail: admin@srmduluth.org, Internet: http://www.srmduluth.org. Head: Lesa Campbell
Science&Tech Museum / Historical Museum - 1970
Rail cars and locomotives 1910 - present, rail-related artefacts 36565

Duluth MN

Duluth Art Institute, 506 W Michigan St, Duluth, MN 55802 - T: (218) 733-7560, Fax: (218) 733-7506, Internet: http://www.computerpro.com/~depot. Head: John Steffl
Fine Arts Museum 36566

Duluth Children's Museum, 506 W Michigan St, Duluth, MN 55802 - T: (218) 733-7543, Fax: (218) 733-7547. Head: Bonnie A. Cusick
Local Museum / Special Museum - 1930
Children's, youth, Saint Louis County heritage, arts 36567

Glensheen Historic Estate, 3300 London Rd, Duluth, MN 55804 - T: (218) 726-8910, Fax: (218) 726-8911, E-mail: glen@d.umn.edu, Internet: http://www.d.umn.edu/glen. Head: William K. Miller
Historical Museum - 1979
Historic neo-Jacobean mansion, carriage house, original furnishings 36568

Lake Superior Maritime Visitors Center, 600 Lake Av, Duluth, MN 55802 - T: (218) 727-2497, Fax: (218) 720-5270, E-mail: Charles.P.Labadie@Lre02.usace.army.mil. Head: Dennis Medjo, C. Patrick Labadie
Historical Museum / Science&Tech Museum - 1973
Marine hist 36569

Lake Superior Railroad Museum, 506 W Michigan St, Duluth, MN 55802 - T: (218) 733-7590, Fax: (218) 733-7596, E-mail: lsrm@cpinternet.com, Internet: http://www.cpinternet.com/~srm
Historical Museum - 1974
Railroad, Duluth Union Depot Bldg 36570

Saint Louis County Historical Museum, 506 W Michigan St, Duluth, MN 55802 - T: (218) 733-7580, Fax: (218) 733-7585, E-mail: slchs@computerpro.com. Head: Nick Wognum, JoAnne Coombe
Local Museum - 1922
Regional history, E. Johnson coll of drawings and paintings, Ojibwe and Sioux beadwork, quillwork, furniture 36571

Tweed Museum of Art, University of Minnesota, 10 University Dr, Duluth, MN 55812 - T: (218) 726-8222, Fax: (218) 726-8503, E-mail: tmva@d.umn.edu, Internet: http://www.d.umn.edu/tma/. Head: Martin DeWitt
Fine Arts Museum / University Museum - 1950
Johnathan Sax coll (American prints), George P. Tweed coll (paintings), sculpture 36572

Dumas AR

Desha County Museum, Hwy 165, Dumas, AR 71639 - T: (870) 382-4222. Head: Martha Clark, Charlotte Shexnayder
Local Museum - 1979
Local history 36573

Dumas TX

Moore County Historical Museum, 810 S Dumas Av, Dumas, TX 79029-4329 - T: (806) 935-3113. Head: Hilary Cordero
Local Museum - 1976
Local hist 36574

Dumfries VA

Weems-Botts Museum, 300 W Duke St, Dumfries, VA 22026 - T: (703) 221-2218, Fax: (703) 221-2218. Head: David Shutt
Local Museum - 1974
Local hist 36575

Duncan OK

Stephens County Historical Society Museum, Hwy 81 and Beech, Fuqua Park, Duncan, OK 73533 - T: (580) 252-0717, Fax: (580) 251-3195. Head: Cary PeeWee
Local Museum - 1971 36576

Dundee IL

Dundee Township Historical Society Museum, 426 Highland Av, Dundee, IL 60118 - T: (847) 428-6996. Head: Jill Engelman
Local Museum - 1964
Local history 36577

Dunedin FL

Dunedin Historical Society Museum, 349 Main St, Dunedin, FL 34697-2393 - T: (813) 736-1176, Fax: (813) 738-1871, E-mail: DUNHIST@compuserve.com, Internet: http://www.ci.dunedin.fl.us. Head: Daniel W. Zantop, Vincent Luisi
Local Museum - 1969
Local history, 1920 Atlantic Coastline Passenger Station, Old Freight Warehouse 36578

Dunkirk IN

The Glass Museum, 309 S Franklin, Dunkirk, IN 47336 - T: (765) 768-6872, Fax: (765) 768-6872, E-mail: marynewsome@netscape.net, Internet: http://www.dunkirkpubliclibrary.com. Head: Gay A. Rife
Decorative Arts Museum - 1979
Glass 36579

DuPont WA

Dupont Historical Museum, 207 Barksdale Av, DuPont, WA 98327 - T: (253) 964-2399, 964-3492, Fax: (253) 964-3554, E-mail: l_overmyer@mindspring.com. Head: Lorraine Overmyer
Local Museum - 1976
Local hist 36580

Durango CO

Animas Museum, 3065 W 2nd Av, Durango, CO 81301 - T: (970) 259-2402, Fax: (970) 259-2402. Head: Robert McDaniel
Local Museum - 1978
Local hist 36581

Strater Hotel, 699 Main Av, Durango, CO 81301 - T: (970) 247-4431, Fax: (970) 259-2208, E-mail: rod@frontier.net, Internet: http://www.strater.com. Head: Rod Barker
Historical Museum - 1887 36582

Durant OK

Fort Washita, 15 miles east of Madill, Durant, OK 74701 - T: (580) 924-6502, Fax: (580) 924-6502, E-mail: ftwashita@ok-history.mus.ok.us, Internet: http://www.texoma-ok.com/trooper/1842.htm. Head: Blake Wade
Historic Site / Open Air Museum / Military Museum - 1967 36583

Durham NC

Bennett Place State Historic Site, 4409 Bennett Memorial Rd, Durham, NC 27705 - T: (919) 383-4345, Fax: (919) 383-4349, E-mail: bennettplace@mindspring.com, Internet: http://wwwah.dcr.state.nc.us/hs/bennett/bennett.htm. Head: Davis Waters
Local Museum - 1962 36584

Duke Homestead State Historic Site, 2828 Duke Homestead Rd, Durham, NC 27705 - T: (919) 477-5498, Fax: (919) 479-7092, E-mail: dukehomestead@mindsoring.com, Internet: http://duke.ncsl.dcr.state.nc.us. Head: Walker S. Stone
Historical Museum - 1974 36585

Duke University Museum of Art, Buchanan Blvd at Trinity, Durham, NC 27708 - T: (919) 684-5135, Fax: (919) 681-8624, E-mail: brevans@duke.edu, Internet: http://www.duke.edu/duma/. Head: Dr. Michael P. Mezzatesta
Fine Arts Museum / University Museum - 1968 36586

Durham Art Guild, 120 Morris St, Durham, NC 27701 - T: (919) 560-2713, Fax: (919) 560-2754, E-mail: artguild1@yahoo.com, Internet: http://www.durhamartguild.org. Head: Lisa Morton
Public Gallery 36587

History of Medicine Collections, Duke University Medical Center Library, Durham, NC 27710 - T: (919) 660-1143, Fax: (919) 681-7599, E-mail: porte004@mc.duke.edu, Internet: http://www.mc.duke.edu/mclibrary
Library with Exhibitions - 1956 36588

North Carolina Central University Art Museum, 1801 Fayetteville Stal University, Durham, NC 27707, mail addr: c/o North Carolina Central University, POB 19555, Durham, NC 27707 - T: (919) 560-6211, Fax: (919) 560-5012, E-mail: Krodgers@wpo.nccu.edu, Internet: http://www.nccu.edu/artmuseum/. Head: Kenneth G. Rodgers
Fine Arts Museum / University Museum - 1971 36589

North Carolina Museum of Life and Science, 433 Murray Av, Durham, NC 27704 - T: (919) 220-5429, Fax: (919) 220-5575, E-mail: tkrakauer@mindspring.com, Internet: http://www.herald-sun.com/ncmls. Head: Thomas Krakauer
Science&Tech Museum / Natural History Museum - 1946 36590

Durham NH

The Art Gallery, University of New Hampshire, Paul Creative Arts Center, 30 College Rd, Durham, NH 03824-3538 - T: (603) 862-3712, Fax: (603) 862-2191, E-mail: art.gallery@unh.edu, Internet: http://www.unh.edu/art-gallery. Head: Vicki C. Wright
Fine Arts Museum / University Museum - 1960 36591

Durham Historic Association Museum, Newmarket Rd and Main St, Durham, NH 03824 - T: (603) 868-5436. Head: Richard Dewing, Craig Brown
Local Museum - 1851 36592

Duxbury MA

Art Complex Museum, 189 Alden St, Duxbury, MA 02331 - T: (781) 934-6634, Fax: (781) 934-5117, E-mail: info@artcomplex.org, Internet: http://www.artcomplex.org. Head: Charles A. Weyerhaeuser
Fine Arts Museum - 1971
Art 36593

Eagle WI

Old World Wisconsin, S103 W37890 Hwy 67, Eagle, WI 53119 - T: (262) 594-6300, Fax: (262) 594-6342, E-mail: owwvisit@idcnet.com, Internet: http://oww.shsw.wisc.edu. Head: Thomas Woods
Ethnology Museum / Historical Museum / Open Air Museum - 1976
Ethnology 36594

Eagle City AK

Eagle Historical Society and Museums, 3rd and Chamberlain, Eagle City, AK 99738 - T: (907) 547-2325, Fax: (907) 547-2232, E-mail: ehsmuseums@aol.com, Internet: http://www.agleak.org. Head: Elva Scott
Local Museum - 1961
Local military and Indians history 36595

Eagle Harbor MI

Keweenaw County Historical Society Museum, Lighthouse Street, M-26, Eagle Harbor, MI 49950 - T: (906) 289-4990. Head: Peter Van Pelt
Historical Museum / Science&Tech Museum - 1981
Marine hist 36596

Eagle River AK

Alaska Museum of Natural History, 11723 Old Glenn Hwy, Eagle River, AK 99577 - T: (907) 694-0819, Fax: (907) 694-0919, E-mail: info@alaskamuseum.org, Internet: http://www.alaskamuseum.org. Head: Kurt Johnson
Natural History Museum - 1992 36597

East Aurora NY

Aurora Historical Society Museum, POB 472, East Aurora, NY 14052 - T: (716) 652-4735
Local Museum - 1951 36598

Elbert Hubbard-Roycroft Museum, 363 Oakwood Av, East Aurora, NY 14052 - T: (716) 652-4735
Local Museum / Decorative Arts Museum - 1962
Books, leathercraft, metal work, furniture, artglass, arts and crafts movement 36599

Millard Fillmore House, 24 Shearer Av, East Aurora, NY 14052 - T: (716) 652-8875
Local Museum - 1951 36600

East Brunswick NJ

East Brunswick Museum, 16 Maple St, East Brunswick, NJ 08816 - T: (732) 257-2313, 257-1508. Head: Mark Nonesteid
Local Museum - 1978
Local and regional hist 36601

East Durham NY

Durham Center Museum, Star Rte 1, East Durham, NY 12423 - T: (518) 239-8461. Head: Dan Clifton
Local Museum - 1960 36602

Irish American Heritage Museum, Rte 145, East Durham, NY 12423 - T: (518) 634-7497, Fax: (518) 634-7497, E-mail: IrishMus@crisny.org, Internet: http://www.IrishAmericanHerMuseum.org. Head: Joseph J. Dolan
Folklore Museum - 1986
Ethnic museum 36603

East Greenwich RI

James Mitchell Varnum House and Museum, 57 Peirce St, East Greenwich, RI 02818 - T: (401) 884-1776, E-mail: k8bcm@home.com, Internet: http://www.varnumcontinentals.org. Head: Bruce C. MacGunnigle
Local Museum - 1938
Historic house 36604

New England Wireless and Steam Museum, 1300 Frenchtown Rd, East Greenwich, RI 02818 - T: (401) 885-0545, Fax: (401) 884-0683, E-mail: newsm@ids.net, Internet: http://users.ids.net/~newsm. Head: Robert W. Merriam
Science&Tech Museum - 1964
Engineering 36605

Varnum Memorial Armory and Military Museum, 6 Main St, East Greenwich, RI 02818 - T: (401) 884-4110, E-mail: k8bcm@home.com, Internet: http://www.varnumcontinentals.org. Head: Bruce C. MacGunnigle
Military Museum - 1913
Military hist 36606

East Hampton NY

Clinton Academy Museum, 151 Main St, East Hampton, NY 11937 - T: (516) 324-6850, Fax: (516) 324-9885. Head: Dr. Karen Hensel
Historical Museum - 1784 36607

East Hampton Historical Society Museum, 101 Main St, East Hampton, NY 11937 - T: (516) 324-6850, Fax: (516) 324-9885. Head: Dr. Karen Hensel
Local Museum - 1921 36608

East Hampton Town Marine Museum, 101 Main St, East Hampton, NY 11937 - T: (516) 267-6544, Fax: (516) 324-9885. Head: Dr. Karen Hensel
Natural History Museum - 1966 36609

Guild Hall Museum, 158 Main St, East Hampton, NY 11937 - T: (516) 324-0806, Fax: (516) 324-2722, E-mail: pr@guildhall.org, Internet: http://guildhall.org. Head: Ruth Appelhof
Fine Arts Museum - 1931 36610

Home Sweet Home Museum, 14 James Ln, East Hampton, NY 11937 - T: (613) 324-0713, Fax: (613) 324-0713. Head: Hugh R. King
Decorative Arts Museum / Local Museum / Historic Site - 1928 36611

Mulford House and Farm, 10 James Ln, East Hampton, NY 11937 - T: (516) 324-6850, Fax: (516) 324-9885. Head: Dr. Karen Hensel
Agriculture Museum / Open Air Museum - 1948 36612

Osborn-Jackson House, 101 Main St, East Hampton, NY 11937 - T: (516) 324-6850, Fax: (516) 324-9885. Head: Dr. Karen Hensel
Decorative Arts Museum / Local Museum - 1979 36613

East Haven CT

Shore Line Trolley Museum, 17 River St, East Haven, CT 06512-2519 - T: (203) 467-6927, Fax: (203) 467-7635, E-mail: beraslm@aol.com, Internet: http://www.bera.org. Head: Donald J. Engel, George Boucher, Theodore Eickmann, Frederick Sherwood
Science&Tech Museum - 1945
Transport technology, operating railway 36614

East Islip NY

Islip Art Museum, 50 Irish Ln, East Islip, NY 11730 - T: (631) 224-5402, Fax: (631) 224-5417, E-mail: info@islipartmuseum.org, Internet: http://www.islipartmuseum.org. Head: Mary Lou Cohalan, Catherine Valenza
Fine Arts Museum - 1973
Art 36615

East Jordan MI

East Jordan Portside Art and Historical Museum, 1787 S M-66 Hwy, East Jordan, MI 49727 - T: (616) 536-2393, Fax: (616) 536-2051, E-mail: JPardee2@Juno.com. Head: Jean Pardee, Cygred Riley
Fine Arts Museum / Local Museum - 1976
Local hist, art 36616

East Lansing MI

Kresge Art Museum, Michigan State University, East Lansing, MI 48824 - T: (517) 355-7631, Fax: (517) 355-6577, E-mail: kamuseum@pilot.msu.edu, Internet: http://www.msu.edu/unit/kamuseum. Head: Dr. Susan J. Bandes
Fine Arts Museum / University Museum - 1959
Drawings, graphics, bronzes, African art, ethnology, ceramics, etchings and engravings, Afro-American art, Eskimo art, decorative arts, baroque art, antiquities 36617

Michigan State University Museum, W Circle Dr, East Lansing, MI 48824-1045 - T: (517) 355-2370, Fax: (517) 432-2846, E-mail: dewhurs1@pilot.msu.edu, Internet: http://museum.msu.edu. Head: Max Hoffman, Dr. C. Kurt Dewhurst
University Museum / Historical Museum / Natural History Museum - 1857
Science, cultural history, folk art, history, archaeology, ethnology, anthropology, paleontology, mammalogy, ornitology 36618

East Liverpool OH

Museum of Ceramics at East Liverpool, 400 E Fifth St, East Liverpool, OH 43920 - T: (330) 386-6001, Fax: (330) 386-0488, Internet: http://www.ohiohistory.org
Decorative Arts Museum - 1980 36619

East Meredith NY

Hanford Mills Museum, POB 99, East Meredith, NY 13757 - T: (607) 278-5744, Fax: (607) 278-6299, E-mail: hanford1@hanfordmills.org, Internet: http://www.hanfordmills.org
Historical Museum / Science&Tech Museum - 1973 36620

East Poultney VT

East Poultney Museums, The Green, East Poultney, VT 05741 - T: (802) 287-5268
Local Museum / Museum of Classical Antiquities - 1954
Antiques, local hist 36621

East Tawas MI

Iosco County Historical Museum, 405 W Bay St, East Tawas, MI 48730 - T: (517) 362-7456, 362-8911. Head: Rosemary Klenow
Local Museum - 1976
Local history, bldg built by J.D. Hawks, 1st president of the Detroit and Mackinaw Railway 36622

East Windsor CT

Connecticut Trolley Museum, 58 North Rd, East Windsor, CT 06088-0360 - T: (860) 627-6540, Fax: (860) 627-6510, E-mail: information@ceraonline.org, Internet: http://www.ceraonline.org. Head: Alex P. Goff
Science&Tech Museum - 1940
Trolley transport system 36623

Scantic Academy Museum, 115 Scantic Rd, East Windsor, CT 06088 - T: (860) 623-3149. Head: Michael Hunt
Local Museum - 1965
General museum 36624

Easton MD

Academy Art Museum, 106 South St, Easton, MD 21601 - T: (410) 822-2787, Fax: (410) 822-5997, E-mail: Academy@expresshost.com, Internet: http://www.art-academy.org. Head: Christopher J. Brownawell
Fine Arts Museum - 1958
Multi-disciplinary arts 36625

Historical Museum of Talbot County, 25 S Washington St, Easton, MD 21601 - T: (410) 822-0773, Fax: (410) 822-7911, E-mail: director@hstc.org, Internet: http://www.hstc.org. Head: Clinton Salt Brown, Joan R. Hoge
Local Museum - 1954
Regional history 36626

Easton PA

Lafayette College Art Gallery, Hamilton and High St, Easton, PA 18042-1768 - T: (610) 250-5361, Fax: (610) 559-4042, E-mail: okayam@lafayette.edu, Internet: http://www.lafayette.edu. Head: Michiko Okaya
Fine Arts Museum / Public Gallery / University Museum - 1983
Art 36627

National Canal Museum, 30 Centre Sq, Easton, PA 18042-7743 - T: (610) 559-6613, Fax: (610) 559-6690, E-mail: ncm@canals.org, Internet: http://canals.org. Head: J. Steven Humphrey
Science&Tech Museum - 1970 36628

Northampton County Historical and Genealogical Society Museum, 107 S Fourth St, Easton, PA 18042 - T: (610) 253-1222, Fax: (610) 253-1222, Internet: http://northamptonctymuseum.org. Head: Grace Fried, Paul A. Goudy
Local Museum - 1906 36629

Eastsound WA

Orcas Island Historical Museum, 181 North Beach Rd, Eastsound, WA 98245 - T: (360) 376-4849, Fax: (360) 376-2994, Internet: http://www.orcasisland.org. Head: Audrey Stupke, Jennifer Vollmer
Local Museum - 1950
Local hist 36630

Eatonton GA

Uncle Remus Museum, 360 Oak St, Hwy 441 S, Eatonton, GA 31024 - T: (706) 485-6856. Head: Norma Watterson
Historical Museum - 1963
House c.1820 slave cabin, furnishings 36631

Eatonville WA

Pioneer Farm Museum and Ohop Indian Village, 7716 Ohop Valley Rd E., Eatonville, WA 98328 - T: (360) 832-6300, Fax: (360) 832-4533. Head: Dean Carpenter
Local Museum / Agriculture Museum - 1975
Agriculture, local hist 36632

Eau Claire WI

Foster Gallery, University of Wisconsin-Eau Claire, 121 Water St, Eau Claire, WI 54702-5008 - T: (715) 836-2328, Fax: (715) 836-4882, E-mail: wagenetk@uwec.edu, Internet: http://www.uwec.edu. Head: Thomas K. Wagner
Fine Arts Museum / University Museum - 1970 36633

Paul Bunyan Logging Camp, 1110 Carson Park Dr, Eau Claire, WI 54703 - T: (715) 835-6200, Fax: (715) 835-6293, E-mail: hank@omni.xgen.net, Internet: http://www.paulbunyancamp.org
Science&Tech Museum - 1934
Logging and lumbering 36634

Ebensburg PA

Cambria County Historical Society Museum, 615 N Center, Ebensburg, PA 15931 - T: (814) 472-6674
Local Museum - 1925 36635

Eckley PA

Eckley Miners' Village, Main St, Eckley, PA 18255 - T: (717) 636-2070, Fax: (717) 636-2938. Head: David Dubick
Historical Museum - 1969
54 houses built in the 1850s as coal patch town including Roman Catholic Church, Episcopal Church, doctor's office, coal breaker, visitor's center and mule barn 36636

Edenton NC

Historic Edenton State Historic Site, 108 N Broad St, Edenton, NC 27932 - T: (252) 482-2637, Fax: (252) 482-3499, E-mail: edentonshs@inteliport.com, Internet: http://www.ah.dcr.state.nc.us/sections/hs/iredell
Historical Museum - 1951 36637

Edgartown MA

Vineyard Museum, Cooke and School Sts, Edgartown, MA 02539 - T: (508) 627-4441, Fax: (508) 627-4436, E-mail: mvhist@vineyard.net, Internet: http://www.vineyard.net/org/mvhs. Head: Bruce Andrews
Open Air Museum / Local Museum - 1922
Thomas Cooke House, 2nd Captain Francis Pease House 36638

Edgerton KS

Lanesfield School, 18745 S Dillie Rd, Edgerton, KS 66021 - T: (913) 893-6645, Fax: (913) 631-6359, Internet: http://www.digitalhistory.com. Head: Mindi Love
Historical Museum - 1967
One-room schoolhouse restored to 1904 appearance 36639

Edgerton WI

Albion Academy Historical Museum, 605 Campus Ln, Edgerton, WI 53534 - T: (608) 884-6598. Head: Clayton Olstad
Local Museum - 1959
Local hist 36640

Edgewater MD

London Town, 839 Londontown Rd, Edgewater, MD 21037 - T: (410) 222-1919, Fax: (410) 222-1918, E-mail: londntwn@clark.net, Internet: http://www.historiclondontown.com. Head: Melissa Heaver, Gregory Stiverson
Historical Museum / Archaeological Museum - 1971
Significant archaelogical site 36641

Edina MN

Mhiripiri Gallery, 3519 W 70th St, Edina, MN 55343 - T: (952) 285-9684, Internet: http://www.shonasculpturemhiripiri.com
Fine Arts Museum - 1986 36642

Edina MO

Knox County Historical Society Museum, Court House, 107 N Fourth St, Edina, MO 63537 - T: (660) 397-2349, Fax: (660) 397-3331. Head: Brent Karhoff
Historical Museum - 1967 36643

Edinburg TX

Hidalgo County Historical Museum, 121 E McIntyre St, Edinburg, TX 78539 - T: (210) 383-6911, Fax: (210) 381-8518, E-mail: hchm@hiline.net, Internet: http://www.riograndeborderlands.org. Head: Shan Rankin
Local Museum - 1967
Local hist 36644

University Galleries, Art Dept., University of Texas Pan American, 1201 W University Dr, Edinburg, TX 78539 - T: (210) 381-2655, Fax: (210) 384-5072, E-mail: galleries@panam.edu, Internet: www.panam.edu/dept/art/pages/artgall.html. Head: Dindy Reich
Fine Arts Museum 36645

Edmond OK

Edmond Historical Society Museum, 431 S Blvd, Edmond, OK 73034 - T: (405) 340-0078, Fax: (405) 340-2771, Internet: http://www.edmondhistory.org. Head: Linda Hopkins, Brenda Granger, Iris Muno Jordan
Local Museum - 1983
Local hist 36646

Edmonds WA

Edmonds Art Festival Museum, 700 Main St, Edmonds, WA 98020 - T: (425) 771-6412
Fine Arts Museum - 1979
Art 36647

Edmonds South Snohomish County Historical Society Museum, 118 Fifth Av N, Edmonds, WA 98020 - T: (425) 774-0900, Fax: (425) 774-6507, Internet: http://www.historicedmonds.org. Head: Joni L. Sein
Local Museum - 1973
Local hist 36648

Edna TX

Texana Museum, 403 N Wells, Edna, TX 77957 - T: (512) 782-5431. Head: Lois Cunning, Lee Doersch
Local Museum - 1967
Local hist 36649

Edwards Air Force Base CA

Air Force Flight Test Center Museum, 95 ABW/MU, 1100 Kincheloe, Edwards Air Force Base, CA 93524-1850 - T: (805) 277-8050, Fax: (805) 277-8051, E-mail: museum@po-box1.edwards.af.mil, Internet: http://afftc.edwards.af.mil/341.html. Head: Doug Nelson
Military Museum / Science&Tech Museum - 1986
Aeronautics 36650

Edwardsville IL

Madison County Historical Museum, 715 N Main St, Edwardsville, IL 62025-1111 - T: (618) 656-7562, Internet: http://library.wustl.edu/-spec/archives/aslaa/madison-historical.html. Head: Suzanne Dietrich
Local Museum - 1924
Local history, housed in John H. Weir home - library 36651

The University Museum, Southern Illinois University Edwardsville, Edwardsville, IL 62026 - T: (618) 650-2996, Fax: (618) 650-2995, E-mail: ebarnet@siue.edu, Internet: http://www.siue.edu/art/museum.html. Head: Eric B. Barnett
Local Museum / University Museum - 1959 36652

Egg Harbor WI

Chief Oshkosh Native American Arts, 7631 Egg Harbor Rd, Egg Harbor, WI 54209 - T: (920) 868-3240. Head: Coleen Bins
Fine Arts Museum - 1975
Native American art 36653

Eglin Air Force Base FL

Air Force Armament Museum, 100 Museum Dr, Eglin Air Force Base, FL 32542-1497 - T: (850) 882-4062, 882-4189, Fax: (850) 882-3990, E-mail: sneddon@eglin.af.mil, Internet: http://www.wg53.eglin.af.mil/armmus. Head: Russell C. Sneddon
Military Museum - 1985
Military 36654

Egypt PA

Troxell-Steckel House and Farm Museum, 4229 Reliance St, Egypt, PA 18052 - T: (610) 435-1074, Fax: (610) 435-9812
Local Museum / Agriculture Museum - 1904 36655

Ekalaka MT

Carter County Museum, 100 Main St, Ekalaka, MT 59324 - T: (406) 775-6886. Head: Warren O. White
Local Museum / Ethnology Museum / Natural History Museum / Folklore Museum - 1936 36656

El Cajon CA

Hyde Art Gallery, Grossmont Community College, 8800 Grossmont College Dr, El Cajon, CA 92020 - T: (619) 644-7299, Fax: (619) 644-7922, E-mail: teresa.markey@gcccd.net, Internet: http://www.grossmont.gcccd.cc.ca.us/home. Head: Ron Tatro
University Museum / Fine Arts Museum - 1961 36657

El Campo TX

El Campo Museum of Art, History and Natural Science, 2350 N Mechanic St, El Campo, TX 77437 - T: (409) 541-5092, Fax: (409) 543-5788
Natural History Museum - 1978
Natural hist 36658

El Dorado AR

South Arkansas Arts Center, 110 E Fifth St, El Dorado, AR 71730 - T: (870) 862-5474, Fax: (870) 862-4921, E-mail: saac@arkansas.net, Internet: http://www.saac-arts.org. Head: George Maguire, Beth James
Fine Arts Museum - 1962
Art gallery 36659

El Dorado KS

Butler County Museum and Kansas Oil Museum, 383 E Central Av, El Dorado, KS 67042 - T: (316) 321-9333, Fax: (316) 321-3619, E-mail: bchs@powwwer.net, Internet: http://www.skyways.org/museums/kom. Head: Rebecca Matticks
Local Museum / Science&Tech Museum - 1956
Kansas oil history, local history 36660

Coutts Memorial Museum of Art, 110 N Main St, El Dorado, KS 67042-0001 - T: (316) 321-1212, Fax: (316) 321-1215, E-mail: coutts@southwind.com, Internet: http://skyways.lib.ks.us/kansas/museums/coutts/. Head: Rhoda Hodges, Terri Scott
Fine Arts Museum - 1970
Fine art, Frederic Remington sculpture coll 36661

El Monte CA

El Monte Historical Society Museum, 3150 N Tyler Av, El Monte, CA 91731 - T: (626) 444-3813
Local Museum - 1958 36662

El Paso CO

United States Air Force Academy Museum, 2346 Academy Dr, USAF Academy, El Paso, CO 80840-9400 - T: (719) 333-2569, Fax: (719) 333-4402
University Museum / Military Museum - 1961
Military 36663

El Paso TX

Americana Museum, 5 Civic Center Plaza, El Paso, TX 79901 - T: (915) 542-0394, Fax: (915) 542-4511
Folklore Museum / Historical Museum 36664

Bridge Center for Contemporary Art, 1112 E Mandell St, El Paso, TX 79902 - T: (915) 532-6707. Head: Richard Baron
Public Gallery - 1986 36665

The Centennial Museum at the University of Texas at El Paso, University Av, Wiggins Rd, El Paso, TX 79968-0533 - T: (915) 747-5565, Fax: (915) 747-5411, E-mail: museum@utep.edu, Internet: http://www.utep.edu/museum/. Head: Florence Schwein
University Museum / Natural History Museum - 1936
Natural hist 36666

Chamizal National Memorial, 800 S San Marcial, El Paso, TX 79905 - T: (915) 532-7273, Fax: (915) 532-7240, Internet: http://www.nps.gov/cham
Local Museum - 1967
Local hist 36667

El Paso Museum of Art, 1 Arts Festival Plaza, El Paso, TX 79901 - T: (915) 532-1707, Fax: (915) 532-1010, E-mail: duvalreeseb@ci.el-paso.tx.us, Internet: http://www.elpasoartmuseum.org. Head: Becky Duval Reese
Fine Arts Museum - 1959
Art 36668

El Paso Museum of History, 12901 Gateway West, El Paso, TX 79928 - T: (915) 858-1928, Fax: (915) 858-4591. Head: René Harris
Historical Museum - 1974
History 36669

Insights - El Paso Science Center, 505 N Santa Fe, El Paso, TX 79901 - T: (915) 542-2990, Fax: (915) 532-7416, E-mail: insighta@dzn.com. Head: Ned Eussepie, Raymond Shubinski
Science&Tech Museum - 1979
Science 36670

International Museum of Art, 1211 Montana St, El Paso, TX 79902 - T: (915) 543-6747, Fax: (915) 543-9222. Head: Michael Kirkwood
Fine Arts Museum
Western, African and Heritage gallery, William Kolliker Gallery 36671

Magoffin Home State Historic Site, 1120 Magoffin Av, El Paso, TX 79901 - T: (915) 533-5147, Fax: (915) 544-4398, Internet: http://www.tpwd.state.tx.us/tpwd.htm. Head: Prestene Dehrkoop, Andrew Sansom, Zane Morgan
Local Museum - 1976
Historic house 36672

National Border Patrol Museum and Memorial Library, 4315 Transmountain Rd, El Paso, TX 79924 - T: (915) 759-6060, Fax: (915) 759-0992, E-mail: nbpm@dzn.com, Internet: http://www.nationalbpmuseum.org. Head: Michael Kirkwood
Historical Museum - 1985 36673

Wilderness Park Museum, 4301 Transmountain Rd, El Paso, TX 79924 - T: (915) 755-4332, Fax: (915) 759-6824. Head: Marc Thompson
Archaeological Museum - 1977 36674

El Reno OK

Canadian County Historical Museum, 300 S Grand, El Reno, OK 73036 - T: (405) 262-5121
Local Museum - 1969 36675

Elberta AL

Baldwin County Heritage Museum, 25521 Hwy 98, Elberta, AL 36530 - T: (334) 986-8375. Head: June Taylor
Local Museum / Agriculture Museum - 1986
Rural hist (farming, forestry and associated crafts) 36676

Elbow Lake MN

Grant County Historical Museum, Hwy 79 E, Elbow Lake, MN 56531 - T: (218) 685-4864, E-mail: gcmnhist@runestone.net. Head: Milton Erlandson, Patricia Benson
Historical Museum - 1944
Regional history 36677

Elgin IL

Elgin Public Museum, 225 Grand Blvd, Elgin, IL 60120 - T: (847) 741-6655, Fax: (847) 931-6787, E-mail: epm@mc.net, Internet: elginpublicmuseum.org. Head: Marty Kellams, Nancy J. Epping
Ethnology Museum / Natural History Museum - 1904
Natural hist 36678

Elgin ND

Grant County Museum, 119 Main St, Elgin, ND 58533 - T: (701) 584-2900. Head: Duane Schatz
Local Museum - 1970 36679

Elizabeth City NC

Museum of the Albemarle, 1116 US Hwy 17 S, Elizabeth City, NC 27909-9806 - T: (252) 335-1453, Fax: (252) 335-0637, E-mail: ncs1583@interpath.com, Internet: http://www.albemarle-nc.com. Head: Ed Merrell
Historical Museum - 1963 36680

Elizabethtown KY

Coca-Cola Memorabilia Museum of Elizabethtown, 321 Peterson Dr, Elizabethtown, KY 42701-9375 - T: (270) 769-3320 ext 328, Fax: (270) 769-3323
Science&Tech Museum - 1977
Company museum 36681

Elizabethtown NY

Adirondack Center Museum, Court St, Elizabethtown, NY 12932 - T: (518) 873-6466. Head: Morris Glen, Reid S. Larson
Local Museum - 1954 36682

Elk City OK

Old Town Museum, 2717 W Hwy 66, Elk City, OK 73644 - T: (405) 225-6266, Fax: (580) 225-1008
Local Museum - 1966 36683

Elk Grove Village IL

Elk Grove Farmhouse Museum, 399 Biesterfield Rd, Elk Grove Village, IL 60007 - T: (847) 439-3994, Fax: (847) 228-3508. Head: Tammy Miller
Local Museum - 1976 36684

Elk River MN

Oliver Kelley Farm, 15788 Kelley Farm Rd, Elk River, MN 55330 - T: (612) 441-6896, Fax: (612) 441-6302, E-mail: Jim.Mattson@MNHS.ORG, Internet: http://www.mnhs.org/sites/ohkf.html. Head: James Mattson
Local Museum / Agriculture Museum - 1849
Agriculture 36685

Elkhart IN

CTS Turner Museum, 905 N West Blvd, Elkhart, IN 46514 - T: (219) 293-7511 ext 296, Fax: (219) 293-6146, E-mail: turnermuseum@ctscorp.com, Internet: http://www.cts.com. Head: Joseph Carlson
Science&Tech Museum - 1979
Company history, technology 36686

Midwest Museum of American Art, 429 S Main St, Elkhart, IN 46515 - T: (219) 293-6660, Fax: (219) 293-6660. Head: Jane Burns
Fine Arts Museum - 1978 36687

National New York Central Railroad Museum, 721 S Main St, Elkhart, IN 46516 - T: (219) 294-3001, Fax: (219) 295-9434, E-mail: artscul@michiana.org, Internet: http://nycrrmuseum.-railfan.net. Head: David M. Bird
Science&Tech Museum - 1987 36688

Ruthmere House Museum, 302 E Beardsley Av, Elkhart, IN 46514 - T: (219) 264-0330, Fax: (219) 266-0474, E-mail: library@ruthmere.com, Internet: http://www.ruthmere.com. Head: Kathleen Gray
Decorative Arts Museum - 1969 36689

RV/MH Heritage Foundation, 801 Benham Av, Elkhart, IN 46516-3369 - T: (219) 293-2344, Fax: (219) 293-3466, E-mail: rvmhhall@aol.com, Internet: http://rv-mh-hall-of-fame.org. Head: Carl A. Ehry
Science&Tech Museum - 1972 36690

Elkhorn WI

Webster House Museum, 9 E Rockwell, Elkhorn, WI 53121 - T: (414) 723-4248. Head: Charlotte Gates
Decorative Arts Museum / Local Museum - 1955
Local hist 36691

Elko NV

Northeastern Nevada Museum, 1515 Idaho St, Elko, NV 89801 - T: (775) 738-3418, Fax: (775) 778-9318, Internet: http://www.nenv-museum.org. Head: Stephanie Alberts-Weber
Fine Arts Museum / Historical Museum / Natural History Museum - 1968
History, natural history, wildlife, art - library, archives 36692

Elkton MD

Historical Museum of Cecil County, 135 E Main St, Elkton, MD 21921 - T: (410) 398-1790, E-mail: history@cchistory.org, Internet: http://www.cchistory.org. Head: U.G. Demond
Local Museum - 1931
Regional history 36693

Ellensburg WA

Clymer Museum of Art, 416 N Pearl St, Ellensburg, WA 98926 - T: (509) 962-6416, Fax: (509) 962-6424, E-mail: clymermuseum@home.com. Head: Diana Tasker
Fine Arts Museum - 1991 36694

Olmstead Place State Park, 921 N Ferguson Rd, Ellensburg, WA 98926 - T: (509) 925-1943, Fax: (509) 925-1943
Local Museum / Agriculture Museum - 1968
Local hist 36695

Ellenton FL

The Judah P. Benjamin Confederate Memorial at Gamble Plantation, 3708 Patten Av, Ellenton, FL 34222 - T: (941) 723-4536, Fax: (941) 723-4538, E-mail: gpshs1@juno.com, Internet: http://www.fcn.state.fl.us
Local Museum / Agriculture Museum - 1926
Home of Robert Gamble, main house of the Gamble sugar plantation 36696

Ellicott City MD

Bando Railroad Station Museum, 2711 Maryland Av, Ellicott City, MD 21043 - T: (410) 461-1945, Internet: http://www.rcf.usc.edu/~gkoma. Head: Janet Kusterer, Ed Williams
Science&Tech Museum - 1976
Transport, railroad stn, first terminus in the U.S 36697

Firehouse Museum, 3829 Church Rd, Ellicott City, MD 21043 - T: (410) 465-0232. Head: Carolyn Klein
Science&Tech Museum - 1991 36698

Ellis Grove IL

Pierre Menard Home - State Historic Site, 4230 Kaskaskta Rd, Ellis Grove, IL 62241-9702, mail addr: 4372 Park Rd, Ellis Grove, IL 62241-9704 - T: (618) 859-3031, Fax: (618) 859-3741, E-mail: menrdhom@midwest.net. Head: Robert Coomer
Historical Museum - 1927
Home of Pierre Menard, the first Lt. Governor of Illinois and U.S. Agent of Indian Affairs 36699

Ellsworth KS

Ellsworth County Museum, 104 W South Main, Ellsworth, KS 67439 - T: (785) 472-3059. Head: Patricia L. Bender
Local Museum - 1961 36700

Rogers House Museum and Gallery, 102 E Main S, Ellsworth, KS 67439 - T: (913) 472-5674. Head: Robert Rogers
Fine Arts Museum / Public Gallery - 1968 36701

Elmhurst IL

Elmhurst Art Museum, 150 Cottage Hill Av, Elmhurst, IL 60126 - T: (630) 834-0202, Fax: (630) 834-0234, E-mail: nbremer@elmhurstartmuseum.org, Internet: http://www.elmhurstartmuseum.org. Head: D. Neil Bremer
Fine Arts Museum - 1981
Art 36702

Elmhurst Historical Museum, 120 E Park Av, Elmhurst, IL 60126 - T: (630) 833-1457, Fax: (630) 833-1326, E-mail: ehm@elmhurst.org, Internet: http://www.elmhurst.org. Head: Brian F. Bergheger
Local Museum - 1952
Local history 36703

Lizzadro Museum of Lapidary Art, 220 Cottage Hill Av, Elmhurst, IL 60126 - T: (630) 833-1616, Fax: (630) 833-1225, Internet: http://www.elmhurst.org. Head: John S. Lizzadro
Special Museum - 1962
Chinese jades, hardstone carvings, gemstones, minerals, earth science 36704

Elmira NY

Arnot Art Museum, 235 Lake St, Elmira, NY 14901 - T: (607) 734-3697, Fax: (607) 734-5687. Head: Laurie Liberatore, John D. O'Hern
Fine Arts Museum - 1913 36705

Chemung Valley History Museum, 415 E Water St, Elmira, NY 14901 - T: (607) 734-4167, Fax: (607) 734-1565. Head: Constance Brennan Barone
Local Museum - 1923 36706

National Soaring Museum, Harris Hill, 51 Soaring Hill Dr, Elmira, NY 14903-9204 - T: (607) 734-3128, Fax: (607) 732-6745, E-mail: nsm@soaringmuseum.org, Internet: http://www.soaringmuseum.org. Head: Robert Ball, L. Little
Science&Tech Museum - 1969 36707

Elsah IL

School of Nations Museum, Principia College, Elsah, IL 62028 - T: (618) 374-2131, Fax: (618) 374-5122, E-mail: bkh@prin.edu. Head: Bonnie Gibbs
University Museum / Local Museum - 1930
Local history, arts, crafts 36708

Village of Elsah Museum, 26 LaSalle, Elsah, IL 62028 - T: (618) 374-1568, Internet: http://www.elsah.org. Head: Jane H. Pfeifer
Local Museum - 1978
Local history housed in 1857 school 36709

Elverson PA

Hopewell Furnace National Historic Site, 2 Mark Bird Ln, Elverson, PA 19520 - T: (610) 582-8773, Fax: (610) 582-2768, E-mail: - hofu_superintendent@nps.gov, Internet: http://www.nps.gov/hofu/index.html. Head: William A. Sanders
Science&Tech Museum - 1938 36710

Ely NV

White Pine Public Museum, 2000 Aultman St, Ely, NV 89301 - T: (702) 289-4710, Internet: http://www.webpanda.com. Head: Terry Walker
Local Museum / Natural History Museum - 1957
Local hist 36711

Elyria OH

Hickories Museum, 509 Washington Av, Elyria, OH 44035 - T: (216) 322-3341, Fax: (440) 322-2817. Head: George Strom
Historical Museum - 1889 36712

Elysian MN

Lesueur County Historical Museum, NE Frank and Second St, Elysian, MN 56028-0240 - T: (507) 267-4620, 362-8350, Fax: (507) 267-4750, E-mail: museum@lchs.mus.mn.us, Internet: http://www.lchs.mus.mn.us. Head: Audrey Knutson
Local Museum - 1966 36713

Emmaus PA

Shelter House, 601 S Fourth St, Emmaus, PA 18049 - T: (610) 965-9258. Head: R. Mitchell Freed
Local Museum - 1951 36714

Empire MI

Empire Area Heritage Group, 11544 S La Core, Empire, MI 49630 - T: (616) 326-5568. Head: Gerard Boiseneau
Local Museum - 1972
Local hist 36715

Emporia KS

Emporia State University Geology Museum, 1200 Commercial St, Emporia, KS 66801 - T: (316) 341-5330. Head: Dr. Michael Morales
Natural History Museum - 1983
Geology 36716

Lyon County Museum, 118 E 6th Av, Emporia, KS 66801 - T: (316) 342-0933, E-mail: lyeomu@valu-line.ne7. Head: Steve Hanschu, J. Greg Jordon
Local Museum - 1938
County history, Carnegie library and Richard Howe home 36717

Norman R. Eppink Art Gallery, Emporia State University, 1200 Commercial, Emporia, KS 66801 - T: (316) 341-5246, Fax: (316) 341-6246, E-mail: perrydon@emporia.edu, Internet: http://www.emporia.edu/m/www/art/eppink.htm. Head: Donald Johnson
Fine Arts Museum / University Museum - 1939
Art gallery 36718

Richard H. Schmidt Museum of Natural History, Emporia State University, 1200 Commercial St, Emporia, KS 66801 - T: (316) 341-5311, Fax: (316) 341-6055, E-mail: mooredwi@esumail.emporia.edu. Head: Dr. Dwight Moore
University Museum / Natural History Museum - 1959
Natural history 36719

Encampment WY

Grand Encampment Museum, 817 Barnett Av, Encampment, WY 82325 - T: (307) 327-5459, 327-5308, Fax: (307) 327-5427, Internet: http://www.prib.com/ENCAMPMENT/GEMueum.html. Head: Doug Tiescen
Science&Tech Museum - 1965
Mining 36720

Encinitas CA

San Dieguito Heritage Museum, 561 S Vulcan Av, Encinitas, CA 92024 - T: (760) 632-9711, Fax: (760) 632-9711. Head: Alice Jacobson, Carol Jensen
Local Museum / Historical Museum - 1988 36721

Enfield NH

Enfield Shaker Museum, 24 Caleb Dyor Ln, Enfield, NH 03748 - T: (603) 632-4346, Fax: (603) 632-4346, E-mail: chosen.vale@valley.net, Internet: http://www.shakermuseum.org. Head: Dr. William D. Moore
Local Museum / Historical Museum - 1986
Historic village 36722

Lockehaven Schoolhouse Museum, E Hill Rd., Enfield, NH 03748 - T: (603) 632-7740. Head: John Goodwin
Local Museum - 1947 36723

Enfield Center NH

Enfield Historical Society Museum, Rte 4A, Enfield Center, NH 03749 - T: (603) 632-7740. Head: John Goodwin
Local Museum - 1991
Local hist 36724

Englewood CO

The Museum of Outdoor Arts, 1000 Englewood Pkwy, Ste 2-230, Englewood, CO 80110 - T: (303) 806-0444, Fax: (303) 806-0504, Internet: http://www.moaonline.org. Head: Cynthia Madden Leitner
Fine Arts Museum - 1982
Art 36725

Enid OK

Museum of the Cherokee Strip, Oklahoma Historical Society, 507 S Fourth St, Enid, OK 73701 - T: (580) 237-1907, Fax: (580) 242-2874, E-mail: mcsi@onenet.net
Historical Museum - 1951 36726

Ephrata PA

Ephrata Cloister, 632 W Main St, Ephrata, PA 17522-1717 - T: (717) 733-6600, Fax: (717) 733-4364, E-mail: mripton@phmc.state.pa.us. Head: Linda Matthews, Michael J. Ripton
Open Air Museum / Religious Arts Museum / Historic Site - 1732
Religious Village Museum comprising of 12 mid-18th century buildings of Germanic architectural style, located on original site of a celibate religious community 36727

Historical Society of the Cocalico Valley Museum, 249 W Main St, Ephrata, PA 17522 - T: (717) 733-1616. Head: Jill Berkes
Historical Museum - 1957 36728

Epping ND

Buffalo Trails Museum, Main St, Epping, ND 58843 - T: (701) 859-4361, Fax: (701) 859-4361, E-mail: hedderich@dia.net
Local Museum - 1966 36729

Erie KS

Mem-Erie Historical Museum, 225 S Main St, Erie, KS 66733 - T: (316) 244-3218, Fax: (316) 244-3332, E-mail: ruthmck@erieks.com. Head: Ruth McKinney-Tandy
Local Museum - 1994
Local hist 36730

Erie PA

Erie Art Museum, 411 State St, Erie, PA 16501 - T: (814) 459-5477, Fax: (814) 452-1744, E-mail: erieartm@erie.net, Internet: http://www.erieartmuseum.org. Head: Dr. Kirk W. Steehler, John L. Vanco
Fine Arts Museum - 1898 36731

Erie Historical Museum, 356 W Sixth St, Erie, PA 16507 - T: (814) 871-5790, Fax: (814) 879-0988, E-mail: ehmp@erie.net. Head: Michael Knecht
Local Museum - 1899 36732

Erie History Center, 417-419 State St, Erie, PA 16501 - T: (814) 454-1813, Fax: (814) 452-1744, E-mail: echs@velocity.net
Local Museum - 1903 36733

Experience Children's Museum, 420 French St, Erie, PA 16507 - T: (814) 453-3743, Fax: (814) 459-9735, E-mail: junep@vpo.net. Head: June Pintea
Ethnology Museum
Children,Youth 36734

United States Brig Niagara, Homeport Erie Maritime Museum, 150 E Front St, Ste 100, Erie, PA 16507 - T: (814) 452-2744, Fax: (814) 455-6760, E-mail: sail@brigniagara.org, Internet: http://www.brigniagara.org. Head: Walter P. Rybka, John Beebe
Military Museum - 1943 36735

Escanaba MI

William Bonifas Fine Arts Center, 700 First Av S, Escanaba, MI 49829 - T: (906) 786-3833, Fax: (906) 786-3840, E-mail: sgibb@chartermi.net, Internet: http://www.bonifasarts.org. Head: Samantha Gibb Roff, Pasqua Warstler
Fine Arts Museum - 1974
Arts 36736

Escondido CA

Escondido Historical Museum → Heritage Walk Museum

Heritage Walk Museum, 321 N Broadway, Escondido, CA 92025 - T: (760) 743-8207, Fax: (760) 743-8267. Head: Wendy Barker
Historical Museum - 1956
Local history, railroad car with model train layout, furnishing, blacksmith shop 36737

Museum California Center for the Arts Escondido, 340 N Escondido Blvd, Escondido, CA 92025 - T: (760) 839-4170, Fax: (760) 743-6472, Internet: http://www.artcenter.org. Head: Ellen Fleurov
Fine Arts Museum - 1992
Art 36738

Essex CT

Connecticut River Museum, 67 Main St, Essex, CT 06426 - T: (860) 767-8269, Fax: (860) 767-7028, E-mail: crm@connix.com, Internet: http://www.connix.com/~crm. Head: Stuart Parnes
Historical Museum / Folklore Museum - 1974
Maritime and River Museum: housed in 1878 wooden warehouse 36739

Essex Historical Museum, POB 123, Essex, CT 06426 - T: (860) 767-7384. Head: William Chatman
Local Museum - 1955
Local history 36740

Essex MA

Essex Shipbuilding Museum, 66 Main St, Essex, MA 01929 - T: (508) 768-7541, Fax: (978) 768-7541, E-mail: info@essexshipbuilding.museum.com. Head: Suzanne O'Brien
Historical Museum / Science&Tech Museum - 1976
Hearse house, maritime history, old Story Yard site where A.D. Story launched 300 fishing schooners 36741

Essington PA

Governor Printz Park, Second and Taylor Aves, Essington, PA 19029 - T: (610) 583-7221, Fax: (610) 459-9586. Head: Brent D. Glass
Local Museum - 1937 36742

Estero FL

Koreshan Historic Site, U.S. 41 at Corkscrew Rd, Estero, FL 33928 - T: (941) 992-0311, Fax: (941) 992-1607, E-mail: j_parks.kshs@juno.com, Internet: http://www.dep.state.fl.us/parks. Head: Jeanne Parks
Special Museum - 1961
Historic buildings, 1894-1977 utopian settlement 36743

Estes Park CO

Estes Park Area Historical Museum, 200 4th St, Estes Park, CO 80517 - T: (970) 586-6256, Fax: (970) 586-6909, E-mail: bkilsdonk@estes.org, Internet: http://estes.on-line.com/epmuseum/. Head: Betty Kilsdonk
Local Museum - 1962
General museum, regional history 36744

Rocky Mountain National Park Museum, 1000 Hwy 36, Estes Park, CO 80517 - T: (970) 586-1340, Fax: (970) 586-1310, E-mail: bill_butler@nps.gov
Natural History Museum - 1915
Natural history, archaeology 36745

Estherville IA

H.G. Albee Memorial Museum, 1720 Third Av, S, Estherville, IA 51334 - T: (712) 362-2750. Head: David Kaltved
Special Museum - 1964 36746

Eufaula AL

Shorter Mansion Museum, 340 N Eufaula Av, Eufaula, AL 36027 - T: (334) 687-3793, Fax: (334) 687-1836, E-mail: pilgrimage@zebra.net, Internet: http://www.zebra.met/~pilgrimage. Head: Calvin Wingo, John Martin
Local Museum - 1965
Local history 36747

Eugene OR

Lane Community College Art Gallery, 4000 E 30 Av, Eugene, OR 97405 - T: (541) 747-4501, Fax: (541) 744-4185. Head: Harold Hoy
University Museum / Fine Arts Museum - 1970 36748

Lane County Historical Museum, 740 W 13 Av, Eugene, OR 97402 - T: (541) 682-4242, Fax: (541) 682-7361, E-mail: lchm@efn.org, Internet: http://www.ichmuseum.org. Head: Evearad Stelfox
Historical Museum - 1951 36749

Maude I. Kerns Art Center, 1910 E 15 Av, Eugene, OR 97403 - T: (541) 345-1571, Fax: (541) 345-6248, E-mail: mkart@pond.net, Internet: http://www.mkartcenter.org. Head: Sandra Dominguez
Fine Arts Museum / Public Gallery - 1962 36750

Museum of Natural History, University of Oregon, 1680 E 15th Av, Eugene, OR 97403-1224 - T: (541) 346-3024, Fax: (541) 346-5334, E-mail: mnh@oregon.uoregon.edu, Internet: http://natural-history.uoregon.edu. Head: C. Melvin Aikens, Patricia Krier, Thomas Connolly
Natural History Museum / Ethnology Museum / Archaeological Museum - 1935
Natural history, archaeology 36751

Oregon Air and Space Museum, 90377 Boeing Dr, Eugene, OR 97402 - T: (541) 461-1101, Internet: http://digiforest.com/~airspace
Science&Tech Museum - 1987
Aviation, space 36752

University of Oregon Museum of Art (closed until 2003), 1430 Johnson Ln, Eugene, OR 97403 - T: (541) 346-0973, Fax: (503) 346-0976, E-mail: uoma@darkwing.uoregon.edu, Internet: http://uoma.uoregon.edu. Head: Del Hawkins
Fine Arts Museum / University Museum - 1930 36753

Willamette Science and Technology Center, 2300 Leo Harris Pkwy, Eugene, OR 97401 - T: (541) 682-7888, Fax: (541) 484-9027, E-mail: wistec@efn.org, Internet: http://www.efn.org/~wistec. Head: Meg Trendler
Natural History Museum / Science&Tech Museum - 1960 36754

Eureka CA

Clarke Memorial Museum, 240 E St, Eureka, CA 95501 - T: (707) 443-1947, Fax: (707) 443-0290. Head: John Winzler, Sondra Harlan
Local Museum - 1960 36755

Eureka KS

Greenwood County Historical Society Museum, 120 W 4th St, Eureka, KS 67045 - T: (316) 583-6682. Head: Alfred Ferguson
Local Museum - 1973
Local hist 36756

Eureka SD

Eureka Pioneer Museum of McPherson County, 1610 J Av, Eureka, SD 57437 - T: (605) 284-2711. Head: Edmund Opp
Local Museum - 1978
Local hist 36757

Eureka UT

Tintic Mining Museum, POB 218, Eureka, UT 84628 - T: (435) 433-6842. Head: J.L. McNulty
Historical Museum - 1974
Mining 36758

Eureka Springs AR

Rosalie House, 282 Spring St, Eureka Springs, AR 72632 - T: (501) 253-7377, E-mail: rosalie@arkansas.net, Internet: http://www.rosaliehouse.com
Historical Museum / Science&Tech Museum - 1973
Home belonging to J.W. Hill, housed first phone system 36759

Evanston IL

Charles Gates Dawes House, Evanston Historical Society Museum, 225 Greenwood St, Evanston, IL 60201 - T: (847) 475-3410, Fax: (847) 475-3599, E-mail: evanstonhs@nwu.edu, Internet: http://collaboratory.acns.nwu.edu/ehs. Head: Lee A. Cabot
Local Museum - 1898
Restored 1894 national historic landmark, home of former Vice President and Nobel laureate Dawes, original 1920s furnishings 36760

Evanston Art Center, 2603 Sheridan Rd, Evanston, IL 60201 - T: (847) 475-5300, Fax: (847) 475-5330. Head: Michele Rowe Shields
Fine Arts Museum - 1929
Contemporary art 36761

The Kendall College Mitchell Museum of the American Indian, 2600 Central Park, Evanston, IL 60201 - T: (847) 495-1030, Fax: (847) 495-0911, E-mail: mitchellmuseum@mindsprung.com, Internet: http://www.mitchellmuseum.org. Head: Janice B. Klein
University Museum / Historical Museum / Ethnology Museum - 1977 36762

Levere Memorial Temple, 1856 Sheridan Rd, Evanston, IL 60201-3837 - T: (847) 475-1856, Fax: (847) 475-2250, E-mail: lburrows@sae.net, Internet: http://www.saefraternity.org. Head: Richard Hopple, Thomas Goodale
Historical Museum - 1929 36763

Mary and Leigh Block Gallery, Northwestern University, 1967 South Campus Dr, Evanston, IL 60208-2410 - T: (847) 491-4000, Fax: (847) 491-2261, E-mail: d-mickenberg@nortwestern.edu, Internet: http://www.blockmuseum.north-western.edu. Head: David Mickenberg
Fine Arts Museum / University Museum - 1851 36764

The Willard House, WCTU Museum, 1730 Chicago Av, Evanston, IL 60201-4585 - T: (847) 328-7500. Head: B. A. Church
Special Museum - 1946
Home of Frances E. Willard (1865-1898) 36765

Evansville IN

Angel Mounds Historic Site, 8215 Pollack Av, Evansville, IN 47715 - T: (812) 853-3956, Fax: (812) 853-6271, E-mail: curator@angelmounds
Archaeological Museum / Folklore Museum - 1972
Archaeology, pre-historic middle Mississippian Indian site 36766

Evansville Museum of Arts and Science, 411 SE Riverside Dr, Evansville, IN 47713 - T: (812) 425-2406, Fax: (812) 421-7506, E-mail: mary@emuseum.org, Internet: http://www.emuseum.org. Head: John W. Streetman
Local Museum / Fine Arts Museum - 1926
General museum - planetarium 36767

Reitz Home Museum, 224 SE First St, Evansville, IN 47713 - T: (812) 426-1871, Fax: (812) 426-2179, E-mail: reitz@evansville.net, Internet: http://www.reitzhome.evansville.net. Head: Tess C. Grimm
Local Museum - 1974 36768

Eveleth MN

United States Hockey Hall of Fame, 801 Hat Trick Av, Eveleth, MN 55734 - T: (218) 744-5167, Fax: (218) 744-2590, E-mail: sersha@ushockeyhall.com, Internet: http://www.ushockeyhall.com. Head: Tom Sersha
Special Museum - 1969
Sports 36769

Evergreen CO

Hiwan Homestead Museum, 4208 S Timbervale Dr, Evergreen, CO 80439 - T: (303) 674-6262, Fax: (303) 670-7746, E-mail: jsteinle@co.jefferson.co.us, Internet: http://www.co.jefferson.co.us/dpt/openspac/hiwan/
Ethnology Museum / Historical Museum / Historic Site - 1974
Local history, Camp Neosho, later renamed Hiwan Ranch Inetrnational antique Doll collection, Southwestern native american pottery - Archiv of local hist 36770

Excelsior MN

Excelsior-Lake Minnetonka Historical Museum, 420 3rd Av, Excelsior, MN 55331 - T: (612) 474-8956. Head: Marlyn Thomson
Local Museum - 1972
Local history 36771

Exeter NH

American Independence Museum, 1 Governors Ln, Exeter, NH 03833-2420 - T: (603) 772-2622, Fax: (603) 772-0861, E-mail: aim@nh.ultranet.com, Internet: http://www.nh.ultranet.com/~aim. Head: Carol Walker Aten
Historical Museum - 1991 36772

Gilman Garrison House, 12 Water St, Exeter, NH 03833 - T: (603) 436-3205, Fax: (617) 227-9204, Internet: http://www.spnea.org
Local Museum - 1965 36773

The Lamont Gallery, Phillips Exeter Academy, Frederic R. Mayer Bldg, 20 Main St, Exeter, NH 03833 - T: (603) 777-3461, Fax: (603) 777-4384, E-mail: gallery@exeter.edu. Head: Samuel Heath
Fine Arts Museum / University Museum - 1953 36774

Exton PA

Thomas Newcomen Museum, 412 Newcomen Rd, Exton, PA 19341 - T: (610) 363-6600, Fax: (610) 363-0612, E-mail: newcomen@libertynet.org, Internet: http://www.libertynet.org/~newcomen/. Head: C. Daniel Hayes, Edward Kottcamp
Science&Tech Museum - 1923 36775

Fabius NY

Pioneer Museum, Highland Forest Rte 80, Fabius, NY 13063 - T: (315) 453-6767, Fax: (315) 453-6762, E-mail: prewiso@emi.com, Internet: http://www.co.onondaga.ny.us/parks.htw. Head: Valerie Bell
Local Museum - 1959 36776

Fairbanks AK

University of Alaska Museum, 907 Yukon Dr, Fairbanks, AK 99775-6960 - T: (907) 474-7505, 474-6939, Fax: (907) 474-5469, E-mail: ffaj@uaf.edu, Internet: http://www.uaf.edu/museum. Head: Aldona Jonaitis, Paul E. Matheus, Leonard J. Kamerling
Fine Arts Museum / University Museum / Local Museum / Natural History Museum - 1929
Natural history, fine art, photography, ethnograpgy, archaeology, paleontology, geology, ornitology, mammals - herbarium 36777

Fairbury NE

Rock Creek Station State Historic Park, 57425 710 Rd, Fairbury, NE 68352 - T: (402) 729-5777. Head: Wayne Brandt
Local Museum / Open Air Museum - 1980 36778

Fairfax VA

Fairfax Museum and Visitor Center, 10209 Main St, Fairfax, VA 22030 - T: (703) 385-8414, Fax: (703) 385-8692
Historical Museum / Natural History Museum - 1992 36779

National Firearms Museum, 11250 Waples Mill Rd, Fairfax, VA 22030 - T: (703) 267-1620, Fax: (703) 267-3913, E-mail: nfmstaff@nrahq.org, Internet: http://www.nrahq.org. Head: Whit Fentem
Science&Tech Museum - 1871
Firearms 36780

Fairfield CT

Connecticut Audubon Birdcraft Museum, 314 Unquowa Rd, Fairfield, CT 06430 - T: (203) 259-0416, Fax: (203) 259-1344, E-mail: birdcraft@snet, Internet: http://www.ctaudubon.org. Head: Christopher B. Nevins, Anne H. Harper
Natural History Museum - 1914 36781

Fairfield Historical Museum, 636 Old Post Rd, Fairfield, CT 06430 - T: (203) 259-1598, Fax: (203) 255-2716, E-mail: asaintpierre@fairfieldhs.org, Internet: http://www.fairfieldhistoricalsociety.org. Head: Steve Young
Local Museum - 1902
Local history - library 36782

Thomas J. Walsh Art Gallery and Regina A. Quick Center for the Arts, Fairfield University, N Benson Rd, Fairfield, CT 06430 - T: (203) 254-4242, Fax: (203) 254-4113. Head: Diana Mille
Fine Arts Museum / University Museum - 1990
Art gallery 36783

Fairfield IA

Fairfield Art Museum, POB 904, Fairfield, IA 52556 - T: (515) 472-2688, 472-6551. Head: Jane McNerney
Fine Arts Museum - 1964
Art association, housed in 1st Carnegie library West of the Mississippi River 36784

Fairfield TX

Freestone County Historical Museum, 302 E Main St, Fairfield, TX 75840 - T: (903) 389-3738, E-mail: fcmuseum@airmail.net. Head: Kathleen McKee
Historical Museum - 1967
Local hist, telephones 36785

Fairfield UT

Camp Floyd, 18035 W 1540 N, Fairfield, UT 84013 - T: (801) 768-8932. Head: J. Ben White
Local Museum - 1855
Historic site, former Army of Utah camp 36786

Fairfield VT

President Chester A. Arthur Historic Site, Chester Arthur St, Fairfield, VT 05455 - T: (802) 828-3051, Fax: (802) 828-3206, E-mail: jdumville@gate.dca.state.vt.us, Internet: http://www.state.vt.us/dca/historic/hp_sites/htm. Head: John P. Dumville
Local Museum - 1953
Local hist 36787

Fairhope AL

Eastern Shore Art Center, 401 Oak St, Fairhope, AL 36532 - T: (334) 928-2228, Fax: (334) 928-5188, E-mail: esac@mindspring.com. Head: Kate Fisher, Robin Fitzhugh
Fine Arts Museum - 1958
Art 36788

Fairmont MN

Pioneer Museum, 304 E Blue Earth Av, Fairmont, MN 56031 - T: (507) 235-5178
Local Museum - 1929
Regional history 36789

Fairmont WV

Pricketts Fort, Rte 3, Fairmont, WV 26554 - T: (304) 363-3030, Fax: (304) 363-3857, E-mail: pfort@host.dmsc.net, Internet: http://www.dmssoft.com/pfort. Head: Richard D. Brown
Local Museum - 1976 36790

Fairplay CO

South Park City Museum, 100 4th, Fairplay, CO 80440 - T: (719) 836-2387, Internet: http://wwws.southparkcity.org. Head: Raymond Dellacroce, Carol A. Davis
Open Air Museum / Local Museum - 1957
Historic village, Colorado mining town 36791

Fairport Harbor OH

Fairport Marine Museum, 129 Second St, Fairport Harbor, OH 44077 - T: (440) 354-4825, E-mail: fhhs@ncweb.com, Internet: http://www.ncweb.com/org/fhlh. Head: Valerie Laczko
Special Museum - 1945 36792

Falcon Heights MN

Gibbs Farm Museum, 2097 W Larpenteur Av, Falcon Heights, MN 55113 - T: (651) 646-8629, Fax: (651) 223-8539, E-mail: admin@rchs.com, Internet: http://www.rchs.com. Head: Howard Guthman, Priscilla Farnham
Agriculture Museum - 1949 36793

Falfurrias TX

The Heritage Museum at Falfurrias, 415 N Saint Mary's St, Falfurrias, TX 78355 - T: (512) 325-2907
Local Museum - 1965
Local hist 36794

Fall River MA

Battleship Massachusetts Museum, Battleship Cove, Fall River, MA 02721 - T: (508) 678-1100, 678-1905, Fax: (508) 674-5597, E-mail: battleship@battleshipcove.com, Internet: http://www.battleshipcove.com. Head: Ernst Cummings
Historical Museum - 1965
Historic ships 36795

Fall River Historical Society Museum, 451 Rock St, Fall River, MA 02720 - T: (508) 679-1071, Fax: (508) 675-5754, Internet: http://www.lizzieborden.org. Head: Elizabeth Denning
Local Museum - 1921
Local history 36796

Marine Museum at Fall River, 70 Water St, Fall River, MA 02721 - T: (508) 674-3533, Fax: (508) 674-3534, Internet: http://www.marinemuseum.org
Historical Museum - 1968
Marine, restored machine shop 36797

Fall River Mills CA

Fort Crook Historical Museum, Fort Crook Av and Hwy 299, Fall River Mills, CA 96028 - T: (530) 336-5110
Historical Museum - 1934 36798

Fallon NV

Churchill County Museum and Archives, 1050 S Maine St, Fallon, NV 89406 - T: (775) 423-3677, Fax: (775) 423-3662, E-mail: ccmuseum@phonewave.net, Internet: http://ccmuseum.org. Head: Jane Pieplow
Local Museum - 1967 36799

Fallsington PA

Historic Fallsington, 4 Yardley Av, Fallsington, PA 19054 - T: (215) 295-6567, Fax: (215) 295-6567, E-mail: histfals@pop.erols.com. Head: Robert L.B. Harman, Linda L. Brinker
Open Air Museum / Local Museum - 1953 36800

Falmouth MA

Falmouth Historical Museum, Palmer Av at Village Green, Falmouth, MA 02541 - T: (508) 548-4857, Fax: (508) 540-0968, E-mail: FHsoc@jomo.com, Internet: http://www.falmouthhistoricalsociety.org. Head: Ann Sears
Local Museum - 1900
Local history 36801

Far Hills NJ

Golf Museum, Liberty Corner Rd, Far Hills, NJ 07931 - T: (908) 234-2300, Fax: (908) 234-0319, Internet: http://www.usga.org
Special Museum - 1935
Golf 36802

Fargo GA

Stephen C. Foster State Park, Rte 1, Fargo, GA 31631, mail addr: POB 131, Fargo, GA 31631 - T: (912) 637-5274, Fax: (912) 637-5587, E-mail: scfost@surfsouth.com
Natural History Museum - 1954
Folk culture, personal artefacts 36803

Fargo ND

Children's Museum at Yunker Farm, 1201 28 Av N, Fargo, ND 58102 - T: (701) 232-6102, Fax: (701) 232-4605, Internet: http://www.childrensmuseum-yunker.org. Head: Kim Brust, Yvette Nasset
Special Museum - 1989 36804

Fargo Air Museum, 1609 19th Av N, Fargo, ND 58109 - T: (701) 293-8043, Fax: (701) 293-8103, Internet: http://www.fargoairmuseum.org. Head: Gerald Beck
Science&Tech Museum 36805

Memorial Union Gallery, Memorial Union-North Dakota State University, Fargo, ND 58105-5476 - T: (701) 231-7900, Fax: (701) 231-8043, E-mail: peg-furshong@ndsu.nodak.edu, Internet: http://www.ndsu.nodak.edu/memorial_union/gallery. Head: Peg Furshong
University Museum / Fine Arts Museum - 1975 36806

Faribault MN

Rice County Museum of History, 1814 NW 2nd Av, Faribault, MN 55021 - T: (507) 332-2121. Head: Ion Velishek
Local Museum / Agriculture Museum - 1926
Local history, agricultural 36807

Farmington CT

Hill-Stead Museum, 35 Mountain Rd, Farmington, CT 06032 - T: (860) 677-4787, Fax: (860) 677-0174, E-mail: hillstead@juno.com, Internet: http://www.hillstead.org. Head: Pamela P. West, Linda Stagleder
Fine Arts Museum - 1946
Art 36808

Museum of the University of Connecticut Health Center, School of Dental Medicine, 263 Farmington Av, Farmington, CT 06030 - T: (860) 679-3211. Head: Jay Christian
University Museum / Special Museum - 1979 36809

Stanley-Whitman House, 37 High St, Farmington, CT 06032 - T: (860) 677-9222, Fax: (860) 677-7758. Head: Lisa Johnson
Local Museum - 1935
Interpretation of 18th-c Farmington 36810

Farmington ME

Nordica Homestead Museum, Holley Rd, Farmington, ME 04938 - T: (207) 778-2042. Head: Tom Sawyer
Local Museum - 1927
Regional history 36811

Farmington NM

Farmington Museum, 3041 E Main St, Farmington, NM 87402 - T: (505) 599-1174, Fax: (505) 326-7572, E-mail: frmngtnmuseum@juno.com
Ethnology Museum / Local Museum - 1980 36812

Farmington PA

Fort Necessity National Battlefield, 1 Washington Pkwy, Farmington, PA 15437 - T: (724) 329-5512, Fax: (724) 329-8682, E-mail: - FONE_Superintendent@nps.gov, Internet: http://www.nps.gov/fone/. Head: Joanne Hanley
Open Air Museum / Military Museum - 1931 36813

Farmington UT

Pioneer Village, 375 N Lagoon Ln, Farmington, UT 84025 - T: (801) 451-8050, Fax: (801) 451-8015. Head: Peter Freed
Local Museum / Open Air Museum - 1954
Historic village 36814

Farmville NC

May Museum and Park, 213 S Main St, Farmville, NC 27828 - T: (252) 753-5814, Fax: (252) 753-2910. Head: Kimberly Barrow
Local Museum - 1991
Local history, decorative art, textiles 36815

Farmville VA

Longwood Center for the Visual Arts, 129 N Main St, Farmville, VA 23901 - T: (804) 395-2206, Fax: (804) 392-6441, E-mail: gcoopers@longwood.lwc.edu, Internet: http://web.lwc.edu/administrative/visualart/index.htm. Head: Kay Johnson Bowles
Fine Arts Museum / University Museum - 1971
Art 36816

Fayette AL

Fayette Art Museum, 530 Temple Av N, Fayette, AL 35555 - T: (205) 932-8727, Fax: (205) 932-8788, E-mail: fam@fayette.net. Head: Jack Black
Fine Arts Museum - 1969 36817

Fayette MO

Ashby-Hodge Gallery of American Art, 411 CMC Sq, Fayette, MO 65248 - T: (660) 248-6334, Fax: (660) 248-2622, E-mail: jgeist@coin.org, Internet: http://www.cmc.edu. Head: Dr. Joe Geist
Fine Arts Museum / University Museum - 1994 36818

Stephens Museum, Central Methodist College, Fayette, MO 65248 - T: (660) 248-6370, 248-6334, Fax: (660) 248-2622, E-mail: delliot@cmc2.cmc.edu, Internet: http://www.cmc.edu. Head: Dana R. Elliott
Natural History Museum / Religious Arts Museum / University Museum - 1879 36819

Fayetteville AR

The University Museum, University of Arkansas, Museum Bldg, Rm 202, Fayetteville, AR 72701 - T: (501) 575-3466, Fax: (501) 575-8766, Internet: http://www.uark.edu/~museinfo/. Head: Dr. Johnnie L. Gentry
University Museum / Ethnology Museum / Natural History Museum - 1873
Ethnology, anthropology, zoology - herbarium 36820

Fayetteville NC

Arts Center, 301 Hay St, Fayetteville, NC 28302 - T: (910) 323-1776, Fax: (910) 323-1727, E-mail: artscncl@fayetteville.com. Head: Libby Seymour
Fine Arts Museum - 1974 36821

Fayetteville Museum of Art, 839 Stamper Rd, Fayetteville, NC 28303 - T: (910) 485-5121, Fax: (910) 485-5233, E-mail: fmastar@fayettevillenc.com, Internet: http://www.fmoa.org. Head: Peggy Vick, Tom Grubb
Fine Arts Museum / Public Gallery - 1971 36822

Museum of the Cape Fear Historical Complex, Corner of Bradford and Arsenal Aves, Fayetteville, NC 28305 - T: (910) 486-1330, Fax: (910) 486-1585, E-mail: mcfhc@fayettevillenc.com
Historical Museum - 1985
History 36823

Fergus Falls MN

Otter Tail County Historical Museum, 1110 Lincoln Av W, Fergus Falls, MN 56537 - T: (218) 736-6038, Fax: (218) 739-3075. Head: Chris Schuelke
Local Museum - 1927
Regional history 36824

Fernandina Beach FL

Amelia Island Museum of History, 233 S Third St, Fernandina Beach, FL 32034 - T: (904) 261-7378, Fax: (904) 261-9701, E-mail: aimh@net-magic.net. Head: Carol Ann Atwood
Historical Museum - 1986 36825

Ferrisburgh VT

Rokeby Museum, Rowland Evans Robinson Memorial Association, 4334 Rte 7, Ferrisburgh, VT 05456 - T: (802) 877-3406, E-mail: rokeby@globalnetisp.net, Internet: http://www.rokeby.org. Head: Jane Williamson
Historic Site - 1962
Historic house 36826

Ferrum VA

Blue Ridge Institute and Museum, Ferrum College, Ferrum, VA 24088 - T: (540) 365-4416, Fax: (540) 365-4419, E-mail: bri@ferrum.edu, Internet: http://www.ferrum.edu. Head: J. Roderick Moore
Folklore Museum - 1971
Farming, folklife 36827

Fessenden ND

Wells County Museum, 305 First St S, Fessenden, ND 58450 - T: (701) 984-2688. Head: Lorraine Rau
Local Museum - 1972 36828

Fifield WI

Old Town Hall Museum, W 7213 Pine St, Fifield, WI 54524 - T: (715) 762-4571. Head: Patricia Schroeder
Local Museum / Historical Museum - 1969
Local hist, logging and farming tools, clothing, books, household 36829

Fillmore CA

Fillmore Historical Museum, 350 Main St, Fillmore, CA 93016 - T: (805) 524-0948, Fax: (805) 524-0516, E-mail: museum@csiway.com. Head: Martha Gentry
Local Museum - 1971 36830

Fillmore UT

Territorial Statehouse State Museum, 50 W Capitol Av, Fillmore, UT 84631 - T: (435) 743-5316, Fax: (435) 743-4723. Head: Gordon Chatland
Historical Museum - 1930
Regional hist 36831

Findlay OH

Hancock Historical Museum, 422 W Sandusky St, Findlay, OH 45840 - T: (419) 423-4433. Head: Kent Weaver, Sue Tucker
Local Museum - 1969 36832

Fishers IN

Conner Prairie House, 13400 Allisonville Rd, Fishers, IN 46038 - T: (317) 776-6000, Fax: (317) 776-6014, E-mail: sphen@conncoll.edu, Internet: http://lymanallyn.conncoll.edu
Historical Museum - 1964
William Conner home; living history, natural history area 36833

Fishers NY

Valentown Museum, Valentown Sq, Fishers, NY 14453 - T: (716) 924-4170. Head: J. Sheldon Fisher
Local Museum - 1940 36834

Fishkill NY

Van Wyck Homestead Museum, 504 Rte 9, Fishkill, NY 12524 - T: (845) 896-9560, E-mail: royjorg@aol.com
Historical Museum - 1962
Artefacts of Rev. war, Hudson valley painting 36835

Fitchburg MA

Fitchburg Art Museum, 185 Elm St, Fitchburg, MA 01420 - T: (978) 345-4207, Fax: (978) 345-2319, E-mail: info@fitchburgartmuseum.org, Internet: http://www.fitchburgartmuseum.org. Head: Peter Timms, Marianne Menger, Roger Dell
Fine Arts Museum - 1925
Art 36836

Fitchburg Historical Society Museum, 50 Grove St, Fitchburg, MA 01420 - T: (978) 345-1157, Fax: (978) 345-2229, E-mail: fitchburghistory@aol.com. Head: Helen Obermeyer Simmons, Betsy Hannula
Historical Museum - 1892
Local history, civil war coll 36837

Flagstaff AZ

Arizona Historical Society Pioneer Museum, 2340 N Fort Valley Rd, Flagstaff, AZ 86001 - T: (520) 774-6272, Fax: (520) 774-1596, E-mail: ahsnad@infomagic.net, Internet: http://www.infomagic.net/ahsnad. Head: Joseph M. Meehan
Historical Museum - 1953 36838

Museum of Northern Arizona, 3101 N Fort Valley Rd, Flagstaff, AZ 86001 - T: (520) 774-5213, Fax: (520) 779-1527, E-mail: info@mna.mus.az.us, Internet: http://www.musnac.org. Head: Dr. Edwin L. Wade
Local Museum - 1928
Local history, anthropology, geology, biology, fine art 36839

Northern Arizona University Art Museum and Galleries, Knoles and McMullen Circle, Bldg 10, N NAU Campus, Flagstaff, AZ 86011-6021 - T: (520) 523-3471, Fax: (520) 523-1424, E-mail: linda.stromberg@nau.edu, Internet: http://www.nau.edu/art_museum. Head: John Burton
University Museum / Fine Arts Museum / Public Gallery - 1961
Art 36840

Riordan Mansion State Historic Park, 409 Riordan Rd, Flagstaff, AZ 86001 - T: (520) 779-4395, Fax: (520) 556-0253, Internet: http://www.pr.state.az.us. Head: John R. Marvin
Local Museum - 1983
Local hist, coll of original craftsman furnishings 36841

Walnut Canyon National Monument, 6400 N Hwy 89, Flagstaff, AZ 86004 - T: (520) 526-1157, Fax: (520) 526-4259. Head: Sam R. Henderson
Historic Site / Archaeological Museum - 1915
Site of prehistoric Indian ruins of the Sinagua Indian culture 36842

Wupatki National Monument, 6400 N Hwy. 89, Flagstaff, AZ 86004, mail addr: HC 33 Box 444A, Flagstaff, AZ 86004 - T: (520) 526-1157, Fax: (520) 526-4259
Historic Site / Archaeological Museum - 1924
Over 2,600 archaeological sites dating from approx. 1100 A.D., Hopi ancestral homeland 36843

Flandreau SD

Moody County Museum, 706 East Pipestone Av, Flandreau, SD 57028 - T: (605) 997-3191, Internet: http://www.rootsweb.com/~sdmoody. Head: Roberta Williamson
Local Museum - 1965
Local hist 36844

Flat Rock NC

Carl Sandburg Home National Historic Site, 1928 Little River Rd, Flat Rock, NC 28731 - T: (704) 693-4178, Fax: (704) 693-4179. Head: Connie Backlund
Local Museum - 1969 36845

Fleming CO

Fleming Historical Museum, Heritage Museum Park, Fleming, CO 80728 - T: (970) 265-3721, 265-2591. Head: Wanda West, Helen Lambert
Local Museum - 1965
Local history 36846

Flemington NJ

Doric House, 114 Main St, Flemington, NJ 08822 - T: (908) 782-1091. Head: Richard H. Stothoff
Local Museum - 1885 36847

Flint MI

Flint Institute of Arts, 1120 E Kearsley St, Flint, MI 48503 - T: (810) 234-1695, Fax: (810) 234-1692, E-mail: info@flintarts.org, Internet: http://www.flintarts.org. Head: John B. Henry
Fine Arts Museum - 1928
African, American, Asian and European art, decorative arts 36848

Sloan Museum, 1221 E Kearsley St, Flint, MI 48503 - T: (810) 237-3450, Fax: (810) 237-3451, E-mail: sloandir@tir.com. Head: Tim Shickles
Historical Museum / Science&Tech Museum - 1966 36849

Flora MS

Mississippi Petrified Forest Museum, 124 Forest Park Rd, Flora, MS 39071 - T: (601) 879-8189, Fax: (601) 879-8165, E-mail: mspforest@aol.com, Internet: http://www.mspetrifiedforest.com. Head: C. J. McNamara
Natural History Museum - 1963 36850

Floral Park NY

Queens County Farm Museum, 73-50 Little Neck Pkwy, Floral Park, NY 11004 - T: (718) 347-3276, Fax: (718) 347-3243, E-mail: info@queensfarm.org, Internet: http://www.queensfarm.org. Head: Amy Fischetti
Agriculture Museum - 1975 36851

Florence AL

Kennedy-Douglass Center for the Arts, 217 E Tuscaloosa St, Florence, AL 35630 - T: (205) 760-6379, Fax: (205) 760-6382, E-mail: BBroach@lloweb.com. Head: Barbara K. Broach
Fine Arts Museum - 1976 36852

Pope's Tavern Museum, 203 Hermitage Dr, Florence, AL 35630 - T: (205) 760-6439
Local Museum - 1968
One of oldest structures in Florence, one-time stagecoach stop, tavern and inn, hospital by Confederate and Union forces 36853

W.C. Handy Home Museum, 620 W College St, Florence, AL 35630 - T: (205) 760-6434. Head: Barbara Kimberlin
Historical Museum - 1968 36854

Florence CO

Florence Price Pioneer Museum, Pikes Peak Av and Front St, Florence, CO 81226 - T: (719) 784-3157
Local Museum - 1964 36855

Florence KS

Harvey House Museum, 221 Marion, Florence, KS 66851 - T: (316) 878-4296, E-mail: timm2@marionco.net. Head: Kristal Timm
Special Museum - 1971
First Fred Harvey Restaurant-Hotel 36856

Florence SC

Florence Museum of Art, Science and History, 558 Spruce St, Florence, SC 29501 - T: (843) 662-3351, E-mail: flomus@bellsouth.net, Internet: http://www.florenceweb.com/museum.htm. Head: Betsy Olsen
Fine Arts Museum / Natural History Museum / Historical Museum - 1936
Art, science, history 36857

Florissant MO

Florissant Valley Historical Society Museum, 1896 Florissant Rd, Florissant, MO 63031 - T: (314) 524-1100. Head: Margaret Connors
Historical Museum - 1958 36858

Old Saint Ferdinand's Shrine, 1 Rue Saint François, Florissant, MO 63031 - T: (314) 921-6900 ext 122. Head: Bill Bray
Religious Arts Museum - 1958 36859

Flovilla GA

Indian Springs State Park Museum, Hwy 42, 5 mi S of Jackson, Flovilla, GA 30216 - T: (770) 504-2277, Fax: (770) 504-2178. Head: Don Coleman
Natural History Museum - 1825
History, photos 36860

Flushing NY

Bowne House, 37-01 Bowne St, Flushing, NY 11354 - T: (718) 359-0528. Head: Douglas F. Bauer
Local Museum - 1945 36861

Frances Godwin and Joseph Ternbach Museum, Queens College, 65-30 Kissena Blvd, Flushing, NY 11367 - T: (718) 997-5000 ext 4747, Fax: (718) 997-5738. Head: Ceil Cleveland
Fine Arts Museum / University Museum - 1957 36862

Kingsland Homestead, Queens Historical Society, Weeping Beech Park, 143-35 37th Av, Flushing, NY 11354 - T: (718) 939-0647, Fax: (718) 539-9885, E-mail: qhs@juno.com, Internet: http://www.preserve.org/queens. Head: Stanley Cogan, Mitchell Grubler
Historical Museum - 1968
Photographs, postcards, maps, personal papers, archtectural renderings, 36863

Queens Historical Museum, 143-35 37th Av, Flushing, NY 11354 - T: (718) 939-0647, Fax: (718) 539-9885, E-mail: qhs@juno.com, Internet: http://www.preserve.org/queens. Head: Stanley Cogan, Joyce A. Cook
Local Museum - 1968
Local history, Kingsland homestead 36864

Flushing Meadows NY

New York Hall of Science, 47-01 111 St, Flushing Meadows, NY 11368 - T: (718) 699-0005, Fax: (718) 699-1341, E-mail: wbrez@nyhallsci.org, Internet: http://www.nyhallsci.org. Head: Dr. Alan J. Friedman
Science&Tech Museum - 1964 36865

Folsom CA

Folsom History Museum, 823 Sutter St, Folsom, CA 95630 - T: (916) 985-2707, Fax: (916) 985-7288. Head: John Messner
Local Museum - 1960 36866

Folsom NM

Folsom Museum, Main St, Folsom, NM 88419 - T: (505) 278-3616, E-mail: bkthompson@bakavalley.com, Internet: http://www.geocities.com/folsom_museum. Head: Vinita Brown
Archaeological Museum - 1967 36867

Fond du Lac WI

Galloway House and Village, 336 Old Pioneer Rd, Fond du Lac, WI 54935 - T: (414) 922-6390
Local Museum - 1955
Historic village 36868

Fonda NY

Native American Exhibit, National Kateri Shrine, Rte 5, 1/2 mile West of Fonda, Fonda, NY 12068 - T: (518) 853-3646, Fax: (518) 853-3371, E-mail: katerei_s@yahoo.com. Head: Kevin Kenny
Historical Museum / Archaeological Museum / Folklore Museum / Religious Arts Museum - 1949
1666-1693 staked out Mohawk Indian castle and 1666-1676 residence of Kateri Tekakwitha 36869

Forest Grove OR

Pacific University Museum, Pacific University, 2043 College Way, Forest Grove, OR 97116 - T: (503) 359-2211, Fax: (503) 359-2252, E-mail: ur@pacificu.edu, Internet: http://www.pacificu.edu
University Museum / Historical Museum / Folklore Museum - 1949 36870

Forsyth MT

Rosebud County Pioneer Museum, 1335 Main St, Forsyth, MT 59327. Head: Cal MacConnel
Local Museum - 1966 36871

Fort Atkinson WI

Hoard Historical Museum, 407 Merchant Av, Fort Atkinson, WI 53538 - T: (920) 563-7769, Fax: (920) 568-3203, E-mail: hartwick@hoardmuseum.org, Internet: http://www.hoardmuseum.org. Head: Sue Hartwick
Local Museum - 1933
Local hist 36872

Fort Benning GA

National Infantry Museum, U.S. Army Infantry School, Bldg 396, Baltzell Av, Fort Benning, GA 31905-5593 - T: (706) 545-6762, Fax: (706) 545-5158, Internet: http://www.benningmwr.com. Head: Frank Hanner
Military Museum - 1959
Military history 36873

Fort Benton MT

Fort Benton Museum of the Upper Missouri, 1801 Front St, Fort Benton, MT 59442 - T: (406) 622-5316, Fax: (406) 622-3725, E-mail: fbmusuems@hotmail.com. Head: John G. Lepley
Local Museum - 1957 36874

Museum of the Northern Great Plains, 20 and Washington, Fort Benton, MT 59442 - T: (406) 622-5133, Fax: (406) 622-3725, E-mail: fbmuseums@hotmail.com. Head: John G. Lepley
Historical Museum - 1989 36875

Fort Bliss TX

Fort Bliss Museum, Pleasonton and Sheridan Rds, Fort Bliss, TX 79916-3802 - T: (915) 568-6940, Fax: (915) 568-6941, E-mail: jroger@bliss.army.mil. Head: Peter M. Poessiger
Military Museum - 1954
Military hist, local installation hist 36876

United States Army Air Defense Artillery Museum, Bldg 5000, Pleasanton Rd, Fort Bliss, TX 79916 - T: (915) 568-5412, Fax: (915) 568-4013
Military Museum - 1975
Military hist 36877

Fort Bragg NC

82nd Airborne Division War Memorial Museum, Gela and Ardennes Sts, Fort Bragg, NC 28307-0119 - T: (910) 432-5307, Fax: (910) 436-4440
Military Museum - 1945 36878

JFK Special Warfare Museum, Ardennes and Marion Sts, Bldg D-2502, Fort Bragg, NC 28307 - T: (910) 432-1533, Fax: (910) 432-4062, E-mail: merrittr@ahqb.soc.mil
Military Museum - 1963 36879

Fort Bridger WY

Fort Bridger State Museum, 37,000 Business Loop I-80, Fort Bridger, WY 82933 - T: (307) 782-3842, Fax: (307) 782-7181, E-mail: lnewma@missc.state.wy, Internet: http://www.fortbridge.com. Head: Bill Gentle
Historical Museum / Historic Site - 1843
Local hist 36880

Fort Calhoun NE

Fort Atkinson State Historical Park, 1 mile E of Hwy 75, Fort Calhoun, NE 68023 - T: (402) 468-5611, Fax: (402) 468-5066, E-mail: ftatkin@ngpc.state.ne.us, Internet: http://ngpc.state.ne.us. Head: John Slader
Military Museum - 1963 36881

Washington County Historical Association Museum, 104 N 14, Fort Calhoun, NE 68023 - T: (402) 468-5740, E-mail: info@newashcohist.org, Internet: http://www.newashcohist.org
Local Museum - 1938 36882

Fort Campbell KY

Don F. Pratt Museum, 5702 Tennessee Av, Fort Campbell, KY 42223-5335 - T: (502) 798-4986, Fax: (502) 798-2605, E-mail: boggsr@emh2.army.mil, Internet: http://www.campbell.army.mil/pratt/. Head: Rex Boggs
Military Museum - 1956
Airborne military, history of 101st ABN Division 36883

Fort Carson CO

3rd Cavalry Museum, Bldg 2160, Barkeley Rd, Fort Carson, CO 80913-5000 - T: (719) 526-1404, 526-2028, Fax: (719) 526-6573, E-mail: paul.martin@carson.army.mil. Head: Paul Martin
Military Museum - 1959
Military hist 36884

Fort Collins CO

Curfman Gallery and Duhesa Lounge, Colorado State University, Fort Collins, CO 80523 - T: (303) 491-6626, Fax: (303) 491-6423, Internet: http://www.colostate.edu. Head: Miriam B. Harris
Fine Arts Museum / Public Gallery - 1968 36885

Discovery Center Science Museum, 703 E Prospect, Fort Collins, CO 80525 - T: (970) 493-2182, 472-3990, Fax: (970) 493-4085, E-mail: dwhite@psd.k12.co.us, Internet: http://www.csmate.colostate.edu/dcsm/. Head: Rich Fisher, Diane White
Science&Tech Museum - 1989
Science 36886

Fort Collins Museum, 201 S College Av, Fort Collins, CO 80524 - T: (970) 482-2787, Fax: (970) 416-2236, E-mail: fcmoca@frii.com, Internet: http://www.ci.fort-collins.co.us/arts_culture/museum. Head: Jeanne Shoaff
Local Museum - 1940
Local history 36887

Gustafson Gallery, Colorado State University, 314 Gifford St, Fort Collins, CO 80523 - T: (970) 491-1983, Fax: (970) 491-4376, E-mail: carlson@cahs.colostate.edu, Internet: http://www.colostate.edu/depts/dm. Head: Dr. Antigone Kotsiopulos
Special Museum / University Museum - 1986
Historical costume and textile 36888

Hatton Gallery, Colorado State University, Visual Arts Bldg, Fort Collins, CO 80523 - T: (970) 491-6774, Fax: (970) 491-0505, E-mail: lfrickman@vines.colostate.edu. Head: Linda Frickman
Fine Arts Museum / University Museum - 1970
Art gallery 36889

Museum of Contemporary Art, 201 S College Av, Fort Collins, CO 80524 - T: (970) 482-2787, Fax: (970) 482-0804, E-mail: fcmoca@frii.com. Head: Jeanne Shoaff
Fine Arts Museum - 1990 36890

One West Art Center → Museum of Contemporary Art

Fort Davis TX

Fort Davis, Hwy 17-118, Fort Davis, TX 79734 - T: (915) 426-3224 ext 27, Fax: (915) 426-3122, Internet: http://www.nps.gov/foda
Military Museum / Historical Museum - 1963
Military hist, Indians wars Western frontier history 36891

Neill Museum, 7th and Court St, Fort Davis, TX 79734 - T: (915) 426-3838, 426-3969. Head: Teda W. Neill
Local Museum - 1960
Local hist 36892

Fort DeRussy HI

United States Army Museum of Hawaii, Battery Randolph, Kalia Rd, Fort DeRussy, HI 96815 - T: (808) 438-2821, Fax: (808) 438-2819, E-mail: fdcura@shafter_emh3.army.mil. Head: Thomas M. Fairfull
Historical Museum / Military Museum - 1976
Military history, Battery Randolph, a Pre-WWI coast artillery defense bastion 36893

Fort Dix NJ

Fort Dix Museum, AFRC-FA-KPS, Fort Dix, NJ 08640 - T: (609) 562-6983, Fax: (609) 562-2164, E-mail: daniel.zimmerman@dix.army.mil. Head: Daniel W. Zimmerman
Military Museum - 1984 36894

Fort Dodge IA

Blanden Memorial Art Museum, 920 Third Av, S, Fort Dodge, IA 50501 - T: (515) 573-2316, Fax: (515) 573-2317, E-mail: blanden@dodgenet.com, Internet: http://www.blanden.org. Head: M. Peters, Charles P. Helsell
Fine Arts Museum - 1930
Art 36895

Fort Dodge Historical Museum, Museum Rd, Fort Dodge, IA 50501 - T: (515) 573-4231, Fax: (515) 573-4231, E-mail: thefort@frontiernet.net, Internet: http://www.fort.org. Head: Dr. E. Ryan, David Parker
Military Museum / Local Museum - 1962
Local and military history 36896

Fort Douglas UT

Fort Douglas Military Museum, 32 Potter St, Fort Douglas, UT 84113 - T: (801) 581-1710, Fax: (801) 581-9846, E-mail: fdouglas@webquyinternet.com, Internet: http://www.fortdouglas.org. Head: Robert Voyles
Military Museum - 1975
Military history, weapons, equipment, uniforms 36897

Fort Duchesne UT

Cultural Rights and Protection/Ute Indian Tribe, Hwy 40, Fort Duchesne, UT 84026 - T: (801) 722-4992, Fax: (801) 722-2083. Head: Betsy Chapoose
Ethnology Museum - 1976
Indian hist 36898

Fort Edward NY

Old Fort House Museum, 29 Lower Broadway, Fort Edward, NY 12828 - T: (518) 747-9600. Head: William Murphy, R. Paul McCarty
Local Museum - 1925 36899

Fort Eustis VA

United States Army Transportation Museum, Besson Hall, Bldg 300, Fort Eustis, VA 23604 - T: (757) 878-1115, Fax: (757) 878-5656, E-mail: bowerb@eustis.army.mil, Internet: http://www.eustis.army.mil/DPTMSEC/museum.htm. Head: Barbara A. Bower
Military Museum / Science&Tech Museum - 1959
Military transportation 36900

Fort Garland CO

Old Fort Garland, S of U.S. 160, on Hwy 159, Fort Garland, CO 81133 - T: (719) 379-3512. Head: Rick Manzanares
Historical Museum / Military Museum - 1858
Military, Pioneer 36901

Fort Gordon GA

United States Army Signal Corps and Fort Gordon Museum, Bldg 29807, Fort Gordon, GA 30905-5293 - T: (706) 791-2818, 791-3856, Fax: (706) 791-6069, E-mail: atzhsm@emh.gordon.army.mil, Internet: http://www.gordon.army.mil/museums. Head: Theodore F. Wise
Military Museum / Science&Tech Museum - 1965
Military, technology, photos 36902

Fort Hood TX

First Cavalry Division Museum, 2218 Headquarters Av, Bldg 2218, Fort Hood, TX 76545 - T: (254) 287-3626, Fax: (254) 287-6423, E-mail: DRAPERS@Hood-emh3.Army.Mil, Internet: http://www.METROT.com/~harry/1st-Team/FtMuseum. Head: Steven C. Draper
Military Museum - 1971
Military hist 36903

Fort Huachuca AZ

Fort Huachuca Museum, Boyd and Grierson Sts, Fort Huachuca, AZ 85613-6000 - T: (520) 533-3898, 533-3638, Fax: (520) 533-5736. Head: James P. Finley
Historical Museum / Military Museum - 1960
Local history, 1877 fort, national historic landmark 36904

Fort Jackson SC

Fort Jackson Museum, 4442 Jackson Blvd, Fort Jackson, SC 29207-5325 - T: (803) 751-7419, Fax: (803) 751-4435
Military Museum - 1974
Military hist 36905

United States Army Chaplain Museum, 10100 Lee Rd, Fort Jackson, SC 29207-7090 - T: (803) 751-8827, Fax: (803) 751-8740, E-mail: mcmanusm@usaches.army.mil. Head: Marcia McManus
Military Museum - 1957 36906

United States Army Finance Corps Museum, ATSG-FSM, Bldg 4392, Fort Jackson, SC 29207 - T: (803) 751-3771, Fax: (803) 751-1749, E-mail: carnesw@jackson.army.mil
Military Museum / Special Museum - 1954
Military 36907

Fort Johnson NY

Old Fort Johnson, 14 Tessiero Dr, Fort Johnson, NY 12070 - T: (518) 843-0300, Internet: http://www.telenet.net/commercial/fortjohnson. Head: David Bellinger
Local Museum - 1905 36908

Fort Jones CA

Fort Jones Museum, 11913 Main St, Fort Jones, CA 96032-0428 - T: (916) 468-5568, Fax: (530) 468-2598. Head: Cecelia Reuter
Local Museum - 1947 36909

Fort Knox KY

Patton Museum of Cavalry and Armor, 4554 Fayette Av, Fort Knox, KY 40121-0208 - T: (502) 624-3812, Fax: (502) 624-2364, E-mail: museum@kno1-emh1.army.mil. Head: John Purdy
Military Museum - 1948
Military 36910

Fort Laramie WY

Fort Laramie National Historic Site, Fort Laramie, WY 82212 - T: (307) 837-2221, Fax: (307) 837-2120, Internet: http://www.nationalparks.org/guide/parks/fort-laramie-1986.htm. Head: James Mack
Military Museum - 1938
Military hist 36911

Fort Lauderdale FL

Bonnet House, 900 N Birch Rd, Fort Lauderdale, FL 33304-3326 - T: (954) 563-5393, Fax: (954) 561-4174, E-mail: bobk@bonnethouse.com, Internet: http://www.bonnethouse.com. Head: Robert R. Kauth
Local Museum / Historic Site - 1987 36912

Broward County Historical Museum, 151 SW 2nd St, Fort Lauderdale, FL 33301 - T: (954) 765-4670, Fax: (954) 765-4437. Head: Wally Elserf
Local Museum - 1972
Historic Commission 36913

Fort Lauderdale Historical Museum, 219 SW 2nd Av, Fort Lauderdale, FL 33302 - T: (954) 463-4431, Fax: (954) 463-4434. Head: Daniel T. Hobby
Local Museum - 1962
Local history 36914

International Swimming Hall of Fame, One Hall of Fame Dr, Fort Lauderdale, FL 33316 - T: (954) 462-6536, Fax: (954) 525-4031, E-mail: ishof@ishof.org, Internet: http://www.ishof.org
Special Museum - 1965
Swimming sports 36915

Museum of Art, 1 E Las Olas Blvd, Fort Lauderdale, FL 33301 - T: (954) 525-5500, Fax: (954) 524-6011, E-mail: museum98@bellsouth.net, Internet: http://www.museumofart.org. Head: Kathleen Harleman
Fine Arts Museum - 1958
Art 36916

Museum of Discovery and Science, 401 SW Second St, Fort Lauderdale, FL 33312-1707 - T: (954) 467-6637 ext 300, Fax: (305) 467-0046, E-mail: brosen@mods.net, Internet: http://www.gsni.com/discsci. Head: Barry H. Rosen, Paul Siboroski, Joe Cytacki, Woody Wilkes
Science&Tech Museum - 1976
Science, technology 36917

Stranahan House, 335 SE Sixth Av, Fort Lauderdale, FL 33303-0207 - T: (954) 524-4736, Fax: (954) 525-2838, E-mail: stranahanl@aol.com, Internet: http://www.stranahanhouse.comtm. Head: Joe Millsaps, Barbara W. Keith
Local Museum - 1981 36918

Fort Leavenworth KS

Fort Leavenworth Historical Museum and Post Museum, Reynolds and Gibbons Sts, Fort Leavenworth, KS 66027 - T: (913) 651-7440
Special Museum / Local Museum - 1950
Local history, postal hist 36919

Frontier Army Museum, 100 Reynolds Av, Fort Leavenworth, KS 66027-2334 - T: (913) 684-3767, 684-3553, Fax: (913) 684-3192, Internet: http://leav-www.army.mil/museum. Head: Stephen J. Allie
Military Museum - 1938
Military 36920

Fort Lee NJ

Fort Lee Historic Park and Museum, Hudson Terrace, Fort Lee, NJ 07024 - T: (201) 461-1776, Fax: (201) 461-7275, E-mail: flhp@intac. Head: Gaspar Santiago
Local Museum - 1976
Local hist 36921

Fort Lee VA

The United States Army Quartermaster Museum, Bldg 5218, A Av, Fort Lee, VA 23801-1601 - T: (804) 734-4203, Fax: (804) 734-4359, Internet: http://www.qmmuseum.lee.army.mil. Head: Tim O'Gorman
Military Museum - 1957
Military hist 36922

United States Army Women's Museum, A Av and 22nd St, Fort Lee, VA 23801 - T: (804) 734-4327, Fax: (804) 734-4337, E-mail: burgessj@lee.army.mil, Internet: http://www.amw.lee.army.mil. Head: Bettie J. Morden, Jerry G. Burgess
Military Museum - 1955
Women military history 36923

Women's Army Corps Museum → United States Army Women's Museum

Fort Leonard Wood MO

United States Army Engineer Museum, Bldg 1607, Fort Leonard Wood, MO 65473 - T: (573) 596-0780, Fax: (573) 596-0169, E-mail: combsk@wood.army.mil, Internet: http://www.Wood.Army.Mil/Museum. Head: Robert K. Combs
Military Museum - 1972 36924

Fort Lewis WA

Fort Lewis Military Museum, Bldg 4320, Fort Lewis, WA 98433-5000 - T: (206) 967-7206. Head: Alan H. Archambault
Military Museum - 1970
Military hist 36925

Fort McKavett TX

Fort McKavett State Historic Park, POB 867, Fort McKavett, TX 76841 - T: (915) 396-2358, Fax: (915) 396-2818, E-mail: mckavett@airmail.net, Internet: http://www.tpwd.state.tx.us. Head: Michael A. Garza
Military Museum - 1968
Military hist 36926

Fort McNair DC

United States Army Center of Military History, 103 Third Av, Bldg 35, Fort McNair, DC 20319-5058 - T: (202) 685-2453, Fax: (202) 685-2113, E-mail: benneje@hqda.army.mil
Military Museum - 1946
Military hist 36927

Fort Madison IA

North Lee County Historic Center and Santa Fe Depot Museum Complex, 10th and Av H, Fort Madison, IA 52627 - T: (319) 372-7661, 372-7363, Fax: (319) 372-1825. Head: Tom Barr, Sheila Sallen
Local Museum / Fine Arts Museum - 1962
Historic Center, located in Santa Fe Railroad depot, caboose, country school, Brush College, 1993 Flood museum, Louis Koch Gallery of historic paintings, furniture 36928

Fort Meade MD

Fort George G. Meade Museum, 4674 Griffin Av, Fort Meade, MD 20755-5094 - T: (301) 677-6966, 677-7054, Fax: (301) 677-2953, E-mail: johnsonr@emh1.ftmeade.army.mil
Military Museum - 1963
Military hist 36929

National Cryptologic Museum, Colony 7 Rd, Fort Meade, MD 20755-6000 - T: (301) 688-5848, 588-5849, Fax: (301) 688-5847, E-mail: www.museum@nsa.gov, Internet: http://www.nsa.gov:8080/museum/. Head: JacK E. Ingram
Military Museum - 1993
Cryptology 36930

Fort Meade SD

Old Fort Meade Museum, POB 164, Fort Meade, SD 57741 - T: (605) 347-9822. Head: Michael Jackley, Beverly Pechan
Military Museum - 1964
Military hist 36931

Fort Mitchell KY

Vent Haven Museum, 33 W Maple, Fort Mitchell, KY 41011 - T: (859) 341-0461, 331-9500, Fax: (859) 341-0461, E-mail: venthaven@home.com, Internet: http://www.venthaven.org
Performing Arts Museum - 1973
Ventriloguial figures and memorabilia 36932

Fort Monmouth NJ

United States Army Communications-Electronics Museum, Kaplan Hall, Bldg 275, Fort Monmouth, NJ 07703 - T: (732) 532-1682, Fax: (732) 532-2637. Head: Mindy Rosewitz
Military Museum / Science&Tech Museum - 1976 36933

Fort Monroe VA

Casemate Museum, 20 Bernard Rd, Fort Monroe, VA 23651-0341 - T: (757) 788-3391, Fax: (757) 788-3886, E-mail: mroczkod@monroe.army.mil, Internet: http://www.tradoc.monroe.army.mil/museum. Head: LeRoy W. Dyment, Dennis P. Mroczkowski
Military Museum - 1951
Military hist 36934

Fort Morgan CO

Fort Morgan Museum, 414 Main City Park, Fort Morgan, CO 80701 - T: (970) 867-6331, Fax: (970) 542-3008, E-mail: ftmormus@ftmorganmus.org, Internet: http://www.ftmorganmus.org/. Head: Marne Jurgemeyer
Local Museum / Music Museum - 1969
General museum, music Glen Miller 36935

Fort Myer VA

The Old Guard Museum, 204 Lee Av, 3rd US Infantry, Fort Myer, VA 22211-1199 - T: (703) 696-6670, 696-4168, Fax: (703) 696-4256, E-mail: bogana@fmmc.army.mil, Internet: http://www.mdw.army.mil/oldguard/. Head: Alan Bogan
Military Museum - 1962
Military hist 36936

Fort Myers FL

Edison and Ford Winter Estates, 2350 McGregor Blvd, Fort Myers, FL 33901 - T: (941) 334-7419, Fax: (941) 332-6684, E-mail: info@edison-ford-state.com, Internet: http://edison-ford-estate.com. Head: Judy Surprise
Historic Site - 1947
1886 wooden vernacular, pre-cut in Maine, brought to Florida by schooner, early light bulbs, early phonographs laboratory with equipment, Edison papers/rubber research 36937

Edison Community College Gallery of Fine Art, 8099 College Pkwy SW, Fort Myers, FL 33919, mail addr: POB 60210, Fort Myers, FL 33906 - T: (941) 489-9313, Fax: (941) 489-9482, E-mail: rbishop@edison.edu, Internet: http://www.edison.edu/. Head: Ron Bishop
Fine Arts Museum / Public Gallery / University Museum - 1979
Art 36938

Fort Myers Historical Museum, 2300 Peck St, Fort Myers, FL 33901 - T: (941) 332-5955, Fax: (941) 332-6637, E-mail: msantiago@cityftmyers.com, Internet: http://www.tntonline.com/dtown/muse.htm. Head: Mildred Santiago
Local Museum / Historical Museum - 1982
Local history, in a 1924 ACL Railroad Depot 36939

Gallery of Fine and Performing Arts, Edison Community College, 8099 College Pkwy SW, Fort Myers, FL 33936-6210 - T: (941) 489-9313, Fax: (941) 489-9482
Public Gallery 36940

Imaginarium Hands-On Museum, 2000 Cranford Av, Fort Myers, FL 33916 - T: (941) 337-3332, Fax: (941) 337-2109, E-mail: cpendleton@cityftmyers.com, Internet: http://www.cityftmyers.com. Head: Chris Pendleton
Science&Tech Museum - 1989
Science and technology 36941

Fort Oglethorpe GA

Chickamauga-Chattanooga National Military Park, U.S. 27 S, Fort Oglethorpe, GA 30742 - T: (706) 866-9241, Fax: (423) 752-5215. Head: Patrick H. Reed
Military Museum - 1890
Military, communication 36942

Fort Peck MT

Fort Peck Museum, Fort Peck Power Plant, Fort Peck, MT 59223 - T: (406) 526-3431, Fax: (406) 526-3431
Natural History Museum 36943

Fort Pierce FL

Harbor Branch Oceanographic Institution, 5600 U.S. 1, N, Fort Pierce, FL 34946 - T: (561) 465-2400 ext 306, Fax: (561) 465-5415, E-mail: tours@hboi.edu, Internet: http://www.hboi.edu. Head: Richard Herman
Natural History Museum / Science&Tech Museum - 1975
Natural hist 36944

Saint Lucie County Historical Museum, 414 Seaway Dr, Fort Pierce, FL 34949 - T: (561) 462-1795, Fax: (561) 462-1877, Internet: http://www.stlucieco.gov. Head: Iva Jean Maddox
Local Museum - 1965 36945

UDT-SEAL Museum, 3300 N State Rd A1A, Fort Pierce, FL 34949-8520 - T: (561) 595-5845, Fax: (561) 595-5847, Internet: http://www.udt-seal.org. Head: James H. Barnes, H.T. Aldhizer
Military Museum - 1985
Military, site where the Navy first trained Frogmen (underwater demolition teams), artifacts, weapons 36946

Fort Plain NY

Fort Plain Museum, 389 Canal St, Fort Plain, NY 13339 - T: (518) 993-2527. Head: G. Wetterau
Local Museum - 1963 36947

Fort Polk LA

Fort Polk Military Museum, Bldg 917, S Carolina Av, Fort Polk, LA 71459-0916 - T: (337) 531-7905, 531-4840, Fax: (337) 531-4202, E-mail: binghamd@polk_emh2.army.mil, Internet: http://polk_emh2.army.mil. Head: David S. Bingham
Military Museum - 1972
Military 36948

Fort Ransom ND

Bjarne Ness Gallery, Bear Creek Hall, Fort Ransom, ND 58033 - T: (701) 973-4461
Fine Arts Museum
American painting, woodcarvings, paintings of Bjarne Ness 36949

Ransom County Historical Society Museum, 101 Mill Rd SE, Fort Ransom, ND 58033-9740 - T: (701) 973-4811
Local Museum - 1972 36950

Fort Recovery OH

Fort Recovery Museum, 1 Fort Site St, Fort Recovery, OH 45846 - T: (800) 283-8920, Fax: (419) 375-4629, E-mail: bmeiring@yahoo.com. Head: Barbara Meiring
Military Museum / Ethnology Museum - 1982 36951

Fort Riley KS

First Territorial Capitol of Kansas, Bldg 693, Huebner Rd, K-18, Fort Riley, KS 66442 - T: (785) 784-5535, E-mail: scott_price@rocketmail.com. Head: Gary R. Dierking
Historical Museum - 1928
Historic House Museum 36952

United States Cavalry Museum, Bldg 205, Fort Riley, KS 66442 - T: (785) 239-2737, Fax: (785) 239-6243, E-mail: vanmetet@riley.army.mil
Military Museum - 1957
Military, housed in a old hospital 1855-1890 (post headquarters 1890-1948), 1st Infantry and 1st Armored division 36953

Fort Rucker AL

United States Army Aviation Museum, Bldg 6000, Fort Rucker, AL 36362 - T: (334) 255-3036, Fax: (334) 255-3054, E-mail: avnmuseum@alanet.com, Internet: http://www.aviationmuseum.org. Head: R.S. Maxham
Military Museum / Science&Tech Museum - 1962 36954

Fort Sam Houston TX

Fort Sam Houston Museum, 1210 Stanley Rd, Fort Sam Houston, TX 78234-5002 - T: (210) 221-1886, Fax: (210) 221-1311, E-mail: ftsammuseum@amedd.army.mil, Internet: http://wwww.army.mil/dptmsec/muse/htm. Head: John M. Manguso
Military Museum / Historical Museum / Historic Site - 1967
Military hist 36955

United States Army Medical Department Museum, Bldg 1046, 2310 Stanley Rd, Fort Sam Houston, TX 78234 - T: (210) 221-6358, Fax: (210) 221-6781, E-mail: ameddmus@aol.com, Internet: http://www.cs.amedd.army.mil/dptmsec/amedd.htm. Head: Thomas O. McMasters
Military Museum / Historical Museum - 1955
Military medicine 36956

Fort Scott KS

Fort Scott National Historic Site, Old Fort Blvd, Fort Scott, KS 66701 - T: (620) 223-0310, Fax: (620) 223-0188, E-mail: FOSC_superintendent@nps.gov, Internet: http://www.nps.gov/fosc
Historic Site - 1978
Restored and reconstructed Fort Scott 36957

Historic Preservation Association of Bourbon County, 117 S Main, Fort Scott, KS 66701 - T: (316) 223-1557. Head: Don Miller
Local Museum / Military Museum - 1973
History, military 36958

Fort Sill OK

Fort Sill Museum, 437 Quanah Rd, Fort Sill, OK 73503-5100 - T: (580) 442-5123, Fax: (580) 442-8120, E-mail: spiveyt@sill.army.mil, Internet: http://www-sill.army.mil/museum. Head: Towana Spivey
Military Museum - 1934
archives 36959

Fort Smith AR

Fort Smith, Parker Av and Third St, Fort Smith, AR 72901 - T: (501) 783-3961, Fax: (501) 783-5307, Internet: http://www.nps.gov./fosm. Head: William N. Black
Historical Museum - 1961
1817-24 Fort Smith, became the Federal Courthouse and Jail 1871-1896 36960

Fort Smith Art Center, 423 N Sixth St, Fort Smith, AR 72901 - T: (501) 784-2787, Fax: (501) 784-9071, E-mail: ftsartcenter@aol.com, Internet: http://www.ftsartcenter.com. Head: Kathy Williams, Michael Richardson
Fine Arts Museum - 1948
Arts 36961

Fort Smith Museum of History, 320 Rogers Av, Fort Smith, AR 72901 - T: (501) 783-7841, Fax: (501) 783-3244, Internet: http://www.fortsmith.com/museum. Head: Ellen F. Campbell
Historical Museum - 1910 36962

Patent Model Museum, 400 N 8th St, Fort Smith, AR 72901 - T: (501) 782-9014, Fax: (501) 782-1555. Head: Carolyn Pollan
Museum of Classical Antiquities - 1976
Rogers-Tilles House 36963

Fort Stewart GA

Fort Stewart Museum, 2022 Frank Cochran Dr, Fort Stewart, GA 31314 - T: (912) 767-7885, 767-4480, Fax: (912) 767-4480
Military Museum - 1977
Military 36964

Fort Stockton TX

Annie Riggs Memorial Museum, 301 S Main St, Fort Stockton, TX 79735 - T: (915) 336-2167, Fax: (915) 336-2402, E-mail: TXRousse@aol.com. Head: Leanna S. Biles
Local Museum - 1955
Local hist 36965

Historic Fort Stockton, 300 E Third, Fort Stockton, TX 79735 - T: (915) 336-2400, Fax: (915) 336-2402, E-mail: TXRousse@aol.com. Head: Leanna S. Biles
Historic Site / Open Air Museum / Military Museum - 1990 36966

Fort Totten ND

Fort Totten State Historic Site-Pioneer Daughters Museum, Fort Totten, ND 58335 - T: (701) 766-4441, Fax: (701) 766-4882
Local Museum / Open Air Museum - 1960
Local hist 36967

Fort Towson OK

Fort Towson Military Park, HC 63, Fort Towson, OK 74735-9273 - T: (580) 873-2634
Military Museum - 1972 36968

Fort Valley GA

A.L. Fetterman Educational Museum, 100 Massee Ln, Fort Valley, GA 31030 - T: (912) 967-2358, 967-2722, Fax: (912) 967-2083, Internet: http://www.acs.home.ml.org. Head: Robert Ehrhart, Ann Blair Brown
Decorative Arts Museum - 1989
Porcelain 36969

Massee Lane Gardens, American Camellia Society, One Massee Lane, Fort Valley, GA 31030 - T: (912) 967-2358, 967-2722, Fax: (912) 967-2083. Head: Robert Ehrhart, Ann Blair Brown
Decorative Arts Museum / Historical Museum - 1945
Horticulture, paintings 36970

Fort Walton Beach FL

Indian Temple Mound Museum, 139 Miracle Strip Pkwy, SE, Fort Walton Beach, FL 32549 - T: (850) 833-9595, Fax: (850) 833-9675, Internet: http://www.fwb.org. Head: Anna M. Peele
Historical Museum / Ethnology Museum - 1962
Anthropology, ethnology of Indian, Indian Temple Mound of Fort Walton Culture, prehistoric Native American cultures of local area 36971

Fort Washakie WY

Shoshone Tribal Cultural Center, 31 First St, Fort Washakie, WY 82514 - T: (307) 332-9106, Fax: (307) 332-3055. Head: Zelda Tillman
Folklore Museum
Indian culture 36972

Fort Washington MD

Fort Washington, 13551 Fort Washington Rd, Fort Washington, MD 20744 - T: (301) 763-4600, Fax: (301) 763-1389. Head: Robert Stanton
Military Museum - 1940
Military, Commandant's house 36973

Fort Washington PA

Childventure Museum, 430 Virginia Dr, Fort Washington, PA 19034 - T: (215) 643-9906. Head: Nina Kardon, Beverly Levine
Special Museum - 1989 36974

Highlands, 7001 Sheaff Ln, Fort Washington, PA 19034 - T: (215) 641-2687, Fax: (215) 641-2556. Head: Margaret Bleecker Blades
Local Museum - 1975 36975

Historical Society of Fort Washington Museum, 473 Bethlehem Pike, Fort Washington, PA 19034 - T: (215) 646-6065. Head: Betty Mackinlay
Historical Museum / Historic Site - 1935
1801 Clifton House 36976

Hope Lodge and Mather Mill, 553 S Bethlehem Pike, Fort Washington, PA 19034 - T: (215) 646-1595, Fax: (215) 628-9471, E-mail: smiller@phmc.state.pa.us, Internet: http://www.ushistory.org/hope
Local Museum / Historic Site / Open Air Museum - 1957 36977

Fort Wayne IN

Allen County-Fort Wayne Historical Society Museum, 302 E Berry St, Fort Wayne, IN 46802 - T: (219) 426-2882, Fax: (219) 424-4419, E-mail: histsociety@fwi.net
Local Museum - 1921
Local history 36978

Fort Wayne Museum of Art, 311 E Main St, Fort Wayne, IN 46802 - T: (219) 422-6467, Fax: (219) 422-1374, E-mail: mail@fwmoa.org, Internet: http://www.fwmoa.org. Head: Patricia Watkinson
Fine Arts Museum - 1922
Art 36979

The Lincoln Museum, 200 E Berry, Fort Wayne, IN 46801-7838 - T: (219) 455-3864, Fax: (219) 455-6922, E-mail: ekehoe@lnc.com, Internet: http://www.thelincolnmuseum.org. Head: Joan L. Flinspach
Historical Museum - 1928
History, civil war 36980

Fort Worth TX

Amon Carter Museum, 3501 Camp Bowie Blvd, Fort Worth, TX 76107-2695 - T: (817) 738-1933, Fax: (817) 377-8523, E-mail: ruthann.rugg@cartermuseum.org, Internet: http://www.cartermuseum.org. Head: Rick Stewart
Fine Arts Museum / Folklore Museum - 1961
Art 36981

Cattle Raisers Museum, 1301 W 7th St, Fort Worth, TX 76102-2665 - T: (817) 332-8551, Fax: (817) 332-8749, Internet: http://www.cattleraisersmuseum.org. Head: Cheri L. Wolfe
Local Museum - 1981
Local hist 36982

Contemporary Art Center of Fort Worth, 500 Commerce St, Fort Worth, TX 76102 - T: (817) 877-5550
Public Gallery 36983

Fort Worth Museum of Science and History, 1501 Montgomery St, Fort Worth, TX 76107 - T: (817) 255-9300 ext 0, Fax: (817) 732-7635, E-mail: webmaster@fwmshz.org, Internet: http://www.fortworthmuseum.org. Head: James P. Diffily, Dennis Gabbard
Historical Museum / Science&Tech Museum - 1941
General Museum 36984

Kimbell Art Museum, 3333 Camp Bowie Blvd, Fort Worth, TX 76107-2792 - T: (817) 332-8451 ext 224, Fax: (817) 877-1264, E-mail: gottlieb@kimbellmuseum.org, Internet: http://www.kimbellart.org. Head: Timothy Potts
Fine Arts Museum - 1972
Art 36985

Log Cabin Village, 2100 Log Cabin Village Lane, Fort Worth, TX 76109 - T: (817) 926-5881, Fax: (817) 922-0246, E-mail: pickark@ci.fort-worth.tx.us, Internet: http://www.sed.tcu.edu/sed/logcabin/wel.html. Head: Kelli L. Pickard
Local Museum / Open Air Museum - 1965
Historic village 36986

Modern Art Museum of Fort Worth (close April 2002, reopen in new location November 2002), 1309 Montgomery St, Fort Worth, TX 76107 - T: (817) 738-9215, Fax: (817) 735-1161, E-mail: carriann@mamfw.org, Internet: http://www.theModern.org. Head: Dr. Marla J. Price
Fine Arts Museum - 1892
Art 36987

Moudy Exhibition Hall, c/o Texas Christian University, Dept. of Art and Art History, Campus Box 298000, Fort Worth, TX 76129 - T: (817) 257-7643, Fax: (817) 257-7399, E-mail: r.watson@tcu.edu. Head: Ronald Watson
University Museum / Fine Arts Museum - 1874 36988

National Cowgirl Museum and Hall of Fame, 111 West 4th St, Ste 300, Fort Worth, TX 76102 - T: (817) 336-4475, Fax: (817) 336-2470, E-mail: susan@cowgirl.net, Internet: http://www.cowgirl.net. Head: Pat Riley
Historical Museum - 1975/2002
Hist of Western American women 36989

Sid Richardson Collection of Western Art, 309 Main St, Fort Worth, TX 76102 - T: (817) 332-6554, Fax: (817) 332-8671, E-mail: info@sidrmuseum.org, Internet: http://www.sidrmuseum.org. Head: Jan Brenneman
Fine Arts Museum - 1982
Art 36990

Forty Fort PA

Nathan Denison House, 35 Denison St, Forty Fort, PA 18704-4390 - T: (717) 288-5531. Head: Louise Robinson
Local Museum - 1970 36991

Fountain MN

Fillmore County Historical Museum, 202 County Rd, Ste 8, Fountain, MN 55935 - T: (507) 268-4449. Head: Jerry D. Henke
Local Museum - 1934 36992

Fountain City IN

Levi Coffin House, 113 U.S. 27 North, Fountain City, IN 47341 - T: (765) 847-2432, Fax: (765) 847-2498. Head: Janice McGuire
Historical Museum - 1967 36993

Four Oaks NC

Bentonville Battleground State Historic Site, 5466 Harper House Rd, Four Oaks, NC 27524 - T: (910) 594-0789, Fax: (910) 594-0222, Internet: http://www.ah.dcr.state.nc.us/hs/bentonri/bentonri.htm. Head: John C. Goode
Military Museum / Open Air Museum - 1961 36994

Fox Island WA

Fox Island Historical Society Museum, 1017 Ninth Av, Fox Island, WA 98333 - T: (253) 549-2461, 549-2239, Fax: (253) 549-2461
Local Museum - 1895
Local hist 36995

Fox Lake WI

Fox Lake Historical Museum, 211 Cordelia St and S College Av, Fox Lake, WI 53933 - T: (920) 928-2172. Head: Donald Frank
Local Museum / Science&Tech Museum - 1970
Railroad, local hist 36996

Framingham MA

Danforth Museum of Art, 123 Union Av, Framingham, MA 01702 - T: (508) 620-0050, Fax: (508) 872-5542. Head: Ronald L. Crusan
Fine Arts Museum - 1975
Art 36997

Framingham Historical Society Museum, 16 Vernon St, Framingham, MA 01701 - T: (508) 872-3780, Fax: (508) 872-3780, E-mail: framhist@juno.com, Internet: http://www.townonline/ine.koz.com/visit/framhistsoc/. Head: Joan Mickelson-Lukach
Local Museum - 1888
Local history 36998

Frances E. Warren Air Force Base WY

Warren ICBM and Heritage Museum, 7405 Marne Loop, 90th SW/MU, Frances E. Warren Air Force Base, WY 82005 - T: (307) 773-2980, Fax: (307) 773-2791, E-mail: Paula.taylor@warren.af.mil, Internet: http://www.pawnee.com/fewmuseum. Head: Paula Bauman Taylor
Military Museum - 1967
Military hist 36999

Franconia NH

New England Ski Museum, Franconia Notch State Park, Pkwy Exit 2, Franconia, NH 03580 - T: (603) 823-7177, Fax: (603) 823-9505, E-mail: staff@skimuseum.org, Internet: http://www.skimuseum.org. Head: Glenn Parkinson, Jeffrey R. Leich
Special Museum - 1977 37000

Frankenmuth MI

Frankenmuth Historical Museum, 613 S Main, Frankenmuth, MI 48734 - T: (517) 652-9701, Fax: (517) 652-9701, Internet: http://www.concentric.net/~dtimmins/musehome.shtml. Head: Daniel Haubenstricker, Sally D. Van Ness
Local Museum / Folklore Museum - 1963
Regional history 37001

Frankfort IN

Clinton County Museum, 301 E Clinton St, Frankfort, IN 46041 - T: (765) 659-2030, 659-4079, Fax: (765) 654-7773, E-mail: elosrebe@aol.com. Head: Nancy Hart
Local Museum - 1980
Local history, housed in Old Stoney, former Frankfort High School building 37002

Frankfort KY

The Executive Mansion, 704 Capitol Av, Frankfort, KY 40601 - T: (502) 564-8004, Fax: (502) 564-5022, E-mail: rlyons@mail.state.ky.us, Internet: http://www.state.ky.us/agencies/gov./mansion. Head: Rex Lyons
Local Museum - 1914
Historic house, residence of 22 of Kentucky's governors 37003

Kentucky Historical Society Museum, 100 W Broadway, Frankfort, KY 40601 - T: (502) 564-1792, Fax: (502) 564-4701, Internet: http://www.kyhistory.org. Head: J. Kevin Graffagnino
Historical Museum - 1836
History, housed in the Kentucky History Center and 1869 Old State Capitol Annex 37004

Kentucky Military History Museum, Old State Arsenal, E Main St, Frankfort, KY 40602-1792 - T: (502) 564-3265, Fax: (502) 564-4054, Internet: http://www.kyhistory.org
Military Museum - 1974
Military 37005

Liberty Hall, 218 Wilkinson St, Frankfort, KY 40601 - T: (502) 227-2560, Fax: (502) 227-3348, E-mail: libhall@dcr.net, Internet: http://www.libertyhall.org. Head: Sara Farley-Harger
Decorative Arts Museum - 1937
Formerly the home of the Kentucky Senator John Brown 37006

The Old Governor's Mansion, 420 High St, Frankfort, KY 40601 - T: (502) 564-5500, Fax: (502) 564-4099
Local Museum - 1798
Historic house 37007

Vest-Lindsey House, 401 Wapping St, Frankfort, KY 40601 - T: (502) 564-3000, 564-6980, Fax: (502) 564-6505. Head: Helen H. Evans
Local Museum - 1978
Historic house 37008

Frankfort SD

Fisher Grove Country School, 17250 Fishers Ln, Frankfort, SD 57440 - T: (605) 472-1212
Local Museum - 1884
Historic building 37009

Franklin IN

Johnson County History Museum, 135 N Main St, Franklin, IN 46131 - T: (317) 736-4655, Fax: (317) 736-5451, E-mail: map@netdirect.net. Head: Mary Ann Plummer
Local Museum - 1931
County history 37010

Franklin ME

Franklin Historical Society Museum, Rte 200, Franklin, ME 04634 - T: (207) 565-2223. Head: Lawrence Button
Local Museum - 1960
Local hist 37011

Franklin NJ

Franklin Mineral Museum, 32 Evans St, Franklin, NJ 07416 - T: (973) 827-3481, Fax: (973) 827-0149, E-mail: rockman@warwick.net, Internet: http://www.geocities.com/CapeCanaveral/Lab/6347/
Natural History Museum / Science&Tech Museum - 1965
Geology, mining 37012

Franklin OH

Harding Museum, 302 Park Av, Franklin, OH 45005 - T: (513) 746-8295. Head: Geofrey Gorsuch
Local Museum - 1965 37013

Franklin TN

Carnton Plantation, 1345 Carnton Ln, Franklin, TN 37064 - T: (615) 794-0903, Fax: (615) 794-6563, E-mail: carnton@mindspring.com, Internet: http://carnton.home.mindspring.com. Head: Angela Calhoun
Local Museum - 1977
Historic house 37014

The Carter House, 1140 Columbia Av, Franklin, TN 37064 - T: (615) 791-1861, Fax: (615) 794-1327, E-mail: julepl9@mail.idt.net, Internet: http://www.carterhouse.org
Local Museum - 1951
Local hist 37015

Franklin Center PA

Franklin Mint Museum, Franklin Mint, Rte 1, Franklin Center, PA 19091 - T: (610) 459-6881 ext 6348, Fax: (610) 459-6463, Internet: http://www.franklinmint.com
Science&Tech Museum / Local Museum - 1973 37016

Franklinville NY

Ischua Valley Historical Society, 9 Pine St, Franklinville, NY 14737 - T: (716) 676-5651. Head: Gertrude H. Schnell
Local Museum - 1966 37017

Frederick MD

The Children's Museum of Rose Hill Manor Park, 1611 N Market St, Frederick, MD 21701-4304 - T: (301) 694-1648, Fax: (301) 694-2595, E-mail: rhmp@co.frederick.md.us, Internet: http://www.frederick.md.us/qovt/parks/rosehill.html. Head: A. Colin Clevenger
Historical Museum - 1972 37018

Historical Museum of Frederick County, 24 E Church St, Frederick, MD 21701 - T: (301) 663-1188, Fax: (301) 663-0526, E-mail: director@fwp.net, Internet: http://www.fwp.net/hsfc. Head: Mark S. Hudson
Local Museum - 1888
Regional history 37019

Monocacy National Battlefield, 4801 Urbana Pike, Frederick, MD 21704 - T: (301) 662-3515, 432-7677, Fax: (301) 662-3420, E-mail: cathy_beeler@nps.gov, Internet: http://www.nps.gov/mono/mo_visit.htm. Head: John Howard
Historic Site - 1907
Dedicated to soldiers who fought in the Battle of Monocacy, July 9, 1864 37020

National Museum of Civil War Medicine, 48 E Patrick St, Frederick, MD 21701 - T: (301) 695-1864, Fax: (301) 695-6823, E-mail: museum@civilwarmed.org, Internet: http://www.CivilWarMed.org. Head: Robert E. Gearinger, JaNeen M. Smith
Special Museum - 1990
Medical hist 37021

Schifferstadt Architectural Museum, 1110 Rosemont Av, Frederick, MD 21701 - T: (301) 663-3885, Fax: (301) 663-3885, Internet: http://www.wam.umd.edu/~marystev/index.html. Head: Charles Gunn-Frederick
Fine Arts Museum - 1974
Architecture 37022

Fredericksburg TX

Admiral Nimitz Museum and Historical Center, 340 E Main St, Fredericksburg, TX 78624 - T: (830) 997-4379 ext 225, Fax: (830) 997-8220, E-mail: nimitzm@ktc.com, Internet: http://www.nimitz-museum.org
Local Museum - 1967
Local hist 37023

Pioneer Museum and Vereins Kirche, 312 W San Antonio St, Fredericksburg, TX 78624 - T: (830) 997-2835, Fax: (830) 997-3891, E-mail: gchs@ktc.com, Internet: http://www.ktc.net/gchs. Head: Kathy Harrison, Paul Camfield
Local Museum - 1936
History 37024

Fredericksburg VA

Belmont, Gari Melchers Estate and Memorial Gallery, 224 Washington St, Fredericksburg, VA 22405 - T: (540) 654-1015, 654-1840, Fax: (540) 654-1785, E-mail: dberreth@mwc.edu, Internet: http://www.mwc.edu/belmont. Head: David S. Berreth
Fine Arts Museum - 1975
Art 37025

Fredericksburg and Spotsylvania National Military Park, 120 Chatham Ln, Fredericksburg, VA 22405 - T: (540) 371-0802, Fax: (540) 371-1907
Military Museum - 1927
Military hist 37026

Fredericksburg Area Museum and Cultural Center, 907-911 Princess Anne St, Fredericksburg, VA 22401 - T: (540) 371-5668, 371-3037, Fax: (540) 373-6569, E-mail: famcc@fls.infi.net, Internet: http://www.famcc.org. Head: Edwin W. Watson
Local Museum - 1985
Local hist 37027

James Monroe Museum and Memorial Library, 908 Charles St, Fredericksburg, VA 22401-5810 - T: (540) 654-1043, Fax: (540) 654-1106, E-mail: -JamesMonroeMuseum@mwc.edu, Internet: http://www.JamesMonroeMuseum.mwc.edu. Head: John N. Pearce
Historical Museum / Library with Exhibitions / Historic Site - 1928
Presidential library, local hist, James Monroe (1785 - 1831, 5th president of the USA) 37028

Kenmore Plantation and George Washington's Ferry Farm, 1201 Washington Av, Fredericksburg, VA 22401 - T: (540) 373-3381, Fax: (540) 371-6066, E-mail: mailroom@kenmore.org, Internet: http://www.kenmore.org. Head: Stacia G. Norman
Local Museum - 1922
Local hist 37029

Mary Washington House, 1200 Charles St, Fredericksburg, VA 22401 - T: (540) 373-1569, Internet: http://www.apva.org. Head: Gail G. Braxton
Local Museum - 1772
Historic house 37030

Ridderhof Martin Gallery, College Av at Seacobeck St, Fredericksburg, VA 22401-5358 - T: (540) 654-1013, Fax: (540) 654-1171, E-mail: gallery@mwc.edu, Internet: http://www.mwc.edu. Head: Dr. Thomas P. Somma
Fine Arts Museum / University Museum - 1956 37031

Rising Sun Tavern, 1304 Caroline St, Fredericksburg, VA 22401 - T: (540) 371-1494, Internet: http://www.apva.org. Head: Gail G. Braxton
Local Museum - 1760
Historic house 37032

Saint James' House, 1300 Charles St, Fredericksburg, VA 22401 - T: (703) 373-1569, Internet: http://www.apva.org. Head: Gail G. Braxton
Local Museum - 1760
Historic house 37033

Fredonia KS

Stone House Gallery, 320 N 7th St, Fredonia, KS 66736 - T: (316) 378-2052, E-mail: stonehouse@trerraworld.net. Head: Joyce Fulghum
Fine Arts Museum - 1967
Art 37034

Wilson County Historical Society Museum, 420 N 7th, Fredonia, KS 66736 - T: (316) 378-3965
Local Museum - 1961
Local history, located in old county jail 37035

Fredonia NY

Historical Museum of the D.R. Barker Library, 20 E Main St, Fredonia, NY 14063 - T: (716) 672-2114, Fax: (716) 679-3547, E-mail: BarkerMu@netsync.net, Internet: http://www.netsync.net/users/BarkerMu. Head: Peter Clark, Christine Drby-Cuadrado
Library with Exhibitions - 1884 37036

Michael C. Rockefeller Arts Center Gallery, State University College, Fredonia, NY 14063 - T: (716) 673-4897, Fax: (716) 673-3810, E-mail: gaaschc@fredonia.edu, Internet: http://www.fredonia.edu. Head: Cynnie Gaasch
Fine Arts Museum / University Museum - 1826 37037

Freeman SD

Heritage Hall Museum, 748 S Main St, Freeman, SD 57029 - T: (605) 925-4237
Local Museum - 1976
Local history, ethnology 37038

Freeport IL

Freeport Arts Center, 121 N Harlem Av, Freeport, IL 61032 - T: (815) 235-9755, Fax: (815) 235-6015, E-mail: arts@mwci.net. Head: Becky Hewitt Connors
Fine Arts Museum - 1975 37039

Silvercreek Museum, 2954 Walnut Rd, Freeport, IL 61032 - T: (815) 232-2350, E-mail: ike.sue@gte.net. Head: Larry Buttel, Rose Reeter, Esther Otto, Betty Bawinkel
Local Museum / Agriculture Museum - 1988
Regional history, in 1906 county poor farm 37040

Stephenson County Historical Society, 1440 S Carroll Av, Freeport, IL 61032 - T: (815) 232-8419, Fax: (815) 297-0313. Head: Suzy Beggin
Historical Museum - 1944
Local and regional history, Jane Addams, Abraham Licoln, underground railroad, school, agriculture 37041

Freeport ME

Freeport Historical Society Museum, 45 Main St, Freeport, ME 04032 - T: (207) 865-3170, Fax: (207) 865-9055, E-mail: FRPhistory@aol.com. Head: Cliff Goodall, Randall Wade Thomas
Library with Exhibitions - 1969
Local hist 37042

Fremont NC

Charles B. Aycock Birthplace State Historic Site, 264 Governor Aycock Rd, Fremont, NC 27830 - T: (919) 242-5581, Fax: (919) 242-6668, E-mail: aycock@ncsl.dcr.state.nc.us, Internet: http://www.ah.dcr.state.nc.us/hs/Aycock/Aycock.htm. Head: Charlotte Brow
Local Museum - 1959 37043

Fremont NE

Louis E. May Museum, 1643 N Nye, Fremont, NE 68025 - T: (402) 721-4515, Fax: (402) 721-8354, E-mail: dchs-may@teknetwork.com
Historical Museum - 1969 37044

Fremont OH

Rutherford B. Hayes Presidential Center, Spiegel Grove, Fremont, OH 43420 - T: (419) 332-2081, Fax: (419) 332-4952, E-mail: hayeslib@rbhayes.org, Internet: http://www.rbhayes.org. Head: Roger D. Bridges
Historical Museum / Library with Exhibitions - 1916
Books, manuscripts, photographic prints 37045

Fresno CA

Discovery Center, 1944 N Winery Av, Fresno, CA 93703 - T: (209) 251-5533, Fax: (209) 251-5531, Internet: http://www.gemworld.com/discoverycenter. Head: Marc Birnbaum, Anne D. Bell
Ethnology Museum / Historical Museum / Natural History Museum / Science&Tech Museum - 1956 37046

Fresno Art Museum, 2233 N First St, Fresno, CA 93703-9955 - T: (559) 441-4221, Fax: (559) 441-4227, E-mail: fam@qnis.net, Internet: http://www.fresnoartmuseum.com. Head: Mary LaFollette
Fine Arts Museum - 1949 37047

Fresno Metropolitan Museum, 1555 Van Ness Av, Fresno, CA 93721 - T: (209) 441-1444, Fax: (209) 441-8607, Internet: http://www.fresnonet.org. Head: Kim Cline
Fine Arts Museum / Local Museum / Natural History Museum - 1984 37048

Kearney Mansion Museum, 7160 W Kearney Blvd, Fresno, CA 93706 - T: (209) 441-0862, Fax: (209) 441-1372, E-mail: frhistsoc@aol.com, Internet: http://www.fcoe.kiz.ca.us/home/histscty.html. Head: Keith Moyer, Zelma Barrett Smith
Local Museum - 1919 37049

Frisco CO

Frisco Historical Society Museum, 120 Main St, Frisco, CO 80443 - T: (970) 668-3428, Fax: (970) 668-3428. Head: Rita Bartram
Local Museum - 1983 37050

Frisco NC

Frisco Native American Museum and Natural History Center, 53536 Hwy 12, Frisco, NC 27936 - T: (252) 995-4440, Fax: (252) 995-4030, E-mail: bfriend1@mindspring.com, Internet: http://www.nativeamericanmuseum.org. Head: Carl Bornfriend
Ethnology Museum - 1986 37051

Fritch TX

Lake Meredith Aquatic and Wildlife Museum, 103 N Robey St, Fritch, TX 79036 - T: (806) 857-2458, Fax: (806) 857-3229, E-mail: lmmuseum@infinitytx.net. Head: Lanelle Poling
Natural History Museum - 1976
Natural hist 37052

Front Royal VA

Warren Rifles Confederate Museum, 95 Chester St, Front Royal, VA 22630 - T: (540) 636-6982, 635-2219, Fax: (540) 635-2219, E-mail: silwood@rma.edu. Head: Suzanne Silek
Military Museum - 1959
Military hist 37053

Fryeburg ME

The Fryeburg Fair Farm Museum, Rte 5 N, Fryeburg, ME 04037 - T: (207) 935-3268, Fax: (207) 935-3662, E-mail: fryefair@hxi.com, Internet: http://www.fryefair.com
Agriculture Museum - 1970
Agriculture 37054

Fullerton CA

Art Gallery, Visual Arts Center, California State University, 800 N State College Blvd, Fullerton, CA 92834-6850 - T: (714) 278-2011, Fax: (714) 278-2390, E-mail: mmcgee@fullerton.edu, Internet: http://www.fullerton.edu. Head: Prof. Mike McGee
Fine Arts Museum / University Museum - 1963 37055

Fullerton Museum Center, 301 N Pomona Av, Fullerton, CA 92832 - T: (714) 738-6545, Fax: (714) 738-3124, E-mail: fmc@ci.fullerton.ca.us, Internet: http://www.ci.fullerton.ca.us/museum. Head: Joseph Felz
Local Museum - 1971 37056

Museum of Anthropology, California State University, Fullerton, CA 92834-6846 - T: (714) 278-2844, 278-3564, Fax: (714) 278-7046, Internet: http://hss.fullerton.edu/anthro/anthro.html. Head: Susan Parman
Ethnology Museum - 1970
Anthropology 37057

Fulton MO

William Woods University Art Gallery, 1 University Av, Fulton, MO 65251 - T: (573) 592-4245. Head: Terry Martin
Fine Arts Museum 37058

Winston Churchill Memorial and Library in the United States, Westminster College, 501 Westminster Av, Fulton, MO 65251 - T: (573) 592-5369, Fax: (573) 592-5222, E-mail: hollraw@jaynet.wcmo.edu, Internet: http://www.wcmo.edu. Head: Dr. Gordon Davis
University Museum / Historical Museum - 1962 37059

Gadsden AL

Center for Cultural Arts, 501 Broad St, Gadsden, AL 35901 - T: (256) 543-2787, Fax: (256) 546-7435, Internet: http://www.culturalarts.org. Head: Robert M. Welch
Fine Arts Museum / Folklore Museum - 1987
Art 37060

Gadsden Museum of Fine Arts, 2829 W Meighan Blvd, Gadsden, AL 35904-1717 - T: (256) 546-7365, E-mail: gadmus.cybertyme. Head: Jim Loftin, Janie Terr
Fine Arts Museum - 1965 37061

Gaffney SC

Winnie Davis Museum of History, Limestone College, 1115 College Dr, Gaffney, SC 29340 - T: (864) 488-8399, Fax: (864) 487-7151, E-mail: chayward@saint.limestone.edu, Internet: http://www.limestone.edu
Historical Museum / University Museum - 1976
History 37062

Gainesville FL

Florida Museum of Natural History, SW 34th St and Hull Rd, Gainesville, FL 32611-7800, mail addr: POB 117800, Gainesville, FL 32611-7800 - T: (352) 392-1721, 846-2000, Fax: (352) 392-8783, 846-0253, Internet: http://flmnh.ufl.edu. Head: Dr. Douglas S. Jones
University Museum / Natural History Museum - 1917
Paleontology, archaeology, ornitology, botany, mammalogy, herpetlogy, art 37063

Morningside Nature Center, 3540 E University Av, Gainesville, FL 32641 - T: (352) 334-2170, Fax: (352) 334-2248. Head: Gloria Ewell, Dr. Clifford Crawford
Agriculture Museum / Open Air Museum / Natural History Museum - 1972 37064

Samuel P. Harn Museum of Art, University of Florida, Gainesville, FL 32611-2700 - T: (352) 392-9826, Fax: (352) 392-3892, E-mail: iwolins@ufl.edu, Internet: http://www.arts.ufl.edu/harn. Head: Inez S. Wolins
Fine Arts Museum / University Museum - 1981
Art 37065

Santa Fe Gallery, Santa Fe Community College, 3000 NW 83rd St, Gainesville, FL 32606 - T: (352) 395-5621, Fax: (352) 395-5581, E-mail: mallory.o'connor@santafe.cc.fl.us
Fine Arts Museum - 1978
Art gallery 37066

University Gallery, University of Florida, Gainesville, FL 32611, mail addr: POB 115803, Gainesville, FL 32611-5803 - T: (352) 392-0201, Fax: (352) 846-0266, E-mail: wyman@ufl.edu, Internet: http://www.arts.ufl.edu. Head: James Wyman
Fine Arts Museum / University Museum - 1965 37067

Gainesville GA

Brenau University Galleries, 1 Centennial Circle, Gainesville, GA 30501 - T: (770) 534-6299, Fax: (770) 538-4599, Internet: http://www.brenau.edu. Head: Jean Westmacott
Fine Arts Museum / University Museum - 1983 37068

Gainesville TX

Morton Museum of Cooke County, 210 S Dixon St, Gainesville, TX 76240 - T: (817) 668-8900, E-mail: mortonmuseum@nortexinfo.net
Local Museum - 1968
Local hist 37069

Gaithersburg MD

The London Brass Rubbing Centre in Washington D.C., 11808 Silent Valley Ln, Gaithersburg, MD 20878 - T: (301) 279-7046. Head: Richard A. Etches, Ann Etches
Decorative Arts Museum - 1977
Arts, crafts 37070

Galax VA

Jeff Matthews Memorial Museum, 606 W Stuart Dr, Galax, VA 24333 - T: (540) 236-7874
Local Museum - 1974
Local hist 37071

Galena IL

Galena-Jo Daviess County Historical Museum, 211 S Bench St, Galena, IL 61036 - T: (815) 777-9129, Fax: (815) 777-9131, E-mail: ghmuseum@galenalink.net, Internet: http://www.galenahistorymuseum.org. Head: Daryl Watson
Local Museum - 1938
Local history, civil war, lead mining, clothing, geology, dolls and toys 37072

Old Market House, Market Sq, Galena, IL 61036 - T: (815) 777-3310, Fax: (815) 777-3310, Internet: http://www.state.il.us/hpa. Head: Daniel F. Tindell
Historical Museum - 1947
Greek Revival-style Market House 37073

United States Grant's Home, 500 Bouthillier St, Galena, IL 61036 - T: (815) 777-3310, Fax: (815) 777-3310, E-mail: ebwgalena@hotmail.com, Internet: http://www.state.il.us/hpa. Head: Terry J. Miller
Historical Museum - 1932
Italianate bracketed style house presented to Gen. Grant in 1865 37074

Galesburg IL

Carl Sandburg State Historic Site, 331 E 3rd St, Galesburg, IL 61401 - T: (309) 342-2361, Fax: (309) 342-2141, E-mail: carl@sandburg.org, Internet: http://www.sandburg.org. Head: Carol Nelson
Historical Museum - 1945
Immigrant railroad worker's cottage 37075

Galesburg Civic Art Center, 114 E Main St, Galesburg, IL 61401 - T: (309) 342-7415, E-mail: artcenter@misslink.net, Internet: http://www.artcenter.com. Head: Julie E. Layer
Public Gallery - 1923 37076

Illinois Citizen Soldier Museum, 1001 Michigan Av, Galesburg, IL 61401 - T: (309) 342-1181
Military Museum - 1988 37077

Galesville MD

Carrie Weedon Natural Science Museum, 911 Galesville Rd, Galesville, MD 20765 - T: (410) 222-1625, Fax: (410) 867-0588. Head: Hugo Gemignani
Natural History Museum / Science&Tech Museum - 1988
Natural history and science 37078

Galeton PA

Pennsylvania Lumber Museum, US Rte 6, Galeton, PA 16922 - T: (814) 435-2652, Fax: (814) 435-6361. Head: Robert Currin
Historical Museum / Natural History Museum - 1970 37079

Galion OH

Brownella Cottage, 132 S Union St, Galion, OH 44833 - T: (419) 468-9338. Head: Jerry A. Lantz
Local Museum - 1981 37080

Galion Historical Museum, 132 S Union St, Galion, OH 44833 - T: (419) 468-9338. Head: Dr. Bernard M. Mansfield
Local Museum - 1986 37081

Gallipolis OH

French Art Colony, 530 First Av, Gallipolis, OH 45631 - T: (740) 446-3834, Fax: (740) 446-3834, E-mail: facart@zoomnet.net. Head: Mary Bea McCalla
Fine Arts Museum - 1971 37082

Our House State Memorial, 434 First Av, Gallipolis, OH 45631 - T: (740) 446-0586
Historical Museum - 1933 37083

Galveston TX

Ashton Villa, 2328 Broadway, Galveston, TX 77550 - T: (409) 762-3933, Fax: (409) 762-1904, E-mail: foundation@galvestonhistory.org, Internet: http://www.galvestonhistory.org
Local Museum - 1974
Historic house 37084

The Bishop's Palace, 1402 Broadway, Galveston, TX 77550 - T: (409) 762-2475, Fax: (409) 762-1801. Head: Tom Hunter
Local Museum - 1886
Historic building 37085

Galveston Arts Center, 2127 Strand, Galveston, TX 77550 - T: (409) 763-2403, Fax: (409) 763-0531, E-mail: galartsctr@aol.com. Head: Clint Willour
Fine Arts Museum
Art 37086

Galveston County Historical Museum, 2219 Market St, Galveston, TX 77550 - T: (409) 766-2340, Fax: (409) 795-2157, E-mail: Jone.Johnson@galvestonhistory.org, Internet: http://www.galvestonhistory.org. Head: Jane C. Johnson
Historical Museum - 1972
Local hist 37087

John Sydnor's 1847 Powhatan House, 3427 Avenue O, Galveston, TX 77550 - T: (409) 763-0077, Fax: (409) 744-1456. Head: Mary Faye Barnes
Local Museum - 1938
Historic house 37088

Lone Star Flight Museum/Texas Aviation Hall of Fame, 2002 Terminal Dr, Galveston, TX 77552-099 - T: (409) 740-7722, Fax: (409) 740-7612, E-mail: flight@lsfm.org, Internet: http://www.lsfm.org. Head: Ralph Royce
Military Museum / Science&Tech Museum - 1986
Aeronautics 37089

Moody Mansion Museum, 2618 Broadway, Galveston, TX 77550 - T: (409) 762-7668, 765-9770, Fax: (409) 762-7055. Head: Betty Massey
Historical Museum / Decorative Arts Museum - 1991
History, decorative arts, costume, textiles 37090

Texas Seaport Museum, Pier 21, 8, Galveston, TX 77550 - T: (409) 763-1877, Fax: (409) 763-3037, E-mail: elissa@galvestonhistory.org, Internet: http://www.tsm-elissa.org. Head: Fred Micks, Kurt Voss
Historical Museum - 1982
Maritime hist 37091

Ganado AZ

Hubbell Trading Post National Historic Site, Hwy 264, Ganado, AZ 86505 - T: (520) 755-3475, Fax: (520) 755-3405, E-mail: E_chamberlin@nps.gov, Internet: http://www.nps.gov/hutr/
Historical Museum / Historic Site - 1967
Historic Site 37092

Garden City KS

Finney County Kansas Historical Museum, Finnup Park, S 4th, Garden City, KS 67846-0796 - T: (316) 272-3664, Fax: (316) 272-3662, E-mail: fico.historical@gcnet.com. Head: Mary Regan
Historical Museum - 1949
Local history - library 37093

Garden City NY

Firehouse Art Gallery, Nassau Community College, 1 Education Dr, Garden City, NY 11530 - T: (516) 572-7165, Fax: (516) 572-7302
University Museum / Fine Arts Museum - 1965 37094

Long Island Children's Museum, 550 Stewart Av, Garden City, NY 11530 - T: (516) 222-0217, Fax: (516) 222-0225, E-mail: licm1@aol.com, Internet: http://www.licm.org. Head: Robert Lemle, Bonnie Dixon
Special Museum - 1990 37095

Gardner MA

Gardner Museum, 28 Pearl St, Gardner, MA 01440 - T: (978) 632-3277. Head: Donald Gearan
Fine Arts Museum / Local Museum - 1978
Local history, Richardson Romanesque brick bldg 37096

Garfield AR

Pea Ridge National Military Park, 15930 Hwy 62, Garfield, AR 72732 - T: (501) 451-8122, Fax: (501) 451-8635, Internet: http://www.nps.gov/peri/. Head: Steve Adams
Military Museum - 1960
Reconstructed Elkhorn tavern 37097

Garnavillo IA

Garnavillo Historical Museum, 205 N Washington, Garnavillo, IA 52049 - T: (319) 964-2341, Fax: (319) 964-2485, E-mail: gsb@netins.net. Head: Kurt Kuenzel
Local Museum - 1965
Local history, housed in a church 37098

Garnett KS

Anderson County Historical Museum, W 6th St, Garnett, KS 66032-0217 - T: (785) 867-2966, 448-5740, E-mail: ancohiso@karza.net. Head: Dorothy L. Lickteig
Local Museum / Folklore Museum - 1968
Local hist, home and carriage house of Dr. Harris, Longfellow school building 37099

Walker Art Collection of the Garnett Public Library, 125 W 4th Av, Garnett, KS 66032 - T: (913) 448-3388, Fax: (913) 448-3936, E-mail: garnett@kanza.net, Internet: http://www.kanza.net/garnett. Head: Douglas Archer
Fine Arts Museum - 1965
Art gallery 37100

Garrett IN

Garrett Historical Museum, Heritage Park, 300 N Randolph St, Garrett, IN 46738 - T: (219) 357-5575, E-mail: jmohre@locl.net
Local Museum / Science&Tech Museum - 1971
Local history, 3 railroad cars, diesel locomotive 37101

Garrison NY

Boscobel Restoration, 1601 Rte 9D, Garrison, NY 10524 - T: (845) 265-3638, Fax: (845) 265-4405, E-mail: info@boscobel.org, Internet: http://www.boscobel.org. Head: Charles T. Lyle
Decorative Arts Museum / Historical Museum - 1955 37102

Gastonia NC

Schiele Museum of Natural History, 1500 E Garrison Blvd, Gastonia, NC 28054-5199 - T: (704) 866-6900, Fax: (704) 866-6041, E-mail: dbrose@schielemuseum.org, Internet: http://www.schielemuseum.org
Natural History Museum / Ethnology Museum - 1960
Natural hist, ethnography, colonial hist 37103

Gate OK

Gateway to the Panhandle, Main St, Gate, OK 73844 - T: (405) 934-2004. Head: L. Ernestine Maphet
Local Museum / Historical Museum - 1975 37104

Gates Mills OH

Gates Mills Historical Society Museum, 7580 Old Mill Rd, Gates Mills, OH 44040 - T: (440) 423-4808, Fax: (440) 423-4808. Head: Harriet Leedy
Local Museum - 1946 37105

Gatlinburg TN

Arrowmont School of Arts and Crafts Collection, 556 Pkwy, Gatlinburg, TN 37738 - T: (423) 436-5860, Fax: (423) 430-4101, E-mail: arrowmnt@aol.com, Internet: http://www.arrowmont.org. Head: Sandra J. Blain
Fine Arts Museum / Decorative Arts Museum - 1945
Arts and crafts 37106

Gaylord MI

Call of the Wild Museum, 850 S Wisconsin Av, Gaylord, MI 49735 - T: (517) 732-4336, Fax: (517) 732-4087. Head: Candiss Van Overbeke, Janis Vollmer
Natural History Museum - 1957
Natural history 37107

Geddes SD

Geddes Historic District Village, Box 97, Geddes, SD 57342 - T: (605) 337-2501. Head: John Steckley
Local Museum - 1969
Local hist, old items from 1850-1910 era 37108

Geneseo NY

Bertha V.B. Lederer Fine Arts Gallery, SUNY at Geneseo, Fine Arts Bldg, 1 College Circle, Geneseo, NY 14454 - T: (716) 245-5814, Fax: (716) 245-5815, E-mail: shanahan@uno.cc.geneseo.edu. Head: Carl Shanahan
Fine Arts Museum / University Museum - 1967 37109

Livingston County Historical Society Museum, 30 Center St, Geneseo, NY 14454 - T: (716) 243-2281, Internet: http://www.rootsweb.com/~nyliving/lchs. Head: Alberta Dunn
Historical Museum - 1876 37110

Geneva IN

Limberlost State Historic Site, 200 East 6th St, Geneva, IN 46740 - T: (219) 368-7428, Fax: (219) 368-7007, E-mail: limberlost@adamswells.com, Internet: http://www.genestrattonporter.net
Special Museum - 1947
Home of Gene Stratton-Porter, author and naturalist 37111

Geneva NY

Prouty-Chew Museum, 543 S Main St, Geneva, NY 14456 - T: (315) 789-5151, Fax: (315) 789-0314, E-mail: genevhst@flare.net
Historical Museum - 1883 37112

Rose Hill Mansion, Rte 96A, Geneva, NY 14456 - T: (315) 789-5151, Fax: (315) 789-0314, E-mail: genevehst@flare.net
Historical Museum - 1968 37113

Geneva OH

Platt R. Spencer Special Collections and Archival Room, 860 Sherman St, Geneva, OH 44041-9101 - T: (440) 466-4521 ext 107, Fax: (440) 466-0162, E-mail: acgs@suite224.net, Internet: http://www.ashtabula.lib.oh.us/geneva.htm. Head: William Tokarczyk
Special Museum - 1988
Archive 37114

Shandy Hall, 6333 S Ridge, Geneva, OH 44041 - T: (216) 466-3680. Head: Byron Robertson
Historical Museum - 1937 37115

Gentryville IN

Colonel William Jones House, 3/4 m W of U.S. Hwy 231, on Boone St, Gentryville, IN 47537 - T: (812) 937-2802, Fax: (812) 937-7038, E-mail: coljones@psci.net, Internet: http://www.state.in.us/ism/sites/jones. Head: Peggy Brooks
Historical Museum - 1976 37116

Georgetown CO

Historic Georgetown, 305 Argentine, Georgetown, CO 80444 - T: (303) 569-2840, Fax: (303) 674-2625, E-mail: preservation@historicgeorgetown.org, Internet: http://www.historicgeorgetown.org. Head: Jeanne Waligroski
Open Air Museum / Local Museum - 1970
William A. Hamill house and office bldg, stable and carriage house, Bowman-White house; Tucker-Rutherford house; Miner's cottage, log cabin 37117

Hotel de Paris Museum, 409 6th Av, Georgetown, CO 80444 - T: (303) 569-2311, Fax: (303) 756-8768, E-mail: mrc6118@aol.com, Internet: http://www.historicgeorgetown.org/georgetown
Historical Museum - 1875 37118

Georgetown DE

Treasures of the Sea Exhibit, Delaware Technical and Community College, Rte 18, Georgetown, DE 19947 - T: (302) 856-5700, Fax: (302) 858-5462, E-mail: treasuresdtcc.edu, Internet: http://www.treasuresofthesea.org. Head: Barbara S. Ridgely
Natural History Museum - 1988 37119

Georgetown SC

Hopsewee Plantation, 494 Hopsewee Rd, Georgetown, SC 29440 - T: (803) 546-7891. Head: Helen B. Maynard
Local Museum - 1970
Historic house, birthplace of Thomas Lynch Jr., signer of the Declaration of Independence 37120

Kaminski House Museum, 1003 Front St, Georgetown, SC 29440 - T: (843) 546-7706, Fax: (843) 546-2126. Head: Katrina P. Lawrimore, Alice Williams
Local Museum - 1973
Historic house 37121

The Rice Museum, Lafayette Park, Front and Screven Sts, Georgetown, SC 29440 - T: (843) 546-7423, Fax: (843) 545-9093, Internet: http://www.distrand.com/rice. Head: James A. Fitch
Historical Museum - 1968
History 37122

Gering NE

North Platte Valley Museum, 11 and J Sts, near Hwys 92 and 71, Gering, NE 69341 - T: (308) 436-5411, E-mail: npvm@actcom.net, Internet: http://www.wyobraskagold.com/npvmuseum/index. Head: John Versluis
Local Museum - 1969 37123

Oregon Trail Museum, Scotts Bluff National Monument, Hwy 92 W, Gering, NE 69341 - T: (308) 436-4340, Fax: (308) 436-7611, Internet: http://www.nps.gov/scbl
Historical Museum - 1919
Geology, prehistory, archaeology, ethnological history, history of Western migration 37124

Scotts Bluff National Monument, 190276 Hwy 92, Gering, NE 69341-0027 - T: (308) 436-4340, Fax: (308) 436-7611
Archaeological Museum - 1919
History 37125

Germantown TN

P.T. Boat Museum, POB 38070, Germantown, TN 38138 - T: (901) 755-8440, Fax: (901) 751-0522, Internet: http://www.ptboats.org. Head: Alyce N. Guthrie
Historical Museum / Military Museum - 1946
Maritime, naval history, at Battleship Cove, WW II - archives 37126

Gettysburg PA

Eisenhower National Historic Site, 250 Eisenhower Farm Ln, Gettysburg, PA 17325 - T: (717) 338-9114, Fax: (717) 338-0821, E-mail: eise_site_manager@nps.gov, Internet: http://www.nps.gov/eise
Historical Museum - 1967
Presidential and retirement home of Dwight D. Eisenhower 37127

Gettysburg National Military Park, 97 Taneytown Rd, Gettysburg, PA 17325 - T: (717) 334-1124, Fax: (717) 334-1891, E-mail: gett_curator@nps.gov, Internet: http://www.nps.gov/gett. Head: Dr. John A. Latschar
Historic Site / Military Museum / Open Air Museum - 1895 37128

Ghent NY

Parker-O'Malley Air Museum, 1571 Rte 66, Ghent, NY 12075 - T: (518) 392-7200, Fax: (518) 392-2408, E-mail: parkeromalley@netscape.net. Head: James E. McMahon
Science&Tech Museum - 1991
Aeronautics 37129

Gig Harbor WA

Gig Harbor Peninsula Historical Society Museum, 4218 Harborview Dr, Gig Harbor, WA 98332 - T: (253) 858-6722, Fax: (253) 853-4211, E-mail: ghphs@harbornet.com, Internet: http://www.gigharbormuseum.org. Head: Chris Fiala Erlich
Historical Museum - 1962
Local hist 37130

Gillett AR

Arkansas Post Museum, 5530 Hwy 165 S, Gillett, AR 72055 - T: (870) 548-2634, E-mail: arkpost@futura.net, Internet: http://www.arkansas.com. Head: Lillie Fuhrman
Local Museum - 1960
Local history 37131

Arkansas Post National Memorial, 1741 Old Post Rd, Gillett, AR 72055 - T: (870) 548-2207, Fax: (870) 548-2431, E-mail: arpo/nps.gov.www, Internet: http://www.gov.nps./arpo. Head: Edward Wood
Historical Museum - 1964 37132

Gillette WY

Campbell County Rockpile Museum, 900 W 2nd St, Gillette, WY 82716 - T: (307) 682-5723, Fax: (307) 686-8528, E-mail: rockpile@vcn.com, Internet: http://www.gillettewyoming.com/rockpile/. Head: Robert J. Kothe
Local Museum - 1974
Local hist 37133

Gilmanton NH

Carpenter Museum of Antique Outboard Motors, POB 459, Gilmanton, NH 03237-0459 - T: (603) 524-7611, Fax: (603) 524-7611, E-mail: amc@cyberportal.net
Special Museum / Science&Tech Museum - 1976
Marine technology 37134

Gilroy CA

Gilroy Historical Museum, 195 Fifth St, Gilroy, CA 95020 - T: (408) 848-0470, 846-0460, Fax: (408) 842-2409. Head: Cathy Mirelez
Local Museum - 1958
Local history 37135

Glasgow MT

Valley County Pioneer Museum, Hwy 2 W, Glasgow, MT 59230 - T: (406) 228-8692, Fax: (406) 228-4601
Historical Museum - 1964 37136

Glastonbury CT

Historical Society of Glastonbury Museum, 1944 Main St, Glastonbury, CT 06033 - T: (860) 633-6890, Fax: (860) 633-6890, E-mail: hsglastonbury@netzero.net. Head: James Bennett, Susan G. Motycka
Historical Museum - 1936 37137

Glen Echo MD

Clara Barton Home, 5801 Oxford Rd, Glen Echo, MD 20812 - T: (301) 492-6245, Fax: (301) 492-5384, E-mail: gwmp_clara_barton_nhs@nps.gov, Internet: http://www.nps.gov/clba
Historical Museum - 1975
Home of Clara Barton, founder of the American Red Cross 37138

Glen Ellen CA

Jack London State Historic Park, House of Happy Walls, 2400 London Ranch Rd, Glen Ellen, CA 95442 - T: (707) 938-5216, Fax: (707) 938-4827, Internet: http://www.parks.sonoma.net
Natural History Museum - 1959 37139

Glen Ellyn IL

Stacy's Tavern Museum and Glen Ellyn Historical Society, 557 Geneva Rd, Glen Ellyn, IL 60137, mail addr: POB 283, Glen Ellyn, IL 60138 - T: (630) 858-8696, Fax: (630) 858-8696, Internet: http://www.glen-ellyn.com/historical/. Head: John Costersian, Barbara Bishop
Local Museum - 1976
1846 Moses Stacy House and Inn, local Glen Ellyn history - archive 37140

Glen Rose TX

Barnard's Mill Art Museum, 307 SW Barnard St, Glen Rose, TX 76043 - T: (817) 897-2611. Head: Richard H. Moore
Fine Arts Museum - 1989
Art 37141

Dinosaur Valley State Park, FM 205, Glen Rose, TX 76043 - T: (817) 897-4588, Fax: (817) 897-3409, E-mail: dinosaur@hcnews.com, Internet: http://www.tpwd.state.tx.us. Head: Billy P. Baker
Natural History Museum - 1969
Paleontology 37142

Somervell County Museum, Elm & Vernon Sts, Glen Rose, TX 76043 - T: (254) 897-4529. Head: Jeanne P. Mack
Local Museum - 1966
Local hist 37143

Glendale CA

Brand Library and Art Galleries, 1601 W Mountain St, Glendale, CA 91201-1200 - T: (818) 548-2051, Fax: (818) 548-5079, Internet: http://library.ci.glendale.ca.us/brand. Head: Jill Conner
Library with Exhibitions / Fine Arts Museum - 1956 37144

Casa Adobe de San Rafael, 1330 Dorothy Dr, Glendale, CA 91202 - T: (818) 548-2000, Fax: (818) 548-3789. Head: Helen Gregory
Historical Museum - 1867 37145

Forest Lawn Museum, 1712 S Glendale Av, Glendale, CA 91205 - T: (323) 254-3131, Fax: (323) 551-5329. Head: Margaret Burton
Local Museum / Historical Museum - 1951 37146

Glenford OH

Flint Ridge State Memorial Museum, 7091 Brownsville Rd SE, Glenford, OH 43739-9609 - T: (800) 283-8707
Natural History Museum - 1933 37147

Glenn Dale MD

Marietta Historic House, 5626 Bell Station Rd, Glenn Dale, MD 20769 - T: (301) 464-5291, Fax: (301) 456-5654, E-mail: smwolfe@pgparks.com. Head: Susan Wolfe
Local Museum - 1988
Federal style brick home 37148

Glens Falls NY

Chapman Historical Museum, 348 Glen St, Glens Falls, NY 12801 - T: (518) 793-2826, Fax: (519) 793-2831
Historical Museum - 1967 37149

Hyde Collection Art Museum, 161 Warren St, Glens Falls, NY 12801 - T: (518) 792-1761, Fax: (518) 792-9197, E-mail: info@hydeartmuseum.org, Internet: http://www.hydeartmuseum.org. Head: Randall Suffolk
Fine Arts Museum - 1952
European and American art by Raphael, Da Vinci, Rubens, Rembrandt, Cézanne, Renoir, Van Gogh, Picasso, Whistler, Eakins, Homer 37150

Glenside PA

Beaver College Art Gallery, Church and Easton Rds, Glenside, PA 19038 - T: (215) 572-2131, Fax: (215) 881-8774, E-mail: torchia@beaver.edu, Internet: http://www.beaver.edu. Head: Richard Torchia
University Museum / Fine Arts Museum - 1853 37151

Glenview IL

Glenview Area Historical Museum, 1121 Waukegan Rd, Glenview, IL 60025 - T: (847) 724-2235
Local Museum - 1965
Local history, housed in original 1864 farm house - library 37152

Hartung's Auto and License Plate Museum, 3623 W Lake St, Glenview, IL 60025 - T: (847) 724-4354. Head: Lee Hartung
Science&Tech Museum - 1971
Automotive, over 150 antique cars, trucks, tractors and motorcycles 37153

Glenville NY

Empire State Aerosciences Museum, 250 Rudy Chase Dr, Glenville, NY 12302 - T: (518) 377-2191, Fax: (518) 377-1959, E-mail: esam@crisny.org, Internet: http://www.cana.cam/esam. Head: Nanci Conley, Robert L. Burroughs
Science&Tech Museum - 1984
Aerosciences and airplane 37154

Glenwood IA

Mills County Museum, Lake Park, Glenwood, IA 51534 - T: (712) 527-5038, 527-9533, E-mail: carriemerritt@hotmail.com. Head: Carrie Merrit
Local Museum - 1957
Local history 37155

Glenwood MN

Pope County Historical Museum, 809 S Lakeshore Dr, Glenwood, MN 56334-1115 - T: (320) 634-3293, Fax: (320) 634-3293, E-mail: pcmuseum@runestone.net. Head: Merlin Peterson
Fine Arts Museum / Historical Museum / Open Air Museum - 1931
Regional history, native American crafts 37156

Globe AZ

Gila County Historical Museum, 1330 N Broad St, Globe, AZ 85502 - T: (520) 425-7385. Head: Dr. Bill Haak
Local Museum / Archaeological Museum - 1972 37157

Gloucester MA

Beauport-Sleeper-McCann House, 75 Eastern Point Blvd, Gloucester, MA 01930, mail addr: 141 Cambridge St, Boston, MA 02114 - T: (978) 283-0800, (617) 227-3956, Fax: (617) 277-2904, E-mail: beauporthouse@spnea.org, Internet: http://www.spnea.org
Historical Museum - 1942
40-room summer cottage 37158

Cape Ann Historical Museum, 27 Pleasant St, Gloucester, MA 01930 - T: (978) 283-0455, Fax: (978) 283-4141, Internet: www.cape-ann.com/historical-museum. Head: Judith McCulloch, Harold Bell
Historical Museum / Fine Arts Museum - 1873
Maritime history, art 37159

Hammond Castle Museum, 80 Hesperus Av, Gloucester, MA 01930 - T: (508) 283-7673, 283-2080, Fax: (508) 283-1643, Internet: http://www.hammondcastle.org
Historical Museum - 1930
Castle built in 1928 37160

The North Shore Arts Association, 197 E Main St at Pirate's Ln, Gloucester, MA 01930 - T: (978) 283-1857, Fax: (978) 282-9189, E-mail: wwwarts@gis.net, Internet: http://www.shore.net/~nya/NSA.html. Head: Trudy J. Allen, Anne Krapish
Association with Coll - 1922
Art gallery   37161

Glover VT

Bread & Puppet Museum, RD2, Rte 122, Glover, VT 05839 - T: (802) 525-3031, 525-6972, Fax: (802) 525-3618. Head: Peter Schumann
Decorative Arts Museum - 1975
Puppets   37162

Gnadenhutten OH

Gnadenhutten Historical Park and Museum, 352 S Cherry St, Gnadenhutten, OH 44629 - T: (614) 254-4143, Fax: (614) 254-4986, E-mail: gnadmuse@tusc.net, Internet: http://www.tusco.net/gnaden. Head: Jack J. McKeown
Local Museum - 1963   37163

Goehner NE

Seward County Historical Society Museum, I-80 Exit 373, Goehner, NE - T: (402) 643-4935, 523-4055, E-mail: drouss//@connect.ccsn.edu
Local Museum / Agriculture Museum - 1978
Local history, agriculture   37164

Goessel KS

Mennonite Heritage Museum, 200 N Poplar St, Goessel, KS 67053 - T: (316) 367-8200. Head: Dwight Schmidt, Kristine Schmucker
Historical Museum - 1974
History   37165

Golden CO

Astor House Hotel Museum, 822 12th St, Golden, CO 80401 - T: (303) 278-3557, Fax: (303) 278-3557, E-mail: ahmuseum@aol.com, Internet: http://www.astorhousemuseum.org
Historical Museum - 1972   37166

Buffalo Bill Memorial Museum, 987.5 Lookout Mountain Rd, Golden, CO 80401 - T: (303) 526-0747, Fax: (303) 526-0197, Internet: http://www.buffalobill.org. Head: Steve Friesen
Historical Museum - 1921
Founded by Johnny Baker, a close friend of Buffalo Bill and an important member of Buffalo Bill's Wild West Show   37167

Colorado Railroad Museum, 17155 W 44th Av, Golden, CO 80403 - T: (303) 279-4591, Fax: (303) 279-4229, Internet: http://www.crrm.org. Head: Charles Albi
Science&Tech Museum - 1958
Railroad   37168

Colorado School of Mines Geology Museum, 16th and Maple, Golden, CO 80401-1887 - T: (303) 273-3823, 273-3815, Fax: (303) 273-3859, E-mail: pbartos@mives.edu, Internet: http://www.magma.mines.edu/academics/geology/museum. Head: Paul I. Bartos
University Museum / Natural History Museum - 1874
Geology, mineralogy   37169

Rocky Mountain Quilt Museum, 1111 Washington Av, Golden, CO 80401 - T: (303) 277-0377, Fax: (303) 215-1636, E-mail: rmqm@worldnet.att.net, Internet: http://www.rmqm.org. Head: Janet Finley
Folklore Museum / Special Museum - 1982
Quilts   37170

Goldendale WA

Klickitat County Historical Society Museum, 127 W Broadway, Goldendale, WA 98620 - T: (509) 773-4303. Head: Denise Morris
Local Museum - 1958
Local hist   37171

Maryhill Museum of Art, 35 Maryhill Museum Dr, Goldendale, WA 98620 - T: (509) 773-3733, Fax: (509) 773-6138, E-mail: maryhill@gorge.net, Internet: http://www.maryhillmuseum.org. Head: Josie E. De Falla
Fine Arts Museum - 1923
Art   37172

Goldsboro NC

Community Arts Council Museum, 901 E Ash St, Goldsboro, NC 27530 - T: (919) 736-3300, Fax: (919) 736-3335. Head: Alice Strickland
Fine Arts Museum - 1971   37173

Goleta CA

Air Heritage Museum of Santa Barbara/Goleta, 601 Firestone Rd, Goleta, CA 93117 - T: (805) 683-8936. Head: H. Ben Walsh
Military Museum / Science&Tech Museum - 1989
Military hist, aviation   37174

South Coast Railroad Museum at Goleta Depot, 300 N Los Carneros Rd, Goleta, CA 93117 - T: (805) 964-3540, Fax: (805) 964-3549, E-mail: director@goletadepot.org, Internet: http://www.goletadepot.org. Head: Gary B. Coombs
Science&Tech Museum - 1983
Southern Pacific railroad depot   37175

Stow House, Museum of Goleta Valley History, 304 N Los Carneros Rd, Goleta, CA 93117 - T: (805) 964-4407, Fax: (805) 681-7217
Historical Museum / Local Museum - 1967   37176

Goliad TX

Goliad State Historical Park, 108 Park Rd, Goliad, TX 77963 - T: (361) 645-3405, Fax: (361) 645-8538. Head: Andrew Sansom
Local Museum / Folklore Museum - 1937
Local hist   37177

Presidio La Bahia, Refugio Hwy, 1 mile south of Goliad on Hwy 183, Goliad, TX 77963 - T: (512) 645-3752, Fax: (512) 645-1706, Internet: http://www.nazarethtoday.com/mhs. Head: Newton M. Warzecha
Military Museum / Historic Site / Archaeological Museum - 1966
Military hist   37178

Gonzales TX

Gonzales Memorial Museum, E Saint Lawrence St, Gonzales, TX 78629 - T: (210) 672-6350. Head: Mary Bea Arnold
Local Museum - 1936
Local hist   37179

Goochland VA

Goochland County Museum, POB 602, Goochland, VA 23063 - T: (804) 556-3966, Fax: (804) 556-4617
Library with Exhibitions - 1968
Land grant parents (1700's)   37180

Goodland KS

High Plains Museum, 1717 Cherry, Goodland, KS 67735 - T: (913) 899-4595. Head: Linda Holton
Historical Museum - 1959
History   37181

Goodwell OK

No Man's Land Historical Museum, 207 W Sewell St, Goodwell, OK 73939 - T: (580) 349-2670, Fax: (580) 349-2670, E-mail: nmlhs@ptsi.net. Head: Dr. Kenneth R. Turner, Gerald Dixon
Historical Museum - 1932   37182

Gordonsville VA

Exchange Hotel Civil War Museum, 400 S Main St, Gordonsville, VA 22942 - T: (540) 832-2944, E-mail: sturkhntr@aol.com, Internet: http://www.gemlink.com/~exchange-hotel/. Head: Andy Daniel
Historical Museum / Military Museum - 1971
Civil war, railroad hotel used as a Confederate receiving hospital   37183

Gorham ME

Baxter House Museum, 71 S St, Gorham, ME 04038 - T: (207) 839-5031, Fax: (207) 839-7749. Head: Linda M. Frinsko
Local Museum - 1908   37184

USM Art Gallery, Campus, 37 College Av, Gorham, ME 04038 - T: (207) 780-5008, Fax: (207) 780-5759, E-mail: cexler@usm.maine.edu, Internet: http://www.usm.maine.edu/~gallery. Head: Carolyn Eyler
Fine Arts Museum / University Museum - 1965
Art   37185

Goshen CT

Goshen Historical Society Museum, 21 Old Middle Rd, Goshen, CT 06756 - T: (860) 491-9610. Head: Margaret K. Wood
Historical Museum - 1955   37186

Goshen NY

Harness Racing Museum and Hall of Fame, 240 Main St, Goshen, NY 10924 - T: (845) 294-6330, Fax: (845) 294-3463, Internet: http://www.harnessmuseum.com. Head: Gail C. Cunard
Special Museum - 1951   37187

Gothenburg NE

Sod House Museum, I-80 and Hwy 47, Gothenburg, NE 69138 - T: (308) 537-2680. Head: Merle Block
Local Museum - 1988
Local hist   37188

Gouverneur NY

Gouverneur Historical Association Museum, 30 Church St, Gouverneur, NY 13642 - T: (315) 287-0570
Historical Museum - 1974   37189

Grafton MA

Willard House and Clock Museum, 11 Willard St, Grafton, MA 01536 - T: (508) 839-3500, Fax: (508) 839-3599, E-mail: willardhouse@erols.com, Internet: http://www.nawcc.org/museum/willard/. Head: Dr. Roger W. Robinson
Science&Tech Museum - 1971
Horology   37190

Grafton VT

Grafton Museum, Main St, Grafton, VT 05146 - T: (802) 843-2584, 843-2594
Local Museum - 1962
Local hist   37191

Grafton Museum of Natural History, 186 Townshend Rd, Grafton, VT 05146 - T: (802) 843-2111, E-mail: info@nature-museum.org, Internet: http://www.nature-museum.org
Natural History Museum - 1987
Natural hist   37192

Granby CT

Salmon Brook Historical Society Museum, 208 Salmon Brook St, Granby, CT 06035 - T: (860) 653-9713, Internet: http://www.harborside.com/home/p/p2241/sbhs.html
Historical Museum - 1959   37193

Grand Canyon AZ

Grand Canyon National Park Museum Collection, Village, South Rim, Grand Canyon, AZ 86023, mail addr: POB 129, Grand Canyon, AZ 86023 - T: (520) 638-7769, Fax: (520) 638-7797, E-mail: GRCA_Museum_Collection@nps.gov. Head: Robert Arnberger
Natural History Museum - 1919
Deep gorge of the Colorado River, 277 mi long, 1-18 mi wide, 1 mi deep   37194

Grand Forks ND

Grand Forks County Historical Society Museum, 2405 Belmont Rd, Grand Forks, ND 58201 - T: (701) 775-2216. Head: Jack Lien, Ted Jelliff
Historical Museum - 1970   37195

North Dakota Museum of Art, Centennial Dr, Grand Forks, ND 58202 - T: (701) 777-4195, Fax: (701) 777-4425, E-mail: ndmuseum@infi.net, Internet: http://www.ndmoa.com. Head: Laurel J. Reuter
Fine Arts Museum - 1970   37196

University of North Dakota Zoology Museum, Dept of Biology, University of North Dakota, Grand Forks, ND 58202 - T: (701) 777-2621, Fax: (701) 777-2623, Internet: http://www.und.edu/dept/biology/undergrad/bio_undergrad.html
University Museum / Natural History Museum - 1883   37197

Grand Haven MI

Tri-Cities Museum, 1 N Harbor, Grand Haven, MI 49417 - T: (616) 842-0700, Fax: (616) 842-0379, E-mail: tcmuseum@grandhaven.com, Internet: http://www.grandhaven.com/museum. Head: Elizabeth Kammeraad
Local Museum - 1962
Regional history   37198

Grand Island NE

Stuhr Museum of the Prairie Pioneer, 3133 W Hwy 34, Grand Island, NE 68801 - T: (308) 385-5316, Fax: (308) 385-5028, Internet: http://www.stuhrmuseum.org. Head: Fred W. Goss
Local Museum - 1961   37199

Grand Junction CO

Children's Museum of Western Colorado, 248 Colorado Av, Grand Junction, CO 81501 - T: (970) 241-5225, Fax: (970) 241-8510
Special Museum - 1984   37200

Museum of Western Colorado, 462 Ute, Grand Junction, CO 81502 - T: (970) 242-0971, Fax: (970) 242-3960, E-mail: sdavis@westcomuseum.org, Internet: http://www.wcmuseum.org. Head: Richard S. Helm
Local Museum - 1966
Cultural and natural history, paleontology, farming   37201

Western Colorado Center for the Arts, 1803 N 7th, Grand Junction, CO 81501 - T: (970) 243-7337, Fax: (970) 243-2482, E-mail: arts@gict.net, Internet: http://www.giartcenter.org. Head: Dan W. Patten
Fine Arts Museum / Decorative Arts Museum - 1953
Arts, crafts   37202

Grand Lake CO

Grand Lake Area Historical Museum, Kauffman House, Lake Av at Pitkin St, Grand Lake, CO 80447-0656 - T: (970) 627-9277
Local Museum - 1973
Regional history   37203

Grand Marais MN

Cook County Historical Museum, 4 N Broadway, Grand Marais, MN 55604 - T: (218) 387-2883, E-mail: cchristsoc@boreal.org. Head: Pat Zankman
Local Museum - 1966
Regional history   37204

Grand Portage, 315 S Broadway, Grand Marais, MN 55604 - T: (218) 387-2788, Fax: (218) 387-2790, E-mail: grpo_admin_clerk@nps.gov, Internet: http://www.nps.gov/grpo. Head: Tim Cochrane
Historical Museum - 1958
18thc reconstructed NW Co. fur trading depot   37205

Johnson Heritage Post, 115 W Wisconsin St, Grand Marais, MN 55604 - T: (218) 387-2314, E-mail: cchristsoc@boreal.org. Head: D. Anderson
Fine Arts Museum - 1966
Art gallery   37206

Grand Rapids MI

Center Art Gallery, c/o Calvin College, 3201 Burton St SE, Grand Rapids, MI 49546 - T: (616) 957-6326, Fax: (616) 957-8551, E-mail: bullock@calvin.edu, Internet: http://www.calvin.edu. Head: Charles Young
Fine Arts Museum / University Museum - 1974
Drawings, prints, sculpture, textiles, ceramics   37207

Gerald R. Ford Library Museum, 303 Pearl St NW, Grand Rapids, MI 49504 - T: (616) 451-9263 ext 21, Fax: (616) 451-9570, E-mail: ford.museum@nara.gov, Internet: http://www.ford.utexas.edu. Head: Dennis Daellenbach
Library with Exhibitions / Historical Museum - 1980
Presidential library   37208

Grand Rapids Art Museum, 155 Division N, Grand Rapids, MI 49503 - T: (616) 831-1000, 831-2929, Fax: (616) 559-0422, E-mail: pr@gr-artmuseum.org, Internet: http://www.gramonline.org. Head: Celeste M. Adams
Fine Arts Museum - 1910
Art   37209

Grand Rapids Children's Museum, 11 Sheldon Av, Grand Rapids, MI 49503 - T: (616) 235-4726, Fax: (616) 235-4728, E-mail: akinsman@grcm.org, Internet: http://www.grcm.org. Head: Teresa L. Thome
Special Museum - 1992   37210

Public Museum of Grand Rapids, 272 Pearl St NW, Grand Rapids, MI 49504-5371 - T: (616) 456-3977, Fax: (616) 456-3873, E-mail: staff@grmuseum.org, Internet: http://www.grmuseum.org. Head: Timothy J. Chester
Local Museum - 1854
Local history, ethnology, natural history, astronomy   37211

Urban Institute for Contemporary Arts, 41 Sheldon Blvd SE, Grand Rapids, MI 49503 - T: (616) 454-7000, Fax: (616) 454-9395, E-mail: info@uica.org, Internet: http://www.uica.org. Head: Gail Philbin, Tom Clinton
Fine Arts Museum - 1977   37212

Grand Rapids MN

Forest History Center, 2609 County Rd 76, Grand Rapids, MN 55744 - T: (218) 327-4482, Fax: (218) 327-4483, E-mail: foresthistory@mnhs.org, Internet: http://www.mnhs.org
Natural History Museum - 1978
Natural hist   37213

Itasca Heritage Center Museum, 10-5th St NW, Grand Rapids, MN 55744-0664 - T: (218) 326-6431, Fax: (218) 326-7083, E-mail: ichs@paulbunyan.net. Head: Art Toms
Local Museum - 1948
Local history   37214

Grandview WA

Ray E. Powell Museum, 313 S Division, Grandview, WA 98930 - T: (509) 882-2070. Head: Jack Norting
Local Museum - 1969
Local hist   37215

Grant NE

Perkins County Historical Society Museum, Central Av, Grant, NE 69140 - T: (308) 352-4019. Head: Delores Swan
Local Museum - 1964   37216

Grants Pass OR

Grants Pass Museum of Art, 229 SW G St, Grants Pass, OR 97526 - T: (541) 479-3290, Fax: (541) 479-1218, E-mail: museum@grantspass.net. Head: Don Brown
Fine Arts Museum / Folklore Museum / Public Gallery - 1979   37217

Wiseman and Fire House Galleries, Rogue Community College, 3345 Redwood Hwy, Grants Pass, OR 97527 - T: (541) 956-7339, Fax: (541) 471-3588, E-mail: tdrake@rogue.cc.or.us, Internet: http://www.rogue.cc.or.us/. Head: Tommi Drake
Fine Arts Museum / University Museum - 1988
Art   37218

Granville NY

Pember Museum of Natural History, 33 W Main St, Granville, NY 12832 - T: (518) 642-1515, Fax: (518) 642-3097, E-mail: pember@adelphia.net, Internet: http://www.pembermuseum.com. Head: Patricia E. Bailey, Dan Wilson
Natural History Museum - 1909 37219

Granville OH

Denison University Art Gallery, Burke Hall, Granville, OH 43023 - T: (740) 587-6255, Fax: (740) 587-5701, E-mail: vanderheijde@cc.denison.edu, Internet: http://www.denison.edu/art/artgallery. Head: Merijn Van Der Heijden
Fine Arts Museum / University Museum - 1946 37220

Granville Historical Museum, 115 E Broadway, Granville, OH 43023 - T: (740) 587-3951, E-mail: - granvillehistorical@juno.com. Head: Richard J. Daly
Historical Museum - 1885 37221

Robbins Hunter Museum, Avery-Downer House, 221 E Broadway, Granville, OH 43023 - T: (740) 587-0430. Head: David Neel
Historical Museum - 1981 37222

Grass Valley CA

North Star Mining Museum, Allison Ranch Rd, Grass Valley, CA 95959 - T: (916) 273-4255. Head: Glenn Jones
Science&Tech Museum
World largest Pelton wheel, models, machinery, tools 37223

Video Museum and Theater, Central Av, Memorial Park, Grass Valley, CA 95959 - T: (916) 274-1126. Head: Ron Sturgell
Science&Tech Museum 37224

Great Bend KS

Barton County Historical Society Village and Museum, 85 S Hwy 281, Great Bend, KS 67530 - T: (316) 793-5125, Fax: (316) 793-5125, Internet: http://www.greatbend.net/gbcc/tourism/bchs. Head: Beverly Komarek
Local Museum / Open Air Museum - 1963
Historic Village 37225

Great Falls MT

C.M. Russell Museum, 400 13 St N, Great Falls, MT 59401 - T: (406) 727-8787, Fax: (406) 727-2402, Internet: http://www.cmrussell.org. Head: Michael Warner
Fine Arts Museum - 1953
Latin American, Mexican and American Indian art, decorative arts, archaeology, ethnology, folk art 37226

High Plains Heritage Center, 422 2nd St S, Great Falls, MT 59405 - T: (406) 452-3462, Fax: (406) 761-3805, E-mail: hphc@montana.com, Internet: http://www.HighPlainsHeritage.org. Head: Cindy Kittredge
Local Museum - 1976
archive 37227

Paris Gibson Square Museum of Art, 1400 First Av N, Great Falls, MT 59401 - T: (406) 727-8255, Fax: (406) 727-8256, E-mail: pgsmoa@mcn.net. Head: Jessica Hunter
Fine Arts Museum - 1976
American art, folk art, decorative art 37228

Greeley CO

Centennial Village Museum, 1475 A St, Greeley, CO 80631 - T: (970) 350-9224, Fax: (970) 350-9570, E-mail: dillc@ci.greeley.co.us, Internet: http://www.ci.greeley.co.us/culture/museums.html
Open Air Museum / Historical Museum - 1976
28 historic structures illustrating the hist of Colorado 37229

Historic Centennial Village → Centennial Village Museum

John Mariani Art Gallery, University of Northern Colorado, Eighth Av and 18 St, Greeley, CO 80639 - T: (970) 351-2184, Fax: (970) 351-2299. Head: Patricia Reubain
Fine Arts Museum / University Museum - 1972 37230

Meeker Home Museum, 1324 9th Av, Greeley, CO 80631 - T: (970) 350-9220, Internet: http://www.greeley.co.us/culture/museums. Head: Chris Dill
Historical Museum - 1929
Home of Nathan Cook Meeker, founder of Greeley 37231

Municipal Archives, 919 7th St, Greeley, CO 80631 - T: (970) 350-9220, Fax: (970) 350-9570, E-mail: museum@ci.greeley.co.us, Internet: http://www.greeleymuseums.com. Head: Chris Dill
Local Museum - 1968
Local history 37232

Green Bay WI

The Children's Museum of Green Bay, Port Plaza Mall, 320 N Adams St, Green Bay, WI 54301 - T: (920) 432-4397, Fax: (920) 432-4566, E-mail: gbcmuseum@yahoo.com, Internet: http://www.cmuseumgb.org. Head: Bobbie Schuette
Special Museum - 1989 37233

Great Expectations → The Children's Museum of Green Bay

Green Bay Packer Hall of Fame, 855 Lombardi Av, Green Bay, WI 54307 - T: (920) 499-4281, Fax: (920) 405-5564, Internet: http://www.packerhalloffame.com. Head: William Brault, Kelly Schiltz
Special Museum - 1969
Sports 37234

Heritage Hill State Park, 2640 S Webster Av, Green Bay, WI 54301 - T: (920) 448-5150 ext 10, Fax: (920) 448-5127, Internet: http://www.netnet.net/heritagehill. Head: Brenda Promis
Local Museum - 1976
Local hist 37235

National Railroad Museum, 2285 S Broadway, Green Bay, WI 54304-4832 - T: (920) 437-7623, Fax: (920) 437-1291, E-mail: staff@nationalrrmuseum.org, Internet: http://www.nationalrrmuseum.org. Head: Jim Reck
Science&Tech Museum - 1957
Railroad 37236

Neville Public Museum of Brown County, 210 Museum Pl, Green Bay, WI 54303 - T: (920) 448-4460 ext 0, Fax: (920) 448-4458, E-mail: be_museum@co.brown.wi.us, Internet: http://www.nevillepublicmuseum.org. Head: Eugene Umberger
Local Museum - 1915
Local hist 37237

Green Lane PA

Goschenhoppen Folklife Museum, Rte 29, Red Men's Hall, Green Lane, PA 18054-0476 - T: (215) 234-8953, E-mail: redmens_hall@goschenhoppen.org, Internet: http://www.goschenhoppen.org
Ethnology Museum / Folklore Museum / Historical Museum - 1965
Folk art and love, local history 37238

Green River WY

Sweetwater County Historical Museum, 80 W Flaming Gorge Way, Green River, WY 82935 - T: (307) 872-6435, Fax: (307) 872-6469, E-mail: swchm@sweetwater.net, Internet: http://www.sweetwatermuseum.org. Head: Ruth Lauritzen
Local Museum - 1967
Local hist 37239

Green Valley AZ

Titan Missile Museum, Duval Mine Rd, Green Valley, AZ 85614 - T: (520) 625-7736, Fax: (520) 625-9845
Science&Tech Museum - 1986
Missiles 37240

Greenbelt MD

Greenbelt Museum, 10b Crescent Rd, Greenbelt, MD 20770 - T: (301) 474-1936, 507-6582, Fax: (301) 441-8248, E-mail: greenbeltmuseum@sturpower.net, Internet: http://otal.umd.edu/~vg/
Historical Museum - 1987
Local history, culture of the 1930s, planned communities 37241

Greenbush WI

Wade House and Wesley Jung Carriage Museum, W 7747 Plank Rd, Greenbush, WI 53026 - T: (920) 526-3271, Fax: (920) 526-3626, E-mail: wadehous@dotnet.net, Internet: http://wadehouse.shsw.wisc.edu. Head: Jeffrey Schultz
Science&Tech Museum - 1953
Transportation 37242

Greencastle IN

DePauw University Anthropology Museum, Harrison Hall, Rm 206, Greencastle, IN 46135 - T: (765) 658-4800, Fax: (765) 658-4177
University Museum / Ethnology Museum - 1984 37243

Greeneville TN

Andrew Johnson National Historic Site, 101 N College St, Greeneville, TN 37743 - T: (423) 638-3551, 639-3711, Fax: (423) 638-9194, 798-0754, E-mail: jim_small@nps.gov, Internet: http://www.nps.gov/anjo/. Head: Jim Small
Historical Museum - 1942
Memorabilia of Andrew Johnson (US-President), history, civil war, furnishings - Tailor Shop Museum 37244

Doak House Museum, Tusculum College, Greeneville, TN 37743 - T: (423) 636-8554, 636-7348, Fax: (423) 638-7166, E-mail: clucas@tusculum.edu, Internet: http://www.tusculum.edu/museum/doak.html. Head: E. Alvin Gerhardt
University Museum / Historical Museum
History 37245

President Andrew Johnson Museum, Tusculum College, Greeneville, TN 37743 - T: (423) 636-7348, Fax: (423) 638-7166, E-mail: agerhard@tusculum.edu, Internet: http://www.tusculum.edu/museum/johnson.html. Head: E. Alvin Gerhardt
University Museum / Historical Museum - 1993
History 37246

Greenfield IA

Iowa Aviation Museum, 2251 Airport Rd, Greenfield, IA 50849 - T: (515) 343-7184, E-mail: aviation@mddc.com, Internet: http://www.netins.net/showcase/jmaas/iapa. Head: Lee Ann Nelson, Ron Havens
Science&Tech Museum - 1990
Aviation 37247

Greenfield IN

James Whitcomb Riley Birthplace and Museum, Riley Home, 250 W Main St, Greenfield, IN 46140 - T: (317) 462-8539, Fax: (317) 462-8556, Internet: http://www.hccn.org/parks/rileyhouse.htm
Historical Museum - 1937 37248

Greenfield MA

Historical Society of Greenfield Museum, 43 Church St, Greenfield, MA 01301 - T: (413) 774-3663
Local Museum - 1907
Local history - library 37249

Greensboro AL

Magnolia Grove-Historic House Museum, 1002 Hobson St, Greensboro, AL 36744 - T: (334) 624-8618, Fax: (334) 624-8618, E-mail: maggrove@westal.net. Head: Gloria Cole
Historical Museum - 1943 37250

Greensboro NC

Green Hill Center for North Carolina Art, 200 N Davie St, Greensboro, NC 27401 - T: (336) 333-7460, Fax: (336) 275-2612, E-mail: info@greenhillcenter.org, Internet: http://www.greenhillcenter.org. Head: Jennifer Moore
Fine Arts Museum - 1974 37251

Greensboro Artists' League Gallery, 200 N Davie St, #7, Greensboro, NC 27401 - T: (336) 333-7485, Fax: (336) 373-7553, E-mail: gal@vacgreensboro.org, Internet: http://www.people-places.com/gal. Head: Susan Andrews
Fine Arts Museum - 1956 37252

Greensboro Historical Museum, 130 Summit Av, Greensboro, NC 27401-3016 - T: (336) 373-2043, Fax: (336) 373-2204, E-mail: linda.evans@ci.greensboro.nc.us, Internet: http://www.greensbo-rohistory.org. Head: William J. Moore
Historical Museum - 1924 37253

Guilford College Art Gallery, 5800 W Friendly Av, Greensboro, NC 27410 - T: (336) 316-2438, Fax: (336) 316-2950, E-mail: thammond@guilford.edu, Internet: http://www.guilford.edu/artgallery. Head: Theresa N. Hammond
Fine Arts Museum - 1990
Art gallery 37254

Guilford Courthouse National Military Park, 2332 New Garden Rd, Greensboro, NC 27410 - T: (336) 288-1776, Fax: (336) 282-2296, E-mail: - www.guco_administration@nps.gov
Military Museum - 1917 37255

Irene Cullis Gallery, Greensboro College, 815 W Market St, Greensboro, NC 27401-1875 - T: (336) 272-7102 ext 301, Fax: (336) 271-6634. Head: Robert Kowski
Fine Arts Museum / University Museum - 1838 37256

Mattye Reed African Heritage Center, N.C.A. & T. State University, Greensboro, NC 27411 - Fax: (336) 334-4378, 334-7837, E-mail: ndegec@ncat.edu. Head: Conchita F. Ndege
Decorative Arts Museum / University Museum / Historical Museum / Folklore Museum - 1968 37257

Natural Science Center of Greensboro, 4301 Lawndale Dr, Greensboro, NC 27455 - T: (336) 288-3769, Fax: (336) 288-0545, E-mail: nscg@nr.infi.net, Internet: http://www.greensboro.com/sciencecenter
Natural History Museum - 1957 37258

Weatherspoon Art Gallery, University of North Carolina at Greensboro, Spring Garden and Tate St, Greensboro, NC 27402-6170 - T: (336) 334-5770, Fax: (336) 334-5907, E-mail: nmdoll@uncg.edu, Internet: http://www.uncg.edu/wag/. Head: Nancy Doll
Fine Arts Museum / University Museum - 1942 37259

Greensburg PA

Westmoreland Museum of American Art, 221 N Main St, Greensburg, PA 15601-1898 - T: (724) 837-1500, Fax: (724) 837-2921, E-mail: info@wmuseumaa.org, Internet: http://www.wmuseumaa.org. Head: Judith H. O'Toole
Fine Arts Museum - 1949 37260

Greentown IN

Greentown Glass Museum, 112 N Meridian, Greentown, IN 46936 - T: (317) 628-6206
Decorative Arts Museum - 1969
Glass 37261

Greenville IL

Bond County Museum, 318 W Winter St, Greenville, IL 62246 - T: (618) 664-1606
Local Museum - 1955
Local history 37262

Greenville NC

Greenville Museum of Art, 802 S Evans St, Greenville, NC 27834 - T: (252) 758-1946, Fax: (252) 758-1946, E-mail: art@greenvillenc.com, Internet: http://gma.greenvillenc.com. Head: C. Barbour Strickland
Fine Arts Museum - 1956 37263

Wellington B. Gray Gallery, East Carolina University, Jenkins Fine Arts Center, Greenville, NC 27858-4353 - T: (252) 328-6336, Fax: (252) 328-6441, E-mail: adamsk@mail.ecu.edu, Internet: http://www.ecu.edu. Head: Gilbert Leebrick
Fine Arts Museum / University Museum - 1978 37264

Greenville OH

Garst Museum, 205 N Broadway, Greenville, OH 45331-2222 - T: (937) 548-5250, Fax: (937) 548-5250. Head: Judy Logan
Historical Museum - 1903 37265

Greenville SC

Bob Jones University Museum and Gallery, 1700 Wade Hampton Blvd, Greenville, SC 29614 - T: (864) 242-5100 ext 1050, Fax: (864) 770-1306, E-mail: art_gallery@bju.edu, Internet: http://www.bju.edu/art_gallery. Head: Erin Jones
Fine Arts Museum / Religious Arts Museum - 1951
Coll of old masters, icons, antiquities, furniture, tapestries 37266

Greenville County Museum of Art, 420 College St, Greenville, SC 29601 - T: (864) 271-7570, Fax: (864) 271-7579, Internet: http://www.greenvil-lemuseum.org. Head: Thomas W. Styron
Fine Arts Museum - 1963
18th & 19th century southern art 37267

Roper Mountain Science Center, 402 Roper Mountain Rd, Greenville, SC 29615 - T: (864) 281-1188, Fax: (864) 458-7034, Internet: http://www.ropermountain.org. Head: Darrell Harrison
Science&Tech Museum / Natural History Museum - 1978
Science 37268

Greenville TX

American Cotton Museum, 600 I-30 E, Greenville, TX 75401 - T: (903) 450-4502, 454-1990, Fax: (903) 454-1990, E-mail: cottonmuseum@cottonmuseum.com, Internet: http://www.cottonmuseum.com. Head: Adrien Witkofsky
Historical Museum - 1987
Cotton tools and machinary, cotton production hist 37269

Greenwich CT

Historical Society Museum of the Town of Greenwich, 39 Strickland Rd, Greenwich, CT 06807 - T: (203) 869-6899, Fax: (203) 869-6727
Local Museum - 1931
Local history - archives 37270

Putnam Cottage, 243 E Putnam Av, Greenwich, CT 06830 - T: (203) 869-9697. Head: Sidney Willis
Historical Museum - 1900 37271

Greenwich NJ

Cumberland County Historical Society Museum, 960 YeGreate St, Greenwich, NJ 08323 - T: (609) 455-4055, E-mail: lumislib@jnlk.com, Internet: http://www.cumberlandhistorical.org. Head: Sara C. Watson
Local Museum - 1908 37272

Greenwood MS

Cottonlandia Museum, 1608 Hwy 82 W, Greenwood, MS 38930 - T: (662) 453-0925, Fax: (662) 455-7556. Head: Robin Seage Person, Virginia White
Agriculture Museum / Archaeological Museum / Fine Arts Museum / Local Museum / Historical Museum - 1969 37273

Greenwood SC

Greenwood Museum → The Museum

The Museum, 106 Main St, Greenwood, SC 29646 - T: (864) 229-7093, Fax: (864) 229-9317, E-mail: themuseum@greenwood.net. Head: Ken Hartlage, M. Lyda Carroll
Local Museum - 1968
Local hist 37274

Gresham OR

Gresham History Museum, 410 N Main Av, Gresham, OR 97030 - T: (503) 661-0347. Head: Pat Stone
Local Museum - 1976
Local history 37275

Greybull WY

Greybull Museum, 325 Greybull Av, Greybull, WY 82426 - T: (307) 765-2444. Head: Wanda L. Bond
Local Museum - 1967
Local hist 37276

Grinnell IA

Faulconer Gallery, 1108 Park St, Grinnell, IA 50112 - T: (641) 269-4660, Fax: (641) 269-4626, E-mail: strongdj@grinnell.edu, Internet: http://www.grinnell.edu/faulconergallery. Head: Lesley Wright
Fine Arts Museum / University Museum - 1998
Art 37277

Grosse Ile MI

Grosse Ile Historical Museum, East River and Grosse Ile Pkwy, Grosse Ile, MI 48138 - T: (734) 675-1250. Head: Art Koester
Local Museum - 1959
Local history 37278

Grosse Pointe Shores MI

Edsel and Eleanor Ford House, 1100 Lake Shore Rd, Grosse Pointe Shores, MI 48236 - T: (313) 884-4222, Fax: (313) 884-5977, E-mail: info@fordhouse.org, Internet: http://www.fordhouse.org
Local Museum / Decorative Arts Museum / Historic Site - 1978
Historic house, decorative art, design, automotive, architecture, landscape design 37279

Groton CT

Submarine Force Museum and Historic Ship Nautilus, Crystal Lake Rd, Groton, CT 06349-5571 - T: (860) 449-3558, Fax: (860) 449-4150, Internet: http://www.ussnautilus.org. Head: Stephen Finnigan
Military Museum / Science&Tech Museum - 1954 37280

Groton MA

Groton Historical Museum, 172 Main St, Groton, MA 01450 - T: (978) 448-2046, Fax: (978) 448-5589. Head: Isabel C. Beal
Historical Museum - 1894
Governor Boutwell House 37281

Grove OK

Har-Ber Village, 4404 W 20 St, Grove, OK 74344 - T: (918) 786-6446, Fax: (918) 787-6213, E-mail: harbervil@aol.com, Internet: http://www.harbervillaga.com. Head: Gary Smith, Jan Norman
Historical Museum - 1968 37282

Groversville NY

Fulton County Museum, 237 N Kingsboro Av, Groversville, NY 12078 - T: (518) 725-2203
Historical Museum - 1891 37283

Guernsey WY

Lake Guernsey Museum, U.S. 26 to State Hwy 317, Guernsey, WY 82214 - T: (307) 836-2334, 836-2900, Fax: (307) 836-3088. Head: John Keck
Local Museum - 1936
Local hist 37284

Guilford CT

Henry Whitfield State Historical Museum, 248 Old Whitfield St, Guilford, CT 06437 - T: (203) 453-2457, Fax: (203) 453-7544. Head: Michael A. McBride
Historical Museum - 1899
First state-owned museum in Connecticut (1899) 37285

Gulf Shores AL

Fort Morgan Museum, 51 Hwy 180 W, Gulf Shores, AL 36542 - T: (334) 540-7125, Fax: (334) 540-7665. Head: Blanton Blankenship
Military Museum - 1967 37286

Gunnison CO

Gunnison County Pioneer and Historical Museum, S Adams St and Hwy 50, Gunnison, CO 81230 - T: (970) 641-4530. Head: August Grosland
Local Museum - 1930
Regional history 37287

Gurdon AR

Hoo-Hoo International Forestry Museum, 207 Main St, Gurdon, AR 71743 - T: (870) 353-4997, Fax: (870) 353-4151, E-mail: hoohoo@dancooks.com, Internet: http://www.hoo-hoo.org. Head: Beth A. Thomas
Ethnology Museum / Fine Arts Museum - 1981
Logging, lumber 37288

Guthrie OK

Oklahoma Territorial Museum, 402 E Oklahoma Av, Guthrie, OK 73044 - T: (405) 282-1889. Head: Michael Bruce
Historical Museum - 1970 37289

State Capital Publishing Museum, 301 W Harrison Av, Guthrie, OK 73044 - T: (405) 282-4123. Head: Michael Bruce
Special Museum / Science&Tech Museum - 1976 37290

Hackensack NJ

Bergen Museum of Art and Science, 25 E Salem St, Ste 405, Hackensack, NJ 07601 - T: (201) 968-1001, Fax: (201) 265-2536, E-mail: BergenMuse@aol.com, Internet: http://www.thebergenmuseum.com. Head: David J. Messer
Fine Arts Museum / Natural History Museum - 1956 37291

New Jersey Naval Museum, 78 River St, Hackensack, NJ 07601 - T: (201) 342-3268, Fax: (201) 342-3268, E-mail: njnavalmuseum@yahoo.com, Internet: http://www.njnm.com. Head: Ronald J. Pellegrino
Military Museum - 1974
Naval military hist 37292

Hackettstown NJ

Hackettstown Historical Society Museum, 106 Church St, Hackettstown, NJ 07840 - T: (908) 852-8797
Local Museum - 1975
Local history, genealogy - library 37293

Haddonfield NJ

Historical Society of Haddonfield Museum, 343 Kings Hwy E, Haddonfield, NJ 08033 - T: (856) 429-7375, Internet: http://www.08033.com
Historical Museum - 1914
library 37294

Indian King Tavern Museum, 233 King's Hwy E, Haddonfield, NJ 08033 - T: (856) 429-6792, Internet: http://www.levins.com/tavern.html. Head: William J. Mason
Historic Site - 1903 37295

Hadley MA

Hadley Farm Museum, 147 Russell St, Hadley, MA 01035 - T: (413) 586-1812
Agriculture Museum - 1930 37296

Porter-Phelps-Huntington Foundation, 130 River Dr, Hadley, MA 01035 - T: (413) 584-4699. Head: Susan J. Lisk, Peter Wells
Historical Museum - 1955
Womens history studies 37297

Hagerstown IN

Wilbur Wright Birthplace and Museum, 1525 N County Rd 750 E, Hagerstown, IN 47346 - T: (765) 332-2495
Historical Museum - 1929 37298

Hagerstown MD

Jonathan Hager House and Museum, 110 Key St, Hagerstown, MD 21740 - T: (301) 739-8393. Head: John Nelson
Folklore Museum - 1962 37299

Miller House Museum, 135 W Washington St, Hagerstown, MD 21740 - T: (301) 797-8782, E-mail: histsoc@intrepid.net, Internet: http://www.rootsweb.com/~mdwchs. Head: Melinda Marsden
Local Museum - 1911
Antiques, local history 37300

Washington County Museum of Fine Arts, City Park, 91 Key St, Hagerstown, MD 21741 - T: (301) 739-5727, Fax: (301) 745-3741, E-mail: wcmfa@aol.com, Internet: http://www.washcomuseum.org. Head: Jean Woods
Fine Arts Museum - 1929
19th and 20th c american art 37301

Hailey ID

Blaine County Historical Museum, 210 N Main St, Hailey, ID 83333 - T: (208) 726-4226 & 8405, E-mail: teddie@micron.net. Head: Ivan Swaner
Local Museum - 1964
Regional history 37302

Haines AK

Alaska Indian Arts, Historic Bldg 13, Fort Seward, Haines, AK 99827 - T: (907) 766-2160, Fax: (907) 766-2105, 766-2160, Internet: http://www.alaskaindianarts.com. Head: Lee D. Heinmiller
Ethnology Museum - 1957
Indian living village 37303

Sheldon Museum, 11 Main St, Haines, AK 99827 - T: (907) 766-2366, Fax: (907) 766-2368, E-mail: curator@sheldonmuseum.org, Internet: http://sheldonmuseum.org. Head: Cynthia L. Jones
Historical Museum / Ethnology Museum - 1924
History, ethnography, Tlingit Indian culture, Eldred Rock Lighthouse Lense 37304

Haines OR

Eastern Oregon Museum on the Old Oregon Trail, Third and Wilcox, Haines, OR 97833 - T: (503) 856-3233
Local Museum / Historical Museum - 1958 37305

Haledon NJ

American Labor Museum, 83 Norwood St, Haledon, NJ 07508 - T: (973) 595-7953, Fax: (973) 595-7291, E-mail: labormuseum@aol.com, Internet: http://community.nj.com/cc/labormuseum. Head: Angelica M. Santomauro
Historical Museum - 1982 37306

Hallowell ME

Harlow Gallery, 160 Water St, Hallowell, ME 04347 - T: (207) 622-3813. Head: Amy Bliss Coleman, Val Howard
Fine Arts Museum / Public Gallery - 1963
Art 37307

Halstead KS

Kansas Health Museum, Kansas Learning Center for Health, 505 Main St, Halstead, KS 67056 - T: (316) 835-2662, Fax: (316) 835-2755, E-mail: reservations@learningcenter.org, Internet: http://www.learningcenter.org. Head: Megan E. Evans
Historical Museum - 1965
Health, education 37308

Hamden CT

Eli Whitney Museum, 915 Whitney Av, Hamden, CT 06517 - T: (203) 777-1833, Fax: (203) 777-1229, E-mail: wb@eliwhitney.org, Internet: http://www.eliwhitney.org. Head: Beverly Hodgson, William Brown
Science&Tech Museum - 1976 37309

Hamilton NJ

Grounds For Sculpture, 18 Fairgrounds Rd, Hamilton, NJ 08619 - T: (609) 586-0616, Fax: (609) 586-0968, E-mail: info@groundsforsculpture.org, Internet: http://www.groundsforsculpture.org. Head: Brooke Barrie
Fine Arts Museum - 1992
Sculptures 37310

International Sculpture Center, 14 Fairground Rd, Ste B, Hamilton, NJ 08619-3447 - T: (609) 689-1051, Fax: (609) 689-1061, E-mail: isc@sculpture.org, Internet: http://www.sculpture.org
Fine Arts Museum / Association with Coll - 1960 37311

John Abbott II House, 2200 Kuser Rd, Hamilton, NJ 08690 - T: (609) 585-1686
Historical Museum - 1976 37312

Kuser Farm Mansion, 390 Newkirk Av, Hamilton, NJ 08610 - T: (609) 890-3630, Fax: (609) 890-3632, E-mail: comments@hamiltonnj.com, Internet: http://www.hamiltonnj.com. Head: John K. Rafferty
Historical Museum - 1979 37313

Hamilton NY

Picker Art Gallery, Colgate University, Hamilton, NY 13346 - T: (315) 228-7634, Fax: (315) 228-7932, E-mail: pickerart@mail.colgate.edu, Internet: http://picker.colgate.edu. Head: Dewey F. Mosby
Fine Arts Museum - 1966 37314

Hamilton OH

Butler County Museum, 327 N Second St, Hamilton, OH 45011 - T: (513) 896-9936, Fax: (513) 896-9930, E-mail: bcomuseum@fuse.net, Internet: http://home.fuse.net/butlercountymuseum/. Head: Marjorie Brown
Historical Museum - 1934 37315

Pyramid Hill Sculpture Park and Museum, 222 High St, Hamilton, OH 45011 - T: (513) 868-3928, Fax: (513) 968-3585, E-mail: pyramidhill@juno.com, Internet: http://www.pyramidhill.org
Fine Arts Museum - 1997
Sculptures, art 37316

Hammond IN

Hammond Historical Museum, 564 State St, Hammond, IN 46320 - T: (219) 931-5100 ext 255, Fax: (219) 931-3474, E-mail: margevans@aol.com. Head: Margaret Evans
Local Museum - 1960
Local history - library 37317

Hammondsport NY

Glenn H. Curtiss Museum, 8419 Rte 54, Hammondsport, NY 14840 - T: (607) 569-2160, Fax: (607) 569-2040
Historical Museum / Science&Tech Museum - 1961 37318

Wine Museum of Greyton H. Taylor, 8843 Greyton H. Taylor Memorial Dr, Hammondsport, NY 14840 - T: (607) 868-4814, Fax: (607) 868-3205, E-mail: bullyhil@ptd.net, Internet: http://www.bullyhill.com. Head: Walter S. Taylor, Jim Caron
Agriculture Museum - 1967 37319

Hammonton NJ

Batsto Village, 4110 Nesco Rd, Hammonton, NJ 08037 - T: (609) 561-0024, Fax: (609) 567-8116, E-mail: whartonsf@netzero.com. Head: Patricia A. Martinelli
Historic Site / Decorative Arts Museum - 1954
33 historic buildings built in the 1800s 37320

Hampden-Sydney VA

The Esther Thomas Atkinson Museum, College Rd, Hampden-Sydney, VA 23943 - T: (804) 223-6134, 223-6000, Fax: (804) 223-6344, Internet: http://www.hsc.edu/pres/museum/
University Museum / Historical Museum - 1968 37321

Hampton NH

Tuck Museum, 40 Park Av, Hampton, NH 03842 - T: (603) 929-0781. Head: Arthur Caira
Historical Museum - 1925 37322

Hampton SC

Hampton County Historical Museum, 702 1st West, 601 South, Hampton, SC 29924 - T: (803) 943-5484
Local Museum / Folklore Museum - 1979
Local hist 37323

Hampton VA

Air Power Park and Museum, 413 W Mercury Blvd, Hampton, VA 23666 - T: (757) 727-1163. Head: John Miller
Military Museum / Science&Tech Museum - 1964
Military aircraft 37324

Hampton University Museum, Hampton University, Hampton, VA 23668 - T: (757) 727-5308, Fax: (757) 727-5170, E-mail: museum@hamptonu.edu, Internet: http://www.hamptonu.edu. Head: Jeanne Zeidler
Fine Arts Museum / University Museum / Historical Museum / Ethnology Museum - 1868
Art, history 37325

Saint John's Church and Parish Museum, 100 W Queensway, Hampton, VA 23669 - T: (757) 722-2567, Fax: (757) 722-0641, Internet: http://homestead.juno.com/stjohns-hampton. Head: Beverly F. Gundry
Local Museum / Historic Site - 1976
Local hist 37326

Virginia Air and Space Center, 600 Settlers Landing Rd, Hampton, VA 23669 - T: (757) 727-0900, Fax: (757) 727-0898, Internet: http://www.vasc.org. Head: Todd C. Bridgford, Duncan McIver
Local Museum / Science&Tech Museum - 1991
Aerospace, regional history 37327

Hancock NH

Hancock Historical Society Museum, 7 Main St, Hancock, NH 03449-6008 - T: (603) 525-9379
Local Museum / Historical Museum - 1903 37328

Hancock's Bridge NJ

Hancock House, 1 Main St, Hancock's Bridge, NJ 08038 - T: (856) 935-3218, Fax: (856) 925-7818. Head: Florence McNelly
Historical Museum 37329

Hanford CA

Fort Roosevelt Natural Science and History Museum, Spruce Court, Hanford, CA 93230 - T: (559) 582-0919, Fax: (559) 582-8970. Head: Audrey Trevaskis, Heidi Arroues
Natural History Museum / Historical Museum - 1969 37330

Hannibal MO

Mark Twain Home and Museum, 208 Hill St, Hannibal, MO 63401 - T: (573) 221-9010, Fax: (573) 221-7975. Head: Henry Sweets, Herbert S. Parham
Historical Museum - 1936 37331

Hanover KS

Hollenberg Pony Express Station Museum, 2889 23rd Rd, Kansas Hwy 243, Hanover, KS 66945-9634 - T: (913) 337-2635, E-mail: hollenberg@networksplus.net, Internet: http://www.history.cc.ukans.edu/heritage/kshs/places/howlenbg. Head: Duane R. Durst
Special Museum
1857 Pony Express stn, comprised of general store, tavern and stage stn 37332

Hanover MI

Lee Conklin Antique Organ History Museum, 105 Fairview, Hanover, MI 49241 - T: (517) 563-8927, Internet: http://www.community.mlive.com/cc/hanover. Head: Ronald McClain
Local Museum / Museum of Classical Antiquities / Music Museum - 1977   37333

Hanover NH

Hood Museum of Art, Dartmouth College, Hanover, NH 03755 - T: (603) 646-2808, Fax: (603) 646-1400, E-mail: hood.museum@dartmouth.edu, Internet: http://www.dartmouth.edu/acad_support/hood/index.html. Head: Derrick R. Cartwright
Fine Arts Museum / University Museum - 1772
Fine arts, anthropology   37334

Hanover VA

Hanover Historical Society Museum, Hwy 301, Court Green, Hanover, VA 23069 - T: (804) 537-5815
Local Museum - 1967
Local hist   37335

Harbor Springs MI

Andrew J. Blackbird Museum, 368 E Main St, Harbor Springs, MI 49740 - T: (231) 526-0612, Fax: (231) 526-6865, E-mail: cityhs@freeway.net. Head: Joyce Shagonaby
Historical Museum / Ethnology Museum - 1952
Indians   37336

Hardwick MA

Hardwick Historical Museum, On Hardwick Common, Hardwick, MA 01037 - T: (413) 477-8734
Local Museum - 1959
Local history   37337

Hardy VA

Booker T. Washington National Monument, 12130 Booker T. Washington Hwy, Hardy, VA 24101 - T: (540) 721-2094, Fax: (540) 721-8311, 721-5128, Internet: http://www.nps.gov/bowa. Head: Rebecca Harriett
Special Museum - 1956
Birthplace & early home of Booker T. Washington   37338

Harleysville PA

Mennonite Heritage Center, 565 Yoder Rd, Harleysville, PA 19438 - T: (215) 256-3020, Fax: (215) 256-3023, E-mail: info@mhep.org., Internet: http://www.mhep.org/. Head: Joel D. Alderfer
Local Museum / Religious Arts Museum - 1974
Local hist - library   37339

Harlingen TX

Lon C. Hill Home, Boxwood at Raintree, Harlingen, TX 78550 - T: (956) 430-8500, Fax: (956) 430-8502, E-mail: rgvmuse@hiline.net, Internet: http://hiline.net/rgvmuse. Head: Linn Keller
Local Museum - 1905
Historic house   37340

Rio Grande Valley Museum, Boxwood at Raintree, Harlingen, TX 78550 - T: (956) 430-8500, Fax: (956) 430-8502, E-mail: rqvmuse@hiline.net. Head: Linn Keller
Local Museum - 1967
Local hist   37341

Harper KS

Harper City Historical Museum, 804 E 12th St, Harper, KS 67058 - T: (316) 896-2824. Head: Gail Bellar
Local Museum - 1959
Local history, housed in a German Apostolic Church   37342

Harpers Ferry IA

Effigy Mounds Museum, 151 Hwy 76, Harpers Ferry, IA 52146 - T: (319) 873-3491, Fax: (319) 873-3743, E-mail: efmo_superintendent@nps.gov, Internet: http://www.nps.gov/efmo. Head: Phyllis Ewing
Archaeological Museum - 1949
Archaeology   37343

Harpers Ferry WV

Harpers Ferry National Historical Park, Fillmore St, Harpers Ferry, WV 25425 - T: (304) 535-6224, Fax: (304) 535-6244, Internet: http://www.nps.gov/hafe/home.htm. Head: Terry Carlstrom
Local Museum - 1944
56 restored buildings and Civil War fortifications   37344

National Historical John Brown Wax Museum, 168 High St, Harpers Ferry, WV 25425 - T: (304) 535-2792. Head: D.D. Kilham
Decorative Arts Museum - 1964   37345

Harpursville NY

Colesville and Windsor Museum at Saint Luke's Church, Maple Av, Harpursville, NY 13787 - T: (607) 655-3174
Historical Museum - 1971   37346

Harrisburg NE

Banner County Historical Museum, 200 N Pennsylvania Av, Harrisburg, NE 69156 - T: (308) 436-5074. Head: Harold Brown
Local Museum / Agriculture Museum - 1969
Regional history   37347

Harrisburg PA

Fort Hunter Mansion, 5300 N Front St, Harrisburg, PA 17110 - T: (717) 599-5751, Fax: (717) 599-5838. Head: Carl A. Dickson
Decorative Arts Museum / Local Museum - 1933
Historic house   37348

Historical Society of Dauphin County Museum, John Harris Simon Cameron Mansion, Harrisburg, PA 17104 - T: (717) 233-3462, Fax: (717) 233-6059, Internet: http://www.visithhc.com/harrismn.html. Head: Richard Parsons
Local Museum - 1869   37349

State Museum of Pennsylvania, Third and North Sts, Harrisburg, PA 17120-0024 - T: (717) 787-4980, Fax: (717) 783-4558, E-mail: museum@statemuseumpa.org, Internet: http://www.statemuseumpa.org. Head: Anita D. Blackaby
Local Museum / Historical Museum - 1905
Archaeology, fine and decorative arts, natural science, paleontology, geology, industry, technology, military history, mammals, native American village, civil war - planetarium, dino lab   37350

Harrison OH

Village Historical Society Museum, 10659 New Biddinger Rd, Harrison, OH 45030 - T: (513) 367-9379. Head: Betty Cookendorfer
Local Museum - 1962   37351

Harrisonburg VA

D. Ralph Hostetter Museum of Natural History, Eastern Mennonite University, 1200 Park Rd, Harrisonburg, VA 22802-2462 - T: (540) 432-4400, 432-4000, Fax: (540) 432-4488, E-mail: mellinac@emu.edu, Internet: http://www.emu.edu/. Head: Christine C. Hill
University Museum / Natural History Museum - 1968
Natural hist   37352

Sawhill Gallery, Duke Hall, James Madison Universit, Main and Grace St, Harrisonburg, VA 22807 - T: (540) 568-6407, Fax: (540) 568-6598. Head: Stuart Downs
Fine Arts Museum / University Museum - 1967
Art   37353

Harrodsburg KY

Morgan Row Museum, 220 S Chiles St, Harrodsburg, KY 40330 - T: (606) 734-5985, Fax: (606) 734-5985. Head: Terry White
Local Museum - 1907   37354

Old Fort Harrod State Park Mansion Museum, POB 156, Harrodsburg, KY 40330 - T: (859) 734-3314, Fax: (859) 734-0794, E-mail: joan.huffman@mail.state.ky.us, Internet: http//www.state.ky.us/agencies/park/ftharrod2.htm. Head: Joan Huffman
Historical Museum - 1925
1830 Greek revival mansion, replica of original fort   37355

Shaker Village of Pleasant Hill, 3501 Lexington Rd, Harrodsburg, KY 40330 - T: (606) 734-5411, Fax: (606) 734-7278, E-mail: lcurry@shakervillageky.org, Internet: http://www.shakervillageky.org. Head: Larrie Spier Curry
Local Museum / Open Air Museum - 1961
Village, agriculture   37356

Harrogate TN

Abraham Lincoln Museum, Hwy 25 E, Cumberland Gap Pkwy, Harrogate, TN 37752 - T: (423) 869-6235, Fax: (423) 869-6350, E-mail: almuseum@inetlmu.lmunet.edu, Internet: http://www.lmunet.edu/museum/index.html. Head: Dr. Charles M. Hubbard
Historical Museum - 1897
History - Library   37357

Hartford CT

Antiquarian and Landmarks Society Museum, 66 Forest St, Hartford, CT 06105-3204 - T: (860) 247-8996, Fax: (860) 249-4907, E-mail: als@hartnet.org, Internet: http://www.hartnet.org/als. Head: William Hosley
Historical Museum - 1936   37358

Connecticut Historical Society Museum, 1 Elizabeth St, Hartford, CT 06105 - T: (860) 236-5621, Fax: (860) 236-2664, E-mail: ask_vs@chs.org, Internet: http://www.chs.org. Head: David M. Kahn
Fine Arts Museum / Decorative Arts Museum / Local Museum / Historical Museum - 1825   37359

Harriet Beecher Stowe Center, 77 Forest St, Hartford, CT 06105 - T: (860) 522-9258, Fax: (860) 522-9259, E-mail: stowelib@hartret.org, Internet: http://www.hartnet.org/stowe. Head: Katherine Kaue
Historical Museum - 1941   37360

Mark Twain House, 351 Farmington Av, Hartford, CT 06105-4498 - T: (860) 247-0998, Fax: (860) 278-8148, E-mail: lgregor@hartnet.org, Internet: http://www.marktwainhouse.org. Head: John Vincent Boyer
Historical Museum - 1929   37361

Menczer Museum of Medicine and Dentistry, 230 Scarborough St, Hartford, CT 06105 - T: (860) 236-5613, Fax: (860) 523-8657
Special Museum - 1974   37362

Museum of Connecticut History, Connecticut State Library, 231 Capitol Av, Hartford, CT 06106 - T: (860) 566-3056, Fax: (860) 566-2133, Internet: http://www.cslnet.ctstateu.edu
Historical Museum - 1910   37363

Old State House, 800 Main St, Hartford, CT 06103 - T: (860) 522-6766, Fax: (860) 522-2812, E-mail: whfaude@snet.net, Internet: http://www.ctoldstatehouse.org. Head: Wilson H. Faude, Robert DeCrescenzo
Fine Arts Museum / Historical Museum - 1975   37364

Wadsworth Atheneum, 600 Main St, Hartford, CT 06103-2990 - T: (860) 278-2670, Fax: (860) 527-0803, E-mail: winfo@wadsworthatheneum.org, Internet: http://www.wadsworthatheneum.org. Head: Kate M. Sellers
Fine Arts Museum - 1842   37365

Widener Gallery, Austin Arts Center, 300 Summit St, Trinity College, Hartford, CT 06106 - T: (860) 297-5232, Fax: (860) 297-5349, E-mail: felice.caivano@mail.trincoll.edu. Head: Noreen Channels
Fine Arts Museum / University Museum - 1964   37366

Hartford WI

Hartford Heritage Auto Museum → Wisconsin Automotive Museum

Wisconsin Automotive Museum, 147 N Rural St, Hartford, WI 53027 - T: (414) 673-7999, E-mail: automu@netwurx.net. Head: Dale W. Anderson
Science&Tech Museum - 1982
Transportation   37367

Hartsville SC

Cecelia Coker Bell Gallery, c/o Art Deptartment, Coker College, 300 E College Av, Hartsville, SC 29550 - T: (843) 383-8156, Fax: (843) 383-8048, E-mail: lmerriman@pascal.coker.edu, Internet: http://www.coker.edu/art/gallery.html. Head: Larry Merriman
University Museum / Fine Arts Museum - 1983   37368

Hartsville Museum, 222 N Fifth St, Hartsville, SC 29550 - T: (843) 383-3005, Fax: (843) 383-2477, E-mail: hvillemuseum@earthlink.net, Internet: http://www.hartsvillesc.com. Head: Patricia J. Wilmot
Local Museum / Fine Arts Museum - 1980
Local hist, art   37369

Harvard IL

Greater Harvard Area Historical Society, 308 N Hart Blvd, Harvard, IL 60033 - T: (815) 943-6770, 943-6141
Local Museum - 1977
Local history   37370

Harvard MA

Fruitlands Museums, 102 Prospect Hill Rd, Harvard, MA 01451 - T: (978) 456-3924, Fax: (978) 456-8078, E-mail: fruitlands@fruitlands.org, Internet: http://www.fruitlands.org. Head: Maudrank Ayson
Fine Arts Museum / Local Museum / Natural History Museum - 1914
Regional history   37371

Harvard Historical Society Collection, 215 Still River Rd, Harvard, MA 01451 - T: (508) 456-8285
Historical Museum - 1897
History   37372

Harwich MA

Brooks Academy Museum, 80 Parallel St, Harwich, MA 02645 - T: (508) 432-8089, E-mail: hhs@capecodhistory.org, Internet: http://www.capecod-history.org. Head: James A. Brown
Local Museum - 1954
Local history   37373

Hastings MI

Historic Charlton Park Village and Museum, 2545 S Charlton Park Rd, Hastings, MI 49058 - T: (616) 945-3775, Fax: (616) 945-0390. Head: Dr. Peter K. Forsberg
Local Museum / Open Air Museum - 1936
Regional history   37374

Hastings NE

Hastings Museum, 1330 N Burlington, Hastings, NE 68901 - T: (402) 461-2399, Fax: (402) 461-2379, E-mail: hastingsmuseum@alltel.com, Internet: http://www.hastingsnet.com/museum. Head: Terry Hunter
Local Museum / Natural History Museum - 1926   37375

Hattiesburg MS

Turner House Museum, 500 Bay, Hattiesburg, MS 39401 - T: (601) 582-1771. Head: David Sheley
Fine Arts Museum / Decorative Arts Museum - 1970
18th c furniture, silver, Persian rugs, paintings (old masters), tapestries   37376

Hatton ND

Hatton-Eielson Museum, 411 Eielson, Hatton, ND 58240 - T: (701) 543-3726
Historical Museum - 1973   37377

Haverhill MA

Haverhill Historical Museum, 240 Water St, Haverhill, MA 01830 - T: (978) 374-4626. Head: Carolyn Singer
Local Museum - 1893
Local history   37378

Havre MT

H. Earl Clack Museum, 306 Third Av, Havre, MT 59501 - T: (406) 265-4000, Fax: (406) 265-7258, E-mail: mcgregord@nmc1.nmclites.edu. Head: Donna McGregor
Archaeological Museum - 1964   37379

Havre de Grace MD

Havre de Grace Decoy Museum, 215 Giles St, Havre de Grace, MD 21078 - T: (410) 939-3739, Fax: (410) 939-3775, Internet: http://www.decoymuseum.com
Folklore Museum - 1983   37380

Steppingstone Museum, 461 Quaker Bottom Rd, Havre de Grace, MD 21078 - T: (410) 939-2299, 419-1762, Fax: (410) 939-2321. Head: Linda M. Noll
Decorative Arts Museum / Agriculture Museum - 1968
Arts and crafts   37381

Hawaii National Park HI

Volcano Art Center, POB 104, Hawaii National Park, HI 96718 - T: (808) 967-8222, Fax: (808) 967-8512, E-mail: vacadm@gte.net, Internet: http://www.volcanoartcenter.org. Head: Marilyn L. Nicholson
Fine Arts Museum / Folklore Museum - 1974   37382

Hays KS

Fort Hays, 1472 Hwy 183, Alt., Hays, KS 67601-9212 - T: (913) 625-6812, Fax: (785) 625-4785, E-mail: thefort@kshs.org, Internet: http://www.kshs.org/places/forthays.htm. Head: Robert Wilhelm
Military Museum - 1965
Military hist   37383

Sternberg Museum of Natural History, Fort Hays State University, 3000 Sternberg Dr, Hays, KS 67601-2006 - T: (785) 628-5516, Fax: (785) 628-4518, E-mail: jchoate@fhsu.edu, Internet: http://www.fhsu.edu/sternberg/. Head: J.R. Choate
University Museum / Natural History Museum - 1926
Mammals, birds, insects, plants, fossils, amphibians, reptiles, fishes - library   37384

Hayward CA

C.E. Smith Museum of Anthropology, 25800 Carlos B Blvd, Hayward, CA 94542-3039 - T: (510) 885-3168 and 3104, Fax: (510) 885-3353, E-mail: gmiller@csuhaywaRdedu, Internet: http://www.csuhaywaRd.edu/cesmith/. Head: Prof. George Miller
Ethnology Museum - 1974
Anthropology   37385

Sulphur Creek Nature Center, 1801 D St, Hayward, CA 94541 - T: (510) 881-6749, Fax: (510) 881-6763, E-mail: slphrcreek@aol.com, Internet: http://www.hard.dst.ca.us
Natural History Museum - 1961   37386

Sun Gallery, Hayward Area Forum of the Arts, 1015 E St, Hayward, CA 94541 - T: (510) 581-4050, Fax: (510) 581-3384, Internet: http://www.sungallery.org. Head: Maria Ochoa, Carol Henire
Fine Arts Museum - 1975   37387

Hayward WI

National Fresh Water Fishing Hall of Fame, Hall of Fame Dr, Hayward, WI 54843 - T: (715) 634-4440, Fax: (715) 634-4440, E-mail: timg@oldcabin.com
Special Museum - 1960
Fishing   37388

Hazelwood MO

Museum of the Western Jesuit Missions, 700 Howdershell Rd, Hazelwood, MO 63031 - T: (314) 837-3525. Head: William B. Faherty
Religious Arts Museum - 1971 37389

Hazleton PA

Greater Hazleton Historical Society Museum, 55 N Wyoming St, Hazleton, PA 18201 - T: (570) 455-8576
Local Museum - 1983
Local hist 37390

Healdton OK

Healdton Oil Museum, 315 E Main St, Healdton, OK 73438 - T: (580) 229-0317. Head: Claude N. Woods
Special Museum / Science&Tech Museum - 1973
Technology Museum 37391

Heavener OK

Peter Conser House, Hodgens off Hwy 59, Heavener, OK 74937 - T: (918) 653-2493, E-mail: hawhope@clnk.com. Head: Blake Wade
Historical Museum - 1970 37392

Helena AR

Delta Cultural Center, 95 Missouri St, Helena, AR 72342 - T: (870) 338-4350, Fax: (870) 338-4358, Internet: http://www.dah.state.ar.us. Head: Kimberly J. Williams
Folklore Museum - 1990
Folk culture 37393

Phillips County Museum, 623 Pecan St, Helena, AR 72342 - T: (870) 338-7790, Fax: (870) 338-7732. Head: Rose Kettler
Local Museum / Military Museum - 1929
County history, military 37394

Helena MT

Holter Museum of Art, 12 E Lawrence St, Helena, MT 59601 - T: (406) 442-6400, Fax: (406) 442-2404, E-mail: holter@mt.net, Internet: http://www.holtermuseum.org. Head: Peter Held
Fine Arts Museum - 1987
Contemporary regional art 37395

Montana Historical Society Museum, 225 N Roberts, Helena, MT 59620-1201 - T: (406) 444-2694, Fax: (406) 444-2696, E-mail: bmaxwell@state.mt.us, Internet: http://www.montanahistoricalsociety.org. Head: Dr. Arnold Olsen
Local Museum - 1865
library 37396

Hellertown PA

Gilman Museum, At the Cave, Hellertown, PA 18055 - T: (610) 838-8767, Fax: (610) 838-2961, E-mail: info@lostcave.com, Internet: http://www.lostcave.com. Head: Robert G. Gilman
Local Museum - 1955
Natural hist, antique weapons 37397

Hempstead NY

Hofstra Museum, 112 Hofstra University, Hempstead, NY 11549-1120 - T: (516) 463-5672, Fax: (516) 463-4743, E-mail: elgkta@hofstra.edu. Head: David C. Christman
Fine Arts Museum / University Museum - 1963 37398

Henderson KY

John James Audubon Museum, Audubon State Park, U.S. Hwy 41 N, Henderson, KY 42419-0576 - T: (270) 827-1893, Fax: (270) 826-2286, E-mail: jaudubon@henderson.net
Special Museum - 1938
Nr migratory bird route, coll on life and work of John James Audubon 37399

Henderson MN

Sibley County Historical Museum, 700 Main St W, Henderson, MN 56044 - T: (507) 248-3434, 248-3234, E-mail: schs@prairie.lakes.com, Internet: http://www.rootsweb.com/~mnsibley. Head: Jerome Petersen
Historical Museum - 1940
Regional history late 1800's to early 1900's, household, agriculture, music, tools 37400

Henderson NV

Clark County Heritage Museum, 1830 S Boulder Hwy, Henderson, NV 89015 - T: (702) 455-7955, Fax: (702) 455-7948, Internet: http://www.co.clark.nv.us
Historical Museum / Science&Tech Museum - 1968 37401

Henderson TX

The Depot Museum Complex, 514 N High St, Henderson, TX 75652 - T: (903) 657-4303, Fax: (903) 657-2679, E-mail: depot514@qte.net, Internet: http://www.depotmuseum.com. Head: Susan Weaver
Historical Museum - 1979
Local hist 37402

Hendersonville NC

Mineral and Lapidary Museum of Henderson County, 400 N Main St, Hendersonville, NC 28792 - T: (828) 698-1977, Fax: (828) 891-6060, E-mail: minlap@henderson.main.nc.us, Internet: http:/www.minlap.org. Head: Larry Hauser
Natural History Museum / Special Museum - 1996
Minerals, fossils 37403

Hendricks MN

Lincoln County Pioneer Museum, 610 W Elm, Hendricks, MN 56136 - T: (507) 275-3537
Local Museum - 1969
Regional history 37404

Henniker NH

New England College Gallery, 7 Main St, Henniker, NH 03242 - T: (603) 428-2329, Fax: (603) 428-7230, E-mail: jhb@nec1.nec.edu
Fine Arts Museum / University Museum - 1988 37405

Hereford AZ

Coronado National Memorial, 4101 E Montezuma Canyon Rd, Hereford, AZ 85615 - T: (520) 366-5515, Fax: (520) 366-5705, Internet: http://www.nps.gov/coro. Head: James Bellamy
Historical Museum - 1952
Tools and Equipment for Science and technology, costumes, paintings 37406

Hereford TX

Deaf Smith County Museum, 400 Sampson, Hereford, TX 79045 - T: (806) 363-7070. Head: Paula Edwards
Local Museum - 1966
Local hist 37407

Herington KS

Tri-County Historical Society and Museum, 800 S Broadway, Herington, KS 67449-3060 - T: (913) 258-2842. Head: Donna L. Adam
Local Museum / Science&Tech Museum - 1975
Local hist, railroad hist 37408

Herkimer NY

Herkimer County Historical Society Museum, 400 N Main St, Herkimer, NY 13350 - T: (315) 866-6413, E-mail: hchs@musp.net, Internet: http://www.herkimerhistory.com. Head: Jeffrey Steele
Historical Museum - 1896 37409

Hermann MO

Deutschheim State Historic Site, 109 W Second St, Hermann, MO 65041 - T: (573) 486-2200, Fax: (573) 486-2249, E-mail: deutschh@ktis.net, Internet: http://www.mostateparks.com/deutschheim.html
Historical Museum - 1979
German Heritage Museum 37410

Historic Hermann Museum, Fourth and Schiller Sts, Hermann, MO 65041 - T: (573) 486-2017, Fax: (573) 486-2017, Internet: http://www.mo.provider/depteconomicdevelopment. Head: Charles Gehrke
Local Museum - 1956 37411

Hermitage TN

The Hermitage - Home of President Andrew Jackson, 4580 Rachel's Ln, Hermitage, TN 37076 - T: (615) 889-2941, Fax: (615) 889-9289. Head: James M. Vaughan
Local Museum - 1889
Historic house 37412

Hershey PA

Hershey Museum, 170 W Hersheypark Dr, Hershey, PA 17033 - T: (717) 534-3439, Fax: (717) 534-8940, E-mail: info@hersheymuseum.org, Internet: http://www.hersheymuseum.org. Head: David L. Parke
Decorative Arts Museum / Historical Museum / Local Museum - 1933
History 37413

Hibbing MN

Hibbing Historical Museum, 400 23rd St and 5th Av E, Hibbing, MN 55746 - T: (218) 263-8522. Head: Heather Jo Maki
Local Museum - 1958
Local history 37414

Hickory NC

Catawba Science Center, 243 Third Av NE, Hickory, NC 28601 - T: (828) 322-8169, Fax: (828) 322-1585, E-mail: msinclair@catawbascience.org, Internet: http://www.catawbascience.org. Head: Mark E. Sinclair
Natural History Museum / Science&Tech Museum - 1975 37415

Hickory Museum of Art, 243 Third Av NE, Hickory, NC 28601 - T: (828) 327-8576, Fax: (828) 327-7281, E-mail: hma@w3link.com, Internet: http://www.hickorymuseumofart.org. Head: Arnold Cogswell, Blair Shuford
Fine Arts Museum - 1944 37416

Hickory Corners MI

Gilmore-CCCA Museum, 6865 W Hickory Rd, Hickory Corners, MI 49060 - T: (616) 671-5089, Fax: (616) 671-5843, E-mail: gcccam@net-link.net, Internet: http://www.gilmorecarmuseum.org/. Head: Thomas A. Kayser
Science&Tech Museum - 1964
Cars 37417

Hicksville NY

Hicksville Gregory Museum, Heitz Pl, Hicksville, NY 11801 - T: (516) 822-7505, Fax: (516) 822-3227, Internet: http://members.aol.com/HGMuseum. Head: Joan Kawecki
Historical Museum / Science&Tech Museum - 1963 37418

Hiddenite NC

Hiddenite Center, Church St, Hiddenite, NC 28636 - T: (828) 632-6966, Fax: (828) 632-3783, E-mail: hidnight@aol.com, Internet: http://www.hiddenite.appstate.edu. Head: Dwaine C. Coley
Fine Arts Museum / Local Museum - 1981
General museum, art 37419

High Falls NY

Delaware and Hudson Canal Historical Society Museum, Mohonk Rd, High Falls, NY 12440 - T: (914) 687-9311, Fax: (914) 868-7875, E-mail: canalmuse@aol.com, Internet: http://www.mhrs.org/kingston/kgndah.html. Head: Vicki Doyle
Historical Museum / Science&Tech Museum - 1966 37420

High Point NC

High Point Museum, High Point Historical Society Inc, 1859 E Lexington Av, High Point, NC 27262 - T: (336) 885-1859, Fax: (336) 883-3284, Internet: http://www.highpointmuseum.org. Head: Barbaara E. Taylor
Historical Museum - 1966 37421

Springfield Museum of Old Domestic Life, 555 E Springfield Rd, High Point, NC 27263 - T: (910) 889-4911. Head: Brenda Haworth
Historical Museum - 1935 37422

Highland KS

Native American Heritage Museum at Highland Mission, 1737 Elgin Rd, Highland, KS 66035 - T: (913) 442-3304, E-mail: nahm@kshs.org, Internet: http://www.kshs.org
Historical Museum / Folklore Museum - 1943
House serving as a mission, dormitory and school for the Iowa, Sac and Fox Indians 37423

Highland Heights KY

Museum of Anthropology, Northern Kentucky University, University Dr, Highland Heights, KY 41099-6210 - T: (859) 572-5259, Fax: (859) 572-5566, Internet: http://www.nku.edu/~anthro/. Head: Dr. James F. Hopgood
Ethnology Museum / Archaeological Museum - 1976
Anthropology 37424

Northern Kentucky University Art Galleries, Nunn Dr, Highland Heights, KY 41099 - T: (859) 572-5148, Fax: (859) 572-6501. Head: David J. Knight
University Museum / Fine Arts Museum - 1968 37425

Highland Park IL

Highland Park Historical Museum, 326 Central Av, Highland Park, IL 60035 - T: (847) 432-7090, Fax: (847) 432-7307, E-mail: hphistoricalsociety@worldnet.att.net, Internet: http://www.highlandpark.org/histsoc. Head: Ellsworth Mills, Charlotte. Shields
Local Museum - 1966
Local history 37426

Hill Air Force Base UT

Hill Aerospace Museum, 7961 Wardleigh Rd, Hill Air Force Base, UT 84506-5842 - T: (801) 777-6868, Fax: (801) 777-6386, Internet: http://www.hill.af.mil/museum. Head: Rick Oliver
Military Museum / Science&Tech Museum - 1985
Aerospace 37427

Hill City SD

Black Hills Museum of Natural History, 217 Main St, Hill City, SD 57745 - T: (605) 574-4505, Fax: (605) 574-2518. Head: Neal L. Larson
Natural History Museum - 1990
Natural hist 37428

Hillsboro KS

Hillsboro Museum, 501 S Ash St, Hillsboro, KS 67063 - T: (316) 947-3775
Local Museum / Agriculture Museum - 1958
Local history, pioneer adobe house, typical Mennonite dwelling 37429

Hillsboro ND

Traill County Historical Society Museum, 306 Caledonia Av, Hillsboro, ND 58045 - T: (701) 436-5571. Head: John Wright
Historical Museum - 1965 37430

Hillsboro OH

Fort Hill Museum, 13614 Fort Hill Rd, Hillsboro, OH 45133 - T: (937) 588-3221. Head: Keith Bengtson
Historical Museum 37431

Highland House Museum, 151 E Main St, Hillsboro, OH 45133 - T: (937) 393-3392. Head: Lenora Gordon, M. Van Frank
Historical Museum - 1965 37432

Hillsboro TX

Texas Heritage Museum, c/o Hill College, 112 Lamar Dr, Hillsboro, TX 76645 - T: (254) 582-2555 ext 258, Fax: (254) 582-7591, Internet: http://hillcollege.hill-college.cc.tx.us. Head: Dr. T. Lindsay Baker
Military Museum - 1964
Military hist 37433

Hillsboro WI

Hillsboro Area Historical Society Museum, Maple St, Hillsboro, WI 54634 - T: (608) 489-3322. Head: Don Schiefelbein
Local Museum - 1958
Local hist 37434

Hillsborough NC

Orange County Historical Museum, 201 N Churton St, Hillsborough, NC 27278 - T: (919) 732-2201
Local Museum - 1957 37435

Hillsborough NH

Franklin Pierce Homestead, Second N.H. Turnpike, Hillsborough, NH 03244 - T: (603) 478-3913, 478-3165, Fax: (603) 464-5401
Historical Museum - 1804
Childhood home of Franklin Pierce, 14th U.S. President 37436

Hilo HI

Lyman House Memorial Museum, 276 Haili St, Hilo, HI 96720 - T: (808) 935-5021, Fax: (808) 969-7685, E-mail: lymanwks@interpac.net, Internet: http://www.Lymanmuseum.org. Head: Paul A. Dahlquist
Local Museum / Folklore Museum - 1931 37437

Hilton Head Island SC

Coastal Discovery Museum, 100 William Hilton Pkwy, Hilton Head Island, SC 29926-3497 - T: (843) 689-6767, Fax: (843) 689-6769, Internet: http://www.hhisland.com/hiltonheadmuseum/. Head: Chris Tenne Pendleton
Historical Museum / Science&Tech Museum - 1985
History and science 37438

Hinckley ME

L.C. Bates Museum, c/o Good Will-Hinckley Home For Boys and Girls, Rte 201, Hinckley, ME 04944 - T: (207) 238-4250, Fax: (207) 453-2515, E-mail: lcbates@mint.net, Internet: http://www.ghh.org. Head: Deborah Staber
Local Museum - 1911
General museum 37439

Hinckley MN

Hinckley Fire Museum, 106 Old Hwy 61, Hinckley, MN 55037 - T: (320) 384-7338, Fax: (320) 384-7338, E-mail: hfire@ecenet.com, Internet: http://www.ci.hinckley.mn.us/firemuseum. Head: Jeanne Coffey
Historical Museum - 1976
Fire fighting, Saint Paul & Duluth Railroad Depot 37440

Hingham MA

Old Ordinary Museum, 21 Lincoln St, Hingham, MA 02043 - T: (781) 749-0013, 749-7721, Internet: http://www.hingham_ma.com/historical/. Head: Iris M. Daigle
Historical Museum - 1914 37441

Hinsdale IL

Hinsdale Historical Society Museum, 15 S Clay St, Hinsdale, IL 60521 - T: (630) 789-2600
Local Museum / Historical Museum - 1981 37442

Hinton WV

Bluestone Museum, Rte 87, Hinton, WV 25951 - T: (304) 466-1454
Natural History Museum - 1972 37443

Ho-Ho-Kus NJ

The Hermitage, 335 N Franklin Turnpike, Ho-Ho-Kus, NJ 07423 - T: (201) 445-8311, Fax: (201) 445-0437, E-mail: info@thehermitage.org, Internet: http://www.thehermitage.org. Head: T. Robins Brown
Historical Museum - 1972
Clothing ant textiles 37444

Hobbs NM

Lea County Cowboy Hall of Fame and Western Heritage Center, 5317 Lovington Hwy, Hobbs, NM 88240 - T: (505) 392-5118, 657-6260, Fax: (505) 392-5871, E-mail: lburnett@nmjc.cc.nm.us. Head: La Jean Burnett
Historical Museum - 1978
History 37445

New Mexico Wing-Confederate Air Force, U.S. Hwy 62-180, Hobbs, NM 88240 - T: (505) 393-6696, Fax: (505) 392-1441, E-mail: hafnau@aol.com. Head: Phil Ross
Military Museum - 1968
World War II aircraft 37446

Hobson MT

Utica Museum, HC 81, Hobson, MT 59452 - T: (406) 423-5531. Head: George Keating
Historical Museum - 1965 37447

Hodgenville KY

Abraham Lincoln Birthplace, 2995 Lincoln Farm Rd, Hodgenville, KY 42748 - T: (502) 358-3137, Fax: (502) 358-3874. Head: Kenneth Apschnikat
Special Museum - 1916
Lincoln family homestead 37448

Hohenwald TN

Meriwether Lewis National Monument, 189 Meriwether Lewis Park, Hohenwald, TN 38462 - T: (931) 796-2675, Fax: (931) 796-5417
Historical Museum - 1936
Death and burial site of Meriwether Lewis 37449

Holbrook NY

Sachem Historical Society Museum, 59 Crescent Circle, Holbrook, NY 11741 - T: (516) 588-3967
Historical Museum - 1963 37450

Holderness NH

Science Center of New Hampshire, Rte 113, Holderness, NH 03245 - T: (603) 968-7194, Fax: (603) 968-2229, E-mail: scnh@lr.net, Internet: http://www.slnsc.org. Head: Will Abbott
Natural History Museum - 1966 37451

Holdrege NE

Phelps County Museum, N Burlington Hwy 183, Holdrege, NE 68949-0164 - T: (308) 995-5015
Local Museum - 1966
Local history - library 37452

Holland MI

Cappon House Museum, 228 W 9th St, Holland, MI 49423 - T: (616) 394-1362, Fax: (616) 394-4756, E-mail: museum@hope.edu, Internet: http://www.hollandmuseum.org. Head: Ann Kiewel
Historical Museum - 1986
Home of Holland's first mayor 37453

DePree Art Center and Gallery, Hope College, 275 Columbia Av, Holland, MI 49423 - T: (616) 395-7000, Fax: (616) 395-7499, Internet: http://hope.edu/academic/art/depree. Head: Dr. John M. Wilson
University Museum / Fine Arts Museum - 1982 37454

First Michigan Museum of Military History, U.S. 31 and New Holland St, Holland, MI 49424 - T: (616) 399-1955. Head: Craig DeSeyter
Military Museum - 1953
Military history 37455

Holland Area Arts Council, 150 W 8th St, Holland, MI 49423 - T: (616) 396-3278, Fax: (616) 396-6298. Head: Doug Padnos, Brenda S. Nienhouse
Fine Arts Museum / Public Gallery - 1967
Arts 37456

Holland Museum, 31 W 10th St, Holland, MI 49423 - T: (616) 394-1362, Fax: (616) 394-4756, E-mail: museum@hope.edu, Internet: http://www.hollandmuseum.org
Local Museum - 1937
Dutch heritage, local history 37457

Windmill Island Municipal Park Museum, 7th St and Lincoln Av, Holland, MI 49423 - T: (616) 355-1030, Fax: (616) 355-1035, E-mail: ad@windmillisland.org, Internet: http://www.windmillisland.org. Head: Ad Van den Akker
Local Museum - 1965
Dutch windmill 37458

Holland VT

Holland Historical Society Museum, Gore Rd, Holland, VT 05830 - T: (802) 895-4440, Fax: (802) 895-4440. Head: Don Spooner, Fleda Judd, Howard Nelson, Julia Carter, Cyril Worth
Local Museum - 1972
Local hist 37459

Holly Springs MS

Marshall County Historical Museum, 220 E College Av, Holly Springs, MS 38635 - T: (601) 252-3669
Historical Museum - 1970 37460

Hollywood CA

Hollywood Guinness World of Records Museum, 6764 Hollywood Blvd, Hollywood, CA 90028 - T: (323) 463-6433, Fax: (323) 462-3953. Head: Spoony Singh
Special Museum - 1991 37461

Hollywood Studio Museum, 2100 Highland Av, Hollywood, CA 90068 - T: (213) 874-2276, Fax: (310) 789-7281. Head: Jola Mart-Shani
Special Museum - 1982
Film industry 37462

Hollywood Wax Museum, 6767 Hollywood Blvd, Hollywood, CA 90028 - T: (213) 462-5991, Fax: (213) 462-3953
Decorative Arts Museum - 1965 37463

Hollywood FL

Art and Culture Center of Hollywood, 1650 Harrison St, Hollywood, FL 33020 - T: (954) 921-3274, Fax: (954) 921-3273, E-mail: acch@bellsouth.net. Head: Cynthia Miller
Fine Arts Museum / Folklore Museum - 1976
Multi-disciplinary Arts Center 37464

Hollywood MD

Sotterley Plantation Museum, Rte 245, Hollywood, MD 20636 - T: (301) 373-2280, 681-0850, Fax: (301) 373-8474, E-mail: sotterleyoffice@mail.ameritel.net, Internet: http://www.sotterley.com. Head: Carolyn J. Laray
Historic Site - 1961
1710 Manor House, outbuildings, illustrating Tidewater Plantation culture 37465

Holmdel NJ

Longstreet Farm, Holmdel Park, Longstreet Rd, Holmdel, NJ 07733 - T: (732) 946-3758, Fax: (732) 946-0750, E-mail: info@monmouthcountyparks.com, Internet: http://www.monmouthcountyparks.com
Agriculture Museum - 1967 37466

Holyoke CO

Phillips County Museum, 109 S Campbell Av, Holyoke, CO 80734 - T: (970) 854-2822, Fax: (970) 854-3811, E-mail: statz@henge.com, Internet: http://www.rootsweb.com/cophilli. Head: Kenneth Oltjenbruns
Local Museum - 1967
Regional history 37467

Holyoke MA

Children's Museum, 444 Dwight St, Holyoke, MA 01040 - T: (413) 536-7048, Fax: (413) 533-2999. Head: Amy Landry, Margaret Boulais
Special Museum - 1981 37468

Wistariahurst Museum, 238 Cabot St, Holyoke, MA 01040 - T: (413) 534-2216, Fax: (413) 534-2344, Internet: http://www.holyoke.org. Head: Sandra Christoforidis
Local Museum / Historical Museum - 1959
Mansion and carriage house, former home of local silk manufacturer William Skinner 37469

Homer AK

Pratt Museum, 3779 Bartlett St, Homer, AK 99603 - T: (907) 235-8635, Fax: (907) 235-2764, E-mail: info@prattmuseum.org, Internet: http://www.prattmuseum.org. Head: Janet V. O'Meara, Michael C. Hawfield
Historical Museum - 1968
Natural history 37470

Homer NY

Homerville Museum, 49 Clinton St, Homer, NY 13077-1024 - T: (607) 749-3105. Head: Kenneth M. Eaton
Historical Museum / Military Museum - 1976 37471

Hominy OK

Drummond Home, 305 N Price, Hominy, OK 74035 - T: (918) 885-2374. Head: Bob L. Blackburn
Historical Museum - 1986
Original furnishing of Drummond family 37472

Honesdale PA

Wayne County Museum, 810 Main St, Honesdale, PA 18431 - T: (570) 253-3240, Fax: (717) 253-5204, E-mail: wchs@ptd.net-director, Internet: http://www.waynehistorypa.org. Head: Sally Talaga
Historical Museum / Historic Site - 1917
History, hist of the Delaware and Hudson Canal - Research library, Farm Museum, room of a county school 37473

Honolulu HI

Bernice Pauahi Bishop Museum, 1525 Bernice St, Honolulu, HI 96817-0916 - T: (808) 847-3511, Fax: (808) 841-8968, E-mail: ajbuto@bishop.bishop.hawaii.org, Internet: http://www.bishop.hawaii.org. Head: Donald Duckworth
Local Museum / Ethnology Museum / Natural History Museum / Special Museum - 1889
Culture, natural history 37474

The Contemporary Museum, 2411 Makiki Heights Dr, Honolulu, HI 96822 - T: (808) 526-1322, Fax: (808) 536-5973, Internet: http://www.tcmhi.org. Head: Georgiana Lagoria
Fine Arts Museum - 1961
Contemporary fine art, historic house, gardens 37475

The Contemporary Museum at First Hawaiian Center, 999 Bishop St, Honolulu, HI 96813, mail addr: 2411 Makiki Heights Dr, HI 96822 - T: (808) 526-1322, Fax: (808) 536-5973, E-mail: awong@tcmhi.org, Internet: http://www.tcmhi.org. Head: Georgianna Lagoria
Fine Arts Museum - 1989
Art 37476

East-West Center, 1601 East-West Rd, Honolulu, HI 96848-1601 - T: (808) 944-7111, Fax: (808) 944-7070, E-mail: feltzb@ewc.hawaii.edu, Internet: http://www.ewc.hawaii.edu
Fine Arts Museum / Historical Museum / Natural History Museum / Folklore Museum - 1961 37477

Hawaii Children's Discovery Center, 111 Ohe St, Honolulu, HI 96813 - T: (808) 592-5437, Fax: (808) 592-5433. Head: Loretta Yajima
Special Museum - 1985 37478

Hawaii Maritime Center, Pier 7, Honolulu, HI 96813 - T: (808) 523-6151, Fax: (808) 536-1519, E-mail: bmoore@bishopmuseum.org. Head: W. Donald Duckworth
Historical Museum - 1988
Maritime history 37479

Honolulu Academy of Arts Gallery, 900 S Beretania St, Honolulu, HI 96814 - T: (808) 532-8700, Fax: (808) 532-8787, E-mail: webmaster@honoluluacademy.org, Internet: http://www.hoholuluacademy.org. Head: George R. Ellis
Fine Arts Museum - 1922
Art - library 37480

Iolani Palace, King and Richards Sts, Honolulu, HI 96813 - T: (808) 522-0822, Fax: (808) 532-1051, E-mail: miuraa@hawaii.edu, Internet: http://alaike.lcc.hawaii.edu/openstudio/iolani/
Historical Museum / Historic Site - 1966
Iolani Palace c. 1982 erected as state residence for Hawaii's last king Kalakaua, Iolani Barracks of the Royal Guard, paintings 37481

Japanese Cultural Center of Hawaii, 2454 S Beretania St, Honolulu, HI 96826 - T: (808) 945-7633, Fax: (808) 944-1123. Head: Kathleen M. Izon
Historical Museum - 1987 37482

King Kamehameha V - Judiciary History Center, 417 S King St, Honolulu, HI 96813-2911 - T: (808) 539-4999, Fax: (808) 539-4996, E-mail: jhc@aloha.net, Internet: http://jhchawaii.org. Head: T. Lani Ma'a Lapilio
Historical Museum - 1989
History, Ali'iolani Hale, Hawaii Supreme Court Bldg 37483

Mission Houses Museum, 553 S King St, Honolulu, HI 96813 - T: (808) 531-0481, Fax: (808) 545-2280, E-mail: mhm@lava.net, Internet: http://www.lava.net/~mhm. Head: Deborah Dunn
Historical Museum - 1920 37484

Moanalua Gardens Foundation, 1352 Pineapple Pl, Honolulu, HI 96819 - T: (808) 839-5334, Fax: (808) 839-3658, E-mail: mgf@pixi.com, Internet: http://mgf-hawaii.com. Head: Marilyn Schoenke
Archaeological Museum - 1970
Archaeology 37485

Queen Emma Summer Palace, 2913 Pali Hwy, Honolulu, HI 96817 - T: (808) 595-3167, Fax: (808) 595-4395
Historical Museum / Decorative Arts Museum - 1915
Former home of Queen Emma and King Kamehameha IV 37486

Ramsay, 1128 Smith St, Honolulu, HI 96817-5194 - T: (808) 537-2787, Fax: (808) 531-6873, E-mail: ramsey@lava.net, Internet: http://www.ramsaymuseum.org. Head: Russ Sowers
Fine Arts Museum
Drawings, painting-American, photography, prints, sculpture 37487

Tennent Art Foundation Gallery, 203 Prospect St, Honolulu, HI 96813 - T: (808) 531-1987. Head: Elaine Tennent
Fine Arts Museum - 1954 37488

University of Hawaii Art Gallery, 2535 The Mall, Honolulu, HI 96822 - T: (808) 956-6888, Fax: (808) 956-9659, E-mail: gallery@hawaii.edu, Internet: http://www.hawaii.edu/artgallery. Head: Tom Klobe
Fine Arts Museum / Public Gallery / University Museum - 1976 37489

USS Arizona Memorial, 1 Arizona Memorial Pl, Honolulu, HI 96818 - T: (808) 422-2771, Fax: (808) 483-8608, Internet: http://www.nps.gov/usar. Head: Kathy Billings
Military Museum - 1980
Military, WW II Memorial 37490

USS Bowfin Submarine Museum, 11 Arizona Memorial Dr, Honolulu, HI 96818 - T: (808) 423-1341, Fax: (808) 422-5201, E-mail: bowfin@aloha.net, Internet: http://www.aloha.net/~bowfin. Head: Gerald Hofwolt
Historical Museum / Military Museum - 1978
Military ship 37491

Hope ND

Steele County Museum, Steele Av and Third St, Hope, ND 58046 - T: (701) 945-2394. Head: Duane Anderson, Russell Ford-Dunker
Local Museum - 1966 37492

Hope NJ

Hope Historical Society Museum, High St, Rte 519, Hope, NJ 07840 - T: (908) 637-4120, Fax: (908) 637-4120. Head: Mary L. Billow
Historical Museum - 1950 37493

Hopewell NJ

Hopewell Museum, 28 E Broad St, Hopewell, NJ 08525 - T: (609) 466-0103
Local Museum - 1924
Colonial furniture, Indian handicrafts, antique china, glass, silver and pewter, parlors, early needlework 37494

Hopewell VA

Flowerdew Hundred Foundation, 1617 Flowerdew Hundred Rd, Hopewell, VA 23860 - T: (804) 541-8897, Fax: (804) 458-7738, E-mail: flowerdew@firstsaga.com, Internet: http://www.flowerdew.org
Archaeological Museum - 1971
Archaeology 37495

Hopkinsville KY

Pennyroyal Area Museum, 217 E Ninth St, Hopkinsville, KY 42240 - T: (502) 887-4270, Fax: (502) 887-4271. Head: Debra L. Pence-Massie
Local Museum - 1975
Local history 37496

Hopkinton NH

New Hampshire Antiquarian Society Museum, 300 Main St, Hopkinton, NH 03229 - T: (603) 746-3825. Head: Elaine P. Loft
Local Museum - 1859 37497

Hoquiam WA

Polson Park and Museum, 1611 Riverside Av, Hoquiam, WA 98550 - T: (360) 533-5862. Head: John Larson
Local Museum - 1976
Local hist 37498

Horicon WI

Satterlee Clark House, 322 Winter St, Horicon, WI 53032 - T: (414) 485-2830. Head: Margaret Bartelt
Local Museum - 1972
Historic house 37499

Hornby NY

Hornby Museum, County Rte 41, Hornby, NY 14813 - T: (607) 962-6620. Head: Richard Johnson
Local Museum - 1958 37500

Horseheads NY

National Warplane Museum, 17 Aviation Dr, Horseheads, NY 14845 - T: (607) 739-8200 ext 221, Fax: (607) 739-8374, E-mail: nwm@warplane.org, Internet: http://www.warplane.org. Head: Stephen Low
Science&Tech Museum / Military Museum - 1983 37501

Horsham PA

Graeme Park, 859 County Line Rd, Horsham, PA 19044 - T: (215) 343-0965, Fax: (215) 343-2223, E-mail: smiller@phmc.state.pa.us, Internet: http://www.phmc.state.pa.us
Local Museum - 1958
Local hist 37502

Hot Springs AR

Mid-America Science Museum, 500 Mid America Blvd, Hot Springs, AR 71913 - T: (501) 767-3461, Fax: (501) 767-1170, E-mail: masm@direclynx.net, Internet: http://www.direclynx.net/~masm. Head: Glenda Eshenroder
Science&Tech Museum - 1971
Science 37503

Hot Springs SD

Fall River County Historical Museum, Rte 1, Hot Springs, SD 57747 - T: (605) 745-5147. Head: Paul Hickock
Local Museum / Decorative Arts Museum - 1961
Local hist 37504

Mammoth Site of Hot Springs, 1800 Highway 18, Bypass, Hot Springs, SD 57747 - T: (605) 745-6017, Fax: (605) 745-3038, E-mail: mammoth@mammothsite.com, Internet: http://www.mammothsite.com. Head: Joe Muller
Natural History Museum - 1975
Paleontology 37505

Hot Sulphur Springs CO

Grand County Museum, 110 E Byers, Hot Sulphur Springs, CO 80451 - T: (970) 725-3939, Fax: (970) 725-0129, E-mail: gcha@rkymtnhi.com, Internet: http://www.grandcountymuseum.com. Head: Barbara Mitchell
Local Museum - 1974
Regional history 37506

Houghton MI

A.E. Seaman Mineral Museum, Michigan Technological University, 1400 Townsend Dr, Houghton, MI 49931 - T: (906) 487-2572, Fax: (906) 487-3027, E-mail: sjdyl@mtu.edu, Internet: http://www.geo.mtu.edu/museum/. Head: Stanley J. Dyl
University Museum / Natural History Museum - 1902
Mineralogy - library 37507

Houston TX

Art League of Houston, 1953 Montrose Blvd, Houston, TX 77006-1243 - T: (713) 523-9530, Fax: (713) 523-4053, E-mail: artleagh@neosoft.com, Internet: http://www.artleague-houston.org. Head: Wade Wilson
Fine Arts Museum - 1948
Art 37508

The Children's Museum of Houston, 1500 Binz, Houston, TX 77004-7112 - T: (713) 522-1138 ext 215/200, Fax: (713) 522-5747, E-mail: rapih@sam.neosoft.com, Internet: http://www.cmhouston.org. Head: Tammie Kahn
Special Museum - 1981
Children's Museum 37509

Contemporary Arts Museum, 5216 Montrose Blvd, Houston, TX 77006-6598 - T: (713) 284-8250, Fax: (713) 284-8275, E-mail: kblanton@kmh.org, Internet: http://www.camh.org. Head: Marti Mayo
Fine Arts Museum - 1948
Art 37510

Cy Twombly Gallery, 1501 Branard St, Houston, TX 77006 - T: (713) 525-9400, Fax: (713) 525-9444, E-mail: public_affairs@menil.org, Internet: http://www.menil.org. Head: Paul Winkler
Fine Arts Museum - 1995
Art 37511

The Heritage Society Museum, 1100 Bagby, Houston, TX 77002 - T: (713) 655-1912, Fax: (713) 655-7527, E-mail: efle@heritagesociety.org, Internet: http://www.heritagesociety.org
Local Museum - 1954
Local hist 37512

Houston Fire Museum, 2403 Milam St, Houston, TX 77006 - T: (713) 524-2526, Fax: (713) 520-7566, E-mail: hfmi@houstonfiremuseum.org, Internet: http://www.houstonfiremuseum.org. Head: Emily Ponte
Historical Museum - 1982
Fire fighting 37513

Houston Museum of Natural Science, 1 Hermann Circle Dr, Houston, TX 77030 - T: (713) 639-4601, 639-4614, 639-4629, Fax: (713) 523-4125, Internet: http://www.hmns.org
Natural History Museum / Science&Tech Museum - 1909
Natural science 37514

Houston Police Museum, 17000 Aldine Westfield Rd, Houston, TX 77073 - T: (281) 230-2361, Fax: (281) 230-2314. Head: Denny G. Hair
Historical Museum - 1981
Police hist 37515

The Menil Collection, 1515 Sul Ross, Houston, TX 77006 - T: (713) 525-9400, Fax: (713) 525-9444, E-mail: menil@neosoft.com, Internet: http://www.menil.org. Head: Paul Winkler
Fine Arts Museum - 1980
Art, antiquities 37516

Museum of American Architecture and Decorative Arts, c/o Houston Baptist University, 7502 Fondren Rd, Houston, TX 77074 - T: (281) 649-3311, Fax: (281) 649-3489. Head: Lynn Miller
Decorative Arts Museum - 1969
Architecture, decorative arts 37517

The Museum of Fine Arts, 1001 Bissonnet, Houston, TX 77265 - T: (713) 526-1361, Fax: (713) 639-7399, Internet: http://www.mfah.org. Head: Peter C. Marzio
Fine Arts Museum - 1900
Multicultural art, European ancient art, American and European decorative art, impressionist and post- impressionist art, African gold, prints, drawings, photos 37518

Museum of Health and Medical Science, John P. McGovern Bldg,1515 Hermann Dr, Houston, TX 77004-7126 - T: (713) 942-7054, Fax: (713) 526-1434, E-mail: info@mhms.org, Internet: http://www.mhms.org. Head: Randy W. Ray
Science&Tech Museum - 1969 37519

National Museum of Funeral History, 415 Barren Springs Dr, Houston, TX 77090 - T: (281) 876-3063, Fax: (281) 876-4403, E-mail: nmfh@itrw.com, Internet: http://www.nmfh.org. Head: Gary Sanders
Historical Museum - 1992 37520

R.A. Vines Environmental Science Center, 8856 Westview Dr, Houston, TX 77055 - T: (713) 365-4175, Fax: (713) 365-4178. Head: Randell A. Beavers
Natural History Museum
Natural science 37521

Rice University Art Gallery, 6100 Main St, Houston, TX 77005 - T: (713) 348-6069, Fax: (713) 348-5980, E-mail: ruag@rice.edu, Internet: http://www.rice.edu/ruag. Head: Kimberly Davenport
University Museum / Public Gallery - 1971
Contemporary art, installation 37522

Rothko Chapel, 3900 Yupon, 1490 Sul Ross, Houston, TX 77006 - T: (713) 524-9839, Internet: http://www.rothkochapel.org. Head: Suna Umari
Religious Arts Museum - 1971
Religious art 37523

Sarah Campbell Blaffer Foundation, 5601 Main St, Houston, TX 77006 - T: (713) 639-7741, Fax: (713) 639-7742, E-mail: jclifton@mfah.org, Internet: http://riceinfo.rice.edu/projects/blaffer/index.html. Head: Dr. James Clifton, Charles W. Hall
Fine Arts Museum - 1964
Art 37524

Sarah Campbell Blaffer Gallery, Art Museum of the University of Houston, Entrance 16 Central Campus, 120 Fine Arts Bldg, Houston, TX 77204-4891 - T: (713) 743-9521, Fax: (713) 743-9525, E-mail: tsultan@uh.edu, Internet: http://www.blaffergallery.org. Head: Terrie Sultan
Fine Arts Museum / University Museum - 1973
Art 37525

Space Center Houston, 1601 NASA Road One, Houston, TX 77058-3696 - T: (281) 244-2105, Fax: (281) 283-7724, Internet: http://www.spacecenter.org. Head: Richard Allen
Science&Tech Museum - 1992
Space technology 37526

Howell NJ

Howell Historical Society Museum, 427 Lakewood-Farmingdale Rd, Howell, NJ 07731 - T: (732) 938-2212, E-mail: howellhist@aol.com, Internet: http://www.howellnj.com/historic/
Historical Museum - 1971 37527

Howes Cave NY

Iroquois Indian Museum, Caverns Rd, Howes Cave, NY 12092 - T: (518) 296-8949, Fax: (518) 296-8955, E-mail: info@iroquoismuseum.org, Internet: http://www.iroquoismuseum.org. Head: Erynne Ansell
Ethnology Museum / Folklore Museum - 1980
Contemporary Iroquois art, ethnology, archaeology 37528

Hubbardton VT

Hubbardton Battlefield Museum, Monument Hill Rd, Hubbardton, VT 05749 - T: (802) 759-2412, 828-3051, Fax: (802) 828-3206, E-mail: jdumville@dca.state.vt.us, Internet: http://www.state.vt.us/dca/historic/hp_sites.htm. Head: John P. Dumville
Historic Site - 1948
Historic site 37529

Hudson NY

American Museum of Fire Fighting, Firemen's Home, 125 Harry Howard Av, Hudson, NY 12534 - T: (518) 828-7695, Fax: (518) 828-1092, Internet: http://www.artcom.com/museums/
Science&Tech Museum - 1925 37530

Olana State Historic Site, State Rte 9-G, Hudson, NY 12534 - T: (518) 828-0135, Fax: (518) 828-6742, Internet: http://www.olana.org
Fine Arts Museum / Historical Museum - 1966 37531

Hudson OH

Historical Society Museum, 22 Aurora St, Hudson, OH 44236-2947 - T: (330) 653-6658, Fax: (330) 650-4693. Head: E. Leslie Polott
Historical Museum - 1910 37532

Hudson WI

The Octagon House, 1004 Third St, Hudson, WI 54016 - T: (715) 386-2654. Head: Marlene Smigel
Local Museum - 1948
Local hist 37533

Hugo CO

Lincoln County Museum, 7th St and 3rd Av, Hugo, CO 80821 - T: (719) 743-2485, Fax: (719) 743-2447. Head: Garald Ensign
Local Museum - 1972
Local hist 37534

Hugo OK

Choctaw Museum, 309 N B St, Hugo, OK 74743 - T: (580) 326-6630, Fax: (580) 326-2305
Science&Tech Museum - 1978
Railroad Museum 37535

Hugoton KS

Stevens County Gas and Historical Museum, 905 S Adams, Hugoton, KS 67951 - T: (316) 544-8751
Historical Museum / Science&Tech Museum - 1961
Original A.T.S.F. depot country store, incl barber shop, grocery store, agricultural and automotive displays 37536

Humboldt IA

Humboldt County Historical Association Museum, POB 162, Humboldt, IA 50548 - T: (515) 332-5280, 332-3449. Head: Tim Smith, Bette Newton
Local Museum - 1962
County history 37537

Huntersville NC

Historic Latta Plantation, 5225 Sample Rd, Huntersville, NC 28078 - T: (704) 875-2312, Fax: (704) 875-1394, Internet: http://www.lattaplanation.org. Head: Elizabeth Myers
Historical Museum - 1972 37538

Huntingdon PA

Huntingdon County Museum, 106 4th St, Huntingdon, PA 16652 - T: (814) 643-5449. Head: Nancy S. Shedd, Joel S. Steel
Local Museum - 1937
Local hist 37539

Swigart Museum, Museum Park, Rte 22 E, Huntingdon, PA 16652 - T: (814) 643-0885, Fax: (814) 643-2857, E-mail: tours@swigartmuseum.com, Internet: http://www.swigartmuseum.com. Head: Patricia B. Swigart, Marjorie E. Cutright
Science&Tech Museum - 1927
Automobiles 37540

Huntington IN

Huntington County Historical Society Museum, 315 Court St, Huntington, IN 46750 - T: (219) 356-7264, Fax: (219) 356-7265. Head: Robert McKinley
Historical Museum - 1932
Local history 37541

Wings of Freedom, 1365 Warren Rd, Huntington, IN 46750 - T: (219) 356-1945, Fax: (219) 356-1315, E-mail: scat@aol.com, Internet: http://www.aol.com/scatvii/page/index.htm
Military Museum / Science&Tech Museum - 1996
Aeronautics, military hist 37542

Huntington NY

Heckscher Museum of Art, 2 Prime Av, Huntington, NY 11743-7702 - T: (516) 351-3250, Fax: (516) 423-2145, E-mail: heckmuse@ix.netcom.com, Internet: http://www.heckscher.org. Head: Anne DePietro
Fine Arts Museum - 1920 37543

Huntington Historical Society Museum, 209 Main St, Huntington, NY 11743 - T: (516) 427-7045, Fax: (516) 427-7056, E-mail: hunthistory@juno.com
Local Museum - 1903 37544

Huntington VT

Birds of Vermont Museum, 900 Sherman Hollow Rd, Huntington, VT 05462 - T: (802) 434-2167, Fax: (802) 434-2167, E-mail: birdsvt@together.net, Internet: http://www.ejhs.k12.vt.us/homepages/birds. Head: Craig Reynolds, Robert N. Spear
Natural History Museum - 1986 37545

Huntington WV

Geology Museum, Marshall University, 3rd Av & Hal Greer Blvd, Huntington, WV 25755 - T: (304) 696-6720. Head: Dr. Dewey D. Sanderson
University Museum / Natural History Museum / Science&Tech Museum - 1837
Geology 37546

Huntington Museum of Art, 2033 McCoy Rd, Huntington, WV 25701 - T: (304) 529-2701, Fax: (304) 529-7447, E-mail: ltipton@hmoa.org, Internet: http://www.hmoa.org. Head: Margaret A. Skove
Fine Arts Museum - 1947
Art 37547

Huntington Beach CA

Huntington Beach International Surfing Museum, 411 Olive Av, Huntington Beach, CA 92648 - T: (714) 960-3483, Fax: (714) 960-1434, E-mail: Intsurfing@earthlink.net, Internet: http://www.surfingmuseum.org. Head: Don Strout
Special Museum - 1987
Surfing, restored Art Deco bldg 37548

Huntington Station NY

Walt Whitman Birthplace State Historic Site, 246 Old Walt Whitman Rd, Huntington Station, NY 11746-4148 - T: (516) 427-5240, Fax: (516) 427-5247, Internet: http://www.nysparks.com. Head: Barbara M. Bart
Historical Museum - 1949 37549

Huntsville AL

Alabama Constitution Village → Earlyworks Museum Complex

Art Galleries at UAH, Dept of Art and Art History, Huntsville, AL 35899 - T: (256) 890-6114, Fax: (256) 890-6411, E-mail: coffeymt@email.uah.edu, Internet: http://www.artuniversityalabama.com. Head: Marylyn Coffey
Fine Arts Museum / University Museum - 1975 37550

Burritt on the Mountain, Aliving Museum, 3101 Burritt Dr, Huntsville, AL 35801 - T: (256) 536-2882, Fax: (256) 532-1784, E-mail: bm-recep@ci.huntsville.al.us, Internet: http://www.burrittmuseum.com. Head: James L. Powers
Local Museum / Historical Museum / Natural History Museum - 1955 37551

Earlyworks Museum Complex, 404 Madison St, Huntsville, AL 35801 - T: (256) 564-8100, Fax: (256) 564-8151, E-mail: info@earlyworks.com, Internet: http://www.earlyworks.com. Head: Dana Lee Tatum
Historical Museum - 1982 37552

Huntsville Museum of Art, 300 Church St S, Huntsville, AL 35801 - T: (256) 535-4350, Fax: (256) 532-1743, E-mail: info@hsumuseum.org, Internet: http://www.hsumuseum.org. Head: Deborah Taylor
Fine Arts Museum - 1970 37553

United States Space and Rocket Center, 1 Tranquility Base, Huntsville, AL 35805 - T: (205) 837-3400, Fax: (205) 837-6137, E-mail: info@spacecamp.com, Internet: http://www.spacecamp.com. Head: Larry Capps
Science&Tech Museum - 1968
Aviation, early space history to space shuttle, missiles, Apollo artefacts 37554

Huntsville TX

Sam Houston Memorial Museum, 1836 Sam Houston Av, Huntsville, TX 77341 - T: (936) 294-1832, Fax: (409) 294-3670, E-mail: SMM_PBN@shsu.edu, Internet: http://www.SAMHOUSTON.org. Head: Patrick B. Nolan
Historical Museum - 1927
History, memorabilia of Sam Houston (1793 - 1863) 37555

Hurley NY

Hurley Patentee Manor, 464 Old Rte 209, Hurley, NY 12443 - T: (845) 331-5414, Fax: (845) 331-5414. Head: Carolyn M. Waligurski, Stephen S. Waligurski
Historical Museum - 1968 37556

Hurley WI

Old Iron County Courthouse Museum, Wisconsin State Historical Society, 303 Iron St, Hurley, WI 54534 - T: (715) 561-2244. Head: Walter Hoepner
Local Museum / Historic Site - 1976
Local hist, iron mining, loging, early family living, historical records 37557

Hurleyville NY

Sullivan County Historical Society Museum, 265 Main St, Hurleyville, NY 12747-0247 - T: (845) 434-8044, Fax: (845) 434-8056, E-mail: schs@warwick.net, Internet: http://www.sullivancounty-history.org. Head: Allan Dampman
Local Museum - 1898 37558

Huron SD

Dakotaland Museum, State Fair Grounds, Huron, SD 57350 - T: (605) 352-2633. Head: K.O. Kauth, Ruby Johannsen
Local Museum - 1960
Bird and animals (stuffed), Local hist 37559

Hurricane WV

Museum in the Community, 3 Valley Park Dr, Hurricane, WV 25526 - T: (304) 562-0484, Fax: (304) 562-4733, E-mail: mitc@newwave.net, Internet: http://www.newware.net/~mitc/. Head: Mark Payne, Cindy Johnson
Fine Arts Museum / Folklore Museum / Ethnology Museum - 1983 37560

Hutchinson KS

Kansas Cosmosphere and Space Center, 1100 N Plum, Hutchinson, KS 67501-1499 - T: (316) 662-2305, Fax: (316) 662-3693, E-mail: cosmo@cosmo.org, Internet: http://www.cosmo.org. Head: Max L. Ary
Science&Tech Museum - 1962
Space museum 37561

Reno County Museum, 100 S Walnut, Hutchinson, KS 67501-0664 - T: (316) 662-1184, Fax: (316) 662-0236, E-mail: rcmuseum@swbell.net, Internet: http://renocounty.museum.com. Head: Jay Smith
Local Museum - 1961
County history 37562

Hyannis NE

Grant County Museum, Grant County Courthouse, Grant and Harrison, Hyannis, NE 69350-9706 - T: (308) 458-2277. Head: Merle Hayward
Local Museum - 1963 37563

Hyde Park NY

Eleanor Roosevelt National Historic Site, Rte 9 G, Hyde Park, NY 12538 - T: (914) 229-9115, Fax: (914) 229-0739, E-mail: rova-superintendent@nps.gov, Internet: http://www.nps.gov/elro
Local Museum - 1977
Val-Kill, home of Eleanor Roosevelt from 1945-1962 37564

Franklin D. Roosevelt Library-Museum, 4079 Albany Post Rd, Hyde Park, NY 12538 - T: (845) 229-8114, Fax: (845) 229-0872, E-mail: library@roosevelt.nara.gov, Internet: http://www.fdrlibrary.marist.edu. Head: Cynthia M. Koch
Historical Museum / Library with Exhibitions - 1940
Culture coll, manuscripts, books, film, photographs, White House records 37565

Home of Franklin D. Roosevelt, Rte 9, Hyde Park, NY 12538 - T: (914) 229-9115, Fax: (914) 229-0739, E-mail: rova_superintendent@nps.gov., Internet: http://www.nps.gov/fofr
Local Museum - 1946 37566

Vanderbilt Mansion, Rte 9, Hyde Park, NY 12538 - T: (914) 229-9116, Fax: (914) 229-0739, Internet: http://www.nps.gov/vana
Historical Museum - 1940 37567

Idabel OK

Museum of the Red River, 812 E Lincoln Rd, Idabel, OK 74745 - T: (508) 286-3616, Fax: (508) 286-3616, Internet: http://www.museumofthe-redriver.org. Head: Henry Moy
Ethnology Museum / Archaeological Museum - 1974 37568

Idaho Springs CO

Heritage Museum, 2060 Colorado Blvd, Idaho Springs, CO 80452 - T: (303) 567-4382
Local Museum - 1964 37569

Underhill Museum, 1318 Miner Rd, Idaho Springs, CO 80452 - T: (303) 567-4709
Science&Tech Museum
Mining, U.S. Mineral Surveyor James Underhill 37570

Ignacio CO

Southern Ute Indian Cultural Center, Hwy 172 North, Ignacio, CO 81137 - T: (970) 563-9583, Fax: (970) 563-4641. Head: Helen Hoskins
Historical Museum / Ethnology Museum / Folklore Museum - 1972
Native American history, ethnology, Indian reservation 37571

Ilion NY

Remington Firearms Museum and Country Store, 14 Hoefler Av, Ilion, NY 13357 - T: (315) 895-3301, Fax: (315) 895-3543. Head: Dennis Sanita
Science&Tech Museum / Special Museum - 1959 37572

Ilwaco WA

Ilwaco Heritage Museum, 115 SE Lake St, Ilwaco, WA 98624 - T: (360) 642-3446, Fax: (360) 642-4615, E-mail: ihm@willapabay.org
Fine Arts Museum / Historical Museum - 1983
History, art 37573

Independence CA

Eastern California Museum, 155 Grant St, Independence, CA 93526 - T: (760) 878-0364, Fax: (760) 878-0412, E-mail: ecmuseum@gnet.com. Head: William H. Michael
Local Museum / Historical Museum / Ethnology Museum / Natural History Museum - 1928 37574

Independence MO

Community of Christ Musuem, The Temple, River and Walnut, Independence, MO 64051 - T: (816) 833-1000, Fax: (816) 521-3089, Internet: http://www.cofchrist.org. Head: Robert A. Gunderson
Religious Arts Museum - 1956 37575

Harry S. Truman Home, 223 N Main St, Independence, MO 64050 - T: (816) 254-2720, Fax: (816) 254-4491, E-mail: james_sanders@nps.gov, Internet: http://www.nps.gov/hstr/. Head: James Sanders
Historical Museum - 1982
Former farm home young Harry S Truman 37576

Harry S. Truman Museum, 500 W Hwy 24 and Delaware Rd, Independence, MO 64050 - T: (816) 833-1400, Fax: (816) 833-4368, E-mail: library@truman.nara.gov, Internet: http://www.trumanlibrary.org. Head: Scott Roley
Historical Museum - 1957
library 37577

John Wornall House Museum, 146 W 61 Terrace, Independence, MO 64113 - T: (816) 444-1858, Fax: (816) 361-8165, E-mail: jwornall@crn.org. Head: Rebecca Fye
Historical Museum / Decorative Arts Museum - 1972
Decorative arts, furniture, architecture 37578

Mormon Visitors Center, 937 W Walnut St, Independence, MO 64050-0000 - T: (816) 836-3466, Fax: (816) 252-6256, Internet: http://www.lds.org. Head: George Romney
Religious Arts Museum - 1970
30 ft mural of Christ, painting, reproductions 37579

National Frontier Trails Center, 318 W Pacific, Independence, MO 64050 - T: (816) 325-7575, Fax: (816) 325-7579, Internet: http://www.frontier-trailscenter.com. Head: John Mark Lambertson
Historical Museum - 1990 37580

Vaile Mansion - Dewitt Museum, 1500 N Liberty St, Independence, MO 64050 - T: (816) 325-7111, Fax: (816) 325-7400, Internet: http://www.ci.independence.mo.us
Local Museum / Historic Site - 1983
Local hist 37581

Indian Rocks Beach FL

Gulf Beach Art Center, 1515 Bay Palm Blvd, Indian Rocks Beach, FL 33785 - T: (813) 596-4331, Fax: (813) 995-1083. Head: Betsy Choetf
Fine Arts Museum - 1978
Art gallery 37582

Indiana PA

Historical and Genealogical Society of Indiana County, 200 S Sixth St, Indiana, PA 15701-2999 - T: (724) 463-9600, Fax: (724) 463-9899, E-mail: clarkhs@microserve.net, Internet: http://www.rootsweb.com/!paicgs/. Head: James Shertzer, Coleen Chambers
Local Museum - 1938
Local hist 37583

The Jimmy Stewart Museum, 845 Philadelphia St, Indiana, PA 15701 - T: (724) 349-6112, Fax: (724) 349-6140, E-mail: curator@jimmy.org, Internet: http://www.jimmy.org. Head: Elizabeth Salome
Special Museum / Performing Arts Museum - 1994
Cinematography 37584

Kipp Gallery, Indiana University of Pennsylvania, 470 Sprowls Hall, 11th St, Indiana, PA 15705 - T: (412) 357-6495, Fax: (412) 357-7778, Internet: http://www.iup.edu. Head: Dr Richard Field
Fine Arts Museum / University Museum - 1970 37585

The University Museum, Sutton Hall, Indiana University of Pennsylvania, Indiana, PA 15705-1087 - T: (724) 357-7930, Fax: (724) 357-2332, Internet: http://www.iup.edu/fa/museum. Head: Joseph Mack
Fine Arts Museum / University Museum - 1981
Art 37586

Indianapolis IN

The Children's Museum of Indianapolis, 3000 N Meridian St, Indianapolis, IN 46208 - T: (317) 924-5431, Fax: (317) 921-4019, E-mail: tcmi@childrensmuseum.org, Internet: http://www.childrensmuseum.org. Head: Dr. Jeffrey Patchen
Ethnology Museum / Local Museum / Natural History Museum - 1925 37587

Eiteljorg Museum of American Indians and Western Art, 500 W Washington, Indianapolis, IN 46204 - T: (317) 636-9378, Fax: (317) 264-1724, E-mail: museum@eiteljorg.org, Internet: http://www.eiteljorg.org. Head: John Vanausdall
Fine Arts Museum / Ethnology Museum / Folklore Museum - 1989
Art Museum 37588

Emil A. Blackmore Museum of the American Legion, 700 N Pennsylvania St, Indianapolis, IN 46204 - T: (317) 630-1356, Fax: (317) 630-1241, E-mail: library@legion.org, Internet: http://www.legion.org/library.htm. Head: Joseph J. Hovish
Military Museum
Military hist 37589

Historic Landmarks Foundation of Indiana, 340 W Michigan St, Indianapolis, IN 46202-3204 - T: (317) 639-4534, Fax: (317) 639-6734, Internet: http://www.historiclandmarks.org. Head: J. Reid Williamson, Amy Kogsbauer
Historical Museum - 1960
Historic Landmarks Headquarters, Morris-Butler House, Huddleston Farmhouse Inn Museum, Cambridge City, Kemper House Wedding Cake House 37590

Hoosier Salon Gallery, 6434 N College Av C, Indianapolis, IN 46220 - T: (317) 253-5340, Fax: (317) 259-1817. Head: Ginger Bievenour
Fine Arts Museum - 1926
Art 37591

Indiana Historical Society Museum, 450 W Ohio St, Indianapolis, IN 46202-3269 - T: (317) 232-1882, 234-1830, Fax: (317) 233-3109, Internet: http://www.indianahistory.org. Head: Peter T. Harstad
Historical Museum - 1830
History - library, exhibition programs 37592

Indiana Medical History Museum, 3045 W Vermont St, Indianapolis, IN 46222 - T: (317) 635-7329, Fax: (317) 635-7349, E-mail: edenharter@aol.com, Internet: http://www.imhm.org. Head: Virginia L. Terpening
Historical Museum - 1969
Medicine, housed in c.1896 pathology laboratory 37593

Indiana State Museum, 202 N Alabama St, Indianapolis, IN 46204 - T: (317) 232-1637, Fax: (317) 232-7090, E-mail: inmuseum@ismhs.org, Internet: http://www.state.in.us/ism. Head: Richard A. Gantz
Local Museum / Historical Museum / Natural History Museum - 1869
General museum, former Indianapolis City Hall, anthropology, culture and natural history 37594

Indiana War Memorials Museum, 431 N Meridian St, Indianapolis, IN 46204 - T: (317) 232-7615, Fax: (317) 233-4285, Internet: http://www.state.in.us/iwm/. Head: Bill Sweeney
Historic Site / Military Museum - 1927
Military, war history, housed in 1927 Indiana War Memorial 37595

Indianapolis Art Center, Churchman-Fehsenfeld-Gallery, 820 E 67th St, Indianapolis, IN 46220 - T: (317) 255-2464, Fax: (317) 254-0486, E-mail: inartctr@netdirect.net, Internet: http://www.indplsartcenter.org/. Head: David S. Thomas
Fine Arts Museum - 1934
Art Teaching Center 37596

Indianapolis Motor Speedway Hall of Fame Museum, 4790 W 16th St, Indianapolis, IN 46222 - T: (317) 481-8500, Fax: (317) 484-6449, E-mail: ebireley@brickyard.com, Internet: http://www.brickyard.com. Head: Ellen K. Bireley
Special Museum / Science&Tech Museum - 1956 37597

Indianapolis Museum of Art, 1200 W 38th St, Indianapolis, IN 46208-4196 - T: (317) 923-1331, Fax: (317) 931-1978, E-mail: ima@indy.net, Internet: http://www.ima-art.org. Head: Bret Waller
Fine Arts Museum / Decorative Arts Museum / Folklore Museum - 1883
Contemporary art, decorative art, paintings, sculptures, drawings, prints, photos, textiles and costumes - library 37598

Lockerbie Street Home of James Whitcomb Riley, 528 Lockerbie St, Indianapolis, IN 46202 - T: (317) 631-5885, Fax: (317) 955-0419. Head: Sandra Crain
Historical Museum - 1922 37599

Morris-Butler House Museum, 1204 N Park Av, Indianapolis, IN 46202 - T: (317) 636-5409, Fax: (317) 636-2630, E-mail: mbhouse@historiclandmarks.org, Internet: http://www.historiclandmarks.org. Head: J. Reid Williamson
Decorative Arts Museum - 1969 37600

National Art Museum of Sport, University Pl, 850 W Michigan St, Indianapolis, IN 46202-5198 - T: (317) 274-3627, Fax: (317) 274-3878, E-mail: arein@iupui.edu, Internet: http://www.namos.iupui.edu. Head: John D. Short
Fine Arts Museum / Special Museum - 1959
Sports art 37601

Phi Kappa Psi Fraternity-Heritage Hall, 510 Lockerbie St, Indianapolis, IN 46202 - T: (317) 632-1852, Fax: (317) 637-1898, E-mail: pkp_hq@phikappapsi.com, Internet: http://www.phikappapsi.com. Head: Tom C. Pennington
Local Museum - 1978 37602

President Benjamin Harrison Home, 1230 N Delaware St, Indianapolis, IN 46202-2598 - T: (317) 631-1888, Fax: (317) 632-5488, E-mail: Harrison@surf-ici.com, Internet: http://www.surf-ici.com/harrison. Head: Phyllis Geeslin
Historical Museum - 1937 37603

Indianola IA

Farnham Galleries, Simpson College, 701 N C St, Indianola, IA 50125 - T: (515) 961-6251, Fax: (515) 961-1498, E-mail: heinicke@storm.simpson.edu. Head: Dr. Kevin Lagree, Dr. Janet Heinicke
Fine Arts Museum / University Museum - 1982 37604

Ingalls KS

Santa Fe Trail Museums of Gray County, 204 S Main St, Ingalls, KS 67853 - T: (620) 335-5220
Local Museum - 1973
Local hist 37605

Interlaken NY

Interlaken Historical Society Museum, Main St, Interlaken, NY 14847 - T: (607) 532-8505
Historical Museum - 1960 37606

International Falls MN

Koochiching County Historical Society Museum, 214 Sixth Av, International Falls, MN 56649 - T: (218) 283-4316, Fax: (218) 283-8243. Head: Edgar S. Oerichbauer
Local Museum - 1958
Regional history, paintings, football memorabilia 37607

Voyageurs National Park Museum, 3131 Hwy 53, International Falls, MN 56649-8904 - T: (218) 283-9821, Fax: (218) 285-7407, E-mail: -voyasuperintendent@nps.gov. Head: Barbara West
Natural History Museum - 1975 37608

Inverness FL

Museum of Citrus County History-Old Courthouse, 532 Citrus Av, Crystel River, Inverness, FL 34450 - T: (352) 341-6429, Fax: (352) 341-6445. Head: Kathy Turner
Local Museum - 1985
Regional history 37609

Iola KS

Allen County Historical Museum, 207 N Jefferson, Iola, KS 66749 - T: (316) 365-3051
Local Museum - 1956
Local history 37610

The Major General Frederick Funston Boyhood Home and Museum, 14 S Washington Av, Iola, KS 66749 - T: (316) 365-3051, 365-6728. Head: Michael Anderson, Bob Hawk
Local Museum - 1995
Local hist 37611

Iowa City IA

Hospitals and Clinics Medical Museum, University of Iowa, 200 Hawkins Dr 8014 RCP, Iowa City, IA 52242 - T: (319) 356-1616, Fax: (319) 356-3862, E-mail: adrienne-drapkin@uiowa.edu, Internet: http://www.vh.org/welcome/UIHC/MedMuseum.html. Head: Adrienne Drapkin
Historical Museum - 1989
Medicine 37612

Plum Grove Historic Home, 1030 Carroll St, Iowa City, IA 52240 - T: (319) 351-5738, Fax: (319) 351-5310. Head: Laurie Robinson
Historical Museum - 1944
Home of Robert Lucas, first governor of Territory of Iowa 37613

University of Iowa Museum of Art, 150 N Riverside Dr, Iowa City, IA 52242 - T: (319) 335-1727, Fax: (319) 335-3677, E-mail: uima@uiowa.edu, Internet: http://www.uiowa.edu/uima. Head: Howard Collinson
Fine Arts Museum - 1967
International art 37614

University of Iowa Museum of Natural History, 10 Macbride Hall, Iowa City, IA 52242 - T: (319) 335-0481, E-mail: mus-nat-hist@uiowa.edu, Internet: http://www.uiowa.edu/~nathist. Head: Julia Golden
University Museum / Natural History Museum - 1858
Natural history 37615

Iowa Falls IA

Callkins Field Museum, 18335 135th St, Iowa Falls, IA 50126-8511 - T: (515) 648-9878, Fax: (515) 648-9878. Head: Duane Rieken
University Museum / Natural History Museum - 1890
Natural science, history 37616

Ipswich MA

Ipswich Historical Society Museum, 54 S Main St, Ipswich, MA 01938 - T: (978) 356-2811, Fax: (978) 356-2817, E-mail: ihs@gis.net. Head: Elizabeth Redmond
Local Museum - 1890
Local history 37617

Ipswich SD

J.W. Parmely Historical Museum, Hwy 12 and Hwy 45, Ipswich, SD 57451 - T: (605) 426-6949. Head: Phyllis M. Herrick
Local Museum - 1931
Local hist 37618

Iraan TX

Iraan Museum, Alley Oop Fantasy Land Park at West City Limits Off Hwy 190, Iraan, TX 79744 - T: (915) 639-8895
Historical Museum / Archaeological Museum - 1965
Archaeology, history 37619

Ironton OH

Lawrence County Gray House Museum, 506 S Sixth St, Ironton, OH 45638-0073 - T: (614) 532-1222. Head: Sharon Kouns
Local Museum / Historic Site - 1925 37620

Ironwood MI

Ironwood Area Historical Museum, 150 N Lowell St, Ironwood, MI 49938 - T: (906) 932-0287, Internet: http://www.portup.com/~joe. Head: Jean Jindrich
Local Museum - 1970
Local hist 37621

Irvine CA

Irvine Museum, 18881 Von Karman, Ste 1250, Irvine, CA 92612 - T: (949) 476-0294, Fax: (949) 476-2437, Internet: http://www.irvinemuseum.org. Head: Jean Stern
Fine Arts Museum - 1992 37622

University Art Gallery, University of California, Irvine, 101 HTC, Irvine, CA 92967-2775 - T: (714) 824-8251, Fax: (714) 824-4197, E-mail: jweiffen@uci.edu, Internet: http://www.beallcenter.uci.edu. Head: Jeanie Weiffenbach
Fine Arts Museum / University Museum - 1965 37623

Irving

The National Museum of Communications (closed) 37624

Irving TX

National Scouting Museum, 1325 W Walnut Hill Ln, Irving, TX 75015-2079 - T: (800) 303-3047, Fax: (912) 580-2059. Head: Dan Matkinl
Special Museum - 1959
History of the Boy Scouts of America, uniforms, Norman Rockwell oils, patches 37625

Ishpeming MI

United States National Ski Hall of Fame and Museum, 610 Palms, Ishpeming, MI 49849 - T: (906) 485-6323, Fax: (906) 486-4570, E-mail: skihall@uplogon.com, Internet: http://www.skihall.com
Special Museum - 1954
Sports 37626

Isle La Motte VT

Isle La Motte Historical Society Museum, Isle La Motte, VT 05463 - T: (802) 928-3173, Fax: (802) 928-3342, E-mail: camiln@surfglobal.net. Head: Bob McEwen
Local Museum - 1925
Local hist 37627

Islesboro ME

Islesboro Historical Museum, 388 Main Rd, Islesboro, ME 04848 - T: (207) 734-6733
Local Museum - 1964
Local history 37628

Sailor's Memorial Museum, Grindle Point, Islesboro, ME 04848-0076 - T: (207) 734-2253, Fax: (207) 734-8394
Historical Museum - 1936
Maritime, 1850 Lighthouse 37629

Ithaca NY

DeWitt Historical Society Museum, 401 E State St, Ithaca, NY 14850 - T: (607) 273-8284, Fax: (607) 273-6107, E-mail: dhs@lakenet.org, Internet: http://www.lakenet.org/dewitt. Head: Matthew Braun
Historical Museum - 1935 37630

Handwerker Gallery of Art, 1170 Gannett Ctr, Ithaca College, Ithaca, NY 14850-7276 - T: (607) 274-3018, Fax: (607) 274-1484, E-mail: jstojanovic@ithaca.edu, Internet: http://www.ithaca.edu/handwerker. Head: Jelena Stojanovic
Fine Arts Museum / University Museum - 1977
Art Gallery 37631

Herbert F. Johnson Museum of Art, Cornell University, Ithaca, NY 14853 - T: (607) 255-6464, Fax: (607) 255-9940, E-mail: museum@cornell.edu, Internet: http://www.museum.cornell.edu. Head: Franklin W. Robinson
Fine Arts Museum / University Museum - 1973 37632

Hinckley Foundation Museum, 410 E Seneca St, Ithaca, NY 14850 - T: (607) 273-7053. Head: Nicole M. Carrier, Tim Bumgardner
Historical Museum / Folklore Museum / Special Museum - 1972 37633

Sciencenter, 601 First St, Ithaca, NY 14850 - T: (607) 272-0600, Fax: (607) 277-7469, E-mail: info@sciencenter.org, Internet: http://www.sciencenter.org. Head: Charles H. Trautmann
Science&Tech Museum - 1983
Science and technology 37634

Jacksboro TX

Fort Richardson, Hwy 281 S, Jacksboro, TX 76458 - T: (940) 567-3506, Fax: (940) 567-5488, E-mail: fortrich@wf.net. Head: Andrew Sansom
Local Museum - 1968
Local hist 37635

Jackson MI

Ella Sharp Museum, 3225 Fourth St, Jackson, MI 49203 - T: (517) 787-2320, Fax: (517) 787-2933, E-mail: ellasharp@dmci.net
Fine Arts Museum / Local Museum - 1964 37636

Jackson MS

Manship House Museum, 420 E Fortification St, Jackson, MS 39202-2340 - T: (601) 961-4724, Fax: (601) 354-6043
Historical Museum - 1980 37637

Mississippi Governor's Mansion, 300 E Capitol, Jackson, MS 39201 - T: (601) 359-3175, Fax: (601) 359-6473. Head: Elbert R. Hilliard
Historical Museum - 1842 37638

Mississippi Museum of Art, 201 E Pascagoula St, Jackson, MS 39201 - T: (601) 960-1515, Fax: (601) 960-1505, E-mail: mmart@netdoor.com, Internet: http://www.msmuseumart.org. Head: R. Andrew Maass
Fine Arts Museum - 1911 37639

Mississippi Museum of Natural Science, 111 N Jefferson St, Jackson, MS 39202 - T: (601) 354-7303, Fax: (601) 354-7227. Head: Libby Hartfield
Natural History Museum - 1934
library 37640

Museum of the Southern Jewish Experience, 4915 I-55 N, Ste 204B, Jackson, MS 39206 - T: (601) 362-6357, Fax: (601) 366-6293, E-mail: information@msje.org, Internet: http://www.msje.org
Religious Arts Museum - 1989 37641

Oaks House Museum, 823 N Jefferson St, Jackson, MS 39202 - T: (601) 353-9339. Head: Frances Morse
Historical Museum - 1960 37642

Old Capitol Museum of Mississippi History, 100 S State, Jackson, MS 39201 - T: (601) 359-6920, Fax: (601) 359-6981, E-mail: ocmuseum@mdah.state.ms.us, Internet: http://www.mdah.state.ms.us. Head: Donna B. Dye
Historical Museum - 1961
State history, household objects, textiles (quilts, clothing), folk art, craft, civil war flags, swords 37643

Smith Robertson Museum, 528 Bloom St, Jackson, MS 39202-4005 - T: (601) 960-1457, Fax: (601) 960-2070
Historical Museum - 1977
Public funds for Blacks in Jackson 37644

Jackson TN

Casey Jones Home and Railroad Museum, Casey Jones Village, Jackson, TN 38305 - T: (901) 668-1222, Fax: (901) 664-7782, E-mail: casey@aeneas.net. Head: Mark Taylor
Science&Tech Museum - 1956
Railroads 37645

Jackson WY

National Museum of Wildlife Art, 2820 Rungius Rd, Jackson, WY 83001 - T: (307) 733-5771, 733-5328, Fax: (307) 733-5787, E-mail: info@wildlifeart.org, Internet: http://www.wildlifeart.org. Head: Dr. Francine Carraro
Fine Arts Museum - 1987
Art 37646

Jacksonport AR

Courthouse Museum, Jacksonport State Park, Jacksonport, AR 72075 - T: (870) 523-2143, Fax: (870) 523-4260, E-mail: jacksonport@arkansas.com, Internet: http://www.arkansas.com. Head: Mark Ballard
Historical Museum - 1965 37647

Jacksonville AL

Dr. Francis Medical and Apothecary Museum, 207 Gayle Av SW, Jacksonville, AL 36265 - T: (205) 435-5091, Fax: (205) 435-4103. Head: Barbara B. Johnson
Historical Museum - 1968 37648

Jacksonville FL

Alexander Brest Museum, 2800 University Blvd N, Jacksonville, FL 32211 - T: (904) 745-7371, Fax: (904) 745-7375. Head: David Lauderdale
Fine Arts Museum / University Museum - 1977
Art 37649

Cummer Museum of Art, 829 Riverside Av, Jacksonville, FL 32204 - T: (904) 356-6857, Fax: (904) 353-4101, E-mail: info@cummer.org, Internet: http://www.cummer.org. Head: Dr. Maarten van de Guchte
Fine Arts Museum - 1958
Art - gardens 37650

Fort Caroline Museum, 12713 Fort Caroline Rd, Jacksonville, FL 32225 - T: (904) 641-7155, Fax: (904) 641-3798, E-mail: FOCA_Interpretation@nps.gov, Internet: http://www.nps.gov/timu. Head: Barbara Goodman
Historical Museum / Natural History Museum - 1953
History, natural history 37651

Kent Campus Museum and Gallery, Florida Community College, 3939 Roosevelt Blvd, Jacksonville, FL 32205 - T: (904) 381-3674, Fax: (904) 381-3490
Fine Arts Museum / University Museum - 1971 37652

Kingsley Plantation, 11676 Palmetto Av, Jacksonville, FL 32226 - T: (904) 251-3537, Fax: (904) 251-3577, E-mail: -TIMU_Kingsley_Plantation@nps.gov, Internet: http://www.cr.nps.gov/nr/21.htm
Historical Museum / Historic Site - 1955
Historic site 37653

Museum of Science and History of Jacksonville, 1025 Museum Circle, Jacksonville, FL 32207-9053 - T: (904) 396-7062, Fax: (904) 396-5799, E-mail: moshfac@jax-inter.net, Internet: http://www.jacksonvillemuseum.com. Head: Margo Dundon
Historical Museum / Science&Tech Museum - 1941
Planetarium 37654

Jacksonville IL

David Strawn Art Gallery, Art Association of Jacksonville, 331 W College Av, Jacksonville, IL 62651-1213 - T: (217) 243-9390, E-mail: strawn@csj.net, Internet: http://www.japl.lib.il.us/community/strawn. Head: Tori Long, Kelly M. Gross
Fine Arts Museum / Public Gallery - 1873 37655

Jaffrey NH

Jaffrey Civic Center, 40 Main St, Jaffrey, NH 03452 - T: (603) 532-6527. Head: Scott Cunningham, Kim Cunningham
Folklore Museum / Local Museum - 1964 37656

Jamaica NY

Jamaica Center for the Performing and Visual Arts, 161-04 Jamaica Av, Jamaica, NY 11432 - T: (718) 658-7400, Fax: (718) 658-7922, E-mail: jamarts@walrus.com. Head: Howard Asch
Fine Arts Museum / Decorative Arts Museum - 1972
Art 37657

Queens Library Gallery, 89-11 Merrick Blvd, Jamaica, NY 11432 - T: (718) 990-0700, Fax: (718) 291-8936, E-mail: mkrazmien@queenslibrary.org, Internet: http://www.queenslibrary.org
Public Gallery - 1995
Art 37658

Jamestown ND

Frontier Village Museum, 17th St, Jamestown, ND 58401 - T: (701) 252-6307, 252-4835, Fax: (701) 252-8089. Head: Charles Tanata
Local Museum - 1959
Local hist 37659

Stutsman County Memorial Museum, 321 Third Av SE, Jamestown, ND 58401-1002 - T: (701) 252-6741
Local Museum / Historical Museum - 1964 37660

Jamestown NY

Art Gallery, James Prendergast Library, 509 Cherry St, Jamestown, NY 14701 - T: (716) 484-7135, Fax: (716) 487-1148, E-mail: reference@cclslib.org, Internet: http://www.cclslib.org/prendergast/. Head: Murray L. Bob
Fine Arts Museum - 1880 37661

Fenton History Center-Museum and Library, 67 Washington St, Jamestown, NY 14701 - T: (716) 664-6256, Fax: (716) 483-7524, E-mail: information@fentonhistorycenter.org, Internet: http://www.fentonhistorycenter.org. Head: Christin L. Stein
Historical Museum - 1964 37662

Forum Gallery, 525 Falconer St, Jamestown, NY 14701 - T: (716) 665-5220 ext 478, Fax: (716) 665-7023, E-mail: colbyjd@jccw22.cc.sunyjcc.edu. Head: James Colby
Public Gallery - 1969 37663

Roger Tory Peterson Institute of Natural History Museum, 311 Curtis St, Jamestown, NY 14701 - T: (716) 665-2473, Fax: (716) 665-3794, E-mail: webmaster@rtpi.org, Internet: http://www.rtpi.org. Head: James M. Berry
Natural History Museum - 1984 37664

Jamestown RI

Jamestown Museum, 92 Narragansett Av, Jamestown, RI 02835 - T: (401) 423-0784. Head: John H. Howard
Local Museum - 1972
Local hist 37665

Watson Farm, 455 North Rd, Jamestown, RI 02835 - T: (401) 423-0005, (617) 227-3956, Fax: (617) 227-9204, Internet: http://www.spnea.org
Folklore Museum / Agriculture Museum
Historic farm 37666

Jamestown VA

Jamestown Visitor Center Museum, Colonial National Historical Park, Jamestown, VA 23081 - T: (757) 229-1733, Fax: (757) 229-4273, Internet: http://www.nps.gov/colo. Head: Alec Gould
Local Museum - 1930
Local hist, first permanent English settlement at Jamestown 37667

Janesville WI

The Lincoln-Tallman Restorations, 440 N Jackson St, Janesville, WI 53545 - T: (608) 752-4519, 756-4509, Fax: (608) 741-9596, Internet: http://www.lincolntallman.org. Head: Laurel Fant, Madge Murphy
Local Museum - 1951
Historic house 37668

Rock County Historical Society Museum, 426 N Jackson St, Janesville, WI 53545 - T: (608) 756-4509, Fax: (608) 741-9596, E-mail: rchs@ticon.net, Internet: http://www.lincolntallman.org. Head: Laurel Fant
Local Museum - 1948
Local hist 37669

Jefferson GA

Crawford W. Long Museum, 28 College St, Jefferson, GA 30549 - T: (706) 367-5307, Fax: (706) 367-5307, Internet: http://www.crawfordlong.org. Head: Tina B. Harris
Historical Museum - 1957
Medical history 37670

Jefferson IA

Jefferson Telephone Museum, 105 W Harrison, Jefferson, IA 50129 - T: (515) 386-2626, 386-4141, Fax: (515) 386-2600. Head: James Daubendiek
Science&Tech Museum - 1960 37671

Jefferson TX

Jefferson Historical Museum, 223 W Austin, Jefferson, TX 75657 - T: (903) 665-2775. Head: Bill McCay
Local Museum - 1948
Local hist 37672

Jefferson WI

Aztalan Museum, N 6264 Hwy Q, Jefferson, WI 53549 - T: (414) 648-8845. Head: Gerald Nease
Local Museum - 1941
Local hist 37673

Jefferson City MO

Cole County Historical Museum, 109 Madison, Jefferson City, MO 65101 - T: (573) 635-1850. Head: Natalie Tackett, William Tackett
Historical Museum - 1941 37674

Missouri State Museum, Missouri State Capitol, Capitol Av, Jefferson City, MO 65101 - T: (573) 751-2854, Fax: (573) 526-2927, Internet: http://www.mostateparks.com. Head: Molly Strode
Historical Museum - 1919 37675

Jeffersonville IN

Howard Steamboat Museum, 1101 E Market St, Jeffersonville, IN 47130 - T: (812) 283-3728, Fax: (812) 283-6049, Internet: http://www.steamboatmuseum.org
Historical Museum / Science&Tech Museum - 1958
Home of Edmonds J. Howard, son of James E. Howard, founder of the Howard Shipyards 1834 37676

Jekyll Island GA

Jekyll Island Museum, 381 Riverview Dr, Jekyll Island, GA 31527 - T: (912) 635-2119, 635-2236, Fax: (912) 635-4420, E-mail: jekyllisland@compuserve.com, Internet: http://www.jekyllisland.com. Head: F. Warren Murphey
Local Museum - 1954
Local history 37677

Jemez Springs NM

Jemez State Monument, 1 mile North of Jemez Springs, State Hwy 4, Jemez Springs, NM 87025 - T: (505) 829-3530, Fax: (505) 829-3530. Head: A. Robert Baca
Local Museum - 1935
Local hist 37678

Jenkintown PA

Abington Art Center, 515 Meetinghouse Rd, Jenkintown, PA 19046 - T: (215) 887-4882, Fax: (215) 887-1402. Head: Laura Burnham
Fine Arts Museum - 1939 37679

Jennings LA

The Zigler Museum, 411 Clara St, Jennings, LA 70546 - T: (318) 824-0114, Fax: (318) 824-0120, E-mail: zigler@fweb.net, Internet: http://www.jeffdavis.org. Head: Dolores Spears, Richard Boisture
Fine Arts Museum - 1963
European and American art 37680

Jericho Corners VT

Jericho Historical Society Museum, Rte 15, Jericho Corners, VT 05465 - T: (802) 899-3225. Head: Wayne Howe
Local Museum - 1971
Local hist 37681

Jerome AZ

Jerome State Historic Park, Arizona State Parks, Douglas Rd, Jerome, AZ 86331, mail addr: POB D, Jerome, AZ 86331 - T: (520) 634-5381, Fax: (520) 639-3132, Internet: http://www.pr.state.az.us. Head: Jon Clow
Historical Museum - 1962
History, mining 37682

Jersey City NJ

Afro-American Historical Society Museum, 1841 Kennedy Blvd, Jersey City, NJ 07305 - T: (201) 547-5262, Fax: (201) 547-5392. Head: Neal E. Brunson
Historical Museum - 1977
History 37683

Courtney and Lemmerman Galleries, New Jersey City University, 2039 Kennedy Blvd, Jersey City, NJ 07305 - T: (201) 200-3214, Fax: (201) 200-3224, E-mail: hbastidas@njcu.edu. Head: Hugo Xavier Bastidas
Fine Arts Museum
Prints, drawings 37684

Jersey City Museum, 350 Montgommery St, Jersey City, NJ 07302 - T: (201) 413-0303, Fax: (201) 413-9922, E-mail: info@jerseycitymuseum.org, Internet: http://www.jerseycitymuseum.org. Head: Nina S. Jacobs
Fine Arts Museum / Local Museum - 1901
Local artifacts, regional art (19th-20th c) 37685

Saint Peter's College Art Gallery, 2641 Kennedy Blvd, Jersey City, NJ 07306 - T: (201) 915-9000, Fax: (201) 413-1669. Head: Oscar Magnan
Fine Arts Museum - 1971
Different art trends 37686

Jim Thorpe PA

Asa Packer Mansion, Packer Hill, Jim Thorpe, PA 18229-0108 - T: (717) 325-3229, Fax: (717) 325-8154. Head: John Dugan
Local Museum - 1913
Local hist, 1860 Victorian mansion 37687

Johnson City TN

Carroll Reece Museum, East Tennessee State University, Johnson City, TN 37614 - T: (423) 439-4392, Fax: (423) 439-4283, E-mail: whiteb@etsu.edu, Internet: http://cass.etsu.edu/museum. Head: Blair White
Fine Arts Museum / University Museum / Historical Museum - 1965
History, art 37688

Elizabeth Slocumb Galleries, Carrol Reece Museum, c/o Dept. of Art, East Tennessee State University, POB 70708, Johnson City, TN 37614-0708 - T: (423) 439-5315, Fax: (423) 439-4393, E-mail: apack@lycos.com, Internet: http://www.etsu-tenn-st.edu/design/. Head: Allison Pack
Fine Arts Museum / University Museum - 1965
Art 37689

Hands On! Regional Museum, 315 E Main St, Johnson City, TN 37601 - T: (423) 928-6508, 928-6509, Fax: (423) 928-6915, E-mail: handson@xtn.net, Internet: http://www.handsonmuseum.org. Head: Duffie Jones
Special Museum / Science&Tech Museum - 1986
Children's museum 37690

Johnson City TX

Lyndon B. Johnson National Historical Park, 100 Ladybird Ln, Johnson City, TX 78636 - T: (830) 868-7128, Fax: (830) 868-0810, Internet: http://www.nps.gov/lyjo. Head: Leslie Starr Hart
Local Museum - 1969
Local hist 37691

Johnstown NY

Johnson Hall, Hall Av, Johnstown, NY 12095 - T: (518) 762-8712, Fax: (518) 762-2330, E-mail: wanda.burch@oprhp.state.ny.us, Internet: http://www.nysparks.com. Head: Wanda Burch
Historical Museum - 1763 37692

Johnstown Historical Society Museum, 17 N William St, Johnstown, NY 12095 - T: (518) 762-7076
Historical Museum - 1892 37693

Johnstown PA

Johnstown Flood Museum, 304 Washington St, Johnstown, PA 15901 - T: (814) 539-1889, Fax: (814) 535-1931, E-mail: jaha@ctcnet.net, Internet: http://www.ctcnet.net/jaha. Head: Richard A. Burkert
Local Museum - 1971
Local hist 37694

Southern Alleghenies Museum of Art at Johnstown, c/o University of Pittsburgh at Johnstown, Pasquerilla Performing Arts Center, Johnstown, PA 15904 - T: (814) 269-7234, Fax: (814) 269-7240, E-mail: ncward@pitt.edu, Internet: http://www.sama-sfc.org. Head: Nancy Ward
Fine Arts Museum - 1982 37695

Joliet IL

Joliet Area Historical Society Museum, 17 E Van Buren St, Joliet, IL 60431 - T: (815) 722-7003. Head: Gene Bogdan
Local Museum - 1981
Local history 37696

Jolon CA

San Antonio Mission, Mission Creek Rd, Jolon, CA 93928 - T: (408) 385-4478, Fax: (408) 386-9332. Head: John Gini
Religious Arts Museum - 1771 37697

Jonesboro AR

Arkansas State University Art Gallery, Caraway Rd, Jonesboro, AR 72467 - T: (870) 972-3050, Fax: (870) 972-3932, E-mail: cspeele@aztec.astate.edu, Internet: http://www.astate.edu/docs/acad/cfa/art/. Head: Curtis Steele
Fine Arts Museum / University Museum - 1967
Art gallery 37698

Arkansas State University Museum, 110 Cooley Dr, Jonesboro, AR 72401 - T: (870) 972-2074, Fax: (870) 972-2793, E-mail: dsessums@cnoctaw.astate.edu. Head: Danny Sessums
University Museum - 1936
University hist 37699

Jonesborough TN

Jonesborough-Washington County History Museum, 117 Boone St, Jonesborough, TN 37659 - T: (423) 753-1015, Fax: (423) 753-6129, E-mail: jbwchm@tricon.net, Internet: http://jonesborough.tricon.net/museum.html. Head: Barry A. Beach
Local Museum - 1982
Local hist 37700

Joplin MO

Dorothea B. Hoover Historical Museum, Schifferdecker Park, Joplin, MO 64802 - T: (417) 623-1180, Fax: (417) 623-6393, E-mail: jopmusm@ipa.net. Head: Brad Belk
Local Museum - 1973
Local history 37701

George A. Spiva Center for the Arts, 222 W Third St, Joplin, MO 64801 - T: (417) 623-0183, Fax: (417) 623-3805, E-mail: artspiva@clandjop.com, Internet: http://www.clandjop.com/~artspiva. Head: Darlene Brown
Fine Arts Museum - 1957 37702

Tri-State Mineral Museum, Schifferdecker Park, Joplin, MO 64801 - T: (417) 623-2341, Fax: (417) 623-6393, E-mail: jopmusm@ipa.net. Head: Brad Belk
Natural History Museum - 1931 37703

Julesburg CO

Fort Sedgwick Depot Museum, 202 W 1st St, Julesburg, CO 80737 - T: (970) 474-2061
Local Museum - 1940
General museum, Union Pacific Railroad depot 37704

Juliette GA

Jarrell Plantation Georgia State Historic Site, Jarrell Plantation Rd, Juliette, GA 31046-2515 - T: (912) 986-5172, Fax: (912) 986-5919, E-mail: jarrell@mylink.net, Internet: http://www.dnr.state.ga.us/dnr/parks
Agriculture Museum - 1974
Living farm 37705

Junction TX

Kimble County Historical Museum, 101 N 4th St, Junction, TX 76849 - T: (915) 446-4219, Fax: (915) 446-2871, E-mail: burtwyatt@sat.net. Head: Frederica Wyatt
Local Museum - 1966
Local hist 37706

Junction City OR

Junction City Historical Society Museum, 655 Holly St, Junction City, OR 97448 - T: (541) 998-2924, Fax: (541) 998-2924
Historical Museum - 1971 37707

Juneau AK

Alaska State Museum, 395 Whittier St, Juneau, AK 99801-1718 - T: (907) 465-2901, Fax: (907) 465-2976, E-mail: bkato@educ.state.ak.us, Internet: http://www.museum.state.ak.us. Head: Karen R. Crane, Nadine Simonelli
Local Museum / Folklore Museum - 1900
General State museum 37708

House of Wickersham, 213 Seventh St, Juneau, AK 99801 - T: (907) 465-4563, Fax: (907) 465-5330, E-mail: separks@alaska.net. Head: William Garry
Historical Museum / Historic Site - 1984 37709

Juneau Douglas City Museum, 114 4th St, Juneau, AK 99801 - T: (907) 586-3572, Fax: (907) 586-3203, E-mail: mary_pat_wyatt@mail.ci.juneau.ak.us, Internet: http://www.juneau.lib.ak.us.parksrec/
Local Museum - 1976
Local history, culture 37710

Jupiter FL

Florida History Museum, 805 N U.S. Hwy 1, Jupiter, FL 33477 - T: (561) 747-6639, Fax: (561) 575-3292, E-mail: fhcm3@bellsouth.net, Internet: http://www.community.gopbi/FLhistory
Historical Museum - 1971
General History, lighthouse, historic homes 37711

Kadoka SD

Jackson-Washabaugh Historical Museum, S Main St, Kadoka, SD 57543 - T: (605) 837-2229, E-mail: radokaci@rapidnet.com
Local Museum - 1980
Local hist 37712

Kailua-Kona HI

Hulihee Palace, 75-5718 Alii Dr, Kailua-Kona, HI 96740 - T: (808) 329-1877, Fax: (808) 329-1321, E-mail: hulihee@ilhawaii.net, Internet: http://www.huliheepalace.org
Decorative Arts Museum / Natural History Museum - 1928
Residence for Hawaiian royalty 37713

Kake AK

Kake Tribal Heritage Foundation, POB 317, Kake, AK 99830 - T: (907) 785-3165, Fax: (907) 790-3258. Head: Henrich Kadake
Open Air Museum / Local Museum - 1986
Local hist 37714

Kalamazoo MI

Alamo Township Museum-John E. Gray Memorial, 8119 N 6th St, Kalamazoo, MI 49009 - T: (616) 344-9579. Head: Jeanette Grabowski
Ethnology Museum / Local Museum - 1969 37715

Gallery II, Western Michigan University, College of Fine Arts, 1903 W Michigan Av, Kalamazoo, MI 49008 - T: (616) 387-2455, 387-2436, Fax: (616) 387-2477, E-mail: exhibitions@wmich.edu, Internet: http://www.wmich.edu/art/exhibitions/. Head: Jacquelyn Ruttinger
Public Gallery / University Museum - 1975
Prints, sculptures 37716

Kalamazoo Aviation History Museum, 3101 E Milham Rd, Kalamazoo, MI 49002 - T: (616) 382-6555, Fax: (616) 382-1813, E-mail: bellis@airzoo.org, Internet: http://www.airzoo.org. Head: Robert E. Ellis, Suzanne D. Parish
Military Museum / Science&Tech Museum - 1977
Aviation 37717

Kalamazoo Institute of Arts, 314 S Park St, Kalamazoo, MI 49007-5102 - T: (616) 349-7775, Fax: (616) 349-9313, E-mail: kialib@iserv.net, Internet: http://www.kiarts.org. Head: James A. Bridenstine
Fine Arts Museum - 1924
Art - school 37718

Kalamazoo Valley Museum, Kalmazzo Valley Community College, 230 N Rose St, Kalamazoo, MI 49007 - T: (616) 373-7990, Fax: (616) 373-7997, E-mail: pnorris@kvcc.edu, Internet: http://www.kvcc.edu/kvm/. Head: Dr. Patrick Norris
Local Museum / Science&Tech Museum - 1927
Participatory, science, technology - planetarium 37719

Kalaupapa HI

Kalaupapa Historical Park, 7 Puahi St, Kalaupapa, HI 96742, mail addr: POB 2222, Kalaupapa, HI 96742 - T: (808) 567-6802, Fax: (808) 567-6729, Internet: http://www.nps.gov/kala/gov. Head: Dean Alexander
Historic Site - 1980
Site of the 1886-present Molokai Island leprosy settlement 37720

Kalida OH

Putnam County Historical Society Museum, 201 E Main St, Kalida, OH 45853 - T: (419) 532-3008
Local Museum - 1873 37721

Kalispell MT

Conrad Mansion Museum, Between Third and Fourth Sts and Woodland Av, Kalispell, MT 59901 - T: (406) 755-2166, E-mail: paivaa@altavista.net, Internet: http://www.conradmansion.com. Head: L.A. Bibler
Historical Museum - 1975 37722

Hockaday Museum of Arts, Second Av E at Third St, Kalispell, MT 59901 - T: (406) 755-5268, Fax: (406) 755-2023, E-mail: hockaday@aboutmontana.net, Internet: http://www.hockadayartmuseum.org. Head: David Lee Eubank
Fine Arts Museum - 1968 37723

Kalkaska MI

Kalkaska County Museum, POB 1178, Kalkaska, MI 49646 - T: (616) 258-7840. Head: Don F. Darke
Local Museum - 1967
Regional history, Grand Rapids and Indiana Railroad depot 37724

Kampsville IL

Center for American Archeology, Hwy 100, Kampsville, IL 62053 - T: (618) 653-4316, Fax: (618) 653-4232, E-mail: caa@caa-archeology.org, Internet: http://www.caa-archeology.org. Head: Cynthia Sutton
Archaeological Museum - 1954
Archaeology 37725

Kane PA

Thomas L. Kane Memorial Chapel, 30 Chestnut St, Kane, PA 16735 - T: (814) 837-9729
Religious Arts Museum - 1970
Religious hist, historic chapel 37726

Kaneohe HI

Hawaii Pacific University Gallery, 45-045 Kamehamcha Hwy, Kaneohe, HI 968744 - T: (808) 544-0287, Fax: (808) 544-1136, E-mail: nellis@hpu.edu, Internet: http://www.hpu.edu. Head: Sanit Khewhok
University Museum / Fine Arts Museum - 1983 37727

Kankakee IL

Kankakee County Historical Society Museum, 801 South Eighth Av, Kankakee, IL 60901 - T: (815) 932-5204, Fax: (815) 932-5204, E-mail: museum@daily-journal.com. Head: Anne L. Chandler
Local Museum - 1906
Local history 37728

Kanopolis KS

Fort Harker Museum, 309 W Ohio St, Kanopolis, KS 67454 - T: (785) 472-3059. Head: Tyra Denny
Military Museum - 1961
Military 37729

Kansas City KS

The Children's Museum of Kansas City, 4601 State Av, Kansas City, KS 66102 - T: (913) 287-8888, Fax: (913) 287-8332, Internet: http://www.kidmuzm.org. Head: Joseph Globoke, Marty Porter
Special Museum - 1984 37730

Clendening History of Medicine Library and Museum, University of Kansas, 3901 Rainbow Blvd, Kansas City, KS 66160-7311 - T: (913) 588-7244, Fax: (913) 588-7060, Internet: http://www.kumc.edu/service/clendening/. Head: Robert L. Martensen
University Museum / Historical Museum - 1945
Medicine 37731

Grinter Place, 1420 S 78th St, Kansas City, KS 66111 - T: (913) 299-0373, E-mail: grinter@kshs.org, Internet: http://www.kshs.org. Head: Eric Page
Historical Museum - 1968
Historic house, built by Moses Grinter, culture, domestic life 37732

Kansas City MO

American Royal Museum, 1701 American Royal Court, Kansas City, MO 64102 - T: (816) 221-9800, Fax: (816) 221-8189, E-mail: AmRoyalEdu@aol.com, Internet: http://www.americanroyal.com. Head: Nancy Perry
Agriculture Museum - 1992
Agriculture, horses 37733

Creative Arts Center, 4525 Oak St, Kansas City, MO 64111 - T: (816) 751-1236, Fax: (816) 761-7154. Head: Marc F. Wilson
Fine Arts Museum 37734

Gallery of Art → John Maxine Belger Center

John Maxine Belger Center, University of Missouri-Kansas City, 203 Fine Arts, 5100 Rockhill Rd, Kansas City, MO 64110-2499 - T: (816) 235-1502, Fax: (816) 235-6528, E-mail: csubler@umkc.edu, Internet: http://www.umkc.edu/gallery. Head: Craig A. Subler
Fine Arts Museum / University Museum - 1975
Contemporary art (20th-21st c) 37735

Kaleidoscope, 2501 McGee, Kansas City, MO 64108 - T: (816) 274-8301, 274-8934, Fax: (816) 274-3148, E-mail: lavery1@hallmark.com, Internet: http://www.hallmarkkaleidoscope.com. Head: Regi Ahrens
Special Museum - 1969
Children's participatory art exhibit 37736

Kansas City Museum, 3218 Gladstone Blvd, Kansas City, MO 64123 - T: (816) 483-8300, Fax: (816) 483-9912, E-mail: du1@csi.com, Internet: http://www.kcmuseum.com. Head: Maria Meyers
Ethnology Museum / Historical Museum / Natural History Museum / Science&Tech Museum - 1939 37737

Kemper Museum of Contemporary Art, 4420 Warwick Blvd, Kansas City, MO 64111-1821 - T: (816) 753-5784, Fax: (816) 753-5806, E-mail: info@kemperart.org, Internet: http://www.kemperart.org. Head: Rachael Blackburn
Fine Arts Museum - 1994
Contemporary art 37738

Leedy-Voulke's Art Center, 2012 Baltimore Av, Kansas City, MO 64108 - T: (816) 474-1919, Fax: (816) 474-1919. Head: Sherry Leedy
Public Gallery
Contemporary arts and crafts 37739

The Nelson-Atkins Museum of Art, 4525 Oak St, Kansas City, MO 64111-1873 - T: (816) 561-4000, Fax: (816) 561-7154, Internet: http://www.nelson-atkins.org. Head: Marc F. Wilson
Fine Arts Museum - 1933
English pottery, Oriental ceramics, paintings, sculpture, contemporary art works, Oriental art and furniture 37740

Roger Guffey Gallery, Federal Reserve Bank of Kansas City, 925 Grand Blvd, Kansas City, MO 64198 - T: (816) 881-2554, Fax: (816) 881-2007, Internet: http://www.kc.frb.org. Head: Thomas M. Hoenig
Fine Arts Museum / Public Gallery - 1985 37741

Shoal Creek Living History Museum, 7000 NE Barry Rd, Kansas City, MO 64156 - T: (816) 792-2655, Fax: (816) 792-3469, E-mail: sclhm@msn.com. Head: Alisha Moore Cole
Open Air Museum - 1975
Architecture, material culture 19th c 37742

Society for Contemporary Photography, 2016 Baltimore Av, Kansas City, MO 64108, mail addr: POB 32284, Kansas City, MO 64171 - T: (816) 471-2115, Fax: (816) 471-2462, E-mail: spc@sky.net, Internet: http://www.spconline.org. Head: Kathy Aron
Fine Arts Museum - 1984 37743

Thomas Hart Benton Home and Studio, 3616 Belleview, Kansas City, MO 64111 - T: (816) 931-5722
Historical Museum - 1977 37744

Thornhill Art Gallery, Avila College, 11901 Wornall Rd, Kansas City, MO 64145 - T: (816) 501-2443, Fax: (816) 501-2459, E-mail: chrismanga@mail.avila.edu, Internet: http://www.avila.edu. Head: Martin Benson
Fine Arts Museum / University Museum - 1978
Japanese woodblock prints 37745

Toy and Miniature Museum of Kansas City, 5235 Oak St, Kansas City, MO 64112 - T: (816) 333-9328, Fax: (816) 333-2055, Internet: http://www.umkc.edu/tmm. Head: Roger Berg
Decorative Arts Museum - 1981
Toys 37746

Kapaa HI

Kauai Children's Discovery Museum, 6458 B. Kahuna Rd, Kapaa, HI 96746 - T: (808) 823-8222, Fax: (808) 821-2558, E-mail: learn2@aloha.net, Internet: http://www.planet-hawaii.com/kcdm. Head: Robin Mazor
Special Museum - 1994 37747

Katonah NY

Caramoor Center for Music and the Arts, Girdle Ridge Rd, Katonah, NY 10536 - T: (914) 232-5035, Fax: (914) 232-5521, E-mail: mercedes@caramoor.com, Internet: http://www.caramoor.com. Head: Howard Herring
Fine Arts Museum / Decorative Arts Museum / Performing Arts Museum - 1946
Eastern and Western art and furnishings, jade coll 37748

John Jay Homestead, Rte 22, 400 Jay St, Katonah, NY 10536 - T: (914) 232-5651, Fax: (914) 232-8085, E-mail: julia.warger@oprhp.state.ny.us. Head: Julia M. Warger
Historical Museum - 1958
Home and farm of chief justice John Jay, portraits, farming 37749

Katonah Museum of Art, Rte 22 at Jay St, Katonah, NY 10536 - T: (914) 232-9555, Fax: (914) 232-3128, E-mail: 103400.373@compuserve.com, Internet: http://www.katonah-museum.org. Head: Susan H. Edwards
Fine Arts Museum - 1953 37750

Kaukauna WI

Charles A. Grignon Mansion, 1313 Augustine St, Kaukauna, WI 54130 - T: (920) 766-3122, Fax: (920) 766-9834, E-mail: ochs@foxvalleyhistory.org, Internet: http://www.foxvalley-history.org. Head: Jo Ellen Wollangk
Local Museum / Folklore Museum - 1837
Historic house 37751

Kawaihae HI

Puukohola Heiau National Historic Site, POB 44340, Kawaihae, HI 96473 - T: (808) 882-7218, Fax: (808) 882-1215, Internet: http://www.nps.gov/puhe
Archaeological Museum - 1972
Ruins of Puukohola Heiau, Temple on the hill of the Puukohla Whale, war temple built 1790-1791 37752

Kearney MO

Jesse James Farm and Museum, 21216 Jesse James Farm Rd, Kearney, MO 64060 - T: (816) 628-6065, Fax: (816) 628-6676, E-mail: jessejames@claycogov.com, Internet: http://home.co.clay.mo.us. Head: Elizabeth Gilliam-Beckett
Local Museum - 1978 37753

Kearney NE

Fort Kearney Museum, 131 S Central Av, Kearney, NE 68847 - T: (308) 234-5200. Head: Marlo L. Johnson
Military Museum - 1950 37754

Fort Kearny State Historical Park, 1020 V Rd, Kearney, NE 68847 - T: (308) 865-5305, Fax: (308) 865-5306, E-mail: ftkrny@ngpsun.ngpc.state.ne.us. Head: Eugene A. Hunt
Military Museum / Historic Site - 1929 37755

Kearney Area Children's Museum, 2013 Av A, Kearney, NE 68847 - T: (308) 236-5437
Special Museum - 1989 37756

Museum of Nebraska Art, 2401 Central, Kearney, NE 68847 - T: (308) 865-8559, Fax: (308) 865-8104, E-mail: monet@unk.edu, Internet: http://monet.unk.edu/mona. Head: Ronald C. Roth
Fine Arts Museum - 1986 37757

Keene NH

Historical Society of Cheshire County Museum, 246 Main St, Keene, NH 03431 - T: (603) 352-1895, Fax: (603) 352-9226, E-mail: hscc@cheshire.net. Head: Alan F. Rumrill
Local Museum - 1927
Local hist, furniture, glass, pottery, maps, photos, silver, toys, paintings 37758

Thorne-Sagendorph Art Gallery, Keene State College, Wyman Way, Keene, NH 03435-3501 - T: (603) 358-2720, Fax: (603) 358-2238, Internet: http://www.keene.edu/tsag. Head: Maureen Ahern
Fine Arts Museum - 1965 37759

Kelly WY

Murie Museum, 1 Ditch Creek Rd, Kelly, WY 83011 - T: (307) 733-4765, Fax: (307) 739-9388, E-mail: info@tetonscience.org, Internet: http://www.tetonscience.org. Head: John C. Shea
Natural History Museum - 1973 37760

Kelso WA

Cowlitz County Historical Museum, 405 Allen St, Kelso, WA 98626 - T: (360) 577-3119, Fax: (360) 423-9987, E-mail: freeced@co.cowlitz.wa.us, Internet: http://www.cowlitzcounty.org/museum. Head: Jim Elliott, David W. Freece
Local Museum - 1953
Local hist 37761

Kenilworth IL

Kenilworth Historical Museum, 415 Kenilworth Av, Kenilworth, IL 60043-1134 - T: (847) 251-2565. Head: Patricia McClaren Babb
Local Museum - 1922
Local history 37762

Kenly NC

Tobacco Farm Life Museum, Hwy 301 N, 709 Church St, Kenly, NC 27542 - T: (919) 284-3431, Fax: (919) 284-9788, E-mail: tobmuseum@bbnp.com, Internet: http://www.tobmuseum.bbnp.com
Local Museum - 1983
Agriculture, heritage, Eastern NC farm family 37763

Kennebunk ME

Brick Store Museum, 117 Main St, Kennebunk, ME 04043 - T: (207) 985-4802, Fax: (207) 985-6887, E-mail: info@brickstoremuseum.org, Internet: http://www.brickstoremuseum.org. Head: Marcene J. Molinaro
Historical Museum - 1936
Paintings, works on paper, fueniture, photographs, costumes, maritime related objekts, 37764

Kennebunkport ME

Kennebunkport Historical Museum, North St, Kennebunkport, ME 04046 - T: (207) 967-2751, Fax: (207) 967-1205, E-mail: kporths@gwi.net, Internet: http://www.kporthistory.org. Head: Ellen D. Moy
Local Museum - 1952
Local history 37765

Seashore Trolley Museum, 195 Log Cabin Rd, Kennebunkport, ME 04046-1690 - T: (207) 967-2712, Fax: (207) 967-2800, E-mail: carshop@gwi.net, Internet: http://www.trolleymuseum.org. Head: Peter Folger
Science&Tech Museum - 1939
Electric railway history and technology, steetcars, mass transit 37766

Kennesaw GA

Kennesaw Civil War Museum, 2829 Cherokee St, Kennesaw, GA 30144 - T: (770) 427-2117, Fax: (770) 429-4538, E-mail: kcwm@juno.com, Internet: http://www.thegeneral.org. Head: Dr. Jeffrey A. Drobney
Historic Site / Historical Museum / Science&Tech Museum - 1972
Civil war, trains, site where the Great Locomotive chase began, the locomotive General 37767

Kennesaw Mountain National Battlefield Park, 900 Kennesaw Mountain Dr, Kennesaw, GA 30152 - T: (770) 427-4686, Fax: (770) 528-8399, E-mail: kmha@mindspring.com, Internet: http://www.nps.gov
Historical Museum / Military Museum - 1917
Civil war history 37768

Kennett MO

Dunklin County Museum, 122 College, Kennett, MO 63857 - T: (573) 888-6620, E-mail: cbrown@sheltonbbs.com. Head: Charles B. Brown
Historical Museum - 1976 37769

Kenosha WI

Kenosha County Museum, 6300 3rd Av, Kenosha, WI 53143 - T: (262) 654-5770, Fax: (414) 654-1730, E-mail: kchs@acronet.net, Internet: http://www.acronet.net/~kchs/kchshome.htm. Head: Robert B. Fuhrman
Local Museum - 1878
Local hist 37770

Kenosha Public Museum, 5608 Tenth Av, Kenosha, WI 53140 - T: (414) 653-4140, Fax: (414) 653-4143, E-mail: mpaulat@kenosha.org, Internet: http://www.kenosha.org. Head: Paula Touhey
Fine Arts Museum / Decorative Arts Museum / Natural History Museum - 1933
Natural hist, art 37771

Kensington CT

New Britain Youth Museum at Hungerford Park, 191 Farmington Av, Kensington, CT 06037 - T: (860) 827-9064, Fax: (860) 827-1266, E-mail: ymhupark@portone.net. Head: Ann F. Peabody
Special Museum - 1984 37772

Kent CT

Sloane-Stanley Museum and Kent Furnace, Rte 7, Kent, CT 06757 - T: (860) 927-3849, Fax: (860) 927-2152. Head: John W. Shannahan
Science&Tech Museum - 1969 37773

Kent OH

Kelso House, 1106 Old Forge Rd, Kent, OH 44240 - T: (330) 673-1058. Head: Edgar L. McCormick
Historical Museum - 1963 37774

Kent State University Art Galleries, School of Art, Kent State University, Kent, OH 44242 - T: (216) 672-7853, Fax: (216) 672-4729 & 9570, E-mail: fsmith@kentvm.kent.edu, Internet: http://www.kent.edu/art/soa-gallery/index.html. Head: Fred T. Smith
Fine Arts Museum / University Museum - 1950 37775

Kent State University Museum, Rockwell Hall, Corner of E Main & S Lincoln Sts, Kent, OH 44242-0001 - T: (330) 672-3450, Fax: (330) 672-3218, E-mail: museum@kent.edu, Internet: http://www.kent.edu/museum/. Head: Jean Druesedow
Decorative Arts Museum - 1981
Costumes and decorative arts 37776

Kenton OH

Hardin County Historical Museum, 223 N Main St, Kenton, OH 43326 - T: (419) 673-7147, E-mail: zeppo@kenton.com, Internet: http://www.kenton.com/keller.hchm. Head: Charles M. Jacobs
Historical Museum - 1984 37777

Kenyon MN

Gunderson House, 107 Gunderson Blvd, Kenyon, MN 55946 - T: (507) 789-6141, 789-6329. Head: Ryan Ugland
Historical Museum - 1895 37778

Keokuk IA

Keokuk River Museum, Foot of Johnson St, Victory Park, Keokuk, IA 52632 - T: (319) 524-4765. Head: Charles Pietscher
Maritime Museum - 1962
Maritime history, housed in Geo. M. Verity Mississippi River Steamboat 37779

Keosauqua IA

Van Buren County Historical Society Museum, 1st St, Keosauqua, IA 52565 - T: (319) 293-3211. Head: Vel Luse
Local Museum - 1960
Local history 37780

Kerby OR

Kerbyville Museum, 24195 Redwood Hwy, Kerby, OR 97531 - T: (541) 592-2076, Fax: (541) 592-3173, Internet: http://www.grantspass.com. Head: Kendell W. Phillips
Local Museum - 1959 37781

Kerrville TX

Cowboy Artists of America Museum, 1550 Bandera Hwy, Kerrville, TX 78028 - T: (830) 896-2553, Fax: (830) 896-2556, E-mail: caam@ktc.com, Internet: http://www.caamuseum.com. Head: Michael W. Duty
Fine Arts Museum - 1983
Art 37782

L.D. Brinkman Art Foundation, 444 Sidney Baker St S, Kerrville, TX 78028 - T: (830) 257-2000, Fax: (830) 257-2030. Head: L.D. Brinkman, Byron C. Smith, Charles C. Thomas
Fine Arts Museum - 1985
Art 37783

Ketchikan AK

Tongass Historical Museum, 629 Dock St, Ketchikan, AK 99901 - T: (907) 225-5600, Fax: (907) 225-5602, E-mail: museumdir@city.ketchikan.ak.us. Head: Michael Naab
Local Museum - 1961
Regional history 37784

Kewaunee WI

Kewaunee County Historical Museum, Court House Sq, 613 Dodge St, Kewaunee, WI 54216 - T: (920) 388-7176, Internet: http://www.rootsweb.com/~wikewaun
Special Museum - 1970
Local hist 37785

Key Biscayne FL

Bill Baggs Cape Florida State Recreation Area, 1200 S Crandon Blvd, Key Biscayne, FL 33149-2713 - T: (305) 361-5811, Fax: (305) 365-0003, E-mail: capefla@gate.net, Internet: http://www.dep.state.fl.us/parks/
Historical Museum - 1935
C.1825 restored Lighthouse, reconstruction of Keeper's house 37786

Key West FL

Audubon House, 205 Whitehead St, Key West, FL 33040 - T: (305) 294-2116, Fax: (305) 294-4513, E-mail: audubon1@flakeysol.com, Internet: http://www.audubonhouse.com. Head: Thomas Kisenwood
Historical Museum - 1960
Early 19th-century home of Capt. John H. Geiger which commemorates John James Audubon visit to Key West in 1832 37787

East Martello Museum, 3501 S Roosevelt Blvd, Key West, FL 33040 - T: (305) 296-3913, Fax: (305) 296-6206. Head: Kevin J. O'Brien
Historical Museum - 1951
History, art, housed in 1861 brick fort 37788

Ernest Hemingway House Museum, 907 Whitehead, Key West, FL 33040 - T: (305) 294-1136, 294-1575, Fax: (305) 294-2755, E-mail: hemingwayhome@prodigy.net, Internet: http://www.hemingwayhome.com. Head: Mike Morawski
Special Museum / Historic Site - 1964
1931-1961 Ernest Hemingway Home in Spanish Colonial Style 37789

Key West Lighthouse Museum, 3501 S. Roosevelt Blvd, Key West, FL 33040 - T: (305) 296-3913, Fax: (305) 296-6206. Head: Kevin J. O'Brien
Science&Tech Museum - 1966
Housed in 1887 lighthouse keepers home, 1846 lighthouse 37790

Mel Fisher Maritime Heritage Museum, 200 Greene St, Key West, FL 33040 - T: (305) 294-2633, Fax: (305) 294-5671, E-mail: info@melfisher.org, Internet: http://www.melfisher.org
Historical Museum - 1982 37791

The Oldest House Museum, 322 Duval St, Key West, FL 33040 - T: (305) 294-9502. Head: David L. Roumm
Historical Museum / Folklore Museum - 1975
Maritime, Conch house, home of local sea captain and wrecker 37792

Keyport NJ

Steamboat Dock Museum, POB 312, Keyport, NJ 07735 - T: (732) 264-7822
Local Museum / Science&Tech Museum - 1976
Local hist 37793

Keyport WA

Naval Undersea Museum, Garnett Way, Keyport, WA 98345-7610 - T: (360) 396-4148, Fax: (360) 396-7944, Internet: http://num.kpt.nuwc.navy.mil. Head: Bill Galvani
Science&Tech Museum / Military Museum - 1979 37794

Keystone SD

Big Thunder Gold Mine, 604 Blair, Keystone, SD 57751 - T: (605) 666-4847, Fax: (605) 666-4566, Internet: http://www.bigthundergoldmine.com. Head: Charles McLain
Science&Tech Museum - 1958
1880s gold mine's equipment 37795

Keystone Area Museum, 410 3rd St, Keystone, SD 57751 - T: (605) 666-4494. Head: Bob Main
Local Museum - 1983
Local hist 37796

Mount Rushmore National Memorial, Hwy 244, Keystone, SD 57751 - T: (605) 574-2523, Fax: (605) 574-2307, E-mail: jim_popovich@nps.gov, Internet: http://www.nps.gov/moru/. Head: Daniel N. Wenk
Historical Museum - 1925
Massive granite sculpture, carved into a mountainside, memorializing the likenesses of the Presidents Washington, Jefferson, Theodore Roosevelt & Lincoln 37797

Parade of Presidents Wax Museum, Highway 609 16-A, Keystone, SD 57751 - T: (605) 666-4455, Fax: (605) 666-4455. Head: Mary Ann Riordan
Decorative Arts Museum - 1970
Wax figures 37798

Keytesville MO

General Sterling Price Museum, 412 Bridge St, Keytesville, MO 65261 - T: (660) 288-3204. Head: Sarah Weaver
Local Museum - 1964 37799

Kilgore TX

East Texas Oil Museum at Kilgore College, Hwy 259 at Ross St, Kilgore, TX 75662 - T: (903) 983-8531, 983-8295, Fax: (903) 983-8600. Head: Joe L. White
Science&Tech Museum / University Museum - 1980
Oil industry 37800

Kill Devil Hills NC

Wright Brothers National Memorial, Virginia Dare Trail-US 158, Kill Devil Hills, NC 27948 - T: (919) 441-7430, Fax: (919) 441-7730, Internet: http://www.nps.gov/wrbr. Head: Mary H. Doll
Science&Tech Museum - 1928 37801

Kimberly OR

John Day Fossil Beds National Monument, HCR 82, Box 126, Kimberly, OR 97848 - T: (541) 987-2333, Fax: (541) 987-2336, E-mail: joda_interpretation@nps.gov, Internet: http://www.nps.gov/joda/
Natural History Museum / Archaeological Museum - 1975
Fossils, geology, cenozoic 37802

Kinderhook NY

Columbia County Historical Society Museum, 5 Albany Av, Kinderhook, NY 12106-0311 - T: (518) 758-9265, Fax: (518) 758-2499. Head: Sharon S. Palmer
Historical Museum / Local Museum - 1916 37803

Martin Van Buren Historic Site, Rte 9H, Kinderhook, NY 12106 - T: (518) 758-9689, Fax: (518) 758-6986, E-mail: superintendent@nps.gov/mava, Internet: http://www.nps.gov/mava
Historical Museum - 1974 37804

King WI

Wisconsin Veterans Museum King, Wisconsin Veterans Home, Hwy QQ, King, WI 54946 - T: (608) 266-1009, Fax: (608) 264-7615. Head: Richard Zeitlin
Military Museum - 1935
Military hist 37805

Kingfield ME

Stanley Museum, School St, Kingfield, ME 04947 - T: (207) 265-2729, Fax: (207) 265-4700, E-mail: stanleym@tdstelme.net, Internet: http://www.stanleymuseum.org. Head: Susan S. Davis
Historical Museum / Science&Tech Museum - 1981
History, transportation, steam car 37806

Kingfisher OK

Chisholm Trail Museum, 605 Zellers Av, Kingfisher, OK 73750 - T: (405) 375-5176, Fax: (405) 375-5176 (call first), E-mail: reneem@ok-history.mus.ok.us, Internet: http://www.ok-history.mus.ok.us/
Local Museum - 1970 37807

Seay Mansion, 11 and Overstreet, Kingfisher, OK 73750 - T: (405) 375-5176, Fax: (405) 375-5176
Historical Museum - 1967 37808

Kingman AZ

Mohave Museum of History and Arts, 400 W Beale, Kingman, AZ 86401 - T: (520) 753-3195, Fax: (520) 753-3195, E-mail: mocohist@ctaz.com, Internet: http://www.ctaz.com/mehovist/museum/index.htm. Head: Chambers Jaynell
Local Museum / Fine Arts Museum - 1961
History, archaeology, art 37809

Kingman KS

Kingman County Historical Museum, 400 N Main, Kingman, KS 67068 - T: (316) 532-2627
Local Museum - 1969
County history, housed in 1888 City Hall 37810

Kings Point NY

American Merchant Marine Museum, United States Merchant Marine Academy, Kings Point, NY 11024-1699 - T: (516) 773-5515, Fax: (516) 482-5340, Internet: http://www.usmma.edu
Historical Museum / Science&Tech Museum - 1978
American Merchant Marine hist 37811

Kingston MA

Major John Bradford House, Maple St and Landing Rd, Kingston, MA 02364 - T: (617) 585-6300. Head: Lilias Cingolani
Historical Museum - 1921 37812

Kingston NY

Hudson River Maritime Museum, 1 Rondout Landing, Kingston, NY 12401 - T: (914) 338-0071, Fax: (914) 338-0583, E-mail: hrmm@ulster.net, Internet: http://www.ulster.net/~hrmm
Historical Museum - 1980 37813

Senate House, 296 Fair St, Kingston, NY 12401 - T: (914) 338-2786, Fax: (914) 334-8173
Fine Arts Museum / Historic Site / Historical Museum - 1887 37814

Kingston RI

University of Rhode Island Fine Arts Center Galleries, University of Rhode Island, 105 Upper College Rd, Ste 1, Kingston, RI 02881-0820 - T: (401) 874-2775, Fax: (401) 874-2007, E-mail: jtolnick@uri.edu, Internet: http://www.uri.edu/artsci/art/gallery. Head: Judith E. Tolnick
University Museum / Fine Arts Museum - 1968 37815

Kingsville TX

John E. Conner Museum, Texas A&M University, 905 W Santa Gertrudis St, Kingsville, TX 78363 - T: (361) 593-2810, Fax: (361) 593-2112. Head: Hal Hau
Local Museum - 1925
Local hist 37816

Kinsley KS

Edwards County Historical Museum, POB 64, Kinsley, KS 67547 - T: (316) 659-2420
Local Museum - 1967
County history 37817

Kinston RI

Pettaquamscutt Museum, 2636 Kingstown Rd, Kinston, RI 02881 - T: (401) 783-1328
Local Museum - 1958
Local hist 37818

Kinzers PA

Rough and Tumble Engineers Museum, Rte 30 1/2 E of Kinzers, Kinzers, PA 17535 - T: (717) 442-4249. Head: Dale Young
Agriculture Museum / Science&Tech Museum - 1948
Agricultural and mechanical technology and hist 37819

Kirksville MO

E.M. Violette Museum, Truman State University, Kirksville, MO 63501-4221 - T: (660) 785-4532, Fax: (660) 785-7415, E-mail: emdoak@truman.edu, Internet: http://www2.truman.edu/pickler/web2000/collections/violette-mus.html. Head: Richard J. Coughlin
University Museum / Historical Museum - 1913
Pickler library, University archives 37820

Still National Osteopathic Museum, 800 W Jefferson, Kirksville, MO 63501 - T: (660) 626-2359, Fax: (660) 626-2984, E-mail: museum@fileserver7.kcom.edu, Internet: http://www.kcom.edu/museum. Head: Jason Haxton
Special Museum - 1978 37821

Kirtland OH

Kirtland Temple Historic Center, 9020 Chillicothe Rd, Kirtland, OH 44094 - T: (440) 256-3318, E-mail: temple@ncweb.com, Internet: http://www.kirtlandtemple.org. Head: Dr. Lachlan MacKay
Historic Site 37822

Kit Carson CO

Kit Carson Historical Society Museum, Park St, Kit Carson, CO 80825 - T: (719) 962-3306. Head: Polly Johnson
Local Museum - 1968
Local history 37823

Klamath Falls OR

Favell Museum of Western Art and Indian Artifacts, 125 W Main St, Klamath Falls, OR 97601 - T: (541) 882-9996, Fax: (541) 850-0125, E-mail: favmusem@internetcds.com, Internet: http://www.favellmuseum. Head: Gene H. Favell
Fine Arts Museum / Ethnology Museum / Archaeological Museum - 1972 37824

Klamath County Museum, 1451 Main St, Klamath Falls, OR 97601 - T: (541) 883-4208, Fax: (541) 884-0666, E-mail: tourklco@cdsnet.net. Head: Pat McMillan
Historical Museum - 1953
Baldwin Hotel Museum Annex 37825

Knoxville IL

Knox County Museum, c/o City Hall, Public Sq, Knoxville, IL 61448 - T: (309) 289-2814, Fax: (309) 289-8825, E-mail: tbould@netins.net, Internet: http://www.netins.net/showcase/knoxhistory
Local Museum - 1954
Local history 37826

Knoxville TN

Beck Cultural Exchange Center, 1927 Dandridge Av, Knoxville, TN 37915-1909 - T: (423) 524-8461, Fax: (423) 524-8462, E-mail: beckcec@korrnet.org, Internet: http://www.korrnet.org/beckcec. Head: Avon W. Rollins, William V. Powell
Folklore Museum / Library with Exhibitions / Historical Museum - 1975
Local Black history 37827

Blount Mansion, 200 W Hill Av, Knoxville, TN 37902 - T: (865) 525-2375, Fax: (865) 546-5315, E-mail: info@blountmansion.org, Internet: http://www.blountmansion.org. Head: C.L. Creech
Local Museum / Historic Site - 1926
Historic house 37828

Confederate Memorial Hall-Bleak House, 3148 Kingston Pike, Knoxville, TN 37919 - T: (423) 522-2371, E-mail: bhpa@korrnet.org. Head: Florence E. Hillis
Local Museum - 1959
Historic house 37829

Crescent Bend Armstrong-Lockett House and William P. Toms Memorial Gardens, 2728 Kingston Pike, Knoxville, TN 37919 - T: (615) 637-3163
Decorative Arts Museum - 1975
Decorative arts 37830

East Tennessee Discovery Center, 516 N Beaman, Chilhowee Park, Knoxville, TN 37914-0204 - T: (423) 594-1494, Fax: (423) 594-1469, E-mail: atdc@vsit.net, Internet: http://funnelweb.utcc.utk/edu/~loganj/etdc. Head: Margaret Maddox
Science&Tech Museum / Natural History Museum - 1960
Science Museum with Planetarium/Kama Health Discovery 37831

East Tennessee Historical Society Museum, 600 Market St, Knoxville, TN 37902 - T: (885) 215-8824, Fax: (615) 544-4319, E-mail: eths@east-tennessee-history.org, Internet: http://www.east-tennessee-history.org. Head: Kent Whitworth, Joseph A. Swann
Local Museum - 1834
Local hist 37832

Ewing Gallery of Art and Architecture, University of Tennessee, Art and Architecture Bldg, 1715 Volunteer Blvd, Knoxville, TN 37996 - T: (865) 974-3200, Fax: (865) 974-3198, E-mail: spangler@utk.edu, Internet: http://sunsite.utk.edu/ewing_gallery. Head: Sam Yates
University Museum / Fine Arts Museum - 1981
Contemporary arts and architecture 37833

Frank H. McClung Museum, University of Tennessee, 1327 Circle Park Dr, Knoxville, TN 37996-3200 - T: (865) 974-2144, Fax: (865) 974-3827, Internet: http://mcclungmuseum.utk.edu. Head: Dr. Jefferson Chapman
University Museum / Local Museum / Natural History Museum - 1961
Local hist, natural hist, SE U.S. archaeology 37834

Governor John Sevier Farm Home, 1220 West Gov. John Sevier Hwy, Knoxville, TN 37920 - T: (423) 573-5508, Fax: (423) 573-9768. Head: Chris Milne, R. Mark Cull
Local Museum - 1941
Historic house, home of Tennessee's first governor John Sevier 37835

Knoxville Museum of Art, 1050 World's Fair Park Dr, Knoxville, TN 37916-1653 - T: (865) 525-6101, Fax: (865) 546-3635, E-mail: kma@esper.com, Internet: http://www.kmaonline.org. Head: Barbara Apking
Fine Arts Museum - 1961
Modern and contemporary art in all media, Mexican folk masks, Thorne miniature, paintings, sculpture, photography, works on paper 37836

Mabry-Hazen House, 1711 Dandridge Av, Knoxville, TN 37915 - T: (423) 522-8661, Fax: (423) 522-8471, E-mail: mabry@korrnet.org, Internet: http://www.korrnet.org/mabry. Head: Robert Freeland
Local Museum - 1992
Historic house 37837

Ramsey House Museum Plantation, 2614 Thorngrove Pike, Knoxville, TN 37914 - T: (865) 546-0745, 694-9224, Fax: (865) 546-0745, E-mail: ramhse@korrnet.org, Internet: http://www.kornet.org/ramhse. Head: Anna McKelvey
Local Museum - 1952
Historic house 37838

Kodiak AK

Alutiiq Museum and Archaeological Repository, 215 Mission Rd, Kodiak, AK 99615 - T: (907) 486-7004, Fax: (907) 486-7048, E-mail: alutiiq2@ptialaska.net, Internet: http://www.alutiiqmuseum.com. Head: Sven Haakanson
Ethnology Museum / Archaeological Museum - 1995
Archaeology 37839

Baranov Museum, Erskine House, 101 Marine Way, Kodiak, AK 99615 - T: (907) 486-5920, Fax: (907) 486-3166, E-mail: baranov@ptialaska.net, Internet: http://www.ptialaska.net/~baranov. Head: Marian Johnson
Local Museum - 1954
Local history, Alexander Baranov (chief manager of Russian American Company), Handwoven grass baskets, Russian American occupation, Kodiak and Aleutian Island hist 37840

Kokomo IN

Elwood Haynes Museum, 1915 S Webster St, Kokomo, IN 46902-2040 - T: (765) 456-7500. Head: Kay J. Frazer
Special Museum - 1967
Home of the inventor Elwood Haynes, Haynes memorabilia, 4 Haynes cars and inventions, exhib. about industrial hist 37841

Howard County Historical Museum, 1200 W Sycamore St, Kokomo, IN 46901 - T: (317) 452-4314, Fax: (765) 452-4581, E-mail: hchs@mail.netusal.net. Head: Kelly Thompson
Historic Site / Local Museum - 1916
Local history 37842

Kotzebue AK

Kotzebue Museum, POB 46, Kotzebue, AK 99752 - T: (907) 442-3747, Fax: (907) 442-3742. Head: Michael Scott
Local Museum - 1967
Local history 37843

Kure Beach NC

Fort Fisher, 1610 Fort Fisher Blvd, Kure Beach, NC 28449 - T: (910) 458-5538, Fax: (910) 458-0477. Head: Barbara G. Hoppe
Historical Museum - 1961 37844

La Conner WA

Museum of Northwest Art, 121 S First St, La Conner, WA 98257 - T: (360) 466-4446, Fax: (360) 466-7431, E-mail: mona@ncia.com, Internet: http://www.museumofnwart.org. Head: Susan Parke
Fine Arts Museum - 1981
Art 37845

Skagit County Historical Museum, 501 S 4th St, La Conner, WA 98257-0818 - T: (360) 466-3365, Fax: (360) 466-1611, E-mail: museum@co.skagit.wa.us, Internet: http://www.skagitcounty.net/museum.htm. Head: Karen Marshall
Local Museum / Folklore Museum - 1959
Local hist 37846

La Crosse KS

Kansas Barbed Wire Museum, W 1st St, La Crosse, KS 67548 - T: (785) 222-9900, Internet: http://www.rushcounty.org/barbedwiremuseum. Head: Bradley Penka
Historical Museum - 1971 37847

Post Rock Museum, Rush Co Historical Society, 202 W First St, La Crosse, KS 67548-0473 - T: (785) 222-2719, 222-3508. Head: James Jecha
Natural History Museum - 1962
Geology, post rock is limestone bedrock used in building, churches, homes 37848

La Crosse WI

Hixon House, 429 N 7th St, La Crosse, WI 54601 - T: (608) 782-1980. Head: Michael J. Erickson
Local Museum - 1898
Historic house 37849

Pump House of Regional Arts, 119 King St, La Crosse, WI 54601 - T: (608) 785-1434, Fax: (608) 785-1432, E-mail: pumphouse@lse.fullfeed.com, Internet: http://www.thepumphouse.org. Head: Jan Engelhardt
Fine Arts Museum - 1980
Arts 37850

Riverside Museum, 410 E Veterans Memorial Dr, La Crosse, WI 54601 - T: (608) 782-1980, E-mail: brjjordan@aol.com. Head: Michael J. Erickson
Local Museum - 1990
Local hist 37851

Swarthout Memorial Museum, 112 S 9th St, La Crosse, WI 54601 - T: (608) 782-1980. Head: Michael J. Erickson
Local Museum - 1898
Local hist 37852

La Fargeville NY

Agricultural Museum at Stone Mills, Rte 180 at Stone Mills, La Fargeville, NY 13656 - T: (315) 658-2353. Head: Richard Shattuck
Agriculture Museum - 1968 37853

La Grange GA

Chattahoochee Valley Art Museum, 112 Hines St, La Grange, GA 30240 - T: (706) 882-3267, Fax: (706) 882-2878. Head: Keith Rasmussen
Fine Arts Museum / Decorative Arts Museum - 1963
Decorative arts, paintings, prints, drawings, graphics, sculpture 37854

La Grange IN

Machan Museum, 405 S Poplar St 4H Fair Grounds, La Grange, IN 46761 - T: (219) 463-2632. Head: Robert Lee Yoder
Local Museum - 1966
Local history 37855

La Grange TX

Fayette Heritage Museum, 855 S Jefferson, La Grange, TX 78945 - T: (409) 968-6418, Fax: (409) 968-5357, E-mail: library@fais.net, Internet: http://lagrange.fais.net/library/museum.html. Head: Kathy Carter
Historical Museum - 1978
Local hist 37856

Nathaniel W. Faison Home and Museum, 1716 Zapalac Rd, La Grange, TX 78945 - T: (409) 249-3265. Head: Ruby J. Burrough
Local Museum - 1960
Local hist 37857

La Habra CA

Children's Museum at La Habra, 301 S Euclid, La Habra, CA 90631 - T: (562) 905-9693, Fax: (562) 905-9698, E-mail: april_morales@lahabracity.com, Internet: http://www.lhcm.org
Special Museum - 1977 37858

La Jolla CA

Museum of Contemporary Art San Diego, 700 Prospect St, La Jolla, CA 92037 - T: (858) 454-3541, Fax: (858) 454-4985, E-mail: info@mcasandiego.org, Internet: http://www.mcasandiego.org. Head: Hugh M. Davies
Fine Arts Museum - 1941 37859

Stuart Collection, University of California-San Diego, 9500 Gilman Dr, La Jolla, CA 92093-0010 - T: (858) 534-2117, Fax: (858) 534-9713, E-mail: mbeebe@ucsd.edu, Internet: http://stuartcollection.ucsd.edu. Head: Mary L. Beebe
Fine Arts Museum / University Museum - 1981 37860

University Art Gallery, University of California, San Diego, 9500 Gilman Dr, La Jolla, CA 92093-0327 - T: (619) 534-0419, 534-2107, Fax: (619) 534-0668, E-mail: uag@ucsd.edu, Internet: http://www.universityartgallery.ucsd.edu. Head: Catherine Palmer, Kathleen Stoughton
Fine Arts Museum / University Museum - 1967
Art gallery 37861

La Junta CO

Bent's Old Fort, 35110 Hwy 194 E, La Junta, CO 81050 - T: (719) 383-5010, Fax: (719) 383-5031, Internet: http://www.nps.gov. Head: Donald C. Hill
Historical Museum - 1963
Living history 37862

Koshare Indian Museum, 115 W 18th, La Junta, CO 81050 - T: (719) 384-4411, Fax: (719) 384-8836, E-mail: linda.powers@ojc.cccoes.edu, Internet: http://www.koshare.org. Head: Linda Powers
Ethnology Museum - 1949
Indian arts and crafts 37863

La Pointe WI

Madeline Island Historical Museum, Woods Av and Main St, La Pointe, WI 54850 - T: (715) 747-2415, Fax: (715) 747-6985, E-mail: madeline@mail.shsw.wisc.edu, Internet: http://www.shsw.wisc.edu. Head: Steven R. Cotherman
Historical Museum - 1958
Local hist, native american, maritime, 19th c. trades 37864

La Porte IN

La Porte County Historical Society Museum, 809 State St, La Porte, IN 46350-3329 - T: (219) 326-6808 ext 276, Fax: (219) 324-9029, E-mail: lpcohist@csinet.net, Internet: http://www.lapcohistsoc.org/
Historical Museum - 1906
Local history 37865

La Porte TX

Battleship Texas, 3527 Battleground Rd, La Porte, TX 77571 - T: (281) 479-2431, Fax: (281) 479-4197, E-mail: barry.ward@tpwd.state.tx.us, Internet: http://www.tpwd.state.tx.us. Head: Barry J. Ward
Historic Site / Military Museum - 1948
Military hist 37866

San Jacinto Museum of History, 1 Monument Circle, La Porte, TX 77571 - T: (281) 479-2421, Fax: (281) 479-6619, E-mail: sjm@sanjacinto-museum.org, Internet: http://sanjacinto-museum.org. Head: George J. Donnelly
Historical Museum - 1938
History 37867

La Puente CA

La Puente Valley Historical Society Museum, 15900 E Main St, La Puente, CA 91744 - T: (818) 336-2382. Head: Mildred Deyoung
Historical Museum - 1960 37868

La Veta CO

Francisco Fort Museum, 306 Main St, La Veta, CO 81055 - T: (719) 742-5501, Fax: (719) 742-5501, E-mail: lvcc@ruralwideweb.com, Internet: http://www.ruralwideweb.com/lvcc.htm. Head: Pamela E. Munrde
Local Museum - 1956
Local history 37869

Lackland Air Force Base TX

History and Traditions Museum, 37 TRW/MU, Bldg 5206, 2051 George Av, Lackland Air Force Base, TX 78236-5218 - T: (210) 671-3055, Fax: (210) 671-0347, E-mail: henry.valdez@lackland.af.mil. Head: E.A. Valdez
Military Museum - 1956
Military hist 37870

Laclede MO

General John J. Pershing Boyhood Home, POB 141, Laclede, MO 64651 - T: (660) 963-2525, Fax: (660) 963-2520. Head: Dr. Douglas Eiken
Historical Museum - 1960
WW I General Pershing 37871

Laconia NH

The Belknap Mill Museum, The Mill Plaza, Laconia, NH 03246 - T: (603) 524-8813, Fax: (603) 528-1228, E-mail: belknap@worldpath.net. Head: Mary Rose Boswell
Fine Arts Museum / Local Museum - 1970
Art, history 37872

Ladysmith WI

Rusk County Historical Society Museum, W 7891 Old 8 Rd, Ladysmith, WI 54848 - T: (715) 532-6450
Local Museum - 1961
Local hist 37873

Lafayette CA

Museum of Vintage Fashion, 1712 Chapparal Ln, Lafayette, CA 94549-1712 - T: (925) 944-1896, E-mail: pattimvf@home.com, Internet: http://www.museumofvintagefashion.org. Head: Patti Parks McClain
Special Museum / Historical Museum - 1978 37874

Lafayette CO

Lafayette Miners Museum, 108 E Simpson St, Lafayette, CO 80026-2322 - T: (303) 665-7030. Head: James D. Hutchison, Elizabeth Hutchison
Science&Tech Museum - 1976
Coal mining 37875

Lafayette IN

Art Museum of Greater Lafayette, 102 S 10th St, Lafayette, IN 47905 - T: (765) 742-1128, Fax: (765) 742-1120, E-mail: glma@glmart.org, Internet: http://www.dcwi.com/~glma. Head: Gretchen Mehring
Fine Arts Museum - 1909
Art if Indiana 37876

Greater Lafayette Museum of Art → Art Museum of Greater Lafayette

Tippecanoe County Historical Museum, 900 South St, Lafayette, IN 47901 - T: (765) 476-8411, Fax: (765) 476-8414, E-mail: mail@tcha.mus.in.us, Internet: http://www.tcha.mus.in.us. Head: Paul Schueler
Local Museum / Historical Museum - 1925
General museum, housed in Moses Fowler Home, nr the site of 1717-91 Fort Ouiatenon, the first fortified European settlement in Indiana 37877

Lafayette LA

Lafayette Museum - Alexandre Mouton House, 1122 Lafayette St, Lafayette, LA 70501 - T: (318) 234-2208. Head: Yvonne D Bienvenu
Local Museum - 1954
Local history 37878

Lafayette Natural History Museum, 637 Girard Park Dr, Lafayette, LA 70503 - T: (318) 268-5544, Fax: (318) 268-5464
Natural History Museum - 1969
Natural history - planetarium, library 37879

University Art Museum, University of Louisiana at Lafayette, E. Lewis and Girard Park Cr., Lafayette, LA 70504 - T: (337) 482-5326, Fax: (318) 482-5907, E-mail: artmuseum@louisiana.edu, Internet: http://www.louisiana.edu/UAM. Head: Herman Mhire
Fine Arts Museum - 1968
Art 37880

Lafox IL

Garfield Farm Museum, 3N016 Garfield Rd, Box 403, Lafox, IL 60147 - T: (630) 584-8485, Fax: (630) 584-8522, E-mail: garfarm@elnet.com, Internet: http://www.garfieldfarm.org. Head: Jerome Martin Johnson
Agriculture Museum - 1977
Historic farm and Inn 37881

LaGrange GA

Lamar Dodd Art Center, LaGrange College, 302 Forrest Av, LaGrange, GA 30240 - T: (706) 882-2911, Fax: (706) 884-6567, E-mail: doddartc@mentor.lgc.peachnet.edu. Head: John D. Lawrence
Fine Arts Museum / University Museum - 1982 37882

Lahaina HI

Lahaina Restoration Foundation, 120 Dickenson, Lahaina, HI 96761 - T: (808) 661-3262, Fax: (808) 661-9309, E-mail: lrf@maui.net, Internet: http://www.lahainarestoration.org. Head: George W. Freeland, Donald Malcolm
Folklore Museum / Open Air Museum - 1962
Historical Houses, Baldwin Home, Masters Reading Rm, Hale Pai Printing House, Wohing Chinese Temple, Hale Paahao Prison, Hale Aloha Church, depicting the life of the Lahaina during the Hawaiian Monarchy (1820-1893) 37883

Lake Bronson MN

Kittson County History Center Museum, County Rd 28, Lake Bronson, MN 56734 - T: (218) 754-4100, E-mail: history@means.net. Head: Cindy Adams
Local Museum / Agriculture Museum - 1973
Regional history 37884

Lake Buena Vista FL

Epcot, Walt Disney World Resort, Lake Buena Vista, FL 32830, mail addr: POB 10000, Lake Buena Vista, FL 32830 - T: (407) 824-4321, Internet: http://www.disneyworld.com. Head: Michael Eisner
Fine Arts Museum - 1971 37885

Lake Charles LA

Children's Museum of Lake Charles, 925 Enterprise Blvd, Lake Charles, LA 70601 - T: (318) 433-9420, Fax: (318) 433-0144, E-mail: dan@child-museum.org, Internet: http://www.child-museum.org. Head: Dan Ellender
Special Museum - 1988 37886

Imperial Calcasieu Museum, 204 W Sallier St, Lake Charles, LA 70601 - T: (318) 432-3793, Fax: (318) 439-6040. Head: Mary June Malus
Fine Arts Museum / Local Museum - 1963
Local history 37887

Lake City MN

Wabasha County Museum, Reads Landing, Lake City, MN 55041 - T: (507) 282-4027, E-mail: fpass_@rconnect.com
Historical Museum - 1965 37888

Lake City SD

Fort Sisseton, 11545 Northside Dr, Lake City, SD 57247-6142 - T: (605) 448-5701, Fax: (605) 448-5572, E-mail: roylakestp@gfp.state.sd.us
Local Museum - 1972
Local hist 37889

Lake George NY

Fort William Henry Museum, Canada St, Lake George, NY 12845 - T: (518) 668-5471, Fax: (518) 668-4926
Military Museum - 1952 37890

Lake George Historical Association Museum, Canada St, Lake George, NY 12845 - T: (518) 668-5044. Head: Grace MacDonald
Fine Arts Museum / Local Museum / Historical Museum - 1964 37891

Lake Junaluska NC

World Methodist Museum, 575 Lakeshore Dr, Lake Junaluska, NC 28745 - T: (828) 456-9432, Fax: (828) 456-9433, E-mail: wmc6@juno.com. Head: Dr. Joe Hale
Religious Arts Museum - 1881 37892

Lake Linden MI

Houghton County Historical Museum Society, 53150 N Hwy M-26, Lake Linden, MI 49945 - T: (906) 296-4121, Fax: (906) 296-9191. Head: Leo W. Chaput
Local Museum - 1961
Regional history 37893

Lake Norden SD

South Dakota Amateur Baseball Hall of Fame, 519 Main Av, Lake Norden, SD 57248 - T: (605) 785-3553, 785-3884, Fax: (605) 785-3315
Special Museum - 1976
Sports 37894

Lake Oswego OR

Oregon Electric Railway Historical Society Museum, 311 N State St, Lake Oswego, OR 97034 - T: (503) 222-2226, Internet: http://www.trainweb.org/oerhs. Head: Greg Bonn
Science&Tech Museum - 1957 37895

Lake Placid NY

John Brown Farm, John Brown Rd, Lake Placid, NY 12946 - T: (518) 523-3900
Agriculture Museum - 1895 37896

Lake Placid-North Elba Historical Society Museum, Averyville Rd, Lake Placid, NY 12946 - T: (518) 523-1608. Head: Gordon Pratt
Historical Museum - 1967 37897

Lake Tomahawk WI

Northland Historical Society Museum, 7247 Kelly Dr, Lake Tomahawk, WI 54539 - T: (715) 277-2629, 277-3476. Head: Susanna G. Myers
Local Museum - 1957
Local hist 37898

Lake Waccamaw NC

Lake Waccamaw Depot Museum, 201 Flemington Av, Lake Waccamaw, NC 28450 - T: (910) 646-1992
Historical Museum / Natural History Museum / Science&Tech Museum - 1977 37899

Lake Wales FL

Lake Wales Depot Museum, 325 S Scenic Hwy, Lake Wales, FL 33853 - T: (941) 678-4209, Fax: (941) 678-4299, E-mail: lwdepot@digital.net, Internet: http://www.cityoflakewales.com. Head: Mimi Reid Hardman
Local Museum - 1976
Local history 37900

Lake Worth FL

Museum of the City of Lake Worth, 414 Lake Av, Lake Worth, FL 33460 - T: (561) 586-1700, Fax: (561) 586-1651. Head: Beverly Mustaine
Local Museum - 1982
Local history 37901

Museum of the Contemporary Art → Palm Beach Institute of Contemporary Art

National Museum of Polo and Hall of Fame, 9011 Lake Worth Rd, Lake Worth, FL 33467 - T: (561) 969-3210, Fax: (561) 964-8299. Head: George DuPont
Special Museum - 1984
Polo sports hist 37902

Palm Beach Institute of Contemporary Art, 601 Lake Av, Lake Worth, FL 33460 - T: (561) 582-0006, Fax: (561) 582-0504, E-mail: info@palmbeachica.org, Internet: http://www.palmbeachica.org. Head: Dr. Michael Rush
Fine Arts Museum - 1989
Art, housed in 1939 art deco movie theatre 37903

Lakefield MN

Jackson County Historical Museum, 307 N Hwy 86, Lakefield, MN 56150-0238 - T: (507) 662-5505. Head: Randy Winters
Local Museum - 1931
Local history 37904

Lakeland FL

Polk Museum of Art, 800 E Palmetto, Lakeland, FL 33801-5529 - T: (941) 688-7743, Fax: (941) 688-2611, E-mail: info@polkmuseumofart.org, Internet: http://www.polkmuseumofart.com. Head: Daniel E. Stetson, Doug Small
Fine Arts Museum - 1966 37905

Sun'n Fun Fly-In, International Sport Aviation Museum, 4175 Medulla Rd, Lakeland, FL 33811 - T: (863) 644-0741, Fax: (863) 648-9264, E-mail: museum@airmuseum.org, Internet: http://www.airmuseum.org. Head: John Burton
Science&Tech Museum - 1989
Aviation 37906

Lakeport CA

Lake County Museum, 255 N Main St, Lakeport, CA 95453 - T: (707) 263-4555, Fax: (707) 263-7918, E-mail: museum@co.lake.ca.us, Internet: http://www.museum.lake.k12.ca.us. Head: Donna J. Howard
Historical Museum - 1936 37907

Lakeview OR

Schminck Memorial Museum, 128 S E St, Lakeview, OR 97630 - T: (541) 947-3134, Fax: (541) 947-3134, E-mail: jenglenn@triax.com. Head: Sherrain Glenn
Local Museum - 1936 37908

Lakewood CO

Lakewood's Heritage Center, 797 S Wadsworth Blvd, Lakewood, CO 80226 - T: (303) 987-7850, Fax: (303) 987-7851. Head: Kris Anderson
Local Museum - 1976
20th c Lakewood history 37909

Lakewood NJ

M. Christina Geis Gallery, Georgian Court College, 900 Lakewood Av, Lakewood, NJ 08701-2697 - T: (732) 364-2200 ext 348, Fax: (732) 905-8571, E-mail: velasquez@georgian.edu. Head: Dr. Geraldine Velasquez
Fine Arts Museum - 1964 37910

Lakewood OH

Cleveland Artists Foundation at Beck Center for the Arts, 17801 Detroit Av, Lakewood, OH 44107 - T: (216) 227-9507, Fax: (216) 228-6050, E-mail: cshearer@clevelandartists.org, Internet: http://www.clevelandartists.org. Head: Christine Fowler Shearer, Leon M. Plevin
Fine Arts Museum - 1984 37911

Oldest Stone House Museum, 14710 Lake Av, Lakewood, OH 44107 - T: (216) 221-7343, E-mail: lkwdhist@bge.net, Internet: http://www.lkwdpl.org/histsoc/. Head: Mazie M. Adams
Historical Museum / Local Museum - 1952 37912

Lamar MO

Harry S. Truman Birthplace State Historic Site, 1009 Truman Av, Lamar, MO 64759 - T: (417) 682-2279, Fax: (417) 682-6304
Historical Museum - 1959 37913

Lamoni IA

Liberty Hall Historic Center, 1300 W Main St, Lamoni, IA 50140 - T: (515) 784-6133, E-mail: alblair@neting.net, Internet: http://www.pbdy.com/libertyhall.html. Head: W.B. Spillman, A.R. Blair
Local Museum - 1976
Local hist 37914

Lancaster CA

Lancaster Museum/Art Gallery, 44801 N Sierra Hwy, Lancaster, CA 93534 - T: (805) 723-6250, Fax: (805) 948-1322. Head: Lyle Norton
Fine Arts Museum / Historical Museum - 1984 37915

Western Hotel Museum, 557 W Lancaster Blvd, Lancaster, CA 93534 - T: (805) 723-6250, Fax: (805) 948-1322. Head: Norma Gurba
Historical Museum 37916

Lancaster NH

Lancaster Historical Society Museum, 226 Main St, Lancaster, NH 03584 - T: (603) 788-3695. Head: Bart P. Sheridan
Historical Museum - 1964 37917

Lancaster OH

The Georgian, 105 E Wheeling St, Lancaster, OH 43130 - T: (740) 654-9923, Fax: (740) 654-9890, E-mail: fheritage@buckeyeinternet.com, Internet: http://www.fairfieldheritage.org. Head: Peggy Smith
Historical Museum / Local Museum - 1976 37918

Lancaster PA

Heritage Center of Lancaster County, 13 W King St, Lancaster, PA 17603-3813 - T: (717) 299-6440, Fax: (717) 299-6916, E-mail: heritage@taonline.com, Internet: http://www.lancaster-heritage.com. Head: Peter S. Seibert
Fine Arts Museum / Decorative Arts Museum / Local Museum - 1976
History, decorative art 37919

Historic Rock Ford, 881 Rock Ford Rd, Lancaster, PA 17602 - T: (717) 392-7223, Fax: (717) 392-7283, E-mail: hhbecker@rockfordplantation.org, Internet: http://www.rockfordplantation.org. Head: Heather Hartman Becker
Local Museum - 1958
Local hist 37920

James Buchanan Foundation for the Preservation of Wheatland, 1120 Marietta Av, Lancaster, PA 17603 - T: (717) 392-8721, Fax: (717) 295-8825, E-mail: wheatland.org, Internet: http://www.wheatland.org. Head: John L. Kraft
Historical Museum - 1936
Restored 1828 Federal mansion, residence of President James Buchanan 37921

Lancaster County Museum, 230 N President Av, Lancaster, PA 17603-3125 - T: (717) 392-4633, Fax: (717) 293-2739, E-mail: lchs@ptd.net, Internet: http://lanclio.org. Head: Thomas R. Ryan
Local Museum - 1886
Local hist 37922

Lancaster Museum of Art, 135 N Lime St, Lancaster, PA 17602 - T: (717) 394-3497, Fax: (717) 394-0101, E-mail: lmart@mindspring.com, Internet: http://www.lancastermuseumart.com. Head: Cindi Morrison
Fine Arts Museum - 1965
Art 37923

Landis Valley Museum, 2451 Kissel Hill Rd, Lancaster, PA 17601 - T: (717) 569-0401 ext 200, Fax: (717) 560-2147. Head: Stephen Miller
Local Museum / Agriculture Museum - 1925
Rural life and culture 37924

The North Museum of Natural History and Science, 400 College Av, Lancaster, PA 17604 - T: (717) 291-3941, Fax: (717) 399-4504
Natural History Museum - 1901
Natural history 37925

Lander WY

Fremont County Pioneer Museum, 630 Lincoln St, Lander, WY 82520 - T: (307) 332-4137, Fax: (307) 332-6498. Head: Todd Guenther
Local Museum - 1908
Local hist 37926

Landing NJ

Lake Hopatcong Historical Museum, Hopatcong State Park, Landing, NJ 07850 - T: (973) 398-2616, Fax: (973) 361-8987, E-mail: lhhistory@worldnet.att.net, Internet: http://www.hopatcong.org/museum. Head: Marilyn Garrity
Historical Museum - 1955 37927

Langhorne PA

Historic Langhorne Museum, 160 W Maple Av, Langhorne, PA 19047 - T: (215) 757-1888, 757-6158, Internet: http://hla.buxcom.net
Historical Museum - 1965 37928

Langtry TX

Judge Roy Bean Visitor Center, Hwy 90, W, Loop 25, Langtry, TX 78871 - T: (915) 291-3340, Fax: (915) 291-3366, E-mail: lytic@dot.state.tx.us. Head: Vernon N. Billings
Local Museum - 1939
Historic building 37929

Lanham-Seabrook MD

Howard B. Owens Science Center, 9601 Greenbelt Rd, Lanham-Seabrook, MD 20706 - T: (301) 918-8750, Fax: (301) 918-8753, E-mail: owens2@erols.com, Internet: http://www.gsfc.nasa.gov/hbowens/. Head: Winnie S. Wooley
Natural History Museum - 1978
Science - planetarium 37930

Lansing IL

Lansing Veterans Memorial Museum, Lansing Municipal Airport, Lansing, IL 60438 - T: (708) 895-1321, Fax: (708) 474-0798. Head: Craig Greenhill
Military Museum - 1991 37931

Lansing MI

Carl G. Fenner Nature Center, 2020 E Mt Hope Rd, Lansing, MI 48910 - T: (517) 483-4224, Fax: (517) 377-0012. Head: Clara Bratton
Natural History Museum - 1959
Natural history 37932

Lansing Art Gallery, 425 S Grand Av, Lansing, MI 48933 - T: (517) 374-6406, Fax: (517) 484-2564, E-mail: lansingartgallery@yahoo.com. Head: Catherine Babcock
Fine Arts Museum / Public Gallery - 1965
Visual arts 37933

Michigan Historical Museum, 717 W Allegan, Lansing, MI 48918 - T: (517) 373-0515, Fax: (517) 241-4738, E-mail: kwiatkowskip@sosmail.state.mi.us, Internet: http://www.sos.state.mi.us/history/. Head: Phillip C. Kwiatkowski
Local Museum - 1879
Regional history 37934

R.E. Olds Transportation Museum, 240 Museum Dr, Lansing, MI 48933 - T: (517) 372-0529, Fax: (517) 372-2901, E-mail: reolds@voyager.net. Head: Duane Allen
Science&Tech Museum - 1981
Transport 37935

Laona WI

Camp Five Museum, 5480 Connor Farm Rd, Laona, WI 54541 - T: (715) 674-3414, Fax: (715) 674-7400. Head: Edward J. Dellin
Science&Tech Museum - 1969
Logging 37936

Laramie WY

The Geological Museum, University of Wyoming, Laramie, WY 82071-3006 - T: (307) 766-2646, Fax: (307) 766-6679, E-mail: uwgeoms@uwyo.edu, Internet: http://www.uwyo.edu.geomuseum. Head: Brent H. Breithaupt
University Museum / Natural History Museum - 1887
Geology 37937

Laramie Plains Museum, 603 Ivinson Av, Laramie, WY 82070-3299 - T: (307) 742-4448, E-mail: laramiemuseum@vcn.com, Internet: http://www.laramiemuseum.org. Head: Daniel A. Nelson
Local Museum - 1966
Local hist 37938

University of Wyoming Anthropology Museum, Anthropology Bldg, 14th and Ivinson St, Laramie, WY 82071 - T: (307) 766-5136, Fax: (307) 766-2473, E-mail: arrow@uwyo.edu, Internet: http://www.uwyo.edu/a&s/anth. Head: Charles A. Reher
University Museum / Ethnology Museum / Archaeological Museum - 1966
Anthropology 37939

University of Wyoming Art Museum, 2111 Willett Dr, Laramie, WY 82071-3807 - T: (307) 766-6622, Fax: (307) 766-3520, E-mail: amsm@uwyo.edu, Internet: http://www.uwyo.edu/artmuseum. Head: Susan Moldenhauer
Fine Arts Museum / University Museum - 1968
Art 37940

Wyoming Territorial Prison and Old West Park, 975 Snowy Range Rd, Laramie, WY 82070 - T: (307) 745-3733, Fax: (307) 745-8620, E-mail: prison@lariat.org, Internet: http://www.wyoprisonpark.org. Head: Pam Malone
Local Museum - 1986
Local hist 37941

Laredo TX

Laredo Children's Museum, P-56 Fort Macintosh, Laredo, TX 78040 - T: (956) 725-2299, Fax: (956) 725-7776, E-mail: lcm@netscorp.net. Head: Olga Gentry, Patricia McDonald
Special Museum / Historical Museum - 1988 37942

Largo FL

Florida Gulf Coast Art Center, 12211 Walshingham Rd, Largo, FL 33778 - T: (727) 518-6833, Fax: (727) 518-1852, Internet: http://www.gulfcoastmuseum.org. Head: Ken Rollins
Fine Arts Museum / Public Gallery - 1936 37943

Heritage Village - Pinellas County Historical Museum, 11909-125 St N, Largo, FL 33774 - T: (727) 582-2123, Fax: (727) 582-2455, Internet: http://www.co.pinellas.fl.us/bcc/heritag.htm. Head: Kendrick T. Ford
Historical Museum / Open Air Museum - 1961
Living history 37944

Larned KS

Fort Larned, Rte 3, Larned, KS 67550 - T: (316) 285-6911, Fax: (316) 285-3571, E-mail: george_elmore@nps.gov, Internet: http://www.nps.gov/fols. Head: Steve Linderer
Historical Museum / Military Museum - 1964
Historic fort on Santa Fe Trail 37945

Santa Fe Trail Museum, Rte 3, Larned, KS 67550 - T: (316) 285-2054, Fax: (316) 285-7491, E-mail: trailctr@larned.net, Internet: http://www.larned.net/trailctr/. Head: Ruth Olson Peters
Historical Museum - 1974
Regional history - library 37946

Las Cruces NM

Branigan Cultural Center, 500 N Water, Las Cruces, NM 88001 - T: (505) 541-2155, Fax: (505) 525-3645, E-mail: bcci@zianet.com, Internet: http://www.lascruces-culture.org. Head: Sharon Bode-Hempton
Fine Arts Museum / Natural History Museum - 1981
Natural hist, art 37947

New Mexico Farm and Ranch Heritage Museum, 4100 Dripping Springs Rd, Las Cruces, NM 88011 - T: (505) 522-4100, Fax: (505) 522-3085, E-mail: cmassey@frh.state.nm.us, Internet: http://www.frhm.org. Head: Mac R. Harris
Agriculture Museum - 1991
Agriculture 37948

New Mexico State University Art Gallery, University Av E. of Solano, Las Cruces, NM 88003-8001 - T: (505) 646-1705, Fax: (505) 646-8036, E-mail: artglry@nmsu.edu, Internet: http://crl.nmsu.edu/users/retablos/collection/FrontPage.html. Head: Charles Lovell
Fine Arts Museum / University Museum - 1973 37949

New Mexico State University Museum, Kent Hall, University Av, Las Cruces, NM 88003 - T: (505) 646-3739, Fax: (505) 646-1419, E-mail: estaski@nmsu.edu, Internet: http://www.nmsu.edu/~museum. Head: Edward Staski
University Museum / Ethnology Museum - 1959 37950

Las Vegas NM

City of Las Vegas and Rough Riders Memorial Museum, 727 Grand Av, Las Vegas, NM 87701 - T: (505) 454-1401 ext 283, Fax: (505) 425-7335. Head: Melanie LaBorwit
Local Museum - 1960
Local history, Spanish-American war 37951

New Mexico Highlands University Fine Arts Gallery, Donelly Library, National Av, Las Vegas, NM 87701 - T: (505) 425-7511, Fax: (505) 454-3338, E-mail: gallery@nmhu.edu. Head: Bob Read
University Museum / Fine Arts Museum - 1956 37952

Las Vegas NV

Donna Beam Fine Art Gallery, University of Nevada, Las Vegas, 4505 Maryland Pkwy, Las Vegas, NV 89154-5002 - T: (702) 895-3893, Fax: (702) 895-3751, E-mail: jschefcik@ccmail.nevada.edu, Internet: http://www.unlv.edu/fine_arts/facilities/donna_beam_gallery. Head: Jerry A. Schefcik
Fine Arts Museum / University Museum - 1962
US works of all media of art (2nd half of 20th c) 37953

Guinness World of Records Museum, 2780 Las Vegas Blvd S, Las Vegas, NV 89109 - T: (702) 792-3766, Fax: (702) 792-0530, E-mail: oli@applevar.com, Internet: http://www.lasvegas/lv/guiness/. Head: Oli Lewis
Special Museum - 1990 37954

Las Vegas Art Museum, 9600 W Sahara Av, Las Vegas, NV 89117 - T: (702) 360-8000, Fax: (702) 360-8080, E-mail: lvam@earthlink.net, Internet: http://www.lvamlastplace.com/exhibits/lvam. Head: James Mann
Fine Arts Museum - 1950 37955

Las Vegas Natural History Museum, 900 Las Vegas Blvd N, Las Vegas, NV 89101 - T: (702) 384-3466, Fax: (702) 384-5343, E-mail: lvnathist@aol.com, Internet: http://www.lvrj.com/communitylink/lvnaturalhistory. Head: Marilyn Gillespie
Natural History Museum - 1989
Natural history, fossils, animals, prints 37956

Liberace Museum, 1775 E Tropicana, Las Vegas, NV 89119 - T: (702) 798-5595 ext 20, Fax: (702) 798-7386, E-mail: sharris@liberace.org, Internet: http://liberace.org. Head: Sandra L. Harris
Special Museum / Music Museum - 1979 37957

Lied Discovery Children's Museum, 833 Las Vegas Blvd N, Las Vegas, NV 89101 - T: (702) 382-3445, Fax: (702) 382-0592, E-mail: edcm@sprintmail.com. Head: Suzanne LeBlanc
Special Museum - 1984 37958

Nevada State Museum, 700 Twin Lakes Dr, Las Vegas, NV 89107 - T: (702) 486-5205, Fax: (702) 486-5172. Head: Shirl R. Naegle
Local Museum - 1982
Local hist 37959

UNLV Barrick Museum, 4505 Maryland Pkwy, Las Vegas, NV 89154-4012 - T: (702) 895-3381, Fax: (702) 895-3094, Internet: http://hrcweb.lv-hrc.nevada.edu. Head: Dr. Donald H. Baepler
University Museum / Natural History Museum - 1967 37960

Laurel MD

The Laurel Museum, 817 Main St, Laurel, MD 20707 - T: (301) 725-7975, Fax: (301) 725-7975, E-mail: laurelmuseum@erols.com, Internet: http://www.laurelhistory.org. Head: Alexandra Roosa
Local Museum - 1996
Local hist 37961

Montpelier Cultur Arts Center, 12826 Laural-Bowie Rd, Laurel, MD 20708 - T: (301) 953-1993, Fax: (301) 206-9682, E-mail: montpeliermansion@smart.net, Internet: http://www.smart.net/~parksrec/montpeli.htm. Head: Richard Zandler
Decorative Arts Museum - 1979 37962

Laurel MS

Lauren Rogers Museum of Art, Fifth Av at Seventh St, Laurel, MS 39440 - T: (601) 649-6374, Fax: (601) 649-6379, E-mail: lrma@c-gate.net, Internet: http://www.lrma.org. Head: George Bassi
Fine Arts Museum - 1923
19th c European art, 18th c Englisg Georgian silver, 18th-19th c Japanese Ukiyo-e Woodblock prints, 19th-20th c American paintings - library 37963

Laurens IA

Pocahontas County Iowa Historical Society Museum, 272 N Third, Laurens, IA 50554 - T: (712) 845-2577
Local Museum - 1977
Regional history, photos, medicine 37964

Laurinburg NC

Indian Museum of the Carolinas, 607 Turnpike Rd, Laurinburg, NC 28352 - T: (910) 276-5880. Head: Dr. Margaret Houston
Archaeological Museum - 1969 37965

Lava Hot Springs ID

South Bannock County Historical Center, 110 E Main St, Lava Hot Springs, ID 83246 - T: (208) 776-5254, Fax: (208) 776-5254. Head: Ruth Ann Olson
Local Museum - 1980
Local history 37966

Lawrence KS

Museum of Anthropology, University of Kansas, Lawrence, KS 66045 - T: (913) 864-4245, Fax: (913) 864-5243. Head: Alfred E. Johnson
University Museum / Ethnology Museum - 1975
Anthropology 37967

Natural History Museum, University of Kansas, Dyche Hall, Lawrence, KS 66045-2454 - T: (785) 864-4540, Fax: (785) 864-5335, E-mail: kunhm@ukans.edu, Internet: http://www.nhm.ukans.edu. Head: Dr. Leonard Krishtalka
Natural History Museum - 1866
Natural history, zoology, ornitology, icthyology, mammalogy, entomology, paleontology, botany, herpetology 37968

Spencer Museum of Art, University of Kansas, 1301 Mississippi St, Lawrence, KS 66045-7500 - T: (785) 864-4710, Fax: (785) 864-3112, E-mail: spencer@ukans.edu, Internet: http://www.ukans.edu/~sma. Head: Andrea S. Norris
Fine Arts Museum / University Museum - 1928
American, European and Asian art, prints, photos, drawings 37969

University of Kansas Ryther Printing Museum, 2425 W 15th St, Lawrence, KS 66049-3903 - T: (785) 864-4341, Fax: (785) 864-7356, E-mail: jgs@ukans.edu. Head: John G. Sayler
Science&Tech Museum - 1955
Antique printing equipment 37970

Watkins Community Museum of History, 1047 Massachusetts St, Lawrence, KS 66044 - T: (785) 841-4109, E-mail: wcmhist@sunflower.com, Internet: http://www.ci.lawrence.ks.us/museums/watkins.html. Head: Dr. Steve Jansen
Local Museum - 1972
Local history 37971

Lawrenceville GA

Gwinnett Historical Society Museum, 185 Crogan St, Lawrenceville, GA 30045 - T: (770) 822-5174, Fax: (770) 822-5174, E-mail: gwhissoc@bellsouth.net, Internet: http://www.gwinnetths.org. Head: Elaine Roberts
Local Museum / Historical Museum - 1966
Local history 37972

Gwinnett History Museum, 455 Perry St, Lawrenceville, GA 30045 - T: (770) 882-5178, Fax: (770) 237-5612, E-mail: triggan@co.gwinnett-ga.us. Head: Angela A. Trigg
Local Museum - 1974
Local hist 37973

Lawrenceville NJ

Rider University Art Gallery, 2083 Lawrenceville Rd, Lawrenceville, NJ 08648-3099 - T: (609) 896-5168, Fax: (609) 896-5232, E-mail: lnaar@rider.edu, Internet: http://www.rider.edu. Head: Harry I. Naar
Fine Arts Museum - 1970 37974

Lawson MO

Watkins Woolen Mill, 26600 Park Rd N, Lawson, MO 64062 - T: (816) 296-3357, Fax: (816) 580-3784, E-mail: dspwatkn@mail.dnr.state.mo.us, Internet: http://www.mobot.org:80/stateparks/watkins.htm. Head: Ann M. Sligar
Agriculture Museum / Science&Tech Museum - 1964 37975

Lawtell LA

Matt's Museum, McClelland St and Hwy 190, Lawtell, LA 70550 - T: (318) 543-7223. Head: Edvin Matt
Local Museum - 1968
General museum 37976

Lawton OK

Museum of the Great Plains, 601 NW Ferris Av, Lawton, OK 73502 - T: (580) 581-3460, Fax: (580) 581-3458, E-mail: mgp@sirinet.net, Internet: http://www.museumgreatplains.org. Head: Richard Welch
Local Museum / Historical Museum - 1961 37977

Le Claire IA

Buffalo Bill Museum of Le Claire, Iowa, 200 N River Dr, Le Claire, IA 52753 - T: (319) 289-5580, Fax: (319) 289-4989
Local Museum / Historical Museum - 1957
Indian preservation 37978

Le Roy NY

Le Roy House and Jell-o Gallery, 23 E Main St, Le Roy, NY 14482 - T: (716) 768-7433, Fax: (716) 768-7579, Internet: http://www.iinc.com/jellomuseum/. Head: Lynne J. Belluscio
Local Museum - 1940 37979

Le Sueur MN

Le Sueur Museum, 709 N 2nd St, Le Sueur, MN 56058 - T: (612) 357-4488. Head: Helen Meyer
Local Museum - 1968
Local history, in first school in Le Sueur 37980

Lead SD

Black Hills Mining Museum, 323 W Main, Lead, SD 57754 - T: (605) 584-1605, E-mail: bhminmus@mato.com, Internet: http://www.mining-museum.blackhills.com
Science&Tech Museum - 1986 37981

Leadville CO

Healy House and Dexter Cabin, 912 Harrison Av, Leadville, CO 80461 - T: (719) 486-0487. Head: Larry Frank
Historical Museum - 1947 37982

Tabor Opera House Museum, 306-310 Harrison Av, Leadville, CO 80461 - T: (719) 486-1147. Head: Evelyn E. Furman
Performing Arts Museum - 1955
Historic theater 37983

Leavenworth KS

Leavenworth County Historical Society Museum, 1128 5th Av, Leavenworth, KS 66048-3212 - T: (913) 682-7759, Fax: (913) 682-2089, E-mail: lvcohistsoc@lvworth.com, Internet: http://leavenworth-net.com/chs. Head: Marianna Spain
Local Museum - 1964
Local history 37984

Lebanon OH

Glendower State Memorial, 105 Cincinnati Av, Lebanon, OH 45036 - T: (513) 932-8560, E-mail: wchs@compuserve.com
Historic Site - 1944 37985

Warren County Historical Society Museum, 105 S Broadway, Lebanon, OH 45036-1707 - T: (513) 932-1817, Fax: (513) 932-8560, E-mail: wchs@goconcepts.com. Head: Mary Payne
Local Museum - 1940 37986

Lebanon PA

The Stoy Museum of the Lebanon County Historical Society, 924 Cumberland St, Lebanon, PA 17042 - T: (717) 272-1473, Fax: (717) 272-7474, E-mail: history@leba.net, Internet: http://www.leba.net/~history2. Head: Philip H. Feather
Local Museum - 1898
Local hist 37987

Lebec CA

Fort Tejon, 4201 Fort Tejon Rd, Lebec, CA 93243 - T: (661) 248-6692, Fax: (661) 248-8373. Head: Donald R. La Katos
Military Museum - 1939 37988

Lecompton KS

Territorial Capital-Lane Museum, 393 N 1900 Rd, Lecompton, KS 66050 - T: (785) 887-6285, Fax: (785) 887-6148, Internet: http://www.nekesc.org/~vista/hislec. Head: Rich McConnell
Historical Museum - 1969
State history 37989

Lee MA

Warehouse Gallery, Council for Creative Projects, 17 Main St, Lee, MA 01238 - T: (413) 243-8030, Fax: (413) 243-8031, E-mail: ccp@ccpexhibits.org, Internet: http://www.ccpexhibits.org. Head: Dr. Gail Gelburd
Fine Arts Museum - 1989 37990

Lee's Summit MO

Missouri Town 1855, 8010 E Park Rd, Lee's Summit, MO 64015 - T: (816) 795-8200 ext 1260, Fax: (816) 795-7938, E-mail: juligor@gw.co.jackson.mo.us, Internet: http://www.co.jackson.mo.us
Open Air Museum - 1963 37991

Leesburg VA

Loudoun Museum, 14-16 Loudoun St, Leesburg, VA 20175 - T: (703) 777-8331, 777-7427, Fax: (703) 737-3861, Internet: http://www.loudounmuseum.org. Head: Peter Kelpinski, Tracy Gillespie
Local Museum - 1967
Local hist 37992

Oatlands, 20850 Oatlands Plantation Ln, Leesburg, VA 20175 - T: (703) 777-3174, Fax: (703) 777-4427, E-mail: oatlands@erols.com, Internet: http://www.oatlands.org. Head: David Y. Boyce
Local Museum - 1965
Historic house 37993

Lehi UT

John Hutchings Museum of Natural History, 55 N Center St, Lehi, UT 84043 - T: (801) 768-7180. Head: J.L. Hutchings
Natural History Museum - 1955
Natural hist 37994

Leland MI

Leelanau Historical Museum, 203 E Cedar St, Leland, MI 49654 - T: (231) 256-7475, Fax: (231) 256-7650, E-mail: info@leelanauhistory.org, Internet: http://www.leelanauhistory.org. Head: R. Marc Livengood
Historical Museum - 1957
Local history 37995

Lenhartsville PA

Pennsylvania Dutch Folk Culture Society Museum, Lenhartsville, PA 19534 - T: (610) 867-6705
Folklore Museum - 1965
Folk culture 37996

Lerna IL

Lincoln Log Cabin, 400 S Lincoln Hwy Rd, Lerna, IL 62440 - T: (217) 345-6489, 345-1845, Fax: (217) 345-6472, E-mail: tomandsarah@lincolnlogcabin.org, Internet: http://www.lincoln-logcabin.org. Head: Tom Vance, Susan Mogerman
Historical Museum - 1929
Reconstructed cabin and farm of Thomas and Sara Lincoln on original site 37997

Moore Home, 400 S Lincoln Hwy Rd, Lerna, IL 62440 - T: (217) 345-6489, 345-1845, Fax: (217) 345-6472, E-mail: tomandsarah@lincolnlogcabin.org, Internet: http://www.lincolnlogcabin.org. Head: Tom Vance
Historical Museum - 1929
Home of Reuben and Matilda Moore, daughter of Sara Lincoln and stepsister of Abraham Lincoln 37998

Leverett MA

Leverett Historical Museum, N Leverett Rd, Leverett, MA 01054 - T: (413) 548-9082. Head: Annette Gibavic
Local Museum - 1963
Local history 37999

Lewes DE

Lewes Historical Society Museum, 110 Shipcarpenter St, Lewes, DE 19958 - T: (302) 645-7670, 645-8988. Head: George Elliott
Local Museum - 1961
Local hist 38000

Lewisburg PA

Edward and Marthann Samek Art Gallery, Bucknell University, Elaine Langone Center, Lewisburg, PA 17837 - T: (570) 577-3792, Fax: (570) 577-3480, E-mail: inthebag@bucknell.edu, Internet: http://www.bucknell.edu/departments/cgallery/. Head: Cynthia Peltier
Fine Arts Museum / University Museum - 1983
Art 38001

Packwood House Museum, 15 N Water St, Lewisburg, PA 17837 - T: (570) 524-0323, Fax: (570) 524-0323, E-mail: packwood@jdweb.com, Internet: http://www.Packwoodhou-semuseum.com. Head: Charles North
Local Museum - 1976
Local hist 38002

Slifer House, Riverwoods, 1 River Rd, Lewisburg, PA 17837 - T: (570) 524-2245, Fax: (570) 524-2245, E-mail: sliferhs@postoffice.ptd.net, Internet: http://slifer.albrightcare.org. Head: Gary W. Parks
Historic Site - 1976 38003

Union County Museum, Union County Courthouse, 2nd and Saint Louis Sts, Lewisburg, PA 17837 - T: (570) 524-8666, Fax: (570) 524-8743, E-mail: hstoricl@ptd.net, Internet: http://www.rootsweb.com. Head: Jeannette Lasansky, Gary Slear
Local Museum - 1906
History, genealogy, oral traditions 38004

Lewisburg WV

Fort Savannah Museum, 100 E Randolph St, Lewisburg, WV 24901 - T: (304) 645-3055. Head: Rosalie S. Detch
Military Museum - 1962
Military hist 38005

North House Museum, 301 W Washington St, Lewisburg, WV 24901 - T: (304) 645-3398, Fax: (304) 645-5201, E-mail: ghs@access.mountain.net, Internet: http://web.mountain.net/~ghs/ghs.html. Head: Joyce Mott, John Garnett
Local Museum / Historical Museum - 1963 38006

Lewiston ID

Luna House Museum, 306 Third St, Lewiston, ID 83501-1860 - T: (208) 743-2535. Head: Richard Riggs
Local Museum - 1960
Local history 38007

Lewiston ME

Bates College Museum of Art, 75 Russell St, Lewiston, ME 04240 - T: (207) 786-6158, Fax: (207) 786-8335, E-mail: museum@bates.edu, Internet: http://www.bates.edu. Head: Genetta McLean
Fine Arts Museum / University Museum - 1986
Art 38008

Lewistown IL

Dickson Mounds Museum, 10956 N Dickson Mounds Rd, Lewistown, IL 61542 - T: (309) 547-3721, Fax: (309) 547-3189, E-mail: jfranke@museum.state.il.us, Internet: http://www.museum.state.il.us/ismsites/dickson/. Head: Dr. Judith A. Franke
Archaeological Museum / Historic Site - 1927
Archaeology, American Indian cultures of Illinois 38009

Lewistown MT

Central Montana Historical Association Museum, 408 NE Main St, Lewistown, MT 59457 - T: (406) 538-5436. Head: Anthony R. Tuss
Historical Museum - 1955 38010

Lewistown PA

McCoy House, 17 N Main St, Lewistown, PA 17044 - T: (717) 242-1022, 248-4711, Fax: (717) 242-1022, E-mail: mchistory@acsworld.net, Internet: http://www.mccoyhouse.com. Head: Joseph E. Deihl
Local Museum - 1921
Historic building 38011

Lexington KY

American Saddle Horse Museum, 4093 Iron Works Pike, Lexington, KY 40511 - T: (606) 259-2746, Fax: (606) 255-2909, Internet: http://www.american-saddlebred.com. Head: Tolley Graves
Special Museum - 1962 38012

Ashland - Henry Clay Estate, 120 Sycamore Rd, Lexington, KY 40502 - T: (606) 266-8581, Fax: (606) 268-7266, E-mail: tgreen0124@aol.com, Internet: http://www.henryclay.org. Head: Terry Green, Mark D. Query
Historical Museum - 1926
1811 estate of Henry Clay, 1857 house of James Clay 38013

Headley-Whitney Museum, 4435 Old Frankfort Pike, Lexington, KY 40510 - T: (606) 255-6653, Fax: (606) 255-8375, E-mail: hwmuseum@mindspring.com, Internet: http://www.headley-whitney.org. Head: Diane C. Wachs
Decorative Arts Museum - 1973
Decorative arts 38014

Hunt-Morgan House, 201 N Mill St, Lexington, KY 40507 - T: (606) 232-3290, Fax: (606) 259-9210. Head: Joanne Binford
Local Museum - 1955 38015

International Museum of the Horse, 4089 Iron Works Pkwy, Lexington, KY 40511 - T: (859) 259-4231, 233-4303, Fax: (859) 225-4613, E-mail: khp@mis.net, Internet: http://www.imh.org. Head: Bill Cooke
Fine Arts Museum / Special Museum - 1978 38016

Lexington Children's Museum, 440 W Short St, Lexington, KY 40507 - T: (859) 258-3253, Fax: (859) 258-3255, E-mail: icm@prodigy.net, Internet: http://www.lexingtonchil-drensmuseum.com. Head: Sara Nees Holcomb
Special Museum - 1990 38017

The Living Arts and Science Center, 362 N Martin Luther King Blvd, Lexington, KY 40508 - T: (606) 252-5222, Fax: (606) 255-7448, E-mail: lasc6898@aol.com, Internet: http://www.livingarts&science.org. Head: Marty Henton
Fine Arts Museum / Ethnology Museum - 1968
Children's art, science 38018

Transylvania Museum, 300 N Broadway, Lexington, KY 40508 - T: (606) 233-8155, Fax: (606) 233-8171, E-mail: jmill@mail.transy.edu, Internet: http://www.transy.edu. Head: Dr. James Miller
Historical Museum - 1882
Science, medicine 38019

University of Kentucky Art Museum, Rose and Euclid, Lexington, KY 40506-0241 - T: (859) 257-5716, Fax: (859) 323-1994, E-mail: amshwf@pop.uky.edu, Internet: http://www.uky.edu. Head: Harriet Fowler
Fine Arts Museum / University Museum - 1976
Art 38020

Lexington MA

Lexington Historical Society Exhibition, POB 514, Lexington, MA 02420 - T: (781) 862-1703, Fax: (781) 862-4920, E-mail: lexhissc@tiac.net, Internet: http://www.lexingtonhistory.org. Head: Gardner Hayward, George S. Comtois
Historical Museum - 1886
Local history, Munroe and Buckman tavern, Hancock-Clarke house, American revolution 38021

Museum of Our National Heritage, The VanGordon-Williams Library and Archives, 33 Marrett Rd, Lexington, MA 02421 - T: (781) 861-6559 ext 100, Fax: (781) 861-9846, E-mail: info@monh.org, Internet: http://www.mnh.org. Head: John H. Ott
Historical Museum - 1971
History 38022

Lexington MO

Battle of Lexington State Historic Site, Ext Hwy 13, Lexington, MO 64067 - T: (660) 259-4654, Fax: (660) 259-2378, E-mail: blex@iland.net, Internet: http://www.mostateparks.com. Head: Janae Fuller
Military Museum / Historical Museum - 1959 38023

Lexington NC

Davidson County Historical Museum, 2 S Main St, Lexington, NC 27292 - T: (336) 242-2035, Fax: (336) 248-4122, E-mail: choffmann@co.davidson.nc.us. Head: Catherine Matthews Hoffmann
Local Museum - 1976 38024

Lexington NE

Dawson County Historical Museum, 805 N Taft St, Lexington, NE 68850-0369 - T: (308) 324-5340, Fax: (308) 324-5340, E-mail: bawcomus@nadix.net. Head: Francis Fagot, Barbara Vondras
Local Museum - 1958 38025

Lexington OH

Richland County Museum, 51 Church St, Lexington, OH 44904 - T: (419) 884-2230. Head: Harold Zehner
Folklore Museum / Local Museum - 1966 38026

Lexington SC

Lexington County Museum, 231 Fox St, Lexington, SC 29072 - T: (803) 359-8369, Fax: (803) 359-0023. Head: Horace E. Harmon
Decorative Arts Museum / Local Museum - 1970
Local hist 38027

Lexington VA

American Work Horse Museum, POB 1051, Lexington, VA 24450 - T: (540) 463-2194, Fax: (540) 464-3507, E-mail: info@horsecenter.org. Head: Robert Reel
Special Museum - 1971
Horses 38028

Gallery of Dupont Hall, Washington & Lee University, Lexington, VA 24450-0303 - T: (540) 463-8861, 463-8859, Fax: (540) 463-8104, E-mail: psimpson@wlu.edu, Internet: http://www.wlu.edu. Head: Kathleen Olson
Fine Arts Museum / University Museum - 1929
Art 38029

George C. Marshall Foundation, VMI Parade Ground, Lexington, VA 24450 - T: (540) 463-7103 ext 225, Fax: (540) 464-5229, E-mail: kemper@vmi.edu, Internet: http://www.gcmarshallfdn.org. Head: Julie Kemper, Albert J. Beveridge
Historical Museum / Military Museum - 1953
Military and political history (20th c) 38030

Lee Chapel and Museum, Washington and Lee University, Lexington, VA 24450-0303 - T: (504) 463-8768, Fax: (540) 463-8741, Internet: http://www.leechapel.wlu.edu. Head: Patricia A. Hobbs
Historical Museum - 1867
Local hist 38031

Reeves Center, Washington and Lee University, Lexington, VA 24450 - T: (540) 463-8744, Fax: (540) 463-8741. Head: Thomas V. Litzenburg
Fine Arts Museum / University Museum - 1982 38032

Rockbridge Historical Society Museum, 101 E Washington St, Lexington, VA 24450 - T: (540) 464-1058. Head: David Reynolds, Alice Williams
Local Museum - 1939
Local hist 38033

Virginia Military Institute Museum, Virginia Military Institute, Jackson Memorial Hall, Lexington, VA 24450 - T: (540) 464-7232, Fax: (540) 464-7112, E-mail: gibsonke@vmi.edu, Internet: http://www.vmi.edu/museum. Head: Keith E. Gibson
Military Museum - 1856
Military hist 38034

Liberal KS

Mid-America Air Museum, 2000 W 2nd St, Liberal, KS 67901 - T: (316) 624-5263, Fax: (316) 624-5454. Head: Gregory P. Kennedy
Science&Tech Museum - 1987
Aviation 38035

Liberty MO

Clay County Historical Museum, 14 N Main, Liberty, MO 64068 - T: (816) 781-8062
Historical Museum - 1965 38036

Jesse James Bank Museum, 103 N Water, Liberty, MO 64068 - T: (816) 781-4458, Fax: (816) 628-6676. Head: Elizabeth Gilliam Beckett
Historical Museum - 1966 38037

Libertyville IL

Libertyville-Mundelein Historical Society, 413 N Milwaukee Av, Libertyville, IL 60048-2280 - T: (847) 362-2330, Fax: (847) 362-0006. Head: Douglass Getchell
Local Museum - 1955
Local history 38038

Ligonier IN

Stone's Tavern Museum, 4946 N State Rd 5 and U.S. 33, Ligonier, IN 46767 - T: (219) 856-2871. Head: Dick Hursey
Historical Museum - 1964
Tavern of 1839 38039

Ligonier PA

Fort Ligonier Museum, 216 S Market St, Ligonier, PA 15658-1206 - T: (724) 238-9701, Fax: (724) 238-9732. Head: J. Martin West
Historical Museum - 1946
History 38040

Lihue HI

Kauai Museum, 4428 Rice St, Lihue, HI 96766 - T: (808) 245-6931, Fax: (808) 245-6864, Internet: http://www.openstudio.hawaii.edu. Head: Carol Lovell
Fine Arts Museum / Historical Museum - 1960
History, art 38041

Lima OH

Allen County Museum, 620 W Market St, Lima, OH 45801 - T: (419) 222-9426, Fax: (419) 222-0649, E-mail: acmuseum@worcnet.gen.oh.us, Internet: http://www.allencountymuseum.org. Head: Patricia F. Smith
Local Museum - 1908 38042

Lincoln IL

Postville Courthouse Museum, 914 Fifth St, Lincoln, IL 62656 - T: (217) 732-8930. Head: Richard Schachtsiek
Historic Site - 1953 38043

Lincoln MA

Codman House - The Grange, Codman Rd, Lincoln, MA 01773 - T: (781) 259-8843, Fax: (781) 259-8843, Internet: http://www.spnea.org. Head: Crystal Flores
Historical Museum - 1969
1740 Georgian mansion, home of Codman family 38044

DeCordova Museum and Sculpture Park, 51 Sandy Pond Rd, Lincoln, MA 01773 - T: (781) 259-8355, Fax: (781) 259-3650, E-mail: info@decardova.org, Internet: http//www.decordova.org. Head: Paul Master-Karnik
Fine Arts Museum / Folklore Museum - 1950
Arts, sculptures, Photography, Paintings 38045

Drumlin Farm, S Great Rd, Lincoln, MA 01773 - T: (781) 259-9500, Fax: (781) 259-7941, Internet: http://www.massaudubon.org. Head: Daniel Hart
Agriculture Museum - 1955
Living farm 38046

Gropius House, 68 Baker Bridge Rd, Lincoln, MA 01773 - T: (781) 259-8098, (617) 227-3956, Fax: (781) 259-9722, E-mail: mzephir@spnea.org, Internet: http://www.sprea.org. Head: Jane Nylander
Historical Museum - 1985
Modern architecture, designed by combining Bauhaus principles with New England building materials 38047

The Thoreau Institute at Walden Woods, 44 Baker Farm, Lincoln, MA 01773 - T: (781) 259-4730, Fax: (781) 259-4730, E-mail: jeff.cramer@walden.org, Internet: http://www.walden.org. Head: Kathi Anderson
Library with Exhibitions - 1991
Regional history, American literature - library 38048

Lincoln NE

Elder Art Gallery, Rogers Center for Fine Arts, Nebraska Wesleyan University, Lincoln, NE 68504-2230 - T: (402) 466-2371, Fax: (402) 465-2179, E-mail: dp@nebrwesleyan.edu. Head: Dr. Donald Paoletta
Fine Arts Museum / University Museum - 1965 38049

Gallery of the Department of Art and Art History, University of Nebraska, 207 Nelle Cochrane Woods Hall, Lincoln, NE 68588-0114 - T: (402) 472-2631, 472-5541, Fax: (402) 472-9746, Internet: http://www.unl.edu. Head: Joseph M. Ruffo
Fine Arts Museum - 1985
Student works 38050

Great Plains Art Collection in the Christlieb Gallery, c/o University of Nebraska-Lincoln, 1155 Q St, Hewit Pl, Lincoln, NE 68588-0250 - T: (402) 472-6220, Fax: (402) 472-2960, E-mail: sgustafson2@unl.edu, Internet: http://www.unl.edu/plains/gallery. Head: James Stubbendieck
Fine Arts Museum / University Museum - 1980 38051

Lincoln Children's Museum, 1420 P St, Lincoln, NE 68508 - T: (402) 477-0128, Fax: (402) 477-2004, E-mail: lbullcm@navix.net, Internet: http://www.lincolnchildrensmuseum.org. Head: Marilyn R. Gorham
Special Museum - 1989 38052

Museum of American Historical Society of Germans from Russia, 631 D St, Lincoln, NE 68502-1199 - T: (402) 474-3363, Fax: (402) 474-7229, E-mail: ahsgr@aol.com, Internet: http://www.ahsgr.org
Historical Museum - 1968 38053

Museum of Nebraska History, 131 Centennial Mall N, Lincoln, NE 68508 - T: (402) 471-4754, Fax: (402) 471-3144, E-mail: ednshs@inetnebr.com, Internet: http://www.nebraska-history.org. Head: Lawrence J. Sommer
Historical Museum - 1878 38054

National Museum of Roller Skating, 4730 South St, Lincoln, NE 68506 - T: (402) 483-7551 ext 16, Fax: (402) 483-1465, E-mail: rllrsktmus@aol.com, Internet: http://www.usacrs.com/museum.htm. Head: Michael Zaidman
Special Museum - 1980 38055

Nebraska Conference United Methodist Historical Center, 5000 Saint Paul Av, Lincoln, NE 68504-2796 - T: (402) 464-5994, Fax: (402) 464-6203, E-mail: mvetter@inebraska.com. Head: Maureen Vetter
Religious Arts Museum - 1968 38056

Sheldon Memorial Art Gallery and Sculpture Garden, c/o University of Nebraska-Lincoln, 12 and R Sts, Lincoln, NE 68588-0300 - T: (402) 472-2461, Fax: (402) 472-4258, E-mail: pjacobs@unlinfo.unl.edu, Internet: http://www.sheldon.unl.edu/. Head: Janice Driesbach
Fine Arts Museum / University Museum - 1963 38057

Thomas P. Kennard House, 1627 H St, Lincoln, NE 68501 - T: (402) 471-4764, Fax: (402) 471-4764, E-mail: museum02@nebraskahistory.org, Internet: http://www.nebraskahistory.org. Head: Larry Sommers
Historical Museum - 1968 38058

University of Nebraska State Museum, 307 Morrill Hall, 14 and U Sts, Lincoln, NE 68588-0338 - T: (402) 472-3779, Fax: (402) 472-8899, E-mail: jestes1@unl.edu, Internet: http://www-museum.unl.edu. Head: Dr. James R. Estes
University Museum / Natural History Museum - 1871
planetarium, library 38059

Lincoln NM

Old Lincoln County Courthouse Museum, Lincoln State Monument, Hwy 380, Lincoln, NM 88338 - T: (505) 653-4372, Fax: (505) 653-4372
Historical Museum - 1937 38060

Lincoln Park MI

Lincoln Park Historical Museum, 1335 Southfield Rd, Lincoln Park, MI 48146 - T: (313) 386-3137, E-mail: citylp@aol.com, Internet: http://www.downriverarts.com
Local Museum - 1972
Local and regional history - library 38061

Lincolnton GA

Elijah Clark Memorial Museum, 2959 McCormick Hwy, Lincolnton, GA 30817 - T: (706) 359-3458, Fax: (706) 359-5856, E-mail: eclark@g-net.net. Head: Dorothy Shields
Special Museum - 1961
Replica of the house of Elijah Clark 38062

Lincroft NJ

Monmouth Museum, College Campus, Newman Springs Rd, Lincroft, NJ 07738 - T: (732) 747-2266, Fax: (732) 747-8592, E-mail: monmuseum@netlabs.net, Internet: http://www.monmouthmuseum.org. Head: Dorothy V. Morehouse
Local Museum - 1963
Culture, art, scientific phenomena 38063

Lind WA

Adams County Historical Society Museum, POB 526, Lind, WA 99341 - T: (509) 677-3393, E-mail: galeirma@ritzcom.net. Head: Irma E. Gfeller
Local Museum - 1963
Local hist 38064

Linden IN

Railway Heritage Network, 207 N Main St, Linden, IN 47955-0061 - T: (765) 339-4896, Fax: (765) 339-4896, E-mail: eutsler@tctc.com. Head: David White
Science&Tech Museum - 1986
Railroad 38065

Lindenhurst NY

Old Village Hall Museum, 215 S Wellwood Av, Lindenhurst, NY 11757-0296 - T: (516) 957-4385. Head: Evelyn M. Ellis
Historical Museum - 1958 38066

Lindsborg KS

Birger Sandzen Memorial Gallery, 401 N First St, Lindsborg, KS 67456-0348 - T: (785) 227-2220, Fax: (785) 227-4170, E-mail: fineart@sandzen.org, Internet: http://www.sandzen.org. Head: Larry L. Griffis
Fine Arts Museum - 1957
Fine art 38067

McPherson County Old Mill Museum, 120 Mill St, Lindsborg, KS 67456 - T: (785) 227-3595, Fax: (785) 227-2810, E-mail: oldmillmuseum@hotmail.com, Internet: http://www.lindsborg.org/oldmill. Head: Lorna Batterson
Historical Museum / Science&Tech Museum - 1959
Local history, mill, genealogy 38068

Linthicum MD

Historical Electronics Museum, 1745 W Nursery Rd, Linthicum, MD 21090 - T: (410) 765-3803, Fax: (410) 765-0240, E-mail: radarmus@erols.com, Internet: http://www.erols.com/radarmus. Head: Katherine Dver Marks
Science&Tech Museum - 1980
Technology 38069

Lisbon OH

Lisbon Historical Society Museum, 117-119 E Washington St, Lisbon, OH 44432 - T: (330) 424-9000, Fax: (330) 424-1861. Head: David Privette
Local Museum - 1938 38070

Lisle IL

Jurica Nature Museum, Benedictine University, 5700 College Rd, Lisle, IL 60532 - T: (630) 829-6545, Fax: (630) 829-6551, E-mail: tsuchy@ben.edu, Internet: http://alt.ben.edu/resources/J-Museum/
University Museum / Natural History Museum - 1970
Natural history 38071

Lisle Station Park, 918-920 Burlington Av, Lisle, IL 60532 - T: (630) 968-0499, Fax: (630) 964-7448. Head: Kim Paetschow
Historical Museum / Historic Site / Open Air Museum - 1978 38072

Litchfield CT

Litchfield Historical Society Museum, 7 South St, Litchfield, CT 06759 - T: (860) 567-4501, Fax: (860) 567-3565, E-mail: lhsoc@snet.net, Internet: http://www.litchfieldhistoricalsociety.org. Head: Catherine Keene Fields
Historical Museum - 1856 38073

White Memorial Conservation Center, 80 Whitehall Rd, Litchfield, CT 06759-0368 - T: (860) 567-0857, Internet: http://www.whitememorialcc.org. Head: Keith R. Cudworth
Natural History Museum - 1964 38074

Litchfield MN

Meeker County Museum and G.A.R. Hall, 308 N Marshall, Litchfield, MN 55355 - T: (320) 693-8911. Head: Dona Brown
Local Museum - 1961
Regional history 38075

Little Falls MN

Charles A. Weyerhaeuser Memorial Museum, 2151 S Lindbergh Dr, Little Falls, MN 56345-0239 - T: (612) 632-4007, Fax: (320) 632-8409. Head: Jan Warner
Local Museum - 1936
Local history - library 38076

Little Falls NY

Herkimer Home, 200 State Rte 169, Little Falls, NY 13365 - T: (315) 823-0398, Fax: (315) 823-0587. Head: William Watkins
Historical Museum - 1913 38077

Little Falls Historical Museum, 319 S Ann St, Little Falls, NY 13365 - T: (315) 823-0643. Head: Esther M. Brown
Historical Museum - 1962
Local memorabilia, genealogy - library 38078

Little Rock AR

The Arkansas Arts Center, MacArthur Park, 9th and Commerce Sts, Little Rock, AR 72202 - T: (501) 372-4000, Fax: (501) 375-8053, E-mail: center@arkarts.org, Internet: http://www.arkarts.com. Head: T. Wolfe, William E. Clark
Fine Arts Museum - 1937
Art, decorative art - children's theater 38079

Arkansas Museum of Science and History - Museum of Discovery, 500 E Markham, Ste 500, Little Rock, AR 72201 - T: (501) 396-7050 ext 200, Fax: (501) 396-7054, E-mail: mod@Aristotle.net, Internet: http://www.amod.org. Head: Bill Bradshaw
Historical Museum / Natural History Museum - 1927
History, science 38080

The Old State House Museum, 300 W Markham St, Little Rock, AR 72201 - T: (501) 324-9685, Fax: (501) 324-9688, E-mail: info@oldstatehouse.com, Internet: http://

www.oldstatehouse.com. Head: Bill Gatewood
Historical Museum - 1952
History, built 1833-1842, first state capitol (1836-1911) 38081

University of Arkansas at Little Rock Art Galleries, Dept of Art, 2801 South University Av, Little Rock, AR 72204-1099 - T: (501) 569-8977, Fax: (501) 569-8775, E-mail: becusham@uair.edu, Internet: http://www.ualr.edu/artdept/index.html
Fine Arts Museum / University Museum - 1972 38082

Littleton CO

Colorado Gallery of the Arts, Araphoe Community College, 2500 W College Dr, Littleton, CO 80160 - T: (303) 797-5649, Fax: (303) 797-5935, Internet: http://www.arapahoe.com
Fine Arts Museum / University Museum - 1979
Art gallery 38083

Littleton Historical Museum, 6028 S Gallup, Littleton, CO 80120 - T: (303) 795-3950, Fax: (303) 730-9818. Head: Mary Allman
Local Museum - 1969
Local history, farms 38084

Livermore IA

Humboldt County Old Settler's Museum, Old Settlers Park, Hwy 222, Livermore, IA 50558 - T: (515) 379-1848
Historical Museum / Museum of Classical Antiquities - 1885
Antiques, settlement 38085

Liverpool NY

Sainte Marie among the Iroquois, Onondaga Lake Pkwy, Liverpool, NY 13088 - T: (315) 453-6767, Fax: (315) 453-6762, E-mail: stemane@nysnet.net, Internet: http://www.co.onondaga.ny.us/parks.htm. Head: Valerie Bell
Open Air Museum - 1933 38086

Salt Museum, Onondaga Lake Park, Liverpool, NY 13088 - T: (315) 453-6767, Fax: (315) 453-6762, E-mail: stemarie@nysnet.net, Internet: http://www.co.onondaga.ny.us/parks.htm
Special Museum - 1934 38087

Livingston MT

Livingston Depot Center, 200 W Park, Livingston, MT 59047 - T: (406) 222-2300, Fax: (406) 222-2401. Head: John Sullivan, Diana L. Seider
Local Museum - 1985
Northern Pacific railroad stn 38088

Yellowstone Gateway Museum of Park County, 118 W Chinook, Livingston, MT 59047 - T: (406) 222-4184, E-mail: museum@ycsi.net, Internet: http://www.avicom.net/parkmuseum/
Local Museum - 1976
Local and regional history and archaeology, railroads 38089

Livingston TX

Alabama-Coushatta Indian Museum, U.S. Hwy 190, between Livingston and Woodville, Livingston, TX 77351 - T: (409) 563-4391, Fax: (409) 563-4397
Ethnology Museum - 1965
Native American hist 38090

Polk County Memorial Museum, 514 W Mill St, Livingston, TX 77351 - T: (409) 327-8192. Head: Harleyne Clamon
Local Museum - 1963
Local hist 38091

Livingston Manor NY

Catskill Fly Fishing Center and Museum, 1031 Old Rte 17, Livingston Manor, NY 12758 - T: (845) 439-4810, Fax: (845) 439-3387, E-mail: flyfish@catskill.net, Internet: http://www.cffcm.org. Head: Paul N. Dahlie
Special Museum - 1981 38092

Loachapoka AL

Lee County Historical Society Museum, 6500 Stage Rd, Loachapoka, AL 36865 - T: (334) 887-3007. Head: John Sugg
Historical Museum - 1968 38093

Lock Haven PA

Heisey Museum, 362 E Water St, Lock Haven, PA 17745 - T: (570) 748-7254, Fax: (570) 748-1590, E-mail: heisey@cub.kcnet.org, Internet: http://www.kcnet.org/~heisey/. Head: David P. Winton
Local Museum / Historical Museum - 1921 38094

Lockport IL

Illinois and Michigan Canal Museum, 803 S State St, Lockport, IL 60441 - T: (815) 838-5080. Head: Marge Greger
Local Museum - 1964
Local history, pioneer settlement 38095

Lockport Gallery, Illinois State Museum, 201 W 10th St, Lockport, IL 60441 - T: (815) 838-7400, Fax: (815) 838-7448, E-mail: jzimmer@museum.state.il.us, Internet: http://www.museum.state.il.us/ismsites/lockport/. Head: Jim L. Zimmer
Fine Arts Museum / Public Gallery - 1987
Art 38096

Lockport NY

Niagara County Historical Center, 215 Niagara St, Lockport, NY 14094-2605 - T: (716) 434-7433, Fax: (716) 434-7433
Local Museum / Historical Museum - 1947
Local history, military, pioneer, Tuscarora trades, Erie Cunnl 38097

Lodi CA

San Joaquin County Historical Museum, 11793 N Micke Grove Rd, Lodi, CA 95240 - T: (209) 331-2055, Fax: (209) 331-2057, E-mail: info@sanjoaquinhistory.org, Internet: http://www.sanjoaquinhistory.org. Head: Michael W. Bennett
Historical Museum / Agriculture Museum - 1966 38098

Logan KS

Dane G. Hansen Memorial Museum, 110 W Main St, Logan, KS 67646 - T: (785) 689-4846, Fax: (785) 689-4892, E-mail: dghansen@ruraltel.net. Head: Lee Sause
Fine Arts Museum / Special Museum - 1973
Art 38099

Logan UT

Nora Eccles Harrison Museum of Art, Utah State University, 4020 Old Main Hill, Logan, UT 84322 - T: (435) 797-0163, Fax: (435) 797-3423, E-mail: jimmel@cc.usu.edu, Internet: www.usu.edu. Head: Jim Edwards
Fine Arts Museum / University Museum - 1982
Art 38100

Logansport IN

Cass County Historical Society Museum, 1004 E Market St, Logansport, IN 46947 - T: (219) 753-3866, Fax: (219) 753-3866
Local Museum - 1907
Local history 38101

Loma MT

House of a Thousand Dolls, 106 First St, Loma, MT 59460 - T: (406) 739-4338. Head: Marion Britton
Decorative Arts Museum - 1979 38102

Lombard IL

Lombard Historical Museum, 23 W Maple, Lombard, IL 60148 - T: (630) 629-1885, Fax: (630) 629-9927, Internet: http://www.tccafe.com/lhm/lhm.html. Head: Joel Van Haaften
Local Museum - 1970
Local hist 38103

Lompoc CA

Lompoc Museum, 200 S H St, Lompoc, CA 93436 - T: (805) 736-3888, Fax: (805) 736-2840. Head: Debra D. Argel
Ethnology Museum - 1969 38104

Lompoc Valley Historical Society Museum, 207 N L St, Lompoc, CA 93438 - T: (805) 735-4626. Head: Oscar Cook
Historical Museum - 1964 38105

La Purisima Mission, 2295 Purisima Rd, Lompoc, CA 93436 - T: (805) 733-3713, Fax: (805) 733-2497, E-mail: lapurmis@lapurisima.sbceo.k12.ca.us
Historical Museum - 1935 38106

London KY

Mountain Life Museum, 998 Levi Jackson Mill Rd, London, KY 40744 - T: (606) 878-8000, Fax: (606) 864-3825, Internet: http://www.kystateparks.com/agencies/parks/levijack.htm. Head: Ed Henson
Historical Museum / Ethnology Museum - 1929
History, ethnography 38107

Londonderry NH

The Children's Metamorphosis, 217 Rockingham Rd, Londonderry, NH 03053 - T: (603) 425-2560, Internet: http://www.discoverthemet.com. Head: Betsy Anderson
Special Museum - 1991
Children's museum 38108

Lone Jack MO

Civil War Museum of Lone Jack, Jackson County, 301 S Bynum Rd, Lone Jack, MO 64070 - T: (816) 566-2272. Head: Charlotte Remington
Military Museum - 1964 38109

Long Beach CA

American Museum of Straw Art, 2324 Snowden Av, Long Beach, CA 90815 - T: (562) 431-3540, Fax: (562) 598-0457, E-mail: strawwdrkz@aol.com, Internet: http://www.strawartmuseum.org. Head: Morgyn Owens-Celli
Decorative Arts Museum / Folklore Museum - 1989
Decorative and folk art 38110

California State University-Long Beach Art Museum, 1250 Bellflower Blvd, Long Beach, CA 90840-1901 - T: (562) 985-5761, Fax: (562) 985-7602, E-mail: uam@csulb.edu, Internet: http://www.csulb.edu/~uam. Head: Constance W. Glenn
Fine Arts Museum / University Museum - 1949 38111

Long Beach Museum of Art, 2300 E Ocean Blvd, Long Beach, CA 90803 - T: (562) 439-2119, Fax: (562) 439-3587, Internet: http://www.lbma.com. Head: Harold B. Nelson, Sandra Darling
Fine Arts Museum - 1950 38112

Queen Mary Museum, 1126 Queens Hwy, Long Beach, CA 90802-6390 - T: (562) 435-3511, Fax: (562) 432-7674, E-mail: queenmry@gte.net, Internet: http://www.queenmary.com. Head: Joseph F. Prevratil, Ronald Smith
Special Museum - 1971
Maritime Museum located aboard the Queen Mary, retired British luxury liner 38113

Rancho Los Alamitos, 6400 Bixby Hill Rd, Long Beach, CA 90815 - T: (562) 431-3541, Fax: (562) 430-9694. Head: Pamela Seager
Historical Museum - 1970 38114

Rancho Los Cerritos, 4600 Virginia Rd, Long Beach, CA 90807 - T: (562) 570-1755, Fax: (562) 570-1893, Internet: http://www.ci.long-beach.ca.us/park/ranchlc.htm. Head: Ellen Calomiris
Historical Museum - 1955 38115

Long Beach WA

World Kite Museum and Hall of Fame, 3rd St NW, Long Beach, WA 98631 - T: (360) 642-4020, Fax: (360) 642-4020, E-mail: jkite@willapabay.org, Internet: http://www.worldkitemuseum.com. Head: Kay Buesing
Special Museum - 1988
Japanese kites, other kites used in science, sport and religion 38116

Long Branch NJ

Long Branch Historical Museum, 1260 Ocean Av, Long Branch, NJ 07740 - T: (732) 222-9879. Head: Edgar N. Dinkelspiel
Local Museum - 1953
1879 Saint James Episcopal Chapel, Church of the Presidents, civil war 38117

Long Island City NY

Isamu Noguchi Garden Museum, 32-37 Vernon Blvd, Long Island City, NY 11106 - T: (718) 721-1932 ext 208, Fax: (718) 278-2348, E-mail: museum@noguchi.org, Internet: http://www.noguchi.org. Head: Shoji Sadao
Fine Arts Museum - 1985 38118

P.S. 1 Contemporary Art Center, 22-25 Jackson Av, Long Island City, NY 11101-5324 - T: (718) 784-2084, Fax: (718) 482-9454, E-mail: mail@ps1.org, Internet: http://www.ps1.org. Head: Alanna Heiss
Fine Arts Museum - 1971
Contemporary art 38119

Long Lake MN

Western Hennepin County Pioneers Museum, 1953 W Wayzata Blvd, Long Lake, MN 55356 - T: (952) 473-6557
Local Museum - 1907
Pioneer museum - archives 38120

Longboat Key FL

Longboat Key Center for the Arts, 6860 Longboat Dr S, Longboat Key, FL 34228 - T: (941) 383-2345, Fax: (941) 383-7915, E-mail: LBKARTS@att.net, Internet: http://www.longboatkeyartscenter.org. Head: Beth Cunningham
Fine Arts Museum / Decorative Arts Museum - 1952 38121

Longmeadow MA

Richard Salter Storrs House, 697 Longmeadow St, Longmeadow, MA 01106 - T: (413) 567-3600
Local Museum - 1899
Local history 38122

Longmont CO

Longmont Museum, 400 Quail Rd, Longmont, CO 80501 - T: (303) 651-8374, Fax: (303) 651-8590, E-mail: martha.clevenger@ci.longmont.co.us, Internet: http://www.ci.longmont.co.us/museum.htm. Head: Martha R. Clevenger
Local Museum - 1940
Regional history 38123

Longview TX

Gregg County Historical Museum, 214 N Fredonia St, Longview, TX 75601 - T: (903) 753-5840, Fax: (903) 753-5854
Local Museum - 1983
Local hist 38124

Longview Museum of Fine Art, 215 E Tyler St, Longview, TX 75601 - T: (903) 753-8103, Fax: (903) 753-8217, E-mail: director@lmfa.org, Internet: http://www.lmfa.org
Fine Arts Museum - 1970
Art 38125

Longview WA

Lower Columbia College Fine Arts Gallery, 1600 Maple St, Longview, WA 98632 - T: (360) 577-2300, Fax: (360) 577-3400, E-mail: twoods@lcc.ctc.edu
Fine Arts Museum / University Museum - 1978
Art 38126

Lookout Mountain TN

Cravens House, Point Park Visitor Center, Lookout Mountain, TN 37350 - T: (423) 821-7786, Fax: (423) 821-7788. Head: Sam Weddle
Local Museum
Historic house 38127

Lopez Island WA

Lopez Island Historical Museum, 28 Washburn Pl, Lopez Village, Lopez Island, WA 98261 - T: (360) 468-3447, 468-2049, E-mail: lopezmuseum@rockisland.com
Historical Museum - 1966
Local hist 38128

Loretto PA

Southern Alleghenies Museum of Art, Saint Francis College Mall, Loretto, PA 15940 - T: (814) 472-3920, Fax: (814) 472-4131, E-mail: sama@sfcpa.edu, Internet: http://SAMA-SFC.org. Head: Michael M. Strueber
Fine Arts Museum - 1975
Visual art 38129

Los Alamos NM

Art Center at Fuller Lodge, 2132 Central Av, Los Alamos, NM 87544 - T: (505) 662-9331, E-mail: artful@losalamos.com, Internet: http://artful.losalamos.com. Head: Gloria Gilmore-House
Fine Arts Museum - 1977 38130

Bradbury Science Museum, 15 and Central, Los Alamos, NM 87544 - T: (505) 665-3339, Fax: (505) 665-6932, E-mail: museum@lanl.gov., Internet: http://bsm.lanl.gov. Head: John S. Rhoades
Natural History Museum - 1963 38131

Los Alamos County Historical Museum, Fuller Lodge Cultural Center, 1921 Juniper St, Los Alamos, NM 87544 - T: (505) 662-6272, Fax: (505) 662-6312, E-mail: historicalsociety@losalamos.com, Internet: http://www.losalamos.com/historicalsociety. Head: Hedy Dunn, Fred Roensch
Historical Museum - 1968
Manhattan Project history 38132

Los Angeles CA

The American Film Institute, 2021 N Western Av, Los Angeles, CA 90027 - T: (323) 856-7600, Fax: (323) 467-4578, Internet: http://www.comafionline.org. Head: Jean Firstenberg
Fine Arts Museum - 1967
Cinematography 38133

Autry Museum of Western Heritage, 4700 Western Heritage Way, Los Angeles, CA 90027-1462 - T: (323) 667-2000, Fax: (323) 660-5721, E-mail: autry@autry-museum.org, Internet: http://www.autry-museum.org. Head: John L. Gray
Historical Museum - 1984 38134

Barnsdall Junior Arts Center, 4814 Hollywood Blvd, Los Angeles, CA 90027 - T: (213) 485-4474, Fax: (213) 485-7456, E-mail: jacbac@earthlink.net, Internet: http://www.culturela.org/communityarts/JAC. Head: Istiharoh Glasgow
Fine Arts Museum - 1966 38135

Beit Hashoah - Museum of Tolerance, 9786 W Pico Blvd, Los Angeles, CA 90035 - T: (310) 553-8403, Fax: (310) 553-8007, E-mail: lgeft@wiesenthal.com, Internet: http://motlc.wiesenthal.com
Historical Museum - 1993
Holocaust, Human Rights 38136

California African-American Museum, 600 State Dr, Exposition Park, Los Angeles, CA 90037 - T: (213) 744-7432, Fax: (213) 744-2050, Internet: http://www.caam.ca.gov. Head: Jai Henderson
Fine Arts Museum / Historical Museum / Ethnology Museum - 1981 38137

California Science Center, 700 State Dr, Los Angeles, CA 90037 - T: (213) 744-7400, Fax: (213) 744-2034, E-mail: 4info@cscmail.org, Internet: http://www.casciencectr.org. Head: Jeffrey N. Rudolph
Science&Tech Museum - 1880 38138

The Carole and Barry Kaye Museum of Miniatures, 5900 Wilshire Blvd, Los Angeles, CA 90036 - T: (323) 937-6464, 937-7766, Fax: (323) 937-2126, E-mail: carolekaye@aol.com, Internet: http://www.museumofminiatures.com. Head: Carole Kaye
Decorative Arts Museum - 1994
Miniatures 38139

County of Los Angeles Fire Museum, 1320 N Eastern Av, Los Angeles, CA 90063-3294 - T: (213) 881-2411, Fax: (818) 249-8165. Head: Paul Schneider
Historical Museum - 1974
Fire-fighting 38140

Fisher Gallery, c/o University of Southern California, 823 Exposition Blvd, Los Angeles, CA 90089-0292 - T: (213) 740-4561, Fax: (213) 740-7676, E-mail: jlavere@bcf.usc.edu, Internet: http://www.usc.edu/fishergallery. Head: Dr. Selma Holo
Fine Arts Museum / University Museum - 1939 38141

Fowler Museum of Cultural History, University of California, Los Angeles, CA 90024 - T: (310) 825-4361, Fax: (310) 206-7007, E-mail: office@fmch.ucla.edu, Internet: http://www.fmch.ucla.edu. Head: Doran H. Ross
Fine Arts Museum / Decorative Arts Museum / Folklore Museum / Ethnology Museum / Archaeological Museum - 1963 38142

Gallery 825, 825 N La Cienega Blvd, Los Angeles, CA 90069 - T: (310) 652-8272, Fax: (310) 652-9251, E-mail: gallery825@laaa.org, Internet: http://www.laaa.org. Head: Ashley Emenegger
Public Gallery - 1925 38143

Grier-Musser Museum, 403 S Bonnie Brae, Los Angeles, CA 90057 - T: (213) 413-1814, E-mail: griermusser@hotmail.com, Internet: http://www.isi.edu/sims/gm/html. Head: Susan Tejada
Historical Museum - 1984 38144

Grunwald Center for the Graphic Arts, University of California, Hammer Museum of Art and Cultural Center, 10899 Wilshire Blvd, Los Angeles, CA 90024-4201 - T: (310) 443-7076, Fax: (310) 443-7099, E-mail: cdixon@arts.ucla.edu, Internet: http://www.hammer.ucla.edu. Head: David Rodes
Fine Arts Museum / University Museum - 1956
Graphic art 38145

Hollywood Bowl Museum, 2301 N Highland Av, Los Angeles, CA 90068 - T: (323) 850-2058, Fax: (323) 850-2066, E-mail: museum@laphil.org, Internet: http://www.hollywoodbowl.org. Head: Dr. Carol Merrill-Mirsky
Music Museum / Performing Arts Museum - 1984
Music and performing arts 38146

Holyland Exhibition, 2215 Lake View Av, Los Angeles, CA 90039 - T: (323) 664-3162. Head: Christine Kirkegaard, Betty J. Shepard
Religious Arts Museum - 1924 38147

J. Paul Getty Museum, 1200 Getty Center Dr, Ste 1000, Los Angeles, CA 90049-1687 - T: (310) 440-7300, Fax: (310) 440-7751, E-mail: info@getty.edu, Internet: http://www.getty.edu. Head: Deborah Gribbon
Fine Arts Museum - 1953 38148

Japanese American National Museum, 369 E First St, Los Angeles, CA 90012 - T: (213) 625-0414, Fax: (213) 625-1770, Internet: http://www.janm.org. Head: Irene Hirano
Historical Museum / Fine Arts Museum - 1985
History, former 1925 Nishi Hongwanji Buddhist Temple 38149

Justice Museum of Art, 7611 S San Pedro St, Los Angeles, CA 90003 - T: (323) 971-9529
Fine Arts Museum 38150

Korean Museum, 176 S Western Av, Los Angeles, CA 90004 - T: (213) 427-0333
Ethnology Museum / Fine Arts Museum 38151

Laband Art Gallery, c/o Loyola Marymount University, 7900 Loyola Blvd, Los Angeles, CA 90045-8346 - T: (310) 338-2880, Fax: (310) 338-6024, E-mail: gfuglie@lmu.edu, Internet: http://www.lmu.edu/colleges/cfa/art/laband. Head: Gordon L. Fuglie
Fine Arts Museum / University Museum - 1985
Coll o figurative art 38152

Los Angeles Children's Museum, 310 N Main St, Los Angeles, CA 90012 - T: (213) 687-8800, Fax: (213) 687-0319, E-mail: lacm@lacm.org, Internet: http://www.lacm.org. Head: Candace Barrett, Douglas R. Ring
Special Museum - 1979 38153

Los Angeles Contemporary Exhibitions, 6522 Hollywood Blvd, Los Angeles, CA 90028-6210 - T: (323) 957-1777, Fax: (323) 957-9025, E-mail: info@artleak.org, Internet: http://www.artleak.org. Head: Irene Tsatsos, Mikel Kaufman
Public Gallery - 1977 38154

Los Angeles County Museum of Art, 5905 Wilshire Blvd, Los Angeles, CA 90036 - T: (323) 857-6000, Fax: (323) 857-6214, E-mail: publicinfo@lacma.org, Internet: http://www.lacma.org
Fine Arts Museum - 1910 38155

Los Angeles Municipal Art Gallery, 4804 Hollywood Blvd, Los Angeles, CA 90027 - T: (213) 485-4581, Fax: (213) 485-8396, E-mail: cadmag@earthlink.net. Head: Thomas McGovern
Fine Arts Museum - 1954
Contemporary fineart and design 38156

Los Angeles Museum of Contemporary Art, 250 S Grand Av, California Plaza, Los Angeles, CA 90012 - T: (213) 621-2766, Fax: (213) 620-8674, Internet: http://www.moca-la.org. Head: Richard Koshalek
Fine Arts Museum - 1979 38157

Los Angeles Museum of the Holocaust, 6006 Wilshire Blvd, Los Angeles, CA 90036 - T: (323) 761-8170, Fax: (323) 761-8174, E-mail: museumgroup@jewishla.org, Internet: http://www.jewishla.org. Head: Marcia Reines Josephy
Historical Museum - 1978
Art, children's art, personal memorabilia, pre war photos and decorative art 38158

Lummis Home El Alisal, 200 E Av 43, Los Angeles, CA 90031 - T: (323) 222-0546, Fax: (323) 222-0771, E-mail: hssc@socalhistory.org, Internet: http://www.socalhistory.org. Head: Siegfried G. Demke, Thomas F. Andrews
Historical Museum - 1883 38159

MAK Center for Art and Architecture, Pearl M. Mackey Apartment House, 1137-1141 S Cochran Av, Los Angeles, CA 90019 - T: (323) 651-1510, Fax: (323) 651-2340, E-mail: makcenter@earthlink.net, Internet: http://www.MAK.at. Head: Daniela Zyman
Fine Arts Museum - 1994 38160

Museum of African American Art, 4005 Crenshaw Blvd, Los Angeles, CA 90008 - T: (213) 294-7071, Fax: (213) 294-7084. Head: Belinda Fontenote-Jamerson
Fine Arts Museum - 1976 38161

Museum of Arts Downtown Los Angeles, 514 S Spring St, Los Angeles, CA 90013 - T: (213) 627-7849
Fine Arts Museum 38162

Museum of Neon Art, 501 W Olympic Blvd, Los Angeles, CA 90015 - T: (213) 489-9918, Fax: (213) 489-9932, E-mail: info@neonmona.org, Internet: http://www.museneon.org. Head: Kim Koga
Fine Arts Museum - 1981 38163

My Jewish Discovery Place Children's Museum of JCCA → Zimmer Children's Museum

Natural History Museum of Los Angeles County, 900 Exposition Blvd, Los Angeles, CA 90007 - T: (213) 763-3412, 763-3466, Fax: (213) 743-4843, E-mail: gward@nhm.org, Internet: http://www.nhm.org. Head: Dr. James L. Powell
Natural History Museum - 1910 38164

New Image Art, 7906 Santa Monica Blvd, Los Angeles, CA 90046 - T: (323) 654-2192, Fax: (323) 654-2192, E-mail: newimgart@aol.com, Internet: http://www.newimagartgallery.com. Head: Marsea Goldberg
Fine Arts Museum - 1995 38165

Otis Gallery, Otis College of Art and Design, 9045 Lincoln Blvd, Los Angeles, CA 90045 - T: (310) 665-6905, 665-6800, Fax: (310) 665-6908, E-mail: exhibit@otisart.edu, Internet: http://www.otisart.edu. Head: Dr. Anne Ayres
Fine Arts Museum - 1940
Art gallery 38166

Plaza de La Raza, 3450 N Mission Rd, Los Angeles, CA 90031 - T: (213) 223-2475, Fax: (213) 223-1804, E-mail: admin@plazaraza.org, Internet: http://www.plazaraza.org. Head: Rose Marie Cano
Fine Arts Museum - 1969 38167

El Pueblo de Los Angeles Historical Monument, 125 Paseo de la Plaza, Ste 400, Los Angeles, CA 90012 - T: (213) 628-1274, Fax: (213) 485-8238. Head: Frank Catania
Historical Museum - 1953 38168

Side Street Projects, 400 S Main St, Los Angeles, CA 90013 - T: (213) 620-8895, Fax: (213) 620-8896, E-mail: sidest@netcom.com, Internet: http://www.sidestreet.org. Head: Karen Atkinson
Fine Arts Museum - 1991 38169

Skirball Cultural Center, Hebrew Union College, 2701 N Sepulveda Av, Los Angeles, CA 90049 - T: (310) 440-4500, Fax: (310) 440-4695, E-mail: nberman@skirball.org, Internet: http://www.skirball.org. Head: Nancy Berman
Fine Arts Museum / Historical Museum - 1913 38170

Southern California Chapter Railway and Locomotive Museum, 6006 Wooster Av, Los Angeles, CA 90056-1434
Science&Tech Museum
Railroad 38171

Southwest Museum, 234 Museum Dr, Los Angeles, CA 90065 - T: (213) 221-2163, Fax: (213) 224-8223, Internet: http://www.southwestmuseum.org. Head: Dr. Duane H. King
Fine Arts Museum / Decorative Arts Museum / Folklore Museum / Ethnology Museum / Archaeological Museum - 1907
library 38172

Travel Town Museum, 5200 Zoo Dr, Los Angeles, CA 90027 - T: (213) 662-5874, Fax: (818) 243-0041, E-mail: lbarth@rap.ci.la.ca.us, Internet: http://www.cityofla.org/dept/rap/grifmet/tt/index.htm. Head: Linda J. Barth
Science&Tech Museum - 1952 38173

UCLA Hammer Museum, 10899 Wilshire Blvd, Los Angeles, CA 90024 - T: (310) 443-7020, Fax: (310) 443-7099, E-mail: hammerinfo@arts.ucla.edu, Internet: http://www.hammer.ucla.edu/. Head: Ann Philbin
Fine Arts Museum / University Museum - 1994 38174

Watts Towers Arts Center, 1727 E 107 St, Los Angeles, CA 90002 - T: (213) 847-4646, Fax: (323) 564-7030, E-mail: cadwattsctr@earthlink.net. Head: Mark S. Greenfield
Fine Arts Museum - 1975 38175

Wells Fargo History Museum, 333 S Grand Av, Los Angeles, CA 90071 - T: (213) 253-7166, Fax: (213) 680-2269
Historical Museum - 1982 38176

Zimmer Children's Museum, 6505 Wilshire Blvd, Los Angeles, CA 90048 - T: (323) 761-8991, Fax: (323) 761-8990, E-mail: sherrik@zimmermuseum.org. Head: Sherri Kadovitz
Special Museum - 1991 38177

Los Banos CA

Ralph Milliken Museum, Merced County Park, US Hwy 152, Los Banos, CA 93635 - T: (209) 826-5505
Folklore Museum / Historical Museum - 1954 38178

Los Gatos CA

Forbes Mill Museum of Regional History, 75 Church St, Los Gatos, CA 95030 - T: (408) 395-7375, Fax: (408) 395-7386, E-mail: lgmuseums@aol.com. Head: Laura Bajuk
Historical Museum - 1965 38179

Los Gatos Museum of Art and Natural History, 4 Taut Av, Los Gatos, CA 95030 - T: (408) 354-2646, Fax: (408) 395-7386, E-mail: lgmuseums@aol.com. Head: Laura Bajuk
Fine Arts Museum / Natural History Museum - 1965 38180

Lost Creek WV

Watters Smith, Duck Creek Rd, Lost Creek, WV 26385 - T: (304) 745-3081, Fax: (304) 745-3631. Head: Larry A. Jones
Local Museum / Agriculture Museum - 1964
Local hist 38181

Loudonville OH

Cleo Redd Fisher Museum, 203 E Main St, Loudonville, OH 44842 - T: (419) 994-4050
Local Museum - 1973
Local history 38182

Louisa VA

Louisa County Historical Museum, 200 Church Av, Louisa, VA 23093 - T: (703) 967-2794, E-mail: lchs@firstva.com, Internet: http://www.ups.edu/biology/museum/. Head: Matt Kersey
Local Museum - 1966
Regional history, in 1868 jail 38183

Louisburg NC

Louisburg College Art Gallery, 501 N Main St, Louisburg, NC 27549 - T: (919) 496-2521, Fax: (919) 496-1788, E-mail: hintonwj@yahoo.com, Internet: http://www.louisburg.edu. Head: William Hinton
Fine Arts Museum / University Museum - 1957
American Impressionist art, Primitive art 38184

Louisville KY

Allen R. Hite Art Institute, University of Louisville, Belknap Campus, Louisville, KY 40292 - T: (502) 852-6794, Fax: (502) 852-6791, E-mail: darrell@louisville.edu, Internet: http://www.art.louisville.edu. Head: Prof. James Grubola
Fine Arts Museum / University Museum - 1946
Art 38185

Archaeological Museum, Louisville Presbyterian Theological Seminary, 1044 Alta Vista Dr, Louisville, KY 40205-1798 - T: (502) 895-3411, Fax: (502) 895-1096. Head: Dr. Eugene March
Archaeological Museum / Religious Arts Museum - 1930
Religion, archaeology 38186

Farmington Historic Home, 3033 Bardstown Rd, Louisville, KY 40205 - T: (502) 452-9920, Fax: (502) 456-1976, Internet: http://www.historicfarmington.org. Head: Carolyn Brooks
Historical Museum - 1958 38187

The Filson Club Historical Society Museum, 1310 S Third St, Louisville, KY 40208 - T: (502) 635-5083, Fax: (502) 635-5086, E-mail: filson@filsonclub.org, Internet: http://www.filsonclub.org. Head: Mark V. Wetherington
Local Museum - 1884
Local history 38188

The Joseph A. Callaway Archaeological Museum, Southern Baptist Theological Seminary, 2825 Lexington Rd, Louisville, KY 40280 - T: (502) 897-4141, Fax: (502) 897-4880, E-mail: jdrinkard@sbts.edu, Internet: http://www.sbtf.edu. Head: Joel F. Drinkard
Archaeological Museum / Religious Arts Museum - 1961
Biblical archaeology 38189

Kentucky Art and Craft Foundation, 609 W Main St, Louisville, KY 40202 - T: (502) 589-0102, Fax: (502) 589-0154, E-mail: kacf@aye.net, Internet: http://www.kentuckycrafts.org. Head: Mary Miller
Decorative Arts Museum / Fine Arts Museum - 1981
Folk art, crafts 38190

Kentucky Derby Museum, 704 Central Av, 1 Churchill Downs, Louisville, KY 40201 - T: (502) 637-1111, Fax: (502) 636-5855, E-mail: info@derbymuseum.org, Internet: http://www.derbymuseum.org. Head: Lynn Ashton
Special Museum - 1985
Thoroughbred racing, equine art, history, science 38191

Locust Grove, 561 Blankenbaker Lane, Louisville, KY 40207 - T: (502) 897-9845, Fax: (502) 897-0103, E-mail: lghh@locustgrove.org, Internet: http://www.locustgrove.org. Head: Julie Parke
Historic Site - 1964
1790 Georgian mansion, home of General George Rogers Clark 38192

Louisville Science Center, 727 W Main St, Louisville, KY 40202 - T: (502) 561-6100, Fax: (502) 561-6145, E-mail: admin@lsclouienet.com, Internet: http://www.louisvillescience.org. Head: Gail R. Becker
Natural History Museum / Science&Tech Museum - 1872
Physical, life and natural science, industrial technology, ethnographic, costumes 38193

Louisville Visual Art Museum, 3005 River Rd, Louisville, KY 40207 - T: (502) 896-2146, Fax: (502) 896-2148, E-mail: feedback@louisvillevisualart.org, Internet: http://www.louisvillevisualart.org. Head: John P. Begley, Frank F. Weisberg
Fine Arts Museum - 1909
Art gallery 38194

Museum of the American Printing House for the Blind, 1839 Frankfort Av, Louisville, KY 40206 - T: (502) 895-2405 ext 365, Fax: (502) 899-2363, E-mail: ctobe@aph.org, Internet: http://www.aph.org. Head: Carol B. Tobe
Historical Museum - 1990 38195

Portland Museum, 2308 Portland Av, Louisville, KY 40212 - T: (502) 776-7678, Fax: (502) 776-9874, E-mail: portmuseum@aol.com. Head: Nathalie Taft Andrews
Local Museum - 1978
Regional history, Beach Grove residence of William Skene 38196

Sons of the American Revolution Museum, 1000 S Fourth St, Louisville, KY 40203 - T: (502) 589-1776, Fax: (502) 589-1671, Internet: http://www.sar.org. Head: William H. Roddis
Historical Museum - 1876
National history 38197

Speed Art Museum, 2035 S Third St, Louisville, KY 40208 - T: (502) 634-2700, Fax: (502) 636-2899, E-mail: info@speedmuseum.org, Internet: http://www.speedmuseum.org. Head: Peter Morrin
Fine Arts Museum - 1925
Art 38198

Loveland CO

Loveland Museum and Gallery, 503 N Lincoln, Loveland, CO 80537 - T: (970) 962-2410, 962-2490, Fax: (970) 962-2910, E-mail: isons@ci.loveland.co.us, Internet: http://www.ci.loveland.co.us. Head: Susan P. Ison
Local Museum / Public Gallery - 1937
Local history, art 38199

Loveland OH

Loveland Historical Museum, 201 Riverside Dr, Loveland, OH 45140 - T: (513) 683-5692, Fax: (513) 683-5692. Head: Janet Beller
Local Museum - 1975
Local hist 38200

Lowell MA

American Textile History Museum, 491 Dutton St, Lowell, MA 01854-4221 - T: (978) 441-0400, Fax: (978) 441-1412, E-mail: msmith@athm.org, Internet: http://www.athm.org. Head: Michael J. Smith
Historical Museum / Science&Tech Museum - 1960
Textile history, machinery and industry, costumes, clothing - library, archive 38201

Lowell National Historical Park, 67 Kirk St, Lowell, MA 01852 - T: (978) 970-5000, Fax: (978) 275-1762, Internet: http://www.nps.gov/lowe. Head: Patrick C. McCrary
Local Museum - 1978
Local hist - Labor 38202

Middlesex Canal Collection, Center for Lowell History, 40 French St, Lowell, MA 01852 - T: (978) 934-4997, Fax: (978) 934-4995. Head: Martha Mayo
Local Museum - 1962
Local history 38203

New England Quilt Museum, 18 Shattuck St, Lowell, MA 01852 - T: (978) 452-4207, Fax: (978) 452-5405, E-mail: nequiltmuseum@erols.com, Internet: http://www.nequiltmuseum.org. Head: Deborah McAdams, Patricia Steuert
Decorative Arts Museum - 1987
Quilts 38204

Whistler House Museum of Art, Lowell Art Association, 243 Worthen St, Lowell, MA 01852 - T: (978) 452-7641, Fax: (978) 454-2421, E-mail: Tomedmonds@whistlerhouse.org, Internet: http://www.whistlerhouse.org. Head: Tom Edmonds
Fine Arts Museum - 1878
Art gallery, birthplace of James A. M. Whistler - Lowell celebrates Kerouac Committee 38205

Lubbock TX

Museum of Texas Tech University, 4th & Indiana St, Lubbock, TX 79409-3191 - T: (806) 742-2442, Fax: (806) 742-1136, E-mail: museum.texastech@ttu.edu, Internet: http://www.ttu.edu/~museum/. Head: Gary Edson
University Museum / Local Museum - 1929
History of Southwestern US, ethnology, natural science, paleontology, fine and contemporary art, Pre-Columbian art coll, archaeology, mammalogy, biodiversity 38206

Science Spectrum, 2579 S Loop 289, Lubbock, TX 79423 - T: (806) 748-1040, Fax: (806) 745-1115, E-mail: spectrum@door.net, Internet: http://www.sciencespectrum.com. Head: Cassandra L. Henry
Science&Tech Museum - 1986
Science 38207

Lubec ME

Roosevelt Campobello, POB 129, Lubec, ME 04652 - T: (506) 752-2922, Fax: (506) 752-6000, E-mail: quirk@fdr.net, Internet: http://www.fdr.net. Head: Christopher Roosevelt
Historical Museum - 1964
Summer home of Pres. Franklin D. Roosevelt 38208

Lucas OH

Malabar Farm State Park, 4050 Bromfield Rd, Lucas, OH 44843 - T: (419) 892-2784, Fax: (419) 892-3988, E-mail: malabar@richnet.net, Internet: http://www.malabarfarm.org. Head: Louis M. Andres
Historical Museum / Agriculture Museum - 1939 38209

Ludington MI

White Pine Village Museum, 1687 S Lakeshore Dr, Ludington, MI 49431 - T: (231) 843-4808, Fax: (231) 843-7089, E-mail: whitepine@masoncounty.net, Internet: http://www.lumanet.org/whitepine. Head: Ronald M. Wood
Open Air Museum / Local Museum - 1937
Local history, reconstructed historical village, 21 bldgs, incl Rose Hawley Museum, Maritime Museum, Abe Nelson Lumbering Museum, Scottville Clown Band's Museum of Music 38210

Ludlow VT

Black River Academy Museum, High St, Ludlow, VT 05149 - T: (802) 228-5050, Fax: (802) 228-7444, E-mail: glbrehm@tds.net
Local Museum - 1972
Local hist 38211

Lufkin TX

The Museum of East Texas, 503 N Second St, Lufkin, TX 75901 - T: (409) 639-4434, Fax: (409) 639-4435. Head: J.P. McDonald
Fine Arts Museum / Historical Museum - 1975
Art, history 38212

Texas Forestry Museum, 1905 Atkinson Dr, Lufkin, TX 75901 - T: (409) 632-9535, 633-6248, Fax: (409) 632-9543, E-mail: info@treetexas.com, Internet: http://www.treetexas.com. Head: Carol Riggs
Natural History Museum - 1972 38213

Lumpkin GA

Bedingfield Inn Museum, Cotton St on the Square, Lumpkin, GA 31815 - T: (912) 838-6419. Head: Sara Singer
Historical Museum - 1965
1836 Stagecoach Inn , costumes, paintings, decorative art, furnishings 38214

Westville Historic Handicrafts Museum, Martin Luther King Dr, Lumpkin, GA 31815 - T: (912) 838-6310, Fax: (912) 838-4000, Internet: http://www.westville.org. Head: Matthew M. Moye
Historical Museum / Open Air Museum - 1966
Historic Village 34 buildings and houses c.1850 38215

Lutherville MD

Fire Museum of Maryland, 1301 York Rd, Lutherville, MD 21093 - T: (410) 321-7500, Fax: (410) 321-5679, E-mail: info@firemuseummd.org, Internet: http://www.firemuseummd.org. Head: Stephen G. Heaver
Historical Museum - 1971
Fire fighting 38216

Lynchburg VA

The Anne Spencer Memorial Foundation, 1313 Pierce St, Lynchburg, VA 24501 - T: (804) 845-1313. Head: Hugh R. Jones
Local Museum - 1977
Local hist 38217

Lynchburg Museum, 901 Court St, Lynchburg, VA 24504 - T: (804) 847-1459, Fax: (804) 528-0162, E-mail: museum@ci.lynchburg.va.us, Internet: http://www.lynchburgmuseum.org. Head: Thomas G. Ledford
Historical Museum - 1976
Local hist 38218

Maier Museum of Art, Randolph-Macon Woman's College, 2500 Rivermont Av, Lynchburg, VA 24503 - T: (804) 947-8000, 947-8136, Fax: (804) 947-8726, E-mail: klawson@rmwc.edu, Internet: http://www.rmwc.edu/maier.edu. Head: Karol Lawson
Fine Arts Museum / University Museum - 1920
Art 38219

Point of Honor, 112 Cabell St, Lynchburg, VA 24504 - T: (804) 847-1459, Fax: (804) 528-0162, E-mail: museum@ci.lynchburg.va.us, Internet: http://www.pointofhonor.org. Head: Mary Jo Tull
Local Museum / Folklore Museum - 1976
Historic house 38220

South River Meeting House, 5810 Fort Av, Lynchburg, VA 24502 - T: (804) 239-2548, 239-1688, Fax: (804) 239-6649
Local Museum - 1757
Historic house 38221

Lyndon KS

Osage County Historical Society, 631 Topeka Av, Lyndon, KS 66451 - T: (785) 828-3477, E-mail: research@kanza.net, Internet: http://www.osagechs.org. Head: Tammy S. Orear
Local Museum - 1963
Local history, family history, library 38222

Lynn MA

Lynn Museum, 125 Green St, Lynn, MA 01902 - T: (781) 592-2465, Fax: (781) 592-0012, E-mail: lynnmuse@shore.net, Internet: http://www.lynnmuseum.org. Head: Sandra Krein
Historical Museum - 1897
Local history, Hyde-Mills house - library 38223

Lyons CO

The Lyons Redstone Museum, 340 High St, Lyons, CO 80540, mail addr: POB 9, CO 80540 Lyons - T: (303) 823-6692, 823-5271, Fax: (303) 823-8257, 823-6692. Head: LaVern M. Johnson
Local Museum / Historic Site - 1973
Local history 38224

Lyons KS

Coronado-Quivira Museum, 105 W Lyon, Lyons, KS 67554 - T: (316) 257-3941. Head: Janel Cook
Local Museum - 1927
General museum 38225

Lyons NY

Wayne County Historical Society Museum, 21 Butternut St, Lyons, NY 14489 - T: (315) 946-4943, Fax: (315) 946-0069, E-mail: wchs4943@aol.com, Internet: http://members.aol.com/wchs4943. Head: Andrea Evangelist
Historical Museum - 1946 38226

Lyons Falls NY

Lewis County Historical Society Museum, High St, Lyons Falls, NY 13368 - T: (315) 348-8089, E-mail: histsoc@northnet.org, Internet: http://web.northnet.org/lewiscountyhistoricalsociety/home.html. Head: Lisa Becker
Historical Museum - 1930 38227

Mabel MN

Steam Engine Museum, Steam Engine Park, Mabel, MN 55954 - T: (507) 493-5350. Head: Tim Mengis
Science&Tech Museum - 1990
Technology 38228

McAllen TX

McAllen International Museum, 1900 Nolana, McAllen, TX 78504 - T: (956) 682-1564, Fax: (956) 686-1813, E-mail: mim@hiline.net, Internet: www.mcallenmuseum.org. Head: John Mueller
Fine Arts Museum / Science&Tech Museum - 1969
Arts and sciences 38229

McCalla AL

Iron and Steel Museum of Alabama, 12632 Confederate Pkwy, McCalla, AL 35111 - T: (205) 477-5711, Fax: (205) 477-9400. Head: Vicki Gentry
Historical Museum - 1970 38230

McClellanville SC

Hampton Plantation, 1950 Rutledge Rd, McClellanville, SC 29458 - T: (803) 546-9361, Fax: (803) 527-4995
Local Museum - 1971
Historic house 38231

McConnells SC

Historic Brattonsville, 1444 Brattonsville Rd, McConnells, SC 29726 - T: (803) 684-2327, Fax: (803) 684-0149. Head: Van Shields
Open Air Museum / Historic Site - 1976
Local hist 38232

McCook NE

High Plains Museum, 421 Norris Av, McCook, NE 69001 - T: (308) 345-3661. Head: Marilyn Hawkins
Historical Museum - 1969 38233

Senator George Norris State Historic Site, 706 Norris Av, McCook, NE 69001-3142 - T: (308) 345-8484, Fax: (308) 345-8484, E-mail: norris@mccooknet.com, Internet: http://www.nebraska-history.org. Head: Lynne Ireland
Historical Museum - 1969 38234

McCutchenville OH

McCutchen Overland Inn, Rte 53 N, McCutchenville, OH 44844 - T: (419) 981-2052
Local Museum - 1967
Historic house 38235

McDade TX

McDade Museum, Main St, McDade, TX 78650 - T: (512) 273-0044. Head: Don Grissom
Local Museum - 1962
Local hist 38236

Macedon NY

Macedon Historical Society Museum, 1185 Macedon Center Rd, Macedon, NY 14502 - T: (716) 388-0629
Historical Museum - 1962 38237

McFarland WI

McFarland Historical Society Museum, 5814 Main St, McFarland, WI 53558 - T: (608) 838-3986
Local Museum - 1964
Local hist 38238

Machias ME

Burnham Tavern, Hannah Weston Chapter, National Society Daughters of the American Revolution, Main St, Machias, ME 04654 - T: (207) 255-4432, E-mail: valdine@juno.com. Head: John R. Atwood, Valdine C. Atwood
Historical Museum - 1910
Tavern from 1770 38239

Machiasport ME

Gates House, Rte N 92, Machiasport, ME 04655-0301 - T: (207) 255-8461, E-mail: franklf@nemalne.com. Head: Jane C. Armstrong
Historical Museum - 1964 38240

Mackinac Island MI

Mackinac Island Museum, Mackinac Island, MI 49757 - T: (906) 847-3328, (517) 373-4296, Fax: (906) 847-3815, E-mail: mackinacparks@state.mi.us, Internet: http://www.mackinac.com/historicparks. Head: Carl R. Nold
Local Museum / Military Museum - 1895
Regional history, archaeology 38241

Stuart House City Museum, Market St, Mackinac Island, MI 49757 - T: (906) 847-8181, E-mail: cmim@freeway.net. Head: Lewis D. Crusoe
Historical Museum / Local Museum - 1930 38242

Mackinaw MI

Fort Machilimackinac, Mill Creek and Point Light Staion, Mackinaw, MI 49757 - T: (906) 847-3328, (517) 373-4296, Fax: (906) 847-3815, (517) 373-4790, E-mail: mackinacparks@state.mi.us, Internet: http://www.mackinac.com/historicparks. Head: Carl R. Nold
Local Museum - 1895
Archaeology, 1780-1895 Fort Mackinac, 1715-1780 Fort Michilimackinac, colonial time, tourism, transportation, lighthouses, native american - Fort Mackinac 38243

Mackinaw City MI

Colonial Michilimackinac, 102 W Straits Av, Mackinaw City, MI 49701 - T: (231) 627-5563, Fax: (231) 436-5410, 436-4210, E-mail: mackinacparks@state.mi.us, Internet: http://www.mackinac.com/historicparks. Head: Carl R. Nold
Historic Site / Open Air Museum - 1959
French and British military outpost and fur-trading village 38244

Historic Mill Creek, Mackinaw City, MI 49701 - T: (231) 436-7301, Fax: (231) 436-5410, 436-4210, E-mail: mackinacparks@state.mi.us, Internet: http://wwwmackinac.com/historicparks. Head: Carl R. Nold
Science&Tech Museum - 1975
18th-c water-powered sawmill 38245

Teysen's Woodland Indian Museum, 300 E Central St, Mackinaw City, MI 49701 - T: (616) 436-7011, 436-7519, Fax: (616) 436-5932. Head: Kenneth Teysen
Ethnology Museum / Folklore Museum - 1950
Local hist 38246

McKinney TX

Bolin Wildlife Exhibit and Antique Collection, 1028 N McDonald, McKinney, TX 75069 - T: (972) 562-2639. Head: Jerry Bolin
Natural History Museum / Museum of Classical Antiquities - 1980
Natural hist 38247

Collin County Farm Museum, 7117 County Rd 166, McKinney, TX 75070 - T: (972) 548-4793, Fax: (972) 542-2265. Head: Randy La Jaunie
Agriculture Museum - 1976
Farming 38248

Heard Natural Science Museum, 1 Nature Pl, McKinney, TX 75069-8840 - T: (972) 562-5566, Fax: (972) 548-9119, E-mail: heardmuseum@texoma.net, Internet: http://www.heardmuseum.org. Head: Steve R. Runnels
Natural History Museum - 1964
Natural science 38249

McLean TX

McLean-Alanreed Area Museum, Main St, McLean, TX 79057 - T: (806) 779-2731
Local Museum - 1969
Local hist 38250

McMinnville OR

Evergreen Aviation Museum, 3850 Three Mile Ln, McMinnville, OR 97128 - T: (503) 434-4180, Fax: (503) 434-4058, E-mail: bill.schaub@evergreenaviation.com, Internet: http://www.sprucegoose.org
Science&Tech Museum - 1992 38251

Macomb IL

Western Illinois University Art Gallery, 1 University circle, Macomb, IL 61455 - T: (309) 298-1587, Fax: (309) 298-2400, E-mail: JR-Graham1@wiu.edu, Internet: http://www.wiu.edu/artgallery. Head: John R. Graham, Donald B. Spancer
Fine Arts Museum / University Museum - 1899
Art 38252

Macon GA

Hay House Museum, 934 Georgia Av, Macon, GA 31201-6708 - T: (912) 742-8155, Fax: (912) 745-4277. Head: Marilyn L. Ashmore
Historical Museum - 1973
Historic House: 1855-59 Italian Renaissance Revival Mansion 38253

Museum of Arts and Sciences, 4182 Forsyth Rd, Macon, GA 31210 - T: (478) 477-3232, Fax: (478) 477-3251, E-mail: info@masmacon.com, Internet: http://www.masmacon.com. Head: Michael Brothers, Claire Smith
Fine Arts Museum / Science&Tech Museum - 1956
plantearium 38254

Ocmulgee National Monument, 1207 Emery Hwy, Macon, GA 31201 - T: (912) 752-8257, Fax: (912) 752-8259, Internet: http://www.nps.gov/ocmu
Archaeological Museum - 1936 38255

Sidney Lanier Cottage, Middle Georgia Historical Society, 935 High St, Macon, GA 31208-3358 - T: (912) 743-3851, Fax: (912) 745-3132. Head: Katherine C. Oliver
Historical Museum / Local Museum - 1964
Regional History, birthplace of poet Sidney Lanier - library 38256

Tubman African-American Museum, 340 Walnut St, Macon, GA 31208 - T: (912) 743-8544, Fax: (912) 743-9063, E-mail: tubman@mindspring.com, Internet: http://www.tubmanmuseum.com. Head: Carey Pickard, Chi Ezekwueche
Historical Museum / Folklore Museum - 1982 38257

McPherson KS

McPherson Museum, 1130 E Euclid, McPherson, KS 67460 - T: (316) 245-2574, Fax: (316) 245-2574. Head: David Flask
Local Museum - 1890
Local history 38258

Madawaska ME

Tante Blanche Museum, U.S. 1, Madawaska, ME 04756 - T: (207) 728-4518. Head: Verna Fortin
Local Museum - 1968
Local hist 38259

Madera CA

Madera County Museum, 210 W Yosemite Av, Madera, CA 93637 - T: (209) 673-0291, Fax: (559) 674-5114
Local Museum / Historical Museum - 1955 38260

Madison CT

Madison Historical Society Museum, 853 Boston Post Rd, Madison, CT 06443 - T: (203) 245-4567, E-mail: achard@cshore.com, Internet: http://www.MadisonCT.com. Head: A.M. Chard
Local Museum / Historical Museum - 1917 38261

Madison FL

North Florida Community College Art Gallery, Turner Davis Dr, Madison, FL 32340 - T: (904) 973-2288, Fax: (904) 973-2288. Head: William F. Gardner
Fine Arts Museum / University Museum - 1975
College Art Gallery 38262

Madison IN

Historic Madison House, 500 West St, Madison, IN 47250 - T: (812) 265-2967, Fax: (812) 273-3941, E-mail: hmihmfi@seidata.com. Head: John E. Galvin
Historical Museum / Science&Tech Museum - 1960 38263

Jefferson County Historical Museum, 615 W First St, Madison, IN 47250 - T: (812) 265-2335, Fax: (812) 273-5023, E-mail: jchs@seidata.com, Internet: http://www.seidata.com/~jchs. Head: John Zubaty
Local Museum - 1850
County history, Madison railroad stn 38264

Lanier State Historic Site, 511 W 1st St, Madison, IN 47250 - T: (812) 265-3526, Fax: (812) 265-3501, E-mail: lanier1@seidata.com
Historical Museum - 1925
Home of J.F.D. Lanier 38265

Shrewsbury Windle House, 301 W 1st St, Madison, IN 47250 - T: (812) 265-4481. Head: Ann S. Windle
Historical Museum - 1948 38266

Madison MN

Lac Qui Parle County Historical Museum, 250 8th Av S, Madison, MN 56256 - T: (612) 598-7678, E-mail: madville@frontiernet.net
Local Museum - 1948
Regional history 38267

Madison NJ

Elizabeth P. Korn Gallery, Drew University, Rte 24, Madison, NJ 07940 - T: (973) 408-3000. Head: Livio Saganic
Fine Arts Museum / Archaeological Museum - 1968
Ancient Near-East archeaology, different arts 38268

Museum of Early Trades and Crafts, Main St at Green Village Rd, Madison, NJ 07940 - T: (973) 377-2982, Fax: (973) 377-7358, E-mail: metc@msn.com, Internet: http://www.rosenet.org/metc. Head: Jean M. Martin
Historical Museum - 1969 38269

Madison SD

Prairie Village, W Hwy 34, Madison, SD 57042 - T: (605) 256-3644, Fax: (605) 256-9616
Local Museum / Open Air Museum - 1966
40 restored buildings 38270

Smith-Zimmermann Museum, 221 NE 8th St, Dakota State University Campus, Madison, SD 57042 - T: (605) 256-5308, Fax: (605) 256-5643, E-mail: smith.zimmermann@dsu.edu, Internet: http://www.smith-zimmermann.dsu.edu. Head: Clyde K. Brashier
Historical Museum - 1952
History of lake County, Ethnic settlers artifacts, Chautaugua, musical instruments, transportation, farm implements 38271

Madison WI

Elvehjem Museum of Art, 800 University Av, Madison, WI 53706-1479 - T: (608) 263-2246, Fax: (608) 263-8188, E-mail: ppowell@lvm.wisc.edu. Head: Dr. Russell Panczenko
Fine Arts Museum / University Museum - 1962
Art 38272

Helen Louise Allen Textile Collection, 1300 Linden Dr, University of Wisconsin, Madison, WI 53706 - T: (608) 262-1162, Fax: (608) 262-5335, Internet: http://sohe.wisc.edu/hlatc. Head: Mary Ann Fitzgerald
Special Museum - 1968
Textiles and costume 38273

Madison Art Center, 211 State St, Madison, WI 53703 - T: (608) 257-0158, Fax: (608) 257-5722, E-mail: mac@itis.com, Internet: http://www.madisonartcenter.org. Head: Stephen Fleischman
Fine Arts Museum - 1901
Art 38274

Madison Children's Museum, 100 State St, Madison, WI 53703 - T: (608) 256-6445, Fax: (608) 256-3226, E-mail: mcm@kidskiosk.org, Internet: http://www.kidskiosk.org. Head: Karen A. Drummer
Special Museum - 1980
Children's museum 38275

State Historical Museum of Wisconsin, 30 N Carroll St, Madison, WI 53703-2707 - T: (608) 264-6555, Fax: (608) 264-6575, E-mail: shsw.museum@ccmail.adp.wisc.edu, Internet: http://www.shsw.wisc.edu. Head: George Voigt
Local Museum - 1846
Local hist 38276

University of Wisconsin Zoological Museum, 250 North Mills St, Madison, WI 53706 - T: (608) 262-3766, Fax: (608) 262-5395, Internet: http://www.wisc.edu/zoology/museum. Head: Dr. John A.W. Kirsch
University Museum / Natural History Museum - 1887
Vertebrate zoology, osteology 38277

The Wisconsin Union Galleries, University of Wisconsin-Madison, 800 Langdon St, Madison, WI 53706 - T: (608) 262-5969, Fax: (608) 262-8862, E-mail: rfrusso@facstaff.wisc.edu, Internet: http://www.sit.wisc.edu/~wudart/. Head: Ralph Russo
Fine Arts Museum - 1928
Art 38278

Wisconsin Veterans Museum Madison, 30 W Mifflin St, Madison, WI 53703 - T: (608) 266-1009, Fax: (608) 264-7615, E-mail: lwolfe@mail.wi.us, Internet: http://badger.state.wi.us/agencies/dva/museum/wvmmain.html. Head: Dr. Richard H. Zeitlin
Military Museum - 1901
Military hist - archive 38279

Mahomet IL

Early American Museum, State Rte 47, Mahomet, IL 61853 - T: (217) 586-2612, Fax: (217) 586-3491, E-mail: early@cu-online.com, Internet: http://www.advance.net/~early. Head: Cheryl Kennedy
Historical Museum / Museum of Classical Antiquities - 1967 38280

Mahwah NJ

Art Galleries of Ramapo College, 505 Ramapo Valley Rd, Mahwah, NJ 07430 - T: (201) 684-7587. Head: Shalom Gorewitz
Fine Arts Museum - 1979
Haitian art, popular art, prints 38281

Maitland FL

Maitland Art Center, 231 W Packwood Av, Maitland, FL 32751-5596 - T: (407) 539-2181, Fax: (407) 539-1198, E-mail: RCmailMAC@aol.com, Internet: http://www.maitartctr.org. Head: James G. Shepp
Fine Arts Museum - 1972
Art 38282

Malden MA

Malden Public Library Art Collection, 36 Salem St, Malden, MA 02148 - T: (781) 324-0218, 388-0800, Fax: (617) 324-4467, E-mail: maldensvp@mbln.lib.ma.us, Internet: http://www.museumca.org/usa/state.html. Head: Dina G. Malgeri
Fine Arts Museum - 1879
Library with special art coll 38283

Malibu CA

Frederick R. Weisman Museum of Art, Pepperdine University, 24255 Pacific Coast Hwy, Malibu, CA 90263 - T: (310) 317-7257, Fax: (310) 456-4556, E-mail: mzakian@pepperdine.edu, Internet: http://www.pepperdine.edu. Head: Michael Zakian
Fine Arts Museum - 1992
Art 38284

Malibu Lagoon Museum, 23200 Pacific Coast Hwy, Malibu, CA 90265 - T: (310) 456-8432. Head: Sandra Mitchell
Historical Museum - 1982 38285

Malone NY

House of History, 51 Milwaukee St, Malone, NY 12953 - T: (518) 483-2750. Head: Jeanette Hotchkiss
Historical Museum - 1903 38286

Malvern AR

The Boyle House - Hot Spring County Museum, 310 E Third St, Malvern, AR 72104 - T: (501) 337-4775. Head: Janis West
Local Museum - 1981
County history 38287

Mammoth Spring AR

Depot Museum of the Mammoth Spring State Park, Box 36, Mammoth Spring, AR 72554 - T: (501) 625-7364, Fax: (870) 625-3255, E-mail: mammothsprg@arkansas.com, Internet: http://www.arkansasstateparks.com
Historical Museum - 1971
Local history, Frisco railroad depot, train memorabilia, Frisco Caboose 38288

Manassas VA

Jennie Dean Memorial, 9601 Prince William St, Manassas, VA 20110 - T: (703) 368-1873, Fax: (703) 257-8406, Internet: http://xroads.virginia.edu/~VAM/vamhome.html. Head: Scott H. Harris
Local Museum - 1995
Local hist 38289

Manassas National Battlefield Park, 6511 Sudley Rd, Rte 234, Manassas, VA 20109 - T: (703) 361-1339, Fax: (703) 361-7106, E-mail: - mana_superintendent@nps.gov, Internet: http://www.nps.gov/mana
Military Museum / Historic Site - 1940
Historic site 38290

Manchester CT

Cheney Homestead, 106 Hartford Rd, Manchester, CT 06040 - T: (860) 643-5588, E-mail: - ManchesterHistory@Juno.com, Internet: http://www.ci.manchester.ct.us/cheney/historic/htm. Head: David Smith
Local Museum - 1969 38291

Lutz Children's Museum, 247 S Main St, Manchester, CT 06040 - T: (860) 649-2838, E-mail: rich@lutzmuseum.org, Internet: http://www.lutzmuseum.org. Head: Richard D. Goodwin
Special Museum - 1953 38292

Manchester MA

Manchester Historical Society Museum, 10 Union St, Manchester, MA 01944 - T: (978) 526-7230
Decorative Arts Museum / Local Museum - 1886
Decorative arts, local history 38293

Manchester NH

Chapel Art Center, Saint Anselm College, 100 Saint Anselm Dr, Manchester, NH 03102 - T: (603) 641-7470, Fax: (603) 641-7116, E-mail: drosenth@anselm.edu, Internet: http://www.anselm.edu. Head: Dr. Donald A. Rosenthal
Fine Arts Museum / University Museum - 1967 38294

Currier Gallery of Art, 201 Myrtle Way, Manchester, NH 03104 - T: (603) 669-6144, Fax: (603) 669-7194, Internet: http://www.currier.org. Head: Susan E. Strickler
Fine Arts Museum - 1929
Architecture, American paintings, drawings, American Indian art, folk art, textiles, woodcarvings, Oriental art, American art, porcelain, silver, tapestries, enamels, Baroque art - library 38295

Lawrence L. Lee Scouting Museum, 40 Blondin Rd, Manchester, NH 03109 - T: (603) 627-1492, 669-8919, Fax: (603) 641-6436, E-mail: administrator@scoutingmuseum.org, Internet: http://www.scoutingmuseum.org. Head: Al Lambert
Folklore Museum - 1969
Scouting 38296

Manchester Historic Association Museum, 129 Amherst St, Manchester, NH 03101 - T: (603) 622-7531, Fax: (603) 622-0822, E-mail: history@mha.mv.com, Internet: http://www.manchester-historic.org. Head: Gail Nessell Colglazier
Historical Museum - 1896 38297

New Hampshire Institute of Art, 148 Concord St, Manchester, NH 03104 - T: (603) 623-0313, Fax: (603) 641-1832, E-mail: nhiart@gsinet.net, Internet: http://www.nhia.edu
Fine Arts Museum - 1898
Arts and science 38298

Manchester VT

The American Museum of Fly Fishing, Seminary Av and Historic 7a, Manchester, VT 05254 - T: (802) 362-3300, Fax: (802) 362-3308, E-mail: amffish@sover.net, Internet: http://www.amff.com. Head: Gary P. Tanner
Special Museum - 1968
Presidential fishing tackle, fly fishing art 38299

Hildene, Rte 7A S, Manchester, VT 05254 - T: (802) 362-1788, Fax: (802) 362-1564, E-mail: info@hildene.org, Internet: http://www.hildene.org. Head: Gerrit W. Kouwenhoven
Local Museum - 1978
Historic house 38300

Southern Vermont Art Center, West Rd, Manchester, VT 05254 - T: (802) 362-1405, Fax: (802) 362-3274, E-mail: info@svac.org, Internet: www.svac.org. Head: Christopher Madkour
Fine Arts Museum / Folklore Museum - 1929
Art 38301

Mangum OK

Old Greer County Museum and Hall of Fame, 222 W Jefferson St, Mangum, OK 73554 - T: (580) 782-2851
Local Museum - 1972 38302

Manhasset NY

Science Museum of Long Island, Leeds Pond Preserve, 1526 N Plandome Rd, Manhasset, NY 11030 - T: (516) 627-9400 ext 10, Fax: (516) 365-8927, E-mail: smli@compuserve.com, Internet: http://ourworld.compuserve.com/homepages/smli. Head: John Loret
Science&Tech Museum - 1963 38303

Manhattan KS

Goodnow Museum, 2224 Stone Post Rd, Manhattan, KS 66502 - T: (785) 565-6490
Historical Museum - 1969
Home of pioneer Kansas educator, Isaac Tichenor Goodnow 38304

Hartford House Museum, 2309 Claflin Rd, Manhattan, KS 66502 - T: (785) 565-6490. Head: D. Cheryl Collins
Historical Museum - 1974
Pre-fabricated house shipped on the Hartford Steamboat to Manhattan, KS 38305

Pioneer Log Cabin Museum, City Park, 11th and Poyntz, Manhattan, KS 66502 - T: (785) 565-6490. Head: D. Cheryl Collins
Historical Museum - 1915 38306

Riley County Historical Museum, 2309 Claflin Rd, Manhattan, KS 66502 - T: (785) 565-6490. Head: D. Cheryl Collins
Local Museum - 1914
County history 38307

Wolf House Museum, 630 Fremont, Manhattan, KS 66502 - T: (785) 565-6490. Head: D. Cheryl Collins
Historical Museum - 1983
1868 boarding house 38308

Manistee MI

Manistee County Historical Museum, 425 River St, Manistee, MI 49660 - T: (231) 723-5531. Head: Steve Harold
Local Museum - 1953
Regional history, A.H. Lyman Drug Co 38309

Manistique MI

Imogene Herbert Historical Museum, Pioneer Park, Deer St, Manistique, MI 49854 - T: (906) 341-8131, 341-5010. Head: Ellen Davenport
Local Museum - 1963
Local history 38310

Manitou Springs CO

Miramont Castle Museum, 9 Capitol Hill Av, Manitou Springs, CO 80829 - T: (719) 685-1011. Head: John Smichny, Bob Yager
Historical Museum - 1976 38311

Manitowoc WI

Pinecrest Historical Village, 924 Pine Crest Ln, Manitowoc, WI 54221-0574 - T: (920) 684-4445, 684-5110, Fax: (920) 684-0573. Head: Robert P. Fay
Local Museum / Open Air Museum - 1970
Local hist 38312

Rahr West Art Museum, 610 N 8th St, Manitowoc, WI 54220 - T: (920) 683-4501, Fax: (920) 683-5047, E-mail: rahrwest@manitowoc.org. Head: Jan Smith
Fine Arts Museum - 1950
Art 38313

Wisconsin Maritime Museum, 75 Maritime Dr, Manitowoc, WI 54220-6823 - T: (920) 684-0218, Fax: (920) 684-0219, E-mail: maritime@lakesfield.net, Internet: http://www.wimaritimemuseum.com. Head: Jay C. Martin
Historical Museum - 1968
Maritime hist 38314

Mankato KS

Jewell County Historical Museum, 201 N Commercial St, Mankato, KS 66956 - T: (913) 378-3218
Local Museum / Agriculture Museum - 1961
Agriculture 38315

Mankato MN

Blue Earth County Historical Museum, 415 Cherry St, Mankato, MN 56001 - T: (507) 345-5566, E-mail: bechs@juno.com, Internet: http://www.ic.mankato.mn.us/reg9/bechs. Head: Jane Tarjeson, James Lundgreen
Local Museum - 1901
Regional history 38316

Carnegie Art Center, Rotunda and Fireplace Galleries, 120 S Broad St, Mankato, MN 56001 - T: (507) 625-2730
Fine Arts Museum
Regional artists 38317

Helson Hall, Minnesota State University, 136 Mankato Av, Mankato, MN 56002 - T: (507) 389-6412, Internet: http://www.mankato.msus.edu/dept/artdept. Head: Harlan Bloomer
Fine Arts Museum
Drawings, American paintings, prints, crafts, bookplates 38318

Manlius NY

Town of Manlius Museum, 101 Scoville Av, Manlius, NY 13104 - T: (315) 682-6660, Fax: (315) 682-6660. Head: Maggie Trespasz
Local Museum - 1976 38319

Mansfield LA

Mansfield State Historc Site, 15149 Hwy 175, 3 mi SE of Mansfield, Mansfield, LA 71052 - T: (318) 872-1474, (888) 677-6267, Fax: (318) 871-4345, E-mail: mansfield@crt.state.la.us, Internet: http://www.crt.state.la.us/crt/parks/
Historical Museum / Military Museum - 1957
Civil War Battlefield 38320

Mansfield MO

Laura Ingalls Wilder-Rose Wilder Lane Historic Home and Museum, 3068 Hwy A, Mansfield, MO 65704 - T: (417) 924-3626, Fax: (417) 924-8580, E-mail: liwhone@windo.missouri.org, Internet: http://www.lauraingallswilderhome.com. Head: Jean C. Coday
Historical Museum - 1957 38321

Mansfield OH

Mansfield Art Center, 700 Marion Av, Mansfield, OH 44903 - T: (419) 756-1700. Head: H. Daniel Butts
Fine Arts Museum - 1946 38322

Manteo NC

Fort Raleigh, US 64-264, Manteo, NC 27954 - T: (919) 473-2111, Fax: (919) 473-2595. Head: Robert Raynolds
Natural History Museum - 1941 38323

Roanoke Island Festival Park, 1 Festival Park, Manteo, NC 27954 - T: (252) 475-1500, Fax: (252) 475-1507, E-mail: rifp.information@ncmail.net, Internet: http://www.roanokeisland.com. Head: Deloris Harrell
Historical Museum - 1983 38324

Mantorville MN

Dodge County Historical Museum, 615 Main, N, Mantorville, MN 55955 - T: (507) 635-5508. Head: Idella M. Conwell
Local Museum - 1876
Regional history, former Episcopal church 38325

Maple Valley WA

Maple Valley Historical Museum, 23015 SE 216th Way, Maple Valley, WA 98038 - T: (425) 432-3470, Fax: (425) 432-3470, E-mail: pilgrim.dsk-c@worldnet.att.net., Internet: http://www.maplevalley.com/community/historical. Head: Mona Pickering
Local Museum - 1972
Local hist, fire engines 38326

Maquoketa IA

Jackson County Historical Museum, 1212 E Quarry, Fairgrounds, Maquoketa, IA 52060-1245 - T: (319) 652-5020, Fax: (319) 652-5020. Head: Toni Kracke
Local Museum / Agriculture Museum - 1964
Local history, agriculture - library 38327

Marathon FL

Crane Point Hammock Museum, 5550 Overseas Hwy, Marathon, FL 33050 - T: (305) 743-7124, Fax: (305) 743-0429, E-mail: tropcranept@aol.com, Internet: http://www.thefloridakeys.com. Head: Deanna S. Lloyd
Natural History Museum - 1990 38328

Tropical Crane Point Hammock Museum → Crane Point Hammock Museum

Marble CO

Marble Historical Museum, 412 W Main St, Marble, CO 81623 - T: (970) 963-1710. Head: Joseph Manz
Local Museum - 1977
Local history 38329

Marblehead MA

Marblehead Historical Museum, 170 Washington St, Marblehead, MA 01945 - T: (781) 631-1768. Head: Elisabeth A. Alles
Local Museum - 1898
Local history, home of Col. Jeremiah Lee 38330

Marbletown NY

Ulster County Historical Society Museum, Rte 209, Marbletown, NY - T: (914) 338-5614. Head: Amanda C. Jones, Agnes R. Kelly
Local Museum / Historical Museum - 1930 38331

Marbury MD

Smallwood's Retreat, Smallwood State Park, Marbury, MD 20658 - T: (301) 743-7613, Fax: (301) 743-9405. Head: Roberta Dorsch
Military Museum - 1954 38332

Marcellus NY

Marcellus Historical Society Museum, 6 Slocombe Av, Marcellus, NY 13108 - T: (315) 673-3112
Historical Museum - 1960 38333

Marfa TX

Chinati Foundation, 1 Cavalry Row, Marfa, TX 79843 - T: (915) 729-4362, Fax: (915) 729-4597, E-mail: chinati@iglobal.net, Internet: http://www.chinati.org. Head: Marianne Stockebrand, Fredericka Hunter
Fine Arts Museum - 1986
Art 38334

Marianna AR

Marianna-Lee County Museum, 67 W Main St, Marianna, AR 72360 - T: (870) 295-2469. Head: Suzy Keasler
Local Museum - 1981
Regional history, housed in the Marianna Elks Club 38335

Marietta GA

Cobb County Youth Museum, 649 Cheatham Hill Dr, Marietta, GA 30064 - T: (770) 427-2563, Fax: (770) 427-1060. Head: Anita S. Barton
Ethnology Museum - 1964
Youth 38336

Marietta Cobb Museum of Art, 30 Atlanta St NE, Marietta, GA 30060 - T: (770) 528-1444, Fax: (770) 528-1440, Internet: http://www.mariettasquare.com. Head: Susanne Katz
Fine Arts Museum - 1986
Art 38337

Marietta OH

Campus Martius: Museum of the Northwest Territory, 601 Second St, Marietta, OH 45750 - T: (740) 373-3750, Fax: (740) 373-3680, E-mail: cmmoriv@marietta.edu, Internet: http://www.ohiohistory.org/places/campus. Head: Gary C. Ness
Historical Museum - 1919 38338

The Castle, 418 Fourth St, Marietta, OH 45750 - T: (740) 373-4180, Fax: (740) 373-4233, E-mail: Castle@marietta.edu, Internet: http://www.castowebdesign.com/thecastle. Head: Lynne Shuman
Local Museum - 1992
Historic house 38339

Ohio River Museum, 601 Front St, Marietta, OH 45750 - T: (614) 373-3750, Fax: (614) 373-3680, E-mail: Cmmoriv@marietta.edu, Internet: http://www.ohiohistory.org/places/ohriver. Head: Gary C. Ness
Historical Museum - 1941 38340

Marilla NY

Marilla Historical Society Museum, 1810 Two Rod Rd, Marilla, NY 14102 - T: (716) 652-5396. Head: Peg Schwenk
Local Museum - 1960 38341

Marineland FL

Marineland Ocean Museum, 9507 Ocean Shore Blvd, Marineland, FL 32086-9602 - T: (904) 471-1111, Fax: (904) 461-0156, E-mail: mor@aug.com, Internet: http://www.marineland.com. Head: David Internoscia
Historical Museum - 1938 38342

Marinette WI

Marinette County Historical Museum, Stephenson Island, U.S. Hwy 41, Marinette, WI 54143 - T: (715) 732-0831. Head: Walter Stepniak
Local Museum - 1962
Local hist 38343

Marion IL

Williamson County Historical Society Museum, 105 S Van Buren, Marion, IL 62959 - T: (618) 997-5863
Local Museum - 1976
County history, housed former county jail and sheriff's home 38344

Marion IN

Marion Public Library Museum, Carnegie Bldg, 600 S Washington St, Marion, IN 46953 - T: (765) 668-2900, Fax: (765) 668-2911, E-mail: mpl@comteck.com, Internet: http://www.marion.lib.in.us. Head: Sue Israel
Local Museum - 1884
Local hist 38345

Marion NC

Historic Carson House, Hwy 70 West of Marion, Marion, NC 28752 - T: (704) 724-4640. Head: Nina Greenlee
Historical Museum - 1964 38346

Marion OH

Harding Home and Museum, 380 Mount Vernon Av, Marion, OH 43302 - T: (740) 387-9630, Fax: (740) 387-9630. Head: Phillip Payne
Historical Museum - 1925 38347

Stengel-True Museum, 504 S State St, Marion, OH 43302 - T: (614) 387-7150. Head: J.C. Ballinger
Local Museum - 1973 38348

Marion VA

Smyth County Museum, 203 N Church St, Marion, VA 24354 - T: (540) 783-7067, 783-7286. Head: Brenda Gwyn, Joan T. Armstrong
Local Museum - 1961
Local hist 38349

Mariposa CA

California State Mining and Mineral Museum, 5005 Fairgrounds Dr, Mariposa, CA 95338 - T: (209) 742-7625, Fax: (209) 966-3597. Head: Shirley Mitchell
Natural History Museum / Science&Tech Museum - 1988 38350

Marlboro MA

Peter Rice Homestead, 377 Elm St, Marlboro, MA 01752 - T: (508) 485-4763
Local Museum - 1962
Local history 38351

Marlboro NY

Gomez Foundation for Mill House, Mill House Rd, Marlboro, NY 12542 - T: (914) 236-3126, Fax: (914) 236-3365, E-mail: gomezmillhouse@juno.com, Internet: http://www.gomez.org. Head: C.F. William Maurer
Decorative Arts Museum / Local Museum - 1984
Historic house 38352

Marlboro VT

Marlboro Museum, N Main St, Marlboro, VT 05344 - T: (802) 257-9265. Head: Whitney Nichols
Local Museum - 1958
Local hist 38353

Marlinton WV

Pocahontas County Museum, Seneca Trail, Marlinton, WV 24954 - T: (304) 799-4973, Fax: (304) 799-6466
Local Museum - 1962
Local hist 38354

Marquette MI

Marquette County Historical Museum, 213 N Front St, Marquette, MI 49855 - T: (906) 226-3571, E-mail: mqtcohis@uproc.lib.mi.us. Head: Frances J. Porter
Local Museum - 1918
Local history - library 38355

Northern Michigan University Art Museum, Lee Hall, 1401 Preque Isle Av, Marquette, MI 49855 - T: (906) 227-1481, Fax: (906) 227-2276, E-mail: wfrancis@nmu.edu, Internet: http://www.nmu.edu/department/admuseum. Head: Wayne Francis
Fine Arts Museum
Contemporary prints ans sculpture, Japanese and American illustrations 38356

Marshall AR

Searcy County Museum, Hwy 27, S, Marshall, AR 72650 - T: (870) 448-5786. Head: Veda Clemons
Local Museum - 1980
Regional history, Old Searcy County Jail 38357

Marshall IL

Clark County Museum, 4th and Maple Sts, Marshall, IL 62441 - T: (217) 826-5365. Head: Jack Huffington
Local Museum - 1969
Local history 38358

Marshall MI

American Museum of Magic, 107 E Michigan St, Marshall, MI 49068 - T: (616) 781-7674. Head: Elaine H. Lund
Performing Arts Museum - 1978 38359

Honolulu House Museum, 107 N Kalamazoo, Marshall, MI 49068 - T: (616) 781-8544, Fax: (616) 789-0371, E-mail: dircherie@aol.com, Internet: http://www.marshallhistoricalsociety.org. Head: Cherie Riser
Local Museum - 1962 38360

Marshall MN

Lyon County Historical Society Museum, 114 N 3rd St, Marshall, MN 56258 - T: (507) 537-6580, Fax: (507) 537-1699. Head: Ellayne Velde-Conyers
Local Museum - 1934
Regional history 38361

Museum of Natural History, Southwest State University, 1501 State St, Marshall, MN 56258 - T: (507) 537-6178, Fax: (507) 537-7154, E-mail: desy@ssu.southwest.msus.edu. Head: Dr. Elizabeth A. Desy
University Museum / Natural History Museum - 1972 38362

Marshall TX

Franks Antique Doll Museum, 211 W Grand Av, Marshall, TX 75670 - T: (903) 935-3065, 935-3070. Head: Clara Franks
Decorative Arts Museum - 1960
Dolls 38363

Harrison County Historical Museum, 707 N Washington, Marshall, TX 75670 - T: (903) 938-2680, Fax: (903) 927-2534, E-mail: museum@ccape.net, Internet: http://www.cets.sfasu.edu/Harrison/. Head: Alex Liebling
Historical Museum - 1965
Local hist 38364

Michelson Museum of Art, 216 N Bolivar, Marshall, TX 75671 - T: (903) 935-9480, Fax: (903) 935-1974, E-mail: leomich@shreve.net, Internet: www.michelsonmuseum.org. Head: Susan Stears
Fine Arts Museum - 1985
Art 38365

Marshalltown IA

Central Iowa Art Museum, Fisher Center, 709 S Center St, Marshalltown, IA 50158 - T: (515) 753-9013. Head: Tim Castle
Fine Arts Museum / Decorative Arts Museum - 1946
Art, ceramics 38366

Historical Society of Marshall County Museum, 202 E Church St, Marshalltown, IA 50158 - Internet: http://www.marshallnet.com/museum. Head: Jeffery Quam, Gary L. Cameron
Local Museum - 1908
Local hist 38367

Marshfield WI

New Visions Gallery, 1000 N Oak Av, Marshfield, WI 54449 - T: (715) 387-5562, E-mail: nvisions@tznet.com. Head: Ann Waisbrot
Fine Arts Museum / Decorative Arts Museum - 1975
Art 38368

Marthaville LA

Louisiana Country Music Museum, State Hwy 1221, Marthaville, LA 71450 - T: (318) 472-6255, Fax: (318) 472-6255. Head: Marsha Gentry
Music Museum - 1981
Musical instrument-shaped bldg 38369

Martin TN

University Museum, The University of Tennessee at Martin, Martin, TN 38238 - T: (901) 587-7454, 587-7464, Fax: (901) 587-7443, E-mail: skairee@utm.edu, Internet: http://fmc.utm.edu/~sairee/museum.htm. Head: Dr. S.K. Airee
University Museum / Local Museum - 1981
Local hist 38370

Martinsburg WV

General Adam Stephen House, 309 East John St, Martinsburg, WV 25402 - T: (304) 267-4434
Local Museum / Folklore Museum / Decorative Arts Museum - 1959
Historic house 38371

Martinsville VA

Piedmont Arts Museum, 215 Starling Av, Martinsville, VA 24112 - T: (540) 632-3221, Fax: (540) 638-3963, E-mail: PAA@PiedmontArts.org, Internet: http://www.piedmontarts.org. Head: Toy L. Cobbe
Fine Arts Museum - 1961
Arts 38372

Virginia Museum of Natural History, 1001 Douglas Av, Martinsville, VA 24112 - T: (540) 666-8600, Fax: (540) 632-6487, E-mail: spike@vmnh.org, Internet: http://www.vmnh.org. Head: Stephen J. Pike
Natural History Museum - 1984
Natural hist 38373

Marylhurst OR

Art Gym at Marylhurst College, Marylhurst College, 17600 Pacific Hwy 43, Marylhurst, OR 97036-0261 - T: (503) 636-8141, Fax: (503) 636-9526, E-mail: artgym@marylhurst.edu, Internet: http://www.marylhurst.edu/. Head: Terri M. Hopkins
Fine Arts Museum / University Museum - 1980 38374

Marysville OH

Union County Historical Society Museum, 246-254 W Sixth St, Marysville, OH 43040 - T: (937) 644-0568. Head: Robert W. Parrott
Local Museum - 1949 38375

Maryville MO

Olive DeLuce Art Gallery, Northwest Missouri State University, 800 University Dr, Maryville, MO 64468 - T: (660) 562-1326, Fax: (660) 562-1346, E-mail: plaber@mail.nwmissouri.edu. Head: Philip Laber
Fine Arts Museum
Contemporary 38376

Maryville TN

Fine Arts Center Gallery, Maryville College, 502 E Lamar Alexander Pkwy, Maryville, TN 37804 - T: (865) 981-8000, 981-8150, Fax: (865) 273-8873, E-mail: sowders@maryvillecollege.edu, Internet: http://www.maryvillecollege.edu. Head: Mark Hall
Public Gallery 38377

Sam Houston Historical Schoolhouse, 3650 Old Sam Houston School Rd, Maryville, TN 37804-5644 - T: (423) 983-1550. Head: Enoch Simerly
Local Museum - 1965
Historic House 38378

Mason City IA

Charles H. MacNider Museum, 303 2nd St, SE, Mason City, IA 50401-3988 - T: (641) 421-3666, Fax: (641) 422-9612, E-mail: macnider@macniderart.org, Internet: http://www.macniderart.org. Head: Richard E. Leet
Fine Arts Museum - 1964
American art incl. Bil Baird puppets 38379

Mason Neck VA

Gunston Hall Plantation, 10709 Gunston Rd, Mason Neck, VA 22079 - T: (703) 550-9220, Fax: (703) 550-9480, E-mail: Historic@GunstonHall.org, Internet: http://www.gunstonhall.org. Head: Thomas A. Lainhoff
Local Museum - 1932
Historic house 38380

Massillon OH

Massillon Museum, 121 Lincoln Way E, Massillon, OH 44646 - T: (330) 833-4061, Fax: (330) 833-2925. Head: John Klassen
Fine Arts Museum / Historical Museum - 1933 38381

Matawan NJ

Burrowes Mansion Museum, 94 Main St, Matawan, NJ 07747 - T: (732) 566-3817, 566-5605
Local Museum - 1976
Local hist 38382

Mattapoisett MA

Mattapoisett Museum and Carriage House, 5 Church St, Mattapoisett, MA 02739 - T: (508) 758-2844
Local Museum - 1959
Local history, Christian meeting House 38383

Maumee OH

Wolcott House Museum Complex, 1031 River Rd, Maumee, OH 43537 - T: (419) 893-9602, Fax: (419) 893-3108, E-mail: mvhs@accesstoledo.com, Internet: http://www.maumee.org/wolcott/wolcott.htm
Historical Museum - 1961 38384

Mauston WI

The Boorman House, 211 N Union St, Mauston, WI 53948 - T: (608) 462-5931. Head: Nancy McCullick
Local Museum - 1963
Historic house 38385

Maxwell IA

Community Historical Museum, Main St, Maxwell, IA 50161 - T: (515) 385-2376
Local Museum - 1964
Local history 38386

Maysville KY

Mason County Museum, 215 Sutton St, Maysville, KY 41056 - T: (606) 564-5865, Fax: (606) 564-4372, E-mail: masonmuseum@maysvilleky.net, Internet: http://www.webpages.maysvilleky.net/masonmuseum. Head: Dawn C. Browning
Fine Arts Museum / Local Museum - 1876
Art, genealogy, local history 38387

Mayville MI

Mayville Area Museum of History and Genealogy, 2124 Ohmer Rd, Mayville, MI 48744 - T: (517) 843-6259, 843-6389. Head: Howard J. Brumley
Local Museum - 1972
History, genealogy 38388

Mayville WI

Mayville Historical Society Museum, 11 N German St, Mayville, WI 53050 - T: (414) 387-5530, Fax: (414) 387-5944. Head: James Schinderle
Local Museum - 1968
Local hist 38389

Mazomanie WI

Mazomanie Historical Society Museum, 118 Brodhead St, Mazomanie, WI 53560 - T: (608) 795-2992, 795-4733, Fax: (608) 795-4576, E-mail: fewolf@blkearth.tds.net, Internet: http://www.mazoarea.com/ypahist.htm
Historical Museum - 1965
Local hist, tool coll 38390

Meade KS

Meade County Historical Society Museum, 200 E Carthage, Meade, KS 67864 - T: (316) 873-2359, 873-2224. Head: Don Goodnight
Local Museum - 1969
General museum 38391

Meadville PA

Baldwin-Reynolds House Museum, 639 Terrace St, Meadville, PA 16335 - T: (814) 333-9882, Fax: (814) 333-8173, E-mail: cchs@ccfls.org, Internet: http://www.visitcrawford.org
Historical Museum - 1883
Historic house 38392

Bowman, Megahan and Penelec Galleries, Allegheny College, N Main St, Meadville, PA 16335 - T: (814) 332-4365, Fax: (814) 724-6834, E-mail: rraczka@allegheny.edu. Head: Robert Raczka
University Museum - 1970 38393

Medford MA

Royall House, 15 George St, Medford, MA 02155 - T: (781) 396-9032. Head: Peter Gittgrian
Historical Museum - 1908
Colonial history, Georgian architecture, American slavery 38394

Tufts University Art Gallery, Aidekman Arts Center, 11 Talbot Av, Medford, MA 02155 - T: (617) 627-3518, Fax: (617) 627-3121, Internet: http://www.tufts.edu/as/gallery. Head: Susan Masuoka
Fine Arts Museum / University Museum - 1955
Art 38395

Medford NJ

Air Victory Museum, 68 Stacy Haines Rd, Medford, NJ 08055 - T: (609) 267-4488, Fax: (609) 702-1852, Internet: http://www.airvictorymuseum.org. Head: Barbara C. Snyder
Science&Tech Museum - 1989
Aeronautics 38396

Medford OK

Grant County Museum, Main and Cherokee Sts, Medford, OK 73759 - T: (580) 395-2822, Fax: (580) 395-2343. Head: Mariann Smrcka
Local Museum / Historical Museum - 1965 38397

Medford OR

Rogue Gallery and Art Center, 40 S Bartlett, Medford, OR 97501 - T: (541) 772-8118, Fax: (541) 772-0294, E-mail: roguegal@medford.com. Head: Judy Barnes
Public Gallery / Fine Arts Museum - 1959 38398

Southern Oregon Historical Society Museum, 106 N Central Av, Medford, OR 97501-5926 - T: (541) 773-6536, Fax: (541) 776-7994, E-mail: director@sohs.org, Internet: http://www.sohs.org. Head: Brad Linder
Historical Museum / Open Air Museum - 1946
library, archive 38399

Media PA

Colonial Pennsylvania Plantation, Ridley Creek State Park, Media, PA 19063 - T: (610) 566-1725. Head: David Stitely
Local Museum - 1973
Local hist 38400

Medicine Lodge KS

Carry A. Nation Home Memorial, 211 W Fowler, Medicine Lodge, KS 67104 - T: (316) 886-5671, Fax: (316) 886-5978. Head: Ann Bell
Historical Museum - 1950
1880-1903 home of Carry A. Nation 38401

Medina OH

John Smart House, 206 N Elmwood St, Medina, OH 44256 - T: (330) 722-1341
Local Museum / Historic Site - 1922 38402

Portholes Into the Past, 4450 Poe Rd, Medina, OH 44256 - T: (330) 725-0402, Fax: (330) 722-2439. Head: Merle H. Mishne
Fine Arts Museum / Public Gallery / Historical Museum / Science&Tech Museum - 1984 38403

Meeker CO

White River Museum, 565 Park St, Meeker, CO 81641 - T: (970) 878-9982. Head: Ardith Douglass
Folklore Museum / Local Museum - 1956
Regional history 38404

Melbourne FL

Brevard Museum of Art and Science, 1463-1520 Highland Av, Melbourne, FL 32935, mail addr: POB 360835, Melbourne, FL 32936-0835 - T: (407) 242-0737, Fax: (407) 242-0798, E-mail: artmuseum@mindspring.com, Internet: http://www.artandscience.org. Head: Sheila Stewart-Leach
Fine Arts Museum / Science&Tech Museum - 1978
Art, science 38405

Melrose LA

Melrose Plantation Home Complex, Melrose General Delivery, Melrose, LA 71452 - T: (318) 379-0055, Fax: (318) 379-0055
Historical Museum / Folklore Museum - 1971
Early Louisiana type plantation, home of Marie Therese Coin-Coin, freed slave who became owner of plantation 38406

Memphis TN

Art Museum of the University of Memphis, 142 Communication & Fine Arts Bldg, Memphis, TN 38152-3200 - T: (901) 678-2224, Fax: (901) 678-5118, E-mail: luebbrs@memphis.edu, Internet: http://www.amum.org. Head: Leslie Luebbers
Fine Arts Museum - 1981
Fine arts 38407

C.H. Nash Museum-Chucalissa Archaeological Museum, 1987 Indian Village Dr, Memphis, TN 38109 - T: (901) 785-3160, Fax: (901) 785-0519, E-mail: MLMOORE@cc.memphis.edu, Internet: http://www.people.memphis.edu/~chucalissa. Head: M.L. Moore
University Museum / Ethnology Museum / Archaeological Museum - 1955
Archaeology, Native American Choctaw & Pre-historic Native Mississippian culture 38408

The Children's Museum of Memphis, 2525 Central Av, Memphis, TN 38104 - T: (901) 458-2678, Fax: (901) 458-4033, E-mail: children@cmom.com, Internet: http://www.cmom.com. Head: Judy Caldwell
Special Museum - 1987 38409

Clough-Hanson Gallery, Rhodes College, Clough Hall, 2000 N Pkwy, Memphis, TN 38112 - T: (901) 843-3442, Fax: (901) 843-3727, E-mail: pacini@rhodes.edu, Internet: http://artslides2.art.rhodes.edu/gallery.html. Head: Marina Pacini
Fine Arts Museum - 1970
Local, regional and national art, textiles, woodcarvings 38410

The Dixon Gallery and Gardens, 4339 Park Av, Memphis, TN 38117 - T: (901) 761-5250, Fax: (901) 682-0943, E-mail: adm1@dixon.org, Internet: http://www.dixon.org. Head: James J. Kamm
Fine Arts Museum - 1976
Imressionist art - library 38411

Fire Museum of Memphis, 118 Adams Av, Memphis, TN 38103 - T: (901) 452-9973, Fax: (901) 452-8338, Internet: http://www.firemuseum.com. Head: Bob Brame
Special Museum - 1993
Fire fighting 38412

Graceland, 3764 Elvis Presley Blvd, Memphis, TN 38116 - T: (901) 332-3322, Fax: (901) 344-3116, E-mail: graceland@memphisonline.com, Internet: http://www.elvis-presley.com. Head: Priscilla Presley, Jack Soden
Music Museum - 1982
Mansion occupied by Elvis Presley from 1957 until his death in 1977 38413

Magevney House, 198 Adams, Memphis, TN 38103 - T: (901) 526-4464. Head: Kate Dixon
Local Museum - 1941
Historic house 38414

Memphis Brooks Museum of Art, 1934 Poplar Av, Overton Park, Memphis, TN 38104-2765 - T: (901) 544-6200, Fax: (901) 725-4071, E-mail: brooks@brooksmuseum.org, Internet: http://www.brooksmuseum.org. Head: Kaywin Feldman
Fine Arts Museum - 1913
Fine arts, paintings, sculpture, glass, textiles, porcelain - library 38415

Memphis College of Art Gallery, Overton Park, 1930 Poplar Av, Memphis, TN 38104 - T: (901) 272-5100, Fax: (901) 272-5104, E-mail: info@mca.edu, Internet: http://www.mca.edu. Head: Jeffrey D. Nesin
Fine Arts Museum / University Museum - 1936
Art 38416

Memphis Pink Palace Museum, 3050 Central Av, Memphis, TN 38111 - T: (901) 320-6369, 320-6398, Fax: (901) 320-6391, E-mail: more_info@memphismuseums.org, Internet: http://www.memphismuseums.org. Head: Dr. Douglas R. Noble, Dan Antonelli
Historical Museum / Natural History Museum / Science&Tech Museum - 1928
Natural hist, science, cultural hist 38417

Mississippi River Museum at Mud Island River Park, 125 N Front St, Memphis, TN 38103 - T: (901) 576-7230, Fax: (901) 576-7235, E-mail: giuntini@memphis.mgicbox.net, Internet: http://www.mudisland.com. Head: Trey Giuntini
Local Museum / Natural History Museum - 1978
Natural and cultural hist of the Lower Mississippi River 38418

National Civil Rights Museum, 450 Mulberry St, Memphis, TN 38103 - T: (901) 521-9699, Fax: (901) 521-9740, Internet: http://www.mecca.org/~crights/ncrn.html. Head: J.R. Hyde, Beverly Robinson
Historical Museum
Modern hist 38419

National Ornamental Metal Museum, 374 Metal Museum Dr, Memphis, TN 38106 - T: (901) 774-6380, Fax: (901) 774-6382, E-mail: metal@wspice.com, Internet: http://www.metalmuseum.org. Head: James A. Wallace
Decorative Arts Museum - 1976
Historic and contemporary decorative & fine art metalwork 38420

Peabody Place Museum and Gallery, 119 S Main St, Memphis, TN 38103 - T: (901) 523-2787
Fine Arts Museum 38421

Mendham NJ

John Ralston Museum, 313 Rte 24, Mendham, NJ 07945 - T: (973) 543-4347. Head: Tracey Kinsell
Historical Museum - 1964 38422

Mendocino CA

Kelley House Museum, 45007 Albion St, Mendocino, CA 95460 - T: (707) 937-5791, Fax: (707) 937-4233, E-mail: kelleyhs@mcn.org, Internet: http://www.homestead.com/kelleyhousemuseum. Head: Katharine Bicknell
Local Museum - 1973
Local hist 38423

Mendota MN

Sibley Historic Site, 1357 Sibley Memorial Hwy, Mendota, MN 55150, mail addr: POB 50772, Mendota, MN 55150 - T: (651) 452-1596, Fax: (651) 452-1238, E-mail: sibleyhouse@mnhs.org, Internet: http://www.mnhs.org/sites. Head: Marveen Minish
Historical Museum - 1910
Henry Hastings Sibley house, dwelling & trading house, later Minnesota's first state governor's house 38424

Menominee MI

Menominee County Historical Museum, 904 11 Av, Menominee, MI 49858 - T: (906) 863-9000. Head: William C. King
Local Museum - 1967
Regional history - library, research center 38425

Menomonee Falls WI

Old Falls Village, N 96 W 15791 County Line Rd, Menomonee Falls, WI 53051 - T: (414) 250-5096, Fax: (414) 250-5097, Internet: http://www.menomoneefalls.us. Head: Debra Zindler
Local Museum - 1966
Historic village 38426

Menomonie WI

John Furlong Gallery, Department of Art and Design, Menomonie, WI 54751 - T: (715) 232-2261, Fax: (715) 232-1346, E-mail: bloedoring@uwstout.edu
Fine Arts Museum / University Museum - 1965
Art 38427

Mentor OH

James A. Garfield National Historic Site, 8095 Mentor Av, Mentor, OH 44060 - T: (440) 255-8722, Fax: (440) 255-8545, E-mail: garfield@wens.org, Internet: http://www.wrhs.org. Head: Edith Serkownek
Historic Site - 1936 38428

Lake County Historical Society Museum, 8610 King Memorial Rd, Mentor, OH 44060 - T: (440) -255-8979, Fax: (440) 255-8980. Head: Christopher H. Gillcrest
Local Museum - 1936 38429

Mequon WI

Concordia University-Wisconsin Art Gallery, 12800 N Lake Shore Dr, Mequon, WI 53097 - T: (414) 243-5700, Fax: (414) 243-4351, E-mail: gstone@bach.cuw.edu, Internet: http://www.cuw.edu. Head: Jeff Shawhan
Fine Arts Museum / University Museum 38430

Crafts Museum, 11458 N Laguna Dr, Mequon, WI 53092 - T: (262) 242-1571. Head: Bob Siegel
Special Museum - 1972
Arts and crafts, wood-carving - woodenshoes, handcarving, ice-harvesting (storage, iceboxes etc.) 38431

Merced CA

Merced County Courthouse Museum, 21st and N Sts, Merced, CA 95340 - T: (209) 723-2401, Fax: (209) 723-8029. Head: Andrea Morris
Local Museum - 1975
Local history 38432

Mercer PA

Mercer County Museum, 119 S Pitt St, Mercer, PA 16137 - T: (724) 662-3490, Internet: http://www.pattiway.net/mchs. Head: William C. Philson, David M. Miller
Historical Museum - 1946
Local hist 38433

Meriden CT

Meriden Historical Society Museum, 424 W Main St, Meriden, CT 06450 - T: (203) 237-5079
Historical Museum / Local Museum / Folklore Museum - 1893 38434

Meridian MS

Jimmie Rodgers Museum, 1725 Jimmie Rodgers Dr, Meridian, MS 39304 - T: (601) 485-4724. Head: Jean Bishop
Folklore Museum - 1976 38435

Meridian Museum of Art, 25th Av and Seventh St, Meridian, MS 39301 - T: (601) 693-1501, Fax: (601) 485-3175. Head: Terence Heder, Bonnie Busbee
Fine Arts Museum - 1969
Drawings, American paintings, prints, sculpture, pottery, photography, decorative art 38436

Merion PA

Barnes Foundation, 300 N Latch's Ln, Merion, PA 19066 - T: (610) 667-0290, Fax: (610) 664-4026, Internet: http://www.barnesfoundation.org. Head: Kimberly Camp
Special Museum / Fine Arts Museum / Decorative Arts Museum
American decorative arts, African sculpture, horticulture, Greek, Roman and Egyptian antiquities, paintings, metalwork 38437

Merrillan WI

Thunderbird Museum, Hatfield N 9517 Thunderbird Ln, Merrillan, WI 54754-8033 - T: (715) 333-5841, E-mail: tbirdm@win.bright.net, Internet: http://www.thunderbirdmuseum.com. Head: Robert Flood, Ellen Flood
Local Museum - 1959
Local hist, Indian Artifacts 38438

Mesa AZ

Arizona Museum For Youth, 35 N Robson, Mesa, AZ 85201 - T: (480) 644-2467/68, Fax: (480) 644-2466, E-mail: azmus4youth@ci.mesa.az.us, Internet: http://www.ci.mesa.az.us/amfy. Head: Barbara Meyerson
Fine Arts Museum - 1980
Children fine arts 38439

Mesa Southwest Museum, 53 N Macdonald, Mesa, AZ 85201 - T: (480) 644-2230, Fax: (480) 644-3424, E-mail: cynthia_diaz@ci.mesa.az.us, Internet: http://www.ci.mesa.az.us/parksrec/msm/. Head: Dr. William Holmes
Fine Arts Museum / Historical Museum / Natural History Museum - 1977
Paleontology, archaeology, ethnology, history and art 38440

Mesa Verde CO

Mesa Verde National Park Museum, Mesa Verde, CO 81330 - T: (970) 529-4465, Fax: (970) 529-4637, Internet: http://www.nps.gov/meve. Head: Larry Wiese
Archaeological Museum - 1917
Archaeology from AD 550-1300, ethnography 38441

Mesilla NM

Gadsden Museum, W Barker Rd and Hwy 28, Mesilla, NM 88046 - T: (505) 526-6293. Head: Mary Veitch Alexander
Historical Museum - 1931
Civil war coll, Indian artifacts, clothing, guns 38442

Metamora IL

Metamora Courthouse, 113 E Partridge, Metamora, IL 61548 - T: (309) 367-4470
Historical Museum - 1845
Courthouse located in the 8th Judicial Circuit that Abraham Lincoln traveled as a circuit lawyer 38443

Metamora IN

Whitewater Canal Historic Site, 19083 Clayborn St, Metamora, IN 47030 - T: (765) 647-6512, Fax: (765) 647-2734, E-mail: wwcshe@bonwell.com. Head: Jay Dishman
Science&Tech Museum - 1845 38444

Metlakatla AK

Duncan Cottage Museum, 501 Tait St, Metlakatla, AK 99926 - T: (907) 886-4441 ext 232, Fax: (907) 886-4134. Head: Lindarae H. Shearer
Historical Museum - 1975 38445

Metropolis IL

Fort Massac, 1308 E 5th St, Metropolis, IL 62960 - T: (618) 524-9321, 524-4712, Fax: (618) 524-9321, E-mail: SMCREE@dnrmail.state.il.us, Internet: http://www.stateofillinois-dnr-fortmassacstatepark. Head: Terry Johnson
Historical Museum - 1908
Located on the site of 1756-1814, Military Post 38446

Mexico MO

American Saddlebred Horse Museum, 501 S Muldrow, Mexico, MO 65265 - T: (573) 581-3910, E-mail: achs@swbell.net. Head: Kathy Adams
Historical Museum - 1970 38447

Audrain Country Historical Museum, Graceland and American Saddlehorse Museums, 501 S Muldrow, Mexico, MO 65265 - T: (573) 581-3910, E-mail: achs@swbell.net. Head: Kathryn Adams
Local Museum - 1952 38448

Miami FL

The Art Museum at Florida International University, University Park, PC 110, Miami, FL 33199 - T: (305) 348-2890, Fax: (305) 348-2762, E-mail: artinfo@fiu.edu, Internet: http://www.fiu.edu. Head: Dahlia Morgan
Fine Arts Museum / University Museum - 1977
Art 38449

Black Heritage Museum, POB 570327, Miami, FL 33257-0327 - T: (305) 252-3535, Fax: (305) 252-3535, E-mail: blkhermu@bellsouth.net, Internet: http://gsni.cvom/bhm.htm
Historical Museum / Folklore Museum - 1987 38450

Cuban Museum of Arts and Culture, 1300 SW 12 Av, Miami, FL 33129 - T: (305) 858-8006, Fax: (305) 858-9639, Internet: http://www.infolatino. Head: Louis Jeffery Collette
Fine Arts Museum / Folklore Museum - 1985 38451

Gold Coast Railroad Museum, 12450 SW 152 St, Miami, FL 33177 - T: (305) 253-0063, Fax: (305) 233-4641, E-mail: gcrm@askchuck.com, Internet: http://www.elink.net/goldcoast. Head: Connie Greer, Alan Deems
Science&Tech Museum - 1957 38452

Historical Museum of Southern Florida, 101 W Flagler St, Miami, FL 33130 - T: (305) 375-1492, Fax: (305) 375-1609, E-mail: hasf@historical-museum.org, Internet: http://www.historical-museum.org. Head: J. Andrew Brian
Historical Museum - 1940 38453

International Art Center, 70 Miracle Mile, Coral Gables, Miami, FL 33134 - T: (305) 567-1750, 471-7383
Public Gallery 38454

Kendall Campus Art Gallery, Miami-Dade Community College, 11011 SW 104th St, Miami, FL 33176-3393 - T: (305) 237-2322, Fax: (305) 237-2901, E-mail: lfontana@kendall.mdcc.edu, Internet: http://www.kendall.mdcc.edu/. Head: Lilia Fontana
Fine Arts Museum / University Museum - 1970
Art gallery 38455

Miami Art Museum of Dade County, 101 W Flagler St, Miami, FL 33130 - T: (305) 375-3000, Fax: (305) 375-1725, E-mail: mamart@co.miami-dade.fl.us, Internet: http://www.miamiartmuseum.org. Head: Suzanne Delehanty
Fine Arts Museum - 1978
Art 38456

Miami Children's Museum, 701 Arena Blvd, Miami, FL 33136 - T: (305) 373-5439, Fax: (305) 373-5431, E-mail: mcmuseum@bellsouth.net, Internet: http://www.miamichildrensmuseum.org. Head: Deborah Spiegelman
Special Museum - 1984 38457

Miami Museum of Science, 3280 S Miami Av, Miami, FL 33129 - T: (305) 646-4200, Fax: (305) 646-4300, E-mail: jsatt@miamisci.org, Internet: http://www.miamisci.org. Head: Russell Etling
Science&Tech Museum - 1949
Seashells, Entomology collection, Pre-Columbian collection, unique fossile heritage - planetarium 38458

Vizcaya Museum, 3251 S Miami Av, Miami, FL 33129 - T: (305) 250-9133 ext 2221, Fax: (305) 285-2004. Head: Richard S. Farwell
Decorative Arts Museum / Historical Museum - 1952
Italian Renaissance-styled Villa, formal gardens 38459

Weeks Air Museum, 14710 SW 128 St, Miami, FL 33196 - T: (305) 233-5197, Fax: (305) 232-4134, Internet: http://www.weekairmuseum.com. Head: Vincent Tirado
Science&Tech Museum - 1987 38460

Miami MO

Van Meter State Park, Rte 122, Miami, MO 65344 - T: (660) 886-7537, Fax: (660) 886-7512
Archaeological Museum - 1990
Missouri Indian village archaeological site 38461

Miami TX

Roberts County Museum, Rte 1, Hwy 60, Miami, TX 79059 - T: (806) 868-3291, Fax: (806) 868-3381. Head: Cecil Gill, Katie Underwood
Local Museum - 1979
Local hist 38462

Miami Beach FL

Art Center of South Florida, 924 Lincoln Rd, Miami Beach, FL 33139 - T: (305) 674-8278, Fax: (305) 674-8772, E-mail: info@artcentersf.org, Internet: http://www.artcentersf.org
Public Gallery 38463

Bass Museum of Art, 2121 Park Av, Miami Beach, FL 33139-1729 - T: (305) 673-7530, Fax: (305) 673-7062, E-mail: bassmus@mail.icanect.net, Internet: http://ci.miami-beach.fl.us/culture/bass/bass.html. Head: Diane W. Camber
Fine Arts Museum - 1964
Art 38464

Jewish Museum of Florida, 301 Washington Av, Miami Beach, FL 33139-6965 - T: (305) 672-5044 ext 10/18, Fax: (305) 672-5933, E-mail: mzerivitz@jewishmuseum.com, Internet: http://www.jewishmuseum.com
Historical Museum - 1995
Jewish hist of Florida 38465

The Wolfsonian, Florida International University, 1001 Washington Av, Miami Beach, FL 33139 - T: (305) 531-1001, Fax: (305) 531-2133, Internet: http://www.wolfsonian.org. Head: Kathy Leff
Special Museum / Decorative Arts Museum / Historical Museum - 1986
Design, decorative arts, architecture, historic Art Deco District - library 38466

Miami Lakes FL

Jay I. Kislak Foundation, 7900 Miami Lakes Dr W, Miami Lakes, FL 33016 - T: (305) 364-4208, Fax: (305) 821-1267, E-mail: adunkelman@kislak.com, Internet: http://www.jayikislak-foundation.org. Head: Jay I. Kislak
Fine Arts Museum / Archaeological Museum - 1988 38467

Michigan City IN

John G. Blank Center for the Arts, 312 E Eighth St, Michigan City, IN 46360 - T: (219) 874-4900, Fax: (219) 872-6829, E-mail: jgbartcenter@adsnet.com. Head: Barbara Stodola
Fine Arts Museum - 1977
Art, housed in the Old Michigan City Library, an Beaux Arts structure of Indiana Limestone 38468

Old Lighthouse Museum, Heisman Harbor Rd, Washington Park, Michigan City, IN 46360 - T: (219) 872-6133. Head: Bruce Gregg
Science&Tech Museum - 1973
Maritime history 38469

Middleborough MA

Middleborough Historical Museum, Jackson St, Middleborough, MA 02346 - T: (508) 947-2596. Head: Dorothy Thayer, Marsha Manchester
Local Museum - 1960
Local history 38470

Robbins Museum of Archaeology, 17 Jackson St, Middleborough, MA 02346-0700 - T: (508) 947-9005, Internet: http://www.geocities.com/Athens/aegean/5154/. Head: Darrell Pinckney
Archaeological Museum - 1939
Archaeology 38471

Middleburg PA

The Snyder County Historical Society Museum, 30 E Market St, Middleburg, PA 17842 - T: (510) 837-6191, Fax: (510) 837-4282. Head: Carolyn Arndt
Historical Museum - 1898
Local hist 38472

Middlebury VT

The Henry Sheldon Museum of Vermont Histoy, 1 Park St, Middlebury, VT 05753 - T: (802) 388-2117, E-mail: shel-mus@panther.middlebury.edu, Internet: http://www.middlebury.edu/~shel-mus. Head: Ann O. Perkins
Fine Arts Museum / Local Museum - 1882
Art, history, furniture, textiles, documents 38473

The Middlebury College Museum of Art, Center for the Arts, Middlebury, VT 05753-6177 - T: (802) 443-5235, Fax: (802) 443-2069, Internet: http://www.middlebury.edu/~museum. Head: Richard H. Saunders
Fine Arts Museum / University Museum - 1968
Art 38474

The Sheldon Art Museum → The Henry Sheldon Museum of Vermont Histoy

Vermont Folklife Center, Painter House, 2 Court St, Middlebury, VT 05753 - T: (802) 388-4964, Fax: (802) 388-1844. Head: Jane C. Beck
Folklore Museum - 1983
Folk art 38475

Middlesboro KY

Cumberland Gap National Historical Park, U.S. 25 E, Middlesboro, KY 40965 - T: (606) 248-2817, Fax: (606) 248-7276, Internet: http://www.nps.gov/cuga. Head: Mark H. Woods
Historical Museum / Archaeological Museum - 1959
History, archaeology 38476

Middleton MA

Lura Watkins Museum, Pleasant St, Middleton, MA 01949 - T: (508) 774-9301. Head: Henry Tragent
Local Museum - 1976
Local history 38477

Middletown CT

Davison Art Center, Wesleyan University, 301 High St, Middletown, CT 06459-0487 - T: (860) 685-2500, Fax: (860) 685-2501, E-mail: swiles@wesleyan.edu, Internet: http://www.wesleyan.edu/dac/home.html. Head: Stephanie Wiles
Fine Arts Museum / University Museum - 1952 38478

Ezra and Cecile Zilkha Gallery, Center for the Arts, Wesleyan University, Middletown, CT 06459-0442 - T: (860) 685-2695, Fax: (860) 685-2061, E-mail: parnold@wesleyan.edu, Internet: http://www.wesleyan.edu/cfazilkha/home.html. Head: Nina Felshin
Fine Arts Museum / University Museum - 1973 38479

Middlesex County Historical Society Museum, 151 Main St, Middletown, CT 06457 - T: (860) 346-0746, Fax: (860) 346-0746. Head: Dione Longley
Local Museum - 1901 38480

Middletown MD

Middletown Valley Historical Society Museum, 305 W Main St, Middletown, MD 21769 - T: (301) 371-7582. Head: J. Dwight Hutchinson, Lydia C. Hutchinson
Local Museum - 1976
Local hist 38481

Middletown NY

Historical Society of Middletown and the Wallkill Precinct, 25 East Av, Middletown, NY 10940 - T: (914) 342-0941, E-mail: enjine@aol.com. Head: Marvin H. Cohen
Historical Museum - 1923 38482

Middletown VA

Belle Grove Plantation, 336 Belle Grove Rd, Middletown, VA 22645 - T: (540) 869-2028, Fax: (540) 869-9638, E-mail: bellegro@shentel.net, Internet: http://www.bellegrove.org. Head: Elizabeth McClung
Local Museum - 1964
Historic house 38483

Middleville MI

Historic Bowens Mills and Pioneer Park, 200 Old Mill Rd, Middleville, MI 49333 - T: (616) 795-7530, Fax: (616) 795-7530, E-mail: oldmill@iserv.net. Head: Carleen Sabin, Owen Sabin
Science&Tech Museum - 1978
1864 water-powered grist and cider mill 38484

Midland MI

Arts Midland Galleries, 1801 W Saint Andrews Rd, Midland, MI 48640 - T: (517) 835-7401, Fax: (517) 631-7890, Internet: http://www.mcfta.org. Head: Bruce Winslow
Fine Arts Museum - 1956
Great Lake regional art, local history photographs - art school 38485

Midland County Historical Museum, 1801 W Saint Andrews Rd, Midland, MI 48640 - T: (517) 631-5930. Head: Gary F. Skory
Local Museum - 1952
Regional history 38486

Midland TX

American Airpower Heritage Museum, 9600 Wright Dr, Midland, TX 79711 - T: (915) 567-3009, Fax: (915) 567-3047, E-mail: director@aahm.org, Internet: http://www.avdigest.com/aahm/aahm.html. Head: Tami O'Bannion
Historical Museum / Military Museum / Science&Tech Museum - 1957
World War II, military aviation 38487

J. Evetts Haley History Center, 1805 W Indiana, Midland, TX 79701 - T: (915) 682-5785, Fax: (915) 685-3512, Internet: http://www.haleylibrary.com
Local Museum - 1976
Local hist 38488

Midland County Historical Museum, 301 W Missouri, Midland, TX 79701 - T: (915) 682-2931, 688-8947
Local Museum - 1930
Local hist 38489

Museum of the Southwest, 1705 W Missouri Av, Midland, TX 79701-6516 - T: (915) 683-2882, 570-7770, Fax: (915) 570-7077, Internet: http://www.museumsw.org. Head: Thomas Jones
Fine Arts Museum / Local Museum - 1965
Local hist, regional art - Planetarium 38490

The Petroleum Museum, 1500 Interstate 20, Midland, TX 79701 - T: (915) 683-4403, Fax: (915) 683-4509, E-mail: twhite@petroleummuseum.org, Internet: http://www.petroleummuseum.org. Head: Ken Burgess, Jane Phares
Historical Museum / Science&Tech Museum - 1967
History, technology - archive 38491

Midway GA

Fort Morris, 2559 Fort Morris Rd, Midway, GA 31320 - T: (912) 884-5999, Fax: (912) 884-5285, E-mail: ftmorris@infoave.net. Head: Arthur C. Edgar jr.
Military Museum - 1978
Military 38492

Midway Museum, U.S. Hwy 17, Midway, GA 31320 - T: (912) 884-5837. Head: W.C. Cox
Local Museum - 1957
Local history 38493

Milan OH

Milan Historical Museum, 10 Edison Dr, Milan, OH 44846 - T: (419) 499-2968, Fax: (419) 499-9004, E-mail: museum@milanhist.org, Internet: http://www.milanhistory.org. Head: Ellen Maurer
Local Museum / Decorative Arts Museum - 1930
38494

Thomas Edison Birthplace Museum, 9 Edison Dr, Milan OH 44846 - T: (419) 499-2135, Fax: (419) 499-3241, E-mail: edisonbp@accnorwalk.com, Internet: http://www.tomedison.org
Historical Museum - 1947
38495

Milford CT

Eells-Stow House, 34 High St, Milford, CT 06460 - T: (203) 874-2664, Fax: (203) 874-5789, E-mail: mhsoc@usa.net, Internet: http://mhsoc.home.ml.org. Head: Pamela S. Hudak
Local Museum - 1930
38496

Milford DE

Milford Historical Society Museum, 501 NW Front St, Milford, DE 19963 - T: (302) 422-5522. Head: Mort Whitehead
Local Museum - 1961
Local hist
38497

Milford Museum, 121 S Walnut St, Milford, DE 19963 - T: (302) 424-1080. Head: John Huntzinger
Local Museum - 1983
Local hist
38498

Milford MI

Milford Historical Museum, 124 E Commerce St, Milford, MI 48381 - T: (248) 685-7308. Head: Mary Lou Gharrity
Local Museum - 1976
Local hist
38499

Milford NJ

Volendam Windmill Museum, 231 Adamic Hill Rd, Holland Township, Milford, NJ 08848 - T: (908) 995-4365. Head: Charles T. Brown
Historical Museum - 1965
38500

Milford OH

Promont, 906 Main St, Milford, OH 45150 - T: (513) 831-4704. Head: Scott Cruse, Susan Cruse
Historical Museum / Local Museum - 1973
38501

Milford PA

Pike County Museum, 608 Broad St, Milford, PA 18337 - T: (570) 296-8126, E-mail: pchs1@ptd.net. Head: Charles Clausen
Local Museum - 1930
Local history
38502

Milledgeville GA

Museum and Archives of Georgia Education, Georgia College and State University, 131 S Clarke St, Milledgeville, GA 31061 - T: (478) 445-4391, E-mail: mhargaden@mail.gcsu.edu. Head: Mary Hargaden
Historical Museum - 1975
History, education
38503

Millersburg PA

Upper Paxton Township Historical Museum, 330 Center St, Millersburg, PA 17061 - T: (717) 692-4084. Head: Nancy L. Wert
Local Museum - 1980
Local history
38504

Millville NJ

Museum of American Glass at Wheaton Village, 1501 Glasstown Rd, Millville, NJ 08332 - T: (856) 825-6800, Fax: (856) 825-2410, E-mail: mail@wheatonvillage.org, Internet: http://www.wheaton-village.org
Decorative Arts Museum - 1968
38505

Millwood VA

Burwell-Morgan Mill, VA 255 & County 723, Millwood, VA 22646 - T: (540) 837-1799, Fax: (540) 955-0285, E-mail: ccha39@hotmail.com
Science&Tech Museum - 1964
38506

Milton MA

Blue Hills Trailside Museum, 1904 Canton Av, Milton, MA 02186 - T: (617) 333-0690 ext 0, Fax: (617) 333-0814, E-mail: bluehills@massaudubon.org, Internet: http://www.massaudubon.org. Head: Norman Smith
Natural History Museum - 1959
Natural history, environment
38507

Captain Forbes House Museum, 215 Adams St, Milton, MA 02186 - T: (617) 696-1815, Fax: (617) 696-1815, Internet: http://key-biz.com/ssn/milton/forbes.html. Head: Christine M. Sullivan
Historical Museum - 1964
38508

Suffolk Resolves House, 1370 Canton Av, Milton, MA 02186 - T: (617) 333-9700, E-mail: mhs1904@aol.com
Local Museum - 1904
Local history
38509

Milton NH

New Hampshire Farm Museum, Rte 125, Plummer's Ridge, Milton, NH 03851 - T: (603) 652-7840, Fax: (603) 652-7840. Head: John Murphy
Agriculture Museum - 1970
38510

Milton WI

Milton House Museum, 18 S Janesville St, Milton, WI 53563 - T: (608) 868-7772, Fax: (608) 868-1698, E-mail: miltonhouse@inwave.com, Internet: http://www.miltonhouse.org. Head: Judy E. Scheehle
Historical Museum - 1948
Local hist
38511

Milwaukee WI

Charles Allis Art Museum, 1801 N Prospect Av, Milwaukee, WI 53202 - T: (414) 278-8295, Fax: (414) 278-0335, Internet: http://www.charlesallismuseum.org
Fine Arts Museum - 1947
Art
38512

Discovery World - The James Lovell Museum of Science, Economics and Technology, 815 N James Lovell St, Milwaukee, WI 53233 - T: (414) 765-9966, Fax: (414) 765-0311, E-mail: hdq@braintools.org, Internet: http://www.braintools.org. Head: Paul J. Krajniak, Michael J. Cudahy
Science&Tech Museum - 1984
Science, economics, technology
38513

Greene Memorial Museum, University of Wisconsin-Milwaukee, 3209 N Maryland Av, Milwaukee, WI 53211 - T: (414) 229-5067, 229-4561, Fax: (414) 229-5452. Head: Rod Watkins
Natural History Museum / University Museum - 1913
Geology
38514

Institute of Visual Arts, University of Wisconsin-Milwaukee, 3253 N Downer Av, Milwaukee, WI 53211 - T: (414) 229-5070, Fax: (414) 229-6785, E-mail: inova@csd.uwm.edu, Internet: http://www.uwm.edu/dept/inova. Head: Peter Doroshenko
Fine Arts Museum / University Museum - 1982
Art
38515

International Clown Hall of Fame and Research Center, The Grand Av Mall 161 W Wisconsin Av, Milwaukee, WI 53203 - T: (414) 319-0848, Fax: (414) 319-1070, E-mail: ichof@clownmuseum.org, Internet: http://www.clownmuseum.org/. Head: Kathryn O'Dell
Performing Arts Museum / Special Museum - 1986
38516

Milwaukee Art Museum, 700 N Art Museum Dr, Milwaukee, WI 53202 - T: (414) 224-3200, Fax: (414) 271-7588, E-mail: mam@mam.org, Internet: http://www.mam.org. Head: Christopher Goldsmith, Russell Bowman
Fine Arts Museum - 1888
Art
38517

Milwaukee County Historical Society Museum, 910 N Old World Third St, Milwaukee, WI 53203 - T: (414) 273-8288, Internet: http://www.milwaukeecountyhistsoc.org. Head: Robert Teske
Local Museum - 1935
Local hist
38518

Milwaukee Public Museum, 800 W Wells St, Milwaukee, WI 53233 - T: (414) 278-2700, Fax: (414) 278-6100, E-mail: jan@mpm.edu, Internet: http://www.mpm@edu. Head: William J. Moynihan
Natural History Museum - 1882
Natural and human hist
38519

Mitchell Gallery of Flight, c/o Mitchell International Airport, 5300 S Howell Av, Milwaukee, WI 53207-6189 - T: (414) 747-4503, Fax: (414) 747-4525, E-mail: info@mitchellgallery.org, Internet: http://www.mitchellgallery.org. Head: Bill Streicher
Science&Tech Museum - 1984
Aviation
38520

Mount Mary College Costume Museum, 2900 N Menomonee River Pkwy, Milwaukee, WI 53222 - T: (414) 258-4810, Fax: (414) 256-1224, E-mail: elliottm@mtmary.edu, Internet: http://www.mtmary.edu. Head: Mary C. Elliott
University Museum / Special Museum - 1928
38521

The Patrick and Beatrice Haggerty Museum of Art, c/o Marquette University, POB 1881, Milwaukee, WI 53201-1881 - T: (414) 288-7290, Fax: (414) 288-5415, E-mail: haggertym@marquette.edu, Internet: http://www.marquette.edu/haggerty. Head: Dr. Curtis L. Carter
Fine Arts Museum / University Museum - 1984
Art
38522

Union-Art Gallery, University of Wisconsin-Milwaukee, 2200 E Kenwood Blvd, Milwaukee, WI 53201 - T: (414) 229-6310, Fax: (414) 229-6709, E-mail: art-gallery@aux.uwm.edu, Internet: http://aux.uwm.edu/union/artgal.htm. Head: Steven D. Jaeger
Fine Arts Museum / University Museum - 1972
Art
38523

Villa Terrace Decorative Arts Museum, 2220 N Terrace Av, Milwaukee, WI 53202 - T: (414) 271-3656, Fax: (414) 271-3986, E-mail: cavtartmuseums@aol.com, Internet: http://www.villaterracemuseum.org. Head: Susan Modder
Decorative Arts Museum - 1967
Decorative arts
38524

Minden NE

Harold Warp Pioneer Village Foundation, 138 E Hwy 6, Minden, NE 68959-0068 - T: (308) 832-1181, Fax: (308) 832-1181, Internet: http://www.pioneer-village.org. Head: Harold G. Warp
Historical Museum - 1953
38525

Kearney County Historical Museum, Sixth and Nebraska Av, Minden, NE 68959 - T: (308) 832-2676. Head: Duane Newbold
Local Museum - 1925
38526

Mineral VA

North Anna Nuclear Information Center, Rte 700, 1022 Haley Dr, Mineral, VA 23117 - T: (804) 771-3200, (540) 894-4394, Fax: (540) 894-0379, Internet: http://www.vapower.com
Science&Tech Museum - 1973
Nuclear energy
38527

Mineral Point WI

Pendarvis, 114 Shake Rag St, Mineral Point, WI 53565 - T: (608) 987-2122, Fax: (608) 987-3738, E-mail: shakerag@mhtc.net. Head: Allen Schroeder
Local Museum / Folklore Museum - 1971
Historic house
38528

Minneapolis MN

American Swedish Institute, 2600 Park Av, Minneapolis, MN 55407 - T: (612) 871-4907, Fax: (612) 871-8682, E-mail: info@americanswedishinst.org, Internet: http://www.americanswedishinst.org. Head: Bruce N. Karstadt
Ethnology Museum - 1929
Ethnic museum
38529

The Bakken, Library and Museum of Electricity in Life, 3537 Zenith Av S, Minneapolis, MN 55416-4623 - T: (612) 926-3878, Fax: (612) 927-7265, E-mail: info@thebakken.org, Internet: http://www.thebakken.org. Head: David J. Rhees
Historical Museum - 1975
History of electricity in medicine, magnetism, culture
38530

Frederick R. Weisman Art Museum, 333 E River Rd, Minneapolis, MN 55455 - T: (612) 625-9494, Fax: (612) 625-9630, Internet: http://www.weisman.umn.edu. Head: Lyndel King
Fine Arts Museum / University Museum - 1934
Paintings, drawings, prints by American artists
38531

Hennepin History Museum, 2303 Third Av S, Minneapolis, MN 55404 - T: (612) 870-1329, Fax: (612) 870-1320, E-mail: hhmuseum@mtn.org, Internet: http://www.hhmuseum.org. Head: Jack Kabrud
Local Museum / Historical Museum - 1938
38532

Humphrey Forum, 301 19 Av S, Minneapolis, MN 55455 - T: (612) 624-5893, Fax: (612) 625-3513, E-mail: ssandell@hhh.umn.edu. Head: Stephen Sandell
Special Museum - 1989
38533

Intermedia Arts Minnesota, 2822 Lyndale Av S, Minneapolis, MN 55408 - T: (612) 871-4444, Fax: (612) 871-2769, E-mail: allstaff@intermediaarts.org, Internet: http://www.intermediaarts.org. Head: Tom Borrup
Fine Arts Museum
38534

James Ford Bell Museum of Natural History, University of Minnesota, 10 Church St SE, Minneapolis, MN 55455 - T: (612) 624-7083, Fax: (612) 626-7704, E-mail: bellmuse@tc.umn.edu, Internet: http://www.umn.edu/bellmuse/. Head: Scott M. Lanyon
Natural History Museum / University Museum - 1872
Frozen tissues, seeds, fossils, mollusks, birds, fishes, mammals, reptiles, amphibians, flowering plants, lichens, mosses, nature art - herbarium
38535

Katherine Nash Gallery, University of Minnesota, 225 19th Av, Lower Concourse, Willey Hall, Minneapolis, MN 55455 - T: (612) 624-6518, Fax: (612) 625-0152, Internet: http://artdept.umn.edu. Head: Nicholas Shank
Public Gallery / University Museum - 1973
Ceramics, paintings, prints, sculpture, metalwork, photography
38536

Minneapolis College of Art and Design Gallery, 2501 Stevens Av S, Minneapolis, MN 55404 - T: (612) 874-3785, Fax: (612) 874-3704, E-mail: brianszott_@mn.mcad.edu., Internet: http://www.mcad.edu/admin/gallery/mcadgallery.html. Head: Brian Szott
Fine Arts Museum / University Museum - 1886
38537

Minneapolis Institute of Arts, 2400 Third Av S, Minneapolis, MN 55404 - T: (612) 870-3000, 870-3046, Fax: (612) 870-3004, E-mail: miagen@artsmia.org, Internet: http://www.artsmia.org/mia. Head: Patricia J. Grazzini
Fine Arts Museum - 1915
38538

Walker Art Center, Vineland Pl, Minneapolis, MN 55403 - T: (612) 375-7622, Fax: (612) 375-7618, E-mail: information@walkerart.org, Internet: http://www.walkerart.org/. Head: Kathy Halbreich
Fine Arts Museum - 1879
38539

Wells Fargo History Museum, Sixth and Marquette Av, Minneapolis, MN 55401 - T: (612) 667-4210, Internet: http://www.wellsfargohistory.com
Historical Museum
38540

Minot ND

Lillian and Coleman Taube Museum of Art, 2 N Main St, Minot, ND 58703 - T: (701) 838-4445, Fax: (701) 839-7225, E-mail: feist@minot.com. Head: Susan Anne Feist
Fine Arts Museum - 1970
Drawings, folk art, paintings, sculptures by local and national artists
38541

Northwest Art Center, Minot State University, 500 W University Av, Minot, ND 58707 - T: (701) 858-3000, Fax: (701) 858-3894, E-mail: nac@misu.nodak.edu. Head: Zoe Spooner
Fine Arts Museum
38542

Ward County Historical Society Museum, North Dakota Fairgrounds, Minot, ND 58702 - T: (701) 839-0785. Head: Gene Egen
Local Museum - 1951
Local hist
38543

Mishawaka IN

Hannah Lindahl Children's Museum, 1402 S Main St, Mishawaka, IN 46544 - T: (219) 254-4540, Fax: (219) 254-4585, E-mail: hlindahl@michianatoday.com, Internet: http://www.hlcm.org. Head: Irene Maenhout, Peggy Marker
Ethnology Museum / Local Museum - 1946
Local history
38544

Mission Hills CA

Historical Museum, 15151 San Fernando Mission Blvd, Mission Hills, CA 91345 - T: (818) 365-1501, Fax: (818) 361-3276. Head: Francis J. Weber
Historical Museum - 1962
38545

San Fernando Mission, 15151 San Fernando Mission Blvd, Mission Hills, CA 91345 - T: (818) 361-0186, Fax: (818) 361-3276. Head: Francis J. Weber
Fine Arts Museum / Historical Museum - 1797
38546

Mississippi State University MS

Cobb Institute of Archaeology Museum, POB AR, Mississippi State University, MS 39762 - T: (662) 325-3826, Fax: (662) 325-8690, E-mail: jds1@ra.msstate.edu, Internet: http://www.cobb.msstate.edu. Head: Joe Seger
Archaeological Museum - 1972
38547

Dunn-Seiler Museum, Dept of Geosciences, Mississippi State University, MS 39762 - T: (601) 325-3915, Fax: (601) 325-2907, E-mail: dewey@geosci.msstate.edu
University Museum / Natural History Museum - 1947
38548

Missoula MT

Art Museum of Missoula, 335 N Pattee, Missoula, MT 59802 - T: (406) 728-0447, Fax: (406) 543-8691, E-mail: museum@artmissoula.org, Internet: http://www.artmissoula.org. Head: Laura J. Millin
Fine Arts Museum - 1975
Architecture, ethnology, American Indian, Afo-American, Western art, African art, decorative arts
38549

Gallery of Visual Arts, University of Montana, Missoula, MT 59812 - T: (406) 243-2813, Fax: (406) 243-4968, Internet: http://www.umt.edu/art/gva.htm
Fine Arts Museum
38550

Historical Museum at Fort Missoula, 322 Fort Missoula, Missoula, MT 59804 - T: (406) 728-3476, Fax: (406) 543-6277, E-mail: ftmslamuseum@montana.com, Internet: http://www.montana.com/ftmslamuseum. Head: Robert M. Brown
Local Museum - 1975
38551

Museum of Fine Arts, School of Fine Arts, University of Montana, Missoula, MT 59812 - T: (406) 243-4970, Fax: (406) 243-5726, E-mail: m.mudd@selway.umt.edu, Internet: http://www.umt.edu/partv/famus. Head: Margaret Mudd
Fine Arts Museum / University Museum - 1956
38552

Paxson Gallery, University of Montana, Missoula, MT 59812 - T: (406) 243-2019, Fax: (406) 243-4968, Internet: http://www.umt.edu/partv/famus. Head: Margaret Mudd
Fine Arts Museum
Contemporary ceramic sculpture and paintings
38553

Philip L. Wright Zoological Museum, University of Montana, Div of Biological Sciences, Missoula, MT 59812 - T: (406) 243-5222, Fax: (406) 243-4184, E-mail: ddyer@selway.umt.edu
University Museum / Natural History Museum - 1909
Research coll - herbarium
38554

Missouri Valley IA

Steamboat Bertrand Museum, DeSoto National Wildlife Refuge, Missouri Valley, IA 51555 - T: (712) 642-4121, Fax: (712) 642-2877, E-mail: r3bertrand@fws.gov, Internet: http://refuges.fws.gov/nwrsfiles/culturalresources/bertrand/
Historical Museum - 1969 38555

Mitchell GA

Hamburg State Park Museum, 60701 Hamburg State Park Rd, Mitchell, GA 30820 - T: (912) 552-2393, Fax: (912) 553-1457, E-mail: hamburg@accucomm.net, Internet: http://www.accucomm.net/~hamburg
Historical Museum / Science&Tech Museum
Industry, 1920 water turbine powered gin and milling complex 38556

Mitchell IN

Spring Mill State Park Pioneer Village and Grissom Memorial, Hwy 60 E, Mitchell, IN 47446 - T: (812) 849-4129, Fax: (812) 849-4004
Historical Museum / Open Air Museum - 1927
Village life, housed in a Grist Mill, flourishing pioneer village in the 1800s 38557

Mitchell SD

Enchanted World Doll Museum, 615 N Main, Mitchell, SD 57301 - T: (605) 996-9896, Fax: (605) 996-0210. Head: Tom Wudel
Decorative Arts Museum - 1977
Dolls 38558

Middle Border Museum of American Indian and Pioneer Life, 1311 S Duff St, Mitchell, SD 57301 - T: (605) 996-2122, Fax: (605) 996-0323, E-mail: fmb@mitchell.net. Head: Chris Hanson
Local Museum / Open Air Museum / Ethnology Museum - 1939
Historic village 38559

Oscar Howe Art Center, 119 W Third Av, Mitchell, SD 57301 - T: (605) 996-4111. Head: Joanita Monteith
Fine Arts Museum / Folklore Museum - 1971
Local and regional artists, paintings by Sioux artists 38560

Moab UT

Dan O'Laurie Canyon Country Museum, 118 E Center, Moab, UT 84532 - T: (435) 259-7985. Head: Tom Stengel
Local Museum - 1958
Local hist, geology, archaeology 38561

Mobile AL

Bragg-Mitchell Mansion, 1906 Springhill Av, Mobile, AL 36608 - T: (334) 471-6364, Fax: (334) 478-3800, E-mail: ginmckean@aol.com, Internet: http://www.braggmitchell.com. Head: Michael Sullivan
Museum of Classical Antiquities / Local Museum - 1987
Antiques, historic house 38562

Eichold-Heustis Medical Museum of the South, 1504 Springhill Av, Mobile, AL 36604 - T: (334) 434-5055, Fax: (334) 434-5080. Head: Mary E. Dodd, Patsy Starkey
Special Museum - 1962 38563

Gulf Coast Exploreum and IMAX Dome, 65 Government St, Mobile, AL 36602 - T: (334) 471-5923, Fax: (334) 471-4686. Head: Scott Osborne
Science&Tech Museum - 1979 38564

Mobile Museum of Art, 401 Civic Center Dr, Mobile, AL 36608, mail addr: POB 8426, Mobile, AL 36689-0426 - T: (251) 208-5200, Fax: (251) 208-5201, E-mail: jbs@mobilemuseumofart.com, Internet: http://www.mobilemuseumofart.com. Head: Joseph B. Schenk
Fine Arts Museum - 1964 38565

Museum of Mobile, 111 S Royal St St, Mobile, AL 36602-1341 - T: (334) 208-7569, Fax: (334) 208-7686, E-mail: museum1@acan.net, Internet: http://www.museumofmobile.com. Head: George H. Ewert
Historical Museum - 1962 38566

Oakleigh House, 300 Oakleigh Pl, Mobile, AL 36604 - T: (334) 432-6161. Head: Jean G. Wentworth
Historical Museum - 1935 38567

Richards-Dar House, 256 N Joachim St, Mobile, AL 36603 - T: (334) 434-7320, 433-3426 ext 51. Head: H.G. Hase
Local Museum - 1972
Historic house 38568

USS Alabama Battleship Memorial Park, 2703 Battleship Pkwy, Mobile, AL 36601 - T: (334) 433-2703, Fax: (334) 433-2777, E-mail: ussalbb60@aol.com, Internet: http://www.ussalabama.com. Head: Bill Tunnell
Military Museum / Open Air Museum - 1963 38569

Mobridge SD

Klein Museum, 1820 W Grand Crossing, Mobridge, SD 57601 - T: (605) 845-7243, E-mail: kleinmuseum@westriv.com. Head: Diane Kindt
Local Museum - 1975
Local hist, native American beadwork, Sitting Bul pictures 38570

Modesto CA

Great Valley Museum of Natural History, 1100 Stoddard Av, Modesto, CA 95350 - T: (209) 575-6196, Fax: (209) 575-6798, E-mail: lcrawford@yosemite.cc.ca.us, Internet: http://yosemite.cc.ca.us/community/great-valley. Head: Mitch Gagos
Natural History Museum - 1973 38571

McHenry Museum, 1402 I St, Modesto, CA 95354 - T: (209) 577-5366, Fax: (209) 491-4313, E-mail: museum@thevision.net, Internet: http://www.thevision.net/
Historical Museum - 1965 38572

Mohall ND

Renville County Historical Society Museum, 504 First St NE, Mohall, ND 58761 - T: (701) 756-6195. Head: Dorothy Aalund
Local Museum / Historical Museum - 1978 38573

Moline IL

Deere Museum, One John Deere Pl, Moline, IL 61265 - T: (309) 765-4881, Fax: (309) 765-4088, Internet: http://www.deere.com. Head: James H. Collins
Science&Tech Museum - 1837
Tractors 38574

Rock Island County Historical Museum, 822-11 Av, Moline, IL 61266-0632 - T: (309) 764-8590. Head: Sue Ann McMaster
Local Museum - 1905
Local history 38575

Monhegan ME

The Monhegan Museum, 1 Lighthouse Hill, Monhegan, ME 04852 - T: (207) 596-7003
Fine Arts Museum / Local Museum / Natural History Museum - 1968
Local history 38576

Monkton MD

Ladew Topiary Gardens Museum, 3535 Jarrettsville Pike, Monkton, MD 21111 - T: (410) 557-9570, 557-9466, Fax: (410) 557-7763, Internet: http://www.ladewgardens.com. Head: Jennifer B. Shattuck
Historic Site - 1977
Manor House, English furniture, fox hunting memorabilia and equestrian-inspired paintings 38577

Monmouth IL

Buchanan Center for the Arts, 64 Public Sq, Monmouth, IL 61462 - T: (309) 734-3033, Fax: (309) 734-3554, E-mail: bca@misslink.net
Fine Arts Museum - 1990 38578

Wyatt Earp Birthplace, 406 S 3rd St and Wyatt Earp Way, Monmouth, IL 61462-1435 - T: (309) 734-6419, Fax: (309) 734-6419, E-mail: wyattearpbirthp@webtv.net, Internet: http://www.misslink.net/misslink/earp.htm
Local Museum - 1986
Local hist 38579

Monmouth OR

Jensen Arctic Museum, Western Oregon University, 590 W Church St, Monmouth, OR 97361 - T: (503) 838-8468, 838-8281, Fax: (503) 838-8289, E-mail: macem@redbaron.wou.edu, Internet: http://www.wou.edu/president/universityadvancement/jensen/. Head: Mariana Mace
University Museum / Folklore Museum - 1985
Arctic culture 38580

Monroe CT

Monroe Historical Society Museum, 433 Barnhill Rd, Monroe, CT 06468 - T: (203) 268-5048
Local Museum / Historical Museum - 1959 38581

Monroe LA

Emy-Lou Biedenharn Foundation, 2006 Riverside Dr, Monroe, LA 71201 - T: (318) 387-5281, Fax: (318) 387-8253, E-mail: bmuseum@bayou.com, Internet: http://www.bmuseum.org. Head: Murray Biedenharn, Ralph Calhoun
Religious Arts Museum / Special Museum - 1971
Bible museum, home of Joseph A. Biedenharn, first bottler of Coca-Cola 38582

Masur Museum of Art, 1400 S Grand, Monroe, LA 71202 - T: (318) 329-2237, Fax: (318) 329-2847, E-mail: masur@ci.monroe.la.us, Internet: http://www.ci.minroe.la.us/mma. Head: Suzanne M. Prudhomme
Fine Arts Museum - 1963
Art 38583

Monroe MI

Monroe County Historical Museum, 126 S Monroe St, Monroe, MI 48161 - T: (734) 240-7780, Fax: (734) 240-7788, E-mail: matthew_switlik@monroemi.org. Head: Matthew C. Switlik
Local Museum - 1939
Regional history, Gen. George A. Custer home 38584

Monroe NY

Museum Village, 1010 Museum Village Rd, Monroe, NY 10950 - T: (845) 782-8248, Fax: (845) 782-6432, Internet: http://www.museumvillage.org. Head: Mark Sutherland
Open Air Museum - 1950 38585

Monroeville AL

Monroe County Heritage Museum, POB 1637, Monroeville, AL 36461 - T: (334) 575-7433, Fax: (334) 575-7934, Internet: http://www.tokilla-mockingbiRdcom. Head: Kathy McCoy
Local Museum - 1990
Local hist 38586

Montague MI

Montague Museum, Church and Meade Sts, Montague, MI 49437 - T: (616) 893-8603. Head: Henry E. Roesler
Local Museum - 1964
Local history, former United Methodist Church 38587

Montclair NJ

Montclair Art Museum, 3 S Mountain Av, Montclair, NJ 07042-1747 - T: (973) 746-5555, Fax: (973) 746-9118, E-mail: mail@montclair-art.com, Internet: http://www.montclair-art.com. Head: Nathanial C. Harris
Fine Arts Museum - 1914
American Indian art, costumes, silver, paintings, drwaings 38588

Montclair Historical Society Museum, 108 Orange Rd, Montclair, NJ 07042 - T: (973) 744-1796, Fax: (973) 783-9419. Head: Susan Godfrey, Pamela A. Fosdich
Local Museum - 1965 38589

Monterey CA

Casa Amesti, 516 Polk St, Monterey, CA 93940 - T: (831) 372-8173. Head: Tom McCuller
Historical Museum - 1953 38590

Colton Hall Museum, City Hall, Pacific St, Monterey, CA 93940 - T: (831) 646-5640, Fax: (831) 646-3422, E-mail: parttimemuseum@c1.monterey.ca.us. Head: Nancy Selfridge
Historical Museum - 1949 38591

Maritime Museum of Monterey, 5 Custom House Plaza, Monterey, CA 93940 - T: (831) 375-2553, Fax: (831) 655-3054, Internet: http://www.mhaamm.org. Head: Linda. Jaffe
Special Museum - 1971 38592

Monterey History and Art Association Museum, 5 Custom House Plaza, Monterey, CA 93940 - T: (831) 372-2608, Fax: (831) 655-3054, Internet: http://www.mhaamm.org. Head: Thomas A. Mercer
Local Museum - 1931 38593

Monterey Museum of Art, 559 Pacific St, Monterey, CA 93940 - T: (831) 372-5477, Fax: (831) 372-5680, E-mail: mtry_art@mbay.net, Internet: http://www.monereyart.org. Head: Richard W. Gadd
Fine Arts Museum - 1959 38594

Monterey State Historic Park, 20 Custom House Plaza, Monterey, CA 93940 - T: (831) 649-7118, Fax: (831) 647-6236, Internet: http://www.mbay.net/~mshp/. Head: Kris N. Quist
Historical Museum / Open Air Museum - 1938 38595

Old Monterey Jail, City Hall, Pacific St, Monterey, CA 93940 - T: (831) 646-5640, Fax: (831) 646-3422. Head: Nancy Selfridge
Local Museum / Historical Museum - 1949 38596

Monterey MA

Bidwell House, Art School Rd, Monterey, MA 01245 - T: (413) 528-6888, Fax: (413) 528-6888, Internet: http://www.berkshireweb.com/bidwellhouse. Head: Anita Carroll-Weldon
Historical Museum - 1990 38597

Monterey VA

Highland Maple Museum, U.S. 220 S, Monterey, VA 24465 - T: (540) 468-2420, 468-2550, Fax: (540) 468-2551. Head: T.E. Billingsley
Agriculture Museum - 1983
Agriculture 38598

Montevideo MN

Chippewa County Historical Society Museum, 151 Pioneer Dr, Montevideo, MN 56265 - T: (320) 269-7636, E-mail: CCHS.June@juno.com, Internet: http://www.montevideomn.com. Head: Evelyn Ostlie
Open Air Museum / Local Museum - 1936 38599

Montgomery AL

First White House of the Confederacy, 644 Washington Av, Montgomery, AL 36130 - T: (334) 242-1861. Head: John H. Napier
Historical Museum - 1900
Historic building 38600

Montgomery Museum of Fine Arts, 1 Museum Dr, Montgomery, AL 36117 - T: (334) 244-5700, Fax: (334) 244-5774, E-mail: mmfa@mindspring.com, Internet: http://www.fineartmuseum.com. Head: Mark M. Johnson, G. Carl Barker
Fine Arts Museum / Folklore Museum - 1930
American paintings and sculptures, Old Master prints, Southern regional art and decorative arts 38601

The Wallace Museum Foundation, 631 S Perry St, Montgomery, AL 36104 - T: (334) 834-1972, Fax: (334) 262-5650, E-mail: info@wallacefoundation.org, Internet: http://www.wallacefoundation.org. Head: Joe Terry
Historical Museum - 1994
Political hist 38602

Montgomery NY

Brick House, Rte 17K, Montgomery, NY 12549 - T: (914) 457-4921, Fax: (914) 457-4906
Historical Museum - 1979 38603

Hill-Hold Museum, 211 Rte 416, Montgomery, NY 12549 - T: (845) 457-4905, Fax: (914) 457-4906, E-mail: stucker@co.orange.ny.us. Head: Suasan A. Tucker
Historic Site - 1976 38604

Monticello AR

Drew County Historical Museum, 404 S Main St, Monticello, AR 71655 - T: (870) 367-7446. Head: Connie Mullis
Local Museum - 1970
Regional history 38605

Monticello IL

Monticello Railway Museum, Interstate 72 at Exit 166, Market St, Monticello, IL 61856 - T: (217) 762-9011, 952-3396, E-mail: mrm@prairienet.org, Internet: http://www.prairienet.org/community/mrm/. Head: Kent McClure, Donna McClure
Science&Tech Museum - 1966
Railways 38606

Piatt County Museum, 315 W Main, Monticello, IL 61856 - T: (217) 762-4731. Head: Tari Bricker
Local Museum - 1965
Local history 38607

Monticello IN

White County Historical Society Museum, 101 S Bluff St, Monticello, IN 47960 - T: (219) 583-3998
Local Museum - 1911
Local history 38608

Montour Falls NY

Schuyler County Historical Society Museum, 108 N Catharine, Montour Falls, NY 14865 - T: (607) 535-9741. Head: Doris Gauvin
Local Museum - 1960 38609

Montpelier OH

Williams County Historical Museum, 619 E Main St, Montpelier, OH 43543 - T: (419) 485-8200
Local Museum - 1956 38610

Montpelier VT

T.W. Wood Gallery and Arts Center, Vermont College, Montpelier, VT 05602 - T: (802) 828-8743, Fax: (802) 828-8855, E-mail: twwood@norwich.edu. Head: Joyce Mandeville
Fine Arts Museum / Public Gallery - 1891
Art 38611

Vermont Historical Society Museum, 109 State St, Pavilion Bldg, Montpelier, VT 05609-0901 - T: (802) 828-2291, Fax: (802) 828-3638, E-mail: vhs@vhs.state.vt.us, Internet: http://www.state.vt.us/vhs. Head: Gainor B. Davis
Local Museum - 1838
Local hist 38612

The Vermont State House, 115 State St, Montpelier, VT 05633 - T: (802) 828-2228, Fax: (802) 828-2424, Internet: http://www.leg.state.vt.us
Decorative Arts Museum / Local Museum - 1808
Historic building 38613

Montpelier Station VA

Montpelier, 11407 Constitution Hwy, Montpelier Station, VA 22957 - T: (540) 672-2728, Fax: (540) 672-0411, Internet: http://www.montpelier.org. Head: Kathleen Stiso Mullins
Local Museum - 1984
Historic house, home of President James Madison 38614

Montreat NC

Presbyterian Church Museum, 318 Georgia Terrace, Montreat, NC 28757 - T: (704) 669-7061, Fax: (704) 669-5369, E-mail: pcusadoh@montreat.edu
Religious Arts Museum - 1927 38615

Montrose CO

Montrose County Historical Museum, Main and Rio Grande, Montrose, CO 81402, mail addr: POB 1882, Montrose, CO 81402 - T: (970) 249-6135, E-mail: stepbackintime@montrose.net
Local Museum - 1974
Regional history 38616

Ute Indian Museum, 17253 Chipeta Dr, Montrose, CO 81401 - T: (970) 249-3098, Fax: (970) 252-8741, E-mail: cj.brafford@state.co.us. Head: C.J. Brafford
Ethnology Museum / Historic Site - 1956
Indian history 38617

Montrose PA

Susquehanna County Historical Society, Two Monument Sq, Montrose, PA 18801 - T: (570) 278-1881, Fax: (570) 278-9336, E-mail: suspulib@epix.net, Internet: http://www.epix.net/~suspulib/
Local Museum - 1890
Local hist 38618

Montville NJ

Montville Township Historical Museum, Taylor Town Rd, Montville, NJ 07045 - T: (973) 334-5604. Head: Carol Larson
Historical Museum - 1963 38619

Moorestown NJ

Perkins Center for the Arts, 395 Kings Hwy, Moorestown, NJ 08057 - T: (856) 235-6488, Fax: (856) 235-6624, E-mail: create@perkinscenter.org, Internet: http://www.perkinscenter.org. Head: Alan Willoughby
Fine Arts Museum - 1977
Art 38620

Moorhead MN

Clay County Museum, 202 First Av N, Moorhead, MN 56560 - T: (218) 299-5520, Fax: (218) 299-5525, E-mail: mpeihl1@funo.com. Head: Paul Harris
Local Museum / Historical Museum - 1932 38621

Comstock Historic House, 506 8th St, Moorhead, MN 56560 - T: (218) 291-4211, 233-1772. Head: Robert J. Loeffler
Local Museum - 1975
Historic house 38622

Mora MN

Kanabec History Center, 805 W Forest Av, Mora, MN 55051 - T: (320) 679-1665, Fax: (320) 679-1673, E-mail: kanabechistory@ncis.com, Internet: http://www.kanabechistory.com. Head: S.L. Nelson, J.L. Franz
Historical Museum - 1977 38623

Moraga CA

Hearst Art Gallery, Saint Mary's College, 1928 Saint Mary's Rd, Moraga, CA 94575 - T: (510) 631-4379, Fax: (510) 376-5128, E-mail: aduesber@stmarys-ca.edu, Internet: http://www.gaelnet.stmarys-ca.edu/gallery. Head: Carrie Brewster
Fine Arts Museum / University Museum - 1977 38624

Moravia NY

Cayuga-Owasco Lakes Historical Society Museum, 14 W Cayuga, Moravia, NY 13118 - T: (315) 497-3096. Head: Sue Stoyell
Local Museum - 1966 38625

Morehead KY

Kentucky Folk Art Center, 102 W First St, Morehead, KY 40351 - T: (606) 783-2204, Fax: (606) 783-5034, E-mail: g.barker@morehead-st.edu, Internet: http://www.kyfolkart.org. Head: Garry Barker
Folklore Museum - 1985
Folk art 38626

Morganton NC

Jailhouse Galleries, Burke Arts Council, 115 E Meeting St, Morganton, NC 28665 - T: (828) 433-7282, Fax: (828) 433-7282, E-mail: burkearts@hci.net, Internet: http://www.burkearts.hci.net
Fine Arts Museum / Decorative Arts Museum 38627

Morgantown WV

Comer Museum, MRB, Rm 311A, Morgantown, WV 26506-6070 - T: (304) 293-4211, Fax: (304) 293-6751, E-mail: jdean@cemrwvu.edu. Head: Jim Dean
Science&Tech Museum - 1990 38628

West Virginia University Mesaros Galleries, Creative Arts Center, Evansdale Campus, West Virginia University, Morgantown, WV 26506-6111 - T: (304) 293-2140 ext 3210, Fax: (304) 293-5731, E-mail: kolson@wvu.edu, Internet: http://www.wvu.edu/~ccarts. Head: J. Bernard Schultz
University Museum / Fine Arts Museum - 1968 38629

Morrilton AR

Museum of Automobiles, Petit Jean Mountain, 8 Jones Ln, Morrilton, AR 72110 - T: (501) 727-5427, Fax: (501) 727-5427. Head: Buddy Hoelzeman, Atley G. Davis
Science&Tech Museum - 1964
Antique automobiles 38630

Morris MN

Stevens County Historical Society Museum, 116 W Sixth St, Morris, MN 56267 - T: (320) 589-1719, E-mail: history@infolink.morris.mn.us. Head: Karen Berget
Historical Museum - 1920 38631

Morristown NJ

Acorn Hall House Museum, 68 Morris Av, Morristown, NJ 07960-4212 - T: (973) 267-3465, Fax: (973) 267-8773. Head: Carol Mann
Historical Museum - 1945 38632

Fosterfields Living Historical Farm, 73 Kahdena Rd, Morristown, NJ 07960 - T: (973) 326-7645, Fax: (973) 631-5023, E-mail: mtexel@morrisparks.net, Internet: http://www.parks.morris.nj.us. Head: Mark Texel
Agriculture Museum - 1978 38633

Historic Speedwell, 333 Speedwell Av, Morristown, NJ 07960 - T: (973) 540-0211, Fax: (973) 540-0476, Internet: http://www.speedwell.org. Head: Kathleen Q. Duane
Historical Museum - 1966 38634

Macculloch Hall Historical Museum, 45 Macculloch Av, Morristown, NJ 07960 - T: (973) 538-2404, Fax: (973) 538-9428, E-mail: macchall@aol.com, Internet: http://www.machall.org. Head: David Breslauer
Local Museum - 1950 38635

The Morris Museum, 6 Normandy Heights Rd, Morristown, NJ 07960 - T: (973) 971-3700, Fax: (973) 538-0154, E-mail: morrismuseum@worldnet.att.net, Internet: http://www.morrismuseum.org
Local Museum - 1913
American Indian, African and Asian art, paintings, sculpture, anthropology, archaeology, costumes, ceramics, crafts, pottery, primitive and decorative art 38636

Morristown National Historical Park, 30 Washington Pl, Morristown, NJ 07960 - T: (973) 539-2016, Fax: (973) 539-8361, E-mail: Joni_Rowe@nps.gov, Internet: http://nps.gov/morr. Head: Clark A. Dixon
Military Museum / Open Air Museum - 1933 38637

Schuyler-Hamilton House, 5 Olyphant Pl, Morristown, NJ 07960 - T: (973) 267-4039
Decorative Arts Museum - 1923 38638

Morristown NY

Red Barn Museum, 518 River Rd E, Morristown, NY 13669 - T: (315) 375-6390. Head: Lorraine B. Bogardus
Open Air Museum - 1971 38639

Morristown TN

Crockett Tavern Museum, 2002 E Morningside Dr, Morristown, TN 37814 - T: (615) 587-9900. Head: Sally B. Bennett
Local Museum - 1958
Local hist 38640

Rose Center Museum, 442 W 2nd N St, Morristown, TN 37816 - T: (423) 586-6205, Fax: (423) 581-4330, E-mail: rosecent@usit.net, Internet: http://www.rosecenter.org. Head: Bill Kornrich
Folklore Museum / Local Museum - 1976
Civic art and culture 38641

Morrisville PA

Pennsbury Manor, 400 Pennsbury Memorial Rd, Morrisville, PA 19067 - T: (215) 946-0400, Fax: (215) 295-2936, E-mail: willpenn17@aol.com, Internet: http://www.pennsburymanor.org. Head: Douglas Miller
Historic Site - 1939
1683 Pennsbury Manor, residence of William Penn, reconstructed in 1939 38642

Morro Bay CA

Morro Bay State Park Museum of Natural History, State Park Rd, Morro Bay, CA 93442 - T: (805) 772-2694, Fax: (805) 772-7129, Internet: http://www.mbspmuseum.org
Natural History Museum - 1962 38643

Moscow ID

The Appaloosa Museum and Heritage Center, 2720 W Pullman Rd, Moscow, ID 83843 - T: (208) 882-5578 ext 279, Fax: (208) 882-8150, E-mail: museum@appaloosa.com, Internet: http://www.appaloosamuseum.org. Head: Stacey Garretson, King Rockhill
Historical Museum / Ethnology Museum - 1973
Local history 38644

McConnell Mansion, 110 S Adams, Moscow, ID 83843 - T: (208) 882-1004, Fax: (208) 882-0759, E-mail: lchs@moscow.com, Internet: http://www.moscow.com. Head: Mary Reed
Historical Museum - 1968
Local history, Governor McConnell - library 38645

Moses Lake WA

Adam East Museum Art Center, 122 W Third, Moses Lake, WA 98837 - T: (509) 766-9395, Fax: (509) 766-9392. Head: Terry Mulkey
Fine Arts Museum - 1957
Art 38646

Mount Clemens MI

Crocker House, 15 Union St, Mount Clemens, MI 48043 - T: (810) 465-2488, Internet: http://www.macombonline.com
Local Museum - 1964
Local history, Crocker House, a Victorian Italianate style house 38647

Michigan Transit Museum, 200 Grand Av, Mount Clemens, MI 48043-5412 - T: (810) 463-1863, Internet: http://www.alexxi.com/mtm. Head: Timothy D. Backhurst
Science&Tech Museum - 1973
Transport, equipment, Grand Trunk depot railroad Museum 38648

Mount Desert ME

Sound School House Museum, 373 Sound Dr, Mount Desert, ME 04660 - T: (207) 276-9323, Fax: (207) 276-4024, E-mail: mdihistory@acadia.net. Head: Jaylene Roths
Historical Museum 38649

Mount Dora FL

Mount Dora Center for the Arts, 138 E 5th Av, Mount Dora, FL 32757 - T: (352) 383-0880, Fax: (352) 383-7753, E-mail: mdca@lcia
Folklore Museum - 1985
Folk art 38650

Mount Gilead NC

Town Creek Indian Mound Historic Site, 509 Town Creek Mound Rd, Mount Gilead, NC 27306 - T: (910) 439-6802, Fax: (910) 439-6441, E-mail: towncreek@ncsl.dcr.state.nc.us, Internet: http://www.ah.dcr.state.nc.us/
Open Air Museum / Historical Museum - 1936 38651

Mount Holly NJ

Historic Burlington County Prison Museum, 128 High St, Mount Holly, NJ 08060 - T: (609) 265-5068, Fax: (609) 265-5782. Head: David A. Kimball
Historical Museum - 1966 38652

Mount Olivet KY

Blue Licks Battlefield Museum, Blue Licks Battlefield Park, Hwy 68, Mount Olivet, KY 41064 - T: (859) 289-5507, Fax: (859) 289-5409, Internet: http://www.state.ky.us/agencies/parks/bluelick.htm
Local Museum - 1928
General museum 38653

Mount Pleasant IA

Harlan-Lincoln House, 101 W Broad St, Mount Pleasant, IA 52641 - T: (319) 385-8021, Fax: (319) 385-6324, E-mail: iwcarch@iwc.edu, Internet: http://www.iwc.edu. Head: Lynn Ellsworth
Historical Museum - 1959
Home of U.S. Senator James Harlan (1876-1899) and the summer home of the Robert Todd Lincoln (1876-1899) - Iowa Wesleyan College
Archives 38654

Midwest Old Settlers and Threshers Association Museum, 405 E Threshers Rd, Mount Pleasant, IA 52641 - T: (319) 385-8937, Fax: (319) 385-0563
Agriculture Museum / Science&Tech Museum - 1950
Agricultural history, technic 38655

Mount Pleasant MI

Museum of Cultural and Natural History, Central Michigan University, Bellows St, 103 Rowe Hall, Mount Pleasant, MI 48859 - T: (517) 774-3829, Fax: (517) 774-2612, E-mail: lynn.fauver@cmich.edu, Internet: http://www.museum.cmich.edu/. Head: Lynn N. Fauver
University Museum / Local Museum - 1970 38656

University Art Gallery, c/o Central Michigan University, Dept. of Art, Wightman 132, Mount Pleasant, MI 48859 - T: (517) 774-3974, 774-3800, E-mail: julia.morrisroe@cmich.edu, Internet: http://www.ccfa.cmich.edu/uag. Head: Julia Morrisroe
Fine Arts Museum 38657

Mount Pleasant OH

Mount Pleasant Historical Society Museum, Union St, Mount Pleasant, OH 43939 - T: (740) 769-2893, Fax: (740) 769-2804, E-mail: kaspenwa@lst.net, Internet: http://users.lst.net/gudzent. Head: Sherry Sawchuk
Local Museum / Historical Museum - 1948 38658

Quaker Yearly Meeting House, Market and South St, Mount Pleasant, OH 43939 - T: (740) 769-2893, E-mail: gudzent@lst.net, Internet: http://users.lst.net/gudzent
Religious Arts Museum - 1814 38659

Mount Pleasant SC

Patriots Point Naval and Maritime Museum, 40 Patriots Point Rd, Mount Pleasant, SC 29464 - T: (803) 884-2727, Fax: (803) 881-4232, E-mail: patriotspt@infoave.net, Internet: http://www.state.sc.us/patpt
Military Museum - 1976
Museum housed in the aircraft carrier USS Yorktown, destroyer USS Laffey, submarine USS Clamagore, Coast Guard cutter Ingham 38660

Mount Prospect IL

Mount Prospect Historical Society Museums, 101 S Maple, Mount Prospect, IL 60056 - T: (847) 392-9006, Fax: (847) 392-8995, E-mail: mphist@aol.com, Internet: http://www.mphist.org. Head: Gavin Kleespies
Historical Museum - 1976
Local history 38661

Mount Pulaski IL

Mount Pulaski Courthouse, 113 S Washington, Mount Pulaski, IL 62548 - T: (217) 792-3919. Head: Richard Schachtsiek
Historical Museum - 1936
Greek Revival County Court House, part of Illinois 8th Judicial Circuit 38662

Mount Vernon IA

Armstrong Gallery, Cornell College, 600 1st St W, Mount Vernon, IA 52314-1098 - T: (319) 895-4491, Fax: (319) 895-5926, E-mail: scolemann@cornell-iowa.edu, Internet: http://www.cornell-iowa.edu. Head: Les Garner
Fine Arts Museum / University Museum - 1853
library 38663

Mount Vernon IL

Mitchell Museum at Cedarhurst, Richview Rd, Mount Vernon, IL 62864 - T: (618) 242-1236, Fax: (618) 242-9530, E-mail: mitchell@midwest.net. Head: Michael J. Beam
Fine Arts Museum - 1973
Art, sculpture park 38664

Mount Vernon VA

Frank Lloyd Wright's Pope-Leighey House, 9000 Richmond Hwy, Mount Vernon, VA 22309 - T: (703) 780-4000, Fax: (703) 780-8509, E-mail: woodlawn@nthp.org, Internet: http://www.nationaltrust.org. Head: Ross Randall
Local Museum / Fine Arts Museum - 1964 38665

Woodlawn Plantation, POB 37, Mount Vernon, VA 22121 - T: (703) 780-4000, Fax: (703) 780-8509, E-mail: woodlawn@nthp.org, Internet: http://www.nthp.org/main/sites/woodlawn.htm. Head: Ross Randall
Local Museum - 1951
Historic house 38666

Mountain Lake MN

Heritage Village, County Rd 1, Mountain Lake, MN 56159 - T: (507) 427-2023, Fax: (507) 427-2640, E-mail: pizzaman@prairie.lakes.com. Head: R.E Patrick
Historical Museum - 1971 38667

Mountain View AR

Ozark Folk Center, Hwy 382, Mountain View, AR 72560 - T: (870) 269-3851, Fax: (870) 269-2909, E-mail: ofc@mvtel.net, Internet: http://www.ozarkfolkcenter.com
Folklore Museum - 1973
Folk arts - library 38668

Mountainair NM

Salinas Pueblo Missions National Monument, Corner of Broadway and Ripley, Mountainair, NM 87036-517 - T: (505) 847-2585, Fax: (505) 847-2441, Internet: http://www.nps.gov/sapu. Head: Glenn Fulfer
Archaeological Museum - 1909
Prehistoric pithouses c. 800 A.D.; prehistoric Indian ruins c. 1100-1670 A.D.; four Spanish mission ruins c. 1622-1672 38669

Mountainside NJ

Trailside Nature and Science Center, 452 New Providence Rd, Mountainside, NJ 07092 - T: (908) 789-3670, Fax: (908) 789-3270. Head: Hollace Hoffman
Natural History Museum - 1941 38670

Mountainville NY

Storm King Art Center, Old Pleasant Hill Rd, Mountainville, NY 10953-0280 - T: (914) 534-3115, Fax: (914) 534-4457, E-mail: SKAC@aol.com, Internet: http://www.skac.org/. Head: David R. Collens
Fine Arts Museum - 1960 38671

Mullens WV

Twin Falls Museum, Hwy Rte 97, Mullens, WV 25882 - T: (304) 294-4000, Fax: (304) 294-5000, Internet: http://wvweb.com/www/twin-falls.html. Head: A. Scott Durham
Local Museum - 1976
Local hist 38672

Mumford NY

Genesee Country Village and Museum, 1410 Flint Hill Rd, Mumford, NY 14511 - T: (716) 538-6822, Fax: (716) 538-2887, E-mail: glazzara@frontiernet.net, Internet: http://www.history.rochester.edu/gcmuseum
Fine Arts Museum / Local Museum - 1966 38673

Muncie IN

Ball State University Museum of Art, Riversite Av at Warwick, Muncie, IN 47306 - T: (765) 285-5242, Fax: (765) 285-5275, Internet: http://www.bsu.edu/artmuseum. Head: Alain Joyaux
Fine Arts Museum / University Museum - 1936
Art 38674

Biology Department Teaching Museum, 2000 University, Muncie, IN 47306 - T: (317) 285-8820, 285-8838, Fax: (317) 285-2351. Head: Dr. Carl E. Warnes
University Museum / Natural History Museum - 1918 38675

Muncie Children's Museum, 515 S High St, Muncie, IN 47305 - T: (765) 286-1660, Fax: (765) 286-1662, E-mail: munciemuseum@home.com, Internet: http://www.muchiechildrensmuseum.com. Head: Lenette Freeman
Ethnology Museum - 1977 38676

National Model Aviation Museum, Academie of Model Aeronautics, 5151 E Memorial Dr, Muncie, IN 47302 - T: (765) 287-1256, Fax: (765) 289-4248, E-mail: michaels@modelaircraft.org, Internet: http://www.modelaircraft.org. Head: Joyce Hager
Special Museum - 1936
Aeronautics - Library 38677

Munising MI

Alger County Heritage Center, 1496 Washington St, Munising, MI 49862 - T: (906) 387-4308. Head: Mary Jo Cook
Local Museum - 1966
Local history 38678

Grand Island Trader's Cabin, Washington St, Munising, MI 49862 - T: (906) 387-4308. Head: Mark Louma
Historical Museum - 1972
Abraham Williams, 1st white settler in Alger County 38679

Munnsville NY

Fryer Memorial Museum, Williams St, Munnsville, NY 13409 - T: (315) 495-5395, 495-6148. Head: Olive S. Boylan
Historical Museum - 1977
Generalogical coll 38680

Munster IN

Northern Indiana Arts Association, 1040 Ridge Rd, Munster, IN 46321 - T: (219) 836-1839, Fax: (219) 836-1863. Head: Michael Spiccia
Fine Arts Museum - 1969
Art 38681

Murdo SD

Pioneer Auto Museum, I-90 and U.S. Hwys 16 and 83, Murdo, SD 57559 - T: (605) 669-2691, Fax: (605) 669-3217, E-mail: pas@pioneerautoshow.com, Internet: http://www.pioneerautoshow.com. Head: David A. Geisler
Science&Tech Museum - 1953
Transportation 38682

Murfreesboro AR

Crater of Diamonds State Park Museum, Rte 1, Murfreesboro, AR 71958 - T: (870) 285-3113
Historic Site - 1972 38683

Ka-Do-Ha Indian Village Museum, 1010 Caddo Dr, Murfreesboro, AR 71958 - T: (870) 285-3736, E-mail: sam@caddotc.com, Internet: http://www.caddotc.com
Ethnology Museum / Archaeological Museum - 1964
Archaeology, on 1,000 A.D. Moundbuilder village and ceremonial center 38684

Murfreesboro NC

Rea Museum, William and Fourth Sts, Murfreesboro, NC 27855 - T: (252) 398-4886, Fax: (252) 398-5871. Head: Kay Mitchell
Historical Museum - 1967 38685

Murfreesboro TN

Baldwin Photographic Gallery, Middle Tennessee State University, Learning Resources Center, Murfreesboro, TN 37132 - T: (615) 898-2085, Fax: (615) 898-5682, E-mail: tjimison@mtsu.edu. Head: Tom Jimison
Fine Arts Museum / University Museum - 1961 38686

Oaklands Historic House Museum, 900 N Maney Av, Murfreesboro, TN 37130 - T: (615) 893-0022, Fax: (615) 896-7233. Head: Carty Roberts
Local Museum - 1959
Historic house 38687

Stones River National Battlefield, 3501 Old Nashville Hwy, Murfreesboro, TN 37129-3094 - T: (615) 893-9501, Fax: (615) 893-9508, E-mail: stri_information@nps.gov, Internet: http://www.nps.gov/stri. Head: Stuart Johnson
Military Museum / Historic Site - 1927
Military hist 38688

Murphy ID

Owyhee County Historical Museum, POB 67, Murphy, ID 83650 - T: (208) 495-2319. Head: James Howard, Byron Johnson
Local Museum - 1960
Local history 38689

Murphy NC

Cherokee County Historical Museum, 205 Peachtree St, Murphy, NC 28906 - T: (828) 837-6792, Fax: (828) 837-6792, E-mail: cchm@grove.net, Internet: http://www.tib.com/cchm
Historical Museum - 1977 38690

Murray KY

University Art Galleries, Murray State University, Price Doyle Fine Arts Center, 15th and Olive Sts, Murray, KY 42071-3342 - T: (502) 762-3052, Fax: (502) 762-3920, E-mail: albert.sperath@murraystate.edu. Head: Albert Sperath
Fine Arts Museum / University Museum - 1971
Art 38691

Wrather West Kentucky Museum, Murray State University, Murray, KY 42071-0009 - T: (502) 762-4771, Fax: (502) 762-4485. Head: Kate A. Reeves
Local Museum - 1982
Regional history 38692

Muscatine IA

Muscatine Art Center, 1314 Mulberry Av, Muscatine, IA 52761 - T: (319) 263-8282, Fax: (319) 263-4702, E-mail: art@muscatine.com, Internet: http://www.muscatineartcenter.org. Head: Barbara C. Longtin
Fine Arts Museum - 1965
Art, housed in Edwardian style Musser mansion, contemporaray gallery 38693

Muskegon MI

Hackley & Hume Historic Site, W Webster Av and Sixth St, Muskegon, MI 49440 - T: (616) 722-7578, Fax: (616) 728-4119, E-mail: info@muskegonmuseum.org, Internet: http://www.muskegonmuseum.org. Head: John H. McGarry
Local Museum - 1971
Historic houses 38694

Muskegon County Museum, 430 W Clay, Muskegon, MI 49440 - T: (213) 722-0278, Fax: (213) 728-4119, E-mail: info@muskegonmuseum.org, Internet: http://www.muskegonmuseum.org. Head: John H. McGarry
Local Museum - 1937
Regional history - children's science museum 38695

Muskegon Museum of Art, 296 W Webster Av, Muskegon, MI 49440 - T: (231) 720-2570, Fax: (231) 720-2585, Internet: http://www.muskegon.kiz.mi.us. Head: Susan Talbot-Stanaway
Fine Arts Museum - 1912
Art - library 38696

USS Silversides and Maritime Museum, 1346 Bluff St, Muskegon, MI 49441 - T: (616) 755-1230, Fax: (616) 755-5883, E-mail: 55236@aol.com
Historical Museum / Military Museum - 1972
Historic Ship of the WW II, navy sub U.S.S. Silversides, USCGC McLane (WMEC 146) 38697

Muskogee OK

Ataloa Lodge Museum, 2299 Old Bacone Rd, Muskogee, OK 74403-1597 - T: (918) 781-7283, Fax: (918) 683-4588, E-mail: jtimothy@bacone.edu, Internet: http://www.bacone.edu. Head: John Timothy
Ethnology Museum / Folklore Museum - 1932 38698

Five Civilized Tribes Museum, Agency Hill, Honor Heights Dr, Muskogee, OK 74401 - T: (918) 683-1701, Fax: (918) 683-3070, E-mail: the5tribesmuseum@azalea.net, Internet: http://www.fivetribes.com. Head: Richard Bradley, Clara Reekie
Historical Museum / Ethnology Museum / Folklore Museum - 1966
American Indian Museum and Art Gallery 38699

Thomas-Foreman Home, 1419 W Okmulgee, Muskogee, OK 74401 - T: (918) 682-6938. Head: Delphia Warren
Historical Museum - 1970 38700

Myrtle Beach SC

Franklin G. Burroughs-Simeon B. Chapin Art Museum, 3100 S Ocean Blvd, Myrtle Beach, SC 29577 - T: (843) 238-2510, Fax: (843) 238-2910, E-mail: villa@sccoast.net. Head: Pat A. Creswell
Fine Arts Museum - 1989
Art 38701

Mystic CT

Mystic Art Association Museum, 9 Water St, Mystic, CT 06355 - T: (860) 536-7601, Fax: (860) 536-0610, E-mail: maa@mystic-art.org, Internet: http://www.mystic-art.org. Head: Willa T. Schuster, Joanne K. Newman
Fine Arts Museum / Folklore Museum - 1914
Art 38702

Mystic Seaport, 75 Greenmanville Av, Mystic, CT 06355-0990 - T: (860) 572-0711, Fax: (860) 572-5327, E-mail: info@mysticseaport.org, Internet: http://www.mysticseaport.org. Head: Douglas H. Teeson
Special Museum - 1929 38703

Nacogdoches TX

Sterne-Hoya Home, 211 S Lanana St, Nacogdoches, TX 75961 - T: (409) 560-5426
Local Museum
Historic house 38704

Stone Fort Museum, Stephen F. Austin State University, Alumni & Griffith Blvds, Stephen F. Austin State University, Nacogdoches, TX 75962, mail addr: POB 6075 (SFASU), TX 75962 Nacogdoches - T: (936) 468-2408, Fax: (936) 468-7084, E-mail: spears@sfasu.edu. Head: Dr. James E. Corbin
Local Museum - 1936
Local hist, Spanish colonial and East Texas prior till 1900 38705

Nageezi NM

Chaco Culture National Historical Park, off Hwy 44 on City Rd 7900/7950, Nageezi, NM 87037 - T: (505) 786-7014, Fax: (505) 786-7061, E-mail: chcu_curation@nps.gov. Head: C.T. Wilson
Archaeological Museum 38706

Nantucket MA

Artists Association of Nantucket Museum, 19 Washington St, Nantucket, MA 02554 - T: (508) 228-0722, 228-0294, Fax: (508) 325-5251, E-mail: aan@nantucket.net, Internet: http://www.nantucketarts.org. Head: Donna Tillotson
Fine Arts Museum - 1945
Art gallery 38707

Hinchman House, Maria Mitchell Association, 7 Milk St, Nantucket, MA 02554 - T: (508) 228-9198, 228-0898, Fax: (508) 228-1031, E-mail: ahunt@mmo.org, Internet: http://www.mmo.org. Head: Kathryn K. Pochman
Natural History Museum - 1902
Natural science, astronomy 38708

Mitchell House, Maria Mitchell Association, 1 Vestal St, Nantucket, MA 02554 - T: (508) 228-9198, 228-2896, Fax: (508) 228-1031, E-mail: kpochman@mmo.org, Internet: http://www.mmo.org. Head: Kathryn K. Pochman
Natural History Museum - 1902
Natural science, astronomy, Maria Mitchell's birthplace - Vestal Street and Loines Observatories, aquarium, science library 38709

Nantucket Historical Association Museum, 15 Broad St, Nantucket, MA 02554-1016 - T: (508) 228-1894, Fax: (508) 228-5618, E-mail: nhainfo@nha.org, Internet: http://www.nha.org. Head: Frank D. Milligan
Local Museum - 1894
Local history - library 38710

Naperville IL

Naper Settlement Museum, 523 S Webster St, Naperville, IL 60540 - T: (630) 420-6010, 305-5250, Fax: (630) 305-5255, E-mail: grouptours@naperville.il.us, Internet: http://www.napersettlement.org. Head: Peggy Frank
Open Air Museum - 1969
Historic village 38711

Naples FL

Naples Museum of Art, 5833 Pelican Bay Blvd, Naples, FL 34108 - T: (941) 597-1900, Fax: (941) 597-8163, E-mail: museum@naplesphilcenter.org, Internet: http://www.naplesphilcenter.org
Public Gallery - 1989 38712

Philharmonic Center for the Arts Galleries → Naples Museum of Art

Teddy Bear Museum of Naples, 2511 Pine Ridge Rd, Naples, FL 34109 - T: (941) 598-2711, Fax: (941) 598-9239, E-mail: info@teddymuseum.com, Internet: http://www.teddymuseum.com. Head: George B. Black
Special Museum - 1990 38713

Nashua IA

Chickasaw County Historical Society Museum, Bradford Village, 2729 Cheyenne Av, Nashua, IA 50658 - T: (641) 435-2567, Fax: (641) 435-2567. Head: Duane Tracy
Local Museum - 1953
Local history 38714

Nashville IN

Brown County Art Gallery and Museum, 1 Artist Dr, Nashville, IN 47448 - T: (812) 988-4609, E-mail: brncagal@indiana.edu, Internet: http://www.brownco.org. Head: Dr. Emanuel Klein
Fine Arts Museum - 1926
Art gallery 38715

Brown County Museum, Museum Ln, Nashville, IN 47448 - T: (812) 988-8768, E-mail: rlaf@iquest.net. Head: Raymond E. Laffin
Local Museum / Open Air Museum - 1957
Local history, museum village 38716

T.C. Steele House, 4220 T.C. Steele Rd, Nashville, IN 47448 - T: (812) 988-2785, Fax: (812) 988-8457, E-mail: tcsteele@bloomington.in.us, Internet: http://www.state.in.us/ism/sites/steele
Fine Arts Museum - 1945
C.1907 T.C. Steele Home, c.1916 Studio 38717

Nashville TN

Belle Meade Plantation, 5025 Harding Rd, Nashville, TN 37205 - T: (615) 356-0501, Fax: (615) 356-2336, E-mail: www.belmeade@bellsouth.net, Internet: http://www.bellemeadeplantation.com. Head: Suzanne S. Iler
Local Museum - 1953
Historic house 38718

Cheekwood Museum of Art, 1200 Forrest Park Dr, Nashville, TN 37205-4242 - T: (615) 356-8000, Fax: (615) 353-0919, E-mail: kwelborn@cheekwood.org, Internet: http://www.cheekwood.org. Head: Dr. John Wetenhall
Fine Arts Museum - 1960
American art , contemporary art and sculpture, american and english decorative arts - library 38719

Country Music Hall of Fame and Museum, 222 Fifth Av S, Nashville, TN 37203 - T: (615) 416-2001, Fax: (615) 255-2245, Internet: http://www.country-musichalloffame.com. Head: Kyle Young
Music Museum - 1964
Country music and historic recording studio 38720

Cumberland Science Museum, 800 Fort Negley Blvd, Nashville, TN 37203 - T: (615) 862-5160, Fax: (615) 862-5178, Internet: http://www.csmisfun.com. Head: Toni Payne, Beth Johnson, B. Matthews
Natural History Museum / Science&Tech Museum - 1944
Natural science, technology - planetarium 38721

Disciples of Christ Historical Society Museum, 1101 19th Av S, Nashville, TN 37212-2196 - T: (615) 327-1444, Fax: (615) 327-1445, E-mail: dishistsoc@aol.com, Internet: http://users.aol.com/dishistsoc. Head: Peter M. Morgan
Religious Arts Museum - 1941
Religious hist 38722

The Fisk University Galleries, Fisk University, 1000 17th Av N, Nashville, TN 37208-3051 - T: (615) 329-8720, 329-8500, Fax: (615) 329-8544. Head: John L. Smith, Opal K.C. Baker
Fine Arts Museum / University Museum - 1949
African, American and European art - Aaron Douglas gallery, Carl van Vechten gallery 38723

Fisk University Galleries, 1000 17th Av N, Nashville, TN 37203-3051 - T: (615) 329-8720, Fax: (615) 329-8544, E-mail: obaker@fisk.edu, Internet: http://www.fisk.edu. Head: Opal Baker
Fine Arts Museum - 1949
African and American art, paintings, drawings, folk art - library 38724

Hartzler-Towner Multicultural Museum, 1104 19th Av, Nashville, TN 37212 - T: (615) 340-7481, Fax: (615) 340-7463, E-mail: museum@scarrittbennett.org, Internet: http://www.scarritt-bennett.org. Head: Herschel Parker
Decorative Arts Museum / Ethnology Museum - 1992
Anthropology 38725

The Parthenon, 2600 West End Av, Nashville, TN 37203 - T: (615) 862-8431, Fax: (615) 880-2265, E-mail: info@parthenon.org, Internet: http://www.parthenon.org. Head: Wesley M. Paine
Fine Arts Museum - 1897
Cowan coll, paintings, artworks 38726

Tennessee State Museum, 505 Deaderick St, Nashville, TN 37243-1120 - T: (615) 741-2692, Fax: (615) 741-7231, E-mail: info@tnmuseum.org, Internet: http://www.tnmuseum.org. Head: Lois S. Riggins-Ezzell
Historical Museum - 1937
State history and art, military history - library 38727

Travellers Rest Historic House Museum, 636 Farrell Pkwy, Nashville, TN 37220 - T: (615) 832-8197, Fax: (615) 832-8169, E-mail: travrest@mindspring.com, Internet: http://www.travellersrest-plantation.org. Head: Jeri Hasselbring
Local Museum - 1955
Local hist 38728

Upper Room Chapel Museum, 1908 Grand Av, Nashville, TN 37212 - T: (615) 340-7206, Fax: (615) 340-7293, E-mail: kkimball@upperroom.org, Internet: http://www.upperroom.org
Religious Arts Museum / Fine Arts Museum - 1953
Bibles from 1577, woodcarving of Da Vinci's last supper, furniture, antiquites, religious art, African, Asian, Arfo-American and African Indian art 38729

Vanderbilt University Fine Arts Gallery, Vanderbilt University, 23rd & W End Avs, Nashville, TN 37203 - T: (615) 322-0605, 343-1704, Fax: (615) 343-3786, E-mail: gallery@vanderbilt.edu, Internet: http://www.vanderbilt.edu/Ans/finearts/gallery.html. Head: Joseph S. Mella
Fine Arts Museum / University Museum - 1961
Asian art, old master print, Italian renaissance painting, Oriental art, rare books - Arts library 38730

Natchez MS

Grand Village of the Natchez Indians, 400 Jefferson Davis Blvd, Natchez, MS 39120 - T: (601) 446-6502, Fax: (601) 446-6503, E-mail: gvni@bkbank.com, Internet: http://mdah.state.ms.us. Head: James F. Barnett
Ethnology Museum / Archaeological Museum - 1976
1700-1730 Natchez Indian ceremonial mound center 38731

Rosalie House Museum, 100 Orleans St, Natchez, MS 39120 - T: (601) 445-4555, Fax: (601) 445-9137, E-mail: manager@rosalie.net, Internet: http://www.rosalie.net. Head: Cheryl Branyan
Historical Museum - 1898
Decorative arts, architecture, family life - historic garden 38732

Natchitoches LA

Bishop Martin Museum, Second and Church Sts, Natchitoches, LA 71457 - T: (318) 352-3422. Head: Kenneth J. Roy
Religious Arts Museum - 1839
Immaculate Conception Church and Rectory 38733

Fort Saint Jean Baptiste, 130 Moreau, Natchitoches, LA 71457 - T: (318) 357-3101, Fax: (318) 357-7055, E-mail: ftstjean@crt.state.la.us, Internet: http://www.crt.state.la.us/crt/parks/ftstjean.html. Head: James Prud'Homme
Historic Site - 1982
Reconstruction of 1732 fort and several bldgs 38734

Naturita CO

Rimrocker Historical Museum of West Montrose County, Town Park, N of Main St, Naturita, CO 81422, mail addr: POB 913, Nucla, CO 81424 - T: (970) 865-2877, E-mail: cookib@aol.com. Head: Mary Helen de Koevend
Local Museum - 1980
Regional history 38735

Nauvoo IL

Joseph Smith Historic Center, 149 Water St, Nauvoo, IL 62354 - T: (217) 453-2246, Fax: (217) 453-6416, E-mail: jshisctr@nauvoo.net, Internet: http://www.joseph-smith.com. Head: Erik I. Hansen
Historical Museum - 1918
Joseph Smith Homestead, Joseph Smith Red Brick Store, Joseph Smith Mansion House 38736

Nauvoo Historical Society Museum, Nauvoo State Park, Nauvoo, IL 62354 - T: (217) 453-6355, Fax: (217) 453-2512
Local Museum - 1953
Local history 38737

Nazareth PA

Whitefield House Museum, Moravian Historical Society, 214 E. Center St, Nazareth, PA 18064 - T: (610) 759-5070, Fax: (610) 759-2461, Internet: http://www.moravianhistoricalsociety.org. Head: Susan M. Dreydoppel
Local Museum / Religious Arts Museum - 1857
Local hist 38738

Nebraska City NE

Arbor Lodge State Historical Park, RR 2, Centennial Av, Nebraska City, NE 68410 - T: (402) 873-7222. Head: Mark Kemper
Historical Museum - 1923 38739

Wildwood Center, Steinhart Park Rd, Nebraska City, NE 68410 - T: (402) 873-6340. Head: Richard B. Wearne
Historical Museum - 1967 38740

Neenah WI

Bergstrom-Mahler Museum, 165 N Park Av, Neenah, WI 54956 - T: (920) 751-4658, 751-4670, Fax: (920) 751-4755. Head: Alex D. Vance
Fine Arts Museum / Decorative Arts Museum - 1954
Art 38741

Neeses SC

Neeses Farm Museum, 6449 Savannah Hwy, Neeses, SC 29107 - T: (803) 247-5811, Fax: (803) 247-5811. Head: Henry Gleaton
Agriculture Museum - 1976
Native American artifacts, pottery, clothing 38742

Neligh NE

Antelope County Historical Museum, Hwy 275, Neligh, NE 68756 - T: (402) 887-4275. Head: Alta J. DeCamp
Local Museum - 1965 38743

Nelsonville OH

Hocking Valley Museum of Theatrical History, 34 Public Sq, Nelsonville, OH 45764 - T: (740) 753-1924. Head: Frederick L. Oremus
Performing Arts Museum - 1978 38744

Neosho MO

Crowder College-Longwell Museum and Camp Crowder Collection, 601 La Clede, Neosho, MO 64850 - T: (417) 451-3223 ext 201, Fax: (417) 451-4280, Internet: http://www.crowder.cc.mo.us. Head: Lori L. Marble
Fine Arts Museum / University Museum - 1970 38745

Neptune NJ

Neptune Township Historical Museum, 25 Neptune Blvd, Neptune, NJ 07754-1125 - T: (732) 775-8241 exe 306, Fax: (732) 774-1132, E-mail: nept_mus@hotmail.com, Internet: http://www.mon.edu/irs/library/melon/neptune/neptune.htm. Head: Evelyn Stryker Lewis
Historical Museum - 1971
Cherokee based Sand Hill Indians, Antarctic explorer Schlossbach, regional history - library 38746

Township of Neptune Hisctorical Museum → Neptune Township Historical Museum

Nevada MO

Bushwhacker Museum, 231 N Main St, Nevada, MO 64772 - T: (417) 667-9602, Fax: (417) 667-5671, E-mail: info@bushwhacker.org, Internet: http://www.bushwhacker.org. Head: Joe C. Kraft
Local Museum / Historical Museum - 1964 38747

Nevada City CA

Firehouse Museum, 214 Main St, Nevada City, CA 95959 - T: (916) 265-5468
Historical Museum - 1947
Relicts of the Donner Party, clothing, furnishings 38748

Miners Foundry Cultural Center, 325 Spring St, Nevada City, CA 95959 - T: (916) 265-5040, Fax: (916) 265-5462. Head: Ellen Davis
Science&Tech Museum - 1989
Mining 38749

Nevada County Historical Society Museum, POB 1300, Nevada City, CA 95959 - T: (530) 265-5468, E-mail: jrose@telis.org, Internet: http://www.nccn.net
Historical Museum - 1945 38750

Transportation Exhibits, First Pioneer Park, Nevada City, CA 95959 - T: (916) 265-5910. Head: Doris Foley
Science&Tech Museum
Railroad cars, beer wagons, old vehicles 38751

New Albany IN

Culbertson Mansion, 914 E Main St, New Albany, IN 47150 - T: (812) 944-9600, Fax: (812) 949-6134, E-mail: culbertson@disknet.com. Head: Joellen Bye
Historical Museum - 1976
W.S. Culbertson Home, a 25-room Victorian mansion 38752

Floyd County Museum, 201 E Spring St, New Albany, IN 47150 - T: (812) 944-7336, Fax: (812) 981-3544. Head: Sally Newkirk
Fine Arts Museum / Local Museum - 1971
Local history, art gallery 38753

New Albany MS

Union County Heritage Museum, 112 Cleveland St, New Albany, MS 38652 - T: (601) 538-0014. Head: Betsy Hamilton
Local Museum - 1991
Local history 38754

New Bedford MA

New Bedford Whaling Museum, 18 Johnny Cake Hill, New Bedford, MA 02740 - T: (508) 997-0046 ext 10, Fax: (508) 997-0018, E-mail: whaling@ma.ultranet.com, Internet: http://www.whalingmuseum.org
Natural History Museum / Local Museum - 1903
Whaling, history 38755

Rotch-Jones-Duff House and Garden Museum, 396 County St, New Bedford, MA 02740 - T: (508) 997-1401, Fax: (508) 997-6846, E-mail: info@rjdmuseum.org, Internet: http://www.rjdmuseum.org. Head: Kate Corkum
Historical Museum - 1984 38756

New Berlin WI

The New Berlin Historical Society Museum, 19765 W National Av, New Berlin, WI 53146 - T: (262) 542-4773
Historical Museum - 1965
Local hist - Restored 1890's local home, school house room of 1863, 1850's Pioneer log home, carriage barn 38757

New Bern NC

Attmore-Oliver House, 510 Pollock St, New Bern, NC 28560 - T: (252) 638-8558, Fax: (252) 638-5773, E-mail: nbhistoricalsoc@coastalnet.com, Internet: http://www.hiddencoast.com/historicnewbern. Head: Joanne Gwaltney
Historical Museum - 1923 38758

New Bern Firemen's Museum, 408 Hancock St, New Bern, NC 28560 - T: (252) 636-4087, Fax: (252) 636-1084, E-mail: firechief-nb@admin.ci.new-bern.nc.us, Internet: http://www4.coastalnet.com/newbern/psafepg6.htm. Head: Bobby Aster
Special Museum - 1955 38759

Tryon Palace, 610 Pollock St, New Bern, NC 28562 - T: (252) 514-4900, Fax: (252) 514-4876, E-mail: tryon_palace@coastalnet.com, Internet: http://www.tryonpalace.org. Head: Kay P. Williams
Historical Museum - 1945 38760

New Braunfels TX

Children's Museum in New Braunfels, New Braunfels Market Pl, New Braunfels, TX 78130 - T: (830) 620-0939, Fax: (830) 606-5724, E-mail: watteam@watteam.org, Internet: http://www.watteam.org. Head: Juli Swift
Special Museum - 1986 38761

Sophienburg Museum, 401 W Coll St, New Braunfels, TX 78130 - T: (830) 629-1572, 629-1900, Fax: (830) 629-3906, E-mail: gertxhst@sat.net, Internet: http://www.new-braunfels.com/sophienburg. Head: Bennie Bock, Michelle Oatman
Local Museum - 1926
Local hist 38762

New Brighton PA

The Merrick Art Gallery, 1100 5th Av, New Brighton, PA 15066 - T: (412) 846-1130, Fax: (724) 846-0413. Head: Cynthia A. Kundar
Fine Arts Museum - 1880
Art 38763

New Britain CT

Museum of Central Connecticut State University, Art Dept, Samuel S.T. Chen Art Center, New Britain, CT 06050 - T: (860) 832-2633, Fax: (860) 832-2634. Head: James Buxton, Rachel Siporin
University Museum / Fine Arts Museum - 1965 38764

New Britain Museum of American Art, 56 Lexington St, New Britain, CT 06052 - T: (860) 229-0257, Fax: (860) 229-3445, E-mail: n@nbmaa.ccsu.edu. Head: Laurene Buckley
Fine Arts Museum - 1903 38765

New Britain Youth Museum, 30 High St, New Britain, CT 06051 - T: (860) 225-3020, Fax: (860) 229-4982, E-mail: nbymdwtn@portone.com. Head: Deborah Pfeiffenberger
Special Museum - 1956 38766

New Brunswick NJ

Buccleuch Mansion, Buccleuch Park, Easton Av, New Brunswick, NJ 08901 - T: (732) 745-5094, E-mail: skenen@telcordia.com. Head: Susan Kenen
Historical Museum / Decorative Arts Museum - 1915 38767

Henry Guest House, 58 Livingston Av, New Brunswick, NJ 08901 - T: (732) 745-5106, Fax: (732) 846-0226. Head: Robert Belvin
Historical Museum - 1760 38768

Hungarian Heritage Center Museum, 300 Somerset St, New Brunswick, NJ 08903 - T: (732) 846-5777, Fax: (732) 249-7033, E-mail: info@ahfoundation.org, Internet: http://www.ahfoundation.org. Head: August J. Molnar
Fine Arts Museum / Folklore Museum - 1954 38769

Jane Voorhees Zimmerli Art Museum, Rutgers State University of New Jersey, New Brunswick, NJ 08901-1248 - T: (732) 932-7237 ext 610, Fax: (732) 932-8201, Internet: http://www.zimmerlimuseum.rutgers.edu. Head: Phillip Dennis Cate
Fine Arts Museum / University Museum - 1966
art library 38770

New Canaan CT

New Canaan Historical Society Museum, 13 Oenoke Ridge, New Canaan, CT 06840 - T: (203) 966-1776, Fax: (203) 972-5917, E-mail: -newcanaan.historical@snet.net, Internet: http://www.nchistory.org. Head: Janet Lindstrom
Local Museum / Historical Museum - 1889 38771

New Canaan Nature Center, 144 Oenoke Ridge, New Canaan, CT 06840 - T: (203) 966-9577, Fax: (203) 966-6536, E-mail: newcanaannature.org, Internet: http://www.newcanaannature.org. Head: Dilip A. Das, Joseph Merrill
Natural History Museum - 1960 38772

Silvermine Guild Arts Center, 1037 Silvermine Rd, New Canaan, CT 06840 - T: (203) 966-9700, Fax: (203) 972-7236, E-mail: sgac@silvermineart.org, Internet: http://www.silvermineart.org. Head: Cynthia Clair
Fine Arts Museum - 1922 38773

New Castle DE

New Castle Historical Society Museum, 4th and Delaware St, New Castle, DE 19720 - T: (302) 322-2794, Fax: (302) 322-8923. Head: Bruce Dalleo
Local Museum - 1934
Local hist 38774

New Castle IN

Henry County Historical Museum, 606 S 14th St, New Castle, IN 47362 - T: (765) 529-4028, E-mail: hchisoc@kiva.net
Local Museum / Historical Museum - 1887
Home of Civil War General William Grose 38775

Indiana Basketball Hall of Fame, 408 Trojan Ln, New Castle, IN 47362 - T: (765) 529-1891, Fax: (765) 529-0273, E-mail: inbkbhof@cioe.com, Internet: http://www.hoopshall.com. Head: Roger Dickinson
Special Museum - 1965 38776

New Castle PA

Hoyt Institute of Fine Arts, 124 E Leasure Av, New Castle, PA 16101 - T: (724) 652-2882, Fax: (724) 657-8786, E-mail: hoyt@lcix.net. Head: Kimberly B. Koller-Jones
Fine Arts Museum - 1965
Art 38777

New City NY

Historical Society of Rockland County Museum, 20 Zukor Rd, New City, NY 10956 - T: (914) 634-9629, Fax: (914) 634-8690, E-mail: hsrockland@aol.com. Head: Sarah E. Henrich
Local Museum - 1965 38778

New Glarus WI

Chalet of the Golden Fleece, 618 2nd St, New Glarus, WI 53574 - T: (608) 527-2614, Fax: (608) 527-2062
Local Museum - 1955
Historic house 38779

Swiss Historical Village, 612 7th Av, New Glarus, WI 53574 - T: (608) 527-2317. Head: Bradley L. Beal
Local Museum / Open Air Museum - 1938
Historic village 38780

New Gloucester ME

Shaker Museum, 707 Shaker Rd, New Gloucester, ME 04260 - T: (207) 926-4597, Internet: http://www.shaker.lib.me.us. Head: Leonard L. Brooks
Historic Site - 1931
Religion, Shaker religious community - library 38781

New Harbor ME

Colonial Pemaquid Historical Site, New Harbor, ME 04554 - T: (207) 677-2423
Archaeological Museum - 1970
Archaeological dig site 38782

New Harmony IN

Historic New Harmony, 506 1/2 Main St, New Harmony, IN 47631 - T: (812) 682-4488, Fax: (812) 682-4313, E-mail: harmony@usi.edu, Internet: http://www.newharmony.org. Head: Connie Weinzapfel
Historic Site - 1973
American history, early natural science, early abolition, early women's movement 38783

New Harmony Gallery of Contemporary Art, University of Southern Indiana, 506 Main St, New Harmony, IN 47631 - T: (812) 682-3156, Fax: (812) 682-4313, E-mail: mhambly@usi.edu. Head: Blake Cook
Fine Arts Museum - 1975 38784

New Harmony State Historic Site, 410 Main St, New Harmony, IN 47631 - T: (812) 682-3271, Fax: (812) 682-5526, E-mail: newharmonyshs@dynasty.net,

Internet: http://www.ai.org/ism. Head: Richard Gantz
Historical Museum - 1937
Site of two early utopian experiments, the communal societies of New Harmony 38785

New Haven CT

John Slade Ely House, 51 Trumbull St, New Haven, CT 06510 - T: (203) 624-8055. Head: Paul Clabby, Dolores Gall
Fine Arts Museum - 1960 38786

Knights of Columbus Headquarters Museum, 1 Columbus Plaza, New Haven, CT 06510-3326 - T: (203) 772-2130, Internet: http://www.kofc-supreme-council.org. Head: Virgil C. Dechant
Historical Museum / Religious Arts Museum - 1982 38787

New Haven Colony Historical Society Museum, 114 Whitney Av, New Haven, CT 06510 - T: (203) 562-4183, Fax: (203) 562-2002, E-mail: dcarter@nhchs.org. Head: Peter Lemon, Bruce Perloth
Local Museum - 1862 38788

Peabody Museum of Natural History, Yale University, 170 Whitney Av, New Haven, CT 06520-8118 - T: (203) 432-5050, Fax: (203) 432-9816, Internet: http://www.peabody.yale.edu. Head: Richard L. Burger
University Museum / Natural History Museum - 1866
Anthropology, paleontology, mineralogy, paleobotany, vertebrates, invertebrates, otnitology, entomology, zoology, botany, meteorits, historic scientific instr. 38789

Yale Center for British Art, 1080 Chapel St, New Haven, CT 06520-8280 - T: (203) 432-2800, Fax: (203) 432-9695, E-mail: bacinfo@yale.edu, Internet: http://www.yale.edu/ycba. Head: Constance Clement
Fine Arts Museum / University Museum - 1977 38790

Yale University Art Gallery, 1111 Chapel St, New Haven, CT 06520 - T: (203) 432-0660, Fax: (204) 432-7159 and 8150, Internet: http://www.cis.yale.edu.edu/yups/yuag. Head: Jack Reynolds
Fine Arts Museum / University Museum - 1832 38791

Yale University Collection of Musical Instruments, 15 Hillhouse Av, New Haven, CT 06520 - T: (203) 432-0822, Fax: (203) 432-8342, E-mail: musinst@pantheon.yale.edu, Internet: http://www.yale.edu/musicalinstruments. Head: Richard Rephann
University Museum / Music Museum - 1900 38792

New Holstein WI

Calumet County Historical Society Museum, 1704 Eisenhower St, New Holstein, WI 53061 - T: (920) 898-1333
Local Museum / Agriculture Museum - 1963
Farming 38793

Pioneer Corner Museum, 2103 Main St, New Holstein, WI 53061 - T: (414) 898-5258. Head: Wendy Cramer
Local Museum - 1961
Local hist 38794

New Hope PA

Lockhouse-Friends of the Delaware Canal, 145 S Main St, New Hope, PA 18938 - T: (215) 862-2021, Fax: (215) 862-2021, E-mail: fodc@erols.com, Internet: http://www.fodc.org. Head: Susan H. Taylor
Local Museum - 1991 38795

Parry Mansion Museum, 45 S Main St, New Hope, PA 18938 - T: (215) 862-5652, 794-5260, Fax: (215) 862-5652
Decorative Arts Museum - 1966
Decorative arts 38796

New Hyde Park NY

Goudreau Museum of Mathematics in Art and Science, Herricks Community Center, 999 Herricks Rd, New Hyde Park, NY 11040-1353 - T: (516) 747-0777, Fax: (516) 747-0777, E-mail: info@mathmuseum.org, Internet: http://www.mathmuseum.org. Head: Beth J. Deaner
Special Museum - 1980
Mathematics 38797

New Iberia LA

The Shadows-on-the-Teche, 317 E Main St, New Iberia, LA 70560 - T: (337) 369-6446, Fax: (337) 365-5213, E-mail: shadows@shadowsont-heteche.org, Internet: http://www.shadowsont-heteche.org. Head: Patricia Kahle
Historic Site - 1961
Plantation home 38798

New Ipswich NH

Barrett House, Forest Hall, Main St, New Ipswich, NH 03071 - T: (603) 878-2517, Fax: (617) 227-9204, Internet: http://www.spnea.org
Historical Museum - 1948 38799

New London CT

Lyman Allyn Art Museum, 625 Williams St, New London, CT 06320 - T: (860) 443-2545, Fax: (860) 442-1280, Internet: http://www.lymanallyn.-conncoll.edu. Head: Charles A. Shepard
Fine Arts Museum - 1930 38800

New London County Historical Society Museum, 11 Blinman St, New London, CT 06320 - T: (860) 443-1209, Fax: (860) 443-1209, E-mail: nlchsinc@aol.com. Head: Alice Sheriff
Local Museum / Historical Museum - 1870 38801

United States Coast Guard Museum, US Coast Guard Academy, 15 Mohegan Av, New London, CT 06320-4195 - T: (860) 444-8511, Fax: (860) 444-8289, E-mail: cherrick@cga.uscg.mil, Internet: http://www.dot.gov/dotinfo/uscg/welcome.html
Historical Museum - 1967 38802

New London NH

New London Historical Society Museum, Little Sunapee Rd, New London, NH 03257-0965 - T: (603) 526-6564. Head: Richard E. Little
Historical Museum - 1954 38803

New London WI

New London Public Museum, 406 S Pearl St, New London, WI 54961 - T: (920) 982-8520. Head: Melvin C. Riley
Local Museum - 1917
Local hist 38804

New Madrid MO

Hunter-Dawson State Historic Site, Dawson Rd, Hwy U, New Madrid, MO 63869 - T: (573) 748-5340, Fax: (573) 748-7228, E-mail: dsphunt@mail.dnr.state.mo.us. Head: Michael Comer
Historic Site - 1967 38805

New Market VA

New Market Battlefield Historical Park, POB 1864, New Market, VA 22844 - T: (540) 740-3101, Fax: (540) 740-3033, E-mail: nmbshpl@shentel.net, Internet: http://www.vmi.edu/museum/nm. Head: Keith E. Gibson
Historic Site / Military Museum - 1967
Military hist 38806

New Milford CT

New Milford Historical Society Museum, 6 Aspetuck Av, New Milford, CT 06776 - T: (860) 354-3069, Internet: http://www.nmhistorical.org
Historical Museum - 1915 38807

New Orleans LA

Academy Gallery, New Orleans Academy of Fine Arts, 5256 Magazine St, New Orleans, LA 70115 - T: (504) 899-8111, Fax: (504) 897-6811, E-mail: noafa@bellsouth.com, Internet: http://www.noafa.com. Head: Dorothy J Coleman
Fine Arts Museum - 1978 38808

Beauregard-Keyes House, 1113 Chartres St, New Orleans, LA 70116 - T: (504) 523-7257, Fax: (504) 523-7257. Head: Marion S. Chambon
Historical Museum - 1970
Louisiana raised cottage, home of Gen. P.G.T. Beauregard and Frances Parkinson Keyes 38809

Confederate Museum, 929 Camp St, New Orleans, LA 70130 - T: (504) 523-4522, Fax: (504) 523-8595, E-mail: memhall@aol.com, Internet: http://www.confederatemuseum.com. Head: Pat Ricci
Military Museum - 1891
Military, housed in 1890 Memorial Hall 38810

Contemporary Arts Center, 900 Camp St, New Orleans, LA 70130 - T: (504) 528-3805, Fax: (504) 528-3828, E-mail: mshalett@cacno.org, Internet: http://www.cacno.org. Head: Jay Weigel
Fine Arts Museum / Public Gallery - 1976
Art 38811

Gallier House, 1118-32 Royal St, New Orleans, LA 70116 - T: (504) 525-5661, Fax: (504) 568-9735, E-mail: hgrimagallier@aol.com, Internet: http://www.gnofn.org/~hggh. Head: Stephen A. Moses
Local Museum - 1969
Decorative arts 38812

Hermann-Grima House, 820 Saint Louis St, New Orleans, LA 70112 - T: (504) 525-5661, Fax: (504) 568-9735, E-mail: hgrimagallier@aol.com, Internet: http://www.gnofn.org/~hggh. Head: Stephen A. Moses
Local Museum - 1971
Early example of American influence on New Orleans architecture 38813

The Historic New Orleans Collection, 533 Royal St, New Orleans, LA 70130 - T: (504) 523-4662, Fax: (504) 598-7108, E-mail: hnocinfo@hnoc.org, Internet: http://www.hnoc.org. Head: Priscilla O'Reilly-Lawrence, John H. Lawrence
Historical Museum - 1966
Hist and culture of Louisiana and Gulf South 38814

Jean Lafitte National Historical Park and Preserve, 365 Canal St, Ste 2400, New Orleans, LA 70130-1142 - T: (504) 589-3882, Fax: (504) 589-3851, E-mail: kathy_lang@nps.gov, Internet: http://www.nps.gov/jela
Military Museum - 1978
Military, site of decisive battle between American and British forces in War of 1812 38815

Louisiana Children's Museum, 420 Julia St, New Orleans, LA 70130 - T: (504) 586-0725, Fax: (504) 529-3666, Internet: http://www.lcm.org. Head: Julia W. Bland
Special Museum - 1981 38816

Louisiana State Museum, 751 Chartres St, New Orleans, LA 70116 - T: (800) 568-6968, Fax: (504) 568-4995, E-mail: cbrown@crt.state.la.us, Internet: http://www.crt.state.la.us/crt/museum/ismnet.htm. Head: James F. Sefcik
Historical Museum - 1906
History, decorative arts, costume, textiles, maps, manuscripts, aviation 38817

New Orleans Museum of Art, 1 Collins Diboll Circle, New Orleans, LA 70124 - T: (504) 488-2631, Fax: (504) 484-6662, E-mail: webmaster@noma.org, Internet: http://www.noma.org. Head: E. John Bullard
Fine Arts Museum - 1910
Art, decorative art, paintings, photos 38818

New Orleans Pharmacy Museum, 514 Rue Chartres, New Orleans, LA 70130-2110 - T: (504) 565-8027, Fax: (504) 565-8028, E-mail: nopharmsm@aol.com, Internet: htpp://www.pharmacymuseum.org
Historical Museum - 1950
Pharmacy, medicine, Louis Joseph Dufilho, Jr., first licensed pharmacist in the U.S 38819

Newcomb Art Gallery, Woldenberg Art Center, Tulane University, New Orleans, LA 70118-5698 - T: (504) 865-5328, Fax: (504) 865-5329, E-mail: smain@tulane.edu, Internet: http://www.tulane.edu/~gallery. Head: Erik Neil
Fine Arts Museum / University Museum - 1886
Art, Newcomb pottery, painting, sculpture, photography 38820

Pitot House Museum, 1440 Moss St, New Orleans, LA 70119 - T: (504) 482-0312, Fax: (504) 482-0312, Internet: http://www.neworleans.com/museum/pitot/
Historical Museum - 1964
1799 French West Indies Plantation style house 38821

Tulane University Art Collection, Tulane University, 7001 Freret St, New Orleans, LA 70118 - T: (504) 865-5685, Fax: (504) 865-5761. Head: Joan G. Caldwell
Fine Arts Museum / University Museum - 1980 38822

New Paltz NY

College Art Gallery → Samuel Dorsky Museum of Art

Huguenot Historical Society Museum, 18 Broadhead Av, New Paltz, NY 12561-1403 - T: (845) 255-1660, Fax: (845) 255-0376, E-mail: hhsoffice@hhs-newpaltz.org, Internet: http://www.hhs-newpaltz.org. Head: John H. Braunlein
Local Museum - 1894
History, architecture, decorative arts - archives 38823

Samuel Dorsky Museum of Art, c/o State University of New York New Paltz, 75 S Manheim Blvd, New Paltz, NY 12561 - T: (914) 257-3844, Fax: (914) 257-3854, E-mail: tragern@matrix.newpaltz.edu, Internet: http://www.newpaltz.edu/museum. Head: Neil C. Trager
Fine Arts Museum / University Museum - 1963
Regional art, photographs, metals, Asian prints, 20th c works on paper 38824

New Philadelphia OH

Schoenbrunn Village State Memorial, State Rte 259, New Philadelphia, OH 44663 - T: (330) 339-3636, Fax: (330) 339-4165, E-mail: schoenbrunn@tusco.net, Internet: http://www.ohiohistory.org/places/schoenbr/index.html. Head: Dr. Gary C. Ness
Open Air Museum / Local Museum - 1923 38825

New Port Richey FL

West Pasco Historical Society Museum, 6431 Circle Blvd, New Port Richey, FL 34652 - T: (727) 847-0680, E-mail: wb2ium@att.net. Head: David Prace
Local Museum - 1983
Local history 38826

New Roads LA

Pointe Coupee Museum, 8348 False River Rd, New Roads, LA 70760 - T: (225) 638-7788, Fax: (504) 638-5555. Head: Olinde S. Haag
Historical Museum - 1976 38827

New Sweden ME

Lars Noak Blacksmith Shop, Larsson/Ostlund Log Home & One-Room Capitol School, Station Rd, New Sweden, ME 04762 - T: (207) 896-5624, 896-3199, Fax: (207) 896-5624. Head: Alwin Espling, Linnea Helstrom, Ralph Ostlund
Local Museum / Open Air Museum - 1989
Historic village 38828

New Sweden Historical Museum, 110 Station Rd, New Sweden, ME 04762 - T: (207) 896-3018, 896-5843. Head: Carolyn Hildebrand
Local Museum - 1925
Local history 38829

New Ulm MN

Brown County Historical Society Museum, 2 N Broadway, New Ulm, MN 56073-1714 - T: (507) 233-2616, Fax: (507) 354-1068, E-mail: bchs@newulmtel.net, Internet: http://www.ic.new-ulm.mn.us/tour/museum.html. Head: Robert Burgess
Local Museum - 1930 38830

New York NY

Abigail Adams Smith Museum → Mount Vernon Hotel Museum

Abrons Arts Center, Henry Street Settlement, 466 Grand St, New York, NY 10002 - T: (212) 598-0400, Fax: (212) 505-8329, Internet: http://www.henrystreetarts.org. Head: Susan Fleminger
Public Gallery
Contemporary Art - photo gallery 38831

Air Gallery, 40 Wooster St, New York, NY 10013 - T: (212) 966-0799, Fax: (212) 941-7508, E-mail: airinfo@airnyc.org. Head: Dena Muller
Fine Arts Museum - 1972 38832

Alternative Museum, 594 Broadway, Ste 402, New York, NY 10012 - T: (212) 966-4444, Fax: (212) 226-2158, E-mail: altmuseum@aol.com, Internet: http://www.alternativemuseum.org. Head: Geno Rodriguez
Fine Arts Museum - 1975 38833

American Academy of Arts and Letters Art Museum, 633 W 155 St, New York, NY 10032-7599 - T: (212) 368-5900, Fax: (212) 491-4615. Head: Virginia Dajani, Louis S. Auchincloss
Fine Arts Museum - 1898 38834

American Bible Society Gallery → Gallery at the American Bible Society

American Craft Museum, 40 W 53 St, New York, NY 10019 - T: (212) 956-3535, Fax: (212) 459-0926, E-mail: ursula.neuman@americancraftmuseum.org, Internet: http://www.americancraftmuseum.org. Head: Holly Hotchner
Fine Arts Museum / Decorative Arts Museum - 1956
Crafts, design, decorative arts 38835

American Folk Art Museum, 45 W 53rd St, New York, NY 10019 - T: (212) 595-9533, 977-7170 ext 309, Fax: (212) 977-8134, E-mail: sflamm@folkartmuseum.org, Internet: http://www.folkartmuseum.org. Head: Gerard C. Wertkin
Folklore Museum - 2001 38836

American Irish Historical Society Museum, 991 Fifth Av, New York, NY 10028 - T: (212) 288-2263, Fax: (212) 628-7927, E-mail: amerirish@earthlink.net, Internet: http://www.aihs.org. Head: William Cobert
Historical Museum - 1897 38837

American Jewish Historical Museum, 15 W 16th St, New York, NY 10001 - T: (212) 294-6160, Fax: (212) 294-6161, E-mail: ajhs@ajhs.org, Internet: http://www.ajhs.org. Head: Ken Bialkin, Michael Feldberg
Folklore Museum / Religious Arts Museum - 1892
Ethnic history 38838

American Museum of Natural History, Central Park W at 79 St, New York, NY 10024 - T: (212) 769-5000, Fax: (212) 496-5018, E-mail: postmaster@amnh.org, Internet: http://www.amnh.org
Natural History Museum - 1869 38839

American Numismatic Society Museum, Broadway and 155 St, New York, NY 10032 - T: (212) 234-3130, Fax: (212) 324-3381, E-mail: info@amnumsoc.org, Internet: http://www.amnumsoc2.org. Head: Ute Wartenberg
Special Museum - 1858 38840

Americas Society Art Gallery, 680 Park Av, New York, NY 10021 - T: (212) 249-8950, Fax: (212) 249-5868, E-mail: exhibitions@as-coa.org, Internet: http://www.americas-society.org. Head: Elizabeth A. Beim, Yona Backer
Fine Arts Museum - 1967 38841

Amos Eno Gallery, 59 Franklin St, New York, NY 10012 - T: (212) 226-5342. Head: Jane Harris
Fine Arts Museum
Contemporary art 38842

Angel Orensanz Foundation, 172 Norfolk St, New York, NY 10002 - T: (212) 780-0175
Public Gallery 38843

Arsenal Gallery, Arsenal Bldg, Fifth Av at 64th St, New York, NY 10021 - T: (212) 360-8163, Fax: (212) 360-1329, E-mail: Adian.Sas@parks.nyc.gov, Internet: http://www.nyc.gov/parks. Head: Adrian Sas
Natural History Museum
Mixed media-park and nature themes 38844

Asia Society Galleries, 725 Park Av, New York, NY 10021 - T: (212) 288-6400, Fax: (212) 517-7246, E-mail: pr@asiasoc.org, Internet: http://www.asiasociety.org. Head: Vishakha N. Desai, Nicholas Platt
Fine Arts Museum - 1956 38845

Asian-American Arts Centre, 26 Bowery, New York, NY 10013 - T: (212) 233-2154, Fax: (212) 766-1287, E-mail: aaartsctr@aol.com, Internet: http://www.artspiral.org. Head: Robert Lee
Fine Arts Museum - 1974
Folk art - research library 38846

The Bard Graduate Center for Studies in the Decorative Arts, Design and Culture, 18 W 86th St, New York, NY 10024 - T: (212) 501-3000, Fax: (212) 501-3079, E-mail: Mulligan@BGC.Bard.edu, Internet: http://www.bgc.bard.edu. Head: Dr. Susan Weber Soros
Decorative Arts Museum / University Museum - 1992
Decorative arts 38847

The Bohen Foundation, 120 Wooster St, New York, NY 10012 - T: (212) 334-2281
Public Gallery 38848

Burden Gallery, Aperture Foundation, 20 E 23 St, New York, NY 10010 - T: (212) 505-5555 ext 325, Fax: (212) 979-7759, E-mail: gallery@aperture.org, Internet: http://www.aperture.org. Head: Michael E. Hoffman
Fine Arts Museum - 1952 38849

Cathedral of Saint John the Divine Museum, 1047 Amsterdam Av, New York, NY 10025 - T: (212) 316-7493
Religious Arts Museum - 1974
Old Master Paintings, decorative arts, silver, tapestries, vestments 38850

Center for Book Arts, 28 W 27th St, New York, NY 10001 - T: (212) 481-0295, Fax: (212) 481-9853, E-mail: info@centerforbookarts.org, Internet: http://www.centerforbookarts.org. Head: Rory Golden
Public Gallery - 1974
Book arts 38851

The Chaim Gross Studio Museum, 526 LaGuardia Pl, New York, NY 10012 - T: (212) 529-4906, Fax: (212) 795-0521
Fine Arts Museum - 1989
Sculpture, watercolours, drawings, prints 38852

Chancellor Robert R. Livingston Masonic Library and Museum, 71 W 23 St, New York, NY 10010-4171 - T: (212) 337-6620, Fax: (212) 633-2639, E-mail: livmalib@pipeline.com, Internet: http://www.rpi.edu/~nichot3/masonry/library. Head: William D. Moore
Historical Museum / Library with Exhibitions - 1856 38853

The Chase Manhattan Bank Art Collections, 270 Park Av, New York, NY 10017 - T: (212) 270-0667, Fax: (212) 270-0725. Head: Manuel Gonzalez
Fine Arts Museum - 1959
17.000 largerly contemporary American works in all media 38854

Children's Museum of Manhattan, 212 W 83 St, New York, NY 10024 - T: (212) 721-1223, Fax: (212) 721-1127, E-mail: mail@cmom.org, Internet: http://www.cmom.org
Special Museum - 1973 38855

China Institute Gallery, 125 E 65 St, New York, NY 10021 - T: (212) 744-8181, Fax: (212) 628-4159, E-mail: gallery@chinainstitute.org, Internet: http://www.chinainstitute.org. Head: Hai Chang Willow
Fine Arts Museum - 1926 38856

The Cloisters, Fort Tryon Park, New York, NY 10040 - T: (212) 928-1146, Fax: (212) 928-1146, E-mail: icma@compuserve.com, Internet: http://www.medievalarts.org. Head: Dorothy F. Glass
Fine Arts Museum / Decorative Arts Museum - 1938
Medieval art 38857

The Collectors Club, 22 E 35 St, New York, NY 10016 - T: (212) 683-0559, Fax: (212) 481-1269. Head: Thomas C. Mazza
Local Museum / Library with Exhibitions - 1896
Medals, awards, engravings prints, early postal equipment 38858

Congregation Emanu-el Museum, 1 E 65th St, New York, NY 10021-6596 - T: (212) 744-1400, Fax: (212) 570-0826. Head: Reva G. Kirschberg-Grossman
Historical Museum
Congregational memorabilia, graphics, Judaica, Paintings 38859

Cooper-Hewitt National Design Museum, 2 E 91 St, New York, NY 10128 - T: (212) 849-8400, Fax: (212) 849-8401, Internet: http://www.si.edu/ndm/. Head: Paul Thompson, Susan Yelavich
Decorative Arts Museum - 1897
300.000 works representing a span of 300 years 38860

Dahesh Museum of Art, 601 Fifth Av, New York, NY 10017 - T: (212) 759-0606, Fax: (212) 759-1235, Internet: http://www.daheshmuseum.org. Head: J. David Farmer
Fine Arts Museum - 1995
European Art (19th-20th c) 38861

Department of Art History & Archaeology Visual Resources Collection, 820-825 Schermerhorn Hall, New York, NY 10027 - T: (212) 854-3044, Fax: (212) 854-7329, Internet: http://www.mcah.columbia.edu/vrc/htm/index.htm. Head: Andrew Gessener
Fine Arts Museum
250.000 photographs - Berenson I-Tatti Archive, Dial Iconographic Index, Haseloff Archive, Bartsch Collection, Gaigleres Collection, Arthur Kingsley Porter Collection, Ware Collection, Courtauld Collection, Marburger Index, Windsor Castle, Chatsworth Collection, Millard Meiss Collection 38862

Dia Center for the Arts, 548 W 22 St, New York, NY 10011 - T: (212) 989-5566, Fax: (212) 989-4055, E-mail: info@diacenter.org, Internet: http://www.diacenter.org. Head: Michael Govan
Fine Arts Museum - 1974
Contemporary American/European art 38863

Drawing Center, 35 Wooster St, New York, NY 10013 - T: (212) 219-2166, Fax: (212) 966-2976, E-mail: drawcent@drawingcenter.org, Internet: http://www.drawingcenter.org. Head: Catherine de Zegher
Fine Arts Museum - 1977 38864

Dyckman Farmhouse Museum, 4881 Broadway at 204 St, New York, NY 10034 - T: (212) 304-9422, Fax: (212) 304-9422, E-mail: info@dyckman.org, Internet: http://www.dyckman.org. Head: Allyson Bowen
Historical Museum - 1915 38865

Eldridge Street Project, 12 Eldridge St, New York, NY 10002 - T: (212) 219-0903, Fax: (212) 966-4782, E-mail: contact@eldridgestreet.org, Internet: http://www.eldridgestreet.org. Head: Amy E. Waterman
Folklore Museum / Religious Arts Museum / Historical Museum - 1986
Jewish culture and hist on the Lower East Side 38866

The Equitable Gallery, 787 Seventh Av, South Gallery, New York, NY 10019 - T: (212) 554-2018, Fax: (212) 554-2456, Internet: http://www.axa-financial.com/aboutus/gallery.html. Head: Pari Stave
Fine Arts Museum / Public Gallery - 1992
19th and 20th century paintings, sculpture and works on paper 38867

The Ernest W. Michel Historical Judaica Collection, c/o UJA-Federation of New York, 130 E 59 St, New York, NY 10022 - T: (212) 836-1720, Fax: (212) 755-9183. Head: Stephen D. Solender
Ethnology Museum / Historical Museum - 1995
History 38868

Eva and Morris Feld Gallery, American Folk Art Museum, 2 Lincoln Sq, New York, NY 10023-6214 - T: (212) 595-9533, Fax: (212) 977-8134, Internet: http://www.folkartmuseum.org. Head: Gerard C. Wertkin
Folklore Museum - 1961 38869

Federal Hall National Memorial, 26 Wall St, New York, NY 10005 - T: (212) 825-6888, Fax: (212) 825-6874, Internet: http://www.nps.gov/feha/
Historical Museum - 1939
Memorabilia of George Washington 38870

Fraunces Tavern Museum, 54 Pearl St, New York, NY 10004 - T: (212) 425-1778, Fax: (212) 509-3467, Internet: http://www.francestavern.org. Head: Marion Grzesiak
Historical Museum - 1907
Decorative arts, textiles, paintings, prints, war memorabilia 38871

Frick Collection, 1 E 70 St, New York, NY 10021 - T: (212) 288-0700, Fax: (212) 628-4417, E-mail: info@frick.org, Internet: http://www.frick.org. Head: Samuel Sachs
Fine Arts Museum / Decorative Arts Museum - 1920
Paintings, sculptures, furniture, decorative art, prints 38872

Gallery at the American Bible Society, 1865 Broadway, New York, NY 10023 - T: (212) 408-1500, 408-1333, Fax: (212) 408-1456, E-mail: gallery@americanbible.org, Internet: http://www.americanbible.org. Head: Dr. Ena Heller
Religious Arts Museum - 1816
Art with biblical themes, religious art 38873

Gallery of Prehistoric Paintings, 30 E 81 St, New York, NY 10028 - T: (212) 861-5152. Head: Douglas Mazonowicz
Fine Arts Museum - 1975
Primitive art - Library 38874

Gay Leslie-Lohman Art Foundation, 131 Prince St, New York, NY 10012 - T: (212) 673-7007
Public Gallery 38875

General Grant National Memorial, Riverside Dr and W 122 St, New York, NY 10027 - T: (212) 666-1640, Fax: (212) 932-9631. Head: Joseph T. Avery
Historical Museum - 1897 38876

Gracie Mansion, East End Av at 88 St, New York, NY 10128 - T: (212) 570-4741, Fax: (212) 988-4854
Historical Museum / Decorative Arts Museum - 1981 38877

Grey Art Gallery, New York University, 100 Washington Sq E, New York, NY 10003 - T: (212) 998-6780, Fax: (212) 995-4024, E-mail: greygallery@nyu.edu, Internet: http://www.nyu.edu/greyart. Head: Lynn Gumpert
Fine Arts Museum / University Museum - 1975
Paintings, sculpture, graphics, contemporary Asian and Middle East art 38878

Guggenheim Museum Soho, 575 Broadway, New York, NY 10012 - T: (212) 423-3500, Fax: (212) 941-8410, Internet: http://www.guggenheim.org. Head: Thomas Krens
Fine Arts Museum / Public Gallery - 1992
Late 19th c and 20th c European and American art, esp. paintings, sculptures, works on paper 38879

Hampden-Booth Theatre Museum, 16 Gramercy Park, New York, NY 10003 - T: (212) 228-7610, Fax: (212) 473-2701
Performing Arts Museum - 1888 38880

Hatch-Billops Collections, 491 Broadway, New York, NY 10012 - T: (212) 966-3231, Fax: (212) 966-3231, E-mail: Hatch-Billops@worldnet.att.net. Head: Camille Billops
Fine Arts Museum - 1975
Collection of primary and secondary resource materials in the Black Cultural Arts - Owen & Edith Dodson Memorial Collection 38881

Herbert and Eileen Bernard Museum, 1 E 65th St, New York, NY 10021 - T: (212) 744-1400, Fax: (212) 570-0826, E-mail: info@emanuelnyc.org, Internet: http://www.emanuelnyc.org
Decorative Arts Museum / Folklore Museum / Religious Arts Museum - 1948
Judaica, Congregation Emanu-El of the City of New York 38882

Hispanic Society of America, 155th St and Broadway, New York, NY 10032 - T: (212) 926-2234, Fax: (212) 690-0743, E-mail: info@hispanicsociety.org, Internet: http://www.hispanic-society.org. Head: Mitchell A. Codding
Fine Arts Museum - 1904
Art, sculpture, furniture, ceramics, metalwork, jewellery 38883

Hunter College Art Galleries, 695 Park Av, New York, NY 10021 - T: (212) 772-4991, Fax: (212) 772-4554, Internet: http://www.hunter.cuny.edu/artgalleries. Head: Sanford Warmfeld
Fine Arts Museum / University Museum - 1984 38884

The Interchurch Center, 475 Riverside Dr, Rm 253, New York, NY 10115 - T: (212) 870-2200, Fax: (212) 870-2440, E-mail: Dennis@interchurch-center.org, Internet: http://www.interchurch-center.org. Head: Mary E. McNamara, Sue M. Dennis
Library with Exhibitions - 1959 38885

International Center of Photography, 1133 Av of the Americans and 43rd Street, New York, NY 10036 - T: (212) 860-1777, Fax: (212) 360-6490, E-mail: info@icp.org, Internet: http://www.icp.org. Head: Willis Hartshorn
Special Museum - 1974 38886

Intrepid Sea-Air-Space Museum, W 46 St and 12 Av, New York, NY 10036 - T: (212) 245-2533, Fax: (212) 245-7289, Internet: http://www.intrepidmuseum.org
Military Museum - 1982 38887

ISE Art Foundation, 555 Broadway, New York, NY 10012 - T: (212) 925-1649
Public Gallery 38888

Japan Society Gallery, 333 E 47 St, New York, NY 10017 - T: (212) 832-1155, Fax: (212) 715-1262, E-mail: amunroe@jpnsoc.org, Internet: http://www.jpnsoc.org. Head: Alexandra Munroe
Fine Arts Museum - 1907 38889

The Jewish Museum, 1109 Fifth Av, New York, NY 10128 - T: (212) 423-3200, Fax: (212) 423-3232, E-mail: jewishmus@aol.com, Internet: http://www.thejewishmuseum.org. Head: Joan Rosenbaum
Fine Arts Museum / Historical Museum / Religious Arts Museum - 1904 38890

Judaica Museum of Central Synagogue, 123 E 55 St, New York, NY 10022 - T: (212) 838-5122, Fax: (212) 644-2168. Head: Livia Thompson
Folklore Museum / Religious Arts Museum - 1962
Judaica, 1870-1872 synagogue and community house 38891

Lladro Museum, 43 W 57th St, New York, NY 10019 - T: (212) 838-9352
Fine Arts Museum 38892

The Lowe Gallery at Hudson Guild, 441 W 26 St, New York, NY 10001 - T: (212) 760-9800. Head: James Furlong
Fine Arts Museum - 1948
Contemporary art 38893

Lower East Side Tenement Museum, 90 Orchard St, New York, NY 10002 - T: (212) 431-0233, Fax: (212) 431-0402, E-mail: lestm@tenement.org, Internet: http://www.wnet.org/tenement
Historical Museum - 1988 38894

Main Gallery of Henry Street Settlement, Abrons Arts Center, 466 Grand St, New York, NY 10002 - T: (212) 598-0400, Fax: (212) 505-8329, Internet: http://www.henrystreetarts.org. Head: Barbara L. Tate
Fine Arts Museum / Public Gallery - 1893 38895

Margaret Thatcher Projects, 529 W 20th St, New York, NY 10011 - T: (212) 675-0222, Internet: http://www.mtprojects.addr.com
Fine Arts Museum 38896

Marie Walsh Sharpe Art Foundation, 443 Greenwich St, New York, NY 10013 - T: (212) 925-3008
Fine Arts Museum 38897

Merchant's House Museum, 29 E Fourth St, New York, NY 10003 - T: (212) 777-1089, Fax: (212) 777-1104, E-mail: nyc1832@aol.com, Internet: http://newyork.citysearch.com/e/v/nycny/0001/27/55/. Head: Margaret Halsey Gardiner
Historical Museum - 1936 38898

Metropolitan Museum of Art, 1000 Fifth Av, New York, NY 10028-0198 - T: (212) 879-5500, Fax: (212) 570-3879, E-mail: webmaster@metmuseum.org, Internet: http://metmuseum.org. Head: Philippe de Montebello, David McKinney
Fine Arts Museum - 1870
Ancient and modern art of Egypt, Greece, Rome, Near and Far East, Europe, Africa, Oceania, pre-Columbian cultures, USA 38899

Miriam and Ira D. Wallach Art Gallery, 116th St and Broadway, New York, NY 10027 - T: (212) 854-7288, 854-2877, Fax: (212) 854-7800, Internet: http://www.columbia.edu/cu/wallach. Head: Sarah Elliston Weiner
Fine Arts Museum / University Museum - 1986
Art gallery in 1897 Schermerhorn hall 38900

Morris-Jumel Mansion, 65 Jumel Terrace, New York, NY 10032 - T: (212) 923-8008, Fax: (212) 923-8947. Head: Peter Apgar
Decorative Arts Museum / Historical Museum - 1904 38901

Mount Vernon Hotel Museum, 421 E 61 St, New York, NY 10021 - T: (212) 838-6878, Fax: (212) 838-7390, E-mail: MVHMuseum@aol.com. Head: Amy Northrop Adamo
Local Museum - 1939/2000 38902

Municipal Art Society, 457 Madison Av, New York, NY 10022 - T: (212) 935-3960, Fax: (212) 753-1816, Internet: http://www.mas.org. Head: Kent Barwick
Fine Arts Museum - 1892
Art 38903

El Museo del Barrio, 1230 Fifth Av, New York, NY 10029 - T: (212) 831-7272, Fax: (212) 831-7927, Internet: http://www.elmuseo.org. Head: Susanna Torruella Leval
Fine Arts Museum - 1969
Works on paper, sculptures, prints, paintings, photography, 16 mm films on history, culture and art - junior museum, 510 seat theatre 38904

Museum at the Fashion Institute of Technology, Seventh Av at 27 St, New York, NY 10001-5992 - T: (212) 217-5705, Fax: (212) 217-5973, E-mail: steeleva@fitsuny.edu, Internet: http://www.fitnyc.suny.edu. Head: Dr. Valerie Steele
Special Museum - 1967
Clothing, textiles 38905

Museum for African Art, 593 Broadway, New York, NY 10012 - T: (212) 966-1313, Fax: (212) 966-1432. Head: Frank Herreman
Ethnology Museum / Fine Arts Museum - 1982 38906

Museum Masters International, 185 E 85th St, New York, NY 10028 - T: (212) 410-6981
Fine Arts Museum 38907

Museum of American Financial History, 26 Broadway, New York, NY 10004-1763 - T: (212) 908-4110, 908-4519, Fax: (212) 908-4601, E-mail: krichar@financialhistory.org, Internet: http://www.financialhistory.org. Head: Brian Thompson
Historical Museum - 1988 38908

Museum of American Folk Art → American Folk Art Museum

Museum of Chinese in the Americas, 70 Mulberry St, New York, NY 10013 - T: (212) 619-4785, Fax: (212) 619-4720, E-mail: moca-org@juno.com, Internet: http://www.moca-nyc.org. Head: Fay Chew Matsuda
Fine Arts Museum / Historical Museum / Folklore Museum - 1980
Chinese history in America 38909

Museum of Jewish Heritage, Living Memorial to the Holocaust, 18 First Pl, New York, NY 10280 - T: (212) 968-1800, Fax: (212) 968-1369, E-mail: aspilka@mjhnyc.org, Internet: http://www.mjhnyc.org. Head: Dr. David Altshuler
Historical Museum / Folklore Museum - 1984
Jewish history, 20th-c memorial to the Holocaust 38910

Museum of Modern Art, 11 W 53 St, New York, NY 10019 - T: (212) 708-9400, Fax: (212) 708-9889, E-mail: comments@moma.org, Internet: http://www.moma.org. Head: Glenn Lowry
Fine Arts Museum - 1929 38911

Museum of Television and Radio, 25 W 52 St, New York, NY 10019 - T: (212) 621-6600, Fax: (212) 621-6700, Internet: http://www.mtr.org
Special Museum / Science&Tech Museum - 1975 38912

Museum of the American Piano, 291 Broadway, New York, NY 10007 - T: (212) 246-4646, E-mail: pianomuseum@pianomuseum.com, Internet: http://www.pianomuseum.com. Head: Kalman Detrich
Music Museum - 1981 38913

Museum of the City of New York, 1220 Fifth Av at 103 St, New York, NY 10029 - T: (212) 534-1672, Fax: (212) 423-0758, 534-5974, E-mail: mcny@mcny.org, Internet: http://www.mcny.org. Head: Robert R. Macdonald
Local Museum - 1923 38914

Museum Quality Finishes, 307 W 38th St, New York, NY 10018 - T: (212) 465-1077
Fine Arts Museum 38915

National Academy of Design Museum, 1083 Fifth Av, New York, NY 10128 - T: (212) 369-4880, Fax: (212) 360-6795, Internet: http://www.nationalacademy.com. Head: Dr. Annette Blaugrund
Fine Arts Museum - 1825 38916

National Arts Club, 15 Gramercy Park S, New York, NY 10003 - T: (212) 475-3424, Fax: (212) 475-3692
Fine Arts Museum - 1898 38917

National Museum of the American Indian, Smithsonian Institution, George Gustav Heye Center, 1 Bowling Green, New York, NY 10004 - T: (212) 514-3700, Fax: (212) 514-3800, Internet: http://www.si.edu/nmai. Head: W. Richard West
Ethnology Museum / Archaeological Museum / Historical Museum / Decorative Arts Museum / Fine Arts Museum - 1916 38918

Neue Galerie New York, 1048 Fifth Av, New York, NY 10011 - T: (212) 627-1455, Fax: (212) 627-0654, Internet: http://www.neuegalerie.org. Head: Gerwald Sonnberger, Renée Price
Fine Arts Museum - 2001
German and Austrian Fine and Decorative Art of the 20th c 38919

Neustadt Museum of Tiffany Art, 124 W 79 St, New York, NY 10024 - T: (212) 874-0872, Fax: (212) 874-0872, E-mail: NMTAmuseum@aol.com. Head: Milton D. Hassol
Fine Arts Museum - 1969 38920

New Museum of Contemporary Art, 583 Broadway, New York, NY 10012 - T: (212) 219-1222, Fax: (212) 431-5328, E-mail: newmu@newmuseum.org, Internet: http://www.newmuseum.org. Head: Lisa Phillips
Fine Arts Museum - 1977 38921

New World Art Center, 250 Lafayette St, New York, NY 10012-4075 - T: (212) 966-4363, Fax: (212) 966-5285, E-mail: nwac_chen@hotmail.com
Fine Arts Museum - 1996
International contemporary art 38922

New York City Fire Museum, 278 Spring St, New York, NY 10013 - T: (212) 691-1303, Fax: (212) 924-0430, Internet: http://www.nyfd.com/museum.html. Head: Geoff Giglierano
Historical Museum - 1987 38923

New York City Police Museum, 25 Broadway, New York, NY 10004 - T: (212) 301-4440, Fax: (212) 425-3660, Internet: http://www.nycpolicemuseum.org. Head: Thomas M. Gambino
Historical Museum - 2000 38924

The New York Historical Society Museum, 2 W 77 St, Central Park W, New York, NY 10024 - T: (212) 873-3400, Fax: (212) 874-8706, E-mail: webmaster@nyhistory.org, Internet: http://www.nyhistory.org. Head: Pamela Dewey
Historical Museum / Local Museum - 1804 38925

New York Public Library for the Performing Arts, 40 Lincoln Center Plaza, New York, NY 10023-7498 - T: (212) 870-1830, Fax: (212) 873-1870, Internet: http://www.nypl.org. Head: Jacqueline Z. Davis
Historical Museum / Performing Arts Museum / Library with Exhibitions / Music Museum - 1965 38926

New York Studio School of Drawing, Painting and Sculpture Gallery, 8 W Eighth St, New York, NY 10011 - T: (212) 673-6466, Fax: (212) 777-0996, E-mail: library@nyss.org, Internet: http://www.nyss.org
Public Gallery - 1964
Drawings, paintings, sculptures 38927

Nicholas Roerich Museum, 319 W 107 St, New York, NY 10025-2799 - T: (212) 864-7752, Fax: (212) 864-7704, E-mail: director@roerich.org, Internet: http://www.roerich.org. Head: Daniel Entin
Fine Arts Museum - 1958
Paintings of Tibet, India, Himalaya area by N. Roerich 38928

Pen and Brush Museum, 16 E 10 St, New York, NY 10003 - T: (212) 475-3669, Fax: (212) 475-6018, E-mail: PenBrush99@aol.com. Head: Lynne Atlas-Wittkin
Fine Arts Museum - 1893
Oil, watercolours, pastel, graphics, sculpture, craft 38929

Pierpont Morgan Library, 29 E 36 St, New York, NY 10016 - T: (212) 685-0008, Fax: (212) 481-3484, E-mail: media@morganlibrary.org, Internet: http://www.morganlibrary.org. Head: Dr. Charles E. Pierce
Fine Arts Museum / Library with Exhibitions - 1924
Paintings, art objects, manuscripts, drawings, prints - Gilbert & Sullivan coll 38930

Pratt Manhattan Gallery, 295 Lafayette St, New York, NY 10012 - T: (718) 636-3517, Internet: http://www.pratt.edu/exhibitions. Head: Eleanor Moretta
Fine Arts Museum / University Museum - 1975
Paintings, sculpture, prints, graphics, decorative art 38931

Queens Museum of Art, New York City Bldg, Flushing Meadows Corona Park, New York, NY 11368-3398 - T: (718) 592-9700, Fax: (718) 592-5778, Internet: http://www.queensmuse.org. Head: Laurene Buckley
Fine Arts Museum - 1972
Paintings, sculpture, prints, photography 38932

Rose Museum at Carnegie Hall, 154 W 57 St, New York, NY 10019 - T: (212) 903-9629, Fax: (212) 582-5518, E-mail: gfrancesconi@carnegihall.org, Internet: http://www.carnegiehall.org. Head: Gino Francesconi
Performing Arts Museum - 1991 38933

Salmagundi Museum of American Art, 47 Fifth Av, New York, NY 10003 - T: (212) 255-7740, Fax: (212) 229-0172, Internet: http://www.salmagundi.org
Fine Arts Museum / Association with Coll - 1871
Paintings, sculptures, photography - library 38934

Scandinavia House, 58 Park Av, New York, NY 10016 - T: (212) 779-3587
Fine Arts Museum 38935

Schomburg Center for Research in Black Culture, N.Y. Public Library, 515 Malcolm X. Blvd, New York, NY 10037-1801 - T: (212) 491-2200, Fax: (212) 491-6760. Head: Howard Dodson
Historical Museum / Ethnology Museum - 1925 38936

Sidney Mishkin Gallery of Baruch College, 135 E 22 St, New York, NY 10010 - T: (212) 802-2690, Internet: http://www.baruch.cuny.edu. Head: Sandra Kraskin
Fine Arts Museum / University Museum - 1981
American and European drawings, paintings, photographs, prints and sculptures 38937

Society of Illustrators Museum of American Illustration, 128 E 63 St, New York, NY 10021-7303 - T: (212) 838-2560, Fax: (212) 838-2561, E-mail: society@societyillustrators.org, Internet: http://www.societyillustrators.org. Head: Terrence Brown
Fine Arts Museum - 1901 38938

Solomon R. Guggenheim Museum, 1071 Fifth Av, New York, NY 10128 - T: (212) 423-3500, Fax: (212) 941-8410, E-mail: visitorinfo@guggenheim.org, Internet: http://www.guggenheim.org. Head: Thomas Krens
Fine Arts Museum - 1937 38939

Sony Wonder Technology Lab, 56th St at Madison Av, New York, NY 10022 - T: (212) 833-8100, Fax: (212) 833-4445, E-mail: stacey-kratz@sonyusa.com, Internet: http://www.sonywondertechlab.com. Head: Courtney White
Science&Tech Museum - 1994
Technology and science 38940

South Street Seaport Museum, 207 Front St, New York, NY 10038 - T: (212) 748-8600, Fax: (212) 748-8725, E-mail: webmaster@southstseaport.org, Internet: http://www.southstseaport.org
Special Museum / Science&Tech Museum - 1967 38941

Statue of Liberty National Monument and Ellis Island Immigration Museum, Liberty Island, New York, NY 10004 - T: (212) 363-7772, Fax: (212) 363-8347, E-mail: stli_museum@nps.gov, Internet: http://www.nps.gov/stli. Head: Diane H. Dayson
Historical Museum / Historic Site - 1924 38942

Studio Museum in Harlem, 144 W 125 St, New York, NY 10027 - T: (212) 864-4500, Fax: (212) 864-4800, E-mail: SMHNY@aol.com, Internet: http://www.studiomuseuminharlem.org. Head: Lowery Stokes Sims
Fine Arts Museum - 1967 38943

Swiss Institute - Contemporary Art, 495 Broadway, New York, NY 10012 - T: (212) 925-2035
Public Gallery 38944

Terrain Gallery, 141 Greene St, New York, NY 10012 - T: (212) 777-4490, Fax: (212) 777-4426, Internet: http://www.terraingallery.org
Fine Arts Museum
Paintings, prints, drawings and photographs with commentary 38945

Theodore Roosevelt Birthplace, 28 E 20 St, New York, NY 10003 - T: (212) 260-1616, Fax: (212) 677-3587, E-mail: - MASI_Theodore_Roosevelt_Birthplace@nps.gov, Internet: http://www.nps.gov/thrb/
Historical Museum - 1923 38946

Trinity Museum of the Parish of Trinity Church, Broadway and Wall St, New York, NY 10006 - T: (212) 602-0800, Fax: (212) 602-9648, E-mail: djette@trinitywallstreet.org, Internet: http://www.trinitywallstreet.org. Head: Daniel Paul Matthews
Religious Arts Museum - 1966 38947

Ukrainian Museum, 203 Second Av, New York, NY 10003 - T: (212) 228-0110, Fax: (212) 228-1947, E-mail: ukrmus@aol.com, Internet: http://www.brama.com/ukrainian_museum
Fine Arts Museum / Folklore Museum / Special Museum - 1976 38948

Visual Arts Museum, 209 E 23 St, New York, NY 10010 - T: (212) 592-2144, Fax: (212) 592-2095, E-mail: fditommaso@adm.schoolofvisualarts.edu, Internet: http://www.schoolofvisualarts.edu. Head: Francis Di Tommaso
Fine Arts Museum - 1971
Photography, fine art, new media, digital graphic design 38949

Whitney Museum of American Art, 945 Madison Av, New York, NY 10021 - T: (212) 570-3600, Fax: (212) 570-1807, Internet: http://www.echonyc.com/~whitney. Head: Maxwell Anderson
Fine Arts Museum - 1930 38950

Yeshiva University Museum, 15 W 16th St, New York, NY 10011 - T: (212) 294-8330, Fax: (212) 294-8335, E-mail: sherskowitz@yum.cjh.edu, Internet: http://www.yu.edu/museum. Head: Sylvia A. Herskowitz
Historical Museum / University Museum / Ethnology Museum / Fine Arts Museum - 1973
Jewish ceremonial objects, Jewish hist, ethnography, art and culture 38951

Newark DE

University Gallery, University of Delaware, Main St at N College Av, Newark, DE 19716 - T: (302) 831-8242, Fax: (302) 831-8251, E-mail: belena.chapp@mvs.udel.edu, Internet: http://seurat.art.udel.edu. Head: Belena S. Chapp
Fine Arts Museum / University Museum - 1978
Art 38952

Newark NJ

New Jersey Historical Society Museum, 52 Park Pl, Newark, NJ 07102 - T: (973) 596-8500, Fax: (973) 596-6957. Head: Dr. Sally Yerkovich
Historical Museum / Local Museum - 1845
library 38953

The Newark Museum, 49 Washington St, Newark, NJ 07101-0540 - T: (973) 596-6550, Fax: (973) 642-0459, Internet: http://www.newarkmuseum.org. Head: Mary Sue Sweeney Price
Local Museum - 1909
Local history, art, natural history, decorative art - planetarium 38954

Newark OH

Licking County Art Gallery, 391 Hudson Av, Newark, OH 43055 - T: (740) 349-8031, Fax: (740) 345-3787. Head: Leah Mitchell
Fine Arts Museum - 1959 38955

Licking County Historical Museum, Veterans Park, N 6th St, Newark, OH 43058-0785 - T: (614) 345-4898, E-mail: lchs@alltel.net. Head: Mike Smith
Local Museum - 1947
Regional history 38956

Moundbuilders State Memorial and Museum, 99 Cooper Av, Newark, OH 43055 - T: (800) 600-7174, Internet: http://www.ohiohistory.org/places/moundld/. Head: James Kingery
Ethnology Museum / Archaeological Museum
Prehistoric Indian Art Museum and Historical Site 38957

National Heisey Glass Museum, 169 W Church St, Newark, OH 43055 - T: (740) 345-2932, Fax: (740) 345-9638, E-mail: heisey@infinet.com, Internet: http://www.heiseymueusm.org
Decorative Arts Museum - 1974 38958

Sherwood-Davidson House, Veterans Park, Sixth St, Newark, OH 43058-0785 - T: (740) 345-6525, E-mail: sherwooddavidson@yahoo.com, Internet: http://www.lickingcountyhistoricalsociety.org. Head: Michael Smith
Local Museum / Historical Museum - 1947 38959

Webb House Museum, 303 Granville St, Newark, OH 43055 - T: (740) 345-8540, E-mail: webbhouse@nextek.net. Head: Mindy Honey Nelson
Historical Museum - 1976 38960

Newark Valley NY

Bement-Billings Farmstead, 9142 Rte 38, Newark Valley, NY 13811 - T: (607) 642-9516, Fax: (607) 642-9516, E-mail: nvhistorical@juno.com, Internet: http://www.tier.net/nvhistory. Head: Harriet Miller
Historical Museum / Historic Site - 1977 38961

Newark Valley Depot Museum, Depot St, Newark Valley, NY 13811 - T: (607) 642-9516, Fax: (607) 642-9516, E-mail: nvhistorical@juno.com, Internet: http://www.tier.net/nvhistory. Head: Harriet Miller
Science&Tech Museum - 1977
Railroad 38962

Newaygo MI

Newaygo County Museum, 85 Water St, Newaygo, MI 49337 - T: (616) 652-9281, Fax: (616) 652-2461
Local Museum - 1968
Regional history 38963

Newbern VA

Wilderness Road Regional Museum, State Rte 611, 5240 Wilderness Rd, Newbern, VA 24126 - T: (540) 674-4835, Fax: (540) 674-1266, E-mail: wrrm@usit.net, Internet: http://www.rootsweb/~vapulask/wrrm/. Head: Ann S. Bailey
Local Museum - 1980
Local hist 38964

Newburgh NY

David Crawford House, 189 Montgomery St, Newburgh, NY 12550 - T: (914) 561-2585. Head: Eugene Embler
Historical Museum - 1884 38965

Washington's Headquarters, Corner of Liberty and Washington Sts, Newburgh, NY 12551-1476 - T: (914) 562-1195
Military Museum - 1850 38966

Newbury MA

Coffin House, 14 High Rd, Newbury, MA 01951 - T: (978) 462-2634, (617) 227-3956, Fax: (617) 227-9204, Internet: http://www.spnea.org
Historical Museum - 1929 38967

Spencer-Peirce-Little Farm, 5 Little's Ln, Newbury, MA 01951 - T: (978) 462-2634, Fax: (978) 462-4022, Internet: http://www.spnea.org. Head: Jane Nylander
Local Museum - 1971
Historic house 38968

Newbury Park CA

Stagecoach Inn Museum Complex, 51 S Ventu Park Rd, Newbury Park, CA 91320 - T: (805) 498-9441, Fax: (805) 498-6375, E-mail: stagecoach@toguide.com, Internet: http://www.toguide.com/stagecoach. Head: Sandra Hildebrandt
Historical Museum - 1967 38969

Newburyport MA

Cushing House Museum, 98 High St, Newburyport, MA 01950 - T: (978) 462-2681, Fax: (978) 462-0134, E-mail: hson@greennet.net, Internet: http://www.greennet.net\clients[redacted]son. Head: Dick Johnson, Audrey Ladd
Local Museum - 1877
Local history 38970

Custom House Maritime Museum, 25 Water St, Newburyport, MA 01950 - T: (978) 462-8681, Fax: (978) 462-8740, E-mail: nms@shore.net. Head: Mark J. Sammons Chandler
Historical Museum - 1969
Local maritime hist, boat building 38971

Newcastle TX

Fort Belknap Museum, Farm to Market 61, Newcastle, TX 76372 - T: (940) 549-1856, Internet: http://www.forttours.com. Head: Dr. K.F. Neighbours
Military Museum - 1851
Military hist 38972

Newcomerstown OH

Temperance Tavern, 221 W Canal St, Newcomerstown, OH 43832 - T: (614) 498-7735. Head: Barbara Scott
Historical Museum / Local Museum / Historic Site - 1923 38973

USS Radford National Naval Museum, 132 W Canal St, Newcomerstown, OH 43832 - T: (740) 498-4446, Fax: (740) 498-8803, E-mail: vane@sota-oh.com, Internet: http://www.ussradford446.org. Head: Vane S. Scott
Special Museum / Military Museum - 2000
USS Radford DD/DDE 446 - Destroyer, WWII (Korea, Vietnam), 3-D Diorama of Rescue at Kula Gulf 38974

Newfield ME

Willowbrook at Newfield, Main St, Newfield, ME 04056 - T: (207) 793-2784. Head: D.F. King
Historical Museum - 1970
Regional history 38975

Newhall CA

William S. Hart County Park and Museum, National History Museum of Los Angeles County, 24151 San Fernando Rd, Newhall, CA 91321 - T: (661) 254-4584, Fax: (661) 254-6499, E-mail: jashley@nhm.orgc.edu, Internet: http://www.hartmuseum.org. Head: Dr. James L. Powell, Bill Crowl
Historical Museum / Historic Site - 1958 38976

Newland NC

Avery County Museum, 1829 Schultz Circle, Newland, NC 28657 - T: (828) 733-7111, E-mail: museum@m-y.net. Head: Frank Hamlin
Local Museum / Folklore Museum - 1977 38977

Newport OR

Oregon Coast History Center, 545 SW Ninth, Newport, OR 97365 - T: (541) 265-7509, Fax: (541) 265-3992, E-mail: coasthistory@newportnet.com, Internet: http://www.newportnet.com/coasthistory/home.htm
Historical Museum - 1948
Maritime objects, logging, coastal hist 38978

Newport RI

Artillery Company of Newport Military Museum, 23 Clarke St, Newport, RI 02840 - T: (401) 846-8488. Head: James Johnsen
Military Museum - 1959
Military hist 38979

International Tennis Hall of Fame Museum, 194 Bellevue Av, Newport, RI 02840 - T: (401) 849-3990, Fax: (401) 849-8780, E-mail: ithf@aol.com, Internet: http://www.tennisfame.org. Head: Melissa Mulrooney
Special Museum - 1954
Sports 38980

The Museum of Newport History, 127 Thames St, Newport, RI 02840 - T: (401) 846-0813, 841-8770, Fax: (401) 846-1853, Internet: http://www.newport-historical.org. Head: Daniel Snydacker
Historical Museum - 1854
Local hist 38981

Museum of Yachting, Fort Adams State Park, Newport, RI 02840 - T: (401) 847-1018, Fax: (401) 847-8320, E-mail: museum@moy.org, Internet: http://www.moy.org. Head: J. Peter Marnane
Special Museum / Science&Tech Museum - 1983
Yachting, sailing 38982

Naval War College Museum, 686 Cushing Rd, Newport, RI 02841-1207 - T: (401) 841-4052, 841-1317, Fax: (401) 841-7689, E-mail: nicolosa@nwc.navy.mil, Internet: http://www.nwc.navy.mil/museum. Head: Anthony S. Nicolosi
Military Museum - 1978
Naval hist 38983

Newport Art Museum, 76 Bellevue Av, Newport, RI 02840 - T: (401) 848-8200, Fax: (401) 848-8205, E-mail: info@newportartmuseum.com, Internet: http://www.newportartmuseum.com. Head: Christine Callahan
Fine Arts Museum - 1912
Drawings, paintings, sculpture, prints, photography 38984

Newport Mansions, 424 Bellevue Av, Newport, RI 02840 - T: (401) 847-1000, Fax: (401) 847-1361, Internet: http://www.NewportMansions.org
Local Museum - 1945
Group of 9 mansions 38985

Redwood Library and Athenaeum, 50 Bellevue Av, Newport, RI 02840 - T: (401) 847-0292, Fax: (401) 841-5680, E-mail: redwood@edgenet.net, Internet: http://www.redwood1747.org. Head: Cheryl V. Helms
Fine Arts Museum - 1747
18th-19th c Anglo-American portraits 38986

Royal Arts Foundation, Belcourt Castle, 657 Bellevue Av, Newport, RI 02840-4280 - T: (401) 846-0669, Fax: (401) 846-5345, E-mail: kevint@belcourt.com, Internet: http://www.belcourtcastle.com. Head: Harle H. Tinney
Decorative Arts Museum / Local Museum - 1957
Historic house, paintings, sculpture, textiles, ceramics 38987

Thames Science Center, 77 Long Wharf, Newport, RI 02840 - T: (401) 849-6966, Fax: (401) 849-7144, E-mail: jane.holdsworth@worldnet.att.net, Internet: http://www.thamesscience.org. Head: Jane A. Holdsworth
Natural History Museum - 1948 38988

Newport Beach CA

Orange County Museum of Art, 850 San Clemente Dr, Newport Beach, CA 92660 - T: (949) 759-1122 ext 200, Fax: (949) 759-5623, E-mail: ocma@pacbell.net, Internet: http://www.ocma.net. Head: Naomi Vine
Fine Arts Museum - 1921 38989

Newport News VA

The Mariners' Museum, 100 Museum Dr, Newport News, VA 23606 - T: (757) 596-2222, Fax: (757) 591-7320, E-mail: info@mariner.org, Internet: http://www.mariner.org. Head: John B. Hightower, Claudia Pennington
Historical Museum / Science&Tech Museum - 1930
Maritime hist 38990

Newsome House Museum, 2803 Oak Av, Newport News, VA 23607 - T: (804) 247-2360, Fax: (804) 928-6754, Internet: http://www.sightsmag.com
Historical Museum - 1991 38991

Peninsula Fine Arts Center, 101 Museum Dr, Newport News, VA 23606 - T: (757) 596-8175, Fax: (757) 596-0807, E-mail: pfac@cvinet.org, Internet: http://www.pfac-va.org. Head: Lisa C. Swenson
Fine Arts Museum - 1962
Arts 38992

Virginia Living Museum, 524 J. Clyde Morris Blvd, Newport News, VA 23601 - T: (757) 595-1900, Fax: (757) 599-4897, Internet: http://www.valivingmuseum.org. Head: Gloria R. Lombardi, David C. Maness, George K. Mathews
Natural History Museum / Special Museum - 1964
Natural hist 38993

The Virginia War Museum, 9285 Warwick Blvd, Huntington Park, Newport News, VA 23607 - T: (757) 247-8523, Fax: (757) 247-8627
Military Museum - 1923
Military hist 38994

Newton IL

Newton Museum, 100 S Vanburen, Newton, IL 62448 - T: (618) 783-8141, 783-3860, Fax: (618) 783-8141, E-mail: newtonpl@pfbnewton.com
Local Museum - 1928
Local history - library 38995

Newton KS

Harvey County Historical Museum, 203 N. Main, Newton, KS 67114 - T: (316) 283-2221, Fax: (316) 283-2221, E-mail: hchs@southwind.net, Internet: http://www2.southwind.net/~hchs. Head: Roger N. Wilson
Historical Museum - 1962
Local history, housed in a Carnegie library bldg 38996

Newton MA

The Jackson Homestead, 527 Washington St, Newton, MA 02158 - T: (617) 552-7238, Fax: (617) 552-7228, E-mail: dolson@ci.newton.ma.us, Internet: http://www.ci.newton.ma.us/jackson. Head: David Olson
Historical Museum - 1950
Local history, Jackson Homestead 38997

Newton City Museum → The Jackson Homestead

Newton NC

Catawba County Museum of History, 1 Court Sq, Newton, NC 28658 - T: (828) 465-0383, Fax: (828) 465-9813, E-mail: ccha@w3link.com. Head: Sidney Halma
Historical Museum - 1949 38998

Newton NJ

Sussex County Historical Society Museum, 82 Main St, Newton, NJ 07860 - T: (973) 383-6010. Head: Robert R. Longcore
Historical Museum - 1904 38999

Newtown PA

Artmobile, Bucks County Community College, Newtown, PA 18940 - T: (215) 968-8432, Fax: (215) 504-8530, E-mail: orlando@bucks.edu. Head: Fran Orlando
Fine Arts Museum / University Museum - 1975 39000

Newtown Historic Museum, Court St and Centre Av, Newtown, PA 18940 - T: (215) 968-4004, E-mail: dcnhh@aol.com, Internet: http://www.newtown.pa.us/historic/nha.html
Historical Museum / Local Museum - 1965
Local history, early 1700s Court Inn 39001

Niagara Falls NY

Schoellkopf Geological Museum, New York State Parks, Niagara Region, Robert Moses State Pkwy near Main St, Niagara Falls, NY 14303-0132 - T: (716) 278-1780, Fax: (716) 278-1744
Natural History Museum - 1971 39002

Niagara University NY

Castellani Art Museum, Niagara University, NY 14109 - T: (716) 286-8200, Fax: (716) 286-8289, E-mail: cam@niagara.edu, Internet: http://www.niagara.edu/~cam. Head: Dr. Sandra H. Olsen
Fine Arts Museum / University Museum - 1973 39003

Niles MI

Fort Saint Joseph Museum, 508 E Main St, Niles, MI 49120 - T: (616) 683-4702, Fax: (616) 684-3930, E-mail: cbainbridge@gtm.net, Internet: http://www.ci.niles.mi.us. Head: Carol Bainbridge
Local Museum - 1932
Local history, Henry A. Chapin carriage house 39004

Niles OH

National McKinley Birthplace Memorial, 40 N Main St, Niles, OH 44446 - T: (330) 652-1704, Fax: (330) 652-5788, E-mail: mckinley@oplin.lib.oh.us, Internet: http://www.mckinley.lib.oh.us. Head: Leonard B. Holloway
Historic Site - 1911 39005

Ninety-Six SC

Ninety-Six National Historic Site, 1103 Hwy 248, Ninety-Six, SC 29666 - T: (864) 543-4068, Fax: (864) 543-2058, Internet: http://www.NPS.gov/NISI. Head: Eric K. Williams
Local Museum / Open Air Museum - 1976
Local hist 39006

Noank CT

Noank Historical Society Museum, 17 Sylvan St, Noank, CT 06340 - T: (860) 536-3021
Local Museum / Historical Museum - 1966 39007

Noblesville IN

Indiana Transportation Museum, 325 Cicero Rd, Noblesville, IN 46061-0083 - T: (317) 773-6000, 776-7881, Fax: (317) 773-5530, E-mail: itm@indy.net, Internet: http://www.itm.org. Head: David E. Witcox
Science&Tech Museum - 1960
Rail transportation and technology, 1930 railroad station from Hobbs 39008

Nogales AZ

Pimeria Alta Historical Society Museum, 136 N Grand Av, Nogales, AZ 85621 - T: (520) 287-4621, Fax: (520) 287-5201. Head: Sigrid Maitrejean
Local Museum - 1948 39009

Norfolk CT

Norfolk Historical Museum, 13 Village Green, Norfolk, CT 06058 - T: (203) 542-5761. Head: Richard Byrne
Local Museum / Historical Museum - 1960 39010

Norfolk VA

The Chrysler Museum of Art, 245 West Olney Rd, Norfolk, VA 23510-1587 - T: (757) 664-6200, Fax: (757) 664-6201, E-mail: museum@chrysler.org, Internet: http://www.chrysler.org. Head: Dr. William J. Hennessey
Fine Arts Museum - 1933
Art 39011

General Douglas MacArthur Memorial, MacArthur Square, Norfolk, VA 23510 - T: (757) 441-2965, Fax: (757) 441-5389, E-mail: macmem@norfolk.infi.net, Internet: http://sites.community-link.org/mac. Head: William J. Davis
Military Museum - 1964
Military hist 39012

Hampton Roads Naval Museum, One Waterside Dr, Norfolk, VA 23510-1607 - T: (804) 444-8971, 322-2987, Fax: (804) 445-1867, E-mail: bapoulliot@cmar.navy.mil, Internet: http://naval-station.norfolk.va.us/navy.html. Head: Elizabeth A. Poulliot, Dennis J. Murphy
Military Museum - 1979
Naval hist 39013

Moses Myers House, 331 Bank St, Norfolk, VA 23510 - T: (757) 664-6283; 664-6255, Fax: (757) 441-2329, E-mail: dbiller@chrysler.org, Internet: http://www.chrysler.org. Head: Dr. William Hennessey
Decorative Arts Museum / Local Museum - 1951
Historic house 39014

Norfolk Historical Society Museum, 810 Front St, Norfolk, VA 23510 - T: (757) 625-1720. Head: Amy Waters Yarsinske
Local Museum - 1965
Local hist 39015

Old Dominion University Gallery, 305 W 21st St, Norfolk, VA 23517 - T: (757) 683-6227, Fax: (757) 683-5923, E-mail: khuntoon@odu.edu, Internet: http://www.odu.edu/al/artsandletters/gallery/index.html. Head: Katherine Huntoon
Fine Arts Museum / University Museum - 1972 39016

Willoughby-Baylor House, 601 E Freemason St, Norfolk, VA 23510 - T: (757) 664-6283, 664-6255, E-mail: dbiller@chrysler.org, Internet: http://www.chrysler.org. Head: Dr. William Hennessey
Decorative Arts Museum / Local Museum - 1962
Historic house 39017

Norman OK

Fred Jones Jr. Museum of Art, University of Oklahoma, 410 W Boyd St, Norman, OK 73019 - T: (405) 325-3272, Fax: (405) 325-7696, Internet: http://www.ou.edu/fjjma. Head: Eric M. Lee
Fine Arts Museum / University Museum - 1936 39018

Norman Cleveland County Historical Museum, 508 N Peters, Norman, OK 73069 - T: (405) 321-0156. Head: Lavina McKinzey
Historical Museum - 1973 39019

Oklahoma Museum of Natural History, University of Oklahoma, 2401 Chautauqua, Norman, OK 73072-7029 - T: (405) 325-4712, Fax: (405) 325-7699, E-mail: smomnh@ou.edu, Internet: http://www.snomnh.ou.edu
University Museum / Natural History Museum - 1899 39020

Norris TN

Museum of Appalachia, Hwy 61, Norris, TN 37828 - T: (865) 494-7680, Fax: (865) 494-8957, E-mail: musofapp@icx.net. Head: John Rice Irwin, Elaine Irwin Meyer
Local Museum / Folklore Museum - 1967
Local hist, folk art 39021

North Andover MA

North Andover Historical Museum, 153 Academy Rd, North Andover, MA 01845 - T: (978) 686-4035, Fax: (978) 686-6616. Head: Carol Majahad
Local Museum - 1913
Local history 39022

North Bend OR

Coos County Historical Society Museum, 1220 Sherman, North Bend, OR 97459 - T: (541) 756-6320, Fax: (541) 756-6320, E-mail: museum@harborside.com. Head: Reg Pullen, Ann Koppy
Local Museum / Historical Museum - 1891 39023

North Bennington VT

The Park-McCullough House, Corner of Park & West Sts, North Bennington, VT 05257 - T: (802) 442-5441, Fax: (802) 442-5442, E-mail: thehouse@sover.net, Internet: http://www.parkmccullough.org. Head: Jane Nicholls
Local Museum - 1968
Historic house 39024

North Blenheim NY

Lansing Manor House Museum, NY State Rte 30, North Blenheim, NY 12131 - T: (518) 827-6121, Fax: (607) 588-9466, E-mail: dicocco@nypa.gov, Internet: http://www.nypa.gov/html/vcblenhe.html. Head: Barbara DiCocco
Historical Museum - 1977 39025

North Brunswick NJ

New Jersey Museum of Agriculture, College Farm Rd and Rte 1, North Brunswick, NJ 08902 - T: (732) 249-2077, Fax: (732) 247-1035, E-mail: info@agriculturemuseum.org, Internet: http://www.agriculturemuseum.org. Head: Richard A. Sgritta
Agriculture Museum - 1984 39026

North Canton OH

Hoover Historical Center, 1875 Easton St NW, North Canton, OH 44720-3331 - T: (330) 499-0287, 499-9200 ext 3041, Fax: (330) 494-4725, E-mail: ahaines@hoover.com, Internet: http://www.hoover.com. Head: Jackie Love
Science&Tech Museum - 1978
Company history, Hoover family home, evolution of vacuum cleaner, Hoover products for WWII 39027

North Conway NH

Conway Scenic Railroad, 38 Norcross Circle, North Conway, NH 03860 - T: (603) 356-5251, Fax: (603) 356-7606, E-mail: info@conwayscenic.com, Internet: http://www.conwayscenic.com. Head: Russell G. Seybold
Science&Tech Museum - 1974
Railroad, wood frame railroad station 39028

Mount Washington Museum, 2936 White Mountain Hwy, North Conway, NH 03860 - T: (603) 356-2137, Fax: (603) 356-3070, E-mail: wdc@mountwashington.org, Internet: http://www.mountwashington.org. Head: Matthew White
Natural History Museum - 1969 39029

Weather Dicovery Center, 2936 White Mountain Hwy, North Conway, NH 03860 - T: (603) 356-2137, Fax: (603) 356-3070, E-mail: wdc@mountwashington.org, Internet: http://www.mountwashington.org. Head: Matthew White
Science&Tech Museum - 2000
Meterology, science, local history 39030

North Dartmouth MA

University Art Gallery, University of Massachusetts-Dartmouth, North Dartmouth, MA 02747 - T: (508) 999-8555, Fax: (508) 999-9279, E-mail: lantonsen@umassd.edu. Head: Lasse B. Antonsen
University Museum / Fine Arts Museum - 1987 39031

North East PA

Lake Shore Railway Museum, 31 Wall St, North East, PA 16428-0571 - T: (814) 825-2724. Head: Charles W. Farrington
Science&Tech Museum - 1956
Railway 39032

North Easton MA

The Children's Museum in Easton, Sullivan Av, North Easton, MA 02356 - T: (508) 230-3789, Fax: (508) 230-7130
Historical Museum - 1988
Fire station in town's historical district 39033

North Freedom WI

Mid-Continent Railway Museum, E 8948 Diamond Hill Rd, North Freedom, WI 53951-0055 - T: (608) 522-4261, Fax: (608) 522-4490, E-mail: midcon@baraboo.com, Internet: http://www.mcrwy.com
Science&Tech Museum - 1959
Railway 39034

North Haven CT

North Haven Historical Society Museum, 27 Broadway, North Haven, CT 06473 - T: (203) 239-7722
Local Museum / Historical Museum - 1957 39035

North Miami FL

Holocaust Documentation and Education Center, 3000 NE 151th St and Biscayne Blvd, North Miami, FL 33181 - T: (305) 919-5690, Fax: (305) 919-5691, E-mail: xholocau@fiu.edu, Internet: http://holocaust.fiu.edu. Head: Harry A. Levy
Historical Museum - 1979
Holocaust oral histories, artifacts, memorabilia   39036

Museum of Contemporary Art, 770 NE 125th St, North Miami, FL 33161 - T: (305) 893-6211, Fax: (305) 891-1472, Internet: http://www.montanbml.org. Head: Bonnie Clearwater
Fine Arts Museum - 1981
Visual contemporary art   39037

North Miami Beach FL

Ancient Spanish Monastery of Saint Bernard de Clairvaux Cloisters, 16711 W Dixie Hwy, North Miami Beach, FL 33160 - T: (305) 945-1462, Fax: (305) 945-6986, E-mail: monastery@earthlink.net, Internet: http://www.spanishmonastery.net. Head: Dr. Ronald Fox
Fine Arts Museum - 1952
Religious art, reconstruction of monastery, built in 1141 in Segovia Spain, with original stones brought to United States by William Randolph Hearst 39038

North Newton KS

Kauffman Museum, Bethel College, 2701 N Main, North Newton, KS 67117-0531 - T: (316) 283-1612, Fax: (316) 283-2107, E-mail: kauffman@bethelks.edu, Internet: http://www.bethelks.edu/kauffman.html. Head: Rachel K. Pannabecker
University Museum / Local Museum / Natural History Museum - 1941
Cultural and natural history   39039

Mennonite Library and Archives Museum, Bethel College, 300 E 27th St, North Newton, KS 67117 - T: (316) 283-2500, 284-5304, Fax: (316) 284-5286, E-mail: mla@bethelks.edu, Internet: http://www.bethelks.edu/services/mla
Religious Arts Museum - 1938
Religion   39040

North Oxford MA

Clara Barton Birthplace, 68 Clara Barton Rd, North Oxford, MA 01537 - T: (508) 987-5375. Head: Shelley Yeager
Historical Museum - 1921
Historic house   39041

North Salem NH

America's Stonehenge, 105 Haverhill Rd, North Salem, NH 03073, mail addr: POB 84, North Salem, NH 03073 - T: (603) 893-8300, Fax: (603) 893-5889, E-mail: amstonehenge@worldnet.att.net, Internet: http://www.stonehengeusa.com. Head: Robert E. Stone
Archaeological Museum - 1958
Archaeology on Mystery Hill, site of 4,000 year old archaeo-astronomical site   39042

North Salem NY

Hammond Museum, Deveau Rd off Rte 124, North Salem, NY 10560 - T: (914) 669-5033, Fax: (914) 669-8221, E-mail: abigail@hammond, Internet: http://www.hammondmuseum.org. Head: Abigail Free
Fine Arts Museum / Decorative Arts Museum / Special Museum - 1957   39043

North Tonawanda NY

Herschell Carrousel Factory Museum, 180 Thompson St, North Tonawanda, NY 14120 - T: (716) 693-1885, Fax: (716) 743-9018. Head: Elizabeth M. Brick
Science&Tech Museum - 1983
Company hist   39044

North Troy VT

Missisquoi Valley Historical Society Museum, Main St, North Troy, VT 05859 - T: (802) 988-4323
Local Museum - 1976
Local hist   39045

North Wildwood NJ

Hereford Inlet Lighthouse, 11 N Central Av, North Wildwood, NJ 08260 - T: (609) 522-4520, Fax: (609) 523-8502, Internet: http://www.the-wildwoods.com. Head: Aldo Palombo
Historical Museum - 1982
Maritime hist   39046

North Wilkesboro NC

Wilkes Art Gallery, 800 Elizabeth St, North Wilkesboro, NC 28659 - T: (336) 667-2841, Fax: (336) 667-9564, E-mail: wilkesartgal@wilkes.net, Internet: http://www.northwilkesboro.com/local. Head: Dee C. Vannoy
Fine Arts Museum / Public Gallery - 1962   39047

North Woburn MA

Rumford Historical Museum, 90 Elm St, North Woburn, MA 01801 - T: (617) 933-0781. Head: Leonard Harmon
Historical Museum - 1877
Count Rumford's birthplace   39048

Northampton MA

Calvin Coolidge Memorial Room of the Forbes Library, 20 West St, Northampton, MA 01060 - T: (413) 587-1014, Fax: (413) 587-1015, Internet: http://www.forbeslibrary.org. Head: Lu Knox
Historical Museum / Library with Exhibitions - 1920
Presidential life and time   39049

Historic Northampton, 46 Bridge St, Northampton, MA 01060 - T: (413) 584-6011, Fax: (413) 584-7956, E-mail: hstnhamp@javanet.com, Internet: http://www.virtual-valley.com/histnhamp. Head: Kerry W. Buckley
Historical Museum - 1905
Local history, Parsons house, Isaac Damon house, Shepherd house, Shepherd barn   39050

Smith College Museum of Art, Elm St at Bedford Tce, Northampton, MA 01063 - T: (413) 585-2760, 585-2770, Fax: (413) 585-2782, E-mail: artmuseum@smith.edu, Internet: http://www.smith.edu/artmuseum. Head: Suzannah Fabing
Fine Arts Museum / University Museum - 1920
Paintings, sculptures, drawings, prints, photographs, decorative arts   39051

Words and Pictures Museum, 140 Main St, Northampton, MA 01060 - T: (413) 586-8545, Fax: (413) 586-9855, E-mail: comics@wordsandpictures.org, Internet: http://www.wordsandpictures.org
Fine Arts Museum - 1991   39052

Northborough MA

Northborough Historical Museum, 50 Main St, Northborough, MA 01532 - T: (508) 393-6298
Local Museum - 1906
General museum, housed in Baptist Church 39053

Northfield MN

Carleton College Art Gallery, 1 N College St, Northfield, MN 55057 - T: (507) 646-4342, Fax: (507) 646-7042, E-mail: lbradley@carleton.edu. Head: Laurel Bradley
Fine Arts Museum
American paintings, photography, prints, woodcuts, Asian art, Greek and Roman antiquities   39054

Exhibition of the Norwegian-American Historical Association, 1510 Saint Olaf Av, Northfield, MN 55057-1097 - T: (507) 646-3221, Fax: (507) 646-3734, E-mail: naha@stolaf.edu, Internet: http://www.naha.stolaf.edu. Head: Kim Holland
Historical Museum - 1925   39055

Northfield Historical Society Museum, 408 Division St, Northfield, MN 55057 - T: (507) 645-9268, E-mail: nhsmuseum@microassist.com. Head: Anneliese Detwiler
Historical Museum / Local Museum - 1975   39056

Steensland Art Museum, Saint Olaf College, 1520 Saint Olaf Av, Northfield, MN 55057 - T: (507) 646-3556, Fax: (507) 646-3776, E-mail: ewaldj@stolaf.edu, Internet: http://www.stolaf.edu/other/steensland. Head: Jill Ewald
Fine Arts Museum - 1976
Prints and paintings, graphics, textiles, religious art, woodcuts, oriental and renaissance art   39057

Northfield OH

Palmer House, 9390 Olde Eight Rd, Northfield, OH 44067 - T: (216) 237-1813. Head: Mildred McCarty
Local Museum / Historical Museum - 1956   39058

Northfield VT

Norwich University Museum, White Chapel, Norwich University, Northfield, VT 05663 - T: (802) 485-2000, 485-2360, Fax: (802) 485-2580, E-mail: GLORD@Norwich.edu. Head: G.T. Lord
University Museum / Historical Museum - 1819
History   39059

Northport NY

Northport Historical Society Museum, 215 Main St, Northport, NY 11768 - T: (516) 757-9859, Fax: (516) 757-9398, E-mail: info@northporthistorical.org, Internet: http://www.northporthistorical.org. Head: Barbra Wells Fitzgerald
Historical Museum - 1962   39060

Northridge CA

California State University-Northridge Art Galleries, 18111 Nordhoff St, Northridge, CA 91330-8299 - T: (818) 677-2226 & 2156, Fax: (818) 677-5910, E-mail: art.gallery@csun.edu, Internet: http://www.csun.edu/artgalleries/. Head: Louise Lewis
Fine Arts Museum / University Museum - 1972   39061

Northumberland PA

Joseph Priestley House, 472 Priestley Av, Northumberland, PA 17857 - T: (570) 473-9474, Fax: (570) 473-7901, E-mail: abashore@phmc.state.pa.us, Internet: http://www.phmc.state.pa.us. Head: William Vandenheuvel
Historical Museum - 1960
Historic house   39062

Norton MA

Watson Gallery, Wheaton College, E Main St, Norton, MA 02766 - T: (508) 286-3578, Fax: (508) 286-3565, E-mail: amurray@wheatonma.edu, Internet: http://www.wheatonma.edu/academic/watson/home.html. Head: Ann H. Murray
Fine Arts Museum / University Museum - 1960   39063

Norwalk CT

Lockwood-Mathews Mansion Museum, 295 West Av, Norwalk, CT 06850 - T: (203) 838-9799, Fax: (203) 838-1434, E-mail: lockmathew@aol.com, Internet: http://www.lockwood-mathews.org. Head: Zachary Studenroth
Local Museum / Historical Museum - 1966   39064

Musical Box Society International Museum, Lockwood Mathews Mansion, Norwalk, CT 06850 - T: (203) 838-1434, Fax: (310) 377-5240, E-mail: biesboech@aol.com, Internet: http://www.mbsi.org
Music Museum - 1949   39065

Norwalk OH

Firelands Historical Society Museum, 4 Case Av, Norwalk, OH 44857 - T: (419) 668-6038
Historical Museum - 1857   39066

Norwich CT

Faith Trumbull Chapter Museum, 42 Rockwell St, Norwich, CT 06360 - T: (860) 887-8737
Local Museum / Historical Museum - 1893   39067

Leffingwell House Museum, 348 Washington St, Norwich, CT 06360 - T: (860) 889-9440, Fax: (860) 887-4551, Internet: http://www.visitne-wengland.com. Head: Ann-Etta Cannon
Local Museum / Historical Museum - 1901   39068

Slater Memorial Museum, 108 Crescent St, Norwich, CT 06360 - T: (860) 887-2506, Fax: (860) 889-6196, E-mail: tabakoffs@norwichfreeacademy.com. Head: Joseph P. Gualtieri
Fine Arts Museum - 1888   39069

Norwich NY

Chenango County Historical Society Museum, 45 Rexford St, Norwich, NY 13815 - T: (607) 334-9227, Fax: (607) 334-9227. Head: Kay Zaia
Historical Museum - 1938   39070

Norwich OH

National Road/Zane Grey Museum, 8850 E Pike, Norwich, OH 43767 - T: (740) 872-3143, Fax: (740) 872-3510, E-mail: zanegrey@globalco.net, Internet: http://www.ohiohistory.org. Head: Alan King
Science&Tech Museum - 1973   39071

Norwich VT

Montshire Museum of Science, Montshire Rd, Norwich, VT 05055 - T: (802) 649-2200, Fax: (802) 649-3637, E-mail: montshire@montshire.net, Internet: http://www.montshire.org. Head: David Goudy
Natural History Museum - 1975   39072

Norwich Historical Society Museum, 37 Church St, Norwich, VT 05055 - T: (802) 649-0124, E-mail: NHS@tpk.net. Head: Jane F. Britton
Local Museum - 1951
Local hist   39073

Norwood NY

Norwood Historical Association Museum, POB 163, Norwood, NY 13668-0163. Head: Gerald LaComb
Historical Museum - 1968   39074

Notre Dame IN

The Snite Museum of Art, University of Notre Dame, M. Krause Circle, Notre Dame, IN 46556-0368 - T: (219) 631-5466, Fax: (219) 631-8501, Internet: http://www.nd.edu/~sniteart. Head: Charles R. Loving
Fine Arts Museum / University Museum - 1842
Ethnographic art, photography, design, native American art   39075

Novato CA

Marin Museum of the American Indian, 2200 Novato Blvd, Novato, CA 94947 - T: (415) 897-4064, Fax: (415) 892-7804. Head: Shirley Schaufel
Ethnology Museum / Archaeological Museum - 1967   39076

Novato History Museum, 815 De Long Av, Novato, CA 94945 - T: (415) 897-4320, Fax: (415) 892-9136, E-mail: gretab@mindspring.com, Internet: http://www.ci.novato.com. Head: Greta Brunschwyler
Local Museum - 1976
Local hist - archive   39077

Nowata OK

Nowata County Historical Society Museum, 121 S Pine St, Nowata, OK 74048 - T: (918) 273-1191. Head: Raymond Cline
Historical Museum - 1969   39078

Oak Brook IL

Graue Mill and Museum, York and Spring Rds, Oak Brook, IL 60522-4533 - T: (630) 655-2090, Fax: (630) 920-9721, E-mail: administrator@grauemill.org, Internet: http://www.grauemill.org. Head: James J. Blaha
Local Museum / Science&Tech Museum - 1950
Local history, housed in 1852 restored waterwheel gristmill   39079

Oak Creek WI

Oak Creek Pioneer Village, S 15th Av & E. Forest Hill Av, Oak Creek, WI 53154 - T: (414) 761-2572, Internet: http://members.aol.com/larryr3670/oc_histr/ochsocie.htm
Local Museum - 1964
Local hist   39080

Oak Park IL

Frank Lloyd Wright Home and Studio, 951 Chicago Av, Oak Park, IL 60302 - T: (708) 848-1976, Fax: (708) 848-1248, E-mail: mercuri@wrightplus.org, Internet: http://www.wrightplus.org. Head: Joan B. Mercuri
Historical Museum - 1974
Residence and Studio of Frank Lloyd Wright 39081

Historical Society of Oak Park and River Forest, 217 S Home Av, Oak Park, IL 60302-3101 - T: (708) 848-6755, Internet: http://www.oprf.com/ophistory/. Head: Frank Lipo, Jan Dressel
Public Gallery / Local Museum - 1968
Regional history, Prairie style mansion, photography   39082

Oak Ridge TN

American Museum of Science and Energy, 300 S Tulane Av, Oak Ridge, TN 37830 - T: (865) 576-3200, Fax: (865) 576-6024, E-mail: info@amse.org, Internet: http://www.amse.org. Head: David J. Bean
Science&Tech Museum - 1949
Science, technology, hist of the Manhattan Project   39083

Children's Museum of Oak Ridge, 461 W Outer Dr, Oak Ridge, TN 37830 - T: (423) 482-1074, Fax: (423) 481-4889. Head: Selma Shapiro
Special Museum - 1973   39084

Oak Ridge Art Center, 201 Badger Av, Oak Ridge, TN 37831-3305 - T: (423) 482-1441, Fax: (423) 482-1441. Head: Leah Marcum-Estes
Fine Arts Museum - 1952
Mary & Alden coll, contemporary regional art 39085

Oakdale CA

Oakdale Museum, 212 W F St, Oakdale, CA 95361 - T: (209) 847-9229, 847-5822, E-mail: museum@chitons.com, Internet: http://oakdalemuseum.homestead.com/museum.html. Head: Glenn Burghardt
Local Museum - 1985
Local history   39086

Oakland CA

African-American Museum, 5606 San Pablo Av, Oakland, CA 94608 - T: (510) 597-5054, Fax: (510) 597-5030, E-mail: AAMLO@juno.com, Internet: http://oak2.ci.oakland.ca.us/aamlol.htm
Historical Museum - 1965   39087

Camron-Stanford House, 1418 Lakeside Dr, Oakland, CA 94612 - T: (510) 444-1876, Fax: (510) 874-7803
Fine Arts Museum / Historical Museum - 1971   39088

CCAC Institute, California College of Arts and Crafts, 5212 Broadway, Oakland, CA 94618 - T: (510) 594-3650, Fax: (510) 594-3761, E-mail: institute@ccac.art.edu, Internet: http://www.ccac.art.edu/institute. Head: Ralph Rugoff
Fine Arts Museum - 1907   39089

Merritt Museum of Anthropology, 12500 Campus Dr, Oakland, CA 94619 - T: (510) 436-2607, Fax: (415) 922-0905, E-mail: 104347.13@compuserve.com. Head: Dr. Barbara Joans
Ethnology Museum - 1973   39090

Mills College Art Museum, 5000 MacArthur Blvd, Oakland, CA 94613 - T: (510) 430-2164, Fax: (510) 430-3168, E-mail: mcam@mills.edu, Internet: http://www.mills.edu/mcam/mcam. Head: Dr. Katherine B. Crum
Fine Arts Museum / University Museum - 1925
Asian textiles, Japanese ceramics, old master prints, 19th-20th c prints drawings   39091

Oakland Museum of California, 1000 Oak St, Oakland, CA 94607 - T: (510) 238-2200, Fax: (510) 238-2258, E-mail: dmpower@museumca.org, Internet: http://www.museumca.org. Head: Dennis M. Power
Fine Arts Museum / Historical Museum / Library with Exhibitions / Natural History Museum - 1969 39092

Pardee Home Museum, 672 11th St, Oakland, CA 94607 - T: (510) 444-2187, Fax: (510) 444-7120. Head: David Nicolai
Historical Museum / Historic Site - 1982
Former residence of Governor George Pardee 39093

Pro Arts Gallery, 461 Ninth St, Oakland, CA 94607 - T: (510) 763-4361, Fax: (510) 763-9425, E-mail: proarts@lmi.net, Internet: http://www.proartsgallery.org. Head: Betty Kano
Fine Arts Museum - 1974 39094

Steven H. Oliver Art Center → CCAC Institute

Western Aerospace Museum, 8260 Boeing St, Oakland, CA 94614 - T: (510) 638-7100, Fax: (510) 638-6530, Internet: http://www.cyberair.com. Head: Ben Hance
Science&Tech Museum - 1980
Aerospace 39095

Oakland IA

Nishna Heritage Museum, 123 Main St, Oakland, IA 51560 - T: (712) 482-6802. Head: Cena Rattenborg
Fine Arts Museum / Local Museum - 1975
Heritage, local history 39096

Oakland MD

Garrett County Historical Museum, 107 S 2nd St, Oakland, MD 21550 - T: (301) 334-3226
Local Museum - 1969
Local history 39097

Oakley ID

Oakley Pioneer Museum, 108 W Main, Oakley, ID 83346 - T: (208) 862-3626. Head: Becky Clark
Local Museum / Museum of Classical Antiquities - 1967
History, antiques 39098

Oakley KS

Fick Fossil and History Museum, 700 W Third St, Oakley, KS 67748 - T: (785) 672-4839, Fax: (785) 672-3497, E-mail: cmullen@ruraltel.net, Internet: http://www.oakley-kansas.com/fick. Head: Cindy Mullen
Historical Museum / Natural History Museum - 1972
Geology, paleontology, history 39099

Oberlin KS

Last Indian Raid Museum, 258 S Penn Av, Oberlin, KS 67749 - T: (913) 475-2712, E-mail: decaturmuseum@nwkansas.com
Historic Site / Historical Museum - 1958
History, nr the site of 1878 last Indian raid on Kansas soil 39100

Oberlin OH

Allen Memorial Art Museum, Oberlin College, 87 N Main St, Oberlin, OH 44074 - T: (440) 775-8665, Fax: (440) 775-6841, E-mail: leslie.miller@oberlin.edu, Internet: http://www.oberlin.edu/allenart. Head: Dr. Sharon F. Patton
University Museum / Fine Arts Museum - 1917 39101

Oberlin Historical and Improvement Organization Museum, 73 1/2 S Professor St, Oberlin, OH 44074 - T: (440) 774-1700, Fax: (440) 774-8061
Local Museum / Historical Museum - 1964 39102

Ocala FL

Discovery Science Center of Central Florida, 50 S Magnolia Av, Ocala, FL 34474 - T: (352) 620-2555, Fax: (352) 620-8951. Head: Dr. Ellen Gilchrist
Historical Museum / Science&Tech Museum - 1993 39103

Don Garlits Museum of Drag Racing, 13700 SW 16th Av, I-75, Exit 67, Ocala, FL 34473 - T: (352) 245-8661, Fax: (352) 245-6895, E-mail: garlits@pig.net, Internet: http://www.garlits.com. Head: Donald G. Garlits
Special Museum - 1976 39104

Silver River Museum, 7189 NE 7th St, Ocala, FL 34470 - T: (352) 236-5401, Fax: (352) 236-7142, E-mail: wingate-e@popmail.firn.edu. Head: Guy Marwick
Natural History Museum / Archaeological Museum / Historical Museum - 1991 39105

Occoquan VA

Historic Occoquan, 413 Mill St, Occoquan, VA 22125 - T: (703) 491-7525. Head: Nellie K. Curtis
Local Museum - 1969
Local history, Miller's cottage of Grist mill 39106

Ocean City NJ

Ocean City Art Center, 1735 Simpson Av, Ocean City, NJ 08226 - T: (609) 399-7628, Fax: (609) 399-7089, E-mail: ocart@prousa.net, Internet: http://www.oceancityartcenter.org. Head: Eunice Bell
Public Gallery - 1967
Paintings 39107

Ocean City Historical Museum, 1735 Simpson Av, Ocean City, NJ 08226 - T: (609) 399-1801, Fax: (609) 399-0544. Head: Paul S. Anselm
Historical Museum - 1964 39108

Ocean Grove NJ

Historical Society Museum of Ocean Grove, New Jersey, 50 Pittman Av, Ocean Grove, NJ 07756 - T: (732) 774-1869. Head: Philip May
Local Museum - 1969
History of Ocean Grove, history of the camp meeting 39109

Ocean Springs MS

Walter Anderson Museum of Art, 510 Washington Av, Ocean Springs, MS 39564 - T: (228) 872-3164, Fax: (228) 875-4494, E-mail: motif@datasync.com, Internet: http://www.motif.org. Head: Clayton Bass
Fine Arts Museum - 1991 39110

William M. Colmer Visitor Center, 3500 Park Rd, Davis Bayou Area, Ocean Springs, MS 39564 - T: (228) 875-9057, Fax: (228) 872-2954, Internet: http://www.nps.gov/guis/
Historical Museum / Natural History Museum - 1970 39111

Oceanside CA

Mission San Luis Rey Museum, 4050 Mission Av, Oceanside, CA 92057 - T: (760) 757-3651, Fax: (760) 757-4613, E-mail: museuminfo@sanluisrey.org, Internet: http://www.sanluisrey.org. Head: Mary C. Whelan
Historical Museum - 1798
Local hist 39112

Oceanville NJ

The Noyes Museum of Art, Lily Lake Rd, Oceanville, NJ 08231 - T: (609) 652-8848, Fax: (609) 652-6166, E-mail: info@noyesmuseum.org, Internet: http://www.noyesmuseum.org. Head: Lawrence R. Schmidt
Fine Arts Museum - 1983 39113

Oconto WI

Oconto County Historical Society Museum, 917 Park Av, Oconto, WI 54153 - T: (920) 834-6206, 834-3860. Head: Diane Nichols
Local Museum - 1940
Local hist 39114

Odessa DE

Historic Houses of Odessa, Delaware, Main St, Odessa, DE 19730 - T: (302) 378-4069, Fax: (302) 378-4050. Head: Steven M. Pulinka
Local Museum - 1958
Historic house 39115

Odessa TX

The Ellen Noel Art Museum of the Permian Basin, 4909 East University Blvd, Odessa, TX 79762 - T: (915) 550-9696, Fax: (915) 368-9226, E-mail: enam@texasonline.net. Head: Marilyn Bassinger
Fine Arts Museum - 1985
Art 39116

The Presidential Museum, 622 N Lee, Odessa, TX 79761 - T: (915) 332-7123, Fax: (915) 498-4021, Internet: www.presidentialmuseum.org. Head: Carey F. Behrends
Historical Museum - 1965
History 39117

Ogallala NE

Front Street Museum, 519 E First, Ogallala, NE 69153 - T: (308) 284-6000, Fax: (308) 284-0865, E-mail: frontstreet@lakemac.net, Internet: http://www.negavision.net/frontstreet. Head: Jan Nielsen
Local Museum - 1964
History 39118

Ogden IA

Hickory Grove Rural School Museum, Don Williams Lake, Ogden, IA 50212 - T: (515) 432-1907, E-mail: bchs@opencominc.com. Head: Charles W. Irwin
Local Museum - 1972
Local hist 39119

Ogden UT

Eccles Community Art Center, 2580 Jefferson Av, Ogden, UT 84401 - T: (801) 392-6935, Fax: (801) 392-5295, E-mail: eccles@ogden4arts.org, Internet: http://www.ogden4arts.org. Head: Sandra H. Havas
Fine Arts Museum - 1959
Art 39120

Fort Buenaventura, 2450 A Av, Ogden, UT 84401 - T: (801) 621-4808, 392-5581, Fax: (801) 392-2431
Local Museum - 1980
Replica of 1848 fort located on site of first permanent white settlement in the Great Basin 39121

Ogden Union Station Museums, 2501 Wall Av, Union Station, Ogden, UT 84401 - T: (801) 629-8595, Fax: (801) 629-8555, E-mail: jeannieyoung@ciogden.ut.us, Internet: http://www.theunionstation.org. Head: Bob Geier
Local Museum - 1978
Art, railroads, cars, firearms, natural history 39122

Weber State University Art Gallery, Art Dept, Weber State University, 2001 University Circle, Ogden, UT 84408-2001 - T: (801) 626-7689, Fax: (801) 626-6976. Head: H. Barens
Fine Arts Museum / University Museum - 1960 39123

Ogdensburg NJ

Sterling Hill Mining Museum, 30 Plant St, Ogdensburg, NJ 07439 - T: (973) 209-7212, Fax: (973) 209-8505, E-mail: shm@tapnet.net, Internet: http://www.sterlinghill.org. Head: Richard Hauck
Science&Tech Museum - 1990
Mining 39124

Ogdensburg NY

Frederic Remington Art Museum, 303 Washington St, Ogdensburg, NY 13669 - T: (315) 393-2425, Fax: (315) 393-4464, E-mail: info@remington-museum.org, Internet: http://www.fredericremington.org. Head: Lowell McAllister
Fine Arts Museum / Decorative Arts Museum - 1923 39125

Ogunquit ME

Ogunquit Museum of American Art, 543 Shore Rd, Ogunquit, ME 03907-0815 - T: (207) 646-4909, Fax: (207) 646-6903. Head: John Dirks, Nicholas S. Strater
Fine Arts Museum - 1952
American art 39126

Oil City LA

Caddo-Pine Island Oil and Historical Society Museum, 207 S Land Av, Oil City, LA 71061 - T: (318) 995-6845, Fax: (318) 995-6848, E-mail: laoilmuseum@earthlink.net, Internet: http://www.sec.state.la.us. Head: H.D. Farrar
Local Museum - 1965
Local hist 39127

Oil City PA

Venango Museum of Art, Science and Industry, 270 Seneca St, Oil City, PA 16301 - T: (814) 676-2007, Fax: (814) 676-2007, E-mail: venangomuseum@venangomuseum.org. Head: Catherine Teig, Barbara Perlstein
Fine Arts Museum / Science&Tech Museum - 1961
Art, science, industry 39128

Ojai CA

Ojai Valley Museum, 130 W Ojai Av, Ojai, CA 93023 - T: (805) 640-1390, Fax: (805) 640-1342, E-mail: ojaivalleymuseum@aol.com. Head: Robin Sim
Local Museum / Natural History Museum / Historic Site / Historical Museum - 1966
Local hist, art, cultural and natural hist 39129

Okemah OK

Territory Town USA, Old West Museum, 5 m W of Okemah, on I-40, Okemah, OK 74859 - T: (918) 623-2599. Head: Louise Parsons
Local Museum - 1967
Western relics, Civil War and Native American artefacts 39130

Oklahoma City OK

45th Infantry Division Museum, 2145 NE 36, Oklahoma City, OK 73111 - T: (405) 424-5313, Fax: (405) 424-3748, E-mail: museum45@aol.com
Military Museum - 1976 39131

Harn Homestead and 1889er Museum, 313 NE 16, Oklahoma City, OK 73104 - T: (405) 235-4058, Fax: (405) 235-4041, Internet: http://connections.-oklahoman.net/harnhomestead/. Head: H. Johnson
Historical Museum - 1976 39132

Hulsey Gallery, Oklahoma City University, Norick Art Center, 2501 N Blackwelder, Oklahoma City, OK 73106 - T: (405) 521-5226, Fax: (405) 557-6029, Internet: http://www.okcu.edu. Head: Kirk Niemeyer
Public Gallery 39133

Individual Artists of Oklahoma, 1 N Hudson, Ste 150, Oklahoma City, OK 73102, mail addr: POB 60824, Oklahoma City, OK 73146 - T: (405) 232-6060, Fax: (405) 232-6061, E-mail: iao@telepath.com, Internet: http://www.iaogallery.org. Head: Shirley Blaschke
Fine Arts Museum 39134

Kirkpatrick Center Museum Complex, 2100 NE 52, Oklahoma City, OK 73111 - T: (405) 427-5461, Fax: (405) 424-1407. Head: Marilyn Ripple
Fine Arts Museum / Ethnology Museum / Local Museum / Natural History Museum - 1978
Air Space Museum, Omniplex, Planetarium, Red Earth Indian Center, Photography Hall of Fame and Museum, Greenhouse, Garden and Kirkpatrick Galleries (17 cultural, art and historical galleries) 39135

Kirkpatrick Science and Air Space Museum at Omniplex, 2100 NE 52 St, Oklahoma City, OK 73111 - T: (405) 602-6664, Fax: (405) 602-3767, E-mail: omniplex@ionet.net, Internet: http://www.omniplex.org. Head: Chuck Schillings
Science&Tech Museum / Natural History Museum - 1958 39136

Melton Art Reference Library Museum, 4300 N Sewell, Oklahoma City, OK 73118 - T: (405) 525-3603, Fax: (405) 525-0396, E-mail: meltonart@aol.com. Head: Suzanne Silvester
Library with Exhibitions / Special Museum - 1979 39137

National Cowboy and Western Heritage Museum, 1700 NE 63 St, Oklahoma City, OK 73111 - T: (405) 478-2250, Fax: (405) 478-4714, Internet: http// www.nationalcowboymuseum.org. Head: Ken Townsend
Historical Museum - 1954 39138

National Softball Hall of Fame and Museum Complex, 2801 NE 50, Oklahoma City, OK 73111 - T: (405) 424-5266, Fax: (405) 424-3855, E-mail: info@softball.org, Internet: http://www.softball.org. Head: Ron Radigonda, Bill Plummer
Special Museum - 1957 39139

Oklahoma City Art Museum, The Fairgrounds, 3113 Pershing Blvd, Oklahoma City, OK 73107 - T: (405) 946-4477, Fax: (405) 946-7671, E-mail: brian@okcartmuseum.com, Internet: http://www.okcartmuseum.com. Head: Carolyn Hill
Fine Arts Museum - 1989
Art 39140

Oklahoma Firefighters Museum, 2716 NE 50, Oklahoma City, OK 73111 - T: (405) 424-3440, Fax: (405) 425-1032, E-mail: osfa@brightok.net, Internet: http://www.brightok.net/~osfa. Head: Jim Minx
Special Museum - 1970 39141

Oklahoma Museum of African American Art, 3919 NW 10th St, Oklahoma City, OK 73107 - T: (405) 942-4896
Fine Arts Museum 39142

Overholser Mansion, NW 15 and Hudson, Oklahoma City, OK 73103 - T: (405) 528-8485
Historical Museum - 1972 39143

State Museum of History, 2100 N Lincoln Blvd, Oklahoma City, OK 73105 - T: (405) 521-2491, Fax: (405) 522-2492, Internet: http://www.ok-history.mus.ok.us. Head: Dr. Bob Blackburn
Historical Museum - 1893
Historic site - Library, Archives 39144

The World Organization of China Painters, 2641 NW 10th St, Oklahoma City, OK 73107 - T: (405) 521-1234, Fax: (405) 521-1265, E-mail: wocporg@theshop.net, Internet: http://www.theshop.net/wocporg. Head: Patricia Dickerson
Fine Arts Museum / Decorative Arts Museum - 1967
Porcelain 39145

Okmulgee OK

Creek Council House Museum, Town Square, 106 W Sixth, Okmulgee, OK 74447 - T: (918) 756-2324, Fax: (918) 756-3671. Head: Debbie Martin
Historical Museum / Ethnology Museum - 1923 39146

Olathe KS

Mahaffie Stagecoach Stop and Farm, 1100 Kansas City Rd, Olathe, KS 66061 - T: (913) 782-6972, Fax: (913) 397-5114, E-mail: mahaffie@unicom.net. Head: Jack L. Tinnell
Historical Museum - 1977
1865 Mahaffie house and stagecoach stop on Santa Fe Trail 39147

Old Bennington VT

Bennington Battle Monument, 15 Monument Circle, Old Bennington, VT 05201 - T: (802) 828-3051, Fax: (802) 447-0550, E-mail: jdumville@gate.dca.state.vt.us, Internet: http://www.state.vt.us/dca/historic/hp_sites.htm
Historic Site - 1891
Historic site located near the site of the Bennington Battle of the Revolutionary War 39148

Old Bethpage NY

Old Bethpage Village Restoration, Round Swamp Rd, Old Bethpage, NY 11804 - T: (516) 572-8401, Fax: (516) 572-8413. Head: James McKenna
Open Air Museum - 1970 39149

Old Chatham NY

Shaker Museum, 88 Shaker Museum Rd, Old Chatham, NY 12136 - T: (518) 794-9100 ext 100, Fax: (518) 794-8621, E-mail: shakeroldchat@taconic.net, Internet: http://www.shakermuseumoldchat.org. Head: Mary Ellen W. Hern
Folklore Museum / Historical Museum - 1950 39150

Old Fort NC

Mountain Gateway Museum, Water and Catawba Sts, Old Fort, NC 28762 - T: (704) 668-9259, Fax: (704) 668-0041. Head: Sam Gray
Local Museum - 1971 39151

Old Lyme CT

Florence Griswold Museum, 96 Lyme St, Old Lyme, CT 06371 - T: (860) 434-5542, Fax: (860) 434-6259, E-mail: flogris@connix.com, Internet: http://www.flogris.org. Head: Jeffrey W. Andersen
Fine Arts Museum / Historical Museum - 1936 39152

Old Shawneetown IL

Shawneetown Historic Site, 280 Washington St, Old Shawneetown, IL 62984-3401 - T: (618) 269-3303
Historical Museum / Open Air Museum - 1917
Historic Building, 1839 4-story Greek Revival Bank 39153

Old Westbury NY

Old Westbury Gardens, 71 Old Westbury Rd, Old Westbury, NY 11568 - T: (516) 333-0048, Fax: (516) 333-6807, Internet: http://www.oldwestbury-gardens.org. Head: Carol Large
Historical Museum / Decorative Arts Museum - 1959 39154

Olivet MI

Armstrong Collection, Olivet College, Art Department, 320 S Main St, Olivet, MI 49076 - T: (616) 749-7000 ext 7661, Fax: (616) 749-7178, Internet: http://www.olivet.edu. Head: Donald Rowe
Fine Arts Museum
American Indian, Mesopotamian, Philippine and Thailand artifacts, primitive arts, sculpture, modern American prints - library 39155

Olustee FL

Olustee Battlefield, U.S. 90, 2 m E, Olustee, FL 32072, mail addr: POB 40, Olustee, FL 32072 - T: (904) 758-0400, Internet: http://extlab1.entvem.ufl.edu/olustee
Historic Site / Military Museum - 1909
State historic site, military 39156

Olympia WA

Bigelow House Museum, 918 Glass Av, Olympia, WA 98506 - T: (360) 357-6198, 753-1215. Head: Gerry Alexander
Local Museum - 1992
Local hist 39157

Evergreen Galleries, Evergreen State College, 2700 Evergreen Pkwy NW, Olympia, WA 98505-0002 - T: (360) 866-6000 ext 6488, Fax: (360) 866-6794, E-mail: alvesb@evergreen.edu, Internet: http://www.evergreen.edu/user/galleries. Head: Peter Ramsey
Fine Arts Museum / University Museum - 1970
Art 39158

Washington State Capital Museum, 211 W 21st Av, Olympia, WA 98501 - T: (360) 753-2580, Fax: (360) 586-8322, E-mail: dvalley@wshs.wa.gov, Internet: http://www.wshs.com
Local Museum - 1941
Local hist 39159

Omaha NE

Artists' Cooperative Gallery, 405 S 11th St, Omaha, NE 68102 - T: (402) 342-9617. Head: Nicholas W. Pella
Fine Arts Museum - 1975
American paintings 39160

Bemis Center for Contemporary Arts, 724 S 12th St, Omaha, NE 68102-3202 - T: (402) 341-7130, Fax: (402) 341-9791, E-mail: bemis@novia.net. Head: Ree Schonlau
Fine Arts Museum
Sculpture, ceramics 39161

Durham Western Heritage Museum, 801 S 10 St, Omaha, NE 68108 - T: (402) 444-5071, Fax: (402) 444-5397, E-mail: info@dwhm.org, Internet: http://www.dwhm.org. Head: Randall Hayes
Local Museum - 1975 39162

Fine Arts Gallery, Creighton University, 2500 California Plaza, Omaha, NE 68178 - T: (402) 280-2509 ext 2831, Fax: (402) 280-2320, E-mail: bohr@creightonuniversity.edu, Internet: http://www.creightonuniversity.edu. Head: G. Ted Bohr
Fine Arts Museum - 1973
Drawings, graphics, paintings, photography, prints, sculpture 39163

General Crook House Museum, 5730 N 30 St, Omaha, NE 68111-1657 - T: (402) 455-9990, Fax: (402) 453-9448, Internet: http://www.radiks.net/~hsdc-lac/. Head: Betty J. Davis
Local Museum - 1956 39164

Great Plains Black Museum, 2213 Lake St, Omaha, NE 68110 - T: (402) 345-2212, Fax: (402) 345-2256, Internet: http://members.aol.com/asmith8955/ahist.htm
Historical Museum - 1975 39165

Joslyn Art Museum, 2200 Dodge St, Omaha, NE 68102-1292 - T: (402) 342-3300, Fax: (402) 342-2376, E-mail: info@joslyn.org, Internet: http://www.joslyn.org. Head: J. Brooks Joyner
Fine Arts Museum - 1931 39166

El Museo Latino, 4701 S 25th St, Omaha, NE 68107-2728 - T: (402) 731-1137, Fax: (402) 733-7012, E-mail: mgarcia@radiks.net, Internet: http://www.elmuseolatino.org. Head: Magdalena A. Garcia
Fine Arts Museum / Folklore Museum / Historical Museum - 1993
Latino art and hist 39167

The Omaha Center for Contemporary Art, 1116 Jackson St, Omaha, NE 68102 - T: (402) 345-9711
Fine Arts Museum 39168

Omaha Children's Museum, 500 S 20 St, Omaha, NE 68102-2508 - T: (402) 342-6164 ext 410, Fax: (402) 342-6165, E-mail: recooper@compuserve.com, Internet: http://www.ocm.org. Head: Rudyard E. Cooper
Special Museum - 1977
Arts, science, humanities 39169

Onancock VA

Kerr Place, 69 Market St, Onancock, VA 23417 - T: (757) 787-8012, E-mail: kerr@esva.net. Head: John H. Verrill
Local Museum - 1957
Local hist 39170

Onchiota NY

Six Nations Indian Museum, County Rte 30, HCR #1, Onchiota, NY 12989 - T: (518) 891-2299, E-mail: redmaple@northnet.org. Head: John Fadden
Ethnology Museum - 1954 39171

Oneida NY

Cottage Lawn, 435 Main St, Oneida, NY 13421-0415 - T: (315) 363-4136, Fax: (315) 363-4136. Head: Thomas J. Keman
Historical Museum - 1895 39172

Oneonta NY

The National Soccer Hall of Fame, 18 Stadium Circle, Oneonta, NY 13820 - T: (607) 432-3351, Fax: (607) 432-8429, E-mail: info@soccerhall.org, Internet: http://www.soccerhall.org. Head: Will Lunn
Special Museum - 1981
Sports hist 39173

Science Discovery Center of Oneonta, State University College, Oneonta, NY 13820-4015 - T: (607) 436-2011, Fax: (607) 436-2654, E-mail: scdisc@oneonta.edu, Internet: http://www.oneonta.edu/~scdisc. Head: Albert J. Read
Science&Tech Museum / Natural History Museum - 1987 39174

Yager Museum, Hartwick College, Oneonta, NY 13820-4020 - T: (607) 431-4480, Fax: (607) 431-4457, E-mail: abramsg@hartwick.edu, Internet: http://www.hartwick.edu. Head: George H.J. Abrams
Fine Arts Museum / University Museum - 1797 39175

Onset MA

Porter Thermometer Museum, 49 Zarahemla Rd, Onset, MA 02558 - T: (508) 295-5504, Fax: (508) 295-8323, E-mail: thermometerman@aol.com, Internet: http://members.aol.com/thermometerman/inoex.html. Head: Barbara A. Porter
Science&Tech Museum / Historical Museum - 1990
Medical, maritime, antique, weather, souvenir thermometers 39176

Ontario CA

Museum of History and Art, 225 S Euclid Av, Ontario, CA 91761 - T: (909) 983-3198, Fax: (909) 983-8978. Head: Theresa Hanley
Local Museum / Fine Arts Museum - 1979
Local history and art 39177

Ontario NY

Town of Ontario Historical and Landmark Preservation Society Museum Complex, Heritage Sq, Ontario Center Rd and Brickchurch Rd, Ontario, NY 14519 - T: (315) 524-8928
Historical Museum / Local Museum - 1969 39178

Ontario OR

Four Rivers Cultural Center, 676 SW 5th Av, Ontario, OR 97914 - T: (541) 889-8191, Fax: (541) 889-7628, E-mail: frcc@micron.net, Internet: http://www.4rcc.com. Head: Ila Staab
Local Museum / Folklore Museum - 1987
Local hist 39179

Ontonagon MI

Ontonagon County Historical Society Museum, 422 River St, Ontonagon, MI 49953-0092 - T: (906) 884-6165, E-mail: ochsmuse@up.lib.mi.us, Internet: http://www.upbiz.com/mi/ochs.html
Local Museum - 1957
Regional history 39180

Oradell NJ

Hiram Blauvelt Art Museum, 705 Kinderkamack Rd, Oradell, NJ 07649 - T: (201) 261-0012, Fax: (201) 391-6418, E-mail: majazi8@att.nzt, Internet: http://www.blauvzitmuszum.com. Head: Dr. Marijane Singer
Fine Arts Museum - 1940
Art 39181

Orange TX

Heritage House of Orange County Museum, 905 W Division, Orange, TX 77630 - T: (409) 886-5385, Fax: (409) 886-0917, E-mail: hhmuseum@exp.net, Internet: http://www.heritagehouseoforange.org
Historical Museum - 1977
Local hist 39182

Stark Museum of Art, 712 Green Av, Orange, TX 77630 - T: (409) 883-6661, Fax: (409) 883-6361, E-mail: starkart@exp.net, Internet: http://www.starkmuseumofart.org. Head: Walter G. Riedel
Fine Arts Museum - 1974
Art 39183

The W.H. Stark House, 610 W Main St, Orange, TX 77630 - T: (409) 833-3513, Fax: (409) 883-3530. Head: Tracy Corley
Local Museum - 1981
Historic house 39184

Orange VA

The James Madison Museum, 129 Caroline St, Orange, VA 22960 - T: (540) 672-1776, Fax: (540) 672-0231, E-mail: info@jamesmadis-onmuseum.org, Internet: http://www.jamesmadis-onmuseum.org. Head: Victoria B. Milton
Historical Museum - 1976
Local hist 39185

Orangeburg SC

I.P. Stanback Museum, South Carolina State University, Orangeburg, SC 29117 - T: (803) 536-7174, 536-8119, Fax: (803) 536-8309. Head: Dr. Leroy Davis, Frank Martin
Fine Arts Museum / University Museum - 1980
Art 39186

Orchard Lake MI

Saint Mary's Galeria, 3535 Indian Trail, Orchard Lake, MI 48324 - T: (248) 683-0345. Head: Marian Owczarski
Fine Arts Museum - 1963
Former Michigan Military Academy, contemporary Polish paintings and sculpture, Polish printing, folk art, tapestries 39187

Orchard Park NY

Orchard Park Historical Society Museum, S-4287 S Buffalo St, Orchard Park, NY 14127 - T: (716) 662-3285. Head: John N. Printy
Historical Museum - 1951 39188

Oregonia OH

Fort Ancient Museum, 6123 State Rte 350, Exits 32 and 36 off I-71, Oregonia, OH 45054 - T: (513) 932-4421, Fax: (513) 932-4843, E-mail: fancient@your-net.com, Internet: http://www.ohiohistory.org
Ethnology Museum / Natural History Museum 39189

Orinda CA

Museum of Robotics, 120 Village Sq, #49, Orinda, CA 94563-2502 - T: (510) 832-6059, 524-1163, Fax: (510) 524-8085, E-mail: ramoroso@hooked.net, Internet: http://www.museumrobotics.org. Head: Richard L. Amoroso
Science&Tech Museum - 1987
Technology, robots 39190

Oriskany NY

Oriskany Battlefield, State Rte 69 W, Oriskany, NY 13424 - T: (315) 768-7224, Fax: (315) 337-3081
Military Museum / Open Air Museum - 1927 39191

Orland ME

Orland Historical Museum, Castine Rd, Orland, ME 04472 - T: (207) 469-2476. Head: David L. Davis
Local Museum - 1966
Local history 39192

Orlando FL

East Campus Galleries, Valencia Community College, 701 N Econlockhatchee Trail, Orlando, FL 32825 - T: (407) 299-5000 ext 2298, Fax: (407) 299-5000 ext 2270, Internet: http://www.valencia.cc.fl.us. Head: Sanford Shugart
Fine Arts Museum - 1967
Art 39193

Orange County Historical Museum, 65 E Central Blv, Orlando, FL 32801 - T: (407) 836-8500, Fax: (407) 836-8550, E-mail: sara.vanarsdel@ocfl.net, Internet: http://www.thehistorycenter.org. Head: Sara Van Arsdel
Local Museum - 1957
Local Central Florida history 39194

Orlando Museum of Art, 2416 N Mills Av, Orlando, FL 32803-1483 - T: (407) 896-4231, Fax: (407) 896-9920, 894-4314, E-mail: info@omart.org, Internet: http://www.omart.org. Head: Marena Grant Morrisey
Fine Arts Museum - 1924
Art 39195

Orleans MA

French Cable Station Museum in Orleans, 41 Rte 28, Orleans, MA 02653 - T: (508) 240-1735, Fax: (508) 240-6099, E-mail: miko@gis.net
Special Museum - 1972
Atlantic Cable Terminal, communications 39196

Ormond Beach FL

Fred Dana Marsh Museum, 2099 N Beach St, Tomoka State Park, Ormond Beach, FL 32174 - T: (904) 676-4045, 676-4050, Fax: (904) 676-4060, Internet: http://www.dep.state.pl.us/parks
Open Air Museum / Natural History Museum - 1967
Village of Nocoroco of the 1605, site of British plantation, Mount Oswald 39197

Ormond Memorial Art Museum, 78 E Granada Blvd, Ormond Beach, FL 32176 - T: (904) 676-3347, Fax: (904) 676-3244, E-mail: omam78e@aol.com, Internet: http://www.state.fl.us/ormond/. Head: Ann Burt
Fine Arts Museum - 1946 39198

Orofino ID

Clearwater Historical Museum, 315 College Av, Orofino, ID 83544-1454 - T: (208) 476-5033, E-mail: chmusuem@clearwater.net, Internet: http://home.valint.net/chmuseum. Head: Bernice Pullen
Local Museum - 1960
Local history, mining, logging, Nez Perce Indians, farming 39199

Orono ME

Hudson Museum, University of Maine, 5476 Maine Center for the Arts, Orono, ME 04469-5746 - T: (207) 581-1901, Fax: (207) 581-1950, E-mail: stephen@maine.maine.edu, Internet: http://www.umaine.edu/hudsonmuseum/. Head: Stephen L. Whittington
Ethnology Museum / Archaeological Museum - 1986
Anthropology 39200

Museum of Art, University of Maine, 109 Carnegie Hall, Orono, ME 04469 - T: (207) 581-3255, Fax: (207) 581-3083, E-mail: umma@umit.maine.edu, Internet: http://umma.umecah.maine.edu. Head: Wally Mason
Fine Arts Museum / University Museum - 1946
Art, housed in a library of Tusco-Doric (Palladian) design 39201

Oroville CA

Oroville Chinese Temple, 1500 Broderick St, Oroville, CA 95965 - T: (530) 538-2415, Fax: (530) 538-2426. Head: Jim P. Carpenter
Historical Museum / Religious Arts Museum - 1863 39202

Osage IA

Mitchell County Historical Museum, N 6th, Osage, IA 50461-8557 - T: (515) 732-4047. Head: Jerry Hemrich
Local Museum / Agriculture Museum - 1965
Local history, agriculture, Cedar Valley seminary 39203

Osceola NE

Polk County Historical Museum, 561 South St, Osceola, NE 68651 - T: (402) 747-7901. Head: D. Ruth Lux
Local Museum - 1967 39204

Oshkosh WI

EAA AirVenture Museum, 3000 Poberezny Rd, Oshkosh, WI 54903-3065 - T: (920) 426-4800, Fax: (920) 426-6765, E-mail: museum@eaa.org, Internet: http://www.eaa.org. Head: Adam. Smith
Science&Tech Museum - 1963
Aviation 39205

Military Veterans Museum, Park Plaza Mall, Oshkosh, WI 54901 - T: (920) 426-8615, Fax: (920) 738-1515. Head: E. Munroe Hjerstedt
Military Museum - 1985 39206

Oshkosh Public Museum, 1331 Algoma Blvd, Oshkosh, WI 54901 - T: (920) 424-4731, Fax: (920) 424-4738, E-mail: info@publicmuseum.oshkosh.net, Internet: http://www.publicmuseum@oshkosh.net. Head: Bradley Larson
Local Museum - 1924
Local hist 39207

Paine Art Center, 1410 Algoma Blvd, Oshkosh, WI 54901-2719 - T: (920) 235-6903, Fax: (920) 235-6303, E-mail: mmueller@paineartcenter.com, Internet: http://www.paine.artcenter.com. Head: Barbara A. Hirschfeld
Fine Arts Museum - 1947
Art Museum 39208

Oskaloosa IA

Nelson Pioneer Farm and Museum, 2294 Oxford Av, Oskaloosa, IA 52577 - T: (515) 672-2989
Historical Museum / Agriculture Museum - 1942
Daniel and Margaret Nelson Home, Nelson barn, local history, agriculture 39209

Oskaloosa KS

Old Jefferson Town, Hwy 59, Oskaloosa, KS 66066 - T: (785) 863-2070, Internet: http://www.digital-history.com/schools/Oskaloosa/Old_Jeff_Town.html. Head: Karen Heady
Local Museum / Open Air Museum - 1966
Seven c.1880 bldgs 39210

Ossineke MI

Dinosaur Gardens Museum, 11160 U.S. 23 S, Ossineke, MI 49766 - T: (517) 471-5477. Head: Frank A. McCourt
Natural History Museum - 1934
Paleontology 39211

Ossining NY

Ossining Historical Society Museum, 196 Croton Av, Ossining, NY 10562 - T: (914) 941-0001, Fax: (914) 941-0001, E-mail: ohsm@worldnet.att.net, Internet: http://home.att.net/~ohsm. Head: Roberta Y. Arminio
Historical Museum / Fine Arts Museum - 1931 39212

Osterville MA

Osterville Historical Museum, 155 W Bay Rd, Osterville, MA 02655 - T: (508) 428-5861, Fax: (508) 428-2241, E-mail: ohs@capecod.net, Internet: http://www.osterville.org. Head: Harry Holway
Local Museum - 1931
Local history 39213

Oswego NY

Fort Ontario, 1 E Fourth St, Oswego, NY 13126 - T: (315) 343-4711, Fax: (315) 343-1430. Head: Patrick A. Wilder
Military Museum - 1949 39214

Richardson-Bates House Museum, 135 E Third St, Oswego, NY 13126 - T: (315) 343-1342. Head: Terrence M. Prior
Historical Museum - 1896 39215

Safe Haven, 3651 County Rte 57, Oswego, NY 13126 - T: (315) 343-1971, E-mail: safehavn@juno.com, Internet: http://www.syracuse.com/safehaven. Head: Scott B. Scanlon
Historical Museum
History 39216

Tyler Art Gallery, State University of New York College of Arts and Science, Oswego, NY 13126 - T: (315) 341-2113, Fax: (315) 341-3439, E-mail: kwasigro@oswego.edu, Internet: http://www.oswego.edu/. Head: David Kwasigroh
Fine Arts Museum / University Museum
Grant Arnold coll 39217

Ottumwa IA

Airpower Museum, 22001 Bluegrass Rd, Ottumwa, IA 52501-8569 - T: (441) 938-2773, Fax: (441) 938-2084, E-mail: aaaapmhq@pcsia.com, Internet: http://www.aaa-apm.org
Science&Tech Museum - 1965
Aeronautics 39218

Wapello County Historical Museum, 210 W Main, Ottumwa, IA 52501 - T: (515) 682-8676. Head: Harold Gipson
Local Museum / Ethnology Museum - 1959
Regional history 39219

Overland Park KS

Gallery of Art, Johnson County Community College, 12345 College Blvd, Overland Park, KS 66210 - T: (913) 469-8500, Fax: (913) 469-2348, E-mail: bhartman@jccc.net, Internet: http://www.jccc.net/gallery. Head: Dr. Charles Carlsen, Bruce Hartman
Fine Arts Museum / University Museum - 1969
Art gallery, Oppenheimer-Stein sculpture coll 39220

Overton NV

Lost City Museum, 721 S Hwy 169, Overton, NV 89040 - T: (702) 397-2193, Fax: (702) 397-8987, E-mail: lostcity@comnett.net, Internet: http://www.comnett.net/~kolson/. Head: Kathryne Olson
Historical Museum / Local Museum - 1935 39221

Owego NY

Tioga County Historical Society Museum, 110 Front St, Owego, NY 13827 - T: (607) 687-2460, Fax: (607) 687-7788, E-mail: tiogamus@clarityconnect.com, Internet: http://www.tier.net/tiogahistory/. Head: Dr. John B. Shafer, JoAnn Lindstrom Llewellyn, Pamela Goddard
Historical Museum / Local Museum - 1914 39222

Owensboro KY

International Bluegrass Music Museum, 101 Daviess St, Owensboro, KY 42303 - T: (502) 926-7891, Fax: (502) 686-7863. Head: Thomas Riggs
Music Museum - 1992
Music hist 39223

Owensboro Area Museum of Science and History, 220 Daviess St, Owensboro, KY 42303 - T: (502) 687-2732, Fax: (502) 687-2738. Head: Ed Allen
Local Museum - 1966
Local history 39224

Owensboro Museum of Fine Art, 901 Frederica St, Owensboro, KY 42301 - T: (502) 685-3181, Fax: (502) 685-3181, E-mail: omfa@mindspring.com. Head: Mary Bryan Hood
Fine Arts Museum - 1977
Art, decorative arts 39225

Owls Head ME

Owls Head Transportation Museum, Rte 73, Owls Head, ME 04854 - T: (207) 594-4418, Fax: (207) 594-4410, E-mail: info@ohtm.org, Internet: http://www.ohtm.org. Head: Charles Chiarchiaro
Science&Tech Museum - 1974
Transport 39226

Owosso MI

Curwood Castle, 224 Curwood Castle Dr, Owosso, MI 48867 - T: (517) 725-0511
Special Museum - 1975
Studio of novelist James Oliver Curwood 39227

Michigan State Trust for Railway Preservation, 600 S Oakwood St, Owosso, MI 48867-0665 - T: (517) 725-9464, Fax: (517) 723-1225, E-mail: twelve25@shianet.org, Internet: http://www.mstrp.com
Science&Tech Museum - 1980
Railroad Transportation and technology 39228

Oxford MA

Oxford Library Museum, 339 Main St, Oxford, MA 01540 - T: (508) 987-6003, Fax: (508) 987-3896, E-mail: tkelley@cwmarsmail.cwmars.org, Internet: http://www.oxfordma.com. Head: Timothy Kelley
Local Museum - 1903
Local history 39229

Oxford MD

Oxford Museum, Morris and Market Sts, Oxford, MD 21654 - T: (410) 226-5331
Local Museum - 1964
Local history 39230

Oxford MI

Northeast Oakland Historical Museum, 1 N Washington St, Oxford, MI 48371 - T: (800) 628-8413, E-mail: mariee1@prodigy.net
Local Museum - 1971
Local history 39231

Oxford MS

University Gallery, c/o University of Mississippi, Bryandt Hall, Oxford, MS 38677 - T: (662) 232-7193, Fax: (662) 232-5013, E-mail: art@sunset.backbone.oldmiss.edu. Head: Margaret Gorove
University Museum / Fine Arts Museum
Student art works 39232

University Museums, c/o University of Mississippi, University Av and Fifth St, Oxford, MS 38677-1848 - T: (662) 915-7073, Fax: (662) 915-7035, E-mail: museums@olemiss.edu, Internet: http://www.olemiss.edu/depts/u_museum. Head: William Griffith
University Museum / Fine Arts Museum - 1977
Local history, classical antiquities, folk art of the American South, antique scientific instruments 39233

Oxford NC

Granville County Museum, 110 Court St, Oxford, NC 27565 - T: (919) 693-9706, Fax: (919) 692-1030, E-mail: gcmuseum@gloryroad.net. Head: Pam Thornton
Local Museum - 1996
Local hist, art, culture, science 39234

Harris Exhibit Hall, 1 Museum Ln, Oxford, NC 27565 - T: (919) 693-9706, Fax: (919) 692-1030, E-mail: gcmuseum@gloryroad.net. Head: Pam Thornton
Public Gallery - 1996 39235

Oxford OH

Miami University Art Museum, Patterson Av, Oxford, OH 45056 - T: (513) 529-2232, Fax: (513) 529-6555, E-mail: kretra@muohio.edu, Internet: http://www.muohio.edu/artmuseum. Head: Robert A. Kret
Fine Arts Museum / University Museum - 1978 39236

William Holmes McGuffey, 410 E Spring St, Oxford, OH 45056 - T: (513) 529-2232, Fax: (513) 529-6555, E-mail: ellisocw@muohio.edu, Internet: http://www.muohio.edu/artmuseum/. Head: Dr. Curtis W. Ellison
Historical Museum - 1960 39237

Oxnard CA

Carnegie Art Museum, 424 S C St, Oxnard, CA 93030 - T: (805) 385-8157, Fax: (805) 483-3654, Internet: http://www.vcnet.com/carnart. Head: Suzanne Bellah
Fine Arts Museum - 1980 39238

Ventura County Maritime Museum, 2731 S Victoria Av, Oxnard, CA 93035 - T: (805) 984-6260, Fax: (805) 984-5970, E-mail: vcmm@aol.com. Head: Mark S. Bacin
Local Museum / Historical Museum - 1991
Maritime and county history 39239

Oxon Hill MD

Oxon Cove Park Museum, 6411 Oxon Hill Rd, Oxon Hill, MD 20745 - T: (301) 839-1177, Fax: (202) 690-0862. Head: Robert Stanton
Agriculture Museum - 1967
Agriculture, farm and farm outbuildings 39240

Oyster Bay NY

Coe Hall, Planting Fields Rd, Oyster Bay, NY 11771-0058 - T: (516) 922-9210, Fax: (516) 922-9226, E-mail: coehall@worldnet.att.net, Internet: http://www.plantingfields.com
Historical Museum - 1979 39241

Earle Wightman Museum, 20 Summit St, Oyster Bay, NY 11771 - T: (516) 922-5032, Fax: (516) 922-6892, E-mail: obhistory@aol.com, Internet: http://members.aol.com/obhistory. Head: Thomas A. Kuehhas
Historical Museum - 1960
Reichnan coll of early American tools, Theodor Roosevelt coll 39242

Oyster Bay Historical Society Museum → Earle Wightman Museum

Raynham Hall Museum, 20 W Main St, Oyster Bay, NY 11771 - T: (516) 922-6808, Fax: (516) 922-7640, E-mail: raynham-hall-museum@global.net. Head: Andrew C. Batten
Decorative Arts Museum / Historical Museum - 1953 39243

Sagamore Hill National Historic Site, 20 Sagamore Hill Rd, Oyster Bay, NY 11771-1899 - T: (516) 922-4788, Fax: (516) 922-4792, Internet: http://www.nps.gov/sahi
Historical Museum - 1963 39244

Ozona TX

Crockett County Museum, 404 Eleventh St, Ozona, TX 76943 - T: (915) 392-2837, Fax: (915) 392-5654, E-mail: ccmuseum@hotmail.com. Head: Mary Geniece Childress
Local Museum - 1939
Local hist 39245

Pacific Grove CA

Pacific Grove Art Center, 568 Lighthouse Av, Pacific Grove, CA 93950 - T: (831) 375-2208, Fax: (831) 375-2208, E-mail: pgart@mbay.net, Internet: http://www.pgartcenter.org
Fine Arts Museum - 1969 39246

Pacific Grove Museum of Natural History, 165 Forest Av, Pacific Grove, CA 93950 - T: (831) 648-5716, Fax: (831) 372-3256, E-mail: pgmuseum@mbay.net, Internet: http://www.pgmuseum.org. Head: Stephen F. Bailey
Natural History Museum - 1881 39247

Pacific Palisades CA

Will Rogers State Historic Park, 1501 Will Rogers State Park Rd, Pacific Palisades, CA 90272 - T: (310) 454-8212, Fax: (310) 459-2031
Historical Museum / Open Air Museum / Natural History Museum - 1944 39248

Pacifica CA

Sanchez Adobe Historic Site, 1000 Linda Mar Blvd, Pacifica, CA 94044 - T: (650) 359-1462, Fax: (650) 359-1462, E-mail: samhist@aol.com, Internet: http://www.sanmateocountyhistory.com. Head: Mitch Postel
Historical Museum / Local Museum - 1947 39249

Paducah KY

Museum of the American Quilter's Society, 215 Jefferson St, Paducah, KY 42001 - T: (270) 442-8856, Fax: (270) 442-5448, E-mail: maqsmus@apex.net, Internet: http://www.quiltmuseum.org. Head: Victoria Faoro
Fine Arts Museum / Decorative Arts Museum - 1991
Arts and crafts, textiles, quilts 39250

William Clark Market House Museum, 121 S Second St, Market House Sq, Paducah, KY 42001 - T: (270) 443-7759. Head: Penny Baucum-Fields
Local Museum - 1968
History, building was used as a farmers market 39251

Yeiser Art Center, 200 Broadway, Paducah, KY 42001-0732 - T: (502) 442-2453, E-mail: yacenter@apex.net, Internet: http://www.yeiser.org. Head: Dan Carver
Fine Arts Museum - 1957 39252

Page AZ

John Wesley Powell Memorial Museum, 6 N Lake Powell Blvd, Page, AZ 86040-0547 - T: (520) 645-9496, Fax: (520) 645-3412, E-mail: director@powellmuseum.org, Internet: http://www.powellmuseum.org. Head: Julia P. Betz
Historical Museum - 1969 39253

Pagosa Springs CO

Fred Harman Art Museum, 2560 W Hwy 160, Pagosa Springs, CO 81147 - T: (970) 731-5785, Fax: (970) 731-4832, E-mail: fharman@pagosa.net, Internet: http://www.harmanartmuseum.com. Head: Fred C. Harman
Fine Arts Museum - 1979 39254

Paicines CA

Pinnacles National Monument, 5000 Hwy 146, Paicines, CA 95043 - T: (408) 389-4485 ext 233, Fax: (408) 389-4489, E-mail: Larry_Whalon@nps.gov, Internet: http://www.nps.gov
Natural History Museum - 1908 39255

Painesville OH

Indian Museum of Lake County-Ohio, Lake Erie College, 391 W Washington, Painesville, OH 44077 - T: (440) 352-1911. Head: Gwen G. King
Ethnology Museum / Archaeological Museum - 1980 39256

Painted Post NY

Erwin Museum, 117 W Water St, Painted Post, NY 14870 - T: (607) 962-7021
Local Museum - 1945 39257

Palm Beach FL

Flagler Museum, Coconut Row and Whitehall Way, Palm Beach, FL 33480 - T: (561) 655-2833, Fax: (561) 655-2826, E-mail: flagler@emi.net, Internet: http://www.flagler.org. Head: John M. Blades
Historical Museum - 1959 39258

The Society of the Four Arts Gallery, 2 Four Arts Plaza, Palm Beach, FL 33480 - T: (561) 655-7227, Fax: (561) 655-7233, E-mail: SFourArts@aol.comts.org, Internet: http://www.sfourarts.org. Head: Robert W. Safrin, Wiley R. Reynolds
Fine Arts Museum - 1936
Art gallery, sculpture garden - library 39259

Palm Coast FL

Florida Agricultural Museum, 1850 Princess Place Rd, Palm Coast, FL 32137 - T: (904) 446-7630, Fax: (904) 922-9444, E-mail: famuseum@pcfl.net. Head: Bruce J. Piatek
Agriculture Museum - 1983
Agriculture 39260

Palm Springs CA

Palm Springs Desert Museum, 101 Museum Dr, Palm Springs, CA 92262 - T: (760) 325-7186, Fax: (760) 327-5069, E-mail: psmuseum@aol.com, Internet: http://www.psmuseum.org. Head: Janice Lyle
Fine Arts Museum / Natural History Museum / Performing Arts Museum - 1938 39261

Palmyra NY

Hill Cumorah Visitors Center and Historic Sites, 603 State Rte 21 S, Palmyra, NY 14522-9301 - T: (315) 597-5851, Fax: (315) 597-0165, Internet: http://www.ggw.org/hillcumorah
Religious Arts Museum - 1830
5 historical sites and places of historic significance in connection with the founding of the Church of Jesus Christ of Latter-day Saints 39262

Historic Palmyra, 132 Market St, Palmyra, NY 14522 - T: (315) 597-6981, Fax: (716) 597-4793, E-mail: bjfhpinc@aol.com, Internet: http://palmyrany.lynet.com. Head: Bonnie Hays
Local Museum / Historical Museum - 1967
Local history, military, textiles, Covelelt and quilts coll, naval admirals, W. Churchill's family, mormon hist 39263

Palmyra VA

The Old Stone Jail Museum, Court Sq, Palmyra, VA 22963 - T: (804) 842-3378, Fax: (804) 842-3374. Head: Ellen Miyagawa
Decorative Arts Museum / Local Museum - 1964
Local hist 39264

Palo Alto CA

Palo Alto Art Center, 1313 Newell Rd, Palo Alto, CA 94303 - T: (650) 329-2366, Fax: (650) 326-6165, Internet: http://www.city.palo-alto.ca.us/palo/city/artsculture/. Head: Linda Craighead
Fine Arts Museum - 1971 39265

Palo Alto Junior Museum, 1451 Middlefield Rd, Palo Alto, CA 94301 - T: (650) 329-2111, Fax: (650) 473-1965, E-mail: rachel_meyer@city.palo-alto.ca.us. Head: Rachel Meyer
Natural History Museum - 1934 39266

Pampa TX

White Deer Land Museum, 112-116 S Cuyler, Pampa, TX 79065 - T: (806) 669-8041, Fax: (806) 669-8030, E-mail: museum@pan-tex.net
Local Museum - 1970
Local hist 39267

Panama City FL

The Junior Museum of Bay County, 1731 Jenks Av, Panama City, FL 32405 - T: (850) 769-6129, Fax: (850) 769-6129, E-mail: jrmuseum@panamacity.com, Internet: http://www.jrmuseum.org. Head: William R. Barton
Ethnology Museum - 1969
Children education 39268

Visual Arts Center of Northwest Florida, 19 E 4th St, Panama City, FL 32401 - T: (850) 769-4451, Fax: (850) 785-9248, E-mail: vac@visualartscenter.org, Internet: http://www.visualart-scenter.org. Head: Kimberly Branscome
Fine Arts Museum / Public Gallery - 1988
Art 39269

Panama City Beach FL

Museum of Man in the Sea, 17314 Panama City Beach Pkwy, Panama City Beach, FL 32413-2020 - T: (904) 235-4101, Fax: (904) 235-4101, E-mail: subraces@panamacity.com, Internet: http://www.panamacity.cpm/~subraces. Head: Douglas R. Hough
Historical Museum / Historic Site - 1981 39270

Panhandle TX

Carson County Square House Museum, Texas Hwy, 207 Fifth St, Panhandle, TX 79068 - T: (806) 537-3524, Fax: (806) 537-5628, E-mail: shm@squarehousemuseum.org, Internet: http://www.squarehousemuseum.org. Head: Dr. Viola Moore
Local Museum - 1965
Local hist 39271

Paramus NJ

New Jersey Children's Museum, 599 Industrial Av, Paramus, NJ 07652 - T: (201) 262-2638, Fax: (201) 262-0560, E-mail: esumers@aol.com, Internet: http://www.njcm.com. Head: Anne R. Sumers
Special Museum - 1992 39272

Paris AR

Logan County Museum, 202 N Vine, Paris, AR 72855 - T: (501) 963-3936
Local Museum - 1975
History, former Logan County Jail 39273

Paris IL

Bicentennial Art Center and Museum, 132 S Central Av, Paris, IL 61944 - T: (217) 466-8130. Head: Janet M. Messenger, Anne J. Johnson
Fine Arts Museum / Public Gallery - 1975 39274

Edgar County Historical Museum, 408 N Main, Paris, IL 61944-1549 - T: (217) 463-5305. Head: Warren Alieff
Local Museum - 1971
Local history, housed in 1872 Arthur House 39275

Paris KY

Hopewell Museum, 800 Pleasant St, Paris, KY 40361 - T: (859) 987-7274, Fax: (859) 987-8107, E-mail: hopemuseum@aol.com. Head: Betsy Kephart
Local Museum - 1995
Local hist 39276

Paris TX

Sam Bell Maxey House, 812 S Church St, Paris, TX 75460 - T: (903) 785-5716, Fax: (903) 739-2924, E-mail: maxeyhouse@1starnet.com
Decorative Arts Museum / Local Museum - 1976
Local hist 39277

Parishville NY

Parishville Museum, Main St, Parishville, NY 13672 - T: (315) 265-7619
Local Museum - 1964 39278

Park Rapids MN

North Country Museum of Arts, Third and Court Sts, Park Rapids, MN 56470 - T: (218) 732-5237. Head: Johanna M. Verbrugghen
Fine Arts Museum - 1977 39279

Park Ridge IL

Wood Library-Museum of Anesthesiology, 520 N Northwest Hwy, Park Ridge, IL 60068-2573 - T: (847) 825-5586, Fax: (847) 825-1692, Internet: http://www.asahq.org
Historical Museum / Special Museum - 1950
Medicine 39280

Park Ridge NJ

Pascack Historical Society Museum, 19 Ridge Av, Park Ridge, NJ 07656 - T: (201) 573-0307. Head: Katharine P. Randall
Local Museum / Historical Museum - 1942 39281

Parker AZ

Colorado River Indian Tribes Museum, Rte 1, Box 23-B, Parker, AZ 85344 - T: (520) 669-9211 ext 1339, Fax: (520) 669-5675. Head: Betty L. Cornelius
Ethnology Museum - 1970
American Indian - library, archive 39282

Parkersburg WV

The Cultural Center of Fine Arts, 725 Market St, Parkersburg, WV 26101 - T: (304) 485-3859, Fax: (304) 485-3850. Head: Jill Chidester
Fine Arts Museum - 1938
Arts 39283

Parrish FL

Florida Gulf Coast Railroad Museum, POB 355, Parrish, FL 34219 - T: (941) 776-9656, Internet: http://www.fgcrrm.org. Head: James Herron
Science&Tech Museum - 1983
Railroad 39284

Parsippany NJ

Craftsman Farms Foundation, 2352 Rte 10 W, Parsippany, NJ 07950 - T: (973) 540-1165, Fax: (973) 540-1167. Head: Tommy McPherson
Historical Museum / Open Air Museum / Agriculture Museum - 1989 39285

Pasadena CA

Kidspace Children's Museum, 390 S El Molino Av, Pasadena, CA 91101 - T: (626) 449-9144, Fax: (626) 449-9985, Internet: http://www.kidspacechildrensmuseum.org. Head: Carol E. Scott
Special Museum - 1979
Handson, arts, science, humanities 39286

Norton Simon Museum, 411 W Colorado Blvd, Pasadena, CA 91105 - T: (626) 449-6840, Fax: (626) 796-4978, E-mail: art@nortonsimon.org, Internet: http://www.nortonsimon.org. Head: Sara Campbell
Fine Arts Museum - 1924 39287

Pacific Asia Museum, 46 N Los Robles Av, Pasadena, CA 91101 - T: (626) 449-2742, Fax: (626) 449-2754, E-mail: PacAsiaMus@aol.com, Internet: http://pacificasiamuseum.org. Head: David L. Kamansky
Fine Arts Museum / Historical Museum / Folklore Museum - 1971 39288

Pasadena Historical Museum, 470 W Walnut St, Pasadena, CA 91103-3594 - T: (626) 577-1660, Fax: (626) 577-1662, E-mail: info@pasadenahistory.org, Internet: http://www.pasadenahistory.org. Head: Don Fedde, Richard S. Cohen
Local Museum - 1924 39289

Pascagoula MS

Old Spanish Fort and Museum, 4602 Fort St, Pascagoula, MS 39567 - T: (228) 769-1505, Fax: (228) 769-1432
Historical Museum - 1949 39290

Pasco WA

Franklin County Historical Museum, 305 N 4th Av, Pasco, WA 99301 - T: (509) 547-3714, Fax: (509) 545-2168, E-mail: fchs@bossig.com. Head: Nancy Ostergaard
Local Museum - 1982
Local hist 39291

Paterson NJ

Passaic County Community College Galleries, Broadway Gallery, 1 College Blvd, Paterson, NJ 07505-1179 - T: (973) 684-6555, Fax: (973) 523-6085, E-mail: mgillan@pccc.cc.nj.us, Internet: http://www.pccc.cc.nj.us/poetry. Head: Maria Mazziotti Gillan
Fine Arts Museum / University Museum - 1968 39292

Passaic County Historical Society Museum, Lambert Castle, Valley Rd, Paterson, NJ 07503-2932 - T: (973) 881-2761, Fax: (973) 357-1070, Internet: http://www.geocities.com/pchslc. Head: Andrew F. Shick
Local Museum - 1926
Local history, Koempel Spoon coll, textiles, paintings, decorative art, folk art - library 39293

Paterson Museum, 2 Market St, Paterson, NJ 07501 - T: (973) 881-3874, Fax: (973) 881-3435, Internet: http://www.thepattersonmuseum.org. Head: Giacomo R. DeStefano
Historical Museum / Natural History Museum / Science&Tech Museum - 1925 39294

Patten ME

Patten Lumberman's Museum, Shin Pond Rd, Patten, ME 04765 - T: (207) 528-2650, Internet: http://www.mainerec.com/logger.html
Historical Museum / Ethnology Museum - 1959
Logging, lumbering 39295

Patterson LA

Louisiana State Museum, 394 Airport Circle, Patterson, LA 70392 - T: (504) 395-7067, Fax: (504) 395-7067. Head: Nicholas Neylon
Science&Tech Museum - 1975
Aviation 39296

Pawhuska OK

Osage County Historical Museum, 700 N Lynn Av, Pawhuska, OK 74056 - T: (918) 287-9924. Head: J.B. Smith
Local Museum - 1964 39297

Pawling NY

Gunnison Museum of Natural History, Quaker Hill, Pawling, NY 12564 - T: (914) 855-5099
Natural History Museum - 1960 39298

Pawnee City NE

Pawnee City Historical Society Museum, Hwy 50/8 East, Pawnee City, NE 68420 - T: (402) 852-3131, Internet: http://www.rootsweb.com/~.nepawnee. Head: Roy Mullin
Local Museum - 1968 39299

Pawtucket RI

Slater Mill Historic Site, 67 Roosevelt Av, Pawtucket, RI 02860 - T: (401) 725-8638, Fax: (401) 722-3040, E-mail: samslater@aol.com, Internet: http://www.slatermill.org. Head: Gail Fowler Mohanty
Science&Tech Museum - 1921
Hist of textile industry 39300

Paxton IL

Ford County Historical Society Museum, 200 West State St, Paxton, IL 60957 - T: (217) 379-4684. Head: Gwen Lindholm
Local Museum - 1967
Local history, housed in County Court House 39301

Paxton MA

Saint Luke's Gallery, Anna Maria College, Moll Art Center, 50 Sunset Ln, Paxton, MA 01612 - T: (508) 849-3300 ext 442, Fax: (508) 849-3408, Internet: http://www.annamaria.edu. Head: Alice Lambert, Elizabeth Killoran
Fine Arts Museum / University Museum - 1968 39302

Peace Dale RI

Museum of Primitive Art and Culture, 1058 Kingstown Rd, Peace Dale, RI 02883 - T: (401) 783-5711. Head: Wallace Campbell, Sarah Peabody Turnbaugh
Ethnology Museum / Archaeological Museum - 1892
Anthropology 39303

Peaks Island ME

Fifth Maine Regiment Center, 45 Seashore Av, Peaks Island, ME 04108 - T: (207) 766-3330, Fax: (207) 766-3083, E-mail: fifthmaine@juno.com, Internet: http://fifthmaine.home.att.net
Military Museum - 1954
Military hist 39304

Pecos TX

West of the Pecos Museum, First at Cedar (U.S. 285), Pecos, TX 79772 - T: (915) 445-5076, Fax: (915) 445-2407
Local Museum - 1962
Local hist 39305

Peebles OH

Serpent Mound Museum, 3850 State Rte 73, Peebles, OH 45660 - T: (937) 587-2796
Ethnology Museum - 1900 39306

Pelham NY

Pelham Art Center, 155 Fifth Av, Pelham, NY 10803 - T: (914) 738-2525, Fax: (914) 738-2686, E-mail: pelhamartcenter@worldnet.att.net. Head: Nina Diefenbach, Yvette Nieves
Fine Arts Museum / Folklore Museum - 1975
Art 39307

Pella IA

Pella Historical Village, 507 Franklin, Pella, IA 50219-0145 - T: (515) 628-2409, Fax: (515) 628-9192, E-mail: pellatt@kdsi.net, Internet: http://www.kdsi.net/~pellatt. Head: Elaine de Boef, Patsy Sadler
Ethnology Museum / Local Museum - 1965
Ethnography (Dutch), 20 historic buildings 39308

Pembina ND

Pembina State Museum, 805 State Hwy 59, Pembina, ND 58271-0456 - T: (701) 825-6840, Fax: (701) 825-6383, E-mail: mbailey@state.nd.us, Internet: http://www.state.nd.us/hist/pembina.htm
Historical Museum - 1962
Fur trade, Meti's 39309

Pembroke MA

Pembroke Historical Museum, Center St, Pembroke, MA 02359 - T: (781) 293-9083
Local Museum - 1950
Local history 39310

Pembroke NC

Native American Resource Center, University of North Carolina at Pembroke, Pembroke, NC 28372 - T: (910) 521-6282, E-mail: knick@nat.uncp.edu, Internet: http://www.uncp.edu/nativemuseum/. Head: Dr. Stanley Knick
University Museum / Ethnology Museum - 1979 39311

Pendleton OR

Umatilla County Historical Society Museum, 108 SW Frazer St, Pendleton, OR 97801 - T: (541) 276-0012, Fax: (541) 276-7989, Internet: http://www.umatillahistory.org. Head: Charles McCullough, Julie Reese
Local Museum - 1974
Local hist 39312

Pendleton SC

Pendleton District Agricultural Museum, Hwy 76, Pendleton, SC 29670 - T: (864) 646-3782, Fax: (864) 646-2506, E-mail: pendtour@innova.net, Internet: http://www.pendleton-district.org. Head: Hurley E. Badders
Agriculture Museum - 1976
Agriculture 39313

Penn Valley CA

Museum of Ancient and Modern Art, POB 975, Penn Valley, CA 95946 - T: (530) 432-3080, Fax: (530) 272-0184, E-mail: info@mam.org, Internet: http://www.mama.org. Head: Zoe Alowan
Fine Arts Museum - 1981
Art 39314

Penn Yan NY

Oliver House Museum, 200 Main St, Penn Yan, NY 14527 - T: (315) 536-7318, Fax: (315) 536-7318, E-mail: ycghs@linkny.com. Head: Idelle Dillon
Local Museum - 1860 39315

Pennsburg PA

Schwenkfelder Library and Heritage Center, 105 Seminary St, Pennsburg, PA 18073-1898 - T: (215) 679-3103, Fax: (215) 679-8175, E-mail: schwenkfeld@netcarrier.com, Internet: http://www.schwenkfelder.com. Head: David W. Luz
Historical Museum - 1913
Local hist 39316

Pensacola FL

Historic Pensacola Village, 120 Church St, Pensacola, FL 32501 - T: (850) 595-5985 ext 103, Fax: (850) 595-5989, E-mail: jdaniels@historicpensacola.org, Internet: http://www.historic-pensacola.org. Head: John P. Daniels
Local Museum - 1967
Local history 39317

National Museum of Naval Aviation, 1750 Radford Blvd, Ste C, Pensacola, FL 32508-5402 - T: (904) 452-3604 ext 119, Fax: (904) 452-3296, E-mail: navalair@amaranth.com, Internet: http://www.naval_air.org. Head: Robert Rasmussen
Military Museum / Science&Tech Museum - 1963
Naval aviation 39318

Pensacola Historical Museum, 115 E Zaragosa St, Pensacola, FL 32501 - T: (850) 434-5455, Fax: (904) 433-1559, E-mail: phstaff@freenet.com, Internet: http://www.penacolahistory.org. Head: Eric Mead, Sandra L. Johnson
Historical Museum - 1960
History, historic Arbona building 39319

Pensacola Museum of Art, 407 S Jefferson St, Pensacola, FL 32501 - T: (850) 432-6247, Fax: (850) 469-1532, E-mail: pma407@aol.com, Internet: http://www.pensacolamuseumofart.org. Head: Maria V. Butler, Linda P. Nolan
Fine Arts Museum - 1954
Art Museum, housed in 1908 old city jail 39320

University of West Florida Art Gallery, University of West Florida, 11000 University Pkwy, Pensacola, FL 32514 - T: (850) 474-2696, Fax: (850) 474-3247, E-mail: dbond@uwf.edu, Internet: http://www.uwf.edu/~art. Head: Debra Bond
Fine Arts Museum / Public Gallery - 1970 39321

Visual Arts Gallery, 1000 College Blvd, Pensacola, FL 32504 - T: (850) 484-2554, Fax: (850) 484-2564, E-mail: apeterson@pjc.cc.fl.us, Internet: http://www.pjc.cc.fl.us. Head: Allan Peterson
Fine Arts Museum / Decorative Arts Museum / University Museum - 1970 39322

Peoria IL

Lakeview Museum of Arts and Sciences, 1125 W Lake Av, Peoria, IL 61614-5985 - T: (309) 686-7000, Fax: (309) 686-0280, E-mail: kathleen@cyberdesic.com, Internet: http://www.lakeview-museum.org. Head: Sheldon Schafer
Fine Arts Museum / Science&Tech Museum - 1965 39323

Peoria Historical Society, 942 NE Glen Oak Av, Peoria, IL 61603 - T: (309) 674-1921, Fax: (309) 674-1882, Internet: http://www.peoriahistorical-society.org. Head: Kathryn Belsley
Historical Museum - 1934
Local history 39324

Wheels O' Time Museum, 11923 N Knoxville Av, Peoria, IL 61612-9636 - T: (309) 243-9020, Fax: (309) 243-5616, E-mail: wotmuseum@aol.com, Internet: http://www.wheelsotime.org. Head: Gary O. Bragg
Science&Tech Museum - 1977
Antique vehicles, clocks, musical devices, tools, toys, farm equipment 39325

Perkasie PA

Pearl S. Buck House, Green Hills Farm, 520 Dublin Rd, Perkasie, PA 18944 - T: (215) 249-0100, Fax: (215) 249-9657, E-mail: info@pearl-s-buck.org, Internet: http://www.pearl-s-buck.org. Head: Sandy Bates, Meredith J. Richardson
Local Museum / Decorative Arts Museum - 1964
Stone farmhouse 39326

Perris CA

Orange Empire Railway Museum, 2201 S A St, Perris, CA 92570 - T: (909) 943-3020, Fax: (909) 943-2676, E-mail: oerm@juno.com, Internet: http://www.oerm.org. Head: Thomas N. Jacobson
Science&Tech Museum - 1956
Railway, historical Santa Fe line from Chicago to San Diego 39327

Perry FL

Forest Capital State Museum, 204 Forest Park Dr, on U.S. 19-98, Perry, FL 32347 - T: (850) 584-3227, Fax: (850) 584-3488, E-mail: forestcapital@perry.gulfnet.com
Natural History Museum / Folklore Museum - 1973
Logging, lumber, timber industry, forestry 39328

Perry OK

Cherokee Strip Museum and Henry S. Johnston Library, 2617 W Fir St, Perry, OK 73077 - T: (405) 336-2405, E-mail: csmuseum@ionet.net
Historical Museum - 1965 39329

Perrysburg OH

Fort Meigs State Memorial, State Rte 65, Perrysburg, OH 43551 - T: (419) 874-4121. Head: Dr. Larry Nelson
Military Museum - 1975 39330

Perryville KY

Perryville Battlefield Museum, 1825 Battlefield Rd, Perryville, KY 40468-0296 - T: (606) 332-8631, Fax: (606) 332-2440, E-mail: kholman@searnet.com, Internet: http://www.state.ky.us/agencies/parks/perryvil.html. Head: Kurt Holman
Military Museum - 1965
Civil War hist 39331

Perryville MD

Rodgers Tavern, E Broad St, Perryville, MD 21903 - T: (410) 642-6066, Fax: (410) 642-6391. Head: Brenda Price
Local Museum - 1956 39332

Perth Amboy NJ

The Royal Governor's Mansion, 149 Kearny Av, Perth Amboy, NJ 08861 - T: (732) 826-5527, Fax: (732) 826-8889. Head: David D. Furman
Local Museum - 1967
Historic house 39333

Peru IN

Circus City Festival Museum, 154 N Broadway, Peru, IN 46970 - T: (765) 472-3918, Fax: (765) 472-2826, E-mail: perucirc@perucircus.com, Internet: http://www.perucircus.com. Head: Dennis See
Performing Arts Museum - 1959
Circus 39334

Grissom Air Museum, 6500 Hoosier Blvd, Peru, IN 46970 - T: (765) 688-2654, Fax: (765) 688-2956, E-mail: info@grissomAirMuseum.com, Internet: http://www.grissomairmuseum.com. Head: John S. Marsh
Military Museum / Science&Tech Museum - 1981
Military hist, aviation 39335

Miami County Museum, 51 N Broadway, Peru, IN 46970 - T: (765) 473-9183, Fax: (317) 473-3880, E-mail: mchs@netusa1.net, Internet: http://www.netusa1.net/~mchs/. Head: Cinnamon Catlin-Legutko
Local Museum / Ethnology Museum - 1916
County history, circus, Miami Indians, transportation 39336

Peshtigo WI

Peshtigo Fire Museum, 400 Oconto Av, Peshtigo, WI 54157 - T: (715) 582-3244
Local Museum - 1962
Local hist 39337

Petaluma CA

Petaluma Adobe State Historic Park, 3325 Old Adobe Rd, Petaluma, CA 94952 - T: (707) 762-4871
Local Museum - 1951
Local hist 39338

Petaluma Wildlife and Natural Science Museum, 201 Fair St, Petaluma, CA 94952 - T: (707) 778-4787, Fax: (707) 778-4787, E-mail: wildlifemuseum@yahoo.com, Internet: http://www.Sonic.net/~museum/. Head: George Grossi, Andrea Gates
Natural History Museum - 1990
Natural science 39339

Peterborough NH

Peterborough Historical Society Museum, 19 Grove St, Peterborough, NH 03458 - T: (603) 924-3235, Fax: (603) 924-3200, E-mail: office.phs@webryder.com. Head: Dorothy Peterson, Ellen S. Derby
Local Museum - 1902 39340

Petersburg AK

Clausen Memorial Museum, 203 Fram St, Petersburg, AK 99833 - T: (907) 772-3598, Fax: (907) 772-2698, E-mail: bigfish@clausenmuseum.alaska.net, Internet: http://www.clausenmuseum.alaska.net. Head: Glorianne DeBoer, Sue McCallum
Historical Museum / Local Museum - 1965
Fishing, fish, boats, local history 39341

Petersburg IL

Lincoln's New Salem Historic Site, R.R. 1, Petersburg, IL 62675 - T: (217) 632-4000, Fax: (217) 632-4010, E-mail: newsalem@fgi.net, Internet: http://www.petersburgil.com. Head: Kim Smith
Local Museum - 1917
New Salem Village, in the 1830s where Lincoln lived as a young man 39342

Petersburg VA

Archibald Graham McIlwaine House, The Petersburg Museums, 325 Cockade Alley, Petersburg, VA 23803 - T: (804) 733-2400, Fax: (804) 861-0883, E-mail: ssavery@techcom.net, Internet: http://www.petersburg-va.org. Head: Suzanne T. Savery
Local Museum - 1984
Historic house 39343

Centre Hill Mansion, The Petersburg Museums, Centre Hill Center, Petersburg, VA 23803 - T: (804) 733-2400, Fax: (804) 861-0883, E-mail: ssavery@techcom.net, Internet: http://www.petersburg-va.org. Head: Suzanne T. Savery
Local Museum - 1976
Historic house 39344

Farmers Bank, The Petersburg Museums, 19 Bollingbrook St, Petersburg, VA 23803 - T: (804) 733-2400, Fax: (804) 732-9212, E-mail: ssavery@techcom.net, Internet: http://www.petersburg-va.org. Head: Suzanne T. Savery
Special Museum - 1974
Banking 39345

Pamplin Park Civil War Site, 6125 Boydton Plank Rd, Petersburg, VA 23803 - T: (804) 861-2408, Fax: (804) 861-2820, E-mail: pamplinpark@mindspring.com, Internet: http://www.pamplinpark.org. Head: A. Wilson Greene, William C. Lazenby
Military Museum - 1994
Military hist 39346

Petersburg Area Art League, 7 Olde St, Petersburg, VA 23803 - T: (804) 861-4611, Fax: (804) 861-3962. Head: James H. Ryan
Fine Arts Museum - 1932
Art 39347

The Petersburg Museums, 15 W Bank St, Petersburg, VA 23803 - T: (804) 733-2404, Fax: (804) 863-0837, E-mail: ssavery@techcom.net, Internet: http://www.petersburg-va.com. Head: Suzanne T. Savery
Local Museum - 1972
Local hist 39348

Petersburg National Battlefield, Rte 36 East, Petersburg, VA 23804 - T: (804) 732-3531, Fax: (804) 732-0835, Internet: http://www.nps.gov/pe_info.htm
Historic Site / Military Museum - 1926
Military hist 39349

Trapezium House, The Petersburg Museums, Market St, Petersburg, VA 23803 - T: (804) 733-2400, Fax: (804) 732-9212, E-mail: ssavery@techcom.net, Internet: http://www.petersburg-va.org. Head: Suzanne T. Savery
Local Museum - 1974
Historic house 39350

Petersham MA

Fisher Museum of Forestry, Harvard University, 326 N Main St, Petersham, MA 01366-0068 - T: (978) 724-3302, Fax: (978) 724-3595, E-mail: jokeefe@fas.harvard.edu, Internet: http://www.iternet.edu/hfr/mus.html. Head: David R. Foster
Natural History Museum / University Museum - 1940
Forest history and ecology 39351

Petersham Historical Museum, N Main St, Petersham, MA 01366 - T: (508) 724-3380. Head: Donald Haines
Local Museum - 1923
Local history 39352

Petoskey MI

Little Traverse Historical Museum, 100 Depot Court, Petoskey, MI 49770 - T: (616) 347-2620, Fax: (616) 347-2875, E-mail: mce@freeway.net. Head: Mary Candace Eaton
Local Museum - 1971
Regional history 39353

Virginia M. McCune Community Arts Center, 461 E Mitchell St, Petoskey, MI 49770 - T: (231) 347-4337, Fax: (231) 347-5414, E-mail: ctac@freeway.net, Internet: http://www.crookedtree.org. Head: Dale Hall
Fine Arts Museum - 1981 39354

Pharr TX

Old Clock Museum, 929 E Preston St, Pharr, TX 78577 - T: (210) 787-1923. Head: Gene Shawn, Barbara Shawn Barber
Science&Tech Museum - 1968
Horology 39355

Philadelphia PA

Academy of Natural Sciences of Philadelphia Museum, 1900 Ben Franklin Pkwy, Philadelphia, PA 19103-1195 - T: (215) 299-1000, Fax: (215) 299-1028, Internet: http://www.acnatsci.org. Head: Seymour S. Preston
Natural History Museum - 1812
Natural science 39356

The African American Museum in Philadelphia, 701 Arch St, Philadelphia, PA 19106-1557 - T: (215) 574-0380, Fax: (215) 574-3110, E-mail: TRour@AAMPmuseum.org, Internet: http://www.aampmuseum.org. Head: Terrie S. Rouse
Local Museum - 1976
Intellectual and material cultural of african and american 39357

American Catholic Historical Society Museum, 263 S Fouth St, Philadelphia, PA 19106 - T: (610) 667-2125, Fax: (215) 204-1663, E-mail: fitz@vm.temple.edu, Internet: htpp://www.amchs.org. Head: James A. Fitzsimmons, James P. McCoy
Historical Museum / Religious Arts Museum - 1884
Religious and American hist 39358

American Swedish Historical Museum, 1900 Pattison Av, Philadelphia, PA 19145 - T: (215) 389-1776, Fax: (215) 389-7701, E-mail: ashm@libertynet.org, Internet: http://www.libertynet.org/ashm
Local Museum / Folklore Museum - 1926
Swedish-American history, art 39359

Artforms Gallery Manuyunk, 106 Levering St, Philadelphia, PA 19127 - T: (215) 483-3030. Head: Ronna Cooper
Fine Arts Museum
Paintings, collage prints, ceramic sculpture, wood & stone sculpture & photography 39360

Arthur Ross Gallery, University of Pennsylvania, 220 S 34 St, Philadelphia, PA 19104-6303 - T: (215) 898-2083, Fax: (215) 573-2045, E-mail: arg@pobox.upenn.edu, Internet: http://www.upenn.edu/arg/. Head: Dr. Dilys V. Winegrad
University Museum / Fine Arts Museum - 1983 39361

Athenaeum of Philadelphia, 219 S 6th St, E Washington Sq, Philadelphia, PA 19106 - T: (215) 925-2688, Fax: (215) 925-3755, E-mail: magee@philaathenaeum.org, Internet: http://www.philaathenaeum.org. Head: Dr. Roger W. Moss
Fine Arts Museum / Decorative Arts Museum - 1814
Art coll, manuscripts, architectural drawings, historic design 39362

Atwater Kent Museum - The History Museum of Philadelphia, 15 S 7th St, Philadelphia, PA 19106 - T: (215) 922-3031, Fax: (215) 922-0708, E-mail: akmexhibit@aol.com, Internet: http://www.philadephiahistory.org. Head: D. Kaye Gapen
Fine Arts Museum / Historical Museum - 1939
History 39363

The Balch Institute for Ethnic Studies, 18 S 7th St, Philadelphia, PA 19106 - T: (215) 925-8090, Fax: (215) 925-8195, E-mail: balchlib@balchinstitute.org, Internet: http://www.balchinstitute.org
Ethnology Museum - 1971
Ethnography 39364

Betsy Ross House, 239 Arch St, Philadelphia, PA 19106 - T: (215) 686-1252, Fax: (215) 686-1256, E-mail: eileenvig@aol.com, Internet: http://www.betsyrosshouse.org. Head: Eileen F. Young-Vignola
Local Museum - 1898
Historic house, craftman's tools, furnishings - American Flag House 39365

Center for the Visual Arts, Brandywine Workshop, 730 S Broad St, Philadelphia, PA 19146 - T: (215) 546-3675, Fax: (215) 546-2825, E-mail: brandwn@libertynet.org, Internet: http://www.blackboard.com/brndywne. Head: Allan L. Edmunds
Fine Arts Museum - 1972 39366

Cigna Museum and Art Collection, 2 Liberty Pl, 1601 Chestnut St, Philadelphia, PA 19192-2078 - T: (215) 761-4907, Fax: (215) 761-5596, E-mail: melissa.hough@cigna.com. Head: Melissa E. Hough
Fine Arts Museum / Historical Museum - 1925
Art, history 39367

Civil War Museum, 1805 Pine St, Philadelphia, PA 19103 - T: (215) 735-8196, Fax: (215) 735-3812, Internet: http://www.libertynet.org/~CWLM. Head: John J. Craft
Historical Museum - 1888
History 39368

Cliveden House, 6401 Germantown Av, Philadelphia, PA 19144 - T: (215) 848-1777, Fax: (215) 438-2892, E-mail: chewhouse@aol.com, Internet: http://www.cliveden.org. Head: Kris S. Kepford
Local Museum / Historic Site - 1972
Historic house, site of the Battle of Germantown 1777 39369

Ebenezer Maxwell Mansion, 200 W Tulpehocken St, Philadelphia, PA 19144 - T: (215) 438-1861, Fax: (215) 438-1861. Head: Joan Frankel
Local Museum - 1975
Local hist 39370

Edgar Allan Poe House, 530-32 N 7th St, Philadelphia, PA 19123 - T: (215) 597-8780, Fax: (215) 597-1901, Internet: http://www.nps.gov/edal
Special Museum - 1935
Edgar Allan Poe brick house 39371

Elfreth's Alley Museum, 126 Elfreths Alley, Philadelphia, PA 19106 - T: (215) 574-0560, Fax: (215) 922-7869, E-mail: info@elfrethsalley.org, Internet: http://www.elfrethsalley.org. Head: Beth Richards
Historic Site - 1934
Historic Buildings 39372

Esther M. Klein Art Gallery, University City Science Center, 3600 Market St, Philadelphia, PA 19104 - T: (215) 387-2255, Fax: (215) 382-0056, E-mail: kleinart@libertynet.org, Internet: http://www.libertynet.org/kleinart
University Museum / Fine Arts Museum - 1976 39373

The Fabric Workshop and Museum, 1315 Cherry St, Philadelphia, PA 19107 - T: (215) 568-1111, Fax: (215) 568-8211, E-mail: fwmuseum@libertynet.org. Head: Marion Boulton Stroud
Fine Arts Museum / Special Museum - 1977
Contemporary art, Studio focusing on fabric and new materials 39374

Fireman's Hall Museum, 147 N 2nd St, Philadelphia, PA 19106-2010 - T: (215) 923-1438, Fax: (215) 923-0479
Historical Museum - 1967
Fire fighting 39375

Fort Mifflin, Fort Mifflin Rd, Philadelphia, PA 19153 - T: (215) 492-1881, Fax: (215) 492-1608. Head: Dori McMunn
Historical Museum / Military Museum - 1962
Historic 1777 fort 39376

The Franklin Institute, 222 N 20th, Philadelphia, PA 19103-1194 - T: (215) 448-1208, 448-1200, Fax: (215) 448-1235, E-mail: ken@franklininstitute.com, Internet: http://www.fi.edu. Head: Dennis M. Wint
Science&Tech Museum - 1824
Science and technology 39377

Fred Wolf Jr. Gallery, Klein Branch Jewish Community Center, 10100 Jamison Av, Philadelphia, PA 19116 - T: (215) 698-7300, Fax: (215) 673-7447. Head: Jay W. Steinberg
Fine Arts Museum / Decorative Arts Museum - 1975 39378

Germantown Historical Society Museum, 5501 Germantown Av, Philadelphia, PA 19144-2291 - T: (215) 844-0514, Fax: (215) 844-2831, E-mail: ghs@libertynet.org, Internet: http://www.liberty.org/ghs/. Head: Eugene Stackhouse, Mary K. Dabney
Historical Museum - 1900
Local hist 39379

The Goldie Paley Gallery, Moore College of Art and Design, 20th St and The Pkwy, Philadelphia, PA 19103 - T: (215) 965-4027, Fax: (215) 568-5921, E-mail: mdougherty@moore.edu, Internet: http://

www.thegalleriesatmoore.orge. Head: Molly Dougherty
Fine Arts Museum - 1948
Art 39380

Grand Army of the Republic Civil War Museum, 4278 Griscom St, Philadelphia, PA 19124-3954 - T: (215) 289-6484, 673-1688, E-mail: garmuslib@aol.com, Internet: http://suvcw.org/garmus.htm. Head: Elmer F. Atkinson
Historical Museum - 1926
Hist of the Civil War 39381

High Wire Gallery, 137 N Second St, Philadelphia, PA 19106 - T: (215) 829-1255, E-mail: malcor@aol.com. Head: Jeff Waring
Fine Arts Museum - 1985 39382

Historical Society of Pennsylvania, 1300 Locust St, Philadelphia, PA 19107-5699 - T: (215) 732-6200, Fax: (215) 732-2680, E-mail: pres@hsp.org, Internet: http://www.hsp.org. Head: David Moltke-Hansen
Local Museum / Library with Exhibitions - 1824
Historical Research Center 39383

Independence National Historical Park, 313 Walnut St, Philadelphia, PA 19106 - T: (215) 597-8787, Fax: (215) 597-5556, E-mail: inde_curatorial@nps.gov, Internet: http://www.nps.gov/inde
Historical Museum / Historic Site - 1948
Local hist 39384

Independence Seaport Museum, Penn's Landing Waterfront, 211 S Columbus Blvd at Walnut St, Philadelphia, PA 19106 - T: (215) 925-5439, Fax: (215) 925-6713, E-mail: seaport@libertynet.org, Internet: http://seaport.philly.com. Head: John S. Carter
Historical Museum - 1961
Maritime hist 39385

Institute of Contemporary Art, University of Pennsylvania, 118 S 36th St, Philadelphia, PA 19104-3289 - T: (215) 898-7108, Fax: (215) 898-5050, E-mail: ica@pobox.upenn.edu, Internet: http://www.icaphila.org. Head: Claudia Gould
Fine Arts Museum / University Museum - 1963
Art 39386

Lemon Hill Mansion, Lemon Hill and Sedgelay Drs, East Fairmount Park, Philadelphia, PA 19130 - T: (215) 232-4337, Fax: (215) 646-8472, Internet: http://www.lemonhill.org. Head: H. Dawson Penniman
Decorative Arts Museum
Decorative arts of Philadelphia 1800 - 1836; local hist 39387

Loudoun Mansion, 4650 Germantown Av, Philadelphia, PA 19144 - T: (215) 686-2067, 677-7830. Head: Ursula Reed
Decorative Arts Museum
Historic house 39388

Mario Lanza Museum, c/o Settlement Music School, 416 Queen St, Philadelphia, PA 19147-3094 - T: (215) 468-3623, Fax: (215) 468-1903, E-mail: nli@mario-lanza-institute.org. Head: Mary Galanti Papola
Music Museum - 1962
Music hist 39389

The Masonic Museum of Pennsylvania, Masonic Temple, 1 N Broad St, Philadelphia, PA 19107-2520 - T: (215) 988-1932, Fax: (215) 988-1972. Head: John H. Platt
Local Museum
Local hist 39390

Muse Art Gallery, 60 N Second St, Philadelphia, PA 19106 - T: (215) 627-5310. Head: Sissy Pizzollo
Fine Arts Museum - 1970 39391

The Museum of Nursing History, Pennsylvania Hospital, 8th and Spruce Sts, Philadelphia, PA 19107 - T: (215) 829-3370
Historical Museum - 1976
Nursing hist 39392

Museum of the Philadelphia Civic Center, 3101 Market St, Philadelphia, PA 19104 - T: (215) 925-8191, Fax: (215) 823-7282
Public Gallery - 1893
Trade 39393

Mutter Museum, College of Physicians of Philadelphia, 19 S 22nd St, Philadelphia, PA 19103-3097 - T: (215) 563-3737 ext 242, Fax: (215) 561-6477, E-mail: worden@collphyphil.org, Internet: http://www.collphyphil.org. Head: Gretchen Worden
Historical Museum - 1863
Medicine 39394

Naomi Wood Collection at Woodford Mansion, 33rd and Dauphin St, E Fairmont Park, Philadelphia, PA 19132 - T: (215) 229-6115
Natural History Museum - 1926 39395

National Exhibits by Blind Artists, 919 Walnut St, Philadelphia, PA 19107 - T: (215) 627-5930
Public Gallery 39396

National Museum of American Jewish History, 55 N 5th St, Independence Mall E, Philadelphia, PA 19106-2197 - T: (215) 923-3812, Fax: (215) 923-0763, E-mail: nmajh@nmajh.org, Internet: http://www.nmajh.org. Head: D. Walter Cohen, Gwen Goodman
Historical Museum / Ethnology Museum / Religious Arts Museum - 1974
Social and ethnic hist 39397

Nexus Foundatoin for Today's Art, 137 N Second St, Philadelphia, PA 19106 - T: (215) 629-1103, E-mail: nexus@libertynet.org. Head: John Murphy
Fine Arts Museum - 1975 39398

The Paley Design Center of Philadelphia University, 4200 Henry Av, Philadelphia, PA 19144 - T: (215) 951-2860, Fax: (215) 951-2662, E-mail: jayh@philau.edu, Internet: http://www.philacol.edu/paley/. Head: Hilary Jay
Decorative Arts Museum - 1978
Textiles hist, costumes, design 39399

Pennsylvania Academy of the Fine Arts Gallery, 118 N Broad St, Philadelphia, PA 19102 - T: (215) 972-7600, Fax: (215) 569-0153, E-mail: pafa@pafa.org, Internet: http://www.pafa.org. Head: Daniel Rosenfeld
Fine Arts Museum - 1805
American art 39400

Philadelphia Art Alliance, 251 S 18th St, Philadelphia, PA 19103 - T: (215) 545-4305, Fax: (215) 545-0767, E-mail: info@philartalliance.org, Internet: http://www.philartalliance.org. Head: Carole Price Shanis, James McClelland
Fine Arts Museum - 1915
Art 39401

Philadelphia Mummers Museum, 1100 S Second St, Philadelphia, PA 19147 - T: (215) 336-3050, Fax: (215) 389-5630, E-mail: mummersmus@aol.com, Internet: http://www.mummers.com. Head: Palma B. Lucas
Decorative Arts Museum / Performing Arts Museum - 1976
Costumes 39402

Philadelphia Museum of Art, 26th St and Benjamin Franklin Pkwy, Philadelphia, PA 19130 - T: (215) 763-8100, Fax: (215) 236-4465, E-mail: pr@philamuseum.org, Internet: http://www.philamuseum.org. Head: Anne d' Harnoncourt
Fine Arts Museum - 1876
Art 39403

Philadelphia Museum of Judaica-Congregation Rodeph Shalom, 615 N Broad St, Philadelphia, PA 19123 - T: (215) 627-6747, Fax: (215) 627-1313, E-mail: rshalom@libertynet.org, Internet: http://www.rodephshalom.org. Head: Joan C. Sall
Religious Arts Museum - 1975
Religion, oldest German synagogue in Western hemisphere 39404

Please Touch Museum, 210 N 21st St, Philadelphia, PA 19103 - T: (215) 963-0667, Fax: (215) 963-0424, E-mail: fstone@pleasetouchmuseum.org, Internet: http://www.pleasetouchmuseum.org
Special Museum - 1976
Children's museum, visual and performing arts, sciences, humanities 39405

Presbyterian Historical Society Museum, 425 Lombard St, Philadelphia, PA 19147 - T: (215) 627-1852, Fax: (215) 627-0509. Head: Frederick J. Heuser
Religious Arts Museum - 1852
Religious hist 39406

The Print Center, 1614 Latimer St, Philadelphia, PA 19103 - T: (215) 735-6090, Fax: (215) 735-5511, E-mail: print@libertynet.org, Internet: http://www.printcenter.org. Head: Christine Filippone
Fine Arts Museum - 1915
Art 39407

Robert W. Ryerss Museum, Burholme Park, 7370 Central Av, Philadelphia, PA 19111 - T: (215) 745-3061, E-mail: Ryerss@netzero.net. Head: Theresa Stuhlman
Historical Museum - 1910
Asian collection 39408

Rodin Museum, Philadelphia Museum of Art, Benjamin Franklin Pkwy at 26th St, Philadelphia, PA 19130 - T: (215) 763-8100, Fax: (215) 235-0050, Internet: http://www.rodinmuseum.org. Head: Anne d' Harnoncourt, George D. Widener
Fine Arts Museum - 1926
Art 39409

Rosenbach Museum, 2010 Delancey Pl, Philadelphia, PA 19103 - T: (215) 732-1600, Fax: (215) 545-7529, E-mail: rml@rosenbach.org, Internet: http://www.rosenbach.org. Head: Derick Dreher
Special Museum - 1953
Rare books 39410

Rosenwald-Wolf Gallery, University of the Arts, 333 S Broad St, Philadelphia, PA 19102 - T: (215) 717-6480, Fax: (215) 875-2238, E-mail: rwg@uarts.edu, Internet: http://www.uarts.edu. Head: Miguel-Angel Corzo
Fine Arts Museum / University Museum - 1876
Art 39411

Saint Joseph's University Gallery, Boland Hall, 5600 City Line Av, Philadelphia, PA 19131-3195 - T: (610) 660-1840, Fax: (610) 660-2278, E-mail: sfenton@sju.edu, Internet: http://www.sju.edu. Head: Dennis Weeks
Fine Arts Museum / University Museum - 1976 39412

La Salle University Art Museum, 20th and Olney Av, Philadelphia, PA 19141 - T: (215) 951-1221, 951-1000, Fax: (215) 951-1488, E-mail: wistar@lasalle.edu, Internet: http://www.lasalle.edu/artmuseum.htm. Head: Daniel Burke
Fine Arts Museum / University Museum - 1975
Art 39413

The Stephen Girard Collection, Founder's Hall, 2101 S College Av, Philadelphia, PA 19121 - T: (215) 787-2680, Fax: (215) 787-2710, Internet: http://www.girardcollege.com
Historical Museum - 1831
Furniture, decorative arts 39414

Taller Puertorriqueno, 2721 N Fifth St, Philadelphia, PA 19133 - T: (215) 426-3311, Fax: (215) 426-5682. Head: Annabella Roige
Fine Arts Museum - 1974 39415

Temple Gallery, Tyler School of Art, Temple University, 45 N Second St, Philadelphia, PA 19106 - T: (215) 925-7379, Fax: (215) 925-7389, E-mail: tylerart@vm.temple.edu. Head: Kevin Melchionne
Fine Arts Museum / University Museum - 1985 39416

United States Mint-Philadelphia, 5th and Arch Sts, Philadelphia, PA 19106 - T: (215) 408-0114, Fax: (215) 408-2700, Internet: http://www.usmint.gov. Head: R.R. Robidoux
Special Museum - 1792
Numismatics 39417

University of Pennsylvania Museum of Archaeology and Anthropology, 33rd and Spruce Sts, Philadelphia, PA 19104-6324 - T: (215) 898-4000, Fax: (215) 898-0657, E-mail: websiters@museum.upenn.edu, Internet: http://www.upenn.edu/museum/. Head: Dr. Jeremy Sabloff
Ethnology Museum / Archaeological Museum - 1887
Archaeology, anthropology 39418

Wagner Free Institute of Science, 1700 W Montgomery Av, Philadelphia, PA 19121 - T: (215) 763-6529, Fax: (215) 763-1299, E-mail: wgninst@hslc.org. Head: Susan Glassman
Natural History Museum - 1855
Natural hist and science 39419

Woodmere Art Museum, 9201 Germantown Av, Philadelphia, PA 19118 - T: (215) 247-0476, Fax: (215) 247-2387, E-mail: ngreene@woodmereartmuseum.org, Internet: http://www.woodmereartmuseum.org. Head: Joseph Nicholson, Michael W. Schantz
Fine Arts Museum - 1940
Art 39420

Wyck Museum, 6026 Germantown Av, Philadelphia, PA 19144 - T: (215) 848-1612, Fax: (215) 848-1690, E-mail: wyck@libertynet.org. Head: John M. Groff
Historical Museum - 1973
Local hist, furniture, glass, ceramics, metals, textiles 39421

Philip SD

Prairie Homestead, HC 1, Box 51, Philip, SD 57567 - T: (605) 433-5400, Fax: (605) 433-5434, E-mail: klcrew@gwtc.net, Internet: http://www.prairiehomestead.com. Head: Keith Crew
Historic Site / Agriculture Museum / Open Air Museum - 1962
Historic house 39422

West River Museum, Center Av, Philip, SD 57567. Head: Arnold Waldon
Local Museum - 1965
Local hist 39423

Phillips ME

Phillips Historical Society Museum, Pleasant St, Phillips, ME 04966 - T: (207) 639-3352, Fax: (207) 639-5258
Local Museum - 1959
Local history 39424

Phillipsburg KS

Old Fort Bissell, Hwy 36, by City Park, Phillipsburg, KS 67661 - T: (913) 543-6212
Local Museum - 1961
Local history 39425

Philomath OR

Benton County Historical Museum, 1101 Main St, Philomath, OR 97370 - T: (541) 929-6230, Fax: (541) 929-6261, E-mail: bchm@peak.org, Internet: http://www.peak.org/~lewisb/Museum.html. Head: William R. Lewis
Local Museum - 1980 39426

Phoenix AZ

Arizona Hall of Fame Museum, 1101 W Washington, Phoenix, AZ 85007 - T: (602) 255-2110, Fax: (602) 255-3314, E-mail: hofguide@dlapr.lib.az.us, Internet: http://www.dlapr.lib.az.us. Head: Michael D. Carman
Local Museum - 1986
Local hist 39427

Arizona Mining and Mineral Museum, 1502 W Washington, Phoenix, AZ 85007 - T: (602) 255-3795, Fax: (602) 255-3777, E-mail: susancelestina@hotmail.com, Internet: http://www.admmr.states.az.us. Head: Doug Sawyer
Natural History Museum / Science&Tech Museum - 1953
Minerals, mining 39428

Arizona Science Center, 600 E Washington, Phoenix, AZ 85004-2394 - T: (602) 716-2000 ext 0, Fax: (602) 716-2099, Internet: http://www.azscience.org. Head: Sheila Grinell, Grant Slinn
Science&Tech Museum - 1984
Science 39429

Arizona State Capitol Museum, 1700 W Washington, Phoenix, AZ 85007 - T: (602) 542-4675, Fax: (602) 542-4690, Internet: http://www.dlapr.lib.az.us. Head: Michael D. Carman
Historical Museum - 1974
Restored Capitol Building 39430

Hall of Flame Museum of Firefighting, 6101 E Van Buren St, Phoenix, AZ 85008-3421 - T: (602) 275-3473, Fax: (602) 275-0896, E-mail: petermolloy@hallofflame.org, Internet: http://www.hallofflame.org. Head: Dr. Peter M. Molloy
Historical Museum - 1961
History of fire fighting 39431

Heard Museum, 2301 N Central Av, Phoenix, AZ 85004 - T: (602) 252-8840, Fax: (602) 252-9757, E-mail: postmaster@heard.org, Internet: http://www.heard.org. Head: Frank H. Goodyear jr.
Fine Arts Museum / Ethnology Museum - 1929
Native cultures, art 39432

Phoenix Art Museum, 1625 N Central Av, Phoenix, AZ 85004-1685 - T: (602) 257-1880, Fax: (602) 253-8662, E-mail: info@phxart.org, Internet: http://www.phxart.org. Head: James K. Ballinger
Fine Arts Museum - 1949
American, European and Asian art, contemporary art 39433

Phoenix Museum of History, 105 N Fifth St, Phoenix, AZ 85004-4404 - T: (602) 253-2734, Fax: (602) 253-2348. Head: Cindy L. Myers
Local Museum - 1923
Phoenix history 39434

Pioneer Arizona Living History Museum, 3901 W Pioneer Rd, Phoenix, AZ 85027-7020 - T: (602) 465-1052, Fax: (602) 465-1029, E-mail: plhm@aol.com, Internet: http://www.pioneer-arizona.com. Head: William D. Gaston
Historical Museum - 1956
Living history complex 39435

Pueblo Grande Museum, 4619 E Washington, Phoenix, AZ 85034-1909 - T: (602) 495-0900, Fax: (602) 495-5645, E-mail: prlpgstf@ci.phoenix.az.us, Internet: http://www.pueblogrande.com. Head: Roger Lidman
Archaeological Museum - 1929
Archaeological site 39436

Pickens SC

Pickens County Museum of Art History, 307 Johnson St, Pickens, SC 29671 - T: (864) 898-5963, Fax: (803) 898-5947, E-mail: picmus@innova.net, Internet: http://www.co.pickens.sc.us/cultural_events.asp. Head: C. Allen Coleman
Fine Arts Museum / Local Museum / Historical Museum / Historic Site - 1976
Art, local hist 39437

Piedmont SD

Petrified Forest of the Black Hills, 8228 Elk Creek Rd, Piedmont, SD 57769-9520 - T: (605) 787-4560, Fax: (605) 787-6477, E-mail: forest@elkcreek.org, Internet: http://www.elkcreek.org. Head: Gerald E. Teachout
Natural History Museum - 1929
Geology 39438

Pierre SD

The Museum of the South Dakota State Historical Society, Cultural Heritage Center, 900 Governors Dr, Pierre, SD 57501-2217 - T: (605) 773-3458, Fax: (605) 773-6041, E-mail: david.hartley@state.sd.us, Internet: http://www.sdhistory.org. Head: David B. Hartley
Historical Museum - 1901
Local hist 39439

South Dakota Discovery Center, 805 W Sioux Av, Pierre, SD 57501 - T: (605) 224-8295, Fax: (605) 224-2865, E-mail: sddcacad@sd.cybernex.net. Head: Bill Bullard, Craig DeTample
Science&Tech Museum - 1989
Science 39440

Pilger NE

Historical Society of Stanton County Museum, 345 N Main St, Pilger, NE 68768-0213 - T: (402) 396-3477, E-mail: rjensen@ncfcomm.com. Head: Jim L. Duncan
Local Museum - 1965 39441

Pilot Knob MO

Fort Davidson State Historic Site, Hwy 21 and Hwy V, Pilot Knob, MO 63663 - T: (314) 546-3454, Fax: (314) 546-2713. Head: David Roggensees
Military Museum - 1969 39442

Pima AZ

Eastern Arizona Museum and Historical Society of Graham County, 2 N Main St, Pima, AZ 85543 - T: (520) 485-3032
Local Museum / Ethnology Museum - 1963
Local history 39443

Pine Bluff AR

Arts and Science Center for Southeast Arkansas, 701 Main St, Pine Bluff, AR 71601 - T: (870) 536-3375, Fax: (870) 536-3380, E-mail: asc@seark.net. Head: Mary Brock
Fine Arts Museum / Performing Arts Museum - 1968
Arts, culture 39444

Pine Bluff/ Jefferson County Historical Museum, 201 E 4th, Pine Bluff, AR 71601 - T: (501) 541-5402, Fax: (501) 541-5405, E-mail: jumuse@ipa.net. Head: Sue Trulock
Local Museum - 1980
History of Pine Bluff and Jefferson County 39445

Pine Ridge AR

Lum and Abner Museum and Jot 'Em Down Store, 4562 Hwy 88 West, Pine Ridge, AR 71966 - T: (870) 326-4442, Fax: (870) 326-4442, E-mail: nstucker@alltel.net, Internet: http://www.lum-abner.com. Head: Noah Lon Stucker, Kathryn Moore Stucker
Science&Tech Museum / Historical Museum - 1971
Historic stores on which the Lum and Abner radio program 1931-55 was based, country store, rural life 39446

Pine Ridge SD

The Heritage Center, c/o Red Cloud Indian School, 100 Mission Dr, Pine Ridge, SD 57770 - T: (605) 867-5491, Fax: (605) 867-1104, E-mail: rcheritage@basec.net, Internet: http://basec.net/rcheritage/. Head: Calvin Jumping Bull, C.M. Simon
Fine Arts Museum / Ethnology Museum - 1967
Native American art 39447

Pinedale WY

Museum of the Mountain Man, 700 E Hennick, Pinedale, WY 82941 - T: (307) 367-4101, Fax: (307) 367-6768, E-mail: museummtman@wyoming.com, Internet: http://www.pinedaleonline.com/mmMuseuM. Head: Dave Bell, Laurie Latta
Historical Museum - 1990
History 39448

Piney Flats TN

Rocky Mount Museum, Rocky Mount Pkwy, 200 Hyder Hill Rd, Piney Flats, TN 37686 - T: (423) 538-7396, Fax: (423) 538-1086, E-mail: rmm@preferred.com, Internet: http://www.pages.preferred.com/~rmm. Head: C. Lee McConnell, John Patterson
Open Air Museum / Local Museum - 1958
Historical village 39449

Piney Woods MS

Laurence C. Jones Museum, Piney Woods Country Life School, Piney Woods, MS 39148 - T: (601) 845-2214, Fax: (601) 845-2604, Internet: http://www.pineywoods.org. Head: Charles H. Beady
Local Museum - 1986
Regional history 39450

Pinson TN

Pinson Mounds State Archaeological Area, 460 Ozier Rd, Pinson, TN 38366 - T: (901) 988-5614, Fax: (901) 424-3909, Internet: http://www.tnstateparks.com/pinson
Archaeological Museum - 1980
Archaeology 39451

Pipestone MN

Pipestone County Historical Museum, 113 S Hiawatha Av, Pipestone, MN 56164 - T: (507) 825-2563, Fax: (507) 825-2563, E-mail: pipctymu@rconnect.com, Internet: http://www.pipestone-minnesota.com/Museum. Head: Rich Gergen, Chris Roelfsema-Hummel
Historical Museum - 1880 39452

Pipestone National Monument, 36 Reservation Av, Pipestone, MN 56164 - T: (507) 825-5464, Fax: (507) 825-5466, E-mail: PIPE_Interpretation@nps.gov, Internet: http://www.NPS.GOV/PIPE
Historical Museum / Ethnology Museum - 1937 39453

Piqua OH

Piqua Historical Area State Memorial, 9845 N Hardin Rd, Piqua, OH 45356-9707 - T: (937) 773-2522, Fax: (937) 773-4311. Head: Andy Hite
Agriculture Museum - 1972 39454

Piscataway NJ

Cornelius Low House/Middlesex County Museum, 1225 River Rd, Piscataway, NJ - T: (732) 745-4177, 745-4489, Fax: (732) 745-4507, E-mail: info@cultureheritage.org, Internet: http://www.culture-heritage.org. Head: Kenneth M. Helsby
Local Museum - 1979
Local hist 39455

East Jersey Olde Towne, River Rd and Hoes Ln, Piscataway, NJ 08855-0661 - T: (732) 463-9077, 329-9159, Fax: (732) 329-2103. Head: Stanley Bresticker
Local Museum / Open Air Museum - 1971
Historic 18th c village 39456

Pittsburg KS

Crawford County Historical Museum, N of 69 Bypass and W 20th St, Pittsburg, KS 66762-8600 - T: (316) 231-1440. Head: Denny Davidson
Local Museum - 1968
General museum 39457

Natural History Museum, Pittsburg State University, Dept. of Biology, Heckert-Wells Hall, Pittsburg, KS 66762 - T: (316) 235-4732, Fax: (316) 235-4194. Head: Dr. S.D. Ford
University Museum / Natural History Museum - 1903
Biology, mammals, birds, insects 39458

Pittsburgh PA

The Andy Warhol Museum, 117 Sandusky St, Pittsburgh, PA 15212-5890 - T: (412) 237-8300, Fax: (412) 237-8340, E-mail: warhol@alphaclp.clpgh.org, Internet: http://www.warhol.org/warhol. Head: Thomas Sokolowski
Fine Arts Museum - 1994
Art, visual arts 39459

Art Institute of Pittsburgh, 420 Allies Blvd, Pittsburgh, PA 15233 - T: (412) 471-2473
Public Gallery 39460

Associated Artists of Pittsburgh Gallery, 937 Liberty Av, Pittsburgh, PA 15222 - T: (412) 263-2710, Fax: (412) 471-1765, E-mail: aap@telerama.com. Head: Rich Brown, Frances Frederick
Fine Arts Museum - 1910
Art 39461

Carnegie Museum of Art, 4400 Forbes Av, Pittsburgh, PA 15213-4080 - T: (412) 622-3131, Fax: (412) 622-3112, Internet: http://www.cmoa.org. Head: Richard Armstrong
Fine Arts Museum - 1895 39462

Carnegie Museum of Natural History, 4400 Forbes Av, Pittsburgh, PA 15213-4080 - T: (412) 622-3131, Fax: (412) 622-8837, Internet: http://www.clpgh.org/cmnh. Head: Dr. Jay Apt, Michael Nelson
Ethnology Museum / Natural History Museum - 1896
Natural hist, anthropology 39463

Carnegie Science Center, 1 Allegheny Av, Pittsburgh, PA 15212-5850 - T: (412) 237-3400, Fax: (412) 237-3309, Internet: http://www.csc.clpgh.org. Head: Ellsworth H. Brown, Seddon Bennington, Tom Flaherty, John Radzilowicz
Science&Tech Museum - 1991
Science and technology 39464

Center for American Music, Stephen Foster Memorial, University of Pittsburgh, Pittsburgh, PA 15260 - T: (412) 624-4100, Fax: (412) 624-7447, E-mail: amerimus@pitt.edu, Internet: http://www.pitt.edu/~amerimus. Head: Deane L. Root
Music Museum - 1937
American music hist, Stephen Collins Foster - Research library 39465

The Frick Art Museum, 7227 Reynolds St, Pittsburgh, PA 15208 - T: (412) 371-0600, Fax: (412) 371-6140, E-mail: ngrabania@frickart.org, Internet: http://www.frickart.org. Head: E. McIntosh
Fine Arts Museum - 1970
Art 39466

The Henry Clay Frick Center, 7227 Reynolds St, Pittsburgh, PA 15208-2923 - T: (412) 371-0600, Fax: (412) 241-5393, E-mail: info@frickart.org, Internet: http://www.frickart.org. Head: E. McIntosh
Fine Arts Museum / Historical Museum - 1990
Art and history 39467

Hermann John A. jr. Memorial Art Museum, 318 Lincoln Av, Pittsburgh, PA 15202 - T: (412) 761-8008
Fine Arts Museum 39468

Historical Society of Western Pennsylvania Museum, 1212 Smallman St, Pittsburgh, PA 15222 - T: (412) 454-6000, 454-6370, Fax: (412) 454-6029, E-mail: hswp@usaor.net, Internet: http://trfn.clpgh.org/hswp
Local Museum - 1879
Urban and regional hist, 20th-century immigrant and ethnic experience, rural life 39469

Mattress Factory Museum, 500 Sampsonia Way, Pittsburgh, PA 15212 - T: (412) 231-3169, Fax: (412) 322-2231, E-mail: info@mattress.org, Internet: http://www.mattress.org
Fine Arts Museum - 1977
Art 39470

Pittsburgh Center for the Arts, 6300 Fifth Av, Pittsburgh, PA 15232 - T: (412) 361-0873, 361-0455, Fax: (412) 361-8338, E-mail: dmadden@pittsburgharts.org, Internet: http://www.pittsburgharts.org. Head: Laura H. Willumsen
Fine Arts Museum - 1945
Local art 39471

Pittsburgh Children's Museum, 10 Childrens Way, Pittsburgh, PA 15212 - T: (412) 322-5059, Fax: (412) 322-4932, E-mail: info@pittsburghkids.org, Internet: http://www.pittsburghkids.org. Head: Anne V. Lewis, Jane Werner, Chris Siefert
Special Museum - 1980 39472

Silver Eye Center for Photography, 1015 E Carson St, Pittsburgh, PA 15203 - T: (412) 431-1810, Fax: (412) 431-5777. Head: Jody Guy
Fine Arts Museum 39473

Society for Contemporary Craft Museum, 2100 Smallman St, Pittsburgh, PA 15222 - T: (412) 261-7003, Fax: (412) 261-1941, Internet: http://www.contemporarycraft.org. Head: Janet L. McCall
Fine Arts Museum / Decorative Arts Museum - 1972
Contemporary crafts 39474

University Art Gallery, University of Pittsburgh, 104 Frick Fine Arts Bldg, Pittsburgh, PA 15260 - T: (412) 648-2400, Fax: (412) 648-2792, E-mail: histart@pitt.edu, Internet: http://www.pitt.edu/~arthome. Head: Prof. David G. Wilkins
University Museum / Fine Arts Museum - 1966 39475

Pittsfield MA

Berkshire Artisans, 28 Renne Av, Pittsfield, MA 01201 - T: (413) 499-9348, Fax: (413) 499-9348, E-mail: berkart@taconic.net, Internet: http://www.berkshireweb.com/artisans/index.html. Head: Daniel M. O'Connell
Fine Arts Museum / Public Gallery - 1976 39476

Berkshire County Historical Society Museum at Arrowhead, 780 Holmes Rd, Pittsfield, MA 01201 - T: (413) 442-1793, Fax: (413) 443-1449, E-mail: info@mobydick.org, Internet: http://www.mobydick.org. Head: Susan Eisley
Local Museum / Special Museum - 1962
Regional history, Pittsfield home of author Herman Melville 1850-1863 39477

The Berkshire Museum, 39 South St, Pittsfield, MA 01201 - T: (413) 443-7171 ext 10, Fax: (413) 443-2135, E-mail: info@berkshire.museum.org, Internet: http://www.berkshiremuseum.org. Head: Marion Grant
Local Museum - 1903
Art, natural science, history - aquarium 39478

Hancock Shaker Village, Rte 20, W Housatonic St, Pittsfield, MA 01202 - T: (413) 443-0188, Fax: (413) 447-9357, E-mail: info@hancockshakervillage.org, Internet: http://www.hancockshakervillage.org
Historic Site / Open Air Museum - 1960
Historic village, 22 buildings with constructions dating back to 1790 - library, archive 39479

Pittsford NY

Historic Pittsford, 18 Monroe Av, Pittsford, NY 14534 - T: (716) 381-2941. Head: Jerry Francis
Local Museum - 1966 39480

Pittsford VT

Pittsford Historical Society Museum, Main St Rte 7, Pittsford, VT 05763 - T: (802) 483-6040, 483-6623, Internet: http://www.pittsford-historical.org
Local Museum - 1980
Local hist 39481

Placerville CA

El Dorado County Historical Museum, 104 Placerville Dr, Fairgrounds, Placerville, CA 95667 - T: (530) 621-5865, Fax: (530) 621-6644. Head: Kaye Murdock
Local Museum - 1939
Local hist 39482

Plainfield NJ

Drake House Museum, 602 W Front St, Plainfield, NJ 07060 - T: (908) 755-5831, Internet: http://members.tripod.com/~drakehouse. Head: Jean Mattson
Local Museum - 1921 39483

Plains TX

Tsa Mo Ga Memorial Museum, 1109 Av H, Plains, TX 79355 - T: (806) 456-8855. Head: P.W. Saint Romain
Local Museum - 1959
Local hist 39484

Plainview TX

Museum of the Llano Estacado, Wayland University, Plainview, TX 79072 - T: (806) 296-4735. Head: Eddie Guffee
University Museum / Local Museum - 1976
Local hist 39485

Plano TX

Heritage Farmstead Museum, 1900 W 15 St, Plano, TX 75075 - T: (972) 881-0140, Fax: (972) 422-6481, E-mail: museum@airmail.net, Internet: http://www.heritagefarmstead.org
Historical Museum - 1974 39486

Plantation FL

Plantation Historical Museum, 511 N Fig Tree Ln, Plantation, FL 33317 - T: (954) 797-2722, Fax: (954) 797-2717, E-mail: museum511@aol.com, Internet: http://www.plantation.org
Local Museum - 1975
Local history 39487

Platteville CO

Fort Vasquez Museum, Colorado Historical Society Regional Museum, 13412 U.S. Hwy 85, Platteville, CO 80651 - T: (970) 785-2832, Fax: (970) 785-9193, E-mail: susan.hoskinson@chs.state.co.us, Internet: http://www.coloradohistory.org. Head: Susan Hoskinson
Historic Site - 1958
Fur trade and Native American, reconstructed adobe fort (1835 trading post) 39488

Platteville WI

The Mining Museum, 405 E Main St, Platteville, WI 53818 - T: (608) 348-3301, Fax: (608) 348-4640. Head: Stephen J. Kleefisch
Science&Tech Museum - 1965
Mining 39489

Rollo Jamison Museum, 405 E Main St, Platteville, WI 53818 - T: (608) 348-3301, Fax: (608) 348-4640. Head: Stephen J. Kleefisch
Historical Museum - 1981
Local hist 39490

Plattsburgh NY

Clinton County Historical Museum, 48 Court St, Plattsburgh, NY 12901 - T: (518) 561-0340, Fax: (518) 561-4616. Head: Cecily Feldman, Shirley L. Koster
Local Museum - 1973 39491

Kent-Delord House Museum, 17 Cumberland Av, Plattsburgh, NY 12901 - T: (518) 561-1035, Fax: (518) 561-1035. Head: Nancy Church, Gary Worthington
Local Museum - 1924 39492

Plattsburgh Art Museum, State University of New York, Plattsburgh, NY 12901 - T: (518) 564-2474, Fax: (518) 564-2473, E-mail: beauhaml@splava.cc.plattsburgh.edu. Head: Edward R. Brohel
Fine Arts Museum / University Museum - 1952 39493

Plattsmouth NE

Cass County Historical Society Museum, 646 Main St, Plattsmouth, NE 68048 - T: (402) 296-4770. Head: George Miller
Local Museum - 1936 39494

Pleasant Hill CA

Diablo Valley College Museum, 321 Golf Club Rd, Pleasant Hill, CA 94523 - T: (925) 685-1230 ext 303, Fax: (925) 685-1551
University Museum / Local Museum - 1960
Science 39495

Pleasanton CA

Amador-Livermore Valley Museum, 603 Main St, Pleasanton, CA 94566 - T: (925) 462-2766. Head: Lynda Greene
Local Museum - 1972
Local hist 39496

Pleasanton KS

Linn County Museum, Dunlap Park, Pleasanton, KS 66075 - T: (913) 352-8739. Head: Ola May Earnest
Local Museum - 1973
County history 39497

Marais Des Cygnes Memorial Historic Site, Rte 2, Pleasanton, KS 66075 - T: (913) 352-6174
Historical Museum
Home of Charles C. Hadsall, used as a fort by John Brown, nr massacre site 39498

Pleasanton TX

Longhorn Museum, 1959 Hwy 97 E, Pleasanton, TX 78064 - T: (830) 569-6313. Head: Mary L. Tondre
Historical Museum - 1976 39499

Pleasantville NY

Reader's Digest Art Gallery, Reader's Digest, Reader's Digest Rd, Pleasantville, NY 10570-7000 - T: (914) 238-1000, Fax: (914) 244-5006
Fine Arts Museum 39500

Pleasantville PA

Historic Pithole City, Drake Well Museum, R.D. 2, Pleasantville, PA 16341 - T: (814) 589-7912, 827-2797, Fax: (814) 827-4888, E-mail: bzolli@state.pa.us, Internet: http://www.drakewell.org. Head: Barbara T. Zolli
Open Air Museum - 1975
Oil wells, model of city in 1865 39501

Plymouth IN

Marshall County Historical Museum, 123 N Michigan St, Plymouth, IN 46563 - T: (219) 936-2306, Fax: (219) 936-9306, E-mail: mchistory@mchistoricalsociety.org, Internet: http://www.mchistoricalsociety.org. Head: Peter Trone, Linda Rippy
Local Museum - 1957
Local history 39502

Plymouth MA

Howland House, 33 Sandwich St, Plymouth, MA 02360 - T: (508) 746-9590, Fax: (508) 866-5056. Head: Harry L. Walen
Archaeological Museum - 1897 39503

Mayflower Society Museum, 4 Winslow St, Plymouth, MA 02360 - T: (508) 746-2590
Local Museum - 1897 39504

Pilgrim Hall Museum, 75 Court St, Plymouth, MA 02360 - T: (508) 746-1620, Fax: (508) 747-4228, E-mail: pegbaker@ici.net, Internet: http://www.pilgrimhall.org
Historical Museum / Local Museum - 1820
Local history 39505

Plimoth Plantation Museum, 137 Warren Av, Plymouth, MA 02362 - T: (508) 746-1622, Fax: (508) 746-3407, Internet: http://www.plimoth.org. Head: Nancy Brennan
Historical Museum - 1947
Outdoor living history 39506

Plymouth Antiquarian Society Museum, 6 Court St, Plymouth, MA 02360 - T: (508) 746-0012, Fax: (508) 746-7908, E-mail: pasm@ici.net. Head: Mary Guidoboni, Donna D. Curtin
Historical Museum - 1919
Historic houses: Harlow Fort house, Spooner house, Hedge house 39507

Richard Sparrow House, 42 Summer St, Plymouth, MA 02360 - T: (508) 747-1240, Fax: (508) 746-9521, E-mail: lcatherton@aol.com, Internet: http://www.sparrowhouse.com. Head: Violet Berry, Lois Atherton
Folklore Museum - 1961
Local crafts 39508

Plymouth MI

Plymouth Historical Museum, 155 S Main St, Plymouth, MI 48170 - T: (734) 455-8940, Fax: (734) 455-7797, E-mail: history@pdl.plymouth.lib.mi.us, Internet: http://www.plymouth.lib.mi.us/~history. Head: Dan LeBlond, Beth A. Stewart
Historical Museum - 1962
Local history, Petz Abraham Lincoln col 39509

Plymouth NH

Karl Drerup Fine Arts Gallery, Dept of Fine Arts, Plymouth State College, Plymouth, NH 03264 - T: (603) 535-2201, Fax: (603) 535-2938, Internet: http://eeyore.plymouth.edu/~rdecicco/art/home.html. Head: Joe Driscoll
University Museum / Fine Arts Museum - 1969 39510

Plymouth WI

Bradley Gallery of Art, W 3718 South Dr, Plymouth, WI 53073 - T: (920) 565-2111, Fax: (920) 565-1206, E-mail: presnellweidner@lakeland.edu, Internet: http://www.lakeland.edu. Head: Denise Presnell-Weidner, William Weidner
Public Gallery - 1988 39511

John G. Voigt House, W 5639 Anokijig Ln, Plymouth, WI 53073 - T: (920) 893-0782, Fax: (920) 893-0873. Head: Jim Scherer
Local Museum - 1850
Historic house 39512

Plymouth Notch VT

President Calvin Coolidge State Historic Site, Plymouth Notch, VT 05056 - T: (802) 672-3773, Fax: (802) 672-3337, E-mail: wjenny@dca.state.vt.us, Internet: http://www.historic-vermont.org
Local Museum - 1951
Early 20th c village, Calvin Coolidge birthplace and homestead 39513

Pocatello ID

Idaho Museum of Natural History, 5th and Dillon, Pocatello, ID 83209 - T: (208) 282-3160, Fax: (208) 282-5893, E-mail: lohserne@isu.edu, Internet: http://www.isu.edu/departments/museum. Head: Dr. E.S. Lohse
University Museum / Natural History Museum - 1934
Natural history 39514

Point Lookout MO

Ralph Foster Museum, College of the Ozarks, Point Lookout, MO 65726 - T: (417) 334-6411 ext 3407, Fax: (417) 335-2618. Head: Annette J. Sain
University Museum / Local Museum - 1930
Local history, art, firearms, natural history 39515

Point Marion PA

Friendship Hill National Historic Site, 223 New Geneva Rd, Point Marion, PA 15474 - T: (724) 725-9190, Fax: 7242) 725-1999, E-mail: lawren-dunn@npg.gov, Internet: http://www.nps.gov/frhi
Historic Site - 1978
Local hist 39516

Point Pleasant OH

Grant's Birthplace State Memorial, US 52 and State Rte 232, Point Pleasant, OH 45153 - T: (513) 553-4911
Local Museum 39517

Point Pleasant WV

Point Pleasant Battle Monument State Park, 1 Main St, Point Pleasant, WV 25550 - T: (304) 675-0869. Head: Stephen Jones
Local Museum / Historic Site - 1901
Historic house and site, where the first battle of the Revolution was fought 39518

West Virginia State Farm Museum, Rte 1, Box 479, Point Pleasant, WV 25550 - T: (304) 675-5737, Fax: (304) 675-5430, E-mail: wvfarmus@ns3.zoomnet.net. Head: Jim Lewis
Agriculture Museum - 1974 39519

Polk City FL

Water Ski Hall of Fame, American Water Ski Educational Foundation, 1251 Noly Cow Rd, Polk City, FL 33868-8200 - T: (863) 324-2472, Fax: (863) 324-3996, E-mail: 102726, 2751@compuserve.com, Internet: http://usawaterski.org. Head: Dr. J.D. Morgan, Carole Lowe
Special Museum - 1968 39520

Polson MT

Miracle of America Museum, 58176 Hwy 93, Polson, MT 59860 - T: (406) 883-6804, E-mail: museum@cyberport.net, Internet: http://www.cyberport.net/museum. Head: W. Gil Mangels
Historical Museum / Science&Tech Museum - 1985
Ethnology, history, farm machinery, steam engine, fishing, cars, tractors, military vehicles, tranportation 39521

Pomeroy OH

Meigs County Museum, 144 Butternut Av, Pomeroy, OH 45769 - T: (740) 992-3810. Head: Margaret Parker
Local Museum - 1960 39522

Ponca City OK

Marland's Grand Home, 1000 E Grand, Ponca City, OK 74601 - T: (580) 767-0427. Head: Kathy Adams
Historical Museum / Historic Site - 1916 39523

Pioneer Woman Statue and Museum, 701 Monument, Ponca City, OK 74604 - T: (580) 765-6108, Fax: (580) 762-2498, E-mail: piown@ok-history.mus.ok.us, Internet: http://www.ok.-history.mus.ok.us. Head: Valerie Haynes
Historical Museum - 1958 39524

Ponce Inlet FL

Ponce DeLeon Inlet Lighthouse, 4931 S Peninsula Dr, Ponce Inlet, FL 32127 - T: (904) 761-1821, Fax: (904) 761-1821, E-mail: lighthouse@ponceinlet.org, Internet: http://www.ponceinlet.org. Head: Ann Caneer
Historical Museum - 1972 39525

Pontiac MI

Creative Arts Center, 47 Williams St, Pontiac, MI 48341 - T: (248) 333-7849, Fax: (248) 333-7841, E-mail: createpont@aol.com. Head: Carol Paster
Fine Arts Museum / Folklore Museum - 1964
Civic art, culture 39526

Pine Grove Historic Museum, 405 Oakland Av, Pontiac, MI 48342 - T: (248) 338-6732, Fax: (248) 338-6731, E-mail: ocphs@wwnet.net, Internet: http://wwnet.net/~ocphs/index.html. Head: Michael Willis
Historical Museum - 1874
Pine Grove, the Governor Moses Wisner House 39527

Poplar Bluff MO

Margaret Harwell Art Museum, 421 N Main St, Poplar Bluff, MO 63901 - T: (573) 686-8002, Fax: (573) 686-8017, E-mail: tina@mham.org, Internet: http://www.mham.org. Head: Ann Cotrell
Fine Arts Museum - 1981 39528

Port Allen LA

West Baton Rouge Museum, 845 N Jefferson Av, Port Allen, LA 70767 - T: (225) 336-2422, Fax: (225) 336-2448, E-mail: wbrmuseum@inetmail.att.net, Internet: http://www.westbatonrougemuseum.com. Head: Caroline Kennedy
Historical Museum - 1968
Regional history 39529

Port Angeles WA

The Museum of Clallam County Historical Society, Lincoln School, Port Angeles, WA 98362 - T: (360) 452-2662. Head: Kathy Monds
Local Museum - 1948
Local hist 39530

Port Angeles Fine Arts Center, 1203 E Lauridsen Blvd, Port Angeles, WA 98362 - T: (360) 457-3532, 457-0411 ext 4590, Fax: (360) 457-3532, E-mail: pafac@olypen.com, Internet: http://www.olympus.net/community/pafac. Head: Mim Foley, Jake Seniuk
Fine Arts Museum / Public Gallery - 1986
Art, coll of sculptures, contemporary art of the Northwest 39531

Port Arthur TX

Museum of the Gulf Coast, 700 Procter St, Port Arthur, TX 77640 - T: (409) 982-7000, Fax: (409) 982-9614. Head: Dr. Sam Monroe, Danny M. Sessums
Local Museum - 1964
Regional history 39532

Port Austin MI

Huron City Museums, 7930 Huron City Rd, Port Austin, MI 48467 - T: (517) 428-4123, Fax: (517) 428-4123, Internet: http://www.wlpf.org. Head: Charles A. Scheffner
Local Museum - 1950
Local hist 39533

Port Clinton OH

Ottawa County Historical Museum, 126 W Third St, Port Clinton, OH 43452 - T: (419) 732-2237, E-mail: ochm@thirdplanet.net. Head: Eugene van Voorhis
Historical Museum - 1932 39534

Port Gamble WA

Port Gamble Historic Museum, 3 Rainier Av, Port Gamble, WA 98364 - T: (360) 297-8074, Fax: (360) 297-7455, E-mail: ssmith@orminc.com, Internet: http://www.ptgamble.com
Historic Site - 1976
Local hist 39535

Port Gibson MS

Grand Gulf Military State Park Museum, Rte 2, Grand Gulf Rd, Port Gibson, MS 39150 - T: (601) 437-5911, Fax: (601) 437-2929, E-mail: park@grandgulf.state.ms.us, Internet: http://www.grandgulfpark.state.ms.us. Head: Dr. David Headley
Military Museum - 1958 39536

Port Hueneme CA

Civil Engineer Corps and Seabee Museum, Bldg 99, Naval Construction Battalion Center, 1000 23rd Av, Port Hueneme, CA 93043-4301 - T: (805) 982-5165, Fax: (805) 982-5595. Head: Lara Bickell
Military Museum - 1947
Military hist 39537

Port Huron MI

Jack R. Hennesey Art Galleries, Saint Clair County Community College, 323 Erie St, Port Huron, MI 48061-5015 - T: (810) 989-5709, Fax: (810) 984-2852, E-mail: dkorffstclair.cc.mi.us, Internet: http://www.stclair.cc.mi.us. Head: David Korff
Fine Arts Museum
Paintings, prints, metal and wooden sculpture 39538

Port Huron Museum, 1115 Sixth St, Port Huron, MI 48060 - T: (810) 982-0891, Fax: (810) 982-0053, E-mail: phmuseum@tir.com, Internet: http://www.phmuseum.org. Head: Stephen R. Williams
Local Museum - 1967
Local history 39539

Port Jefferson NY

Historical Society of Greater Port Jefferson Museum, 115 Prospect St, Port Jefferson, NY 11777 - T: (516) 473-2665, Internet: http://www.portjeffhistorical.org
Local Museum - 1967 39540

Port Jervis NY

Minisink Valley Historical Society Museum, 125-133 W Main St, Port Jervis, NY 12771 - T: (914) 856-2375, Fax: (914) 856-1049, Internet: http://www.minisink.org. Head: Charles Swartwont, Peter Osborne
Local Museum - 1889 39541

Port Orange FL

Hungarian Folk-Art Museum, 546 Ruth St, Port Orange, FL 32127 - T: (904) 767-4292, Fax: (904) 788-6785. Head: Dr. Michael J. Horvath
Folklore Museum - 1979 39542

Port Saint Joe FL

Constitution Convention State Museum, 200 Allen Memorial Way, Port Saint Joe, FL 32456 - T: (850) 229-8029, Fax: (850) 229-8029, Internet: http://www.dep.state.fl.us/parks/. Head: Eddie Ranew
Local Museum - 1955
History 39543

Port Sanilac MI

Sanilac County Historical Museum, 228 S Ridge St, Port Sanilac, MI 48469 - T: (810) 622-9946, Fax: (810) 622-9946, E-mail: nlm@greatlakes.net. Head: Art Schlichting
Historical Museum - 1964
Local history 39544

Port Townsend WA

Jefferson County Historical Society Museum, 210 Madison St, Port Townsend, WA 98368 - T: (360) 385-1003, Fax: (360) 385-1042, E-mail: -jchsmuseum.olympus.net.com. Head: Harry Dudley, Dr. Niki R. Clark
Historical Museum - 1951
Northwest Coast history and prehistory 39545

Port Townsend Marine Science Center, Fort Worden State Park, 532 Battery Way, Port Townsend, WA 98368-3431 - T: (360) 385-5582, Fax: (360) 385-7248, E-mail: ptmsc@olympus.net, Internet: http://www.olympus.net/ptmsc. Head: Andrew Palmer
Military Museum - 1983
Marine hist 39546

Puget Sound Coast Artillery Museum at Fort Worden, Bldg 201, Fort Worden State Park, Port Townsend, WA 98368 - T: (360) 385-3295, Fax: (360) 385-2328, E-mail: artymus@olypen.com. Head: Donald F. McLarney
Military Museum - 1976
Military hist 39547

Port Washington NY

Polish American Museum, 16 Belleview Av, Port Washington, NY 11050 - T: (516) 883-6542, Fax: (516) 767-1936
Fine Arts Museum / Decorative Arts Museum / Historical Museum - 1977 39548

Sands-Willets House, 336 Port Washington Blvd, Port Washington, NY 11050 - T: (516) 365-9074
Local Museum - 1962 39549

Portage WI

Fort Winnebago Surgeons Quarters, W 8687 St, Hwy 33 E, Portage, WI 53901 - T: (608) 742-2949
Local Museum - 1938
Local hist 39550

The Historic Indian Agency House, Hwy 33, Portage, WI 53901-3116 - T: (608) 742-6362
Decorative Arts Museum / Local Museum / Historic Site - 1932
Historic house and site 39551

Portales NM

Blackwater Draw Museum, 7 miles north of ENMU campus on Hwy 70, Portales, NM 88130 - T: (505) 562-2202, Fax: (505) 562-2305, E-mail: matthew.hillsman@enmu.edu, Internet: http://www.enmu.edu. Head: Dr. John Montgomery
Archaeological Museum - 1969
1932 America's first multi-cultural, paleoindian archaeological site 39552

Gallery of the Department of Art, Eastern New Mexico University, Portales, NM 88130 - T: (505) 562-2510, Fax: (505) 562-2362, Internet: http://www.enmu.edu. Head: Jim Bryant
Fine Arts Museum / University Museum - 1935
Students artworks 39553

Miles Mineral Museum, Eastern New Mexico University Campus, Portales, NM 88130 - T: (505) 562-2651, Fax: (505) 562-2192, E-mail: -jim.constantopoulos@enmu.edu, Internet: http://www.enmu.edu/~constanj/milesmuseum.htm. Head: Dr. Jim Constantopoulos
University Museum / Natural History Museum - 1969 39554

Natural History Museum, Eastern New Mexico University, Portales, NM 88130 - T: (505) 562-2723, Fax: (505) 562-2192, E-mail: jennifer.frey@enmu.edu, Internet: http://www.enmu.edu/~freyj/museum/home.htmnaturalhistory.htm. Head: Dr. Jennifer K. Frey
University Museum / Natural History Museum - 1968 39555

Roosevelt County Museum, Eastern New Mexico University, Portales, NM 88130 - T: (505) 562-2592, Fax: (505) 562-2578
Local Museum - 1934 39556

Porterville CA

Porterville Historical Museum, 257 N D St, Porterville, CA 93257 - T: (559) 784-2053. Head: Helen Trueblood
Historical Museum - 1965
History 39557

Portland ME

Children's Museum of Maine, 142 Free St, Portland, ME 04101 - T: (207) 828-1234, Fax: (207) 828-5726, Internet: http://www.childrensmuseumofme.org. Head: Harry Pringle, Suzanne Olson
Special Museum - 1976 39558

Institute of Contemporary Art, Maine College of Art, 522 Congress St, Portland, ME 04101 - T: (207) 879-5742 ext 229, Fax: (207) 772-5069, E-mail: ica@meca.edu, Internet: http://www.meca.edu/ica. Head: Mark Bessire
Fine Arts Museum - 1983
Art 39559

Maine Historical Society Museum, 485 Congress St, Portland, ME 04101 - T: (207) 879-0427, Fax: (207) 775-4301, E-mail: info@mainehistory.org, Internet: http://www.mainehistory.com. Head: Richard D'Abate
Local Museum - 1822
Regional history 39560

Portland Museum of Art, 7 Congress Sq, Portland, ME 04101 - T: (207) 775-6148, Fax: (207) 773-7324, E-mail: pma@maine.rr.com, Internet: http://www.portlandmuseum.org. Head: Daniel E. O'Leary
Fine Arts Museum - 1882
Maine's largest art museum, prints, drawings, sculpture, photos 39561

Tate House, 1270 Westbrook St, Portland, ME 04102 - T: (207) 774-9781, Fax: (207) 774-6177, E-mail: tate@gwi.net, Internet: http://www.nentug.org/museums/tatehouse. Head: Lynn Glover, Kristen Crean
Historical Museum - 1931 39562

Victoria Mansion, 109 Danforth St, Portland, ME 04101 - T: (207) 772-4841, Fax: (207) 772-6290, E-mail: victoria@maine.rr.com, Internet: http://www.portlandarts.com/victoriamansion. Head: David Brisk, Robert Wolterstorff
Local Museum / Decorative Arts Museum - 1943 39563

Wadsworth-Longfellow House, 485 Congress St, Portland, ME 04101 - T: (207) 774-0427, Fax: (207) 775-4301, E-mail: post@mainehistory.org, Internet: http://www.mainehistory.org. Head: Richard D'Abate
Special Museum - 1822
Boyhood home of poet Henry Wadsworth Longfellow 39564

Portland OR

American Advertising Museum, 211 NW Fifth Av, Portland, OR 97209 - T: (503) AAM-0000, Fax: (503) 274-2576, E-mail: admuseum@aol.com, Internet: http://www.admuseum.org. Head: Steve Karakas
Special Museum - 1984 39565

Blue Sky, Oregon Center for the Photographic Arts, 1231 NW Hoyt St, Portland, OR 97209 - T: (503) 225-0210. Head: Chris Rauschenberg
Public Gallery 39566

Children's Museum → Portland Children's Museum Second Generation

Contemporary Crafts Association Museum, 3934 SW Corbett Av, Portland, OR 97201 - T: (503) 223-2654, Fax: (503) 223-0190, E-mail: ccg3934@aol.com. Head: Edgar Darcy
Decorative Arts Museum - 1936
Fine crafts 39567

Douglas F. Cooley Memorial Art Gallery, Reed College, 3203 SE Woodstock Blvd, Portland, OR 97202-8199 - T: (503) 771-1112, Fax: (503) 777-7798, E-mail: s.fillin-yelt@reed.edu, Internet: http://www.reed.edu
Fine Arts Museum - 1989 39568

Oregon History Center, 1200 SW Park Av, Portland, OR 97205 - T: (503) 222-1741, Fax: (503) 221-2035, E-mail: orhist@ohs.org, Internet: http://www.ohs.org. Head: Norma Paulus, Marsha Matthews, Susan Seyl, Richard Engeman
Historical Museum / Local Museum - 1873 39569

Oregon Museum of Science and Industry, 1945 SE Water Av, Portland, OR 97214 - T: (503) 797-4000, Fax: (503) 797-4566, Internet: http://www.omsi.edu
Natural History Museum / Science&Tech Museum - 1944 39570

Pittock Mansion, 3229 NW Pittock Dr, Portland, OR 97210 - T: (503) 823-3623, Fax: (503) 823-3619, E-mail: pkdanc@ci.portland.or.us, Internet: http://www.pittockmansion@mediaforte.com. Head: Michael Henley, Daniel T. Crandall
Local Museum / Historic Site - 1965
18th, 19th and early 20th c decorative arts, coll of Thomas Hill paintings 39571

Portland Art Museum, 1219 SW Park Av, Portland, OR 97205 - T: (503) 226-2811, Fax: (503) 226-4842, E-mail: info@pam.org, Internet: http://www.portlandartmuseum.org. Head: John E. Buchanan
Fine Arts Museum - 1892 39572

Portland Children's Museum Second Generation, 4015 SW Canyon Rd, Portland, OR 97221 - T: (503) 223-6500, Fax: (503) 223-6600, E-mail: vstanford@ci.portland.or.us, Internet: http://www.portlandcm2.org. Head: Verne Stanford
Special Museum - 1949
Creative youth 39573

State of Oregon Sports Hall of Fame, 321 SW Salmon, Portland, OR 97204 - T: (503) 227-7466, Fax: (503) 227-6925. Head: Stan Link
Special Museum - 1978 39574

World Forestry Center, 4033 SW Canyon Rd, Portland, OR 97221 - T: (503) 228-1367, Fax: (503) 228-3624, E-mail: mail@worldforest.org, Internet: http://www.worldforest.org/~wfc. Head: John L. Blackwell
Natural History Museum - 1964 39575

Portsmouth NH

Children's Museum of Portsmouth, 280 Marcy St, Portsmouth, NH 03801 - T: (603) 436-3853, Fax: (603) 436-7706, E-mail: staff@childrens-museum.org, Internet: http://www.childrens-museum.org. Head: Xanthi Gray
Historical Museum - 1983 39576

Governor John Langdon House, 143 Pleasant St, Portsmouth, NH 03801 - T: (603) 436-3205, Fax: (617) 227-9204, Internet: http://www.spnea.org
Local Museum - 1947 39577

MacPheadris/Warner House, 150 Daniel St, Portsmouth, NH 03802-0895 - T: (603) 436-5909. Head: Dr. Robert Barth
Local Museum - 1931 39578

Moffatt-Ladd House, 154 Market St, Portsmouth, NH 03801 - T: (603) 430-7968, Fax: (603) 431-9063, E-mail: moffatt-ladd@juno.com. Head: Laura Donohoe, Dr. Babara Ward
Historic Site - 1911 39579

Portsmouth Athenaeum, 9 Market Sq, Portsmouth, NH 03801 - T: (603) 431-2538, Fax: (603) 431-7180, E-mail: athenaeum@juno.com. Head: Ellie Sanderson, Jane M. Porter
Historical Museum - 1817
Maritinme history, ship models, paintings, portraits - library 39580

Rundlet-May House, 364 Middle St, Portsmouth, NH 03801 - T: (603) 436-3205, Fax: (617) 227-9204, Internet: http://www.spnea.org
Local Museum - 1971 39581

Strawbery Banke, 454 Court St, Portsmouth, NH 03801, mail addr: POB 300, Portsmouth, NH 03802-0300 - T: (603) 433-1100, Fax: (603) 433-1129
Local Museum - 1958 39582

Wentworth-Coolidge Mansion, Little Harbor Rd, Portsmouth, NH 03801 - T: (603) 436-6607, Fax: (603) 436-1036. Head: Molly Bolster
Historical Museum - 1954
Home of first British Colonial Governor of New Hampshire 39583

Wentworth Gardner and Tobias Lear Houses, 50 Mechanic St, Portsmouth, NH 03801 - T: (603) 436-4406, Internet: http://www.seacoastnh.com/wentworth. Head: William Manfull
Local Museum / Decorative Arts Museum - 1941
Historic House from 1760, early Georgian architecture 39584

Portsmouth OH

Southern Ohio Museum and Cultural Center, 825 Gallia St, Portsmouth, OH 45662 - T: (740) 354-5629, Fax: (740) 354-4090, E-mail: museum@zoomnet.net, Internet: http://www.somuseum.aol. Head: C. Clayton Johnson
Fine Arts Museum / Folklore Museum - 1977 39585

Portsmouth RI

Portsmouth Museum, 870 E Main Rd and Union St, Portsmouth, RI 02871 - T: (401) 683-9178. Head: Herbert Hall
Local Museum - 1938
Local hist 39586

Portsmouth VA

The Hill House, Portsmouth Historical Association, 221 North St, Portsmouth, VA 23704 - T: (804) 393-0241. Head: Alice C. Hanes
Fine Arts Museum / Historical Museum / Museum of Classical Antiquities - 1957
Local hist, historic house, furnishings 39587

Portsmouth Museums, Court House Gallery, 420 High St, Portsmouth, VA 23704 - T: (757) 393-8983, Fax: (757) 393-5228, Internet: http://www.ci.portsmouth.va.us
Fine Arts Museum / Military Museum / Historical Museum - 1974 39588

Virginia Sports Hall of Fame, 420 High St, Portsmouth, VA 23704 - T: (757) 393-8031, Fax: (757) 393-5228, E-mail: webbe@ci.portsmouth.va.us. Head: Jimmy Williams, Eddie Webb
Special Museum - 1971
Sports 39589

Visual Arts Center, Tidewater Community College, 340 High St, Portsmouth, VA 23704 - T: (757) 822-6999, Fax: (757) 822-6800, E-mail: tciotta@tc.cc.va.us, Internet: http://www.tc.cc.va.us
Performing Arts Museum 39590

Poteau OK

Robert S. Kerr Museum, 1507 S McKenna, Poteau, OK 74953 - T: (918) 647-9579, Fax: (918) 647-3952
Local Museum - 1968 39591

Potsdam NY

Roland Gibson Gallery, State University of New York College at Potsdam, 44 Pierrepont Av, Potsdam, NY 13676 - T: (315) 267-3290, Fax: (315) 267-4884. Head: Dan Mills
Fine Arts Museum / University Museum - 1968 39592

Pottstown PA

Pottsgrove Manor, 100 West King St, Pottstown, PA 19464-6318 - T: (610) 326-4014, Fax: (610) 326-9618, Internet: http://www.montco.pa.org. Head: Robert K. Study
Local Museum - 1988
Historic house 39593

Pottsville AR

Potts Inn Museum, Town Sq, Pottsville, AR 72801 - T: (501) 968-1877
Local Museum - 1978
1850-1858 home and stage stop of Kirkbride Potts 39594

Poughkeepsie NY

Frances Lehman Loeb Art Center, Vassar College, 124 Raymond Av, Poughkeepsie, NY 12604-0703 - T: (845) 437-5237, Fax: (845) 437-7304, E-mail: jamundy@vassar.edu, Internet: http://departments.vassar.edu/~fllac/. Head: James Mundy
Fine Arts Museum - 1864 39595

Samuel F.B. Morse Historic Site, 370 South Rd, Poughkeepsie, NY 12601 - T: (914) 454-4500, Fax: (914) 485-7122, E-mail: morse-historic-site@worldnet.att.net, Internet: http://www.morsehistoricsite.org. Head: Frances S. Reese, Raymond J. Armater
Local Museum - 1979 39596

Pound Ridge NY

Pound Ridge Museum, 255 Westchester Av, Pound Ridge, NY 10576 - T: (914) 764-4333, Fax: (914) 764-7642. Head: Joyce Butterfield
Historical Museum / Local Museum - 1970 39597

Prairie du Chien WI

Prairie du Chien Museum at Fort Crawford, 717 S Beaumont Rd, Prairie du Chien, WI 53821 - T: (608) 326-6960. Head: Delores Igou
Local Museum - 1955
Local hist 39598

Villa Louis Historic Site, 521 Villa Louis Rd, Prairie du Chien, WI 53821 - T: (608) 326-2721, Fax: (608) 326-5507, E-mail: villalou@pearl.mhtc.net. Head: Michael Douglass
Local Museum - 1936
Local hist 39599

Prairie du Rocher IL

Fort de Chartres Museum, Prairie du Rocher, IL 62277 - T: (618) 284-7230. Head: Darrell Duensing
Historic Site / Military Museum - 1913
Original site of the French Fort de Chartes built in 1753 39600

Prairie du Sac WI

Sauk Prairie Area Historical Society Museum, 565 Water St, Prairie du Sac, WI 53578
Local Museum - 1961
Local hist 39601

Prairie Grove AR

Prairie Grove Battlefield, 506 E Douglas, Prairie Grove, AR 72753 - T: (501) 846-2990, Fax: (501) 846-4035, E-mail: pgbspeds@pgtc.net. Head: Ed Smith
Historic Site - 1957
Civil war, Dec. 7, 1862 Battle of Prairie Grove 39602

Prattsburgh NY

Narcissa Prentiss House, 7226 Mill Pond Rd, Prattsburgh, NY 14873 - T: (607) 522-4537. Head: Reva Davis
Local Museum - 1940 39603

Prescott AZ

The Bead Museum, 138 S Montezuma, Prescott, AZ 86303 - T: (520) 445-2431, Fax: (520) 445-2431, E-mail: liese@northlinks.com
Decorative Arts Museum - 1985
Jewelry 39604

Phippen Museum, 4701 Hwy 89 N, Prescott, AZ 86301 - T: (520) 778-1105, Fax: (520) 778-4524, E-mail: phippen@primenet.com, Internet: http://www.phippenmuseum.org. Head: Deborah Reeder
Fine Arts Museum - 1984
Art of the American West 39605

Sharlot Hall Museum, 415 W Gurley St, Prescott, AZ 86301 - T: (520) 445-3122, Fax: (520) 776-9053, E-mail: sharlot@sharlothall.lib.az.us, Internet: http://www.sharlot.org. Head: Richard Sims
Local Museum - 1929
Regional history 39606

Smoki Museum, 147 N Arizona St, Prescott, AZ 86304-0224 - T: (520) 445-1230, E-mail: smoki@futureone.com, Internet: http://www.smoki.com. Head: Paul V. Long jr.
Ethnology Museum - 1935
Anthropology, American Indian art and culture 39607

Presidio TX

Fort Leaton State Historic Park, River Rd FM 170, Presidio, TX 79845 - T: (915) 229-3613, Fax: (915) 229-4814, E-mail: fortleatonshp@brooksdata.net, Internet: http://tpwd.state.tx.us. Head: Andrew Sansom
Local Museum - 1977
Local hist, birding, bats, adobe structure maintained, 2 wheel ox-cart 39608

Price UT

College of Eastern Utah Art Gallery, 451 E 400 N, Price, UT 84501 - T: (435) 637-2120, Fax: (435) 637-4102, Internet: http://www.ceu.edu
Fine Arts Museum / University Museum - 1937
Art 39609

College of Eastern Utah Prehistoric Museum, 155 E Main St, Price, UT 84501 - T: (435) 613-5060, Fax: (435) 637-2514, E-mail: dburge@ceu.edu, Internet: http://www.ceu.edu. Head: Don Burge
University Museum / Ethnology Museum / Natural History Museum - 1961
Anthropology, geology 39610

Princeton IA

Buffalo Bill Cody Homestead, 28050 230th Av, Princeton, IA 52768 - T: (319) 225-2981, Fax: (319) 381-2805. Head: Roger Kean
Local Museum - 1970
Historic house, boyhood home of Buffalo Bill Cody 39611

Princeton IL

Bureau County Historical Society Museum, 109 Park Av, W, Princeton, IL 61356-1927 - T: (815) 875-2184. Head: Barbara Hansen
Local Museum - 1911
Local history 39612

Princeton MO

Casteel-Linn House and Museum, 902 E Oak St, Princeton, MO 64673 - T: (816) 748-3905. Head: Joe Dale Linn
Local Museum - 1982
Local hist 39613

Mercer County Genealogical and Historical Society Museum, 601 Grant, Princeton, MO 64673 - T: (660) 748-3725. Head: Randy Ferguson
Local Museum - 1965 39614

Princeton NJ

Historical Society of Princeton Museum, 158 Nassau St, Princeton, NJ 08542 - T: (609) 921-6748, Fax: (609) 921-6939, Internet: http://www.princetonol.com/groups/histsoc/. Head: T. Jeffery Clarke, Gail F. Stern
Local Museum - 1938 39615

Princeton University Art Museum, Princeton University, Princeton, NJ 08544-1018 - T: (609) 258-3788, Fax: (609) 258-5949, E-mail: artmuseum@princeton.edu, Internet: http://www.princeton.edu/artmuseum. Head: Susan M. Taylor
Fine Arts Museum / University Museum - 1882
Ancient Mediterranean, British and American art, Chinese ritual bronze vessels, Far Eastern art, Pre-Columbian and African art - Index of Christian art, library 39616

Princeton University Museum of Natural History (closed until about 2005), Guyot Hall, Princeton University, Princeton, NJ 08544-1003 - T: (609) 258-4102, Fax: (609) 258-1334
University Museum / Natural History Museum - 1805 39617

Rockingham, 108 CR 518, Princeton, NJ 08540 - T: (609) 921-8835, Fax: (609) 921-8835, E-mail: peggi@superlink.net, Internet: http://www.rockingham.net
Historic Site - 1896
1710 Berrien Mansion, Washington's headquarters while Continental Congress was in session in Princeton in 1738 39618

Thomas Clarke House-Princeton Battlefield, 500 Mercer Rd, Princeton, NJ 08540-4810 - T: (609) 921-0074, Fax: (609) 921-0074, E-mail: pbsp@aol.com. Head: John K. Mills
Historical Museum / Military Museum - 1976 39619

Prineville OR

A.R. Bowman Memorial Museum, 246 N Main St, Prineville, OR 97754 - T: (541) 447-3715, Fax: (541) 447-3715, E-mail: bowmuse@netscape.net, Internet: http://www.bowmanmuseum.org. Head: William Weberg, Gordon Gillespie
Local Museum - 1971 39620

Proctor VT

Vermont Marble Exhibition, 52 Main St, Proctor, VT 05765 - T: (800) 427-1396, Fax: (802) 459-2948, E-mail: vmecss@sover.net, Internet: http://www.vermont-marble.com. Head: Marsha Hemm
Natural History Museum / Science&Tech Museum - 1933
Mining, geology 39621

Prospect ME

Fort Knox, State Hwy 174, Prospect, ME 04981 - T: (207) 469-7719, Fax: (207) 469-7719. Head: Mike Wilusz
Military Museum / Historic Site - 1943 39622

Prospect Park PA

Morton Homestead, 100 Lincoln Av, Prospect Park, PA 19076 - T: (215) 583-7221, (717) 783-9935, Fax: (717) 783-1073. Head: Toni Collins
Local Museum - 1939
Local hist 39623

Providence RI

Annmary Brown Memorial, 21 Brown St, Providence, RI 02912 - T: (401) 863-1994, E-mail: carol_cramer@brown.edu, Internet: http://www.brown.edu/facilities/university_library/lihs/amb.html
Fine Arts Museum / University Museum - 1905
Art 39624

Betsey Williams Cottage, Roger Williams Park, Providence, RI 02905 - T: (401) 785-9457, Fax: (401) 461-5146. Head: Tracey K. Brussat
Local Museum - 1871
Historic house 39625

Culinary Archives and Museum, Johnson and Wales University, 315 Harborside Blvd, Providence, RI 02905 - T: (401) 598-2805, Fax: (401) 598-2807, Internet: http://www.culinary.org. Head: John Bowen, Barbara Kuck
University Museum / Special Museum - 1989 39626

David Winton Bell Gallery, List Art Center, Brown University, 64 College St, Providence, RI 02912 - T: (401) 863-2932, 863-2929, Fax: (401) 863-9323. Head: Jo-Ann Conklin
Fine Arts Museum / University Museum - 1971
Art 39627

Edward M. Bannister Gallery, Rhode Island College, 600 Mount Pleasant Av, Providence, RI 02908 - T: (401) 456-9765, Fax: (401) 456-9718, E-mail: domalley@ric.edu, Internet: http://www.ric.edu/bannister. Head: Dennis M. O'Malley
Fine Arts Museum - 1978
Visual arts 39628

Governor Henry Lippitt House Museum, 199 Hope St, Providence, RI 02906 - T: (401) 453-0688
Local Museum - 1991
Local hist 39629

Governor Stephen Hopkins House, Hopkins and Benefit Sts, Providence, RI 02903 - T: (401) 421-0694. Head: Patricia D. Harris
Local Museum - 1707
Historic house, 1707 Governor Stephen Hopkins home 39630

Museum of Art, Rhode Island School of Design, 224 Benefit St, Providence, RI 02903-2723 - T: (401) 454-6500, Fax: (401) 454-6556, E-mail: museum@risd.edu, Internet: http://www.risd.edu. Head: Phillip Johnston
Fine Arts Museum / University Museum - 1877
European porcelain, Oriental textiles, ancient Oriental and ethnographic art, modern Latin American art, contempotary graphics 39631

Museum of Natural History, Roger Williams Park, Providence, RI 02905 - T: (401) 785-9457, Fax: (401) 461-5146, Internet: http://ids.net/~cormack_pl/museum.html. Head: Tracey Keough
Natural History Museum - 1896
Natural hist - planetarium 39632

Providence Children's Museum, 100 South St, Providence, RI 02903 - T: (401) 273-5437, Fax: (401) 273-1004, E-mail: provcm@childrenmuseum.org, Internet: http://www.childrenmuseum.org. Head: Anne Maxwell Livingston, Janice O'Donnell
Special Museum - 1976
Children's museum 39633

Rhode Island Black Heritage Society Exhibition, 202 Washington St, Providence, RI 02903, mail addr: POB 1656, Providence, RI 02901 - T: (401) 751-3490, Fax: (401) 751-0040. Head: Walter Stone, Joaquina B. Teixeira
Fine Arts Museum / Historical Museum - 1975
Afro-American history and art 39634

Rhode Island Historical Society Exhibition, Aldrich House, 110 Benevolent St, Providence, RI 02906 - T: (401) 331-8575, Fax: (401) 351-0127. Head: Murney Gerlach
Local Museum - 1822
Local hist - library 39635

Roger Williams National Memorial, 282 N Main St, Providence, RI 02903 - T: (401) 521-7266, Fax: (401) 521-7239, E-mail: rowl_interpretation@nps.gov, Internet: http://www.nps.gov/rowi. Head: Michael Creasey
Local Museum - 1965
Local hist 39636

Wheeler Gallery, 228 Angell St, Providence, RI 02906 - T: (401) 421-9230. Head: Sue Carroll
Fine Arts Museum
Contemporary paintings, sculpture, photography, prints, ceramics, glass, installations 39637

Provincetown MA

Pilgrim Monument and Provincetown Museum, High Pole Hill, Provincetown, MA 02657 - T: (508) 487-1310, Fax: (508) 487-4702, E-mail: cturley@pilgrimmonument.org, Internet: http://www.pilgrim-monument.org
Local Museum - 1892
Local history 39638

Provincetown Art Museum, 460 Commercial St, Provincetown, MA 02657 - T: (508) 487-1750, Fax: (508) 487-4372, E-mail: paam@capecod.net, Internet: http://www.paam.org. Head: Robyn Watson
Fine Arts Museum - 1914
Art 39639

Provincetown Heritage Museum, 356 Commercial St, Provincetown, MA 02657 - T: (508) 487-7098. Head: Dale A. Fanning
Fine Arts Museum / Local Museum - 1976
Local history, housed in Methodist church 39640

Provo UT

Brigham Young University Earth Science Museum, ERTH Bldg, Provo, UT 84602-3300 - T: (801) 378-3939, Fax: (801) 378-7919, E-mail: klstadtman@geology.byu.edu, Internet: http://www.cpms.byu.edu/esm. Head: Kenneth L. Stadtman
University Museum / Natural History Museum - 1987
Paleontology 39641

Brigham Young University Museum of Art, N Campus Dr, Provo, UT 84602-1400 - T: (801) 378-8256, 378-8257, Fax: (801) 378-8222, E-mail: moasecretary@byu.edu, Internet: http://www.byu.edu/moa. Head: Campbell B. Gray
Fine Arts Museum / University Museum - 1993
Art 39642

Brigham Young University Museum of Peoples and Cultures, 700 N 100 E, Allen Hall, Provo, UT 84602 - T: (801) 378-6112, Fax: (801) 378-7123, E-mail: programs@ucs-exch.byn.edu, Internet: http://fhss.byu.edu/anthro/mopc/main.htm. Head: Dr. Marti Lu Allen
Ethnology Museum - 1946
Anthropology, ethnology 39643

Monte L. Bean Life Science Museum, 290 MLBM Bldg, Brigham Young University, Provo, UT 84602 - T: (801) 378-5052, Fax: (801) 378-3733, E-mail: office@museum.byu.edu, Internet: http://www.bioag.byu.edu/mlbean. Head: Dr. H. Duane Smith
Natural History Museum / Science&Tech Museum - 1978
Science 39644

Pryor MT

Chief Plenty Coups Museum, Pryor, MT 59066 - T: (406) 252-1289, Fax: (406) 252-6668, E-mail: plentycoups@plentycoups.org, Internet: http://www.plentycoups.org. Head: Rich Furber
Ethnology Museum - 1972
Ethnography of Crow Indians, paintings, drawings 39645

Pueblo CO

El Pueblo Museum, 324 W 1st St, Pueblo, CO 81003 - T: (719) 583-0453, Fax: (719) 583-0453
Local Museum - 1959
Local history 39646

Pueblo County Historical Society Museum, 217 S Grand Av, Pueblo, CO 81003 - T: (719) 542-1851. Head: Thomas Cummins, Patricia Crum
Local Museum - 1986
Edward H. Broadhead Library 39647

Rosemount Museum, 419 W 14th St, Pueblo, CO 81003 - T: (719) 545-5290, Fax: (719) 545-5291, E-mail: kreynolds@firstworld.net, Internet: http://www.rosemount.org. Head: William T. Henning
Local Museum - 1967
John A. Thatcher residence; Henry Hudson Holly 39648

Sangre de Cristo Arts Center and Buell Children's Museum, 210 N Santa Fe Av, Pueblo, CO 81003 - T: (719) 543-0130, Fax: (719) 543-0134, E-mail: artctr@ris.net, Internet: http://www.sdc-arts.org. Head: Maggie Divelbiss
Fine Arts Museum / Special Museum - 1972
Art education 39649

Pulaski VA

Fine Arts Center for New River Valley, 21 W Main St, Pulaski, VA 24301 - T: (540) 980-7363, Fax: (540) 994-5631, E-mail: facnrv@swva.net. Head: Michael B. Dowell
Fine Arts Museum / Public Gallery - 1978
Art 39650

Pullman WA

Charles R. Conner Museum, Washington State University, Pullman, WA 99164-4236 - T: (509) 335-3515, Fax: (509) 335-3184, E-mail: crcm@mail.wsu.edu, Internet: http://www.sci.wsu.edu/cm. Head: Dr. Paul C. Schroeder
Natural History Museum - 1894
Zoology, natural history 39651

Museum of Anthropology, Department of Anthropology, Washington State University, Pullman, WA 99164-4910 - T: (509) 335-3441, Fax: (509) 335-3999. Head: William Andrefsky
University Museum / Ethnology Museum - 1966
Anthropology 39652

Museum of Art, Washington State University, Pullman, WA 99164-7460 - T: (509) 335-1910, Fax: (509) 335-1908, E-mail: artmuse@wsu.edu, Internet: http://www.wsu.edu/artmuse
Fine Arts Museum / University Museum - 1973
Art 39653

Punta Gorda FL

Florida Adventure Museum, 260 W Retta Esplanade, Punta Gorda, FL 33950 - T: (941) 639-3777, Fax: (941) 639-3505, E-mail: museum@sunline.net, Internet: http://www.charlotte-florida.com/museum. Head: Lori Tomlinson
Local Museum - 1969
Local and military history, science 39654

Purchase NY

Neuberger Museum of Art, Purchase College, State University of New York, 735 Anderson Hill Rd, Purchase, NY 10577-1400 - T: (914) 251-6100, Fax: (914) 251-6101, E-mail: neuberger@purchase.edu, Internet: http://www.neuberger.org. Head: Lucinda H. Gedeon
Fine Arts Museum / University Museum - 1974 39655

Putney VT

Putney Historical Society Museum, Town Hall, Putney, VT 05346 - T: (802) 387-5862
Local Museum / Folklore Museum - 1959
Local hist 39656

Puunene HI

Alexander and Baldwin Sugar Museum, 3957 Hansen Rd, Puunene, HI 96784 - T: (808) 871-8058, Fax: (808) 871-7663, E-mail: sugarmus@maui.net, Internet: http://www.sugarmuseum.com. Head: Stephen Onaga, Gaylord Kubota
Historical Museum / Agriculture Museum - 1980
Agriculture 39657

Puyallup WA

Ezra Meeker Mansion, 312 Spring St, Puyallup, WA 98371 - T: (253) 848-1770, Internet: http://www.meekermansion.org. Head: Dorothy Cardon
Historic Site - 1970
Historic house located at end of the Oregon Trail 39658

Paul H. Karshner Memorial Museum, 309 4th St, Puyallup, WA 98372 - T: (253) 841-8748, Fax: (253) 841-8660, E-mail: reckerson@puyallup.kil.wa.us. Head: Rosemary Eckerson
Historical Museum - 1930
History 39659

Quantico VA

United States Marine Corps Air-Ground Museum, 2014 Anderson Av, Quantico, VA 22134 - T: (703) 784-2606, Fax: (703) 784-5856
Military Museum - 1940
Military hist 39660

Quincy CA

Plumas County Museum, 500 Jackson St, Quincy, CA 95971 - T: (530) 283-6320, Fax: (530) 283-6081, E-mail: pcmuseum@psln.com, Internet: http://www.pluma.s.ca.us. Head: Scott J. Lawson
Local Museum - 1964
Local hist 39661

Quincy IL

The Gardner Museum of Architecture and Design, 332 Maine St, Quincy, IL 62301 - T: (217) 224-6873, Fax: (217) 224-3303, E-mail: gmadqcy@dstream.net. Head: Kent Slack
Historical Museum / Decorative Arts Museum - 1974
Architecture, design, housed in Richardsonian Romanesque Old Public Library 39662

Historical Society of Quincy and Adams County Museum, 425 S 12th St, Quincy, IL 62301 - T: (217) 222-1835. Head: Hal Oakley, Philip Germann
Historical Museum - 1896
Local history, in home of former Governor of Illinois John Wood, also founder of Quincy 39663

Quincy Art Center, 1515 Jersey St, Quincy, IL 62301 - T: (217) 223-5900, Fax: (217) 223-6950, E-mail: qac@qsni.net, Internet: http://www.quincynet.com/artcenter. Head: Julie D. Nelson
Fine Arts Museum - 1923 39664

The Quincy Museum, 1601 Maine St, Quincy, IL 62301 - T: (217) 224-7669, Fax: (217) 224-9323. Head: Bill Bergman, Steve Adams
Local Museum / Natural History Museum - 1966
Natural and local history 39665

Quincy MA

Adams National Historical Park, 135 Adams St, Quincy, MA 02169 - T: (617) 773-1177, 770-1175, Fax: (617) 471-9683, E-mail: ADAMSuperintendent@nps.gov, Internet: http://www.nps.gov/adam. Head: Marianne Peak
Historical Museum - 1927 39666

Quincy Historical Museum, Adams Academy Bldg, 8 Adams St, Quincy, MA 02169 - T: (617) 773-1144, Fax: (617) 472-4990. Head: Joyce Baker, E. Fitzgerald
Local Museum - 1893
Local history - library 39667

Racine WI

Charles A. Wustum Museum of Fine Arts, 2519 Northwestern Av, Racine, WI 53404 - T: (414) 636-9177, Fax: (414) 636-9231, Internet: http://www.wustum.org. Head: Bruce W. Pepich
Fine Arts Museum - 1941
Arts 39668

Racine Heritage Museum, 701 S Main St, Racine, WI 53403-1211 - T: (414) 636-3926, Fax: (414) 636-3940, Internet: http://www.racine.org/rcmuseum.html. Head: Mary Ellen Conaway
Historical Museum / Science&Tech Museum - 1960
Southeast Wisconsin industrial and product hist 39669

Radford VA

Radford University Art Museum, 200 Powell Hall, Radford, VA 24142 - T: (540) 831-5475, 831-5754, Fax: (540) 831-6799, E-mail: sarbury@radford.edu, Internet: http://www.radford.edu/~rumuseum. Head: Steve Arbury
Fine Arts Museum / University Museum - 1985
Art 39670

Radford University Galleries → Radford University Art Museum

Radium Springs NM

Fort Selden State Monument, Fort Selden Junction 185 and Interstate 25 on Exit 19, Radium Springs, NM 88054 - T: (505) 526-8911, Fax: (505) 526-8911, E-mail: selden@zia.nct.com. Head: Nathan Stone
Military Museum - 1973 39671

Raleigh NC

Contemporary Art Museum, 336 Fayetteville St, Raleigh, NC 27601, mail addr: POB 66, Raleigh, NC 27602-0066 - T: (919) 836-0088, Fax: (919) 836-2239, E-mail: dd@camnc.org, Internet: http://www.camnc.org. Head: Denise Dickens
Fine Arts Museum - 1983 39672

Mordecai Historic Park, 1 Mimosa St, Raleigh, NC 27604 - T: (919) 834-4844, Fax: (919) 834-7314, E-mail: CapPresInc@aol.com. Head: Gary G. Roth
Open Air Museum / Historical Museum - 1972 39673

North Carolina Museum of Art, 2110 Blue Ridge Rd, Raleigh, NC 27607-6494 - T: (919) 839-6262, Fax: (919) 733-8034, E-mail: hmckinney@ncmamail.dcr.state.nc.us, Internet: http://www.ncartmuseum.org. Head: Lawrence J. Wheeler
Fine Arts Museum - 1956 39674

North Carolina Museum of History, 5 E Edenton St, Raleigh, NC 27601-1011 - T: (919) 715-0200, Fax: (919) 733-8655, E-mail: jcw@moh.dcr.state.nc.us, Internet: http://nchistory.dcr.state.nc.us/museums. Head: Eve Williamson, James C. McNutt
Historical Museum - 1902 39675

North Carolina State Museum of Natural Sciences, 102 N Salisbury St, Raleigh, NC 27603 - T: (919) 733-7450, Fax: (919) 733-1573, E-mail: betsy_bennett@mail.enr.state.nc.us, Internet: http://www.naturalsciences.org. Head: Dr. Betsy Bennett, Roy G. Campbell, Dr. Stephen Busack
Natural History Museum - 1879 39676

North Carolina State University Gallery of Art and Design, Visual Arts Center, Cates Av, Raleigh, NC 27695-7306 - T: (919) 515-3503, Fax: (919) 515-6163, E-mail: Charlotte_Brown@ncsu.edu, Internet: http://www.fis.ncsu.edu/visualarts/. Head: Dr. Charlotte V. Brown
University Museum / Fine Arts Museum - 1979
Coll of American, Indian, Asian & pre-Columbian textiles; ceramics, furniture, product design 39677

Frankie G. Weems Gallery & Rotunda Gallery, Meredith College, Gaddy-Hamrick ArtCenter, 3800 Hillsborough St, Raleigh, NC 27607-5298 - T: (919) 760-8465, Fax: (919) 760-2347, E-mail: bankerm@meredith.edu. Head: Maureen Banker
Public Gallery
American art, special exhibitions 39678

Ralls TX

Ralls Historical Museum, 801 Main St, Ralls, TX 79357 - T: (806) 253-2425. Head: Linda Isbell, Georgia M. Nipp
Local Museum - 1970
Local hist 39679

Ramah NM

El Morro National Monument, Hwy 53, 43 miles west of Grants, Ramah, NM 87321 - T: (505) 783-4226, Fax: (505) 783-4689. Head: P. Eringen
Historical Museum / Archaeological Museum - 1906 39680

Rancho Cucamonga CA

Casa de Rancho Cucamonga, 8810 Hemlock St, Rancho Cucamonga, CA 91730 - T: (909) 989-4970. Head: Alan Reid
Local Museum - 1972
Historic house 39681

Wignall Museum and Gallery, Chaffey College, 5885 Haven Av, Rancho Cucamonga, CA 91737-3002 - T: (909) 941-2388, Fax: (909) 466-2863, E-mail: veaton@bunny.chaffey.cc.ca.us. Head: Virginia M. Eaton
Fine Arts Museum - 1972
Art 39682

Rancho Mirage CA

Children's Discovery Museum of the Desert, 71-701 Gerald Ford Dr, Rancho Mirage, CA 92270 - T: (760) 321-0602, Fax: (760) 321-1605, E-mail: info@cdmod.org, Internet: http://www.cdmod.org. Head: Betty Barker, LeeAnne Vanderbeck
Special Museum - 1987
Children's Museum 39683

Heartland - The California Museum of the Heart, 39600 Bob Hope Dr, Rancho Mirage, CA 92270 - T: (760) 324-3278, Fax: (760) 346-1867. Head: Rebbecca Rogeway, Adam Rubinstein
Historical Museum - 1988
Heart health 39684

Rancho Palos Verdes CA

Palos Verdes Art Center, 5504 W Crestridge Rd, Rancho Palos Verdes, CA 90275 - T: (310) 541-2479, Fax: (310) 541-9520, E-mail: artcenter@palosverdes.com, Internet: http://www.pvartcenter.org. Head: Jacqueline S. Marks, Scott Ward
Fine Arts Museum - 1931
Art 39685

Randleman NC

Saint Paul Museum, 411 High Point St, Randleman, NC 27317 - T: (336) 498-2447. Head: Louise Hudson
Local Museum - 1966 39686

Randolph NJ

Historical Museum of Old Randolph, 30 Carrel Rd, Randolph, NJ 07869 - T: (973) 989-7095. Head: Cecile Wilder, Linda Pawchuak
Local Museum
Local history 39687

Randolph VT

Chandler Gallery, Chandler Music Hall and Cultural Center, Main St, Randolph, VT 05060 - T: (802) 728-9878, 728-3840, Fax: (802) 728-3840, E-mail: chandler@quest-net. Head: Janet Watton, Beth Hary Keenhold
Fine Arts Museum - 1979
Art 39688

Rankin TX

Rankin Museum, 101 W Main St, Rankin, TX 79778 - T: (915) 693-2758, 693-2422, Fax: (915) 693-2303, E-mail: jcpg@yahoo.com, Internet: http://www.rootsweb.com/~txupton/. Head: Judy Greer
Local Museum - 1974
Local hist 39689

Rapid City SD

Dahl Arts Center, 713 Seventh St, Rapid City, SD 57701 - T: (605) 394-4101, Fax: (605) 394-6121, E-mail: rcacaafd@rapidnet.com. Head: Carrie Cisle, Don Hotalling
Fine Arts Museum - 1974
Art 39690

Minnilusa Pioneer Museum, 222 New York St, Rapid City, SD 57701 - T: (605) 394-6099, Fax: (605) 394-6940, Internet: http://www.sdsmp.edu/journey/. Head: Robert E. Preszler
Local Museum - 1938
Local hist 39691

Museum of Geology, South Dakota School of Mines and Technology, 501 E St, Rapid City, SD 57701 - T: (605) 394-2467, Fax: (605) 394-6131, E-mail: pbjork@msmailgw.sdsmt.edu, Internet: http://www.sdsmt.edu/services/museum/museum1.htm. Head: Philip R. Bjork
University Museum / Natural History Museum - 1885
Natural hist 39692

Sioux Indian Museum, 222 New York St, Rapid City, SD 57701 - T: (605) 394-2381, Fax: (605) 348-6182, Internet: http://www.journeymuseum.com
Fine Arts Museum / Folklore Museum - 1939
Indian art 39693

Raton NM

Raton Museum, 216 S First St, Raton, NM 87740 - T: (505) 445-8979. Head: Roger Sanchez
Local Museum / Historical Museum / Military Museum - 1939 39694

Ravenna OH

Portage County Historical Society Museum, 6549 N Chestnut St, Ravenna, OH 44266 - T: (330) 296-3523, Internet: http://www2.clearlight.com/~pchs. Head: Jeff Jones
Local Museum - 1951 39695

Rawlins WY

Carbon County Museum, 904 W Walnut St, Rawlins, WY 82301 - T: (307) 328-2740. Head: Joyce J. Kelley
Local Museum - 1940 39696

Raymond MS

Marie Hull Gallery, Hinds Community College, Raymond, MS 39154 - T: (601) 857-3275, Fax: (601) 857-3392, Internet: http://www.hinds.cc.ms.us. Head: Gayle McCarty
Fine Arts Museum
Prints, sculpture, paintings 39697

Reading MA

Parker Tavern Museum, 103 Washington St, Reading, MA 01867 - T: (781) 944-4030. Head: Beth Anderson
Historical Museum - 1916
Headquarters for Scotch Highlanders prisoners of war during American revolution 39698

Reading OH

Reading Historical Society Museum, 22 W Benson St, Reading, OH 45215 - T: (513) 761-8535. Head: Thomas Dwyer
Local Museum - 1988
Local hist 39699

Reading PA

Freedman Gallery, Albright College, 1621 N 13th St, Reading, PA 19604 - T: (610) 921-7541, 921-7715, Fax: (610) 921-7768, Internet: http://www.albright.edu. Head: Christopher Youngs
Fine Arts Museum / University Museum - 1976
Art 39700

Historical Society of Berks County Museum, 940 Centre Av, Reading, PA 19601 - T: (610) 375-4375, Fax: (610) 375-4376. Head: Harold E. Yoder
Local Museum - 1869
Local hist 39701

Reading Public Museum and Art Gallery, 500 Museum Rd, Reading, PA 19611-1425 - T: (610) 371-5850, Fax: (610) 371-5632, E-mail: registra@ptd.net, Internet: http://www.readingpublicmuseum.org. Head: Dr. Robert P. Metzger
Fine Arts Museum / Natural History Museum / Science&Tech Museum - 1904
Art and science 39702

Reading VT

Reading Historical Society Museum, Main St, Rte 106, Reading, VT 05062 - T: (802) 484-5005. Head: Jonathan Springer
Local Museum - 1953
Local hist 39703

Readsboro VT

Readsboro Historical Society Museum, Main St, Readsboro, VT 05350 - T: (802) 423-5432. Head: Betty Bolognani
Local Museum - 1972
Local hist 39704

Red Bluff CA

William B. Ide Adobe State Historic Park, 21659 Adobe Rd, Red Bluff, CA 96080 - T: (530) 529-8599, Fax: (530) 529-8598, E-mail: bgrace@rbuhsd.k12.ca.us, Internet: http://www.ideadobe.-tehama.k12.ca.us. Head: Kare Hislop
Local Museum - 1951
1850 adobe cabin, memorial to William B. Ide, president of the California Republic 39705

Red Cloud NE

Webster County Historical Museum, 721 W Fourth Av, Red Cloud, NE 68970 - T: (402) 746-2444. Head: Nancy Sherwood, Helen Mathew
Local Museum - 1965 39706

Willa Cather State Historic Site, 326 N Webster, Red Cloud, NE 68970 - T: (402) 746-2653, Fax: (402) 746-2652, Internet: http://www.willacather.org. Head: John Swift, Steven P. Ryan
Local Museum - 1978 39707

Red Wing MN

Goodhue County Historical Society Museum, 1166 Oak St, Red Wing, MN 55066 - T: (651) 388-6024, Fax: (651) 388-3577, E-mail: goodhuec@clear.lakes.com, Internet: http://www.goodhuehistory.mus.mn.us. Head: Char Henn
Historical Museum - 1869 39708

Redding CA

Carter House Natural Science Museum, 48 Quartz Hill, Redding, CA 96003 - T: (530) 243-8850, Fax: (530) 243-8898. Head: Judith LaLouche
Science&Tech Museum - 1977
Natural science 39709

Shasta College Museum, 11555 Old Oregon Trail, Redding, CA 96003 - T: (530) 225-4669, 225-4754, Fax: (530) 225-4990, E-mail: museum@snowcrest.net, Internet: http://www.shastacollege.edu. Head: Michael Small
Local Museum / University Museum - 1970
Local hist 39710

Turtle Bay Museums, 800 Auditorium Dr, Redding, CA 96001 - T: (530) 243-8850, Fax: (530) 243-8898, E-mail: info@turtlebay.org, Internet: http://www.turtlebay.org
Historical Museum / Fine Arts Museum / Natural History Museum - 1990
History, art, natural hist 39711

Redlands CA

Kimberly Crest House, 1325 Prospect Dr, Redlands, CA 92373 - T: (909) 792-2111, Fax: (909) 798-1716, E-mail: kimcrest@empirenet.com, Internet: http://e2.empirenet.com/~kimcrest/. Head: Pam Aday, Steven T. Spiller
Decorative Arts Museum / Local Museum - 1981
Historic house 39712

Lincoln Memorial Shrine, 125 W Vine St, Redlands, CA 92373 - T: (909) 798-7632, 798-7636, Fax: (909) 798-7566, E-mail: archives@aksmiley.org, Internet: http://www.aksmiley.org
Historical Museum - 1932
History 39713

San Bernardino County Museum, 2024 Orange Tree Ln, Redlands, CA 92374 - T: (909) 307-2669, Fax: (909) 307-0539, E-mail: p.oles@co.san-bernardino.ca.us, Internet: http://www.sbcountymuseum.org. Head: Dr. Persijs Kolberg
Local Museum / Natural History Museum - 1959
Local hist 39714

Redmond WA

Marymoor Museum of Eastside History, 6046 W Lake Sammamish Pkwy, Redmond, WA 98073 - T: (206) 885-3684, E-mail: marymoormuseum@juno.com. Head: Nancy Way, Karen Holt Luetjen
Local Museum - 1965
Local hist 39715

Redwood City CA

San Mateo County Historical Museum, 777 Hamilton St, Redwood City, CA 94063 - T: (650) 299-0104, Fax: (650) 299-0141, E-mail: samhist@aol.com, Internet: http://www.sanmateocountyhistory.com. Head: Mitchell Postel
Historical Museum - 1935
Local hist 39716

Redwood Falls MN

Redwood County Historical Society Museum, State Hwy 19 W, Redwood Falls, MN 56283 - T: (507) 637-3329, Fax: (507) 637-2828
Historical Museum - 1949 39717

Refugio TX

Refugio County Museum, 102 W West St, Refugio, TX 78377 - T: (512) 526-5555, Fax: (512) 526-4943. Head: Nan Linney
Local Museum - 1983
Local history 39718

Regent ND

Hettinger County Historical Society Museum, Main St, Regent, ND 58650 - T: (701) 563-4547. Head: Alois Gion
Local Museum / Ethnology Museum - 1962 39719

Rehoboth Beach DE

Rehoboth Art League, 12 Dodds Ln, Rehoboth Beach, DE 19971 - T: (302) 227-8408, Fax: (302) 227-4121, Internet: http://www.rehobothartleague.org. Head: Nancy Alexander
Fine Arts Museum - 1938
Art 39720

Reno NV

National Automobile Museum, Harrah Collection, 10 Lake St S, Reno, NV 89501 - T: (775) 333-9300, Fax: (775) 333-9309, Internet: http://www.automuseum.org. Head: Jackie L. Frady
Science&Tech Museum - 1989 39721

Nevada Historical Society Museum, Vevada Department Museums and Library, 1650 N Virginia St, Reno, NV 89503 - T: (702) 688-1191, Fax: (702) 688-2917, Internet: http://www.clan.lib.nv.us./docs/museums/hist/soc.htm. Head: Peter L. Bandurraga
Historical Museum - 1904
Library 39722

Nevada Museum of Art, 160 W Liberty St, Reno, NV 89501 - T: (775) 329-3333, Fax: (775) 329-1541, E-mail: art@nma.reno.nv.us, Internet: http://www.nevadaart.org. Head: Steven S. High
Fine Arts Museum / Public Gallery - 1931
library 39723

Sheppard Fine Arts Gallery, University of Nevada, Reno, Church Fine Arts Complex, Mail Stop 224, Reno, NV 89557 - T: (702) 784-6682, Fax: (702) 784-6655, E-mail: art@scs.unr.edu, Internet: http://www.unr.edu. Head: Edward Martinez
Fine Arts Museum / University Museum - 1960 39724

Wilbur D. May Museum, 1502 Washington St, Reno, NV 89503 - T: (702) 785-5961, Fax: (702) 785-4707. Head: Barbie Strubel, Gene Sullivan
Local Museum - 1985
Local hist 39725

W.M. Keck Museum, Mackay School of Mines, University of Nevada, Reno, NV 89557 - T: (702) 784-6052, Fax: (702) 784-1766
University Museum / Natural History Museum - 1908 39726

Rensselaer NY

Crailo State Historic Site, 9 1/2 Riverside Av, Rensselaer, NY 12144 - T: (518) 463-8738, Fax: (518) 463-8738. Head: Donnarae Gordon
Local Museum - 1924 39727

Renton WA

Renton Museum, 235 Mill Av S, Renton, WA 98055-2133 - T: (425) 255-2330, Fax: (425) 277-4400, E-mail: rtnmuseum@aol.com. Head: Steve Anderson
Local Museum - 1966
Local hist 39728

Renville MN

Historic Renville Preservation Commission Museum, POB 681, Renville, MN 56284 - T: (612) 329-3545. Head: Jane Rice
Historical Museum - 1976 39729

Republic KS

Pawnee Indian Village, Rte 1, Republic, KS 66964 - T: (785) 361-2255, Fax: (785) 361-2255, E-mail: piv@kshs.org, Internet: http://www.kshs.org. Head: Richard Gould
Ethnology Museum / Archaeological Museum / Historical Museum - 1967
Archaeology, preserved Pawnee site 39730

Republic MO

Wilson's Creek National Battlefield, 6424 W Farm Rd, Republic, MO 65738 - T: (417) 732-2662, Fax: (417) 732-1167, Internet: http://www.nps.gov/wicr. Head: Malcolm J. Berg
Military Museum - 1960 39731

Reston VA

The Greater Reston Arts Center, 11911 Freedom Dr, Reston, VA 20190 - T: (703) 471-9242, Fax: (703) 471-0952, E-mail: graceart@erols.com. Head: Suzi Jones, Anne Brown
Fine Arts Museum / Folklore Museum - 1974
Civic art and culture 39732

Rexburg ID

Upper Snake River Valley Historical Museum, 51 N Center, Rexburg, ID 83440 - T: (208) 356-9101, Fax: (208) 356-3379, E-mail: dhc@srv.net. Head: David Morris, Louis Clements
Fine Arts Museum / Local Museum - 1965
Local history - library 39733

Rhinebeck NY

Rhinebeck Aerodrome Museum, Stone Church Rd and Norton Rd, Rhinebeck, NY 12572 - T: (845) 752-3200, Fax: (914) 758-6481, E-mail: info@oldrhinebeck.org, Internet: http://www.oldrhinebeck.org. Head: John Costa
Science&Tech Museum - 1977
Aeronautics 39734

Rhinelander WI

Rhinelander Logging Museum, Pioneer Park, Martin Lynch Dr, Rhinelander, WI 54501 - T: (715) 362-2193, 369-5004. Head: Walt Krause
Folklore Museum / Science&Tech Museum - 1932
Pioneer logging industry 39735

Rialto CA

Rialto Museum, 201-205 N Riverside Av, Rialto, CA 92376 - T: (909) 875-1750, 875-4634. Head: Bette Hughbanks
Folklore Museum / Local Museum - 1971
Local hist 39736

Richey MT

Richey Historical Museum, POB 218, Richey, MT 59259 - T: (406) 773-5656. Head: Donald Handlos
Historical Museum - 1973 39737

Richfield Springs NY

Petrified Creatures Museum of Natural History, Rte 20, Richfield Springs, NY 13439 - T: (315) 858-2868, Fax: (315) 858-2868, E-mail: stellapcm@yahoo.com, Internet: http://www.cooperstown-chamber.org. Head: Stella C. Mlecz
Natural History Museum / Open Air Museum - 1934 39738

Richland WA

Columbia River Exhibition of History, Science and Technology, 95 Lee Blvd, Richland, WA 99352 - T: (509) 943-9000, Fax: (509) 943-1770, E-mail: gwen@crehst.org, Internet: http://www.crehst.org. Head: Gwen I. Leth
Science&Tech Museum - 1963
Science, nuclear hist 39739

Richland Center WI

A.D. German Warehouse, 300 S Church St, Richland Center, WI 53581 - T: (608) 647-2808. Head: Harvey W. Glanzer, Bethel I. Caulkins
Fine Arts Museum
Architecture by Lloyd Wright, enginering/ architectural models 39740

Richlands NC

Onslow County Museum, 301 S Wilmington St, Richlands, NC 28574 - T: (910) 324-5008, Fax: (910) 324-2897, E-mail: ocmuseum@co.onslow.nc.us. Head: Albert Potts
Local Museum - 1976 39741

Richmond CA

Richmond Art Center, 2540 Barrett Av, Civic Center Plaza, Richmond, CA 94804 - T: (510) 620-6772, Fax: (510) 620-6771, Internet: http://www.therichmondartcenter.org. Head: Larry Kennings, Rachel Osajima
Fine Arts Museum - 1936
Art 39742

Richmond Museum of History, 400 Nevin Av, Richmond, CA 94802 - T: (510) 235-7387, Fax: (510) 235-4345. Head: Lois H. Boyle, Kathleen Rupley
Local Museum - 1952
Local hist 39743

Richmond IN

Joseph Moore Museum, Earlham College, Richmond, IN 47374 - T: (765) 983-1303, Fax: (765) 983-1497, E-mail: johni@earlham.edu, Internet: http://www.earlham.edu. Head: Dr. John B. Iverson
University Museum / Natural History Museum - 1887
Natural history 39744

Richmond Art Museum, 350 Hub Etchison Pkwy, Richmond, IN 47375 - T: (765) 966-0256, Fax: (765) 973-3738, Internet: http://www.richmondartmuseum.org. Head: Kathleen D. Martin
Fine Arts Museum - 1898
Art 39745

Wayne County Historical Museum, 1150 N A St, Richmond, IN 47374 - T: (317) 962-5756, Fax: (765) 939-0909, E-mail: micheleb@infocom.com. Head: Michele Bottorff
Local Museum - 1930
General museum, housed in Hicksite Friends Meeting House 39746

Richmond KY

Fort Boonesborough Museum, 4375 Boonesboro Rd, Richmond, KY 40475 - T: (606) 527-3131, Fax: (606) 527-3328, E-mail: phil.gray@mail.state.ky.us, Internet: http://www.kystateparks.com. Head: Lilly Newman
Historical Museum - 1974
History 39747

White Hall Historic Site, 500 White Hall Shrine Rd, Richmond, KY 40475 - T: (606) 623-9178, Fax: (606) 626-8489
Local Museum / Decorative Arts Museum - 1971
Historic house Georgian style bldg, added to in the Italianate style 39748

Richmond ME

CHTJ Southard House Museum, 75 Main St, Richmond, ME 04357 - T: (207) 737-8202, Fax: (207) 737-8772, E-mail: fcmain@ctel.net, Internet: http://www.southardhousemuseum.com. Head: Carolyn Cooper Case
Local Museum - 1990 39749

Richmond TX

Fort Bend Museum, 500 Houston, Richmond, TX 77469 - T: (281) 342-6478, Fax: (281) 342-2439. Head: Michael R. Moore
Local Museum - 1967
Local hist 39750

Richmond VA

1708 Gallery, 103 E Broad St, Richmond, VA 23219 - T: (804) 643-7829, Fax: (804) 643-7829, E-mail: artgallery1708@mindspring.com, Internet: http://www.1708gallery.com. Head: Peter S. Calvert
Public Gallery - 1978 39751

Agecroft Hall, 4305 Sulgrave Rd, Richmond, VA 23221 - T: (804) 353-4241, Fax: (804) 353-2151, Internet: http://www.agecrofthall.com. Head: Richard W. Moxley
Local Museum - 1969
Historic house 39752

The American Historical Foundation Museum, 1142 W Grace St, Richmond, VA 23220 - T: (804) 353-1812, Fax: (804) 353-0689. Head: Robert A. Buerlein
Historical Museum / Military Museum - 1982
Military, history 39753

Anderson Gallery, c/o School of the Arts, Virginia Commonwealth University, 907 1/2 W Franklin St, Richmond, VA 23284-2514 - T: (804) 828-1522, Fax: (804) 828-8585, E-mail: jcaperto@atlas.vcu.edu, Internet: http://www.vcu.edu/artweb/gallery/. Head: Ted Potter
Fine Arts Museum / University Museum - 1969
Art 39754

Artspace, 6 E Broad St, Richmond, VA 23219 - T: (804) 782-8672, Fax: (804) 782-9880, Internet: http://www.artspacegallery.org. Head: Christina Newton
Public Gallery 39755

Beth Ahabah Museum and Archives, 1109 W Franklin St, Richmond, VA 23220 - T: (804) 353-2668, Fax: (804) 358-3451, Internet: http://www.bethahabah.org/museum. Head: Gail Straus, Shirley S. Belkowitz
Historical Museum - 1977
Jewish hist 39756

Children's Museum of Richmond, 2626 W Broad St, Richmond, VA 23220 - T: (804) 474-2667, Fax: (804) 474-7099, E-mail: nmiller@c-mor.org, Internet: http://www.c.mor.org. Head: Stanley K. Joynes, Nan L. Miller
Special Museum - 1977
Children's museum 39757

Edgar Allan Poe Museum, 1914-16 E. Main St, Richmond, VA 23223 - T: (804) 648-5523, Fax: (804) 648-8729, E-mail: -edgarallanpoemuseum@erols.com, Internet: http://www.poemuseum.org. Head: John P.C. Moon
Local Museum / Special Museum - 1922
Historic house 39758

Folk Art Society of America, 1904 Byrd Av, Richmond, VA 23230 - T: (804) 285-4532, Fax: (804) 285-4532, E-mail: fasa@folkart.org, Internet: http://www.folkart.org. Head: Ann Oppenhimer
Library with Exhibitions - 1987
Folk art 39759

Hand Workshop Art Center, 1812 W Main St, Richmond, VA 23220 - T: (804) 353-0094, Fax: (804) 353-8018. Head: Susan Glasser
Fine Arts Museum - 1963 39760

John Marshall House, 818 E Marshall St, Richmond, VA 23219 - T: (804) 648-7998, Fax: (804) 775-0802, E-mail: JMHAPVA@AOL.com, Internet: http://apva.org. Head: Elisabeth Kostelny
Local Museum - 1790
Local hist 39761

Lora Robins Gallery of Design from Nature, University of Richmond, Richmond, VA 23173 - T: (804) 289-8460; 8762, Fax: (804) 287-6467
University Museum / Natural History Museum - 1977
Geology, natural hist 39762

Marsh Art Gallery, University of Richmond, Richmond, VA 23173 - T: (804) 289-8276, Fax: (804) 287-1894, E-mail: rwaller@richmond.edu, Internet: http://www.arts.richmond.edu/~marshart. Head: Richard Waller
Fine Arts Museum / University Museum - 1968 39763

Maymont, 1700 Hampton St, Richmond, VA 23220 - T: (804) 358-7166, Fax: (804) 358-9994, Internet: http://www.maymont.org. Head: Dale C. Wheary, Mark S. Rich
Decorative Arts Museum / Local Museum - 1925
Historic house 39764

The Museum of the Confederacy, 1201 E Clay St, Richmond, VA 23219-1615 - T: (804) 649-1861, Fax: (804) 644-7150, E-mail: info@moc.org, Internet: http://www.moc.org. Head: Robin Edward Reed
Historical Museum - 1896
Confederate military, artefacts, flags, documents 39765

Richmond National Battlefield Park, 3215 E Broad St, Richmond, VA 23223 - T: (804) 226-1981, Fax: (804) 771-8522, Internet: http://www.nps.gov/rich. Head: Cynthia MacLeod
Military Museum - 1936
Civil War hist 39766

Science Museum of Virginia, 2500 W Broad St, Richmond, VA 23220-2054 - T: (804) 367-6552, Fax: (804) 367-2511, Internet: http://www.smv.mus.va.us. Head: Adrienne G. Hines, Walter R.T. Witschey
Science&Tech Museum - 1970
Science, aviation 39767

The Valentine Museum - Richmond History Center, 1015 E Clay St, Richmond, VA 23219-1590 - T: (804) 649-0711, Fax: (804) 643-3510, E-mail: valmus@mindspring.com, Internet: http://www.valentinemuseum.com. Head: William J. Martin
Historical Museum / Decorative Arts Museum - 1892
Urban hist 39768

Virginia Baptist Historical Society Museum, Boatwright Library, University of Richmond, Richmond, VA 23173 - T: (804) 289-8434, Fax: (804) 289-8953. Head: Robert F. Woodward, Fred Anderson
Local Museum - 1876
Baptist hist 39769

Virginia Historical Society Museum, 428 North Blvd, Richmond, VA 23220 - T: (804) 358-4901, Fax: (804) 342-2399, E-mail: charles@vahistorical.org, Internet: http://www.vahistorical.org. Head: Dr. Charles F. Bryan, Scott Burrell
Historical Museum - 1831
State hist 39770

Virginia Museum of Fine Arts, 2800 Grove Av, Richmond, VA 23221-2466 - T: (804) 340-1400, Fax: (804) 340-1548, E-mail: webmaster@vmfa.state.va.us, Internet: http://www.vmfa.state.va.us. Head: Dr. Michael Brand
Fine Arts Museum / Folklore Museum - 1934
Art 39771

Wilton House Museum, The National Society of the Colonial Dames of America in the Commonwealth of Virginia, 215 S Wilton Rd, Richmond, VA 23226 - T: (804) 282-5936, Fax: (804) 288-9805, E-mail: wiltonhouse@mindspring.com, Internet: http://www.wiltonhousemuseum.org. Head: Sylvia B. Evans
Decorative Arts Museum - 1934
Local hist, decorative arts 39772

Richmond Hill GA

Fort McAllister, 3894 Fort McAllister Rd, Richmond Hill, GA 31324 - T: (912) 727-2339, 727-3614, Fax: (912) 727-3614, E-mail: ftmcallr@g-net.net. Head: Daniel Brown
Military Museum - 1958
1861 Confederate fort 39773

Ridgecrest CA

Maturango Museum of the Indian Wells Valley, 100 E Las Flores Av, Ridgecrest, CA 93555 - T: (760) 375-6900, Fax: (760) 375-0479, E-mail: matmus@ridgenet.net, Internet: http://www.maturango
Local Museum - 1962
Local hist 39774

Ridgefield CT

Aldrich Museum of Contemporary Art, 258 Main St, Ridgefield, CT 06877 - T: (203) 438-4519, Fax: (203) 438-0198, E-mail: general@aldrichart.org, Internet: http://www.aldrichart.org. Head: Kathleen O'Grady, Harry Philbrick
Fine Arts Museum - 1964 39775

Keeler Tavern Museum, 132 Main St, Ridgefield, CT 06877 - T: (203) 438-5485, 431-0815, Fax: (203) 438-9953. Head: Anne Smith
Historical Museum - 1965
Local hist 39776

Ridgeland MS

Mississippi Crafts Center, Natchez Trace Pky, Ridgeland, MS 39157 - T: (601) 856-7546, Fax: (601) 856-7546. Head: Ann Baker, Martha Garrott
Decorative Arts Museum / Folklore Museum - 1975 39777

Ridgewood NJ

Schoolhouse Museum, 650 E Glen Av, Ridgewood, NJ 07450 - T: (201) 652-4584
Local Museum - 1949 39778

Rifle CO

Rifle Creek Museum, 337 East Av, Rifle, CO 81650 - T: (970) 625-4862. Head: Crystal Anderson, Kim Fazzi
Local Museum - 1967
General museum 39779

Rincon GA

Georgia Salzburger Society Museum, 2980 Ebenezer Rd, Rincon, GA 31326 - T: (912) 754-7001, Fax: (912) 754-7001, Internet: http://www.msstate.edu/Archives/History/salzb/index.html. Head: Gregory Ardsdorff
Local Museum - 1925 39780

Ringwood NJ

The Forges and Manor of Ringwood, 1304 Sloatsburg Rd, Ringwood, NJ 07456 - T: (973) 962-2240, Fax: (973) 962-2247, E-mail: ringwood@warwick.net. Head: Elbertus Prol
Local Museum - 1935
Local history, industrial history 39781

Rio Hondo TX

Texas Air Museum, 1 Mile E Rio Hondo, Rio Hondo, TX 78583 - T: (956) 748-2112, Fax: (956) 425-3500, Internet: http://www.cyberair.com. Head: John Houston
Science&Tech Museum - 1986 39782

Ripley OH

Rankin House State Memorial, Liberty Hill, Ripley, OH 45167 - T: (937) 392-4188
Local Museum - 1938 39783

Ripon WI

Little White Schoolhouse, 303 Blackburn St, Ripon, WI 54971 - T: (920) 748-6764, Fax: (920) 748-6784, E-mail: racc@vbl.com, Internet: http://www.ripon-wi.com. Head: Loren Boon, Ellen C. Sormsen
Historical Museum - 1951
Historic house, Birthplace of Republican Party 39784

Ripon Historical Society Museum, 508 Watson St, Ripon, WI 54971 - T: (920) 748-5354
Historical Museum - 1899
Local hist 39785

Rittman OH

Rittman Historical Society Museum, 393 W Sunset Dr, Rittman, OH 44270 - T: (330) 925-7572
Local Museum - 1960 39786

River Edge NJ

Steuben House Museum, 1201 Main St, River Edge, NJ 07661 - T: (201) 343-9492, 487-1739, Fax: (201) 498-1696, Internet: http://www.carroll.com/bchs. Head: Kevin Wright
Local Museum - 1902
Artifacts of the Bergen Dutch 1680-1914 39787

River Falls WI

Gallery 101, University of Wisconsin-River Falls, River Falls, WI 54022 - T: (715) 425-3266, Fax: (715) 425-0657, E-mail: michael.a.padgett@uwrf.edu, Internet: http://www.uwrf.edu. Head: Michael Padgett
Fine Arts Museum - 1973
Art 39788

Riverdale Park MD

Riversdale Mansion, 4811 Riverdale Rd, Riverdale Park, MD 20737 - T: (301) 864-0420, Fax: (301) 927-3498, E-mail: dayedwardparksrec@smart.net, Internet: http://www.smart.net/~parksrec
Local Museum - 1949 39789

Riverhead NY

Hallockville Museum Farm, 6038 Sound Av, Riverhead, NY 11901 - T: (516) 298-5292, Fax: (516) 298-0144, E-mail: hallockville@peconic.net. Head: James Pim, John Eilertsen
Agriculture Museum - 1975 39790

Suffolk County Historical Society Museum, 300 W Main St, Riverhead, NY 11901 - T: (631) 727-2881, Fax: (631) 727-3467, E-mail: histsoc@suffolk.lib.ny.us. Head: John Sprayue, Wallace W. Broege
Local Museum - 1886
Indians, ceramics, decorative arts, whaling, early crafts, trade tools 39791

Riverside CA

California Museum of Photography, 3824 Main St, Riverside, CA 92501 - T: (909) 787-4787, Fax: (909) 787-4797, E-mail: jgreen@citrus.ucr.edu, Internet: http://www.cmp.ucr.edu/. Head: Jonathan Green
Fine Arts Museum / University Museum - 1973
Photography 39792

Entomology Research Museum, c/o Department of Entomology, University of California, Riverside, CA 92521-0314 - T: (909) 787-4385, 787-4315, Fax: (909) 787-3086, 787-3681, Internet: http://insects.ucr.edu/entmus/entmus.html. Head: Dr. Timothy D. Paine
University Museum / Natural History Museum - 1962
Entomology 39793

March Field Museum, 22550 Van Buren Blvd, Riverside, CA 92518-6463 - T: (909) 697-6602, Fax: (909) 697-6605, E-mail: marfldmu@pe.net, Internet: http://www.pe.net/~marfldmu. Head: Hal Austin, Steven P. Clark
Military Museum / Science&Tech Museum - 1979
Military hist 39794

Mission Inn Museum, 3696 Main St, Riverside, CA 92501 - T: (909) 788-9556, Fax: (909) 781-8201, E-mail: missioninnmuseum@pe.net, Internet: http://www.missioninnmuseum.com. Head: J. Worden
Local Museum
Local hist 39795

Riverside Art Museum, 3425 Mission Inn Av, Riverside, CA 92501 - T: (909) 684-7111, Fax: (909) 684-7332, E-mail: ram@riversideartmuseum.com, Internet: http://www.riversideartmuseum.com. Head: Bobbie Powell
Fine Arts Museum - 1935
Art 39796

Riverside Municipal Museum, 3580 Mission Inn Av, Riverside, CA 92501 - T: (909) 782-5273, Fax: (909) 369-4970, E-mail: resparza@ci.riverside.ca.us, Internet: http://www.ci.riverside.ca.us/museum. Head: Richarad R. Esparza
Local Museum - 1924
Local hist 39797

Sweeney Art Gallery, University of California, Watkins House, 3701 Canyon Crest Dr, Riverside, CA 92521 - T: (909) 787-3755 ext 1465, Fax: (909) 787-3798, E-mail: katherine.warren@ucr.edu, Internet: http://sweeney.ucr.edu. Head: Katherine V. Warren
University Museum / Fine Arts Museum - 1963 39798

World Museum of Natural History, 4700 Pierce St, Riverside, CA 92515-8247 - T: (909) 785-2209, Fax: (909) 785-2901, E-mail: ballen@lasierra.edu, Internet: http://www.lasierra.edu/wmnh. Head: William M. Allen
Natural History Museum - 1971
Natural history, reptiles, birds, Indian artifacts 39799

Riverton WY

Riverton Museum, 700 E Park Av, Riverton, WY 82501 - T: (307) 856-2665. Head: Loren Jost
Local Museum - 1956
Local hist 39800

Roanoke VA

Art Museum of Western Virginia, One Market Sq, Roanoke, VA 24011-1436 - T: (540) 342-5760, Fax: (540) 342-5798, E-mail: info@artmuseumroanoke.org, Internet: http://artmuseumroanoke.org. Head: Dr. Judy L. Larson
Fine Arts Museum - 1951
Art 39801

Catholic Historical Society of the Roanoke Valley Museum, 400 W Campbell Av, Roanoke, VA 24016 - T: (540) 982-0152. Head: Margaret M. Cochener
Religious Arts Museum - 1983 39802

History Museum of Western Virginia, One Market Sq, Roanoke, VA 24011 - T: (540) 342-5770, Fax: (540) 224-1256, E-mail: history@roanoke.infi.net, Internet: http://history-museum.org. Head: Robert H. Kulp, D. Kent Chrisman
Historical Museum - 1957
History 39803

Science Museum of Western Virginia, 1 Market Sq, Roanoke, VA 24011 - T: (540) 342-5778, Fax: (540) 224-1240, E-mail: sthompson@smwv.org, Internet: http://www.smwv.org. Head: John Grove, Kenneth J. Schutz, Leslie Bochenski
Natural History Museum / Science&Tech Museum - 1970
Science 39804

Virginia Museum of Transportation, 303 Norfolk Av, Roanoke, VA 24016 - T: (540) 342-5670, Fax: (540) 342-6898, E-mail: info@vmt.org, Internet: http://www.vmt.org. Head: Katherine F. Strickland
Science&Tech Museum - 1963
Transportation, trains, automobiles, carriages, aviation equipment 39805

Rochester IN

Fulton County Historical Society Museum, 37 E 375 N, Rochester, IN 46975 - T: (219) 223-4436, E-mail: wwillard@rtcol.com, Internet: http://www.icss.net/~fchs. Head: Shirley Willard
Local Museum / Open Air Museum / Historical Museum - 1963
Round Barn, Potawatomi Trail of Death, Reference Room 17 rooms of permanent displays, village with 11 buildings 39806

Rochester MI

Meadow Brook Art Gallery, Oakland University, 209 Wilson Hall, Rochester, MI 48309-4401 - T: (248) 370-3005, Fax: (248) 370-4208, E-mail: watson@oakland.edu, Internet: http://www.oakland.edu/mbag. Head: Dick Goody
Fine Arts Museum / University Museum - 1959
African, Pre-Columbian and Oriental art, furniture 39807

Rochester MN

Olmsted County Historical Society Museum, 1195 W Circle Dr SW, Rochester, MN 55902 - T: (507) 282-9447, Fax: (507) 289-5481, E-mail: ochs@olmstedhistory.com, Internet: http://www.olmsted-history.com. Head: John Hunziker
Historical Museum - 1926
archives 39808

Rochester Art Center, 320 E Center St, Rochester, MN 55904 - T: (507) 282-8629, Fax: (507) 282-7737, Internet: http://www.rochesterusa.com/artcenter. Head: Betty Shigaki
Fine Arts Museum - 1946
Contemporary visual arts and crafts 39809

Rochester NY

Baker-Cederberg Museum, Rochester General Hospital, 1425 Portland Av, Rochester, NY 14621-3095 - T: (716) 922-3521, Fax: (716) 922-5292, E-mail: phil.maples@viahealth.org, Internet: http://www.viahealth.org/archives. Head: Philip G. Maples
Science&Tech Museum - 1947
Local history, Company museum 39810

DAR-Hervey Ely House, 11 Livingston Park, Rochester, NY 14608 - T: (716) 232-4509
Decorative Arts Museum / Local Museum - 1894 39811

International Museum of Photography and Film, George Eastman House, 900 E Av, Rochester, NY 14607 - T: (716) 271-3361, Fax: (716) 271-3970, Internet: http://www.eastman.org. Head: Anthony Bannon
Fine Arts Museum - 1947
Photography, motion pictures 39812

Mercer Gallery, Monroe Community College, 1000 E Henrietta Rd, Rochester, NY 14623 - T: (716) 292-2021, Fax: (716) 427-2749, E-mail: KFarrell@zodiac.monroecc.edu, Internet: http://www.monroecc.edu. Head: Kathleen Farrell
Fine Arts Museum / University Museum
Art 39813

Rochester Historical Society Museum, 485 East Av, Rochester, NY 14607 - T: (716) 271-2705. Head: Elizabeth G. Holahan
Local Museum - 1861 39814

Rochester Museum, 657 East Av, Rochester, NY 14607-2177 - T: (716) 271-4320, Fax: (716) 271-6546, E-mail: katebennett@rmsc.org, Internet: http://www.rmsc.org. Head: Kate Bennett
Historical Museum / Natural History Museum / Science&Tech Museum - 1912 39815

Strong Museum, 1 Manhattan Sq, Rochester, NY 14607 - T: (716) 263-2700, Fax: (716) 263-2493, Internet: http://www.strongmuseum.org. Head: G. Rollie Adams
Historical Museum - 1968 39816

Susan B. Anthony House, 17 Madison St, Rochester, NY 14608 - T: (716) 235-6124 ext 10, Fax: (716) 235-6212, Internet: http://susanbanthonyhouse.org. Head: Lorie Barnum
Local Museum - 1946 39817

University of Rochester Memorial Art Gallery, 500 University Av, Rochester, NY 14607 - T: (716) 473-7720 ext 3000, Fax: (716) 473-6266, E-mail: maginfo@mag.rochester.edu, Internet: http://www.rochester.edu/MAG/. Head: Grant Holcomb
Fine Arts Museum / University Museum / Decorative Arts Museum - 1913 39818

Rochester Hills MI

Rochester Hills Museum at Van Hoosen Farm, 1005 Van Hoosen Rd, Rochester Hills, MI 48306 - T: (248) 656-4663, Fax: (248) 608-8198, E-mail: rhmuseum@ameritech.net, Internet: http://www.rochesterhills.org. Head: Patrick McKay
Local Museum / Historical Museum - 1979
Local hist 39819

Rock Hill SC

Museum of York County, 4621 Mount Gallant Rd, Rock Hill, SC 29732-9905 - T: (803) 329-2121, Fax: (803) 329-5249, E-mail: myco@infoave.net, Internet: http://web.cetlink.net/~myco/mycohome.html. Head: W. Van Shields
Local Museum - 1950
Local hist, African amimals, art and ethnography, local art, archaeology and natural history 39820

Winthrop University Galleries, Rutledge Bldg, Rock Hill, SC 29733 - T: (803) 323-2126, Fax: (803) 323-2333, E-mail: stanteyt@winthrop.edu, Internet: http://www.winthrop.edu/vpa. Head: Tom Stanley
Fine Arts Museum
Visual arts and design 39821

Rock Island IL

Augustana College Art Gallery, 7th Av and 38th St, Rock Island, IL 61201-2296 - T: (309) 794-7231, Fax: (309) 794-7678, E-mail: armaurer@augustana.edu, Internet: http://www2.augustana.edu/resource/gallery. Head: Sherry C. Maurer
Fine Arts Museum - 1983
Art 39822

Black Hawk State Historic Site, Hauberg Indian Museum, Illinois Rte 5, Rock Island, IL 61201 - T: (309) 788-9536, Fax: (309) 788-9865, E-mail: hauberg-museum@juno.com. Head: Elizabeth Carvey-Stewart
Historic Site / Historical Museum - 1927
1740-1831 site of the main villages of the Sauk and Fox Nations 39823

Colonel Davenport Historical Foundation, Hillman St, Rock Island Arsenal, Rock Island, IL 61201 - T: (309) 764-6471, 388-9657, E-mail: coldav1833@yahoo.com, Internet: http://www.dav1833@aol.com. Head: Susan Wolters
Local Museum - 1978
Local hist 39824

Fryxell Geology Museum, Swenson Hall of Science, Augustana College, Rock Island, IL 61201 - T: (309) 794-7318, Fax: (309) 794-7564, E-mail: glhammer@augustana.edu, Internet: http://www.augustana.edu. Head: William R. Hammer
Natural History Museum - 1929
Geology 39825

Rock Island Arsenal Museum, Attn SMARI-CFS-M, 1 Rock Island Arsenal, Rock Island, IL 61299-5000 - T: (309) 782-5021, Fax: (309) 782-3598, Internet: http://www.ria.army.mil/. Head: Kris G. Leinicke
Military Museum - 1905
Military 39826

Rock Springs WY

Community Fine Arts Center, 400 C St, Rock Springs, WY 82901 - T: (307) 362-6212, Fax: (307) 382-4101, E-mail: cfac@rock.sw1.k12.wy.us. Head: Debora Thaxton Soule
Fine Arts Museum - 1938
Arts 39827

Rock Springs Historical Museum, 201 B St, Rock Springs, WY 82901 - T: (307) 362-3138, Fax: (307) 352-1516. Head: Cyndi Sullivan, Jack Smith
Local Museum - 1988
Local hist 39828

Rockford IL

Burpee Museum of Natural History, 737 N Main St, Rockford, IL 61103 - T: (815) 965-3433, Fax: (815) 965-2703, E-mail: info@burpee.org, Internet: http://www.burpee.org. Head: Robert Tilson, Dr. Wallace A. Steffan, Tom Little
Natural History Museum - 1942
Natural history, new Robert Solem wing 39829

Discovery Center Museum, 711 N Main St, Rockford, IL 61103 - T: (815) 963-6769, Fax: (815) 968-0164, E-mail: webmaster@discoverycentermuseum.org, Internet: http://www.discoverycentermuseum.org. Head: Russ Anderson, Sarah Wolf, Jan Aschim
Special Museum - 1981 39830

Midway Village and Museum, 6799 Guilford Rd, Rockford, IL 61107 - T: (815) 397-9112, Fax: (815) 397-9156
Open Air Museum - 1970
History Village, 24-building turn-of-the-century complex 39831

Rockford Art Museum, 711 N Main St, Rockford, IL 61103-6999 - T: (815) 968-2787, Fax: (815) 968-0164, E-mail: staff@rockfordartmuseum.com, Internet: http://www.rockfordartmuseum.org. Head: Lorie Langan
Fine Arts Museum - 1913
Art 39832

Rockford College Art Gallery/Clark Arts Center, 5050 E State, Rockford, IL 61108 - T: (815) 226-4034, Fax: (815) 394-5167. Head: Maureen Gustafson
Fine Arts Museum / University Museum - 1847
Art 39833

Tinker Swiss Cottage Museum, 411 Kent St, Rockford, IL 61102 - T: (815) 964-2424, Fax: (815) 964-2466, Internet: http://www.tinkercottage.com. Head: Dr. M. Constance Tucker, Laura Bachelder
Local Museum / Decorative Arts Museum - 1943
1865 Swiss-style home built by Robert H. Tinker 39834

Rockhill Furnace PA

Railways to Yesterday, Rockhill Trolley Museum, East Broad Top Railroad, State Rte 994, Rockhill Furnace, PA 17249 - T: (814) 447-9576, E-mail: s.gurley@prodigy.net, Internet: http://www.rockhilltrolley.org. Head: Joel Salomon
Science&Tech Museum - 1960
Transportation, specialization in collecting, restoring and maintaining cars that operated in Pennsylvania, trolley cars from Johnstown, Philadelphia, York, Scranton 39835

Rockland ME

Shore Village Museum, 104 Limerock St, Rockland, ME 04841 - T: (207) 594-0311, Fax: (207) 594-9581, E-mail: knb@ime.net. Head: Kenneth N. Black
Historical Museum - 1977
Maritime, lighthouse 39836

William A. Farnsworth Art Museum and Wyeth Center, 352 Main St, Rockland, ME 04841-0466 - T: (207) 596-6457, Fax: (207) 596-0509, E-mail: farnsworth@midcoast.com, Internet: http://www.farnsworthmuseum.org. Head: Christopher B. Crosman
Fine Arts Museum - 1948
American art, Louise Nevelson coll - library, Wyeth study center 39837

Rockport MA

Rockport Art Association Museum, 12 Main St, Rockport, MA 01966 - T: (978) 546-6604, Fax: (978) 546-9767. Head: Carol Linsky
Fine Arts Museum - 1921
Arts 39838

Sandy Bay Historical Museums, 40 King St, Rockport, MA 01966 - T: (508) 546-9533
Local Museum - 1925
Local history, Sewall-Scripture house, old castle 39839

Rockport ME

Center for Maine Contemporary Art, 162 Russell Av, Rockport, ME 04856 - T: (207) 236-2875, Fax: (207) 236-2490, E-mail: mca@midcoast.com, Internet: http://www.artsmaine.org. Head: Sheila Crosby Tasker
Fine Arts Museum - 1952
Contemporary art 39840

Rockport TX

Texas Maritime Museum, 1202 Navigation Circle, Rockport, TX 78382-2773 - T: (361) 729-1271, Fax: (361) 729-9938. Head: Clayton Black, Mindy Durham
Historical Museum - 1980
Maritime 39841

Rockton IL

Macktown Living History Site and Whitman Trading Post, Macktown Forest Preserve, Hwy 75 W, Rockton, IL 61072 - T: (815) 877-6100, Fax: (815) 877-6124, E-mail: wcfpd@wcfpd.org, Internet: http://www.wcfpd.org. Head: Ray Ferguson, Marilyn Mohring
Local Museum - 1952
Two-story farm house, home to one of the first white settlers in Winnebago County, 1846 Whitman Trading Post 39842

Rockville MD

Jane L. and Robert H. Weiner Judaic Museum, 6125 Montrose Rd, Rockville, MD 20852 - T: (301) 881-0100, Fax: (301) 881-5512, Internet: http://www.jccgw.org. Head: Michael Witkes
Fine Arts Museum / Religious Arts Museum - 1925
Judaica 39843

Latvian Museum, 400 Hurley Av, Rockville, MD 20850 - T: (301) 340-1914, Fax: (301) 340-8732, E-mail: alainfo@alausa.org. Head: Anna Graudina-Zadina
Ethnology Museum / Folklore Museum - 1980
Latvian historic and cultural development from Ice Age to 20th c 39844

Montgomery County Historical Society Museum, 103 W Montgomery Av, Rockville, MD 20850-4212 - T: (301) 340-2825, Fax: (301) 340-2871, E-mail: info@montgomeryhistory.org, Internet: http://www.montgomeryhistory.org. Head: Mary Anne Tuohey, Mary Kay Harper
Local Museum / Historical Museum - 1944
Beall-Dawson House, 1852 Stonestreet Medical Museum, local history 39845

Rockwell City IA

Calhoun County Museum, 150 W High St, Rockwell City, IA 50579 - T: (712) 297-8139, 297-8585
Local Museum - 1956
Regional history 39846

Rocky Ford CO

Rocky Ford Historical Museum, 1005 Sycamore Av, Rocky Ford, CO 81067 - T: (719) 254-6737
Local Museum - 1940
Local history 39847

Rocky Hill CT

Academy Hall Museum of the Rocky Hill Historical Society, 785 Old Main St, Rocky Hill, CT 06067 - T: (860) 563-6704, 529-1438. Head: Sandra Brown
Local Museum - 1962
Local hist 39848

Rocky Mount NC

Rocky Mount Arts Center, 1173 Nashville Rd, Rocky Mount, NC 27803 - T: (252) 972-1163, Fax: (252) 972-1563, E-mail: jackson@ci.rocky-mount.nc.us, Internet: http://www.ci.rocky-mount.nc.us/artscenter. Head: Jerry Jackson
Fine Arts Museum - 1956 39849

Rocky Mount Children's Museum, 1610 Gay St, Rocky Mount, NC 27804 - T: (919) 972-1167, Fax: (919) 972-1232, Internet: http://www.ci.rocky-mount.nc.us/museum.html. Head: Candy L. Madrid
Special Museum - 1952 39850

Roebuck SC

Walnut Grove Plantation, 1200 Otts' Shoals Rd, Roebuck, SC 29376 - T: (864) 576-6546, Fax: (864) 576-4058. Head: Susan Dunlap, Susan Turpin
Historical Museum - 1961
Historic house 39851

Rogers AR

Daisy International Air Gun Museum, 2111 S 8th St, Rogers, AR 72756 - T: (501) 636-1200, Fax: (501) 636-1601, E-mail: info@daisy.com, Internet: http://www.daisy.com. Head: Adam J. Blalock
Science&Tech Museum / Military Museum - 1966
Air guns 39852

Rogers Historical Museum, 322 S Second St, Rogers, AR 72756 - T: (501) 621-1154, Fax: (501) 621-1155, E-mail: museum@rogersarkansas.com, Internet: http://www.rogersarkansas.com/museum. Head: Gaye K. Bland
Local Museum / Historical Museum - 1975
Hawkins house, local history 39853

Rohnert Park CA

University Art Gallery, Sonoma State University, 1801 E Cotati Av, Rohnert Park, CA 94928 - T: (707) 664-2295, Fax: (707) 664-4333, E-mail: art.gallery@sonoma.edu, Internet: http://www.sonoma.edu/artgallery/. Head: Michael Schwager
Fine Arts Museum / University Museum - 1977
Art 39854

Rolla MO

Ed Clark Museum of Missouri Geology, 111 Fairgrounds Rd, Rolla, MO 65401 - T: (573) 368-2100, Fax: (573) 368-2111
Natural History Museum - 1963 39855

Rolla Minerals Museum, University of Missouri, 125 McNutt Hall, UMR Campus, Rolla, MO 65401 - T: (573) 341-4616, Fax: (573) 341-6935
University Museum / Natural History Museum - 1870 39856

Rome GA

Chieftains Museum, 501 Riverside Pkwy, Rome, GA 30161 - T: (706) 291-9494, Fax: (706) 291-2410, E-mail: chmuseum@bellsouth.net. Head: Ansley Saville
Ethnology Museum / Historical Museum / Archaeological Museum - 1969
Plantation house belonging to Cherokee leader Major Ridge, native American archaeology 39857

Rome NY

Erie Canal Village, 5789 New London Rd, RT46/49, Rome, NY 13440 - T: (315) 337-3999, Fax: (315) 339-7755, Internet: http://www.eriecanal-village.com
Local Museum / Historic Site / Open Air Museum - 1973 39858

Rome Art and Community Center, 308 W Bloomfield St, Rome, NY 13440 - T: (315) 336-1040, Fax: (315) 336-1090, E-mail: racc@borg.com, Internet: http://www.borg.com/~racc. Head: Ann Peach Lynch, Maureen Dunn Murphy
Fine Arts Museum - 1967 39859

Rome Historical Society Museum, 200 Church St, Rome, NY 13440 - T: (315) 336-5870, Fax: (315) 336-5912
Local Museum - 1936 39860

Rome City IN

Gene Stratton-Porter House, 1205 Pleasant Point, Rome City, IN 46784, mail addr: Box 639, Rome City, IN 46784 - T: (219) 854-3790, Fax: (219) 854-9102
Historical Museum 39861

Roosevelt AZ

Tonto National Monument, Hwy 88, Roosevelt, AZ 85545 - T: (520) 467-2241, Fax: (520) 467-2225. Head: Lee Baiza
Archaeological Museum - 1907
Archaelogy 39862

Rosanky TX

Central Texas Museum of Automotive History, Hwy 304, Rosanky, TX 78953 - T: (512) 237-2635, Fax: (512) 754-2424, Internet: http://www.tourtexas.com/rosanky. Head: Richard L. Burdick
Science&Tech Museum - 1982
Transportation 39863

Roseau MN

Roseau County Historical Museum, 110 Second Av NE, Roseau, MN 56751 - T: (218) 463-1918, Fax: (218) 463-3795, E-mail: roseau@wiktel.com, Internet: http://www.angelfire.com/mn/rehistsocmuseum
Historical Museum - 1927 39864

Roseburg OR

Douglas County Museum of History and Natural History, 123 Museum Dr, Roseburg, OR 97470 - T: (541) 957-7007, Fax: (541) 957-7017, E-mail: museum@co.douglas.or.us, Internet: http://www.co.douglas.or.us/museum. Head: Stacey B. MacDonald
Local Museum / Natural History Museum - 1968 39865

Lane House, 544 SE Douglas Av, Roseburg, OR 97470 - T: (541) 459-1393. Head: Jane Clarke
Historical Museum - 1953 39866

Roselle IL

Law Enforcement Museum, POB 72835, Roselle, IL 60172 - T: (847) 795-1547, Fax: (847) 795-2469, E-mail: rurbigred@aol.com, Internet: http://www.w8ca.com/lema. Head: Ronald C. Van Raalte
Special Museum - 1989
Law, crime, police deaths 39867

Roselle NJ

Sons of the American Revolution, 101 W Ninth Av, Roselle, NJ 07203-1926 - T: (908) 245-1777
Military Museum - 1889 39868

Rosendale NY

A.J. Snyder Estate, 668 Rte 213, Rosendale, NY 12472-0150 - T: (845) 658-9900, Fax: (845) 658-9277, E-mail: mail@centuryhouse.org, Internet: http://www.centuryhouse.org. Head: Dietrich Werner
Historical Museum / Science&Tech Museum - 1988 39869

Roslyn NY

Van Nostrand-Starkins House, 221 Main St, Roslyn, NY 11576 - T: (516) 625-4363, Fax: (516) 625-4363, E-mail: RoslynLandmarkSociety@juno.com. Head: Donald Kavanash, Donna Kianka
Historical Museum - 1976 39870

Roslyn Harbor NY

Nassau County Museum of Art, 1 Museum Dr, Roslyn Harbor, NY 11576 - T: (516) 484-9338, Fax: (516) 484-0710, E-mail: nassaumuseum@yahoo.com, Internet: http://www.nassaumuseum.org. Head: Constance Schwartz
Fine Arts Museum - 1989 39871

Roswell GA

Bulloch Hall, 180 Bulloch Av, Roswell, GA 30075 - T: (770) 992-1731, 992-1951, Fax: (770) 587-1840. Head: Pam Billingsley
Folklore Museum - 1978
Historic c.1839 Antebellum Greek Revival House and Cottage 39872

Roswell NM

General Douglas L. McBride Museum, New Mexico Military Institute, 101 West College Blvd, Roswell, NM 88201-8107 - T: (505) 624-8220, Fax: (505) 624-8107, Internet: http://www.nmmi.cc.nm.us. Head: Glede Holman
Military Museum - 1983
Military 39873

Historical Center for Southeast New Mexico, 200 N Lea Av, Roswell, NM 88201 - T: (505) 622-8333, Fax: (505) 622-8333
Local Museum - 1976 39874

Roswell Museum and Art Center, 100 W 11, Roswell, NM 88201 - T: (505) 624-6744 ext 10, Fax: (505) 624-6765, E-mail: rufe@roswellmuseum.org, Internet: http://www.roswellmuseum.org. Head: Laurie J. Rufe
Fine Arts Museum / Local Museum - 1937
Regional and Native American fine arts and crafts, graphics, Western history, ethnology, folk art 39875

Round Top TX

Festival-Institute Museum, State Hwy 237, Round Top, TX 78954 - T: (409) 249-3129, Fax: (409) 249-5078, E-mail: festhill@fais.net, Internet: http://www.fais.net/~festinst. Head: James Dick
Fine Arts Museum / Decorative Arts Museum - 1971
Art 39876

Roundup MT

Musselshell Valley Historical Museum, 524 First W Roundup, Roundup, MT 59072 - T: (406) 323-1403, Fax: (406) 323-1518. Head: Bonnie DeMaio
Local Museum - 1972 39877

Rowe MA

Kemp-McCarthy Memorial Museum, 288 Zoar Rd, Rowe, MA 01367-9774 - T: (413) 339-4700, 339-4729, Fax: (413) 339-0190, E-mail: rowehistorical@netzero.net. Head: Alan Bjork
Local Museum - 1963 39878

Rowley MA

Rowley Historical Museum, 233 Main St, Rowley, MA 01969 - T: (508) 948-7483, Internet: http://www.tiac.net/users/mcmahon. Head: Edward DesJardins
Local Museum - 1918
Local history 39879

Roxbury MA

Roxbury Historical Museum, 183 Roxbury St, John Eliot Sq, Roxbury, MA 02119 - T: (617) 445-3399, Fax: (617) 445-5883. Head: Antonio Menefee
Local Museum - 1901
Local history, Dillaway-Thomas house 39880

Royalton VT

Royalton Historical Society Museum, 4184 Rte 14, Royalton, VT 05068 - T: (802) 828-3051, Fax: (802) 828-3206, E-mail: jdumville@gate.dca.state.vt.us
Local Museum - 1967
Local hist 39881

Rugby ND

Geographical Center Historical Museum, 1 Block E Hwy. US #2 and ND #3, Rugby, ND 58368 - T: (701) 776-6414, Internet: http://www.artcom.com/museum/. Head: Richard Blessum
Local Museum - 1964 39882

Rugby TN

Historic Rugby, State Hwy 52, Rugby, TN 37733 - T: (423) 628-2441, Fax: (423) 628-2266, E-mail: rugbytn@highland.net, Internet: http://www.historucrugby.htm. Head: Gerald Walker, Barbara Stagg
Local Museum - 1966
Historic village 39883

Ruidoso Downs NM

Museum of the Horse, 841 Hwy 70 W, Ruidoso Downs, NM 88346 - T: (505) 378-4142, Fax: (505) 378-4166, E-mail: moth@zianet.com, Internet: http://www.zianet.com/museum. Head: Bruce B. Eldredge
Natural History Museum / Historical Museum - 1990
Horses 39884

Rushville IL

Schuyler Jail Museum, 200 S Congress St, Rushville, IL 62681 - T: (217) 322-6975
Local Museum - 1968
Local history, housed in Schuyler Jail 39885

Russell KS

Deines Cultural Center, 820 N Main St, Russell, KS 67665 - T: (785) 483-3742, Fax: (785) 483-4397, E-mail: deinescenter@russellks.net. Head: Nance Selbe
Fine Arts Museum - 1990
Art 39886

Fossil Station Museum, 331 Kansas St, Russell, KS 67665 - T: (913) 483-3637, E-mail: rchs@russellks.net, Internet: http://www.rchs.russellks.net. Head: Jeff McCoy
Local Museum / Science&Tech Museum - 1969
Local hist 39887

Gernon House and Blacksmith Shop, 818 N Kansas St, Russell, KS 67665 - T: (913) 483-3637, E-mail: rchs@russellks.net, Internet: http://www.rchs.russellks.net. Head: Jeff McCoy
Local Museum - 1979
Historic buildings 39888

Heym-Oliver House, 503 Kansas St, Russell, KS 67665 - T: (913) 483-3637, E-mail: rchs@russellks.net, Internet: http://www.rchs.russellks.net
Ethnology Museum / Historical Museum - 1968 39889

Oil Patch Museum, Interstate 70 and Hwy 281, Russell, KS 67665 - T: (913) 483-6640, E-mail: rchs@russellks.net, Internet: http://www.rchs.russellks.net. Head: Jeff McCoy
Science&Tech Museum - 1973
Industrial oil production 39890

Russell Springs KS

Butterfield Trail Historical Museum, Broadway and Hilts, Russell Springs, KS 67755 - T: (913) 751-4242. Head: Jarett Hanemza
Historical Museum - 1964
Local history, housed in the Logan County Courthouse and Jail 39891

Ruston LA

Lincoln Parish Museum, 609 N Vienna St, Ruston, LA 71270 - T: (318) 251-0018. Head: William Davis Green
Local Museum - 1975
Local hist 39892

Louisiana Tech Museum, Louisiana Tech University, Ruston, LA 71272 - T: (318) 257-2264, 257-2737, Fax: (318) 257-4735, E-mail: caesar@latech.edu. Head: C. Wade Meade
University Museum / Local Museum - 1982 39893

Rutherford NJ

Meadowlands Museum, 91 Crane Av, Rutherford, NJ 07070 - T: (201) 935-1175, Fax: (201) 935-9791. Head: Jackie Bunker-Lohrenz
Local Museum / Natural History Museum - 1961
Regional rocks and minerals, history 39894

Rutland VT

New England Maple Museum, POB 1615, Rutland, VT 05701 - T: (802) 483-9414, Fax: (802) 775-1650. Head: Thomas H. Olson, Dona A. Olson
Agriculture Museum - 1977
Local hist 39895

Rye NY

Rye Historical Society Museum, 1 Purchase St, Rye, NY 10580 - T: (914) 967-7588. Head: Elizabeth Reynolds, Phyllis Dillon
Local Museum - 1964 39896

Sabetha KS

Albany Historical Museum, 415 Grant, Sabetha, KS 66534 - T: (785) 284-3446, 284-3529. Head: Kenny Alderfer
Local Museum - 1965
Local history 39897

Sackets Harbor NY

Sackets Harbor Battlefield State Historic Site, 505 W Washington St, Sackets Harbor, NY 13685 - T: (315) 646-3634, Fax: (315) 646-1203. Head: Stephen R. Wallace
Military Museum / Open Air Museum - 1933 39898

Saco ME

Saco Museum, York Institute Museum, 371 Main St, Saco, ME 04072 - T: (207) 283-0684, Fax: (207) 283-0754, Internet: http://www.org/history. Head: Marilyn Solvay
Fine Arts Museum - 1867
Art 39899

Sacramento CA

California State Capitol Museum, State Capitol, Sacramento, CA 95814 - T: (916) 324-0333, Fax: (916) 445-3628, E-mail: st.capmus@cwo.com, Internet: http://www.assembly.ca.gov/Museum/VirTour.htm. Head: Jonathan Williams
Historical Museum - 1981
History 39900

California State Indian Museum, 2618 K St, Sacramento, CA 95816 - T: (916) 324-0971, Fax: (916) 322-5231, Internet: http://www.parks.ca.gov
Historical Museum - 1940
California Native American culture and hist 39901

California State Railroad Museum, 111 I St, Sacramento, CA 95814-2265 - T: (916) 445-7387, 323-8075, Fax: (916) 327-5655, E-mail: csrmlibrary@csrmf.org, Internet: http://www.csrmf.org
Science&Tech Museum - 1976
Railroad 39902

Crocker Art Museum, 216 O St, Sacramento, CA 95814 - T: (916) 264-5423, Fax: (916) 264-7372, E-mail: cam@cityofsacramento.org, Internet: http://www.crockerartmuseum.org. Head: Lial A. Jones
Fine Arts Museum - 1885
Art 39903

Discovery Museum, 101 I St, Sacramento, CA 95814 - T: (916) 264-7057, Fax: (916) 264-5100, Internet: http://www.thediscovery.org. Head: Evangeline Higginbotham
Historical Museum / Science&Tech Museum - 1994
History, science and technology 39904

Governor's Mansion State Historic Park, 1526 "H" St, Sacramento, CA 95814 - T: (916) 323-3047, Fax: (916) 322-4775, Internet: http://www.cal-parks.ca.gov. Head: Janelle Miller
Local Museum / Historical Museum / Historic Site - 1967
Local hist 39905

La Raza/Galeria Posada, 704 O St, Sacramento, CA 95814 - T: (916) 446-5133, Fax: (916) 446-5801, E-mail: marisa@galeriaposada.org, Internet: http://www.galeriaposada.org. Head: Gina Montoya, Marisa Gutiérez
Local Museum - 1972 39906

Sutter's Fort, 2701 L St, Sacramento, CA 95816 - T: (916) 445-4422, Fax: (916) 442-8613, E-mail: suttersfortelp@cwo.com, Internet: http://www.parks.ca.gov
Historical Museum / Historic Site - 1839
Local hist, pre gold rush 39907

Towe Auto Museum, 2200 Front St, Sacramento, CA 95818 - T: (916) 442-6802, Fax: (916) 442-2646, E-mail: info@toweautomuseum.org, Internet: http://www.toweautomuseum.org. Head: Kristin Hartley
Science&Tech Museum / Historical Museum - 1982
Transportation, coll of cars 1900 - 1970s 39908

University Art Center, 2601 J St, Sacramento, CA 95816 - T: (916) 443-5721
Public Gallery 39909

Wells Fargo History Museum, 400 Capitol Mall, Sacramento, CA 95814 - T: (916) 440-4161, Fax: (916) 492-2931, E-mail: kalnins@wellsfargo.com, Internet: http://www.wellsfargo-history.com
Historical Museum - 1992 39910

Wells Fargo History Museum Old Sacramento, 1000 Second St, Sacramento, CA 95814 - T: (916) 440-4263, Internet: http://www.wellsfargo-history.com
Historical Museum - 1984
Company hist 39911

Safety Harbor FL

Safety Harbor Museum of Regional History, 329 Bayshore Blvd S, Safety Harbor, FL 34695 - T: (727) 726-1668, Fax: (727) 725-9938, E-mail: shmuseum@ij.net, Internet: http://www.safety-harbor-museum.org. Head: Batty J. Quibell, Lisa Flamand
Historical Museum / Archaeological Museum - 1970 39912

Safford AZ

Discovery Park, 1651 Discovery Park Blvd, Safford, AZ 85546 - T: (520) 428-6260, Fax: (520) 428-8081, E-mail: discover@discoverypark.com, Internet: http://www.discoverypark.com. Head: Ed Sawyer
Science&Tech Museum - 1995
Science 39913

Graham County Historical Museum, 808 8th Av, Safford, AZ 85546 - T: (520) 348-3212. Head: Russ Murdock, Betty Graham Lee
Local Museum - 1962
Local history 39914

Sag Harbor NY

Sag Harbor Whaling and Historical Museum, 200 Main St, Sag Harbor, NY 11963 - T: (516) 725-0770, Fax: (516) 725-0770, Internet: http://www.sagharborwhalingmuseum.org. Head: David H. Cory
Special Museum / Historical Museum - 1936 39915

Saginaw MI

Castle Museum of Saginaw County History, 500 Federal Av, Saginaw, MI 48607 - T: (517) 752-2861, Fax: (517) 752-1533. Head: Charles Hoover
Historical Museum - 1948
Regional history 39916

Saginaw Art Museum, 1126 N Michigan Av, Saginaw, MI 48602 - T: (517) 754-2491, Fax: (517) 754-9387, Internet: http://www.SaginawArtMuseum.org. Head: Sheila K. Redmann
Fine Arts Museum - 1947
Art, former residence of Clark L. Ring family, Charles Adams platt designed 39917

Saguache CO

Saguache County Museum, Hwy 285, Saguache, CO 81149 - T: (719) 655-2557. Head: Evelyn Croft
Local Museum - 1958
Pioneer site 39918

Saint Augustine FL

Castillo de San Marcos Museum, 1 S Castillo Dr, Saint Augustine, FL 32084 - T: (904) 829-6506, Fax: (904) 823-9388, E-mail: casa_administration@nps.gov. Head: Gordon J. Wilson
Historical Museum / Historic Site - 1935
Museum housed in 1672-95 restored Spanish Castillo de San Marcos 39919

Fort Matanzas, 8635 A1A S, Saint Augustine, FL 32086 - T: (904) 471-0116, 829-6506, Fax: (904) 471-7605. Head: Gordon J. Wilson
Historical Museum - 1935
Site of first European battle for control of New World 39920

Lightner Museum, 75 King St, Saint Augustine, FL 32085-0334 - T: (904) 824-2874, Fax: (904) 824-2712, E-mail: lightner@aug.com, Internet: http://www.lightnermuseum.org. Head: Robert W. Harper
Local Museum - 1948
Housed in 1887 Alcazar Hotel 39921

Oldest House Museum Complex, 14 Saint Francis St, Saint Augustine, FL 32084 - T: (904) 824-2872, Fax: (904) 824-2569, E-mail: oldhouse@aug.com, Internet: http://www.oldcity.com/oldhouse. Head: Taryn Rodriguez-Boette
Historical Museum / Military Museum - 1918
Military, Gonzalez-Alvarez House, Tovar House, Webb Museum of Florida history 39922

Saint Augustine Historical Society Museum, 271 Charlotte St, Saint Augustine, FL 32084 - T: (904) 824-2872, Fax: (909) -824-2569, E-mail: oldhouse@aug.com, Internet: http://www.oldcity.com/oldhouse. Head: Taryn Rodríguez-Boette
Local Museum - 1883
Local history - library 39923

Saint Augustine Lighthouse and Museum, 81 Lighthouse Av, Saint Augustine, FL 32080 - T: (904) 829-0745, Fax: (904) 808-1248, E-mail: staugl@aug.com, Internet: http://www.staugustine-lighthouse.com. Head: Kathy Allen Fleming
Historical Museum / Historic Site - 1988 39924

The Spanish Quarter Museum, 29 St George St, Saint Augustine, FL 32084 - T: (904) 825-6830, Fax: (904) 825-6874, E-mail: sqmuse@aug.com. Head: Chuck Dale
Folklore Museum - 1959
Restored village, traditional 18th c life skills 39925

World Golf Hall of Fame, 1 World Golf Pl, Saint Augustine, FL 32082 - T: (904) 940-4000, Fax: (904) 940-4394, Internet: http://www.wgv.com. Head: Bruce Lucker
Special Museum - 1974 39926

Saint Bonaventure NY

F.Donald Kenney Museum and Art Study Wing, Saint Bonaventure University, Saint Bonaventure, NY 14778 - T: (716) 375-4030, Fax: (716) 375-2690, E-mail: bracker@sbu.edu, Internet: http://www.sbu.edu. Head: Barbara Racker
Fine Arts Museum / University Museum - 1856 39927

Saint Bonaventure Art Collection → F.Donald Kenney Museum and Art Study Wing

Saint Charles IL

Saint Charles Heritage Center, 2 E Main St, Saint Charles, IL 60174 - T: (630) 584-6967, Fax: (630) 377-4487, E-mail: stcmuseum@aol.com, Internet: http://www.stchistory.http://www.org. Head: Brian Henry, Jeanne Schultz Angel
Local Museum - 1940
Local hist 39928

Saint Charles MO

First Missouri State Capitol, 200-216 S Main St, Saint Charles, MO 63301 - T: (636) 940-3322, Fax: (636) 940-3324, E-mail: Dspfrst@mail.DNR.state.mo.us, Internet: http://www.mostateparks.com/firstcapitol.htm. Head: David Klostermeier
Historical Museum - 1971 39929

Saint Charles County Historical Society Museum, 101 S Main St, Saint Charles, MO 63301-2802 - T: (636) 946-9828, E-mail: scchs@mail.win.org, Internet: http://www.win.org/library/other/historical_society. Head: Dr. Daniel T. Brown
Local Museum - 1956 39930

Saint Cloud MN

Atwood Memorial Center, Saint Cloud State University, 720 Fourth Av S, Saint Cloud, MN 56301 - T: (320) 255-4636, Fax: (320) 529-1669, Internet: http://www.stcloudstate.edu/~atwood. Head: Janice Courtney
Fine Arts Museum - 1967
Central Minnesota artists 39931

Evelyn Payne Hatcher Museum of Anthropology, 213A Stewart Hall, Saint Cloud State University, Saint Cloud, MN 56301 - T: (320) 255-2294, Fax: (320) 654-5198
Ethnology Museum / Archaeological Museum - 1972 39932

Kiehle Gallery, Saint Cloud State University, 720 Fourth Av S, Saint Cloud, MN 56301 - T: (320) 255-4283, Fax: (320) 529-1669, Internet: http://www.stcloudstate.edu/!utb. Head: Joseph Akin
Fine Arts Museum
Paintings, prints, sculpture, photographs 39933

Stearns History Museum, 235 S 33 Av, Saint Cloud, MN 56301-3752 - T: (320) 253-8424, Fax: (320) 253-2172, E-mail: info@stearns-museum.org, Internet: http://www.stearns-museum.org. Head: David F. Ebnet
Historical Museum - 1936 39934

Saint Croix VI

Christiansted National Historic Site, Danish Custom House, Kingswharf-Christiansted, Saint Croix, VI 00821 - T: (809) 773-1460, Fax: (809) 773-5995. Head: Joel A. Tutein
Local Museum - 1962
Local hist 39935

Saint Francis SD

Buechel Memorial Lakota Museum, Saint Francis Indian Mission, 350 S Oak St, Saint Francis, SD 57572 - T: (605) 747-2745, Fax: (605) 747-5057. Head: J. Charmayne Young
Ethnology Museum / Folklore Museum - 1915
Lakota Indian culture 39936

Saint George UT

Brigham Young's Winter Home, 67 West 200 North, Saint George, UT 84770 - T: (801) 673-5181, 673-2517, Fax: (801) 652-9589
Local Museum - 1975
Historic house, Brigham Young winter home 39937

Saint Helens OR

Columbia County Historical Society Museum, Old County Courthouse, Saint Helens, OR 97051 - T: (503) 397-3868, Fax: (503) 397-7257. Head: R.J. Bob Brown
Local Museum - 1969 39938

Saint Ignace MI

Father Marquette National Memorial and Museum, 720 Church St, Saint Ignace, MI 49781 - T: (906) 643-8620, 643-9394, Fax: (906) 643-9329. Head: Wayne Burnett
Religious Arts Museum - 1980
Local hist 39939

Saint Ignatius MT

Flathead Indian Museum, 1 Museum Ln, Saint Ignatius, MT 59865 - T: (406) 745-2951, Fax: (406) 745-2961. Head: Jeanine Allard
Ethnology Museum - 1974 39940

Saint James MO

Maramec Museum, Maramec Spring Park, 21880 Maramec Spring Dr, Saint James, MO 65559 - T: (573) 265-7124, Fax: (573) 265-8770, E-mail: tjf@tigernet.missouri.org. Head: Danny Marshall
Historical Museum / Folklore Museum / Science&Tech Museum - 1971 39941

Saint Johns MI

Clinton County Historical Society Museum, 106 Maple Av, Saint Johns, MI 48879 - T: (517) 224-2894, 224-7402. Head: Catherine Rumbaugh
Historical Museum - 1978
Local hist 39942

Saint Johnsbury VT

Fairbanks Museum and Planetarium, 1302 Main St, Saint Johnsbury, VT 05819 - T: (802) 748-2372, Fax: (802) 748-1893, E-mail: fairbanks.museum@connriver.net, Internet: http://www.fairbanksmuseum.org. Head: Charles C. Browne
Local Museum / Natural History Museum - 1889
Local hist, ethnological coll 39943

Saint Johnsville NY

Fort Klock Historic Restoration, Rte 5, Saint Johnsville, NY 13452 - T: (518) 568-7779. Head: Alice Edmunds
Local Museum - 1964 39944

Saint Joseph MI

The Curious Kids' Museum, 415 Lake Blvd, Saint Joseph, MI 49085 - T: (616) 983-2543, Fax: (616) 983-3317, E-mail: ckm@curiouskidsmuseum.org, Internet: http://www.curiouskidsmuseum.org. Head: Patricia Adams
Science&Tech Museum / Historical Museum - 1988
Science, history, culture, technology 39945

Krasl Art Center, 707 Lake Blvd, Saint Joseph, MI 49085-1398 - T: (616) 983-0271, Fax: (616) 983-0275, E-mail: info@krasl.org, Internet: http://www.krasl.org. Head: Darwin R. Davis
Fine Arts Museum - 1963
Sculpture 39946

Saint Joseph MN

Benedicta Arts Center, College of Saint Benedict, 37 S College Av, Saint Joseph, MN 56374 - T: (612) 363-5777, Fax: (612) 363-6097, E-mail: amthompson@csbsju.edu. Head: Anna M. Thompson
Fine Arts Museum / University Museum - 1963
Contemporary coll of crafts, drawings, paintings, prints and sculpture, East Asian and African colls 39947

Saint Joseph MO

Albrecht-Kemper Museum of Art, 2818 Frederick Av, Saint Joseph, MO 64506 - T: (816) 233-7003, Fax: (816) 233-3413, E-mail: akma@albrecht-kemper.org, Internet: http://www.albrecht-kemper.org. Head: Terry Oldham
Fine Arts Museum - 1914
Paintings, drawings, prints, sculpture 39948

Glore Psychiatric Museum, 3406 Frederick Av, Saint Joseph, MO 64506 - T: (816) 387-2310, Fax: (816) 387-2170, E-mail: glore_museum@mail.dmh.state.mo.us. Head: Scott Clark
Special Museum - 1967 39949

Jesse James Home Museum, 12 and Penn Sts, Saint Joseph, MO 64502 - T: (816) 232-8206, Fax: (816) 232-8206, Internet: http://www.st.joseph.net/ponyexpress. Head: Gary Chilcote
Historic Site - 1939
1879 house where Jesse James was killed in 1882 39950

Patee House Museum, 1202 Penn St, Saint Joseph, MO 64502 - T: (816) 232-8206, Fax: (816) 232-8206, Internet: http://www.stjoseph.net/ponyexpress. Head: Gary Chilcote
Science&Tech Museum - 1964
Pony Express headquarters, trains, cars, fire trucks, antique town 39951

Pony Express Museum, 914 Penn St, Saint Joseph, MO 64503 - T: (816) 279-5059, (800) 530-5940, Fax: (816) 233-9370, Internet: http://www.ponyexpress.org. Head: Richard N. DeShon, F. Burns McAndrew
Local Museum - 1959 39952

Saint Joseph Museum, 11th and Charles Sts, Saint Joseph, MO 64502 - T: (816) 232-8471, Fax: (816) 232-8482, E-mail: sjm@stjosephmuseum.org, Internet: http://www.stjosephmuseum.org. Head: Richard A. Nolf
Historical Museum / Ethnology Museum / Natural History Museum - 1927
American Indian art,anthropology, archaeology, ethnology, costumes, Eskimo art, native American art - library 39953

Saint Leonard MD

Jefferson Patterson Museum, 10515 Mackall Rd, Saint Leonard, MD 20685 - T: (410) 586-8500, Fax: (410) 586-0080, E-mail: jppm@dhcd.state.md.us. Head: Richard Fischer, Michael A. Smolek
Local Museum - 1983
Cultural heritage of people living in the Chesapeake Bay region, archaeology, agriculture, local history 39954

Saint Louis MO

Atrium Gallery, 7638 Forsyth Blvd, Saint Louis, MO 63105 - T: (314) 726-1066, Fax: (314) 726-5444, E-mail: atrium@earthlink.net, Internet: http://www.gallery-guide.com/gallery/atrium/. Head: Carolyn P. Miles
Public Gallery / Folklore Museum - 1986 39955

Boatmen's National Bank Art Collection, 1 Boatmen's Plaza, 800 Market St, Saint Louis, MO 63101 - T: (888) 279-3121
Fine Arts Museum
Political series by Caleb Bingham, transportation series by Oscar E. Berninghause, watercolours 39956

Campbell House Museum, 1508 Locust St, Saint Louis, MO 63103 - T: (314) 421-0325, Fax: (314) 421-0113, E-mail: campbellhousemuseum@worldnet.att.net. Head: Janice K. Broderick
Decorative Arts Museum / Historical Museum - 1943 39957

Chatillon-DeMenil Mansion, 3352 DeMenil Pl, Saint Louis, MO 63118 - T: (314) 771-5828, Fax: (314) 771-3475, E-mail: demenil@stlouis.missouri.org. Head: Robert Printz, Graff Marcia
Local Museum - 1965 39958

Concordia Historical Institute Museum, 801 DeMun Av, Saint Louis, MO 63105 - T: (314) 505-7900, Fax: (314) 505-7901, E-mail: chi@chi.lcms.org, Internet: http://chi.lcms.org. Head: Daniel Preus
Religious Arts Museum - 1927
History of American Lutheranism 39959

Craft Alliance Gallery, 6640 Delmar Blvd, Saint Louis, MO 63130 - T: (314) 725-1177, Fax: (314) 725-2068, E-mail: tzmmyp@craftalliance.org, Internet: http://www.craftalliance.org. Head: Sharon M. McPherron
Fine Arts Museum / Decorative Arts Museum - 1962 39960

The Dinosaur Museum, Science Center, Saint Louis, MO 63110 - T: (314) 289-4400
Natural History Museum - 1991 39961

Eugene Field House and Saint Louis Toy Museum, 634 S Broadway, Saint Louis, MO 63102 - T: (314) 421-4689, Fax: (314) 588-9328, E-mail: efhouse@swbell.org. Head: William Piper, Frances Kerber Walrond
Local Museum / Decorative Arts Museum - 1936 39962

The Forum for Contemporary Art, 3540 Washington Av, Saint Louis, MO 63103 - T: (314) 535-4660, Fax: (314) 535-1226, E-mail: forum@inlink.com, Internet: http://www.forumart.org. Head: Elizabeth Wright Millard
Public Gallery - 1980
Photographs, paintings 39963

Gallery 210, University of Missouri Saint Louis, 210 Lucas Hall, Saint Louis, MO 63121 - T: (314) 516-5000, Fax: (314) 516-5816. Head: Terry Suhre
Fine Arts Museum - 1972
Contemporary art 39964

General Daniel Bissell House, 10225 Bellefontaine Rd, Saint Louis, MO 63137 - T: (314) 868-0973, 554-5790, Fax: (314) 868-8435, E-mail: jd_magurany@stlouisco.com, Internet: http://st-louiscountyparks.com. Head: J.D. Magurany
Historic Site - 1960
Historic house 39965

International Bowling Museum and Hall of Fame, 111 Stadium Plaza, Saint Louis, MO 63102 - T: (314) 231-6340, Fax: (314) 231-4054, E-mail: bowling@anet-stl.com, Internet: http://www.bowlingmuseum.com. Head: Gerald W. Baltz
Special Museum - 1977 39966

Jefferson Barracks, 533 Grant Rd, Saint Louis, MO 63125-4121 - T: (314) 544-5714, 544-5790, Fax: (314) 638-5009, E-mail: jd_magurany@stlouisco.com, Internet: http://www.st-louiscountyparks.comw/jb.html. Head: J.D. Magurany
Military Museum - 1826
Military post - Gen. Daniel Bissell house, Fort Belle 39967

Jefferson National Expansion Memorial, 11 N Fourth St, Saint Louis, MO 63102 - T: (314) 655-1600, Fax: (314) 655-1639, E-mail: -jeff_superintendent@nps.gov, Internet: http://www.nps.gov/jeff. Head: David Grove
Historical Museum - 1935 39968

Laumeier Sculpture Park and Museum, 12580 Rott Rd, Saint Louis, MO 63127 - T: (314) 821-1209, Fax: (314) 821-1248, E-mail: info@laumeier.org, Internet: http://www.laumeier.org. Head: Clara Coleman
Fine Arts Museum - 1976
Contemporary sculpture coll 39969

Magic House, Saint Louis Children's Museum, 516 S Kirkwood Rd, Saint Louis, MO 63122 - T: (314) 822-8900, Fax: (314) 822-8930, Internet: http://www.magichouse.com. Head: Herb Jones, Elizabeth Fitzgerald, Kelley Jay
Special Museum - 1979 39970

Missouri Historical Society Museum, Lindell and De Baliviere, Saint Louis, MO 63112-0040 - T: (314) 746-4599, Fax: (314) 454-3162, E-mail: info@mohistory.org, Internet: http://www.mohistory.org. Head: Dr. Robert R. Archibald, Myron Freedman, Martha Clevenger, Eric Sandweiss
Historical Museum - 1866 39971

Morton J. May Foundation Gallery, Maryville University, 13550 Conway Rd, Saint Louis, MO 63141 - T: (314) 529-9300, 529-9381, Fax: (314) 529-9940, E-mail: nrice@maryville.edu. Head: Nancy N. Rice
Fine Arts Museum / University Museum
American paintings 39972

Museum of the Dog, 1721 S Mason Rd, Saint Louis, MO 63131 - T: (314) 821-3647, Fax: (314) 821-7381, E-mail: dogarts@aol.com. Head: Barbara Jedda McNab
Fine Arts Museum - 1981
Fine arts 39973

Museum of Transportation, 3015 Barrett Station Rd, Saint Louis, MO 63122 - T: (314) 965-7998, Fax: (314) 965-0242. Head: Donald Morice, James Worton
Science&Tech Museum - 1944 39974

Old Cathedral Museum, 209 Walnut, Saint Louis, MO 63102 - T: (314) 231-3251, Fax: (314) 231-4280, Internet: http://www.catholic-forum.com/stlouisking/. Head: Bernard Sandheinrich
Religious Arts Museum - 1970 39975

Saint Louis Art Museum, 1 Fine Arts Dr, Forest Park, Saint Louis, MO 63110-1380 - T: (314) 721-0067, Fax: (314) 721-6172, E-mail: infotech@slam.org, Internet: http://www.slam.org. Head: Brent Benjamin
Fine Arts Museum - 1906
Prints, drawings, photographs, Oceanian, African, Pre-Columbian and American Indian objects, paintings, sculpture, European decorative art, Chinese bronzes and porcelain - Richardson Memorial Library 39976

Saint Louis Artists' Guild Museum, 2 Oak Knoll Park, Saint Louis, MO 63105 - T: (314) 727-6266, Fax: (314) 727-9190, Internet: http://www.stlouisartistsguild.org. Head: Bill Wilson, Anne Murphy
Fine Arts Museum - 1886 39977

Saint Louis Science Center Museum, 5050 Oakland Av, Saint Louis, MO 63110 - T: (314) 289-4400, Fax: (314) 289-4420, E-mail: gjasper@slsc.org, Internet: http://www.slc.org. Head: Douglas R. King
Public Gallery / Science&Tech Museum - 1959 39978

Soldiers' Memorial Military Museum, 1315 Chestnut St, Saint Louis, MO 63103 - T: (314) 622-4550, Fax: (314) 622-4237. Head: Ralph D. Wiechert
Military Museum - 1938 39979

Washington University Gallery of Art, Forsyth and Skinker Blvds, Saint Louis, MO 63130 - T: (314) 935-4523, Fax: (314) 935-7282, E-mail: wuga@aismail.wustl.edu, Internet: http://galleryofart.wustl.edu. Head: Dr. Mark S. Weil
Fine Arts Museum / University Museum - 1881
Modern artists incl Miro, Ernst, Picasso, Leger, Moore, old masters, 19th-20th c paintings, sculpture, drawings, prints 39980

Saint Marks FL

San Marcos de Apalache Historic Site, 148 Old Fort Rd, Saint Marks, FL 32355-0027 - T: (850) 922-6007, Fax: (850) 488-0366, E-mail: sanmarcos@nettally.com, Internet: http://www.dep.state.fl.us/parks. Head: Virginia Wetherell, Fran P. Mainella
Historical Museum / Historic Site - 1964
Second-oldest fortification in Florida 39981

Saint Martinville LA

Oliver House Museum, 1200 N Main St, Saint Martinville, LA 70582 - T: (800) 677-2900, Fax: (318) 394-3754, E-mail: longfellow@crt.state.la.usa
Historical Museum - 1931
History, old plantation house of French and Carribean architecture 39982

Saint Mary City MD

Dwight Frederick Boyden Gallery, Saint Mary's College of Maryland, Saint Mary's College of Maryland, Saint Mary City, MD 20686 - T: (301) 862-0226, 862-0246, Fax: (301) 862-0958, E-mail: vcpage@osprey.smcm.edu, Internet: http://www.smcm.edu/academics/gallery/. Head: Casey Page
Fine Arts Museum / University Museum - 1839
Art gallery 39983

Saint Marys PA

Historical Society of Saint Marys and Benzinger Township Museum, Municipal Building, Erie Av, Saint Marys, PA 15857 - T: (814) 834-6525. Head: Richard Dornisch
Local Museum - 1960
Local hist 39984

Saint Mary's City MD

Historic Saint Mary's City, Rte. 5, Saint Mary's City, MD 20686 - T: (301) 862-0960, Fax: (301) 862-0968, E-mail: kbstanford@osprey.smcm.edu, Internet: http://www.smcm.edu/hsmc/. Head: Martin E. Sullivan Chandler
Special Museum - 1966
Outdoor living history 39985

Saint Matthews SC

Calhoun County Museum, 303 Butler St, Saint Matthews, SC 29135 - T: (803) 874-3964, Fax: (803) 874-4790, E-mail: calmus@oburg.net. Head: Debbie Roland
Local Museum - 1954
Local hist 39986

Saint Michaels MD

Chesapeake Bay Maritime Museum, Navy Point, Saint Michaels, MD 21663 - T: (410) 745-2916, Fax: (410) 745-6088, E-mail: letters@cbmm.org, Internet: http://www.cbmm.org. Head: John R. Valliant, Melissa McLeod
Historical Museum - 1965
Regional maritime history 39987

Saint Paul MN

Alexander Ramsey House, 265 S Exchange St, Saint Paul, MN 55102 - T: (612) 296-8760, Fax: (612) 296-0100, E-mail: janet.budack@mnhs.org, Internet: http://www.mnhs.org. Head: Janet Budack
Local Museum / Decorative Arts Museum - 1964
Late 19th-century upper class Victorian mansion 39988

American Museum of Asmat Art, 3510 Vivian Av, Saint Paul, MN 55126-3852 - T: (651) 287-1132, Fax: (651) 287-1130, E-mail: rgambone@crosier.org, Internet: http://www.asmat.org. Head: Robert L. Gambone
Fine Arts Museum / Ethnology Museum - 1974
Ethnological art 39989

College of Visual Arts Gallery, 344 Summit Av, Saint Paul, MN 55102 - T: (651) 290-9379, Fax: (651) 224-8854. Head: Colleen Mullins
Fine Arts Museum - 1948
Contemporary art from local artists 39990

Goldstein Museum, c/o University of Minnesota, Dept. of Design, 244 McNeal Hall, 1985 Buford Av, Saint Paul, MN 55108 - T: (612) 624-7434, Fax: (612) 624-2750, E-mail: lshen@che2.che.umn.edu, Internet: http://goldstein.che.umn.edu. Head: Dr. Lindsay Shen
Decorative Arts Museum / University Museum - 1976
Historic costumes, 20th c designer garments, decorative arts, furniture, glass, metal, ceramics, textiles 39991

Hamline University Galleries, Dept of Art, Hamline University, 1536 Hewitt Av, Saint Paul, MN 55104 - T: (651) 523-2386, Fax: (651) 523-3066, E-mail: llasansky@gw.hamline.edu, Internet: http://www.hamline.edu/depts/art. Head: Leonardo Lasansky
Fine Arts Museum / University Museum - 1850
Modern works 39992

Historic Fort Snelling, Fort Snelling History Center, Saint Paul, MN 55111 - T: (612) 726-1171, Fax: (612) 725-2429, E-mail: ftsnelling@mnhs.org, Internet: http://www.mnhs.org/places/sites/hfs
Military Museum / Open Air Museum - 1970
Military hist 39993

James J. Hill House, 240 Summit Av, Saint Paul, MN 55102 - T: (651) 296-8205, Fax: (651) 297-5655, Internet: http://www.mnhs.org. Head: Craig Johnson
Local Museum - 1978
Historic house 39994

Julian H. Sleeper House, 66 Saint Albans St, S, Saint Paul, MN 55105 - T: (651) 225-1505. Head: Dr. Seth C. Hawkins
Decorative Arts Museum - 1993
Eastlake-Vernacular House, moved to present site in 1911, President Garfield memorabilia, furniture, pottery 39995

Macalester College Art Gallery, 1600 Grand Av, Saint Paul, MN 55105 - T: (651) 696-6416, Fax: (651) 696-6266, E-mail: gallery@macalester.edu, Internet: http://www.macalester.edu. Head: Devin A. Colman
Fine Arts Museum / Decorative Arts Museum / University Museum - 1964
Regional artists, Asian and British ceramics, African art 39996

Minnesota Children's Museum, 10 W Seventh St, Saint Paul, MN 55102 - T: (651) 225-6001, Fax: (651) 225-6006. Head: Carleen Rhodes
Ethnology Museum - 1979 39997

Minnesota Historical Society Museum, 345 Kellogg Blvd W, Saint Paul, MN 55102-1906 - T: (651) 296-6126, (800) 657-3773, Fax: (651) 297-3343, E-mail: fname./name@mnhs.org, Internet: http://www.mnhs.org. Head: Nina M. Archabal
Historical Museum / Historic Site - 1849 39998

Minnesota Museum of American Art, 505 Landmark Center, 75 W Fifth St, Saint Paul, MN 55102-1486 - T: (651) 292-4355, Fax: (651) 292-4340, E-mail: mmaa@mtn.org, Internet: http://www.mtn.org/mmaa. Head: Bruce Lilly
Fine Arts Museum - 1927
American art, Paul Manship, contemporary art of Upper Midwest, 19th-20th c and native art 39999

Science Museum of Minnesota, 120 Kellogg Blvd W, Saint Paul, MN 55102-1208 - T: (612) 221-9444, Fax: (612) 221-4777, E-mail: postmaster@sci.mus.mn.us, Internet: http://www.sci.mus.mn.us. Head: Paul Maurer
Local Museum / Natural History Museum / Science&Tech Museum - 1907 40000

Saint Paul OR

Robert Newell House, DAR Museum, 8089 Champoeg Rd NE, Saint Paul, OR 97137 - T: (503) 678-5537
Local Museum / Historic Site - 1959 40001

Saint Peter MN

E. St. Julien Cox House, 500 S Washington, Saint Peter, MN 56082 - T: (507) 931-2160, Fax: (507) 931-0172, E-mail: nicolletco@aol.com, Internet: http://www.nchs.st-peter.mn.us/. Head: Carl Aanonsen, Wayne E. Allen
Historical Museum - 1971 40002

Treaty Site History Center, 1851 N Minnesota Av, Saint Peter, MN 56082 - T: (507) 931-2160, Fax: (507) 931-0172, E-mail: nicolletco@aol.com, Internet: http://www.nchs.st_peter.mn.us/. Head: Wayne E. Allen
Historical Museum - 1928 40003

Saint Petersburg FL

Florida Holocaust Museum, 55 5th St, Saint Petersburg, FL 33701 - T: (813) 820-0100 ext 221, Fax: (813) 821-8435, E-mail: ldwasser@flholocaustmuseum.org, Internet: http://www.flholocaustmuseum.org. Head: Larry Wasser
Historical Museum - 1989
History 40004

Museum of Fine Arts Saint Petersburg, Florida, 255 Beach Dr, NE, Saint Petersburg, FL 33701 - T: (727) 896-2667, Fax: (727) 894-4638, E-mail: michaelm@fine-arts.org, Internet: http://www.fine-arts.org. Head: Michael Milkovich
Fine Arts Museum - 1961
Art 40005

Saint Petersburg Museum of History, 335 Second Av NE, Saint Petersburg, FL 33701 - T: (727) 894-1052, E-mail: spmh@ij.net, Internet: http://www.ij.net/spmh/. Head: Sam Bond
Local Museum - 1920
Local history 40006

Salvador Dali Museum, 1000 Third St S, Saint Petersburg, FL 33701 - T: (813) 823-3767, Fax: (813) 894-6068, E-mail: info@salvadordalimuseum.org, Internet: http://www.salvadordalimuseum.org. Head: Marshall Rousseau
Fine Arts Museum - 1954 40007

Saint Simons Island GA

The Arthur J. Moore Methodist Museum, Arthur Moore Dr, Saint Simons Island, GA 31522 - T: (912) 638-4050, Fax: (912) 634-0642, E-mail: methmuse@darientel.net. Head: Mary L. Vice
Religious Arts Museum - 1965
Religious, nr Oglethorpe, John and Charles Wesley's activities in 1736 40008

Fort Frederica, Rte 9, Saint Simons Island, GA 31522 - T: (912) 638-3639, Fax: (912) 638-3639, E-mail: -fofr_visitor_center@nps.gov, Internet: http://www.nps.gov. Head: Mike Tennent
Historical Museum - 1936 40009

The Glynn Art Association Museum, 319 Mallery St, Saint Simons Island, GA 31522 - T: (912) 638-8770, Fax: (912) 634-2787, E-mail: glynnart@pierimage.com, Internet: http://www.glynnart.org. Head: Mary T. Garrison, Lynda Dalton-Gallagher
Fine Arts Museum / Public Gallery - 1948
Art 40010

Museum of Coastal History → Saint Simons Island Lighthouse Museum

Saint Simons Island Lighthouse Museum, 101 12th St, Saint Simons Island, GA 31522-0636 - T: (912) 638-4666, Fax: (912) 638-6609, E-mail: ssilight@darientel.net, Internet: http://www.saintsimonslighthouse.org. Head: Patricia A. Morris
Local Museum / Historical Museum - 1965
History, civil war 40011

Sainte Genevieve MO

Bolduc House Museum, 125 S Main St, Sainte Genevieve, MO 63670 - T: (573) 883-3105. Head: Lorraine Stange
Local Museum - 1770 40012

Felix Valle State Historic Site, 198 Merchant St, Sainte Genevieve, MO 63670 - T: (573) 883-7102, Fax: (573) 883-9630, E-mail: dspvalle@mail.dnr.state.mo.us. Head: James Baker
Historic Site - 1970 40013

Sainte Genevieve Museum, Merchant and DuBourg Sts, Sainte Genevieve, MO 63670 - T: (573) 883-3461. Head: James Baker, Ruby A. Stephens
Local Museum - 1935 40014

Salamanca NY

Seneca-Iroquois National Museum, 794-814 Broad St, Allegany Indian Reservation, Salamanca, NY 14779 - T: (716) 945-1738, Fax: (716) 945-1760, E-mail: senirogm@localnet.com, Internet: http://www.senecamuseum.org. Head: Michele Dean Stock
Ethnology Museum - 1977 40015

Salem IN

Stevens Museum, 307 E Market St, Salem, IN 47167 - T: (812) 883-6495. Head: Willie Harlen
Local Museum / Open Air Museum - 1897
Local history, 1824 John Hay birthplace, pionner village - library 40016

Salem MA

The House of the Seven Gables, 54 Turner St, Salem, MA 01970 - T: (978) 744-0991, Fax: (978) 741-4350, E-mail: postmaster@7gables.org, Internet: http://www.7gables.org. Head: Stanley Brechfielt
Historical Museum / Open Air Museum - 1910
17th, 18th and 19th-century architecture, Nathaniel Hawthorne 40017

Peabody Essex Museum, E India Sq, Salem, MA 01970 - T: (800) 745-4054, 745-9500, Fax: (978) 744-6776, E-mail: pem@pem.org, Internet: http://www.pem.org. Head: Dan L. Monroe
Fine Arts Museum / Local Museum - 1799
Asian, Oceanic, African arts and cultures, native American art and archaeology, maritime arts and history, architecture, decorative arts, natural history - library 40018

Salem 1630 Pioneer Village, Forest River Park, West Av, Salem, MA 01970 - T: (978) 745-0525, 744-0991, Fax: (978) 741-4350. Head: Thomas Neel, K. David Gross
Local Museum / Open Air Museum - 1930
Reproduction of a fishing village 40019

Salem Maritime National Historic Site, 174 Derby St, Salem, MA 01970 - T: (978) 740-1650, Fax: (978) 740-1655, Internet: http://www.nps.gov/sama
Historic Site - 1937
Maritime, commerce and World trade 40020

Salem Witch Museum, 19-1/2 Washington Sq N, Salem, MA 01970 - T: (978) 744-1692, Fax: (978) 745-4414, E-mail: facts@salemwitchmuseum.com, Internet: http://www.salemwitchmuseum.com. Head: Patricia MacLeod
Historical Museum - 1971
History 40021

Salem NJ

Salem County Historical Society Museum, 79-83 Market St, Salem, NJ 08079 - T: (609) 935-5004, Fax: (609) 935-0728, Internet: http://www.salemcounty.com/historicalsociety. Head: Kathleen M. McCarthy, James F. Turk
Local Museum - 1884 40022

Salem OH

Salem Historical Society Museum, 208 S Broadway Av, Salem, OH 44460 - T: (330) 337-8514, Internet: http://www.salemohio.com/historicalsociety/. Head: Carolyn Caldwell, Josephine Rupe
Local Museum - 1971 40023

Salem OR

A.C. Gilbert's Discovery Village, 116 Marion St NE, Salem, OR 97301-3437 - T: (503) 371-3631, Fax: (503) 316-3485, E-mail: info@acgilbert.org, Internet: http://www.acgilbert.org. Head: Pamela Vorachek
Special Museum - 1987 40024

Bush House Museum and Bush Barn Art Center, 600 Mission St SE, Salem, OR 97302 - T: (503) 581-2228, Fax: (503) 371-3342, Internet: http://www.salemart.org. Head: Julie Larson
Fine Arts Museum / Local Museum - 1919 40025

The Gilbert House Children's Museum → A.C. Gilbert's Discovery Village

Mission Mill Museum, 1313 Mill St, Salem, OR 97301 - T: (503) 585-7012, Fax: (503) 588-9902, E-mail: missionm@teleport.com, Internet: http://www.missionmill.org
Local Museum - 1964
Local hist 40026

Salem VA

Salem Museum, 801 E Main St, Salem, VA 24153 - T: (540) 389-6760, E-mail: salemmuseum@intrlink.com, Internet: http://www.intrlink.com/shs/. Head: Inez Good, Mary Hill
Local Museum - 1992 40027

Salida CO

Salida Museum, 406 1/2 W Rainbow Blvd, Salida, CO 81201 - T: (719) 539-4602. Head: Judy Micklich
Local Museum - 1954
Local hist 40028

Salina KS

Salina Art Center, 242 S Santa Fe, Salina, KS 67402-0743 - T: (785) 827-1431, Fax: (785) 827-0686, E-mail: artcentr@midusa.net, Internet: http://www.salinaartcenter.org. Head: Wendy Moshier
Fine Arts Museum - 1978
Art 40029

Smoky Hill Museum, 211 W Iron Av, Salina, KS 67401 - T: (785) 309-5776, Fax: (785) 826-7414, E-mail: dee.harris@salina.org, Internet: http://www.smokyhillmuseum.org. Head: Dee Harris
Historical Museum - 1983
History 40030

Salinas CA

National Steinbeck Center, 1 Main St, Salinas, CA 93901 - T: (831) 796-3833, Fax: (831) 796-3828, E-mail: steinbeck@steinbeck.org, Internet: http://www.steinbeck.org. Head: Kim Greer
Local Museum / Special Museum / Agriculture Museum - 1983
Literature, local hist, agriculture 40031

Salisbury MD

Salisbury State University Galleries, 1101 Camden Av, Salisbury State University, Salisbury, MD 21801 - T: (410) 543-6271, 543-6000, Fax: (410) 548-3002, E-mail: kabasile@ssu.edu. Head: Kenneth Basile
Fine Arts Museum / University Museum - 1962
Art 40032

Salisbury University → The Ward Museum of Wildfowl Art

The Ward Museum of Wildfowl Art, 909 S Schumaker Dr, Salisbury, MD 21804-8743 - T: (410) 742-4988, Fax: (410) 742-3107, E-mail: ward@wardmuseum.org, Internet: http://www.wardmuseum.org. Head: Kenneth A. Basile
Fine Arts Museum - 1976
Art 40033

Salisbury NC

Horizons Unlimited Supplementary Educational Center, 1636 Parkview Circle, Salisbury, NC 28144 - T: (704) 639-3004, Fax: (704) 639-3015. Head: Cynthia B. Osterhus
Local Museum / Natural History Museum - 1967 40034

Rowan Museum, 202 N Main St, Salisbury, NC 28144 - T: (704) 633-5946, Fax: (704) 633-9858, E-mail: rowanmuseum@tarheel.net, Internet: http://www.tarheel.net/rowanmuseum. Head: Edward Norvell, Kaye Brown Hirst
Historical Museum - 1953 40035

Waterworks Visual Arts Center, 1 Water St, Salisbury, NC 28144 - T: (704) 636-1882, Fax: (704) 636-1895, E-mail: waterworks@salisbury.net, Internet: http://www.waterworks.org. Head: Jane Gamwell, Denny H. Mecham
Fine Arts Museum / Public Gallery - 1959 40036

Salisbury NH

Salisbury Historical Society Museum, Salisbury Heights, Rte 4, Salisbury, NH 03268 - T: (603) 648-2774
Local Museum - 1966 40037

Sallisaw OK

Sequoyah Cabin, Rte 1, Box 141, Sallisaw, OK 74955 - T: (918) 775-2413, Fax: (918) 775-2413, E-mail: SeqCabin@ipa.net. Head: Bob Blackburn
Local Museum - 1936 40038

Salmon ID

Lemhi County Historical Museum, 210 Main, Salmon, ID 83467 - T: (208) 756-3342
Local Museum - 1963
Local history 40039

Salt Lake City UT

Atrium Gallery, 209 E 500 S, Salt Lake City, UT 84111 - T: (801) 524-8200
Public Gallery 40040

Beehive House, 67 E South Temple, Salt Lake City, UT 84111 - T: (801) 240-2681. Head: Margaret Adams
Religious Arts Museum - 1961
Historic house, Brigham Young's residence and office 40041

Chase Home Museum of Utah Folk Art, Liberty Park, Salt Lake City, UT - T: (801) 533-5760, 236-7555, Fax: (801) 533-4202, E-mail: cedison@dced.st.ut.us, Internet: http://www.arts.utah.org. Head: Bonnie Stephens
Folklore Museum - 1986
Folk art 40042

The Children's Museum of Utah, 840 N 300 West, Salt Lake City, UT 84103 - T: (801) 328-3383, Fax: (801) 328-3384, Internet: http://www.childmuseum.org
Special Museum - 1979 40043

Daughters of Utah Pioneers Pioneer Memorial Museum, 300 N Main St, Salt Lake City, UT 84103-1699 - T: (801) 538-1050, Fax: (801) 538-1119, E-mail: dupmuseum@juno.com
Local Museum - 1901
Pioneer hist 40044

Museum of Church History and Art, 45 N West Temple St, Salt Lake City, UT 84150-1003 - T: (801) 240-2299, Fax: (801) 240-5342, Internet: www.lds.org. Head: Glen M. Leonard
Religious Arts Museum - 1869
Religious art and hist 40045

Salt Lake Art Center, 20 S West Temple, Salt Lake City, UT 84101 - T: (801) 328-4201, Fax: (801) 322-4323. Head: Ric Collier
Fine Arts Museum - 1931
Art 40046

This Is The Place Heritage Park, 2601 Sunnyside Av, Salt Lake City, UT 84108 - T: (801) 582-7353, Fax: (801) 584-8325, Internet: http://www.thisistheplace.org. Head: Carol Nixon
Open Air Museum - 1947
Local hist 40047

Utah Museum of Fine Arts, 370 S 1530 E, University of Utah, Salt Lake City, UT 84112 - T: (801) 581-7332, 581-7049, Fax: (801) 585-5198, Internet: http://www.utah.edu/umfa. Head: E.F. Sanguinetti
Fine Arts Museum / University Museum - 1951
Art 40048

Utah Museum of Natural History, University of Utah, Salt Lake City, UT 84112 - T: (801) 581-6927, Fax: (801) 585-3684. Head: Sarah B. George
Natural History Museum - 1963
Natural hist 40049

Utah State Historical Society Museum, 300 Rio Grande St, Salt Lake City, UT 84101-1182 - T: (801) 533-3500, Fax: (801) 533-3503, E-mail: ushs@history.state.ut.us, Internet: http://www.history.state.ut.us. Head: Max J. Evans
Historical Museum - 1897
History 40050

Wheeler Historic Farm, 6351 S 900 E, Salt Lake City, UT 84121 - T: (801) 264-2241, Fax: (801) 264-2213, Internet: http://www.wheelerfarm.com
Local Museum / Agriculture Museum - 1976
Historic farm representing the initial statehood period and typical of Utah agriculture in 1898 40051

San Andreas CA

Calaveras County Museum and Archives, 30 N Main St, San Andreas, CA 95249 - T: (209) 754-3910, Fax: (209) 754-1086. Head: Donna Schantz
Local Museum - 1936
County hist 40052

San Angelo TX

Children's Art Museum, 36 E Twohig St, San Angelo, TX 76903 - T: (915) 658-4084, Fax: (915) 659-2407, E-mail: kimberly@wcc.net, Internet: http://web2.airmail.net/samfa
Fine Arts Museum / Special Museum - 1994 40053

Helen King Kendall Memorial Art Gallery, c/o San Angelo Art Club, 119 W First St, San Angelo, TX 76903 - T: (915) 653-4405. Head: Jean McFerrin
Fine Arts Museum - 1948 40054

San Angelo Museum of Fine Arts, One Love St, San Angelo, TX 76903 - T: (915) 653-3333, Fax: (915) 659-2407, E-mail: samfa@airmail.net, Internet: http://web2.airmail.net/samfa. Head: Frank Rose, Howard Taylor
Fine Arts Museum - 1981
Art 40055

San Antonio TX

The Alamo, 300 Alamo Plaza, San Antonio, TX 78205 - T: (210) 225-1391, Fax: (210) 354-3602, E-mail: bbreuer@thealamo.org, Internet: http://www.thealamo.org. Head: Brad Breuer
Historic Site / Military Museum - 1905
Site of the Battle of the Alamo 40056

Art Gallery, The University of Texas at San Antonio, 6900 N Loop, San Antonio, TX 78249-0641 - T: (210) 458-4352, Fax: (210) 458-4356, E-mail: jdiaz@utsa.edu. Head: Ron Boling
Fine Arts Museum / University Museum - 1982 40057

Buckhorn Museum, 318 E Houston St, San Antonio, TX 78205 - T: (210) 247-4002, Fax: (210) 247-4020, Internet: http://www.buckhornmuseum.com. Head: Scott Smith
Natural History Museum - 1881
Natural hist 40058

Casa Navarro, 228 S Laredo St, San Antonio, TX 78207 - T: (210) 226-4801, Fax: (210) 226-4801, E-mail: navarro@txdirect.net, Internet: http://www.tpwd.state.tx.us/park/jose
Historical Museum - 1975
Furnishings, Hispanic family 40059

Contemporary Art for San Antonio Blue Star Art Space, 116 Blue Star, San Antonio, TX 78204 - T: (210) 227-6960, Fax: (210) 229-9412, Internet: www.bluestarartspace.org. Head: Carla Stellwes
Fine Arts Museum - 1986 40060

Guadalupe Cultural Arts Center, 1300 Guadalupe St, San Antonio, TX 78207 - T: (210) 271-0379, Fax: (210) 271-3480, Internet: www.guadalupeculturalarts.org. Head: Maria Elena-Torralva
Fine Arts Museum - 1979 40061

Hertzberg Circus Museum, San Antonio Public Library, 210 W Market St, San Antonio, TX 78205 - T: (210) 207-7819, Fax: (210) 207-4468, E-mail: roconnor@ci.sat.tx.us, Internet: http:///www.sat.lib.tx.us(Hertzberg/hzmain.html. Head: Robert O'Connor
Performing Arts Museum - 1942
Circus, popular culture, hist of American circus, 40062

Magic Lantern Castle Museum, 1419 Austin Hwy, San Antonio, TX 78209 - T: (210) 805-0011, Fax: (210) 822-1226, E-mail: castle@magiclanterns.org, Internet: http://www.magiclanterns.org. Head: Jack Judson
Science&Tech Museum - 1991
Magic laterns, glass slides, related materials - library 40063

Marion Koogler McNay Art Museum, 6000 N New Braunfels Av, San Antonio, TX 78209-0069 - T: (210) 824-5368, Fax: (210) 824-0218, E-mail: sbailey@mcnayart.org, Internet: http://www.mcnayart.org. Head: William J. Chiego
Fine Arts Museum - 1950
Fine arts 40064

San Antonio Children's Museum, 305 E Houston St, San Antonio, TX 78205 - T: (210) 212-4453, Fax: (210) 242-1313, E-mail: chris@sakids.org, Internet: http://www.sakids.org. Head: Lisa Holt, Chris Sinick
Special Museum - 1992 40065

San Antonio Museum of Art, 200 W Jones Av, San Antonio, TX 78215-1406 - T: (210) 978-8111, Fax: (210) 978-8182, E-mail: samoa@world-net.net, Internet: http://www.sa-museum.org. Head: George W. Neubert
Fine Arts Museum - 1981
Art 40066

Southwest School of Art and Craft Exhibition, 300 Augusta St, San Antonio, TX 78205 - T: (210) 224-1848, Fax: (210) 224-9337, E-mail: info@swschool.org, Internet: http://www.swschool.org. Head: Paula Owen
Fine Arts Museum / Historic Site - 1965
Contemporary art 40067

Spanish Governor's Palace, 105 Military Plaza, San Antonio, TX 78205 - T: (210) 224-0601, Fax: (210) 207-7946. Head: Malcom Matthew
Historical Museum - 1749
Historic building 40068

Steves Homestead Museum, 509 King William St, San Antonio, TX 78204 - T: (210) 225-5924, Fax: (210) 224-6168, E-mail: conserve@saconservation.org, Internet: http://www.saconservation.org. Head: Paula D. Piper, Bruce MacDougal
Historical Museum / Historic Site - 1924
Steves Homestead 1876, Wulff House, 1840-1860 Yturri-Edmunds Historic Site 40069

Witte Museum, 3801 Broadway, San Antonio, TX 78209 - T: (210) 357-1900, 357-1898, Fax: (210) 357-1882, Internet: http://www.wittemuseum.org. Head: Jim McNutt
Historical Museum - 1926
History 40070

Yturri-Edmunds Historic Site, 107 King William St, San Antonio, TX 78204-1399 - T: (210) 224-6163, Fax: (210) 224-6168, E-mail: conserve@saconservation.org, Internet: http://www.saconservation.org. Head: Bruce MacDougal
Historic Site - 1924
Historic houses 40071

San Bernardino CA

Robert V. Fullerton Art Museum, California State University, 5500 University Pkwy, San Bernardino, CA 92407 - T: (909) 880-5493, Fax: (909) 880-7680, E-mail: ekivsch@csusb.edu. Head: Eva Kirsch
Fine Arts Museum - 1965
Art 40072

San Diego CA

Cabrillo National Monument, 1800 Cabrillo Memorial Dr, Point Loma, San Diego, CA 92106 - T: (619) 557-5450, 222-8211, Fax: (619) 557-5469, Internet: http://www.nps.gov/cabr/
Historical Museum / Historic Site - 1913
Historic site commemorating the exploration of California coast and San Diego Bay by Juan Rodriguez Cabrillo in 1542 40073

Children's Museum, Museo de Los Ninos, 200 W Island Av, San Diego, CA 92101 - T: (619) 233-8792, Fax: (619) 233-8796. Head: Robert L. Sain
Special Museum - 1981 40074

Command Museum, Marine Corps Recruit Depot, 1600 Henderson Av, Bldg 26, San Diego, CA 92140-5010 - T: (619) 524-6719, Fax: (619) 524-0076, E-mail: mccurtisb@sandiego.usmc.mil, Internet: http://www.sdo.usmc.mil/museum.nsf. Head: Allen Ruppoport, Michael Zacker, Barbara S. McCurtis
Military Museum - 1987
Military 40075

E.C. Allison Research Center, Department of Geological Sciences, San Diego State University, San Diego, CA 92182-1020 - T: (619) 594-6978, Fax: (619) 594-4372, E-mail: allison.center@geology.sdsu.edu, Internet: http://www.geology.sdsu.edu. Head: Dr. George L. Kennedy
University Museum / Natural History Museum - 1971
Paleontology and Geology Study Collections Museum and Library 40076

Junipero Serra Museum, 2727 Presidio Dr, Presidio Park, San Diego, CA 92103 - T: (619) 297-3258, Fax: (619) 297-3281, Internet: http://edweb.sdsu.edu/SDS.HistSoc.html. Head: Dr. Ann Bethel
Local Museum - 1928
Local hist 40077

Marston House, 3525 7th Av, San Diego, CA 92138 - T: (619) 232-6203, Fax: (619) 232-6297, Internet: http://www.sandiegohistory.org. Head: Bob Witty
Local Museum - 1928
Local hist 40078

Mingei International Museum, 1439 El Prado, Balboa Park, San Diego, CA 92101 - T: (619) 239-0003, Fax: (619) 239-0605, E-mail: mingei@mingei.org, Internet: http://www.mingei.org. Head: Martha W. Longenecker
Folklore Museum / Fine Arts Museum / Decorative Arts Museum - 1974
Folk art, craft, design from India, Japan, Indonesia, Mexico, Ethiopia and China, Palesinian costumes, Pre-Columbiana 40079

Mission San Diego de Alcala, 10818 San Diego Mission Rd, San Diego, CA 92108 - T: (619) 283-7319, Fax: (619) 283-7762. Head: Mary C. Whelan
Local Museum - 1769
First rectory and residence of Fray Junipero Serra 40080

Museum of Contemporary Art San Diego, 1001 Kettner Blvd, San Diego, CA 92101 - T: (858) 454-3541, Fax: (858) 454-4985, E-mail: info@mcasandiego.org, Internet: http://www.mcasandiego.org. Head: Hugh M. Davies, Dr. Charles G. Lochrane
Fine Arts Museum 40081

Museum of Death, 437 19th St, San Diego, CA 92102 - T: (619) 338-8153
Special Museum 40082

Museum of Photographic Arts, 1649 El Prado, Balboa Park, San Diego, CA 92101 - T: (619) 238-7559, Fax: (619) 238-8777, E-mail: info@mopa.org, Internet: http://www.mopa.org. Head: Arthur Ollman
Fine Arts Museum - 1983
Photographic arts 40083

Old Town San Diego State Historic Park, c/o c/o San Diego Coast District, 9609 Waples, San Diego, CA 92121 - T: (619) 642-4200, Fax: (619) 642-4222. Head: Edward Navarro
Local Museum - 1967
Local hist 40084

Reuben H. Fleet Science Center, 1875 El Prado, Balboa Park, San Diego, CA 92101 - T: (619) 238-1233, Fax: (619) 685-5771, Internet: http://www.rhfleet.org. Head: Dr. Jeffrey W. Kirsch, Dennis Mammana
Science&Tech Museum - 1973 40085

San Diego Aerospace Museum, 2001 Pan American Plaza, Balboa Park, San Diego, CA 92101 - T: (619) 234-8291 ext 10, Fax: (619) 233-4526, Internet: http://www.aerospacemuseum.org. Head: Gordon L. Witter, Edwin D. McKellar
Science&Tech Museum - 1961
Aviation 40086

San Diego Automotive Museum, 2080 Pan American Plaza, Balboa Park, San Diego, CA 92101-1636 - T: (619) 231-2886, Fax: (619) 231-9869, E-mail: sdauto@cts.com, Internet: http://www.sdautomuseum.org. Head: Art Bishop
Science&Tech Museum - 1987 40087

San Diego Hall of Champions Sports Museum, 2131 Pan America Plaza, Balboa Park, San Diego, CA 92101 - T: (619) 234-2544, Fax: (619) 234-4543, E-mail: sdhoc@socal.wanet.com, Internet: http://www.sandiegosports.org. Head: Bill Adams
Special Museum - 1961
Sports 40088

San Diego Historical Society Museum, 1649 El Prado Casa de Balboa, Balboa Park, San Diego, CA 92101-1621 - T: (619) 232-6203 ext 100, Fax: (619) 232-6297, Internet: http://www.sandiegohistory.org. Head: Robert M. Witty
Local Museum - 1928
Local hist 40089

San Diego Maritime Museum, 1492 N Harbor Dr, San Diego, CA 92101 - T: (619) 234-9153, Fax: (619) 234-8345, E-mail: ashley@sdmaritime.com, Internet: http://www.sdmaritime.com. Head: William Dysart, Raymond E. Ashley
Science&Tech Museum - 1948
Museum housed in three ships (1863 Star of India, 1898 ferryboat Berkeley, 1904 steam yacht Medea) 40090

San Diego Model Railroad Museum, 1649 El Prado, San Diego, CA 92101 - T: (619) 696-0199, Fax: (619) 696-0239, E-mail: sdmodrailm@abac.com, Internet: http://www.sdmodel-railroadm.com. Head: Joe Cesare, John A. Rotsart
Science&Tech Museum - 1980
Railroad 40091

San Diego Museum of Art, Balboa Park, 1450 El Prado, San Diego, CA 92101 - T: (619) 232-7931, Fax: (619) 232-9367, E-mail: library2@class.org, Internet: http://www.samart.org. Head: Dr. Don Bacigalupi
Fine Arts Museum - 1925
Art 40092

San Diego Museum of Man, 1350 El Prado, Balboa Park, San Diego, CA 92101 - T: (619) 239-2001, Fax: (619) 239-2749, Internet: http://www.museumofman.org. Head: Dr. Douglas Sharon
Ethnology Museum / Archaeological Museum - 1915
Anthropology 40093

San Diego Natural History Museum, 1788 El Prado, Balboa Park, San Diego, CA 92101 - T: (619) 232-3821 ext 216, Fax: (619) 232-0248, E-mail: mhager@sdnhm.org, Internet: http://www.sdnhm.org. Head: Dr. Michael W. Hager, Dr. Exequiel Ezcurra, Tim Murray, Denise Brook Schwartz
Natural History Museum - 1874
Natural hist 40094

Sushi Performance and Visual Art, 320 11 Av, San Diego, CA 92101 - T: (619) 235-8466, Fax: (619) 235-8552. Head: Vicki Wolf
Fine Arts Museum / Public Gallery - 1980 40095

Timken Museum of Art, 1500 El Prado, Balboa Park, San Diego, CA 92101 - T: (619) 239-5548, Fax: (619) 233-6629, Internet: http://gort.ucsd.edu/sj/timken/. Head: John Petersen
Fine Arts Museum - 1965
Art 40096

University Art Gallery, San Diego State University, 5500 Campanile Dr, San Diego, CA 92182-4805 - T: (619) 594-5171, Fax: (619) 594-1217, E-mail: artgallery@sdsu.edu, Internet: http://www.sdsu.edu/artgallery. Head: Tina Yapelli
Fine Arts Museum / University Museum - 1977
Art 40097

Villa Montezuma Museum, 1925 K St, San Diego, CA 92102 - T: (619) 232-6203, 239-2211, Fax: (619) 232-6297, Internet: http://edweb.sdsu.edu/sdhs
Local Museum - 1928
Local hist 40098

Wells Fargo History Museum, 2733 San Diego Av, San Diego, CA 92110 - T: (619) 238-3929
Science&Tech Museum - 1990
Company hist 40099

San Francisco CA

Adan E. Treganza Anthropology Museum, Dept. of Anthropology, San Francisco State University, 1600 Holloway Av, San Francisco, CA 94132 - T: (415) 338-1642, Fax: (415) 338-0530, E-mail: yamamoto@sfsu.edu, Internet: http://www.sfsu.edu/~anthro/treganza.htm. Head: Yoshiko Yamamoto
University Museum / Archaeological Museum / Natural History Museum - 1958
Anthropology 40100

American Indian Contemporary Arts, 23 Grant Av, San Francisco, CA 94108 - T: (415) 989-7003, Fax: (415) 989-7025. Head: Janeen Antoine
Fine Arts Museum - 1983 40101

Ansel Adams Center for Photography, 655 Mission St, San Francisco, CA 94105 - T: (415) 495-7000, Fax: (415) 495-8517, E-mail: staff@friendsofphotography.org, Internet: http://www.friendsofphotography.org. Head: Deborah Klochko
Fine Arts Museum - 1967 40102

Asian Art Museum of San Francisco, Golden Gate Park, San Francisco, CA 94118 - T: (415) 379-8800, Fax: (415) 668-8928, E-mail: pr@asianart.org, Internet: http://www.asianart.org. Head: Dr. Emily J. Sano
Fine Arts Museum - 1966/2001
Art 40103

Califonia Palace of the Legion of Honor, 100 34th Av, San Francisco, CA 94121 - T: (415) 750-3600, Fax: (415) 750-3656, Internet: http://www.legionofhonor.org. Head: Harry S. Parker
Fine Arts Museum - 1924
Ancient and European arts, sculptures 40104

California Academy of Sciences Museum, Golden Gate Park, San Francisco, CA 94118-4599 - T: (415) 221-5100, Fax: (415) 750-7346, E-mail: llacarrubba@calacademy.org, Internet: http://www.calacademy.org. Head: Dr. John Pearse, J. Patrick Kociolek, Dr. Terry Gosliner
Natural History Museum - 1853
Natural hist 40105

Cartoon Art Museum, 814 Mission St, San Francisco, CA 94103 - T: (415) 227-8666, Fax: (415) 243-8666, E-mail: toonart@wenet.net, Internet: http://www.cartoonart.org. Head: Rod Gilchrist
Fine Arts Museum - 1984
Cartoon art 40106

Center for the Arts at Yerba Buena Gardens → Yerba Buena Center for the Arts

Chinese Culture Center of San Francisco, 750 Kearny St, San Francisco, CA 94108 - T: (415) 986-1822, Fax: (415) 986-2825, E-mail: info@c-c-c.org, Internet: http://www.c-c-c.org. Head: Hon Seng Cheng
Fine Arts Museum / Folklore Museum - 1965
Art 40107

The Exploratorium, 3601 Lyon St, San Francisco, CA 94123 - T: (415) 563-7337, Fax: (415) 561-0307, E-mail: pubinfo@exploratorium.edu, Internet: http://www.exploratium.edu. Head: Goery Delacote
Fine Arts Museum / Science&Tech Museum / Ethnology Museum - 1969
Science, art, human perception 40108

The Friends of Photography at the Ansel Adams Center, 650 Mission St, San Francisco, CA 95105 - T: (415) 495-7000, Fax: (415) 495-8517, E-mail: staff@friendsofphotography.org, Internet: http://www.friendsofphotography.org. Head: Deborah Klochko
Fine Arts Museum
Photography 40109

Haas-Lilienthal House, 2007 Franklin St, San Francisco, CA 94109 - T: (415) 441-3000, Fax: (415) 441-3015, E-mail: info@sfheritage.org, Internet: http://www.sfheritage.org. Head: Bruce Judd
Local Museum - 1973
Historic house 40110

The Jewish Museum San Francisco, 121 Steuart St, San Francisco, CA 94105 - T: (415) 591-8800, Fax: (415) 591-8815, E-mail: info@jmsf.org, Internet: http://www.jmsf.org. Head: Connie Wolf
Fine Arts Museum - 1984 40111

The Mexican Museum (closed until Fall 2003), Fort Mason Center, Bldg D, Laguna and Marina Blvd, San Francisco, CA 94123 - T: (415) 202-9700, Fax: (415) 441-7683, E-mail: emmalouise@mexicanmuseum.org, Internet: http://www.mexicanmuseum.org. Head: Lorraine Garcia-Nakata
Fine Arts Museum / Folklore Museum - 1975
Fine arts 40112

M.H. de Young Memorial Museum, The Fine Arts Museums of San Francisco (closed until 2005 for rebuilding), 75 Tea Garden Dr, Golden Gate Park, San Francisco, CA 94118 - T: (415) 750-3600, 750-3615, Fax: (415) 750-7692, Internet: http://www.thinker.org. Head: Harry S. Parker
Fine Arts Museum - 1894
Fine Arts 40113

Mission Cultural Center for Latino Arts, 2868 Mission St, San Francisco, CA 94110 - T: (415) 821-1155, Fax: (415) 648-0933. Head: Jennie Rodriquez
Fine Arts Museum / Folklore Museum - 1977
Civic art 40114

Museo Italoamericano, Fort Mason Center, Bldg C, San Francisco, CA 94123 - T: (415) 673-2200, Fax: (415) 673-2292, E-mail: museo@finstworld.net, Internet: http://www.museoitaloamericano.org
Fine Arts Museum / Folklore Museum - 1978
Contemporary Italian, Italian-American art, Italian culture 40115

Museum of Craft and Folk Art, Bldg A, Fort Mason Center, San Francisco, CA 94123 - T: (415) 775-0990/91, Fax: (415) 775-1861, E-mail: weldon@mocfa.org, Internet: http://www.mocfa.org. Head: J. Weldon Smith
Folklore Museum - 1983
Worldwide tribal, contemporary craft and folk art, outsider art 40116

Museum of Russian Culture, 2450 Sutter St, San Francisco, CA 94115 - T: (415) 921-4082. Head: Dmitri G. Brauns
Historical Museum - 1948
Ethnic hist 40117

The Museum of Vision, c/o Foundation of the American Academy of Ophthalmology, 655 Beach St, Ste 300, San Francisco, CA 94109-1336 - T: (415) 447-0297, Fax: (415) 561-8533, E-mail: tschmitz@aao.org, Internet: http://www.eyenet.org. Head: Licia A. Wells
Special Museum - 1980
Medical hist, medical instruments, ophthalmology, rare books 40118

New Langton Arts, 1246 Folsom St, San Francisco, CA 94103 - T: (415) 626-5416, Fax: (415) 255-1453, E-mail: nla@newlangtonarts.org, Internet: http://www.newlangtonarts.org. Head: Susan Miller
Public Gallery - 1975 40119

Randall Museum, 199 Museum Way, San Francisco, CA 94114 - T: (415) 554-9600, Fax: (415) 554-9609, E-mail: info@randallmuseum.org, Internet: http://www.randallmuseum.org. Head: Amy Dawson
Special Museum - 1937
Children's museum 40120

San Francisco African American Historical and Cultural Society Museum, Fort Mason Center, Bldg C, San Francisco, CA 94123 - T: (415) 441-0640. Head: Eric DuPree
Folklore Museum / Historical Museum - 1955
African American culture 40121

San Francisco Art Institute Galleries, 800 Chestnut St, San Francisco, CA 94133 - T: (415) 771-7020, Fax: (415) 749-1036, E-mail: exhibitions@sfai.edu, Internet: http://www.sfai.edu. Head: Ella King Torrey
Fine Arts Museum - 1871
Art 40122

San Francisco Camerawork, 1246 Folsom St, San Francisco, CA 94103 - T: (415) 863-1001, Fax: (415) 863-1015, E-mail: sfcamera@sfcamerawork.org, Internet: http://www.sfcamerawork.org. Head: Marnie Gillett
Fine Arts Museum / Public Gallery - 1974
Photography 40123

San Francisco Craft and Folk Art Museum → Museum of Craft and Folk Art

San Francisco Fire Department Museum, 655 Presidio Av and Bush St, San Francisco, CA 94115 - T: (415) 558-3546, 563-4630
Special Museum - 1964
Fire museum, specializing in San Francisco history 40124

San Francisco Maritime National Historical Park, Hyde Street Pier, San Francisco, CA 94109 - T: (415) 556-1659, Fax: (415) 556-1624, E-mail: lynn_cullivan@nps.gov, Internet: http://www.nps.gov/safr. Head: William G. Thomas
Historical Museum / Science&Tech Museum - 1951
Maritime hist - historic douments, archives, libraray 40125

San Francisco Museum of Modern Art, 151 Third St, San Francisco, CA 94103 - T: (415) 357-4000, Fax: (415) 357-4037, E-mail: conmassistant@sfmoma.org, Internet: http://www.sfmoma.org. Head: David A. Ross
Fine Arts Museum - 1935
Modern art 40126

Southern Exposure Gallery, 401 Alabama St, San Francisco, CA 94110 - T: (415) 863-2141, Fax: (415) 863-1841, E-mail: soex@soex.org, Internet: http://www.soex.org. Head: N. Trisha Lagaso
Public Gallery - 1974 40127

Tattoo Art Museum, 841 Columbus Av, San Francisco, CA 94133 - T: (415) 775-4991, Fax: (707) 462-4433, E-mail: lyletutt@pacific.net, Internet: http://www.lyletuttle.com. Head: Lyle Tuttle
Special Museum - 1974 40128

Telephone Pioneer Communications Museum of San Francisco, 140 New Montgomery St, San Francisco, CA 94105 - T: (415) 542-0182, Fax: (415) 661-1077. Head: Alison Moore
Science&Tech Museum - 1968
Telephone hist 40129

Wells Fargo History Museum, 420 Montgomery St, San Francisco, CA 94163 - T: (415) 396-2619, 396-4157, Fax: (415) 391-8644, E-mail: fontaine@wellsfargo.com, Internet: http://www.wellsfargo-history.com. Head: Charles LaFontaine
Historical Museum - 1929
Company history, Wells Fargo Bank's headquarters 40130

Women's Heritage Museum, 870 Market St, #547, San Francisco, CA 94102 - T: (415) 433-3026. Head: Elizabeth Colton, Jeanne McDonnell
Historical Museum - 1985 40131

Yerba Buena Center for the Arts, 701 Mission St, San Francisco, CA 94103 - T: (415) 978-2700, Fax: (415) 978-9635, E-mail: info@yerbabuenarts.org, Internet: http://www.yerbabuenaarts.org. Head: John Killacky
Fine Arts Museum / Performing Arts Museum - 1986 40132

San Gabriel CA

San Gabriel Mission Museum, 428 S Mission Dr, San Gabriel, CA 91776 - T: (626) 457-3048, Fax: (626) 282-5308. Head: Denis Gallo
Religious Arts Museum - 1771
Religious hist 40133

San Jacinto CA

San Jacinto Museum, 181 E Main St, San Jacinto, CA 92583 - T: (909) 654-4952. Head: Phil Brigandi
Local Museum - 1939
Local hist 40134

San Jose CA

Children's Discovery Museum of San Jose, 180 Woz Way, San Jose, CA 95110 - T: (408) 298-5437 ext 0, Fax: (408) 298-6826, Internet: http://www.cdm.org. Head: Sally Osberg
Special Museum - 1982 40135

History San José, 1650 Senter Rd, San Jose, CA 95112-2599 - T: (408) 287-2290, Fax: (408) 287-2291, Internet: http://www.historysanjose.org
Historical Museum - 1950
History 40136

Military Medal Museum, 448 N San Pedro St, San Jose, CA 95110-2232 - T: (408) 298-1100
Military Museum - 1978
Military hist 40137

The Natalie & James Thompson Gallery, School of Art and Design, San Jose State University, San Jose, CA 95192-0089 - T: (408) 924-4328, Fax: (408) 924-4326, Internet: http://www.sjsu.edu. Head: Jo Farb Hernández
Fine Arts Museum / University Museum - 1959
Art 40138

Rosicrucian Egyptian Museum, 1342 Naglee Av, San Jose, CA 95191-0001 - T: (408) 947-3600, Fax: (408) 947-3638, E-mail: director@rcegyptmus.org, Internet: http://www.rosicrucian.org. Head: Julie Scot
Historical Museum - 1929
Egyptian hist 40139

San Jose Institute of Contemporary Art, 451 S First St, San Jose, CA 95113 - T: (408) 283-8155, Fax: (408) 283-8157, E-mail: info@sjica.org. Head: Cathy Kimball
Fine Arts Museum - 1980 40140

San Jose Museum of Art, 110 S Market St, San Jose, CA 95113 - T: (408) 271-6840, Fax: (408) 294-2977, E-mail: info@sjmusart.org, Internet: http://www.sjmusart.org. Head: Daniel T. Keegan
Fine Arts Museum - 1969
Art 40141

San Jose Museum of Quilts and Textiles, 110 Paseo de San Antonio, San Jose, CA 95112-3639 - T: (408) 971-0323 ext 16, Fax: (408) 971-7226, E-mail: jane@sjquiltmuseum.org, Internet: http://www.sjquiltmuseum.org. Head: Jane Przybysz, Robin Treen
Decorative Arts Museum - 1977
Quilts and textiles 40142

San Jose State University Art Galleries → The Natalie & James Thompson Gallery

Youth Science Institute, 16260 Alum Rock Av, San Jose, CA 95127 - T: (408) 258-4322, Fax: (408) 358-3683, Internet: http://www.ysi-ca.org. Head: Anne Dunham
Natural History Museum - 1953
Natural hist 40143

San Juan Bautista CA

San Juan Bautista State Historic Park, 2nd St, Washington and Mariposa Sts, San Juan Bautista, CA 95045-0787 - T: (831) 623-4881, 623-4526, Fax: (831) 623-4612, E-mail: sjbshp@hollinet.com
Historical Museum - 1933
Local hist 40144

San Juan Capistrano CA

Mission San Juan Capistrano Museum, Ortega Highway and Camino Capistrano, San Juan Capistrano, CA 92693 - T: (949) 234-1300, Fax: (949) 443-2061, E-mail: museum@fea.net, Internet: http://www.sanjuancapistrano.com/missionsjc. Head: Gerry Miller
Historic Site - 1980
Local hist, archaeology, native american, period rooms 40145

San Luis Obispo CA

Mission San Luis Obispo de Tolosa, 751 Palm St, San Luis Obispo, CA 93401 - T: (805) 543-6850, 781-8220, Fax: (805) 781-8214, Internet: http://www.sloforsale.com/missionslo. Head: Frank Thome
Religious Arts Museum - 1772
Religious hist 40146

San Luis Obispo County Historical Museum, 696 Monterey St, San Luis Obispo, CA 93401 - T: (805) 543-0638, Fax: (805) 543-6659, Internet: http://www.slonet.org/vv/ipslochm/. Head: Bruce Miller
Local Museum - 1956
Local hist 40147

San Marcos CA

Boehm Gallery, 1140 W Mission Rd, San Marcos, CA 92069 - T: (760) 744-1150 ext 2304, Fax: (760) 744-8123, Internet: http://www.palomar.edu. Head: Harry Bliss, Vicki Cole
Fine Arts Museum - 1964
Art 40148

San Marino CA

El Molino Viejo Museum, 1120 Old Mill Rd, San Marino, CA 91108 - T: (626) 449-5450. Head: Stephen Taber, Margaret O. Eley
Local Museum - 1816
Local hist 40149

Huntington Art Collections, 1151 Oxford Rd, San Marino, CA 91108 - T: (626) 405-2125, Fax: (626) 405-0225, E-mail: webmaster@huntington.org, Internet: http://www.huntington.org. Head: Edward Nygren
Fine Arts Museum - 1919
Art 40150

San Martin CA

Wings of History Air Museum, 12777 Murphy Av, San Martin, CA 95046 - T: (408) 683-2290, Fax: (408) 683-2291, E-mail: frankhnich@aol.com, Internet: http://www.wingsofhistory.org. Head: Gayle Womack
Science&Tech Museum - 1983 40151

San Mateo CA

Coyote Point Museum for Environmental Education, 1651 Coyote Point Dr, San Mateo, CA 94401 - T: (650) 342-7755, Fax: (650) 342-7853, Internet: http://www.coyoteptmuseum.org. Head: Jefferey P. Cooper-Smith
Natural History Museum - 1953
Natural science 40152

San Miguel CA

Mission San Miguel, 775 Mission St, San Miguel, CA 93451 - T: (805) 467-3256, Fax: (805) 467-2448, Internet: http://missionsanmiguel.org. Head: William Short
Religious Arts Museum - 1797
Religion 40153

San Pedro CA

Fort MacArthur Museum, 3601 S Gaffey St, San Pedro, CA 90731 - T: (310) 548-2631, Fax: (310) 241-0847, E-mail: director@ftmac.org, Internet: http://www.ftmac.org. Head: Stephen R. Nelson
Open Air Museum / Military Museum - 1985 40154

Los Angeles Maritime Museum, Berth 84, foot of 6th St, San Pedro, CA 90731 - T: (310) 548-7618, Fax: (310) 832-6537, E-mail: museum@lamaritimemuseum.org, Internet: http://www.lamaritimemuseum.org
Historical Museum - 1980
Maritime, former Los Angeles municipal ferry building, ship building, US Navy 40155

San Rafael CA

Falkirk Cultural Center, 1408 Mission Av, San Rafael, CA 94901 - T: (415) 485-3328, Fax: (415) 485-3404, E-mail: cadney@aol, Internet: http://www.falkirkculturalcenter.org. Head: Jane Lange
Fine Arts Museum / Folklore Museum - 1974
Contemporary arts 40156

Marin County Historical Society Museum, 1125 B St, San Rafael, CA 94901 - T: (415) 454-8538, Internet: http://www.marinweb.com/marinhistory/. Head: Merry Alberigi
Local Museum - 1935
Local hist 40157

Schwartz Collection of Skiing Heritage, 1099 D St, Penthouse A, San Rafael, CA 94901-2843 - T: (415) 256-9300, Fax: (415) 256-9400, E-mail: info@picturesnow.com, Internet: http://www.picturesnow.com. Head: Gary Schwartz
Special Museum - 1986
Sports 40158

San Simeon CA

Hearst San Simeon State Historical Monument, 750 Hearst Castle Rd, San Simeon, CA 93452 - T: (805) 927-2020, Fax: (805) 927-2031. Head: Deborah A. Weldon
Local Museum - 1957
Local hist 40159

Sandown NH

Sandown Historical Museum, Rte 121-A, Sandown, NH 03873 - T: (603) 887-4520. Head: Paul M. Densen
Local Museum - 1977
Local history, railroad stn 40160

Sandpoint ID

Bonner County Historical Museum, 611 S Ella Av, Sandpoint, ID 83864 - T: (208) 263-2344, Fax: (208) 263-2344, E-mail: bchsmuseum@nidlink.com, Internet: http://www.sandpoint.com/museum. Head: John Hunt
Historical Museum - 1972
Local history 40161

Sandusky OH

Follett House Museum, 404 Wayne St, Sandusky, OH 44870 - T: (419) 625-3834, Fax: (419) 625-4574, E-mail: comments@sandusky.lib.oh.us, Internet: http://www.sandusky.lib.oh.us/
Local Museum - 1902 40162

Sandwich IL

Sandwich Historical Society Museum, 315 E Railroad, Sandwich, IL 60548 - T: (815) 786-7936. Head: Roger Peterson
Local Museum - 1969
Local history, housed in sturdy old structure locally known as the Old Stone Mill 40163

Sandwich MA

Heritage Plantation of Sandwich, 67 Grove St and Pine St, Sandwich, MA 02563 - T: (508) 888-3300, Fax: (508) 888-9535, E-mail: heritage@heritageplantation.org, Internet: http://www.heritageplantation.org. Head: Gene A. Schott
Local Museum - 1969
General museum, military, cars 40164

Old Hoxie House, Rte 130, Water St, Sandwich, MA 02563 - T: (508) 888-1173. Head: Barbara L. Gill
Historical Museum - 1960
Oldest restored house on Cape Cod 40165

Sandwich Glass Museum, 129 Main St, Sandwich, MA 02563 - T: (508) 888-0251, Fax: (508) 888-4941, E-mail: glass@sandwichglassmuseum.org, Internet: http://.www.sandwichglassmuseum.org. Head: Bruce A. Courson
Decorative Arts Museum / Historical Museum - 1907
Glass history 40166

Thornton W. Burgess Museum, 4 Water St, Sandwich, MA 02563 - T: (508) 888-4668, Fax: (508) 888-1919, E-mail: twbmuseum@capecod.net, Internet: http://www.thornton-burgess.org. Head: Jeanne Johnson
Local Museum / Natural History Museum - 1976
History, nature 40167

Yesteryears Doll and Toy Museum, Main and River Sts, Sandwich, MA 02563 - T: (508) 888-1711. Head: Diane Costa
Decorative Arts Museum - 1961
Dolls, toys 40168

Sandy Hook NJ

Fort Hancock Museum, Sandy Hook Unit, Gateway National Recreation Area, Sandy Hook, NJ 07732 - T: (732) 872-5970, Fax: (732) 872-2256
Natural History Museum - 1968 40169

Sandy Spring MD

Sandy Spring Museum, 17901 Bentley Road, Sandy Spring, MD 20860 - T: (301) 774-0022, Fax: (301) 774-8149, E-mail: dheibein@sandyspringmuseum.org, Internet: http://www.sandyspringmuseum.org. Head: Debbie Heibein
Local Museum / Historical Museum - 1980
Local history, quaker, farming 40170

Sanford FL

Museum of Seminole County History, 300 Bush Blvd, Sanford, FL 32773 - T: (407) 321-2489, Fax: (407) 665-5220, Internet: http://www.co.seminole.fl.us. Head: Karen Jacobs
Glass Museum - 1983 40171

Sanford Museum, 520 E First St, Sanford, FL 32771 - T: (407) 302-1000, Fax: (407) 330-5666
Decorative Arts Museum / Historical Museum / Special Museum - 1957 40172

Sanford NC

House in the Horseshoe, 324 Alston House Rd, Sanford, NC 27330-8713 - T: (910) 947-2051, Fax: (910) 947-2051 (call first), E-mail: horseshoe@ac.net, Internet: http://www.ah.dcr.state.nc.us/sections/hs/horsesho. Head: Guy Smith
Local Museum - 1972
Furnished house from 1772 40173

Sanibel FL

Bailey-Matthews Shell Museum, 3075 Sanibel-Captiva Rd, Sanibel, FL 33957 - T: (941) 395-2233, Fax: (941) 395-6706, E-mail: shell@shellmuseum.org, Internet: http://www.shellmuseum.org. Head: José H. Leal
Natural History Museum - 1986 40174

Sankt Louis MO

Cecille R. Hunt Gallery, Webster University, 8342 Big Bend Blvd, Sankt Louis, MO 63119 - T: (314) 968-7171, E-mail: langtk@websteruniv.edu, Internet: http://www.webster.edu/dept/finearts/art. Head: Tom Lang
Fine Arts Museum - 1950
Local, national and international art in all media 40175

Sanset TX

Cowboy Museum → Old West Museum

Old West Museum, Hwy 287 at Lawhorn Ln, Sanset, TX 76270 - T: (940) 872-9698, Fax: (940) 872-8504, E-mail: sunsettradingpost@earthlink.net. Head: Jack Glover
Local Museum / Historical Museum - 1956
Local hist, early Texas 40176

Santa Ana CA

The Bowers Museum of Cultural Art, 2002 N Main St, Santa Ana, CA 92706 - T: (714) 567-3600, 3601, Fax: (714) 567-3603, E-mail: pkeller@bowers.org, Internet: http://www.bowers.org
Fine Arts Museum - 1936
Art 40177

Old Courthouse Museum, 211 W Santa Ana Blvd, Santa Ana, CA 92701 - T: (714) 834-3703, Fax: (714) 834-2280, E-mail: duellm@pfRdco.orange.ca.us, Internet: http://www.ocparks.com. Head: Robert Selway
Local Museum - 1987
County history 40178

Santa Ana College Art Gallery, 1530 W 17th St, Santa Ana, CA 92706 - T: (714) 564-5615, 564-5600, Fax: (714) 564-5629, E-mail: sacarts@mail.rancho.cc.ca.us. Head: Mayde Herberg
Fine Arts Museum / University Museum - 1970 40179

Santa Barbara CA

The Santa Barbara Historical Museum, 136 E De la Guerra St, Santa Barbara, CA 93101 - T: (805) 966-1601, Fax: (805) 966-1603. Head: George M. Anderjack
Local Museum - 1932
Local hist 40180

Santa Barbara Museum of Art, 1130 State St, Santa Barbara, CA 93101-2746 - T: (805) 963-4364, Fax: (805) 966-6840, E-mail: info@sbmuseart.org, Internet: http://www.sbmuseart.org. Head: Robert H. Frankel
Fine Arts Museum - 1941
Art 40181

Santa Barbara Museum of Natural History, 2559 Puesta del Sol Rd, Santa Barbara, CA 93105 - T: (805) 682-4711, Fax: (805) 569-3170, E-mail: info@sbnature2.org, Internet: http://www.sbnature.org
Natural History Museum - 1916
Natural hist 40182

University Art Museum, University of California Santa Barbara, Santa Barbara, CA 93106-7130 - T: (805) 893-2951, 893-2724, Fax: (805) 893-3013, E-mail: uam@humanitas.ucsb.edu, Internet: http://uam.ucsb.edu. Head: Marla C. Berns
Fine Arts Museum / University Museum - 1959
Art 40183

Santa Clara CA

De Saisset Museum, Santa Clara University, 500 El Camino Real, Santa Clara, CA 95053-0550 - T: (408) 554-4528, Fax: (408) 554-7840, Internet: http://www.scu.edu/deSaisset. Head: Rebecca M. Schapp
Fine Arts Museum / University Museum / Historical Museum - 1955
Art, history 40184

Triton Museum of Art, 1505 Warburton Av, Santa Clara, CA 95050 - T: (408) 247-3754, Fax: (408) 247-3796, E-mail: triton246@aol.com, Internet: http://www.tritonmuseum.org. Head: George Rivera
Fine Arts Museum - 1965
Art 40185

Santa Cruz CA

Museum of Art and History, 705 Front St, Santa Cruz, CA 95060 - T: (408) 429-1964, Fax: (408) 429-1954, E-mail: admin@santacruzmah.org, Internet: http://www.santacruzmah.org. Head: Joan Dunn, Charles Hilger
Fine Arts Museum / Historical Museum - 1981
Art, history 40186

Santa Cruz Art League Museum, 526 Broadway, Santa Cruz, CA 95060 - T: (408) 426-5787, Fax: (408) 426-5789, E-mail: scal.org, Internet: http://www.scal.org. Head: Stephanie Schriber
Fine Arts Museum - 1919
Art 40187

Santa Cruz City Museum of Natural History, 1305 E Cliff Dr, Santa Cruz, CA 95062 - T: (408) 429-3760, Fax: (408) 469-4371, E-mail: scmuseum@cruzio.com, Internet: http://www.cruzio.com/~scmuseum. Head: Greg Moyce
Natural History Museum - 1904
Regional natural hist 40188

Santa Fe NM

American Bicycle and Cycling Museum, POB 8533, Santa Fe, NM 87504 - T: (505) 989-7634, Fax: (505) 989-7634. Head: Sandra Vaillancourt
Science&Tech Museum - 1991 40189

Center for Contemporary Arts of Santa Fe, 1050 Old Pecos Trail, Santa Fe, NM 87501 - T: (505) 982-1338, Fax: (505) 982-9854, Internet: http://www.pla.bart.org. Head: Guy Ambrosino, Jerry Barson
Fine Arts Museum - 1985 40190

El Rancho de Las Golondrinas Museum, 334 Los Pinos Rd, Santa Fe, NM 87505 - T: (505) 471-2261, Fax: (505) 471-5623, E-mail: mail@golondrinas.org, Internet: http://www.golondrinas.org. Head: George B. Paloheimo
Open Air Museum - 1970 40191

Georgia O'Keeffe Museum, 217 Johnson St, Santa Fe, NM 87501 - T: (505) 995-0785, Fax: (505) 983-1759, E-mail: main@okeeffemuseum.org, Internet: http://www.okeeffemuseum.org. Head: George G. King
Fine Arts Museum - 1997
Modern art, paintings 40192

Governor's Gallery, State Capitol Bldg, Rm 400, Santa Fe, NM 87503 - T: (505) 827-3089, Fax: (505) 827-3026, E-mail: gov@gov.state.nm.us, Internet: http://www.governor.state.nm.us. Head: Dr. J. Edson Way
Fine Arts Museum - 1973 40193

Institute of American Indian Arts Museum, 108 Cathedral Pl, 83 Avon Nu Po Rd, Santa Fe, NM 87501 - T: (505) 988-6281, Fax: (505) 988-6273, E-mail: datencio@iaiancad.org, Internet: http://www.iaiacad.org. Head: Thomas Atencio
Ethnology Museum / Fine Arts Museum - 1962 40194

Liquid Paper Correction Fluid Museum, Rte 1, Santa Fe, NM 87501 - T: (505) 455-3848. Head: Michael Nesmith, Marcia J. Summers
Science&Tech Museum - 1980
Industrial hist 40195

Museum of Fine Arts, 107 W Palace, Santa Fe, NM 87501 - T: (505) 827-4452, Fax: (505) 476-5036, E-mail: mjebsen@mnm.state.nm.us. Head: Mary Jebsen
Fine Arts Museum - 1917
Art 40196

Museum of Indian Arts and Culture, 710 Camino Lejo, Santa Fe, NM 87501 - T: (505) 476-1250, Fax: (505) 476-1330, E-mail: info@miaclab.org, Internet: http://www.miaclab.org. Head: Duane Anderson
Fine Arts Museum / Ethnology Museum / Folklore Museum - 1909
Anthropology, ethnology and Indian art 40197

Museum of International Folk Art, 706 Camino Lejo, Santa Fe, NM 87505, mail addr: POB 2087, NM 87505-2087 Santa Fe - T: (505) 476-1200, Fax: (505) 476-1300, Internet: http://www.moifa.org. Head: Dr. Joyce Ice
Folklore Museum - 1953
International folk art 40198

Museum of New Mexico, 113 Lincoln Av, Santa Fe, NM 87501 - T: (505) 476-5060, Fax: (505) 476-5088, E-mail: mnmreg@nm-us.campus.mci.net, Internet: http://www.state.nm.us/moifa. Head: Thomas A. Livesay
Local Museum / Historical Museum - 1909 40199

Palace of the Governors, Museum of New Mexico, Plaza, Santa Fe, NM 87501, mail addr: POB 2087, Santa Fe, NM 87504-2087 - T: (505) 476-5100, Fax: (505) 476-5104, Internet: http://www.state.nm.us/moifa. Head: Thomas Chavez
Local Museum - 1909
Local hist 40200

Santa Fe Children's Museum, 1050 Old Pecos Trail, Santa Fe, NM 87501 - T: (505) 989-8359, Fax: (505) 989-7506, E-mail: children@trail.com, Internet: http://www.sfchildmuseum.org. Head: Mary Amelia Howell, Ellen Biderman, Ellyn Feldman, Londi Carbajal
Special Museum / Historical Museum - 1985 40201

Santuario de Guadalupe, 100 S Guadalupe St, Santa Fe, NM 87501 - T: (505) 988-2027. Head: Emilio I. Ortiz
Religious Arts Museum - 1975 40202

Site Santa Fe, 1606 Paseo de Peralta, Santa Fe, NM 87501 - T: (505) 989-1199
Historic Site 40203

Wheelwright Museum of the American Indian, 704 Camino Lejo, Santa Fe, NM 87505 - T: (505) 982-4636, Fax: (505) 989-7386, E-mail: pr@wheelwright.org, Internet: http://www.wheelwright.org. Head: Jonathan Batkin
Folklore Museum / Ethnology Museum - 1937 40204

Santa Fe Springs CA

Hathaway Ranch Museum, 11901 E Florence Av, Santa Fe Springs, CA 90670 - T: (562) 944-7372, Fax: (562) 946-0708. Head: Nadine Hathaway
Local Museum - 1986 40205

Santa Maria CA

Santa Maria Museum of Flight, 3015 Airpark Dr, Santa Maria, CA 93455 - T: (805) 922-8758, Fax: (805) 922-8958. Head: K.R. Weber
Science&Tech Museum - 1984
Aeronautics 40206

Santa Maria Valley Historical Society Museum, 616 S Broadway, Santa Maria, CA 93454 - T: (805) 922-3130
Local Museum - 1955
Local hist 40207

Santa Monica CA

California Heritage Museum, 2612 Main St, Santa Monica, CA 90405 - T: (310) 392-8538, Fax: (310) 396-0547, E-mail: calmuseum@earthlink.net. Head: Tobi Smith
Historical Museum / Decorative Arts Museum / Fine Arts Museum - 1977
California History 40208

Santa Monica Museum of Art, Bergamot Stn, 2525 Michigan Av, Santa Monica, CA 90404 - T: (310) 586-6488, Fax: (310) 586-6487, E-mail: smmuseum@netvip.com, Internet: http://www.smmoa.org. Head: Elsa Longhauser
Fine Arts Museum - 1985
Contemporary art, historic former train stn 40209

Santa Paula CA

California Oil Museum, 1001 E Main St, Santa Paula, CA 93060, mail addr: POB 48, Santa Paula, CA 93060 - T: (805) 933-0076, Fax: (805) 933-0096, E-mail: info@oilmuseum.net, Internet: http://www.oilmuseum.net. Head: Mike Nelson
Science&Tech Museum - 1950
Oil Industry 40210

Santa Paula Union Oil Museum → California Oil Museum

Santa Rosa CA

Jesse Peter Museum, Santa Rosa Junior College, 1501 Mendocino Av, Santa Rosa, CA 95401 - T: (707) 527-4479, Fax: (707) 524-1861, E-mail: foley_benson@garfield.santarosa.edu, Internet: http://www.santarosa.edu/museum. Head: Foley C. Benson
Ethnology Museum - 1932
Native American art 40211

Luther Burbank Home, Santa Rosa Av, Santa Rosa, CA 95402 - T: (707) 524-5445, Fax: (707) 524-5827, E-mail: burbankhome@flash.netdex.com, Internet: http://www.ci.santa-rosa.ca.us/rp/burbank/
Local Museum - 1979
Historic house 40212

Sonoma County Museum, 425 Seventh St, Santa Rosa, CA 95401 - T: (707) 579-1500, Fax: (707) 579-4849, E-mail: scm@pon.net, Internet: http://www.pressdemo.com/scmuseum
Local Museum - 1976
Local hist 40213

Saranac Lake NY

Robert Louis Stevenson Memorial Cottage, 11 Stevenson Ln, Saranac Lake, NY 12983 - T: (518) 891-1462. Head: John M. Delahant
Special Museum - 1920 40214

Sarasota FL

Art Center Sarasota, 707 N Tamiami Trail, Sarasota, FL 34236-4050 - T: (941) 365-2032, Fax: (941) 366-0585, E-mail: visualartcenter@aol.com, Internet: http://www.artsarasota.org. Head: Lisa-Marie Confessore
Fine Arts Museum / Public Gallery / Association with Coll - 1926 40215

Crowley Museum, 16405 Myakka Rd, Sarasota, FL 34240 - T: (941) 322-1000, Fax: (941) 322-1000, E-mail: crowleymuseum@aol.com, Internet: http://www.crowleymuseumnaturectr.org. Head: Judy Ball, Debbie Dixon
Historical Museum / Natural History Museum - 1974
History, natural history 40216

The John and Mable Ringling Museum of Art, State Art Museum of Florida, 5401 Bay Shore Rd, Sarasota, FL 34243 - T: (941) 359-5700, Fax: (941) 359-5745, E-mail: ringling@ringling.org, Internet: http://www.ringling.org. Head: John Wetenhall
Fine Arts Museum / Decorative Arts Museum - 1927
Archaeology, folk culture, costumes and textiles, decorative arts, paintings, photographs, prints, drawings, graphic arts, sculpture, furnishings, botany 40217

Selby Gallery, Ringling School of Art and Design, 2700 N Tamiami Trail, Sarasota, FL 34234 - T: (941) 359-7563, Fax: (941) 359-7517, E-mail: selby@ringling.edu, Internet: http://www.rsad.edu/. Head: Kevin Dean
University Museum - 1986
Library 40218

The Turner Museum, 5747 Summerside Ln, Sarasota, FL 34231-8370 - T: (941) 924-5622, Fax: (941) 924-5622, E-mail: budapest1924@aol.com. Head: Douglass J.M. Graham
Fine Arts Museum - 1973
Art of J.M.W. Turner (1775-1851) 40219

Saratoga CA

Montalvo Center for the Arts, 15400 Montalvo Rd, Saratoga, CA 95070 - T: (408) 961-5800, Fax: (408) 961-5850, E-mail: echallener@villamontalvo.org, Internet: http://www.villamontalvo.org. Head: Elisbeth Challener
Fine Arts Museum - 1930
Art 40220

Saratoga WY

Saratoga Museum, 104 Constitution Av, Saratoga, WY 82331 - T: (307) 326-5511, Internet: http://members.xoom.com/kaikin/welcome. Head: Pat Bensen
Local Museum / Archaeological Museum - 1978
Local hist 40221

Saratoga Springs NY

The Children's Museum at Saratoga, 36 Phila St, Saratoga Springs, NY 12866 - T: (518) 584-5540, Fax: (518) 584-6049, E-mail: cmas@netheaven.com. Head: Ashley Edwards
Special Museum - 1989 40222

Historical Society of Saratoga Springs Museum, Casino, Congress Park, Saratoga Springs, NY 12866 - T: (518) 584-6920, Fax: (518) 581-1477, E-mail: historicalsociety@juno.com, Internet: http://www.saratogahistory.org. Head: John Carpener McKee
Decorative Arts Museum / Local Museum - 1883 40223

National Museum of Dance, 99 S Broadway, Saratoga Springs, NY 12866 - T: (518) 584-2225, Fax: (518) 584-4515, E-mail: info@dancemuseum.org, Internet: http://www.dancemuseum.org. Head: Toni Smith
Performing Arts Museum - 1986 40224

National Museum of Racing and Hall of Fame, 191 Union Av, Saratoga Springs, NY 12866 - T: (518) 584-0400, Fax: (518) 584-4574, E-mail: nmrhof96@race.saratoga.ny.us, Internet: http://racingmuseum.org. Head: Peter Hammell
Special Museum - 1950 40225

Schick Art Gallery, c/o Skidmore College, Skidmore Campus, 815 N Broadway, Saratoga Springs, NY 12866-1632 - T: (518) 584-5000 ext 2370, Fax: (516) 580-5029, E-mail: damiller@skidmore.edu. Head: David Miller
Fine Arts Museum / University Museum - 1926 40226

Saugerties NY

Opus 40 and the Quarryman's Museum, 50 Fite Rd, Saugerties, NY 12477 - T: (914) 246-3400, Fax: (914) 246-1997. Head: Don Bell, Pat Richards
Fine Arts Museum / Local Museum - 1978 40227

Saugus MA

Saugus Iron Works, 244 Central St, Saugus, MA 01906 - T: (781) 233-0050, Fax: (781) 231-9012, Internet: http://www.nps.gov/sair. Head: Steve Kesselman
Science&Tech Museum - 1954
Blast furnace, forge and slitting mill 40228

Sauk Centre MN

Sinclair Lewis Museum, I94 and US 71, Sauk Centre, MN 56378 - T: (320) 352-5201. Head: Roberta Olson
Historical Museum - 1960 40229

Saukville WI

Ozaukee County Historical Society Pioneer Village, 4880 Hwy I, Saukville, WI 53080 - T: (414) 377-4510. Head: Ralph D. Luedtke
Open Air Museum / Local Museum - 1960
Pioneer village 40230

Sault Sainte Marie MI

Sault de Sainte Marie Historical Sites, 501 E Water St, Sault Sainte Marie, MI 49783 - T: (906) 632-3658, Fax: (906) 632-9344. Head: John P. Wellington, J.H. Hobaugh
Historical Museum / Science&Tech Museum - 1967
Maritime hist 40231

Saum MN

First Consolidated School in Minnesota, Main St, Saum, MN 56650 - T: (218) 647-8673. Head: Arnold Wolden
Historical Museum - 1962
1903 original log school, 1912 Saum School 40232

Saunderstown RI

Casey Farm, Route 1A, Saunderstown, RI 02874 - T: (617) 227-3956, Fax: (617) 227-9204, Internet: http://www.spnea.org. Head: Elizabeth Igleheart
Open Air Museum / Local Museum - 1955
Historic homestead 40233

The Gilbert Stuart Museum, 815 Gilbert Stuart Rd, Saunderstown, RI 02874 - T: (401) 294-3001, Fax: (401) 294-3869, Internet: http://www.gilbertstuartmuseum.org
Fine Arts Museum - 1930
Historic house, birthplace of artist Gilbert Stuart 40234

Sausalito CA

Bay Area Discovery Museum, Fort Baker, 557 McReynolds Rd, Sausalito, CA 94965 - T: (415) 487-4398, Fax: (415) 332-9671, E-mail: info@badm.org, Internet: http://www.badm.org. Head: Bill Paterson, Bonnie Pitman
Special Museum - 1984 40235

Savannah GA

Archives Museum - Temple Mickve Israel, 20 E Gordon St, Savannah, GA 31401 - T: (912) 233-1547, Fax: (912) 233-3086, E-mail: Rabbelzer@aol.com, Internet: http://www.Mickveisrael.org. Head: Joel Greenberg
Religious Arts Museum - 1974
Congregation Mickve Israel Synagogue, oldest Jewish congregation in the South 40236

Davenport House Museum, 324 E State St, Savannah, GA 31401 - T: (912) 236-8097, Fax: (912) 233-7706, E-mail: davenport@g-net.net. Head: Chris Johnson, Scott M. Brown
Historical Museum / Historic Site - 1955
Historic House 40237

Fort Pulaski National Monument, U.S. Hwy 80 E, Savannah, GA 31410 - T: (912) 786-5787, Fax: (912) 786-6023, Internet: http://www.nps.gov/fopu/. Head: John D. Breen
Military Museum - 1924 40238

Georgia Historical Society Museum, 501 Whitaker St, Savannah, GA 31499 - T: (912) 651-2128, Fax: (912) 651-2831, E-mail: ghs@history.com, Internet: http://www.georgiahistory.com. Head: Dr. W. Todd Groce
Local Museum - 1839
Regional history 40239

Juliette Gordon Low Birthplace, 10 E Oglethorpe Av, Savannah, GA 31401 - T: (912) 233-4501, Fax: (912) 233-4659, E-mail: birthplace@girlscouts.org, Internet: http://www.girlscouts.org/birthplace. Head: Fran Powell Harold
Historical Museum - 1956
1818-1821 Wayne-Gordon House 40240

Old Fort Jackson, 1 Fort Jackson Rd, Savannah, GA 31404 - T: (912) 232-3945, Fax: (912) 236-5126, E-mail: fortjackson@chsgeorgia.org, Internet: http://www.chsgeorgia.org. Head: Phillip R. Brinson, Scott Smith
Military Museum - 1975
Military 40241

Owens-Thomas House, 124 Abercorn, Savannah, GA 31401 - T: (912) 233-9743, Fax: (912) 233-0102, E-mail: chamberlainc@telfair.org, Internet: http://www.telfair.org. Head: Diane B. Lesko
Historical Museum - 1951
Original carriage house with slave quarters and walled garden 40242

Telfair Museum of Art, 121 Barnard St, Savannah, GA 31401 - T: (912) 232-1177, Fax: (912) 232-6954, E-mail: mooreb@telefair.org, Internet: http://www.telfair.org. Head: Diane B. Lesko
Fine Arts Museum / Science&Tech Museum - 1875 40243

William Scarbrough House, Ships of the Sea Museum, 41 Martin Luther King Blvd, Savannah, GA 31401 - T: (912) 232-1511, Fax: (912) 234-7363, Internet: http://www.shipsofthesea.org. Head: Jeff Fulton
Historical Museum - 1966
Maritime history, housed in 1819 Regency style house 40244

Wormsloe State Historic Site, 7601 Skidaway Rd, Savannah, GA 31406 - T: (912) 353-3023, Fax: (912) 353-3023. Head: Joe H. Thompson
Archaeological Museum - 1973
Ruins of 1739 fortified house 40245

Savannah MO

Andrew County Museum, 202 E Duncan Dr, Savannah, MO 64485-0012 - T: (816) 324-4720, Fax: (816) 324-5271, E-mail: andcomus@ccp.com, Internet: http://www.artcom.com/museums/. Head: Harold Johnson, Patrick S. Clark
Local Museum - 1972 40246

Saxton PA

Captain Phillips' Rangers Memorial, Pennsylvania Hwy 26, Saxton, PA 16678 - T: (717) 787-3602, Fax: (717) 783-1073
Historic Site - 1959
Site of July 16, 1780, Indian massacre of members of Capt. Phillips' militia 40247

Scarborough ME

Scarborough Historical Museum, 649A U.S. Rte 1, Dunstan, Scarborough, ME 04074 - T: (207) 883-3539. Head: Rodney Laughton
Local Museum - 1961
Local history 40248

Scarsdale NY

Scarsdale Historical Society Museum, 937 Post Rd, Scarsdale, NY 10583 - T: (914) 723-1744, Fax: (914) 723-2185, Internet: http://www.scarsdalenet.com/historicalsociety. Head: Beverley Brigandi
Local Museum - 1973 40249

Weinberg Nature Center, 455 Mamaroneck Rd, Scarsdale, NY 10583 - T: (914) 722-1289, Fax: (914) 723-4784. Head: Lois Weiss, Walter D. Terrell
Natural History Museum - 1958 40250

Schaefferstown PA

Historic Schaefferstown, N Market St, Schaefferstown, PA 17088 - T: (717) 866-6152. Head: Ed Bixler
Agriculture Museum / Local Museum - 1966
Local hist 40251

Schaumburg IL

Motorola Museum, 1297 E Algonquin Rd, Schaumburg, IL 60196 - T: (847) 576-6400, Fax: (847) 576-6401, E-mail: asd003@email.mot.com. Head: Sharon Darling
Science&Tech Museum - 1991 40252

Volkening Heritage Farm at Spring Valley, 1111 E Schaumburg Rd, Schaumburg, IL 60194 - T: (847) 985-2100, Fax: (847) 985-9692, Internet: http://www.parkfun.com. Head: Jerry Handlon
Natural History Museum / Agriculture Museum / Historical Museum - 1983
Living history farm, German-American farmlife of the 1880s 40253

Schenectady NY

Schenectady County Historical Society Museum, 32 Washington Av, Schenectady, NY 12305 - T: (518) 374-0263, Internet: http://www.schist.org. Head: William Dimpelfeld
Local Museum - 1905 40254

Schenectady Museum, 15 Nott Terrace Heights, Schenectady, NY 12308 - T: (518) 382-7890, Fax: (518) 382-7893, E-mail: schdymuse@schenectadymuseum.org, Internet: http://www.schenectadymuseum.org. Head: Bart A. Roselli
Local Museum - 1934 40255

Schoharie NY

Old Stone Fort Museum Complex, N Main St, Schoharie, NY 12157 - T: (518) 295-7192, Fax: (518) 295-7187, E-mail: schosf@telenet.net. Head: Carle J. Kopecky
Local Museum / Historical Museum - 1889
Local history, American war for independence - Library, archives 40256

Schoharie Colonial Heritage Association Museum, 1743 Palatine House, Spring St, Schoharie, NY 12157 - T: (518) 295-7505, Fax: (518) 295-6001, E-mail: scha@midtel.net, Internet: http://www.midtel.net/~scha. Head: Judith Warner
Local Museum - 1963 40257

Schwenksville PA

Pennypacker Mills, 5 Haldeman Rd, Schwenksville, PA 19473 - T: (610) 287-9349, Fax: (610) 287-9657, Internet: http://www.montcopa.org/culture/history.htm. Head: Ella Aderman
Science&Tech Museum - 1981
Historic house 40258

Scituate MA

Scituate Historical Museum, Laidlaw Historical Center, Scituate, MA 02066 - T: (781) 545-1083, Fax: (781) 545-8287, Internet: http://www.21plink.net/~history. Head: David S. Ball
Local Museum - 1916
Local history 40259

Scobey MT

Daniels County Museum and Pioneer Town, 7 County Rd, Scobey, MT 59263 - T: (406) 487-5965, Fax: (406) 487-2849, E-mail: charlynt@nemontel.net. Head: Edgar Richardson, Chet Solberg, Lee Cook, Sue Leibrand, Justin Hanson, Mike Stableton, Frank Edwards, Paul Landeraaen
Local Museum - 1965 40260

Scotia CA

The Pacific Lumber Company Museum, 125 Main St, Scotia, CA 95565 - T: (707) 764-2222, Fax: (707) 764-4150, Internet: http://www.palco.com. Head: Mary Bullwinkel
Historical Museum - 1959
Logging and lumber industry 40261

Scotia NY

Scotia-Glenville Children's Museum, 303 Mohawk Av, Scotia, NY 12302 - T: (518) 346-1764, Fax: (518) 377-6593, E-mail: sgcminfo@crisny.org. Head: Dr. Frank B. Strauss, Claudia McLaughlin
Special Museum - 1978 40262

Scotland SD

Scotland Heritage Chapel and Museum, 811 6th St, Scotland, SD 57059 - T: (605) 583-2344. Head: Marvin Thum
Local Museum / Religious Arts Museum - 1976
Local and religious hist 40263

Scott AR

Plantation Agriculture Museum, 4815 Hwy 161, Scott, AR 72142 - T: (501) 961-1409, E-mail: bswad@aristotle.net. Head: Ben H. Swadley
Agriculture Museum / Local Museum - 1989
Agriculture, local hist 40264

Toltec Mounds Archeological State Park, 490 Toltec Mounds Rd, Scott, AR 72142 - T: (501) 961-9442, Fax: (501) 961-9221, E-mail: toltecmounds@aristotle.net, Internet: http://www.wwn.cast.vark.edn/~shelly/html/parkin/toltecvisitpg.html. Head: Henry Thomason
Archaeological Museum - 1975
Archaeology 40265

Scottdale PA

West Overton Museums, West Overton Village, Scottdale, PA 15683 - T: (724) 887-7910, Fax: (724) 882-5010, E-mail: womuseum@westol.com. Head: Donald J. Snyder, Rodney Sturtz
Open Air Museum / Local Museum - 1928
Rural industrial village 40266

Scottsdale AZ

Fleischer Museum, 17207 N Perimeter Dr, Scottsdale, AZ 85255 - T: (480) 585-3108, Fax: (480) 563-6192, E-mail: jhoeffel@ffca.com, Internet: http://www.fleischer.org. Head: Donna H. Fleischer
Fine Arts Museum - 1990
Art 40267

Rawhide Old West Museum, 23023 N Scottsdale Rd, Scottsdale, AZ 85255 - T: (602) 502-5600, Fax: (602) 502-1301, Internet: http://www.rawhide.com. Head: Victor Ostrow
Local Museum - 1972
Local hist 40268

Scottsdale Museum of Contemporary Art, 7380 E Second St, Scottsdale, AZ 85251 - T: (480) 874-4610, Fax: (480) 874-4699, E-mail: info@sccarts.org, Internet: http://www.scottsdalearts.org. Head: Valerie Vadala-Homer
Fine Arts Museum / Public Gallery - 1975
Contemporary art, architecture, design 40269

Sylvia Plotkin Judaica Museum, 10460 N 56th St, Scottsdale, AZ 85253 - T: (480) 951-0323, Fax: (480) 951-7150, E-mail: museum@templebethisrael.org, Internet: http://www.sylviaplotkinjudaicamuseum.org. Head: Pamela Levin
Religious Arts Museum - 1966
Religious antiques, housed in Temple belonging to oldest Jewish Congregation in the Phoenix area 40270

Scranton PA

The Catlin House Museum, 232 Monroe Av, Scranton, PA 18510 - T: (717) 344-3841, Fax: (717) 344-3815. Head: Alan Sweeney, Maryann Moran
Local Museum - 1886
Local hist 40271

Everhart Museum, 1901 Mulberry St, Scranton, PA 18510-2390 - T: (717) 346-7186, Fax: (717) 346-0652, E-mail: exdir@everhart.museum.org, Internet: http://Everhart-museum.org. Head: Dr. Michael C. Illuzzi
Fine Arts Museum / Natural History Museum / Science&Tech Museum - 1908
Art, science and natural hist 40272

Marywood University Art Galleries, 2300 Adams Av, Scranton, PA 18509 - T: (717) 348-6278, Fax: (717) 340-6023. Head: Mary Reap, Sandra Ward Povse
Fine Arts Museum / University Museum - 1924 40273

Pennsylvania Anthracite Heritage Museum, RR 1, Bald Mountain Rd, Scranton, PA 18504 - T: (717) 963-4804, 963-4845, Fax: (717) 963-4194, Internet: http://www.phmc.state.pa.vs. Head: Steven Ling
Historical Museum - 1975
History 40274

Steamtown National Historic Site, 150 S Washington Av, Scranton, PA 18503 - T: (570) 340-5200, Fax: (570) 340-5309, Internet: http://www.nps.gov/stea. Head: Terry R. Gess
Science&Tech Museum - 1986
Transportation and technology 40275

Seaford DE

Governor Ross Plantation, N Pine St, Seaford, DE 19973 - T: (302) 628-9500, 629-4269, 628-0400, Fax: (302) 628-9501. Head: Claudia Melson
Local Museum - 1977
Local hist 40276

Seaford NY

Seaford Historical Museum, 3890 Waverly Av, Seaford, NY 11783 - T: (516) 826-1150. Head: Joshua Soren
Local Museum - 1968 40277

Searsport ME

Penobscot Marine Museum, 5 Church St, Searsport, ME 04974-0498 - T: (207) 548-2529, Fax: (207) 548-2520, E-mail: museumoffices@penobscotmarinemuseum.org, Internet: http://www.penobscotmarinemuseum.org. Head: Renny A. Stackpole
Historical Museum - 1936
Maritime hist, 3 sea captain's homes and Town Hall, paintings - Phillips library, Carver gallery 40278

Seattle WA

Burke Museum of Natural History and Culture, University of Washington Campus, Seattle, WA 98195 - T: (206) 543-7907, Fax: (206) 685-3039, E-mail: recept@u.washington.edu, Internet: http://www.washington.edu/burkemuseum/index.html. Head: Dr. Karl Hutterer
Ethnology Museum / Natural History Museum / Folklore Museum - 1885
Anthropology, natural hist, art 40279

Center for Wooden Boats, 1010 Valley St, Seattle, WA 98109 - T: (206) 382-2628, Fax: (206) 382-2699, E-mail: cwb@cwb.org, Internet: http://www.cwb.org. Head: William Van Vlack, Bob Perkins
Science&Tech Museum - 1978
Boats 40280

Center on Contemporary Art, 65 Cedar St, Seattle, WA 98121 - T: (206) 728-1980, E-mail: nwannual@hotmail.com. Head: Elisabeth Shepherd
Fine Arts Museum 40281

The Children's Museum, 305 Harrison St, Seattle, WA 98109 - T: (206) 441-1768, Fax: (206) 448-0910. Head: Irwin Goverman, Cynthia Captain
Special Museum - 1981
Children's museum 40282

Frye Art Museum, 704 Terry Av, Seattle, WA 98104 - T: (206) 622-9250, Fax: (206) 223-1707, E-mail: fryeart@aol.com, Internet: http://www.fryeart.org. Head: Richard L. Cleveland, Richard V. West
Fine Arts Museum - 1952
Art 40283

Henry Art Gallery, University of Washington, 15th Av NE and NE 41st St, Seattle, WA 98195, mail addr: Box 351410, Seattle, WA 98195-1410 - T: (206) 543-2280/81, Fax: (206) 685-3123, E-mail: hartg@u.washington.edu, Internet: http://www.henryart.org. Head: Richard Andrews
Fine Arts Museum / University Museum - 1927
Art 40284

King County Art Gallery, 506 2nd Av, Rm 1115, Seattle, WA 98104 - T: (206) 296-8671, Fax: (206) 296-8629, E-mail: jimkelly@metrokc.gov, Internet: http://www.metrokc.gov/exec/culture. Head: Jim Kelly
Fine Arts Museum / Public Gallery - 1967
Art 40285

Klondike Gold Rush National Historical Park, 117 S Main, Seattle, WA 98104 - T: (206) 553-7220, Fax: (206) 553-0614. Head: Willie Russell
Historical Museum - 1979
History 40286

Memory Lane Museum at Seattle Goodwill, 1400 S Lane St, Seattle, WA 98144 - T: (206) 329-1000, Fax: (206) 726-1502, E-mail: goodwill@seattlegoodwill.org, Internet: http://www.seattle-goodwill.org. Head: Jill Jones
Local Museum - 1968
Local hist 40287

Museum of Flight, 9404 E Marginal Way, Seattle, WA 98108 - T: (206) 764-5700, Fax: (206) 764-5707, Internet: http://www.museumofflight.org. Head: Ralph A. Bufano, Joan Piper
Science&Tech Museum / Special Museum - 1964
Aeronautics 40288

Museum of History and Industry, 2700 24th Av, Seattle, WA 98112 - T: (206) 324-1126, Fax: (206) 324-1346, E-mail: mjh@historymuse-nw.org, Internet: http://www.historymuse-nw.org. Head: Sonya L. Ralph
Historical Museum - 1914
History, industry 40289

Nordic Heritage Museum, 3014 NW 67th St, Seattle, WA 98117 - T: (206) 789-5708, Fax: (206) 789-3271, E-mail: nordic@intelistip.com, Internet: http://www.nordicmuseum.com. Head: Marianne Forssblad
Special Museum - 1979
Local hist, nordic hist, nordic american art 40290

Pacific Arts Center, 810 18th Av, Seattle, WA 98122 - T: (206) 328-1221, Fax: (206) 328-1244. Head: Marty Spiegel
Fine Arts Museum - 1983
Art 40291

Pacific Science Center, 200 2nd Av N, Seattle, WA 98109 - T: (206) 443-2001, Fax: (206) 443-3631, E-mail: webmaster@pacsci.org, Internet: http://www.pacsci.org. Head: Lawrence P. Horowitz, George P. Moynihan, David Taylor
Science&Tech Museum - 1962
Science, technology 40292

Seattle Art Museum, 100 University St, Seattle, WA 98101-2902 - T: (206) 625-3255, Fax: (206) 654-3135, E-mail: webmaster@seattleartmuseum.org, Internet: http://www.seattleartmuseum.org. Head: Mimi Gardner Gates
Fine Arts Museum - 1917
Art 40293

Seattle Asian Art Museum, Volunteer Park, 1400 E Prospect, Seattle, WA 98112-3303 - T: (206) 625-8900, Fax: (206) 654-3191, E-mail: webmaster@seattleartmuseum.org, Internet: http://www.seattleartmuseum.org. Head: Mimi Gardner Gates
Fine Arts Museum - 1917
Art 40294

Shoreline Historical Museum, 749 N 175th St, Seattle, WA 98133 - T: (206) 542-7111, Fax: (206) 542-4645, E-mail: shorelinehistorical@juno.com. Head: Margaret Boyce
Local Museum - 1976
Local hist 40295

Wing Luke Asian Museum, 407 Seventh Av, Seattle, WA 98104 - T: (206) 623-5124, Fax: (206) 623-4559, E-mail: folks@wingluke.org, Internet: http://www.wingluke.org. Head: Ron Chew
Fine Arts Museum / Ethnology Museum / Historical Museum - 1967
Asian Pacific American hist, art and culture 40296

Sebago ME

The Jones Museum of Glass and Ceramics, 35 Douglas Mountain Rd, Sebago, ME 04029 - T: (207) 787-3370, Fax: (207) 787-2800. Head: John H. Holverson
Decorative Arts Museum - 1978
Glass, ceramics 40297

Sebewaing MI

Luckhard Museum - The Indian Mission, 612 E. Bay St, Sebewaing, MI 48759 - T: (517) 883-2539. Head: Jim Bunke
Local Museum / Religious Arts Museum - 1957
Historic house, mission home 40298

Sebring FL

Civilian Conservation Corps Museum, Highlands Hammock State Park, 5931 Hammock Rd, Sebring, FL 33872 - T: (941) 386-6094, Fax: (941) 386-6095, E-mail: hammock@strato.net, Internet: http://www.dep.state.fl.us/park/central/highlands.html. Head: Peter Anderson
Historical Museum / Natural History Museum - 1994
Housed in 1930s building constructed of heavy native timbers, lumber cut and fabricated 40299

Highlands Museum of the Arts, 351 W Center Av, Sebring, FL 33870 - T: (941) 385-5312, Fax: (941) 655-3240, E-mail: haleague@strato.net. Head: Gene Brenner, Jeanne A. Watkins
Fine Arts Museum - 1986
Art 40300

Second Mesa AZ

Hopi Cultural Museum, Rte 264, Second Mesa, AZ 86043 - T: (520) 734-6650, Fax: (520) 734-6650. Head: Anna Silas
Local Museum / Folklore Museum - 1970 40301

Sedalia MO

Pettis County Historical Society Museum, c/o Sedalia Public Library, 311 W Third St, Sedalia, MO 65301-4399 - T: (660) 826-1314. Head: Rhonda Chalfant
Local Museum - 1943 40302

Sedan KS

Emmett Kelly Historical Museum, 202 E Main, Sedan, KS 67361 - T: (316) 725-3470. Head: Roger Floyd
Local Museum / Performing Arts Museum - 1967
Clowns, history, local history 40303

Sedgwick ME

Sedgwick-Brooklin Historical Museum, Rte 172, Sedgwick, ME 04676 - T: (207) 359-2547. Head: Robert Sargent
Local Museum - 1963
Regional history 40304

Sedona AZ

Sedona Arts Center, Hwy 89A at Art Barn Rd, Sedona, AZ 86336 - T: (520) 282-3809, Fax: (520) 282-1516, E-mail: sac@sedona.net. Head: Craig O. Thompson
Fine Arts Museum / Folklore Museum - 1961
Art 40305

Seguin TX

Fiedler Memorial Museum, Texas Lutheran University, Seguin, TX 78155 - T: (830) 372-8000, Fax: (830) 372-8188, Internet: http://www.txlutheran.edu. Head: Evelyn Fiedler Streng
Natural History Museum / Science&Tech Museum - 1973
Geology 40306

Selinsgrove PA

Lore Degenstein Gallery, Susquehanna University, 514 University Av, Selinsgrove, PA 17870-1001 - T: (570) 372-4059, 374-0101, Fax: (570) 372-2775, E-mail: livingst@susqu.edu, Internet: http://www.susqu.edu. Head: Dr. Valerie Livingston
Fine Arts Museum / University Museum - 1993
Art 40307

Selkirk NY

Bethlehem Historical Association Museum, 1003 River Rd, Selkirk, NY 12158 - T: (518) 767-9432. Head: Parker D. Mathusa
Local Museum - 1965 40308

Selma AL

Sturdivant Hall, 713 Mabry St, Selma, AL 36701 - T: (334) 872-5626, E-mail: smuseum@zebra.net. Head: Archie T. Reeves
Local Museum - 1957
Historic house 40309

Senatobia MS

Heritage Museum Foundation of Tate County, POB 375, Senatobia, MS 38668 - T: (601) 562-8559, Fax: (622) 562-5786, E-mail: dperkins@gmi.net. Head: Deborah Perkins
Local Museum - 1977
History, agriculture, art, folklore 40310

Seneca SC

World of Energy at Keowee-Toxaway, 7812 Rochester Hwy, Seneca, SC 29672 - T: (864) 885-4600, Fax: (864) 885-4605
Science&Tech Museum - 1969
Energy and electricity 40311

Seneca Falls NY

National Women's Hall of Fame, 76 Fall St, Seneca Falls, NY 13148 - T: (315) 568-8060, Fax: (315) 568-2976, E-mail: womenshall@aol.com, Internet: http://www.greatwomen.org. Head: Mary Gratton
Local Museum - 1969 40312

Seneca Falls Historical Society Museum, 55 Cayuga St, Seneca Falls, NY 13148 - T: (315) 568-8412, Fax: (315) 568-8426, E-mail: sfhs@flare.ner, Internet: http://www.welcome.to/sfhs/. Head: Frances T. Barbieri
Local Museum - 1904 40313

Sequim WA

Museum and Arts Center in the Sequim Dungeness Valley, 175 W Cedar, Sequim, WA 98382 - T: (360) 683-8110, Fax: (360) 683-8364. Head: Eugene Pember, Margaret DeWitt
Fine Arts Museum / Decorative Arts Museum / Historical Museum - 1992 40314

Setauket NY

Gallery North, 90 N Country Rd, Setauket, NY 11733 - T: (631) 751-2676, Fax: (631) 751-0180, E-mail: gallerynorth@aol.com, Internet: http://www.gallerynorth.org. Head: Elizabeth Goldberg, Collen W. Hanson
Public Gallery - 1965 40315

Sewanee TN

The University Gallery of the University of the South, 735 University Av, Sewanee, TN 37383-1000 - T: (931) 598-1223, Fax: (615) 598-1145, E-mail: aende@sewanne.edu, Internet: http://www.sewanee.edu/gallery/gallery. Head: Arlyn Ende
Fine Arts Museum / University Museum - 1965
Paintings, prints, drawings, graphics, sculpture, photos, furniture, silver, stained glass 40316

Seward AK

Resurrection Bay Historical Society Museum → Seward Museum

Seward Museum, 336 Third Av, Seward, AK 99664 - T: (907) 224-3902. Head: Lee E. Poleske
Local Museum - 1967 40317

Seward NE

Marxhausen Art Gallery, Concordia University, 800 N Columbia Av, Seward, NE 68434 - T: (402) 643-3651, Fax: (402) 643-4073, Internet: http://www.cune.edu/art/flgall.html. Head: James Bockelman
Fine Arts Museum / University Museum - 1951
Contemporary print multiples 40318

Sewickley PA

International Images, 514 Beaver St, Sewickley, PA 15143 - T: (412) 741-3036, Fax: (412) 741-8606. Head: Elena Kornetchuk, Charles M. Wiebe
Fine Arts Museum - 1978 40319

Seymour WI

Seymour Community Museum, Depot St, Seymour, WI 54165 - T: (414) 833-2868
Local Museum - 1976
Local hist 40320

Shady Side MD

Captain Salem Avery House Museum, 1418 EW Shadyside Rd, Shady Side, MD 20764 - T: (410) 867-4486, E-mail: mdaly4942@aol.com, Internet: http://www.averyhouse.org
Historical Museum - 1988
Waterman's house 40321

Shaftsbury VT

Shaftsbury Historical Society Museum, Historic 7A, Shaftsbury, VT 05262 - T: (802) 447-7488. Head: Robert J. Williams, Phil McQuade
Local Museum - 1967
Local hist 40322

Shaker Heights OH

Shaker Historical Society Museum, 16740 S Park Blvd, Shaker Heights, OH 44120 - T: (216) 921-1201, Fax: (216) 921-2615, E-mail: shakhist@wviz.org, Internet: http://www.cwru.edu/affil/shakhist/shaker.htm. Head: Norma Rodgers, Cathie Winans
Local Museum - 1947 40323

Sharon MA

Kendall Whaling Museum, 27 Everett St, Sharon, MA 02067 - T: (781) 784-5642, Fax: (781) 784-0451, E-mail: ehazen@kwm.org, Internet: http://www.kwm.org. Head: Stuart M. Frank
Natural History Museum - 1956
History, maritime history, photos 40324

Sharon NH

Sharon Arts Center, 457 Rte 123, Sharon, NH 03458-9014 - T: (603) 924-7256, Fax: (603) 924-6074, E-mail: sharonarts@sharonarts.org, Internet: http://www.sharonarts.org. Head: Randall Hoel
Fine Arts Museum / Public Gallery - 1947 40325

Sharpsburg MD

Antietam National Battlefield, Rte 65 N, Sharpsburg, MD 21782 - T: (301) 432-5124, Fax: (301) 432-4590, E-mail: keith-snyder@nps.gov, Internet: http://www.nps.gov/anti. Head: Terry Carlstrom
Historic Site / Military Museum - 1890
Site of 1862 Civil War Maryland Campaign and battle of Antietam or Sharpsburg 40326

Chesapeake and Ohio Canal Tavern Museum, 16500 Shepherdstown Park, Sharpsburg, MD 21782 - T: (301) 739-4200, Fax: (301) 714-2232, E-mail: doug.stover@nps.gov, Internet: http://www.nps.gov/choh. Head: Douglas D. Faris
Historical Museum - 1954
Great Falls Tavern, brick railroad station, with operating steam locomotive ride, Ferry Hill slave plantation 40327

Shaw Island WA

Shaw Island Historical Society Museum, Blind Bay Rd, Shaw Island, WA 98286 - T: (360) 468-4068
Local Museum - 1966
Local hist 40328

Shawnee KS

Johnson County Museums, 6305 Lackman Rd, Shawnee, KS 66217 - T: (913) 631-6709, Fax: (913) 631-6359, E-mail: jcmuseum@jocoks.com, Internet: http://www.digitalhistory.com
Local Museum - 1967
County history 40329

Shawnee OK

Mabee-Gerrer Museum of Art, 1900 W MacArthur Dr, Shawnee, OK 74801-2499 - T: (405) 878-5300, Fax: (405) 878-5133, E-mail: info@mabeegerrermuseum.org. Head: Joi Grissom, Debby Williams
Fine Arts Museum - 1917 40330

Sheboygan WI

John Michael Kohler Arts Center, 608 New York Av, Sheboygan, WI 53081 - T: (920) 458-6144, Fax: (920) 458-4473, Internet: http://www.jmkac.org. Head: Ruth Kohler
Fine Arts Museum - 1967
Art 40331

Sheboygan County Historical Museum, 3110 Erie Av, Sheboygan, WI 53081 - T: (920) 458-1103, Fax: (920) 458-5152. Head: Ed Falck, Robert Harker
Historical Museum - 1954
Local hist 40332

Sheffield Lake OH

103rd Ohio Volunteer Infantry Memorial, 5501 E Lake Rd, Sheffield Lake, OH 44054 - T: (440) 949-2790
Military Museum - 1972 40333

Shelburne VT

National Museum of the Morgan Horse, 122 Bostwick Rd, Shelburne, VT 05482 - T: (802) 985-8665, Fax: (802) 985-5242, E-mail: morgans@together.net
Special Museum - 1988
Horses 40334

Shelburne Museum, 5555 Shelburne Rd, Shelburne, VT 05482 - T: (802) 985-3346, Fax: (802) 985-2331, E-mail: museinfo@together.net, Internet: http://www.shelburnemuseum.org. Head: Hope Alswanis
Local Museum - 1947
Local hist 40335

Shelby MT

Marias Museum of History and Art, 206 12 Av N, Shelby, MT 59474 - T: (406) 434-2551, Fax: (406) 434-5422
Fine Arts Museum / Historical Museum - 1963 40336

Shelby NC

Cleveland County Historical Museum, Court Sq, Shelby, NC 28150 - T: (704) 482-8186, Fax: (704) 482-8186. Head: Ginny Hughes, L. Wilson
Local Museum - 1976 40337

Shelbyville IN

Louis H. and Lena Firn Grover Museum, 52 W Broadway, Shelbyville, IN 46176 - T: (317) 392-4634. Head: Norman Barnett, June Barnett
Local Museum - 1980
Local history 40338

Shelter Island NY

Shelter Island Historical Society Museum, 16 S Ferry Rd, Shelter Island, NY 11964 - T: (516) 749-0025, Fax: (516) 749-1825, E-mail: sihissoc@hamptons.com, Internet: http://www.shelterisland-histsoc.org. Head: W.M. Anderson, Louise Green
Historical Museum - 1965
archives 40339

Shepherdstown WV

Historic Shepherdstown Museum, 129e German St, Shepherdstown, WV 25443, mail addr: POB 1786, Shepherdstown, WV 25443 - T: (304) 876-0910, Fax: (304) 876-2679, E-mail: hsc@intrepid.net, Internet: http://www.intrepid.net/~hsc
Local Museum
Local hist 40340

Sheridan AR

Grant County Museum, 521 Shackleford Rd, Sheridan, AR 72150 - T: (870) 942-4496. Head: Elwin L. Goolsby
Local Museum - 1970 40341

Sherwood WI

High Cliff General Store Museum, 7526 N Lower Cliff Rd, Sherwood, WI 54169-0001 - T: (414) 989-1636. Head: Alice Bishop, Todd Bishop
Local Museum - 1974
Local hist 40342

Shevlin MN

Clearwater County Historical Museum, Hwy 2 W, Shevlin, MN 56676 - T: (218) 785-2000, Fax: (218) 785-2440. Head: Harry Larson
Local Museum - 1967
Local history 40343

Shiloh TN

Shiloh National Military Park and Cemetery, Hwy 22, Shiloh, TN 38376 - T: (901) 689-5275, Fax: (901) 689-5450, E-mail: shil_interpretation@nps.gov
Military Museum - 1894
Military hist 40344

Shiner TX

Edwin Wolters Memorial Museum, 306 S Av, Shiner, TX 77984 - T: (512) 594-3774, 594-3362, Fax: (512) 594-3566
Local Museum - 1963
Local hist 40345

Shippensburg PA

Shippensburg Historical Society Museum, 52 W King St, Shippensburg, PA 17257 - T: (717) 532-6727, Internet: http://www.ship.edu/~pegill/shs.html
Local Museum - 1944
Local hist 40346

Shreveport LA

Louisiana State Exhibit Museum, 3015 Greenwood Rd, Shreveport, LA 71109 - T: (318) 632-2020, Fax: (318) 632-2056. Head: Forrest Dunn
Historical Museum - 1937
General museum, State hist 40347

Meadows Museum of Art, Centenary College, 2911 Centenary Blvd, Shreveport, LA 71104 - T: (318) 869-5169, Fax: (318) 869-5730, E-mail: ddufilho@beta.centenary.edu, Internet: http://www.centenary.edu. Head: Diane Dufilho
Fine Arts Museum / University Museum - 1976
Art 40348

Pioneer Heritage Center, LSU-Shreveport, 1 University Pl, Shreveport, LA 71115 - T: (318) 797-5332, Fax: (318) 797-5395, E-mail: mplummer@pilot.1sus.edu. Head: Marguerite R. Plummer
Historical Museum - 1977
History Complex 40349

R.S. Barnwell Memorial Garden and Art Center, 601 Clyde Fant Pkwy, Shreveport, LA 71101 - T: (318) 673-7703, Fax: (318) 673-7707. Head: Clay Brock, Shelly Ragle
Fine Arts Museum / Public Gallery - 1970 40350

The R.W. Norton Art Gallery, 4747 Creswell Av, Shreveport, LA 71106 - T: (318) 869-0435, E-mail: norton@softdisk.com, Internet: http://www.softdisk.com/comp/norton. Head: Richard W. Norton jr.
Fine Arts Museum - 1946
Art 40351

Sci-Port Discovery Center, 820 Clyde Fant Pkwy, Shreveport, LA 71101 - T: (318) 424-3466, Fax: (318) 222-5592, E-mail: apeek@sciport.org, Internet: http://www.sciport.org. Head: Andre Peek
Science&Tech Museum - 1994
Science 40352

Shullsburg WI

Badger Mine and Museum, 279 Estey, Shullsburg, WI 53586 - T: (608) 965-4860. Head: Tim Strang
Local Museum - 1964
Local hist 40353

Sibley IA

McCallum Museum, 5th St and 8th Av, Sibley, IA 51249 - T: (712) 754-3882, E-mail: verstoff@rconnect. Head: Jan Stofferan
Local Museum - 1956
Local history 40354

Sibley MO

Fort Osage National Historic Landmark, 105 Osage St, Sibley, MO 64088 - T: (816) 795-8200 ext 1260, Fax: (816) 795-7938, E-mail: juligor@gw.co.jackson.mo.us, Internet: http://www.co.jackson.mo.us. Head: Bettie Yahn Kramer
Local Museum - 1948 40355

Sidney NE

Fort Sidney Museum and Post Commander's Home, 6th Av and Jackson St, Sidney, NE 69162 - T: (308) 254-2150. Head: Bob Buhrdorf, Mildred Johnson, Norman Spicer, LaVerne Thomas, Lois Heizer, Evelyn Geu, Geraldine Talich
Military Museum - 1954
Military hist 40356

Sidney NY

Sidney Historical Association Museum, 21 Liberty St, Room 218, Sidney, NY 13838 - T: (607) 563-8787
Local Museum - 1945 40357

Siloam Springs AR

Siloam Springs Museum, 112 N Maxwell, Siloam Springs, AR 72761 - T: (501) 524-4011, E-mail: ssmuseum@ipa.net. Head: Bill Osgood, Donald Warden
Historical Museum - 1969
Local history, textiles 40358

Silver City NM

Francis McCray Gallery, Western New Mexico University, 1000 College Av, Silver City, NM 88062 - T: (505) 538-6614, 538-6515, Fax: (505) 538-6316. Head: Gloria Maya
Fine Arts Museum / University Museum - 1960
Art 40359

Silver City Museum, 312 W Broadway, Silver City, NM 88061 - T: (505) 538-5921, Fax: (505) 388-1096, E-mail: scmuseum@zianet.com, Internet: http://www.zianet.com/silverweb/museum. Head: Susan Berry
Local Museum - 1967 40360

Western New Mexico University Museum, Fleming Hall, 10 St, Silver City, NM 88062 - T: (505) 538-6386, Fax: (505) 538-6178, Internet: http://www.wnmw.edu/univ/museum.htm. Head: Dr. Cynthia Ann Bettison
University Museum / Ethnology Museum - 1974 40361

Silver Cliff CO

Silver Cliff Museum, 606 Main St, Silver Cliff, CO 81252 - T: (719) 783-2615, Fax: (719) 783-2615
Local Museum - 1959
Local history 40362

Silverton CO

Mayflower Gold Mill, 1 Main St N, Silverton, CO 81433 - T: (970) 387-5838. Head: Beverly Rich
Science&Tech Museum
Local history 40363

San Juan County Historical Museum, 1557 Greene St, Silverton, CO 81433 - T: (970) 387-5838. Head: Beverly Rich
Local Museum - 1964
Local history 40364

Simi CA

R.P. Strathearn Historical Park, 137 Strathearn Pl, Simi, CA 93065 - T: (805) 526-6453, Fax: (805) 526-6462, E-mail: havens1@ix.netcom.com. Head: John Childress, Patricia Havens
Local Museum - 1970
Local hist 40365

Simsbury CT

Simsbury Historical Society Museum, 800 Hopmeadow St, Simsbury, CT 06070 - T: (860) 658-2500, Fax: (860) 658-2500, E-mail: -simburyhistorical@juno.com. Head: Dawn Hutchins Bobyrk
Local Museum - 1911
Local hist 40366

Sioux City IA

Sioux City Art Center, 225 Nebraska St, Sioux City, IA 51101-1712 - T: (712) 279-6272 ext 208, Fax: (712) 255-2921, Internet: http://www.sc-artcenter.com
Fine Arts Museum - 1914
Art 40367

Sioux City Public Museum, 2901 Jackson St, Sioux City, IA 51104-3697 - T: (712) 279-6174, Fax: (712) 252-5615, E-mail: scpm@sioux-city.org, Internet: http://www.sioux-city.org/museum
Local Museum - 1886
General local history, Peirce mansion, Sergeant Floyd River Museum, Loren D. Callendar gallery 40368

Trinity Heights - Saint Joseph Center-Museum, 2509 33rd St, Sioux City, IA 51105 - T: (712) 239-8670. Head: Bernard F. Cooper
Fine Arts Museum - 1992
Woodcarving 40369

Sioux Falls SD

Battleship South Dakota Memorial, 12th and Kiwanis St, Sioux Falls, SD 57104 - T: (605) 367-7141, 367-7060. Head: David Witte
Military Museum - 1968
Military hist 40370

Delbridge Museum, 805 S Kiwanis Av, Sioux Falls, SD 57104-3714 - T: (605) 367-7003, Fax: (605) 367-8340, E-mail: tylera@gpzoo.org. Head: Edward D. Asper, Tyler Ahnemann
Natural History Museum - 1957
Natural hist 40371

Eide-Dalrymple Gallery, Augustana College, 29th St and S Grange Av, Sioux Falls, SD 57197 - T: (605) 274-4609, Fax: (605) 274-4368, E-mail: hannus@inst.augie.edu, Internet: http://www.augie.edu/archlab/al.html. Head: L. Adrien Hannus
Fine Arts Museum - 1960
Primitive art, Japanese woodcuts, European prints, New Guinea masks 40372

Jim Savage Art Gallery and Museum, 3301 E 26th St, Village Sq, Sioux Falls, SD 57103 - T: (605) 332-7551, Fax: (605) 332-7551. Head: Barb Van Laar
Fine Arts Museum
Woodcarving 40373

Sioux Empire Medical Museum, 1100 S Euclid Av, Sioux Falls, SD 57117-5039 - T: (605) 333-6397. Head: Thenetta Nield
Historical Museum - 1975
Medical hist, regional health care, uniforms, nursing school, hospital life, iron lung 40374

Siouxland Heritage Museums, 200 W 6th St, Sioux Falls, SD 57104-6001 - T: (605) 367-4210, Fax: (605) 367-6004, Internet: http://www.minnehahacounty.org. Head: William J. Hoskins
Local Museum - 1926
Local hist 40375

Washington Pavillion of Arts and Science, 301 S Main St, Sioux Falls, SD 57104 - T: (605) 367-7397, Fax: (605) 731-2402, E-mail: vac@washington-pavilion.org, Internet: http://www.washington-pavilion.org
Fine Arts Museum / Folklore Museum / University Museum - 1961
Art 40376

Sisseton SD

Tekakwitha Fine Arts Center, 401 S 8th Av W, Sisseton, SD 57262-0208 - T: (605) 698-7058, Fax: (605) 698-3801. Head: Harold D. Moore
Fine Arts Museum - 1969
Dakotah Sioux art, former dormitory of the Tekakwitha Indian Childrens' home 40377

Sitka AK

Isabel Miller Museum, 330 Harbor Dr, Sitka, AK 99835 - T: (907) 747-6455, Fax: (907) 747-6588, E-mail: sitkahis@ptialaska.net, Internet: http://www.sitka.org. Head: Gerry Young
Local Museum - 1957 40378

Sheldon Jackson Museum, 104 College Dr, Sitka, AK 99835 - T: (907) 747-8981, Fax: (907) 747-3004, E-mail: Peter_Corey@eed.state.ak.us, Internet: http://www.museums.state.ak.us
Ethnology Museum - 1888
Alaska native cultures 40379

Sitka National Historical Park, 106 Metlakatla St, Sitka, AK 99835 - T: (907) 747-6281, Fax: (907) 747-5938
Local Museum - 1910
Local hist 40380

Skowhegan ME

Skowhegan History House, Elm St, Skowhegan, ME 04976 - T: (207) 474-6632, 474-2415
Historical Museum - 1937 40381

Slidell LA

Slidell Art Center, 444 Erlanger St, Slidell, LA 70458 - T: (504) 646-4375, Fax: (504) 646-4231, E-mail: parsons@gs.verio.net. Head: Suzanne C. Parsons
Fine Arts Museum - 1989 40382

Smackover AR

Arkansas Museum of Natural Resources, 3853 Smackover Hwy, Smackover, AR 71762 - T: (501) 725-2877, Fax: (501) 725-2161, E-mail: amnr@cei.net, Internet: http://www.minipages.com/smackover/ao&b.htm. Head: Don Lambert
Historical Museum / Science&Tech Museum - 1977
History, technology 40383

Smithfield VA

Isle of Wight Courthouse, 130 Main St, Smithfield, VA 23430 - T: (804) 357-3502, Fax: (804) 775-0802, Internet: http://www.apva.org. Head: Martin Kirwan King, Peter Dan Grover
Local Museum - 1750
Historic building 40384

Smithtown NY

Smithtown Historical Society Museum, 5 N Country Rd, Smithtown, NY 11787 - T: (516) 265-6768, Fax: (516) 265-6768. Head: Bradley L. Harris, Louise P. Hall
Local Museum - 1955 40385

Smithville TN

Appalachian Center for Crafts, 1560 Craft Center Dr, Smithville, TN 37166 - T: (615) 597-6801, Fax: (615) 597-6803. Head: Ward Doubet
Ethnology Museum - 1979 40386

Snohomish WA

Blackman Museum, 118 Av B, Snohomish, WA 98290 - T: (360) 568-5235. Head: Mitch Cornelison
Local Museum - 1969
Local hist 40387

Snow Hill MD

Julia A. Purnell Museum, 208 W Market St, Snow Hill, MD 21863 - T: (410) 632-0515, Fax: (410) 632-0515, E-mail: purrellmuseum@hotmail.com, Internet: http://www.intercom.net/local/snowhill/snowhill.html. Head: Mary Saint Hippolyte
Local Museum - 1942
History of American/ Worcester County, folk art, furniture, jewelry, machines, tools 40388

Snyder TX

Scurry County Museum, 4200 College Av, Snyder, TX 79549 - T: (915) 573-6107, Fax: (915) 573-9321, E-mail: scm@snydertex.com. Head: Charlene Akers
Local Museum - 1970
Local hist 40389

Socorro NM

New Mexico Bureau of Mines Mineral Museum, New Mexico Tech, 801 Leroy Pl, Socorro, NM 87801 - T: (505) 835-5140, Fax: (505) 835-6333, E-mail: vwlueth@nmt.edu, Internet: http://geoinfo.nmt.edu. Head: Virgil W. Lueth
Natural History Museum - 1926 40390

Sodus Point NY

Sodus Bay Historical Society Museum, 7606 N Ontario St, Sodus Point, NY 14555 - T: (315) 483-4936, E-mail: sodusbay@ix.netcom.com, Internet: http://www.peachey.com/soduslight. Head: Eugene P. Seymour, Patricia Kalima
Local Museum - 1979
Local hist 40391

Solomons MD

Calvert Marine Museum, 14200 Solomons Island Rd, Solomons, MD 20688 - T: (410) 326-2042, Fax: (410) 326-6691, E-mail: information@calvertmarinemuseum.com, Internet: http://www.calvertmarinemuseum.com. Head: C. Douglass Alves
Historical Museum / Natural History Museum / Special Museum - 1969
Marine, Drum Point Lighthouse on waterfront, seafood packing house 40392

Solvang CA

Old Mission Santa Ines, 1760 Mission Dr, Solvang, CA 93463 - T: (805) 688-4815, Fax: (805) 686-4468, Internet: http://www.missionsantaines.org
Local Museum - 1804
Historic building 40393

Somers NY

Somers Historical Society Museum, Elephant Hotel, Rtes 100 and 202, Somers, NY 10589 - T: (914) 277-4977, Fax: (914) 277-4977
Historical Museum - 1956
Early American circus 40394

Somers Point NJ

Atlantic County Historical Society Museum, 907 Shore Rd, Somers Point, NJ 08244 - T: (609) 927-5218
Local Museum - 1913 40395

Somers Mansion, 1000 Shore Rd, Somers Point, NJ 08244 - T: (609) 927-2212, Fax: (609) 927-1827, E-mail: history54@msn.com
Local Museum - 1941 40396

Somerset PA

Somerset Historical Center, 10649 Somerset Pike, Somerset, PA 15501 - T: (814) 445-6077, Fax: (814) 443-6621
Local Museum - 1969
Local hist 40397

Somerville MA

Somerville Museum, One Westwood Rd, Somerville, MA 02143 - T: (617) 666-9810. Head: Regina M. Pisa
Local Museum - 1897
Local history 40398

Somerville NJ

Old Dutch Parsonage, 38 Washington Pl, Somerville, NJ 08876 - T: (908) 725-1015
Local Museum - 1947 40399

Wallace House, 38 Washington Pl, Somerville, NJ 08876 - T: (908) 725-1015
Decorative Arts Museum / Local Museum - 1947 40400

Somesville ME

Mount Desert Island Historical Museum, 2 Oak Hill Rd, Somesville, ME 04660 - T: (207) 244-5043, Fax: (207) 244-3991, E-mail: jroths@acadia.net. Head: Anne Mazlish, Jaylene Roths
Local Museum - 1931
Local history 40401

Sonoma CA

Sonoma State Historic Park, 20 E Spain St, Sonoma, CA 95476 - T: (707) 938-1519, Fax: (707) 938-1406
Local Museum - 1906
Local hist 40402

South Bend IN

College Football Hall of Fame, 111 S Saint Joseph St, South Bend, IN 46601 - T: (219) 235-5581, Fax: (219) 235-5720, E-mail: bernie.kish@collegefootball.org, Internet: http://www.college-football.org
Special Museum - 1978 40403

Copshaholm House Museum and Historic Oliver Gardens, Northern Indiana Center for History, 808 W Washington, South Bend, IN 46601 - T: (219) 235-9664, Fax: (219) 235-9059, E-mail: nich@michiana.org, Internet: http://www.centerforhistory.org
Local Museum - 1990
Local hist 40404

Northern Indiana Center for History, 808 W Washington, South Bend, IN 46601 - T: (219) 235-9664, Fax: (219) 235-9059, E-mail: nich@michiana.org, Internet: http://www.centerforhistory.org. Head: Cheryl Taylor Bennett
Ethnology Museum / Historical Museum - 1994
History, children's interactive museum, Voyages, history of the Saint Joseph River Valley Region, Changing gallery, Carroll gallery, Leighton gallery, traveling 40405

South Bend Regional Museum of Art, 120 S Saint Joseph St, South Bend, IN 46601 - T: (219) 235-9102, Fax: (219) 235-5782, E-mail: sbrma@sbt.infi.net, Internet: http://www.sbt.infi.net/~sbrma. Head: Susan R. Visser
Fine Arts Museum - 1947
American art 40406

Studebaker National Museum, 525 S Main St, South Bend, IN 46601 - T: (219) 235-9714, Fax: (219) 235-5522, E-mail: stumuseum@skyenet.net, Internet: http://www.studebakermuseum.org. Head: Ronald Radecki
Science&Tech Museum - 1977
Industry 40407

Worker's Home Museum, Northern Indiana Center for History, 808 W Washington St, South Bend, IN 46601 - T: (219) 235-9664, Fax: (219) 235-9059, E-mail: nich@michiana.org, Internet: http://www.centerforhistory.org
Historical Museum - 1994
History 40408

South Bend WA

Pacific County Historical Museum, 1008 W Robert Bush Dr, South Bend, WA 98586-0039 - T: (360) 875-5224, Fax: (360) 875-5224, E-mail: museum@willapabay.org, Internet: http://www.pacificco-history.org. Head: Vincent Shaudys, Bruce Weilepp
Local Museum - 1970
Local hist 40409

South Berwick ME

Sarah Orne Jewett House, 5 Portland St, South Berwick, ME 03908 - T: (603) 436-3205, (617) 227-3956, Fax: (617) 227-9204, Internet: http://www.spnea.org. Head: Andrea Strassner
Special Museum - 1931
Residence of the author Sarah Orne Jewett 40410

South Boston VA

South Boston-Halifax County Museum of Fine Arts and History, 1540 Wilborn Av, South Boston, VA 24592 - T: (804) 572-9200, E-mail: sbhcm@halifax.com, Internet: http://www2.halifax.com/museum
Local Museum / Fine Arts Museum - 1981
Regional history, art 40411

South Dartmouth MA

Children's Museum in Dartmouth, 276 Gulf Rd, South Dartmouth, MA 02748 - T: (508) 993-3361, Fax: (508) 993-3332. Head: Robert Howland, Ronald Mayer
Ethnology Museum / Historical Museum - 1952 40412

South Deerfield MA

Yankee Candle Car Museum, Rte 5, South Deerfield, MA 01373 - T: (413) 665-2020, Fax: (413) 665-2399, Internet: http://www.yankeecandle.com. Head: Steve Smith
Science&Tech Museum - 1995
Transportation 40413

South Hadley MA

Mount Holyoke College Art Museum, Lower Lake Rd, South Hadley, MA 01075-1499 - T: (413) 538-2245, Fax: (413) 538-2144, E-mail: artmuseum@mtholyoke.edu, Internet: http://www.mtholyoke.edu/go/artmuseum. Head: Marianne Doezema
Fine Arts Museum / University Museum - 1875
Art 40414

South Haven MI

Michigan Maritime Museum, 260 Dyckman Av, South Haven, MI 49090 - T: (616) 637-8078, Fax: (616) 637-1594, E-mail: mmmuseum@accn.org, Internet: http://www.michiganmaritimemuseum.org. Head: Dr. Barbara K. Kreuzer
Historical Museum - 1976
Maritime history - library 40415

South Hero VT

South Hero Bicentennial Museum, Rte 2, South Hero, VT 05486 - T: (802) 372-6615, 672-5552, E-mail: lmjshut@aol.com. Head: Barbara Winch
Local Museum - 1974
Local hist 40416

South Holland IL

South Holland Historical Museum, Box 48, South Holland, IL 60473 - T: (708) 596-2722. Head: Pauline Schaap
Local Museum - 1969
Local history 40417

South Milwaukee WI

South Milwaukee Historical Society Museum, 717 Milwaukee Av, South Milwaukee, WI 53172 - T: (414) 768-8790, 762-8852
Local Museum - 1972
Local hist 40418

South Natick MA

Historical and Natural History Museum of Natick, 58 Eliot St, South Natick, MA 01760 - T: (508) 647-4841, Fax: (508) 651-7013, E-mail: elliot@ma.ultranet.com, Internet: http://www.ultranet.com/~elliot/
Local Museum - 1870
Local history, American Indian artifacts, natural history - library 40419

South Orange NJ

Seton Hall University Museum, 400 South Orange Av, South Orange, NJ 07079 - T: (973) 761-9459, Fax: (973) 275-2368, E-mail: krafther@lanmail.shu.edu, Internet: http://www.shu.edu. Head: Charlotte Nichols
University Museum / Archaeological Museum - 1963
Archaeology 40420

South Pass City WY

South Pass City State Historic Site, 125 South Pass Main St, South Pass City, WY 82520 - T: (307) 332-3684, Fax: (307) 332-3688
Local Museum - 1967
Local hist 40421

South Saint Paul MN

Dakota County Historical Society Museum, 130 Third Av N, South Saint Paul, MN 55075 - T: (651) 451-6260, Fax: (651) 552-7265, E-mail: dchs@mtn.org. Head: Steve Larson, Gregory A. Page
Historical Museum - 1939 40422

South Sudbury MA

Longfellow's Wayside Inn Museum, Wayside Inn Rd, South Sudbury, MA 01776 - T: (978) 443-1776;, Fax: (978) 443-8041, E-mail: inkeeper@wayside.org, Internet: http://www.wayside.org. Head: Guy R. LeBlanc
Local Museum - 1716
Local history 40423

South Sutton NH

South Sutton Old Store Museum, 12 Meeting House Hill Rd, South Sutton, NH 03273 - T: (603) 927-4472
Historical Museum - 1954 40424

South Union KY

Shaker Museum, 850 Shaker Museum Rd, South Union, KY 42283 - T: (502) 542-4167, 542-7734, Fax: (502) 542-7558, E-mail: shakmus@logantele.com, Internet: http://www.logantele.com/~shakmus/. Head: Tommy Hines
Historical Museum - 1960
Site of 1807 South Union Shaker village 40425

South Williamsport PA

Peter J. McGovern Little League Baseball Museum, Rte 15, South Williamsport, PA 17701 - T: (570) 326-3607, Fax: (570) 326-2267, Internet: http://www.littleleague.org. Head: Cynthia A. Stearns
Special Museum - 1982
Sports, Little League 40426

Southampton NY

Parrish Art Museum, 25 Job's Ln, Southampton, NY 11968 - T: (631) 283-2118 ext 12, Fax: (631) 283-7006, E-mail: fergusone@parrishart.org, Internet: http://thehamptons.com. Head: Trudy C. Kramer
Fine Arts Museum - 1898 40427

Southold NY

Southold Historical Society Museum, Main Rd and Maple Ln, Southold, NY 11971 - T: (516) 765-5500, Fax: (516) 765-5500. Head: Maureen Ostermann
Local Museum - 1960 40428

Southold Indian Museum, Bayview Rd, Southold, NY 11971 - T: (516) 765-5577, E-mail: indianmuseum@juno.com, Internet: http://www.i2.i-2000.com/~skindoc/. Head: Walter L. Smith
Ethnology Museum / Archaeological Museum - 1925 40429

Southwest Harbor ME

Wendell Gilley Museum, Main St and Herrick Rd, Southwest Harbor, ME 04679 - T: (207) 244-7555, Fax: (207) 244-7555, E-mail: gilleymu@acadia.net, Internet: http://www.acadia.net/gilley. Head: Steven C. Rockefeller, Nina Z. Gormley
Fine Arts Museum / Folklore Museum - 1981
Folk art, woodcarving 40430

Spalding ID

Nez Perce National Historical Park, Hwy 95, Spalding, ID 83540 - T: (208) 843-2261, Fax: (208) 843-2001, E-mail: bob_chenoweth@nps.gov, Internet: http://www.nps.gov/doug_eury
Natural History Museum / Ethnology Museum / Historical Museum - 1965
Prehistoric occupation, Indian ethnographic colls, photos, Dugout canoes, lawyer family coll, 1877 war - archives, research center 40431

Sparta WI

Monroe County Local History Room and Library, 200 W Main St, Sparta, WI 54656 - T: (608) 269-8680, Fax: (608) 269-8921, E-mail: mclhr@centurytel.net, Internet: http://co.monroe.wi.us
Local Museum - 1977 40432

Spartanburg SC

Milliken Gallery, Converse College, 580 E Main St, Spartanburg, SC 29302 - T: (864) 585-6421, Fax: (864) 596-9158, Internet: http://www.converse.edu. Head: Jim Creal
Fine Arts Museum / University Museum - 1971
Art 40433

Regional Museum of Spartanburg County, 100 E Main St, Spartanburg, SC 29306 - T: (864) 596-3501, Fax: (864) 596-3501, E-mail: regionalmuseum@mindspring.com, Internet: http://www.spartanarts.org/history
Local Museum - 1961
Local hist 40434

The Sandor Teszler Gallery, Wofford College, 429 N Church St, Spartanburg, SC 29303-3663 - T: (864) 597-4300, Fax: (864) 597-4329, E-mail: coburnoh@wofford.edu, Internet: http://www.sandorteszlerlibrary.org. Head: Oakley H. Coburn
University Museum / Library with Exhibitions
Art, crafts, sciences, social sciences - library 40435

Spartanburg County Museum of Art, 385 S Spring St, Spartanburg, SC 29306 - T: (803) 582-7616, Fax: (803) 948-5353, E-mail: museum@spartanarts.org, Internet: http://www.sparklenet.com/museumofart. Head: Mike Kohler, Theresa Mann
Fine Arts Museum - 1969
Arts 40436

Spartanburg Science Center, 385 S Spring St, Spartanburg, SC 29306 - T: (864) 583-2777, Fax: (864) 948-5353. Head: John F. Green
Natural History Museum / Science&Tech Museum - 1978
Natural hist, science, exotic tortoises, reptiles, fossils, skulls, rocks, minerals, insects, shells, bird nests 40437

Spearfish SD

Ruddell Gallery, Black Hills State University, 1200 University St, Spearfish, SD 57799 - T: (605) 642-6104 ext 6111, Fax: (605) 642-6105. Head: Jim Knutsen
Fine Arts Museum - 1936
Photography, regional, visual artists - library 40438

Spencer NC

North Carolina Transportation Museum, 411 S Salisbury Av, Spencer, NC 28159 - T: (704) 636-2889, Fax: (704) 639-1881, E-mail: nctrans@tarheel.net, Internet: http://www.ci.salisbury.nc.us/nctrans/. Head: Elizabeth Smith
Science&Tech Museum - 1977
1896 Southern Railway steam primary staging and repair facility complex containing 20 structures, 37 bay roundhouse, turntable and 90,000 feet back shop 40439

Spencerport NY

Ogden Historical Society Museum, 568 Colby St, Spencerport, NY 14559 - T: (716) 352-0660. Head: Ted Rogers
Local Museum - 1958 40440

Spillville IA

Bily Clock Museum and Antonin Dvorak Exhibition, 323 S Main, Spillville, IA 52168 - T: (319) 562-3569, Fax: (319) 562-4373, Internet: http://www.spillville.ia.us
Special Museum - 1923
Clocks 40441

Spiro OK

Spiro Mounds Archaeological Center, Rte 2, Box 339AA, Spiro, OK 74959 - T: (918) 962-2062, Fax: (918) 962-2062, E-mail: spiromds@ipa.net. Head: Dennis Peterson
Archaeological Museum - 1978
Archaeology 40442

Spokane WA

Cheney Cowles Museum, 2316 First Av, Spokane, WA 99204 - T: (509) 456-3931 ext 102, Fax: (509) 456-7690, Internet: http://www.tincan.org/~ccm. Head: Glenn Mason
Local Museum / Folklore Museum - 1916
Local hist 40443

Jundt Art Museum, Gonzaga University, 502 E Boone Av, Spokane, WA 99258-0001 - T: (509) 323-6611, Fax: (509) 323-5525, E-mail: patnode@calvin.gonzaga.edu, Internet: http://www.gonzaga.edu/jundt/index.html. Head: J. Scott Patnode
Fine Arts Museum / University Museum - 1995
Art 40444

Spotsylvania County VA

Spotsylvania Historical Museum, POB 64, Spotsylvania County, VA 22553 - T: (540) 582-7167. Head: John E. Pruitt, Martha C. Carter
Local Museum - 1962
Local hist 40445

Spring Green WI

The House on the Rock, 5754 Hwy 23, Spring Green, WI 53588 - T: (608) 935-3639, Fax: (608) 935-9472. Head: Susan Donaldson
Local Museum - 1961
Historical house 40446

Spring Valley MN

Methodist Church Museum - a Laura Ingalls Wilder Site, c/o Spring Valley Historical Society, 220 W Courtland St, Spring Valley, MN 55975 - T: (507) 346-7659, Fax: (507) 346-7249, Internet: http://www.ci.spring-valley.mn.us. Head: Donald Larson
Historical Museum - 1956 40447

Springdale AR

Shiloh Museum of Ozark History, 118 W Johnson Av, Springdale, AR 72764 - T: (501) 750-8165, Fax: (501) 750-8171, E-mail: shiloh@springdaleark.org, Internet: http://www.springdaleark.org/shiloh. Head: Bob Besom
Historical Museum - 1965 40448

Springdale PA

Rachel Carson Homestead, 613 Marion Av, Springdale, PA 15144-1242 - T: (724) 274-5459, Fax: (724) 275-1259, E-mail: homestead@rachelcarson.org, Internet: http://www.rachelcarson.org. Head: Mark Tomlinson
Local Museum - 1975
Historic house 40449

Springdale UT

Zion National Park Museum, Zion Canyon Headquarters, Springdale, UT 84767-1099 - T: (435) 772-0166, Fax: (435) 772-3426, Internet: http://www.nps.gov/zion
Historical Museum - 1919
Natural and human hist - archives 40450

Springfield IL

The Dana-Thomas House, 301 E Lawrence Av, Springfield, IL 62703 - T: (217) 782-6773, Fax: (217) 788-9450. Head: Dr. Donald P. Hallmark
Decorative Arts Museum - 1981
Frank Lloyd Wright prairie period house, art glass and furniture, decorative art, social history (20th c) 40451

Illinois State Museum, Spring and Edwards Sts, Springfield, IL 62706-5000 - T: (217) 782-7440, Fax: (217) 782-1254, Internet: http://www.museum.state.il.us/. Head: Dr. R. Bruce McMillan, Kent Smith, Dr. Judith A. Franke
Fine Arts Museum / Local Museum / Ethnology Museum / Natural History Museum - 1877
Natural history, anthropology, geology, botany, zoology, decorative art, art 40452

Lincoln Home, 413 S 8th St, Springfield, IL 62701-1905 - T: (217) 492-4241, Fax: (217) 492-4673, E-mail: liho_superintendent@nps.gov, Internet: http://www.nps.gov/liho
Historical Museum / Historic Site - 1972
Home of Abraham Lincoln, 16th Pres. of the United States 40453

Lincoln Tomb, Oak Ridge Cemetery, Springfield, IL 62702 - T: (217) 782-2717, Fax: (217) 524-3738
Historic Site - 1874
1874 the tomb of Abraham Lincoln 40454

The Pearson Museum, 801 N Rutledge, Springfield, IL 62702 - T: (217) 785-2128, 782-4261, Fax: (217) 782-9132, E-mail: bmason@siumed.edu, Internet: http://www.siumed.edu/medhum/html/The_Pearson_Museum/the_pearson_museum.htm. Head: Phillip V. Davis
University Museum / Historical Museum - 1974
Medical hist 40455

Springfield Art Gallery, 700 N Fourth St, Springfield, IL 62702 - T: (217) 523-2631, Fax: (217) 523-3866, E-mail: spiartassc@aol.com. Head: Dean Adkins
Fine Arts Museum / Public Gallery - 1913 40456

Springfield KY

Lincoln Homestead, 5079 Lincoln Park Rd, Springfield, KY 40069 - T: (606) 336-7461, Fax: (606) 336-0659, E-mail: Gary.Feldman@mail.state.ky.us
Historic Site - 1936 40457

Springfield MA

Connecticut Valley Historical Museum, 220 State St, Springfield, MA 01103 - T: (413) 263-6800 ext 304, Fax: (413) 263-6898, E-mail: info@spfldlibmus.org, Internet: http://www.quadrangle.org. Head: John Hamilton
Historical Museum - 1927
Regional history 40458

George Walter Vincent Smith Art Museum, 220 State St, Springfield, MA 01103 - T: (413) 263-6800, Fax: (413) 263-6898, E-mail: info@spfldlibmus.org, Internet: http://www.quadrangle.org. Head: Joseph Carvalho, Heather Haskell
Fine Arts Museum / Decorative Arts Museum - 1895
Japanese decorative arts, Chinese cloisonné, Middle Eastern rugs, American paintings of the 19th c 40459

Museum of Fine Arts, 220 State St, Springfield, MA 01103 - T: (413) 263-6800, Fax: (413) 263-6898, E-mail: info@spfldlibmus.org, Internet: http://www.quadrangle.org. Head: Joseph Carvalho, Heather Haskell
Fine Arts Museum - 1933
American and European painting, sculptures, decorative art 40460

Naismith Memorial Basketball Hall of Fame, 1150 W Columbus Av, Springfield, MA 01105 - T: (413) 781-6500, Fax: (413) 781-1939, Internet: http://www.hoophall.com. Head: John Doleva
Special Museum - 1968
Sports 40461

Springfield Armory Museum, 1 Armory Sq, Springfield, MA 01105-1299 - T: (413) 734-8551, Fax: (413) 747-8062, E-mail: spar_interpretation@nps.gov, Internet: http://www.nps.gov
Special Museum - 1870 40462

Springfield Science Museum, 220 State St, Springfield, MA 01103 - T: (413) 263-6800, Fax: (413) 263-6898, Internet: http://www.quadrangle.org. Head: David Stier
Science&Tech Museum - 1859
African, Native American, minerals 40463

Springfield MO

History Museum for Springfield-Greene County, 830 Boonville, Springfield, MO 65802 - T: (417) 864-1976, Fax: (417) 864-2019, E-mail: shanna_boyle@ci.springfield.mo.us, Internet: http://www.historymuseumsgc.org. Head: Shanna Boyle
Local Museum / Historical Museum - 1975
Local hist 40464

Springfield Art Museum, 1111 E Brookside Dr, Springfield, MO 65807 - T: (417) 837-5700, Fax: (417) 837-5704, E-mail: watercolourusa@ci.springfield.mo.us, Internet: http://www.ci.springfield.mo.us/egov/art. Head: Jerry A. Berger
Fine Arts Museum - 1928
Decorative art, drawings, photography, paintings, prints, sculpture - library 40465

Springfield NJ

Springfield Historical Society Museum, 126 Morris Av, Springfield, NJ 07081 - T: (973) 376-4784. Head: Margaret Bandrowski
Local Museum - 1954 40466

Springfield OH

Clark County Historical Society Museum, 117 S Fountain Av, Springfield, OH 45504 - T: (937) 324-0657, Fax: (937) 324-1992. Head: Floyd Barmann
Local Museum - 1897 40467

Springfield Museum of Art, 107 Cliff Park Rd, Springfield, OH 45501 - T: (937) 325-4673, Fax: (937) 325-4674, E-mail: smoa@main-net.com, Internet: http://www.spfld-museum-of-art.org. Head: Mark Chepp
Fine Arts Museum - 1946 40468

Springfield OR

Springfield Museum, 590 Main St, Springfield, OR 97477 - T: (541) 726-3677, Fax: (541) 726-3689, E-mail: kjensen@ci.springfield.or.us. Head: Kathleen A. Jensen
Local Museum - 1981
Local hist 40469

Springfield VT

Eureka School House, State Rte 11, Springfield, VT 05156 - T: (802) 828-3051, Fax: (802) 828-3206, E-mail: jdumville@gate.dca.state.vt.us, Internet: http://www.state.vt.us/dca/historic/hp_sites.htm. Head: William Jenney
Local Museum - 1968
Historic house 40470

Miller Art Center, 9 Elm Hill, Springfield, VT 05156 - T: (802) 885-2415, E-mail: glenshee@excite.com. Head: Amanda L. Page, Robert McLaughlin
Fine Arts Museum - 1956
Art 40471

Springs PA

Springs Museum, Rte 669, Springs, PA 15562 - T: (814) 662-2625. Head: Joseph Bender
Local Museum - 1957
Local hist 40472

Springville NY

Warner Museum, 98 E Main St, Springville, NY 14141 - T: (716) 592-5546. Head: David C. Batterson
Local Museum - 1953 40473

Springville UT

Springville Museum of Art, 126 E 400 S, Springville, UT 84663 - T: (801) 489-2727, Fax: (801) 489-2739, E-mail: sharon@admn.shs.nebo.edu, Internet: http://www.sma.nebo.edu. Head: Dr. Vern G. Swanson
Fine Arts Museum - 1903
Utah art 40474

Spruce Pine NC

Museum of North Carolina Minerals, Milepost 331, Blue Ridge Pkwy at Hwy 226, Spruce Pine, NC 28777 - T: (704) 765-2761, Fax: (704) 765-0974. Head: Jill Hawk
Natural History Museum - 1955 40475

Staatsburg NY

Mills Mansion State Historic Site, Old Post Rd, Staatsburg, NY 12580 - T: (914) 889-8851, Fax: (914) 889-8321. Head: Eleanor Williamson
Local Museum - 1938 40476

Stamford CT

Stamford Historical Society Museum, 1508 High Ridge Rd, Stamford, CT 06903 - T: (203) 322-1565, Fax: (203) 322-1607, E-mail: ebaulsir@ix.netcom.com, Internet: http://www.stamford-history.org
Local Museum / Decorative Arts Museum - 1901
History, decorative arts 40477

Stamford Museum, 39 Scofieldtown Rd, Stamford, CT 06903 - T: (203) 322-1646, Fax: (203) 322-0408, E-mail: smnc@stamfordmuseum.org, Internet: http://www.stamfordmuseum.org. Head: Kenneth Marchione, Keith Williamson, Sharon Blume
Fine Arts Museum / Natural History Museum - 1936
Natural hist, art 40478

Whitney Museum of American Art at Champion, 1 Champion Plaza, Stamford, CT 06921 - T: (203) 358-7652, Fax: (203) 358-2975
Fine Arts Museum - 1981
Art 40479

Standish ME

Marrett House, Rte 25, Standish, ME 04084 - T: (207) 642-3032, (617) 227-3956, Fax: (617) 227-9204, Internet: http://www.spnea.org
Historical Museum - 1944 40480

Stanfield NC

Reed Gold Mine State Historic Site, 9621 Reed Mine Rd, Stanfield, NC 28163 - T: (704) 721-4653, Fax: (704) 721-4657, E-mail: reedmine@ctc.net, Internet: http://www.itpi.dpi.state.nc.us/reed. Head: Don McNeely
Science&Tech Museum - 1971 40481

Stanford CA

Iris & B. Gerald Cantor Center for Visual Arts at Stanford University, Lomita Dr. and Museum Way, Stanford, CA 94305-5060 - T: (650) 723-4177, Fax: (650) 725-0464, Internet: http://www.stanford.edu/dept/ccva. Head: Thomas K. Seligman
Fine Arts Museum / University Museum - 1885
Art 40482

Stanford KY

William Whitley House, 625 William Whitley Rd, Stanford, KY 40484 - T: (606) 355-2881, Fax: (606) 355-2778, E-mail: ron.langdon@mail.state.ky.us. Head: Ron Langdon
Historical Museum - 1938
1792 William Whitley House, the first brick home W of the Alleghenies 40483

Stanford MT

Judith Basin County Museum, 19 Third S, Stanford, MT 59479 - T: (406) 566-2974. Head: Florence Harris, Oliver Olson, Ruth Hardenbrook, Lorraine Boeck, Mary Mikeson
Local Museum - 1966 40484

Stanton ND

Knife River Indian Villages National Historic Site, County Rd 37, Stanton, ND 58571 - T: (701) 745-3309, Fax: (701) 745-3708, Internet: http://www.nps.gov/knri. Head: Bill Lutz
Local Museum - 1974
Local hist 40485

Stanton TX

Martin County Historical Museum, 207 E Broadway, Stanton, TX 79782 - T: (915) 756-2722
Local Museum - 1969
County hist 40486

Starkville MS

Oktibbeha County Heritage Museum, 206 Fellowship St, Starkville, MS 39759 - T: (601) 323-0211. Head: George Lewis
Historical Museum - 1979 40487

Staten Island NY

Alice Austen House Museum, Alice Austen Park, 2 Hylan Blvd, Staten Island, NY 10305 - T: (718) 816-4506, Fax: (718) 815-3959. Head: Grace Petrone, Nancy E. Fiske
Local Museum - 1985
Local hist 40488

Conference House, 7455 Hylan Blvd, Staten Island, NY 10307 - T: (718) 984-6046. Head: Madalen Bertolini, Geraldine Bennetti
Local Museum - 1927 40489

Garibaldi and Meucci Museum of the Order Sons of Italy in America, 420 Tompkins Av, Staten Island, NY 10305 - T: (718) 442-1608, Fax: (718) 442-8635. Head: Anne Alarcon
Local Museum - 1956 40490

Historic Richmond Town, 441 Clarke Av, Staten Island, NY 10306 - T: (718) 351-1611, Fax: (718) 351-6057, Internet: http://www.historicrichmondtown.org. Head: John Guild
Historical Museum - 1935
Historic village incl 28 historic buildings from late 17th c to early 20th c 40491

Jacques Marchais Museum of Tibetan Art, 338 Lighthouse Av, Staten Island, NY 10306 - T: (718) 987-3500, Fax: (718) 351-0402, Internet: http://www.tibetanmuseum.com. Head: Elizabeth Rogers
Fine Arts Museum / Ethnology Museum / Folklore Museum - 1945 40492

The John A. Noble Collection, 1000 Richmond Terrace, Staten Island, NY 10301 - T: (718) 447-6490, Fax: (718) 447-6056, E-mail: jancol@admin.con2.com, Internet: http://mcns10.med.nyu.edu/noble/noble.collection.html. Head: Erin Urban
Fine Arts Museum / Historical Museum - 1986
Art, maritime history 40493

Snug Harbor Cultural Center, 1000 Richmond Terrace, Staten Island, NY 10301 - T: (718) 448-2500, Fax: (718) 442-8534, E-mail: newhousecenter@hotmail.com. Head: Olivia Georgia
Open Air Museum / Folklore Museum / Historic Site / Fine Arts Museum / Performing Arts Museum - 1976 40494

Staten Island Children's Museum, 1000 Richmond Terrace, Staten Island, NY 10301 - T: (718) 273-2060, Fax: (718) 273-2836, E-mail: adm@kidsmuseum.com, Internet: http://www.kidsmuseum.com. Head: Nancy Ferrara, Dina R. Rosenthal
Special Museum - 1974 40495

Staten Island Ferry Collection, Staten Island Institute of Arts and Sciences, Ferry Terminal Waiting Room, Saint George, Staten Island, NY 10301 - T: (718) 720-9268, Fax: (718) 273-5683
Historical Museum / Science&Tech Museum - 1993
History 40496

Staten Island Historical Society Museum, 441 Clarke Av, Staten Island, NY 10306 - T: (718) 351-1611, Fax: (718) 351-6057. Head: B. Shepherd
Local Museum - 1856 40497

Staten Island Institute of Arts and Sciences, 75 Stuyvesant Pl, Staten Island, NY 10301-1998 - T: (718) 727-1135, Fax: (718) 273-5683
Fine Arts Museum / Natural History Museum - 1881 40498

Statesboro GA

Georgia Southern University Museum, Rosenwald Bldg, Statesboro, GA 30460 - T: (912) 681-5444, Fax: (912) 681-0729, E-mail: dharvey@gasou.edu, Internet: http://www2.gasou.edu/musenews. Head: Richard Smith
University Museum / Natural History Museum - 1980
Natural and cultural history of the Coastal Plain 40499

Statesville NC

Fort Dobbs State Historic Site, US 21, 1 mile off I-40 to SR 1930, West 1 1/2 miles on 1930, Statesville, NC 28677 - T: (704) 873-5866. Head: Louise Huston
Military Museum / Open Air Museum - 1969 40500

Iredell Museum of Arts & Heritage, 1335 Museum Rd, Statesville, NC 28625 - T: (704) 873-4734, Fax: (704) 873-4407, E-mail: imuseum@statesville.net, Internet: http://www.iredellmuseum.com. Head: Mary Bradford
Fine Arts Museum / Natural History Museum / Science&Tech Museum - 1956 40501

Staunton VA

Hunt Gallery, Mary Baldwin College, Market and Vine Sts, Staunton, VA 24401 - T: (540) 887-7196. Head: Paul Ryan
Fine Arts Museum / University Museum - 1842
Art gallery 40502

Museum of American Frontier Culture, 1250 Richmond Rd, Staunton, VA 24401 - T: (540) 332-7850, Fax: (540) 332-9989, Internet: http:http://www.frontiermuseum.org. Head: John A. Walters
Historical Museum - 1982
European and American folklife and culture, focusing on Germany, England, Northern Ireland, America and immigration & culture 40503

Staunton Augusta Art Center, 1 Gyspy Hill Park, Staunton, VA 24401 - T: (540) 885-2028, Fax: (540) 885-6000, E-mail: saartcenter@aol.com. Head: Margo McGirr
Fine Arts Museum - 1961
Art 40504

Woodrow Wilson Birthplace and Museum, 20 N Coalter St, Staunton, VA 24401 - T: (540) 885-0897, Fax: (540) 886-9874, E-mail: woodrow@cfw.com, Internet: http://www.woodrowwilson.org. Head: Patrick Clarke
Historical Museum - 1938
Historic house, birthplace of Woodrow Wilson, academic and social life, presidential history 40505

Steeles Tavern VA

Cyrus H. McCormick Memorial Museum, Box 100, Steeles Tavern, VA 24476 - T: (540) 377-2255, Fax: (540) 377-5850, E-mail: steeles@vt.edu. Head: G.L. Jubb
Local Museum - 1956
Local hist 40506

Steilacoom WA

Steilacoom Historical Museum, 112 Main St, Steilacoom, WA 98388-0016 - T: (253) 584-4133. Head: David J. Welch
Local Museum - 1970
Local hist 40507

Stephenville TX

Stephenville Historical House Museum, 525 E Washington St, Stephenville, TX 76401 - T: (254) 965-5880, E-mail: llohr@our-town.com. Head: Lavinia Lohrmann
Local Museum - 1965
Local hist 40508

Sterling CO

Overland Trail Museum, Junction I-76 and Hwy 6 E, Sterling, CO 80751-0400 - T: (970) 522-3895, Fax: (970) 521-0632, E-mail: hagemeier@sterlingcolo.com, Internet: http://www.sterlingcolo.com
Local Museum - 1936
Regional history 40509

Sterling IL

Sterling-Rock Falls Historical Society Museum, 1005 E 3rd St, Sterling, IL 61081 - T: (815) 622-6215, E-mail: srfhs@coiinc.com
Local Museum - 1959
Local history - library, archives 40510

Sterling NY

Sterling Historical Society Museum, Rte 104A, Sterling, NY 13156 - T: (315) 947-6461. Head: Don H. Richardson
Local Museum - 1976 40511

Steubenville OH

Jefferson County Historical Association Museum, 426 Franklin Av, Steubenville, OH 43952 - T: (740) 283-1133. Head: Eleanor Naylor
Local Museum - 1976 40512

Stevens Point WI

The Museum of Natural History, 900 Reserve St, University of Wisconsin, Stevens Point, WI 54481 - T: (715) 346-4224, 346-2858, Fax: (715) 346-4213, E-mail: emarks@uwsp.edu, Internet: http://www.uwsp.edu/museum/
Natural History Museum / University Museum - 1966
Natural hist 40513

Stillwater MN

Warden's House Museum, 602 N Main St, Stillwater, MN 55082 - T: (612) 439-5956, E-mail: ptp2001@aol.com. Head: Nancy Goodman, Joan Daniels
Historical Museum - 1941 40514

Stillwater NY

Saratoga National Historical Park, 648 Rte 32, Stillwater, NY 12170 - T: (518) 664-9821, Fax: (518) 664-3349, E-mail: sara_info@nps.gov, Internet: http://www.nps.gov/sara. Head: Gina Johnson
Military Museum / Open Air Museum - 1938
Site of the Battles of Saratoga, Sept. 19 and Oct. 7, 1777 40515

Stillwater OK

Gardiner Art Gallery, 108 Bartlett Center, Oklahoma State University, Stillwater, OK 74078 - T: (405) 744-9086, Fax: (405) 744-5767, E-mail: nwilkin@okway.okstate.edu, Internet: http://www.okstate.edu/artsci/art/gallery.html. Head: B.J. Smith
Fine Arts Museum / University Museum - 1965 40516

National Wrestling Hall of Fame, 405 W Hall of Fame Av, Stillwater, OK 74075 - T: (405) 377-5243, Fax: (405) 377-5244, E-mail: nwhof@fullnet.net. Head: Myron Roderick, Tony Linville
Special Museum - 1976 40517

Oklahoma Museum of Higher Education, Old Central, Oregon State University, NE of University and Hester, Stillwater, OK 74078-0705 - T: (405) 744-2828. Head: David Swank
Special Museum / University Museum - 1980 40518

Stockbridge MA

Chesterwood Museum, 4 Williamsville Rd, Stockbridge, MA 01262-0827 - T: (413) 298-3579, Fax: (413) 298-3973, E-mail: chesterwood@nthp.org, Internet: http://www.chesterwood.org. Head: Paul W. Ivory
Historic Site - 1955
Summer estate of Daniel Chester French 40519

Merwin House Tranquility, 14 Main St, Stockbridge, MA 01262 - T: (413) 298-4703, (617) 227-3956, Fax: (617) 227-9204, Internet: http://www.spnea.org. Head: Carol Colby
Decorative Arts Museum / Local Museum - 1966 40520

The Mission House, Main St, Stockbridge, MA 01262 - T: (413) 298-3239, Fax: (413) 298-5239, E-mail: westregion@ttor.org, Internet: http://www.thetrustees.org. Head: Steve M(â"cMahon
Religious Arts Museum - 1948
1739 home of Rev. John Sergeant, first missionary to the Stockbridge Indians 40521

Naumkeag House, Prospect Hill, Stockbridge, MA 01262 - T: (413) 298-3239, Fax: (413) 298-5239, E-mail: westregion@ttor.org, Internet: http://www.thetrustees.org. Head: Stephen McMahon
Historical Museum - 1959
Shingle style house, summer home of Joseph Hodges Choate, U.S. Ambassador to the Court of Saint James 40522

Norman Rockwell Museum at Stockbridge, 9 Glendale Rd, Stockbridge, MA 01262 - T: (413) 298-4100, Fax: (413) 298-4142, E-mail: info@nrm.org, Internet: http://www.nrm.org. Head: Laurie Norton Moffatt
Fine Arts Museum / Special Museum - 1967
Art, education, art appreciation inspired by Norman Rockwell 40523

Stockbridge Library Historical Room, Library, Stockbridge, MA 01262 - T: (413) 298-5501, E-mail: ballen@cwmars.org
Historical Museum - 1939
Local history 40524

Stockholm ME

Stockholm Historical Society Museum, 350 Main St, Stockholm, ME 04783 - T: (207) 896-5759. Head: Albertine Dufour
Local Museum - 1976
Local history 40525

Stockton CA

Children's Museum of Stockton, 402 W Weber Av, Stockton, CA 95203 - T: (209) 465-4386, Fax: (209) 465-4394, E-mail: children@sonnet.com, Internet: http://www.sonnet.com/usr/children. Head: Alan MacIsaac
Special Museum - 1991 40526

The Haggin Museum, 1201 N Pershing Av, Stockton, CA 95203 - T: (209) 462-4116, Fax: (209) 462-1404, E-mail: info@hagginmuseum.org, Internet: http://hagginmuseum.org. Head: Tod Ruhstaller
Fine Arts Museum / Historical Museum - 1928
Art, history 40527

Stone Mountain GA

Georgia's Stone Mountain Park, Hwy 78, Stone Mountain, GA 30086, mail addr: POB 778, Stone Mountain, GA 30086 - T: (404) 498-5690 and 5600, Fax: (404) 498-5607, Internet: http://www.stonemountainpark.org. Head: Curtis Branscome
Local Museum / Natural History Museum - 1958 40528

Stonington CT

Captain Nathaniel B. Palmer House, 40 Palmer St, Stonington, CT 06378 - T: (860) 535-8445. Head: Michael Davis
Local Museum / Special Museum - 1996
Historic house 40529

Old Lighthouse Museum, 7 Water St, Stonington, CT 06378 - T: (860) 535-1440
Local Museum - 1925
Local hist 40530

Stony Brook NY

Long Island Museum of American Art, History & Cariages, 1200 Rte 25A, Stony Brook, NY 11790 - T: (631) 751-0066, Fax: (631) 751-0353, E-mail: mail@longislandmuseum.com, Internet: http://www.longislandmuseum.org
Fine Arts Museum / Historical Museum - 1935
American art, hist of transportation 40531

Museum of Long Island Natural Sciences, Earth and Space Sciences Bldg, State University of New York at Stony Brook, Stony Brook, NY 11794-2100 - T: (516) 632-8230, Fax: (516) 632-8240, E-mail: Pamela.Stewart@sunysb.edu, Internet: http://www.molins.sunysb.edu. Head: Pamela Stewart
University Museum / Natural History Museum - 1973 40532

Museums at Stony Brook → Long Island Museum of American Art, History & Cariages

University Art Gallery, Staller Center for the Arts, State University of New York at Stony Brook, Stony Brook, NY 11794-5425 - T: (516) 632-7240, Fax: (516) 632-7354, E-mail: rcooper@notes.cc.sunysb.edu. Head: Rhonda Cooper
Fine Arts Museum / University Museum - 1975 40533

Stony Point NY

Stony Point Battlefield State Historic Site, Park Rd off US Rte 9W, Stony Point, NY 10980 - T: (914) 786-2521, E-mail: spbattle@ric.lhric.org, Internet: http://www2.1hric.org/spbattle/spbattle.htm. Head: Don Loprieno
Military Museum / Open Air Museum - 1897
Site of raid on British stronghold by Brigadier Gen. Anthony Wayne on July 15, 1779 40534

Storm Lake IA

Witter Gallery, 609 Cayuga St, Storm Lake, IA 50588 - T: (712) 732-3400, E-mail: wittergallery@yahoo.com. Head: Joleen Dentlinger
Fine Arts Museum - 1972
Art 40535

Storrs CT

Connecticut State Museum of Natural History, 2019 Hillside Rd, Unit 1023ook Rd, Storrs, CT 06269-1023 - T: (860) 486-4460, Fax: (860) 486-0827, E-mail: mnhadm05@uconnvm.uconn.edu, Internet: http://www.mnh.uconn.edu. Head: Ellen J. Censky
University Museum / Natural History Museum - 1982
Natural hist 40536

Mansfield Historical Society Museum, 954 Storrs Rd, Storrs, CT 06268 - T: (860) 872-8558, E-mail: info@mansfield-history.org, Internet: http://www.mansfield-history.org. Head: Fred A. Cazel, Ann Galonska
Local Museum - 1961
Local hist 40537

The William Benton Museum of Art, University of Connecticut, 245 Glenbrook Rd, Storrs, CT 06269-2140 - T: (860) 486-4520, Fax: (860) 486-0234, Internet: http://www.benton.uconn.edu. Head: Salvatore Scalora
Fine Arts Museum / University Museum - 1966
Art 40538

Story WY

Fort Phil Kearny, Hwy 87, Story, WY 82842 - T: (307) 684-7629, Fax: (307) 684-7967, E-mail: sreisc@missc.state.wy.us, Internet: http://www.com.net/philkearny. Head: Jahn Kock
Military Museum - 1913
Military hist 40539

Stoughton MA

Stoughton Historical Museum, Lucius Clapp Memorial, 6 Park St, Stoughton, MA 02072 - T: (617) 344-5456
Local Museum - 1895
Local history 40540

Stoutsville MO

Mark Twain Birthplace Museum, 37352 Shrine Rd, Stoutsville, MO 65283 - T: (573) 565-3449, Fax: (573) 565-3718, E-mail: dsptwab@mail.dns.state.mo.us, Internet: http://www.mostatesports.com/twainsite.htm. Head: John Huffman
Historical Museum - 1960 40541

Stow MA

Randall Library Museum, 19 Crescent St, Stow, MA 01775 - T: (978) 897-8572, Fax: (978) 897-7379, E-mail: stow@mln.lib.ma.us. Head: Susan C. Wysk
Local Museum - 1892
Regional history 40542

Stow West 1825 School Museum, Harvard Rd, Stow, MA 01775 - T: (978) 897-7417. Head: C.G. Schwarzkopf
Local Museum - 1974 40543

Stowe VT

Helen Day Art Center, School St, Stowe, VT 05672 - T: (802) 253-8358, Fax: (802) 253-2703, E-mail: helenday@stowe.nu, Internet: http://www.helenday.com. Head: Ellen Thorndike, Mickey Myers
Fine Arts Museum - 1981
Art 40544

Strafford VT

Justin Smith Morrill Homestead, 214 Justin Morrill Memorial Hwy, Strafford, VT 05072 - T: (802) 828-3051, Fax: (802) 828-3206, E-mail: jdumville@dca.state.vt.us, Internet: http://www.state.vt.us/dca/historic/hp_sites.htm. Head: John P. Dumville
Historic Site - 1969
Historic house, agricultural buildings 40545

Strasburg CO

Comanche Crossing Historical Museum, 56060 E Colfax, Strasburg, CO 80136 - T: (303) 622-4690
Local Museum / Science&Tech Museum - 1969
Regional history, site where the first continuous chain of rails was completed by the Kansas Pacific Railroad, Aug. 15, 1870 40546

Strasburg PA

The National Toy Train Museum, 300 Paradise Lane, Strasburg, PA 17579 - T: (717) 687-8976, 687-8623, Fax: (717) 687-0742, E-mail: toytrain@collectors.org, Internet: http://www.traincollectors.org. Head: Gordon L. Wilson
Special Museum - 1954
Toy and model trains 40547

Railroad Museum of Pennsylvania, 300 Gap Rd, Strasburg, PA 17579 - T: (717) 687-8629, Fax: (717) 687-0876, E-mail: frm@redrose.net, Internet: http://www.rrhistorical.com/frm. Head: David W. Dunn
Science&Tech Museum - 1963
Transportation, passanger and freight locomotives, railcars, PA railroad history - library, archives 40548

Strasburg VA

Strasburg Museum, 440 E King St, Strasburg, VA 22657 - T: (540) 465-3428, 465-3175. Head: Nicholas Racey
Folklore Museum - 1970
Local hist 40549

Stratford CT

The Stratford Historical Society and Catherine B. Mitchell Museum, 967 Academy Hill, Stratford, CT 06497 - T: (203) 378-0630, Fax: (203) 378-2562
Local Museum - 1925
Local hist 40550

Stratford VA

Robert E. Lee Memorial Association, Stratford, VA 22558 - T: (804) 493-8038, Fax: (804) 493-0333, E-mail: shpedu@stratfordhall.org, Internet: http://www.stratfordhall.org. Head: Hugh G. Van der Veer, Thomas C. Taylor
Historic Site / Historical Museum - 1929
Local hist 40551

Strawberry Point IA

Wilder Memorial Museum, 123 W Mission, Strawberry Point, IA 52076 - T: (319) 933-4615
Local Museum / Decorative Arts Museum - 1970
Local hist, dolls, antiques, art, tools 40552

Stroudsburg PA

Driebe Freight Station, 537 Ann St, Stroudsburg, PA 18360-2012 - T: (570) 424-1776, Fax: (570) 421-9199, E-mail: mcha@ptd.net. Head: F. Andrew Wolf, Candace McGreevy
Local Museum - 1921
Local hist 40553

Quiet Valley Living Historical Farm, 1000 Turkey Hill Rd, Stroudsburg, PA 18360 - T: (570) 992-6161, E-mail: qvfarm@ptdprolog.net. Head: Alice Wicks, Gary Oiler, Sue Oiler
Agriculture Museum - 1963
Historic farm 40554

Stroud Mansion, 900 Main St, Stroudsburg, PA 18360-1604 - T: (717) 421-7703, Fax: (717) 421-9199, E-mail: mcha@ptdprolog.net, Internet: http://www.mcha.stroudsburg.com. Head: F. Andrew Wolf, Candace McGreevy
Local Museum - 1921
Historic house 40555

Stuart FL

Elliott Museum, 825 NE Ocean Blvd, Stuart, FL 34996 - T: (561) 225-1961, Fax: (561) 225-2333, E-mail: hsmc@bellsouth.net, Internet: http://www.goodnature.org/elliottmuseum. Head: Rob Blount
Local Museum - 1961 40556

Gilbert's Bar House of Refuge, 301 SE MacArthur Blvd, Stuart, FL 34996 - T: (561) 225-1961, Fax: (561) 225-2333, E-mail: hsmc@bellsouth.net, Internet: http://www.goodnature.org/elliotmuseum. Head: Tom Prestegard
Historical Museum - 1875 40557

Sturbridge MA

Old Sturbridge Village, 1 Old Sturbridge Village Rd, Sturbridge, MA 01566 - T: (508) 347-3362, Fax: (508) -347-0375, E-mail: osv@osv.org, Internet: http://www.osv.org. Head: Alberta Sebolt George
Open Air Museum / Local Museum - 1946
Re-created rural New England village 40558

Sturgeon Bay WI

Door County Maritime Museum, 120 N Madison Av, Sturgeon Bay, WI 54235 - T: (920) 743-5958, Fax: (920) 743-9483, E-mail: dcmm@itol.com, Internet: http://www.dcmm.org. Head: Dan Austad
Science&Tech Museum - 1969
Maritime hist 40559

Door County Museum, 18 N 4th and Michigan St, Sturgeon Bay, WI 54235 - T: (414) 743-5809
Local Museum - 1939
Local hist 40560

The Farm, 4285 Hwy 57, Sturgeon Bay, WI 54235 - T: (920) 743-6666, Fax: (920) 743-6447, E-mail: thefarm@door.pi.net, Internet: http://www.thefarmindoorcounty.com. Head: Carl Scholz
Agriculture Museum - 1965
Agriculture 40561

Miller Art Center, 107 S 4th Av, Sturgeon Bay, WI 54235 - T: (920) 746-0707, Fax: (920) 746-0865, E-mail: oehlertbb@aol.com, Internet: http://www.doorcountyarts.com. Head: Bonnie Hartmann
Fine Arts Museum / Public Gallery - 1975
Art 40562

Stuttgart AR

Stuttgart Agricultural Museum, 921 E Fourth St, Stuttgart, AR 72160 - T: (870) 673-7001, Fax: (870) 673-3959, Internet: http://www.aiea.ualr.edu/dina/cities/stuttgart
Folklore Museum / Agriculture Museum - 1972
Science of rice, hay and soybean agriculture, farm family 40563

Suffolk VA

Suffolk Museum, 118 Bosley Av, Suffolk, VA 23434 - T: (757) 925-6311, Fax: (757) 538-0833. Head: Lisa W. Mizelle
Fine Arts Museum / Public Gallery - 1986
Art 40564

Sugar Land TX

The Museum of Southern History, 14070 SW Freeway, Sugar Land, TX 77478-3553, mail addr: POB 2190, Sugar Land, TX 77487-2190 - T: (281) 269-7171, Fax: (218) 269-7179, E-mail: snoddys@snbtx.com. Head: Suzie Snoddy
Historical Museum / Military Museum / Museum of Classical Antiquities - 1978 40565

Suisun City CA

The Western Railway Museum, 5848 State Hwy 12, Suisun City, CA 94585 - T: (707) 374-2978, Fax: (707) 374-6742, Internet: http://www.wrm.org. Head: Loring Jensen
Science&Tech Museum - 1946
Electric railways 40566

Suitland MD

Airmen Memorial Museum, 5211 Auth Rd, Suitland, MD 20746 - T: (301) 899-8386, Fax: (301) 899-8136, E-mail: staff@assahq.org. Head: James D. Staton
Military Museum - 1986
Military 40567

Sullivan's Island SC

Fort Sumter National Monument, 1214 Middle St, Sullivan's Island, SC 29482 - T: (843) 883-3123 ext 24, Fax: (843) 883-3910, E-mail: -fosu_ranger_activitie@nps.gov, Internet: http://www.nps.gov/fosu. Head: Fran Norton
Military Museum - 1948
Military hist 40568

Sulphur LA

Brimstone Museum, 800 Picard Rd, Sulphur, LA 70663 - T: (337) 527-7142, Fax: (337) 527-0860, E-mail: westcal@usunwired.net. Head: Glenda Vincent
Local Museum - 1975
Local history 40569

Summersville WV

Carnifex Ferry Battlefield State Park and Museum, State Hwy 129, Summersville, WV 26651 - T: (304) 872-0825, Internet: http://wvweb.com/www/carnifax.ferry.html. Head: Mark Mengele
Local Museum
Local hist 40570

Summerville SC

Old Dorchester State Historic Site, 300 State Park Rd, Summerville, SC 29485 - T: (843) 873-1740, Fax: (843) 873-1740, E-mail: old_dorchester_sp@prt.state.sc.us, Internet: http://www.southcarolinaparks.com. Head: John Durst
Local Museum - 1960
Archaeological site of 18th-century Village of Dorchester 40571

Summit NJ

New Jersey Center for Visual Arts, 68 Elm St, Summit, NJ 07901 - T: (908) 273-9121, Fax: (908) 273-1457, Internet: http://www.njmuseums.com/njcva/index.htm. Head: Joan Duffey Good
Fine Arts Museum - 1933 40572

Sumter SC

South Carolina National Guard Museum, 395 N Pike Rd, Sumter, SC 29150 - T: (803) 806-1107, Fax: (803) 806-1121, E-mail: tng151fa@sc-ngnet.army.mil. Head: Roy Pipkin
Military Museum - 1982
Military hist 40573

The Sumter County Museum, 122 N Washington St, Sumter, SC 29150 - T: (803) 775-0908, Fax: (803) 775-0908. Head: Katherine Richardson
Local Museum - 1976
Local hist 40574

Sumter Gallery of Art, 421 N Main St, Sumter, SC 29151 - T: (803) 775-0543, Fax: (803) 778-2787. Head: Priscilla F. Haile
Fine Arts Museum - 1970
Paintings, etchings, drawings by Elizabeth White 40575

Sun Prairie WI

Sun Prairie Historical Museum, 115 E Main St, Sun Prairie, WI 53590 - T: (608) 837-2511, Fax: (608) 825-6879
Local Museum - 1967
Local hist 40576

Sunbury PA

The Northumberland County Historical Society Museum, The Hunter House, 1150 N Front St, Sunbury, PA 17801 - T: (570) 286-4083. Head: Scott A. Heintzelman, Jane DuPree Richardson
Local Museum - 1925
Local hist 40577

Sundance WY

Crook County Museum and Art Gallery, 309 Cleveland St, Sundance, WY 82729 - T: (307) 283-3666, Fax: (307) 283-1091, E-mail: crcogallery@vcm.com. Head: Linda Evans
Fine Arts Museum / Local Museum - 1971
Local hist, art 40578

Sunnyvale CA

Lace Museum, 552 S Murphy Av, Sunnyvale, CA 94086 - T: (408) 730-4695, E-mail: sherrigd@thelacemuseum.org, Internet: http://www.thelacemuseum.org. Head: Cherie Helm
Special Museum - 1980 40579

Sunnyvale Historical Museum, 235 E California Av, Sunnyvale, CA 94086 - T: (408) 749-0220, Fax: (408) 732-4726. Head: Janet G. Camp
Local Museum - 1973
Local hist 40580

Superior MT

Mineral County Museum, Second Av E, Superior, MT 59872 - T: (406) 822-4626, E-mail: mrshezzie@blackfoot.net. Head: Cathryn J. Strombo
Local Museum - 1975
Local and natural hist, geology, forest, mining, mullan rd. 40581

Superior WI

Fairlawn Mansion and Museum, 906 E 2nd St, Superior, WI 54880 - T: (715) 394-5712, Fax: (715) 394-2043, Internet: http://www.visitsuperior.com. Head: Dr. Richard A. Sauers
Decorative Arts Museum - 1963
Pattison Family hist 40582

Old Fire House and Police Museum, 402 23 rd Av, Superior, WI 54880 - T: (715) 394-5712, Fax: (715) 394-2043
Special Museum - 1983
Superior polic & fire dept. hist, Wisconsin fire & police hall of fame 40583

S.S. Meteor Maritime Museum, 300 Marina Dr, Superior, WI 54880 - T: (715) 394-5712, Fax: (715) 394-2043. Head: Dr. Richard A. Sauers
Science&Tech Museum
Whaleback ships, american steel barge, port hist 40584

Suquamish WA

Suquamish Museum, Sandy Hook Rd, Suquamish, WA 98392 - T: (360) 394-5275, Fax: (360) 598-6295, E-mail: suamuseum@hotmail.com, Internet: http://www.suquamish.nsn.us. Head: Alexis Barry, Marilyn Jones
Ethnology Museum - 1983
Indian hist 40585

Surprise AZ

West Valley Art Museum, Sun Cities Museum of Art, 17420 N Av of the Arts, Surprise, AZ 85374 - T: (602) 972-0635, Fax: (602) 972-0456, E-mail: jdavis@wvam.org, Internet: http://www.wvam.org. Head: Dr. G. Sanford, G: Goldstein, Wallen A. Steffan
Fine Arts Museum - 1980
Art 40586

Surry VA

Chippokes Farm and Forestry Museum, 695 Chippokes Park Rd, Surry, VA 23883 - T: (757) 294-3439, Fax: (804) 371-8500, E-mail: cffmuseum@dcr.state.va.us. Head: Frederick M. Quayle
Agriculture Museum / Natural History Museum - 1990 40587

Smith's Fort Plantation, 217 Smith's Fort Ln, Rte 31, Surry, VA 23883 - T: (757) 294-3872. Head: Peter Dan Grover
Local Museum - 1925
Historic house 40588

Surry County VA

Bacon's Castle, 465 Bacon's Castle Trail, Surry County, VA 23883 - T: (757) 357-5976, 648-1889, Fax: (804) 775-0802, Internet: http://www.apva.org. Head: Martin Kirwan King, Elizabeth Kostelny
Local Museum - 1665
Local hist, oldest brick house in North America 40589

Sussex NJ

Space Farms Zoological Park and Museum, Beemerville Rd, Sussex, NJ 07461 - T: (201) 875-3223, Fax: (201) 875-9397, Internet: http://www.spacefarms.com. Head: Fred Space
Local Museum / Natural History Museum - 1927 40590

Swampscott MA

Atlantic 1 Museum, 33 Roy St, Swampscott, MA 01907 - T: (781) 592-7446. Head: Rowe Austin, Richard Maitland
Historical Museum - 1965
Fire-Fighting 40591

John Humphrey House, 99 Paradise Rd, Swampscott, MA 01907. Head: Barbara Whalen
Local Museum - 1921
Local history 40592

Sweet Briar VA

Sweet Briar College Art Gallery, Sweet Briar College, Sweet Briar, VA 24595 - T: (804) 381-6248, Fax: (804) 381-6173, E-mail: rmlane@sbc.edu, Internet: http://www.artgallery.sbc.edu/. Head: Rebecca Massie Lane
Fine Arts Museum / Public Gallery / University Museum - 1901
Art 40593

Sweet Briar Museum, Sweet Briar College, Sweet Briar, VA 24595 - T: (804) 381-6248, 381-6262, Fax: (804) 381-6173, E-mail: rmlane@sbc.edu, Internet: http://www.sbc.edu. Head: Rebecca Massie-Lane
University Museum / Local Museum - 1985
Local hist 40594

Sweetwater TX

City County Pioneer Museum, 610 E Third St, Sweetwater, TX 79556 - T: (915) 235-8547. Head: Franzas Cupp
Local Museum - 1968
Local hist 40595

Syracuse NE

Otoe County Museum of Memories, 366 Poplar, Syracuse, NE 68446 - T: (402) 269-3482
Local Museum - 1972 40596

Syracuse NY

Erie Canal Museum, 318 Erie Blvd E, Syracuse, NY 13202 - T: (315) 471-0593, Fax: (315) 471-7220. Head: Persijs Kolberg
Local Museum - 1962 40597

Everson Museum of Art, 401 Harrison St, Syracuse, NY 13202 - T: (315) 474-6064, Fax: (315) 474-6943, Internet: http://www.everson.org. Head: Sandra Trop
Fine Arts Museum - 1896
Ceramics, American painting 40598

Joe and Emily Lowe Art Gallery, Syracuse University, Shaffer Art Bldg, Syracuse, NY 13244-1230 - T: (315) 443-4098, Fax: (315) 443-1303, E-mail: jhart@vpa.syr.edu, Internet: http://vpa.syr.edu/schools/soad/art.htm. Head: Dr. Edward A. Aiken, Dr. Alfred T. Collette
Fine Arts Museum / University Museum - 1952 40599

Milton J. Rubenstein Museum of Science and Technology, 500 S Franklin St, Syracuse, NY 13202-1245 - T: (315) 425-9068, Fax: (315) 425-9072, Internet: http://www.most.org. Head: Lawrence Leatherman, Stephen A. Karon
Natural History Museum / Science&Tech Museum - 1978 40600

Onondaga Historical Association Museum, 321 Montgomery St, Syracuse, NY 13202 - T: (315) 428-1864, Fax: (315) 471-2133, E-mail: ohamail@juno.com, Internet: http://www.cnyhistory.org. Head: Peter Apgar
Local Museum - 1862 40601

Syracuse University Art Collection, Sims Hall, Syracuse, NY 13244 - T: (315) 443-4097, Fax: (315) 443-9225, E-mail: djiacono@syr.edu, Internet: http://sumweb.syr.edu/suart/. Head: Dr. Alfred T. Collette
Fine Arts Museum - 1871
American art 1915-1965, prints, photography 40602

Table Rock NE

Table Rock Historical Society Museum, 414-416 Houston St, Table Rock, NE 68447 - T: (402) 839-4135, Fax: (402) 839-4135, E-mail: fv64137@navix.net. Head: Floyd Vrtiska
Local Museum - 1965 40603

Tacoma WA

Camp 6 Logging Museum, 5 Mile Dr, Point Defiance Park, North End of Pearl St, Tacoma, WA 98407 - T: (253) 752-0047, E-mail: camp6museum@harbornet.com, Internet: http://www.camp-6-museum.org/alcYY2.html. Head: Don Olson
Special Museum - 1964
Logging and lumber industry (buildings, cars and operational logging railroad from logging camps) 40604

Fort Nisqually Historic Site, 5400 N Pearl St, Tacoma, WA 98407 - T: (253) 591-5339, Fax: (253) 305-1005, E-mail: fortnisqually@tacomaparks.com. Head: Melissa S. McGinnis
Local Museum - 1937
Local hist 40605

Historic Fort Steilacoom, 9601 Steilacoom Blvd SW, Tacoma, WA 98498-7213 - T: (253) 756-3928, E-mail: fortsteil@yahoo.com, Internet: http://www.homel.gte.net/5white/fort_steilacoom.html. Head: Walter T. Neary
Military Museum - 1983
Military hist 40606

James R. Slater Museum of Natural History, University of Puget Sound, Tacoma, WA 98416 - T: (206) 756-3798, Fax: (206) 756-3352, E-mail: dpaulson@ups.edu, Internet: http://www.ups.edu/biology/museum/museum.htm/. Head: Dr. Dennis R. Paulson
University Museum / Natural History Museum - 1926
Natural hist 40607

Kittredge Art Gallery, University of Puget Sound, 1500 N Lawrence, Tacoma, WA 98416 - T: (253) 879-2806, Fax: (253) 879-3500, Internet: http://www.ups.edu. Head: Greg Bell
University Museum / Fine Arts Museum - 1961 40608

Tacoma Art Museum, 1123 Pacific Av, Tacoma, WA 98402 - T: (253) 272-4258, Fax: (253) 627-1898, E-mail: info@tacomaartmuseum.org, Internet: http://www.tacomaartmuseum.org. Head: Janeanne Upp
Fine Arts Museum - 1891
Art 40609

Thomas Handforth Gallery, 1102 Tacoma Av, Tacoma, WA 98402 - T: (253) 591-5666, Fax: (253) 591-5470, E-mail: ddomkoshi@tpl.lib.wa.us, Internet: http://www.tpl.lib.wa.us
Fine Arts Museum / Public Gallery - 1886
Art 40610

Washington State Historical Society Museum, 1911 Pacific Av, Tacoma, WA 98402 - T: (253) 272-3500, Fax: (253) 272-9518, Internet: http://www.wshs.org. Head: David Lamb, David L. Nicandri
Local Museum - 1891
Local hist 40611

Tahlequah OK

Cherokee Heritage Centre, Willis Rd, Tahlequah, OK 74465 - T: (918) 456-6007, Fax: (918) 456-6165, Internet: http://www.netsites.net/cnhs. Head: Mary Ellen Meredith
Historical Museum / Ethnology Museum / Folklore Museum - 1963 40612

Murrell Home, 3 miles S of Tahlequah, 1 mile E of SH 82, Tahlequah, OK 74464 - T: (918) 456-2751, Fax: (918) 456-2751, E-mail: shirleyp@intellex.com. Head: Shirley Pettengill
Local Museum - 1948 40613

Tahoe City CA

Gatekeeper's Museum and Marion Steinbach Indian Basket Museum, 130 W Lake Blvd, Tahoe City, CA 96145 - T: (530) 583-1762, Fax: (530) 583-8992. Head: Miriam Biro
Local Museum - 1969
Local hist, American Indian basketry 40614

Tahoma CA

Ehrman Mansion, Sugarpine Point State Park, Hwy 89, Tahoma, CA 96142 - T: (916) 525-7982, Fax: (916) 525-0138
Local Museum / Natural History Museum - 1965 40615

Vikingsholm, Emerald Bay State Park, Hwy 89, Tahoma, CA 96142 - T: (916) 525-7232, Fax: (916) 525-6730
Historic Site - 1953 40616

Talkeetna AK

Talkeetna Historical Society Museum, First Alley and Village Airstrip, Talkeetna, AK 99676 - T: (907) 733-2487, Fax: (907) 733-2484
Local Museum - 1972
Local hist 40617

Tallahassee FL

Florida State University Museum of Fine Arts, 250 Fine Arts Bldg, Rm 250, Tallahassee, FL 32306-1140 - T: (850) 644-6836, Fax: (850) 644-7229, E-mail: apcraig@mailer.fsu.edu, Internet: http://www.fsu.edu/~svad/FSUMuseum/FSU_Museum.html. Head: Allys Palladino-Craig
Fine Arts Museum - 1950
Decorative arts, paintings, photographs, prints, drawings, graphics, sculpture 40618

Lake Jackson Mounds, 3600 Indian Mounds Rd, Tallahassee, FL 32303-2348 - T: (850) 562-0042, Fax: (850) 488-0366, E-mail: lakejackson@nettally.com, Internet: http://www.dep.state.fl.us/parks/
Historic Site / Archaeological Museum - 1970
Archaeology, 1200-1500 ceremonial center 40619

LeMoyne Art Foundation, 125 N Gadsden St, Tallahassee, FL 32301 - T: (850) 222-8800, Fax: (850) 224-2714, E-mail: art@lemoyne.org, Internet: http://www.lemoyne.org. Head: Anneliese Oppenheim, MaryBeth Foss
Fine Arts Museum - 1964 40620

Museum of Florida History, 500 S Bronough St, Tallahassee, FL 32399-0250 - T: (850) 488-1484, Fax: (850) 921-2503, E-mail: wrichey@mail.dos.state.fl.us, Internet: http://www.dos.state.fl.us/dhr/museum. Head: Jeana Brunson
Historical Museum / Archaeological Museum - 1967
History Museum 40621

Tallahassee Museum of History and Natural Science, 3945 Museum Dr, Tallahassee, FL 32310-6325 - T: (850) 575-8684, Fax: (850) 574-8243, E-mail: rdaws@tallahasseemuseum.org, Internet: http://www.tallahasseemuseum.org. Head: Russell S. Daws
Local Museum / Natural History Museum - 1957 40622

Tampa FL

Children's Museum of Tampa, 7550 North Blvd, Tampa, FL 33604 - T: (813) 935-8441, Fax: (813) 915-0063. Head: Sally Shifke, Candace Ostrander
Special Museum - 1987 40623

Contemporary Art Museum, University of South Florida, 4202 E Fowler Av, Tampa, FL 33620 - T: (813) 974-2849, Fax: (813) 974-5130, E-mail: mmiller@chckhov.arts.usf.edu, Internet: http://www.arts.usf.edu/museum. Head: Margaret A. Miller
Fine Arts Museum / University Museum - 1968
Contemporary art 40624

Cracker Country Museum, 4800 N Hwy 301, Tampa, FL 33680 - T: (813) 621-7821, Fax: (813) 740-3518. Head: Rip Stalvey
Local Museum / Open Air Museum - 1979 40625

Henry B. Plant Museum, 401 W Kennedy Blvd, Tampa, FL 33606 - T: (813) 254-1891 ext 22, Fax: (813) 258-7272, E-mail: cgandee@alpha.utampa.edu, Internet: http://www.plantmuseum.com. Head: Cynthia Gandee
Historical Museum / Decorative Arts Museum - 1933
History and Decorative Arts Museum: housed in 1891 Tampa Bay Hotel 40626

Lee Scarfone Gallery → Scarfone/ Hartley Galleries

Scarfone/ Hartley Galleries, University of Tampa, 401 W Kennedy, Tampa, FL 33606 - T: (813) 253-3333 and 6217, Fax: (813) 258-7211, E-mail: dcowden@alpha-utampa.edu. Head: Dorothy C. Cowden
Fine Arts Museum / University Museum - 1977
Fine Arts 40627

Tampa Bay History Center, 225 S Franklin St, Tampa, FL 33602 - T: (813) 228-0097, Fax: (813) 223-7021, E-mail: thistory@gte.net, Internet: http://www.homel.gte.net/thistor. Head: Mark Gruetzmacher, Elizabeth L. Dunham
Historical Museum - 1989
Local hist, militaria, paleoindian archeology, seminole material culture 40628

Tampa Museum of Art, 600 N Ashley Dr, Tampa, FL 33602 - T: (813) 274-8130, Fax: (813) 274-8732, E-mail: tm22@ci.tampa.fl.us, Internet: http://www.tampamuseum.com. Head: Emily S. Kass
Fine Arts Museum - 1979
Contemporary art 40629

Ybor City State Museum, 1818 Ninth Av E, Tampa, FL 33605 - T: (813) 247-6323, Fax: (813) 242-4010, E-mail: director@ybormuseum.org, Internet: http://www.ybormuseum.org. Head: Melinda N. Chavez
Historical Museum / Local Museum - 1980
Ethnically divere immigrants in Ybor City, cigar industry, mutual aid societies 40630

Tamworth NH

Remick Country Doctor Museum and Farm, 58 Cleveland Hill Rd, Tamworth, NH 03886 - T: (603) 323-7591, Fax: (603) 323-8382, E-mail: -Remick.foundation@RSCS.net, Internet: http://www.remickmuseum.org. Head: Robert Cottrell
Local Museum - 1993
Local hist 40631

Taos NM

Governor Bent Museum, 117 Bent St, Taos, NM 87571 - T: (505) 758-2376, Fax: (505) 758-2376, E-mail: gnideon@laplaza.com. Head: Faye S. Noeding
Historical Museum - 1958 40632

Harwood Foundation of the University of New Mexico, 238 Ledoux St, Taos, NM 87571-6004 - T: (505) 758-9826, Fax: (505) 758-1475, E-mail: scarlton@unm.edu, Internet: http://www.nmculture.org. Head: Robert M. Ellis
Fine Arts Museum / University Museum - 1923 40633

Kit Carson Historic Museums, 222 Ledoux St, Taos, NM 87571 - T: (505) 758-0505, Fax: (505) 758-0330, E-mail: thm@taoshistoricmuseums.com, Internet: http://www.taoshistoricmuseums.com. Head: Karen S. Young
Local Museum - 1949
Ernest Blumenschein home 40634

Millicent Rogers Museum of Northern New Mexico, 1504 Museum Rd, Taos, NM 87571 - T: (505) 758-2462, Fax: (505) 758-5751, E-mail: mrm@newmex.com, Internet: http://www.millicen-trogers.org. Head: William D. Ebie
Fine Arts Museum / Ethnology Museum - 1953 40635

Stables Art Gallery of Taos Art Association, 133 N Pueblo Rd, Taos, NM 87571 - T: (505) 758-2036, Fax: (505) 751-3305, E-mail: taa@taos.newmex.com, Internet: http://www.taosnet.com/taa/. Head: Betsy Carey
Fine Arts Museum - 1953 40636

Tappan NY

Tappantown Historical Society Museum, Box 71, Tappan, NY 10983 - T: (914) 359-7790. Head: Ginny McCarthy
Historical Museum - 1965 40637

Tarboro NC

Blount-Bridgers House/Hobson Pittman Memorial Gallery, 130 Bridgers St, Tarboro, NC 27886 - T: (252) 823-4159, Fax: (252) 823-6190, E-mail: eccac@coastalnet.com, Internet: http://www.2.coastalnet.com/~83f3w5rm. Head: Meade B. Horne
Fine Arts Museum - 1982
Art 40638

Tarrytown NY

Historical Society of the Tarrytowns Museum, 1 Grove St, Tarrytown, NY 10591 - T: (914) 631-8374
Local Museum - 1889 40639

Lyndhurst, 635 S Broadway, Tarrytown, NY 10591 - T: (914) 631-4481, Fax: (914) 631-5634, E-mail: lyndhurst@nthp.org, Internet: http://www.lyndhurst.org. Head: Susanne Brendel-Pandich
Local Museum - 1964 40640

Taunton MA

Old Colony Historical Museum, 66 Church Green, Taunton, MA 02780 - T: (508) 822-1622. Head: Katheryn P. Viens
Historical Museum - 1853
History 40641

Taylors Falls MN

Historic W.H.C. Folsom House, 272 W Government Rd, Taylors Falls, MN 55084 - T: (612) 465-3125. Head: William W. Scott
Historical Museum - 1968 40642

Tazewell VA

Historic Crab Orchard Museum and Pioneer Park, Rte 19 and Rte 460, Tazewell, VA 24651 - T: (540) 988-6755, Fax: (540) 988-9400, E-mail: histcrab@netscope.net, Internet: http://histcrab.netscope.net. Head: Ross Weeks
Folklore Museum / Historical Museum - 1978
Central Appalachian history 40643

Teague TX

Burlington-Rock Island Railroad Museum, 208 S 3rd Av, Teague, TX 75860 - T: (254) 739-2645, Internet: http://www.mexia.com/railroad/index.htm. Head: H.A. Ellisor
Science&Tech Museum - 1969
Railroad 40644

Tecumseh NE

Johnson County Historical Society Museum, Third and Lincoln Sts, Tecumseh, NE 68450 - T: (402) 335-3258. Head: John R. Fisher, Boyd Mattox
Local Museum - 1962 40645

Tekamah NE

Burt County Museum, 319 N 13 St, Tekamah, NE 68061 - T: (402) 374-1505. Head: Velma Cooper
Local Museum - 1967 40646

Temecula CA

Temecula Valley Museum, 28314 Mercedes St, Temecula, CA 92593 - T: (909) 676-0021, Fax: (909) 506-6871, E-mail: ottw@cityoftemecula.org
Local Museum - 1985 40647

Tempe AZ

Arizona Historical Society Museum, Central Arizona Division, 1300 N College Av, Tempe, AZ 85281 - T: (602) 929-9499, Fax: (602) 967-5450, E-mail: ahs@ahs.lib.az.us, Internet: http://www.tempe.gov/ahs. Head: Richard Oldham, Reba Wells Grandrud
Local Museum - 1973
Regional history 40648

Arizona State University Art Museum, 10th St and Mill Av, Nelson Fine Arts Center, Tempe, AZ 85287-2911 - T: (602) 965-2787, Fax: (602) 965-5254, Internet: http://asuartmuseum.asu.edu. Head: Marilyn Zeitlin
Fine Arts Museum / University Museum - 1950 40649

Center for Meteorite Studies, Arizona State University, Tempe, AZ 85287-2504 - T: (602) 965-6511, Fax: (602) 965-2747, E-mail: cmoore@asu.edu. Head: Carleton B. Moore
University Museum / Natural History Museum - 1961
Meteorite Museum 40650

Museum of Anthropology, Arizona State University, Tempe, AZ 85287-2402 - T: (480) 965-6213, Fax: (480) 965-7671, E-mail: anthro.museum@asu.edu
Ethnology Museum - 1959
Anthropology, archaeology, ethnography 40651

Tempe Arts Center, POB 549, Tempe, AZ 85280-0549 - T: (602) 968-0888, Fax: (602) 968-0888. Head: Claudia Anderson
Fine Arts Museum - 1982
Art 40652

Tempe Historical Museum, 809 E Southern Av, Tempe, AZ 85282 - T: (480) 350-5100, Fax: (480) 350-5150, Internet: http://www.tempe.gov/museum
Local Museum - 1972
Local history 40653

Temple TX

Railroad and Heritage Museum, 315 W Av B, Temple, TX 76501 - T: (254) 298-5172, Fax: (254) 298-5171, E-mail: mirving@ci.temple.tx.us, Internet: http://www.ci.temple.tx.us/mus. Head: Leon Jezek, Mary L. Irving
Historical Museum / Science&Tech Museum - 1973
Transportation, history, Santa Fe, MKT and TX railroads - archives 40654

Slavonic Benevolent Order of the State of Texas Museum, 520 N Main St, Temple, TX 76501 - T: (254) 773-1575, Fax: (254) 774-7447. Head: Howard B. Leshikar
Ethnology Museum / Historical Museum - 1971
Czech history, culture and genealogy 40655

Templeton MA

Narragansett Historical Society Museum, 1 Boynton Rd, Templeton, MA 01468 - T: (978) 939-2251
Local Museum - 1928
Regional history 40656

Tenafly NJ

African Art Museum of the S.M.A. Fathers, 23 Bliss Av, Tenafly, NJ 07670 - T: (201) 894-8611, Fax: (201) 541-1280, E-mail: smausa-e@1x.netcom.com, Internet: http://www.smafathers.org. Head: Robert J. Koenig
Ethnology Museum - 1963 40657

Tequesta FL

Lighthouse Gallery and Art of School, 373 Tequesta Drv, Tequesta, FL 33469-3027 - T: (561) 746-3101, Fax: (561) 746-3241, Internet: http://www.artsforyou.org. Head: Margaret Inserra

Fine Arts Museum - 1965
Drawings, painting-American, photography, sculpture, watercolors, bronzes, ceramics, collages, calligraphy 40658

Terra Alta WV

Americana Museum, 401 Aurora Av, Terra Alta, WV 26764 - T: (304) 789-2361. Head: Ruth E. Teets, James W. Teets, Robert G. Teets
Local Museum - 1968
Local hist 40659

Terre Haute IN

Eugene V. Debs Home, 451 N Eighth St, Terre Haute, IN 47807 - T: (812) 232-2163, 237-3443, Fax: (812) 237-8072, E-mail: soking@scifac.indstate.edu, Internet: http://www.eugenevdebs.com
Historical Museum - 1962 40660

Paul Dresser Memorial Birthplace, First and Farrington Sts, Terre Haute, IN 47802 - T: (812) 235-9717, Fax: (812) 235-9717, E-mail: vchs@iquest.net, Internet: http://web.indstate.edulcommunity/uchs/. Head: Marylee Hagan
Historical Museum - 1967 40661

Swope Art Museum, 25 S 7th St, Terre Haute, IN 47807-3692 - T: (812) 238-1676, Fax: (812) 238-1677, E-mail: swope@thnet.com, Internet: http://www.swope.org. Head: Kent Ahrens
Fine Arts Museum - 1942
19th-20th c american art 40662

University Art Gallery, Indiana State University, Center for Performing and Fine Arts, 7th and Chestnut St, Terre Haute, IN 47809 - T: (812) 237-3787, Fax: (812) 237-4369, E-mail: artdept@ruby.indstate.edu, Internet: http://www.indstate.edu. Head: Joe Houston
Fine Arts Museum / Public Gallery / University Museum - 1939
Paintings, sculpture 40663

Vigo County Historical Museum, 1411 S 6th St, Terre Haute, IN 47802 - T: (812) 235-9717, Fax: (812) 235-9717, E-mail: vchs@iquest.net, Internet: http://web.indstate.edu/. Head: Marylee Hagan
Local Museum - 1958
General museum, brick two story Italianate bldg 40664

Terryville CT

Lock Museum of America, 230 Main St, Terryville, CT 06786 - T: (860) 589-6359, Fax: (860) 589-6359, Internet: http://www.lockmuseum.com/
Science&Tech Museum - 1972
Hist of locks 40665

Teutopolis IL

Teutopolis Monastery Museum, Rte 40 and S. Garrott St, Teutopolis, IL 62467, mail addr: 106 W Water St, Teutopolis, IL 62467 - T: (217) 857-3227, Fax: (217) 857-3227. Head: Edward Jansen
Local Museum / Religious Arts Museum - 1975
Local history 40666

Texarkana TX

Ace of Clubs House, 420 Pine St, Texarkana, TX 75501 - T: (903) 793-4831, Fax: (903) 793-7108, E-mail: gcvanderpool@cableone.net, Internet: http://www.texarkmuseums.org. Head: Guy C. Vanderpool
Local Museum / Decorative Arts Museum - 1985
Wilbur Smith research library and archives 40667

Texas City TX

The Mainland Museum of Texas City → Texas City Museum

Texas City Museum, 409 Sixth St, Texas City, TX 77592 - T: (409) 948-9570, Fax: (409) 948-9570. Head: Linda Turner
Historical Museum / Science&Tech Museum - 1991
History, industry 40668

The Dalles OR

Fort Dalles Museum, 500 W 15 St, The Dalles, OR 97058 - T: (541) 296-4547. Head: Sam Woolsey
Military Museum - 1951 40669

Wasco County Historical Museum, 5000 Discovery Dr, The Dalles, OR 97058 - T: (541) 296-8600, Fax: (541) 298-8660, E-mail: everyone@gorgediscovery.org, Internet: http://www.gorgediscovery.org. Head: Dr. Carol Mortland
Local Museum - 1997
Local hist 40670

Wonder Works Children's Museum, 419-East Second, The Dalles, OR 97058 - T: (541) 296-2444, Fax: (541) 298-1408. Head: Betsy Hege
Special Museum / Science&Tech Museum - 1977 40671

Thermopolis WY

Wyoming Pioneer Home, 141 Pioneer Home Dr, Thermopolis, WY 82443 - T: (307) 864-3151, Fax: (307) 864-2934
Local Museum - 1950
Local hist 40672

Thetford VT

Thetford Historical Society Museum, Bicentennial Bldg, 16 Library Rd, Thetford, VT 05074 - T: (802) 785-2068. Head: Charles Latham
Local Museum / Agriculture Museum - 1943
Local hist 40673

Thomaston ME

General Henry Knox Museum, Rte 1 and Rte 131, Thomaston, ME 04861 - T: (207) 354-8062, Fax: (207) 354-3501, Internet: http://www.midcoast.com/generalknoxmuseum/. Head: Christopher Mould, Jana Wood
Historical Museum - 1931
Montpelier home of Major General Henry Knox 40674

Thomaston Historical Museum, Lower Knox St, Thomaston, ME 04861 - T: (207) 354-2295, 354-8835, E-mail: catsmeow@mint.net, Internet: http://www.mint.net/thomastonhistoricalsociety. Head: Eve Anderson
Local Museum - 1971
Local history, 1794 Henry Knox farmhouse 40675

Thomasville GA

Lapham-Patterson House, 626 N Dawson St, Thomasville, GA 31792 - T: (912) 225-4004, Fax: (912) 227-2419, E-mail: lphouse@rose.net
Historical Museum - 1974
Historic Victorian House c.1884 40676

Pebble Hill Plantation, U.S. 319 S, Tallahassee Rd, Thomasville, GA 31792 - T: (912) 226-2344, Fax: (912) 226-0780, E-mail: php@rose.net, Internet: http://www.pebblehill.com. Head: John Parker
Local Museum - 1983
Historic house 40677

Thousand Oaks CA

Conejo Valley Art Museum, POB 1616, Thousand Oaks, CA 91358 - T: (805) 373-0054, 492-2147, Fax: (805) 492-7677. Head: Maria E. Dessornes
Fine Arts Museum - 1975
Art 40678

Ticonderoga NY

Fort Ticonderoga, Fort Rd, Ticonderoga, NY 12883 - T: (518) 585-2821, Fax: (518) 585-2210, E-mail: mail@fort-ticonderoga.org, Internet: http://www.fort-ticonderoga.org. Head: Nicholas Westbrook
Military Museum - 1908
Military history (18th c), tourism (19th c) 40679

Tiffin OH

Seneca County Museum, 28 Clay St, Tiffin, OH 44883 - T: (419) 447-5955, Fax: (419) 443-7940. Head: Fran Flat, Rosalie Adams
Local Museum - 1942 40680

Tifton GA

Georgia Agrirama-19th Century Living History Museum, Interstate 75 Exit 20 at 8th St, Tifton, GA 31793 - T: (912) 386-3344, Fax: (912) 386-3386. Head: Teresa Veazey
Agriculture Museum / Ethnology Museum - 1972 40681

Tillamook OR

Tillamook County Pioneer Museum, 2106 Second St, Tillamook, OR 97141 - T: (503) 842-4553, Fax: (503) 842-4553, E-mail: wjensen@pacifier.com, Internet: http://www.oregoncoast.com/Piormus.htm. Head: M. Wayne Jensen
Local Museum - 1935 40682

Tinley Park IL

Tinley Park Historical Society Museum, 6727 W 174 St, Tinley Park, IL 60477 - T: (708) 429-4210, Fax: (708) 444-5099, E-mail: lrtphist@lincolnnet.net, Internet: http://www.lincolnnet.net/users/lrtphist. Head: Brad L. Bettenhausen
Local Museum - 1974 40683

Tishomingo OK

Chickasaw Council House Museum, Court House Sq, Tishomingo, OK 73460 - T: (580) 371-3351. Head: Sherman Fraiser
Ethnology Museum / Historic Site / Folklore Museum - 1970 40684

Titusville NJ

Johnson Ferry House Museum, Washington Crossing State Park, 355 Washington Xing Penn Rd, Titusville, NJ 08560-1517 - T: (609) 737-2515, Fax: (609) 737-0627
Local Museum - 1912 40685

Titusville PA

Drake Well Museum, R.D. 3, Titusville, PA 16354-8902 - T: (814) 827-2797, Fax: (814) 827-4888, E-mail: drakewell@usachoice.net, Internet: http://www.drakewell.org. Head: William Dixon, Brent D. Glass
Local Museum / Science&Tech Museum - 1934
Site of first commercially successful oil well 40686

Tobias NE

Tobias Community Historical Society Museum, Main St, Tobias, NE 68453 - T: (402) 243-2356. Head: Judith K. Rada
Local Museum - 1968 40687

Toccoa GA

Traveler's Rest State Historic Site, 8162 Riverdale Rd, Toccoa, GA 30577 - T: (706) 886-2256. Head: Steven Turk
Historical Museum - 1955
1833 former stagecoach inn 40688

Toledo IA

Tama County Historical Museum, 200 N Broadway, Toledo, IA 52342 - T: (641) 484-6767, E-mail: tracers@pcpartner.net. Head: Joyce Wiese
Local Museum - 1942
Local history, housed in a former County Jail 40689

Toledo OH

Toledo Museum of Art, 2445 Monroe St, Toledo, OH 43620 - T: (419) 255-8000, Fax: (419) 255-5638, E-mail: informationtoledomuseum.org, Internet: http://www.toledomuseum.org. Head: Dr. Roger M. Berkowitz
Fine Arts Museum - 1901 40690

Toledo Museum of Science, 2700 Broadway, Toledo, OH 43609 - T: (419) 385-5721, Fax: (419) 389-8670, E-mail: andi.norman@toledozoo.rog, Internet: http://www.toledozoo.org. Head: William V.A. Dennler
Natural History Museum - 1899 40691

Tolland CT

The Benton Homestead, Metcalf Rd, Tolland, CT 06084 - T: (860) 872-8673. Head: Stewart R. Joslin, Gail W. White
Local Museum - 1969
Historic house 40692

Tolland County Jail and Warden's Home Museum, 52 Tolland Green, Tolland, CT 06084 - T: (860) 870-9599. Head: Stewart Joslin, Mary LaFontaine
Local Museum - 1856
Local hist 40693

Tomball TX

Tomball Community Museum Center, 510 N Pine St, Tomball, TX 77375 - T: (281) 444-2449. Head: Ben Scholl, Jean Alexander
Local Museum - 1961
Historic house 40694

Tome NM

Tome Parish Museum, POB 100, Tome, NM 87060-0100 - T: (505) 865-7497, Fax: (505) 865-7497. Head: Carl Feil
Religious Arts Museum - 1966 40695

Toms River NJ

Ocean County Historical Museum, 26 Hadley Av, Toms River, NJ 08754-2191 - T: (908) 341-1880, Fax: (732) 341-4372
Local Museum - 1950 40696

Tonalea AZ

Navajo National Monument, End of 564 N Rte, Tonalea, AZ 86044-9704 - T: (520) 672-2366, 672-2367, Fax: (520) 672-2345. Head: Rose James
Archaeological Museum - 1909
Archaeology 40697

Tonawanda NY

Historical Society of the Tonawandas Museum, 113 Main St, Tonawanda, NY 14150-2129 - T: (716) 694-7406. Head: Willard B. Dittmar
Historical Museum - 1961 40698

Tonkawa OK

A.D. Buck Museum of Natural History and Science, Northern Oklahoma College, 1220 E Grand, Tonkawa, OK 74653 - T: (405) 628-6200, Fax: (405) 628-6209, E-mail: rackerso@nocaxp.north-ok.edu. Head: Rex D. Ackerson
University Museum / Historical Museum / Natural History Museum - 1913 40699

Topeka KS

Alice C. Sabatini Gallery, Topeka and Shawnee County Public Library, 1515 W 10th, Topeka, KS 66604-1374 - T: (785) 580-4516, 580-4400, Fax: (785) 580-4496, E-mail: lpeters@tscpl.lib.ks.us, Internet: http://www.tscpl.org. Head: Larry D. Peters, David. L. Leaman
Fine Arts Museum / Public Gallery - 1870
American ceramics, prints, paintings, antique/modern glass paperweights, West African cultural objects, wood carving, Chinese pewter, decorative objects - library 40700

Combat Air Museum, Forbes Field, Hangar 602, Topeka, KS 66619 - T: (785) 862-3303, Fax: (785) 862-3304, E-mail: camtopeka@aol.com, Internet: http://www.combatairmuseum.org. Head: Adam Trupp
Military Museum / Science&Tech Museum - 1976
Topeka Army Air Field, later Forbes AFB, now Forbes Field 40701

Kansas Museum of History, 6425 SW Sixth St, Topeka, KS 66615-1099 - T: (785) 272-8681 ext 401, Fax: (785) 272-8682, E-mail: webmaster@kshs.org, Internet: http://www.kshs.org. Head: Robert J. Keckeisen
Decorative Arts Museum / Historical Museum - 1875
History, decorative art 40702

Mulvane Art Museum, 17th and Jewell Sts, Topeka, KS 66621-1150 - T: (785) 231-1124, Fax: (785) 234-2703, E-mail: soppelsa@washburn.edu, Internet: http://www.washburn.edu/mulvane. Head: Robert T. Soppelsa
Fine Arts Museum / University Museum - 1922
Art 40703

Toppenish WA

Confederated Tribes and Bands of the Yakama Indian Nation - Cultural Heritage Center Museum, 100 Speelyi Loop, Toppenish, WA 98948 - T: (509) 865-2800, Fax: (509) 865-5749, E-mail: marilyn@yakama.com, Internet: http://www.wolfenet.com/~yingis/hert.html. Head: Marilyn Malatare
Historical Museum / Ethnology Museum - 1980
Indian culture and hist 40704

Toppenish Museum, 1 S Elm St, Toppenish, WA 98948 - T: (509) 865-4510, Fax: (509) 865-3864. Head: Marian Ross
Local Museum - 1975
Local hist 40705

Topsfield MA

Topsfield Historical Museum, 1 Howlett St, Topsfield, MA 01983 - T: (978) 887-9724, E-mail: topshist@tial.net, Internet: http://www.tial.net/users/topshist
Historical Museum - 1894
Local history 40706

Torrey UT

Capitol Reef National Park Visitor Center, Capitol Reef National Park, Torrey, UT 84775 - T: (435) 425-3791 ext 111, Fax: (435) 425-3026, E-mail: -care_interpretation@nps.gov, Internet: http://www.nps.gov/care. Head: Albert J. Hendricks
Natural History Museum - 1968
Natural hist, Native American ethnology 40707

Torrington CT

Torrington Historical Society Museum, 192 Main St, Torrington, CT 06790 - T: (860) 482-8260. Head: Mark McEachern
Local Museum - 1944
Local hist 40708

Tougaloo MS

Tougaloo College Art Collection, Tougaloo, MS 39174 - T: (601) 977-7743, Fax: (601) 977-7714, E-mail: art@tougaloo.edu, Internet: http://www.tougaloo.edu/artcolony. Head: Ronald Schnell
Fine Arts Museum / University Museum - 1963 40709

Towanda PA

Bradford County Historical Society Museum, 109 Pine St, Towanda, PA 18848 - T: (717) 265-2240, E-mail: bchs@cyber-guest.com. Head: Henry G. Farley
Local Museum / Historical Museum - 1870
Local hist - Library 40710

French Azilum, R.R. 2, Towanda, PA 18848 - T: (717) 265-3376, Internet: http://www.frenchazilum.org. Head: William Knowles
Local Museum - 1954
Historic house, 1793-1803 refuge of the French Royalists 40711

Townsend TN

Cades Cove Open-Air Museum, Great Smoky Mountains National Park, Townsend, TN 37882 - T: (423) 436-1275
Local Museum / Open Air Museum - 1951
Cable Mill Area and other historic structures typical of Southern Appalachia at turn of the 20th century 40712

Towson MD

Asian Arts and Culture Center, Towson University, Towson, MD 21252 - T: (410) 704-2807, Fax: (410) 704-4032, E-mail: sshieh@towson.edu, Internet: http://www.towson.edu/tu/asianarts. Head: Suewhei Shieh
Fine Arts Museum - 1971
Art 40713

Hampton National Historic Site Museum, 535 Hampton Ln, Towson, MD 21286 - T: (410) 823-1309, Fax: (410) 823-8394, E-mail: -laurie_coughlan.nps.gov, Internet: http://www.nps.gov/hamp
Historical Museum - 1948
Late Georgian Mansion incl slave quarters, agricultural-industrial complex 40714

Trappe PA

Museum of the Historical Society of Trappe, Pennsylvania, 301 Main St, Trappe, PA 19426 - T: (215) 489-7560
Local Museum - 1964
Local hist 40715

Traverse City MI

Con Foster Museum, 181 E Grandview Pkwy, Traverse City, MI 49684 - T: (616) 922-4905. Head: Steve Harold, Ann Hoopfer
Local Museum - 1934
Local history 40716

Dennos Museum Center of Northwestern Michigan College, 1701 E Front St, Traverse City, MI 49686 - T: (231) 995-1055, Fax: (231) 995-1597, E-mail: dmc@nmc.edu, Internet: http://www.dennosmuseum.org. Head: Eugene A. Jenneman
Fine Arts Museum / University Museum - 1991
Art 40717

Trenton MI

Trenton Historical Museum, 306 Saint Joseph, Trenton, MI 48183 - T: (313) 675-4340, Fax: (313) 675-4088. Head: Tod Davis
Local Museum - 1962
Local history 40718

Trenton NJ

College of New Jersey Art Gallery, Holman Hall, Trenton, NJ 08650-4700 - T: (609) 771-2615, Fax: (609) 771-2633, E-mail: masterjp@tcnj.edu, Internet: http://www.tcnj.edu/~tcag. Head: Prof. Dr. Lois Fichner-Rathus
Fine Arts Museum
Drawings, prints, photography, sculpture, African arts, crafts 40719

The Gallery, Mercer County Community College, 1200 Old Trenton Rd, Trenton, NJ 08690 - T: (609) 586-4800 ext 3589, Internet: http://www.mccc.edu/gallery. Head: Henry Hose
Fine Arts Museum - 1971
Cybis coll, paintings, sculpture, ceramics, Mexican art, folk art - library 40720

Invention Factory Science Center, 650 S Broad St, Trenton, NJ 08611 - T: (609) 396-2002, Fax: (609) 396-0676. Head: Judy Winkler
Science&Tech Museum
Science, Technology, Industry 40721

New Jersey State Museum, 205 W State St, Trenton, NJ 08625-0530 - T: (609) 292-6300, Fax: (609) 599-4098, E-mail: lorraine.williams@sos.state.nj.us, Internet: http://www.state.nj.us/state/museum/musidx.html. Head: Lorraine E. Williams
Local Museum / Historical Museum - 1895
Culture, archaeology, ethnology, science, fine and decorative arts 40722

Old Barracks Museum, Barrack St, Trenton, NJ 08608 - T: (609) 396-1776, Fax: (609) 777-4000, E-mail: barracks@voicenet.com, Internet: http://www.barracks.org. Head: Richard Patterson
Military Museum - 1902
American decorative arts (1750-1820), archaeology, tools and household equipment, military artifacts 40723

Trenton City Museum, Cadwalader Park, 319 E State St, Trenton, NJ 08608 - T: (609) 989-3632, Fax: (609) 989-3624, E-mail: bhill@ellarslie.org, Internet: http://www.ellarslie.org. Head: Brian O. Hill
Local Museum - 1971
Ceramics, porcelain 40724

William Trent House, 15 Market St, Trenton, NJ 08611 - T: (609) 989-3027, Fax: (609) 278-7890. Head: Derik Sutphin, Ann M. Hermann
Local Museum - 1939 40725

Trinidad CO

A.R. Mitchell Memorial Museum of Western Art, 150 E Main St, Trinidad, CO 81082 - T: (719) 846-4224, Fax: (719) 846-2004, E-mail: themitch@smi.net. Head: Richard Louder, James Baker
Fine Arts Museum - 1979
Western art 40726

Baca House, Trinidad History Museum, 300 E Main, Trinidad, CO 81082 - T: (719) 846-7217, Fax: (719) 846-4550, Internet: http://www.trinidadco.com/thm. Head: Georgianna Contiguglia, Paula Manini
Historical Museum - 1870 40727

Bloom Mansion, Trinidad History Museum, 300 E Main, Trinidad, CO 81082 - T: (719) 846-7217, Fax: (719) 846-4550, Internet: http://www.trinidadco.com/thm. Head: Georgianna Contiguglia, Paula Manini
Local Museum / Decorative Arts Museum - 1955 40728

Louden-Henritze Archaeology Museum, Trinidad State Junior College, 600 Prospect St, Trinidad, CO 81082 - T: (719) 846-5508, Fax: (719) 846-5667, E-mail: loretta.martin@tsjc.cccoes.edu. Head: Loretta Martin
University Museum / Archaeological Museum - 1955 40729

Santa Fe Trail Museum, Trinidad History Museum, 300 E Main, Trinidad, CO 81082 - T: (719) 846-7217, Fax: (719) 846-4550, Internet: http://www.trinidadco.com/thm. Head: Georgianna Contiguglia, Paula Manini
Historical Museum - 1955 40730

Troy AL

Pike Pioneer Museum, 248 U.S. 231 N, Troy, AL 36081 - T: (334) 566-3597. Head: Gussie Gibson, Charlotte Gibson
Local Museum / Agriculture Museum - 1969
Agriculture 40731

Troy MI

Troy Museum and Historic Village, 60 W Wattles Rd, Troy, MI 48098 - T: (248) 524-3570, Fax: (248) 524-3572, E-mail: museum@ci.troy.mi.us. Head: Loraine Campbell
Open Air Museum / Historical Museum - 1927
History Museum 40732

Troy NY

Junior Museum, 105 Eighth St, Troy, NY 12180 - T: (518) 235-2120, Fax: (518) 235-6836, E-mail: info@juniormuseum.org, Internet: http://www.juniormuseum.org. Head: Joseph Herwick
Special Museum - 1954
Art hist 40733

Rensselaer County Historical Society Museum, 59 Second St, Troy, NY 12180 - T: (518) 272-7232, Fax: (518) 273-1264, E-mail: rchs@crisny.org, Internet: http://www.crisny.org/not-for-profit/rchs. Head: Donna Hassler
Local Museum - 1927 40734

Troy OH

Overfield Tavern Museum, 201 E Water St, Troy, OH 45373 - T: (937) 335-4019. Head: Robert Patton
Local Museum - 1966 40735

Truckee CA

Donner Memorial State Park and Emigrant Trail Museum, 12593 Donner Pass Rd, Truckee, CA 96161 - T: (530) 582-7892, Fax: (530) 582-7893, E-mail: ranger301@jps.net
Historic Site / Historical Museum - 1962 40736

Truth or Consequences NM

Geronimo Springs Museum, 211 Main St, Truth or Consequences, NM 87901 - T: (505) 894-6600, Fax: (505) 894-1968. Head: Jim Brannon, Ann Welborn
Historical Museum - 1972 40737

Tubac AZ

Tubac Center of the Arts, 9 Plaza Rd, Tubac, AZ 85646-1911 - T: (520) 398-2371, Fax: (520) 398-9511, E-mail: artcntr@flash.net, Internet: http://azarts.asu.edu/tubac. Head: Ken Parkinson, Colleen C. Lester
Fine Arts Museum - 1963 40738

Tuckerton NJ

Barnegat Bay Decoy and Baymen's Museum, 137 W Main St, Tuckerton, NJ 08087 - T: (609) 296-8868, Fax: (609) 296-5810, E-mail: BaymensMuseum@internetmci.com, Internet: http://www.icsglobal.com/baymens-museum. Head: Malcolm J. Robinson, John Gormley
Folklore Museum - 1989
Maritime culture 40739

Tucson AZ

The Aquary Museum, POB 57006, Tucson, AZ 85732-7066 - T: (520) 318-1460. Head: Y.Z. Painter-De Monte
Natural History Museum - 1976 40740

Arizona Gallery, 5101 N Oracle Rd, Tucson, AZ 85704 - T: (520) 888-8788
Public Gallery 40741

Arizona Historical Society Museum, Headquarters and Southern Arizona Division, 949 E 2nd St, Tucson, AZ 85719 - T: (520) 628-5774 ext 169, Fax: (520) 628-5695, E-mail: azhist@azstarnet.com, Internet: http://www.azstarnet.com/~azhist/index.html. Head: Felipe Jacome
Historical Museum - 1884
History 40742

Arizona-Sonora Desert Museum, 2021 N Kinney Rd, Tucson, AZ 85743-8918 - T: (520) 883-1380, Fax: (520) 883-2500, Internet: http://www.desertmuseum.org. Head: Stephen K. Brigham, Mark A. Dimmitt, Gary Nabhan, D. Peter Siminski
Natural History Museum - 1952
Natural history 40743

Arizona State Museum, University of Arizona, Tucson, AZ 85721-0026 - T: (520) 621-6302, Fax: (520) 621-2976, E-mail: darlene@al.arizona.edu, Internet: http://www.statemuseum.arizona.edu. Head: George J. Gumerman
University Museum / Ethnology Museum / Archaeological Museum - 1893
Anthropology, archaeology, ethnology of the American Southwest and northern Mexico 40744

Center for Creative Photography, University of Arizona, 130 North Olive Rd, Tucson, AZ 85721-0103 - T: (520) 621-7968, Fax: (520) 621-9444, E-mail: oncenter@ccp.arizona.edu, Internet: http://www.creativephotography.org. Head: Amy Rulle
Fine Arts Museum / Public Gallery / University Museum - 1975
Art - Archives, Library 40745

Degrazia Gallery and Foundation, 6300 N Swan Rd, Tucson, AZ 85718 - T: (520) 299-9191, 545-2185, Fax: (520) 299-1381. Head: Lorraine Drachman, John Reyes
Fine Arts Museum - 1977
Art 40746

Dinnerware Contemporary Art Gallery, 135 E Congress St, Tucson, AZ 85701 - T: (520) 792-4503, Fax: (520) 792-4503, E-mail: dinnerware@theriver.com, Internet: http://www.dinnerwarearts.com. Head: Chris Morrey, Barbara McLaughlin
Fine Arts Museum - 1979 40747

Doll Museum, 4940 E Speedway Blvd, Tucson, AZ 85712 - T: (520) 323-0018
Special Museum 40748

Flandrau Science Center, 1601 E University Blvd, Tucson, AZ 85721-0091 - T: (520) 621-4515, Fax: (520) 621-8451, E-mail: yestok@u.arizona.edu, Internet: http://www.flandrau.org. Head: William L. Buckingham
Science&Tech Museum - 1975
Science - planetarium, observatory 40749

The Franklin Museum, 1405 E Kleindale Rd, Tucson, AZ 85719 - T: (520) 326-8038, E-mail: hhff2@aol.com, Internet: http://www.FranklinCar.org. Head: Bourke A. Runton
Science&Tech Museum - 1992
Franklin vehicles 1904-1934, 25 cars, air cooled motors 1938-1975, H.H Franklin company hist 1892-1936 40750

International Wildlife Museum, 4800 W Gates Pass Rd, Tucson, AZ 85745 - T: (520) 629-0100, Fax: (520) 618-3561, E-mail: lwm@compuserve.com, Internet: http://www.thewildlifemuseum.org. Head: Richard Fedele
Natural History Museum - 1988
Natural history 40751

Pima Air and Space Museum, 6000 E Valencia Rd, Tucson, AZ 85706 - T: (520) 574-0462, Fax: (520) 574-9238, E-mail: pimaair@azstarnet.com, Internet: http://www.pimaair.org. Head: William T. Healy, Edward D. Harrow
Historical Museum / Science&Tech Museum - 1966
Aeronautics, space, Arizona aviation Hall of Fame 40752

Tucson Children's Museum, 200 S Sixth Av, Tucson, AZ 85701 - T: (520) 792-9985, Fax: (520) 792-0639, E-mail: tuchimu@azstarnet.com, Internet: http://www.azstarnet.com/~tuchimu. Head: Beth Walkup
Special Museum - 1986 40753

Tucson Museum of Art and Historic Block, 140 N Main Av, Tucson, AZ 85701 - T: (520) 624-2333, Fax: (520) 624-7202, E-mail: info@tucsonarts.com, Internet: http://www.tucsonarts.com. Head: Robert A. Yassin
Fine Arts Museum - 1924
Art 40754

University of Arizona Mineral Museum, Flandrau Science Center, Gould-Simpson Bldg, Tucson, AZ 85721 - T: (520) 621-4227, 621-4849, Fax: (520) 621-8451, E-mail: wetmore@laplatas.geo.-arizona.edu
University Museum / Natural History Museum - 1891
Mineralogy 40755

The University of Arizona Museum of Art, Park and Speedway, Tucson, AZ 85721, mail addr: POB 210002, Tucson, AZ 85721-0002 - T: (520) 621-7567, Fax: (520) 621-8770, E-mail: azs@u.arizona.edu, Internet: http://artmuseum.arizona.edu/art.html. Head: Lee Karpiscak
Fine Arts Museum / University Museum - 1955
Art 40756

University of Arizona Student Union Galleries, Center for Student Invovement and Leadership, Student Union Rm 404, Tucson, AZ 85721 - T: (520) 621-5853, Fax: (520) 621-6930, E-mail: ceagan@u.arizona.edu, Internet: http://www.arts.arizona.edu/galleries/jg.html
Fine Arts Museum / University Museum - 1971 40757

Western Archeological and Conservation Center, 1415 N Sixth Av, Tucson, AZ 85705 - T: (520) 670-6501, Fax: (520) 670-6525
Local Museum - 1952
Archaeology, ethnography, history, natural science 40758

Tucumcari NM

Tucumcari Historical Research Institute Museum, 416 S Adams, Tucumcari, NM 88401 - T: (505) 461-4201. Head: Duane Moore
Local Museum - 1958
Local history, folk art, pictures 40759

Tujunga CA

McGroarty Cultural Art Center, 7570 McGroarty Terrace, Tujunga, CA 91042 - T: (818) 352-5285, E-mail: director@mcgroartyarts.org, Internet: http://www.mcgroartyarts.org
Public Gallery 40760

Tulelake CA

Lava Beds National Monument, Indian Wells Headquarters, Tulelake, CA 96134 - T: (530) 667-2282, Fax: (530) 667-2737, Internet: http://www.nps.gov/labe/. Head: Craig Dorman
Natural History Museum - 1925
Natural hist 40761

Tulia TX

Swisher County Museum, 127 SW Second St, Tulia, TX 79088 - T: (806) 995-2819. Head: Linda Foster, Billie Sue Gayler
Local Museum - 1965
Local hist 40762

Tulsa OK

Gershon & Rebecca Fenster Museum of Jewish Art, POB 52188, Tulsa, OK 74152-0188 - T: (918) 299-1366, Fax: (919) 294-8338, E-mail: fenster.museum@ibm.net, Internet: http://www.jewishmuseum.net. Head: Diana Aaronson
Historical Museum / Special Museum / Religious Arts Museum - 1966 40763

Gilcrease Museum, 1400 Gilcrease Museum Rd, Tulsa, OK 74127-2100 - T: (918) 596-2700, Fax: (918) 596-2770, E-mail: gilcreas@ionet.net, Internet: http://www.gilcrease.org. Head: J. Brooks Joyner
Fine Arts Museum / Historical Museum - 1949 40764

Philbrook Museum of Art, 2727 S Rockford Rd, Tulsa, OK 74114-4104 - T: (918) 749-7941, Fax: (918) 743-4230, E-mail: mmanhart@philbrook.org, Internet: http://www.philbrook.org. Head: Marcia Y. Manhart, Christine Knop Kallenberger
Fine Arts Museum - 1938 40765

Tulsa Zoo and Living Museum, 5701 E 36 St, Tulsa, OK 74115 - T: (918) 669-6222, Fax: (918) 669-6260, E-mail: zoo@ci.tulsa.ok.us, Internet: http://www.tulsazoo.org. Head: Larry Nunley
Natural History Museum - 1927 40766

Tupelo MS

Natchez Trace Parkway Study Collection, 2680 Natchez Trace Pkwy, Tupelo, MS 38801 - T: (601) 680-4004, Fax: (601) 680-4033, Internet: http://www.nps.gov/. Head: Wendell Simpson
Natural History Museum - 1938 40767

Tupelo Artist Guild Gallery, 211 W Main St, Tupelo, MS 38801 - T: (662) 844-2787, Fax: (662) 844-9751, E-mail: tag@netbci.com. Head: Tina Lutz
Fine Arts Museum - 1989
Art 40768

Tuscaloosa AL

Alabama Museum of Natural History, Smith Hall, University of Alabama Campus, Tuscaloosa, AL 35487-0340 - T: (205) 348-7550, Fax: (205) 348-9292, E-mail: ftucker@rosie.aalan.ua.edu, Internet: http://www.ua.edu/history.htm. Head: Dr. Richard Diehl
University Museum / Natural History Museum - 1847
Natural hist 40769

Children's Hands-On Museum, 2213 University Blvd, Tuscaloosa, AL 35403 - T: (205) 349-4235, Fax: (205) 349-4276. Head: Kathleen Hughes
Special Museum - 1984 40770

Gorgas House, Capstone Dr and 9th Av, Tuscaloosa, AL 35487-0266 - T: (205) 348-5906, 348-9473, Fax: (205) 348-9292, E-mail: ftucker@rosie.aalan.ua.edu, Internet: http://www.ua.edu/gorgasmain.html. Head: Dr. Richard Diehl
Local Museum - 1954
Historic house 40771

The Old Tavern Museum, 500 28th Av-Capitol Park, Tuscaloosa, AL 35401 - T: (205) 758-2238, Fax: (205) 758-8163. Head: Hannah Brown
Local Museum - 1965
Local hist 40772

Paul W. Bryant Museum, 300 Bryant Dr, Tuscaloosa, AL 35487-0385 - T: (205) 348-4668, Fax: (205) 348-8883, E-mail: kgaddy@rosie.aalan.ua.edu, Internet: http://www.ua.edu/bryant.htm. Head: Kenneth Gaddy
Special Museum - 1985
Sports 40773

Sarah Moody Gallery of Art, University of Alabama, 103 Garland Hall, Tuscaloosa, AL 35487 - T: (205) 348-1890, 348-5967, Fax: (205) 348-9642, E-mail: wdooley@woodsquad.as.ua.edu, Internet: http://www.as.ua.edu/art/indexart.html. Head: Bill Dooley
Fine Arts Museum / University Museum - 1967
Art 40774

Tuscumbia AL

Alabama Music Hall of Fame, 617 Hwy 72 W, Tuscumbia, AL 35674 - T: (256) 381-4417, Fax: (256) 381-1031, E-mail: alamhof@hiwaay.net, Internet: http://www.alamhof.org. Head: David A. Johnson
Music Museum - 1982
Music 40775

Ivy Green - Birthplace of Helen Keller, 300 W N Commons, Tuscumbia, AL 35674 - T: (256) 383-4066, Fax: (256) 383-4068. Head: Sue Pilkilton
Local Museum - 1952
Historic house 40776

Tennessee Valley Art Association, 511 N Water St, Tuscumbia, AL 35674 - T: (205) 383-0533, Fax: (205) 383-0535, E-mail: tvac@hiwaay.net, Internet: http://www.tvac.riverartists.com. Head: Mary Settle Cooney
Fine Arts Museum / Folklore Museum - 1963
Art 40777

Tuskegee Institute AL

George Washington Carver Museum, 1212 Old Montgomery Rd, Tuskegee Institute, AL 36088-0010 - T: (334) 727-6390, 727-3200, Fax: (334) 727-4597. Head: Robyn Harris, Willie C. Madison
Historical Museum / Natural History Museum - 1941
History, science 40778

Tuskegee Institute National Historic Site, 1212 Old Montgomery Rd, Tuskegee Institute, AL 36087 - T: (334) 727-6390, Fax: (334) 727-4597, Internet: http://www.nps.gov/quin/index.htm. Head: Willie C. Madison
Historical Museum - 1941
African American hist 40779

Twin Falls ID

Herrett Center for Arts and Science, College of Southern Idaho, 315 Falls Av, Twin Falls, ID 83303-1238 - T: (208) 733-9554 ext 2655, Fax: (208) 736-4712, E-mail: herritt@csi.edu, Internet: http://www.csi.edu. Head: James C. Woods
University Museum / Ethnology Museum / Natural History Museum - 1952
Anthropology, ethnology, Indian art - Faulkner Planetarium 40780

Two Harbors MN

Lake County Historical Society Museum, 520 South Av, Two Harbors, MN 55616 - T: (218) 834-4898. Head: Rachelle Malonly
Historical Museum - 1926 40781

Split Rock Lighthouse Historic Site, 3713 Split Rock Lighthouse Rd, Two Harbors, MN 55616 - T: (218) 226-6372, Fax: (218) 226-6373, E-mail: splitrock@mnhs.org, Internet: http://www.mnhs.org. Head: Lee Radzak
Local Museum - 1976
Local hist 40782

Tybee Island GA

Tybee Museum and Lighthouse, 30 Meddin Dr, Tybee Island, GA 31328 - T: (912) 786-5801, Fax: (912) 786-6538
Historical Museum - 1960
History, in old Spanish-American War Coastal Defense Battery, Tybee Island lighthouse and cottages 40783

Tyler TX

Smith County Historical Society Museum, 125 S College Av, Tyler, TX 75702 - T: (903) 592-5993, Fax: (903) 592-5993, E-mail: schs@tyler.net, Internet: http://www.tyler.net/schs/. Head: Zelda Boucher
Local Museum - 1959
Local hist 40784

Tyler Museum of Art, 1300 S Mahon Av, Tyler, TX 75701 - T: (903) 595-1001, Fax: (903) 595-1055, E-mail: tma@etgs.com, Internet: www.ty-lermuseum.org. Head: Kimberley B Tomio
Fine Arts Museum - 1971
Art 40785

Tyringham MA

Santarella Museum and Gardens, 75 Main Rd, Tyringham, MA 01264 - T: (413) 243-3260, Fax: (413) 243-9178, Internet: http://www.santarella.org. Head: Candy Talbert, Michael Atkins
Fine Arts Museum - 1953
Art, former studio of Sir Henry Hudson Kitson 40786

Ukiah CA

Grace Hudson Museum and The Sun House, 431 S Main St, Ukiah, CA 95482 - T: (707) 467-2836, Fax: (707) 467-2835, E-mail: ghmuseum@jps.net, Internet: http://www.gracehudsonmuseum.org. Head: Sherrie Smith-Ferri
Local Museum / Fine Arts Museum - 1975
Historic house, art, history, anthropology, Grace Hudson art work, California Indian ethnography, coll about Pomo Indians 40787

Held-Poage Memorial Home, 603 W Perkins St, Ukiah, CA 95482-4726 - T: (707) 462-6969, 462-2039. Head: Lila J. Lee
Local Museum - 1970
Local hist 40788

Uncasville CT

Tantaquidgeon Indian Museum, Rte 32, 1819 Norwich-New London Rd, Uncasville, CT 06382 - T: (860) 848-9145
Historical Museum / Ethnology Museum - 1931
Indian hist and culture 40789

Union IL

Illinois Railway Museum, 7000 Olson Rd, Union, IL 60180 - T: (815) 923-4391 ext 16, Fax: (815) 923-2006, Internet: http://www.irm.org. Head: James D. Johnson, Nick Kallas
Science&Tech Museum - 1953
Railways, housed in Marengo, Illinois rail depot 40790

McHenry County Historical Society Museum, 6422 Main St, Union, IL 60180 - T: (815) 923-2267, Fax: (815) 923-2271. Head: Nancy J. Fike
Local Museum - 1963
Local history 40791

Union ME

Matthews Museum of Maine Heritage, Union Fairgrounds, Union, ME 04862 - T: (207) 785-3321, Fax: (207) 785-3321, E-mail: mitchell@tidewater.net. Head: John Crabtree
Local Museum - 1965
Local history 40792

Union NJ

James Howe Gallery, Kean University, Vaughn Eames Hall, Morris Av, Union, NJ 07083 - T: (908) 527-2307, 527-2347, Fax: (908) 527-2804, Internet: http://www.library.kean.edu. Head: Alec Nicolescu
Fine Arts Museum / University Museum - 1971
Paintings, prints, sculpture, photographs, design and furniture 40793

Union OR

Union County Museum, 333 S Main St, Union, OR 97883 - T: (541) 562-6003, Fax: (541) 562-5196, Internet: http://www.visitlagrande.com
Local Museum - 1969 40794

Union SC

Rose Hill Plantation State Historic Site, 2677 Sardis Rd, Union, SC 29379 - T: (864) 427-5966, Fax: (864) 427-5966, E-mail: -rose_hill_plantation_sp@prt.state.sc.us, Internet: http://www.southcarolinaparks.com
Local Museum - 1960
Local hist 40795

Union Gap WA

Central Washington Agricultural Museum, 4508 Main St, Union Gap, WA 98903 - T: (509) 457-8735, 248-0432. Head: Robert Eschbach
Agriculture Museum - 1979
Agriculture 40796

University Center MI

Marshall M. Fredericks Sculpture Museum, Saginaw Valley State University, Arbury Arts Center, University Center, MI 48710 - T: (517) 790-5667, Fax: (517) 791-7721, E-mail: panhorst@svsu.edu, Internet: http://www.svsu.edu/mfsm. Head: Dr. Michael W. Panhorst
Fine Arts Museum / University Museum - 1988
Sculptures 40797

University Park IL

Nathan Manilow Sculpture Park, Governors State University, Wagner House, University Park, IL 60466 - T: (708) 534-5000, Fax: (708) 534-8959, E-mail: b-goldbe@govst.edu, Internet: http://www.govst.edu/sculpture. Head: Beverly Goldberg
University Museum / Open Air Museum - 1969 40798

University Park PA

The Frost Entomological Museum, c/o Department of Entomology, The Pennsylvania State University, 501 A.S.I. Bldg, University Park, PA 16802 - T: (814) 863-2863, Fax: (814) 865-3048, E-mail: KC_KIM@psu.edu, Internet: http://www.ento.psu.edu/home/frost. Head: Dr. K.C. Kim
Natural History Museum - 1968
Natural hist 40799

Palmer Museum of Art, The Pennsylvania State University, Curtin Rd, University Park, PA 16802-2507 - T: (814) 865-7672, Fax: (814) 863-8608, E-mail: pjm19@psu.edu, Internet: http://www.psu.edu/dept/palmermuseum/. Head: Jan Keene Muhlert
Fine Arts Museum / University Museum - 1972
Art 40800

Upland CA

Cooper Regional History Museum, 217 E A St, Upland, CA 91785-0772 - T: (909) 982-8010, E-mail: info@culturalcenter.org, Internet: http://www.culturalcenter.org. Head: Max A. Van Balgooy, Phil Born
Local Museum - 1965
Local hist 40801

Upland PA

Caleb Pusey House, 15 Race St, Upland, PA 19015 - T: (610) 874-5665. Head: Harold R. Poden
Local Museum - 1960
Local hist 40802

Upper Marlboro MD

Darnall's Chance, 14800 Gov. Oden Bowie Dr, Upper Marlboro, MD 20772 - T: (301) 952-8010, Fax: (301) 952-1773
Local Museum / Museum of Classical Antiquities - 1988
Darnall and Carroll family home 40803

W. Henry Duvall Tool Museum, Patuxent River Park, 16000 Croom Airport Rd, Upper Marlboro, MD 20772-8395 - T: (301) 627-6074, Fax: (301) 952-9754. Head: Greg Lewis
Science&Tech Museum - 1983
Tools 40804

Upper Montclair NJ

Montclair State University Art Galleries, Life Hall, 1 Normal Av, Upper Montclair, NJ 07043 - T: (973) 655-5113, Fax: (973) 655-5279, E-mail: pacel@montclair.edu, Internet: http://www.montclair.edu/pages/arts. Head: Dr. Lorenzo Pace
Fine Arts Museum / University Museum - 1973
Contemporary East Indian art, Japanese expressionism in paper - Calcia library 40805

Upper Sandusky OH

Indian Mill Museum State Memorial, 7417 Wyandot County Rd 47, Upper Sandusky, OH 43351 - T: (419) 294-3349, 294-4022
Historic Site - 1967 40806

Wyandot County Historical Society Museum, 130 S Seventh St, Upper Sandusky, OH 43351-0372 - T: (419) 294-3857
Local Museum / Historical Museum - 1929 40807

Upton NY

Science Museum, Brookhaven National Laboratory, Upton, NY 11973-5000 - T: (516) 344-4049, Fax: (516) 344-7098, E-mail: jtempel@bnl.gov, Internet: http://www.pubaf.bnl.gov/museum.html. Head: Janet Tempel
Science&Tech Museum - 1977
Science 40808

Urbana IL

Museum of Natural History, University of Illinois at Urbana-Champaign, Natural History Bldg, 1301 W Green St, Urbana, IL 61801 - T: (217) 333-2360, Fax: (217) 244-9419, E-mail: ksheahan@uiuc.edu, Internet: http://www.spurlock.uiuc.edu/. Head: Dr. Douglas J. Brewer
University Museum / Natural History Museum - 1870
Natural history 40809

Spurlock Museum, University of Illinois at Urbana-Champaign, 600 S Gregory St, Urbana, IL 61801 - T: (217) 333-2360, Fax: (217) 344-9419, E-mail: ksheahan@uiuc.edu, Internet: http://www.spurlock.uiuc.edu. Head: Dr. Douglas Brewer
University Museum / Historical Museum / Natural History Museum - 1911
General Museum 40810

Urbana OH

Champaign County Historical Museum, 809 E Lawn Av, Urbana, OH 43078 - T: (937) 653-4517. Head: Barbara Sour
Local Museum - 1934 40811

Urbandale IA

Living History Farms Museum, 2600 NW 111th St, Urbandale, IA 50322 - T: (515) 278-5286, Fax: (515) 278-9808, Internet: http://www.lhf.org. Head: Steve Green, Joe Anderson
Agriculture Museum - 1967
Agriculture 40812

Utica IL

LaSalle County Historical Society Museum, Mill and Canal, Utica, IL 61373 - T: (815) 667-4861, Fax: (815) 667-5121, E-mail: museum@megsinet.org. Head: Bill Gish, Mary C. Toraason
Local Museum - 1967
Local history, housed in 1848 pre-Civil War stone warehouse 40813

Starved Rock State Park, POB 509, Utica, IL 61373 - T: (815) 667-4906, 667-5356, Fax: (815) 667-5354, E-mail: starvedrockvc@ivi.net
Historical Museum - 1911
Former Indian village of Illinois Indians, 1673-1760 French occupation and 1683 French Fort Saint Louis 40814

Utica NY

Children's Museum of History, Natural History and Science at Utica, New York, 311 Main St, Utica, NY 13501 - T: (315) 724-6129, Fax: (315) 724-6120, Internet: http://www.museum4kids.com. Head: Duke Mosakowski, Anthony Clementi
Special Museum / Natural History Museum - 1963 40815

Munson-Williams-Proctor Arts Institute Museum of Art, 310 Genesee St, Utica, NY 13502 - T: (315) 797-0000 ext 2140, Fax: (315) 797-5608, E-mail: pschweiz@mwpi.edu, Internet: http://www.mwpi.edu. Head: Dr. Paul D. Schweizer
Fine Arts Museum - 1919 40816

Oneida County Historical Society Museum, 1608 Genesee St, Utica, NY 13502-5425 - T: (315) 735-3642, Fax: (315) 732-0806, E-mail: ochs@borg.com, Internet: http://www.midyork.org/ochs. Head: Kevin Marken
Local Museum - 1876 40817

Uvalde TX

Garner Memorial Museum, 333 N Park St, Uvalde, TX 78801 - T: (830) 278-5018
Local Museum - 1960
Historic house, home of Vice President John N. Garner 40818

Vacaville CA

Vacaville Museum, 213 Buck Av, Vacaville, CA 95688 - T: (707) 447-4513, Fax: (707) 447-2661, E-mail: vacmuseum@aol.com, Internet: http://www.vacavillemuseum.org. Head: Shawn Lum
Local Museum - 1981
Local hist 40819

Vail CO

Colorado Ski Museum, 231 S Frontage Rd, Vail, CO 81657 - T: (970) 476-1876, Fax: (970) 476-1879, E-mail: skimuse@vail.net, Internet: http://vailsoft.com/museum/. Head: Margie J. Plath
Special Museum - 1976
Ski and Snowboard history, Hall of Fame 40820

Vails Gate NY

Knox's Headquarters State Historic Site, Forge Hill Rd at Rte 94, Vails Gate, NY 12584 - T: (914) 561-5498, Fax: (914) 561-6577, E-mail: nwc@orn.net. Head: Michael J. Clark
Military Museum - 1922 40821

New Windsor Cantonment State Historic Site and National Purple Heart Hall of Honor, Rte 300 and Temple Hill Rd, Vails Gate, NY 12584 - T: (914) 561-1765, Fax: (914) 561-6577, E-mail: nwc@orn.net, Internet: http://www.thepurpleheart.com. Head: Michael J. Clark
Local Museum - 1967 40822

Valdese NC

Museum of Waldensian History, Waldensian Presbyterian Church, Valdese, NC 28690 - T: (704) 874-2531, Fax: (704) 874-0880, E-mail: waldensian@nci.net. Head: Jewell P. Bounous
Religious Arts Museum - 1955 40823

Valdez AK

The Valdez Museum, 217 Egan Av, Valdez, AK 99686-0008 - T: (907) 835-2764, Fax: (907) 835-5800, E-mail: vldzmuse@alaska.net, Internet: http://www.alaska.net/~vldzmuse/index.html. Head: Tabitha Gregory
Local Museum - 1976
Local hist 40824

Valdosta GA

Valdosta State University Fine Arts Gallery, College of the Arts, Valdosta, GA 31698 - T: (912) 333-5835, Fax: (912) 245-3799, E-mail: kgmurray@valdosta.edu, Internet: http://www.valdosta.edu/art. Head: Karin G. Murray
Fine Arts Museum / University Museum - 1906 40825

Valentine NE

Cherry County Historical Society Museum, Main St and Hwy 20, Valentine, NE 69201 - T: (402) 376-2015
Local Museum - 1928 40826

Vallejo CA

Vallejo Naval and Historical Museum, 734 Marin St, Vallejo, CA 94590 - T: (707) 643-0077, Fax: (707) 643-2443, E-mail: valmuse@pacbell.net, Internet: http://www.vallejomuseum.org. Head: Carol Larson, James E. Kern
Local Museum - 1974
Local hist 40827

Valley NE

Valley Community Historical Society Museum, 218 W Alexander St, Valley, NE 68064 - T: (402) 359-2678. Head: Marianne Nielsen
Local Museum - 1966 40828

Valley City ND

Barnes County Historical Museum, 315 Central Av N, Valley City, ND 58072 - T: (701) 845-0966, Fax: (701) 845-4755. Head: George Amann
Local Museum - 1930 40829

Valley Forge PA

The Valley Forge Museum, Rte 23, Valley Forge, PA 19481-0122 - T: (610) 783-0535, Fax: (610) 783-0957, E-mail: vfhs@ix.netcom.com, Internet: http://www.libertynet.org/iha/valleyforge
Historic Site / Historical Museum - 1918
History, museum located on the site of Valley Forge encampment area 40830

Valley Forge National Historical Park, POB 953, Valley Forge, PA 19482-0953 - T: (610) 783-1000, 783-1077, Fax: (610) 783-1053, Internet: http://www.nps.gov/vafo. Head: Arthur L. Stewart
Historical Museum / Historic Site - 1893
1777-1778 site of Continental Army winter encampment 40831

Valparaiso FL

Heritage Museum, 115 Westview Av, Valparaiso, FL 32580 - T: (850) 678-2615, Fax: (850) 678-2615. Head: Christian S. LaRoche
Local Museum - 1970
Local history 40832

Valparaiso IN

Brauer Museum of Art, Valparaiso University Center for the Arts, Valparaiso, IN 46383-6349 - T: (219) 464-5365, Fax: (219) 464-5244, Internet: http://www.valpo.edu/artmuseum. Head: Gregg Hertzlieb
Fine Arts Museum / University Museum - 1953
Art 40833

Porter County Old Jail Museum, Old Jail Bldg, 153 Franklin St, Valparaiso, IN 46383 - T: (219) 465-3595
Local Museum / Special Museum - 1916
Local history, criminology 40834

Van Buren AR

Bob Burns Museum, 813 Main St, Old Frisco Depot, Van Buren, AR 72956 - T: (501) 474-2761, Fax: (501) 474-5084, E-mail: vanburen@vanburen.org, Internet: http://www.vanburen.org. Head: Lance Lanier
Historical Museum - 1994 40835

Van Horn TX

Culberson County Historical Museum, 212 W Broadway, Van Horn, TX 79855 - T: (915) 283-8028. Head: Robert Stuckey
Local Museum - 1975
Local hist 40836

Vancouver WA

Archer Gallery, Clark College, 1800 E McLoughlin Blvd, MS-13, Vancouver, WA 98663 - T: (360) 992-2370, 992-2246, Fax: (360) 992-2828, E-mail: mhirsch@hawkins.clark.edu, Internet: http://www.clark.edu/. Head: Marjorie Hirsch
Fine Arts Museum - 1978
Art 40837

Clark County Historical Museum, 1511 Main St, Vancouver, WA 98660 - T: (360) 695-4681, Fax: (360) 695-4034, E-mail: dfenton@fvhscc.org. Head: William Hidden, David Fenton
Historical Museum - 1917
Local hist 40838

Fort Vancouver National Historic Site, 1501 E Evergreen Blvd, Vancouver, WA 98661 - T: (360) 696-7655, Fax: (360) 696-7657, E-mail: -FOVA_Interpretation@nps.gov, Internet: http://www.nps.gov
Local Museum - 1948
Local hist 40839

Pearson Air Museum, 1115 E Fifth St, Vancouver, WA 98661 - T: (360) 694-7026, Fax: (360) 694-0824, E-mail: pearson@pacifier.com, Internet: http://www.pearsonairmuseum.org. Head: John Donnelly
Science&Tech Museum - 1987 40840

Vandalia IL

The Little Brick House, 621 St Clair, Vandalia, IL 62471 - T: (618) 283-0024
Historical Museum - 1960
1840-1860 James W. Berry property 40841

Vandalia State House, 315 W Gallatin St, Vandalia, IL 62471 - T: (618) 283-1161. Head: Robert Coomer
Historic Site - 1836
1836 Vandalia Statehouse is the oldest Capitol building in the state of Illinois 40842

Vasa MN

Vasa Lutheran Church Museum, County Rd 7, Vasa, MN 55089 - T: (612) 258-4327. Head: Everett Lindquist
Religious Arts Museum - 1930 40843

Vaughan MS

Casey Jones Museum, Main St, Vaughan, MS 39179 - T: (601) 673-9864, Fax: (601) 653-6693
Science&Tech Museum - 1980 40844

Ventura CA

San Buenaventura Mission Museum, 225 E Main St, Ventura, CA 93001-2622 - T: (805) 643-4318, Fax: (805) 643-7831, E-mail: Mission@anacapa.net, Internet: http://www.anacapa.net/~Tmission. Head: Patrick J. O'Brien
Local Museum - 1782
Local hist 40845

Ventura County Museum of History and Art, 100 E Main St, Ventura, CA 93001 - T: (805) 653-0323 ext 11, Fax: (805) 653-5267, E-mail: director@vcmha.org, Internet: http://www.vcmha.org
Fine Arts Museum / Historical Museum - 1913
History, art 40846

Vergennes VT

The Lake Champlain Maritime Museum, 4472 Basin Harbor Rd, Vergennes, VT 05491 - T: (802) 475-2022, Fax: (802) 475-2953, E-mail: info@lemm.org, Internet: http://www.lcmm.org. Head: Arthur B. Cohn
Archaeological Museum - 1985
Maritime and nautical archaeology 40847

Vermilion OH

Inland Seas Maritime Museum of The Great Lakes Historical Society, 480 Main St, Vermilion, OH 44089 - T: (440) 967-3467, Fax: (440) 967-1519, E-mail: glhs1@inlandseas.org, Internet: http://www.inlandseas.org. Head: Anthony F. Fugaro, Christopher Gillerist
Historical Museum - 1944 40848

Vermillion SD

Shrine to Music Museum, 414 E Clark St, Vermillion, SD 57069-2390 - T: (605) 677-5306, Fax: (605) 677-5073, E-mail: smm@usd.edu, Internet: http://www.usd.edu/smm. Head: Dr. Andre P. Larson
Music Museum - 1973
Musical instruments 40849

University Art Galleries, Warren M. Lee Center, University of South Dakota, Vermillion, SD 57069 - T: (605) 677-5481, Fax: (605) 677-5988, E-mail: jday@usd.edu, Internet: http://www.usd.edu/cfa/cfa.html. Head: John A. Day
Fine Arts Museum / University Museum - 1976 40850

W.H. Over Museum, 1110 Ratingen St, Vermillion, SD 57069 - T: (605) 677-5228, Internet: http://www.usd.edu/whom/. Head: Robert Noiva, Dorothy E. Neuhaus
Local Museum / Natural History Museum - 1883
Local hist 40851

Vernal UT

Utah Field House of Natural History State Park, 235 E Main St, Vernal, UT 84078 - T: (435) 789-3799, Fax: (435) 789-4883, E-mail: ufsp@state.ut.us, Internet: http://www.nr.state.ut.us/parks/www1/utaf.htm. Head: Steven Sroka
Natural History Museum - 1946
Natural hist 40852

Vernon TX

Red River Valley Museum, 4600 College Dr W, Vernon, TX 76384 - T: (817) 553-1848, Fax: (817) 553-1849, E-mail: museum@chipshot.net, Internet: http://www.chipshot.net/museum. Head: Lou Byrd, Ann G. Huskinson
Historical Museum / Science&Tech Museum / Fine Arts Museum - 1963
History, science, fine arts 40853

Vernon VT

Vernon Historical Museum and Pond Road Chapel, Rte 142 and Pond Rd, Vernon, VT 05354 - T: (802) 254-8015. Head: Robert E. Johnson
Local Museum - 1968
Local hist 40854

Vernon Hills IL

Cuneo Museum, 1350 N Milwaukee, Vernon Hills, IL 60061 - T: (847) 362-3042, 362-3054, Fax: (847) 362-4130. Head: James Bert
Fine Arts Museum / Historical Museum - 1991 40855

Vero Beach FL

Center for the Arts, 3001 Riverside Park Dr, Vero Beach, FL 32963 - T: (407) 231-0707, Fax: (407) 231-0938, E-mail: info@verocfta.org, Internet: http://www.verocfta.org. Head: John Z. Lofgren
Fine Arts Museum - 1979
Art audiovisual and film, decorative arts, paintings, photographs, prints, drawings, graphic arts, sculpture 40856

McLarty Treasure Museum, 13180 N A1A, Vero Beach, FL 32963, mail addr: 9700 S A1A, Melbourne Beach, FL 32951 - T: (561) 589-2147, Fax: (407) 984-4854. Head: Beverly Wotring
Historical Museum / Special Museum - 1970
History, Film, Spanish Shipwreck 40857

Versailles IN

Ripley County Historical Society Museum, Water and Main, Versailles, IN 47023. Head: Beatrice Boyd
Local Museum - 1930
Local history 40858

Vestal NY

Vestal Museum, 328 Vestal Pkwy E, Vestal, NY 13850 - T: (607) 748-1432, E-mail: vestalhistory@tier.net, Internet: http://www.tier.net/vestalhistory
Local Museum / Science&Tech Museum - 1976 40859

Vevay IN

Switzerland County Historical Society Museum, Main and Market Sts, Vevay, IN 47043 - T: (812) 427-3560. Head: Martha Bladen
Local Museum - 1925
General county history 40860

Vicksburg MS

Cairo Museum, 3201 Clay St, Vicksburg, MS 39180 - T: (601) 636-2199, Fax: (601) 638-7329, Internet: http://www.nps.gov/vick
Historical Museum / Military Museum / Natural History Museum - 1980 40861

Cedar Grove Mansion Inn, 2200 Oak St, Vicksburg, MS 39180 - T: (601) 636-1000, Fax: (601) 634-6126, Internet: http://cedargroveinn.com. Head: Ted Mackey, Estel Mackey
Historical Museum - 1959 40862

Old Court House Museum, 1008 Cherry St, Vicksburg, MS 39183 - T: (601) 636-0741. Head: Gordon A. Cotton
Local Museum - 1947 40863

Vicksburg National Military Park Museum, 3201 Clay St, Vicksburg, MS 39180 - T: (601) 636-0583, Fax: (601) 636-9497. Head: William O. Nichols
Military Museum / Open Air Museum - 1899 40864

Victor NY

Ganondagan State Historic Site, 1488 Victor Bloomfield Rd, Victor, NY 14564 - T: (716) 924-5848, Fax: (716) 742-1732
Historical Museum - 1972 40865

Victoria TX

McNamara House Museum, 502 N Liberty, Victoria, TX 77901 - T: (512) 575-8227, Fax: (512) 575-8228, E-mail: vrma@viptx.net, Internet: http://www.viptx.net/museum/. Head: Lexey Fender, Emma H. Burnett
Historical Museum - 1959 40866

Nave Museum, 306 W Commercial, Victoria, TX 77901 - T: (512) 575-8227, Fax: (512) 575-8228, E-mail: vrma@viptx.net, Internet: http://www.viptx.net/museum/. Head: Emma H. Burnett
Fine Arts Museum - 1976
Art 40867

Victorville CA

The Roy Rogers-Dale Evans Museum, 15650 Seneca Rd, Victorville, CA 92392 - T: (760) 243-4548, Fax: (760) 245-2009, E-mail: administrator@royrogers.com, Internet: http://www.royrogers.com. Head: Roy Rogers, Cheryl Rogers-Barnett
Special Museum - 1967
Lives and careers of Western entertainers Roy Rogers and Dale Evans 40868

Vinalhaven ME

The Vinalhaven Historical Society Museum, High St, Vinalhaven, ME 04863 - T: (207) 863-4410, E-mail: vhhissoc@midcoast.com, Internet: http://www.midcoast.com/~vhhissoc. Head: Wyman Philbrook
Historical Museum - 1963
Local history 40869

Vincennes IN

George Rogers Clark Park Museum, 401 S Second St, Vincennes, IN 47591 - T: (812) 882-1776, Fax: (812) 882-7270, E-mail: -gero_administration.nsp.gov, Internet: http://www.nps.gov/gero. Head: Dale Phillips
Natural History Museum - 1967
American hist, American Revolution, military hist 18th c, frontier hist 18th c 40870

William H. Harrison Museum/ Grouseland, 3 W Scott St, Vincennes, IN 47591 - T: (812) 882-2096
Historical Museum / Historic Site - 1911
Local history, William Henry Harrison mansion, Grouseland 40871

Virginia Beach VA

Adam Thoroughgood House, 1636 Parish Rd, Virginia Beach, VA 23455 - T: (757) 664-6283, 664-6255, Fax: (757) 460-9415, E-mail: dbiller@chrysler.org, Internet: http://www.chrysler.org. Head: Dr. William Hennessey
Decorative Arts Museum / Local Museum - 1961
Historic house 40872

Atlantic Wildfowl Heritage Museum, 1113 Atlantic Av, Virginia Beach, VA 23451 - T: (757) 437-8432, Fax: (757) 437-9055, E-mail: atlanticwilfowl@rcn.com, Internet: http://www.awhm.org. Head: Janet Forbes
Fine Arts Museum / Folklore Museum - 1995
Art and artifact concerning wildfowl 40873

Cape Henry Lighthouse, Fort Story, off Rte 60, Virginia Beach, VA 23459 - T: (757) 422-9421, Internet: http://www.apva.org. Head: Martin Kirwan King, Peter Dan Grover
Local Museum - 1791
Local hist 40874

Contemporary Art Center of Virginia, 2200 Parks Av, Virginia Beach, VA 23451 - T: (757) 425-0000, Fax: (757) 425-8186, E-mail: info@cacv.org, Internet: http://www.cacv.org. Head: Kevin Grogan
Fine Arts Museum - 1952
Art 40875

Francis Land House, 3131 Virginia Beach Blvd, Virginia Beach, VA 23452 - T: (804) 431-4000, Fax: (804) 431-3733, E-mail: mreed@city.virginia-beach.va.us. Head: Joseph J. Owens
Local Museum - 1986
Historic house 40876

Lynnhaven House, Association for the Preservation of Virginia Antiquities, 4405 Wishart Rd, Virginia Beach, VA 23455 - T: (757) 456-0351, 460-1688, Fax: (757) 456-0997, E-mail: ahb@bueche.com, Internet: http://www.apucz.org
Historic Site - 1976
Historic house 40877

Virginia Beach Maritime Museum, 24th St and Atlantic Av, Virginia Beach, VA 23451 - T: (757) 422-1587, Fax: (757) 491-8609, E-mail: FTylerVB2@aol.com, Internet: http://www.va-beach.com/old_coast. Head: Fielding L. Tyler
Science&Tech Museum - 1981
Maritime hist 40878

Virginia Marine Science Museum, 717 General Booth Blvd, Virginia Beach, VA 23451 - T: (757) 437-4949, Fax: (757) 437-4976, E-mail: fish@city.virginia-beach.va.us, Internet: http://www.vmsm.com. Head: Lynn B. Clements
Natural History Museum - 1986
Marine science 40879

Virginia City MT

Virginia City Madison County Historical Museum, Wallace St, Virginia City, MT 59755 - T: (406) 843-5500
Local Museum - 1958 40880

Virginia City NV

Nevada State Fire Museum and Comstock Firemen's Museum, 117 S C St, Virginia City, NV 89440 - T: (775) 847-0717, Fax: (775) 847-9010, E-mail: mtwain1861@reno.quik.com, Internet: http://www.comstockfiremuseum.com. Head: Michael E. Nevin
Special Museum - 1979
Antique fire Apparatus 40881

Viroqua WI

Vernon County Museum, 410 S Center St, Viroqua, WI 54665 - T: (608) 637-7396, E-mail: vcmuseum@frontiernet.net, Internet: http://www.frontiernet.net/~vcmuseum
Local Museum - 1942
Local hist 40882

Visalia CA

Tulare County Museum, 27000 S Mooney Blvd, Visalia, CA 93277 - T: (209) 733-6616, 733-6612, Fax: (209) 737-4582. Head: Kathy Howell
Local Museum - 1948
Local hist 40883

Vista CA

Antique Gas and Steam Engine Museum, 2040 N Santa Fe Av, Vista, CA 92083 - T: (760) 941-1791, Fax: (760) 941-0690, E-mail: rod@nctimes.net, Internet: http://www.agsem.com. Head: Rod Groenewold
Historical Museum - 1976
Industrial hist 40884

Volga City Park SD

Brookings County Museum, Samara Av, Volga City Park, SD 57071 - T: (605) 627-9149. Head: Lawrence Barnett
Local Museum - 1968
Local hist 40885

Volo IL

Volo Antique Auto Museum and Village, 27582 Volo Village Rd, Volo, IL 60073 - T: (815) 385-3644, Fax: (815) 385-0703, Internet: http://www.voloautomuseum.com. Head: Greg Grams
Science&Tech Museum / Folklore Museum - 1970
Automobile, village life 40886

Vulcan MI

Iron Mountain Iron Mine, Hwy U.S. 2, Vulcan, MI 49892 - T: (906) 774-7914, E-mail: ironmine@uplogon.com, Internet: http://www.ironmountainironmine.com. Head: Albert H. Carollo, Eugene R. Carollo
Science&Tech Museum - 1956
Mining, Menominee iron range 40887

Wabasso MN

Wabasso Historical Society Museum, South and Maple, Wabasso, MN 56293 - T: (507) 342-5759. Head: Eleanor Daub
Historical Museum - 1973 40888

Waco TX

Armstrong Browning Library, Baylor University, Eighth and Speight Sts, Waco, TX 76798 - T: (254) 710-3566, Fax: (254) 710-3552, E-mail: rita_patteson@baylor.edu, Internet: http://www.browninglibrary.org. Head: Mairi C. Rennie
University Museum / Library with Exhibitions - 1918
Library of Browningiana 40889

The Art Center of Waco, 1300 College Dr, Waco, TX 76708 - T: (254) 752-4371, Fax: (254) 752-3506, E-mail: artcenter@clearsource.net. Head: Amme Garrett
Fine Arts Museum - 1972
Art 40890

Dr. Pepper Museum and Free Enterprise Institute, 300 S Fifth, Waco, TX 76701 - T: (817) 757-2433, Fax: (817) 757-2221, E-mail: joec@drpeppermuseum.com, Internet: http://drpeppermuseum.com. Head: Joe Cavanaugh
Science&Tech Museum - 1989 40891

The Earle-Harrison House, 1901 N Fifth St, Waco, TX 76708 - T: (254) 753-2032, Fax: (360) 397-8896, E-mail: earleharrison@texnet.net. Head: Stanley A. Latham
Local Museum - 1956 40892

Museum of Texas, 715 Columbus, Waco, TX 76702 - T: (254) 753-7395, Fax: (254) 753-2944
Historical Museum - 1936
History 40893

The Satirical World Art Museum, 201 J.H. Kulgen Hwy, Waco, TX 76706 - T: (888) 413-4064, Fax: (254) 754-0709. Head: Robert Dippel
Fine Arts Museum - 1996
Art 40894

Strecker Museum Complex, S 4th St, Baylor University, Waco, TX 76798 - T: (254) 710-1233, Fax: (254) 710-1173, E-mail: Calvin_Smith@baylor.edu, Internet: http://diogenes.baylor.edu/WWWproviders/Strecker_Museum/. Head: Calvin B. Smith
University Museum / Historical Museum / Natural History Museum - 1893
Natural Science, history 40895

Texas Ranger Hall of Fame and Museum, Fort Fisher Park, Interstate 35 and the Brazos River, Waco, TX 76703 - T: (254) 750-8631, Fax: (254) 750-8629, E-mail: trhf@eramp.net, Internet: http://www.texasranger.org. Head: Byron A. Johnson
Historical Museum - 1968
Texas Ranger hist 40896

Texas Sports Hall of Fame, 1108 S University Parks Dr, Waco, TX 76706 - T: (254) 756-1633, Fax: (254) 756-2384, E-mail: info@hallofame.org, Internet: http://www.hallofame.org. Head: Steve Fallon
Special Museum - 1989
Sports 40897

Waconia MN

Carver County Historical Society Museum, 555 W First St, Waconia, MN 55387-1203 - T: (612) 442-4234, Fax: (612) 442-3025, E-mail: historical@co.carver.mn.us. Head: Leanne Brown
Historical Museum - 1940 40898

Wadesboro NC

Anson County Historical Society Museum, 206 E Wade St, Wadesboro, NC 28170 - T: (704) 694-6694, Fax: (704) 694-3763, E-mail: achs@vnet.net. Head: Paul Ricketts
Local Museum - 1962 40899

Wahoo NE

Saunders County Historical Museum, 240 N Walnut, Wahoo, NE 68066 - T: (402) 443-3090, Internet: http://www.co.saunders.ne.us/museum.html. Head: Kenneth Schoen, Raymond Screws
Historical Museum - 1963 40900

Wahpeton ND

Richland County Historical Museum, Second St and Seventh Av N, Wahpeton, ND 58075 - T: (701) 642-3075. Head: Elaine Wold
Local Museum - 1946 40901

Wailuku HI

Bailey House Museum, Mauri Historical Society, 2375a Main St, Wailuku, HI 96793 - T: (808) 244-3326, Fax: (808) 242-3920, E-mail: baileyhouse@aloha.net, Internet: http://www.mauimuseum.org. Head: Roselyn Lighfoot
Historical Museum - 1951 40902

Wakefield MA

Wakefield Historical Museum, Americal Civic Center, 467 Main St, Wakefield, MA 01880 - T: (781) 245-0549, Internet: http://www.wakefieldma.org
Local Museum - 1890
Local history 40903

Walden NY

Jacob Walden House, 34 N Montgomery St, Walden, NY 12586 - T: (845) 778-5862. Head: Patricia Eisley
Local Museum - 1958 40904

Walla Walla WA

Fort Walla Walla Museum, 755 Myra Rd, Walla Walla, WA 99362 - T: (509) 525-7703, Fax: (509) 525-7798, E-mail: fortw2@bmi.net, Internet: http://www.bmi.net/fortw2. Head: James Payne
Historical Museum - 1968
Pioneer village, agriculture, local hist 40905

Sheehan Gallery at Whitman College, Olin Hall, 814 Isaacs st, Walla Walla, WA 99362 - T: (509) 527-5249, Fax: (509) 527-5039, E-mail: mitcheb@whitman.edu, Internet: http://www.whitman.edu/sheehan. Head: Ben Mitchell
Fine Arts Museum / University Museum - 1972
Art 40906

Wallace ID

Wallace District Mining Museum, 509 Bank St, Wallace, ID 83873 - T: (208) 556-1592. Head: Donald C. Springer, John Amonson
Science&Tech Museum - 1956 40907

Wallingford CT

Wallingford Historical Society Museum, 180 S Main St, Wallingford, CT 06492 - T: (203) 294-1996. Head: Robert N. Beaumont
Local Museum / Historical Museum - 1916
Local hist 40908

Walnut Creek CA

Bedford Gallery at the Dean Lesher Regional Center for the Arts, 1601 Civic Dr, Walnut Creek, CA 94596 - T: (510) 295-1417, Fax: (510) 943-7222, E-mail: lederer@ci.walnut.creek.ca.us, Internet: http://www.ci.walnut.creek.ca.us
Fine Arts Museum / Folklore Museum - 1963
Art 40909

Lindsay Wildlife Museum, 1931 1st Av, Walnut Creek, CA 94596 - T: (925) 935-1978, Fax: (925) 935-8015, E-mail: webmaster@wildlife-museum.org, Internet: http://www.wildlife-museum.org. Head: Marc Kaplan, Eunice E. Valentine
Natural History Museum - 1955
Natural hist, live native Califonia wildlife 40910

Walnut Grove MN

Laura Ingalls Wilder Museum and Tourist Center, 330 Eighth St, Walnut Grove, MN 56180 - T: (507) 859-2358 and 2155, Internet: http://www.walnutgrove.org. Head: Shirley Knakmuhs
Local Museum - 1975 40911

Walsenburg CO

The Walsenburg Mining Museum and Fort Francisco Museum of La Veta, 400 Main St, Walsenburg, CO 81089-2002 - T: (719) 738-1065, 738-1081, Fax: (719) 738-2506, E-mail: esheldon@rmi.net. Head: Jeanette Johannessen
Science&Tech Museum - 1987
Mining 40912

Walterboro SC

Colleton Museum, 239 N Jeffries Blvd, Walterboro, SC 29488 - T: (803) 549-2303, Fax: (803) 549-7215, E-mail: museum@lowcountry.com. Head: Martha Creighton
Local Museum - 1985
Local hist 40913

South Carolina Artisans Center, 334 Wichman St, Walterboro, SC 29488 - T: (843) 549-0011, Fax: (843) 549-7433, E-mail: artisan@lowcountry.com, Internet: http://www.southcarolinacenter.org. Head: Denise P. Simmons
Decorative Arts Museum / Folklore Museum - 1994
Arts and crafts, drawings, ceramics, decorative and folk arts 40914

Waltham MA

Charles River Museum of Industry, 154 Moody St, Waltham, MA 02154 - T: (781) 893-5410, Fax: (781) 891-4536, Internet: http://www.crmi.org/~crmi. Head: Arthur Nelson, Karen M. LeBlanc
Science&Tech Museum - 1980
Textile, industry, innovation 40915

Gore Place, 52 Gore St, Waltham, MA 02453 - T: (781) 894-2798, Fax: (781) 894-5745, E-mail: gpsinc@erols.com, Internet: http://www.goreplace.org. Head: Susan Robertson
Historical Museum - 1935 40916

Rose Art Museum, Brandeis University, 415 South St, Waltham, MA 02254-9110 - T: (781) 736-3434, Fax: (781) 736-3439, Internet: http://www.brandeis.edu/rose. Head: Joseph D. Ketner
Fine Arts Museum / University Museum - 1961
Art 40917

Waltham Historical Museum, 190 Moody St, Waltham, MA 02154 - T: (781) 891-5815
Local Museum - 1913
Local history, 1813 Francis Cabot Lowell Mill 40918

The Waltham Museum, 196 Charles St, Waltham, MA 02543 - T: (781) 893-8017. Head: Albert A. Arena
Local Museum - 1971
Local history, 1870 James Baker house 40919

Wamego KS

The Columbian Museum and Art Center, 521 Lincoln Av, Wamego, KS 66547 - T: (785) 456-2029, Fax: (785) 456-9498, E-mail: ctheatre@kansas.net, Internet: http://www.wamego.com. Head: Barbara Hopper
Fine Arts Museum / Decorative Arts Museum - 1990
Decorative arts 40920

Wapakoneta OH

Neil Armstrong Air and Space Museum, I-75 and Bellefontaine Rd, Wapakoneta, OH 45895 - T: (419) 738-8811, Fax: (419) 738-3361, E-mail: namu@bright.net, Internet: http://ohiohistory.org. Head: John Zwez
Science&Tech Museum - 1972 40921

Warm Springs GA

Little White House Historic Site, 401 Little White House Rd, Warm Springs, GA 31830 - T: (706) 655-5870, Fax: (706) 655-5872, E-mail: lwhs@peachnet.campus.mci.net, Internet: http://www.georgianet.org/dnr/parts. Head: Frankie Mewborn
Historical Museum - 1946
Georgia home of Pres. Roosevelt, where he died April 12, 1945 40922

Warm Springs OR

The Museum at Warm Springs, 2189 Hwy 26, Warm Springs, OR 97761 - T: (514) 553-3331, Fax: (514) 553-3338, E-mail: museum@madras.net
Ethnology Museum - 1991
Tribal culture, ethnology, archaeology, history, folklore 40923

Warner OK

Wallis Museum at Connors State College, Rte 1, Box 1000, Warner, OK 74469 - T: (918) 463-2931, Fax: (918) 463-6272, E-mail: rmcclur@connors.cc.ok.us. Head: Don Nero
University Museum / Local Museum - 1963 40924

Warner Robins GA

Museum of Aviation at Robins Air Force Base, Hwy 247 and Russell Pkwy, Warner Robins, GA 31099 - T: (912) 923-6600, Fax: (912) 923-8807. Head: Elizabeth Garcia
Science&Tech Museum - 1984
Aviation 40925

Warren ME

Warren Historical Museum, 225 Main St, Warren, ME 04864 - T: (207) 273-3343
Local Museum - 1964
Regional history 40926

Warren MI

Ukrainian-American Museum, Ukrainian Cultural Center, 26601 Ryan Rd, Warren, MI 48091 - T: (810) 757-8130, 757-7910, 264-9524, Fax: (810) 757-8684
Folklore Museum / Local Museum / Historical Museum / Special Museum - 1958
Cultural Center 40927

Warren MN

Marshall County Historical Society Museum, POB 103, Warren, MN 56762 - T: (218) 745-4803. Head: Delvin Potucek, Ethel Thorlacius
Historical Museum - 1920 40928

Warren OH

John Stark Edwards House, 303 Monroe St NW, Warren, OH 44483 - T: (330) 394-4653
Local Museum - 1938 40929

Warren PA

Crary Art Gallery, 511 Market St, Warren, PA 16365 - T: (814) 723-4523. Head: Ann Lesser
Fine Arts Museum - 1977 40930

Warren County Museum, 210 Fourth Av, Warren, PA 16365 - T: (814) 723-1795, E-mail: warrenhistory@allegany.com, Internet: http://nathan.allegany.com/warrenhistory/. Head: John Mangus, Rhonda J. Hoover
Local Museum - 1900
Local hist 40931

Warrensburg MO

Art Center Gallery, Central Missouri State University, 217 Clark St, Warrensburg, MO 64093-5246 - T: (660) 543-4498, Fax: (660) 543-8006, E-mail: gallatin@cmsu1.cmsu.edu, Internet: http://www.cmsu.edu. Head: Morgan Dean Gallatin
Fine Arts Museum - 1984 40932

Central Missouri State University Archives and Museum, James C. Kirkpatrick, Warrensburg, MO 64093-5040 - T: (660) 543-4649. Head: John W. Sheets
University Museum / Local Museum / Natural History Museum - 1968 40933

Johnson County Historical Society Museum, 302 N Main St, Warrensburg, MO 64093 - T: (660) 747-6480. Head: Clayta Downing
Local Museum - 1920 40934

Warrenton VA

The Old Jail Museum, 10 Waterloo St, Warrenton, VA 20188 - T: (540) 347-5525. Head: Jackie Lee
Local Museum - 1964
Local history, jail 40935

Warsaw NY

Warsaw Historical Museum, 15 Perry Av, Warsaw, NY 14569 - T: (716) 786-2030. Head: David M. Lane
Local Museum - 1938 40936

Warwick MD

Old Bohemia Historical Museum, Bohemia Church Rd, Warwick, MD 21912 - T: (302) 378-5800, Fax: (302) 378-5808. Head: Thomas A. Flowers
Local Museum / Religious Arts Museum - 1953
Religious artifacts (liturgical vessels, vestments, prayer books, devotional articles), farm conveyances and tools, historic cemetery 40937

Warwick NY

Historical Society of the Town of Warwick Museum, POB 353, Warwick, NY 10990 - T: (914) 986-4872. Head: John Lee
Historical Museum - 1906 40938

Pacem in Terris, 96 Covered Bridge Rd, Warwick, NY 10990 - T: (914) 986-4329. Head: Dr. Frederick Franck
Local Museum - 1972 40939

Warwick RI

Art Department Gallery, Community College of Rhode Island, 400 East Av, Warwick, RI 02886 - T: (401) 825-2220, Fax: (401) 825-1148, Internet: http://www.ccri.cc.ri.us. Head: Nichola Sevigney
Public Gallery - 1972 40940

Warwick Museum of Art, Kentish Artillery Armory, 3259 Post Rd, Warwick, RI 02886 - T: (401) 737-0010, Fax: (401) 737-1796. Head: Bill Reif
Fine Arts Museum - 1973
Art 40941

Waseca MN

Farmamerica, County Rds 2 and 17, Waseca, MN 56093 - T: (507) 835-2052, Fax: (507) 835-2053, E-mail: farmamer@mnic.net, Internet: http://www.farmamerica.org. Head: Kathleen L. Backer
Agriculture Museum - 1978 40942

Waseca County Historical Society Museum, 315 Second Av NE, Waseca, MN 56093 - T: (507) 835-7700, E-mail: director@historical.waseca.mn.us, Internet: http://www.historical.waseca.mn.us. Head: Donald Wynnemer, Margaret Sinn
Historical Museum - 1938
library, archives 40943

Washburn ND

McLean County Historical Society Museum, 605 Main St, Washburn, ND 58577 - T: (701) 462-3744, E-mail: vmerkel@westriv.com. Head: Dan Wieklander
Local Museum - 1967 40944

Washington AR

Old Washington Museum, Franklin St, Washington, AR 71862 - T: (870) 983-2684, 983-2278
Historical Museum - 1973
History, located in 1824 town 40945

Washington CT

Gunn Memorial Library and Museum, Wykeham Rd, Washington, CT 06793 - T: (860) 868-7756, Fax: (860) 868-7247, E-mail: gunnmus@biblio.org, Internet: http://www.biblio.org/gunn/. Head: Jean Chapin
Local Museum - 1899
Local hist 40946

Washington DC

American Red Cross Museum, 1730 E St NW, Washington, DC 20006 - T: (202) 639-3300, Fax: (202) 628-1362, E-mail: askmuseum@usa.redcross.org, Internet: http://www.redcross.org. Head: Steven E. Shulman
Historical Museum
Paintings, decorative arts, uniforms, manuscripts, memorabilia - archives 40947

Anacostia Museum, 1901 Fort Pl SE, Washington, DC 20020 - T: (202) 287-3369, Fax: (202) 287-3183, Internet: http://www.si.edu. Head: Steven C. Newsome
Fine Arts Museum / Historical Museum - 1967
African American hist and culture 40948

Archives of American Art, Smithsonian Institution, 370 L'Enfant Promenade, Ste 704, Washington, DC 20560-0937 - T: (202) 314-3903, Fax: (202) 314-3988, E-mail: aaaenref@aaa.si.edu, Internet: http://www.archivesofamericanart.si.edu. Head: Dr. Richard J. Wattenmaker
Library with Exhibitions - 1954
Letters and diaries of artists and craft persons, critics, works on paper, photographs, recorded interviews 40949

Art Museum of the Americas, 201 18th St NW, Washington, DC 20006 - T: (202) 458-6016/19, Fax: (202) 458-6021, E-mail: fsader@oas.org, Internet: http://www.oas.org. Head: Ana Maria Escallon
Fine Arts Museum - 1976
Latin American contemporary art 40950

Arthur M. Sackler Gallery, 1050 Independence Av, Washington, DC 20560 - T: (202) 357-4880, Fax: (202) 357-4911, Internet: http://www.si.edu/asia. Head: Dr. Milo C. Beach
Fine Arts Museum / Folklore Museum - 1982
Art 40951

Arts Club of Washington, James Monroe House, 2017 I St NW, Washington, DC 20006 - T: (202) 331-7282, Fax: (202) 857-3678, E-mail: artsclub@erols.com. Head: Linda Cassell
Fine Arts Museum - 1916
Art 40952

B'nai B'rith Klutznick National Jewish Museum, 1640 Rhode Island Av NW, Washington, DC 20036 - T: (202) 857-6583, Fax: (202) 857-1099, E-mail: museum@bnaibrith.org. Head: Elizabeth Ressin Beiman
Fine Arts Museum / Folklore Museum - 1957
Folk art and fine art 40953

Capital Children's Museum, 800 3rd St NE, Washington, DC 20002 - T: (202) 675-4120, Fax: (202) 675-4140, Internet: http://www.ccm.org. Head: Catherine Martens
Special Museum - 1974 40954

The Corcoran Gallery of Art, 500 17th St and New York Av, Washington, DC 20006 - T: (202) 639-1700, Fax: (202) 639-1768, Internet: http://www.corcoran.edu. Head: David C. Levy
Fine Arts Museum - 1869
Art 40955

Daughters of the American Revolution Museum, 1776 D St NW, Washington, DC 20006 - T: (202) 879-3241, Fax: (202) 628-0820, E-mail: museum@dar.org, Internet: http://www.dar.org. Head: Diane L. Dunkley
Decorative Arts Museum / Historical Museum - 1890
Decorative arts, history 40956

Decatur House Museum, 748 Jackson Pl NW, Washington, DC 20006 - T: (202) 842-0920, Fax: (202) 842-0030, E-mail: decatur_house@nthp.org. Head: Paul C. Reber
Decorative Arts Museum - 1956
Decorative art, porcellain 40957

Department of the Treasury Museum, 15th and Pennsylvania NW, Washington, DC 20220 - T: (202) 622-1250, Fax: (202) 622-2294, E-mail: paula.mohr@do.treas.gov, Internet: http://www.ustreas.gov/curator
Decorative Arts Museum / Fine Arts Museum / Historical Museum 40958

Dimock Gallery, c/o George Washington University, 730 21st St NW, Washington, DC 20052 - T: (202) 994-1525, 994-7091, Fax: (202) 994-1632, E-mail: ldmiller@gwu.edu, Internet: http://www.gwu.edu/~dimock. Head: Lenore D. Miller
Fine Arts Museum / University Museum - 1966
Art 40959

Discovery Creek Children's Museum of Washington DC, 4954 MacArthur Blvd NW, Washington, DC 20007 - T: (202) 364-3111, Fax: (202) 364-3114, E-mail: discoverycreek@capaccess.org, Internet: http://www.discoverycreek.org. Head: Susan M. Seligmann
Special Museum - 1941 40960

District of Columbia Arts Center, 2438 18th St NW, Washington, DC 20009 - T: (202) 462-7833, Fax: (202) 328-7099, E-mail: dcac@dcartscenter.org, Internet: http://www.dcartscenter.org. Head: B. Stanley
Public Gallery - 1989 40961

Dumbarton House, 2715 Que St NW, Washington, DC 20007-3071 - T: (202) 337-2288, Fax: (202) 337-0348, E-mail: pr@dumbartonhouse.org. Head: William S. Birdseye
Historical Museum - 1891
Historic house 40962

Dumbarton Oaks Collections, Harvard University, 1703 32nd St NW, Washington, DC 20007 - T: (202) 339-6400, Fax: (202) 339-6419, E-mail: dumbartonoaks@doaks.org, Internet: http://www.doaks.org. Head: Edward Keenan
Fine Arts Museum - 1940
Art 40963

Explorers Hall, National Geographic Society, 1145 17th St NW, Washington, DC 20036 - T: (202) 857-7588, 857-7456, Fax: (202) 857-5864, Internet: http://www.nationalgeographic.com. Head: John M. Fahey, Susan E.S. Norton
Natural History Museum / Science&Tech Museum - 1964
Science, geography, expedition equipment 40964

Federal Reserve Board Art Gallery, 20 and C Sts NW, Washington, DC 20551 - T: (202) 452-3000, Fax: (202) 452-3102. Head: Mary Anne Goley
Fine Arts Museum - 1975 40965

Fondo Del Sol, Visual Art and Media Center, 2112 R St NW, Washington, DC 20008 - T: (202) 483-2777, Fax: (202) 658-1078. Head: W. Marc Zuver
Public Gallery - 1973 40966

Ford's Theatre, Lincoln Museum, 511 10th St NW, Washington, DC 20004 - T: (202) 426-6924, Fax: (202) 426-1845, E-mail: ford's_theatre@nps.gov, Internet: http://www.nps.gov/foth/index.htm. Head: Terry Carlstrom
Performing Arts Museum - 1933
History 40967

Frederick Douglass National Historic Site, 1411 W St SE, Washington, DC 20020 - T: (202) 426-5961, 426-1452, Fax: (202) 426-0880, E-mail: NACE_Frederick_Douglass_NHS@nps.gov, Internet: http://www.cr.nps.gov/csd/exhibits/douglass. Head: Kym Elder
Historic Site - 1916
History 40968

Freer Gallery of Art, Jefferson Dr at 12th St SW, Washington, DC 20560 - T: (202) 357-4880, Fax: (202) 357-4911, E-mail: arnolje@asia.si.edu, Internet: http://www.si.edu/asia. Head: Dr. Milo C. Beach
Fine Arts Museum - 1906
Art 40969

Georgetown University Art Collection, 3700 O St NW, Washington, DC 20057-1006 - T: (202) 687-4406, Fax: (202) 687-4452, E-mail: llw@georgetown.edu
Fine Arts Museum / University Museum - 1789
Art 40970

Heurich House Museum, 1307 New Hampshire Av NW, Washington, DC 20036 - T: (202) 785-2068, Fax: (202) 887-5785, E-mail: heurich@ibm.net, Internet: http://www.hswdc.org. Head: Barbara Franco
Local Museum - 1894
Local hist 40971

Hillwood Museum, Hillwood Museum Foundation, 4155 Linnean Av NW, Washington, DC 20008 - T: (202) 686-8500, Fax: (202) 966-7846, E-mail: admin@hillwoodmuseum.org, Internet: http://www.hillwoodmuseum.org. Head: Frederick J. Fisher
Decorative Arts Museum - 1976
Decorative art - Library, archives 40972

Hirshhorn Museum and Sculpture Garden, Smithsonian Institution, Seventh St and Independence Av SW, Washington, DC 20560 - T: (202) 357-3091, Fax: (202) 786-2682, E-mail: lawrence_s@hmsg.si.edu, Internet: http://www.si.edu/hirshhorn. Head: James T. Demetrion
Fine Arts Museum - 1966
Art 40973

Howard University Gallery of Art, 2455 6th St NW, Washington, DC 20059 - T: (202) 806-7047, Fax: (202) 806-9258, Internet: http://www.howarduniversity.edu. Head: Dr. Tritobia H. Benjamin
Fine Arts Museum / University Museum - 1928
Art 40974

Howard University Museum, Moorland Spingarn Research Center, 500 Howard Pl NW, Washington, DC 20059 - T: (202) 806-7239, Fax: (202) 806-6405. Head: Dr. Thomas C. Battle
University Museum / Historical Museum - 1914
Black hist 40975

The Kreeger Museum, 2401 Foxhall Rd NW, Washington, DC 20007 - T: (202) 337-3050, Fax: (202) 337-3051, E-mail: publicretatins@kreegermuseum.com, Internet: http://www.kreegermuseum.com. Head: Judy A. Greenberg
Fine Arts Museum - 1994
Art 40976

Lillian and Albert Small Jewish Museum, 701 Third St NW, Washington, DC 20001 - T: (202) 789-0900, Fax: (202) 789-0485, E-mail: info@jhsgw.org. Head: Paula Goldmann, Laura C. Apelbaum
Religious Arts Museum / Historical Museum - 1975 40977

Mary McLeod Bethune House, 1318 Vermont Av NW, Washington, DC 20005 - T: (202) 673-2402, Fax: (202) 673-2414, Internet: http://www.nps.gov/mamc. Head: Terry Carlstrom
Local Museum - 1979 40978

Meridian International Center - Cafritz Galleries, 1624-30 Crescent Pl NW, Washington, DC 20009 - T: (202) 939-5568, Fax: (202) 319-1306, E-mail: nmatthew@meridian.org, Internet: http://www.meridan.org. Head: Walter L. Cutler, Nancy Matthews
Fine Arts Museum / Folklore Museum - 1960
International arts and culture 40979

Museum of Contemporary Art, 1054 31st St NW, Washington, DC 20007 - T: (202) 342-6230
Fine Arts Museum 40980

National Air and Space Museum, Smithsonian Institution, Sixth St and Independence Av SW, Washington, DC 20560 - T: (202) 357-1552, Fax: (202) 786-2262, Internet: http://www.nasm.edu. Head: John R. Dailey
Science&Tech Museum - 1946
Aeronautics 40981

National Building Museum, 401 F St NW, Washington, DC 20001 - T: (202) 272-2448, Fax: (202) 272-2564, E-mail: jdixon@nbm.org, Internet: http://www.nbm.org. Head: Susan Henshaw Jones
Fine Arts Museum - 1980
Architecture 40982

National Gallery of Art, Constitution Av at Fourth St. NW, Washington, DC 20565 - T: (202) 737-4215, Fax: (202) 842-2356, E-mail: rstevenson@nga.gov, Internet: http://www.nga.gov. Head: Robert H. Smith, Earl A. Powell
Fine Arts Museum - 1937
Art 40983

National Museum of African Art, Smithsonian Institution, 950 Independence Av SW, Washington, DC 20560-0708 - T: (202) 357-4600, Fax: (202) 357-4879, E-mail: NMAFAweb@nmafa.si.edu, Internet: http://www.si.edu/nmafa. Head: Roslyn A. Walker
Fine Arts Museum / Folklore Museum - 1964
Art 40984

National Museum of American History, 14th St and Constitution Av NW, Washington, DC 20560 - T: (202) 357-2700, Fax: (202) 357-1853, Internet: http://nmah.si.edu. Head: Spencer R. Crew
Historical Museum - 1846
American hist 40985

National Museum of American Jewish Military History, 1811 R St NW, Washington, DC 20009 - T: (202) 265-6280, Fax: (202) 462-3192, E-mail: jwv@erols.com, Internet: http://www.penfed.org/jwv. Head: Harvey S. Friedman, Herb Rosenbleeth
Historical Museum / Military Museum - 1958
American Jewish military hist 40986

National Museum of Health and Medicine, Armed Forces Institute of Pathology, 6900 Georgia Av and Elder St NW, Washington, DC 20307 - T: (202) 782-2200, Fax: (202) 782-3573, E-mail: nmhminfo@afip.osd.mil, Internet: http://www.natmedmuse.afip.org. Head: Adrianne Noe
Historical Museum - 1862
Medical hist, human anatomy, neuroanatomy, civil war surgery, microscopes, AIDS 40987

National Museum of Natural History, 10th St and Constitution Av NW, Washington, DC 20560 - T: (202) 357-1300, Fax: (202) 357-4779, Internet: http://nmnh.si.edu. Head: Robert W. Fri
Natural History Museum - 1846
Natural hist 40988

The National Museum of Women in the Arts, 1250 New York Av NW, Washington, DC 20005 - T: (202) 783-5000, Fax: (202) 393-3235, Internet: http://www.nmwa.org
Fine Arts Museum / Folklore Museum - 1981
Art 40989

National Portrait Gallery, 750 Ninth St NW, Ste 8300, Washington, DC 20560-0973 - T: (202) 275-2738, Fax: (202) 275-1887, E-mail: npgweb@npg.si.edu, Internet: http://www.npg.si.edu. Head: Marc Pachter
Fine Arts Museum / Historical Museum - 1962
Art 40990

National Postal Museum, Smithsonian Institution, 2 Massachusetts Av NE, Washington, DC 20560-0570 - T: (202) 633-2700, Fax: (202) 633-9393, E-mail: npm@npm.si.edu, Internet: http://www.si.edu/postal. Head: James H. Bruns
Special Museum - 1993
Postal hist 40991

National Society of the Children of the American Revolution Museum, 1776 D St NW, Washington, DC 20006 - T: (202) 638-3153, Fax: (202) 737-3162, E-mail: hq@nscar.org, Internet: http://www.nscar.org. Head: Joanne Scheifer
Historical Museum - 1895
History 40992

The Octagon, 1799 New York Av NW, Washington, DC 20006-5292 - T: (202) 638-3221, Fax: (202) 879-7764, E-mail: platzere@aiamail.aia.org, Internet: http://www.archifoundation.org. Head: Eryl J. Wentworth, Sherry C. Birk
Fine Arts Museum - 1942
Architecture 40993

The Old Stone House, 3051 Main St NW, Washington, DC 20007 - T: (202) 426-6851, Fax: (202) 426-0125, E-mail: old_stone_house@nps.gov, Internet: http://www.nps.gov/rocr. Head: Terry Carlstrom
Local Museum - 1950
Historic house 40994

The Phillips Collection, 1600 21st St NW, Washington, DC 20009-1090 - T: (202) 387-2151, Fax: (202) 387-2436, E-mail: webmaster@phillipscollection.org, Internet: http://www.phillipscollection.org. Head: Jay Gates
Fine Arts Museum - 1918
Art 40995

Renwick Gallery of the Smithsonian American Art Museum, Smithsonian Institution, Pennsylvania Av at 17th St NW, Washington, DC 20006 - T: (202) 357-2700, Fax: (202) 275-1715, E-mail: info@saam.si.edu, Internet: http://www.americanart.si.edu. Head: Elizabeth Broun
Fine Arts Museum / Decorative Arts Museum - 1972
American craft 40996

Sewall-Belmont House, 144 Constitution Av NE, Washington, DC 20002 - T: (202) 546-3989, Fax: (202) 546-3997. Head: Mary Langelan
Historical Museum - 1929
Women's History Portrait Gallery, residence of Albert Gallatin 1801-1813 and Alice Paul 1929-1972 40997

Smithsoniam American Art Museum (closed until fall 2004), 8th and G Sts NW, Washington, DC 20560-0970 - T: (202) 275-1500, E-mail: info@saam.si.edu, Internet: http://AmericanArt.si.edu. Head: Dr. Elizabeth Broun
Fine Arts Museum - 1846
Art 40998

Smithsonian Institution, 1000 Jefferson Dr SW, Washington, DC 20560 - T: (202) 357-2700, 633-9126, Fax: (202) 786-2515, E-mail: info@info.si.edu, Internet: http://www.si.edu. Head: Ira Michael Heyman
Local Museum / Science&Tech Museum / Natural History Museum / Folklore Museum - 1846
Museum, education and research complex: 16 museums and galleries, institutes including: Archives of American Art, Astrophysical Observatory, Environmental Research Center, Tropical Research Institute, Marine Station 40999

Society of the Cincinnati Museum, 2118 Massachusetts Av, Washington, DC 20008-2810 - T: (202) 785-2040, Fax: (202) 293-3350. Head: Kathleen Betts
Fine Arts Museum / Historical Museum - 1783
History and art 41000

Studio Gallery, 2108 R St NW, Washington, DC 20008 - T: (202) 232-8734, Fax: (202) 232-5894, E-mail: info@studiogallerydc.com, Internet: http://www.studiogallerydc.com. Head: Jana Lyons
Fine Arts Museum - 1964 41001

The Supreme Court of the United States Museum, One First St, NE, Washington, DC 20543 - T: (202) 479-3298, Fax: (202) 479-2926, Internet: http://www.supremecourtus.gov
Historical Museum - 1973
Historic Agency and Building 41002

The Textile Museum, 2320 S St NW, Washington, DC 20008 - T: (202) 667-0441, Fax: (202) 483-0994, E-mail: info@textilemuseum.org, Internet: http://www.textilemuseum.org. Head: Ursula E. McCracken
Special Museum - 1925
Textiles 41003

United States Capitol, Capitol, Washington, DC 20515 - T: (202) 228-1222, Fax: (202) 228-1893, Internet: http://www.aoc.gov
Fine Arts Museum - 1793
Paintings, sculpture, decorative art, photography 41004

United States Department of the Interior Museum, 1849 C St NW, Washington, DC 20240 - T: (202) 208-4743, Fax: (202) 208-1535, Internet: http://www.doi.gov/museum
Historical Museum / Ethnology Museum - 1938 41005

United States Holocaust Memorial Museum, 100 Raoul Wallenberg Pl SW, Washington, DC 20024-2150 - T: (202) 488-0400, Fax: (202) 488-2690, Internet: http://www.ushmm.org. Head: Sara J. Bloomfield, Brewster Chamberlain, Martin Goldman, Raye Farr, Genya Markon, Radu Ioanid, Joan Ringelheim, Steve Goodell
Historical Museum - 1980
History - archives 41006

United States Marine Corps Museum, Marine Corp Historical Center, 1254 Charles Morris St SE, Washington, DC 20374-5040 - T: (202) 433-3534, 433-2484, Fax: (202) 433-7265. Head: Michael F. Monigan
Historical Museum / Military Museum - 1940
Military history 41007

United States Senate Commission on Art Collection, Rm S-411, U.S. Capitol Bldg, Washington, DC 20510-7102 - T: (202) 224-2955, Fax: (202) 224-8799, E-mail: curator@sec.senate.gov, Internet: http://www.senate.gov/curator/collections.htm
Fine Arts Museum / Decorative Arts Museum - 1968
Paintings, sculpture, prints, furnishing 41008

Washington Dolls House and Toy Museum, 5236 44th St NW, Washington, DC 20015 - T: (202) 363-6400, Fax: (202) 237-1659. Head: Flora Gill Jacobs
Decorative Arts Museum - 1975
Antique Toy ans Dolls 41009

Washington National Cathedral, Cathedral Church of Saint Peter and Saint Paul, Massachusetts and Wisconsin Av, NW, Washington, DC 20016-5098 - T: (202) 537-8991, 537-6200, Fax: (202) 364-6600, E-mail: tours@cathedral.org, Internet: http://www.cathedral.org/cathedral
Religious Arts Museum - 1893
Gothic design Cathedral, Episcopal Cathedral, structure 41010

Watkins Gallery, American University, 4400 Massachusetts NW Av, Washington, DC 20016 - T: (202) 885-1064, 885-1670, Fax: (202) 885-1132, E-mail: rhaynie@american.edu, Internet: http://www.american.edu/academic.depts/cas/art/watkins. Head: Ron Haynie
Fine Arts Museum / University Museum - 1945
Art 41011

The White House, 1600 Pennsylvania Av NW, Washington, DC 20500 - T: (202) 456-2550, Fax: (202) 456-6820, Internet: http://www.whitehousehistory.org
Historical Museum - 1792
Hist, politics 41012

Woodrow Wilson House, 2340 S St NW, Washington, DC 20008 - T: (202) 387-4062 ext 14, Fax: (202) 483-1466, E-mail: wilson_house@nthp.org, Internet: http://www.nthp.org. Head: Frank J. Aucella
Historical Museum - 1963
Home of President Wilson 41013

Washington GA

Robert Toombs House, 216 E Robert Toombs Av, Washington, GA 30673 - T: (706) 678-2226, Fax: (706) 678-7515, E-mail: toombs@g-net.net. Head: Marty Fleming
Natural History Museum - 1974 41014

Washington Historical Museum, 308 E Robert Toombs Av, Washington, GA 30673-2038 - T: (706) 678-2105
Local Museum - 1959
1836 Barnett-Slaton House, local history 41015

Washington LA

Washington Museum, 402 N Main St, Washington, LA 70589 - T: (318) 826-3627
Local Museum - 1972
Local history 41016

Washington PA

David Bradford House, 175 S Main St, Washington, PA 15301 - T: (724) 222-3604. Head: Mary Ellen Chaney
Local Museum - 1960
Historic house 41017

Olin Art Gallery, Washington and Jefferson College, 285 E Wheeling St, Washington, PA 15301 - T: (724) 223-6546, Fax: (724) 223-5271, E-mail: htaylor@washjeff.edu, Internet: http://www.washjeff.edu. Head: Ronald F. Sherhofer
Fine Arts Museum / University Museum - 1980 41018

Pennsylvania Trolley Museum, 1 Museum Rd, Washington, PA 15301-6133 - T: (724) 228-9675, Fax: (724) 228-9675, E-mail: ptm@pa-trolley.org, Internet: http://www.pa-trolley.org. Head: Scott R. Becker
Science&Tech Museum - 1949
Railway 41019

Washington County Museum, Le Moyne House, 49 E Maiden St, Washington, PA 15301 - T: (724) 225-6740, Fax: (724) 225-8495, E-mail: infa@wchspa.org, Internet: http://www.wchspa.org
Local Museum - 1900
Le Moyne House, a national historic landmark of the undergroud railroad incl historic house, doctor's office, gardens, crematory 41020

Washington TX

Barrington Living History Farm, Brazos Park, 23100 Barrington Ln, Washington, TX 77880 - T: (979) 878-2214, Fax: (979) 878-2810, E-mail: -washington.brazos@tpwd.state.tx.us, Internet: http://www.tpwd.state.tx.us/park/parks.htm. Head: Tom Scaggs
Agriculture Museum - 1936
Historic house, home of Anson Jones, last president of the Republic of Texas 41021

Star of the Republic Museum, Blinn College, Washington-On-The-Brazos State Historical Park, Washington, TX 77880 - T: (409) 878-2461, Fax: (936) 878-2462, E-mail: star@acmail.blinncol.edu, Internet: http://www.starmuseum.org. Head: Houston McGaugh
Historical Museum - 1970
Texas hist 1836-1846 41022

Washington Crossing PA

Washington Crossing Historic Park, 1112 River Rd, Washington Crossing, PA 18977 - T: (215) 493-4076, Fax: (215) 493-4820. Head: Eric F. Castle
Historical Museum - 1917
Historic Site 41023

Washington Green CT

The Institute For American Indian Studies (IAIS), 38 Curtis Rd, Washington Green, CT 06793-0260 - T: (860) 868-0518, Fax: (860) 868-1649, E-mail: -instituteamer.indian@snet.net, Internet: http://www.amerindianinstitute.org. Head: Alberto C. Meloni
Ethnology Museum / Archaeological Museum - 1975
American Indian culture and archaeology 41024

Wasilla AK

Dorothy G. Page Museum, 323 Main St, Wasilla, AK 99654 - T: (907) 373-9071, Fax: (907) 373-9072, E-mail: museum@ci.wasilla.ak.us. Head: John Cramer
Local Museum - 1966
Local hist 41025

Water Mill NY

Water Mill Museum, 41 Old Mill Rd, Water Mill, NY 11976 - T: (516) 726-4625. Head: Marlene Haresign
Local Museum - 1942 41026

Waterbury CT

The Mattatuck Museum of the Mattatuck Historical Society, 144 W Main St, Waterbury, CT 06702 - T: (203) 753-0381, Fax: (203) 756-6283, E-mail: mattatuckmuseum@cybergary.net, Internet: http://www.mattatuckmuseum.org. Head: Terry P. Cassidy, Sharon Drubner
Fine Arts Museum / Historical Museum - 1877
History and art Temple 41027

Waterbury Center VT

Green Mountain Club, Rte. 100, Waterbury Center, VT 05677 - T: (802) 244-7037, Fax: (802) 244-5867, E-mail: gmc@sover.net. Head: Rolf Anderson, Ben Rose
Local Museum - 1910 41028

Waterford NY

Waterford Historical Museum, 2 Museum Ln, Waterford, NY 12188 - T: (518) 238-0809. Head: Dr. James Lefebvre
Local Museum - 1964 41029

Waterloo IA

Grout Museum of History and Science, Rensselaer Russell House Museum, Snowden House, Bluedorn Science Imaginarium, 503 South St, Waterloo, IA 50701 - T: (319) 234-6357, Fax: (319) 236-0500, E-mail: grout@cedarnet.org, Internet: http://www.cedarnet.org/grout. Head: Billie K. Bailey
Historical Museum / Natural History Museum - 1933
History, science - planetarium 41030

Rensselaer Russell House Museum, 520 W 3rd St, Waterloo, IA 50701 - T: (319) 233-0262, Fax: (319) 236-0500. Head: Roger P. Olesen, Billie K. Bailey
Historical Museum - 1861
Historic house built in Italianate architectural style 41031

Waterloo Center of the Arts, 225 Commercial St, Waterloo, IA 50701 - T: (319) 291-4490, Fax: (319) 291-4270, E-mail: museum@warterloo-ia.org, Internet: http://www.wplwloo.lib.ia.us/arts. Head: Cammie V. Scully
Fine Arts Museum
Haitian art, Mid-West regional art 41032

Waterloo NY

Memorial Day Museum of Waterloo, 35 E Main St, Waterloo, NY 13165 - T: (315) 539-0533, Fax: (315) 539-7798. Head: James T. Hughes
Military Museum - 1966 41033

Peter Whitmer Sr. Home and Visitors Center, 1451 Aunkst Rd, Waterloo, NY 13165 - T: (315) 539-2552, Internet: http://www.ggw.org/hillcumorah. Head: Jerry Hess
Historic Site - 1980 41034

Terwilliger Museum, 31 E Williams St, Waterloo, NY 13165 - T: (315) 539-0533, Fax: (315) 539-7798, E-mail: ssnyder@lakenet.org, Internet: http://www.waterloony.com/library.html. Head: James T. Hughes
Local Museum / Historical Museum - 1960 41035

Watertown CT

Watertown Historical Society Museum, 22 DeForest St, Watertown, CT 06795 - T: (860) 274-1634, E-mail: faitc@juno.com
Local Museum - 1947
Local hist 41036

Watertown MA

Armenian Museum of America, 65 Main St, Watertown, MA 02472 - T: (617) 926-2562, Fax: (617) 926-0175, E-mail: almainc@aol.com, Internet: http://www.almainc.org. Head: Mildred Nahabedian
Ethnology Museum / Folklore Museum - 1971
Library 41037

Museum on the History of Blindness, Perkins School for the Blind, 175 North Beacon St, Watertown, MA 02472 - T: (617) 972-7250, Fax: (617) 923-8076, Internet: http://www.perkins.pvt.k12.ma.us
Special Museum - 1829 41038

Watertown NY

Jefferson County Historical Society Museum, 228 Washington St, Watertown, NY 13601 - T: (315) 782-3491, Fax: (315) 782-2913. Head: Fred H. Rollins
Local Museum - 1886 41039

Sci-Tech Center of Northern New York, 154 Stone St, Watertown, NY 13601 - T: (315) 788-1340, Fax: (315) 788-2738, E-mail: scitech@imcnet.net. Head: David Stanley, John Kunz
Science&Tech Museum - 1982
Science and technology 41040

Watertown SD

Codington County Heritage Museum, 27 First Av, Watertown, SD 57201 - T: (605) 886-7335, Fax: (605) 882-4383, E-mail: cchs@dailypost.com, Internet: http://www.cchmuseum.org. Head: Tim Hoheisel
Local Museum - 1974
Local hist 41041

Mellette House, 421 Fifth Av, Watertown, SD 57201 - T: (605) 886-4730. Head: Prudence K. Calvin
Local Museum - 1943
Historic house, home of Arthur Calvin Mellette, first Governor of South Dakota 41042

Watertown WI

Octagon House, 919 Charles St, Watertown, WI 53094 - T: (920) 261-2796, Internet: http://members.tripod.com/~watertownhs. Head: William Jannke, Linda Werth
Local Museum - 1933
Historic house 41043

Waterville ME

Colby College Museum of Art, 5600 Mayflower Hill, Waterville, ME 04901 - T: (207) 872-3000, 872-3228, Fax: (207) 872-3807, Internet: http://www.colby.edu/museum. Head: William Cotter, Hugh J. Gourley
Fine Arts Museum / University Museum - 1959
Art 41044

Redington Museum, 64 Silver St, Waterville, ME 04901 - T: (207) 872-9439, Internet: http://www.redingtonmuseum.org
Historical Museum - 1903
Local history, residence of Asa Redington 41045

Watervliet NY

The Watervliet Arsenal Museum, Watervliet Arsenal, Rte 32, Watervliet, NY 12189-4050 - T: (518) 266-5805, Fax: (518) 266-5011, Internet: http://www.wva.army.mil. Head: Rosemarie A. Hutchinson
Military Museum - 1975
Military hist 41046

Watford City ND

Pioneer Museum, 104 Park Av W, Watford City, ND 58854 - T: (701) 842-2990. Head: Clyde Holman
Historical Museum - 1968 41047

Watonga OK

T.B. Ferguson Home, 519 N Weigel, Watonga, OK 73772 - T: (580) 623-5069
Local Museum - 1972 41048

Watrous NM

Fort Union National Monument, Rte 161, Watrous, NM 87753 - T: (505) 425-8025, Fax: (505) 454-1155, E-mail: foun_administration@nps.gov, Internet: http://www.nps.gov/foun/. Head: Harry C. Myers
Military Museum - 1956 41049

Watseka IL

Iroquois County Historical Society Museum, 103 West Cherry St, Watseka, IL 60970 - T: (815) 432-2215. Head: Rolland Light
Local Museum - 1967
Local history, housed in Old Iroquois County Courthouse 41050

Watsonville CA

Pajaro Valley Historical Museum, 332 E Beach St, Watsonville, CA 95076 - T: (408) 722-0305. Head: Raymon Hoffman
Local Museum - 1940
Local hist 41051

Wauconda IL

Lake County Museum, Rte 176, Fairfield Rd, Wauconda, IL 60084 - T: (847) 526-7878, Fax: (847) 526-0024, E-mail: lcmuseum@co.lake.il.us, Internet: http://www.co.lake.i1.us/forest. Head: Janet Gallimore
Local Museum - 1976
Local and regional history 41052

Waukegan IL

Haines Museum, 1917 N Sheridan Rd, Bowen Park, Waukegan, IL 60079 - T: (847) 336-1859, 360-4772, Fax: (847) 360-4743, Internet: http://www.waukeganparks.org. Head: Steve Kolber
Local Museum - 1968
Local history 41053

Waukesha WI

Waukesha County Museum, 101 W Main St, Waukesha, WI 53186-4811 - T: (262) 521-2859, Fax: (262) 521-2865, E-mail: exdirector@voyager.net. Head: Susan K. Baker
Local Museum - 1911
Local hist - research center 41054

Waupaca WI

Hutchinson House Museum, End of S Main St, South Park, Waupaca, WI 54981 - T: (715) 258-5958, 258-7726, 258-8238. Head: Don Duesterbeck
Local Museum - 1956
Local hist 41055

Waurika OK

Chisholm Trail Historical Museum, US 81 and State Rte 70, Waurika, OK 73573 - T: (405) 228-2166, Fax: (405) 228-3290. Head: Gin Dodson
Local Museum - 1965 41056

Wausau WI

Leigh Yawkey Woodson Art Museum, 700 N 12th St, Wausau, WI 54403-5007 - T: (715) 845-7010, Fax: (715) 845-7103, E-mail: museum@lywam.org, Internet: http://www.lywam.org. Head: Kathy Kelsey Foley
Fine Arts Museum / Decorative Arts Museum - 1973
Art 41057

Marathon County Historical Society Museum, 410 McIndoe St, Wausau, WI 54403 - T: (715) 848-6143, Fax: (715) 848-0576, Internet: http://www.g02america.com/historicalmuseum. Head: Mary Jane Hettingg
Local Museum - 1952
Local hist 41058

Wauseon OH

Fulton County Historical Museum, 229 Monroe St, Wauseon, OH 43567 - T: (419) 337-7922
Local Museum - 1883 41059

Wauwatosa WI

Lowell Damon House, 2107 Wauwatosa Av, Wauwatosa, WI 53213 - T: (414) 273-8288, Internet: http://www.milwaukeecountyhistsoc.org. Head: Michael J. Klinker, Harry H. Anderson
Local Museum - 1941
Historic house 41060

Waverly TN

World O' Tools Museum, 2431 Hwy 13, Waverly, TN 37185 - T: (931) 296-3218. Head: Hunter M. Pilkinton
Science&Tech Museum - 1973
Tools and related items 41061

Waverly VA

Miles B. Carpenter Museum, 201 Hunter St, Waverly, VA 23890 - T: (804) 834-2151, 834-3327. Head: Shirley S. Yancey
Folklore Museum / Agriculture Museum - 1986
Folk art, peanuts 41062

Waxahachie TX

Ellis County Museum, 201 S College St, Waxahachie, TX 75165 - T: (972) 937-0681, Fax: (972) 937-3910, E-mail: ecmuseum@azmail.net. Head: David Hudgins, Shannon Simpson
Local Museum - 1967
Local hist 41063

Waxhaw NC

Museum of the Alphabet, Jaars Summer Institute of Linguistics, 6409 Davis Rd, Waxhaw, NC 28173 - T: (704) 843-6066, Fax: (704) 843-6200, E-mail: info@jaars.org, Internet: http://www.jaars.org. Head: LaDonna Mann
Special Museum - 1990
Alphabet 41064

Waycross GA

Okefenokee Heritage Center, 1460 N Augusta Av, Waycross, GA 31503 - T: (912) 285-4260, Fax: (912) 283-2858, E-mail: ohc@acces.net, Internet: http://www.okeheritage.org. Head: T. Henry Clarke, Catherine Larkins
Fine Arts Museum / Historical Museum - 1975
History, art 41065

Southern Forest World Museum, 1440 N Augusta Av, Waycross, GA 31503 - T: (912) 285-4056, Fax: (912) 283-2858, Internet: http://www.okefeno-keeswamp.com. Head: Earl Smith
Science&Tech Museum / Natural History Museum - 1981
Forestry 41066

Wayland MA

Wayland Historical Museum, 12 Cochituate Rd, Wayland, MA 01778 - T: (508) 358-7959, Internet: http://towonline.koz.com/visit/waylandhistoricalsoc
Historical Museum - 1954
General museum 41067

Wayne MI

City of Wayne Historical Museum, 1 Town Sq, Wayne, MI 48184 - T: (313) 722-0113. Head: Virginia Presson
Local Museum - 1966
Local history 41068

Wayne NE

Nordstrand Visual Arts Gallery, Wayne State College, 1111 Main St, Wayne, NE 68787 - T: (402) 375-7000, Fax: (402) 375-7204. Head: Prof. Pearl Hansen, Prof. Marlene Mueller
Public Gallery - 1977 41069

Wayne NJ

Ben Shahn Galleries, c/o William Paterson University of New Jersey, 300 Pompton Rd, Wayne, NJ 07470 - T: (973) 720-2654, Fax: (973) 720-3290, E-mail: einreinhofern@wpunj.edu, Internet: http://www.wpunj.edu. Head: Nancy Einreinhofer
University Museum / Fine Arts Museum - 1969 41070

Dey Mansion, Washington's Headquarters Museum, 199 Totowa Rd, Wayne, NJ 07470 - T: (201) 696-1776, Fax: (973) 696-1365
Military Museum - 1934 41071

Van Riper-Hopper House, Wayne Museum, 533 Berdan Av, Wayne, NJ 07470 - T: (973) 694-7192, Fax: (973) 872-0586, Internet: http:///http://www.waynetownship.com/. Head: Bob Brubaker, Cecilia Paccioretti
Local Museum / Archaeological Museum - 1964 41072

Wayne PA

The Finley House, 113 W Beech Tree Ln, Wayne, PA 19087 - T: (610) 688-2668, 688-4455. Head: J. Bennett Hill
Local Museum - 1948
Local hist 41073

Wayne Art Center, 413 Maplewood Ave, Wayne, PA 19087 - T: (610) 688-3553, Fax: (610) 995-0478, E-mail: wayneart@worldnet.att.net, Internet: http://www.wayneart.com. Head: Nancy Campbell
Public Gallery - 1930 41074

Waynesboro PA

Renfrew Museum, 1010 E Main St, Waynesboro, PA 17268 - T: (717) 762-4723, Fax: (717) 762-4707, E-mail: renfrew@innernet.net, Internet: http://www.innernet.net/renfrew
Decorative Arts Museum - 1973
Decorative arts 41075

Waynesburg PA

Greene County Historical Museum, 918 Rolling Meadows Rd, Waynesburg, PA 15370 - T: (724) 627-3204, Fax: (724) 627-3204, E-mail: museum@greenepa.net, Internet: http://www.greenepa.net/~museum/. Head: Paul Maytk
Local Museum - 1925
Local hist 41076

Weathersfield VT

Museum of the Weathersfield Historical Society, Weathersfield Center Rd, Weathersfield, VT 05156 - T: (802) 263-5230, 263-5361, Fax: (802) 263-9263, E-mail: efh@sover.net. Head: Sally Harris
Local Museum - 1951
Local hist 41077

Weaverville CA

J.J. Jackson Memorial Museum, 508 Main St, Weaverville, CA 96093 - T: (530) 623-5211. Head: Hal E. Goodyear
Local Museum - 1968
Local hist 41078

Weaverville Joss House State Historic Park, Weaverville, CA 96093 - T: (916) 623-5284
Local Museum - 1956
Historic house 41079

Weedsport NY

Old Brutus Historical Society Museum, 8943 N Seneca St, Weedsport, NY 13166 - T: (315) 834-9342. Head: Jean Woodcock
Local Museum - 1967 41080

Weeping Water NE

Weeping Water Valley Historical Society Museum, 215 W Eldora Av, Weeping Water, NE 68463 - T: (402) 267-4925, E-mail: wd85407@navix.net. Head: Doris Duff
Local Museum - 1969 41081

Wellesley MA

Davis Museum, Wellesley College, 106 Central St, Wellesley, MA 02481-8203 - T: (781) 283-2051, Fax: (781) 283-2064, Internet: http://www.wellesley.edu/DavisMuseum/. Head: Dennis McFadden
Fine Arts Museum / University Museum - 1889
Art 41082

Wellesley Hills MA

Wellesley Historical Society, 229 Washington St, Wellesley Hills, MA 02481 - T: (781) 235-6690, Fax: (781) 235-6690, Internet: http://www.wellesleyhsoc.com. Head: Felix Juliani, Laurel Nilsen
Local Museum - 1925
Local history, Dadmun-McNamara house, oldham lace coll , Denton Butterfly and moth coll 41083

Wellfleet MA

Wellfleet Historical Society Museum, 266 Main St, Wellfleet, MA 02667 - T: (508) 349-9157, (367) 413-2469
Local Museum - 1953
Local history 41084

Wellington KS

Chisholm Trail Museum, 502 N Washington, Wellington, KS 67152 - T: (316) 326-3820, 326-7466. Head: Richard M. Gilfillan
Historical Museum - 1964
History, first hospital in Wellington 41085

Wellington OH

Spirit of '76 Museum, 201 N Main St, Wellington, OH 44090 - T: (440) 647-4367. Head: Michael Giar
Historical Museum - 1968 41086

Wells ME

Historical Society of Wells and Ogunquit Museum, 938 Post Rd, Wells, ME 04090 - T: (207) 646-4775, Fax: (207) 646-0832, E-mail: wohistory@cybertours.com
Historical Museum - 1954
Regional history 41087

Wells Auto Museum, 1181 Post Rd, Wells, ME 04090 - T: (207) 646-9064, E-mail: wellsauto@aol.com. Head: Jonathan H. Gould
Science&Tech Museum - 1954
Automobile 41088

Wellsville UT

Ronald V. Jensen Living Historical Farm, 4025 S Hwy, 89-91, Wellsville, UT 84339 - T: (801) 245-4064, 797-1143, Fax: (801) 797-1153. Head: R. Summers
Agriculture Museum / Local Museum - 1979
Historic farm 41089

Wenatchee WA

Gallery '76, 1300 5th St, Wenatchee, WA 98801 - T: (509) 664-2521, Fax: (509) 664-2538, Internet: http://www.ctc.edu. Head: Rae Dana
Fine Arts Museum - 1976
Art 41090

North Central Washington Museum, 127 S Mission, Wenatchee, WA 98801 - T: (509) 664-3340, Fax: (509) 664-3356, E-mail: kwilliams@cityofwenatchee.com, Internet: http://www.museumwsb.wednet.edu. Head: Dr. Keith Williams
Local Museum - 1939
Local hist 41091

Wenham MA

Wenham Museum, 132 Main St, Wenham, MA 01984 - T: (978) 468-2377, Fax: (978) 468-1763, E-mail: info@wenhammuseum.org, Internet: http://www.wenhammuseum.org. Head: Elizabeth R. Colt, Emily Stearns
Local Museum - 1921
Social history, dolls, toys, model trains, costumes, textiles, photography 41092

West Allis WI

West Allis Historical Society Museum, 8405 West National Av, West Allis, WI 53227-1733 - T: (414) 541-6970. Head: John R. Clow
Local Museum - 1966
Local hist 41093

West Bend WI

Washington County Historical Society Museum, 340 S Fifth Av, West Bend, WI 53095 - T: (414) 335-4678, Fax: (414) 335-4612, E-mail: wchs@historyisfun.com, Internet: http://www.historyisfun.com. Head: Chip Beckford
Local Museum - 1937
Local hist 41094

West Bend Art Museum, 300 S 6th Av, West Bend, WI 53095 - T: (414) 334-9638, Fax: (414) 334-8080, E-mail: director@wbartmuseum.com, Internet: http://www.wbartmuseum.com. Head: Thomas D. Lidtke
Fine Arts Museum - 1961
Wisconsin Art from 1800 - 1950, Carl von Marr coll 41095

West Branch IA

Herbert Hoover National Historic Site, 110 Parkside Dr, West Branch, IA 52358 - T: (319) 643-2541, Fax: (319) 643-5367, E-mail: dan_banta@nps.gov, Internet: http://www.nps.gov/heho. Head: Carol E. Kohan
Historic Site - 1965
Birthplace of Herbert Hoover, graves of President and Mrs. Hoover 41096

Herbert Hoover Presidential Library-Museum, 210 Parkside Dr, West Branch, IA 52358 - T: (319) 643-5301, Fax: (319) 643-5825, E-mail: library@hoover.nara.gov, Internet: http://www.hoover.nara.gov. Head: Timoth Walch
Library with Exhibitions - 1962
Presidential library - Archive 41097

West Chester PA

American Helicopter Museum & Education Center, 1220 American Blvd, West Chester, PA 19380 - T: (610) 436-9600, Fax: (610) 436-8642, Internet: http://www.helicoptermuseum.org. Head: Ann Barton Brown
Science&Tech Museum - 1993
Aeronautics 41098

Chester County Historical Society Museum, 225 N High St, West Chester, PA 19380 - T: (610) 692-4800, Fax: (610) 692-4357, E-mail: cchs@chesco.com, Internet: http://www.chestercohi-storical.org. Head: Roland H. Woodward
Local Museum - 1893
Local hist 41099

West Chicago IL

Kruse House Museum, 527 Main St, West Chicago, IL 60185 - T: (630) 231-0564. Head: Lance Conkright
Local Museum - 1976
Local history, housed in 1917 Kruse House 41100

West Chicago City Museum, 132 Main St, West Chicago, IL 60185 - T: (630) 231-3376, 293-2266, Fax: (630) 293-3028, Internet: http://www.westchicago.org. Head: LuAnn Bombard
Local Museum - 1976
Town history 41101

West Fargo ND

Cass County Historical Society Museum, 1351 W Main Av, West Fargo, ND 58078 - T: (701) 282-2822, Fax: (701) 282-7606, E-mail: bonanzaville@fargocity.com, Internet: http://www.fargocity.com/Bonanzaville. Head: Sandra Fuchs, Kathy Anderson
Local Museum - 1967 41102

Red River and Northern Plains Regional Museum, 1351 W Main Av, West Fargo, ND 58078 - T: (701) 282-2822, Fax: (701) 282-7606, E-mail: bonanzaville@fargocity.com, Internet: http://www.fargocity.com/bonanzaville. Head: Sandra Fuchs, Kathy Anderson
Local Museum / Open Air Museum - 1954 41103

West Frankfort IL

Frankfort Area Historical Museum, 2000 E Saint Louis St, West Frankfort, IL 62896 - T: (618) 932-6159
Local Museum - 1972
Local history 41104

West Glacier MT

Glacier National Park Museum, Glacier National Park, West Glacier, MT 59936 - T: (406) 888-7936, Fax: (406) 888-7808, E-mail: deivdve-shaw@nps.gov
Natural History Museum / Historical Museum / Archaeological Museum - 1930 41105

West Hartford CT

Joseloff Gallery, Hartford Art School, Harry Jack Gray Center, University of Hartford, 200 Bloomfield Av, West Hartford, CT 06117 - T: (860) 768-4090, Fax: (860) 768-5159, E-mail: bgreen@mail.hartfoRdedu. Head: Zina Davis
Fine Arts Museum / University Museum - 1970 41106

Museum of American Political Life, University of Hartford, 200 Bloomfield Av, West Hartford, CT 06117 - T: (860) 768-4090, Fax: (860) 768-5159, E-mail: bgreen@mail.hartford.edu. Head: Zina Davis
Historical Museum - 1989 41107

Noah Webster House/Museum of West Hartford History, 227 S Main St, West Hartford, CT 06107-3430 - T: (860) 521-5362, Fax: (860) 521-4036, E-mail: vfzoe@snet.net, Internet: http://www.ctstateu.ed/~noahweb/noahwebster.html. Head: Bill French, Vivian F. Zoe
Historical Museum - 1965
Local hist 41108

Saint Joseph College Art Study Gallery, 1678 Asylum Av, West Hartford, CT 06117 - T: (203) 232-4571, Fax: (203) 233-5695, E-mail: vuccello@sjc.edu. Head: Winifred E. Coleman, Vincenza Uccello
Fine Arts Museum / University Museum - 1932 41109

Science Center of Connecticut, 950 Trout Brook Dr, West Hartford, CT 06119 - T: (806) 231-2824, Fax: (806) 232-0705, E-mail: science.ctr@snet.net, Internet: http://www.sciencecenterCT.org. Head: Linda K. Johnson, Hank Gruner
Science&Tech Museum - 1927
Science and technology 41110

West Henrietta NY

New York Museum of Transportation, 6393 E River Rd, West Henrietta, NY 14586 - T: (716) 533-1113, Internet: http://www.transportation.mus.ny.us/. Head: T.H. Strang
Science&Tech Museum - 1974 41111

West Hollywood CA

MAK Center for Art and Architecture, Schindler House, 835 N Kings Rd, West Hollywood, CA 90069-5409 - T: (323) 651-1510, Fax: (323) 651-2340, E-mail: makcenter@earthlink.net, Internet: http://www.MAK.at. Head: Peter Noever
Fine Arts Museum - 1994 41112

West Lafayette IN

Purdue University Galleries, 1396 Physics Bldg, West Lafayette, IN 47907-1396 - T: (765) 494-3061, Fax: (765) 496-2817, E-mail: gallery@purdue.edu, Internet: http://www.sla.purdue.edu/galleries. Head: Martin Craig
Fine Arts Museum / University Museum - 1978
Art gallery 41113

West Liberty OH

Piatt Castles, 10051 Township Rd 47, West Liberty, OH 43357 - T: (937) 465-2821, Fax: (937) 465-2821, E-mail: macochee@logan.net. Head: Margaret Piatt
Local Museum / Folklore Museum - 1912 41114

West Liberty WV

Women's History Museum, 108 Walnut St, West Liberty, WV 26074 - T: (304) 336-7159, Fax: (304) 336-7893, E-mail: womenshist@earthlink.net, Internet: http://www.womens-history-museum.com. Head: Jeanne Schramm
Historical Museum - 1990
Women's hist 41115

West Orange NJ

Edison National Historic Site, Main St at Lakeside Av, West Orange, NJ 07052 - T: (973) 736-0550, Fax: (973) 736-8496, E-mail: - edis_superintendent@nps.gov, Internet: http://www.nps.gov/edis. Head: Maryanne Gerbauckas
Historical Museum - 1956 41116

West Palm Beach FL

Historical Museum of Palm Beach County, 400 N Dixie Hwy, West Palm Beach, FL 33401 - T: (561) 832-4164, Fax: (561) 832-7965. Head: Ken Brower, Kristin H. Gaspari
Local Museum - 1937 41117

Norton Museum of Art, 1451 S Olive Av, West Palm Beach, FL 33401 - T: (561) 832-5196, Fax: (561) 659-4689, E-mail: museum@norton.org, Internet: http://www.norton.org. Head: Christina Orr-Cahall
Fine Arts Museum - 1940
Chinese and contemporary art 41118

South Florida Science Museum, 4801 Dreher Trail N, West Palm Beach, FL 33405 - T: (561) 832-1988, Fax: (561) 833-0551, E-mail: rollings@sfsm.org, Internet: http://www.sfsm.org. Head: James R. Rollings
Science&Tech Museum - 1959 41119

West Park NY

Slabsides, off John Burroughs Dr, West Park, NY 12493 - T: (212) 769-5169, Fax: (212) 769-5329, E-mail: breslof@amnh.org, Internet: http://www.nimidz.amnh.org/burroughs. Head: Frank Knight
Historical Museum - 1921 41120

West Point NY

Constitution Island Association Museum, POB 41, West Point, NY 10996 - T: (914) 446-8676, E-mail: - executivedirector@constitutionisland.org, Internet: http://www.constitutionisland.org. Head: Richard de Koster
Historical Museum - 1916 41121

West Point Museum, United States Military Academy, Bldg 2110, West Point, NY 10996 - T: (845) 938-2203, Fax: (845) 938-7478, Internet: http://www.usma.edu. Head: Michael E. Moss
Military Museum - 1854 41122

West Saint Paul MN

North Star Scouting Memorabilia, POB 18341, West Saint Paul, MN 55118 - T: (612) 771-9066, E-mail: dickcarroll@juno.com. Head: Richard E. Carroll
Historical Museum - 1976 41123

West Salem WI

Hamlin Garland Homestead, 357 W Garland St, West Salem, WI 54669 - T: (608) 786-1399. Head: Errol Kindschy
Local Museum - 1976
Historic house 41124

Palmer/Gullickson Octagon Home, 360 N Leonard, West Salem, WI 54669 - T: (608) 786-1399. Head: Errol Kindschy
Local Museum - 1976
Local history 41125

West Sayville NY

Long Island Maritime Museum, 86 West Av, West Sayville, NY 11796 - T: (516) 854-4974, Fax: (516) 854-4979. Head: R. Douglas Shaw
Special Museum - 1966 41126

West Springfield MA

Storrowton Village Museum, 1305 Memorial Av, West Springfield, MA 01089 - T: (413) 787-0136, Fax: (413) 787-0127, E-mail: storrow@thebige.com, Internet: http://www.thebige.com. Head: Dennis Picard
Open Air Museum / Historical Museum - 1929
Historic village 41127

West Union IA

Fayette County Historical Museum, 100 N Walnut St, West Union, IA 52175 - T: (319) 422-5797. Head: Ruth Brooks, Laura Janssen
Local Museum - 1975
History, genealogy 41128

Westbrook CT

The Company of Military Historians Museum → Military Historians Museum

Military Historians Museum, N Main St, Westbrook, CT 06498 - T: (860) 399-9460
Military Museum - 1949
Military uniforms 41129

Westbury NY

Historical Society of the Town of North Hempstead Museum, 461 Newton St, Westbury, NY 11590 - T: (516) 333-3151. Head: Frances McKenna
Historical Museum - 1963 41130

Western Springs IL

Western Springs Museum, 4211 Grand Av, Western Springs, IL 60558 - T: (708) 246-9230
Local Museum - 1967
Local history, housed in a Old Water Tower 41131

Westerville OH

Hanby House, 160 W Main St, Westerville, OH 43081 - T: (614) 895-6017
Local Museum - 1937 41132

The Ross C. Purdy Museum of Ceramics, 735 Ceramic Pl, Westerville, OH 43081 - T: (614) 890-4700, Fax: (614) 899-6109, E-mail: info@acers.org, Internet: http://www.acers.org
Decorative Arts Museum - 1977
Ceramics 41133

Westfield MA

Jasper Rand Art Museum, 6 Elm St, Westfield, MA 01085 - T: (413) 568-7833, Fax: (413) 568-1558, E-mail: pcramer@exit3.com, Internet: www.ci.-westfield.ma.us/athen.thml. Head: James A. Rogers, Patricia T. Cramer
Fine Arts Museum - 1927
Art gallery 41134

Westfield NJ

Miller-Cory House Museum, 614 Mountain Av, Westfield, NJ 07090 - T: (908) 232-1776, Fax: (908) 232-1740, E-mail: mc@westfieldnj.com, Internet: http://www.westfieldnj.com. Head: Thomas Sherry, John Petersen
Local Museum - 1972 41135

Westfield NY

McClurg Mansion, Main and Portage Sts, Westfield, NY 14787 - T: (716) 326-2977. Head: Roderick A. Nixon, Nancy Brown
Local Museum - 1883 41136

Westfield WI

Cochrane-Nelson House, 125 Lawrence St, Westfield, WI 53964
Local Museum - 1979
Historic house 41137

Westminster MD

Carroll County Farm Museum, 500 S Center St, Westminster, MD 21157 - T: (410) 848-7775, Fax: (410) 876-8544, Internet: http://www.carr.lib.md.us/carroll/carroll.htm
Public Gallery / Historic Site / Agriculture Museum - 1965 41138

Union Mills Homestead and Grist Mill, 3311 Littles Town Pike, Westminster, MD 21158 - T: (410) 848-2288, Fax: (410) 848-2288. Head: James M. Shriver, Esther L. Shriver
Science&Tech Museum - 1797 41139

Westminster VT

Westminster Historical Society Museum, Main St, Westminster, VT 05158 - T: (802) 387-5778. Head: Virginia Lisai, Karen Larsen
Local Museum - 1966
Local hist 41140

Weston CT

The Coley Homestead and Barn Museum, 104 Weston Rd, Weston, CT 06883 - T: (203) 226-1804, 544-9636, Fax: (203) 227-4268. Head: Sandra O'Brien
Local Museum / Agriculture Museum - 1961
Agriculture 41141

Weston MA

Golden Ball Tavern Museum, 662 Boston Post Rd, Weston, MA 02493 - T: (781) 894-1751, Fax: (781) 862-9178, E-mail: joanb5@aol.com. Head: William Wiseman, Dr. Joan P. Bines
Local Museum - 1964
Historic house 41142

Museum of the Weston Historical Society, 358 Boston Post Rd, Weston, MA 02493 - T: (761) 237-1447, Fax: (781) 237-1471, E-mail: verandy@aol.com. Head: William Martin
Historical Museum - 1963
Local history 41143

Spellman Museum of Stamps and Postal History, Regis College, 235 Wellesley St, Weston, MA 02493 - T: (781) 768-8367, Fax: (781) 768-7332. Head: Viki Sand
Special Museum - 1960
Philatelic, postal services 41144

Weston VT

Farrar-Mansur House and Old Mill Museum, Main St, Weston, VT 05161 - T: (802) 824-6781, Fax: (802) 824-4072
Local Museum - 1933
Historic house 41145

Weston WV

WVU Jackson's Mill Historic Area, Rte I, Box 210-WVU, Weston, WV 26452 - T: (304) 269-5100, Fax: (304) 269-3409, E-mail: chardman@wvu.edu, Internet: http://www.jacksonmill.com. Head: Dean Hardman
Historic Site - 1968
Local hist, Boyhood home of "Stonewall" Jackson 41146

Westport CT

Westport Historical Museum, 25 Avery Pl, Westport, CT 06880 - T: (203) 222-1424, Fax: (203) 221-0981, E-mail: westporth@snet.org, Internet: http://www.townline.com/westporthistorical/whspage7.htm. Head: Ann E. Sheffer, Sheila C. O'Neill
Local Museum - 1899
Diorama of historic downtown, costumes - archives 41147

Wethersfield CT

The Webb-Deane-Stevens Museum, 211 Main St, Wethersfield, CT 06109 - T: (860) 529-0612, Fax: (860) 571-8636, Internet: http://www.webb-deane-stevens.org. Head: Jennifer S. Eifrig, Phyllis Greenberg
Local Museum - 1919
Local hist 41148

Wethersfield Museum, 150 Main St, Wethersfield, CT 06109 - T: (860) 529-7656, Fax: (860) 529-9105, E-mail: director@wethhist.org, Internet: http://www.wethhist.org. Head: Thomas Giardini, Brenda Milkofsky
Historical Museum - 1932
Local hist 41149

Wewoka OK

Seminole Nation Museum, 524 S Wewoka Av, Wewoka, OK 74884 - T: (405) 257-5580. Head: Lewis Johnson
Folklore Museum / Ethnology Museum / Historical Museum - 1974 41150

Wharton TX

Wharton County Historical Museum, 3615 N Richmond Rd, Wharton, TX 77488 - T: (409) 532-2600, Fax: (409) 532-2600. Head: Celeta Moses, Sylvia B. Ellis
Local Museum - 1979
Local hist 41151

Wheat Ridge CO

Wheat Ridge Sod House Museum, 4610 Robb St, Wheat Ridge, CO 80033 - T: (303) 421-9111, Fax: (303) 467-2539, E-mail: wrhissoc@aol.com. Head: Claudia R. Worth
Historical Museum - 1970
Sod house 41152

Wheaton IL

Billy Graham Center Museum, 500 E College Av, Wheaton, IL 60187 - T: (630) 752-5909, Fax: (630) 752-5916, Internet: http://www.wheaton.edu/bgc/museum/. Head: James D. Stambaugh
Religious Arts Museum - 1975 41153

Du Page County Historical Museum, 102 E Wesley St, Wheaton, IL 60187 - T: (630) 682-7343, Fax: (630) 682-6549, E-mail: museum@mcs.net, Internet: http://www.co.dupage.il.us/museum/. Head: Susan E. Stob
Historical Museum - 1967
County history exhibits with changing costumes and hands-on history for children 41154

The First Division Museum at Cantigny, 1 S 151 Winfield Rd, Wheaton, IL 60187-6097 - T: (630) 260-8185, Fax: (630) 260-9298, E-mail: fdmuseum@xnet.com, Internet: http://www.rrmtf.org/firstdivision. Head: John F. Votaw
Military Museum - 1960
Military hist 41155

Robert R. McCormick Museum at Cantigny, 1 S 151 Winfield Rd, Wheaton, IL 60187 - T: (630) 260-8159, Fax: (630) 260-8160, E-mail: emanyon@tribone.com, Internet: http://www.cantignypark.com. Head: Ellen Manyonton
Historical Museum - 1955
Joseph Medill, editor of the Chicago Tribune, Col. Robert R.McCormick (grandson of Medill) editor and publisher of the Chicago Tribune, hisory of journalism 41156

Wheaton History Center, 606 N Main St, Wheaton, IL 60189-0373 - T: (630) 682-9472, Fax: (630) 682-9913, E-mail: wtnhistory@aol.com, Internet: http://www.wheaton.lib.il.us/whc. Head: Alberta Adamson
Local Museum - 1986
Local hist, slavery, underground railroad 41157

Wheaton MN

Traverse County Historical Society Museum, 1201 Broadway, Wheaton, MN 56296 - T: (320) 563-4110. Head: Clarence Juelich
Historical Museum - 1977 41158

Wheeling WV

The Museums of Oglebay Institute, Oglebay Park, Wheeling, WV 26003 - T: (304) 242-7272, Fax: (304) 242-4203. Head: Dr. Frederick A. Lambert, Holly H. McCluskey
Local Museum - 1930
Local hist 41159

West Virginia Independence Hall, 1528 Market St, Wheeling, WV 26003 - T: (304) 238-1300, Fax: (304) 238-1302, E-mail: gerry.reilly@wvculture.org, Internet: http://www.wvculture.org. Head: Gerry Reilly
Local Museum - 1964
Historic building 41160

West Virginia Northern Community College Alumni Association Museum, 1704 Market St, Wheeling, WV 26003-3699 - T: (304) 233-5900 ext 4265, Fax: (304) 232-0965. Head: Joan Weiskircher
Local Museum - 1984
Local hist 41161

Whippany NJ

Yesteryear Museum, Regina Pl and Harriet Dr, Whippany, NJ 07981-1906 - T: (973) 386-1920, E-mail: leemunsick@aol.com
Science&Tech Museum / Special Museum / Ethnology Museum - 1970 41162

White Sulphur Springs MT

Meagher County Historical Association Castle Museum, 310 Second Av SE, White Sulphur Springs, MT 59645 - T: (406) 547-2324. Head: Dale McAfee
Local Museum - 1967 41163

White Sulphur Springs WV

President's Cottage Museum, Rte 60 W, White Sulphur Springs, WV 24986 - T: (304) 536-1110 ext 7314/7198, Fax: (304) 536-7854, Internet: http://www.greenbrier.com. Head: Ted J. Kleisner
Local Museum - 1932
Local hist 41164

Whitewater WI

Whitewater Historical Museum, 275 N Tratt St, Whitewater, WI 53190 - T: (414) 473-2966. Head: Dr. Alfred S. Kolmos
Local Museum - 1974
Local hist 41165

Whitingham VT

Whitingham Historical Museum, Stimpson Hill, Whitingham, VT 05342-0125 - T: (802) 368-2448. Head: Stella Stevens
Local Museum - 1973
Local hist 41166

Wichita KS

Edwin A. Ulrich Museum of Art, Wichita State University, 1845 Fairmount, Wichita, KS 67260-0046 - T: (316) 978-3664, Fax: (316) 978-3898, E-mail: David.Butler@wichita.edu, Internet: http://www.twsu.edu/~ulrich. Head: David Butler
Fine Arts Museum / University Museum - 1974
Art 41167

Indian Center Museum, 650 N Seneca, Wichita, KS 67203 - T: (316) 262-5221, Fax: (316) 262-4216, E-mail: icm@southwind.net, Internet: http://www.theindiancenter.com/museum.htm. Head: Dr. David Hughes, Jerry Martin
Ethnology Museum / Folklore Museum - 1975
Native American museum, old Indian council grounds 41168

Kansas Aviation Museum, 3350 S George Washington Blvd, Wichita, KS 67210 - T: (316) 683-9242, Fax: (316) 683-0573, E-mail: kam3350@juno.com, Internet: http://www.saranap.com/kam.html. Head: Bob Knight, Donald L. Livengood
Science&Tech Museum - 1991
Aviation 41169

Old Cowtown Museum, 1871 Sim Park Dr, Wichita, KS 67203 - T: (316) 264-0671, Fax: (316) 264-2937, E-mail: cowtown@southwind.net, Internet: http://www.old-cowtown.org. Head: Stephanie Payton
Local Museum / Open Air Museum - 1952
Open air living history, 1865-1880 era of Wichita and Sedgwick County Kansas 41170

Omnisphere and Science Center, 220 S Main, Wichita, KS 67202 - T: (316) 337-9174. Head: Janice McKinney
Science&Tech Museum - 1976
Science 41171

Wichita Art Museum, 619 Stackman Dr, Wichita, KS 67203 - T: (316) 268-4921, Fax: (316) 268-4980, E-mail: wam@feist.com, Internet: http://www.wichitaartmuseum.org. Head: Charles K. Steiner
Fine Arts Museum - 1935
Art 41172

Wichita Center for the Arts, 9112 E Central, Wichita, KS 67206 - T: (316) 634-2787, Fax: (316) 634-0593, E-mail: arts@wcfta.com, Internet: http://www.wcfta.com. Head: Howard W. Ellington
Fine Arts Museum - 1920
Arts 41173

Wichita-Sedgwick County Historical Museum, 204 S Main, Wichita, KS 67202 - T: (316) 265-9314, Fax: (316) 265-9319. Head: Carolyn Conley, Robert A. Puckett
Local Museum - 1939
Local history, old City Hall 41174

Wichita Falls TX

Kell House Museum, 900 Bluff St, Wichita Falls, TX 76301 - T: (940) 723-2112. Head: Lawrence Linehan
Historic Site - 1981
Local hist 41175

Wichita Falls Museum and Art Center, 2 Eureka Circle, Wichita Falls, TX 76308 - T: (940) 692-0923, Fax: (940) 696-5358, E-mail: wfmuseum@wf.net, Internet: www.wfmuseum.org. Head: Jeff Desborough
Fine Arts Museum / Local Museum - 1964
Art, local hist 41176

Wickenburg AZ

Desert Caballeros Western Museum, 21 N Frontier St, Wickenburg, AZ 85390 - T: (520) 684-2272, Fax: (520) 684-5794, E-mail: info@westernmuseum.org, Internet: http://www.westernmuseum.org. Head: Michael J. Ettema
Fine Arts Museum / Historical Museum - 1960
History 41177

Wickliffe KY

Wickliffe Mounds, 94 Green St, Wickliffe, KY 42087 - T: (270) 335-3681, E-mail: wmounds@brtc.net, Internet: http://campus.murraystate.edu/org/wmrc/wmrc.htm. Head: Kit W. Wesler
Archaeological Museum - 1932
Archaeology 41178

Wilber NE

Wilber Czech Museum, 102 W Third, Wilber, NE 68465 - T: (402) 821-2183. Head: Irma Ourecky
Local Museum / Folklore Museum - 1962
Czechoslovakian cultures, dolls, clothing, pictures 41179

Wilberforce OH

National Afro-American Museum and Cultural Center, 1350 Brush Row Rd, Wilberforce, OH 45384-0578 - T: (937) 376-4944, Fax: (937) 376-2007, E-mail: naamcc@erinet.com, Internet: http://winslo.ohio.gov/ohswww/places/afroam/. Head: Vernon Courtney
Historical Museum / Folklore Museum - 1972
African American history 41180

Wild Rose WI

Pioneer Museum, Main St, Wild Rose, WI 54984
Local Museum - 1964
Pioneer hist 41181

Wildwood NJ

Boyer Museum and National Marbles Hall of Fame, 3907 Pacific Av, Wildwood, NJ 08260 - T: (609) 523-0277. Head: Robert J. Scully
Local Museum / Historical Museum - 1963 41182

Wilkes-Barre PA

Luzerne County Historical Museum, 69 S Franklin St, Wilkes-Barre, PA 18701 - T: (510) 823-6244, Fax: (510) 823-9011, E-mail: ichs@epix.net, Internet: http://www.whgs.org. Head: Lawrence Neumann, Jesse Teitelbaum
Historical Museum / Natural History Museum - 1858
History, geology 41183

Sordoni Art Gallery, Wilkes University, 150 S River St, Wilkes-Barre, PA 18766 - T: (717) 408-4325, Fax: (717) 408-7733. Head: Stanley I. Grand
Fine Arts Museum - 1973
Art 41184

Willcox AZ

Chiricahua Museum, HCR 2, Willcox, AZ 85643-6500 - T: (520) 824-3560, Fax: (520) 824-3421
Natural History Museum - 1924
Natural history, historical artifacts 41185

Williamsburg VA

Abby Aldrich Rockefeller Folk Art Museum, 307 S England St, Williamsburg, VA 23185 - T: (757) 220-7670, Fax: (757) 565-8915, E-mail: cweekley@cwf.org, Internet: http://www.colonialwilliamsburg.org. Head: Carolyn Weekley
Fine Arts Museum - 1957
Art 41186

Bassett Hall, Francis St, Williamsburg, VA 23185 - T: (757) 229-1000, Fax: (757) 220-7173, Internet: http://www.history.org. Head: Carolyn Weekley
Local Museum - 1979
Historic house 41187

Colonial Williamsburg, 134 N Henry St, Williamsburg, VA 23185, mail addr: POB 1776, Williamsburg VA 23187-1776 - T: (757) 229-1000, Fax: (757) 220-7286, E-mail: 1brown@cwf.org, Internet: http://www.colonialwilliamsburg.org. Head: Colin Campbell
Local Museum - 1926
Historic town 41188

Jamestown Settlement, Rte 31 S, Williamsburg, VA 23187 - T: (757) 253-4838, Fax: (757) 253-5299, Internet: http://www.historyisfun.org. Head: Philip G. Emerson
Historical Museum - 1957
Local hist, America's first permanent English colony, Powhatan Indians 41189

Muscarelle Museum of Art, College of William and Mary, Williamsburg, VA 23185 - T: (757) 221-2710, Fax: (757) 221-2711, E-mail: bgkelm@wm.edu, Internet: http://www.wm.edu/muscarelle. Head: Bonnie G. Kelm
Fine Arts Museum - 1983
Art 41190

The Twentieth Century Gallery, 219 North Boundary St, Williamsburg, VA 23185 - T: (757) 229-4949. Head: Gene Chis
Fine Arts Museum - 1959
Art 41191

Williamsport PA

Thomas T. Taber Museum, 858 W 4th St, Williamsport, PA 17701-5824 - T: (717) 326-3326, Fax: (717) 326-3689, E-mail: lchsmuse@csrlink.net, Internet: http://www.lycoming.org/ichsmuseum. Head: Bruce C. Buckle, Sandra B. Rife
Local Museum / Historical Museum - 1895
Regional hist 41192

Williamstown MA

Chapin Library of Rare Books, Stetson Hall, Williams College, Williamstown, MA 01267 - T: (413) 597-2462, Fax: (413) 597-2929, E-mail: robert.l.volz@williams.edu, Internet: http://www.williams.edu/resources/chapin. Head: Robert L. Volz
Library with Exhibitions - 1923 41193

Sterling and Francine Clark Art Institute, 225 South St, Williamstown, MA 01267 - T: (413) 458-9545, Fax: (413) 458-2318, E-mail: info@clarkart.edu, Internet: http://www.clarkart.edu. Head: Michael Conforti
Fine Arts Museum - 1950
Decorative art, sculptures, paintings, drawings, prints, photography 41194

Williams College Museum of Art, 15 Lawrence Hall Dr , Ste 2, Williamstown, MA 01267-2566 - T: (413) 597-2037, Fax: (413) 458-9017, E-mail: WCMA@williams.edu, Internet: http://www.williams.edu/WCMA/. Head: Linda Shearer
Fine Arts Museum / University Museum - 1926
Art 41195

Williamstown WV

Fenton Glass Museum, 420 Caroline Av, Williamstown, WV 26187 - T: (304) 375-7772, Fax: (304) 375-7833, E-mail: askfenton@fentonartglass.com, Internet: http://www.fentonartglass.com. Head: Dr. Frank M. Fenton
Decorative Arts Museum - 1977 41196

Willimantic CT

Windham Textile and History Museum, 157 Union-Main St, Willimantic, CT 06226 - T: (860) 456-2178, Internet: http://www.milmuseum.org. Head: Charlotte Patros, Beverly York
Historical Museum / Science&Tech Museum - 1985 41197

Williston ND

Fort Buford State Historic Site, Buford Rd, Williston, ND 58801 - T: (701) 572-9034, Internet: http://www.state.nd.us/hist/. Head: Merl Paaverud
Military Museum - 1962 41198

Fort Union Trading Post National Historic Site, 15550 Hwy 1804, Williston, ND 58801 - T: (701) 572-9083, Fax: (701) 572-7321, Internet: http://www.nps.gov/fous. Head: Andy Barta
Historical Museum - 1966 41199

Frontier Museum, Hwy 2 N, Williston, ND 58801 - T: (701) 572-9751. Head: Ruth Robinson
Local Museum - 1958 41200

Willits CA

Mendocino County Museum, 400 E Commercial St, Willits, CA 95490 - T: (707) 459-2736, Fax: (707) 459-7836, E-mail: museum@zapcom.net. Head: Daniel Taylor
Local Museum - 1972
Local hist 41201

Willmar MN

Kandiyohi County Historical Society Museum, 610 Hwy 71 NE, Willmar, MN 56201 - T: (612) 235-1881, E-mail: kandhist@wecnet.com, Internet: http://www.freepages.genealogy-rootsweb.com/~kchs/23/index.html. Head: Mona Nelson-Balcer
Historical Museum - 1898 41202

Willow Run Airport MI

Yankee Air Museum, H-2041 A St, Willow Run Airport, MI 48111 - T: (734) 483-4030, Fax: (734) 483-5076, E-mail: yankeeairmuseum@provide.net, Internet: http://www.yankeeairmuseum.org
Military Museum / Science&Tech Museum - 1981
Aeronautics, Ford Willow Run bomber plant airplane hangar - research library, aircraft restoration 41203

Wilmette IL

Kohl Children's Museum, 165 Green Bay Rd, Wilmette, IL 60091 - T: (847) 256-6056, Fax: (847) 256-2921, E-mail: kom165@aol.com, Internet: http://www.kohlchildrensmuseum.org. Head: Sheridan Turner
Ethnology Museum - 1985 41204

Wilmette Historical Museum, 609 Ridge Rd, Wilmette, IL 60091 - T: (847) 853-7666, Fax: (847) 853-7706, Internet: http://www.wilmette.com/museum. Head: Kathy Hussey-Arntson
Local Museum - 1947
Local history 41205

Wilmington CA

Banning Residence Museum, 401 E Main St, Wilmington, CA 90744 - T: (310) 548-7777, Fax: (310) 548-2644, Internet: http://www.banning.org. Head: Jeffrey Herr
Local Museum - 1974
Local hist 41206

Drum Barracks Civil War Museum, 1052 Banning Blvd, Wilmington, CA 90744 - T: (310) 548-7509, Fax: (310) 548-2946, E-mail: sogle@raplacity.org. Head: Susan F. Ogle
Military Museum / Historical Museum - 1987
Military, civil war, Southern Califonia history - library 41207

Wilmington DE

Delaware Art Museum, 2301 Kentmere Pkwy, Wilmington, DE 19806 - T: (302) 571-9590, Fax: (302) 571-0220, E-mail: lmonty@delart.org, Internet: http://www.delart.org. Head: Stephen T. Bruni
Fine Arts Museum - 1912
American art, English Pre-Raphaelite art 41208

Delaware Museum of Natural History, 4840 Kennett Pike, Wilmington, DE 19807 - T: (302) 658-9111, Fax: (302) 658-2610, Internet: http://www.delmnh.org. Head: Scott F. Nelson, Geoff Halfpenny
Natural History Museum - 1957
Natural hist 41209

The Hagley Museum, Buck Rd E, Wilmington, DE 19807-0630 - T: (302) 658-2400, Fax: (302) 658-0568, E-mail: danmuir@udel.edu, Internet: http://www.hagley.lib.de.us. Head: Glenn Porter
Historical Museum / Science&Tech Museum - 1952
History, technology 41210

Hendrickson House Museum and Old Swedes Church, 606 Church St, Wilmington, DE 19801 - T: (302) 652-5629, Fax: (302) 652-8615, E-mail: oldswedes@aol.com, Internet: http://www.oldswedes.org. Head: Philip Hoge, Jo Thompson
Local Museum - 1947
Historic house and nation's oldest church 41211

Historical Society of Delaware Museum, 505 Market St, Wilmington, DE 19801 - T: (302) 655-7161, Fax: (302) 655-7844, E-mail: hsd@dca.net, Internet: http://www.hsd.org. Head: Gordon A. Pfeiffer, Barbara E. Benson
Local Museum - 1864
Local hist 41212

Nemours Mansion and Gardens, 1600 Rockland Rd, Wilmington, DE 19803 - T: (302) 651-6912, Fax: (302) 651-6933, E-mail: sjelinek@nemours.org, Internet: http://www.nemours.org. Head: Paddy Dietz
Historical Museum - 1977
Historic house 41213

Rockwood Museum, 610 Shipley Rd, Wilmington, DE 19809 - T: (302) 761-4340, Fax: (302) 761-4345, Internet: http://www.new-castle.de.us. Head: Diane Baker
Decorative Arts Museum / Local Museum - 1976
Local hist 41214

Wilmington NC

Battleship North Carolina, Battleship Dr, Eagles Island, Wilmington, NC 28402 - T: (910) 251-5797, Fax: (910) 251-5807, E-mail: ncbb55@aol.com, Internet: http://www.battleshipnc.com. Head: David R. Scheu
Military Museum - 1961 41215

Bellamy Mansion Museum of History and Design Arts, 503 Market St, Wilmington, NC 28401 - T: (910) 251-3700, Fax: (910) 763-8154, E-mail: bellamy@ltinet.com, Internet: http://www.presnc.org. Head: Jonathan Noffke
Decorative Arts Museum / Historical Museum / Fine Arts Museum - 1993 41216

Burgwin-Wright Museum, 224 Market St, Wilmington, NC 28401 - T: (910) 762-0570, Fax: (910) 762-8750, E-mail: burgwinw@bellsouth.net, Internet: http://www.geocities.com/PicketFence/Garden/4354. Head: Susan E. Hart
Historical Museum - 1770
Colonial townhome, English and American antiques and works of art (18th-19th c) 41217

Cape Fear Museum, 814 Market St, Wilmington, NC 28401-4731 - T: (910) 341-4350, Fax: (910) 341-4037, E-mail: ssullivan@co.new-hanover.nc.us, Internet: http://www.co.new-hanover.nc.us/cfm. Head: Ruth Haas
Historical Museum / Natural History Museum - 1898 41218

Lower Cape Fear Historical Society Museum, 126 S Third St, Wilmington, NC 28401 - T: (910) 762-0492, Fax: (910) 763-5869, E-mail: latimer@wilmington.net, Internet: http://www.latimer.wilmington.org. Head: Connie Knox, Cathy Myerow
Decorative Arts Museum / Local Museum - 1956 41219

Poplar Grove Historic Plantation, 10200 U.S. Hwy 17 N, Wilmington, NC 28411 - T: (910) 686-4868, Fax: (910) 686-4309. Head: Forrest Lewis, Nancy Simon
Local Museum - 1980
Historic house 41220

Saint John's Museum of Art, 114 Orange St, Wilmington, NC 28401 - T: (910) 763-0281, Fax: (910) 341-7981, E-mail: info@stjohnsmuseum.com, Internet: http://www.stjohnsmuseum.com. Head: C. Reynolds Brown
Fine Arts Museum - 1962 41221

USS North Carolina Battleship Memorial → Battleship North Carolina

Wilmington Railroad Museum, 501 Nutt St, Wilmington, NC 28401 - T: (910) 763-2634, Fax: (910) 763-2634. Head: Dr. Frank E. Funk, Sadie Ann Hood
Special Museum - 1979
Railroad 41222

Wilson AR

Hampson Museum, 2 Lake Dr, Wilson, AR 72395 - T: (870) 655-8622, E-mail: hampson@arkansas.net. Head: Corinne Fletcher
Archaeological Museum - 1961
Archaeology 41223

Wilson NC

Barton Museum, Barton College Station, Wilson, NC 27893 - T: (252) 399-6477. Head: Chris Wilson
Fine Arts Museum / University Museum - 1965 41224

Wilson NY

Wilson Historical Museum, 645 Lake St, Wilson, NY 14172 - T: (716) 751-9331, Fax: (716) 751-6141, E-mail: agaffiliat@aol.com
Local Museum - 1972 41225

Wilton CT

Weir Farm, 735 Nod Hill Rd, Wilton, CT 06897 - T: (203) 834-1896, Fax: (203) 834-2421, E-mail: - wefa_interpretation@nps.gov, Internet: http://www.nps.gov/wefa/
Local Museum - 1990
Art and history 41226

Wilton Heritage Museum, 249 Danbury Rd, Wilton, CT 06897 - T: (203) 762-7257, Fax: (203) 762-3297. Head: Nicki Brown, Marilyn Gould
Local Museum - 1938
Local hist 41227

Wilton NH

Frye's Measure Mill, 12 Frye Mill Rd, Wilton, NH 03086 - T: (603) 654-6581, 654-5345, Internet: http://www.fryesmeasuremill.com. Head: Pamela Savage, Harland Savage
Historical Museum / Science&Tech Museum - 1858
Industry, measure mill, shaker, colonial boxes 41228

Wimberley TX

Pioneer Town, 333 Wayside Dr, Wimberley, TX 78676 - T: (512) 847-3289, Fax: (512) 847-6705. Head: Raymond L. Czichos
Local Museum - 1956
Reproduction of c.1880 old West Town 41229

Winchendon MA

Winchendon Historical Museum, 50 Pleasant St, Winchendon, MA 01475 - T: (508) 297-0300
Local Museum - 1930
Local history - library 41230

Winchester MA

Arthur Griffin Center for Photographic Art, 67 Shore Rd, Winchester, MA 01890 - T: (781) 729-1158, Fax: (781) 721-2765, E-mail: photos@griffincenter.org, Internet: http://www.griffincenter.org. Head: Katherine Cordova
Fine Arts Museum - 1992
Photographic art 41231

Winchester TN

Franklin County Old Jail Museum, 400 Dinah Shore Blvd, Winchester, TN 37398 - T: (615) 967-0524. Head: Nancy Hall
Local Museum - 1973
Local hist 41232

Winchester VA

Winchester-Frederick County Historical Society Museum, 1340 S Pleasant Valley Rd, Winchester, VA 22601 - T: (540) 662-6550, Fax: (540) 662-6991, E-mail: wfchs@shentel.net, Internet: http://www.visitthevalley.org. Head: Robert K. Woltz
Local Museum - 1930
Local hist 41233

Winder GA

Fort Yargo, Georgia Hwy 81, Winder, GA 30680 - T: (770) 867-3489, Fax: (770) 867-7517. Head: Edwill R. Holcomb
Historical Museum / Historic Site - 1954
Restored blockhouse used during the Creek Indian Wars 41234

Windom MN

Cottonwood County Historical Society Museum, 812 Fourth Av, Windom, MN 56101 - T: (507) 831-1134, Fax: (507) 831-2665. Head: L. Tjentland, Linda Fransen
Historical Museum - 1901 41235

Windsor NC

Historic Hope Foundation, 132 Hope House Rd, Windsor, NC 27983 - T: (252) 794-3140, Fax: (252) 794-5583, E-mail: hopeplantation@coastalnet.com, Internet: http://www.albemarle-nc.com/hope/. Head: John C.P. Tyler
Decorative Arts Museum / Local Museum - 1965 41236

Windsor NY

Old Stone House Museum, 22 Chestnut St, Windsor, NY 13865 - T: (607) 655-1491. Head: Charles L. English
Local Museum - 1970 41237

Windsor VT

American Precision Museum, 196 Main St, Windsor, VT 05089 - T: (802) 674-5781, Fax: (802) 674-2524, E-mail: apm@sover.net. Head: Suzanne Richardson
Science&Tech Museum - 1966
Industrial hist, engineering 41238

Windsor Locks CT

New England Air Museum of the Connecticut Aeronautical Historical Association, Bradley International Airport, Windsor Locks, CT 06096 - T: (860) 623-3305, Fax: (860) 627-2820, E-mail: staff@neam.org, Internet: http://www.neam.org. Head: Michael P. Speciale
Science&Tech Museum - 1959
Aeronautics 41239

Winfield KS

The Cowley County Historical Museum, 1011 Mansfield St, Winfield, KS 67156 - T: (316) 221-4811, Fax: (316) 221-0793. Head: Brad Light
Local Museum - 1931
General museum 41240

Winlock WA

John R. Jackson House, Lewis and Clark State Park, Winlock, WA 98596 - T: (360) 864-2643. Head: Cleve Pinnix
Local Museum - 1915
Historic house 41241

Winnabow NC

Brunswick Town State Historic Site, 8884 Saint Philips Rd SE, Winnabow, NC 28479 - T: (910) 371-6613, Fax: (910) 383-3806. Head: James A. Bartley
Local Museum - 1958 41242

Winnebago MN

Winnebago Area Museum, 18 First Av NE, Winnebago, MN 56098 - T: (507) 893-4660. Head: Marion Muir
Historical Museum / Archaeological Museum - 1977 41243

Winnetka IL

Winnetka Historical Museum, 1140 Elm St, Winnetka, IL 60093 - T: (847) 501-6025, Fax: (847) 501-3221, E-mail: winnetkahistory@cs.com, Internet: http://www.winnetkahistory.com. Head: Joan Evanich, Vancy Judge
Local Museum - 1988
Local history 41244

Winnsboro SC

Fairfield County Museum, 231 S Congress St, Winnsboro, SC 29180 - T: (803) 635-9811
Local Museum - 1963
Local hist 41245

Winona MN

Winona County Historical Museum, 160 Johnson St, Winona, MN 55987 - T: (507) 454-2723, Fax: (507) 454-0006, E-mail: wchs@luminet.net, Internet: http://www.winonanet.com/orgs/wchs. Head: Mark F. Peterson
Historical Museum - 1935 41246

Winslow AZ

Homolovi Ruins State Park, 87 North State Rte, Winslow, AZ 86047 - T: (520) 289-4106, Fax: (520) 289-2021, E-mail: homolovi@pr.state.az.us, Internet: http://www.pr.state.az.us
Archaeological Museum - 1986
Archaeology 41247

Winston-Salem NC

Diggs Gallery at Winston-Salem State University, 601 Martin Luther King Jr. Dr, Winston-Salem, NC 27110 - T: (336) 750-2458, 750-2000, Fax: (336) 750-2463. Head: Belinda Tate
Fine Arts Museum / University Museum - 1990
Art 41248

Museum of Anthropology, Wingate Rd, Winston-Salem, NC 27109-7267 - T: (336) 758-5282, Fax: (336) 758-5116, E-mail: moa@wfu.edu, Internet: http://www.wfu.edu/MOA. Head: Dr. Mary Jane Berman
University Museum / Ethnology Museum - 1962 41249

Museum of Early Southern Decorative Arts, 924 S Main St, Winston-Salem, NC 27101 - T: (336) 721-7360, Fax: (336) 721-7367. Head: Paula Locklair
Decorative Arts Museum - 1965 41250

Old Salem, 600 S Main St, Winston-Salem, NC 27101 - T: (336) 721-7300, Fax: (336) 721-7335, E-mail: webmaster@oldsalem.org, Internet: http://www.oldsalem.org
Open Air Museum / Local Museum - 1950 41251

Reynolda House, Museum of American Art, 2250 Reynolda Rd, Winston-Salem, NC 27106-1765 - T: (336) 725-5325, Fax: (336) 721-0991, E-mail: reynolda@ols.net, Internet: http://www.reynoldahouse.org. Head: John Neff
Fine Arts Museum - 1964 41252

Sciworks, 400 Hanes-Mill Rd, Winston-Salem, NC 27105 - T: (336) 767-6730, Fax: (336) 661-1777, E-mail: bssanford@sciworks.org, Internet: http://www.sciworks.org. Head: Anne O. Armfield, Beverly S. Sanford, Tom Wilson
Natural History Museum / Science&Tech Museum - 1964 41253

Southeastern Center for Contemporary Art, 750 Marguerite Dr, Winston-Salem, NC 27106 - T: (336) 725-1904, Fax: (336) 722-6059, E-mail: general@secca.org, Internet: http://www.secca.org. Head: Vicki C. Kopf
Fine Arts Museum - 1956 41254

Wake Forest University Fine Arts Gallery, Art Dept, Wake Forest University, Winston-Salem, NC 27109 - T: (336) 758-5795, Fax: (336) 758-6014, E-mail: faccinto@wfu.edu, Internet: http://www.wfu.edu/Academic-departments/Art/gall_index.html. Head: Victor Faccinto
Fine Arts Museum / University Museum - 1976 41255

Winter Park FL

The Charles Hosmer Morse Museum of American Art, 445 N Park Av, Winter Park, FL 32789 - T: (407) 645-5311, Fax: (407) 647-1284, Internet: http://www.morsemuseum.org. Head: Dr. Laurence J. Ruggiero
Fine Arts Museum - 1942
American art 41256

The George D. and Harriet W. Cornell Fine Arts Museum, Rollins College, 1000 Holt Av, Winter Park, FL 32789-4499 - T: (407) 646-2526, Fax: (407) 646-2524, E-mail: ablumenthal@rollins.edu, Internet: http://www.rollins.edu/cfam. Head: Arthur R. Blumenthal
Fine Arts Museum / University Museum - 1978
Art 41257

Winterset IA

Birthplace of John Wayne, 224 S 2nd St, Winterset, IA 50273 - T: (515) 462-1044. Head: David Trask, Jan Pergoli
Historical Museum - 1981
Historic house, birthplace of film star John Wayne 41258

Madison County Historical Society Museum, 815 S 2nd Av, Winterset, IA 50273 - T: (515) 462-2134. Head: Carol Bass
Local Museum - 1904
Local history 41259

Winterset Art Center, John Wayne Dr, Winterset, IA 50273 - T: (515) 462-3226. Head: Laura Ingram
Fine Arts Museum - 1958
Art, housed in an Underground Railway stop during the Civil War 41260

Winterthur DE

Winterthur Museum, Rte 52, Winterthur, DE 19735 - T: (302) 888-4600, 448-3883, Fax: (302) 888-4880, Internet: http://www.winterthur.org. Head: Dwight P. Lanmon
Decorative Arts Museum / Historical Museum - 1930
Decorative arts, cultural history 41261

Winterville GA

Carter-Coile Country Doctors Museum, 111 Marigold Lane, Winterville, GA 30683, mail addr: POB 306, Winterville, GA 30683 - T: (706) 742-8600, Fax: (706) 742-5476
Historical Museum - 1971
Medicine, office by Dr. Warren Carter and Dr. Frank Coile 41262

Wiscasset ME

Castle Tucker House Museum, Lee St at High St, Wiscasset, ME 04578 - T: (207) 882-7364, Internet: http://www.spnea.org
Historical Museum - 1974 41263

Maine Art Gallery, Warren St, Wiscasset, ME 04578 - T: (207) 882-7511. Head: John Lorence, Phyllis Wicks
Fine Arts Museum / Public Gallery - 1958
Art gallery 41264

Musical Wonder House, 18 High St, Wiscasset, ME 04578 - T: (207) 882-7163, Fax: (207) 882-6373, E-mail: music@musicalwonderhouse.com, Internet: http://www.musicalwonderhouse.com/. Head: Danilo Konvalinka
Music Museum - 1963
Mechanical musical instr 41265

Nickels-Sortwell House, 121 Main St, Rte US1, Wiscasset, ME 04578 - T: (207) 882-6218, (617) 227-3956, Fax: (617) 227-9204, Internet: http://www.spnea.org
Historical Museum - 1958 41266

The Old Lincoln County Jail and Museum, 133 Federal St, Wiscasset, ME 04578 - T: (207) 882-6817, Internet: http://www.wiscasset.net/icha. Head: Benjamin Kirkland, Lwwarence Bacon
Local Museum / Folklore Museum - 1954
Regional history 41267

Wisconsin Rapids WI

South Wood County Historical Museum, 540 Third St, Wisconsin Rapids, WI 54494 - T: (715) 423-1580, Fax: (715) 423-6369, E-mail: museum@wctc.net, Internet: http://www.swch-museum.com. Head: J. Marshall Buehler, Pam Walker
Local Museum - 1955
Local hist 41268

Wisdom MT

Big Hole National Battlefield, 10 miles W of Wisdom Mount on Hwy 43, Wisdom, MT 59761 - T: (406) 689-3155, Fax: (406) 689-3151, Internet: http://www.nps.gov/biho. Head: Jon G. James
Military Museum / Open Air Museum / Historic Site - 1910 41269

Wolf Point MT

Wolf Point Area Historical Society Museum, 220 Second Av S, Wolf Point, MT 59201 - T: (406) 653-1912. Head: Alma Hall
Local Museum / Folklore Museum / Agriculture Museum - 1970
Early-day settlers, Assinaboine and Sioux culture, grain farming, livestock ranching 41270

Wolfeboro NH

Clark House Museum Complexty Museum, S Main St, Wolfeboro, NH 03894, mail addr: POB 1066, Wolfeboro, NH 03894 - T: (603) 569-4997. Head: Dianne Rogers
Local Museum / Historical Museum - 1925
Schoolhouse, firehouse, pre-revolutionary farm house 41271

Libby Museum, Rte 109 N, Wolfeboro, NH 03894 - T: (603) 569-1035, Internet: http://www.wolfeboroonline.com/libby. Head: Patricia F. Smith
Historical Museum / Natural History Museum - 1912 41272

Wolfeboro Historical Society Museum → Clark House Museum Complexty Museum

Wright Museum, Center St, Rte 28, Wolfeboro, NH 03894 - T: (603) 569-1212, Fax: (603) 569-6326, E-mail: wrmuseum@aol.com, Internet: http://wrightmuseum.org. Head: Denis I. Runeyt, Joyce Shea
Historical Museum - 1984
History 41273

Womelsdorf PA

Conrad Weiser Homestead, 28 Weiser Rd, Womelsdorf, PA 19567-9718 - T: (610) 589-2934, Fax: (610) 589-9458. Head: James Lewars
Historic Site - 1928
Historic house 41274

Woodbridge CT

Amity and Woodbridge Historical Society Museum, 1907 Litchfield Turnpike, Woodbridge, CT 06525 - T: (203) 387-2823. Head: Donald Menzies
Local Museum - 1936
Local hist 41275

Woodbury CT

The Glebe House Museum, Hollow Rd, Woodbury, CT 06798 - T: (203) 263-2855, Fax: (203) 263-6726, E-mail: shmgjg@wtco.net. Head: Frank Coburn
Local Museum - 1923
Local hist 41276

Woodbury KY

Green River Museum, Park St, Woodbury, KY 42261 - T: (502) 526-2133
Historical Museum - 1982
History 41277

Woodbury NJ

Gloucester County Historical Society Museum, 58 N Broad St, Woodbury, NJ 08096 - T: (609) 848-8531, E-mail: gchs@citnet.com, Internet: http://www.rootsweb.com/~njglouce/gchs. Head: Dorothy Range
Local Museum - 1903 41278

Woodland CA

Yolo County Historical Museum, 512 Gibson Rd, Woodland, CA 95695 - T: (530) 666-1045. Head: Monika Stengert
Local Museum - 1979
Local history - library 41279

Woodruff SC

Thomas Price House, 1200 Oak View Farms Rd, Woodruff, SC 29388 - T: (864) 576-6546, 476-2483, Fax: (864) 576-4058. Head: Susan Dunlap, Susan Turpin
Local Museum - 1972
Historic building 41280

Woodside CA

Woodside Store Historic Site, 3300 Tripp Rd, Woodside, CA 94062 - T: (650) 851-7615, 574-6441, Fax: (650) 851-7615. Head: Norm Brook, Mitchell P. Postel
Local Museum - 1954
Local hist 41281

Woodstock CT

Bowen House/Roseland Cottage, Rte 169, on the Common, Woodstock, CT 06281 - T: (860) 928-4074, Fax: (860) 963-2208, E-mail: prusso@spnea.org, Internet: http://www.SPNEA.org. Head: Pam Russo, Dick Russo
Local Museum - 1970
Historic houses 41282

Woodstock Historical Society Museum, 523 Rte 169, Woodstock, CT 06281 - T: (860) 928-1035. Head: Cheryl Wakely
Local Museum - 1967
Local hist 41283

Woodstock NY

Center for Photography at Woodstock, 59 Tinker St, Woodstock, NY 12498 - T: (845) 679-7747, Fax: (845) 679-6337, E-mail: info@cpw.org, Internet: http://www.cpw.org. Head: Colleen Kenyon, Kathleen Kenyon
Fine Arts Museum - 1977 41284

Woodstock Artists Gallery, 28 Tinker St, Woodstock, NY 12498 - T: (914) 679-2940, Fax: (914) 679-2940 (call first), E-mail: waa@mhv.net, Internet: http://www.ulster.net/~waa. Head: Linda Freaney
Fine Arts Museum - 1920 41285

Woodstock VT

Billings Farm and Museum, River Rd and Rte 12, Woodstock, VT 05091 - T: (802) 457-2355, Fax: (802) 457-4663, E-mail: Billings.Farm@Valley.Net, Internet: http://www.billingsfarm.org. Head: David A. Donath
Local Museum / Agriculture Museum - 1976
Local hist 41286

Woodstock Historical Society Museum, 26 Elm St, Woodstock, VT 05091 - T: (802) 457-1822, Fax: (802) 457-2811, E-mail: whs@sover.net. Head: Corwin Sharp
Local Museum - 1943
Local hist 41287

Woodville TX

Allan Shivers Museum, 302 N Charlton, Woodville, TX 75979 - T: (409) 283-3709, Fax: (409) 283-5258. Head: Rosemary Bunch
Local Museum - 1963
Historic house 41288

Heritage Village Museum, Hwy 190 W, Woodville, TX 75979 - T: (409) 283-2272, Fax: (409) 283-2194. Head: Ofiera Gazzaway
Local Museum
Local hist 41289

Woodward OK

Plains Indians and Pioneers Museum, 2009 Williams Av, Woodward, OK 73801 - T: (580) 256-6136, Fax: (580) 256-2577, E-mail: pipm@swbell.net
Local Museum - 1966 41290

Wooster OH

The College of Wooster Art Museum, Ebert Art Center, Wooster, OH 44691 - T: (330) 263-2495, Fax: (330) 263-2633, E-mail: kzurko@acs.wooster.edu, Internet: http://www.wooster.edu/. Head: Kathleen McManus Zurko
Fine Arts Museum / University Museum - 1930 41291

Wayne County Historical Society Museum, 546 E Bowman St, Wooster, OH 44691 - T: (330) 264-8856, Fax: (330) 264-8856, E-mail: host@waynehistorical.org, Internet: http://www.waynehistorical.org/. Head: Marilyn Schantz
Local Museum - 1954 41292

Worcester MA

EcoTarium, 222 Harrington Way, Worcester, MA 01604 - T: (508) 929-2700, Fax: (508) 929-2701, E-mail: info@ecotarium.org, Internet: http://www.ecotarium.org/. Head: Laura H. Myers
Natural History Museum - 1825
Environmental museum 41293

Higgins Armory Museum, 100 Barber Av, Worcester, MA 01606-2444 - T: (508) 853-6015, Fax: (508) 852-7697, E-mail: higgins@higgins.org, Internet: http://www.higgins.org. Head: Michael Pagano
Special Museum - 1928
Arms, armor, history, art 41294

Iris and B. Gerald Cantor Art Gallery, College of the Holy Cross, 1 College St, Worcester, MA 01610 - T: (508) 793-3356, Fax: (508) 793-3030, E-mail: cantor@holycross.edu, Internet: http://www/holycross.edu/departments/cantor/website/cantor.html. Head: Ellen Lawrence
University Museum / Fine Arts Museum - 1983
Art 41295

New England Science Center → EcoTarium

Salisbury Mansion, 40 Highland St, Worcester, MA 01609 - T: (617) 753-8278, Fax: (508) 753-8278, E-mail: worchistmu@aol.com. Head: William D. Wallace
Local Museum - 1875
Local history, Stephen Salisbury home 41296

Worcester Art Museum, 55 Salisbury St, Worcester, MA 01609-3196 - T: (508) 799-4406 ext 0, Fax: (508) 798-5646, E-mail: information@warcesterart.org, Internet: http://www.worchesterart.org. Head: James A. Welu
Fine Arts Museum - 1896
American and Asian art, prints, drawings 41297

Worcester Center for Crafts, Krikorian Gallery, 25 Sagamore Rd, Worcester, MA 01605 - T: (508) 753-8183, Fax: (508) 797-5626, E-mail: wcc@worcestercraftcenter.org, Internet: http://www.worcestercraftcenter.org. Head: Maryon Attwood
Decorative Arts Museum / Public Gallery - 1856
Arts, contemporary American craft 41298

Worcester Historical Museum, 30 Elm St, Worcester, MA 01609 - T: (617) 753-8278, Fax: (508) 753-9070, E-mail: worchistmu@aol.com. Head: Joan O. Vorster, William D. Wallace
Local Museum - 1875
Local history 41299

Worcester PA

Peter Wentz Farmstead, Shearer Rd, Worcester, PA 19490 - T: (610) 584-5104, Fax: (610) 584-6860, Internet: http://www.montcopa.org. Head: Dick Anderl
Historic Site - 1976
Historic building 41300

Worthington MN

Nobles County Art Center Gallery, 407 12 St, Worthington, MN 56187 - T: (507) 372-8245. Head: Martin Bunge, Jean Bunge
Fine Arts Museum - 1960
International art 41301

Nobles County Historical Society Museum, 407 12 St, Ste 2, Worthington, MN 56187 - T: (507) 376-4431, Fax: (507) 376-3005, E-mail: nchs@frontiernet.net. Head: Alan Swanson, Roxann L. Polzine
Historical Museum - 1933 41302

Worthington OH

Ohio Railway Museum, 990 Proprietors Rd, Worthington, OH 43085 - T: (614) 885-7345, Internet: http://www.trainweb.org/orm. Head: Warren W. Hyer
Science&Tech Museum - 1945 41303

Worthington Historical Society Museum, 50 W New England Av, Worthington, OH 43085 - T: (614) 885-1247, Fax: (614) 885-1040, E-mail: worthsoc@aol.com. Head: Victoria Bergesen
Historical Museum - 1955 41304

Wray CO

Wray Museum, 205 E Third St, Wray, CO 80758-0161 - T: (970) 332-5063. Head: Lou Ann Deterding
Local Museum / Archaeological Museum - 1969
Local history 41305

Wright-Patterson Air Force Base OH

United States Air Force Museum, 1100 Spaatz St, Wright-Patterson Air Force Base, OH 45433-7102 - T: (937) 255-3286, Fax: (937) 255-3910, E-mail: usaf.museum@wpafb.af.mil, Internet: http://www.wpafb.af.mil/museum/. Head: Charles D. Metcalf
Military Museum - 1923 41306

Wyandotte MI

Wyandotte Museum, 2610 Biddle Av, Wyandotte, MI 48192 - T: (734) 324-7297, Fax: (734) 324-7283, E-mail: wymuseum@ili.net, Internet: http://www.angelfire.com/mi/wymuseum. Head: Marc Partin
Local Museum - 1958
Local history, Ford-MacNichol home 41307

Wyckoff NJ

James A. McFaul Environmental Center of Bergen County, Crescent Av, Wyckoff, NJ 07481 - T: (201) 891-5571. Head: Wolfgang Albrecht
Natural History Museum - 1967 41308

Wyoming NY

Middlebury Historical Society Museum, 22 S Academy St, Wyoming, NY 14591-9801 - T: (716) 495-6582
Local Museum - 1941 41309

Wytheville VA

Rock House Museum, 205 Tazwell St, Wytheville, VA 24382 - T: (540) 223-3330, Fax: (540) 223-3315. Head: Francis Emerson
Local Museum - 1970
Local hist 41310

Xenia OH

Greene County Historical Society Museum, 74 W Church St, Xenia, OH 45385 - T: (513) 372-4606, Fax: (372) 372-5660, E-mail: gchsxo@aol.com. Head: Richard Strous
Local Museum - 1929 41311

Yakima WA

Larson Museum and Gallery, c/o Yakima Valley Community College, S 16th Av and Nob Hill Blvd, Yakima, WA 98902 - T: (509) 574-4875, Fax: (509) 574-6826, E-mail: chassen@yvcc.wa.us, Internet: http://www.yucc.cc.wa.us/~larson. Head: Carol Hassen
Fine Arts Museum - 1949
Art 41312

Yakima Valley Museum, 2105 Tieton Dr, Yakima, WA 98902 - T: (509) 248-0747, Fax: (509) 453-4890, E-mail: info@yakimavalleymuseum.org, Internet: http://www.yakimavalleymuseum.org. Head: John A. Baule
Local Museum - 1952
Local hist 41313

Yale OK

Jim Thorpe Home, 706 E Boston, Yale, OK 74085 - T: (918) 387-2815
Local Museum - 1973 41314

Yankton SD

Dakota Territorial Museum, 610 Summit St, Yankton, SD 57078 - T: (605) 665-3898, Fax: (605) 665-6314, E-mail: mmorriso@willinet.net. Head: Douglas Sall
Local Museum - 1961
Local hist, paintings, sculpture 41315

Yarmouth ME

Museum of Yarmouth History, Merrill Memorial Library, Main St, Yarmouth, ME 04096 - T: (207) 846-6259, E-mail: yarhistory@omnisystem.com. Head: Marilyn J. Hinkley
Local Museum - 1958
Local history 41316

Yarmouth Port MA

Historical Society of Old Yarmouth Museum, 11 Strawberry Ln, Yarmouth Port, MA 02675 - T: (508) 362-3021. Head: Clifford Cosgrove, Barbara Milligan Ryan
Decorative Arts Museum / Historical Museum - 1953
Local history 41317

Winslow Crocker House, 250 Main St, Rte 6A, Yarmouth Port, MA 02675, mail addr: 141 Cambridge St, Boston, MA 02114 - T: (508) 362-4385, (617) 227-3956, Fax: (617) 227-9204, E-mail: sporter@spnea.org, Internet: http://www.spnea.org. Head: Sara Porter, Jim McGuinness
Local Museum / Decorative Arts Museum - 1935 41318

Yates Center KS

Woodson County Historical Museum, 208 W Mary, Yates Center, KS 66783 - T: (316) 625-2371, Fax: (316) 625-2996, E-mail: rcalll@kscable.com, Internet: http://skyways.lib.ks.us/kansan/towns/YatesCenter/museum
Local Museum - 1965
Historic church, country school, log cabin 41319

Yazoo City MS

Yazoo Historical Museum, 332 N Main St, Yazoo City, MS 39194 - T: (601) 746-2273. Head: Sam Olden
Historical Museum - 1977 41320

Yellow Springs OH

Glen Helen Ecology Institute Trailside Museum, 505 Corry St, Yellow Springs, OH 45387 - T: (937) 767-7375, Fax: (937) 767-6659
Natural History Museum - 1951 41321

Yonkers NY

Hudson River Museum of Westchester, 511 Warburton Av, Yonkers, NY 10701-1899 - T: (914) 963-4550, Fax: (914) 963-8558, E-mail: hrm@hrm.org, Internet: http://www.hrm.org. Head: Philip Verre
Fine Arts Museum / Local Museum / Folklore Museum - 1919 41322

York ME

Old York Historical Museum, 207 York St, York, ME 03909-0312 - T: (207) 363-4974, Fax: (207) 363-4021, E-mail: oyhs@oldyork.org, Internet: http://www.oldyork.org. Head: F. Scott Stevens
Local Museum - 1984
Historic buildings, local history 41323

York NE

Anna Bemis Palmer Museum, 211 E Seventh St, York, NE 68467 - T: (402) 363-2630, Fax: (402) 363-2601. Head: Jim Krejci
Historical Museum - 1967 41324

York PA

Fire Museum of York County, 757 W Market St, York, PA 17404 - T: (717) 845-5665, 843-0464. Head: George E. Kroll
Historical Museum - 1973
Fire fighting, Royal Fire Stn 6 41325

The Historical Society of York County Museum, 250 E Market St, York, PA 17403 - T: (717) 848-1587, Fax: (717) 812-1204, Internet: http://www.yorkheritage.org. Head: Gayle Petty-Johnson
Local Museum - 1895
Local hist 41326

Yorktown TX

Yorktown Historical Museum, 144 W Main St, Yorktown, TX 78164 - T: (512) 564-2174
Local Museum - 1978
Local hist 41327

Yorktown VA

On the Hill Cultural Arts Center, 121 Alexander Hamilton Blvd, Yorktown, VA 23690 - T: (757) 898-3076. Head: Tom Coll
Fine Arts Museum - 1976
Art 41328

Watermen's Museum, 309 Water St, Yorktown, VA 23690 - T: (804) 887-2641, Fax: (804) 888-2089. Head: George A. Zavoonick
Special Museum - 1980
Seafood industry 41329

Yorktown Visitor Center Museum, Colonial National Historical Park, Old Rte 238 and Colonial Pkwy, Yorktown, VA 23690 - T: (757) 898-3400, 253-4838, Fax: (757) 898-6346, 253-5299, Internet: http://www.nps.gov/colo. Head: Alac Gould
Historic Site / Historical Museum - 1930
Site of the last decisive battle of the American Revolution, America's struggle for independence 41330

Yorktown Heights NY

Yorktown Museum, 1974 Commerce St, Yorktown Heights, NY 10598 - T: (914) 962-2970, Fax: (914) 962-4379, Internet: http://www.yorktownmuseum.org
Local Museum - 1966 41331

Yosemite National Park CA

The Yosemite Museum, Museum Bldg, Yosemite National Park, CA 95389 - T: (209) 372-0281, 379-1282, Fax: (209) 372-0255, E-mail: yose_museum@nps.gov
Local Museum / Ethnology Museum / Natural History Museum - 1915
History, ethnography and natural science 41332

Youngstown NY

Old Fort Niagara, Fort Niagara State Park, Youngstown, NY 14174 - T: (716) 745-7611, Fax: (716) 745-9141, E-mail: ofn@oldfortniagara.org, Internet: http://www.oldfort-niagara.org. Head: Ginger McNally, Robert L. Emerson
Military Museum / Open Air Museum - 1927 41333

Youngstown OH

Arms Family Museum of Local History, 648 Wick Av, Youngstown, OH 44502 - T: (330) 743-2589, Fax: (330) 743-7210. Head: H. William Lawson
Local Museum - 1961 41334

Butler Institute of American Art, 524 Wick Av, Youngstown, OH 44502 - T: (330) 743-1711, Fax: (330) 743-9567, E-mail: butler@cisnet.com, Internet: http://www.butlerart.com. Head: Louis A. Zona
Fine Arts Museum - 1919 41335

Yountville CA

Napa Valley Museum, 55 Presidents Circle, Yountville, CA 94599 - T: (707) 944-0500, Fax: (707) 945-0500, E-mail: nvmuse@aol.com, Internet: http://www.napavalleymuseum.org. Head: Eric Nelson
Fine Arts Museum / Local Museum / Natural History Museum - 1973
Local History, art and natural science 41336

Ypsilanti MI

Ford Gallery and Slide Collection, Eastern Michigan University, Art Dept., 114 Ford Hall, Ypsilanti, MI 48197 - T: (734) 487-1268, Fax: (734) 487-2324, E-mail: art.department@emich.edu, Internet: http://www.art.acad.emich.edu/. Head: Larry Newhouse
Fine Arts Museum 41337

Ypsilanti Historical Museum, 220 N Huron St, Ypsilanti, MI 48197 - T: (734) 482-4990, Fax: (313) 483-7481
Local Museum - 1960
Local history 41338

Yreka CA

Klamath National Forest Interpretive Museum, 1312 Fairlane Rd, Yreka, CA 96097 - T: (530) 842-6131, Fax: (530) 842-6327, Internet: http://llbean.com/parksearch/parks/html/7757gd.htm
Natural History Museum - 1981 41339

Siskiyou County Museum, 910 S Main St, Yreka, CA 96097 - T: (530) 842-3836, Fax: (530) 842-3166. Head: Michael Hendryx
Local Museum - 1950
Local hist 41340

Yuba City CA

Community Memorial Museum of Sutter County, 1333 Butte House Rd, Yuba City, CA 95993 - T: (530) 822-7141, Fax: (530) 822-7291, E-mail: museum@syix.com, Internet: http://www.syix.com/museum. Head: Julie Stark
Historical Museum - 1975
Regional history 41341

Yucaipa CA

Mousley Museum of Natural History, 35308 Panorama Dr, Yucaipa, CA 92399 - T: (909) 790-3163. Head: Gregory Maxwell
Natural History Museum - 1970
Natural history 41342

Yucaipa Adobe, 32183 Kentucky St, Yucaipa, CA 92399 - T: (909) 798-8570, Fax: (909) 798-8585, E-mail: adeegan@co.san-bernardino.ca.us, Internet: http://www.co.san-bernardino.ca.us/ccr/museum/. Head: Paul J. Oles
Local Museum - 1958
Local history 41343

Yucca Valley CA

Hi-Desert Nature Museum, 57116 29 Palms Hwy, Yucca Valley, CA 92284 - T: (619) 369-7212, Fax: (619) 369-1605, E-mail: hdnm@hotmail.com. Head: Eileen Galloway, Jim Demersman
Natural History Museum - 1964
Natural history 41344

Yuma AZ

Century House Museum and Garden, 240 S Madison Av, Yuma, AZ 85364 - T: (520) 782-1841, Fax: (520) 783-0680, E-mail: azhistyuma@cybertrails.com. Head: Megan Reid
Historical Museum - 1963
History, housed in 1870s residences 41345

Yuma Territorial Prison Museum, One Prison Hill Rd, Yuma, AZ 85364-8792 - T: (520) 783-4771, Fax: (520) 783-7442, E-mail: jmasterson@pr.state.az.us, Internet: http://www.pr.state.az.us
Local Museum - 1940 41346

Zanesville OH

Dr. Increase Mathews House, 304 Woodlawn Av, Zanesville, OH 43701 - T: (740) 454-9500. Head: Linda Smucker
Local Museum - 1970 41347

Zanesville Art Center, 620 Military Rd, Zanesville, OH 43701 - T: (740) 452-0741, Fax: (740) 452-0797, E-mail: zac@cyberzane.com. Head: Carl Minning, Philip Alan LaDouceur
Fine Arts Museum - 1936 41348

Zelienople PA

Zelienople Historical Museum, 243 S Main St, Zelienople, PA 16063 - T: (724) 452-9457, E-mail: zeliehistory@fyi.net, Internet: http://www.fyi/~zhs. Head: Joyce M. Bessor
Local Museum - 1975
Historic houses - library 41349

Zion IL

Zion Historical Museum, 1300 Shiloh Blvd, Zion, IL 60099 - T: (847) 746-2427, 872-4566. Head: Carol Ruesch
Local Museum - 1967
Shiloh House, residence of the founder of the city of Zion 41350

Zionsville IN

Munce Art Center, 205 W Hawthorne St, Zionsville, IN 46077 - T: (317) 873-6862. Head: Edie Kellar Mahaney
Public Gallery - 1981
Fine art class center 41351

P.H. Sullivan Museum and Genealogy Library, 225 W Hawthorn St, Zionsville, IN 46077 - T: (317) 873-4900. Head: Edie Kellar Mahaney
Local Museum / Folklore Museum - 1973
Local history, woman's guild 41352

Zolfo Springs FL

Cracker Trail Museum, Hwy 17 and State Rd 64, Zolfo Springs, FL 33890 - T: (941) 735-0119, Fax: (941) 773-0107
Natural History Museum - 1966 41353

Uzbekistan

Afčona

Memorialnyj Muzej Abu Ali Ibn Sina (Abu Ali Ibn Sina Memorial Museum), 705000 Afčona - T: (065) 3545142. Head: Kiem Choriev
Special Museum 41354

Andižan

Andižanskij Kraevedčeskij Muzej (Andizhan Regional Museum), Pl Babura, Andižan. Head: G.G. Gafurov
Local Museum 41355

Literaturnyj Muzej Andižana (Andizhan Literary Museum), Oktjabrskaja ul 256, Andižan. Head: R.A. Tilliabaev
Special Museum 41356

Angren

Angrenskij Kraevedčeskij Muzej (Angren Regional Museum), 69, District 5-1a, Angren. Head: L.L. Kerimova
Local Museum 41357

Buchara

Bucharskij Gosudarstvennyj Muzej (Buchara State Museum), Ul Afrasiaba 2, Buchara - T: (065) 2241349, Fax: 2241349, E-mail: robert@bukhara.net. Head: Robert V. Almeev
Decorative Arts Museum / Historical Museum / Archaeological Museum / Fine Arts Museum / Natural History Museum - 1922
Textiles, carpets, gold embroidery, decorative arts, coins, seals, manuscripts, armour, photo coll (pre and post Soviet revolution, Soviet era documents, agricultural equipment, pre-revolutionary medical instruments, music, archeology, religion - 10 special museums 41358

Sitorai Mochi-Khosa, Buchara
Decorative Arts Museum 41359

Chiva

Itčan Qala Davlat Muzej Qo'riqxonasi (Itcan-Kala National Reserve Museum), A. Baltaev 41, Chiva - T: (062) 3753169, Fax: 3753169, E-mail: maqsud@tkt.uz, Internet: http://www.uztour.narod.ru. Head: B. Davletov
Local Museum
Local history, architecture 41360

Čirčik

Kraevedčeskij Muzej Čirčika (Circik Regional Museum), Ul Sverdlova 14, 702100 Čirčik - T: 63451. Head: V. Kolosov
Local Museum 41361

Fergana

Kraevedčeskij Muzej Fergana (Fergana Regional Museum), Pervomajskaja ul 18, 712000 Fergana - T: (03732) 43191, 43870. Head: L. Goulyants
Local Museum 41362

Muzej Hamza Hakim-Žade Niazy (Hamza Hakim Žade Niazy Memorial Museum), Hamzaabad, 712000 Fergana der. Shohirmadon - T: (03732) 26681. Head: A. Hamzaev
Special Museum / Historical Museum 41363

Jangi-Jul

Dom-muzej Usman Jusupov (Usman Jusupov Memorial Museum), Ul Dačnaja 6, Jangi-Jul
Special Museum 41364

Karši

Kaškadarinskij Kraevedčeskij Muzej (Kackadariinsk Regional Museum), Ul Kalinina 309, Karši. Head: B.R. Artykov
Local Museum 41365

Kattakurgan

Istoriko-Kraevedčeskij Muzej Kattagurgana (Kattakurgan Historical and Regional Museum), Ul Karla Marksa 70, Kattakurgan. Head: A. Dzalilov
Historical Museum / Local Museum 41366

Kokand

Dom-muzej Hamza Hakim-zade Niazy (Hamza Hakim-zade Niazy House Museum), Ul Matbuot 28, Kokand. Head: I. Rahmatulaev
Local Museum 41367

Literaturnyj Muzej G. Guliama iz Fergana (Literary Museum G. Guliam from Fergana), Sovetskaya ul 2, Kokand. Head: I. Bekmuradov
Special Museum 41368

Margelan

Memorialnyj Muzej Juldaš Ahunbabaev (Memorial Museum of Yuldash Akhunbabayev), Margelan - T: (03732) 333206. Head: Alijonov Ganijon
Historical Museum - 1964 41369

Namangan

Kraevedčeskij Muzej Namangana (Namangan Regional Museum), Ul Luxemburgovoj 70, Namangan. Head: K. Dadabaev
Local Museum 41370

Nukus

Gosudarstvennyj Kraevedčeskij Muzej Karalpakii (Karalpacia State Regional Museum), ul Karla Marksa 2, 742000 Nukus - T: (022) 23751. Head: Kalbay Chanazarov
Local Museum 41371

Gosudarstvennyj Muzej Iskusstv Respubliki Karakalpakstan (State Art Museum of Karakalpakstan), pr Doslyk 127, 742000 Nukus - T: (061) 2222556, Fax: 2222556, E-mail: museum@online.ru, Internet: http://www.webcenter.ru/~museum/. Head: Marinika Babanazarova
Fine Arts Museum - 1966
Karakalpak applied art, art of ancient Khorezm, Russian avantgarde of 1910-1930 - library, archive 41372

Karakalpakskij Istoričeskij Muzej (Karapalk Historical Museum), ul Rachmatova 3, 74200 Nukus
Historical Museum
Uzbek hist, military hist 41373

Samarkand

Gosudarstvennyj Muzej Istorii Kultury i Iskusstva Uzbekistana (Museum of Culture and Art History of Uzbekistan), Pl Registan, 703000 Samarkand - T: (0662) 353896. Head: N. Mahmudor
Historical Museum / Fine Arts Museum - 1874
Cultural history, fine art, ceramics, archeology, costumes - library, archive 41374

International Museum of Peace and Solidarity, 56 Mustaqillik St, Central Recreation Park, Samarkand, mail addr: POB 76, 703000 Samarkand - T: (0662) 331753, Fax: 331753, E-mail: imps@online.ru, Internet: http://www.friends-partners.org/~ccsi/nisorgs/uzbek/peacemsm.htm. Head: Anatoly Ionesov
Special Museum 41375

Kraevedčeskij Muzej (Museum of Local History), ul Kašidov 51, 703000 Samarkand - T: (0662) 330365
Archaeological Museum / Historical Museum - 1981
Archeology 41376

Sadriddin Aini Memorial Museum, Ul Registanskaya 7b, 703000 Samarkand - T: (0662) 355153. Head: A. Ganiev
Historical Museum - 1964
Literature, history 41377

Ulug-Beg Memorial Museum, Ulug-Beg Observatory, 703000 Samarkand - T: (0662) 350345. Head: N. Akramov
Historical Museum - 1964 41378

Taškent

Gosudarstvennyj Muzej Iskusstv (State Museum of Art), ul Proletarskaja 16, 700060 Taškent - T: (03712) 323444. Head: D.S. Rusibaev
Fine Arts Museum - 1918
Art, architecture, sculpture, fine arts, graphics, music, theatre, ethnography - library 41379

Historical Museum of Uzbekistan M.T. Oibek, ul Rašidova 3, 700047 Taškent - T: (03712) 391083. Head: K.Ch. Inojatov
Historical Museum - 1922
Hist of the Central Asian area, exhibits on the life of Central Asiatic life ranging from primitive communal societies to the present time - library 41380

Literaturnyj Muzej Alisher Navoj (Alisher Navoi State Museum of Literature), Navoi 69, 700011 Taškent - T: (0712) 410275, Fax: 1440061, E-mail: A_navoi@uzsci.net, Internet: http://www.uzsci.net. Head: S.R. Khasanov
Special Museum 41381

Mouhtar Ashrafi Museum, C-1, Dom 15, kv 25, 700000 Taškent - T: (071) 1332384, Fax: 322731. Head: G. Hamraeva
Music Museum - 1982
Collection of classic music disks and music hall for concerts, collection of classic Uzbek music instruments 41382

Museum of the History of Termurids, Amir Temur ul 1, 700000 Taškent - T: (071) 21320211, E-mail: wfrd@online.ru. Head: Nozim Khabibullaev
Ethnology Museum 41383

Muzej Obščestvennogo Zdorovja Uzbekistana (Uzbekistan Public Health Museum), Ul Kujbyševa 30, 700060 Taškent. Head: S. Karimov
Special Museum 41384

Respublikanskij Prirodovedčeskij Muzej (Republican Museum of Nature), Ul Salbana 16, 700000 Taškent. Head: A. Kajdarov
Natural History Museum 41385

Sergej Borodin Muzej, Ul Ordžonikidze 18, 700000 Taškent - T: (03712) 1330932, Fax: 406264, E-mail: Kalohc@aol-com. Head: N. Chebanova
Special Museum - 1978
Coins, books, Sergey Borodin 41386

Tashkent Historical Museum of the People of Uzbekistan, ul Kuibyševa 15, 700047 Taškent - T: (03712) 335733. Head: G.R. Rašidov
Historical Museum - 1876 41387

Termez

Surchandarinskij Kraevedčeskij Muzej (Surhandarinsk Regional Museum), Festivalnaja pl 1, 732006 Termez. Head: Y. Ismailov
Local Museum 41388

Vanuatu

Port Vila

Michoutouchkine Pilioko Foundation, POB 224, Port Vila - T: 23053, Fax: 24224
Fine Arts Museum / Ethnology Museum 41389

Vanuatu Cultural Centre and National Museum, POB 184, Port Vila - T: 22129, Fax: 26590, E-mail: kaljoralsenta@vanuatu.gov.vu, Internet: http://artalpha.anu.edu.au/web/arc/vks/vks.htm. Head: Ralph Regenvanu
Ethnology Museum - 1959
Local art and ethnography 41390

Vatican City

Città del Vaticano

Archivio Segreto Vaticano, 00120 Città del Vaticano - T: (003906) 69883314. Head: Josef Metzler
Library with Exhibitions 41391

Cappelle, Sale e Gallerie Affrescate, Musei Vaticani, Viale Vaticano, 00120 Città del Vaticano - T: (003906) 69883332. Head: Dr. Francesco Buranelli, Dr. Fabrizio Mancinelli
Fine Arts Museum 41392

Collezione d'Arte Religiosa Moderna, Musei Vaticani, Palazzo Apostolico Vaticano, 00120 Città del Vaticano. Head: Dr. Arnold Nesselrath
Fine Arts Museum - 1973
Paintings, sculptures, drawings 41393

Galleria degli Arazzi, Musei Vaticani, Viale Vaticano, Palazzo Apostolico Vaticano, 00120 Città del Vaticano
Fine Arts Museum
Tapestry coll 41394

Monumenti Musei e Gallerie Pontificie, Viale Vaticano, 00120 Città del Vaticano - T: (003906) 69883333, Fax: 69885061. Head: Dr. Francesco Buranelli
Early 16th c 41395

Museo Chiaramonti e Braccio Nuovo, Musei Vaticani, Palazzo Apostolico Vaticano, 00120 Città del Vaticano. Head: Dr. Paolo Liverani
Fine Arts Museum
Statues of the Nile, of Demosthenes and of the Augustus 'of Prima Porta', Greek and Roman art 41396

Museo Gregoriano Egizio, Musei Vaticani, Palazzo Apostolico Vaticano, 00120 Città del Vaticano
Museum of Classical Antiquities - 1839
Egyptian antiquities discovered in Rome, Roman imitations of Egyptian statues from Hadrian's villa in Hadrian's Tivoli 41397

Museo Gregoriano Etrusco, Musei Vaticani, Palazzo Apostolico Vaticano, 00120 Città del Vaticano. Head: Dr. Maurizio Sannibale
Decorative Arts Museum - 1837
Bronzes, terracottas, jewellery and Greek vases from Etruscan tombs 41398

Museo Gregoriano Profano, Musei Vaticani, Palazzo Apostolico Vaticano, 00120 Città del Vaticano. Head: Dr. Paolo Liverani
Fine Arts Museum - 1844
Roman sculptures 41399

Museo Missionario Etnologico, Musei Vaticani, Palazzo Apostolico Lateranese, Piazza San Giovanni 4, 00184 Città del Vaticano. Head: Roberto Zagnoli
Ethnology Museum - 1926
Ethnographical coll 41400

Museo Padiglione delle Carozza, Museo Storico (Carriage Museum), Vatican Gardens, 00120 Città del Vaticano. Head: Pietro Amato
Science&Tech Museum - 1973
Carriages, berlins and first cars used by the Popes 41401

Museo Pio Clementino, Musei Vaticani, Palazzo Apostolico Vaticano, 00120 Città del Vaticano. Head: Dr. Paolo Liverani
Fine Arts Museum
Greek and Roman art 41402

Museo Pio Cristiano, Musei Vaticani, Viale Vaticano, 00120 Città del Vaticano - T: (003906) 69883041, Fax: 69885061, E-mail: secreteria.musei@scv.va. Head: Dr. Giandomenico Spinola
Museum of Classical Antiquities - 1854
Large coll of sarcophargi, Latin and Greek inscriptions from Christian cemeteries and basilicas, early Christian art 41403

Museo Profano, Biblioteca Apostolico Vaticano, 00120 Città del Vaticano - T: (003906) 6985051. Head: Dr. Giovanni Morello
Fine Arts Museum / Decorative Arts Museum - 1767
Bronze sculptures and minor arts of the classical era 41404

Museo Sacro, Biblioteca Apostolico Vaticano, 00120 Città del Vaticano - T: (003906) 6985051. Head: Dr. Giovanni Morello
Religious Arts Museum - 1756 41405

Museo Storico Artistico, Tesoro, Basilica di San Pietro, Capitolo di San Pietro, 00120 Città del Vaticano - T: (003906) 69881840, Fax: 69883465. Head: Ennio Francia
Religious Arts Museum
Sacred vestments, silver and goldsmith work 41406

Museo Storico Vaticano (Historical Museum), Palazzo Apostolico Lateranese, Piazza San Giovanni 4, 00184 Città del Vaticano. Head: Pietro Amato
Historical Museum - 1973
Arms, uniforms and armour of the pontificial court and Army Court 41407

Pinacoteca Vaticana, Musei Vaticani, Palazzo Apostolico Vaticano, 00120 Città del Vaticano. Head: Dr. Arnold Nesselrath
Fine Arts Museum - 1932
Paintings by Giotto, Fra Angelico, Raphael, Leonardo da Vinci, Titian and Caravaggio, the Raphael tapestries 41408

Venezuela

Aragua

Museo Ornitológico, Via Ocumare de la Costa, Parque Nacional Rancho Grande, Aragua 2112
Natural History Museum
Ornithology 41409

Barcelona

Museo de la Tradición, Calle Juncal 3-45, Barcelona 6001
Historical Museum / Fine Arts Museum - 1969
17th, 18th, and 19th c painting and sculpture, authentic 19th c weapons, 19th c documents and furniture - library 41410

Barquisimeto

Museo de Barquisimeto, Carrera 15 entre Calles 25 y 26, Barquisimeto 3001 - T: (0251) 310557, 317479, Fax: 310889, E-mail: fundamuseo@cantv.net, Internet: http://www.geocities.com/Athens/Forum/4330/. Head: Francisco Blavia
Local Museum 41411

Caracas

Casa Natal de El Libertador Simón Bolívar (Simón Bolívar's Birthplace), Calle San Jacinto a Calle Traposos, Caracas - T: (0212) 5412563. Head: Josefina de Sandoval
Historical Museum
Murals by Tito Salas depicting the life of Simón Bolívar and the events of the Independence Movement 41412

Colección Ornitológica W.H. Phelps, Blvd de Sabana Grande, Edificio Gran Sabana, Caracas 1050 - T: (0212) 7615631, Fax: 7633695, E-mail: mlentino@reacciun.ve. Head: Kathleen D. Phelps
Natural History Museum
Ornithology 41413

Galeria de Arte de la UCV, Universidad Central de Venezuela, Adyacente al Aula Magna, Caracas - T: (0212) 619811
Fine Arts Museum 41414

Galería de Arte Nacional, Plaza de los Museos, Los Caobos, Caracas 1050 - T: (0212) 5781818, Fax: 5781661, E-mail: fgan@infoline.wtfe.com
Public Gallery - 1976
Venezuelan visual art from pre-Hispanic time to the present 41415

Museo Alejandro Otero, Complejo Cultural la Rinconada, Caracas 1010-A - T: (0212) 6820941/1841, Fax: 6820023, 6820428, E-mail: museotero@cantv.net. Head: Marinelly Bello Morales
Fine Arts Museum 41416

Museo Armando Reverón, Apdo 6928, Carmelitas, Caracas 1010 - T: (0212) 578290, Fax: 5765308
Local Museum 41417

Museo Arte Visuales Alejanoro Otero Mavao → Museo Alejandro Otero

Museo Arturo Michelena Mam, Calle Urapal 82, Altagracia, Caracas 1010 - T: (0212) 814802, 8625853/3957
Special Museum
19th c home of the printer Arturo Michelena, memorabilia, documents 41418

Museo Audiovisual, Parque Central, Edificio Tacagua, Caracas 1010, mail addr: c/o Academia Nacional de Ciencias y Artes del Cine y la Televisión, Apdo 17030, Caracas - T: (0212) 5731046, 5737757. Head: Prof. Oscar Moraña, Sandra Ramón Vilarasau
Science&Tech Museum
Exhibition of technical audiovisual instruments and apparatus used in T.V. radio, and theatre - library, archives 41419

Museo Bolivariano (Bolívar Museum), Calle San Jacinto a Calle Trapasos, Caracas 1010 - T: (0212) 5459828. Head: Flor Zambrano de Gentile
Special Museum - 1911
Personal memorabilia of revolutionary hero Simón Bolívar (1783-1830), portraits, historical paintings of Bolívar contemporaries - library 41420

Museo Caracas, Esquina de Monjas, Consejo Municipal, Caracas - T: (0212) 5456706
Local Museum 41421

Museo Cuadra de Bolívar, Calle Piedras a Calle Bárcenas, Caracas 1010
Historical Museum
Murals by Titos Salas depicting the struggle for independence, correspondence and documents by Bolívar 41422

Museo de Arquitectura, Av Francisco de Miranda, Ed. Torre La Primera Piso 10, Caracas 1071 - T: (0212) 2620327/2171
Local Museum 41423

Museo de Arte Colonial, Quinta de Anauco, Av Panteón, Caracas 1011 - T: (0212) 518650, Fax: 518517, E-mail: infoanauco@quintadeanauco.org.ve, Internet: http://www.quintadeanauco.org.ve. Head: Carlos F. Duarte
Fine Arts Museum / Decorative Arts Museum - 1942
Paintings, sculpture, furniture, china of the Venezuelar Colonial period - library 41424

Museo de Arte Contemporáneo de Caracas, Zona Cultural, Parque Central Eduardo Anuco Nivel Lecuna, Caracas 1010, mail addr: Apdo 17093, Caracas 1010 - T: (0212) 5738289, Fax: 5771883. Head: Sofia Imber
Fine Arts Museum / Decorative Arts Museum - 1973
Venezuelan and international works of art, sculpture, painting, arts and crafts, Calder's tapestries, works by Soto and Vasarely - library 41425

Museo de Arte Popular de Petare Mapp, Calle Guanchez c/c Lino Clemente, Centro Histórico de Petare, Caracas 1073 - T: (0212) 218741, 218335
Folklore Museum 41426

Museo de Bellas Artes de Caracas, Plaza Morelos, Parque Los Caobos, Caracas 1050 - T: (0212) 5710169, Fax: 5712119, E-mail: fmba@reacciun.ve, Internet: http://www.museodebellasartes.org. Head: Marisela Montes
Fine Arts Museum - 1938
Venezuelan paintings from the end of the 19th c to the present, inter-American coll of paintings and sculptures, European paintings, coll of prints and drawings, contemporary sculpture, Chinese porcelain, Egyptian art - library 41427

Museo de Ciencias, Plaza de los Museos, Parque Los Caobos, Caracas 1010, mail addr: Apdo 5883, Caracas 1010 - T: (0212) 5775094, 5770232, Fax: 5711265, E-mail: mciencia@reacciun.ve, Internet: http://www.museo-de-ciencias.org. Head: Sergio Antillano Armas
Natural History Museum / Science&Tech Museum - 1875
Special collections: archaeology, ethnography, herpetology, invertebrates, ichthyology, ornithology, paleontology, physical anthropology, mineralogy, scientific instruments, theriology, toys - library, documentation center 41428

Museo de la Fundación John Boulton, Av Universidad esq. El Chorro piso 11, Caracas
Local Museum 41429

Museo de Los Niños de Caracas, Parque Central, Nivel Bolívar, Caracas 1010-A - T: (0212) 5734112, 5753022, Fax: 5754302, E-mail: mninos@cantv.net, Internet: http://www.museodelosninos.org.ve. Head: Alicia Pietri de Caldera
Special Museum / Science&Tech Museum 41430

Museo del Oeste, Parque del Oeste, Parroquia Sucre Catia, Caracas - T: (0212) 811111/19 ext 230
Local Museum 41431

Museo del Teclado, Parque Central, Ed. Tacagua nivel Mezzanina, Caracas 1010 - T: (0212) 5720713/9024
Local Museum 41432

Museo del Transporte Guillermo José Schael, Av Francisco de Miranda, al lado del Parque del Este, Caracas 1071-009 - T: (0212) 2342234, Fax: 2390652, E-mail: teremach@telcel.net.ve. Head: Alfredo Schael
Science&Tech Museum - 1970
History of transportation in Venezuela, early motor vehicles, railway history - automobile saloon, aircrafts hangar, carriage saloon, two train stations, library and documental section 41433

Museo Jacobo Borges, Parque del Oeste, Av. Sucre, Catia, Estación Gato Negro, Caracas 1030 - T: (0212) 8620427/8101, Fax: 8623821
Local Museum 41434

Museo Pedagógico de Historia del Arte, c/o Instituto del Arte, Facultad de Humanidades y Educación, Ciudad Universitaria, Caracas
Fine Arts Museum / University Museum
Paintings, Latin American art 41435

Museo Sacro, Calle Torre a Calle Gradillas al lado de la Catedral, Caracas 1010 - T: (0212) 8616562
Religious Arts Museum 41436

Museo Venezolano de Electricidad, Av Sanz, El Marqués, Caracas 1071 - T: (0212) 2088411
Science&Tech Museum 41437

Sala Cadafe, Av Sanz, Ed. Cadafe, El Marqués, Caracas 1071 - T: (0212) 22625, 208500
Local Museum 41438

Catia La Mar

Meseta de Mamo, Escuela Naval de Venezuela, Catia La Mar 1162
Historical Museum / Science&Tech Museum - 1965
History, ethnography, technology 41439

Ciudad Bolívar

Museo de Arte Moderno Jesús Soto, Av Germania, Ciudad Bolívar 8001, mail addr: Apdo 211, Ciudad Bolívar 8001-A - T: (0285) 24474, 20518, Fax: 25854, E-mail: museosoto@cantv.net. Head: Ivanova Decán Gambús
Fine Arts Museum - 1973
20th c art, mainly by Venezuelan and European artists, Jesús Soto, Constructivism, kinetic art, new realism 41440

Museo de Ciudad Bolívar, Casa del Correo del Orinoco, Ciudad Bolívar 8001
Local Museum
Local history 41441

Colonia Tovar

Museo de Historia y Artesanía de la Colonial Tovar, Calle del Museo, Colonia Tovar 1030
Local Museum - 1970
Art, history, natural history, anthropology, ethnography, archaeology, geology 41442

El Tocuyo

Museo Colonial, El Tocuyo
Local Museum - 1945
Relics relating mainly to the colonial period 41443

La Asunción

Museo Nueva Cádiz, Calle Independencia, La Asunción 6311
Local Museum
History, ethnography, natural history, archaeology 41444

La Guaira

Museo Fundación John Boulton, Calle Bolívar 180, La Guaira 1160
Historical Museum - 1970 41445

Los Teques

Museo J.M. Cruxent, c/o Depto Antropología del Instituto Venezolano de Investigaciones Científicas, Carretera Panamericana, Los Teques 1201 - T: (0212) 5041227, Fax: 5041085, E-mail: svidal@ivic.ivic.ve. Head: Silvia M. Vidal
Ethnology Museum / Archaeological Museum - 1959
Archaeology, ethnology 41446

Maracaibo

Museo Urdaneta Histórico Militar (Museum of Military History), Maracaibo 4001 - T: (0261) 226778. Head: Prof. J.C. Borges Rosales
Military Museum - 1936
Military hist 41447

Maracay

Museo Aeronáutico Colonel Luis Hernan Paredes, Av Las Delicias y Av 19 de Abril, Maracay 2101 - T: (0243) 333812, Fax: 333812. Head: Juan C. Flores
Science&Tech Museum - 1963
Aeronautical history 41448

Museo de Antropología e Historia, Fundación Lisandro Alvarado, Blvd La Alcaldía a la Plaza Girardot, Maracay 2101, mail addr: Apdo 4518, Maracay 2101-A - T: (0243) 2472521. Head: Henriqueta Peñalver Gómez
Ethnology Museum / Historical Museum / Archaeological Museum - 1964
Pre-Columbian archeology, Venezuelan ethnology, anthropology, and history, vertebrate paleontology, religious art - library 41449

Museo Mario Abreu, Av 19 de Abril, Complejo Cultural Santos Michelena, Maracay 2107 - T: (0243) 336980, Fax: 338534
Local Museum 41450

Mérida

Museo de Arte Colonial, Av 3, entre Calles 18 y 19, Mérida 5101
Fine Arts Museum 41451

Museo de Arte Moderno, Calle Flamboyán, Santa María, frente a la Plaza Beethoven, Mérida 5101
Fine Arts Museum - 1969
Modern Venezuelan art 41452

Museo del Estado de Mérida, c/o Universidad de Mérida, Mérida 5101
Local Museum
Regional ethnography and history 41453

Porlamar

Museo de Arte Contemporáneo Francisco Narváez, Calle Igualdad, Porlamar 6301
Fine Arts Museum
Painings, sculptures 41454

Trujillo

Museo Cristóbal Mendoza, Trujillo 3150
Historical Museum 41455

Valencia

Ateneo de Valencia, Av Bolívar Nort, Valencia 2001 - T: (0241) 8580046, 8581962
Fine Arts Museum 41456

Casa Museo Páez, Loc. 99-20, Av Boyacá, Valencia 2001 - T: (0241) 8571272
Local Museum 41457

Museo de Arte e Historia Casa de Los Celis, Av Soublette, Valencia 2001 - T: (0241) 8421245
Historical Museum / Archaeological Museum 41458

Vietnam

Da-Nang

National Museum of Cham Sculpture, 02 Tiêũ La St, Da-Nang - T: (051) 21951, Fax: 21279
Archaeological Museum - 1915
Champá sculpture and architectural fragments from various periods and places, late 7th-15th c, in Central Vietnam, objects were collected from the temples y Hinduism and Buddhism of Champákinydom 41459

Ha Noi

Air Force Museum, Truong Chinh, Ha Noi
Military Museum 41460

Anti-Aircraft Museum, Truong Chinh, Ha Noi - T: (04) 8522658
Military Museum 41461

Bao Tàng Dân Tôc Hoc Viêt Nam (Vietnam Museum of Ethnology), Nguyen van Huyen St, Cau Giay, Ha Noi - T: (04) 8360350, Fax: 8360351, E-mail: vmel8@hn.vnn.vn. Head: Prof. Dr. Hguyen Van Huy
Ethnology Museum 41462

Bao Tàng Quan Doi (Army Museum), 28a Dien Bien Phu, Ha Noi - T: (04) 7334682. Head: Ma Luong Le
Military Museum
Military hist 41463

Bien Phong Museum, 2 Tran Hung Dao, Ha Noi - T: (04) 8213835
Local Museum 41464

Geology Museum, 6 Pham Ngu Lao, Ha Noi - T: (04) 8266802, 8249112, Fax: 9331496, E-mail: danht-btdc@fpt.vn, Internet: http://www.idm.gov.vn. Head: Prof. Dr. Trinh Dzanh
Natural History Museum 41465

Hanoi Museum, 5b Ham Long, Ha Noi - T: (04) 8263982
Local Museum
Local history 41466

Ho Chi Minh Museum and Mausoleum, Ba Dinh Sq, Ha Noi - T: (04) 8455435. Head: Ha Huy Giap
Special Museum - 1977
Life and work of President Ho Chi Minh 41467

Museum of Women, 36 Ly Thuong Kiet, Ha Noi - T: (04) 8259129
Ethnology Museum 41468

Vien Bao Tang Lich Sa Viet Nam (The National Museum of Vietnamese History), 1 Pham Ngu Lao, Ha Noi - T: (04) 8252853, 8242433, Fax: 8252853. Head: Phạm Quoc Quan
Historical Museum
Hist of Viet Nam from prehistoric times till 1945 41469

Viet Nam Revolution Museum, 25 Tong Dan, Ha Noi - T: (04) 8254323, 8254151, Fax: 9342064, E-mail: phammaihung@yahoo.com. Head: Prof. Dr. Pham Mai Hung
Military Museum / Historical Museum - 1959
Revolutionary hist of Viet Nam 41470

Vietnam Museum of Fine Arts, 66 Nguyen Thai Hoc, Ha Noi - T: (04) 8231085. Head: Cao Trong Thiem
Fine Arts Museum - 1966
Folk drawings, modern paintings and sculptures, lacquers and silks, bronzes and stones, ancient ceramics, oil paintings, wood carvings - library, departments of research, propaganda and storage 41471

Hai Phong

Bao Tàng Hai Phong (Haiphong Museum), Hai Phong
Local Museum - 1959
Local hist 41472

Ho Chi Minh City

Geological Museum, 31 Han Thuyan St, Ho Chi Minh City
Natural History Museum
Mineralogy, fossils 41473

Revolutionary Museum Ho Chi Minh City, 65 Ly Tu Trong, Ho Chi Minh City - T: (08) 8298250. Head: Cong Van Pham
Historical Museum - 1978
History, revolutionary movement and War of Liberation - library 41474

Saigon Gallery, 5 Ton Duc Thang St, Ho Chi Minh City - T: (08) 297102, Fax: 298540
Public Gallery 41475

Thong Nhat Palace, 133 Nam Ky Khoi Nghia, Ho Chi Minh City - T: (08) 294991
Fine Arts Museum 41476

Hong-Gai

Hong Quang Museum, Hong-Gai
Local Museum
Local history 41477

Hung-Yen

Hung-Yen Museum, Hung-Yen
Local Museum
Local history and archaeology 41478

Lam Dong

Lam Dong Museum, Lam Dong
Local Museum
Modern history of Vietnam, Vietnamese popular arts 41479

Nhatrang

Oceanographic Museum, Institute of Oceanography, 01 Cauda, Nhatrang - T: (058) 590032/36, Fax: 590034, E-mail: haiduong@dng.vnn.vn. Head: Dr. Nguyen Tac An
Natural History Museum - 1923

Coll of marine fishes, sea weeds, coelenterates, sponges, polychaetes, crustacean, mollusks, echinoderms, reptiles, sea-birds, sea-mammals etc (about 20 000 specimens of 10 000 species) 41480

Phu Khanh

Phu Khanh Museum, Phu Khanh
Local Museum
Local history before the founding of the Communist Party 41481

Thai Nguyen

Bao Tàng Dân Van Hóa Các Dân Tôc Viêt Nam (Museum of Cultures of Vietnam's Ethnic Groups), 359 Duong Gu Minh St, Thai Nguyen - T: (0280) 855781, 852182, Fax: 752940, E-mail: mangocdung@yahoo.com. Head: Ha Thi Nu
Ethnology Museum - 1960
Cultures of Vietnamese 54 ethnic groups in Viet Nam, clouthes, textiles, musical instruments, tools, things of life, argiculture, houses 41482

Thua Thien Hue

Ho Chi Minh Memorial House, Duong No, Thua Thien Hue 47000
Special Museum 41483

Ho Chi Minh Museum, 06 Le Loi, Thua Thien Hue 47000 - T: (054) 822152, 820250
Special Museum 41484

Thua Thien Hue Museum, 01-23 Thang Tam St, Thua Thien Hue 47000 - T: (054) 822397, 823159. Head: Pham Xuân Phuong
Archaeological Museum / Ethnology Museum - 1982
Cham sculptures (10th-11th c), ethnological objects, hist of the old capital 41485

Vinh

Nghe-Tinh Museum, Vinh
Historical Museum
Hist of the Nghe-Tinh 'Soviet' uprising 1930-31 41486

Yemen

Aden

Crater Folk Museum, Tawila, Aden
Folklore Museum
Architecture, handicrafts, traditional costumes, musical instruments 41487

Ethnographical Museum, Garden, nr Tanks, Aden
Ethnology Museum 41488

Military Museum, Sayla Rd, Crater, Aden
Military Museum
Historic weapons 41489

National Museum, Crater, Aden
Archaeological Museum
Archaeological find in an old sultan's palace 41490

National Museum of Antiquities, Tawahi, Aden
Museum of Classical Antiquities
South Arabian antiques dating back to pre-Islamic times 41491

The Tanks of Aden, On the Volcanic Slopes, Aden
Science&Tech Museum
18 cisterns from 1st c AD 41492

Al-Mukalla

Al-Mukalla Museum, Al-Mukalla
Folklore Museum
Folk costumes, traditional handicrafts 41493

Sanaa

Military Museum, Tahrir Sq, Sanaa
Military Museum 41494

National Museum, Dar as-Sa'd, nr Tahrir Sq, Sanaa, mail addr: POB 2606, Sanaa - T: (01) 271648. Head: Ahmed Naji Sari
Historical Museum / Archaeological Museum / Folklore Museum
South Arabian antiques of the pre-Islamic and Islamic periods, folklore, artefacts of ancient kingdoms of Saba, Ma'in, Ma'rib and Himyar 41495

Seiyun

Seiyun in Wadi Hadhramaut Museum, Seiyun - T: (05) 5402258
Local Museum / Archaeological Museum / Folklore Museum
Housed in a former Sultans palace, handicrafts, folklore items, antiques found in the region 41496

Taizz

Taizz Museum, Taizz
Local Museum
Housed in a former Imams palace, items pertaining to the 1962 Revolution and the events that led up to it 41497

Wadi Baihan

Baihan Al Qasab Museum, Wadi Baihan
Archaeological Museum
Antiques found in the Qataban region dating back to pre-Islamic times 41498

Yugoslavia

Aleksinac

Zavičajni Muzej Aleksinac (Local Museum), Mome Popoviće 20, 18220 Aleksinac - T: (018) 871618. Head: Slavoljub Matejić
Local Museum
Ethnography 41499

Arandjelovac

Muzej u Arandjelovcu (Arandjelovac Museum), Čede Plećevića 19, 34300 Arandjelovac - T: (034) 712415. Head: Zoran Josić
Local Museum - 1981
Palaeontology, archaeology, ethnology, hist, modern art (ceramics), hist of the revolution - Risovača Cave (palaeolithic museum) 41500

Bački Petrovac

Narodni Muzej (National Museum), Maršala Tita 18, 21470 Bački Petrovac - T: (021) 78168. Head: Jaroslav Caji
Historical Museum / Ethnology Museum / Fine Arts Museum
Ethnography, local contemporary painting 41501

Bar

Memorijalna Galerija Veliša Lekovića (Veliš Lekovič Memorial Gallery), Setalište Kralja Nikole 1, 81350 Bar - T: (085) 27949. Head: Koviljka Calasan
Fine Arts Museum
Paintings, memorabilia on painter V. Leković 41502

Zavičajni Muzej, Setalište Kralja Nikole 1, 81350 Bar - T: (085) 27355. Head: Dušan Marić
Local Museum
Natural history, archaeology, ethnography, history, technology 41503

Bečej

Gradski Muzej i Galerija (Municipal Museum and Gallery), Maršala Tita 43, 21220 Bečej - T: (021) 815765. Head: Jovan Medurić
Local Museum / Fine Arts Museum 41504

Bela Crkva

Kulturno Prosvetni Centar Bela Crkva-Muzejska Jedinica, Proleterska 4, 26340 Bela Crkva - T: 851173. Head: Radoje Sporea
Local Museum
Archaeology, ethnography, numismatics 41505

Beograd

Etnografski Muzej (Ethnographical Museum), Studentski trg 13, 11000 Beograd - T: (011) 3281888, 625140, Fax: 621284, E-mail: etnombeg@eunet.yu. Head: Mitar Mihić
Ethnology Museum - 1901
Ethnology, architecture, Serbian mythology, crafts, ceramics, folk costumes, jewelry, hunting and fishing, weapons, religious items, music instruments, textiles, weaving, paintings, medicine, economic and social history documents, toys, agriculture - library, Manak's mansion 41506

Galerija Fresaka (Fresco Gallery), Cara Uroša 20, 11000 Beograd - T: (011) 621491. Head: Jevta Jevtović
Fine Arts Museum
Medieval frescoes, casts, medieval art and architecture, sculpture 41507

Galerija Nauke i Technike Srpske Akademije Nauka i Umetnosti (Gallery of Science and Technique of the Serbian Academy of Sciences and Arts), Bure Jakš ica 2, 11000 Beograd - T: (011) 328340, Fax: 328479, Internet: http://www.sanu.ac.yu
Science&Tech Museum 41508

Galerija Srpske Akademije Nauka i Umetnosti (Gallery of the Serbian Academy of Sciences and Arts), Knez Mihailova 35, 11000 Beograd - T: (011) 180671, 630789, 3342400 ext 130, Fax: 182825, E-mail: galSANU@bib.sanu.ac.yu, Internet: http://www.sanu.ac.yu/ciril/galerija/GalSanu.htm. Head: Dr. Dinko Davidov
Fine Arts Museum / Public Gallery - 1968
19th to 20th c paintings, drawings, engravings and sculptures of member-artists of the Serbian Academy of Sciences and Arts 41509

Istorijski Muzej Srbije (Historical Museum of Serbia), ul Nemanjina 24, 11000 Beograd - T: (011) 3616267, Fax: 3616268, E-mail: imus@infosky.net. Head: Andrej Vujnović
Historical Museum - 1963
Archaeology, ethnography, manuscripts, posters, documents, flags, maps, pictures, postcards, rare books, seals, medals, weapons, numismatics, 18th-20th c art, uniforms, applied art, photographs, memorials - archives 41510

Jevrejski Istorijski Muzej (Jewish Historical Museum), ul Kralja Petra 71a, 11000 Beograd, mail addr: PP 841, 11001 Beograd - T: (011) 622634, Fax: 626674, E-mail: muzej@eunet.yu, Internet: http://www.jim-bg.org. Head: Milica Mihailović
Historical Museum - 1948
History of Yugoslav Jewry, Jewish culture, religious art, archaeology - archives 41511

Jugoslavenska Galerija Reprodukcija i Umetničkih Dela, ul Dositejeva 1, 11000 Beograd
Fine Arts Museum 41512

Memorijalni Centar Josip Broz Tito → Muzej Istorije Jugoslavije

Muzej Afričke Umetnosti-Zbirka Vede i Dr. Zdravka Pečara, Zbirka Vede i Dr. Zdravka Pečara (Museum of African Arts), Andre Nikolića 14, 11000 Beograd - T: (011) 651654
Ethnology Museum - 1977
Articles used for cult, magical, decorative and everyday purposes, masks, ancestor carvings and other cult objects, musical instruments, textiles, weapons, household utensils and miniature weights, Coll of Dogon art, bronze weights for weighing gold from Ghana, Nomoli stone sculptures from Guinea and Bassari ceramic jugs from Senegal - library, educational department 41513

Muzej Grada Beograda (The Belgrade City Museum), Zmaj Jovina 1, 11000 Beograd - T: (011) 637954, 637844, 630825, Fax: 637954, E-mail: museumbg@EUnet.yu, Internet: http://www.mgb.org.yu. Head: Saša Todorović
Local Museum - 1903
Hist of Belgrade, archaeology, prehistory, 19th-20th c art, cultural and political hist, architecture, antiquities, ceramics, metalwork - library, documentation centre, conservation labratory 41514

Muzej Istorije Jugoslavije (Museum of Yugoslav History), Trg Nikole Pašića 11, 11000 Beograd - T: (011) 3231926, Fax: 3235689, E-mail: muzejij@sezampro.yu, Internet: http://www.muzejistorijeju-goslavieje.org. Head: Ljiljana Cetinić
Historical Museum - 1996
Josip Broz Tito Legacy, funds of the Museum of Revolution, fine and applied arts, numismatics, old weapons, military equipment, archeology, ethnology, philately, films - Library & archive of Josip Broz Tito and of Museum of Revolution 41515

Muzej Jugoslavenska Kinoteka (Museum of the Yugoslav Cinema), ul Kneza Mihaila 19, 11000 Beograd
Special Museum
History of Yugoslavian cinematography, photography, films, posters 41516

Muzej Nauke i Tehnike (Museum of Science and Technology), Knez Mihailova 35, 11000 Beograd - T: (011) 187360, 3281479, Fax: 3281479, E-mail: iqm@eunet.yu. Head: Borislav Šurdić
Science&Tech Museum - 1989
Hist of sciences and technology, architecture, electric engineering, measure used in the 18th and 19th c - library, audio and video tape library 41517

Muzej Nikole Tesle (Nikola Tesla Museum), Krunska 51, 11000 Beograd - T: (011) 438137, Fax: 436408, E-mail: ntmuseum@eunet.yu, Internet: http://www.teslamuseum.org. Head: Maria Sesić
Science&Tech Museum - 1952
Memorabilia on physicist Nikola Tesla (1856-1943), hist of science and of electrotechnics - library 41518

Muzej Pozorišne Umetnosti (Museum of Performing Arts), Gospodar Jevremova 19, 11000 Beograd - T: (011) 626630, Fax: 628920, E-mail: mpus@eunet.yu. Head: Miodrag Djukić
Performing Arts Museum - 1950
Serbian theatre hist, programs, stage scenery, photos, posters - library 41519

Muzej Primenjene Umetnosti (Museum of Applied Art), Vuka Karadžića 18, 11000 Beograd - T: (011) 626494, 626841, 626461, Fax: 629121, E-mail: mpu@yubc.net. Head: Ivanka Zorić
Decorative Arts Museum - 1950
Furniture, ceramics, porcelain, glass, textiles, costumes, bookbinding, wood carving, metalwork, contemporary applied arts - library 41520

Muzej Rečnog Brodarstva (Museum of Shipbuilding), ul Kneza Miloša 82, 11000 Beograd
Science&Tech Museum
History of shipbuilding - archives 41521

Muzej Savremene Umetnosti (Museum of Contemporary Art), Ušće Save b.b., 11070 Beograd - T: (11) 3116965, 3113514, Fax: 3112955, E-mail: msub@eunet.yu. Head: Radislav Trkulja
Fine Arts Museum
Yugoslavian paintings, sculptures, graphics, tapestry, drawings, photos, video, foreign graphics - library, photo and video documentation 41522

Muzej Srpske Pravoslavne Crkve (Museum of the Serbian Orthodox Church), Kralj Petar Prvi 5, 11000 Beograd - T: (011) 3282594, 3282595, Fax: 638875, E-mail: muzejspc@sezampro.yu, Internet: http://www.spc.org.yu/latin/muzej.html. Head: Slobodan Mileusnić
Religious Arts Museum - 1936
History of Serbian Orthodox Church, icons, sacramental seals, portraits, vestments, manuscripts, engravings, seals 41523

Narodni Muzej (National Museum), trg Republike 1a, 11000 Beograd - T: (011) 624322, Fax: 627721. Head: Bojana Borić-Brešković
Historical Museum - 1844
National hist, prehistorical, classical, and medieval archaeology, Turkish period, epigraphs, medieval frescoes, icons, manuscripts, Yugoslavian art, Dutch, Italian, French painting, numismatics, 16th-20th c Yugoslavian and foreign graphic art, Oriental art - library 41524

Pedagoški Muzej (Museum of Education), Uzun Mirkova 14, 11000 Beograd - T: (011) 627538, Fax: 625621. Head: Branislava Jordanović
Special Museum - 1896
History of education - archives 41525

Prirodnjački Muzej (Natural History Museum), ul Njegoševa 51, 11000 Beograd, mail addr: PP 401, 11000 Beograd - T: (011) 3442265, Fax: 3442265, E-mail: nhbeo@beotel.yu. Head: Dr. Voislav Vasić
Natural History Museum - 1895
Botany, zoology, ornithology, entomology, herpetology, geology, mineralogy, paleontology, petrography - library 41526

PTT Muzej Zajednice Jugoslovenskih Pošta, Telegrafa i Telefona, Palmotićeva 2, 11000 Beograd - T: (011) 3210325, Fax: 3346264, E-mail: zjptt@eunet.yu. Head: Dragoljub Popski
Science&Tech Museum 41527

Umetnička Zbirka Flögel, Srpskih Vladara 21, 11000 Beograd - T: (011) 330754
Special Museum 41528

Vojni Muzej Beograd (Military Museum of Belgrade), Kalemagdan b.b., 11000 Beograd - T: (011) 3343441, 3344915, Fax: 3344915. Head: Dragan Jerković
Military Museum - 1878
Oriental and European arms, flags, uniforms, medals, military equipment, World War I, Balcan Wars, Turkish period, National Liberation War (1941-1945), gravures, war paintings, hunting arms - library 41529

Vukov i Dositejev Muzej, Gospodar Jevremova 21, 11000 Beograd - T: (011) 625161, E-mail: muzejvd@infosky.net. Head: Bojana Borić Brešković
Special Museum
Memorabilia of the Serbian writers Karadžić, Vuk, reformer of written Serbian language, and Obradović Dositej 41530

Zeleznički Muzej (Railway Museum), Nemanjina 6, 11000 Beograd - T: (011) 688722. Head: Milan Radivojević
Science&Tech Museum - 1950
Hist of national railway system, paintings - library, archives 41531

Bileća

Zavičajni Muzej (Local Museum), Dvorišta b.b., 79320 Bileća - T: 73018. Head: Milorad Nosovic
Local Museum
Local history 41532

Bor

Muzej Rudarstva i Metalurgije (Museum of Mining and Metallurgy), Moše Pijade 19, 19210 Bor, mail addr: PP 45, 19210 Bor - T: (030) 22145, 23560, 24963, Fax: 22145, E-mail: office@museumbor.org.yu, Internet: http://www.museumbor.org.yu. Head: Sladjana Djurdjekanović
Science&Tech Museum - 1951
Archaeology, ethnography, history, geology, mining - library 41533

Narodni Muzej (National Museum), 12210 Bor. Head: Ilija Janković
Local Museum / Archaeological Museum / Ethnology Museum
Archaeology, ethnography 41534

Budva

Arheološka Zbirka (Archaeological Collection), Crkva sv Marije, 81310 Budva
Archaeological Museum
Phoenician, Greek and Roman finds from a necropolis near by 41535

Muzej Budva, Stari Grad, 81310 Budva - T: (086) 44304. Head: Stanko Papović
Local Museum 41536

Čačak

Narodni Muzej Čačak (National Museum of Cacak), Cra Dušana 1, 32000 Čačak - T: (032) 222169, Fax: 44077, E-mail: caamuzej@Eunet.yu, Internet: http://www.cacakmuzej.org.yu. Head: Nevenka Bojović
Local Museum - 1952
Archaeology, history, art, ethnography 41537

Umetnička Galerija Nadežda Petrović, Cara Dušana 4, 32000 Čačak - T: (032) 22375, Fax: 22375. Head: Ivan Lukić
Fine Arts Museum - 1961
Yugoslavian contemporary art 41538

Čajetina

Muzejska Zbirka pri Narodnoj Biblioteki Dimitrije Tucović (Museum Collection of the Dimitrij Tucović National Library), ul Maršala Tita 8, 31310 Čajetina, mail addr: PP 56, 31310 Čajetina
Natural History Museum / Archaeological Museum / Ethnology Museum / Historical Museum
Natural history, archaeology, ethnology, memorabilia of Dmitrij Tucović 41539

Čelarevo

Stalna Izložba Stilskog Namještaja 18.-19. St. (Exhibition of 18th-19th Century Furniture), Dvorac u Čelarevu, 21413 Čelarevo
Decorative Arts Museum
18th-19th c furnishings 41540

Cetinje

Etnografski Muzej Crne Gore, 81250 Cetinje
Ethnology Museum
Costumes, domestic utensils, regional ethnography 41541

Manastirski Muzej (Monastery Museum), Manastir 58, 81250 Cetinje - T: (086) 31703. Head: Marko Kalanj
Religious Arts Museum
Art, religious items 41542

Narodni Muzej Crne Gore, Novice Cerovića b.b., 81250 Cetinje - T: (086) 31682, Fax: 31682, E-mail: general.director@museumsscg.org. Head: Petar Čuković
Local Museum
Regional history 41543

Njegošev Muzej (Njegoš's Museum), Cetinje. Head: Janko Lepičić
Local Museum
Local exhibits 41544

Danilovgrad

Zavičajni Muzej (Local Museum), Lazara Djurovića b.b., 81410 Danilovgrad - T: (081) 81284. Head: Momčilo Saletić
Local Museum
Local history 41545

Dečane

Manastirska Zbirka-Riznica Manastira Dečane, 38322 Dečane
Religious Arts Museum
Largest monastic Serbian church near the Albanian border, 13th-20th c manuscripts, icons, 15th c bells, crosses, ornaments 41546

Djakovica

Regionali Muzej (Regional Museum), Borisa Kidriča 40, 38320 Djakovica - T: (039) 25473. Head: Mosar Bindija
Local Museum 41547

Doboj

Zavičajni Muzej (Local Museum), ul V. Nazora 4, 74000 Doboj - T: 31220. Head: Dobrila Bjelić
Local Museum
Natural history, archaeology, ethnography, national revolutionary history 41548

Foča

Gradski Muzej (Municipal Museum), ul Maršala Tita 11, 71480 Foča. Head: Rasim Halilagić
Local Museum
Coll in an old caravanserai including Bosnian popular art, costumes, peasant household utensils 41549

Fojnica

Franjevački Samostan (Franciscan Monastery), Rupnovac 4, 71270 Fojnica - T: (071) 87029. Head: Ivica Alilović
Religious Arts Museum
Numismatics, religious items, art, ethnography - library 41550

Herceg-Novi

Umjetnička Galerija Josip-Bepo Benkovic (Art Gallery), ul Marka Vojnovića 4, 85340 Herceg-Novi - T: (088) 44400, Fax: 22080, E-mail: galerijahn@cg.yu, Internet: http://www.rastko.org.yu/rastko-bo/muzej. Head: Djordje Capin
Fine Arts Museum
Paintings by Yugoslav artists 41551

Zavičajni Muzej (Regional Museum), Mirka Komnenovica 9, 85340 Herceg-Novi - T: (088) 22485, Fax: 22080, E-mail: muzej@cg.yu, Internet: http://www.rastko.org.yu/rastko-bo/muzej. Head: Djordje Capin
Local Museum
Archaeological, ethnological, historical coll - lapidarium 41552

Ivangrad

Polimski Muzej (Regional Museum), Balabando b.b., 84300 Ivangrad - T: (084) 61075. Head: Dragiša Boričić
Local Museum
Natural history, archaeology, ethnography, history, numismatics, paleography, heraldry, art, photography - archives 41553

Jagodina

Zavičajni Muzej u Jagodini (Regional Museum Jagodina), Kneginje Milice 82, 35000 Jagodina - T: (035) 223308, 231328, Fax: 223308, E-mail: jagmus@ptt.yu. Head: Branislav Cvetković
Local Museum - 1954
Regional history, archaeology, ethnography, culture, neolithic, iron age, numismatics, weapons 7th-17th c, glass and silverware 19th c, ethnology (Serbian), medieval manuscripts, postbyzantine icons, natural hist 41554

Jaša Tomić

Zavičajni Muzej (Local Museum), 23230 Jaša Tomić
Local Museum
Local history 41555

Jasenovo

Etnološka Muzejska Zbirka (Ethnographical Museum), 26346 Jasenovo
Ethnology Museum
Anthropology, ethnography 41556

Kikinda

Narodni Muzej Kikinda (Kikinda National Museum), Titov trg 21, 23300 Kikinda - T: (023) 521239. Head: Milorad Girić
Local Museum
Archaeology, ethnography, labour movement, history 41557

Knić

Muzejska Zbirka (Museum Collection), 34240 Knić
Local Museum
Prehistory, local history 41558

Kosovska Mitrovica

Gradski Muzej (City Museum), Lole Ribara ul bb, 38220 Kosovska Mitrovica. Head: Maja Pajović
Local Museum
Archaeology, ethnography, paintings 41559

Kotor

Pomorski Muzej Crne Gore (Maritime Museum Montenegro), trg Bokeljske Mornarice 321, 81330 Kotor - T: (082) 11216. Head: Jovan Martinović
Special Museum - 1900
Navigation, cultural hist, history, books - archives 41560

Riznica Srpske Pravoslavne Crkve u Kotoru (Treasure House of Serbian-Orthodox Church), Srpska Pravoslavna Crkva, 81330 Kotor - T: (082) 25406. Head: Momičilo Krivokapič
Religious Arts Museum 41561

Kovačica

Galerija Naivnih Slikara (Gallery of Naive Art), Maršala Tita 46, 26210 Kovačica - T: (013) 761112. Head: Pavel Severini
Fine Arts Museum 41562

Kragujevac

Muzej Stara Livnica, Zastava Namenski Proizvodi (Old Foundry Museum), trg Topolivaca Br 4, 34000 Kragujevac - T: (034) 211304 ext 2446, Fax: 216931. Head: Radmila Milivojević
Military Museum - 1953
Old armaments, automobiles, military equipment 41563

Muzej Zavoda Crvena Zastava, Spanskih Boraca 4, 34000 Kragujevac - T: (034) 224011
Science&Tech Museum 41564

Narodni Muzej (National Museum), ul Vuka Karadžića 1, 34000 Kragujevac - T: (034) 331782, Fax: 331782. Head: Miroslav Banović
Local Museum / Archaeological Museum / Ethnology Museum / Fine Arts Museum - 1949
Prehistoric, Roman, and medieval archaeology, ethnography, art history, Byzantine art, Serbian painting (18th-20th c), local history - library, photo laboratory, prep lab 41565

Spomen-Park Kragujevački Oktobar (Memorial Museum The October 21st), Desankin Venac b.b., 34000 Kragujevac - T: (034) 332089, Fax: 336112, E-mail: muzej21@infosky.net. Head: Nenad Djordjević
Local Museum 41566

Kraljevo

Narodni Muzej Kraljevo (Kraljevo Public Museum), trg Sv. Save 2, 36000 Kraljevo - T: (036) 21540, 337960, Fax: 21540, 337960. Head: Dragan Drašković
Local Museum - 1950
Ethnology, hist, numismatics, art, copies of 13th c frescoes, archaeology, ancient mining and metallurgy, pottery 41567

Krupanj

Memorijalni Muzeji Bela Crkva i Stolice, 15314 Krupanj - T: 68033. Head: Milorad Stajčić
Special Museum 41568

Kruševac

Narodni Muzej Kruševac (Kruševac Regional Museum), Stevana Visokog 15, 37000 Kruševac - T: (037) 29172, Fax: 29172. Head: Ema Radulović
Local Museum - 1951
Prehistory, antiquities, medieval history and art, Turkish slavery, ethnography, old history and history of revolution, Kosovo battle as theme in contemporary art, modern art, coins and medals 41569

Lesak kod Tetova

Spomen-Muzej Prosvetitelja i Pisca Kirila Pejčinovića, 91220 Lesak kod Tetova
Historical Museum 41570

Leskovac

Narodni Muzej (National Museum), Stojana Ljubića 2, 16000 Leskovac - T: (016) 2975. Head: Hranislav Rakić
Local Museum
History, archaeology, ethnology, numismatics, art 41571

Majdanpek

Zbirka Rudnika Majdanpek (Majdanpek Mining Collection), 19250 Majdanpek
Natural History Museum
Mineralogy, petrography 41572

Mrkonjić Grad

Spomen Muzej Prvog Zasjedania ZAVNOBiH-a, Maršala Tita 1, 70260 Mrkonjić Grad - T: (070) 12708. Head: Ismet Caho
Historical Museum 41573

Negotin

Muzej Krajine Negotin (Negotin National Museum), Vere Radosavljević 1, 19300 Negotin - T: (019) 52072. Head: Bozidar Blagojević
Local Museum
Archaeology, ethnography, icons 41574

Nikšić

Nikšićki Muzej, ul Moše Pijade 19, 81400 Nikšić
Local Museum
Natural history, archaeology, ethnography, numismatics, history, weapons, art 41575

Zavičajni Muzej (Local Museum), trg Saka Petrovića 1, 81400 Nikšić - T: (083) 24442. Head: Niko Martinović
Local Museum
Red Cave coll from the prehistoric site 41576

Niš

Koncentracioni Logor 12. Februar (Concentration Camp February 12), 18000 Niš
Historical Museum
Memorabilia relating to the former concentration camp 41577

Narodni Muzej Niš (Regional Museum Niš), Stanka Paunovića 14, 18000 Niš - T: (018) 22532, 22047
Local Museum
History, prehistory, archaeology, numismatics, medieval-modern Yugoslavian art, ethnography, labour movement, National Liberation War 41578

Novi Dojran

Ribarsko-Biološka Zbirka (Marine Biology Collection), 91485 Novi Dojran
Natural History Museum
Ichthyology, marine biology, fishing 41579

Novi Pazar

Galerija Sopoćanska Vidjenja, trg Maršala Tita 1, 36300 Novi Pazar - T: (020) 25808. Head: Dragomir Vukašinović
Fine Arts Museum 41580

Muzej Ras, Nemanjina b.b., 36300 Novi Pazar, mail addr: PP 58, 36300 Novi Pazar - T: (020) 25795, Fax: 25795. Head: Dragica Premović-Aleksić
Local Museum
Archaeology, history, ethnography - library 41581

Novi Sad

Galerija Matice Srpske (Picture Gallery of the Serbian Cultural Association), trg Galerija 1, 21000 Novi Sad - T: (021) 421455, Fax: 421456, E-mail: galmats@eunet.yu. Head: Leposava Selmić
Fine Arts Museum - 1847
Coll of Serbian art 18th - 20th cc 41582

Muzej Grada Novog Sada (Novi Sad City Museum), Petrovaradin-Tvrđava 4, 21000 Novi Sad - T: (021) 432055, 433613, Fax: 433145, E-mail: muzgns@EUnet.yu. Head: Ilija Komnenović
Local Museum
Archaeology, ethnography, cultural history, contemporary art, crafts, applied art, weapons, numismatics 41583

Muzej Radničkog Pokreta i Narodne Revolucije, Dunavska 37, 21000 Novi Sad
Historical Museum / Military Museum 41584

Muzej Savremene Likovne Umetnosti (Museum of Contemporary Art), Jevrejska 21, 21000 Novi Sad - T: (021) 613897, Fax: 611463, E-mail: muzejnovisad@ptt.yu. Head: Dragomir Ugren
Fine Arts Museum
Sculpture and paintings mainly by Yugoslav artists 41585

Spomen-Zbirka Pavla Beljanskog (Pavlo Beljanski Memorial Museum), trg Galerija 2, 21000 Novi Sad - T: (021) 28185. Head: Dr. Vera Jovanović
Fine Arts Museum - 1961
20th c Serbian art - library 41586

Vojvodjanski Muzej (Vojvodina Museum), Dunavska 35-37, 21000 Novi Sad - T: (021) 26766, Fax: 25059. Head: Dr. Ljubivoje Cerović
Local Museum - 1947
Hist of Voivodina, ethnology, archaeology - library 41587

Zavičajna Galerija (Gallery of Local Art), Petrovaradin-Tvrdžava, 21000 Novi Sad
Fine Arts Museum
Contemporary paintings by Serbian artists 41588

Zbirka Poduzeća Naftagas (Naftagas Collection), 21000 Novi Sad
Natural History Museum
Geology 41589

Odžaci

Školska Zbirka Odžaci, Osnovna Škola Boris Kidrić, 25250 Odžaci
Archaeological Museum
Prehistorical archaeology 41590

Oplenac kod Topole

Crkva-Muzej na Oplencu (Church Collection), 34360 Oplenac kod Topole
Religious Arts Museum 41591

Pančevo

Narodni Muzej (National Museum), trg Kralja Petra I br 7, 26000 Pančevo - T: (013) 46471. Head: Rosa Svirčević
Local Museum - 1923
Local hist, natural hist, archaeology, ethnography, art 41592

Perast

Muzej Grada Perasta, Obala Marka Martinovića 158, 81336 Perast - T: (082) 72084. Head: Aleksander Lološević
Local Museum
Archaeology, ethnography, history of navigation 41593

Zbirka Crkve Gospe od Skrpjela (Collection of the Church of Our Lady of Skrpjela), 81336 Perast
Religious Arts Museum
Archaeology, religious items, paintings 41594

Zbirka Crkve Sv. Nikole, 81336 Perast
Religious Arts Museum
Vestments, paintings, icons 41595

Petrovaradin

Muzej, Muzej Grada Novog Sada, Petrovaradinska Tvrdjava 4, 21131 Petrovaradin - T: 433613
Local Museum 41596

Pirot

Muzej Ponišavlja Pirot (Pirot Ethnographical Museum), Moše Pijade br 49, 18300 Pirot - T: (010) 22339. Head: Radmila Vlatković
Ethnology Museum
Anthropology, local ethnography 41597

Pljevlja

Zavičajni Muzej (Local Museum), trg 13 Jula br 12, 84210 Pljevlja. Head: Despa Kosorić
Local Museum
Local history, archaeology, ethnography 41598

Podgorica

Arheološka Zbirka Crne Gore, Vuka Karadžića 8, 81000 Podgorica - T: (081) 23187. Head: Olivera Zižić
Archaeological Museum
Archaeological finds from excavations in the district 41599

Centar Savremene Umjetnosti Crne Gore (Contemporary Art Centre of Montenegro), PP 70, 81000 Podgorica - T: (081) 225043, 225049, Fax: 225131, E-mail: CSUCG@CG.YU, Internet: http://www.CSUCG.CG.YU. Head: Derviš Selhanović
Fine Arts Museum 41600

Moderna Galerija, ul Miljana Vukovar 27, 81000
Podgorica
Fine Arts Museum
Modern paintings and graphics mainly by Yugoslav
artists 41601

Muzeji i Galerije Podgorica (Museum of the City of
Podgorica), Vuka Karadžića 8, 81000 Podgorica
Local Museum / Fine Arts Museum
Ethnography, cultural history, National
Liberation War 41602

Prirodnjački Muzej Crne Gore (Natural History
Museum of Montenegro), Trg Nikole Kovačevića 7,
81000 Podgorica - T: (081) 633184,
E-mail: prmuzej@cg.yu. Head: Ondrej Vizi
Natural History Museum 41603

Požarevac

Galerija Milene Pavlović Barilli, dr Voje Dulića 14,
12000 Požarevac - T: (012) 224173, Fax: 224173,
Internet: http://www.barilli.co.yu. Head: Jelica
Milojković
Fine Arts Museum - 1962
Sculpture and paintings by Yugoslav artists,
paintings by Milena Pavlović-Barilli 41604

Muzej Kulturne Istorije (Museum of Cultural History),
ul Nemanjina 9, 12000 Požarevac
Historical Museum
Cultural history 41605

Narodni Muzej (National Museum), ul Voje Dulića 10,
12000 Požarevac - T: (012) 223597, Fax: 223597.
Head: Miroljub Manojlović
Local Museum - 1895
Archaeology, ethnography, prehistory, medieval
history, art, antiquities, numismatics 41606

Prčanj

Privatna Zbirka Marija Lukovića (Marija Lukovića
Private Collection), Broj 153, 81335 Prčanj
Fine Arts Museum / Decorative Arts Museum /
Historical Museum
Paintings, numismatics, stamps, furniture, old
documents, weapons, navigation items 41607

Zbirka Župne Crkve (Church Collection), 81335
Prčanj
Religious Arts Museum
Religious art, old and contemporary Yugoslavian
painting, sculpture 41608

Priština

Muzej Kosova, trg Bratstva i Jedinstva 13, 38000
Priština - T: (038) 30700, 30709. Head: Stanko
Prica
Historical Museum - 1951
Prehistory, antiquities, Middle Ages, ethnology,
natural history, history, numismatics 41609

Prizren

Arheološki Muzej, Gragice Nekič 158, 38400 Prizren
- T: (029) 22244. Head: Nataša Sutakovič
Archaeological Museum 41610

Muzej Orijentalnih Rukopisa (Museum of Oriental
Manuscripts), Sinan Pašina Džamija, 38400 Prizren
Historical Museum
Oriental manuscripts 41611

Muzeu i Lidhjes së Prizrenit (Prizren League
Museum), Sheshi i Lidhjes së Prizrenit, 38400
Prizren - T: (029) 31487. Head: Parim Kosova
Local Museum
History of the Albanian nation 41612

Prokuplje

Narodni Muzej Toplice, Ratka Pavlovića 11, 18400
Prokuplje - T: (027) 21694. Head: Bozidar Djevori
Local Museum
Natural history, archaeology, ethnography,
numismatics, labour movement, history 41613

Raška

Riznica Manastira Studenica (Monastery Collection),
36350 Raška
Religious Arts Museum 41614

Ruma

Zavičajni Muzej (Local Museum), ul Glavna 182,
22400 Ruma - T: (022) 424888. Head: Radisav
Dordević
Local Museum
Archaeology, ethnography, local history, art 41615

Sabac

Narodni Muzej Sabac (Sabac National Museum),
Masarikova 13, 15000 Sabac - T: (015) 24245.
Head: Dragan Dimitrić
Local Museum
Natural history, archaeology, ethnography,
numismatics, cultural history, paintings 41616

Senta

Senćanski Muzej (Senta Museum), trg Maršala Tita
5-7, 24400 Senta
Local Museum
Biology, archaeology, ethnology, numismatics,
regional history 41617

Sid

Galerija Slika Save Sumanovića, Lenjinova 7, 22240
Sid - T: 72614. Head: Nadežda Grozdanić
Fine Arts Museum 41618

Muzej Naivne Umetnosti (Ilijanum Museum of Naive
Art), Moše Pijade 23, 22240 Sid. Head: Ljubica
Janković
Fine Arts Museum
Naive art 41619

Smederevo

Muzej u Smederevu, Omladinska 4, 11300
Smederevo - T: (011) 22138. Head: Milosav Colović
Local Museum
Local history 41620

Smederevska Palanka

Memorijalni Muzej u Goši, Industrijska 70, 11420
Smederevska Palanka - T: (026) 831360. Head:
Zivadin Djordjević
Fine Arts Museum 41621

Narodni Muzej (National Museum), trg Heroja br 5,
11420 Smederevska Palanka - T: (026) 31037.
Head: Mirjana Marković
Local Museum / Fine Arts Museum / Ethnology
Museum - 1966
Serbian painting 19th-20th c, art hist, Neolithic
settlements in the valley of the river Jasenica,
numismatics (Roman period), coll of aprons and
distaffs, ethnology 41622

Sombor

Galerija Milan Konjović, trg Svetog Trojstva 2, 25000
Sombor - T: (025) 22563. Head: Irma Lang
Fine Arts Museum 41623

Gradski Muzej Sombor (Sombor Municipal Museum),
trg Republike 4, 25000 Sombor - T: (025) 32728,
Fax: 32728, E-mail: muzej@gms.co.yu. Head:
Branimir Mašulovic
Local Museum - 1883
Archaeology, local crafts, decorative arts,
ethnography, numismatics - library 41624

Sremska Kamenica

Muzej Jovana Jovanovića-Zmaja, ul Zmaj Jovina 1,
21208 Sremska Kamenica
Local Museum 41625

Sremska Mitrovica

Galerija Lazar Vozarević, Vuka Karadžića 4, 22000
Sremska Mitrovica - T: (022) 221492. Head: Djordje
Panić
Fine Arts Museum 41626

Muzej Srema (Museum of Srem), Vuka Karadžića 3,
22000 Sremska Mitrovica - T: (022) 221150. Head:
Negovan Vitomirović
Local Museum - 1946
Numismatics, ethnography, art 41627

Opštinski Muzej (Regionalmuseum), Muharema
Bekteši 21, 38220 Sremska Mitrovica - T: (022)
23509. Head: Sulejman Murati
Local Museum 41628

Sremski Karlovci

Gradski Muzej, Muzej Grada Novog Sada (Municipal
Museum), ul Patrijarcha Rajačića 16, 21205
Sremski Karlovci - T: (021) 881637
Local Museum
Local history 41629

Srpska Crnja

Memorijalni Muzej Džuro Jakšić (Džuro Jakšić
Memorial Museum), Borisa Kidriča 62, 23220
Srpska Crnja - T: 811326, 811960. Head: Vesna
Mijin
Special Museum
Memorial to writer and painter Džuro Jakšić 41630

Stari Trg

Mineraloška Zbirka Rudnika Trepča (Mineralogical
Collection), 38226 Stari Trg
Natural History Museum
Mining, mineralogy, local mining industry 41631

Subotica

Gradski Muzej (Municipal Museum), trg Slobode 1,
24000 Subotica - T: (024) 555228, Fax: 555228.
Head: Milka Mikuska
Local Museum - 1892
Archaeology, ethnography, history, coins, art,
biology - library 41632

Svetozarevo

**Galerija Samoukih Likovnih Umetnika
Svetozarevo**, Boška Djuričića 10, 35000
Svetozarevo - T: (035) 23419. Head: Koviljka
Smiljković
Fine Arts Museum 41633

Tjentište

Spomen Kuća Bitke na Sutjesci, 71490 Tjentište -
T: (073) 73110. Head: Alija Berberkić
Historical Museum 41634

Topola

Istorijski Muzej (Historical Museum), Milorada Panića
4, 34310 Topola - T: (034) 811280. Head: Radiša
Pavlićević
Historical Museum
Serbian history 1804-1817 41635

Trebinje

Zavičajni Muzej (Local Museum), Alekse Santića 1,
79300 Trebinje. Head: Marijan Sivrić
Local Museum
Local history 41636

Ulcinj

Muzej Ulcinj, Stari Grad, 81360 Ulcinj - T: (085)
84313. Head: Pavle Mašanović
Local Museum 41637

Zavičajni Muzej (Local Museum), 81360 Ulcinj
Local Museum
Local history, cultural history 41638

Užice

Narodni Muzej (National Museum), ul Maršala Tita
18, 31000 Užice - T: (031) 23035. Head: Angelina
Stanimitović
Local Museum
Archaeology, prehist, antiquities, ethnography,
archives 41639

Valjevo

Narodni Muzej Valjevo (National Museum), Trg
vojvode Mishica 3, 14000 Valjevo - T: (014) 221041,
224641, E-mail: office@museum.org.yu,
Internet: http://www.museum.org.yu. Head: Vladimir
Krivoshejev
Local Museum
Regional archeology, history and arts,
ethnology 41640

Vranje

Narodni Muzej (National Museum), ul Pionirska 2,
18500 Vranje - T: (017) 25046. Head: Miodrag
Mitrović
Local Museum
Archaeology, ethnography 41641

Vršac

Narodni Muzej (National Museum), Andje Ranković
19, 26300 Vršac - T: (013) 822569, Fax: 822569,
Internet: http://www.vrsac.com/kultura/muzej.htm.
Head: Anica Medaković
Local Museum
Natural hist, geology, archaeology, ethnography,
regional hist, art, folklore, numismatics 41642

Zbirka Eparhije Banatski (Banatski Collection),
Eparhija Banatska, 26300 Vršac
Religious Arts Museum
Portraits, religious items 41643

Zaječar

Narodni Muzej (Regional Museum), ul Moše Pijade 2,
19000 Zaječar, mail addr: PP 58, 19000 Zaječar -
T: (019) 422930. Head: Bora N. Dimitrijević
Local Museum - 1951
Archaeology, ethnography, local hist, paintings,
archaeological coll (Late Roman site Felix
Romuliana, Imperial Palace of the Emperor Galerius)
- library 41644

Zemun

Zavičajni Muzej Zemuna (Local Museum Zemun), ul
Maršala Tita 9, 11081 Zemun, mail addr: PP 72,
11081 Zemun - T: (011) 217752. Head: Miodrag
Dabižić
Local Museum - 1954
Local history, portraits of inhabitants of
Zemun 41645

Zrenjanin

Narodni Muzej (National Museum), ul Subotićeva 1,
23000 Zrenjanin - T: (023) 61841, Fax: 34020.
Head: Branko Onjin
Local Museum - 1906
Archaeology, ethnography, art hist, folklore, labour
movement and natural hist 41646

Savremena Galerija Umetničke Kolonije Ečka, trg
Slobode 7, 23000 Zrenjanin - T: (023) 62593,
Fax: 62566, E-mail: maximus@mgnet.co.yu,
Internet: http://www.galerija.co.yu. Head: Prof.
Dragan Ćuk
Fine Arts Museum
Contemporary paintings mainly by Yugoslav
artists 41647

Zambia

Choma

Choma Museum, Lusaka/Livingstone Rd, Choma,
mail addr: POB 630189, Choma - T: (032) 20394,
Fax: 20394, E-mail: cmcc@coppernet.zm. Head:
Mwimanji Ndota Chellah
Local Museum
Material culture of the peoples inhabiting Southern
Zambia, ethnographic hist of the Southern
Province 41648

Limulunga

Nayuma Museum, POB 96, Limulunga - T: (07)
221421, Fax: 221351
Local Museum 41649

Livingstone

Livingstone Museum, National Museum of Zambia,
Mosi-oa-Tunya Rd, Livingstone, mail addr: POB
60498, Livingstone - T: (03) 323566, Fax: 324429,
E-mail: livmus@zamnet.zm. Head: K.V. Katanekwa
Local Museum - 1934
Natural hist, exhibits, general hist, fine arts, relics of
Dr Livingstone, archaeology, ethnography, zoology -
library 41650

Railway Museum, 140 Chishimba Falls Rd,
Livingstone, mail addr: POB 60124, Livingstone -
T: (03) 321820, Fax: 324509, E-mail: nhcc@
zamnet.zm. Head: N.M. Katanekwa
Science&Tech Museum - 1987
Vintage steam locomotives, wooden passenger
carriages, and other memorabialia associated with
the site 41651

Victoria Falls Field Museum, Mosi-Oa-Tunya Rd,
Livingstone, mail addr: POB 60124, Livingstone -
T: (03) 323662, Fax: 323653, E-mail: nhcc@
zamnet.zm. Head: N.M. Katanekwa
Local Museum
Displays illustrating formation of the Victoria Falls,
Stone Age implements 41652

Lusaka

National Archives of Zambia, Ridgeway, Lusaka,
mail addr: POB 50010, Lusaka - T: (01) 254081,
Fax: 254080, E-mail: naz@zamnet.zm. Head: N.M.
Mutiti
Historical Museum
Stamps and coins, local history, photographs 41653

Mbala

Moto Moto Museum, Lucheche Rd, Mbala, mail addr:
POB 420230, Mbala - T: (04) 450098, Fax: 450243,
E-mail: motomoto@zamnet.zm. Head: Flexon M.
Mizinga
Ethnology Museum / Historical Museum - 1974
Research in ethnography and cultural history,
educational and exhibition programmes, prehistory -
library 41654

Ndola

Copperbelt Museum, Buteko Av, Ndola, mail addr:
POB 71444, Ndola - T: (02) 617450, Fax: 617450.
Head: Sibanyama Mudenda
Science&Tech Museum - 1962
Displays on the copper mining industry, nature and
ecology, geology, ethnography 41655

Zimbabwe

Bulawayo

Khami Ruins Site Museum, POB 240, Bulawayo -
T: (09) 60045, Fax: 64019, E-mail: monuments@
telconet.co.zw. Head: A. Kumirai
Open Air Museum / Archaeological Museum
Ruins of one of Mambo dynasty capitals (15th to
early 19th c), archaeological finds from the
area 41656

Matopos National Park Site Museums, Bulawayo
Archaeological Museum
Prehistoric rock paintings, Stone Age tools, grave of
Cecil Rhodes 41657

National Gallery Bulawayo, 75 Main St, Bulawayo,
mail addr: POB 1993, Bulawayo - T: (09) 70721,
Fax: 63343, E-mail: sabona@telcenet.co.zw. Head:
Dr. Yvonne Vera
Fine Arts Museum / Decorative Arts Museum - 1974
Works of contemporary English and South African
artists, loan exhibitions, Ndebele and Tonga baskets,
Zimbabwean art and craft, works of Zimbabwean
and Sadc artists 41658

Natural History Museum of Zimbabwe, Leopold Takawira Av and Park Rd, Bulawayo, mail addr: POB 240, Bulawayo - T: (09) 60045, Fax: 64019, E-mail: natmuse@telconet.co.zw. Head: A. Kumirai
Natural History Museum - 1901
Zoology coll covering Ethiopian region and Southern Africa - library, herbarium 41659

Gweru

Zimbabwe Military Museum, Lobengula Av, Gweru, mail addr: POB 1300, Gweru - T: (054) 22816, Fax: 20321, E-mail: museum@internet.co.zw. Head: T. Tsomondo
Military Museum - 1974
Weapons, military vehicles, uniforms, and equipment, aircraft and aviation uniforms and equipment, archaeology, mining, monuments 41660

Harare

Macgregor Museum, Causeway, Harare, mail addr: c/o Geological Survey Department, POB CY210, Harare - T: (04) 726342/3, Fax: 253626, E-mail: zgs@samara.co.zw, Internet: http://

www.zimgeosurv.co.zw. Head: F. Mugumbare
Natural History Museum - 1940
Eonomic minerals, displays dealing with the Deweras and Umkondo groups, geology of Zimbabwe, great dyke, alcali ring complex rocks 41661

Museum of Human Sciences, Civic Centre, Rotten Row, Causeway, Harare, mail addr: POB CY 33, Harare - T: (04) 751797/98, Fax: 774207, E-mail: nmmz@pci.co.zw. Head: Tafirenyika Masona
Ethnology Museum / Archaeological Museum - 1902
National coll of Iron and Stone Age artifacts, rock paintings, ethnographic coll - library 41662

National Gallery of Zimbabwe, 20 Julius Nyerere Way, Harare - T: (04) 704666, Fax: 704668, E-mail: ngallery@harare.iafrica.com. Head: Prof. George P. Kahari
Fine Arts Museum - 1957
Traditional African art, Zimbabwean stone sculpture ('shona sculpture') - library 41663

Inyanga

Nyahokwe Ruins Site Museum, Inyanga
Open Air Museum / Archaeological Museum
Relics of Iron Age, locally found relics of Ziwa culture 41664

Kwekwe

National Mining Museum, POB 512, Kwekwe - T: (055) 23741, Fax: (054) 20321, E-mail: museum@harare.iafrica.com. Head: T. Tsomondo
Science&Tech Museum - 1984
Mining antiquities, Globe and Phoenix Mining Company founded in 1895 41665

Marondera

Children's Library Museum, The Green, Marondera - T: 3356
Special Museum
Objects illustrating man and his implements from the early Stone Age to pioneering days, rocks and minerals, local birds 41666

Masvingo

Great Zimbabwe Monument, POB 1060, Masvingo - T: (39) 62080, Fax: 63310. Head: E. Matenga
Archaeological Museum
Zimbabwe Iron Age archaeology, Zimbabwe birds 41667

Mutare

Mutare Museum, Aerodrome Rd, Mutare - T: (020) 63630, 63005, Fax: 61100, E-mail: mutarmus@ecoweb.co.zw. Head: Traude Allison Rogers
Local Museum - 1959
Archaeology, history, national coll of transport antiquites and firearms, local flora and fauna 41668

Raylton

National Railways of Zimbabwe Museum, Prospect Av and First St, Raylton, mail addr: POB 596, Bulawayo
Science&Tech Museum
Former Rhodesian Railways steam locomotives, coaches, and freight cars 41669

Museum Associations

Algeria

Comitée National de ICOM de Algérie, c/o Musée National du Bardo, 3 Av F.D. Roosevelt, Alger 16000 - T: (021) 747641, Fax: 742453   41670

Andorra

International Council of Museums, Andorran National Committee, c/o Patrimoni Cultural, Carretera de Bixessarri s/n, Aixovall - T: 844141, Fax: 844343, E-mail: pca.gov@andorra.ad   41671

Angola

ICOM Angola, Rua Major Kanyangulu 77, Luanda, mail addr: c/o Instituto Nacional do Património Cultural, CP 1267, Luanda - T: (2) 331139, Fax: 332575, E-mail: ipc@snet.co.ao   41672

Argentina

Comisión Nacional de Museos y de Monumentos, Av de Mayo 556, C1084AAN Buenos Aires - T: (011) 43316151   41673

ICOM Argentina, Calle Florida 681, C1005AAM Buenos Aires - T: (011) 3141963, 3148759, Fax: 3148759, E-mail: icom@abaconet.com.ar   41674

Australia

Australia ICOMOS, 221 Burwood Hwy, Burwood, Vic. 3125 - T: (03) 92517131, Fax: 92517158, E-mail: austicomos@deakin.edu.au, Internet: http://www.comocs.org/australia   41675

Council of Australian Art Museum Directors, c/o National Gallery of Australia, GPOB 1150, Canberra, ACT 2601 - T: (02) 62406400, Fax: 62406529   41676

Council of Australian Museum Directors, c/o Tasmanian Museum, 40 Macquarie St, Hobart, Tas. 7000 - T: (03) 62114177, Fax: 62114112   41677

Heritage Collections Council, c/o Dept. of Communications, Information Technology and the Arts, GPOB 2154, Canberra, ACT 2601 - T: (02) 62711094, Fax: 62711122, E-mail: hcc.mail@dcita.gov.au   41678

ICOM Asia-Pacific Organization, University of Canberra, Belconnen, ACT 2616, mail addr: POB 1 - T: (06) 201-2199, Fax: 201-5999, E-mail: galla@science.canberra.edu.au   41679

ICOM Australia, 17 Mason St, Hawthorn, Victoria, Vic. 3122 - T: (03) 98186020, Fax: 98186020, E-mail: margaretanderson@bigpond.com   41680

International Committee for University Museums and Collections (UMAC), c/o Peter Stanbury, Macquarie University, Macquarie, NSW 2109 - T: (02) 98507431, Fax: 98507565, E-mail: peterstanbury@mq.edu.au, Internet: http://www.icom.org/umac   41681

Museums Australia, POB 266, Civic Square, ACT 2608 - T: (02 62085044, Fax: 62085015, E-mail: ma@museumsaustralia.org.au, Internet: http://www.museumsaus-tralia.org.au   41682

Austria

ICDAD International Committee for Decorative Arts and Design Museums, c/o Dr. E. Schmuttermeier, MAK Wien, Stubenring 5, 1010 Wien - T: (01) 71136234, Fax: 71136234, E-mail: e.schmuttermeier@mak.at   41683

ICOM Österreich, c/o Münzkabinett, KHM, Burgring 5, 1010 Wien - T: (01) 52524380, Fax: 52524353, E-mail: guenther.dembski@khm.at   41684

Museumsverband, Verband österreichischer Museen, Galerien, Schau- und Studiensammlungen, Feldegg 1, 4742 Pram - T: (07736) 62610, Fax: 62614, E-mail: olaf.bockhorn@univie.ac.at   41685

MuSiS - Verein zur Unterstützung der Museen und Sammlungen in der Steiermark, Strauchergasse 16, 8020 Graz - T: (0316) 738605, Fax: 738605, E-mail: musis@utanet.at, Internet: http://homepage.sime.com/musis   41686

Oberösterreichischer Musealverein, Ursulinenhof, Landstr 31, 4020 Linz - T: (0732) 770218, Fax: 794120   41687

Österreichischer Museumsbund, c/o Kunsthistorisches Museum, Burgring 5, 1010 Wien - T: (01) 52524350, Fax: 52524352, E-mail: -elisabeth.herrmann@khm.at, Internet: http://www.khm.at/static/page1037.html   41688

Verband Österreichischer Privatmuseen, Moor-Hof, 4654 Bad Wimsbach-Neydharting - T: (07245) 5573, Fax: (0732) 77178125   41689

Bangladesh

ICOM Bangladesh, Shahbagh, Dhaka, mail addr: c/o Bangladesh National Museum, Dept. History, POB 355, Dhaka 1000 - T: (02) 505575, 869396, E-mail: mofa@bangla.net   41690

Barbados

Barbados Museum and Historical Society, The Garrison, Saint Michael - T: (246) 436-1956, Fax: (246) 429-5946, E-mail: museum@caribsurf.com, Internet: http://www.barbmus-org.bb   41691

ICOM Barbados, c/o National Cultural Foundation, West Tce, Saint James - T: (246) 424-0909, 428-9383, Fax: (246) 424-0916, E-mail: crhncf@sunbeach.net   41692

Museums Association of the Caribbean, POB 112, Bridgetown - T: (246) 228-2024, Fax: (246) 228-2024, E-mail: macsecretariat@caribsurf.com   41693

Belarus

ICOM Belarussian National Commitee, Bogdanoviča ul 15, 220029 Minsk - T: (017) 2347261, Fax: 2347261, E-mail: icom.org@musbel.belpak.minsk.by   41694

Belgium

L' Association Francophone des Musées de Belgique, c/o Musée d'Art Moderne et d'Art Contemporain, 3 Parc de la Boverie, 4020 Liège - T: 043430403, Fax: 043441907, E-mail: mamac@skynet.be, Internet: http://www.muse.ucl.ac.be/Icom/AFMB.html. Head: Françoise Dumont   41695

Association Internationale des Musées d'Armes et d'Histoire Militaire (International Association of Museums of Arms and Military History), c/o Musée d'Armes de Liège, Halles du Nord, 4 Rue de la Boucherie, 4000 Liège - T: 042219416/17, Fax: 042219401, E-mail: claude.gaier@museedarmes.be, Internet: http://www.klm-mra.be/icomam/index.htm   41696

European Collaborative for Science, Industry and Technology Exhibitions, 63 Blvd du Triomphe, 1160 Bruxelles - T: 026475098, Fax: 026475098, E-mail: wststaveloz@ecsite.net, Internet: http://www.ecsite.net   41697

Forum Européen des Conseillers et Consultants de Musée (European Museum Advisers Conference), 15 Rue du Paroissien, 1000 Bruxelles - T: 025536843, E-mail: leon.smets@wvc.vlaanderen.be   41698

International Association of Custom Museums, c/o Nationaal Museum, Kattendijkdok OK 22, 2000 Antwerpen - T: 032292260, Fax: 032292261, Internet: http://www.etat.lu/IACM   41699

Vlaamse Museumvereniging, Plaatsnijdersstr 2, 2000 Antwerpen - T: 032160360, Fax: 032570861, E-mail: info@museumvereniging.be, Internet: http://www.musweb.be   41700

Benin

ICOM Bénin, c/o Université Nationale du Bénin, BP 526, Cotonou - T: 333690, Fax: 334239   41701

Bolivia

ICOM Bolivia, Apdo 2093, La Paz - T: (02) 352004, Fax: 433552, E-mail: cvp-tda@ceibo.entelnet.bo   41702

Bosnia and Herzegovina

ICOM Bosnia-Hercegovina, Filosofskij Fakultet, 71000 Sarajevo - T: (033) 667846, Fax: 667873   41703

Botswana

ICOM Botswana, c/o Dept. of National Museum, Munuments and Art Gallery, Private Bag 00114, Gaborone - T: 374616, Fax: 302797   41704

Brazil

Comitê Brasileiro do ICOM, Av Independência 867, Porto Alegre 90035-076 - T: (051) 3111188, 3113853, Fax: 3119351, E-mail: icombr@terra.com.br, Internet: http://www.icom.org.br   41705

Bulgaria

Associacija Muzej, c/o Nacionalen politechniceskij muzej, ul Opălčenska 66, 1303 Sofia - T: (02) 313004, Fax: 314036, E-mail: polytechnic@museum.web.bg   41706

Bulgarian Museum Chamber, bul Vitoša 2, 1000 Sofia, mail addr: c/o Nacionalen istoričeski muzej, POB 1351, 1000 Sofia - T: (02) 9802258, 9816600, Fax: 980024, E-mail: nim@einet.bg   41707

ICOM Bulgaria, c/o Nacionalen politechniceskij muzej, ul Opălčenska 66, 1303 Sofia - T: (02) 324050, 313004, Fax: 314036, E-mail: bnc_icom@abv.bg   41708

Burkina Faso

ICOM Burkina Faso, c/o Direction du Patrimoine Culturel, BP 2727, Ouagadougou - T: 317475, Fax: 316808, E-mail: patrimoine@mcc.gov.bf   41709

Burundi

ICOM Burundi, c/o R. Nzobambona, BP 1095, Bujumbura - T: (022) 2250, Fax: 6231   41710

Cambodia

ICOM Cambodia, c/o Vann Molyvann, Ministre d'Etat, Résidence du Conseil des Ministres, Phnom Penh - T: (023) 880623, Fax: 880623, E-mail: apsara.adta@bigpond.com.kh   41711

Cameroon

ICOM Cameroon, c/o Université de Yaoundé, BP 755, Yaoundé - T: 230614, Fax: 306176, E-mail: jessomba@camnet.cm   41712

Canada

Alberta Museums Association, 9829 103 St, Edmonton, Alta. T5K 0X9 - T: (780) 424-2626, Fax: (780) 425-1679, E-mail: info@museumsalberta.ab.ca, Internet: http://www.museumsalberta.ab.ca   41713

Association Museums New Brunswick, 503 Queen St, Fredericton, N.B. E3B 4Y2 - T: (506) 452-2908, Fax: (506) 459-0481, E-mail: muse@nbnet.nb.ca, Internet: http://www.amnb.nb.ca   41714

Association of Manitoba Museums, 153 Lombard Av, Ste 206, Winnipeg, Man. R3B 0T4 - T: (204) 947-1782, Fax: (204) 942-3749, E-mail: amm@escape.ca, Internet: http://www.escape.ca/~amm   41715

British Columbia Museums Association, 514 Government St, Victoria, B.C. V8V 4X4 - T: (250) 387-3315, Fax: (250) 387-1251, E-mail: bcma@MuseumsAssn.bc.ca, Internet: http://www.MuseumsAssn.bc.ca/~bcma/   41716

Canadian Art Museum Directors Organization, 280 Metcalfe St, Ste 400, Ottawa, Ont. K2P 1R7 - T: (613) 567-0099, Fax: (613) 233-5438, E-mail: info@museums.ca, Internet: http://www.museums.ca   41717

Canadian Federation of Friends of Museums, c/o Art Gallery of Ontario, 317 Dundas St W, Toronto, Ont. M5T 1G4 - T: (416) 979-6650, Fax: (416) 979-6674, E-mail: cffm_fcam@ago.net   41718

Canadian Museums Association, 280 Metcalfe St, Ste 400, Ottawa, Ont. K2P 1R7 - T: (613) 567-0099, Fax: (613) 233-5438, E-mail: info@museums.ca, Internet: http://www.museums.ca   41719

Commonwealth Association of Museums, POB 30192, Chinook Postal Outlet, Calgary, Alta. T2H 2V9 - T: (403) 938-3190, Fax: (403) 938-3190, E-mail: irvinel@fclc.com, Internet: http://www.maltwood.uvic.ca/cam   41720

Community Museums Association of Prince Edward Island, POB 22002, Charlottetown, P.E.I. C1A 9S2 - T: (902) 892-8837, Fax: (902) 628-6331, E-mail: cmapei@isn.net   41721

ICFA International Committee for Fine Art Museums, c/o Dr. C. Johnston, National Gallery, 380 Sussex Dr, Ottawa, K1N 9N4 - T: (613) 990-8689, Fax: (613) 990-8689   41722

ICOM Museums Canada, c/o Canadian Museums Association, 280 Metcalfe St, Ste 400, Ottawa, Ont. K2P 1R7 - T: (613) 567-0099, Fax: (613) 233-5438, Internet: http://www.icom.org   41723

Museum Association of Newfoundland and Labrador, One Springdale St, Saint John's, mail addr: POB 5785, Saint John's, Nfld. A1C 5X3 - T: (709) 722-9034, Fax: (709) 722-9035, E-mail: uokshevsky@nf.aibn.com, Internet: http://manl.nf.ca   41724

Museums Association of Saskatchewan, 1836 Angus St, Regina, Sask. S4T 1Z4 - T: (306) 780-9279, Fax: (306) 780-9463, E-mail: mas@saskmuseums.org, Internet: http://www.saskmuseums.org   41725

Ontario Museum Association, 50 Baldwin St, Toronto, Ont. M5T 1L4 - T: (416) 348-8672, Fax: (416) 348-0438, E-mail: omachin@planeteer.com, Internet: http://www.museumsontario.ca   41726

Organization of Military Museums of Canada, POB 323, Gloucester, Ont. K1C 1S7 - T: (613) 737-3223, 996-6799, Fax: (613) 737-0821, E-mail: don.carrington@sympatico.ca, Internet: http://www.ommc.ca   41727

Société des Musées Québécois, CP 8888, Succ Centre-Ville, Montréal, P.Q. H3C 3P8 - T: (514) 987-3264, Fax: (514) 987-3379, Internet: http://www.smq.qc.ca   41728

United States-International Council on Monuments and Sites, 401 F St, Ste 331, Washington, DC 20001 - T: (202) 842-1866, Fax: (202) 842-1861, E-mail: edelage@usicomos.org, Internet: http://www.usicomos.org 41729

Yukon Historical and Museums Association, 3126 3 Av, Whitehorse, Y.T. Y1A 1E7 - T: (867) 667-4704, Fax: (867) 667-4506, E-mail: yhma@yknet.yk.ca, Internet: http://www.yukonalaska.com/yhma 41730

Central African Republic

ICOM Répubique Centralafricaine, c/o Musée National Barthélémy Bogonda, BP 1053, Bangui - T: 615367, 613533, Fax: 611085 41731

Chad

ICOM du Tchad, c/o Arcives Nationales et du Patrimoine, BP 5394, N'Djamena - T: 524445, Fax: 525538 41732

Chile

ICOM Chile, c/o Museo de Arte Contemporáneo, Parque Forestal s/n, Santiago - T: (02) 6380390, Fax: 2712046, E-mail: banados@reuna.cl 41733

China, People's Republic

Chinese Association of Natural Science Museums, c/o Beijing Natural History Museum, 126 Tien Chiao St, 100050 Beijing - T: (010) 754431 41734

Chinese Society of Museums, 29 May the 4th St, 100009 Bejing - T: (010) 65132255666, Fax: 65123119 41735

ICOM China, c/o Chinese Society of Museums, 29 May 4th St, 100009 Beijing - T: (010) 65132255666, 64005531, Fax: 65123119, E-mail: museums@public3.bta.net.cn 41736

China, Republic

Chinese Association of Museums, Taipei, 49 Nanhai Rd, Taipei - T: (02) 23610270, Fax: 23890718, E-mail: cam@moe.nmh.gov.tw, Internet: http://www.cam.org.tw 41737

Colombia

Asociación Columbiana de Museos y Comité Nacional del Consejo Internacional de Museos, ACOM-ICOM, c/o Institutos y Casas de Cultura, Calle 103a No 19-47, Santafé de Bogotá - T: (91) 6104235, 2367088, Fax: 2186146 41738

Comoros

ICOM Comores, c/o Ali Mohamed Gou, BP 169, Moroni - T: 744187, 733980, Fax: 744189, 732222, E-mail: cndrs@snpt.km 41739

Congo, Democratic Republic

ICOM République Democratique du Congo, c/o Musées universitaires, Université de Kinshasa, BP 840, Kinshasa XI - E-mail: cerdasunikin@compuserve.com 41740

ICOMAC Regional Organization for Central Africa, BP 13933, Kinshasa - T: (012) 60263, 60008, Fax: 43675 41741

Congo, Republic

ICOM Republique Congo, c/o Prof. P. Makambila, BP 1786, Brazzaville - T: 810708, Fax: 811828 41742

Costa Rica

ICOM Costa Rica, c/o Ecological Centre and Resort, Apdo 1124, San José 1000 - T: 2561611, 2613462, Fax: 2552197, E-mail: Isanroma@ecouncil.ac.cr 41743

ICOM Latin America and the Caribbean Regional Organization, c/o Dirección General de Museos, Apdo 10277-1000, San Jose 1000 - T: 2553051, Fax: 2552197, E-mail: Isanroma@terra.ecouncil.ac.cr 41744

Côte d'Ivoire

ICOM Côté d'Ivoire, c/o Musée National du Costume, BP 311, Grand Bassam - T: 301370, 301415, Fax: 213359 41745

Croatia

Hrvatski Nacionalni Komitet ICOM, c/o Muzej Suvremene Umjetnosti, Habdelićeva 2, 10000 Zagreb - T: (01) 4851930, Fax: 4851931, E-mail: msu@msu.tel.hr 41746

Hrvatsko Muzejsko Društvo, Habdelićeva 2, 10000 Zagreb - T: (01) 48511808, Fax: 4851977, E-mail: hmd@hrmud.hr, Internet: http://www.hrmud.hr 41747

Savez muzejskih društava Hrvatske, Mesnička 5, Muzejski dokum centar, 10000 Zagreb - T: (01) 426534 41748

Cuba

ICOM Cuba, c/o Museo Nacional, Trocadero, esq Morro y Prado, Habana Vieja - T: (07) 639042, 613856, Fax: 613857, E-mail: musna@cubarte.cult.cu 41749

Cyprus

ICOM Cyprus, c/o S. Hadjisavvas, Ministry of Communication and Works, Department of Antiquities, Nicosia - T: (22) 303142, Fax: 303148 41750

Czech Republic

Association of Czech Moravian and Silesian Museums, Kostelní 44, 170 00 Praha 7 - T: (02) 3804346, Fax: 3804347 41751

Association of Museums and Galleries of Czech Republic, Kostelní 42, 170 00 Praha - T: (02) 20399314, Fax: 20399201, E-mail: amg@vol.cz, Internet: http://www.cz-museums.cz 41752

Czech Council of ICOM, c/o Moravské zemské muzeum, Zelný trh 6-8, 659 37 Brno - T: (05) 42215759, Fax: 42210493, E-mail: icom@mzm.cz, Internet: http://www.mzm.cz/icom 41753

Societas Museologia, Hlavní 13, 737 01 Český Těšín - T: (0659) 56795, Fax: 55060 41754

Denmark

CIDOC International Committee for Documentation, c/o Lene Rold, National Museum, Frederiksholms Kanal 12, 1220 København - T: 33473885, Fax: 33473307, E-mail: lene.rold@natmus.dk 41755

Danish National Council of Museums, c/o Fur Museum, Nederby 28, 7884 Fur - T: 97593411, Fax: 97593917, E-mail: stenstrop@hotmail.com, Internet: http://www.dmol.dk 41756

Dansk ICOM, The Danish National Committee of the International Council of Museums, c/o J. Breinegaad, Danmarks Teknike Museum, Øle Romers Vej, 3000 Helsingør - T: 49222611, Fax: 49226211, E-mail: breine@post6.tele.dk 41757

Dansk Kulturhistorisk Museums Forening (Association of Danish Cultural Museums), Kronborg 10a, 3000 Helsingør, mail addr: POB 108, 3000 Helsingør - T: 49213466, Fax: 49217062, E-mail: krexa@image.dk, Internet: http://www.dkm-mus.dk 41758

Foreningen af Danske Kunstmuseer (Association of Danish Art Museums), Kronborg 10a, 3000 Helsingør, mail addr: POB 108, 3000 Helsingør - T: 49213466, Fax: 49217062, E-mail: krexa@image.dk 41759

Foreningen af Danske Museumsmaend (Association of Danish Museum Curators), c/o Zoologisk Museum, Universitetsparken 15, 2100 København Ø - T: 31354111, Fax: 35321010 41760

Foreningen af Danske Naturhistoriske Museer, c/o Svendborg Zoologiske Museum, Dronningemaen 30, 5700 Svendborg - T: 62210650, Fax: 62218417, E-mail: zoojas@svendborg-kom.dk 41761

Foreningen af Danske Naturvidenskabelige Museer, c/o Fiskeri- og Søfartsmuseet, Tarphagevej, 6710 Esbjerg V - T: 75150666, Fax: 75153057, E-mail: tougaard@inet.uni-c.dk 41762

ICLM International Committee for Literary Museums, c/o M. Wirenfeldt-Asmussen, Karen Blixen Museet, Rundsted Strandvej 111, 2960 Rungsted Kyst - T: 45571057, Fax: 45571058, E-mail: karen-blixen@dinesen.dk 41763

Museumstjenesten (Danish Museum Service), Sjørupvej 1, Lysgaard, 8800 Viborg - T: 86666766, Fax: 86667611, E-mail: mtj@museumstjenesten.com, Internet: http://www.museumstjenesten.com 41764

Skandinavisk Museumsforbund, Danske Afdeling, c/o Jens Peter Munk, Reykjaviksg 2, 2300 København S - T: 32961171 41765

Dominican Republic

ICOM República Dominicana, Ouestre Cul de Sac 27, Residencial Victoria, Santo Domingo, mail addr: Apdo B302, Santo Domingo - T: 5488348 41766

Ecuador

ICOM Ecuador, Almagro 1550 y Pradera, Quito - T: (02) 220610, 526335, Fax: 507705, E-mail: fpak@uio.satnet.net 41767

Egypt

ICOM Arab, Dept. of Egyptology, Faculty of Archaeology, Cairo University, Giza - T: (02) 5678108, Fax: 5675660, E-mail: a_nurelding@hotmail.com 41768

ICOM Egypt, 4d Fakhri Abdel Nour St, Abbasiya - T: (02) 839637, 2838084, Fax: 2831117 41769

Estonia

Estonian Museums Association, c/o Marika Valk, Eesti Kunstimuuseum, Kiriku pl 1, 10130 Tallinn - T: (02) 449340, Fax: 442094, E-mail: muuseum@ekm.estnet.ee 41770

ICOM Estonia, c/o Museum of Estonian Architecture, 2 Ahtri St, 10151 Tallinn - T: 6257000, Fax: 6257003, E-mail: karin@architektu-rimuseum.ee 41771

Fiji

Pacific Islands Museums Association, c/o J. Bacciochi, Fiji Museum, POB 2023, Suva - T: 315944, Fax: 305143, E-mail: secretariat@pacificislandsmuseum.org, Internet: http://www.finearts.mcc.edu/pima 41772

Finland

ICOM Finland, c/o The Finnish National Gallery, Kaivokatu 2, 00100 Helsinki - T: (09) 17336384, Fax: 17336344, E-mail: maija.ekosaari@fng.fi, Internet: http://www.museoliitto.fi/icom 41773

International Committee for Museums and Collections of Modern Art, c/o Tuula Arkio, Finnish National Galleries, Kaivokatu 2, 00100 Helsinki - T: (09) 17336253, Fax: 17336227, E-mail: tuula.arkio@fng.fi, Internet: http://www.cimam.org 41774

Skandinaviskt Museiförbund - Skandinaavinen Museoliitto, Finnish Section, Sofiankatu 4, 00170 Helsinki, mail addr: c/o Helsingin Kaupunginmuseo, PL 4300, 00099 Helsinki - T: (09) 1693442, Fax: 667665, E-mail: irma.savolainen@hel.fi 41775

Suomen Museoammattilaiset, c/o Porvoon Museo, Typopajatie 13, 06150 Porvoo - T: (015) 580589, Fax: 582283 41776

Suomen Museoliitto (Finnish Museums Association), Annankatu 16b, 00120 Helsinki - T: (09) 649001, Fax: 608330, E-mail: museoliitto@museoliitto.fi, Internet: http://www.museoliitto.fi 41777

France

Association des Conservateurs et du Personnel Scientifique des Musées de la Ville de Paris, c/o Musée d'Art Moderne, 9 Rue Gaston-de-Saint-Paul, 75116 Paris - T: 0153674000, Fax: 0147233598 41778

Association des Musées Automobiles de France, 6 Pl de la Concorde, 75008 Paris - T: 0143124311, Fax: 0143124343, Internet: http://www.amaf.asso.fr 41779

Association Européenne des Musées d'Histoire des Sciences Médicales (AEMHSM), c/o Musée d'Histoire de la Médecine, 12 Rue de l'Ecole-de-Médecine, 75006 Paris - T: 0140461693, Fax: 0140461892, E-mail: clin@univ-paris5.fr, Internet: http://www.aemhsm.org 41780

Association Générale des Conservateurs des Collections Publiques de France, 6 Av du Mahatma Gandhi, 75116 Paris - T: 0144176090, Fax: 0144176060, E-mail: maigret@mnhn.fr 41781

Association Internationale des Musées d'Hisoire (International Association of Museums of History), c/o Musée d'Histoire Contemporaine, Hôtel des Invalides, 75007 Paris - T: 0145519302, Fax: 0144189384 41782

Association Museum Shop and Industry Europe - France, 45 Av George V, 75008 Paris - T: 0153576200, Fax: 0153576201 41783

Association pour le Respect de l'Intégrité du Patrimoine Artistique, 97 Blvd Rodin, 92130 Issy-les-Moulineaux - E-mail: aripa@wanadoo.fr, Internet: http://www.aripa-nuances.org 41784

Association pour les Musées de Marseille, 2 Rue de la Charité, 13002 Marseille - T: 0491145842, Fax: 0491145881, E-mail: ass.musees.marseille@wanadoo.fr 41785

Comité National Français de l'ICOM, 13 Rue Molière, 75001 Paris - T: 0142613202, Fax: 0142613202, E-mail: icomfrance@wanadoo.fr, Internet: http://www.culture.fr/icom-france 41786

Direction de Musées de France, 6 Rue des Pyramides, 75041 Paris Cedex 1 - T: 0140153649, Fax: 0147304482, E-mail: maigret@cimrsl.mnhn.fr 41787

Fédération des Ecomusées et des Musées de Société, 2 Av Arthur Gaulard, 25000 Besançon - T: 0381832255, Fax: 0381810892, E-mail: fems@wanadoo.fr 41788

Fédération des Maisons d'Ecrivain et des Patrimoines Littéraires, Médiathèque, Blvd Lamarck, 180001 Bourges Cedex - T: 0248232250, Fax: 0248245064, E-mail: maisonsecrivain@yahoo.com, Internet: http://www.litterature-lieux.com 41789

Fédération Française des Sociétés d'Amis de Musées, 16-18 Rue de Cambrai, 75019 Paris - T: 0142096610, Fax: 0142094471, E-mail: info@amis-musees.fr, Internet: http://www.amis-musees.fr 41790

ICMAH International Committee for Archaeology and History Museums, c/o Jean-Yves Marin, Musée de Normandie, Logis des Gouverneurs Château, 14000 Caen - T: 0231304750, Fax: 0231304769, E-mail: mdn@ville-caen.fr 41791

ICOM Europe, Maison de l'UNESCO, 1 Rue Miollis, 75732 Paris Cedex 15 - T: 0147340500, Fax: 0143067862, E-mail: secretariat@icom.org, Internet: http://www.icom.org 41792

International Council of Museums ICOM, Maison de l'UNESCO, 1 Rue Miollis, 75732 Paris Cedex 15 - T: 0147340500, Fax: 0143067862, E-mail: secretariat@icom.org, Internet: http://www.icom.org 41793

International Council on Monuments and Sites, 49-51 Rue de la Fédération, 75015 Paris - T: 0145676770, Fax: 0145660622, E-mail: secretariat@icomos.org, Internet: http://www.icomos.org 41794

International Society of Libraries and Museums of Performing Arts, 1 Rue de Sully, 75004 Paris - T: 0142770239, Fax: 0142770163, Internet: http://www/theatrelibrary.org/sibnmas/ 41795

France

Réunion des Musées Nationaux, 49 Rue Etienne-Marcel, 75039 Paris Cedex 01 - T: 0140134800, Fax: 0140134861, Internet: http://www.rmn.fr 41796

France

World Federation of Friends of Museums, 4 Rue Auguste Dorchain, 75015 Paris - T: 0145672637, Fax: 0145672637 41797

Germany

Arbeitsgemeinschaft kirchlicher Museen und Schatzkammern, Domerschulstr 2, 97070 Würzburg - T: (0931) 386261, Fax: 3862626, E-mail: kunstreferat@bistum-wuerzburg.de 41798

Association of Castles and Museums around the Baltic Sea, c/o Landesmuseum Schloß Gottorf, 24837 Schleswig - T: (0462) 18130, Fax: 1813202 41799

Association of European Open Air Museums, c/o Westfälisches Freilichtmuseum Hagen, Mäckingerbach, 58091 Hagen, Westfalen - T: (02331) 780710, Fax: 780720, E-mail: wfh-md@freilichtmuseum-hagen.de, Internet: http://www.freilichtmuseum-hagen.de 41800

Bundesverband Museumspädagogik e.V., c/o B. Commanduer, Rheinisches Industriemuseum, Alte Dombach, 51465 Bergisch Gladbach - T: (02202) 9366813, Fax: 9366821, E-mail: beacommandeur@t-online.de 41801

Deutsche Burgenvereinigung e.V., Marksburg, 56338 Braubach - T: (02627) 536, Fax: 8866, E-mail: info@deutsche-burgen.org, Internet: http://www.deutsche-burgen.org 41802

Deutscher Museumsbund, Staatliche Kunstsammlungen Dresden, c/o Deutsches Hygiene-Museum, Lingnerpl 1, 01069 Dresden - T: (0351) 4914700, Fax: 4914777, E-mail: office@museumsbund.de, Internet: http://www.museumsbund.de 41803

Düsseldorfer Museumsverein e.V., c/o Dr. Spennemann, Deutsche Bank 24, Königsallee 45-47, 40189 Düsseldorf - T: (0211) 8832458, Fax: 883379, E-mail: gert.spennemann@db.com 41804

Hessischer Museumsverband e.V., Kölnische Str 44-46, 34117 Kassel - T: (0561) 78896740, Fax: 78896800, E-mail: - www.museumsverband_hessen@sparkassenversicherung.de 41805

ICOFOM International Committee for Museology, c/o Dr. H.K. Vieregg, Bayerische Staatsgemäldesammlungen, Barer Str 29, 80799 München - T: (089) 23805196, Fax: 23805197, E-mail: vieregg@mpz.bayern.de 41806

ICOM International Council of Museums, Deutsches Nationalkomitee, In der Halde 1, 14195 Berlin - T: (030) 69504525, Fax: 69504526, E-mail: icom-deutschland@t-online.de, Internet: http://www.icom-deutschland.de 41807

International Association of Agricultural Museums, AIMA, c/o Hans Haas, Bergisches Freilichtmuseum, Schloss Heiligenhoven, 51789 Lindlar - T: (02266) 90100, Fax: 9010200, E-mail: t.trappe@lvr.de, Internet: http://www.bergisches-freilandmuseum.lvr.de 41808

International Committee for Museums and Collections of Natural History, c/o Gerhard Winter, Naturmuseum Senckenberg, Senckenberganlage 25, 60325 Frankfurt am Main - T: (069) 7542356, Fax: 7542331, E-mail: gwinter@sng.uni-frankfurt.de, Internet: http://www.senckenber.uni-frankfurt.de/icom/nh-board.html 41809

Museumspädagogische Gesellschaft e.V., c/o Museumsdienst Köln, Richartzstr 2-4, 50667 Köln - T: (0221) 22126636, Fax: 22124544 41810

Museumsverband Baden-Württemberg e.V., c/o Stadtmuseum im Gelben Haus, Hafenmarkt 7, 73728 Esslingen - T: (0711) 35123240, Fax: 35123229, E-mail: museumsverband-bw@web.de 41811

Museumsverband für Niedersachsen und Bremen e.V., Fössestr 99, 30453 Hannover - T: (0511) 2144983, Fax: 21449344, E-mail: kontakt@mvnb.de, Internet: http://www.mvnb.de 41812

Museumsverband in Mecklenburg-Vorpommern e.V., Heidberg 15, 18273 Güstrow - T: (03843) 344736, Fax: 344743, E-mail: info@museumsverband-mv.de, Internet: http://www.museumsverband-mv.de 41813

Museumsverband Sachsen-Anhalt e.V., Käthe-Kollwitz-Str 11, 06406 Bernburg - T: (03471) 628116, Fax: 628983, 628116, E-mail: - museumsverbandsachsen-anhalt@t-online.de, Internet: http://www.mv-sachsen-anhalt.de 41814

Museumsverband Schleswig-Holstein e.V., c/o Medizin- und Pharmaziehistorische Sammlung Kiel, Brunswiker Str 2, 24105 Kiel - T: (0431) 8805720, Fax: 8805727, E-mail: jhwolf@med-hist.uni-kiel.de, Internet: http://www.museumsverband-sh.de 41815

Museumsverband Thüringen e.V., Greizer Str 37, 07545 Gera - T: (0365) 22515, Fax: 2900436 41816

Museumsverbund Südniedersachsen e.V., Ritterplan 7-8, 37073 Göttingen - T: (0551) 4002883, Fax: 4003135 41817

Museumsverein Aachen, Wilhelmstr 18, 52070 Aachen - T: (0241) 479800, Fax: 37075, E-mail: info@suermondt-ludwig-museum.de, Internet: http://www.suermondt-ludwig-museum.de 41818

Museumsverein Düren e.V., Hoeschpl 1, 52349 Düren - T: (02421) 252559, 252561, Fax: 252560, E-mail: museum.dueren@t-online.de, Internet: http://www.artcontent.de/dueren 41819

Museumsverein für das Fürstentum Lüneburg, Wandrahmstr 10, 21335 Lüneburg - T: (04131) 43891, Fax: 405497 41820

Museumsverein Hameln e.V., Osterstr 9, 31785 Hameln - T: (05151) 202219, Fax: 202815 41821

Museumsverein Kassel e.V., c/o Schloß Wilhelmshöhe, 34131 Kassel - T: (0561) 93777, Fax: 9377666, E-mail: info@hrz.museum-kassel.de 41822

Museumsverein Mönchengladbach, Abteistr 27, 41061 Mönchengladbach - T: (02161) 252647, Fax: 252659 41823

Sächsischer Museumsbund e.V., Wilsdruffer Str 2, 01067 Dresden - T: (0351) 4906056, Fax: 4951288 41824

Verband Rheinischer Museen, Schloßpl 2, 42659 Solingen - T: (0212) 2422611/12, Fax: 2422640, E-mail: schloss.burg@t-online.de 41825

Vereinigung westfälischer Museen, Rothenburg 30, 48143 Münster 41826

Wetterauer Museumsgesellschaft e.V., Haagstr 16, 61169 Friedberg, Hessen - T: (06031) 88215/18, Fax: 18396 41827

Ghana

Organization of Museums, Monuments and Sites of Africa OMMSA, POB 3343, Accra 41828

Greece

Byzantine Museums, c/o Ministry of Culture, Bouboulinos Od 20-22, 106 82 Athinai - T: (01) 3304030, Fax: 3304009, E-mail: protocol@dbmm.culture.gr 41829

ICOM Grèce, Aghion Assomaton 15, 105 53 Athinai - T: (01) 03239414, Fax: 3239414, E-mail: icom@otenet.gr 41830

Greenland

NUKAKA - Sammenslutningen af Lokalmuseer i Grønland (Association of Local Museums in Greenland), Jukkorsuup Aqq 9, 3911 Sisimiut, mail addr: c/o Sisimiut Museum, Postboks 308, 3911 Sisimiut - T: 865087, Fax: 864475, E-mail: sismus@greennet.gl, Internet: http://www.museum.gl 41831

Semmenslutningen af Grønlandske Lokalmuseer, c/o Narsaq Museum, Postboks 39, 3921 Narsaq - T: 661659, Fax: 661744, E-mail: narsaq.museum@greennet.gl 41832

Guadeloupe

Musées Départementaux de la Guadeloupe, 24 Rue Peynier, 97110 Pointe-à-Pitre - T: 820804, Fax: 837839 41833

Guatemala

Asociación de Museos de Guatemala, c/o Museo Universitario de San Carlos, 9a Av 9-79, Zona 1, Guatemala City - T: 2327666, 2320721, Fax: 2320721, E-mail: amg@hotmail.com 41834

Haiti

ICOM Comité Haïtien, 3 Rue Baussan, Port-au-Prince, mail addr: BP 1214, Port-au-Prince - T: 2451509, Fax: 2454535, E-mail: geraldalexis@hotmail.com 41835

Hungary

Hungarian Museums Association, c/o P. Deme, Magyar Nemzeti Múzeum, Muzeum krt 14-16, 1088 Budapest - T: (01) 3277762, Fax: 3177806, E-mail: demep@hnm.hu 41836

ICOM Hungary, Wesselenyi ú 20-22, 1077 Budapest - T: (01) 4847125, Fax: 4847126, E-mail: - erzsebet.kocziANSzentpeteri@nkom.gov.hu 41837

Iceland

Association of Icelandic Curators, c/o National Museum of Iceland, Svourgotu 41, 101 Reykjavik - T: 5528967, Fax: 5528967 41838

Felag Islenska Safnmanna (Museum Association of Iceland), c/o Byggos- og Listasafn, Tryggvagata 23, 800 Selfoss 41839

ICOM Iceland, c/o Listasafn Así, Freyjugötu 41, 101 Reykjavik - T: 5115353, Fax: 5115354, E-mail: listasi@centrum.is 41840

Scandinavian Museum Association, Icelandic Section, c/o National Museum of Iceland, Svourgotu 41, 101 Reykjavik 41841

India

CECA International Committee for Education and Cultural Action of Museums, c/o Ganga S. Rautela, Nehru Science Centre, Dr. E. Moses Rd, Mumbai 400018 - T: (022) 4932668, Fax: 4932668, E-mail: nscm@giasbm01.vsnl.net.in 41842

CIMUSET International Committee for Science and Technology Museums, c/o P.K. Bhaumik, National Science Centre, Bhairon Rd, Pragati Maidan, Gate 1, Delhi 110001 - T: (011) 3371263, 3371945, Fax: 3371263, E-mail: nscd@giasdl01.vsnl.net.in 41843

ICOM India, c/o Indian Museum, 27 Jawaharlala Nehru Rd, Kolkata 700016 - T: (033) 2495669, 2499902, Fax: 2495669, E-mail: imbot@cal2.vsnl.net.in 41844

Indian Association for the Study of Conservation of Cultural Property, c/o National Museum Institute, Janpath, Delhi 110011 - T: (011) 3016098, 3792217, Fax: 3019821, 3011901 41845

Museums Association of India, c/o National Museum, Janpath, Delhi 110011 - T: (011) 383568 41846

Iran

ICOM Iran, c/o Iranian Cultural Heritage Organization, Azadi Av and Zanpan St, Teheran 13445 - T: (021) 6013527, 6013530, Fax: 6013498, E-mail: mozhganahmadieh@hotmail.com 41847

Ireland

Irish Museums Association, c/o Chester Beatty Library, Dublin Castle, Dublin, 2 - T: (01) 4070764, E-mail: docarroll@cbl.ie, Internet: http://www.cbl.ie 41848

Irish Science Centres Association Network, c/o National Museum Institute, Ballsbridge, Dublin 4 - E-mail: secretary@iscan.ie, Internet: http://www.iscan.ie 41849

Israel

Israel National Committee of ICOM, POB 45134, Haifa - T: (04) 8527892, 8552223, Fax: 8527892, E-mail: icom@netvision.net.il, Internet: http://www.rakia.com/icom 41850

Museum Association of Israel, POB 33288, Tel Aviv 61332 41851

Italy

Associazione Nazionale dei Musei dei Enti Locali ed Istituzionali, Via Tiziano 323, 25124 Brescia - T: 0302300307, Fax: 0302300307 41852

Associazione Nazionale dei Musei Italiani, Piazza San Marco 49, 00186 Roma - T: 066791343, Fax: 066791343 41853

Associazione Nazionale Musei Scientifici, Via G. La Pira 4, 50121 Firenze - T: 0552757460, Fax: 0552737373 41854

DEMHIST-International Committee for Historic House Museums, c/o Museo Bagatti Valsecchi, Via Santo Spirito 10, 20121 Milano - T: 0276006132, Fax: 0276014859, E-mail: demhist@museobagatti-valsecci.org, Internet: http://www.museobagatti-valsecchi.org/icom/demhis_e.htm 41855

ICOM, The International Council of Museums, Comitato Nazionale Italiano, c/o Museo della Scienza e della Tecnologia, Via San Vittore 19-21, 20123 Milano - T: 0248555338, Fax: 0243919840, E-mail: icomit@iol.it, Internet: http://www.museoscienza.it/icom 41856

International Centre for the Study of the Preservation and the Restoration of Cultural Property (ICCROM), Via di San Michele 13, 00153 Roma - T: 06585531, Fax: 0658553349, E-mail: iccrom@iccrom.org, Internet: http://www.iccrom.org 41857

Japan

Japanese Council of Art Museums, c/o Gunma-kenritsu Kindai Bijutsukan, 239 Iwahana-machi, Takasaki 370-1293 - T: (027) 3465560, Fax: 3464064   41858

Japanese National Committee for ICOM, c/o Japanese Association of Museums, Shoyu Kaikan Bldg, 3-3-1 Kasumigaseki, Chiyoda-ku, Tokyo 100-8925 - T: (03) 35917190, Fax: 35917170, E-mail: webmaster@j-muse.or.jp, Internet: http://www.museum.or.jp/icom-japan/   41859

Nihon Hakubutsukan Kyokai (Japanese Association of Museums), Shoyu Kaikan Bldg, 3-3-1 Kasumigaseki, Chiyoda-ku, Tokyo 100-8925 - T: (03) 35917190, Fax: 35917170, E-mail: webmaster@j-muse.or.jp, Internet: http://www.j-muse.or.jp   41860

Jordan

ICOM Jordan, c/o Department of Antiquities, POB 88, Amman - T: (06) 4623398, Fax: 4615848   41861

Kenya

ICOM Kenya, c/o National Museums of Kenya, POB 40658, Nairobi - T: (020) 3742131/4, Fax: 3741424, E-mail: prnmk@users.africaonline.co.ke   41862

International Confederation, c/o Museum Hill, POB 38706, Nairobi - T: (020) 3748668, Fax: 3748928, E-mail: africom@museums.or.ke, Internet: http://www.african-museums.org   41863

International Council of African Museums, c/o Museum Hill, POB 38706, Nairobi - T: (020) 3748668, Fax: 3748928, E-mail: africom@museums.or.ke, Internet: http://www.african-museums.org   41864

Kenya Museum Society, c/o Museum Hill, POB 40658, 00100 Nairobi - T: (020) 3742131 ext 289, E-mail: info@knowkenya.org   41865

Programme for Museum Development in Africa, Old Law Courts Bldg, Nkrumah Rd, Mombasa - T: (011) 2224846   41866

Korea, Republic

Korean Museum Association, c/o National Museum of Korea, 1-57 Sejong-no, Chongno-gu, Seoul 110-050 - T: (02) 7350230, 3985190, Fax: 7350231   41867

Korean National Committee of the International Council of Museums (ICOM), c/o National Museum of Korea, 1-57 Sejong-no, Chongno-gu, Seoul 110-050 - T: (02) 7350230, 3985190, Fax: 7350231, E-mail: office@icomkorea.org, Internet: http://user.collian.net/~pll/public_html/ICOMKorea/ 41868

Latvia

ICOM Latvijas Nacionālā komiteja, c/o A. Ozola, Tukums Museum, Harmonijas iela 7, Tukums, 3100 - T: (031) 82390, Fax: 22707, E-mail: tuktie@tukums.panes.lv   41869

Latvijas Muzeju Asociācija (Latvian Museums Association), Smilšu iela 20, Rīga, 1868 - T: 72227335, Fax: 72227335, E-mail: muzasoc@acad.latnet.lv   41870

Lebanon

ICOM Liban, c/o Leila Badre, Musée de l'Université Americaine, BP 11-0236/9, Beirut - T: (01) 340549, Fax: 4781995, E-mail: badre@aub.edu.lb   41871

Libya

ICOM Libyan Arab Jamahiriya, c/o Jamahiriya Museum, Es Saray El-Hamara, Tripoli - T: (021) 4449065, Fax: 4440166   41872

Lithuania

ICOM Lithuania, c/o Lithuanian Art Museum, Rudininku 8, 2024 Vilnius - T: (02) 617941   41873

Luxembourg

ICOM Luxembourg, c/o Musée National d'Histoire et d'Art, Marché-aux-Poissons, 2345 Luxembourg - T: 479330/31, Fax: 479271, 479330, E-mail: musee@mha.etat.lu, Internet: http://www.mnha.lu   41874

Macedonia

ICOM F.Y.R. Macedonia, c/o Prirodonaučen Muzej, Bul Ilinden 86, Skopje 1000 - T: (02) 116453, Fax: 117669   41875

Muzejsko Društvo na Makedonija, c/o Muzej na Grad Skopje, Mito Hadzi Vasilev bb, 1000 Skopje - T: (02) 115367   41876

Madagascar

ICOM Madagascar, 17, rue Dr Villette, Isoraka, mail addr: c/o Musée d'Art et d'Archéologie, BP 564, Antananarivo 101 - T: (20) 2232317, Fax: 2232317, E-mail: vohitra@refer.mg   41877

Malaysia

ICOM Malaysia, c/o Dr. Kamarul Baharin Bin Buyong, Jalan Damansara, 50566 Kuala Lumpur - T: (03) 2826255, Fax: 2827294   41878

Mali

ICOM Mali, c/o Musée National, BP 159, Bamako - T: 223486, Fax: 231909, E-mail: musee@malinet.ml   41879

ICOM Regional Organization for West Africa, BP 159, Bamako - T: 223489, Fax: 231909, E-mail: musee@malinet.ml   41880

Mauritania

ICOM Mauritanie, c/o Musée de Ouadane, BP 1368, Nouakchott - T: (2) 256017, Fax: 255275, 252802, E-mail: ouldabidinesidi@hotmail.com   41881

Mauritius

ICOM Mauritius, c/o Mauritius Institute, Chaussée, Port Louis - T: 2120639, Fax: 2125717, E-mail: mimuse@intnet.mu   41882

Mexico

ICOM-México, Valerio Trujano 2, Colonia Guerrero, 06000 México - T: (55) 5104377, Internet: http://www.arts-history.mx/museos/icom   41883

Monaco

ICOM Monaco, c/o Musée Océanographique, Av Saint-Martin, Monaco-Ville, 98000 Monaco - T: 93153600, Fax: 93505297   41884

Morocco

ICOM Maroc, c/o Direction du Patrimoine Culturel, 17 Rue Michlifen, Agdal, Rabat - T: (07) 671381, Fax: 671397   41885

Namibia

Museums Association of Namibia, POB 147, Windhoek - T: (061) 22840, Fax: 222544   41886

Netherlands

Brabantse Museumstichting, Ringbaan Oost 8, 5013 CA Tilburg - T: (013) 5355565, Fax: 5810608, E-mail: bms@bart.nl, Internet: http://www.brabant-museumland.nl   41887

Dutch Museum Advisors Liaison Group, Mariapl 23, 3511 LK Utrecht - T: (030) 2343880, Fax: 2328624   41888

European Association of Open Air Museums, c/o Nederlands Openluchtmuseum, Postbus 64g, 6800 AP Arnhem - T: (026) 3576250, Fax: 3576147, E-mail: j.vaessen@openluchtmuseum.nl, Internet: http://www.openluchtmuseum.nl   41889

IAMAM International Association of Museums of Arms and Military History History Museums, c/o J.P. Puype, Koninklijk Nederlands Leger- en Wapenmuseum, Korte Geer 1, 2611 CA Delft - T: (015) 2150500, Fax: 2150544, E-mail: jpp@geweldig.net, Internet: http://www.klm_mra.be/ICOMAM/index.htm   41890

ICAMT International Committee for Architecture and Museums Techniques, c/o J. Verschuuren, Brabantse Museumstichting, Ringbaan 8-17, 5013 CA Tilburg - T: (013) 5355565, Fax: 5810608, E-mail: bmsjv@bart.nl   41891

ICME International Committee for Ethnography Museums, c/o H. Leyten, Reinwardt Academie, Dapperstr 315, 1093 BS Amsterdam - T: (020) 6922111, Fax: 6926836, E-mail: h.leyten@mus.ahk.nl   41892

ICOM Netherlands, c/o M. Ch. Van de Sman, Postbus 74683, 1070 BR Amsterdam - T: (020) 6701100, Fax: 6701101   41893

International Committee for Monetary Museums, c/o Het Nederlands Muntmuseum, Leidseweg 90, 3500 Utrecht - T: (030) 2910482, Fax: 2910467, E-mail: ICOMON@coins.nl   41894

International Confederation of Architectural Museums, c/o Nederlands Architectuurinstituut, Museumpark 25, 3015 CB Rotterdam - E-mail: mwilling@nai.nl, Internet: http://www.icam-web.org   41895

Nederlandse Kastelenstichting, Markt 24, 3961 BC Wijk bij Duurstede - T: (0343) 578995, Fax: 591403, E-mail: info@kastelen.nl, Internet: http://www.kastelen.nl   41896

De Nederlandse Museumvereniging (Netherlands Museums Association), Postbus 74683, 1070 BR Amsterdam - T: (020) 3053760, Fax: 6701101, E-mail: info@museumvereniging.nl, Internet: http://www.museumvereniging.nl   41897

Netherlands Museums Advisors Foundation, Stationsstr 29, 9401 KX Assen - T: (0592) 305934, Fax: 305940, E-mail: p.witteveen@drenthe.nl   41898

New Zealand

Art Galleries and Museums Association of New Zealand, c/o Te Papa Tongarewa, Cable St, Wellington 6020 - T: (04) 3817000, Fax: 3817080, E-mail: mail@tepapa.govt.nz, Internet: http://www.tepapa.govt.nz   41899

ICOM New Zealand, POB 836, Kerikeri 0470 - T: (09) 4074443, Fax: 4073454, E-mail: spark@historic.co.nz   41900

Museum Directors Federation, POB 6401, Te Aro, Wellington 6001 - T: (04) 3844473, Fax: 3851198   41901

Museums Aotearoa, 105 The Terrace, Wellington 6035, mail addr: POB 10928, Wellington 6035 - T: (04) 4991313, Fax: 4996313, E-mail: mail@museums-aotearoa.org.nz, Internet: http://www.museums-aotearoa.org.nz   41902

New Zealand Historic Places Trust, 63 Boulcott St, Wellington - T: (04) 4724341, Fax: 49909669, E-mail: information@historic.org.nz, Internet: http://www.historic.org.nz   41903

Wellington Museums Trust, Queens Wharf Jervois Quay, Wellington 6001 - T: (04) 4710919, E-mail: trust@wmt.org.nz   41904

Niger

ICOM Comité National du Niger, BP 10457, Niamey - T: 724597, Fax: 722336, 723685, E-mail: loutou@internet.ne   41905

Nigeria

ICOM Nigeria, Old Residency, Calabar, mail addr: c/o National Commision for Museums and Monuments, PMB 1180, Calabar - T: (087) 223476/79, Fax: 220111   41906

Museums Association of Nigeria, c/o National Museum, PMB 12556, Lagos - T: (01) 632878, 636005, 636075   41907

National Commission for Museums and Monuments, Plot 2018, Cotonou Crescent, Wuse Zone 6, Abuja, mail addr: PMB 171, Garki, Abuja - T: (09) 5230801, 5238253, Fax: 5238254   41908

Norway

ICOM Norge, c/o Trondelag Folkemuseum, Postboks 1107, 7002 Trondheim - T: 73890102, Fax: 73890150, E-mail: kwik@online.no   41909

International Association of Transport and Communication Museums, c/o Banmuseet, 262 52 Ängelholm - T: (0431) 442170, Fax: 442179, E-mail: lars-olov.karlsson@banverket.se, Internet: http://www.iatm.org   41910

International Committee for Museums and Collections of Musical Instruments, c/o C. Weinheimer, Ringve Museum, Postboks 3064 Lade, 7441 Trondheim - T: 73922411, Fax: 73920422, E-mail: corinna.weinheimer@ringve.museum.no, Internet: http://www.org/cimcim   41911

Norges Museumsforbund, Ullevålsv 11, 0165 Oslo - T: 22201402, Fax: 22112337, E-mail: museumsnytt@museumsforbundet.no, Internet: http://www.museumsforbundet.no   41912

Norsk Museumsutvikling (Norwegian Museums Development), Postboks 8045, 0030 Oslo - T: 23239440, Fax: 23239441   41913

Norske Kunst- og Kulturhistoriske Museer, Ullevålsv 11, 0165 Oslo - T: 22201402, Fax: 22201122   41914

Norske Museumspedagogiske Forening (closed)   41915

Norske Naturhistoriske Museers Landsforbund (closed)   41916

Skandinavisk Museumsforbund, Norwegian Section, Universitetets Oldsahsamling, 0164 Oslo - T: (02) 22859536, E-mail: erla.hohler@iahn.vio.no   41917

Pakistan

The Museums Association of Pakistan, c/o Bait al-Hikmah, Hamardy University, Sharae Madinat al-Hikmah, Karachi 74700 - T: (021) 6996001/02, Fax: 6350574, E-mail: huvc@cyber.net.pk   41918

Panama

Comisión Nacional de Arqueología y Monumentos Historicos, Plaza 5 de Mayo, 662 Panamá City - T: 621438   41919
ICOM Panamá, Casco Viejo, entre Calle 5ta y 6ta, Panamá City, mail addr: c/o Museo del Canal Interoceánico de Panamá, Apdo 1213, Zona 1, Panamá City - T: 2111994/95, Fax: 2111649/50, E-mail: pcmuseum@sinfo.net   41920

Paraguay

ICOM Paraguay, c/o Centro de Conservación del Patrimonio Cultural, Almacén Viola, JE O'Leary 1 y Barranco del Río, Asunción - T: (021) 446829, Fax: 446829, E-mail: patricom@pol.com.py   41921

Peru

ICOM Peru, Jr. Camaná 459, Lima 1 - T: (01) 4602770, Fax: 4277678, E-mail: acastel@pucp.edu.pe   41922

Philippines

ICOM Philippines, c/o National Historical Institute, T.M. Kalaw St, Ermita, Manila - T: (02) 5230995, 5242250, Fax: 5250144, E-mail: sca@ncca.gov.ph   41923
Museum Volunteers of the Philippines, Dasmariñas, POB 8052, 1222 Makati - E-mail: MVPhilippines@hotmail.com, Internet: http://mvphilippines.hypermart.net   41924

Poland

ICOM Poland, c/o Muzeum Narodowe, Marcinkowskiego 9, Poznań - T: (061) 8525969, Fax: 8515898, E-mail: mnoffice@man.poznan.pl   41925
Zarzad Muzeów i Ochrony Zabytków, ul Krakowskie Przedmieście 15-17, 00-171 Warszawa   41926

Portugal

Associação Portugesa de Museologia, c/o Panteão Nacional, Campo Santa Clara, 1100 Lisboa   41927
ICOM Portugal, c/o Commissão Nacional Portugesa, Apdo 23323, 1171-801 Lisboa - T: (01) 3813180, Fax: 3813187   41928
Instituto Português de Museus, Palacio Nacional da Ajuda, Ala Sul, 1349-021 Lisboa - T: 213650800, Fax: 213647821, E-mail: dd.dsm@ipmuseus.pt, Internet: http://www.museus.pt   41929

Romania

Confederatia Asociatillor de Muzeografi din România, Pisto Presei Libre 1, 70000 Bucureşti   41930

ICOM Romania, c/o Muzeul National de Istorie Natural, Soseaua Kiseleff 1, 79744 Bucureşti - T: (01) 3128826, Fax: 3128886, E-mail: mihaist@antipa.ro   41931
Societatea profesorilor de muzica si desen din România, Str Stirbei Voda 33, 70732 Bucureşti - T: (01) 6142610   41932

Russia

Museum Council, Ul D. Ulyanova 19, 117036 Moskva - T: (095) 1251121, Fax: 1260630, E-mail: i_zaitseva@hotmail.com   41933
Rossijskij Komitet Meždunarodnogo Soveta Muzeev (IKOM Rossii), Volchonka bul 3-4, 129010 Moskva - T: (095) 2036090, Fax: 2030480, E-mail: icom_russia@chat.ru, Internet: http://www.prof.museum.ru/icom   41934

St. Lucia

INTERCOM International Committee for Museums Management, c/o L. Gill, Archaeological and Historical Society, 85 Chaussee Rd, Castries - T: (758) 451-9251, Fax: (758) 451-9324, E-mail: gilll@candw.lc   41935

Senegal

ICOM Sénégal, c/o Musée Historique de Gorée, BP 206, Dakar - T: 8251990, Fax: 8244918, E-mail: layetoure@hotmail.com   41936

Seychelles

Association of Museums of the Indian Ocean, c/o National Musuem of Seychelles, POB 720, Victoria - T: 321333, Fax: 323183, E-mail: seymus@seychelles.net   41937
ICOM Seychelles, c/o National Museum, POB 720, Victoria - T: 321333, Fax: 323183, E-mail: seymus@seychelles.net   41938

Singapore

ICOM Singapore, c/o National Heritage Board, 61 Stamford Rd, 02-01 Stamford Court, Singapore 178892 - T: 3327994, Fax: 3323228, E-mail: siamkim_lim@nhb.gov.sg   41939

Slovakia

ICOM Slovakia, c/o Slovenská Národná Galéria, Riečna 1, 815 13 Bratislava - T: (07) 54430746, Fax: 54433971, E-mail: uz@sng.sk   41940
Zväz Muzei na Slavensku (Slovak Museums Association), c/o Slovenské Múzeum Ochrany Prírody a Jaskyniarstva, Školská 4, 031 01 Liptovský Mikuláš   41941

Slovenia

Društvo muzealcev Slovenije, c/o Narodni muzej Ljubljana, Prešernova 20, 1000 Ljubljana - T: (01) 2518862   41942
ICOM Slovenia, c/o SEM, Castle Museum, Gori crane 38, 1215 Medvode - E-mail: ralf.ceplak@guest.arnes.si   41943
ICR International Committee for Regional Museums, c/o I. Zmuc, Mestni Muzej, Gosposka 15, 1000 Ljubljana - T: (01) 2522930, Fax: 2522946   41944

Skupnost Muzejev Slovenije (Museums Association of Slovenia), c/o T. Cepić, Mestni Muzej, Gosposka 15, 1000 Ljubljana   41945
Slovensko Konservatorsko Drustvo (Association of Conservators of Slovenia), Trzaska 4, 1000 Ljubljana - T: (01) 1256079, 1255040, Fax: 1254198   41946
Slovensko Muzejsko Drustvo (Association of Museum Curators of Slovenia), Kongresni Trg 1, 1000 Ljubljana - T: (01) 4213267, Fax: 4213287   41947

South Africa

ICOM South Africa, c/o Johannesburg Art Gallery, POB 23561, Joubert Park 2044 - T: (011) 7253130, Fax: 7206000, E-mail: pdube@mj.org.za   41948
Suider-Afrikaanse Museum-Assosiasie (South African Museums Association), POB 699, Grahamstown 6140 - T: (046) 6361340, Fax: 6222962, E-mail: sama@imaginet.co.za, Internet: http://sama.museums.org.za   41949

Spain

Amigos de los Museos, La Rambla 99, 08002 Barcelona - T: 933014379   41950
Asociación Española de Archiveros, Bibliotecarios, Museólogos y Documentalistas, Calle Recoletos 5, 28001 Madrid - T: 915751727, Fax: 915751727   41951
Asociación Española de Museólogos, Av Reyes Católicos 6, 28040 Madrid - T: 915430917, Fax: 915440225, E-mail: aem@museologia.net, Internet: http://www.museologia.net   41952
Associació del Museo de la Ciència i de la Tècnica i d'Arqueologia Industrial de Catalunya, Rambla d'Egara 270, 08221 Terrassa - T: 937803787, Fax: 937806089, E-mail: associaciomct@eic.ictnet.es   41953
European Federation of Associations of Industrial and Technical Heritage, c/o Museo de la Ciència i de la Tècnica, Rambla d'Egara 270, 08221 Terrassa - T: 937803787, Fax: 937806089, E-mail: associaciomct@eic.ictnet.es   41954
ICOM-CE Spain, c/o Museo Casa de la Moneda, Calle Doctor Esquerdo 36, 28071 Madrid - T: 915666646, Fax: 915666809, E-mail: info@icom-ce.org, Internet: http://www.icom-ce.org   41955
ICOM Spain, c/o Museo Casa de la Moneda, Calle Jorge Juan 106, 28071 Madrid - T: 915666533, Fax: 915666809, E-mail: museo@fnmt.es   41956
International Committee for Museology, c/o Andrea A. García Sastre, Museu Nacional d'Art de Catalunya, Parc de Montjuïc, 08038 Barcelona - T: 936220360, Fax: 936220369, E-mail: wagarcia@correu.gencat.es, Internet: http://www.umu.se/nordic.museology/icofom.html   41957
Vlaamse Vereniging voor Industriële Archeologie, Postbus 30, 9000 Gent - T: 56253373, Fax: 56255173, E-mail: vvia@conservare.be   41958

Sri Lanka

ICOM Sri Lanka, c/o Dept. of National Museums, POB 854, Colombo 7 - T: (01) 695366, Fax: 695366, E-mail: nmdep@slt.lk   41959

Swaziland

ICOM Swaziland, c/o National Museum, POB 100, Lobamba H107 - T: 61178/79, Fax: 61875, E-mail: staff@swazimus.org.sz   41960

Sweden

ICOM Sweden, c/o Riksuitställningar, Alsnög 7, 116 41 Stockholm - T: (08) 6916000, Fax: 6916020, E-mail: mats.widbom@riksutstallningar.se   41961
Skandinaisk Museumsforbund, Swedish Section, c/o Nordiska Museet, Djurgårdsvägen 6-16, 115 93 Stockholm - Fax: (08) 51954580   41962

Svenska Museiföreningen (Swedish Museums Association), Fridhemsg 68, 112 46 Stockholm - T: (08) 6533988, 6536034, Fax: 6530170, E-mail: info@museif.a.se, Internet: http://www.museif.a.se   41963
Sveriges Museimannaförbund (Swedish Association of Museum Curators), Box 760, 131 24 Nacka - T: (08) 4662400, Fax: 4662424, E-mail: dik@akademikerhuset.se   41964

Switzerland

Conseil International des Musées - Comité National Suisse, c/o L. Homberger, Gablerstr 15, 8002 Zürich - T: 012024528, Fax: 012025201, E-mail: lorenz.homberger@rietb.stzh.ch   41965
Museumsgesellschaft, Limmatquai 62, 8022 Zürich - T: 012514233   41966
Stiftung Schweizer Museumspass, Hornbachstr 50, 8034 Zürich - T: 013898456, Fax: 013898400, E-mail: wyler@aruno.com, Internet: http://www.museums.ch   41967
Verband der Museen der Schweiz, Association des Musées Suisses, c/o Schweizerisches Landesmuseum, Postfach 6789, 8032 Zürich - T: 012186588, Fax: 012186589, E-mail: contact@vms-ams.ch, Internet: http://www.vms-ams.ch   41968

Tanzania

ICOM Tanzania, c/o National Museums of Tanzania, POB 511, Dar-es-Salaam - T: (022) 2122030, Fax: 2700437, E-mail: hq@netmus.org.tz   41969

Thailand

ICOM Thailand, c/o S. Charoenpot, National Museum Division, Na Phra That Rd, Bankok 10200 - T: (02) 2211135, Fax: 2249911, E-mail: patchanet@mozart.ine.co.th   41970

Togo

ICOM Togo, c/o Musée National des Sites et Monuments, BP 12156, Lomé - T: 216807, Fax: 221839   41971

Turkey

ICOM Turkish National Committee, c/o Anitlar ve Müzeler Genel Müdürlüğü, Meclis Binasi, 06100 Ulus - T: (0312) 3104286, Fax: 3111417   41972

Ukraine

ICOM Ukraine, c/o Lviv Art Gallery, ul Stefanika 3, 79000 Lviv - T: (0322) 7223948, 2252378, Fax: 723009, 2253257   41973

United Kingdom

24 Hour Museum, The Campaign for Museums, 35-37 Grosvenor Gardens, London SW1W 0BX - T: (020) 72339796, Fax: 72336770, E-mail: cfm@24hourmuseum.org.uk, Internet: http://www.24hourmuseum.org.uk   41974
Alchemy: The Group for Collections Management in Yorkshire and Humberside, c/o Wakefield Museum, Wood St, Wakefield WF1 2EW - T: (01924) 305351   41975

Area Museums Service for South Eastern England, Ferroners House, Barbican, London EC2Y 8AA - T: (020) 76000219, Fax: 76002581 41976

Association for British Transport and Engineering Museums, c/o Science Museum, Exhibition Rd, London SW7 2DD - T: (020) 79388234 41977

Association of British Transport and Engineering Museums, 20 Linnell Rd, Rugby CV21 4AN - T: (01788) 542861 41978

Association of Independent Museums, c/o D. Lees, Bethnal Green Museum of Childhood, Cambridge Heath Rd, London E2 9PA - T: (020) 89835222, Fax: 89835207, E-mail: d.lees@vam.ac.uk, Internet: http://www.aimus.org.uk 41979

Association of Railway Preservation Societies, 3 Orchard Close, Watford WD1 3DU - T: (01923) 221280, Fax: 241023 41980

AVICOM International Committee for Autovisual and New Technologies Museums, c/o Stephen Done, Museum and Tour Centre, Anfield Rd, Liverpool L4 0TH - T: (0151) 2640160, Fax: 2639792, E-mail: done.lfcmuseum@btinernet.com 41981

British Association of Friends of Museums, The Old Post Office, High St, Butleigh, Glastonbury BA6 8SU - T: (01458) 850520, Fax: 850034, E-mail: a.heeleybafm@btinternet.com, Internet: http://www.bafm.org.uk 41982

British Aviation Preservation Council, c/o Nick Forder, Museum of Science and Industry, Liverpool Rd, Castlefield, Manchester M3 4FP - T: (0161) 8322244, Fax: 8345135, E-mail: n.forder@msim.org.uk 41983

Campaign for Museums, 35-37 Grosvenor Gardens, London SW1W 0BX - T: (020) 72339796, Fax: 72336770, E-mail: cfm@24hourmuseum.org.uk, Internet: http://www.24hourmuseum.org.uk 41984

Care of Collections Forum, c/o Falkirk Museums Service, 7-11 Abbotsinch Rd, Grangemouth FK3 9UX - T: (01324) 504689, Fax: 503771, E-mail: carol.john@which.net 41985

Council for Museums, Archives and Libraries, 16 Queen Anne's Gate, London SW1H 9AA - T: (020) 72731444, Fax: 72731404, E-mail: info@resource.gov.uk, Internet: http://www.resource.gov.uk 41986

Council of Museums in Wales, The Courtyard, Letty St, Cardiff CF24 4EL - T: (029) 20225432, Fax: 20668516, E-mail: info@cmw.org.uk, Internet: http://www.cmw.org.uk 41987

Dundee Art Galleries and Museum Association, c/o Frances Towns, 37 Ancrum Dr, Dundee, DD2 2JG - T: (01382) 668720 41988

East Midlands Museums Service, Courtyard Bldgs, Wollaton Park, Nottingham NG8 2AE - T: (0115) 9854534, Fax: 9280038, E-mail: emms@emms.org.uk, Internet: http://www.emms.org.uk 41989

English Heritage, East Midlands Region, 44 Demgate, Northampton NN1 1UH - T: (01604) 735400, Fax: 735401, Internet: http://www.english-heritage.org.uk 41990

English Heritage, North East Region, 41-44 Sandhill, Newcastle-upon-Tyne NE1 3JF - T: (0191) 2691200, Fax: 2611130, Internet: http://www.english-heritage.org.uk 41991

English Heritage North West Region, 3 Chepstow St, Manchester M1 5EW - T: (0161) 2421400, Fax: 2421401, Internet: http://www.english-heritage.org.uk 41992

European Museum Forum, POB 913, Bristol BS99 5ST - T: (0117) 9238897, Fax: 9732437, E-mail: -EuropeanMuseumForum@compuserve.com, Internet: http://www.msim.org.uk/l-connect 41993

European Museum of the Year Award, c/o European Museum Forum, POB 913, Bristol BS99 5ST - T: (0117) 9238897, Fax: (0117) 9732437, E-mail: -europeanmuseumforum@compuserve.com, Internet: http://www.msim.org.uk 41994

Federation of Museums and Art Galleries in Wales, Ceredigion Museum, Terrace Rd, Aberystwyth SY23 2AQ - T: (01970) 633088, Fax: 633084 41995

Group for Costume and Textile Staff in Museums, c/o Christine Rew, Aberdeen Art Gallery and Museums, Schoolhill, Aberdeen AB10 1FQ - T: (01224) 523702, Fax: 632133, E-mail: chrisr_aberdeen@yahoo.com 41996

Group for Directors of Museums, c/o Grosvenor Museum, 27 Grosvenor St, Chester CH1 2DD - T: (01244) 402012, Fax: 347587, E-mail: s.matthews@chestercc.gov.uk 41997

Group for Education in Museums, c/o Emma Webb, Royal Museum, Chambers St, Edinburgh EH1 1JF - T: (0131) 2257534, Fax: 2204819, E-mail: ewebb@nms.ac.uk, Internet: http://www.gem.org.uk/ 41998

ICOM Northern Ireland, c/o Ulster Museum, Robert Heslip, Botanic Gardens, Belfast BT9 5AB - T: (028) 90383015, Fax: 90383013, E-mail: robert.heslip.um@nics.gov.uk 41999

ICTOP International Committee for Personnel Training, c/o I. Newton, National Museums and Galleries, 127 Dale St, Liverpool L19 3PT - T: (0151) 4784671, Fax: 4784672 42000

Institution of Professionals, Managers & Specialists, 75-79 York Rd, London SE1 7AQ - T: (020) 79026649, Fax: 74012241, E-mail: leightonA@ipms.org.uk, Internet: http://www.ipms.org.uk 42001

International Association of Libraries and Museums of Performing Arts, c/o Claire Hudson, Theatre Museum, 1e Tavistock St, London - T: (020) 79434720, Fax: 79434777, E-mail: sibmas@geldner.net, Internet: http://www.theatrelibrary.org/sibmas/sibmas.html 42002

International Committee for Costume Museums, c/o J. Marschner, Royal Ceremonial Dress Collection, Kensington Palace, London W8 4PX - T: (020) 79379561, Fax: 73760198, E-mail: joanna.marschner@hrp.org.uk 42003

International Confederation of Architectural Museums, c/o Victoria and Albert Museum, Cromwell Rd, London SW7 2RL - T: (020) 79388500, Fax: 79388615 42004

International Council of Museums - UK National Committee, c/o Aidan Walsh, Northern Ireland Museums Council, 66 Donegall Pass, Belfast BT7 1BU - T: (028) 90550215, Fax: 90550216, E-mail: dir@nimc.co.uk 42005

Leicestershire Museums, Arts and Records Service, County Hall, Glenfield LE8 3RA - T: (0116) 2656794, Fax: 2656788, E-mail: hbroughton@leics.gov.uk, Internet: http://www.leics.gov.uk 1849 42006

London Federation of Museums and Art Galleries, Saint John's Gate, London EC1M 4DA - T: (020) 72536644, Fax: 74908835 42007

mda, Museum Documentation Association, Jupiter House, Station Rd, Cambridge CB1 2JD - T: (01223) 315760, Fax: 362521, E-mail: mda@mda.org.uk, Internet: http://www.mda.org.uk 42008

Midlands Federation of Museums and Art Galleries, Ironbridge Gorge Museum, Ironbridge, Telford TF8 7AW - T: (01952) 432751, Fax: 432237, E-mail: igmt@aol.com 42009

MPR International Committee for Museums Marketing, c/o B. Hope, National Museums and Galleries, 127 Dale St, Liverpool L69 3LA - T: (0151) 4784611, Fax: 4784777, E-mail: bhope@nmgmepp1.demon.co.uk 42010

Museum Ethnographers Group, Pitt Rivers Museum Research Centre, 64 Banbury Rd, Oxford OX2 6PN - T: (01865) 284661, Fax: 284657, E-mail: chantal.knowles@prm.ox.ac.uk 42011

Museum Professionals Group, c/o Carolyn Abel, Grange Museum of Community History, On the Neasden Roundabout, Neasden Ln, Neasden, London NW10 1QB - T: (020) 84528311, E-mail: carolyn-abel@hotmail.com 42012

Museum Trading and Publishing Group, c/o Colchester Museum Resource Centre, 14 Ryegate Rd, Colchester CO1 1YG - T: (01206) 282931, Fax: 282925 42013

Museums and Galleries Disability Association, c/o Hove Museum and Art Gallery, 19 New Church Rd, Hove BN3 4AB - T: (01273) 292828, Fax: 292827, E-mail: abigail.thomas@brighton-hove.gov.uk, Internet: http://www.magda.org.uk 42014

Museums and Galleries of Northern Ireland, Botanic Gardens, Belfast BT9 5AB - T: (028) 90383000, Fax: 90383006 42015

Museums Association, 42 Clerkenwell Close, London EC1R 0PA - T: (020) 72501837, Fax: 72501959, E-mail: info@museumsassociation.org, Internet: http://www.museumsassociation.org 42016

Museums in Essex Committee, Essex Record Office, Wharf Rd, Chelmsford CM2 6YT - T: (01245) 244612, 244613, Fax: 244655, E-mail: deborah.boden@essexcc.gov.uk 42017

Museums North, Northern Federation of Museums and Art Galleries, Sir William Gray House, Clarence Rd, Hartlepool TS24 8BT - T: (01429) 523443, Fax: 523477, E-mail: arts-museums@hartlepool.gov.uk 42018

Museums Weapons Group, Royal Armouries, Armouries Dr, Leeds LS10 1LT - T: (0113) 2201867, Fax: 2201871, E-mail: grimer@armouries.org.uk 42019

National Heritage: The Museums Action Movement, 9a North St, Clapham, London SW4 0HN - T: (020) 77206789, Fax: 79781815 42020

National Museum Directors' Conference, c/o Imperial War Museum, Lambeth Rd, London SE1 6HZ - T: (020) 74165000, E-mail: nmdc@iwm.org.uk, Internet: http://www.nationalmuseums.org.uk 42021

Network of European Museum Organisations, c/o Museum Association, 42 Clerkenwell Close, London EC1R 0PA - T: (020) 72501789, Fax: 72501929, E-mail: mark@museumsassociation.org, Internet: http://www.ne-mo.org 42022

North East Museums, House of Recovery, Bath Ln, Newcastle-upon-Tyne NE4 5SQ - T: (0191) 2221661, Fax: 2614725, E-mail: nems@nems.co.uk, Internet: http://www.northeast-museums.org 42023

North West Federation of Museums and Art Galleries, Boat Museum, South Pier Rd, Ellesmere Port CH65 4FW - T: (0151) 3555017, Fax: 3554079, Internet: http://www.nwfed.org.uk 42024

North Western Federation of Museums and Art Galleries, c/o Museum of Science and Industry in Manchester, Liverpool Rd, Castlefield, Manchester M3 4FP - T: (0161) 8322244 42025

Northern Ireland Museums Council, 66 Donegall Pass, Belfast BT7 1BU - T: (028) 90550215, Fax: 90550216, E-mail: info@nimc.co.uk, Internet: http://www.nimc.co.uk 42026

Science and Industry Collections Group, Science Museum, Exhibition Rd, London SW7 2DD - T: (020) 79424155, Fax: 79424103, E-mail: j.britton@nmsi.ac.uk, Internet: http://www.sicg.org.uk 42027

Scottish Museums Council, County House, 20-22 Torphichen St, Edinburgh EH3 8JB - T: (0131) 2297465, Fax: 2292728, E-mail: inform@scottishmuseums.org.uk, Internet: http://www.scottishmuseums.org.uk 42028

Scottish Museums Federation, c/o Alison Reid, South Lanarkshire Council, Council Offices, Almada St, Hamilton ML3 0AA - T: (01698) 455714, Fax: 454861 42029

Society of County Museum Officers, c/o Somerset Museums Service, Castle Green, Taunton TA1 4AA 42030

Society of Decorative Art Curators, c/o Decorative Art Department, National Museums and Galleries on Merseyside, 127 Dale St, Liverpool L69 3LA - T: (0151) 4784261/62, Fax: 4784693 42031

Society of Museum Archaeologists, c/o Andover Museum, 6 Church Close, Andover SP10 1DP - T: (01264) 366283, Fax: 339152, E-mail: musmda@hants.gov.uk, Internet: http://www.socmuarch.org.uk 42032

South Eastern Federation of Museums and Art Galleries, 2 Sackville St, Hayes, Bromley BR2 7JT - T: (020) 84622228, E-mail: pwboreham@ukonline.co.uk 42033

South Midlands Museums Federation, Stevenage Museum, Saint Georges Way, Stevenage SG1 1XX - T: (01438) 218883, Fax: 218882, E-mail: museum@stevenage.gov.uk 42034

South West Museums Council, Creech Castle, Bathpool TA1 2DX - T: (01823) 259696, Fax: 270933, E-mail: general@swmuseums.co.uk, Internet: http://www.swmuseums.co.uk 42035

South Western Federation of Museums and Art Galleries, c/o Stephen Bird, Pump Room, Stall St, Bath BA1 1LZ - T: (01225) 477750, Fax: 477271, E-mail: stephen_bird@bathnes.gov.uk 42036

Standing Conference on Archives and Museums, c/o Suffolk County Council, Saint Andrew House, County Hall, Ipswich IP4 1LJ - T: (01473) 584572, Fax: 584549, E-mail: heather.needham@libher.suffolk.gov.uk 42037

Touring Exhibitions Group, 29 Point Hill, Greenwich, London SE10 8QW - T: (020) 86912660, Fax: 83331987, E-mail: admin@teg-net.org.uk, Internet: http://www.teg-net.org.uk 42038

University Museums Group, c/o University of Liverpool Art Gallery, Liverpool L69 3BX - T: (0151) 7942348, Fax: 7942343, E-mail: acompton@liverpool.ac.uk 42039

Visual and Art Galleries Association, The Old School, High St, Witcham, Ely CB6 2LQ - T: (01353) 776356, Fax: 775411, E-mail: admin@vaga.co.uk, Internet: http://www.vaga.co.uk 1978 42040

Welsh Federation of Museums and Art Galleries, c/o Monmouth Museum, Priory St, Monmouth NP5 3XA - T: (01600) 3519 42041

West Midlands Regional Museums Council, Hanbury Rd, Stoke Prior, Bromsgrove B60 4AD - T: (01527) 872258, Fax: 576960, E-mail: wmrmc@wm-museums.co.uk, Internet: http://www.wm-museums.co.uk 42042

Yorkshire and Humberside Federation of Museums and Art Galleries, c/o Neil Jacques, North Lincolnshire Council, Mewson House, Station Rd, Brigg DN20 8XJ - T: (01724) 297254, Fax: 297258, E-mail: neil.jacques@northlincs.gov.uk 42043

Yorkshire Museums Council, Farnley Hall, Hall Ln, Leeds LS12 5HA - T: (0113) 2638909, Fax: 2791479, E-mail: info@yhmc.org.uk, Internet: http://www.yorkshiremuseums.org.uk 42044

Uruguay

ICOM Uruguay, Calle José Ellauri 1050, 11300 Montevideo - T: (02) 7071674, Fax: 7071674, E-mail: icomuy@usa.net 42045

U.S.A.

African American Museums Association, c/o Dr. M.Burroughs, Dusable Museum, 740 E 56th Pl, Chicago, IL 60637 - T: (312) 947-0600, Fax: (312) 947-0677, Internet: http://www.artnoir.com/aaam.html 42046

Alabama Museums Association, POB 870340, Tuscaloosa, AL 35487 - T: (205) 348-7554, Fax: (205) 348-9292, E-mail: jhall@bama.ua.edu 42047

American Association for Museum Volunteers, c/o Denver Museum of Natural History, 2001 Colorado Blvd, Denver, CO 80205 - T: (303) 370-6419, Fax: (303) 331-6492, E-mail: schristian@dmnh.org 42048

American Association for State and Local History, 1717 Church St, Nashville, TN 37203-2991 - T: (615) 320-3203, Fax: (615) 327-9013, E-mail: history@aaslh.org, Internet: http://www.aaslh.org 42049

American Association of Museums, 1575 Eye St NW, Ste 400, Washington, DC 20005 - T: (202) 289-1818, Fax: (202) 289-6578, E-mail: marketing@aam-us.org, Internet: http://www.aam-us.org 42050

American Institute for Conservation of Historic and Artistic Works, 1717 K St NW, Ste 200, Washington, DC 20006 - T: (202) 452-9545, Fax: (202) 452-9328, E-mail: info@aic-faic.org, Internet: http://www.aic.faic.org 42051

Arkansas Museums Association, c/o HRMS, Arkansas State Parks, 6900 Cantrell Rd, Ste M27, Little Rock, AR 72207 - T: (501) 663-7839, Fax: (501) 396-7054, E-mail: mkbynum@amod.org 42052

Association for Living History, Farm and Agricultural Museums, c/o Judith Sheridan, 8774 Rte 45 NW, North Bloomfield, OH 44450 - Fax: (440) 685-4410, E-mail: sheridan@orwell.net, Internet: http://www.alhfam.org 42053

Association of African American Museums, POB 427, Wilberforce, OH 45384 - T: (937) 376-4611, Fax: (937) 376-2007, E-mail: naamcc@erinet.com 42054

Association of Art Museum Directors, 41 E 65 St, New York, NY 10021 - T: (212) 249-4423, Fax: (212) 535-5039, E-mail: aamd@amn.org, Internet: http://www.aamd.org 42055

Association of Children's Museums, 1300 L St NW, Ste 975, Washington, DC 20005 - T: (202) 898-1080, Fax: (202) 898-1086, E-mail: acm@childrensmuseums.org, Internet: http://www.aym.org 42056

Association of College and University Museums and Galleries, c/o Oklahoma Museum of Natural History, 1335 Asp Av, Norman, OK 73019-0606 - T: (405) 325-1009, Fax: (405) 325-7699, E-mail: pbtirrell@ou.edu 42057

Association of Indiana Museums, POB 24428, Indianapolis, IN 46224-0428 - T: (317) 882-5649, Fax: (317) 865-7662, E-mail: wildcat@iquest.net 42058

Association of Midwest Museums, POB 11940, Saint Louis, MO 63112 - T: (314) 454-3110, Fax: (314) 454-3112, E-mail: mmcdirect2@aol.com 42059

Association of Railway Museums, c/o Pennsylvania Trolley Museum, 725 W Chestnut St, Washington, PA 15301-4623 - T: (724) 228-9256, Fax: (724) 228-9675 42060

Association of Science-Museum Directors, c/o San Diego Natural History Museum, 1788 El Prado, San Diego, CA 92101 - T: (619) 232-3821, Fax: (619) 232-0248, E-mail: mhager@sdnhm.org 42061

Association of Science-Technology Centers, 1025 Vermont Av NW, Ste 500, Washington, DC 20001-3516 - T: (202) 783-7200, Fax: (202) 783-7207, E-mail: info@astc.org, Internet: http://www.astc.org 42062

Association of South Dakota Museums, 200 W Sixth St, Sioux Falls, SD 57102 - T: (605) 367-4210, Fax: (605) 367-6004 42063

Association of Systematics Collections, 1725 K St NW, Ste 601, Washington, DC 20006 - T: (202) 835-9050, Fax: (202) 835-7334, E-mail: general@nscalliance.org, Internet: http://www.ascoll.org 42064

California Association of Museums, 2002 N Main St, Santa Ana, CA 92706 - T: (714) 567-3645, Fax: (714) 480-0053, E-mail: cam@calmuseums.org 42065

Colorado-Wyoming Association of Museums, 400 Clarendon Av, Sheridan, WY 82801 - T: (307) 674-4589, Fax: (307) 672-1720, E-mail: admin@cwamit.org, Internet: http://www.cwamit.org 42066

Connecticut Museum Association, POB 78, Roxbury, CT 06783 - T: (860) 354-3543 42067

Council for Museum Anthropology, Exthology, University of Arizona, Tucson, AZ 85721 - T: (520) 621-6281, Fax: (520) 621-2976, E-mail: parezo@u.arizona.edu 42068

Council of American Jewish Museums, 12 Eldridge St, New York, NY 10002 - T: (212) 219-0903, Fax: (212) 966-4782, E-mail: aemsy@aol.com
42069

Council of American Maritime Museums, POB 636, Saint Michaels, MD 21663 - T: (410) 745-2916, Fax: (410) 745-6088, E-mail: jvalliant@cbmm.org
42070

Florida Art Museum Directors Association, 1990 Sand Dollar Ln, Vero Beach, FL 32963 - T: (561) 388-2428, Fax: (561) 388-9313, E-mail: fmda@steds.org
42071

Florida Association of Museums, POB 10951, Tallahassee, FL 32302-2951 - T: (850) 222-6028, Fax: (850) 222-6112, E-mail: Fam@Flamuseums.org
42072

Georgia Association of Museums and Galleries, c/o Fernbank Science Center, 156 Heaton Park Dr, Atlanta, GA 30307 - T: (404) 378-4311, Fax: (404) 370-1336, E-mail: david.dundee@fernbank.edu
42073

Hawaii Museums Association, POB 4125, Honolulu, HI 96812-4125 - T: (808) 254-4292, Fax: (808) 254-4153, E-mail: dpope@lava.net
42074

ICMS International Committee for Museums Security, c/o W. Faulk, Getty Conservation Institute, 1200 Getty Center Dr, Str 700, Los Angeles, CA 90049-1684 - T: (310) 440-6547, Fax: (310) 440-6979, E-mail: wfaulk@getty.edu
42075

ICOM United States of America, 1700 Soscol Av, Napa, CA 94559 - T: (707) 257-3603, Fax: (707) 257-8601, E-mail: ploar@theamericancenter.org
42076

Idaho Association of Museums, c/o Idaho State Historical Museum, 7111 McMullen Rd, Boise, ID 83709 - T: (208) 334-2120, Fax: (208) 334-2775
42077

Illinois Association of Museums, 1 Old State Capitol Plaza, Springfield, IL 62701-1507 - T: (217) 524-7080, Fax: (217) 785-7937, E-mail: mturner@hpa084r1.state.il.us
42078

Institute of Museum and Liberary Services, 1100 Pennsylvania Av, NW, Washington, DC 20506 - T: (202) 606-8539, E-mail: imlsinof@imls.gov, Internet: http://www.imls.gov
42079

Intermuseum Conservation Association, Allen Art Bldg, Oberlin, OH 44074 - T: (216) 775-7331
42080

International Association of Museum Facility Administrators, 11 W 53rd St, New York, NY 10019, mail addr: POB 1505, Washington, DC 20013-1505 - T: (212) 708-9413, Fax: (212) 333-1169, E-mail: vinnie-magorrian@moma.org, Internet: http://www.iamfa.org
42081

International Committee for Egyptology in ICOM - CIPEG, c/o Dr. Regine Schulz, Walters Art Museum, 600 N Charles St, Baltimore, MD 21201-5185 - T: (410) 547-9000 ext 255, Fax: (410) 752-4797, E-mail: rschulz@thewalters.org
42082

International Committee for Exhibition Exchange, c/o Anne R. Gossett, Smithsonian Institution, 1100 Jefferson Dr SW, Ste 705, Washington, DC 20560 - T: (202) 633-9220, Fax: (202) 786-2777, E-mail: argossett@intg.si.edu, Internet: http://www.exhibitionsonline.org/icee
42083

International Committee for Glass Museums, c/o Dr. J.A. Page, Corning Museum of Glass, 1 Glass Centere, Corning, NY 14830-2253 - T: (607) 974-8312, Fax: (607) 974-8473, E-mail: pageja@cmog.org
42084

International Congress of Maritime Museums, c/o Stuart Pames, Connecticut River Museum, 67 Main St, Essex, CT 06426 - T: (860) 767-8269, Fax: (860) 767-7028, E-mail: StuPames@aol.com
42085

International Council of Museums Committee of AAM, 1575 Eye St NW, Ste 400, Washington, DC 20005 - T: (202) 289-1818, Fax: (202) 289-6578, E-mail: international@aam-us.org, Internet: http://www.aam-us.org/international
42086

International Movement for a New Museology, c/o WAN Museum, POB 1009, Zuni, NM 87327 - T: (505) 782-4403, Fax: (505) 782-2700, E-mail: aamhc@zuni.k12.nm.us
42087

International Museum Theatre Alliance, c/o Museum of Science, Science Park, Boston, MA 02114 - T: (617) 589-0449, Fax: (617) 589-0454, E-mail: imtal@mos.org, Internet: http://www.mos.org/imtal
42088

Iowa Museum Association, 3219 Hudson Rd, Cedar Falls, IA 50614-0199 - T: (319) 273-2188, Fax: (319) 273-6924, E-mail: suegrosbol@uni.edu
42089

Kansas Museums Association, 6425 SW 6th Av, Topeka, KS 66615-1099 - T: (785) 272-8681, Fax: (785) 272-8682, E-mail: starr@kshs.org
42090

Kentucky Association of Museums, POB 9, Murray, KY 42071-0009 - T: (270) 762-3052, Fax: (270) 762-3920
42091

Louisiana Association of Museums, 1609 Moreland Av, Baton Rouge, LA 70808-1173 - T: (225) 383-6800, Fax: (225) 383-6880
42092

Maine Association of Museums, 37 Community Dr, Augusta, ME 04330 - T: (207) 623-8428, Fax: (207) 626-5949
42093

Maryland Association of History Museums, POB 56, Annapolis, MD 21404-1806
42094

Michigan Museums Association, POB 10067, Lansing, MI 48901-0067 - T: (517) 482-4055, Fax: (517) 482-7997, E-mail: ashby.ann@acd.net
42095

Mid-Atlantic Association of Museums, POB 817, Newark, DE 19715-0817 - T: (302) 731-1424, Fax: (302) 731-1432
42096

Minnesota Association of Museums, POB 14825, Minneapolis, MN 55414-0825 - T: (612) 624-0089, Fax: (612) 626-7704, E-mail: davis136@tc.umn.edu
42097

Mississippi Museums Association, 640 S Canal St, Box E, Natchez, MS 39120 - T: (601) 446-6502, Fax: (601) 446-6503
42098

Missouri Museums Association, 3218 Gladstone Blvd, Kansas City, MO 64123-1199 - T: (816) 483-8300
42099

Montana Association of Museums, Rte 1, Box 1206A, Hardin, MT 59034
42100

Mountain-Plains Museums Association, POB 8321, Durango, CO 81301-0203 - T: (970) 259-7866, Fax: (979) 259-7867, E-mail: mpma@frontier.net
42101

Museum Association of Arizona, POB 63902, Phoenix, AZ 85082-3902 - T: (602) 966-9680, E-mail: ann.alger@asu.edu
42102

Museum Association of Montana, c/o Glacier National Park, West Glacier, MT 59936 - T: (406) 888-7936, Fax: (406) 888-7808
42103

Museum Association of New York, 189 Second St, Troy, NY 12180 - T: (518) 273-3400, Fax: (518) 273-3416
42104

Museum Computer Network, 1550 S Coast Hwy, Ste 201, Laguna Beach, CA 92651 - T: (877) 626-3800, Fax: (949) 376-3456, Internet: http://www.mcn.edu
42105

Museum Education Roundtable, 621 Pennsylvania Av SE, Washington, DC 20003 - T: (202) 547-8378, Fax: (202) 547-8344, E-mail: merorg@msn.com, Internet: http://www.mer-online.org
42106

Museum Trustee Association, 2100 19th St NW, Ste 300, Washington, DC 20036 - T: (202) 857-1180, Fax: (202) 857-1111, E-mail: amanda_ohlke@dc.sba.com
42107

Museums Alaska, POB 242323, Anchorage, AK 99524 - T: (907) 243-4714, Fax: (907) 243-4714, E-mail: matthews@alaska.net
42108

Nebraska Museums Association, 208 16th St, Aurura, NE 68818-3009 - T: (402) 694-4032, Fax: (402) 694-4035
42109

New England Museum Association, c/o Boston National Historic Park, Charlestown Navy Yard, Boston, MA 02129 - T: (617) 242-2283, Fax: (617) 241-5794
42110

New Jersey Association Museums, POB 877, Newark, NJ 07101-0877 - T: (888) 356-6526, Fax: (973) 748-6607
42111

New Mexico Association of Museums, POB 5800, Albuquerque, NM 87185-1490 - T: (505) 284-3232, Fax: (505) 284-3244, E-mail: jkwalth@sandia.gov
42112

North Carolina Museums Council, POB 2603, Raleigh, NC 27602 - T: (336) 767-6730, Fax: (336) 661-1777
42113

Northeast Mississippi Museums Association, POB 993, Corinth, MS 38835 - T: (662) 287-3120, E-mail: nemma@tsixrhodes.com
42114

Northeast Texas Museums Association, POB 8290, Marshall, TX 75671 - T: (903) 935-9480, Fax: (903) 935-1975, E-mail: tam@io.com
42115

Northern California Association of Museums, California State University, CA 95929 - T: (916) 898-5861, Fax: (916) 898-6824, E-mail: Kjohnson@savax.csuchico.edu
42116

Ohio Museums Association, 567 E Hudson St, Columbus, OH 43211 - T: (614) 298-2030, Fax: (614) 298-2068, E-mail: ohmuseassn@juno.com
42117

Oklahoma Museums Association, 2100 NE 52nd St, Oklahoma City, OK 73111 - T: (405) 424-7757, Fax: (405) 424-1407, E-mail: oma@ionet.net
42118

Oregon Museums Association, POB 1718, Portland, OR 97207 - T: (503) 823-3623, Fax: (503) 823-3619, E-mail: pkdanc@ci.portland.or.us
42119

Pennsylvania Federation of Museums and Historical Organizations, POB 1026, Harrisburg, PA 17108-1026 - T: (717) 787-3253, Fax: (717) 772-4698, E-mail: phmc.state.pa.us
42120

Rhode Island Museum Network, 58 Walcott St, Pawtucket, RI 02860
42121

Small Museums Association, POB 1425, Clinton, MD 20735 - Internet: http://www.smallmuseum.org
42122

South Carolina Federation of Museums, POB 100107, Columbia, SC 29202 - T: (803) 898-4925, Fax: (803) 898-4969, E-mail: scfm@museum.state.sc.us
42123

Southeastern Museums Conference, POB 3494, Baton Rouge, LA 70821 - T: (225) 383-5042, Fax: (225) 343-8669, E-mail: SEMCdirect@aol.com
42124

Tennessee Association of Museums, 200 Hyder Hill, Piney Flats, TN 37686 - T: (615) 538-7396
42125

Texas Association of Museums, 3939 Bee Caves Rd, Bldg A, Ste 1-B, Austin, TX 78746 - T: (512) 328-6812, Fax: (512) 327-9775, E-mail: tam@io.com
42126

Utah Museums Association, POB 2077, Salt Lake City, UT 84110-2077 - T: (801) 799-1414, Fax: (801) 797-3423, E-mail: Lpier@cc.usu.edu
42127

Vermont Museum and Gallery Alliance, POB 489, Woodstock, VT 05091 - T: (802) 457-2671
42128

Virginia Association of Museums, 2800 Grove Av, Richmond, VA 23221 - T: (804) 649-8261, Fax: (804) 649-8262, E-mail: vam@rmond.mindspring.com
42129

Volunteer Committees of Art Museum, One Collins Diboll Circle, New Orleans, LA 70179, mail addr: c/o New Orleans Museum of Art, POB 19123, New Orleans, LA 70179-0123 - T: (504) 737-6301, Fax: (504) 738-5103
42130

Washington Museum Association, POB 5817, Factoria Station, Bellevue, WA 98006 - T: (360) 466-3365, Fax: (360) 466-1611, E-mail: wma@harbornet.com
42131

Western Museums Association, POB 13314-578, Oakland, CA 94661 - T: (510) 428-1380, Fax: (510) 655-2015, E-mail: director@westmuse.org
42132

Wisconsin Federation of Museums, 700 N 12th St, Wausau, WI 54403 - T: (715) 845-7010, Fax: (715) 845-7103
42133

Uzbekistan

ICOM Uzbekistan, c/o Museum of the History of Termurids, Amir Temur ul 1, 700000 Taškent - T: (071) 21320211, E-mail: unesco@natcom.org.uz
42134

Venezuela

ICOM Venezuela, c/o Institut for Cultural Heritage, Apdo 17376, Caracas 1014-A - T: (0212) 4831272, Fax: 4831272, E-mail: mtoledo@reacciun.ve
42135

Yugoslavia

Društvo muzejskih radnika Vojvodine, Dunavska 35, 21000 Novi Sad - T: 26766
42136

Jugoslovenski Nacionalni Komitet - ICOM-YU, c/o Muzej Nauke i Tehnike, Knez Mihailova 35, 11000 Beograd - Fax: (011) 187360, 3281479, E-mail: iqm@eunet.yu
42137

Muzejsko Društvo SR Crne Gore - Cetinje, Muzeji Cetinje, 81250 Cetinje - T: 22046
42138

Muzejsko Društvo Srbije, c/o Narodni Muzej, Trg Republike 1, 11000 Beograd - T: (050) 624322
42139

Zambia

ICOM Zambia, c/o Livingstone Museum, POB 60498, Livingstone - T: (03) 324427/28, Fax: 324509, E-mail: livmus@zamnet.zm
42140

Zimbabwe

ICOM Zimbabwe, c/o National History Museum, POB 240, Bulawayo - T: (09) 60045, 60046, Fax: 64019, E-mail: natmuse@telcontet.co.zw
42141

National Museums and Monuments of Zimbabwe, 107 Rotten Row, Harare, mail addr: POB CY 1485, Harare - T: (04) 752876, Fax: 753-085, E-mail: natmus@utande.co.zw, Internet: http://www.zimheritage.co.zw
42142

Southern African Development Community Association of Museums and Monuments, c/o National Museums and Monuments of Zimbabwe, POB CY 1485, Harare - T: (04) 752876, Fax: 753-085, E-mail: natmus@baobab.cszim.co.zw
42143

Alphabetical
Index to Museums

Galerie d'Art Stewart Hall, Pointe-Claire 05614
Galerie de Carbonnier, Castillonnès 09901
Galerie de Catalans Illustres, Barcelona 28782
Galerie de Lange, Emmen 25015
Galerie de l'École d'Art, Marseille 11637
Galerie de l'École Nationale des Beaux-Arts, Nancy 12018
Galerie de l'École Régionale des Beaux-Arts, Nantes 12032
Galerie de l'Office du Tourisme, Cahors 09810
Galerie de l'UQAM, Québec 05667
Galerie de Minéralogie, Paris 12293
Galerie de Paléobotanique, Paris 12294
Galerie de Paléontologie, Paris 12295
Galerie der Begegnung, Linz 02223
Galerie der Bezirksbibliothek Rheinhausen, Duisburg 15463
Galerie der Freien Akademie Feldkirchen, Feldkirchen in Kärnten 01824
Galerie der Hochschule für Graphik und Buchkunst, Leipzig 17033
Galerie der JENOPTIK AG, Jena 16597
Galerie der Marktgemeinde Sankt Johann in Tirol, Sankt Johann in Tirol 02554
Galerie der Mitte, Linz 02224
Galerie der Sammlung Berthold-Sames, Oberaudorf 17767
Galerie der Stadt, Bad Wimpfen 14540
Galerie der Stadt Backnang, Backnang 14373
Galerie der Stadt Fellbach, Fellbach 15692
Galerie der Stadt Plochingen, Plochingen 17997
Galerie der Stadt Remscheid, Remscheid 18136
Galerie der Stadt Salzburg im Mirabellgarten, Salzburg 02517
Galerie der Stadt Schwaz, Schwaz 02623
Galerie der Stadt Sindelfingen, Sindelfingen 18502
Galerie der Stadt Stuttgart, Stuttgart 18628
Galerie der Stadt Traun, Traun 02707
Galerie der Stadt Tuttlingen, Tuttlingen 18768
Galerie der Stadt Vöcklabruck, Vöcklabruck 02737
Galerie der Stadt Waiblingen Kameralamt, Waiblingen 18877
Galerie der Stadt Wels, Wels 02782
Galerie der Stadt Wendlingen am Neckar, Wendlingen am Neckar 19042
Galerie des Beaux-Arts, Bordeaux 09628
Galerie des Bildungshauses Sodalitas, Tainach 02682
Galerie des Estampes, Rouen 12832
Galerie des Jenaer Kunstvereins, Jena 16598
Galerie des Kultur- und Festspielhauses Wittenberge, Wittenberge 19148
Galerie des Kunstvereins Neustadt an der Weinstraße, Neustadt an der Weinstraße 17676
Galerie des Landkreises Rügen, Putbus 18029
Galerie des Peintres, Jupille-sur-Meuse 03501
Galerie des Polnischen Instituts Düsseldorf, Düsseldorf 15439
Galerie des Sculptures, Beauport 04523
Galerie des Transports, Marseille 11638
Galerie d'Exposition d'Art et d'Histoire, Villaries 13970
Galerie d'Exposition de la Direction des Musées, Rabat 24561
Galerie d'Exposition sur la Bourse, Paris 12296
Galerie Dominion, Montréal 05367
Galerie Dorée du Comte de Toulouse, Paris 12297
Galerie du Bastion, Antibes 09200
Galerie du Château, Nice 12092
Galerie du Conseil Général du Bas-Rhin, Strasbourg 13593
Galerie du Musée Montebello, Trouville-sur-Mer 13785
Galerie du Panthéon Bouddhique du Japon et de la Chine, Paris 12298
Galerie Elizabeth LeFort, Cheticamp 04704
Galerie Felixe Jeneweina, Kutná Hora 07418
Galerie Fernand Léger, Ivry-sur-Seine 10867
Galerie Freihausgasse, Villach 02729
Galerie für Zeitgenössische Kunst Leipzig, Leipzig 17034
Galerie Georges-Goguen, Moncton 05341
Galerie Gersag Emmen, Emmenbrücke 30746
Galerie Gmünd, Gmünd, Kärnten 01881
Galerie Goethe 53, München 17469
Galerie Grünstraße, Berlin 14714
Galerie Günther Frey, Radenthein 02458
Galerie Handwerk, München 17470
Galerie Haus 23, Cottbus 15227
Galerie Haus Dacheröden, Erfurt 15604
Galerie Hausruck, Altenhof am Hausruck 01661
Galerie Hinter dem Rathaus, Wismar 19142
Galerie Hlavního Města Prahy, Praha 07559
Galerie im 44er Haus, Leonding 02205
Galerie im Adalbert Stifter-Haus, Linz 02225
Galerie im Alten Rathaus, Prien 18024
Galerie im Amtshaus, Bad Wurzach 14551
Galerie im Bildhauerhaus und Skulpturenwanderweg, Einöde 01790
Galerie im Bürger- und Gemeindezentrum Hofstetten-Grünau, Hofstetten, Pielach 02033
Galerie im Bürgerhaus, Gröbenzell 16094
Galerie im Bürgerhaus, Haigerloch 16174
Galerie im Bürgerhaus, Neunkirchen, Saar 17656
Galerie im Bürgerspital, Drosendorf an der Thaya 01766
Galerie im Cranach-Haus, Lutherstadt Wittenberg 17204
Galerie im Einstein, Berlin 14715
Galerie im Ermelerspeicher, Schwedt 18429
Galerie im Fontanehaus, Berlin 14716
Galerie im Franck-Haus, Marktheidenfeld 17275
Galerie im Gemeinschaftshaus, Berlin 14717
Galerie im Hörsaalbau, Leipzig 17035
Galerie im Kehrwiederturm, Hildesheim 16424
Galerie im Körnerpark, Berlin 14718
Galerie im Körnerpark, Berlin 14719
Galerie im Kreishaus, Wetzlar 19080
Galerie im Kulturhaus Spandau, Berlin 14720
Galerie im Malzhaus, Plauen 17990
Galerie im Nachtwächterhaus, Poysdorf 02424
Galerie im Parkhaus, Berlin 14721
Galerie im Prediger, Schwäbisch Gmünd 18404
Galerie im Rathaus Köpenick, Berlin 14722
Galerie im Schloß Porcia, Spittal an der Drau 02644
Galerie im Stadtturm, Gmünd, Kärnten 01882
Galerie im Taxispalais, Innsbruck 02058
Galerie im Teisenhoferhof der Malschule Motiv Wachau, Weißenkirchen in der Wachau 02773
Galerie im Theater am Saumarkt, Feldkirch 01819
Galerie im Traklhaus, Salzburg 02518
Galerie im Troadkasten, Pram 02428
Galerie im Turm, Berlin 14723
Galerie im Volkspark, Halle, Saale 16187
Galerie im Willy-Brandt-Haus, Berlin 14724
Galerie in der Alten Schule, Berlin 14725
Galerie in der Hauptschule, Ulrichsberg 02722
Galerie Inkatt, Bremen 15055
Galerie Jamborův Dům, Tišnov 07664
Galerie K & S, Berlin 14726
Galerie Křižovníků, Praha 07560
Galerie Kulturzentrum Lerchhaus, Eibiswald 01788
Galerie Kunst der Gegenwart, Salzburg 02519
Galerie Kunsthoken der Stadt Quedlinburg, Quedlinburg 18033
Galerie Kunstlade, Zittau 19282
Galerie Lapidaire du Palais, Liège 03539
Galerie L'Aquarium, Valenciennes 13841
Galerie Le Carré, Bayonne 09451
Galerie l'Industrielle-Alliance, Montréal 05368
Galerie Loisel Grafik, Pörtschach am Wörther See 02417
Galerie Ludvika Kuby, Březnice 07250
Galerie M, Berlin 14727
Galerie Malovaný Dům, Třebíč 07669
Galerie Marktschlößchen, Halle, Saale 16188
Galerie Města Blanska, Blansko 07239
Galerie Montcalm, Outaouais 05065
Galerie Münsterland, Emsdetten 15571
Galerie Municipale au Palais Montcalm, Québec 05668
Galerie Municipale Dada-Cave, Esch-sur-Alzette 24217
Galerie Municipale d'Art Contemporain Julio-Gonzalez, Arcueil 09227
Galerie Municipale du Château d'Eau, Toulouse 13722
Galerie Municipale Renoir, Nice 12093
Galerie-Musée de l'Auberge Champenoise, Moussy 11973
Galerie-Musée Le Petit Chapitre, Fosses-la Ville 03387
Galerie Muzeum w Cieszynie, Cieszyn 26675
Galerie N, Dahn 15255
Galerie Nationale de la Tapisserie et de l'Art Textile, Beauvais 09483
Galerie Nationale du Jeu de Paume, Paris 12299
Galerie Palais Walderdorff, Trier 18740
Galerie Palette Röderhaus, Wuppertal 19238
Galerie Parterre, Berlin 14728
Galerie Permanente, Bon-Secours 03185
Galerie Peters-Barenbrock im Haus Elisabeth von Eicken, Ostseebad Ahrenshoop 17893
Galerie Port-Maurice, Saint-Léonard 05834
Galerie Portyč, Písek 07523
Galerie Profil, Cham 15187
Galerie-Rotunde, Bonn 14979
Galerie Rudolfinum, Praha 07561
Galerie Sala Terrena, Mödling 02298
Galerie Sans Nom, Moncton 05342
Galerie Schloß Lamberg, Steyr 02657
Galerie Schloß Rimsingen, Breisach am Rhein 15045
Galerie Skell, Schmiedeberg, Osterzgebirge 18362
Galerie Spitalgasse, Weiden, Oberpfalz 18953
Galerie Stephanie Hollenstein, Lustenau 02249
Galerie Stift Eberndorf, Eberndorf 01776
Galerie Taisei, Tokyo 23599
Galerie Talstrasse, Halle, Saale 16189
Galerie Taurine, Nîmes 12119
Galerie Torhaus Rombergpark, Dortmund 15380
Galerie Umění, Ostrov nad Ohří 07514
Galerie Umění Karlovy Vary, Karlovy Vary 07383
Galerie und Weinmuseum Schloß Gamlitz, Gamlitz 01856
Galerie Výtvarného Umění, Havlíčkův Brod 07330
Galerie Výtvarného Umění, Hodonín 07336
Galerie Výtvarného Umění, Náchod 07474
Galerie Výtvarného Umění, Ostrava 07508
Galerie Výtvarného Umění, Roudnice nad Labem 07622
Galerie Výtvarného Umění Litoměřice, Litoměřice 07438
Galerie Weberhaus, Weiz 02780
Galerie zum alten Ötztal, Oetz 02369
Galeries Nationales du Grand Palais, Paris 12300
Galerieverein Leonberg e.V., Leonberg, Württemberg 17083
Galerija Antuna Augustinčića, Klanjec 07003
Galerija Božidar Jakac, Kostanjevica na Krki 28335
Galerija Fresaka, Beograd 41507
Galerija Hlebine-Muzejska Zbirka, Hlebine 06992
Galerija Jaki, Nazarje 28371
Galerija Jerolim, Stari Grad 07078
Galerija Klovićevi Dvori, Zagreb 07101
Galerija Lazar Vozarević, Sremska Mitrovica 41626
Galerija Likovnih Samorastnikov, Trebnje 28393
Galerija Likovnih Umetnosti, Slovenj Gradec 28386
Galerija Matice Srpske, Novi Sad 41582
Galerija Mestne Hiše, Kranj 28336
Galerija Milan Konjović, Sombor 41623
Galerija Milene Pavlović Barilli, Požarevac 41604
Galerija Murska Sobota, Murska Sobota 28369
Galerija Naivnih Slikara, Kovačica 41562
Galerija Nauke i Technike Srpske Akademije Nauka i Umetnosti, Beograd 41508
Galerija Portreta Tuzla, Tuzla 03899
Galerija s Darenija Fond 13 Veka Bălgarija, Šumen 04343
Galerija Samoukih Likovnih Umetnika Svetozarevo, Svetozarevo 41633
Galerija Sebastijan, Dubrovnik 06983
Galerija Škuc, Ljubljana 28343
Galerija Slika, Motovun 07028
Galerija Slika Save Sumanovića, Sid 41618
Galerija Sopoćanska Vidjenja, Novi Pazar 41580
Galerija Srpske Akademije Nauka i Umetnosti, Beograd 41509
Galerija Umjetnina, Split 07071
Galerija Zavjetnih Slika Brodova, Dubrovnik 06984
Galerije Sivčeva Hiša, Radovljica 28380
Galesburg Civic Art Center, Galesburg 37076
Galion Historical Museum, Galion 37081
Galle National Museum, Galle 29987
Gallen-Kallela Museum, Espoo 08313
Galleria Alberoni, Piacenza 22177
Galleria Civica, Valdagno 22767
Galleria Civica Anna e Luigi Parmiggiani, Reggio Emilia 22298
Galleria Civica d'Arte Contemporanea, Suzzara 22619
Galleria Civica d'Arte Contemporanea, Termoli 22638
Galleria Civica d'Arte Moderna e Contemporanea, Sassoferrato 22546
Galleria Civica d'Arte Moderna e Contemporanea, Verona 22834
Galleria Civica d'Arte Moderna e Contemporanea di Torino, Torino 22666
Galleria Colonna, Roma 22336
Galleria Communale d'Arte Moderna, Spoleto 22600
Galleria Comunale d'Arte, Cagliari 21263
Galleria Comunale d'Arte, Prato 22258
Galleria Comunale d'Arte Moderna, Verucchio 22845
Galleria Comunale d'Arte Moderna e Contemporanea, Roma 22337
Galleria Comunale d'Arte Risorgimento, Imola 21738
Galleria Comunale S. Croce, Cattolica 21369
Galleria Corsini, Firenze 21590
Galleria d'Arte Contemporanea, Ascoli Piceno 21098
Galleria d'Arte Contemporanea, Assisi 21106
Galleria d'Arte dell'Opera Bevilacqua la Masa, Venezia 22793
Galleria d'Arte Moderna, Firenze 21591
Galleria d'Arte Moderna, Santhià 22529
Galleria d'Arte Moderna, Udine 22752
Galleria d'Arte Moderna Arnoldo Bonzagni, Cento 21378
Galleria d'Arte Moderna Carlo Rizzarda, Feltre 21540
Galleria d'Arte Moderna di Bologna, Bologna 21186
Galleria d'Arte Moderna e Contemporanea, Bagheria 21125
Galleria d'Arte Moderna e Contemporanea, Bergamo 21155
Galleria d'Arte Moderna Moretti, Civitanova Alta 21441
Galleria d'Arte Moderna Ricci-Oddi, Piacenza 22178
Galleria d'Arte Rocca Sforzesca, Imola 21739
Galleria d'Arte Sacra dei Contemporanei, Milano 21903
Galleria degli Arazzi, Città del Vaticano 41394
Galleria degli ex Voto del Santuario, Livorno 21791
Galleria degli Uffizi, Firenze 21592
Galleria del Costume, Firenze 21593
Galleria dell'Accademia, Firenze 21594
Galleria dell'Accademia Albertina di Belle Arti, Torino 22667
Galleria dell'Accademia di Belle Arti, Napoli 22010
Galleria dell'Accademia di Belle Arti Tadini, Lovere 21807
Galleria dell'Accademia Nazionale di San Luca, Roma 22338
Galleria dello Spedale degli Innocenti, Firenze 21595
Galleria di Palazzo Bianco, Genova 21683
Galleria di Palazzo degli Alberti, Prato 22259
Galleria di Palazzo Reale, Genova 21684
Galleria di Palazzo Rosso, Genova 21685
Galleria di Palazzo Torriglia, Chiavari 21405
Galleria Doria Pamphilj, Roma 22339
Galleria e Mostra del Presepe nel Mondo, Santuario di Montevergine 22530
Galleria Estense, Modena 21940
Galleria Giorgio Franchetti alla Ca' d'Oro, Venezia 22794
Galleria Municipale, Francavilla al Mare 21653
Galleria Nazionale, Parma 22126
Galleria Nazionale d'Arte Antica, Trieste 22740
Galleria Nazionale d'Arte Antica Palazzo Barberini, Roma 22340
Galleria Nazionale d'Arte Antica Palazzo Corsini, Roma 22341
Galleria Nazionale d'Arte Moderna-Arte Contemporanea, Roma 22342
Galleria Nazionale delle Marche, Urbino 22761
Galleria Nazionale dell'Umbria, Perugia 22153
Galleria Nazionale di Arte Moderna e Contemporanea, San Marino 28147
Galleria Nazionale di Palazzo Spinola, Genova 21686
Galleria Palatina, Firenze 21596
Galleria Pallavicini, Roma 22343
Galleria Regionale d'Arte Contemporanea L. Spazzapan, Gradisca d'Isonzo 21715
Galleria Regionale della Sicilia, Palermo 22105
Galleria Regionale di Palazzo Bellomo, Siracusa 22587
Galleria Rinaldo Carnielo, Firenze 21597
Galleria Sabauda, Torino 22668
Galleria Spada, Roma 22344
Galleria Storica del Lloyd Triestino, Trieste 22741
Gallerie dell'Accademia, Venezia 22795
The Galleries, Woking 34865
Galleries of Justice, Nottingham 34094
The Gallery, Gateshead 33055
The Gallery, Luton 33845
The Gallery, Mississauga 05335
The Gallery, Trenton 40720
Gallery 101, Ottawa 05544
Gallery 101, River Falls 39788
Gallery 13 Centuries Bulgaria, Šumen 04343
Gallery 181, Ames 35077
Gallery 2, Chicago 36018
Gallery 210, Saint Louis 39964
Gallery 44, Toronto 06054
Gallery '76, Wenatchee 41090
Gallery 825, Los Angeles 38143
Gallery Abarth, Yamanakako 23756
Gallery Arcturus, Toronto 06055
Gallery at the American Bible Society, New York 38873
The Gallery at UTA, Arlington 35152
Gallery Connexion, Fredericton 04922
Gallery II, Bradford 32352
Gallery II, Kalamazoo 37716
Gallery I.I.I., Winnipeg 06299
Gallery Lambton, Sarnia 05862
Gallery North, Setauket 40315
Gallery of Antonín Chittussi, Ronov nad Doubravou 07621
Gallery of Art, Cedar Falls 35877
Gallery of Art, Dickinson 36523
Gallery of Art, Overland Park 39220
Gallery of British Columbia Ceramics, Vancouver 06151
Gallery of Contemporary Art, Colorado Springs 36183
Gallery of Costume, Manchester 33885
Gallery of Dupont Hall, Lexington 38029
Gallery of Fine and Performing Arts, Fort Myers 36940
Gallery of Fine Arts, Split 07071
Gallery of Fine Arts Litoměřice, Litoměřice 07438
Gallery of Horyu-ji Treasures, Tokyo 23600
Gallery of Local Art, Novi Sad 41588
Gallery of Modern Art, Glasgow 33075
Gallery of Modern Art, Zagreb 07114
Gallery of Modern Greek Art of Kalamata, Kalamata 19481
Gallery of Murska Sobota, Murska Sobota 28369
Gallery of Naive Art, Kovačica 41562
Gallery of Naive Art, Zlatar 07128
Gallery of Plastic Arts, Stará Lubovňa 28301
Gallery of Prehistoric Paintings, New York 38874
Gallery of Sailor's Votive Paintings, Dubrovnik 06984
Gallery of Šariš, Prešov 28285
Gallery of Science and Technique of the Serbian Academy of Sciences and Arts, Beograd 41508
Gallery of Szombathely, Szombathely 20052
Gallery of the Department of Art, Portales 39553
Gallery of the Department of Art and Art History, Lincoln 38050
Gallery of the Knights of the Cross, Praha 07560
Gallery of the Municipality of Patras, Patrai 19609
Gallery of the Royal Scottish Academy, Edinburgh 32917
Gallery of the Saidye Bronfman Centre for the Arts, Montréal 05369
Gallery of the Serbian Academy of Sciences and Arts, Beograd 41509
Gallery of the Society for Epirot Studies, Ioannina 19466
Gallery of the Society for Macedonian Studies, Thessaloniki 19674
Gallery of Traditional Japanese Toys, Takayama 23558
Gallery of Traditional Ornamental Art, Minsk 03075
Gallery of Visual Arts, Missoula 38550
Gallery Oldham, Oldham 34115
Gallery on the Roof, Regina 05702
Gallery One One One, Winnipeg 06300
Gallery Stratford, Stratford 05970
Gallier House, New Orleans 38812
Gallo-Romeins Museum, Tongeren 03764
Gallo-Romeins Museum, Velzeke-Ruddershove 03790
Galloway Deer Museum, Clatteringshaws 32632
Galloway House and Village, Fond du Lac 36868
Galloway Station Museum, Edson 04861
Galtebosamlingen, Spydeberg 26315
Galveston Arts Center, Galveston 37086
Galveston County Historical Museum, Galveston 37087
Galway Arts Centre, Galway 20774
Galway City Museum, Galway 20777
Galway City Museum, Galway 20775
Gambia National Museum, Banjul 14143

745

Alphabetical Index: Mabe

Livingstone and Stanley Memorial, Tabora 31529
Livingstone Museum, Livingstone 41650
Livonijas Ordeņa Pils Tornis, Tukums 24117
Livrustkammaren, Stockholm 30358
Lixnaw Agricultural Museum, Lixnaw 20807
Lizauli Cultural Village, Lizauli 24615
Lizzadro Museum of Lapidary Art, Elmhurst 36704
Ljungbergmuseet, Ljungby 30197
Ljungby Gamla Torg Hembygdsmuseum, Ljungby 30198
Ljusdalsbygdens Museum, Ljusdal 30199
LKAB Gruvmuseum, Kiruna 30166
Lladro Museum, New York 38892
Llanberis Lake Railway, Llanberis 33551
Llancaiach Fawr Living History Museum, Nelson 34002
Llandudno Museum and Art Gallery, Llandudno 33556
Llangollen Motor Museum, Llangollen 33568
Llanidloes Museum, Llanidloes 33570
Llanyrafon Farm, Cwmbran 32730
Llechwedd Slate Caverns, Blaenau Ffestiniog 32298
La Llonja, Palma de Mallorca 29468
Lloyd George Museum and Highgate, Llanystumdwy 33572
Lloyd's Nelson Collection, London 33693
Llywernog Silver-Lead Mine Museum, Ponterwyd 34205
L.N. Tolstoy Country Estate Museum, Moskva 27915
L.N. Tolstoy State Museum, Moskva 27826
L.N. Tolstoy State Museum, Moskva 27827
Lobaumuseum, Wien 02899
Lobdengau-Museum, Ladenburg 16926
Lobkovicky Palác, Praha 07570
Lobkovicz Palace, Praha 07570
Local and Maritime Museum, Newhaven 34038
Local Antiquities Museum, Chitradurga 20192
Local History Collection, Aberfoyle Park 00687
Local History Museum, Buzsák 19867
Local History Museum, Krivoj Rog 31915
Local History Museum, Mezőkövesd 19941
Local History Museum in Pöytyä, Pöytyä 08785
Local History Museum of Sárkös, Decs 19874
Local Museum, Aleksinac 41499
Local Museum, Ashkelon 20862
Local Museum, Bhanpura 20163
Local Museum, Bileća 03883
Local Museum, Bileća 41532
Local Museum, Brú 20089
Local Museum, Dakovo 06979
Local Museum, Danilovgrad 41545
Local Museum, Doboj 41548
Local Museum, Höfn 20098
Local Museum, Jalta 31905
Local Museum, Jaša Tomić 41555
Local Museum, Kibbutz Ma'abarot 20955
Local Museum, Kibbutz Sasa 20959
Local Museum, Našice 07029
Local Museum, Nikšić 41576
Local Museum, Ogulin 07035
Local Museum, Otočac 07040
Local Museum, Pljevlja 41598
Local Museum, Považská Bystrica 28284
Local Museum, Prijedor 03890
Local Museum, Ruma 41615
Local Museum, Skiptvet 26300
Local Museum, Staročerkassk 28091
Local Museum, Stykkishólmur 20126
Local Museum, Travnik 03897
Local Museum, Trebinje 41636
Local Museum, Ulcinj 41638
Local Museum, Visoko 03902
Local Museum L. Štúra, Uhrovec 28314
Local Museum of Beit Shean, Beit Shean 20869
Local Museum of History and Culture, Lugansk 31929
Local Museum of Perniö, Perniö 08769
Local Museum Ozalj, Ozalj 07041
Local Museum Poreč, Poreč 07043
Local Museum Zemun, Zemun 41645
Local Studies Collection, Marrickville 01201
Localbahnmuseum, Innsbruck 02065
Localbahnmuseum Bayerisch Eisenstein, Bayerisch Eisenstein 14606
Loch Ness 2000 Exhibition, Drumnadrochit 32814
Lochwinnoch Community Museum, Lochwinnoch 33574
Lock Museum of America, Terryville 40665
Lockehaven Schoolhouse Museum, Enfield 36723
Lockerbie Street Home of James Whitcomb Riley, Indianapolis 37599
Locke's Distillery Museum, Kilbeggan 20783
Lockhouse-Friends of the Delaware Canal, New Hope 38795
Lockport Gallery, Lockport 38096
Lockwood-Mathews Mansion Museum, Norwalk 39064
Locust Grove, Louisville 38192
Łódź Archidiocesan Museum, Łódź 26891
Lödöse Museum, Lödöse 30201
Löfstad Slott, Norrköping 30252
Löhe-Zeit-Museum, Neuendettelsau 17629
Lönnströmin Taidemuseo, Rauma 08827
Lötschentaler Museum, Kippel 30891
Lövångers Sockenmuseum, Lövånger 30202
Löwen-Drogerie und Museum, Oelsnitz, Vogtland 17824
Lofotmuseet, Kabelvåg 26130
Log Cabin Museum, Murray Harbour 05416
Log Cabin Village, Fort Worth 36986
The Log Farm, Nepean 05437
Logan Art Gallery, Logan 01172
Logan County Museum, Paris 39273
Logan Museum of Anthropology, Beloit 35432
Lohgerber-, Stadt- und Kreismuseum, Dippoldiswalde 15342
Lohilammen Museo, Sammatti 08862
Lohjan Museo, Lohja 08634
Lohrbacher Heimatstuben, Mosbach, Baden 17418
Lohtajan Kotiseutumuseo, Lohtaja 08636
Loimaan Kotiseutumuseo, Loimaa 08637
Lok Virsa, Islamabad 26400
Løkken Museum, Løkken 07959
Lokmuseet, Grängesberg 30108
Lokomotiefdepot Leuven, Kessel-Lo 03506
Lolland-Falsters Stiftsmuseum, Maribo 07965
Lolland-Falsters Traktor- og Motormuseum, Eskildstrup 07796
Lom Heimbygdslag, Lom 26170
Lombard Historical Museum, Lombard 38103
Lompoc Museum, Lompoc 38104
Lompoc Valley Historical Society Museum, Lompoc 38105
Lon C. Hill Home, Harlingen 37340
London Borough of Bromley Museum, Orpington 34122
London Brass Rubbing Centre, London 33694
The London Brass Rubbing Centre in Washington D.C., Gaithersburg 37070
London Canal Museum, London 33695
London Federation of Museums and Art Galleries, London 42007
London Fire Brigade Museum, London 33696
London Historical Museum, London 05230
London Institute Gallery, London 33697
London Irish Rifles Regimental Museum, London 33698
London Motorcycle Museum, Greenford 33161
London Museum of Archaeology, London 05231
London Regional Children's Museum, London 05232
London Scottish Regimental Museum, London 33699
London Sewing Machine Museum, London 33700
London Town, Edgewater 36641
London Toy and Model Museum, London 33701
Londonderry Mines Museum, Londonderry 05236
London's Transport Museum, London 33702
Lone Star Flight Museum/Texas Aviation Hall of Fame, Galveston 37089
Long Beach Museum of Art, Long Beach 38112
Long Branch Historical Museum, Long Branch 38117
Long Eaton Tower Hall, Long Eaton 33821
Long Island Children's Museum, Garden City 37095
Long Island Culture History Museum, Commack 36234
Long Island Maritime Museum, West Sayville 41126
Long Island Museum of American Art, History & Cariages, Stony Brook 40531
Long Shop Museum, Leiston 33496
Long Warehouse, Coalbrookdale 32640
Longboat Key Center for the Arts, Longboat Key 38121
Longdale Craft Centre and Museum, Ravenshead 34275
Longfellow National Historic Site, Cambridge 35790
Longfellow's Wayside Inn Museum, South Sudbury 40423
Longgang Ke Jia Folklorish Museum, Shenzhen 06714
Longhorn Museum, Pleasanton 39499
Longhua Mausoleum of Fallen Heroes, Shanghai 06692
Longleat House, Warminster 34745
Longmont Museum, Longmont 38123
Longquanyi District Museum, Chengdu 06500
Longreach Power House Museum, Longreach 01174
Longstreet Farm, Holmdel 37466
Longview Museum of Fine Art, Longview 38125
Longwood Center for the Visual Arts, Farmville 36816
Longyear Museum, Chestnut Hill 35990
La Lonja, Zaragoza 29951
Look Out Discovery Centre, Bracknell 32346
Loosduins Museum De Korenschuur, Den Haag 24905
Lopez Island Historical Museum, Lopez Island 38128
Lopez Memorial Museum, Pasig 26582
Lora Robins Gallery of Design from Nature, Richmond 39762
Lord Howe Island Museum, Lord Howe Island 01176
Lord Selkirk Settlement, Charlottetown 04688
Lord Strathcona's Horse Museum, Calgary 04633
Lore Degenstein Gallery, Selinsgrove 40307
Lørenskog Bygdemuseum, Skårer 26292
Lørenskog Bygdetun, Lørenskog 26175
Lorenzo State Historic Site, Cazenovia 35873
Lorn Museum, Ledaig 33460
Lorne Scots Regimental Museum, Brampton 04574
Los Alamos County Historical Museum, Los Alamos 38132
Los Angeles Children's Museum, Los Angeles 38153
Los Angeles Contemporary Exhibitions, Los Angeles 38154
Los Angeles County Museum of Art, Los Angeles 38155
Los Angeles Maritime Museum, San Pedro 40155
Los Angeles Municipal Art Gallery, Los Angeles 38156
Los Angeles Museum of Contemporary Art, Los Angeles 38157
Los Angeles Museum of the Holocaust, Los Angeles 38158
Los Gatos Museum of Art and Natural History, Los Gatos 38180
Loseley House, Guildford 33170
Loški Muzej, Škofja Loka 28385
Lossiemouth Fisheries and Community Museum, Lossiemouth 33827
Lost City Museum, Overton 39221
Lostwithiel Museum, Lostwithiel 33828
Lotherton Hall, Aberford 31994
Lottan Torppa, Lokalahti 08639
Louden-Henritze Archaeology Museum, Trinidad 40729
Loudoun Mansion, Philadelphia 39388
Loudoun Museum, Leesburg 37992
Lough Gur Village, Shannon 20833
Louhisaaren Kartanolinna, Askainen 08303
Louhisaari Manor, Askainen 08303
Louis Couperus Museum, Den Haag 24906
Louis E. May Museum, Fremont 37044
Louis H. and Lena Firn Grover Museum, Shelbyville 40338
Louis Spohr-Gedenk- und Forschungsstätte, Kassel 16678
Louis Tussaud Wax Museum, København 07923
Louis Tussaud's Waxworks Museum, Niagara Falls 05456
Louisa County Historical Museum, Louisa 38183
Louisburg College Art Gallery, Louisburg 38184
Louisiana Arts and Science Center, Baton Rouge 35365
Louisiana Association of Museums, Baton Rouge 42092
Louisiana Children's Museum, New Orleans 38816
Louisiana Country Music Museum, Marthaville 38369
Louisiana Museum of Modern Art, Humlebæk 07887
Louisiana Naval War Memorial U.S.S. Kidd, Baton Rouge 35366
Louisiana Old State Capitol, Center for Political and Governmental History, Baton Rouge 35367
Louisiana State Exhibit Museum, Shreveport 40347
Louisiana State Museum, New Orleans 38817
Louisiana State Museum, Patterson 39296
Louisiana State University Museum of Art, Baton Rouge 35368
Louisiana Tech Museum, Ruston 39893
Louisville Science Center, Louisville 38193
Louisville Visual Art Museum, Louisville 38194
Lounais-Hämeen Museo, Forssa 08319
Louth Museum, Louth 33835
Lovački Muzej, Zagreb 07112
Loveland Historical Museum, Loveland 38200
Loveland Museum and Gallery, Loveland 38199
Lovely Lane Museum, Baltimore 35318
Loviisa Town Museum, Loviisa 08641
Loviisan Kaupungin Museo, Loviisa 08641
Lovriner Stube, Donauwörth 15361
Low Parks Museums, Hamilton 33190
Lowe Art Museum, Coral Gables 36265
The Lowe Gallery at Hudson Guild, New York 38893
Lowell Damon House, Wauwatosa 41060
Lowell National Historical Park, Lowell 38202
Lower Cape Fear Historical Society Museum, Wilmington 41219
Lower Columbia College Fine Arts Gallery, Longview 38126
Lower Danube Museum, Călăraşi 27535
Lower East Side Tenement Museum, New York 38894
Lower Fort Garry, Selkirk 05891
Lower Methil Heritage Centre, Lower Methil 33837
Lowestoft and East Suffolk Maritime Museum, Lowestoft 33839
Lowestoft Museum, Lowestoft 33840
Lowewood Museum, Hoddesdon 33279
The Lowry Gallery, Salford 34403
Loxton District Historical Village, Loxton 01179
Loyal Edmonton Regiment Military Museum, Edmonton 04843
Loyalist Cultural Centre, Bath 04513
Loyalist House Museum, Saint John 05802
Lu Xun Museum In Shaoxing, Shaoxing 06708
Lublin Archidiocesan Museum, Lublin 26910
Lubuskie Muzeum Wojskowe w Zielonej Górze z/s w Drzonowie, Letnica 26881
Luchou Museum, Luchou 06634
Luckhard Museum - The Indian Mission, Sebewaing 40298
Lucy Maud Montgomery Birthplace, Charlottetown 04689
Luda Bērziņa Memoriālais Muzejs, Jūrmala 24030
Ludlow Museum, Ludlow 33843
Ludvika Gammelgård och Gruvmuseum, Ludvika 30203
Ludvika Old Homestead and Museum of Mining, Ludvika 30203
Ludwig-Doerfler-Galerie, Schillingsfürst 18333
Ludwig-Forum für Internationale Kunst, Aachen 14166
Ludwig Galerie Schloß Oberhausen, Oberhausen, Rheinland 17773
Ludwig-Gebhard-Museum, Tiefenbach, Oberpfalz 18710
Ludwig-Harms-Haus, Hermannsburg 16393
Ludwig Museum Budapest - Museum of Contemporary Art, Budapest 19826
Ludwig Museum im Deutschherrenhaus, Koblenz 16773
Ludwig-Roselius-Museum für Ur- und Frühgeschichte, Worpswede 19208
Ludwig-Thoma-Haus, Tegernsee 18687
Ludwig Wittgenstein-Dauerausstellung, Kirchberg am Wechsel 02102
Ludza Museum of Local Studies, Ludza 24042
Ludzas Novadpētniecības Muzejs, Ludza 24042
Lüderitz Museum, Lüderitz 24616
Lügenmuseum Schloß Gantikow, Gantikow 15892
Luftfahrt-Museum Laatzen-Hannover, Laatzen 16921
Luftwaffenmuseum der Bundeswehr, Berlin 14791
Lugouqiao Display Center, Beijing 06447
Luis E. Peña G. Collection, Santiago 06382
Luis Muñoz Rivera Museum, Barranquitas 27453
Luisenhütte, Balve 14574
Lullingstone Roman Villa, Eynsford 32994
Lum and Abner Museum and Jot 'Em Down Store, Pine Ridge 39446
Lummis Home El Alisal, Los Angeles 38159
Lumsden and District Museum, Lumsden 25827
Lumsden Heritage Museum, Lumsden 05248
Luna House Museum, Lewiston 38007
Lunacharski Apartment Museum, Moskva 27889
Lundar Museum, Lundar 05249
Lunds Konsthall, Lund 30212
Lundströmska Gården, Sigtuna 30298
Lundy's Lane Historical Museum, Niagara Falls 05457
Lunenburg Art Gallery, Lunenburg 05251
Lungauer Heimatmuseum Tamsweg, Tamsweg 02683
Lungauer Landschaftsmuseum, Mauterndorf 02277
Lunt Roman Fort, Baginton 32105
Luonnonhistoriallinen Museo, Porvoo 08798
Luontomuseo, Kokkola 08522
Luontotalo Arkki, Pori 08792
Luopioinen Museum, Luopioinen 08644
Luopioisten Museo, Luopioinen 08644
Luopioisten Torpparimuseo, Luopioinen 08645
Luostarinmäen Käsityöläismuseo, Turku 08964
Luostarinmäki Handicraft Museum, Turku 08964
Luotsitupa, Uusikaupunki 08989
Luoyang City Folklorish Museum, Luoyang 06637
Luoyang City Museum, Luoyang 06638
Lura Watkins Museum, Middleton 38477
Lurens, Lovisa 08643
Luseland and Districts Museum, Luseland 05252
Lushun Museum, Dalian 06516
Lushun Snakes Dao Natural Museum, Dalian 06517
Lushun Su Jun Mausoleum of Fallen Heroes, Dalian 06518
Lusto-Suomen-metsämuseo ja metsätietokeskus, Punkaharju 08807
Lusto - The Finnish Forest Museum, Punkaharju 08807
Luther Burbank Home, Santa Rosa 40212
Luther-Stube Mansfeld, Mansfeld, Südharz 17251
Lutheran Church Museum, Budapest 19814
Lutherhalle Wittenberg, Lutherstadt Wittenberg 17205
Lutherhaus, Eisenach 15529
Lutherstube, Möhra 17388
Luton Museum and Art Gallery, Luton 33846
Lutz Children's Museum, Manchester 38292
Lutz Mountain Meeting House, Moncton 05343
Luusuan Kylämuseo, Luusua 08647
Luvian Kotiseutumuseo, Luvia 08648
Luxor Museum of Ancient Art, Al-Uqsur 08188
Luxton Museum of the Plains Indian, Banff 04500
Luzerne County Historical Museum, Wilkes-Barre 41183
Lviv Art Gallery, Lviv 31933
Lviv Historical Museum, Lviv 31934
The Lyceum - Alexandria's History Museum, Alexandria 35042
Lyceum Museum, Puškin 28001
Lydd Town Museum, Lydd 33851
Lydiard House, Swindon 34630
Lyly Signal Depot Museum, Lyly 08649
Lylyn Viestivarikon Museo, Lyly 08649
Lyman Allyn Art Museum, New London 38800
Lyman House Memorial Museum, Hilo 37437
Lyme Hall, Disley 32770
Lyme Regis Philpot Museum, Lyme Regis 33854
Lyn and Exmoor Museum, Lynton 33857
Lynchburg Museum, Lynchburg 38218
Lyndhurst, Tarrytown 40640
Lyndon B. Johnson National Historical Park, Johnson City 37691
Lyndon Baines Johnson Museum, Austin 35272
Lyndon House Art Center, Athens 35198
Lynn Canyon Ecology Centre, North Vancouver 05490
Lynn Lake Mining Town Museum, Lynn Lake 05253
Lynn Museum, Lynn 38223
Lynnhaven House, Virginia Beach 40877
Lynnwood Arts Centre, Simcoe 05929
Lyon County Historical Society Museum, Marshall 38361
Lyon County Museum, Emporia 36717
Lyonel-Feininger-Galerie, Quedlinburg 18037
The Lyons Redstone Museum, Lyons 38224
Lytham Hall, Lytham Saint Anne's 33858
Lytham Heritage Centre, Lytham Saint Anne's 33859
Lytham Lifeboat Museum, Lytham Saint Anne's 33860
Lytham Windmill Museum, Lytham Saint Anne's 33861
Lyttelton Historical Museum, Christchurch 25752
Lytton Museum, Lytton 05254
Lyuben Karavelov Memorial House, Koprivštica 04218
M. Christina Geis Gallery, Lakewood 37910
M. Sarians Museum, Erevan 00675
Maagdenhuismuseum, Antwerpen 03108
Maarten Maartenshuis, Doorn 24956
Maarten Van Rossum Museum, Zaltbommel 25671
Maatilamuseo Luhdinsola, Naantali 08694
Mabee-Gerrer Museum of Art, Shawnee 40330

Maison du Parc Naturel du Vercors, Chichilianne 10095
Maison du Parc Naturel Régional de Camargue, Saintes-Maries-de-la-Mer 13347
Maison du Parc Naturel Régional de Lorraine, Bisping 09571
Maison du Parc Naturel Régional de Maine-Normandie, Carrouges 09884
Maison du Parc Naturel Régional des Ballons des Vosges, Munster 11999
Maison du Parc Naturel Régional des Vosges du Nord, La Petite-Pierre 11009
Maison du Parc Naturel Régional du Haut-Languedoc, Roquebrun 12810
Maison du Parc Naturel Régional du Luberon, Apt 09215
Maison du Patrimoine, Carhaix-Plouguer 09868
Maison du Patrimoine, La Garde 10980
Maison du Patrimoine, L'Alpe-d'Huez 11100
Maison du Patrimoine, Lampaul-Guimiliau 11105
Maison du Patrimoine, Le Crès 11197
Maison du Patrimoine, Le Relecq-Kerhuon 11263
Maison du Patrimoine, Marsannay-la-Côte 11627
Maison du Patrimoine, Montlieu-la-Garde 11882
Maison du Patrimoine, Tusson 13809
Maison du Patrimoine, Villard-de-Lans 13969
Maison du Patrimoine, Wimmenau 14106
Maison du Patrimoine d'Oloron et du Haut Béarn, Oloron-Sainte-Marie 12188
Maison du Patrimoine et de la Fraise, Plougastel-Daoulas 12560
Maison du Patrimoine Maritime, Camaret-sur-Mer 09823
Maison du Pays des Étangs, Tarquimpol 13652
Maison du Pays Welche, Fréland 10613
La Maison du Père Mousset, Vrigny 14088
Maison du Peuple, Vénissieux 13908
Maison du Platin, La Flotte-en-Ré 10979
Maison du Portal, Levens 11353
Maison du Potier, Cox 10253
Maison du Protestantisme, Nîmes 12120
Maison du Recteur et de la Paroisse, Loqueffret 11445
Maison du Rh"ne, Givors 10675
Maison du Roi, Bruxelles 03254
Maison du Sabot Neufchâtelois, Neufchâtel-en-Saosnois 12070
Maison du Saint-Curé, Ars-sur-Formans 09262
Maison du Saint-Nectaire, Saint-Nectaire 13162
Maison du Sauvetage, Grand-Fort-Philippe 10703
Maison du Seigle, Menessaire 11712
Maison du Spectacle La Bellone, Bruxelles 03255
Maison du Terroir, Châteauponsac 10036
Maison du Terroir, Saint-Martin-Lacaussade 13140
Maison du Tourisme et du Vin de Pauillac, Pauillac 12473
Maison du Val de Villé, Albé 09107
Maison du Vieux-Zinal, Zinal 31432
Maison du Vin, Tilburg 25537
Maison Dumulon, Rouyn-Noranda 05761
La Maison Enchantée - Le Monde Magique des Automates, Amboise 09142
Maison Espagnole de Bouvignes, Dinant 03356
Maison et Atelier de Jean-François Millet, Barbizon 09417
Maison Européenne de la Photo, Paris 12310
Maison-Expo de Compagnonnage, Nîmes 12121
Maison Familiale de Bossuet, Seurre 13515
Maison-Forte Musée, Bazincourt-sur-Saulx 09458
Maison-Forte Musée, Filain 10535
Maison Francis Jammes, Orthez 12226
Maison Guillaume de Rubroek, Rubrouck 12860
Maison Hamel-Bruneau, Sainte-Foy 05854
Maison Hansi, Riquewihr 12760
Maison Henri-II, La Rochelle 11030
Maison Henri IV, Cahors 09811
Maison J.A. Vachon, Sainte-Marie 05856
Maison Jacques Prévert, Omonville-la-Petite 12190
Maison Jean-Giono, Manosque 11579
Maison Jean-Vilar, Avignon 09356
Maison Jeanne d'Arc, Orléans 12214
Maison Lamontagne, Rimouski 05740
Maison Lansyer, Loches (Indre-et-Loire) 11422
Maison Littéraire de Victor Hugo, Bièvres 09557
Maison Louis-Hippolyte Lafontaine, Boucherville 04561
Maison Maillou, Québec 05669
Maison Marie Henry, Clohars-Carnoët 10141
Maison Médard-Bourgault, Saint-Jean-Port-Joli 05796
Maison Municipale Louis-David, Andernos-les-Bains 09165
Maison-Musée de Charles Maurras, Martigues 11667
Maison-Musée de George Sand, Gargilesse-Dampierre 10641
Maison-Musée de Jeanne Jugan, Cancale 09835
Maison-Musée de Kerlard, Ile-de-Groix 10847
Maison-Musée de la Canne, Les Trois-Ilets 24368
Maison-Musée de la Nature, Marcillé-Robert 11595
Maison-Musée de la Truffe et du Tricastin, Saint-Paul-Trois-Châteaux 13186
Maison-Musée de la Vie d'Autrefois et des Métiers, La Pesse 11008
Maison-Musée de la Vie des Etangs, Saint-Viatre 13283
Maison-Musée des Arômes, Montguers 11873
Maison-Musée des Charcot, Neuilly-sur-Seine 12074
Maison-Musée des Sciences, Lettres et Arts, Cholet 10105
Maison-Musée du Canal, Ecuisses 10403
Maison-Musée du Parc Naturel Régional du Haut-Jura, Lajoux 11098
Maison-Musée du Paysan, Touvois 13769
Maison-Musée du Sabotier, La Chapelle-des-Marais 10943
Maison-Musée du Saumon et de la Rivière, Brioude 09754
Maison-Musée du Sel, Noirmoutier-en-l'Ile 12143
Maison-Musée du Vigneron de Champagne, Saint-Imoges 13049
Maison-Musée Ted Jacobs, Les Cerqueux-sous-Passavent 11317
Maison-Musée Vivant des Papillons Exotiques, Hunawihr 10834
Maison Naïve, Louviers 11483
Maison Natale-Bibliothèque du Président Gaston-Doumergue, Aigues-Vives 09074
Maison Natale de Claude Gellée, Chamagne 09950
Maison Natale de Jean Giraudoux, Bellac 09500
Maison Natale de Jeanne d'Arc et Centre Johannique, Domrémy-la-Pucelle 10353
Maison Natale de la Religieuse Sophie Barat, Joigny (Yonne) 10881
Maison Natale de Saint-Vincent-de-Paul, Saint-Vincent-de-Paul 13286
Maison Natale de Sainte Marie-Madeleine-Postel, Barfleur 09422
Maison Natale du Brave Crillon, Murs 12007
Maison Natale du Père Brothier, La Ferté-Saint-Cyr 10971
Maison Nationale Bonaparte, Ajaccio 09098
Maison Nationale de la Pêche et de l'Eau, Ornans 12221
La Maison Oléronaise, Le Grand-Village-Plage 11209
Maison Papillorama au Jardin Zoologique, Saint-Jean-Cap-Ferrat 13051
Maison Rurale de l'Outre-Forêt, Kutzenhausen 10916
Maison Saint-Dominique, Fanjeaux 10505
Maison-Souvenir de George Sand, Nohant-Vic 12140
Maison Stendhal, Grenoble 10737
Maison Tavel, Genève 30805
Maison Tournaisienne, Tournai 03772
Maison Traditionnelle de la Boucherie, Limoges 11396
Maison Vincent Van Gogh, Cuesmes 03330
Maison Visinand, Montreux 31013
Les Maisons de Bouteilles, Richmond 05730
Maitland Art Center, Maitland 38282
Maitland City Art Gallery, Maitland, New South Wales 01186
Maitland Museum, Maitland, South Australia 01187
Majdanpek Mining Collection, Majdanpek 41572
The Major General Frederick Funston Boyhood Home and Museum, Iola 37611
Major John Bradford House, Kingston 37812
Majorelle Museum, Marrakech 24557
MAK Center for Art and Architecture, Los Angeles 38160
MAK Center for Art and Architecture, West Hollywood 41112
MAK - Museum für Aktuelle Kunst, Groß-Umstadt 16107
MAK - Österreichisches Museum für angewandte Kunst, Wien 02900
Makarenko Museum, Moskva 27858
Makasiinimuseo, Polvijärvi 08790
Makerere Art Gallery, Kampala 31877
Makonde Art Museum, Bammental 14592
Makris Collection, Volos 19703
Maksim Bogdanovich Literature Museum, Minsk 03079
Mala Galerija, Ljubljana 28344
Malabar Farm State Park, Lucas 38209
Malacañang Palace Presidential Museum, Manila 26552
Malacca Museums Corporation, Malacca 24314
Malacological Museum, Makarska 07025
Malahide Castle, Malahide 20813
Malakološki Muzej, Makarska 07025
Malatya Devlet Güzel Sanatlar Galerisi, Malatya 31798
Malatya Müzesi, Malatya 31799
Malatya Museum, Malatya 31799
Malatya Sabancı Culture Center, Malatya 31800
Malatya Sabancı Kültür Merkezi, Malatya 31800
Malatya State Gallery, Malatya 31798
Malay Ethnographic Museum, Kuala Lumpur 24298
Malay Technology Museum, Bandar Seri Begawan 04134
Malaysian Aboriginal Museum, Melaka 24324
Malaysian Youth Museum, Melaka 24318
Malazgirt Culture Center, Malazgirt 31801
Malazgirt Kültür Merkezi, Malazgirt 31801
Malda Museum, Malda 20352
Malden Public Library Art Collection, Malden 38283
Maldon and District Agricultural and Domestic Museum, Goldhanger 33122
Maldon District Museum, Maldon 33879
Maldon Museum, Maldon 01188
Malé Máslovické Muzeum Másla, Vodochody 07705
Måleriyrkets Museum, Stockholm 30359
Malermuseum Wetzikon, Wetzikon 31381
Malerstübchen Willingshausen, Willingshausen 19128
Malibu Lagoon Museum, Malibu 38285
Malki Museum, Banning 35338
Mall Galleries, London 33704
Malla Bleikvasslis Samlinger, Bleikvasslia 26042
Mallaig Heritage Centre, Mallaig 33880
Mallala and Districts Historical Museum, Mallala 01189
Mallalieu Motor Museum, Christ Church 03064
Mallawy Museum, Mallawy 08247
La Malmaison, Cannes 09842
Malmö Konsthall, Malmö 30222
Malmö Konstmuseum, Malmö 30223
Malmö Museer, Malmö 30224
Malmska gården, Jakobstad 08418
Malojaroslavskij Muzej Voennoj Istorii 1812 Goda, Malojaroslavec 27782
Malokarpatské Vinohradnicke Múzeum, Pezinok 28278
Malouinière-Musée, Saint-Malo (Ille-et-Vilaine) 13119
Maloyaroslavets Museum of History of the War of 1812, Malojaroslavec 27782
Malteser-Museum Mailberg, Mailberg 02250
Malton Museum, Malton 33883
Maltwood Art Museum and Gallery, Victoria 06199
Malungs Gammelgård, Malung 30229
Malura-Museum, Unterdießen 18798
Malvar Historical Landmark, Santo Tomás 26592
Malvern Museum, Great Malvern 33154
Mamco, Genève 30806
Mamie Doud Eisenhower Birthplace, Boone 35571
Mammoth Site of Hot Springs, Hot Springs 37505
Man and His Work Center in Memory of S. Avitsur, Tel Aviv 21003
Man and Telecommunication Museum, Edmonton 04844
Man and the Living World Museum, Ramat Gan 20979
Man From Snowy River Folk Museum, Corryong 00936
MAN Museum, Augsburg 14348
Manassas National Battlefield Park, Manassas 38290
Manastirli Palace and Nilometer, Cairo 08214
Manastirska Zbirka-Riznica Manastira Dečane, Dečane 41546
Manastirski Muzej, Cetinje 41542
Manatee Village Historical Park Museum, Bradenton 35632
Manawatu Art Gallery, Palmerston North 25863
Manchester City Art Gallery, Manchester 33889
Manchester Historic Association Museum, Manchester 38297
Manchester Historical Society Museum, Manchester 38293
Manchester Jewish Museum, Manchester 33890
Manchester Museum, Manchester 33891
Manchester Museum of Transport, Manchester 33892
Manchester Transport Museum, Manchester 33893
Manchester United Museum and Tour Centre, Manchester 33894
Manchester University Medical School Museum, Manchester 33895
Mandal Bymuseum, Mandal 26177
Mandal og Opplands Folkemuseum, Mandal 26178
Mander and Mitchenson Theatre Collection, London 33705
Mandurah Community Museum, Mandurah 01192
Mané-Katz Museum, Haifa 20889
Maneżnaja Exhibition Hall, Moskva 27838
Mangapps Farm Railway Museum, Burnham-on-Crouch 32450
Manggha Centrum Sztuki i Techniki Japońskiej, Kraków 26819
Mangyslak Historical and Regional Museum, Sevčenko 23840
Mangyslak State Park Museum Sites and Monuments of Mangyslak and Ustyrt, Sevčenko 23839
Maniitsup Katersugaasivia, Maniitsoq 19719
Manila Police Department Museum, Manila 26553
Manilla Historical Royce Cottage Museum, Manilla 01193
Maniototo Early Settlers Museum, Naseby 25842
Manipur State Museum, Imphal 20276
Manisa Devlet Güzel Sanatlar Galerisi, Manisa 31802
Manisa Müzesi, Manisa 31803
Manisa Museum 600=Saruhan Bey Mah Murat Cad No. 107, Manisa 31803
Manisa Salihli Culture Center, Salihli/Manisa 31821
Manisa Salihli Kültür Merkezi, Salihli/Manisa 31821
Manisa State Gallery, Manisa 31802
Manistee County Historical Museum, Manistee 38309
Manitoba Agricultural Hall of Fame Inc., Brandon 04583
Manitoba Agricultural Museum, Austin 04479
Manitoba Amateur Radio Museum, Brandon 04584
Manitoba Automobile Museum, Elkhorn 04867
Manitoba Children's Museum, Winnipeg 06305
Manitoba Electrical Museum, Winnipeg 06306
Manitoba Museum of Man and Nature, Winnipeg 06307
Manitoba Sports Hall of Fame and Museum, Winnipeg 06308
Manitou Pioneer Museum, Neilburg 05434
Manitoulin Historical Society Museum, Gore Bay 04960
Manjimup Timber Museum, Manjimup 01194
Manly Art Gallery and Museum, Manly 01195
Mann-Simons Cottage, Columbia 36207
Manneken-Pis-Museum, Geraardsbergen 03422
Mannenzaal van het Sint Pieters en Bloklands Gasthuis, Amersfoort 24666
Mannerheim Museo, Helsinki 08367
Manning Regional Art Gallery, Taree 01517
Manno Art Museum, Osaka 23426
Manoir Automobile, Lohéac 11431
Manoir de Kerazan, Loctudy 11427
Manoir de Kernault, Mellac 11704
Manoir de la Ville de Martigny, Martigny 30992
Manoir de Veygoux, Scénomusée des Combrailles, Charbonnières-les-Varennes 09988
Manoir du Huis Bois-Maison P.N.R. du Boulonnais, Le Wast 11284
Manoir Leboutillier, Anse-au-Griffon 04456
Manoir Mauvide-Jenest, Saint-Jean 05794
Manoir-Musée, Vains 13830
Manoir-Musée de Villers, Saint-Pierre-de-Manneville 13198
Manor Cottage Heritage Centre, Southwick 34531
Manor Farm, Bursledon 32458
Manor House, Donington-le-Heath 32783
Manor House, Sandford Orcas 34415
The Manor House in Łopuszna, Łopuszna 26903
Manor House Museum, Kettering 33370
Manor House Museum and Art Gallery, Ilkley 33314
Manor Museum, Manor 05268
Manos Faltaitis Museum, Skyros 19657
Mansfeld-Galerie, Lutherstadt Eisleben 17198
Mansfeld-Museum Hettstedt, Hettstedt, Sachsen-Anhalt 16414
Mansfelder Bergwerksbahn e.V., Benndorf 14643
Mansfield Art Center, Mansfield 38322
Mansfield Costume Study Centre, Colchester 32655
Mansfield Historical Society Museum, Storrs 40537
Mansfield Museum and Art Gallery, Mansfield 33903
Mansfield State Historc Site, Mansfield 38320
Manship House Museum, Jackson 37637
Manx Museum, Douglas, Isle of Man 32797
Manyal Palace Museum, Cairo 08215
Manyara Museum, Manyara 31524
Manzoni Villa, Lecco 21780
Mao Dun Former Residence, Beijing 06448
Maple Ridge Art Gallery, Maple Ridge 05275
Maple Ridge Museum, Maple Ridge 05276
Maple Sugar Museum, Art Gallery and Pioneer Home, Sundridge 05989
Maple Syrup Museum, Saint Jacobs 05792
Maple Valley Historical Museum, Maple Valley 38326
Mappa Mundi and Chained Library, Hereford 33256
Mapua Fire Engine Museum, Mapua 25828
Mapungubwe Museum, Pretoria 28582
Maquettenmuseum, Koersel 03508
Maragheh Museum, Maragheh 20629
Marais Des Cygnes Memorial Historic Site, Pleasanton 39498
Maramec Museum, Saint James 39941
Maramureş District Museum, Baia Mare 27490
Marathon County Historical Society Museum, Wausau 41058
Mårbacka Manor, Sunne 30410
Marble Hill House, Twickenham 34701
Marble Historical Museum, Marble 38329
Marble Mountain Community Museum, West Bay 06246
Marble Palace Art Gallery and Zoo, Kolkata 20181
Marblehead Historical Museum, Marblehead 38330
Marburger Universitätsmuseum für Kunst und Kulturgeschichte, Marburg 17260
Marc Chagall Kunsthuis, Amsterdam 24706
Marcela M. Agoncillo Historical Landmark, Taal 26595
Marcella Sembrich Opera Museum, Bolton Landing 35565
Marcellus Historical Society Museum, Marcellus 38333
March and District Museum, March 33905
March Field Museum, Riverside 39794
March-Museum, Vorderthal 31365
Marchfeldmuseum, Weikendorf 02768
Marcos Foundation Museum, San Miguel 26590
Mardi Gras Museum, Biloxi 35497
Mardin Müzesi, Mardin 31804
Mardin Museum, Mardin 31804
Mareeba District Rodeo Museum, Mareeba 01198
Mareeba Heritage Museum, Mareeba 01199
Margaree Salmon Museum, North East Margaree 05487
Margaret Fort Trahern Gallery, Clarksville 36106
Margaret Harvey Gallery, Saint Albans 34353
Margaret Harwell Art Museum, Poplar Bluff 39528
Margaret Hutchinson Compton Gallery, Cambridge 35791
Margaret Laurence Home, Neepawa 05432
The Margaret Mitchell House & Museum, Atlanta 35220
Margaret Thatcher Projects, New York 38896
Margarete-Steiff-Museum, Giengen 15966
Margaretha Museum, Laag Keppel 25213
Margate Caves, Margate 33908
Margret-Knoop-Schellbach-Museum, Körle 16832
Margrove - South Cleveland Heritage Centre, Boosbeck 32330
Marguerite d'Youville Museum, Montréal 05376
Maria de Lisitzin Fine Art and Historical Museum, Porvoo 08799
Mariager Museum, Mariager 07963
Marian and Religious Museum, Brooklyn 35702
Marianna-Lee County Museum, Marianna 38335
Mariánské Lázně Municipal Museum, Mariánské Lázně 07455
Marias Museum of History and Art, Shelby 40336
Maribor National Liberation Museum, Maribor 28362
Marie Curie Museum, Warszawa 27221
Marie Hull Gallery, Raymond 39697
Marie Rawdon Museum, Matjiesfontein 28542
Marie Walsh Sharpe Art Foundation, New York 38897

Middendorpshuis, Den Ham 24932
Middle Border Museum of American Indian and Pioneer Life, Mitchell 38559
Middle Eastern Culture Centre in Japan, Mitaka 23315
Middle Lake Museum, Middle Lake 05308
Middleborough Historical Museum, Middleborough 38470
The Middlebury College Museum of Art, Middlebury 38474
Middlebury Historical Society Museum, Wyoming 41309
Middlesbrough Art Gallery, Middlesbrough 33946
Middlesex Canal Collection, Lowell 38203
Middlesex County Historical Society Museum, Middletown 38480
Middleton Place Foundation, Charleston 35936
Middleton Top Engine House, Middleton-by-Wirksworth 33948
Middletown Valley Historical Society Museum, Middletown 38481
Middleville Museum, Lanark 05183
Midland Air Museum, Baginton 32106
Midland County Historical Museum, Midland 38486
Midland County Historical Museum, Midland 38489
Midland Motor Museum, Bridgnorth 32378
Midland Railway Centre, Ripley, Derbyshire 34308
Midland Warplane Museum, Warwick 34748
Midlands Art Centre, Birmingham 32273
Midlands Federation of Museums and Art Galleries, Telford 42009
Midsomer Norton and District Museum, Radstock 34261
Midtsønderjyllands Museum, Gram 07826
Midttunet, Skei i Jølster 26296
Midway Museum, Midway 38493
Midway Village and Museum, Rockford 39831
Midwest Museum of American Art, Elkhart 36687
Midwest Old Settlers and Threshers Association Museum, Mount Pleasant 38655
Mie-kenritsu Bijutsukan, Tsu 23725
Mie-kenritsu Hakubutsukan, Tsu 23726
Mie Prefectural Art Museum, Tsu 23725
Mie Prefectural Museum, Tsu 23726
Miegunyah Pioneer Women's Memorial House Museum, Bowen Hills 00810
Miejska Galeria Sztuki, Łódź 26889
Miele-Museum, Gütersloh 16140
Miellerie des Gorges de la Loire, Roche-la-Molière 12778
Miervalda Ķemera Muzejs, Jūrmala 24031
Mies-Pilsner-Heimatmuseum, Dinkelsbühl 15338
Mies van der Rohe Haus, Berlin 14795
Mieszkanie-Pracownia Kazimiery Iłłakowiczówny, Poznań 27014
Migration Museum, Adelaide 00700
migros museum für gegenwartskunst, Zürich 31455
Mihály Babits Memorial Museum, Szekszárd 20027
Mihály Zichy Memorial Museum, Zala 20075
Miho Museum, Koga 23176
Mijnmuseum, Beringen 03175
Mikkeli Art Museum, Mikkeli 08674
Mikkelin Taidemuseo, Mikkeli 08674
Miklós Borsos Collection, Győr 19889
Mikumi Museum, Mikumi 31526
Mikve, Montpellier 11901
Milam County Historical Museum, Cameron 35810
Milan Historical Museum, Milan 38494
Milas Culture Center, Milas 31807
Milas Kültür Merkezi, Milas 31807
Milas Müzesi, Milas 31808
Milas Museum, Milas 31808
Milchwirtschaftliches Museum, Kiesen 30889
Milden Community Museum, Milden 05313
Mildenhall and District Museum, Mildenhall, Suffolk 33949
Mildred M. Mahoney Silver Jubilee Dolls' House Gallery, Fort Erie 04898
Mildura Arts Centre, Mildura 01242
Miles and District Historical Museum, Miles 01244
Miles B. Carpenter Museum, Waverly 41062
Miles Mineral Museum, Portales 39554
Milevské Muzeum, Milevsko 07461
Milford Haven Museum, Milford Haven 33950
Milford Historical Museum, Milford 38499
Milford Historical Society Museum, Milford 38497
Milford Museum, Milford 38498
Mili Weber-Haus, Sankt Moritz 31182
Milieu Educatie Centrum, Eindhoven 25001
Milieucentrum De Grote Rivieren, Heerewaarden 25123
Militärgeschichtliche Ortssammlung, Schnifis 02612
Militärgeschichtliches Museum, Ardagger 01672
Militärhistorisches Museum der Bundeswehr, Dresden 15415
Militärmuseet Skansen Kronan, Göteborg 30100
Militair Historisch Museum De Veteraan, Eefde 24986
Militaire Luchtvaart Museum, Soesterberg 25506
Military Academy Museum, Seoul 23938
Military Aviation Museum, Tangmere 34639
Military Communications and Electronics Museum, Kingston 05141
Military Heritage Museum, Lewes 33504
Military Historians Museum, Westbrook 41129
Military Historical Museum, Praha 07601
Military History Museum, Melbourne 01225
Military History Museum War of Liberation 1877-1878, Bjala 04150
Military Medal Museum, San Jose 40137
Military Medical Museum, Sankt-Peterburg 28070
Military Museum, Aden 41489
Military Museum, Białystok 26625
Military Museum, Cairo 08216
Military Museum, El-Alamein 08239
Military Museum, İstanbul 31744
Military Museum, Jakarta 20498
Military Museum, Kingston 22899
Military Museum, Macau 06645
Military Museum, Sanaa 41494
Military Museum, Teheran 20656
Military Museum, Ulaanbaatar 24540
Military Museum Fort, Bloemfontein 28418
Military Museum Manege, Helsinki 08369
Military Museum of Belgrade, Beograd 41529
Military Museum of Devon and Dorset, Dorchester 32788
Military Museum of Finland, Helsinki 08382
Military Museum of Southern New England, Danbury 36371
Military Technology Museum, Lešany u Týnce nad Sázavou 07427
Military Vehicle Museum, Newcastle-upon-Tyne 34032
Military Veterans Museum, Oshkosh 39206
Militia History Museum, Sankt-Peterburg 28054
Mill Green Museum and Mill, Hatfield 33216
Mill Grove Audubon Wildlife Sanctuary, Audubon 35243
Mill House Cider Museum and Dorset Collection of Clocks, Owermoigne 34126
Mill Museum, Juuka 08433
Mill-Museum, Rautalampi 08831
Mill Museum, Sappee 08864
Mill Museum, Värtsilä 09004
Mill of the Castle, Amsterdam 24708
Mill Trail Visitor Centre, Alva 32041
Millard Fillmore House, East Aurora 36600
Millenium Underground Museum, Budapest 19838
Millennium Galleries, Sheffield 34461
Millenniumi Földalatti Vasúti Múzeum, Budapest 19838
Miller Art Center, Springfield 40471
Miller Art Center, Sturgeon Bay 40562
Miller Bakehouse Museum, Palmyra 01343
Miller-Cory House Museum, Westfield 41135
Miller House Museum, Hagerstown 37300
Miller Museum of Geology, Kingston 05142
Millesgården, Lidingö 30187
Millet and District Museum, Millet 05315
Millgate Museum, Newark-on-Trent 34014
Millicent National Trust Museum, Millicent 01247
Millicent Rogers Museum of Northern New Mexico, Taos 40635
Milliken Gallery, Spartanburg 40433
Millmount Museum and Tower, Drogheda 20732
Mills College Art Museum, Oakland 39091
Mills County Museum, Glenwood 37155
Mills Mansion State Historic Site, Staatsburg 40476
Mills Observatory Museum, Dundee 32837
Millstreet Local Museum, Millstreet 20816
Millwall FC Museum, London 33711
Milne Bay Military Museum, Toowoomba 01539
Milner House, Chatham, Ontario 04701
Milton Blacksmith Shop Museum, Milton 05317
Milton House Museum, Milton 38511
Milton J. Rubenstein Museum of Science and Technology, Syracuse 40600
Milton Keynes Gallery, Milton Keynes 33958
Milton Keynes Museum of Industry, Milton Keynes 33959
Milton's Cottage, Chalfont Saint Giles 32567
Milwaukee Art Museum, Milwaukee 38517
Milwaukee County Historical Society Museum, Milwaukee 38518
Milwaukee Public Museum, Milwaukee 38519
Minbing Weapon Equipment Display Center, Tongzhou 06745
Mindener Museum für Geschichte, Landes- und Volkskunde, Minden, Westfalen 17375
Mine de Sel du Bouillet, Bex 30626
La Mine-Image, La Motte-d'Aveillans 11003
Mine Témoin d'Alès, Alès 09116
Minera Lead Mines, Minera 33962
Mineral and Gem Geological Museum, Parrsboro 05566
Mineral and Lapidary Museum of Henderson County, Hendersonville 37403
Mineral County Museum, Superior 40581
Mineral Museum, Butte 35766
Mineral Resources Divisional Museum, Dodoma 31523
Mineralenexpositie De Siersteen, Oostwold, Leek 25362
Mineralien-Fossilien-Bergbau, Langenlois 02176
Mineralien-Fossilien-Museum, Neckartenzlingen 17597
Mineralien-Kabinett der TU Braunschweig, Braunschweig 15035
Mineralien Museum, Seedorf (Uri) 31226
Mineralien-Museum Andreas Gabrys, Lam 16936
Mineralien-Museum Zirbenhof, Ebene Reichenau 01772
Mineralien-Sammlung, Hohenwarth 16481
Mineralien- und Heimatmuseum, Pleystein 17995
Mineralienmuseum Essen, Essen 15658
Mineralienmuseum Pforzheim-Dillweißenstein, Pforzheim 17974
Mineraliensammlung, Lauingen 17000
Mineralienschau, Afritz 01645
Mineralienschau, Vohenstrauß 18860
Mineralogical Collection, Stari Trg 41631
Mineralogical Museum of Ecole des Mines d'Alès, Alès 09119
Mineralogical Museum of Harvard University, Cambridge 35792
Mineralogical Museum of Lavrion, Lavrion 19545
Mineralogical Museum of the Institute of Geological Sciences, Wrocław 27285
Mineralogičeskij Muzej im. A.E. Fersmana Akademii Nauk Rossii, Moskva 27849
Mineralogisch-Geologisch Museum, Delft 24882
Mineralogisch-Geologische Gesteins-Sammlung, Schwarzenfeld 18428
Mineralogisch Museum, Grouw 25086
Mineralogisch Museum, Schoten 03705
Mineralogisch-Petrografische Sammlungen der Eidgenössischen Technischen Hochschule, Zürich 31456
Mineralogisch-petrographische Sammlung der Universität Leipzig, Leipzig 17046
Mineralogische Sammlung, Erlangen 15622
Mineralogische Schau- und Lehrsammlung, Tübingen 18759
Mineralogisches Museum der Philipps-Universität Marburg, Marburg 17261
Mineralogisches Museum der Universität, Würzburg 19221
Mineralogisches Museum der Universität Bonn, Bonn 14987
Mineralogisches Museum der Universität Hamburg, Hamburg 16229
Mineralogisches Museum (Kristalle und Gesteine), Münster 17549
Mineralogy Museum, Bangkok 31545
Mineralogy Museum Baia Mare, Baia Mare 27489
Mineralogy, Petrography and Vulcanology Museum, Catania 21362
Mineraloška Zbirka Rudnika Trepča, Stari Trg 41631
Mineraloško-Petrografski Muzej, Zagreb 07113
Miners Foundry Cultural Center, Nevada City 38749
Mines d'Asphalte de la Presta, Travers 31319
Ming Shu Wangling Museum, Chengdu 06501
Mingcheng Yuan Shi Museum, Nanjing 06660
Mingei International Museum, San Diego 40079
Mingenew Museum, Mingenew 01248
Minhauzena Muzejs, Dunte 24014
Mini-Château, Amboise 09143
Mini-Musée de l'Aviation, Mèze 11756
Mini-Musée de l'Ossuaire, Pleyben 12549
Mini-Musée Ferroviaire, La Seyne-sur-Mer 11055
Mini-Musée Historique, Rodemack 12793
Mini Musée Militaria, Paris 12312
Miniature English Village and Brass Rubbing Centre, Flaxton 01013
Miniatuurstad, Antwerpen 03109
La Miniera, Desio 21503
Minimundus, Klagenfurt 02121
Minimuseum, Groningen 25078
Minimuseum De Trapper, Drachten 24969
Mining and Iron Works Museum, Złoty Stok 27323
Mining Industry House, Braddon 00819
Mining Museum, Bogatynia 26640
Mining Museum, Gelnica 28233
Mining Museum, Nowa Ruda 26950
Mining Museum, Ostrava 07509
Mining Museum, Outokumpu 08746
Mining Museum, Pécs 19974
Mining Museum, Petroşani 27616
The Mining Museum, Platteville 39489
Mining Museum, Příbram 07609
Mining Museum, Rožňava 28289
Mining Museum, Sala 30293
Mining Museum, Salgótarján 19986
Mining Museum, Sankt-Peterburg 28023
Mining Skansen Museum Queen Louise, Zabrze 27301
Miniota Municipal Museum, Miniota 05322
Minischeepvaartmuseum, Ouwerkerk 25386
Minisink Valley Historical Society Museum, Port Jervis 39541
Minjasafn Austurlands, Egilsstadir 20092
Minjasafn Egils Ólafssonar, Patreksfjördur 20105
Minjasafnid Burstarfelli, Vopnafjördur 20130
Minjasafnida á Akureyri, Akureyri 20083
Minlaton National Trust Museum, Minlaton 01249
Minneapolis College of Art and Design Gallery, Minneapolis 38537
Minneapolis Institute of Arts, Minneapolis 38538
Minnedosa and District Co-Operative Museum, Minnedosa 05323
Minnesota Association of Museums, Minneapolis 42097
Minnesota Children's Museum, Saint Paul 39997
Minnesota Historical Society Museum, Saint Paul 39998
Minnesota Museum of American Art, Saint Paul 39999
Minnie Thomson Memorial Museum, Stratford 05971
Minnilusa Pioneer Museum, Rapid City 39691
Minobusan Homotsukan, Minobu 23308
Minories Art Gallery, Colchester 32656
Minowa Museum, Minowa 23309
Minster Abbey, Minster 33963
Minster Abbey Gatehouse Museum, Sheerness 34454
Mint Museum, Osaka 23427
Mint Museum of Art, Charlotte 35948
Mint Museum of Craft and Design, Charlotte 35949
Minto Museum, Minto 05324
Minton Museum, Stoke-on-Trent 34578
Minusinskij Muzej im. N.M. Martjanova, Minusinsk 27787
Minute Man National Historical Park, Concord 36239
Miracle of America Museum, Polson 39521
Miramar Zeemuseum, Vledder 25599
Miramichi Natural History Museum, Miramichi 05325
Miramont Castle Museum, Manitou Springs 38311
Mirasaka Peace Museum of Art, Mirasaka 23310
Mirehouse, Keswick 33367
Miriam and Ira D. Wallach Art Gallery, New York 38900
Mirror and District Museum, Mirror 05327
Mishima Taisha Treasure House, Mishima 23312
Mishkan Le'Omanut, Ein Harod 20877
Mishkan Le'Omanut, Holon 20897
Misijné Múzeum Nitra, Nitra 28271
Misora Hibari Memorial House, Kyoto 23250
Missiemuseum Steijl, Steijl 25516
Mission and Folklore Museum, Polanica Zdrój 27009
Mission Bell Museum, Coweta 36304
Mission Cultural Center for Latino Arts, San Francisco 40114
Mission Gallery, Swansea 34628
The Mission House, Stockbridge 40521
Mission Houses Museum, Honolulu 37484
Mission Inn Museum, Riverside 39795
Mission Mill Museum, Salem 40026
Mission Museum, Helsinki 08365
Mission Museum, Krosno 26858
Mission Museum, Mission 05329
Mission San Carlos Borromeo Del Rio Carmelo, Carmel 35845
Mission San Diego de Alcala, San Diego 40080
Mission San Juan Capistrano Museum, San Juan Capistrano 40145
Mission San Luis Obispo de Tolosa, San Luis Obispo 40146
Mission San Luis Rey Museum, Oceanside 39112
Mission San Miguel, San Miguel 40153
Missionary Museum, King William's Town 28531
Missionary Museum of the N.G. Kerk, Stellenbosch 28619
Missions-Ethnographisches Museum St. Gabriel, Mödling 02299
Missions-Museum der Pallottiner Limburg, Limburg an der Lahn 17108
Missionsmuseum, Sankt Ottilien 18312
Missionsmuseum, Schwarzach am Main 18423
Missionsmuseum Bug, Bamberg 14581
Missionsmuseum der Mariannhiller Missionare, Würzburg 19222
Missionsmuseum der Spiritaner Knechtsteden, Dormagen 15368
Missionsmuseum des päpstlichen Missionswerks der Kinder in Deutschland, Aachen 14167
Missisquoi Museum, Stanbridge East 05957
Missisquoi Valley Historical Society Museum, North Troy 39045
Mississagi Strait Lighthouse Museum, Meldrum 05296
Mississippi Baptist Historical Commission Museum, Clinton 36151
Mississippi County Historical Society Museum, Charleston 35920
Mississippi Crafts Center, Ridgeland 39777
Mississippi Governor's Mansion, Jackson 37638
Mississippi Museum of Art, Jackson 37639
Mississippi Museum of Natural Science, Jackson 37640
Mississippi Museums Association, Natchez 42098
Mississippi Petrified Forest Museum, Flora 36850
Mississippi River Museum, Dubuque 36563
Mississippi River Museum at Mud Island River Park, Memphis 38418
Mississippi University for Women Museum, Columbus 36224
Mississippi Valley Textile Museum, Almonte 04437
Missouri Historical Society Museum, Saint Louis 39971
Missouri Museums Association, Kansas City 42099
Missouri State Museum, Jefferson City 37675
Missouri Town 1855, Lee's Summit 37991
Místní Muzeum, Kopidlno 07402
Místní Muzeum, Libáň 07430
Místní Muzeum, Městec Králové 07457
Místní Muzeum, Mladá Vožice 07465
Místní Muzeum, Netolice 07481
Místní Muzeum, Netvořice 07482
MIT-List Visual Arts Center, Cambridge 35793
The MIT Museum, Cambridge 35794
Mitchell County Historical Museum, Osage 39203
Mitchell Gallery of Flight, Milwaukee 38520
Mitchell House, Nantucket 38709
Mitchell Museum at Cedarhurst, Mount Vernon 38664
Mitko Palauzov Memorial House, Gabrovo 04185
Mito Geijutsukan Gendai Bijutsu Center, Mito 23319
Mitsubishi Automobile Gallery, Okazaki 23408
Mitsuke School Historical Site, Iwata, Shizuoka 23095
Mitsukuni and Nariaki Tokugawa Memorial Collection, Mito 23320
Mittamuseo, Virrat 09042
Mittelalterliches Foltermuseum, Rüdesheim am Rhein 18265
Mittelalterliches Kriminalmuseum, Rothenburg ob der Tauber 18241
Mittelalterliches Museum, Wien 02903

Musée de la Vigne et du Vin, Curtil-Vergy 10278
Musée de la Vigne et du Vin, Gruissan 10756
Musée de la Vigne et du Vin, Igé 10843
Musée de la Vigne et du Vin, Lézignan-Corbières 11359
Musée de la Vigne et du Vin, Lods 11430
Musée de la Vigne et du Vin, Loupiac 11462
Musée de la Vigne et du Vin, Mareau-aux-Près 11603
Musée de la Vigne et du Vin, Onzain 12191
Musée de la Vigne et du Vin, Prayssas 12653
Musée de la Vigne et du Vin, Vaux-en-Beaujolais 13891
Musée de la Vigne et du Vin d'Anjou, Saint-Lambert-du-Lattay 13083
Musée de la Vigne et du Vin de Franche-Comté, Arbois 09220
Musée de la Vilaine Maritime, La Roche-Bernard 11020
Musée de la Villa Romaine de Pully, Pully 31107
Musée de la Ville de Lachine, Lachine 05175
Musée de la Ville de Molsheim, Molsheim 11790
Musée de la Ville de Saverne, Saverne 13448
Musée de la Ville de Strasbourg, Strasbourg 13604
Musée de la Ville d'Eaux, Spa 03740
Musée de la Villemarque et des Traditions Bretonnes, Quimperlé 12690
Musée de la Viscose, Échirolles 10398
Musée de la Viticulture, Barizey 09424
Musée de la Viticulture, Durban-Corbières 10391
Musée de la Viticulture, Lhomme 11362
Musée de la Viticulture, Mirepeisset 11780
Musée de la Viticulture, Montlouis-sur-Loire 11884
Musée de la Viticulture, Santenay 13389
Musée de la Viticulture et des Arts Populaires, Portel-des-Corbières 12635
Musée de la Viticulture et Renaissance du Vignoble, Contz-les-Bains 10205
Musée de la Voie Étroite et des Chemins de Fer de Montagne, Saint-Georges-de-Commiers 13009
Musée de la Voie Sacrée, Souilly 13565
Musée de la Voiture de Course, Savigny-les-Beaune 13455
Musée de la Voiture Hippomobile et de la Citadelle de Bourg, Bourg-sur-Gironde 09680
Musée de la Volaille de Bresse, Romenay 12804
Musée de l'Abbaye, Echternach 24213
Musée de l'Abbaye de Bourgueil, Bourgueil 09693
Musée de l'Abbaye de Clairvaux, Ville-sous-la-Ferté 13978
Musée de l'Abbaye de Port-Royal, Magny-lès-Hameaux 11550
Musée de l'Abbaye d'Orval, Villers-devant-Orval 03799
Musée de l'Abbaye Romane, La Sauve-Majeure 11052
Musée de l'Abbaye Sainte-Croix, Les Sables-d'Olonne 11340
Musée de l'Abbé Saunière, Rennes-le-Château 12732
Musée de l'Abeille, Bedoues 09493
Musée de l'Abeille, Château-Richer 04696
Musée de l'Abeille, Tilff 03762
Musée de l'Abeille et de la Cire, Toulouse 13726
Musée de l'Abeille et du Braconnage, Salbris 13353
Musée de l'Abri, Hatten 10795
Musée de l'Absinthe, Auvers-sur-Oise 09336
Musée de l'Academie de la Val d'Isère, Moutiers (Savoie) 11979
Musée de l'Affiche de la Carte Postale et de l'Art Graphique, Toulouse 13727
Musée de l'Agriculture Catalane, Saint-Michel-de-Llotes 13150
Musée de l'Agriculture de Montagne, Saint-Paul-sur-Ubaye 13185
Musée de l'Agriculture Traditionnelle et de l'Artisanat de nos Campagnes, Lahamaide 03519
Musée de l'Air et de l'Espace, Le Bourget (Seine-Saint-Denis) 11180
Musée de l'Alambic, Quimper 12687
Musée de l'Alambic, Saint-Desirat 12966
Musée de l'Alambic Louis Roque, Souillac 13562
Musée de l'Albanais, Rumilly 12864
Musée de l'Algérie Française, Perpignan 12500
Musée de l'Alta Rocca, Levie 11356
Musée de l'Amérique Française, Québec 05672
Musée de l'Ancien Collège des Jésuites, Reims 12712
Musée de l'Ancien Havre, Le Havre 11214
Musée de l'Ancienne Abbaye, Stavelot 03745
Musée de l'Ancienne Abbaye de Landévennec, Landévennec 11108
Musée de l'Ancienne Cathédrale, Noyon 12159
Musée de l'Ancienne Chartreuse de la Verne, Collobrières 10159
Musée de l'Ancienne Scierie, Saint-George 31152
Musée de Langres, Langres 11117
Musée de l'Apéritif Noilly-Prat, Marseillan 11630
Musée de l'Apothicairerie, Bazas 09455
Musée de l'Apothicairerie des Hôpitaux Généraux Royaux, Saint-Germain-en-Laye 13020
Musée de l'Arc de Triomphe, Paris 12355
Musée de l'Archerie Traditionnelle, Ayssenes 09377
Musée de l'Archiconfrérie Notre-Dame de la Miséricorde, Pellevoisin 12483
Musée de l'Architecture Locale, Le Rozier 11267
Musée de l'Ardenne, Charleville-Mézières 09993
Musée de l'Ardoise, Fumay 10627
Musée de l'Ardoise, Renazé 12725
Musée de l'Ardoise, Trélazé 13780
Musée de l'Areuse, Boudry 30647
Musée de l'Argonne, Sainte-Menehould 13332
Musée de l'Ariège, Foix 10554
Musée de l'Arles Antique, Arles 09245
Musée de l'Armagnac, Condom 10196
Musée de l'Arme Blanche et Conservatoire de l'Épée, Monistrol-sur-Loire 11799
Musée de l'Armée, Damascus 31498
Musée de l'Armée, Paris 12356
Musée de l'Armée des Alpes, Sospel 13556
Musée de l'Armée Russe, Paris 12357
Musée de l'Art Africain, Sailly 12875
Musée de l'Art Campanaire, Labergement-Sainte-Marie 11079
Musée de l'Art Culinaire, Villeneuve-Loubet 14024
Musée de l'Art Différencié, Liège 03550
Musée de l'Art Forain et de la Musique Mécanique, Conflans-en-Jarnisy 10197
Musée de l'Art Wallon, Liège 03551
Musée de l'Artillerie, Draguignan 10377
Musée de l'Artisanat et des Traditions Rurales, Brebotte 09718
Musée de l'Artisanat Rural Ancien, Tigy 13694
Musée de l'Assistance Publique, Bruxelles 03273
Musée de l'Assistance Publique-Hôpitaux de Paris, Paris 12358
Musée de l'Atelier de Rosa-Bonheur, Thomery 13672
Musée de l'Atelier de Saintonge, Pont-l'Abbé-d'Arnoult 12601
Musée de l'Attelage, Marquillies 11622
Musée de l'Attelage et du Cheval, Sérignan (Hérault) 13501
Musée de l'Audiovisuel, Montarcher 11822
Musée de l'Auditoire, Joinville (Haute-Marne) 10884
Musée de l'Auditoire, Sainte-Suzanne 13338
Musée de l'Auld Alliance Franco-Écossaise, Aubigny-sur-Nère 09291
Musée de l'Automobile, Grenoble 10742
Musée de l'Automobile, Martigny 30994
Musée de l'Automobile, Muriaux 31040
Musée de l'Automobile, Plan-les-Ouates 31093
Musée de l'Automobile, Puteaux 12673
Musée de l'Automobile, Valençay 13835
Musée de l'Automobile, Velaine-en-Haye 13897
Musée de l'Automobile Ancienne, Buis-sur-Damville 09774
Musée de l'Automobile de Limoges, Limoges 11398
Musée de l'Automobile de Vendée, Talmont-Saint-Hilaire 13631
Musée de l'Automobile du Mans, Le Mans 11224
Musée de l'Automobile et Militaires, La Réole 11016
Musée de l'Automobile Française, Reims 12713
Musée de l'Automobile La Belle Époque, Pont-l'Évêque 12603
Musée de l'Automobile Miniature, Fontenay-sur-Mer 10574
Musée de l'Automobile Miniature et des Poupées Anciennes, Nointel (Oise) 12141
Musée de l'Automobile Sportive, Sanary-sur-Mer 13383
Musée de l'Automobiliste, Mougins 11960
Musée de l'Avallonnais, Avallon 09352
Musée de l'Aviation, Savigny-les-Beaune 13456
Musée de l'Aviation Charles-Noetinger, Villeneuve-de-la-Raho 14018
Musée de l'Aviation Légère de l'Armée de Terre, Dax 10295
Musée de l'Échevinage, Saintes 13341
Musée de l'Éclairage au Gaz, Paris 12359
Musée de l'École, Auron 09324
Musée de l'École, Bourges 09684
Musée de l'Ecole, Bruxelles 03274
Musée de l'École, Carcassonne 09861
Musée de l'Ecole, Chartres 10005
Musée de l'École, Châtelus (Allier) 10047
Musée de l'Ecole, Echery 10397
Musée de l'Ecole 1900, Saint-Martin-des-Olmes 13136
Musée de l'Ecole Biblique et Archéologique Française, Jerusalem 26432
Musée de l'Ecole d'Autrefois, Villeneuve-d'Ascq 14012
Musée de l'École de Barbizon - Auberge Ganne, Barbizon 09418
Musée de l'Ecole de Nancy, Nancy 12022
Musée de l'École des Mines, Saint-Étienne 12982
Musée de l'École en Montagne, Pontis 12615
Musée de l'Ecole et de la Mine, Harnes 10790
Musée de l'École Nationale d'Art Décoratif, Aubusson 09294
Musée de l'Ecole Navale, Lanvéoc-Poulmic 11128
Musée de l'Ecole Rurale, Trégarvan 13774
Musée de l'École Rurale d'Auvergne, Messeix 11738
Musée de l'Écologie des Rives de l'Adour, Orist 12211
Musée de l'Église de Lorris, Lorris 11450
Musée de l'Eglise Notre-Dame, Montréal 05380
Musée de l'Elysée, Lausanne 30929
Musée de l'Empéri, Salon-de-Provence 13373
Musée de l'Ephèbe, Agde 09064
Musée de l'Epicerie d'Autrefois, Lignerolles 11373
Musée de l'Épicerie Gosselin, Saint-Vaast-la-Hougue 13276
Musée de l'Escrime Charles Debeur, Bruxelles 03275
Musée de l'Espace, Kourou 14133
Musée de l'Estérel, Les Adrets-de-l'Estérel 11299
Musée de l'Établissement des Constructions Navales de Ruelle, Ruelle 12863
Musée de l'Étain, Angers 09176
Musée de l'Etang de Thau, Bouzigues 09705
Musée de l'Evéché, Sion 31245
Musée de l'Evêché, Verdun (Meuse) 13919
Musée de l'Eventail, Paris 12360
Musée de l'Evolution du Style Plantagenêt, Angers 09177
Musée de l'Habitat Rural Passé et des Traditions, La Garnache 10984
Musée de l'Habitat Troglodytique, Graufthal 10725
Musée de l'Heure et du Feu, Villerest 14032
Musée de l'Histoire de France, Paris 12361
Musée de l'Histoire de France à travers son Armée, Montet et Bouxal 11861
Musée de l'Histoire de la Forêt d'Ardenne, Saint-Hubert 03695
Musée de l'Histoire de la Médecine, Vandœuvre-les-Nancy 13867
Musée de l'Histoire de la Médecine de Toulouse, Toulouse 13728
Musée de l'Histoire de la Poterie, Bouconville-Vauclair 09653
Musée de l'Histoire de la Poterie, La Chapelle-des-Pots 10944
Musée de l'Histoire de l'Eau et des Egouts, Paris 12362
Musée de l'Histoire de l'Emigration Percheronne au Canada, Tourouvre 13752
Musée de l'Histoire des Bastides et de l'Evolution de l'Habitat, Bassoues 09432
Musée de l'Histoire du Costume, Scey-sur-Saône-et-Saint-Albin 13464
Musée de l'Histoire du Fer, Jarville 10874
Musée de l'Histoire et de la Vie Salmiennes, Vielsalm 03796
Musée de l'Histoire Industrielle et Sociale de la Région Bruxelloise, Bruxelles 03276
Musée de l'Histoire Vivante Parc Montreau, Montreuil (Seine-Saint-Denis) 11926
Musée de l'Histore Estudiantine, Assens 30540
Musée de l'Holographie, Paris 12363
Musée de l'Homme, Paris 12364
Musée de l'Homme de Neandertal, La Chapelle-aux-Saints 10937
Musée de l'Homme et de sa Montagne, Sainte-Croix-Vallée-Française 13308
Musée de l'Hôpital, Yssingeaux 14121
Musée de l'Hôpital Psychiatrique, Brumath 09766
Musée de l'Horlogerie, Saint-Nicolas-d'Aliermont 13164
Musée de l'Horlogerie, Villedieu-les-Poêles 13986
Musée de l'Horlogerie du Haut-Doubs, Morteau 11953
Musée de l'Horlogerie et de l'Emaillerie, Genève 30811
Musée de l'Horlogerie et du Décolletage, Cluses 10144
Musée de l'Hospice Comtesse, Lille 11383
Musée de l'Hospice Saint-Roch, Issoudun 10862
Musée de l'Hôtel Bellevue, Bruxelles 03277
Musée de l'Hôtel de Berny, Amiens 09154
Musée de l'Hôtel de Vermandois, Senlis 13493
Musée de l'Hôtel de Ville, Hondschoote 10827
Musée de l'Hôtel-Dieu, Beaune 09479
Musée de l'Hôtel-Dieu, Porrentruy 31097
Musée de l'Hôtel Lallemant, Bourges 09685
Musée de l'Hôtel Sandelin, Saint-Omer 13167
Musée de l'Huître, Marennes 11605
Musée de l'Humour, Palavas-les-Flots 12241
Musée de Lignan et du Canton de Créon, Lignan-de-Bordeaux 11372
Musée de l'Iguanodon, Bernissart 03178
Musée de l'Ile de France, Sceaux 13462
Musée de l'Ile d'Oleron Aliénor d'Aquitaine, Saint-Pierre-d'Oléron 13200
Musée de l'Imagerie Populaire, Pfaffenhoffen 12517
Musée de l'Imagerie Publicitaire sur le Chocolat, Pontlevoy 12617
Musée de l'Impression sur Etoffes, Mulhouse 11989
Musée de l'Imprimerie, Billom 09562
Musée de l'Imprimerie, Bordeaux 09634
Musée de l'Imprimerie, Nantes 12037
Musée de l'Imprimerie de Lyon, Lyon 11518
Musée de l'Industrie du Verre, du Fer et du Bois, Hennezel-Clairey 10809
Musée de l'Industrie Horlogère et Mécanique "Frédéric-Japy", Beaucourt 09467
Musée de l'Industrie Régionale de la Chaussure, Saint-André-de-la-Marche 12894
Musée de l'Infanterie, Montpellier 11906
Musée de l'Insigne et de la Symbolique Militaire, Vincennes 14055
Musée de l'Insolite, Cabrerets 09786
Musée de l'Insolite, Font-Romeu-Odeillo-Via 10556
Musée de l'Insolite, Loriol-sur-Drôme 11448
Musée de l'Institut de Géologie et de Géoscience de Rennes, Rennes (Ille-et-Vilaine) 12729
Musée de l'Institut d'Égyptologie, Strasbourg 13605
Musée de l'Institut du Monde Arabe, Paris 12365
Musée de l'Institut Villien, Avesnes-sur-Helpe 09355
Musée de l'Invasion Aéroportée, Bénouville 09512
Musée de l'Observatoire, Paris 12366
Musée de l'Océanie, Saint-Symphorien-sur-Coise 13267
Musée de Lodève, Lodève 11429
Musée de l'Œuvre de la Madeleine, Vézelay 13943
Musée de l'Oeuvre Notre-Dame, Strasbourg 13606
Musée de Logbiermé, Trois-Ponts 03783
Musée de l'Olive, Clermont-l'Hérault 10135
Musée de l'Olivier, Les Baux-de-Provence 11309
Musée de l'Olivier, Nyons 12163
Musée de l'Opéra National de Paris, Paris 12367
Musée de l'Optique, Biesheim 09555
Musée de l'Optométrie, Bures-sur-Yvette 09777
Musée de l'Or, Jumilhac-le-Grand 10903
Musée de l'Oratoire Saint-Joseph, Montréal 05381
Musée de l'Ordre de la Libération, Paris 12368
Musée de l'Ordre de Malte, Bardonnex 30560
Musée de l'Orfevrerie de la Communaute Française, Seneffe 03706
Musée de Lourdes, Lourdes 11469
Musée de l'Outil, Espezel 10458
Musée de l'Outil, Turquant 13806
Musée de l'Outil à Bois, Peaugres 12478
Musée de l'Outil à la Ferme, Juvigné 10907
Musée de l'Outil Champenois, Dormans-en-Champagne 10357
Musée de l'Outil et de la Vie au Village, Saint-Privat-des-Prés 13212
Musée de l'Outil et des Métiers, Tinténiac 13698
Musée de l'Outil et des Vieux Métiers, La Celle-Guenand 10931
Musée de l'Outil et du Balnéaire Romain, Wy-Dit-Joli-Village 14116
Musée de l'Outillage, Coussac-Bonneval 10246
Musée de l'Outillage Agricole et Viticole du Château Aney, Cussac-Fort-Médoc 10282
Musée de l'Outillage et des Techniques Traditionnelles de la Taille de Pierre, Coucouron 10222
Musée de l'Outillage Miniature, Cohennoz 10153
Musée de l'Outillage Rural et Bourguignon, Cruzille-en-Mâconnais 10273
Musée de Louvain-la-Neuve, Louvain-la-Neuve 03570
Musée de Luluabourg, Luluabourg 06934
Musée de l'Uniforme Legionnaire, Puyloubier 12675
Musée de l'Uniforme Militaire Français et du Vieux Bourbon, Bourbon-Lancy 09667
Musée de l'Union Compagnonnique des Devoirs Unis, Nantes 12038
Musée de l'Université de Fianarantsoa, Fianarantsoa 24268
Musée de l'Université de Tuléar, Tuléar 24272
Musée de l'Uranium, Lachaux 11084
Musée de Machines Agricoles Miniatures, Guerlesquin 10767
Musée de Mahdia, Mahdia 31617
Musée de Maquettes Animées sur les Ateliers, Métiers et Scènes de Jadis, Vallon-en-Sully 13853
Musée de Marine, Faranui 14134
Musée de Maroua, Maroua 04416
Musée de Matériel Agricole, Saint-Laurent-des-Autels 13090
Musée de Matériel Viticole, Saint-Laurent-des-Autels 13091
Musée de Matière Médicale, Paris 12369
Musée de Matour, Matour 11676
Musée de Mayombe, Kinshasa 06928
Musée de Mbandaka, Mbandaka 06935
Musée de Megève, Megève 11698
Musée de Melun, Melun 11708
Musée de Minéralogie, Strasbourg 13607
Musée de Minéralogie de l'Ecole des Mines de Paris, Paris 12370
Musée de Minéralogie et de Géologie, Bruxelles 03278
Musée de Mobilier Breton, Saint-Vougay 13290
Musée de Modèles Réduits, La Rochelle 11033
Musée de Modélisme, Savigny-les-Beaune 13457
Musée de Montmartre, Paris 12371
Musée de Monuments d'Allumettes et d'Artisanat, La Réole 11017
Musée de Moulages, Strasbourg 13608
Musée de Musiques, L'Auberson 30544
Musée de Natitingou, Natitingou 03846
Musée de Noé, Roujan 12849
Musée de Nogent, Nogent-sur-Marne 12137
Musée de Normandie, Caen 09798
Musée de Notre-Dame-de-Paris, Paris 12372
Musée de Paléontologie, La Voulte-sur-Rhône 11071
Musée de Paléontologie, Menat 11709
Musée de Paléontologie, Villeurbanne 14043
Musée de Paléontologie Humaine de Terra Amata, Nice 12099
Musée de Palmyra, Palmyra 31504
Musée de Payerne et Abbatiale, Payerne 31087
Musée de Peinture, Rodilhan 12797
Musée de Peinture Contemporaine, Vars 13880
Musée de Peinture J. Drevon, Saint-Jean-de-Bournay 13056
Musée de Peinture Louis-Français, Plombières-les-Bains 12551
Musée de Peinture Mario-Prassinos, Saint-Rémy-de-Provence 13231
Musée de Peintures Cazin, Samer 13381
Musée de Peintures Contemporaines Hors du Temps, Pierrefeu (Alpes-Maritimes) 12524
Musée de Peintures de Monsieur Paul Ricard, Le Brusc 11184
Musée de Peyne, Laurède 11146
Musée de Pharmacie, Paris 12373
Musée de Pharmacie Dusquenoy, Illkirch-Graffenstaden 10857
Musée de Picardie, Amiens 09155
Musée de Pierre-Corneille, Le Petit-Couronne 11248
Musée de Plein Air, Saint-Vallier-de-Thiey 13280
Musée de Plein Air, Seurre 13516
Musée de Plein Air de Rothéneuf, Rothéneuf 12830
Musée de Plein Air des Maisons Comtoises, Nancray 12017
Musée de Pont-Aven, Pont-Aven 12592

Museo Diocesano de Arte Sacro, Teruel 29761
Museo Diocesano de Bellas Artes, Córdoba 28980
Museo Diocesano de Huesca, Huesca 29149
Museo Diocesano de San Sebastián, Donostia-San Sebastián 29017
Museo Diocesano di Arte Sacra, Mileto 21935
Museo Diocesano di Arte Sacra, Nicotera 22036
Museo Diocesano di Arte Sacra, Orte 22071
Museo Diocesano di Arte Sacra, Palermo 22111
Museo Diocesano di Arte Sacra, San Miniato 22497
Museo Diocesano di Arte Sacra, Volterra 22886
Museo Diocesano di Arte Sacra di Italo Bolano, Marina di Campo 21848
Museo Diocesano di Arte Sacra San Gregorio Barbarigo, Padova 22093
Museo Diocesano di Osimo, Osimo 22077
Museo Diocesano di Pienza, Pienza 22193
Museo Diocesano e Catedralicio de Mondoñedo, Mondoñedo 29363
Museo Diocesano e Collezione dei Presepi, Bressanone 21246
Museo Diocesano e Gallerie del Tiepolo, Udine 22755
Museo Diocesano e Tesoro della Cattedrale, Troia 22748
Museo Diocesano Inercomunale di Arte Sacra, Castignano 21360
Museo Diocesano Inercomunale di Arte Sacra, Monalto Marche 21961
Museo Diocesano Inercomunale di Arte Sacra, Rotella 22438
Museo Diocesano Intercomunale di Arte Sacra, Comunanza 21464
Museo Diocesano Intercomunale di Arte Sacra, Grottammare 21724
Museo Diocesano Intercomunale di Arte Sacra, Monteprandone 21990
Museo Diocesano Intercomunale di Arte Sacra, Ripatransone 22319
Museo Diocesano Regina Coeli, Santillana del Mar 29687
Museo Diocesano Teatino, Chieti 21414
Museo Diocesano Tridentino, Trento 22717
Museo do Humor, Fene 29054
Museo do Mosteiro de San Paio de Antealtares, Santiago de Compostela 29682
Museo do Moucho, Cerceda 28946
Museo do Pobo Galego, Santiago de Compostela 29683
Museo Doctor Francia, Yaguarón 26468
Museo Documental, Guernica y Luno 29134
Museo Doganale Svizzero, Gandria 30789
Museo Dolores Olmedo Patiño, México 24450
Museo Domenicani, Taggia 22621
Museo Don Benito Juárez, México 24451
Museo Don Giovanni Verità, Modigliana 21954
Museo Donizettiano, Bergamo 21159
Museo Duca di Martina, Napoli 22024
Museo Dupré, Fiesole 21564
Museo e Archivio Capitolare, Assisi 21109
Museo e Centro di Documentazione Fotografica, Venezia 22812
Museo e Certosa di San Martino, Napoli 22025
Museo e Chiostri Monumentali di Santa Maria Novella, Firenze 21620
Museo e Grotte dei Balzi Rossi, Ventimiglia 22828
Museo e Istituto Florentino di Preistoria, Firenze 21621
Museo e Pinacoteca Civica, Alessandria 21051
Museo e Pinacoteca Civica, Todi 22650
Museo e Pinacoteca Civica del Broletto, Novara 22049
Museo e Pinacoteca Civici, Teramo 22633
Museo e Pinacoteca Civici, Vasto 22784
Museo e Pinacoteca Comunali, Gubbio 21730
Museo e Pinacoteca del Santuario Madonna delle Grazie, Rimini 22312
Museo e Pinacoteca Diocesana, Camerino 21288
Museo Ecuatoriano de Ciencias Naturales, Quito 08166
Museo-Eerola, Tuulos 08978
Museo Efrain Martínez, Popayán 06875
Museo Egizio, Torino 22687
Museo El Alero, Aristóbulo del Valle 00108
Museo El Castillo Diego Echavarría, Medellín 06857
Museo El Hombre y la Naturaleza, San Juan 00562
Museo El Reencuentro, Darregueira 00317
Museo Elisarion, Minusio 31007
Museo Emidiano, Agnone 21031
Museo Enrico Butti, Viggiù 22867
Museo Entomológco Mariposas del Mundo, San Miguel 00570
Museo Epper, Ascona 30538
Museo Eritreo Bottego, Parma 22133
Museo Ermita de Santa Elena, Irún 29158
Museo Ernest Hemingway, La Habana 07151
Museo Ernesto Laroche, Montevideo 34940
Museo Escobar María Goretti, Pasto 06869
Museo Escolar Agrícola de Pusol, Elche 29032
Museo Escolar de Ciencias Naturales Carlos A. Merti, San Antonio de Areco 00539
Museo Escuela del Mar Itxas Natura, Zarautz 29965
Museo Específico de la Academia de Artillería, Segovia 29700
Museo Específico de la Academia de Caballería, Valladolid 29860
Museo Específico de la Academia de Infantería, Toledo 29775
Museo Específico de la Academia General Militar, Zaragoza 29960
Museo Específico de la Brigada Paracaidista, Alcalá de Henares 28665
Museo Específico de la Legión de Ceuta, Ceuta 28952
Museo Estudio Diego Rivera, México 24452
Museo Ethnográfico de las Obras Misionales Pontificias, Buenos Aires 00195
Museo Etiopico, Frascati 21654
Museo Etnográfico, Alcubilla del Marqués 28676
Museo Etnografico, Aprica 21076
Museo Etnográfico, Atauta 28736
Museo Etnográfico, Camporrobles 28905
Museo Etnográfico, Castrojeriz 28941
Museo Etnográfico, Grado 29103
Museo Etnográfico, Grandas de Salime 29123
Museo Etnográfico, La Habana 07152
Museo Etnografico, Montodine 22000
Museo Etnografico, Morigerati 22005
Museo Etnografico, Parma 22134
Museo Etnografico, Premana 22267
Museo Etnográfico, Quintana Redonda 29544
Museo Etnográfico, Rollamienta 29573
Museo Etnográfico, Romanillos de Medinaceli 29574
Museo Etnografico, Sampeyre 22469
Museo Etnográfico, Torreandaluz 29790
Museo Etnografico, Trebisacce 22712
Museo Etnografico, Ultimo 22758
Museo Etnografico Africa Mozambico, Bari 21138
Museo Etnografico Africano, San Lorenzo in Campo 22492
Museo Etnográfico Andrés Barbero, Asunción 26462
Museo Etnografico Castello D'Albertis, Genova 21700
Museo Etnografico Coumboscuro della Civiltà Provenzale in Italia, Sancto Lucia de Coumboscuro 22507
Museo Etnográfico da Limia, Vilar de Santos 29903
Museo Etnográfico de Amurrio Felix Murga, Amurrio 28703
Museo Etnográfico de Azuaga de la Sierra y la Campiña, Azuaga 28754
Museo Etnográfico de Cantabria, Muriedas 29393
Museo Etnográfico de Colombia, Santafé de Bogotá 06909
Museo Etnográfico de los Valles de Campoo, Canduela 28910
Museo Etnográfico de Oyón, Oyón 29447
Museo Etnografico dei Cimbri, Selva di Progno 22558
Museo Etnografico del Carretto Siciliano, Terrasini 22643
Museo Etnografico del Cologio Nacional Mejia, Quito 08167
Museo Etnografico del Pinerolese, Pinerolo 22206
Museo Etnografico del Ponente Ligure, Cervo 21389
Museo Etnográfico del Pueblo de Asturias, Gijón 29087
Museo Etnográfico del Reino de Pamplona, Val de Ollo 29824
Museo Etnografico della Civiltà Contadina, Colorno 21457
Museo Etnografico della Lunigiana, Villafranca in Lunigiana 22870
Museo Etnografico della Trinità, Botticino 21232
Museo Etnografico delle Alpi Occidentali, Boves 21233
Museo Etnografico di Servola, Trieste 22744
Museo Etnográfico e da Historia de San Paio de Narla, San Paio de Narla-Friol 29622
Museo Etnografico e del Folclore Valsesiano, Borgosesia 21229
Museo Etnografico Extremeño González Santana, Olivenza 29412
Museo Etnografico G. Fontana, Sappada 22531
Museo Etnografico G. Pitrè, Palermo 22112
Museo Etnográfico Juán B. Ambrosetti, Buenos Aires 00196
Museo Etnográfico Leones Ildefonso Fierro, León 29190
Museo Etnográfico Liste, Oseira 29434
Museo Etnográfico Madre Laura, Medellín 06858
Museo Etnográfico Miguel Angel Builes, Medellín 06859
Museo Etnográfico Municipal Dámaso Arce, Olavarría 00453
Museo Etnográfico Piedad Isla, Cervera de Pisuerga 28949
Museo Etnografico Romagnolo, Russi 22451
Museo Etnografico Romagnolo Benedetto Pergoli, Forli 21645
Museo Etnográfico Rural, Valderrueda 29828
Museo Etnográfico Rural y Comarcal, Prioro 29532
Museo Etnografico Siciliano Giuseppe Pitrè, Palermo 22113
Museo Etnográfico Sotelo Blanco, Santiago de Compostela 29684
Museo Etnográfico Textil Pérez Enciso, Plasencia 29509
Museo Etnografico Tiranese, Madonna di Tirano 21825
Museo Etnográfico y Archivo Histórico Enrique Squirru, Azul 00115
Museo Etnográfico y Arqueológico, Tzintzuntzan 24520
Museo Etnográfico y Colonial Juan de Garay, Santa Fé 00594
Museo Etnológico, Barca 28770
Museo Etnológico, Bejis 28835
Museo Etnológico, Bielsa 28849
Museo Etnológico, Boltaña 28862
Museo Etnológico, San Juan de Plan 29614
Museo Etnológico Aljibes de Gasparito, Rojales 29572
Museo Etnológico Casa Mazo, Valle de Hecho 29870
Museo Etnológico de la Diputación, Castellón de la Plana 28935
Museo Etnológico de Morella y del Meastrazgo, Morella 29383
Museo Etnológico de Navarra Julio Caro Baroja, Ayegui 28747
Museo Etnologico della Montagna Pistoiese, Cutigliano 21499
Museo Etnológico Misional C.M.F., Santa Isabel 08261
Museo Etnologico Missionario, Fiesole 21565
Museo Etnológico Popular, Fuensanta 29068
Museo Etnolológico Anselmo Buil, Blecua 28859
Museo Etrusco, Asciano 21097
Museo Etrusco, Chiusi Città 21423
Museo Etrusco, San Gimignano 22481
Museo Etrusco di Villa Giulia, Roma 22391
Museo Etrusco Gasparri, Populonia 22242
Museo Etrusco Guarnacci, Volterra 22887
Museo Etrusco Pompeo Aria, Marzabotto 21852
Museo Etrusco Ranuccio Bianchi Bandinelli, Colle di Val d'Elsa 21451
Museo Ettore Pomarici Santomasi, Gravina di Puglia 21717
Museo Europeo dei Trasporti Ogliari, Ranco 22282
Museo Evaristo Valle, Gijón 29088
Museo Evocativo y de Bellas Artes Osvaldo Gasparini, San Antonio de Areco 00540
Museo Extremeño e Iberoamericano de Arte Contemporáneo, Badajoz 28758
Museo F. Renzi, San Giovanni in Galilea 22484
Museo Fallero, Valencia 29841
Museo Farmacéutico, Matanzas 07167
Museo Farmacobotánica, Buenos Aires 00197
Museo Faryluk, Aristóbulo del Valle 00109
Museo Fernán Félix de Amador, Luján 00409
Museo Ferroviario, Alcázar de San Juan 28669
Museo Ferroviario de Gualeguaychú, Gualeguaychú 00353
Museo Ferrucciano, Gavinana 21675
Museo Filatélico del Banco de la República, Medellín 06860
Museo Florencio de la Fuente, Huete 29151
Museo Florencio Molina Campos, Moreno 00446
Museo Florentino Ameghino, Bolívar 00132
Museo Folklórico, La Rioja 00391
Museo Folklórico Araucano de Cañete Juan A. Ríos M., Cañete 06364
Museo Folklórico de Tejicóndor, Medellín 06861
Museo Folklórico Provincial, San Miguel de Tucumán 00576
Museo Folklórico Regional de Humahuaca, Humahuaca 00356
Museo Fondazione C. Faina e Museo Civico Palazzo Faina, Orvieto 22076
Museo Forense, Roma 22392
Museo Fournier de Naipes de Alava, Vitoria-Gasteiz 29935
Museo Francescano, Gubbio 21731
Museo Francescano, Roma 22393
Museo Francesco Baracca, Lugo 21817
Museo Francesco Borgogna, Vercelli 22832
Museo Francesco Cilea, Palmi 22122
Museo Franciiscos Campos, Guayaquil 08139
El Museo Francisco Oller y Diego Rivera, Buffalo 35741
Museo Franz Mayer, México 24453
Museo Frida Kahlo, México 24454
Museo Friulano di Storia Naturale, Udine 22756
Museo Fuerte Independencia, Tandil 00620
Museo Fundación John Boulton, La Guaira 41445
Museo Fundación Naum Komp, Buenos Aires 00198
Museo Gabriela Mistral de Vicuña, Vicuña 06404
Museo Galego do Xoguete, Allariz 28687
Museo Galleria di Villa Borghese, Roma 22394
Museo Garda, Ivrea 21757
Museo Garibaldino, Caprera 21305
Museo Garibaldino della Campagna dell'Agro Romano per la Liberazione di Roma 1867, Mentana 21876
Museo Gauchesco Ricardo Güiraldes, San Antonio de Areco 00541
Museo General Belgrano, Buenos Aires 00199
Museo General de Arequito, Arequito 00107
Museo General Lavalle, General Pinto 00347
Museo Geográfico Einstein, San Juan 00563
Museo Geologico, Castell'Arquato 21345
Museo Geológico, Laspaules 29180
Museo Geológico de la Universidad Nacional de Ingeniería del Perú, Lima 26500
Museo Geológico del Seminario, Barcelona 28786
Museo Geologico G.G. Gemmellaro, Palermo 22114
Museo Geológico José Royo y Gómez, Santafé de Bogotá 06910
Museo Geologico Paleontologico G. Capellini, Bologna 21210
Museo Geominero, Madrid 29277
Museo Germán Guglielmetti, Benito Juárez 00130
Museo Giannettino Luxoro, Genova 21701
Museo Giovanni Boldini, Ferrara 21556
Museo Gregoriano Egizio, Città del Vaticano 41397
Museo Gregoriano Etrusco, Città del Vaticano 41398
Museo Gregoriano Profano, Città del Vaticano 41399
Museo Gregorio Aguilar Barea, Chontales 25958
Museo Guillermo Perez Chiriboga del Banco Central, Quito 08168
Museo Gustavo de Maeztu, Estella 29047
Museo Hans Multscher e Museo Civico, Vipiteno 22874
Museo Hermann Hesse, Montagnola 31010
Museo Hermanos Nacif Weiss, Rivadavia 00514
Museo Hidráulico los Molinos del Río Segura, Murcia 29390
Museo Historiador Hernández Galiano, Tostado 00629
Museo Historico, Riobamba 08181
Museo Histórico, Zapala 00667
Museo Histórico 26 de Julio, Santiago de Cuba 07182
Museo Histórico Arqueológico, A Coruña 28994
Museo Histórico Arqueológico Guillermo Magrassi, Mar del Plata 00418
Museo Histórico, Arqueológico y de Arte Pedro Balduín, San Pedro de Jujuy 00584
Museo Historico Bae Calderon, Guayaquil 08140
Museo Historico Casa de la Convención de Rionegro, Rionegro 06879
Museo Historico Casa de los Tratados, Cuenca 08128
Museo Histórico, Colonial y de Bellas Artes y Museo de Ciencias Naturales Regional Mesopotámico, Mercedes 00436
Museo Histórico Comunal, Villa Trinidad 00665
Museo Histórico Comunal de San Genaro Norte, San Genaro Norte 00553
Museo Histórico Comunal y de la Colonización Judía Rabino Aaron H. Goldman, Moisés Ville 00443
Museo Histórico Conventual San Carlos, San Lorenzo 00567
Museo Histórico Cultural Juan Santamaría, Alajuela 06941
Museo Histórico de Acapulco, Acapulco 24383
Museo Histórico de Antioquia, Medellín 06862
Museo Histórico de Arenaza, Arenaza 00106
Museo Histórico de Arrecifes, Arrecifes 00111
Museo Histórico de Arte, Morón 00448
Museo Histórico de Cañuelas, Cañuelas 00251
Museo Histórico de Cartagena Casa de la Inquisición, Cartagena 06840
Museo Histórico de Cera, Buenos Aires 00200
Museo Histórico de Corrientes Manuel Cabral de Mayo y Alpoín, Corrientes 00312
Museo Histórico de Entre Ríos Martiniano Leguizamón, Paraná 00460
Museo Histórico de Guatraché, Guatraché 00354
Museo Histórico de la Administración Española, Alcalá de Henares 28666
Museo Histórico de la Ciudad, Valencia 29842
Museo Histórico de la Ciudad de Buenos Aires Brigadier-General Cornelio de Saavedra, Buenos Aires 00201
Museo Histórico de la Colonia San Carlos, San Carlos Centro 00544
Museo Histórico de la Dirección General Impositiva, Buenos Aires 00202
Museo Histórico de la Honorable Cámara de Diputados de la Nación, Buenos Aires 00203
Museo Histórico de la Iglesia, Buenos Aires 00204
Museo Histórico de la Policía de la Provincia de Misiones, Posadas 00475
Museo Histórico de la Policia de Mendoza, Mendoza 00430
Museo Histórico de la Prefectura Naval Argentina, Tigre 00624
Museo Histórico de la Provincia, Santiago del Estero 00608
Museo Histórico de la Provincia de Catamarca, San Fernando del Valle de Catamarca 00548
Museo Histórico de La Rioja, La Rioja 00392
Museo Histórico de Laborde, Laborde 00393
Museo Histórico de Navarro, Navarro 00449
Museo Histórico de Osorno, Osorno 06376
Museo Histórico de Ranchos, Ranchos 00493
Museo Histórico de Requena y su Comarca, Requena 29551
Museo Histórico de San Francisco, Santa Fé 00595
Museo Histórico de Sitio, Dolores Hidalgo 24394
Museo Histórico del Regimiento de Granaderos a Caballo General San Martín, Buenos Aires 00205
Museo Histórico del Transporte Carlos Hillner Decoud, Quilmes 00486
Museo Histórico Etnológico, Llosa de Ranes 29219
Museo Histórico Ferroviario Escribano Alfredo Rueda, Rueda 00526
Museo Histórico Franciscano, San Salvador de Jujuy 00587
Museo Histórico Fuerte Barragan, Ensenada 00331
Museo Histórico General Julio de Vedia, 9 de Julio 00096
Museo Histórico José Hernández-Chacra Pueyrredón, Villa Ballester 00651
Museo Histórico La Gallareta Forestal, La Gallareta 00372
Museo Histórico Local, Cañete de las Torres 28912
Museo Histórico Local, Fuente Tojar 29070
Museo Histórico Local, Montoro 29381
Museo Histórico Manuel A. Moreira, Laboulaye 00394
Museo Histórico Militar, Asunción 26463
Museo Histórico Militar del Perú, Callao 26473
Museo Histórico-Minero Don Felipe de Borbón y Grecia, Madrid 29278
Museo Histórico Municipal, Bahía Blanca 00118
Museo Histórico Municipal, Cádiz 28890
Museo Histórico Municipal, La Habana 07153
Museo Histórico Municipal, Salto 34963
Museo Histórico Municipal, San Fernando 29609
Museo Histórico Municipal Alfredo E. Múlgura, General Belgrano 00344
Museo Histórico Municipal Andrés A. Roverano, Santo Tomé 00612

Alphabetical Index: Muse

Museo Municipal José A. Mulazzi, Tres Arroyos 00632
Museo Municipal José Manuel Maciel, Coronda 00305
Museo Municipal José María Labrador, Nerva 29400
Museo Municipal Lino Enea Spilimbergo, Unquillo 00638
Museo Municipal Lorenzo Coullaut-Valera, Marchena 29332
Museo Municipal Manuel Torres, Marín 29334
Museo Municipal Mariano Benlliure, Crevillente 29000
Museo Municipal Mateo Hernández, Béjar 28834
Museo Municipal Paula Florido, 25 de Mayo 00095
Museo Municipal Primeros Pobladores, San Martín de los Andes 00569
Museo Municipal Punta Hermengo, Miramar 00442
Museo Municipal Ramón María Aller Ulloa, Lalín 29179
Museo Municipal Remigio Crespo Toral, Cuenca 08130
Museo Municipal Sala Dámaso Navarro, Petrer 29505
Museo Municipal Taurino, Córdoba 28982
Museo Municipal Ulpiano Checa, Colmenar de Oreja 28969
Museo Municipal Victorio Macho, Palencia 29456
Museo Municpal Dr. Santos F. Tosticarelli, Casilda 00259
Museo Mural Diego Rivera, México 24457
Museo Muratoriano, Modena 21951
Museo Nacional Centro de Arte Reina Sofía, Madrid 29281
Museo Nacional David J. Guzmán, San Salvador 08260
Museo Nacional de Aeronáutica, Buenos Aires 00216
Museo Nacional de Antropología, Madrid 29282
Museo Nacional de Antropología, Madrid 29283
Museo Nacional de Antropología, México 24458
Museo Nacional de Antropología, Montevideo 34947
Museo Nacional de Antropología, Santafé de Bogotá 06912
Museo Nacional de Antropología y Arqueología, Lima 26501
Museo Nacional de Arqueología, La Paz 03869
Museo Nacional de Arqueología Marítima, Cartagena 28926
Museo Nacional de Arqueología y Etnología, Guatemala City 19753
Museo Nacional de Arquitectura, Madrid 29284
Museo Nacional de Arquitectura, México 24459
Museo Nacional de Arte, La Paz 03870
Museo Nacional de Arte, México 24460
Museo Nacional de Arte Decorativo, Buenos Aires 00217
Museo Nacional de Arte Hispanomusulmán, Granada 29120
Museo Nacional de Arte Moderno, Guatemala City 19754
Museo Nacional de Arte Oriental, Buenos Aires 00218
Museo Nacional de Arte Romano, Mérida 29352
Museo Nacional de Artes Decorativas, Madrid 29285
Museo Nacional de Artes e Industrias Populares, México 24461
Museo Nacional de Artes Visuales, Montevideo 34948
Museo Nacional de Bellas Artes, Buenos Aires 00219
Museo Nacional de Bellas Artes, Habana Vieja 07165
Museo Nacional de Bellas Artes, Montevideo 34949
Museo Nacional de Bellas Artes de Santiago de Chile, Santiago 06391
Museo Nacional de Bellas Artes y Antigüedades, Asunción 26465
Museo Nacional de Caza, Real Bosque de Riofrío 29547
Museo Nacional de Cerámica y de las Artes Suntuarias, Valencia 29843
Museo Nacional de Ciencias Naturales, Madrid 29286
Museo Nacional de Colombia, Santafé de Bogotá 06913
Museo Nacional de Costa Rica, San José 06949
Museo Nacional de Escultura, Valladolid 29861
Museo Nacional de Etnografía y Folklore, La Paz 03871
Museo Nacional de Ferrocarriles, Puebla 24502
Museo Nacional de Historia, Guatemala City 19755
Museo Nacional de Historia, Lima 26502
Museo Nacional de Historia, México 24462
Museo Nacional de Historia Colonial, Omoa 19780
Museo Nacional de Historia de la Medicina Eduardo Estrella, Quito 08171
Museo Nacional de Historia Natural, Guatemala City 19756
Museo Nacional de Historia Natural, Montevideo 34950
Museo Nacional de Historia Natural, Santiago 06392
Museo Nacional de Historia Natural de la Ciudad de México, México 24463
Museo Nacional de la Acuarela, México 24464
Museo Nacional de la Campana de Alfabetización, La Habana 07156
Museo Nacional de la Cerámica, La Habana 07157
Museo Nacional de la Ciencia y la Tecnología, Madrid 29287
Museo Nacional de la Cultura Peruana, Lima 26503
Museo Nacional de la Dirección Regional del Banco Central del Ecuador, Quito 08172
Museo Nacional de la Estampa, México 24465
Museo Nacional de la Histórico del Traje, Buenos Aires 00220
Museo Nacional de la Revolución, México 24466
Museo Nacional de las Culturas, México 24467
Museo Nacional de las Intervenciones, México 24468
Museo Nacional de las Populares, México 24469
Museo Nacional de los Ferrocarriles Mexicanos, México 24470
Museo Nacional de Música, La Habana 07158
Museo Nacional de Nicaragua, Managua 25960
Museo Nacional de Panamá, Panamá City 26448
Museo Nacional de Reproducciones Artísticas, Madrid 29288
Museo Nacional de San Carlos, México 24471
Museo Nacional de Tegucigalpa, Tegucigalpa 19784
Museo Nacional de Virreinato, Tepotzotlán 24512
Museo Nacional del Grabado, Buenos Aires 00221
Museo Nacional del Hombre, Buenos Aires 00222
Museo Nacional del Petróleo, Comodoro Rivadavia 00273
Museo Nacional del Prado, Madrid 29289
Museo Nacional Jesútico de Jesús María, Jesús María 00362
Museo Nacional Justo José de Urquiza, Concepción del Uruguay 00276
Museo Nacional Tihuanacu, La Paz 03872
Museo Nacional y Centro de Estudios Históricos Ferroviarios, Buenos Aires 00223
Museo Nacional y Centro de Investigación de Altamira, Santillana del Mar 29688
Museo Nacional y Zoológico La Aurora, Guatemala City 19757
Museo Nahim Isaias B., Guayaquil 08142
Museo Nájerillense, Nájera 29396
Museo Napoleonico, Arcole 21080
Museo Napoleónico, La Habana 07159
Museo Napoleonico, Rivoli Veronese 22323
Museo Napoleonico, Roma 22395
Museo Natural de Historia y Geografía, Santo Domingo 08111
Museo Natural Dr. Carlos A. Marelli, Colón 00272
Museo Naturalistica-Archeologico, Vicenza 22858
Museo Naturalistico del Lago, Montepulciano 21992
Museo Naturalistico Provinciale, Sondrio 22592
Museo Naval, Madrid 29290
Museo Naval de Cartagena, Cartagena 28927
Museo Naval de la Nación, Tigre 00625
Museo Naval de la Zona Marítima del Cantábrico, Ferrol 29056
Museo Naval de Viña del Mar, Viña del Mar 06407
Museo Naval del Puerto de la Cruz, Puerto de la Cruz 29537
Museo Naval Puerto Belgrano, Puerto Belgrano 00480
Museo Naval - Untzi Museoa, Donostia-San Sebastián 29019
Museo Navale, Napoli 22026
Museo Navale Internazionale del Ponente Ligure, Imperia 21748
Museo Navale Romano, Albenga 21047
Museo Nazionale, Ravenna 22289
Museo Nazionale, Tuscania 22750
Museo Nazionale, Venafro 22788
Museo Nazionale Archeologico, Civitavecchia 21443
Museo Nazionale Archeologico, Ferrara 21558
Museo Nazionale Archeologico, Sarsina 22538
Museo Nazionale Archeologico, Tarquinia 22628
Museo Nazionale Archeologico dell'Abruzzo, Chieti 21415
Museo Nazionale Atestino, Este 21522
Museo Nazionale Cagliari, Cagliari 21267
Museo Nazionale Cerite, Cerveteri 21388
Museo Nazionale Concordiese, Portogruaro 22251
Museo Nazionale d'Abruzzo, L'Aquila 21772
Museo Nazionale d'Arte Orientale, Roma 22396
Museo Nazionale degli Strumenti Musicali, Roma 22397
Museo Nazionale del Bargello, Firenze 21625
Museo Nazionale del Cinema, Torino 22688
Museo Nazionale del Compendio Garibaldino di Caprera, La Maddalena 21760
Museo Nazionale del Palazzo di Venezia, Roma 22398
Museo Nazionale del Risorgimento Italiano, Torino 22689
Museo Nazionale del San Gottardo, San Gottardo 31166
Museo Nazionale della Montagna Duca degli Abruzzi, Torino 22690
Museo Nazionale della Residenza Napoleonica dei Mulini, Portoferraio 22248
Museo Nazionale della Residenza Napoleonica di Villa San Martino, Portoferraio 22249
Museo Nazionale della Scienza e della Tecnica Leonardo da Vinci, Milano 21922
Museo Nazionale della Siritide, Policoro 22229
Museo Nazionale dell'Agro Picentino, Pontecagnano 22238
Museo Nazionale dell'Arma della Cavalleria, Pinerolo 22207
Museo Nazionale delle Arti e Tradizioni Roma, Roma 22399
Museo Nazionale delle Paste Alimentari, Roma 22400
Museo Nazionale dell'Età Neoclassica in Romagna, Faenza 21531
Museo Nazionale di Castel Sant'Angelo, Roma 22401
Museo Nazionale di Reggio Calabria, Reggio di Calabria 22297
Museo Nazionale di San Matteo, Pisa 22216
Museo Nazionale di Villa Guinigi, Lucca 21812
Museo Nazionale Domenico Ridola, Matera 21870
Museo Nazionale Jatta, Ruvo di Puglia 22453
Museo Nazionale Preistorico ed Etnografico Luigi Pigorini, Roma 22402
Museo Nazionale Romano-Terme di Diocleziano, Roma 22403
Museo Néstor, Las Palmas de Gran Canaria 29482
Museo ng Bangko Sentral ng Pilipinas, Manila 26556
Museo ng Kalinangang Pilipino, Manila 26557
Museo ng Maynila, Manila 26558
Museo Nicanor Piñole, Gijón 29090
Museo Nicola Antonio Manfroce, Palmi 22123
Museo Notarial Argentino, Buenos Aires 00224
Museo Nuestra Señora de Carrodilla, Luján de Cuyo 00410
Museo Nueva Cádiz, La Asunción 41444
Museo Numantino, Soria 29738
Museo Numismático, La Habana 07160
Museo Numismático de la Casa Nacional de la Moneda, Lima 26504
Museo Numismático del Banco de la Nación Argentina, Córdoba 00297
Museo Numismático del Banco Naciónal, Buenos Aires 00225
Museo Numismatico della Zecca, Roma 22404
Museo Numismático Dr. José Evaristo Uriburu, Buenos Aires 00226
Museo Nuovo, Roma 22405
Museo Obispo Fray José Antonio de San Alberto, Córdoba 00298
Museo Obispo Vellosillo, Ayllón 28749
Museo Oceanografico dell'Istituto Talassografico, Taranto 22626
Museo Ochoa, Valencia 29844
Museo Odontológico Dr. Jorge E. Dunster, Corrientes 00313
Museo O'Higginiano y de Bellas Artes de Talca, Talca 06397
Museo Omar Rayo, Roldanillo 06880
Museo Oncativo, Oncativo 00455
Museo Onsernonese, Loco 30957
Museo Oraziano, Licenza 21788
Museo Organológico Folklórico Musical, Santafé de Bogotá 06914
Museo Oriental, Valladolid 29862
Museo Orientale, Tagliacozzo 22622
Museo Orientale Ca' Pesaro, Venezia 22814
Museo Orlando Binaghi, Moreno 00447
Museo Ornitológico, Aragua 41409
Museo Ornitologico e di Scienze Naturali, Ravenna 22290
Museo Ornitologico F. Foschi, Forlì 21646
Museo Ornitológico Patagónico, El Bolsón 00324
Museo Oscar María de Rojas, Cardenas 07134
Museo Ostetrico, Bologna 21214
Museo Ostiense, Ostia Antica 22081
Museo Ostiense, Scavi di Ostia, Roma 22406
Museo Pablo Gargallo, Zaragoza 29961
Museo Pablo Serrano, Zaragoza 29962
Museo Pachacamac, Lima 26505
Museo Padiglione delle Carozza, Città del Vaticano 41401
Museo Padre Coll, Buenos Aires 00227
Museo Palacio de Don Pedro I, Astudillo 28735
Museo-Palacio de Fuensalida, Toledo 29776
Museo-Palacio del Emperador Carlos V, Cuacos de Yuste 29001
Museo Palatino, Roma 22407
Museo Palazzina Storica, Peschiera del Garda 22169
Museo Paleocristiano, Aquileia 21078
Museo Paleontologico, L'Aquila 21773
Museo Paleontológico, Miño de Medinaceli 29355
Museo Paleontologico, Monfalcone 21965
Museo Paleontologico, Montevarchi 21997
Museo Paleontologico, Voghera 22882
Museo Paleontológico, Arqueológico e Histórico de la Ciudad de Deán Funes, Deán Funes 00318
Museo Paleontológico Egidio Feruglio, Trelew 00630
Museo Paleontológico Municipal, Valencia 29845
Museo Paleontologico Parmense, Parma 22135
Museo Paleontológico y Petrolero Astra, Comodoro Rivadavia 00274
Museo Paleoveneto, Pieve di Cadore 22198
Museo Pampeano de Chascomús, Chascomús 00263
Museo Pampeano del Pergamino, Pergamino 00466
Museo Parlamentario, Buenos Aires 00228
Museo Parrocchiale, Castell'Arquato 21347
Museo Parrocchiale, Mogliano Marche 21955
Museo Parrocchiale del Santuario del Santissimo Crocifisso, Buggiano 21255
Museo Parrocchiale della Chiesa Collegiata, Mercatello sul Metauro 21880
Museo Parrocchiale di Arte Sacra, Ponte in Valtellina 22235
Museo Parrocchiale di Santa Maria delle Grazie, Salerno 22463
Museo Parroquial, La Almunia de Doña Godina 28695
Museo Parroquial, Alquezar 28696
Museo Parroquial, Barco de Avila 28832
Museo Parroquial, Benabarre 28839
Museo Parroquial, Bocairente 28860
Museo Parroquial, Celanova 28945
Museo Parroquial, Cervera de Pisuerga 28950
Museo Parroquial, Ecija 29024
Museo Parroquial, Espejo 29043
Museo Parroquial, Ezcaray 29051
Museo Parroquial, Hondarribia 29143
Museo Parroquial, Madrid 29291
Museo Parroquial, Medina de Rioseco 29346
Museo Parroquial, Miranda del Castañar 29356
Museo Parroquial, Paradas 29487
Museo Parroquial, Pastrana 29493
Museo Parroquial, Roda de Isábena 29568
Museo Parroquial, Santa Gadea del Cid 29654
Museo Parroquial, Santa María del Campo 29660
Museo Parroquial, Segovia 29701
Museo Parroquial Colegiata de San Miguel, Aguilar de Campoo 28653
Museo Parroquial de Arte Sacro y Etnología, Anso 28704
Museo Parroquial de Monterroso, Monterroso 29377
Museo Parroquial de San Cosme y San Damián, Covarrubias 28998
Museo Parroquial de San Félix, Girona 29093
Museo Parroquial de San Martiño de Mondoñedo, Foz 29064
Museo Parroquial de San Martiño de Mondoñedo, San Martiño de Mondoñedo-Foz 29617
Museo Parroquial de Santa Eulalia, Paredes de Nava 29490
Museo Parroquial de Zurbarán, Marchena 29333
Museo Parroquial San Pedro, Cisneros 28957
Museo Parroquial Santa María del Salvador, Chinchilla 28954
Museo Parroquial Santa María La Real, Xunqueira de Ambia 29940
Museo Participativo de Ciencias, Buenos Aires 00229
Museo Particular Los Abuelos, Franck 00339
Museo Patria Chica, Realicó 00496
Museo Pavese di Scienze Naturali, Pavia 22144
Museo Pecharromán, Pasarón de la Vera 29491
Museo Pedagógico Carlos Stuardo Ortiz, Santiago 06393
Museo Pedagógico Ciencias Naturales Jesús María Hernando, Valladolid 29863
Museo Pedagógico de Arte Infantil, Madrid 29292
Museo Pedagógico de Artes Visuales, Gálvez 00342
Museo Pedagógico de Historia del Arte, Caracas 41435
Museo Pedagógico José Pedro Varela, Montevideo 34951
Museo Pedagógico Nacional, México 24472
Museo Pedro Ara, Córdoba 00299
Museo Pedro Suro, Dolores 00321
Museo Penitenciario Argentino, Buenos Aires 00230
Museo Pepoli, Trapani 22709
Museo per la Storia dell'Università di Pavia, Pavia 22145
Museo Pérez Comendador-Leroux, Hérvas 29142
Museo Permanente delle Truppe Alpine Mario Balocco, Biella 21169
Museo Petrográfico del Servicio Nacional de Geología y Minería, Quito 08173
Museo Picasso, Buitrago del Lozoy 28867
Museo Piersanti, Matelica 21869
Museo Pietro Canonica, Stresa 22610
Museo Pietro Micca, Torino 22691
Museo Pinacoteca A. Salvucci, Molfetta 21959
Museo-Pinacoteca Comunale, Mogliano Marche 21956
Museo Pinacoteca Santa Casa, Loreto 21805
Museo Pinacoteca Villa Groppallo, Vado Ligure 22765
Museo Pio Clementino, Città del Vaticano 41402
Museo Pio Collivadino, Banfield 00123
Museo Pio Cristiano, Città del Vaticano 41403
Museo Pío del Río Ortega, Valladolid 29864
Museo Pio IX e Pinacoteca d'Arte Sacra Senigallia, Senigallia 22561
Museo Pittori Naif Italiani, Luzzara 21819
Museo Playa Girón, Matanzas 07169
Museo Plebano, Agno 30504
Museo Poldi Pezzoli, Milano 21923
Museo Policial, Avila 28741
Museo Polifacético Regional Vottero, Laguna Larga 00395
Museo Pomposiano, Codigoro 21446
Museo Popoli e Culture, Milano 21924
Museo Postal, México 24473
Museo Postal Cubano, La Habana 07161
Museo Postal y Filatélico de Correos del Perú, Lima 26506
Museo Postal y Telegráfico, Madrid 29293
Museo Postal y Telegráfico Doctor Ramon J. Carcano, Buenos Aires 00231
Museo Postale, Filatelico-Numismatico, San Marino 28155
Museo Preistorico della Val Varatello, Toirano 22651
Museo Preistorico e Lapidario, Verucchio 22847
Museo Presidente José Evaristo Uriburu, Salta 00533
Museo Prisión Modelo, Nueva Gerona 07170
Museo Privado de Arqueología Regional Julio Gironde, Carmen de Patagonés 00256
Museo Prof. Dr. Juan Augusto Olsacher, Zapala 00668
Museo Profano, Città del Vaticano 41404
Museo Progressivo d'Arte Contemporanea, Livorno 21793
Museo Provincial, Jaén 29165
Museo Provincial, Lugo 29230
Museo Provincial, Teruel 29762
Museo Provincial Arqueológico Eric Boman, Santa María de Catamarca 00602
Museo Provincial de Arqueología Wagner, Santiago del Estero 00609
Museo Provincial de Artes de La Pampa, Santa Rosa 00603
Museo Provincial de Bellas Artes, Corrientes 00314
Museo Provincial de Bellas Artes, Salta 00534
Museo Provincial de Bellas Artes Dr. Pedro E. Martínez, Paraná 00462
Museo Provincial de Bellas Artes Emiliano Guiñazu - Casa de Fader, Luján de Cuyo 00411

791

Alphabetical Index: Sall

Schreinermuseum, Altishofen 30518
Schreinermuseum, Ettiswil 30763
Schrift- und Heimatmuseum Bartlhaus, Pettenbach 02394
Schriftmuseum J.A. Dortmond, Amsterdam 24734
Schubert-Gedenkstätte Geburtshaus, Wien 02958
Schubert-Gedenkstätte Sterbewohnung, Wien 02959
Schüttesägemuseum, Schiltach 18337
Schützenhaus Glaucha, Halle, Saale 16197
Schützenmuseum der Königlich privilegierten Feuerschützengesellschaft Weilheim, Weilheim, Oberbayern 18977
Schützenscheibenmuseum, Scheibbs 02606
Schützenscheibensammlung, Mainbernheim 17223
Schulgeschichtliche Sammlung, Bremen 15066
Schulgeschichtliche Sammlung, Magdeburg 17218
Schulgeschichtliche Sammlung im Main-Taunus-Kreis, Kriftel 16880
Schulheimatmuseum, Asbach-Bäumenheim 14308
Schulhistorische Sammlung Cruismannschule, Bochum 14944
Schullandheim Sassen, Sassen, Vorpommern 18316
Schulmuseum, Bad Kissingen 14455
Schulmuseum, Frankfurt/Oder 15783
Schulmuseum, Hundisburg 16527
Schulmuseum Bergisch Gladbach, Bergisch Gladbach 14664
Schulmuseum des Bezirkes Urfahr-Umgebung, Bad Leonfelden 01707
Schulmuseum des Bezirks Unterfranken, Bad Bocklet 14403
Schulmuseum Friedrichshafen am Bodensee, Friedrichshafen 15846
Schulmuseum Fronau, Roding 18192
Schulmuseum Lilienthal, Lilienthal 17104
Schulmuseum Mozartschule Rheingönheim, Ludwigshafen am Rhein 17155
Schulmuseum Nordwürttemberg in Kornwestheim, Kornwestheim 16856
Schulmuseum Nürnberg, Nürnberg 17757
Schulmuseum Steinhorst, Steinhorst, Niedersachsen 18591
Schulmuseum und Hallenhaus, Middelhagen, Rügen 17360
Schulmuseum Vechelde, Vechelde 18818
Schulmuseum - Werkstatt für Schulgeschichte Leipzig, Leipzig 17058
Schulmuseum Wildenhain, Wildenhain bei Großenhain, Sachsen 19114
Schulstub'n-Glockenhäusl, Sankt Peter am Wimberg 02575
Schultehuis, Diever 24946
Schulze-Delitzsch-Haus, Delitzsch 15288
Schumacher Gallery, Columbus 36232
Schumann-Haus, Leipzig 17059
Schutterskamer, Sneek 25503
Schuyler County Historical Society Museum, Montour Falls 38609
Schuyler-Hamilton House, Morristown 38638
Schuyler Jail Museum, Rushville 39885
Schuyler Mansion State Historic Site, Albany 35002
Schwäbisches Bauern- und Technikmuseum, Eschach 15631
Schwäbisches Bauernhofmuseum Illerbeuren, Kronburg 16889
Schwäbisches Handwerkermuseum, Augsburg 14355
Schwäbisches Krippenmuseum im Jesuitenkolleg, Mindelheim 17369
Schwäbisches Schnapsmuseum, Bönnigheim 14960
Schwäbisches Schützenmuseum, Kronburg 16890
Schwäbisches Turmuhrenmuseum, Mindelheim 17370
Schwäbisches Volkskundemuseum und Bauernhofmuseum Staudenhaus, Gessertshausen 15962
Schwälmer Dorfmuseum, Schrecksbach 18393
Schwartz Collection of Skiing Heritage, San Rafael 40158
Schwartz Heritage House, Altona 04440
Schwartzsche Villa, Berlin 14838
Schwarz-Afrika-Museum, Vilshofen 18855
Schwarzachtaler Heimatmuseum, Neunburg vorm Wald 17650
Schwarzenberger Skulpturenpark, Schwarzenberg am Böhmerwald 02620
Schwarzwälder Freilichtmuseum Vogtsbauernhof, Gutach, Schwarzwaldbahn 16149
Schwarzwälder Mineralienmuseum, Neubulach 17621
Schwarzwälder Mühlenmuseum, Grafenhausen 16058
Schwarzwälder Trachtenmuseum, Haslach 16299
Schwarzwald-Museum, Triberg 18734
Schwazer Silberbergwerk, Schwaz 02626
Schweine-Museum, Bad Wimpfen 14546
Schweinfurth Memorial Art Center, Auburn 35240
Schweizer Filmmuseum, Basel 30585
Schweizer Jazzmuseum, Uster 31338
Schweizer Kamm-Museum, Mümliswil 31029
Schweizer Kindermuseum, Baden 30555
Schweizer Museum für Wild und Jagd, Utzenstorf 31340
Schweizerische Landesbibliothek, Bern 30616
Schweizerische Theatersammlung, Bern 30617
Schweizerisches Alpines Museum, Bern 30618
Schweizerisches Dampfmaschinenmuseum Vaporama, Thun 31310
Schweizerisches Feuerwehrmuseum, Basel 30586
Schweizerisches Freilichtmuseum für ländliche Kultur, Brienz, Bern 30653
Schweizerisches Gastronomie-Museum, Thun 31311
Schweizerisches Meteoriten-und Mineralienmueum, Schönenwerd 31213
Schweizerisches Museum für Landwirtschaft und Agrartechnik Burgrain, Alberswil 30511
Schweizerisches Schützenmuseum, Bern 30619
Schweizerisches Sportmuseum, Basel 30587
Schweizerisches Zentrum für Volkskultur, Burgdorf 30675
Schwemmgut-Museum, Finsing 15705
Schwenkfelder Library and Heritage Center, Pennsburg 39316
Schwerkolt Cottage Museum, Mitcham 01250
Schwörhaus, Esslingen 15671
Schwules Museum, Berlin 14839
Sci-Port Discovery Center, Shreveport 40352
Sci-Tech Center of Northern New York, Watertown 41040
Science and Industry Collections Group, London 42027
Science and Technology Museum, Yazd 20662
Science and Technology Museum of Atlanta, Atlanta 35229
Science Center of Connecticut, West Hartford 41110
Science Center of Iowa, Des Moines 36493
Science Center of New Hampshire, Holderness 37451
Science Center of West Virginia, Bluefield 35549
Science Centre and Manawatu Museum, Palmerston North 25865
Science Centre for Education, Bangkok 31552
Science Discovery Center of Oneonta, Oneonta 39174
Science Museum, Kabul 00006
Science Museum, London 33777
Science Museum, Tokyo 23612
Science Museum, Upton 40808
Science Museum of Long Island, Manhasset 38303
Science Museum of Minnesota, Saint Paul 40000
Science Museum of Virginia, Richmond 39767
Science Museum of Western Virginia, Roanoke 39804
Science Museum Osaka, Osaka 23438
Science Museum Wroughton, Wroughton 34897
Science North, Sudbury 05984
Science Spectrum, Lubbock 38207
Science Station Museum, Cedar Rapids 35887
Sciencenter, Ithaca 37634
Scienceworks, Spotswood 01465
Scienceworks Museum, Melbourne 01232
Scientific Collections, Forssa 08320
Scientific Researches Museum, Cairo 08233
Scironian Museum of Costas Polychronopoulos, Mégara 19561
SciTech Museum, Aurora 35260
Scituate Historical Museum, Scituate 40259
Sciworks, Winston-Salem 41253
Scolton Manor Museum, Haverfordwest 33220
Scone and Upper Hunter Historical Museum, Scone 01442
Scone Palace, Perth 34173
Scotch Whisky Heritage Centre, Edinburgh 32947
Scotia-Glenville Children's Museum, Scotia 40262
Scotland Heritage Chapel and Museum, Scotland 40263
Scotland Street School Museum, Glasgow 33095
Scotland's Secret Bunker, Saint Andrews 34364
The Scott Gallery, Hawick 33225
Scott Polar Research Institute Museum, Cambridge 32508
Scottish Fisheries Museum, Anstruther 32052
Scottish Football Museum, Glasgow 33096
Scottish Industrial Railway Centre, Dalmellington 32735
Scottish Infantry Divisional Museum, Penicuik 34159
Scottish Jewish Museum, Glasgow 33097
Scottish Maritime Museum, Irvine 33337
Scottish Mining Museum, Newtongrange 34059
Scottish Museum of Woollen Textiles, Walkerburn 34726
Scottish Museums Council, Edinburgh 42028
Scottish Museums Federation, Hamilton 42029
Scottish National Gallery of Modern Art and Dean Gallery, Edinburgh 32948
Scottish National Portrait Gallery, Edinburgh 32949
Scottish Rugby Union Museum, Edinburgh 32950
Scottish Traditions of Dance, Edinburgh 32951
Scotts Bluff National Monument, Gering 37125
Scottsdale Museum of Contemporary Art, Scottsdale 40269
Scout Museum of Finland, Turku 08970
Scouting Museum de Ducdalf, Rotterdam 25446
Scriver Museum of Montana Wildlife and Hall of Bronze, Browning 35713
Scryption, Tilburg 25543
Scugog Shores Historical Museum, Port Perry 05637
Scuola Dalmata dei SS. Giorgio e Trifone, Venezia 22822
Scuola Grande Arciconfraternita di San Rocco, Venezia 22823
Scuola Grande Arciconfraternita S.M. del Carmelo, Venezia 22824
Scuola Grande di San Giovanni Evangelista, Venezia 22825
Scurry County Museum, Snyder 40389
Ščusev Museum, Chişinău 24527
Sea Museum, Toba 23572
Sea World, Durban 28465
Seafood Museum, Qingdao 06679
Seaford Historical Museum, Seaford 40277
Seaford Museum of Local History, Seaford 34436
Seaforth Highlanders of Canada Regimental Museum, Vancouver 06163
Seagate Gallery, Dundee 32842
Seal Island Light Museum, Barrington 04510
Search Centre, Gosport 33134
Searcy County Museum, Marshall 38357
Seashore Trolley Museum, Kennebunkport 37766
Seat of the Patriarch, Moskva 27932
Seaton Delaval Hall, Seaton 34437
Seattle Art Museum, Seattle 40293
Seattle Asian Art Museum, Seattle 40294
Seay Mansion, Kingfisher 37808
Sebastian-Kneipp-Museum, Bad Wörishofen 14550
Sebežskij Muzej Prirody, Sebež 28078
Sebnitzer Kunstblumen- und Heimatmuseum Prof. Alfred Meiche, Sebnitz 18449
Seção de Numismática do Estado do Amazonas, Manaus 03954
Second Street Gallery, Charlottesville 35957
Second World War Experience Centre, Leeds 33473
Secwepemc Museum, Kamloops 05099
Sederholm House of Helsinki City Museum, Helsinki 08379
Sederholmin Talo, Helsinki 08379
Sedgewick Museum and Gallery, Sedgewick 05889
Sedgwick-Brooklin Historical Museum, Sedgwick 40304
Sedgwick Museum of Geology, Cambridge 32509
Sedona Arts Center, Sedona 40305
Seedamm Kulturzentrum, Pfäffikon (Schwyz) 31089
Seelackenmuseum, Sankt Veit im Pongau 02594
Seemuseum in der Kornschütte, Kreuzlingen 30905
Seevogel-Museum Neusiedlersee, Rust, Burgenland 02510
Sefel Collection, Volos 19704
Segantini-Museum, Sankt Moritz 31183
Segedunum Roman Fort, Bath and Museum, Wallsend 34729
Segontium Roman Museum, Caernarfon 32485
Segwun Heritage Centre, Gravenhurst 04983
Şehir Müzesi, Beşiktaş 31681
Seigfred Gallery, Athens 35203
Seiji Togo Memorial Yasuda Kasai Museum of Art, Tokyo 23662
Seikado Library and Art Museum, Tokyo 23663
Seinäjoen Luonto-Museo, Seinäjoki 08873
Seinäjoki Natural History Museum, Seinäjoki 08873
Seisonkaku, Kanazawa 23127
Seiyun in Wadi Hadhramaut Museum, Seiyun 41496
Sejarah Mesjid Banten Museum, Banten 20470
Sejong College Museum, Seoul 23947
Sekelskiftesmuseét, Laxå 30185
Sekitan Kinenkan, Ube 23730
Sekkeh, Teheran 20659
Sekkeh Museum, Kerman 20626
Selbu Bygdemuseum, Selbu 26289
Selby Gallery, Sarasota 40218
Selçuk Müzesi, Konya 31793
Seljuk Museum, Konya 31793
Selkirk Local History Collection, Castlegar 04677
Sellner Glashütte, Lohberg 17130
Selly Manor Museum, Birmingham 32276
Selsey Lifeboat Museum, Selsey 34446
Semenovskij Gosudarstvennyj Kraevedčeskij Muzej, Semenov 28079
Seminole Canyon State Historical Park, Comstock 36236
Seminole Nation Museum, Wewoka 41150
Semipalatinsk Historical and Regional Museum, Semipalatinsk 23838
Semipalatinskij Istoriko-Kraevedčeskij Muzej, Semipalatinsk 23838
Semmelweis Museum of the History of Medicine, Budapest 19857
Semmelweis Orvostörténeti Múzeum, Budapest 19857
Semmenslutningen af Grønlandske Lokalmuseer, Narsaq 41832
Semsey Andor Múzeum, Balmazujváros 19795
Senate House, Kingston 37814
Senator George Norris State Historic Site, McCook 38234
Senćanski Muzej, Senta 41617
Sendai City Museum, Sendai 23492
Sendai Music Box Museum, Sendai 23491
Sendai-shi Hakubutsukan, Sendai 23492
Sendergalerie Dobl, Dobl 01761
Seneca County Museum, Tiffin 40680
Seneca Falls Historical Society Museum, Seneca Falls 40313
Seneca-Iroquois National Museum, Salamanca 40015
Senj Municipal Museum, Senj 07058
Senko-ji Treasure House, Ono 23418
Sennerei-Museum, Unterwasser 31335
Sen'oku Hakukokan Museum, Kyoto 23270
Sensen- und Heimatmuseum, Achern 14182
Senshu-Bunko Museum, Tokyo 23664
Sensler Museum, Tafers 31297
Senta Museum, Senta 41617
Seoul Municipal Museum of Art, Seoul 23948
Seoul National University Museum, Seoul 23936
Sepänmäen Käsityömuseo, Mäntsälä 08651
Sepänmäki Handicraft Museum, Mäntsälä 08651
Sepah Bank Coin Museum, Teheran 20659
Sequoyah Cabin, Sallisaw 40038
Serbian Church Museum, Szentendre 20041
Serbian Heritage Museum of Windsor, Windsor, Ontario 06285
Serbski muzej - Sorbisches Museum, Bautzen 14603
Serbski muzej - Sorbisches Museum, Panschwitz-Kuckau 17930
Serbski muzej/ Wendisches Museum, Cottbus 15230
Serengeti Museum, Serengeti 31528
Sergačskij Kraevedčeskij Muzej, Sergač 28080
Sergei Paradjanov Museum, Erevan 00679
Sergej Borodin Muzej, Taškent 41386
Sergiev-Posad State History and Art Museum-Reserve, Sergiev Posad 28082
Sergievo-Posadskij Gosudarstvennyj Istoriko-chudožestvennyj Muzej Zapovednik, Sergiev Posad 28082
Serpent Mound Museum, Peebles 39306
Serpentine Gallery, London 33778
Serpentine Vintage Tractors and Machinery Museum, Serpentine 01444
Serpentinsteinmuseum Zöblitz, Zöblitz 19287
Serpuchovskij Muzej Istorii i Iskusstva, Serpuchov 28083
Serviceton Historic Railway Station, Serviceton 01445
Sesquicentennial Museum, Toronto 06086
Session Cottage Museum, Turriff 34699
Setagaya Art Museum, Tokyo 23665
Setagaya-kuritsu Bijutsukan, Tokyo 23665
Setesdalsbanen Stiftelsen, Vennesla 26376
Setesdalsmuseet, Rysstad 26276
Seto Ceramics Center, Seto 23496
Seto City Folk Historical Material Museum, Seto 23495
Seto Inland Sea Folk History Museum, Takamatsu, Kagawa 23539
Seto-shi Rekishi Minzoku Shiryokan, Seto 23495
Seto Tojiki, Seto 23496
Seton Centre, Carberry 04660
Seton Hall University Museum, South Orange 40420
Settlers Museum, Brewarrina 00822
Settlers Museum, Himeville 28497
Settlers' Museum, Mahone Bay 05261
Seurasaaren Ulkomuseo, Helsinki 08380
Seurasaari Open Air Museum, Helsinki 08380
Seven Oaks House Museum, Winnipeg 06320
Sevenoaks Museum and Gallery, Sevenoaks 34449
Severn Valley Railway, Bewdley 32232
Severočeské Muzeum v Liberci, Liberec 07433
Severoossetinskij Literaturnyj Muzej im. K.L. Četagurova, Vladikavkaz 28126
Seville Great House and Heritage Park, Ocho Rios 22908
Sewall-Belmont House, Washington 40997
Seward County Historical Society Museum, Goehner 37164
Seward House, Auburn 35241
Seward Museum, Seward 40317
Sewerby Hall Art Gallery and Museum, Bridlington 32384
Sexton's Cottage Museum, Crows Nest 00943
Seymour and District Historical Museum, Seymour 01446
Seymour Art Gallery, North Vancouver 05494
Seymour Community Museum, Seymour 40320
Sezon Museum of Modern Art, Karuizawa 23129
S.F. Klonowic Museum of the Sulmierzyce Region, Sulmierzyce 27122
S.H. Ervin Gallery, Sydney 01503
Shaanxi History Museum, Xian 06770
Shackerstone Railway Museum, Shackerstone 34450
Shades of the Past, Carbonear 04662
The Shadows-on-the-Teche, New Iberia 38798
Shaftesbury Abbey and Museum, Shaftesbury 34451
Shaftesbury Town Museum, Shaftesbury 34452
Shaftsbury Historical Society Museum, Shaftsbury 40322
Shaheed-e-Azam Bhagat Singh Museum, Khatkar Kalan 20305
Shaker Heritage Society Museum, Albany 35003
Shaker Historical Society Museum, Shaker Heights 40323
Shaker Museum, New Gloucester 38781
Shaker Museum, Old Chatham 39150
Shaker Museum, South Union 40425
Shaker Village of Pleasant Hill, Harrodsburg 37356
Shakespeare Birthplace Trust, Stratford-upon-Avon 34598
Shakespeare's Globe Exhibition, London 33779
Shalyapin House Museum, Moskva 27806
Shalyapin Memorial Museum, Sankt-Peterburg 28042
Shambles Museum, Newent 34037
Shambyu Museum, Shambyu 24626
Shamrock and Cotehele Quay Museum, Saint Dominick 34369
Shamrock Museum, Shamrock 05898
Shan Rong Cultural Display Center, Beijing 06465
Shan State Museum, Taunggyi 24600
Shand House Museum, Windsor, Nova Scotia 06283
Shandong Provincial Museum, Jinan 06614
Shandong Stone Engraving Art Museum, Jinan 06615
Shandy Hall, Coxwold 32696
Shandy Hall, Geneva 37115
Shanghai History Museum, Shanghai 06696
Shanghai Luxun House, Shanghai 06697
Shanghai Museum, Shanghai 06698
Shanghai Natural History Museum, Shanghai 06699
Shankar's International Dolls Museum, Delhi 20224
Shannon Railway Station Museum, Shannon 25889
Shantou Archaeology Museum, Shantou 06704
Shantytown, Greymouth 25799
Shaoguan City Museum, Shaoguan 06706
Sharia Museum, Cairo 08234
Sharjah Archaeology Museum, Sharjah 31969

Wan Zhou District Museum, Chongqing 06513
Wanapum Dam Heritage Center, Beverly 35483
Wandle Industrial Museum, Mitcham 33966
Wandsworth Museum, London 33803
Wang Jian Mu Museum, Chengdu 06505
Wangaratta Exhibitions Gallery, Wangaratta 01574
Wangaratta Museum, Wangaratta 01575
Wangmiao Display Center, Dujiangyan 06525
Wannenmachermuseum, Emsdetten 15572
Wanuskewin Heritage Park, Saskatoon 05879
Wapello County Historical Museum, Ottumwa 39219
War and Peace Exhibition, Oban 34111
War in the Pacific National Historical Park, Asan 19746
War Memorial Carillon Tower and Military Museum, Loughborough 33833
War Memorial Gallery of Fine Arts, Sydney 01508
War Museum, Addis Ababa 08283
War Museum, Athinai 19417
War Museum, Yangon 24608
War Museum of the Boer Republics, Bloemfontein 28425
War Room and Motor House Collection, Harrogate 33201
Ward County Historical Society Museum, Minot 38543
Ward Museum, Ward 25926
The Ward Museum of Wildfowl Art, Salisbury 40033
Ward O'Hara Agricultural Museum of Cayuga County, Auburn 35242
Warden's House Museum, Stillwater 40514
Ware Museum, Ware 34742
Warehouse Gallery, Lee 37990
Warhol Family Museum of Modern Art, Medzilaborce 28265
Warkworth and District Museum, Warkworth 25927
Warmia and Mazuries Museum, Olsztyn 26975
Warner Archive, Milton Keynes 33960
Warner Museum, Springville 40473
Warooka and District Museum, Warooka 01576
Warracknabeal Historical Centre, Warracknabeal 01578
Warragul and District Historical Museum, Warragul 01579
Warrandyte Historical Museum, Warrandyte 01580
Warren County Historical Society Museum, Lebanon 37986
Warren County Museum, Warren 40931
Warren Historical Museum, Warren 40926
Warren ICBM and Heritage Museum, Frances E. Warren Air Force Base 36999
Warren Rifles Confederate Museum, Front Royal 37053
Warrick County Museum, Boonville 35573
Warrington Museum and Art Gallery, Warrington 34747
Warrnambool Art Gallery, Warrnambool 01581
Warsaw Agriculture University Experimental Forest Station - Museum of Forestry and Wood, Rogów 27068
Warsaw Historical Museum, Warsaw 40936
Warta and River Warta Museum, Warta 27251
Wartburg, Eisenach 15533
Warther Museum, Dover 36549
Warwick Castle, Warwick 34752
Warwick Doll Museum, Warwick 34753
Warwick Museum of Art, Warwick 40941
Warwick Regional Art Gallery, Warwick 01583
Warwickshire Museum, Warwick 34754
Warwickshire Museum of Rural Life, Moreton Morrell 33983
Warwickshire Yeomanry Museum, Warwick 34755
Wasco County Historical Museum, The Dalles 40670
Het Wase Pijprokerssalon, Sint-Niklaas 03722
Waseca County Historical Society Museum, Waseca 40943
Waseda Daigaku Tsubouchi Hakushi Kinen Engeki Hakubutsukan, Tokyo 23702
Waseda University Tsubouchi Memorial Theatre Museum, Tokyo 23702
Washington County Historical Association Museum, Fort Calhoun 36882
Washington County Historical Society Museum, West Bend 41094
Washington County Museum, Akron 34989
Washington County Museum, Washington 41020
Washington County Museum of Fine Arts, Hagerstown 37301
Washington Crossing Historic Park, Washington Crossing 41023
Washington Dolls House and Toy Museum, Washington 41009
Washington Historical Museum, Washington 41015
Washington Museum, Washington 41016
Washington Museum Association, Bellevue 42131
Washington National Cathedral, Washington 41010
Washington Old Hall, Washington, Tyne and Wear 34758
Washington Pavillion of Arts and Science, Sioux Falls 40376
Washington State Capital Museum, Olympia 39159
Washington State Historical Society Museum, Tacoma 40611
Washington University Gallery of Art, Saint Louis 39980
Washington's Headquarters, Newburgh 38966
Waskada Museum, Waskada 06222
Wasserburg Haus Kemnade, Hattingen 16309
Wasserkraftmuseum Leitzachwerk, Feldkirchen-Westerham 15691
Wasserkunst von 1535, Bad Arolsen 14381
Wasserleitungsmuseum, Reichenau an der Rax 02477
Wasserleitungsmuseum, Wildalpen 02994
Wassermühle Kuchelmiß, Kuchelmiß 16896
Wasserschloß Mitwitz, Mitwitz 17385
Wassertor-Museum, Isny 16590
Wasserwelt Erlebnismuseum, Ostseebad Binz 17904
Wastlbauernhof, Siegsdorf 18493
Wastlmühle, Lainbach 02168
Wasyl Negrych Pioneer Homestead, Gilbert Plains 04944
Wat Ko Museum, Phetchaburi 31580
Wat Phra Thart Lampang Luang Museum, Lampang 31565
Wat Sisaket, Vientiane 23985
Watari Museum of Contemporary Art, Tokyo 23703
Watari-Um, Tokyo 23703
Watchet Market House Museum, Watchet 34759
Water Barracks, Bratislava 28218
Water Mill, Mikkeli 08671
Water Mill Museum, Water Mill 41026
Water Museum, Moskva 27917
Water Ski Hall of Fame, Polk City 39520
Water Supply Museum, Sutton Poyntz 34621
Water Supply Museum of Riga, Ādaži 23986
Water Tower Museum, Gunnedah 01068
Waterford Historical Museum, Waterford 41029
Waterford Treasures at the Granary, Waterford 20849
Waterfront Museum, Poole 34216
Waterloo Center of the Arts, Waterloo 41032
Watermen's Museum, Yorktown 41329
Watermill Museum, Vääksy 09002
Watertown Historical Society Museum, Watertown 41036
The Watervliet Arsenal Museum, Watervliet 41046
Waterways Museum, Goole 33127
Waterwheel Museum, Salisbury 01436
Waterworks Museum - Hereford, Hereford 33260
Waterworks Visual Arts Center, Salisbury 40036
Watford Museum, Watford 34761
Watkins Community Museum of History, Lawrence 37971
Watkins Gallery, Washington 41011
Watkins Woolen Mill, Lawson 37975
Watson Crossley Community Museum, Grandview 04979
Watson Farm, Jamestown 37666
Watson Gallery, Norton 39063
Watson Museum, Rajkot 20402
Watson's Mill, Manotick 05270
Watters Smith, Lost Creek 38181
Watts Gallery, Compton, Surrey 32665
Watts Towers Arts Center, Los Angeles 38175
Wauchope District Historical Museum, Wauchope 01585
Waukesha County Museum, Waukesha 41054
Wawel Royal Castle - State Art Collections, Kraków 26852
Wawota and District Museum, Wawota 06235
Wax Museum, Byblos 24147
Waxworks Museum, Moskva 27929
Wayland Historical Museum, Wayland 41067
Wayne Art Center, Wayne 41074
Wayne County Historical Museum, Richmond 39746
Wayne County Historical Society Museum, Lyons 38226
Wayne County Historical Society Museum, Wooster 41292
Wayne County Museum, Honesdale 37473
Wayne State University Museum of Anthropology, Detroit 36514
Wayne State University Museum of Natural History, Detroit 36515
Wayside Folk Museum, Zennor 34925
Wayville Latvian Museum, Brooklyn Park 00841
W.C. Handy Home Museum, Florence 36854
Weald and Downland Open Air Museum, Singleton 34490
Weapons Museum, Eskilstuna 30067
Weardale Museum, Weardale 34762
Weather Dicovery Center, North Conway 39030
Weatherspoon Art Gallery, Greensboro 37259
Weaver's Cottage, Kilbarchan 33377
Weavers Cottage Museum, Airdrie 32007
Weavers' House, Hollókő 19904
Weavers' Triangle Visitor Centre, Burnley 32455
Weaverville Joss House State Historic Park, Weaverville 41079
Weaving and Silk Museum, Bussières 09779
The Webb-Deane-Stevens Museum, Wethersfield 41148
Webb House Museum, Newark 38960
Weber State University Art Gallery, Ogden 39123
Weberei- und Heimatmuseum, Laichingen 16935
Weberei- und Heimatmuseum Ruedertal, Schmiedrued 31209
Webereimuseum, Breitenberg, Niederbayern 15047
Webereimuseum, Haslach 02004
Weberhaus Marlesreuth, Naila 17581
Weberhausmuseum, Schauenstein 18321
Webermuseum, Heidenreichstein 02010
Weberstube Jonsdorf, Kurort Jonsdorf 16914
Webster County Historical Museum, Red Cloud 39706
Webster House Museum, Elkhorn 36691
Wedgwood Museum, Stoke-on-Trent 34582
Wednesbury Museum and Art Gallery, Wednesbury 34764
Weeks Air Museum, Miami 38460
Weems-Botts Museum, Dumfries 36575
Frankie G. Weems Gallery & Rotunda Gallery, Raleigh 39678
Weenen Museum, Weenen 28641
Weeping Water Valley Historical Society Museum, Weeping Water 41081
Weera Puran Appu Museum, Moratuwa 29991
Weg des Friedens, Purgstall an der Erlauf 02449
Wegmachermuseum, Wasserburg am Inn 18937
Wegwijs Museum, Bakkum 24787
Wehrgeschichtliches Museum Rastatt, Rastatt 18065
Wei Huanggong Display Center, Changchun 06482
Weicheltmühle, Reichenau bei Dippoldiswalde 18117
Weidmann Cottage Heritage Centre, Muswellbrook 01288
Wein- und Heimatmuseum, Durbach 15473
Weinbau-Museum, Chur 30705
Weinbau- und Heimatmuseum, Klingenberg am Main 16763
Weinbau- und Landwirtschaftsmuseum, Hadersdorf 01980
Weinbaumuseum, Flörsheim-Dalsheim 15718
Weinbaumuseum, Oetwil am See 31075
Weinbaumuseum, Reidling 02483
Weinbaumuseum Alte Kelter, Erlenbach, Kreis Heilbronn 15629
Weinbaumuseum am Zürichsee, Au, Zürich 30542
Weinbaumuseum der Winzergenossenschaft, Ortenberg, Baden 17862
Weinbaumuseum im Herrenhof, Neustadt an der Weinstraße 17680
Weinbaumuseum Jenins, Jenins 30886
Weinbaumuseum Meersburg, Meersburg 17312
Weinbaumuseum Stuttgart-Uhlbach, Stuttgart 18650
Weinberg Nature Center, Scarsdale 40250
Weingreen Museum of Biblical Antiquities, Dublin 20764
Weingutmuseum Hoflößnitz, Radebeul 18044
Weinlandmuseum, Asparn an der Zaya 01682
Weinmuseum, Güssing 01965
Weinmuseum, Vaihingen 18813
Weinmuseum Kitzeck, Kitzeck im Sausal 02111
Weinmuseum Prellenkirchen, Prellenkirchen 02436
Weinmuseum Schlagkamp-Desoye Senheim, Senheim 18480
Weinstadtmuseum Krems, Krems 02151
Weinviertler Museumsdorf, Niedersulz 02348
Weinviertler Naturmuseum, Jetzelsdorf 02081
Weinviertler Oldtimermuseum Poysdorf, Poysdorf 02426
Weir Farm, Wilton 41226
Weißenhorner Heimatmuseum, Weißenhorn 19031
Weissenstein-Museum, Weissenstein bei Solothurn 31378
Weißgerbermuseum, Doberlug-Kirchhain 15349
Weisův Dům, Veselí nad Lužnicí 07699
Weizmann Archives and House, Rehovot 20983
The Welch Regiment Museum of The Royal Regiment of Wales (41st/ 69th Foot), Cardiff 32533
Welholme Galleries, Great Grimsby 33153
Welkom Museum, Welkom 28642
Wella Museum, Darmstadt 15273
Welland Historical Museum, Welland 06237
Wellbrook Beetling Mill, Cookstown 32674
Wellcome Museum of Medical Science, London 33804
Wellesbourne Wartime Museum, Wellesbourne 34767
Wellesley Historical Society, Wellesley Hills 41083
Wellfleet Historical Society Museum, Wellfleet 41084
Wellingborough Heritage Centre, Wellingborough 34769
Wellings Landsbymuseum, Lintrup 07956
Wellington Aviation Museum, Moreton-in-Marsh 33982
Wellington B. Gray Gallery, Greenville 37264
Wellington Community Historical Museum, Wellington, Ontario 06238
Wellington County Museum, Fergus 04886
Wellington Courthouse Museum, Wellington 01587
Wellington Museum, London 33805
Wellington Museums Trust, Wellington 41904
Wells Auto Museum, Wells 41088
Wells County Historical Museum, Bluffton 35550
Wells County Museum, Fessenden 36828
Wells Fargo History Museum, Los Angeles 38176
Wells Fargo History Museum, Minneapolis 38540
Wells Fargo History Museum, Sacramento 39910
Wells Fargo History Museum, San Diego 40099
Wells Fargo History Museum, San Francisco 40130
Wells Fargo History Museum Old Sacramento, Sacramento 39911
Wells Museum, Wells 06241
Wells Museum, Wells 34770
Wells Walsingham Light Railway, Wells-next-the-Sea 34772
Welser Puppenweltmuseum, Wels 02787
Welsh Federation of Museums and Art Galleries, Monmouth 42041
Welsh Industrial and Maritime Museum, Cardiff 32534
Welsh Slate Museum, Llanberis 33552
Welshpool and Llanfair Light Railway, Llanfair Caereinion 33563
Weltkulturerbe Völklinger Hütte, Völklingen 18857
Welwyn Roman Baths, Welwyn 34775
Wen Tianxiang Temple, Beijing 06470
Wendell Gilley Museum, Southwest Harbor 40430
Wenham Museum, Wenham 41092
Wenmiao Museum, Tianjin 06741
Wentworth-Coolidge Mansion, Portsmouth 39583
Wentworth Gardner and Tobias Lear Houses, Portsmouth 39584
Wenzel-Hablik-Museum, Itzehoe 16593
Weoley Castle, Birmingham 32280
Werberger Stuben, Motten 17421
Werdenfelser Museum, Garmisch-Partenkirchen 15901
Wereldmuseum Rotterdam, Rotterdam 25450
Werkhof Bistrica, Sankt Michael 02567
Werksmuseum Achse, Rad und Wagen, Wiehl 19094
Werksmuseum der Amazonen-Werke, Gaste 15903
Werksmuseum der Firma Linke-Hofmann-Busch GmbH, Salzgitter 18293
Werksmuseum der MTU, München 17531
Werksmuseum der Waechtersbacher Keramik, Brachttal 15009
Werksmuseum Koenig & Bauer AG, Würzburg 19231
Werkspoor Museum, Amsterdam 24745
Werkzeugmuseum Zur Eisenbahn, Ermatingen 30754
Werner-Berg-Galerie der Stadt Bleiburg, Bleiburg 01732
Werner-Egk-Begegnungsstätte, Donauwörth 15363
Werra-Kalibergbau-Museum, Heringen, Werra 16390
Werribee and District Historical Museum, Werribee 01589
Wesley's House and Museum, London 33806
Wesselstuerne, København 07938
West Allis Historical Society Museum, West Allis 41093
West Baton Rouge Museum, Port Allen 39529
West Bend Art Museum, West Bend 41095
West Berkshire Museum, Newbury 34024
West Blatchington Windmill, Hove 33298
West Bohemian Gallery in Plzeň, Plzeň 07530
West Bohemian Museum, Plzeň 07531
West Chicago City Museum, West Chicago 41101
West Coast Historical Museum, Hokitika 25808
West Coast Maritime Museum, Tofino 06029
West Coast Museum of Flying, Sidney 05923
West Coast Pioneer's Memorial Museum, Zeehan 01632
West Cork Regional Museum, Clonakilty 20718
West End Gallery, Edmonton 04858
West Gate Towers, Canterbury 32523
West Highland Museum, Fort William 33037
West Java Museum, Bandung 20464
West Kalimantan Museum, Pontianak 20563
West Kilbride Museum, West Kilbride 34781
West Midlands Police Museum, Birmingham 32281
West Midlands Regional Museums Council, Bromsgrove 42042
West-Moravian Museum in Třebíč, Třebíč 07670
West-Moravian Museum in Třebíč - Museum Jemnice, Jemnice 07366
West Norway Museum of Decorative Art, Bergen 26037
West of the Pecos Museum, Pecos 39305
West Overton Museums, Scottdale 40266
West Park Museum and Art Gallery, Macclesfield 33867
West Parry Sound District Museum, Parry Sound 05567
West Pasco Historical Society Museum, New Port Richey 38826
West Point Lighthouse Museum, O'Leary 05516
West Point Museum, West Point 41122
West River Museum, Philip 39423
West Somerset Railway, Minehead 33961
West Somerset Rural Life Museum, Allerford 32024
West Sumatrian Museum, Padang 20551
West Torrens Railway, Aviation and Signal Telegraph Museum, Brooklyn Park 00842
West Valley Art Museum, Surprise 40586
West Vancouver Museum, West Vancouver 06250
West Virginia Independence Hall, Wheeling 41160
West Virginia Northern Community College Alumni Association Museum, Wheeling 41161
West Virginia State Farm Museum, Point Pleasant 39519
West Virginia State Museum, Charleston 35941
West Virginia University Mesaros Galleries, Morgantown 38629
West Wales Arts Centre, Fishguard 33022
West Wycombe Motor Museum, West Wycombe 34785
West Wycombe Park House, West Wycombe 34786
Westallgäuer Heimatmuseum, Weiler-Simmerberg 18976
Westbury Manor Museum, Fareham 33005
Western Aerospace Museum, Oakland 39095
Western Archeological and Conservation Center, Tucson 40758
Western Australian Maritime Museum, Fremantle 01024
Western Australian Medical Museum, Subiaco 01481
Western Australian Museum, Perth 01358
Western Australian Museum Geraldton, Geraldton 01035
Western Canada Aviation Museum, Winnipeg 06327
Western Colorado Center for the Arts, Grand Junction 37202
Western Development Museum, Saskatoon 05880
Western Gallery, Bellingham 35421
Western Hennepin County Pioneers Museum, Long Lake 38120
Western Heritage Center, Billings 35494
Western Hotel Museum, Lancaster 37916
Western Illinois University Art Gallery, Macomb 38252

Personality Index

Musäus, Johann Karl August 18990
Musil, Alois 07713
Musil, Robert 02123
Musrepov, Gabit 23818
Muthesius, Hermann 14800
Myers, W.J. 32982
Mylonas, Alex 19359
Näf, Matthias 31072
Nagaoka, Kounito 04170
Nansen, Fridtjof 26220
Napoléon I 01753, 03561, 09098, 09103, 09205, 10570, 22395, 31160
Napoléon III 31160
Narvárez, Francisco 41454
Nash, John 32397
Nash, Thomas 34596
Natsagdorj, Dashdorjiyn 24545
Naumann, J.F. 16837
Necker, Jacques 30715
Negroli, Filippo 29303
Nehru, Jawaharlal 20222
Neidhardt von Gneisenau, August Wilhelm Anton Graf 15999Graf
Nekrassov, Nikolaj A. 28037
Nelimarkka, Eero 08295
Nelson, Lord Horatio 33975, 34243
Němcová, Božena 07278, 07280, 07491
Němejc, Augustin 07480
Nemirovič-Dančenko, Vladimir I. 27896, 27891
Nerdrum, Odd 26164
Nesch, Rolf 26244
Netti, Francesco 21139
Neuber, Friederike Caroline 18118
Neubrand, Philipp 15583
Neukams, Gottfried 16884
Neumann, Balthasar 19225, 19219, 17307
Neuss, Wolfgang 14740
Newman, Chris 16786
Newton, Isaac 33142
Newton, John 34117
Niazy, Hamza Hakim-Zadé 41363, 41367
Nicholson, Ben 34605, 33359
Niebuhr, Carsten 17325
Niekerk, Chris Van 28426
Nielsen, Carl 07760, 07988
Nielsen Hauge, Hans 26270
Nielsen, Jens 07876
Niemeyer-Holstein, Otto 16857, 18227
Niemeyer, Oscar 04002
Nietzsche, Friedrich 17589, 18995
Nightingale, Florence 32097, 33640
Nilsen, Torstein 26048
Noakowski, Stanisław 26949
Nobel, Alfred 30369
Noble, Roberto 00232
Noguchi, Hideyo 23072
Nøis, Hilmar 26263
Nolde, Emil 17641
Nonagase, Banka 23748
Nonell y Monturiol, Isidro 28791
Nordenskiöld, Adolf Erik 08717
Nordheim, Sondre 26190
Nordlander, Anna 30309
Nouveau, Henri 12620
Novák, Vítězslav 07381
Nováková, Tereza 07612
Novalis 16603, 19029, 19093
Nowak,Arthur 02044
Nowowiejski, Feliks 26613
Núñez, Rafael 06837
Oates, Frank 34440
Oates, Lawrence 34440
Oberkampf, Christophe-Philippe 10895
Oberlin, Jean-Frédéric 14091
Oberth, Hermann 15696
O'Carolan 20714
O'Connor, James 20850
Österreich, Maximilian Franz von 14472
Ohmann, Friedrich 01688, 02393
Ohmeyer, Maria 02424
Oille, Lucille 05310
Okakura, Tenshin 23155
Ólafsson, Sigurjón 20119
Olbracht, Ivan 07635
Oldenburg, Claes 16810
Oldenburg, Ernst 18796
Ondříček, František 07245
O'Neill Verner, Elizabeth 35929
Onley, Toni 06199
Opie, Robet 33116
Opitz, Theodor 30942
Oppenheim, Meret 31254
Opsomer, I. Baron 03558
Orff, Carl 15321
Orkan, Władisław 27012, 27055
Orozco, José Clemente 24448, 24431, 24399
Orthman, Thomas 06854
Ortiz Echagüe, Antonio 00257
Ossietzky, Karl von 15493
Ost, Alfred 03471, 03842, 25419
Ostrovskij, Aleksandr 27818
Ostrovskij, Nikolaj Alekseevič 27805, 27868, 31947
Ostwald, Wilhelm 16111
Otero Pedrayo, Ramón 29805
Otto, Nikolaus August 16772
Overbeck, Gerta 16239
Owen, Robert 34007, 34063
Pacheco, Francisco 09904
Pahl, Manfred 17225

Palacios, Alfredo L. 00149
Palacios, Pedro 00376
Palacký, František 07338
Palamas, Kostis 19416
Palauzov, Dimitär Trifonov 04185
Palissy, Bernard 14452
Palitzsch, Johann Georg 15405
Pallas, P.S. 14806
Palma, Jacopo 22087
Panaitescu-Perpessicius, Dumitru 27499
Pancera, Ella 01699
Pander, Pier 25232
Pankok, Bernhard 17554
Pankok, Otto 16524
Pannini, Giovanni Paolo 22177
Paolo Veronese 21685, 22087, 22796, 22856
Papanastassiou, Alexandros 19547
Pappenheim, Gottfried Heinrich Graf zu 17935
Paracelsus, Theophrastus 30549
Parapunov, Nikola 04273
Pardo Bazán, Emilia 28987
Parmigianino 22126, 21640
Parnell, Charles Stewart 20826
Parry, Joseph 33934
Parthenis, K. 19693
Pass, Alfred A. de 28451
Pasternak, Boris 27822
Pasteur, Louis 09218, 10346, 12438
Patton, George S. 24219
Pátzay, Pál 19914
Paul, Jean 14616, 14617
Pavelic, Myfanwy 06199
Pavlov, A.P. 27819
Pavlov, Ivan Petrovič 28004
Pavlović-Barilli, Milena 41604
Pearse, Patrick 20758
Pecharromán, Ricardo 29491
Pechstein, Max 19298
Pedersen, Carl-Henning 07852
Peltonen, Vihtori 09006
Pengelly, William 34682
Perantinos, Nikolaos 19413
Pérez Galdós, Benito 29477
Pérez, Genaro 00296
Perkins, Simeon 05220
Permeke, Constant 03496
Peroutka, Ferdinand 07644
Perraudin, Jean-Pierre 30959
Perugino 11521, 12023
Peské, Jean 10158
Pestalozzi, Johann Heinrich 30674, 31422
Peter I, the Great 25663, 28021
Petersson Döderhultarn, Axel 30276
Petőfi, Sándor 19927, 19787, 19926
Petrarca, Francesco 10560, 21093
Pettoruti, Emilio 00497
Petzval, Johann 28299
Peukert, August 16259
Peyton, Elizabeth 19186
Pezzani, Costante 16338
Pfaff, Michael 16772
Pflug, Johann Baptist 14886
Pfohl, Alexander 16155
Piaf, Edith 12403
Pič, Ladislav 07473
Picabio, Francis 11669
Picard, Max 18386
Picasso, Pablo 12023, 12424, 16810, 31129, 07887, 12502, 09820, 31452, 12980, 37150, 26036, 12420, 15444, 18643, 10727, 11724, 23742, 14011, 03570, 09207, 09247, 11521, 12439, 13848, 13849, 14834, 17546, 23003, 23748, 28825, 28867, 29470, 30363, 30981, 32948, 38939
Piechowski, W. 26932
Pieck, Anton 25112
Piero della Francesca 22510
Piette, Ludovic 12619
Piffetti, Pietro 22670
Pijnenburg, R. 25282
Pilioko, Aloi 41389
Pilon, Veno 28320
Piotrowski, Maksymilian Piotrowski 26651
Pirandello, Luigi 21032, 22330
Piranese, Canaletto 11422
Pisanello 21160
Pisano, Giovanni 22086
Pissarro, Camille 34127, 34733, 23742, 12619
Pissarro, Lucien 12619
Pitman, I. 32164
Pius X 22306
Plantin, Christopher 03111
Plateau, J. 03411
Platter, Felix 30561
Plechanov, Georgi 27776
Plessis, Jean de 12750
Poey, Felipe 07148
Pol, Wincenty 26912
Polenz, Wilhelm von 15242
Poliakoff, Serge 12420
Polke, Sigmar 16810, 07887, 12980
Pollock, Jackson 31457
Polychronopoulos, Costas 19561
Ponce de León, Juan 08101
Popov, Aleksandr Stepanovič 28040
Porras, Belisario 26438
Porsche, Ferdinand 01884, 18640
Porumbescu, Ciprian 27655
Post, Frans 03985

Potter, Beatrix 33227, 34426
Pound, Ezra 22647
Poussin, Nicolas 02800, 33633, 22341, 11300
Powell-Cotton, P.H.G. 32252
Pozzi, Carlo 17307
Pretorius, M.W. 28572
Prieto, Gregorio 29825
Princess Beatrice 34046
Princip, Gavrilo 03884
Proust, Marcel 10856
Prus, B. 26943
Przybyszewski, Stanisław 26746
Puccini, Giacomo 21809, 22700, 22852
Pückler-Muskau, Hermann Fürst von 14477, 15226
Pueyrredón, Juan Martín de 00556
Pufendorf, Samuel Freiherr von 19303
Pułaski, Kazimir 27189
Pulitzer, Joseph 19938
Purrmann, Hans 16625, 18284, 16967
Puškin, Aleksandr Sergeevič 27786, 27823, 27839, 28000, 28001, 28057, 28063, 28139, 31908
Puvis de Chavannes 24471
Quezon, Manuel L. 26587
Quinós, Bernardo Cesáreo de 00476
Raabe, Wilhelm 15038, 15634
Račić, Josip 07114
Radetzky, Joseph Wenzel Graf 02127
Radiščev, Aleksandr Nikolaevič 28076
Radziwill, Franz 17851, 18815
Raffaello 12281, 21592, 22339, 34127, 02800, 22760
Raimund, Ferdinand 01973, 02421
Rainer, Arnulf 02227
Rais, Karel Václav 07425, 07519
Rakovski, Georgi S. 04223
Raman, C.V. 20179
Ramoneda, Francisco 00355
Ran-In-Ting 06825
Ransome, Arthur 32669
Raphaël 13611, 21596, 37150
Rapin, Aimée 31087
Rasmussen, Knud 07888
Rathgeber, Valentin 17770
Rauch, Christian Daniel 14379
Rauf, H. Abdul 20499
Rauschenberg, Robert 06854, 14738
Ravel, Maurice 11868
Ravilious, Eric 34349
Raynaud, Jean-Pierre 23604
Razin, Stepan Timofeevič 27959, 28091
Redon, Odile 12420
Redouté, H.-J. 03698
Redouté, P.-J. 03698
Rees, Lloyd 00764
Reger, Max 15017
Reich, Ferdinand 15799
Reichardt, Johann Friedrich 16191
Reid, George A. 06289
Reiffenstuel, Hans 17973
Reinhardt, Ad 01919
Reis, Philipp 15921, 15843
Rembrandt 02800, 33802, 15410, 32933, 33633, 02890, 02855, 33731, 32260, 37150, 02169, 08008, 12415, 20004, 24692, 24712, 24731, 24908, 25244, 33682
Renan, Ernest 13776
Rendl, Georg 02357
Reni, Guido 21940, 22341, 21685, 22331
Renner, Karl 01879
Renoir, Auguste 21833, 37150
Renoudot, Théophraste 11456
Renz, Ernst Jakob 18016
Repin, Ilja Efimovič 28003
Rerich, Elena Ivanovna 27848
Rerich, Ju.N. 27848
Rerich, Nikolai 24101
Rerich, Nikolaj Konstantinovič 27848
Rerich, Svjatoslav Nikolaevič 27848
Reuter, Fritz 15530, 15351
Reventlow, C.D.F. 07886
Reynolds, Joshua 33682, 32260
Rhodes, Cecil John 28549, 32289
Ribera, Jusepe de 22341
Riccio, Andrea 22087
Rice, Edmund Ignatius 20846
Richards, Ceri 34626
Richelieu, Armand 12750
Richmond, J.C. 25844
Richter, Gerhard 16810, 16760, 26214, 12980
Richter, Johann Paul Friedrich 14616
Rie, Lucie 34088
Riebeeck, Jan Van 24870
Riehl, Elli 01791
Riemenschneider, Tilman 16883, 19219
Ries, Adam 14285
Riesener, Johann Heinrich 15981
Rietschel, Ernst 15427
Rietti, Ciro 00142
Rigaud, Hyacinthe 21685, 12502
Riley, Bridget 33359
Rilke, Rainer Maria 31237
Rimski-Korsakov, Nikolaj Andreevič 28041, 28106
Rinckart, Martin 15523
Ringelnatz, Joachim 15493
Rio Branco, Baron of 04058
Rippl-Rónai, József 19912, 19913
Rist, Pipilotti 18994
Ritter, Johann Wilhelm 16603

Rivel, Charly 18016
Rivera, Diego 24431, 24454, 24401, 24426, 24448
Rizal, José 26523, 26527, 26531
Rizzarda, Carlo 21540
Robbi, Andrea 31238
Robbia, Luca della 21595, 21562
Robert, Hubert 13839
Robertson, David 33954
Robinson, Joy 34753
Roca, Julio A. 00233
Rocha, Dardo 00386
Rochow, Friedrich Eberhard von 18084
Rodin, Auguste 12980, 32949, 09096, 09820, 09947, 11745, 12317, 15427, 23023
Rodt, Christoph 18805
Röder, Paul 17279
Röntgen, Wilhelm Conrad 18134, 19227
Roerich, Nicholas 38928
Roesch, Carl 30729
Rojas, Ricardo 00151
Romanino, Girolamo 22087
Romney, George 33359
Rømer, Ole 08075
Romero de Torres, Julio 28981
Romulo, Carlos P. 26538
Roosevelt, Franklin D. 06243
Rops, Felicien 03625
Rosa, Salvator 21940
Rosegger, Peter 01655, 01656, 02155, 02156
Rossetti, Dante Gabriel 34127, 33791
Rossi, Gino 22726
Rossini, Gioacchino 22159, 22162
Roth, Diter 18628
Rothenstein, Michael 34349
Rother, Richard 16758
Rothko, Mark 23748, 23129
Rousseau, Henri 14959
Rousseau, Jean-Jacques 30795, 09956, 10557, 11892, 30816, 31021, 31050
Rousseau, Théodore 23175
Rożek, Marcin 27276
Rubens, Pieter Paul 02800, 12023, 33802, 21833, 33633, 02890, 02855, 14320, 32260, 21596, 37150, 33585, 24471, 25500, 03133, 03135, 13611, 21063, 24179
Rubin, Reuven 21008
Rubinstein, N.G. 27897, 27922
Rude, Olaf 07966
Rückert, Friedrich 15207
Rückriem, Ulrich 18209
Ruisdael, Salomon Van 24908
Runeberg, Johan Ludvig 08797
Runeberg, Walter 08801
Runge, Friedlieb Ferdinand 17859
Runge, Philipp Otto 19190, 19191
Rupchan, Peter 05878
Ruppe, Hugo 17271
Rusiñol, Santiago 29730
Ruskin, John 33359, 32497, 32668, 32669, 33440
Russell, George 32066
Russell, John 33167
Rutherford, A.C. 04849
Ryba, Jakub Jan 07624
Ryggen, Hannah 26349
Ryokan 23098
Ryti, Risto 08401
Saar, Ferdinand von 02821
Saarinen, Eliel 08511
Sabā, Abdul Hassan 20658
Sacharov A.D. 27855
Sachsen-Weimar, Ernst August Herzog von 15369
Saeki, Yuzo 23748
Sáenz, Manuela 06886
Saint-Saëns, Camille 10314
Sakatsoume, Atsouo 04170
Šaljapin, Fëdor 27806, 28042
Salzillo, Francisco 29392
Salzmann, Christian Gotthilf 18368
Samuels, G.J. 25735
San Martín, José de 00205
Sand, George 10949, 12140
Sandby, Paul 01075
Sander, August 18488
Santa María, Andrés de 06913
Santamaría, Andrés de 06854
Sarian, M. 00675
Sarmiento, Domingo Faustino 00135, 00208, 00560
Sarpaneva, Timo 08406
Satie, Erik 12442
Saul, Petre 03604
Saura, Antonio 16786, 03604
Saussure, H.B. de 30813
Savio, Manuel Nicolás Aristóbulo 00244
Saxe-Coburg-Gotha, Albert Prince of 32874
Scharff, Edwin 17613
Scheffel, Joseph Victor von 18046
Scheffer, Ary 12354
Scheidt, Samuel 16191
Scheinflugová, Olga 07644
Schelling, Friedrich 16603
Scheving, Gunnlaugur 20110
Schiavo, Paolo 21581
Schiele, Egon 02230, 02714, 07287
Schiering, Kurt 17271
Schiestl, Rudolf 15865
Schikaneder, Emanuel 02895
Schill, Ferdinand von 18611
Schiller, Friedrich 18987, 14599, 15425, 16605, 17057, 17154, 17253, 17254, 18999

Subject Index

List of Subjects

Agricultural Implements and Machinery
Agriculture
Amber
Anthropology → Ethnology
Apiculture → Bees
Archaeology
Archaeology, Christian and Medieval
Archaeology, Far Eastern
Archaeology, Greek and Roman
Archaeology, Ibero-American
Archaeology, Near and Middle Eastern
Architecture
Arms and Armour
Art
Art, African
Art, American
Art, Asian
Art, Australian
Art, European
Art, Greek and Roman
Art, Latin American
Art, Medieval
Art, Modern and Contemporary
Art, Oriental
Art, Russian
Astronomy
Automobiles → Vehicles
Aviation
Baking and Cookery
Balneology
Banks and Banking
Baskets
Bees
Bells
Biology
Birds
Boats and Shipping
Bones
Books, Book Art and Manuscripts
Botany
Brewing
Bronzes
Bullfights
Buttons
Cabaret → Performing Arts
Calligraphy
Cameras → Optics
Carpets
Carriages and Carts
Cartography
Carts → Carriages and Carts
Carving, Wood → Wood Carving
Castles and Fortresses
Ceramics → Porcelain and Ceramics
Chemistry
China (Porcelain) → Porcelain and Ceramics
Cigarettes → Tobacco
Cinematography
Circus → Performing Arts

Clocks and Watches → Horology
Clothing and Dress
Coaches → Carriages and Carts
Coffee → Tea and Coffee
Coins → Numismatics
Cookery → Baking and Cookery
Copper
Cosmetics
Costume → Clothing and Dress
Crafts → Handicraft
Criminology
Dairy Products
Dance → Performing Arts
Decorative and Applied Arts
Distilling → Wines and Spirits
Dolls and Puppets
Drawing
Ecology
Economics
Education
Egyptology
Electricity
Embroidery → Needlework
Enamel Works
Energy
Engraving → Graphic Arts
Entomology → Insects
Epitaphs → Inscriptions and Epitaphs
Ethnology
Expeditions → Scientific Expeditions
Explosives
Eyeglasses → Optics
Faience → Porcelain and Ceramics
Farms and Farming
Fashion → Clothing and Dress
Festivals
Fire Fighting and Rescue Work
Firearms → Arms and Armour
Fishing and Fisheries
Folk Art
Folklore
Food
Forest Products
Fortresses → Castles and Fortresses
Fossils
Fresco Painting → Mural Painting and Decoration
Fur → Hides and Skins
Furniture and Interior
Games → Toys and Games
Gas → Petroleum Industry and Trade
Gems → Precious Stones
Genealogy
Geography
Geology
Glass and Glassware
Globes → Cartography
Gold and Silver
Graphic Arts
Gravestones → Tombs

853

Handicapped
Handicraft
Heraldry → Genealogy
Hides and Skins
History
History, Early → Prehistory and Early History
History, Local and Regional
History, Maritime → Boats and Shipping
History, Medieval
History, Modern
History, Social → Social Conditions
Horology
Horses
Horticulture
Household Articles
Hunting
Hygiene → Medicine and Hygiene
Icons
Incunabula → Books, Book Art and Manuscripts
Indian Artifacts
Industry
Inscriptions and Epitaphs
Insects
Instruments of Torture
Ironwork → Metalwork
Ivory
Jewellery → Precious Stones
Judaica
Keys → Locks and Keys
Lace → Needlework
Lacquerwork
Lamps and Lighting
Language and Literature
Law
Lead and Tin Figures
Leather
Literature → Language and Literature
Locks and Keys
Lumber → Forest Products
Machines and Machinery
Majolica → Porcelain and Ceramics
Mammals
Man, Prehistoric
Manuscripts → Books, Book Art and Manuscripts
Maps → Cartography
Marine Archaeology
Marine Biology → Oceanography
Masks
Mass Media
Medals → Numismatics
Medicine and Hygiene
Metals and Metallurgy
Metalwork
Meteorites
Military History
Mills
Mineralogy
Miniature Painting
Mining Engineering
Mollusks
Monasteries
Money → Numismatics
Mosaics

Mummies
Mural Painting and Decoration
Museology
Music and Musical Instruments
Naive Art → Folk Art
Natural History
Needlework
Numismatics
Oceanography
Oenology → Wines and Spirits
Office Equipment
Oil → Petroleum Industry and Trade
Opera → Performing Arts
Optics
Ornithology → Birds
Painted and Stained Glass
Painting
Painting, 17th C.
Painting, 18th C.
Painting, 19th C.
Painting, 20th C.
Painting, English
Painting, European
Painting, French
Painting, German
Painting, Italian
Painting, Latin American
Painting, Medieval
Painting, Netherlandish
Painting, Renaissance
Painting, Spanish
Paleontology → Fossils
Paper
Peasant Life and Traditions
Performing Arts
Petroleum Industry and Trade
Pets
Pewter
Pharmacy
Philately → Postage Stamps
Philosophy
Photography
Physics
Pipes, Tobacco → Tobacco
Plaster Casts
Playing Cards
Police → Criminology
Politics and Government
Porcelain and Ceramics
Portraits
Postage Stamps
Postal Services
Posters
Pottery, Earthenware → Porcelain and Ceramics
Precious Stones
Prehistory and Early History
Press → Mass Media
Printing
Prints → Graphic Arts
Prisons → Criminology
Puppets → Dolls and Puppets
Radio → Mass Media
Railroads

Rare Books → Books, Book Art and Manuscripts
Religious Art and Symbolism
Religious History and Traditions
Reptiles
Rescue Equipment → Fire Fighting and Rescue Work
Rocks → Mineralogy
Salt
Sarcophagi → Tombs
Scientific Apparatus and Instruments
Scientific Expeditions
Sculpture
Shells
Shipping → Boats and Shipping
Shoes
Silk
Silver → Gold and Silver
Skeletons → Bones
Social Conditions
Speleology
Spirits → Wines and Spirits
Sports and Recreation
Stained Glass → Painted and Stained Glass
Stelae → Tombs
Stoves
Stucco
Sugar
Tapestries
Tea and Coffee
Technology
Telecommunications → Postal Services
Television → Mass Media

Terracotta
Textiles
Theatre → Performing Arts
Tin Figures → Lead and Tin Figures
Tobacco
Tombs
Tools
Tourism
Toys and Games
Trades and Guilds
Transport
Travel → Tourism
Treasuries
Typography → Books, Book Art and Manuscripts
Uniforms, Military
Vehicles
Veterinary Medicine
Viticulture → Wines and Spirits
Voyages of Discovery → Scientific Expeditions
Wallpaper
Water
Wax, Molded
Weapons → Arms and Armour
Weaving
Weights and Measures
Whaling → Fishing and Fisheries
Wines and Spirits
Wood → Forest Products
Wood Carving
Zoology

Agricultural Implements and Machinery

Australia
Ardrossan Historical Museum, Ardrossan 00738
Cleve National Trust Museum, Cleve 00912
Donald Agricultural Museum, Donald 00970
Doug Kerr Vintage Museum, Oaklands 01331
Farming Through the Ages, Whyte Yarcowie 01597
Mingenew Museum, Mingenew 01248
Pearn's Steam World, Westbury 01592

Austria
Bäuerliches Gerätemuseum und Venezianer-Gatter, Innervillgraten 02052
Bauern- und Heimatmuseum Haigermoos, Sankt Pantaleon 02571
Freilichtmuseum Stehrerhof - Dreschmaschinenmuseum, Neukirchen an der Vöckla 02333
Landtechnikmuseum, Leiben 02193
Landwirtschaftliches Museum und Pfarrer Franz Engel-Museum, Prinzendorf 02440
Museum für landwirtschaftliche Geräte, Grafenwörth 01902
Schloßmuseum, Sigharting 02637
Troadkasten, Freinberg 01838
Troadkasten Fornach, Fornach 01832

Belgium
Heemmuseum De Kaeck, Wommelgem 03831

Canada
Antique Tractor Museum and Frontier Village, Maple Creek 05271
Backus Heritage Village, Port Rowan 05638
British Columbia Farm Machinery and Agricultural Museum, Fort Langley 04902
Crossroads Museum, Oyen 05562
Frobisher Thresherman's Museum, Frobisher 04933
Heritage Farm Village, North Battleford 05480
Keystone Pioneer Museum, Roblin 05748
Minnie Thomson Memorial Museum, Stratford 05971
Missisquoi Museum, Stanbridge East 05957
Musée Saint-Joseph, Saint-Joseph 05825
Saanich Historical Artifacts Society, Saanichton 05764
Swords and Ploughshares Museum, Manotick 05269
Teeterville Pioneer Museum, Teeterville 06009
Thompson Museum, Readlyn 05686
Whitemouth Municipal Museum, Whitemouth 06269

Denmark
Blaavandshuk Egnsmuseum, Oksbøl 07998

Finland
Helsingin Yliopiston Maatalousmuseo, Helsinki 08354

France
Musée de la Vie Rurale, Steenwerck 13579
Musée des Champs, Saint-Ségal 13251

Germany
Altdenzlinger Heimethüs mit Otto-Raupp-Stube, Denzlingen 15297
Bachgau-Museum, Großostheim 16118
Bäuerliches Heimatmuseum der Landtechnik, Geiselhöring 15910
Bauern- und Waldmuseum, Haidmühle 16168
Bauerngerätemuseum des Stadtmuseums, Ingolstadt 16562
Bauernhaus-Museum, Ruhmannsfelden 18271
Bauernhausmuseum des Landkreises Erding, Erding 15594
Bauernhofmuseum Hof, Kirchanschöring 16740
Bauernmuseum Liebenau, Liebenau bei Dippoldiswalde 17098
Bauernmuseum Mühlhausen, Villingen-Schwenningen 18844
Bauernmuseum Ostdorf, Balingen 14567
Bauernmuseum Pfarrscheuer, Bösingen 14962
Dorfmuseum Weckbach, Weilbach 18969
Freilichtmuseum Ostenfelder Bauernhaus, Husum, Nordsee 16530
Freilichtmuseum Scherzenmühle Weidenberg, Weidenberg 18955
Gerätesammlung Georg Bauer, Stadtlauringen 18569
Gerätesammlung Koch, Königsberg in Bayern 16818
Gottlieb-Häußler-Heimatmuseum, Filderstadt 15703
Heimat- und Bergbaumuseum, Nentershausen, Hessen 17599
Heimat- und Hafnermuseum, Heidenheim, Mittelfranken 16350
Heimatmuseum, Dietenhofen 15324
Heimatmuseum, Weissach im Tal 19019
Heimatmuseum Beutelsbach, Weinstadt 19011
Heimatmuseum Grafenau Schloß Dätzingen, Grafenau, Württemberg 16056
Heimatmuseum Grimmen "Im Mühlentor", Grimmen 16093
Heimatmuseum Holzgerlingen, Holzgerlingen 16491
Heimatmuseum Niederaichbach, Niederaichbach 17695
Heimatmuseum Stadtsteinach, Stadtsteinach 18572
Heimatmuseum Waldaschaff, Waldaschaff 18881
Heimatmuseum Weiler, Schorndorf, Württemberg 18387
Heimatmuseum Wertach, Wertach 19058
Heimatstuben im Oberen Tor, Scheinfeld 18325
Historische Ochsentretanlage im Brunnenhausmuseum, Schillingsfürst 18332
Kreisagrarmuseum, Dorf Mecklenburg 15364
Landmaschinenmuseum - Sammlung Speer, Rimbach bei Eggenfelden 18179
Landtechnik-Museum Gut Steinhof, Braunschweig 15034
Museum Bad Füssing, Bad Füssing 14434
Museum für bäuerliche Arbeitsgeräte des Bezirks Oberfranken, Bayreuth 14622
Museum Wildberg, Wildberg, Württemberg 19113
Museumshof Lerchennest - Friedrich-der-Große-Museum, Sinsheim 18509
Museumsscheune, Bremervörde 15086
Museumsstadl, Bernried, Niederbayern 14875
Privatmuseum Hans Klein, Prichsenstadt 18023
Privatsammlung Leo Gesell, Triefenstein 18737
Riedenburger Bauernhofmuseum, Riedenburg 18169
Schlepper-, Auto- und Gerätemuseum Hesse, Aidhausen 14201
Schulheimatmuseum, Asbach-Bäumenheim 14308
Sensen- und Heimatmuseum, Achern 14182
Stadtmuseum Schloss Wolfsburg, Wolfsburg 19187
Städtische Sammlungen, Adelsheim 14188
Traktoren-Museum Kempen, Horn-Bad Meinberg 16506
Werksmuseum der Amazonen-Werke, Gaste 15903

Ireland
An Dun Transport and Heritage Museum, Ballinahown 20689
Lixnaw Agricultural Museum, Lixnaw 20807
Threshing Museum, Mullinahone 20820

Israel
Museum of Pioneer Settlement, Kibbutz Yif'at 20961

Namibia
Helmeringhausen Museum, Helmeringhausen 24612

Netherlands
Agrarisch Bedrijfsmuseum De Brink, Veenklooster 25581
Boerenwagenmuseum, Buren, Gelderland 24861
Fries Landbouw Museum, Exmorra 25036
Histo-Mobil, Giethoorn 25053
Nationaal Museum Historisch Landbouwtechniek, Wageningen 25621
Plumershuuske, Diepenheim 24944
Streekmuseum Hoeksche Waard, Heinenoord 25134
Het Trekkermuseum, Nisse 25328

New Zealand
Pigeon Valley Steam Museum, Wakefield 25921

Norway
Egge Museum, Steinkjer 26324
Jærmuseet, Nærbø 26197

South Africa
Settlers Museum, Himeville 28497

Switzerland
Heimatmuseum, Aesch, Basel-Land 30502
Heimatmuseum, Attiswil 30541
Musée Agricole, Coffrane 30707
Musée Romand de la Machine Agricole, Gingins 30826
Ortsmuseum Albisrieden, Zürich 31468
Ortsmuseum Wiesendangen, Wiesendangen 31386
Schweizerisches Museum für Landwirtschaft und Agrartechnik Burgrain, Alberswil 30511

United Kingdom
Combe Mill Beam Engine and Working Museum, Long Hanborough 33822
Fife Folk Museum, Ceres 32565
Greenfield Valley Museum, Greenfield 33160
Lackham Museum of Agriculture and Rural Life, Lacock 33431
Laidhay Croft Museum, Dunbeath 32831
March and District Museum, March 33905
Museum of Lincolnshire Life, Lincoln 33519
Northfield Farm Museum, New Pitsligo 34009
Sheppy's Farm and Cider Museum, Bradford-on-Tone 32356
Sussex Farm Museum, Heathfield 33232
Walton Hall Museum, Linford 33523
Wilmington Priory, Wilmington 34830

U.S.A.
Deere Museum, Moline 38574
Midwest Old Settlers and Threshers Association Museum, Mount Pleasant 38655
The National Agricultural Center and Hall of Fame, Bonner Springs 35568

Agriculture

Argentina
Museo de la Máquina Agrícola, Esperanza 00334
Museo Pampeano del Pergamino, Pergamino 00466

Australia
Avondale Discovery Farm, Beverley 00790
Churchill Island Agricultural Museum, Newhaven 01311
Court House Museum, Stroud 01479
Cunderdin Municipal Museum, Cunderdin 00948
Geralka Rural Farm, Spalding 01464
Gledswood Farm Museum and Homestead, Catherine Fields 00888
Gulf Station Historic Farm, Yarra Glen 01623
Maffra Sugarbeet Museum, Maffra 01183
Maitland Museum, Maitland, South Australia 01187
North Western Agricultural Museum, Warracknabeal 01577
Old Council Chambers Museum, Cleve 00913
Old School Museum, Streaky Bay 01478
Roseworthy Agricultural Museum, Roseworthy 01425
Rouse Hill Estate, Rouse Hill 01428
Trentham Agricultural and Railway Museum, Trentham 01550
Waterwheel Museum, Salisbury 01436
Wyalkatchem C.B.H. Agricultural Museum, Wyalkatchem 01617

Austria
Agrargeschichtliche Sammlung, Wels 02781
Alpsennereimuseum, Hittisau 02029
Bauernmuseum im Grottenhof, Kaindorf an der Sulm 02087
Bauernmuseum Sollinger-Bauer, Maria Schmolln 02261
Bergbauernmuseum, Alpbach 01654
Denkmalhof Gererhof, Annaberg 01669
Denkmalhof Maurerbauernhof, Zederhaus 03015
Freilichtmuseum, Bad Tatzmannsdorf 01712
Freilichtmuseum Mondseer Rauchhaus, Mondsee 02308
Heimatmuseum im alten Bruderhaus und in der Dechanathofscheune, Altenmarkt im Pongau 01662
Kärntner Freilichtmuseum, Maria Saal 02260
Kapuzinerturm, Radstadt 02460
Kurmuseum des Österreichischen Moorforschungsinstituts, Bad Wimsbach-Neydharting 01716
Landwirtschaftsmuseum Schloß Ehrental, Klagenfurt 02120
Lavanttaler Obstbaumuseum, Sankt Paul 02573
Mentlhof-Bergbauernmuseum, Heiligenblut 02012
Moor- und Torfmuseum, Heidenreichstein 02007
Mostviertler Bauernmuseum, Amstetten 01665
Nationalparkmuseum, Mittersill 02296
Obermühlviertler Denkmalhof Unterkagerer, Auberg 01684
Ötztaler Freilichtmuseum, Längenfeld 02167
Rauchstubenhaus, Sankt Johann im Saggautal 02553
Urgeschichtliches Freilichtmuseum Keltendorf Mitterkirchen, Mitterkirchen 02294

Belgium
Bardelaere Museum, Lembeke 03527
Havesdonckhoeve, Bornem 03190
Karrenmuseum, Essen 03375
Musée de l'Agriculture Traditionnelle et de l'Artisanat de nos Campagnes, Lahamaide 03519
Musée du Cheval, de la Vie Rurale et du Tabac, Thuillies 03759
Museum Kempenland, Lommel 03565
Museum Rufferdinge, Landen 03521
Nationaal Hopmuseum De Stadsschaal, Poperinge 03661

Brazil
Museu Municipal Visconde de Guarapuava, Guarapuava 03940

Bulgaria
Nacionalen Selskostopanski Muzej, Sofia 04330

Canada
1910 Boomtown, Saskatoon 05864
Agricultural Museum of New Brunswick, Sussex 05993
Antique Tractor Museum and Frontier Village, Maple Creek 05271
Beckoning Hills Museum, Boissevain 04549
Blair House Museum, Kentville 05118
Blockhouse Museum, Merrickville 05304
Bradley Museum, Mississauga 05334
Brownvale North Peace Agricultural Museum, Brownvale 04601
Canada Agriculture Museum, Ottawa 05533
Central Butte District Museum, Central Butte 04680
Cole Harbour Heritage Farm Museum, Cole Harbour 04726
Comber and District Historical Society Museum, Comber 04729
Compton County Historical Museum, Eaton Corner 04827
Gaspesian British Heritage Village, New Richmond 05445
Grain Academy, Museum, Calgary 04629
Greater Sudbury Heritage Museum, Sudbury 05983
Hanna Pioneer Museum, Hanna 05038
Historic Hat Creek Ranch, Cache Creek 04616
Historic O'Keefe Ranch, Vernon, British Colombia 06182
Historic Stewart Farmhouse, Surrey 05990
International Fox Museum, Summerside 05987
Keillor House Museum, Dorchester 04799
Kelowna Museum, Kelowna 05111
Kilby Historic Store and Farm, Harrison Mills 05043
Kings Landing Historical Settlement, Prince William 05660
Lac Sainte-Anne and District Pioneer Museum, Sangudo 05861
The Log Farm, Nepean 05437
MacPherson's Mill and Farm Homestead, New Glasgow 05443
Manitoba Agricultural Hall of Fame Inc., Brandon 04583
Manitoba Agricultural Museum, Austin 04479
Mayne Island Museum, Mayne Island 05290
Museum of the Cariboo Chilcotin, Williams Lake 06276
Ontario Agricultural Museum, Milton 05318
Orwell Corner Historic Village, Orwell 05523
Peace River Centennial Museum, Peace River 05571
Pouce Coupe Museum, Pouce Coupe 05643
River View Ethnographic Museum, Bear River 04521
Ross Farm Museum, New Ross 05446
Salt Spring Island Museum, Ganges 04937
South Peace Centennial Museum, Beaverlodge 04526
Story of People, Yorkton 06348
Victoria County Museum, Baddeck 04490

Chile
Museo de Arte y Artesanía de Linares, Linares 06374

Cuba
Museo La Isabelica, Santiago de Cuba 07183

Czech Republic
Kotulova Dřevěnka, Havířov 07327
Národní Zemědělské Muzeum Praha, Kačina 07379
Zemědělská Sbírka na Zámku Kačina, Kutná Hora 07421
Zemědělské Muzeum Ohrada, Ohrada 07497

Denmark
Bov Museum, Padborg 08004
Dansk Landbrugsmuseum, Auning 07765
Det Danske Hedeselskabs Museum, Viborg 08093
Erichsens Gaard, Bornholms Museum, Rønne 08021
Fjordmuseet, Jyllinge 07894
Frilandsmuseet i Maribo, Maribo 07964
Den Fynske Landsby, Odense 07992
Glud Museum, Horsens 07881
Herning Museum, Herning 07855
Landbrugs- og Interiørmuseet, Farsø 07808
Landbrugsmuseet Melstedgård, Gudhjem 07833
Landbrugsmuseet Skarregaard, Nykøbing Mors 07980
Sydhimmerlands Museum, Nørager 07972
Vestfyns Hjemstavnsgård, Glamsbjerg 07825

Egypt
Cotton Museum, Cairo 08206

Finland
Aaronpiha, Tokrajärvi 08951
Bragegården, Vaasa 08993
Etelä-Pohjanmaan Maakuntamuseo, Seinäjoki 08872
Isonkyrön Kotiseutumuseo, Isokyrö 08414
Jan Karlsgarden, Sund 08905
Jokioisten Pappilamuseo, Jokioinen 08426
Kaarlelan Kotiseutumuseo, Kaarlela 08443
Kalannin Kotiseutumuseo, Kalanti 08453
Karjalainen Kotitalo, Imatra 08411
Kauhajoen Museo, Kauhajoki 08476
Kaunislehdon Talomuseo, Hyrynsalmi 08402
Kemin Museo, Kemi 08487
Keuruun Kotiseutumuseo, Keuruu 08499
Kokemäen Maatalousmuseo, Kokemäki 08517
Laurinmäen Torpparimuseo, Janakkala 08422
Luopioisten Museo, Luopioinen 08644
Murtovaaran Talomuseo, Valtimo 09011
Mustialan Maataloushistoriallinen Museo, Mustiala 08686
Pielisen Museo, Lieksa 08622
Pienmäen Talomuseo, Niemisjärvi 08706
Pöljän Kotiseutumuseo, Pöljä 08783
Pyhäjoen Kotiseutumuseo, Pyhäjoki 08814
Reipin Museo, Pirkkala 08782
Reppuniemen Ulkomuseo, Pöytyä 08786
Ruoveden Kotiseutumuseo, Ruovesi 08851
Rymättylän Kotiseutumuseo, Rymättylä 08853
Someron Museo, Somero 08893
Talonpoikaismuseo Yli-Kirra, Punkalaidum 08809
Tenala Hembyggds Museum, Tenala 08943
Urjalan Museo, Urjalankylä 08985
Vöyrin Kotiseutumuseo, Vöyri 09048
Yläneen Kotiseutumuseo, Yläne 09051

France
Ecomusée de l'Ile de Groix, Ile-de-Groix 10846
Ecomusée du Pays de Rennes, Rennes (Ille-et-Vilaine) 12726
Musée Agricole, Semussac 13486
Musée Comtois, Besançon 09526
Musée d'Art et d'Histoire de Toul, Toul 13708
Musée de la Ferme du Contentin, Sainte-Mère-Eglise 13333
Musée Départemental de l'Abbaye de Saint-Riquier, Saint-Riquier 13238
Musée des Vallées Cévenoles, Saint-Jean-du-Gard 13070
Musée Olivier-de-Serres, Mirabel (Ardèche) 11770
Musée Troglodytique, Louresse 11480

Germany
Agrar- und Freilichtmuseum, Crimmitschau 15238
Agrarhistorisches Museum, Schlepzig 18343
Agrarmuseum, Greußen 16082
Albrecht-Daniel-Thaer-Gedenkstätte-Landesausstellung, Reichenow 18119

Agriculture

Baudenkmal Hopfenhaus - Landwirtschaftliche Gerätesammlung - Alt-Seilerei - Ostdeutsche Heimatstube, Aidlingen 14202
Bauernhaus-Museum, Lindberg 17113
Bauernhausmuseum Amerang des Bezirks Oberbayern, Amerang 14269
Bauernhausmuseum Hattingen, Hattingen 16304
Bauernhofmuseum, Buchhofen 15118
Bauernhofmuseum Jexhof des Landkreises Fürstenfeldbruck, Schöngeising 18379
Bauernmuseum Landkreis Bamberg, Frensdorf 15826
Bergisches Freilichtmuseum für Ökologie und bäuerlich-handwerkliche Kultur, Lindlar 17117
Bodanrück-Bauernmuseum, Allensbach 14221
Denkmalhof Rauchhaus Möllin, Möllin 17389
Deutsches Hirtenmuseum, Hersbruck 16407
Deutsches Landwirtschaftsmuseum, Stuttgart 18626
Europäisches Spargelmuseum, Schrobenhausen 18395
Fränkisches Freilandmuseum, Bad Windsheim 14548
Freilandmuseum Ammerländer Bauernhaus, Bad Zwischenahn 14553
Freilandmuseum Grassemann Naturpark-Infostelle, Warmensteinach 18928
Freilichtmuseum, Diesdorf, Altmark 15320
Freilichtmuseum, Stade 18559
Freilichtmuseum Alt Schwerin, Alt Schwerin 14227
Freilichtmuseum Domäne Dahlem, Berlin 14708
Freilichtmuseum Hessenpark, Neu-Anspach 17608
Freilichtmuseum Klausenhof, Herrischried 16404
Freilichtmuseum Lehde, Lehde bei Lübbenau 17012
Freilichtmuseum Massing, Massing 17294
Hanf-Museum, Berlin 14740
Haselünner Heimathäuser, Haselünne 16297
Heimatmuseum Buchenberg, Buchenberg bei Kempten 15117
Heimatmuseum der Marktgemeinde Wiggensbach, Wiggensbach 19111
Heimatmuseum im Hartmannhaus, Marktoberdorf 17278
Heimatmuseum im Wolfschneiderhof, Taufkirchen, Kreis München 18683
Hopfen-Erlebnis-Hof, Altmannstein 14249
Isinger Dorfmuseum - Alte Kelter, Tübingen 18757
Jura-Bauernhof-Museum, Hitzhofen 16439
Kulturzentrum Sinsteden des Kreises Neuss, Rommerskirchen 18209
Landwirtschaftliches Museum Wetzlar, Wetzlar 19083
Landwirtschafts- und Heimatmuseum, Karben 16641
Landwirtschaftsmuseum, Rhede, Ems 18157
Landwirtschaftsmuseum, Weil am Rhein 18963
Landwirtschaftsmuseum Hof Espe, Bad Berleburg 14395
Mühlen- und Landwirtschaftsmuseum, Jever 16611
Museum der Elbinsel Wilhelmsburg, Hamburg 16231
Museum Dermbach, Dermbach 15298
Museum für Landtechnik und Landarbeit, Emmerthal 15567
Museum Großauheim, Hanau 16259
Museum Hüsli- Sammlung Schwarzwälder Volkskunst, Grafenhausen 16057
Museum im Schafhof Bayerns Landwirtschaft seit 1800, Freising 15822
Museum im Schlößle, Freiberg am Neckar 15797
Museum Reichenau, Reichenau, Baden 18115
Museumsdorf Volksdorf mit Spiekerhus, Hamburg 16238
Museumsscheune Fränkische Schweiz, Hollfeld 16489
Niederbayerisches Landwirtschaftsmuseum, Regen 18089
Oberfränkisches Bauernhofmuseum, Zell, Oberfranken 19267
Oberpfälzer Freilandmuseum Neusath-Perschen, Nabburg 17577
Oberschwäbisches Museumsdorf Kreisfreilichtmuseum Kürnbach, Bad Schussenried 14513
Obstbaumuseum, Werder, Havel 19048
Ostfriesisches Landwirtschaftsmuseum, Krummhörn 16895
Riedmuseum, Rastatt 18061
Schäfertanz-Kabinett, Rothenburg ob der Tauber 18244
Schlesisch-Oberlausitzer Dorfmuseum, Markersdorf bei Görlitz 17267
Schleswig-Holsteinisches Freilichtmuseum e.V., Molfsee 17408
Schleswig-Holsteinisches Landwirtschaftsmuseum und Dithmarscher Bauernhaus, Meldorf 17326
Schlossmuseum Reckahn, Reckahn 18084
Schwäbisches Bauernhofmuseum Illerbeuren, Kronburg 16889
Schwäbisches Volkskundemuseum und Bauernhofmuseum Staudenhaus, Gessertshausen 15962
Schwarzwälder Freilichtmuseum Vogtsbauernhof, Gutach, Schwarzwaldbahn 16149
Stadtmuseum Herrenmühle, Hammelburg 16255
Tauberländer Dorfmuseum, Weikersheim 18960
Technisches Museum Ölmühle, Pockau 18001
Volkskundliches Gerätemuseum, Arzberg, Oberfranken 14307
Westfälisches Freilichtmuseum Detmold, Detmold 15313

Hungary
Georgikon Majormúzeum, Keszthely 19924
Magyar Mezőgazdasági Múzeum, Budapest 19832
Magyar Mezőgazdasági Múzeum, Budapest 19833
Paprika Múzeum, Kalocsa 19907
Paprikamúzeum, Szeged 20015

India
Museum of the Agricultural College and Research Institute, Coimbatore 20194
Victoria and Albert Museum, Mumbai 20179

Indonesia
Museum Subak Bali, Kediri 20527
Subak Museum, Banjar Senggulan 20468

Ireland
Ballinamore Local Museum, Ballinamore 20690
Crover Folk Museum, Mount Nugent 20819
Irish Agricultural Museum, Wexford 20851
Roscrea Heritage Centre, Roscrea 20829

Israel
Dagon Collection, Haifa 20884
Landscapes of the Holy Land Park, Tel Aviv 21002

Italy
Centro di Documentazione sulla Storia dell'Agricoltura e della Frutticoltura della Bassa Ravennate "Adolfo Bonvicini", Massa Lombarda 21857
Museo Agricolo, Castelfranco Veneto 21341
Museo del Po, Monticelli d'Ongina 21998
Museo della Civiltà Contadina, Bentivoglio 21153
Museo della Civiltà Contadina ed Artigiana della Calabria, Monterosso Calabro 21993
Museo della Civiltà Contadina Valle dell'Aniene, Roviano 22445
Museo della Vita e del Lavoro, Cecina e Marina 21375
Museo dell'Agricoltura del Piemonte, Torino 22678
Museo dell'Agricoltura Meridionale, Carditello 21311
Museo di Storia dell'Agricoltura, Cesena 21399
Museo Lombardo di Storia dell'Agricoltura, Sant'Angelo Lodigiano 22521
Raccolta Permanente sulla Lavorazione della Canapa, Buonconvento 21258

Japan
Hida Minzoku-mura, Takayama 23552
Hokkaido Daigaku Nogakubu Hakubutsukan, Sapporo 23467
Jingu Nogyokan, Ise 23079
Nara-kenritsu Minzoku Hakubutsukan, Yamatokoriyama 23757
Nihon Miuka Shuraku Hakubutsukan, Toyonaka 23722
Shizuoka Archaeological Museum, Shizuoka 23516
Yomitan Township History and Folk Art Hall, Yomitanson 23779

Korea, Republic
Agricultural Museum, Seoul 23914
Chonju National Museum, Chonju 23886

Malaysia
Agricultural Museum, Jasin 24284

Netherlands
Boerderijmuseum De Lebbenbrugge, Borculo 24824
Boerenbondsmuseum, Gemert 25048
Boerenmuseum Zelhem, Zelhem 25677
Fruitteeltmuseum, Kapelle 25201
't Fûgelhûs, Piaam 25392
Hagedoorns Plaatse, Epe 25028
Heemkundemuseum Paulus Van Daesdonck, Ulvenhout 25549
Huize Betje Wolff, Middenbeemster 25296
International Soil Reference and Information Centre, Wageningen 25620
Landbouw- en Juttersmuseum Swartwoude, Buren, Friesland 24860
Landbouwmuseum Hand en Span, Oirschot 25342
Museum Bebinghehoes, Exloo 25035
Museum Broeker Veiling, Broek op Langedijk 24848
Museum in de Veenen, Vinkeveen 25595
Museum Oud-Ede, Ede 24983
Museum Saet en Cruyt, Andijk 24749
Museumboerderij, Heeswijk Dinther 25128
Museumboerderij de Karstenhoeve, Ruinerwold 25456
Museumboerderij Welgelegen, Heiligerlee 25133
Museumsboerderij Oud Noordwijk, Noordwijk, Zuid-Holland 25335
Nationaal Asperge- en Champignonmuseum De Locht, Horst 25182
Openlucht Laagveenderij Museum Damshûs, Nij Beets 25320
Openluchtmuseum Ellert en Brammert, Schoonoord 25480
Oudheidkamer Horst, Horst 25183
Peelmuseum, Ospel 25370
Pluimvee Museum, Barneveld 24790
Streek- en Landbouwmuseum Schouwen-Duiveland, Dreischor 24971
Streeklandbouwmuseum Agrimuda, Sint Anna ter Muiden 25483
Streeklandbouwmuseum Agrimuda, Sluis 25501
Streekmuseum Crimpenerhof, Krimpen aan den IJssel 25212
Streekmuseum De Acht Zaligheden, Eersel 24993
Streekmuseum Het Land van Axel, Axel 24781
Streekmuseum Tholen en Sint-Philipsland, Sint Annaland 25484
Veen Park, Barger Compascuum 24789
Vlasbewerkingsmuseum It Braakhok, Ee 24985
Westlands Museum voor Streek- en Tuinbouwhistorie, Honselersdijk 25171
Wieringer Museumboerderij, Den Oever 24936

New Zealand
Agricultural Heritage Museum, Hamilton 25801
East Coast Museum of Technology, Gisborne 25792
Norsewood Pioneer Museum, Norsewood 25849
Tuapeka Goldfields Museum, Lawrence 25822
Waiuku Museum, Waiuku 25920

Norway
Åfjord Bygdetun, Åfjord 26001
Ål Bygdemuseum, Ål 26002
Andøymuseet, Risøyhamn 26263
Askim Bygdemuseet, Askim 26018
Aurskog-Høland Bygdetun, Hemnes i Høland 26109
Bagn Bygdesamling, Bagn 26020
Bardu Bygdetun, Salangsdalen 26279
Brudavollen Bygdetun, Ørsta 26212
Bygdetunet Jutulheimen, Vågåmo 26366
Bygland Museet, Bygland 26054
Eidsvoll Bygdemuseet, Eidsvoll Verk 26069
Enebakk Museet, Enebakk 26072
Folkenborg Museum, Mysen 26195
Fossmotunet - Målselv Bygdemuseum, Moen 26185
Fyresdal Bygdemuseet, Fyresdal 26092
Gamle Hvam Museum, Årnes 26015
Gamle Kvernes Bygdemuseum, Kvernes 26152
Glomdalsmuseet, Elverum 26070
Gol Bygdemuseet, Gol 26096
Granvin Bygdemuseet, Granvin 26097
Grødaland Bygdetun, Varhaug 26370
Grytøy Bygdetun, Lundenes 26176
Haltdalen Bygdetun, Haltdalen 26102
Havråtunet, Lonevåg 26172
Hedmarksmuseet og Domkirkeodden, Hamar 26103
Hemsedal Bygdatun, Hemsedal 26110
Hol Bygdemuseet, Hol i Hallingdal 26113
Hordamuseet, Fana 26078
Huldreheimen, Bykle 26055
Jærmuseet, Nærbø 26197
Kongsvold Bygdetun, Moen 26186
Kvæford Bygdetun, Borkenes 26047
Kviteseid Bygdetun, Kviteseid 26154
Landbruksmuseet for Møre og Romsdal, Vikebukt 26381
Lands Museet, Dokka 26057
Lårdal Bygdemuseum, Høydalsmo 26125
Lom Heimbygdslag, Lom 26170
Lørenskog Bygdemuseum, Skårer 26292
Mandal og Opplands Folkemuseum, Mandal 26178
Meråker Bygdemuseum, Meråker 26181
Mosvik - Sæteråsgården, Mosvik 26194
Namsdalsmuseet, Namsos 26198
Ner Hole Museum, Åndalsnes 26010
Nordre Husan, Alvdal 26008
Norsk Landbruksmuseum, Ås 26016
Odalstunet, Skarnes 26293
Orkdal Bygdetun, Fannrem 26079
Osterøy Museum, Lonevåg 26173
Rakkestad Bygdetun, Rakkestad 26256
Rennebu Bygdetun, Rennebu 26259
Rindal Bygdemuseum, Rindalsskogen 26262
Rissa Bygdemuseum, Rissa 26264
Roan Bygdetun, Roan 26267
Sætersgårds Samlinger Dølmotunet, Tolga 26340
Sigdal og Eggedal Museum, Prestfoss 26254
Skedsmo Bygdetun, Skedsmokorset 26294
Skiptvet Bygdemuseum, Skiptvet 26300
Sørli Museum, Sørli 26311
Spydeberg Bygdetun, Spydeberg 26316
Stenneset Bygdetun, Mo i Rana 26184
Sunndal Bygdemuseum, Sunndalsøra 26332
Sunnfjord Museum, Førde 26088
Toten Økomuseum, Bøverbru 26050
Toten Økomuseum, Kapp 26132
Trøgstad Bygdemuseum, Trøgstad 26343
Trysil Bygdemuseum, Trysil 26356
Tylldalen Bygdetun, Tylldalen 26359
Velfjord Bygdemuseum, Hommelstø 26117
Vestfold Fylkesmuseum, Tønsberg 26341
Volda Bygdetun, Volda 26385
Voss Folkemuseum, Skulestadmo 26303

Pakistan
Agricultural Museum, Faisalabad 26394

Poland
Muzeum Narodowe Rolnictwa i Przemysłu Rolno-Spożywczego w Szreniawie, Komorniki 26801
Muzeum Rolnictwa im. ks. Krzysztofa Kluka, Ciechanowiec 26673

Portugal
Agricultural Museum of Entre Douro e Mino, Vila do Conde 27448
Jardim-Museu Agrícola Tropical, Lisboa 27382

Romania
Muzeul Satului, Bucureşti 27527

Russia
Povčenno-agronomičeskij Muzej im. V.R. Viljamsa, Moskva 27936

Slovakia
Slovenské Polnohospodárske Múzeum, Nitra 28273

Slovenia
Muzej Tomaža Godca, Bohinjska Bistrica 28323
Planšarski Muzej, Bohinjsko Jezero 28324

South Africa
Bathurst Agricultural Museum, Grahamstown 28483
Howick Museum, Howick 28498
Willem Prinsloo Museum, Rayton 28604

Spain
Museu d'Eines del Camp Masia de Can Deu, Sabadell 29584
Museu del Pagès, Linyola 29198

Sweden
Hägnan Friluftsmuseet i Gammelstad, Gammelstad 30090
Kulturhistoriska Museet i Bunge, Farösund 30076

Switzerland
Alpmuseum Riederalp, Riederalp 31128
Dorfmuseum, Bottmingen 30646
Heimatmuseum, Balgach 30558
Heimatmuseum Nutli-Hüschi, Klosters 30892
Mazot-Musée de Plan-Cerisier, Martigny 30993
Sennerei-Museum, Unterwasser 31335
Ständerhaus, Buus 30677
Strohhaus, Muhen 31037

United Kingdom
Aberdeenshire Farming Museum, Mintlaw 33964
Acton Scott Historic Working Farm, Church Stretton 32628
Agricultural Museum, Coate 32646
Agricultural Museum Brook, Dover 32800
Agriculture Museum Brook, Brook 32430
Almond Valley Heritage Centre, Livingston 33549
Ardress Farm Museum, Annaghmore 32050
Barleylands Farm Museum, Billericay 32248
Battle and Farm Museum, Naseby 33999
Beamish, North of England Open Air Museum, Beamish 32182
Brattle Farm Museum, Staplehurst 34552
Bwlch Farm Stable Museum, Llanelli 33560
Bygones at Holkham, Wells-next-the-Sea 34771
Bygones Museum, Claydon 32633
Church Farm Museum, Skegness 34493
Cogges Manor Farm Museum, Witney 34862
Corfe Castle Museum, Corfe Castle 32676
Countryside Museum, East Budleigh 32872
Easton Farm Park, Easton 32896
Ellisland Farm, Ellisland 32961
Farm and Folk Museum, Lanreath 33445
Farmland Museum and Denny Abbey, Waterbeach 34760
Farmlife Centre, Thornhill, Central 34667
Gower Heritage Centre, Gower 33137
Guernsey Folk Museum, Câtel 32558
Hampshire Farm Museum, Botley 32335
Hamptonne Country Life Museum, Saint Lawrence 34386
Hirsel Homestead Museum, Coldstream 32661
Kingsbury Watermill Museum, Saint Albans 34352
Leslie Hill Open Farm, Ballymoney 32121
Llanyrafon Farm, Cwmbran 32730
Maldon and District Agricultural and Domestic Museum, Goldhanger 33122
Manor Farm, Bursledon 32458
Museum of English Rural Life, Reading 34282
Museum of Farming Life, Ellon 32962
Museum of Rural Industry, Sticklepath 34559
Museum of Scottish Country Life, East Kilbride 32879
Newham Grange Leisure Farm Museum, Middlesbrough 33947
Norfolk Rural Life Museum and Union Farm, Gressenhall 33164
Normanby Park Farming Museum, Scunthorpe 34434
Orkney Farm and Folk Museum, Harray 33195
Orkney Farm and Folk Museum in Kirbuster, Birsay 32282
Park Farm Museum, Milton Abbas 33957
Pitstone Green Farm Museum, Pitstone 34191
Plantation of Ulster Visitor Centre, Draperstown 32811
Rural Life Centre, Farnham 33012
Sacrewell Farm and Country Centre, Thornhaugh 34666
Shetland Croft House Museum, Dunrossnes 32851
Somerset Rural Life Museum, Glastonbury 33103
South Molton and District Museum, South Molton 34502
Stacey Hill Museum, Wolverton 34871
Tingwall Agricultural Museum, Gott 33135
Upminster Tithe Barn, Upminster 34712
Upper Wharfdale Folk Museum, Grassington 33146
Warwickshire Museum of Rural Life, Moreton Morrell 33983
Whaley Thorns Heritage Centre and Museum, Whaley Thorns 34801
Wimpole Hall and Home Farm, Arrington 32073
Yorkshire Museum of Farming, York 34924

U.S.A.
The 100th Meridian Museum, Cozad 36306
The Accokeek Foundation, Accokeek 34980
Adams County Museum, Brighton 35663
Agricultural Museum at Stone Mills, La Fargeville 37853
Alexander and Baldwin Sugar Museum, Puunene 39657
American Maple Museum, Croghan 36323
The Apple Trees Museum, Burlington 35746
Baldwin County Heritage Museum, Elberta 36676
Banner County Historical Museum, Harrisburg 37347

Barrington Living History Farm, Washington 41021
Billings Farm and Museum, Woodstock 41286
Blackberry Farm-Pioneer Village, Aurora 35257
Calumet County Historical Society Museum, New Holstein 38793
Carroll County Farm Museum, Westminster 41138
Central Washington Agricultural Museum, Union Gap 40796
Chippokes Farm and Forestry Museum, Surry 40587
The Coley Homestead and Barn Museum, Weston 41141
Collin County Farm Museum, McKinney 38248
Craftsman Farms Foundation, Parsippany 39285
Delaware Agricultural Museum and Village, Dover 36543
Drumlin Farm, Lincoln 38046
Erie Canal Village, Rome 39858
The Farm, Sturgeon Bay 40561
Farm House Museum, Ames 35076
Farmamerica, Waseca 40942
The Farmers' Museum, Cooperstown 36256
Florida Agricultural Museum, Palm Coast 39260
Fort Walla Walla Museum, Walla Walla 40905
Fosterfields Living Historical Farm, Morristown 38633
The Fryeburg Fair Farm Museum, Fryeburg 37054
Garfield Farm Museum, Lafox 37881
Georgia Agrirama-19th Century Living History Museum, Tifton 40681
Gibbs Farm Museum, Falcon Heights 36793
Grant-Kohrs Ranch National Historic Site, Deer Lodge 36436
Hadley Farm Museum, Hadley 37296
Hale Farm and Village, Bath 35364
Hallockville Museum Farm, Riverhead 39790
Highland Maple Museum, Monterey 38598
Hillsboro Museum, Hillsboro 37429
Historic Schaefferstown, Schaefferstown 40251
Hofwyl-Broadfield Plantation, Brunswick 35721
Homestead National Monument of America, Beatrice 35386
Huddleston Farmhouse Inn Museum, Cambridge City 35800
Jarrell Plantation Georgia State Historic Site, Juliette 37705
Jewell County Historical Museum, Mankato 38315
John Brown Farm, Lake Placid 37896
Jourdan-Bachman Pioneer Farm, Austin 35271
Kittson County History Center Museum, Lake Bronson 37884
Kiwanis Van Slyke Museum Foundation, Caldwell 35775
Landis Valley Museum, Lancaster 37924
Landmark Park, Dothan 36535
Leaming's Run Garden and Colonial Farm, Cape May Court House 35836
Living History Farms Museum, Urbandale 40812
Longstreet Farm, Holmdel 37466
Malabar Farm State Park, Lucas 38209
Marjorie Kinnan Rawlings State Historic Site, Cross Creek 36327
Midwest Old Settlers and Threshers Association Museum, Mount Pleasant 38655
Miles B. Carpenter Museum, Waverly 41062
Mitchell County Historical Museum, Osage 39203
Mountain Farm Museum, Cherokee 35975
Mulford House and Farm, East Hampton 36612
The National Agricultural Center and Hall of Fame, Bonner Springs 35568
National Apple Museum, Biglerville 35491
Neeses Farm Museum, Neeses 38742
Nelson Pioneer Farm and Museum, Oskaloosa 39209
New Hampshire Farm Museum, Milton 38510
New Jersey Museum of Agriculture, North Brunswick 39026
New Mexico Farm and Ranch Heritage Museum, Las Cruces 37948
New Sweden Farmstead Museum, Bridgeton 35658
Northeastern Montana Threshers and Antique Association Museum, Culbertson 36335
Old Trail Museum, Choteau 36067
Oliver Kelley Farm, Elk River 36685
Olmstead Place State Park, Ellensburg 36695
Oxon Cove Park Museum, Oxon Hill 39240
Pawnee City Historical Society Museum, Pawnee City 39299
Pendleton District Agricultural Museum, Pendleton 39313
Pike Pioneer Museum, Troy 40731
Pioneer Farm Museum and Ohop Indian Village, Eatonville 36632
Pioneer Florida Museum, Dade City 36348
Piqua Historical Area State Memorial, Piqua 39454
Plantation Agriculture Museum, Scott 40264
Queens County Farm Museum, Floral Park 36851
Quiet Valley Living Historical Farm, Stroudsburg 40554
Rice County Museum of History, Faribault 36807
Ronald V. Jensen Living Historical Farm, Wellsville 41089
Rough and Tumble Engineers Museum, Kinzers 37819
Seward County Historical Society Museum, Goehner 37164
Shaker Village of Pleasant Hill, Harrodsburg 37356
Silvercreek Museum, Freeport 37040
Slate Run Living Historical Farm, Ashville 35185
Sotterley Plantation Museum, Hollywood 37465
State Agricultural Heritage Museum, Brookings 35690
Steppingstone Museum, Havre de Grace 37381
Stonefield Historic Site, Cassville 35863
Stuttgart Agricultural Museum, Stuttgart 40563
Thetford Historical Society Museum, Thetford 40673
Tobacco Farm Life Museum, Kenly 37763
Troy Museum and Historic Village, Troy 40732
Volkening Heritage Farm at Spring Valley, Schaumburg 40253
Ward O'Hara Agricultural Museum of Cayuga County, Auburn 35242
Watters Smith, Lost Creek 38181
West Virginia State Farm Museum, Point Pleasant 39519
Wheeler Historic Farm, Salt Lake City 40051
Wolf Point Area Historical Society Museum, Wolf Point 41270
WVU Jackson's Mill Historic Area, Weston 41146

Amber

Denmark

Ravmuseet, Oksbøl 07999

Germany

Bernstein Museum, Bad Füssing 14432
Deutsches Bernsteinmuseum, Ribnitz-Damgarten 18163

Russia

Amber Museum, Kaliningrad 27742

Sweden

Bärnstensmuseet, Höllviken 30129

Anthropology → Ethnology

Apiculture → Bees

Archaeology

Albania

Archeological Museum of Durrës, Durrës 00015
National Museum of Archaeology, Tiranë 00037

Algeria

Musée Archéologique, Cherchell 00052
Musée d'Archéologie, Béjaia 00048
Musée d'Hippone, Annaba 00047
Musée du Temple de Minerve, Tebessa 00066
Musée National des Antiquités, Alger 00043
Musée Régional d'Archéologie, Sétif 00062
National Archaeologic Museum, Sétif 00063

Angola

Museu Nacional de Arqueologia, Benguela 00077

Argentina

Instituto de Investigaciones Arqueológicas y Museo Prof. Mariano Gambier, Albardón 00099
Museo Arqueológico, Aguilares 00098
Museo Arqueológico, Tafí del Valle 00617
Museo Arqueológico Adán Quiroga, San Fernando del Valle de Catamarca 00546
Museo Arqueológico del Instituto de Arqueología y Etnología, Mendoza 00426
Museo Arqueológico Provincial Andalgalá, Andalgalá 00104
Museo Arqueológico Provincial Condor Huasi (interim), Belén 00129
Museo Etnográfico Juán B. Ambrosetti, Buenos Aires 00196
Museo Histórico de La Rioja, La Rioja 00392
Museo Privado de Arqueología Regional Julio Gironde, Carmen de Patagonés 00256

Armenia

State History Museum of Armenia, Erevan 00683

Australia

Abbey Museum of Art and Archaeology, Caboolture 00862
John Elliott Classics Museum, Hobart 01086
Museum of Classical Archaeology, Adelaide 00701
Nicholson Museum, Sydney 01502

Austria

Archäologisches Museum, Klosterneuburg 02129
Archäologisches Museum Lavant, Lienz 02210
Ausgrabungen Wüstung Hard, Thaya 02699
Freilichtmuseum Römervilla in Brederis, Rankweil 02467
Keltenmuseum Gracarca, Sankt Kanzian 02556
Museen im Wehrturm, Perchtoldsdorf 02386
Museum von Abgüssen und Originalsammlung, Innsbruck 02068
Provinzialrömische Sammlung und Antikenkabinett, Graz 01920
Römermuseum Teurnia, Lendorf 02197
Römermuseum Wallsee-Sindelburg, Wallsee 02762
Rollettmuseum, Baden bei Wien 01722
Salzburger Museum Carolino Augusteum, Salzburg 02531
Stadtmuseum Wels, Wels 02786
Städtisches Kießling-Museum, Drosendorf an der Thaya 01768
Turmmuseum, Pillichsdorf 02399
Ur-und frühgeschichtliche Sammlungen, Graz 01932
Urgeschichtliches Freilichtmuseum Keltendorf Mitterkirchen, Mitterkirchen 02294

Bahrain

Bahrain National Museum, Manama 03044

Bangladesh

Archaeological Museum, Mahastangarh 03056
Archaeological Museum, Paharpur 03058
Dhaka Museum, Dhaka 03052
Dinajpur Museum, Dinajpur 03055
Rangpur Archaeological Museum, Rangpur 03060

Belarus

Muzej Staražytna Belaruskaj Kultury, Minsk 03080

Belgium

Archeologisch Museum, Grobbendonk 03430
Archeologisch Museum, Brugge 03207
Archeologisch Museum Abdij, Affligem 03087
Archeologisch Museum Van Bogaert-Wauters, Hamme 03439
Espace Gallo-Romain, Ath 03148
Gallo-Romeins Museum, Tongeren 03764
Gemeentelijk Museum, Melle 03594
Gemeentemuseum, Temse 03751
Musée Archéologique, Namur 03618
Musée Archéologique, Science, Pêche et Folklore, Durbuy 03362
Musée Athois, Ath 03149
Musée Cantonnal, Wavre 03816
Musée Communal Georges Mulpas, Elouges 03369
Musée d'Archéologie, Nivelles 03635
Musée d'Archéologie et Folklore, Verviers 03791
Musée d'Archéologie Préhistorique de l'Université de Liège, Liège 03544
Musée de la Pierre et Site des Carrières, Maffle 03575
Musée des Fagnes, Roly 03685
Musée des Francs et de la Famenne, Marche-en-Famenne 03579
Musée d'Histoire et d'Archéologie, Warneton 03812
Musée du Malgré-Tout, Treignes 03782
Musée du Monde Souterrain, Han-sur-Lesse 03442
Musée du Vieux-Cimetière, Soignies 03735
Musée et Patrimoine Hastière, Hastière-par-Delà 03454
Musée Gallo-Romain, Rumes 03690
Musée Royal de Mariemont, Morlanwelz-Mariemont 03612
Museum 't Nieuwhuys Hoegaarden, Hoegaarden 03467
Museum voor Oudheidkunde, Geraardsbergen 03424
Rietgaverstede, Nevele 03630
Stedelijk Museum Aalst, Aalst 03085
Stedelijk Museum Brusselport, Mechelen 03589
Stedelijk Ostmuseum, Hoogstraten 03471
Vleeshuismuseum, Dendermonde 03343

Bosnia and Herzegovina

Humačka Arheološko Zbirka, Ljubuški 03886
Muzej Grada Zenice, Zenica 03903
Muzej Istične Bosnë, Tuzla 03900
Muzej Republike Srpske, Banja Luka 03879
Zavičajni Muzej, Prijedor 03890
Zemaljski Muzej, Sarajevo 03896

Brazil

Museu de Arqueologia e Etnologia da Universidade de São Paulo, São Paulo 04107
Museu Paranaense, Curitiba 03930

Bulgaria

Archaeological Preserve Nicopolis ad Istrum, Veliko Tărnovo 04371
Archeologičeska Ekspozicija Kreposta, Silistra 04287
Archeologičeski Muzej, Plovdiv 04262
Archeologičeski Muzej, Varna 04359
Archeologičeski Muzej, Veliko Tărnovo 04372
Archeologičeski Rezervat Starijat Grad Šumen, Šumen 04342
Gradski Archeologičeski Muzej, Nesebâr 04241
Gradski Istoričeski Muzej, Asenovgrad 04139
Gradski Istoričeski Muzej, Botevgrad 04154
Gradski Istoričeski Muzej, Karnobat 04204
Istoričeski Muzej, Blagoevgrad 04152
Istoričeski Muzej, Razgrad 04271
Istoričeski Muzej, Velingrad 04385
Istoričeski Muzej Targovište, Targovište 04353
Istoričeskij Muzej, Tutrakan 04358
Muzej Rafail Popov, Madara 04232
Nacionalen Istoriko-archeologičeski Rezervat s Muzej Veliki Preslav, Veliki Preslav 04370
Nikopolis ad Istrum-Antičen grad, Selo Nikjup 04283
Okražen Istoričeski Muzej, Chaskovo 04163
Okražen Istoričeski Muzej, Sliven 04300
Peštera Rabiša Muzej, Vidin 04391
Regionalen Istoričeski Muzej, Stara Zagora 04340
Regionalen Istoričeski Muzej Varna, Varna 04368

Cameroon

Musée du Palais, Foumban 04414

Canada

Fort George and Buckingham House, Saint Paul 05839
Kingston Archaeological Centre, Kingston 05138
Murray's Museum of History, Neepawa 05433
Musée Canadien des Civilisations, Outaouais 05065
Museum of Archaeology and Ethnology, Burnaby 04611
Parc Archéologique de la Pointe-du-Buisson, Melocheville 05300
Pointe-à-Callière - Musée d'Archéologie et d'Histoire de Montréal, Montréal 05392
Prince of Wales Northern Heritage Centre, Yellowknife 06345
Red Bay Historic Site, Red Bay 05687
Royal British Columbia Museum, Victoria 06204
Ska-Nah-Doht Iroquoian Village and Museum, Mount Brydges 05412
Strathcona Archaeological Centre, Edmonton 04851
Surrey Museum, Surrey 05992
XA Ytem Museum, Mission 05330
Yukon Beringia Interpretive Centre, Whitehorse 06267

Central African Republic

Musée Labasso, Bangassou 06351

Chile

Museo Arqueológico R.P. Gustavo Le Paige S.J., San Pedro de Atacama 06381
Museo Arqueológico San Miguel de Azapa, Arica 06363
Museo de Hualpén, Concepción 06368
Museo Regional de Atacama, Copiapó 06370
Museo Regional de Iquique, Iquique 06372

China, People's Republic

Hong Kong Museum of History, Hong Kong 06580
Inner Mongolia Museum, Huhehot 06600
Municipal Museum, Baoji 06414

Colombia

Casa de Bolívar, Bucaramanga 06832
Casa Museo Don Juan de Vargas, Tunja 06920
Museo Arqueológico, Ipiales 06850
Museo Arqueológico, Manizales 06852
Museo Arqueológico, Sogamoso 06917
Museo Escobar María Goretti, Pasto 06869
Museo Nacional de Colombia, Santafé de Bogotá 06913

Congo, Democratic Republic

Musée de Mbandaka, Mbandaka 06935

Croatia

Archeological and Natural History Museum, Brijuni 06970
Arheološka Zbirka, Metković 07027
Arheološka Zbirka Osor, Nerezine 07030
Brački Muzej, Škrip 07065
Centar za Zaštitu Kulturne Baštine Otoka Hvara, Hvar 06994
Collection of the Dominican Priory, Stari Grad 07077
Creski Muzej, Cres 06978
Glyptothèque, Zagreb 07102
Gradski Muzej Makarska, Makarska 07024
Gradski Muzej Siska, Sisak 07064
Gradski Muzej Virovitica, Virovitica 07090
Muzej Cetinjske Krajine, Sinj 07062
Muzej Franjevačkog Samostana Košljun, Punat 07047
Muzej Grada, Šibenik 07060
Muzej Grada Koprivnice, Koprivnica 07006
Muzej Korčula, Korčula 07010
Muzej Medjimurja, Čakovec 06973
Muzej Moslavine, Kutina 07021
Narodni Muzej Labin, Labin 07022
Senj Municipal Museum, Senj 07058
Zavičajni Muzej, Biograd na Moru 06966
Zavičajni Muzej, Otočac 07040
Zbirka Umjetnina KAIROS, Trogir 07085
Zupski Ured, Ston 07080

Cuba

Museo Arqueológico Guamuhaya, Trinidad 07186
Museo Casa Natal de Carlos Manuel de Céspedes, Bayamo 07131
Museo Chorro de Maita, Banes 07130
Museo de la Provincia de Granma, Bayamo 07132
Museo de la Revolución y Granma Memorial, La Habana 07150
Museo Municipal de Regla, La Habana 07155
Museo Municipal de Trinidad, Trinidad 07188
Museo Provincial de Holguín, Holguín 07166
Museo Provincial de Villaclara, Santa Clara 07178

Cyprus

Kourion Museum, Episkopi 07191
Larnaca District Archaeological Museum, Larnaka 07194
Larnaca District Museum, Larnaka 07195
Paphos District Archaeological Museum, Paphos 07215
Pierides Museum, Larnaka 07196
Temple of Aphrodite, Koukila 07192

Cyprus Turk

Archaeological and Natural Science Museum, Güzelyurt 07224

Czech Republic

Archeological Open Air Museum in Březno u Loun, Louny 07447
Archeologické Muzeum, Břeclav 07248

Archaeology

Archeologické Pracoviště, Opava 07501
Archeologické Sbírky, Plzeň 07526
Jihomoravské Muzeum ve Znojmě, Znojmo 07739
Kamenný Dům, Kutná Hora 07419
Měnínská Brána, Brno 07257
Městské Muzeum, Čelákovice 07277
Městské Muzeum, Dačice 07307
Městské Muzeum, Jesenice u Rakovnika 07367
Městské Muzeum, Mnichovo Hradiště 07466
Městské Muzeum, Nové Strašecí 07489
Městské Muzeum, Počátky 07532
Městské Muzeum, Valašské Klobouky 07688
Městské Muzeum, Veselí nad Moravou 07700
Městské Muzeum a Galerie, Břeclav 07249
Městské Muzeum a Galerie J. Karse, Velvary 07698
Městské Vrbasovo Muzeum, Ždánice 07725
Moravské Zemské Muzeum, Brno 07260
Muzeum Kouřimska, Kouřim 07407
Muzeum Mohelnice, Mohelnice 07467
Muzeum Prostějovska, Prostějov 07613
Muzeum Východních Čech v Hradci Králové, Hradec Králové 07351
Národní Kulturní Památník - Valy, Mikulčice 07458
Okresní Muzeum, Blovice 07241
Okresní Muzeum, Pelhřimov 07521
Okresní Muzeum, Vysoké Mýto 07715
Okresní Muzeum a Galerie, Jičín 07370
Ostravské Muzeum, Ostrava 07511
Regionální Muzeum v Kolíně, Kolín 07400
Východočeské Muzeum, Pardubice 07518

Denmark
Aalborg Historiske Museum, Aalborg 07745
Den Antikvariske Samling, Ribe 08010
Arkaeologisk Museum, Korsør 07945
Blaabjerg Egnsmuseum, Nørre Nebel 07973
Danmarks Kloster Museum, Ry 08033
Djurslands Museum - Dansk Fiskerimuseum, Grenå 07827
Hobro Museum, Hobro 07865
Klosterlund Museet, Engesvang 07790
Kulturhistorisk Museum, Randers 08008
Langelands Museum, Rudkøbing 08031
Lindholm Høje Museet, Nørresundby 07974
Museet ved Danevirke, Dannewerk 07779
Økomuseum Samsø, Samsø 08035
Vendsyssel Historiske Museum, Hjørring 07863
Viborg Stiftsmuseum, Viborg 08097

Ecuador
Museo Arqueología y Etnología, Quito 08153
Museo Municipal, Guayaquil 08141

Eritrea
Archaeological Museum, Asmara 08262

Ethiopia
Aksum Archaeology Museum, Aksum 08284
National Museum, Addis Ababa 08281

Faroe Islands
Føroya Fornminnissavn, Tórshavn 08288

Fiji
Fiji Museum, Suva 08291

Finland
Aboa Vetus - Arkeologis-historiallinen Museo, Turku 08958
Liedon Vanhalinna, Vanhalinna 09014

France
Aître Saint-Saturnin, Blois 09594
L'Archéodrome de Bourgogne, Meursault 11747
Archéosite de Glanum/Les Antiques, Saint-Rémy-de-Provence 13227
Archéosite Gallo-Romain des Flaviers, Mouzon 11980
Circuits-Exposition de Musée de Cerdagne, Eyne 10494
Collections Archéologiques, Parmain 12461
Dépôt de Fouilles Gallo-Romaines et Préhistoriques de Montmaurin, Montmaurin 11888
Expositions du Château, Pierrefonds 12527
Musée Alfred-Bonno, Chelles 10076
Musée Antoine Vivenel, Compiègne 10182
Musée Archéologique, Artenay 09264
Musée Archéologique, Bray-sur-Seine 09717
Musée Archéologique, Briord 09752
Musée Archéologique, Brumath 09765
Musée Archéologique, Champagnole 09969
Musée Archéologique, Corseul 10217
Musée Archéologique, Dijon 10326
Musée Archéologique, Eauze 10395
Musée Archéologique, Ernée 10443
Musée Archéologique, Escolives-Sainte-Camille 10448
Musée Archéologique, Lectoure 11288
Musée Archéologique, Nîmes 12122
Musée Archéologique, Pons 12586
Musée Archéologique, Saint-Gilles-du-Gard 13032
Musée Archéologique, Saintes 13340
Musée Archéologique, Soyons 13576
Musée Archéologique, Strasbourg 13597
Musée Archéologique, Vachères 13825
Musée Archéologique d'Argentomagus, Saint-Marcel (Indre) 13125
Musée Archéologique de la Porte du Croux, Nevers 12086
Musée Archéologique de la Région de Breteuil, Breteuil 09737
Musée Archéologique de l'Institut Catholique, Toulouse 13724
Musée Archéologique de Minerve, Yzeures-sur-Creuse 14128
Musée Archéologique Départemental, Saint-Bertrand-de-Comminges 12913
Musée Archéologique Départemental du Val-d'Oise, Guiry-en-Vexin 10773
Musée Archéologique du Gatinais, Montargis 11824
Musée Archéologique - Eglise Saint-Laurent, Grenoble 10738
Musée Archéologique et de Paléontologie, Minerve 11768
Musée Archéologique et d'Histoire Locale, Saint-Emilion 12975
Musée Archéologique et Lapidaire, Blois 09596
Musée Archéologique Municipal, Montségur-le-Château 11934
Musée Archéologique Municipal Henri-Prades, Lattes 11143
Musée Auguste Jacquet, Beaucaire 09462
Musée Baroncelli, Saintes-Maries-de-la-Mer 13348
Musée Calvet, Avignon 09358
Musée Campanaire, L'Isle-Jourdain 11412
Musée Cappon, Marans 11582
Musée Centre Européen de Préhistoire, Tautavel 13653
Musée Champollion, Figeac 10532
Musée Charbonneau-Lassay, Loudun 11455
Musée Charles-Portal, Cordes 10209
Musée Crozatier, Le Puy-en-Velay 11259
Musée Danicourt, Péronne 12494
Musée d'Archéologie, Izernore 10868
Musée d'Archéologie, Le Pègue 11247
Musée d'Archéologie, Lons-le-Saunier 11442
Musée d'Archéologie et d'Art Populaire, Bricquebec 09746
Musée d'Archéologie et d'Art Populaire René-Bauberot, Châteauponsac 10037
Musée d'Archéologie et d'Histoire, Les Vans 11344
Musée d'Archéologie Méditerranéenne, Marseille 11640
Musée d'Archéologie Sous-Marine, Saint-Raphaël 13224
Musée d'Art, Senlis 13491
Musée d'Art et d'Archéologie, Aurillac 09319
Musée d'Art et d'Archéologie, Laon 11129
Musée d'Art et d'Histoire, Chaumont (Haute-Marne) 10061
Musée d'Art et d'Histoire de Toul, Toul 13708
Musée d'Art et d'Histoire du Vieux Pérouges, Pérouges 12495
Musée d'Art et d'Histoire Labenche, Brive-la-Gaillarde 09757
Musée de Brou, Bourg-en-Bresse 09675
Musée de la Castre, Cannes 09844
Musée de la Société Archéologique et Historique de la Charente, Angoulême 09185
Musée de la Société Polymathique du Morbihan, Vannes (Morbihan) 13871
Musée de la Tour aux Puces, Thionville 13670
Musée de la Vallée de l'Ubaye, Barcelonnette 09419
Musée de l'Ancienne Abbaye de Landévennec, Landévennec 11108
Musée de l'Ardenne, Charleville-Mézières 09993
Musée de l'Ariège, Foix 10554
Musée de Lodève, Lodève 11429
Musée de Melun, Melun 11708
Musée de Moulages, Strasbourg 13608
Musée de Provins et du Provinois, Provins 12666
Musée de Tauroentum, Saint-Cyr-les-Lecques 12958
Musée de Traditions Populaires et d'Archéologie, Chauvigny 10066
Musée de Vendôme d'Art et d'Histoire, Vendôme 13906
Musée Départemental d'Archéologie Jérôme-Carcopino, Aléria 09114
Musée Départemental de l'Oise, Beauvais 09484
Musée Départemental des Antiquités de la Seine-Maritime, Rouen 12835
Musée Départemental des Hautes-Alpes, Gap 10639
Musée des Antiquités Nationales, Saint-Germain-en-Laye 13022
Musée des Arts Décoratifs, Saumur 13430
Musée des Beaux-Arts, Blois 09599
Musée des Beaux-Arts, Dole 10345
Musée des Beaux-Arts et d'Archéologie, Rennes (Ille-et-Vilaine) 12730
Musée des Beaux-Arts et d'Archéologie, Vienne (Isère) 13953
Musée des Beaux-Arts et d'Archéologie, Troyes 13792
Musée des Beaux-Arts et d'Archeologie Joseph Déchelette, Roanne 12770
Musée des Moulages, Montpellier 11908
Musée d'Evreux, Evreux 10483
Musée d'Histoire Naturelle, Rouen 12837
Musée Dobrée, Nantes 12041
Musée du Berry, Bourges 09687
Musée du Biterrois, Béziers 09548
Musée du Châtillonnais, Châtillon-sur-Seine 10056
Musée du Cloître, Tulle 13801
Musée du Colombier, Alès 09118
Musée du Louvre, Paris 12396
Musée du Nord de la Vendée, Montaigu (Vendée) 11818
Musée du Noyonnais, Noyon 12160
Musée du Patrimoine, Néris-les-Bains 12066
Musée du Pays de Sarrebourg, Sarrebourg 13406
Musée du Perigord, Périgueux 12492
Musée du Trophée des Alpes, La Turbie 11065
Musée E. Chenon, Château-Meillant 10017
Musée Historique, Haguenau 10785
Musée Historique, Mulhouse 11995
Musée Historique et Archéologique de l'Orléanais, Orléans 12218
Musée Intercommunal d'Histoire et d'Archéologie, Louvres 11485
Musée Jeanne d'Aboville, La Fère 10964
Musée La Diana, Montbrison 11847
Musée Languédocien, Montpellier 11915
Musée Municipal, Châlons-en-Champagne 09947
Musée Municipal, Digne 10321
Musée Municipal, Nuits-Saint-Georges 12161
Musée Municipal, Saint-Amand-les-Eaux 12885
Musée Municipal, Saint-Dizier 12974
Musée Municipal Ancienne Abbaye Saint-Léger, Soissons 13541
Musée Municipal d'Archéologie et du Vin de Champagne, Épernay 10433
Musée Municipal de Millau, Millau 11764
Musée Municipal des Beaux-Arts, Valence (Drôme) 13839
Musée Municipal d'Étampes, Etampes 10468
Musée Municipal Méditeranéen de Cassis, Cassis 09889
Musée Pierre Tauziac, Montcaret 11848
Musée Pincé, Angers 09182
Musée Rolin, Autun 09329
Musée Saint-Raymond, Toulouse 13738
Musée Saint-Remi, Reims 12719
Musée Savoisien, Chambéry 09958
Musée Site Départemental d'Archéologie de Bavay, Bavay 09441
Musée Westercamp, Wissembourg 14110
Musée Ziem, Martigues 11669
Musées de la Cour d'Or, Metz 11743

Gambia
Gambia National Museum, Banjul 14143

Georgia
Tbilisi State Museum of Anthropology and Ethnography, Tbilisi 14159

Germany
Alamannenmuseum, Weingarten, Württemberg 19006
Antikenmuseum der Universität Leipzig, Leipzig 17026
Antikensammlung der Friedrich-Alexander-Universität Erlangen-Nürnberg, Erlangen 15618
Archäologiemuseum, Künzing 16900
Archäologiemuseum im Fränkischen Freilandmuseum, Bad Windsheim 14547
Archäologisch-Ethnographische Lehr- und Studiensammlung des Instituts für Altamerikanistik und Ethnologie der Universität Bonn, Bonn 14968
Archäologische Sammlung, Essen 15647
Archäologische Sammlung der Stadt Weißenhorn, Weißenhorn 19030
Archäologische Sammlung mit Heimatvertriebenenstube und Kruk-Sammlung, Königsbrunn 16820
Archäologisches Freilichtmuseum Oerlinghausen, Oerlinghausen 17826
Archäologisches Landesmuseum, Schleswig 18344
Archäologisches Landesmuseum Baden-Württemberg, Konstanz 16845
Archäologisches Landesmuseum Mecklenburg-Vorpommern, Groß Raden 16104
Archäologisches Museum, Donauwörth 15357
Archäologisches Museum, Rimpar 18180
Archäologisches Museum der Stadt Kelheim, Kelheim 16704
Archäologisches Museum Essenbach, Essenbach 15666
Archäologisches Museum Gablingen, Gablingen 15884
Archäologisches Museum im Rathaus, Weichering 18951
Archäologisches Museum in der Feldmühle, Rennertshofen 18141
Archäologisches Zentrum Hitzacker, Hitzacker 16437
Badisches Landesmuseum Karlsruhe, Karlsruhe 16647
Burg Neuhaus, Wolfsburg 19183
Clemens-Sels-Museum, Neuss 17664
Die Eulenburg, Rinteln 18184
Federseemuseum Bad Buchau, Bad Buchau 14408
Glauberg-Museum, Glauburg 15987
Haus zum Stockfisch - Stadtmuseum, Erfurt 15606
Hegau-Museum, Singen, Hohentwiel 18505
Heimatmuseum Adlhoch-Haus, Altdorf, Niederbayern 14229
Heimatmuseum Schlitz, Schlitz 18354
Heimatmuseum Zusmarshausen, Zusmarshausen 19292
Heinrich-Schliemann-Museum, Ankershagen 14282
Heuneburgmuseum, Herbertingen 16381
Keltenhaus, Taufkirchen, Kreis München 18684
Keltenmuseum Hochdorf/Enz, Eberdingen 15475
Keltisch-Römisches Museum, Manching 17240
Kreismuseum, Finsterwalde 15707
Landesmuseum Koblenz, Koblenz 16772
Landesmuseum Mainz, Mainz 17232
Münzkabinett und Archäologische Lehrsammlung der Universität Rostock, Rostock 18228
Museum Abodiacum, Denklingen 15296
Museum der Stadt Ettlingen, Ettlingen 15676
Museum der Stadt Worms, Worms 19200
Museum für Archäologie und Volkskunde, Kösching 16834
Museum für Archäologie, Völkerkunde und Naturkunde, Mannheim 17245
Museum für Kunst und Kulturgeschichte der Stadt Dortmund, Dortmund 15384
Museum in der Kaiserpfalz, Paderborn 17925
Museum Roemervilla, Bad Neuenahr-Ahrweiler 14481
Museum Römervilla, Grenzach-Wyhlen 16081
Rhön-Museum, Fladungen 15712
Robertinum, Halle, Saale 16196
Römer und Bajuwaren Museum Burg Kipfenberg, Kipfenberg 16739
Römermuseum Multerer, Grabenstätt 16051
Römermuseum Stettfeld, Ubstadt-Weiher 18773
Saalburgmuseum, Bad Homburg 14446
Sammlung Antiker Kleinkunst, Jena 16604
Torfmuseum, Neustadt am Rübenberge 17671
Ur- und Frühgeschichtliche Sammlung, Erlangen 15628
Wall-Museum, Oldenburg in Holstein 17847
Wikinger Museum Haithabu, Busdorf 15163
Wittelsbachermuseum Aichach, Aichach 14199
Zumsteinhaus mit Römischem Museum und Naturkunde-Museum, Kempten 16719

Ghana
Ghana National Museum, Accra 19307
Museum of Archaeology, Legon 19315

Gibraltar
Gibraltar Museum, Gibraltar 19317

Greece
Archeological Museum, Chaironeia 19425
Archeological Museum, Delos 19436
Archeological Museum, Mykonos 19574
Vaos Collection, Athinai 19420

Greenland
Avanersuup Katersugaasivia, Qaanaaq 19724

Grenada
Grenada National Museum, Saint George's 19732

Hungary
Arany János Múzeum, Nagykőrös 19953
Balassa Bálint Múzeum, Esztergom 19880
Balatoni Múzeum, Keszthely 19922
Csongrádi Múzeum, Csongrád 19870
Déri Múzeum, Debrecen 19871
Dobó István Vármúzeum, Eger 19877
Dráva Múzeum, Barcs 19796
Erkel Ferenc Múzeum, Gyula 19894
Ferenczy Károly Múzeum, Szentendre 20034
Göcseji Múzeum, Zalaegerszeg 20077
Hajdúsági Múzeum, Hajdúböszörmény 19896
Hansági Múzeum, Mosonmagyaróvár 19950
Herman Ottó Múzeum, Miskolc 19945
Intercisa Múzeum, Dunaújváros 19876
Jász Múzeum, Jászberény 19906
Jósa András Múzeum, Nyíregyháza 19958
Katona József Múzeum, Kecskemét 19917
Kubinyi Ferenc Múzeum, Szécsény 20010
Kuny Domokos Múzeum, Tata 20056
Laczkó Dezsoë Múzeum, Veszprém 20071
Magyar Nemzeti Múzeum, Budapest 19835
Mátyás Király Múzeum, Visegrád 20074
Móra Ferenc Múzeum, Szeged 20014
Rákóczi Múzeum, Sárospatak 19989
Reneszánsz Kőtár, Pécs 19979
Smidt Múzeum, Szombathely 20051
Szent István Király Múzeum, Székesfehérvár 20024
Tatabánya Múzeum, Tatabánya 20058
Tornyai János Múzeum, Hódmezővásárhely 19900
Tragor Ignác Múzeum, Vác 20064
Vármúzeum, Esztergom 19884
Wosinsky Mór Megyei Múzeum, Szekszárd 20029
Xantus János Múzeum, Győr 19893

Iceland
Minjasafn Austurlands, Egilsstadir 20092
Thjódminjasafn Islands, Gardabaer 20095

India
Archaeological Museum, Amaravati 20149
Archaeological Museum, Bijapur 20176
Archaeological Museum, Bodh Ghaya 20179
Archaeological Museum, Delhi 20207
Archaeological Museum, Guntur 20252
Archaeological Museum, Gwalior 20254
Archaeological Museum, Halebidu 20257
Archaeological Museum, Hardwar 20262
Archaeological Museum, Jaunpur 20284
Archaeological Museum, Kamalapur 20297
Archaeological Museum, Khajuraho 20304
Archaeological Museum, Nalanda 20376
Archaeological Museum, Pune 20392
Archaeological Museum, Sanchi 20407
Archaeological Museum of Patiala, Patiala 20382
Archaeological Museum Red Fort Delhi, Delhi 20208
Archaeological Site Museum, Alampur 20141
Archaeology Museum, Chennai 20186
Archeological Museum, Trichur 20433
Central Museum, Indore 20277
Central Museum, Nagpur 20375
Chitrapur Math Museum, Shirali 20418
District Archaeological Museum, Dhar 20229
District Museum, Gulbarga 20251
District Museum, Hassan 20265
District Museum, Pillalamari 20388
District Museum, Shimoga 20417
Gandhi Centenary Museum, Karimnagar 20301
Ganga Government Museum, Bikaner 20177

Archaeology, Christian and Medieval

Archaeology, Far Eastern

Archaeology, Greek and Roman

Museum Mistra, Mystras 19577
Museum of Casts and Archeological Collection, Thessaloniki 19681
Museum Papageorgiou, Limenaria 19549
P. and Al. Canellopoulos Museum, Athinai 19415
Perachora Museum, Perachora 19612
Sefel Collection, Volos 19704
Vassiliou Collection, Thessaloniki 19685

Hungary
Aquincumi Múzeum, Budapest 19803
Görög-Római Szobormásolatok Múzeuma, Tata 20055
Gorsium Szabadtéri Múzeum, Székesfehérvár 20020
Román Kori Kőtár, Pécs 19980

Ireland
University College Dublin Classical Museum, Dublin 20762

Israel
Local Museum, Ashkelon 20862
Museum of Regional and Mediterranean Archaeology, Nir-David 20972

Italy
Antiquarium, Brescello 21239
Antiquarium, Cabras 21262
Antiquarium, Numana 22055
Antiquarium, Palazzolo Acreide 22100
Antiquarium, Porto Torres 22246
Antiquarium, Santa Flavia 22512
Antiquarium, Santa Maria Capua Vetere 22513
Antiquarium, Sant'Antioco 22524
Antiquarium, Trapani 22708
Antiquarium Comunale, Orbetello 22066
Antiquarium Comunale, Roma 22326
Antiquarium Comunale, Sutri 22617
Antiquarium di Himera, Termini Imerese 22636
Antiquarium e Zona Archeologica, Lugagnano Val d'Arda 21816
Antiquarium e Zona Archeologica, Ribera 22304
Antiquarium Etrusco, Colle di Val d'Elsa 21448
Antiquarium Municipale, Manduria 21835
Antiquarium Nazionale, Formia 21650
Antiquarium Palatino, Roma 22328
Antiquarium Statale, Locri 21796
Civico Museo Archeologico, Acqui Terme e Bagni 21027
Civico Museo Archeologico, Bergamo 21154
Civico Museo Archeologico e di Scienze Naturali 'Federico Eusebio', Alba 21042
Cripta e Museo di Sant'Anastasio, Asti 21114
Domus Clementina, Castiglione a Casauria 21355
Hospice du Grand Saint Bernard, Aosta 21070
Musei Capitolini, Roma 22352
Museo Antiquarium, Falerone 21534
Museo Archeologico, Cecina e Marina 21374
Museo Archeologico, Cesena 21391
Museo Archeologico, Faenza 21527
Museo Archeologico, Gropello Cairoli 21719
Museo Archeologico, Milano 21904
Museo Archeologico, Foligno 21634
Museo Archeologico Ad Quintum, Collegno 21453
Museo Archeologico al Teatro Romano, Verona 22836
Museo Archeologico dell'Agro Nocerino, Nocera Inferiore 22039
Museo Archeologico di Vallecamonica, Cividate Camuno 21439
Museo Archeologico e Paleontologico, Asti 21116
Museo Archeologico Girolamo Rossi, Ventimiglia 22827
Museo Archeologico Nazionale, Adria 21029
Museo Archeologico Nazionale, Aquileia 21077
Museo Archeologico Nazionale, Chieti 21412
Museo Archeologico Nazionale, Chiusi Città 21421
Museo Archeologico Nazionale, Gioia del Colle 21708
Museo Archeologico Nazionale, Metaponto 21888
Museo Archeologico Nazionale, Napoli 22011
Museo Archeologico Nazionale, Paestum 22098
Museo Archeologico Nazionale, Parma 22128
Museo Archeologico Nazionale, Quarto d'Altino 22271
Museo Archeologico Nazionale, Taranto 22625
Museo Archeologico Nazionale, Venosa 22826
Museo Archeologico Nazionale, Vibo Valentia 22853
Museo Archeologico Nazionale di Palestrina, Palestrina 22117
Museo Archeologico Oliveriano, Pesaro 22161
Museo Archeologico Provinciale, Bari 21134
Museo Archeologico Provinciale F. Ribezzo, Brindisi 21247
Museo Archeologico Regionale, Agrigento 21033
Museo Archeologico Regionale A. Salinas, Palermo 22108
Museo Archeologico Romano, Isernia 21753
Museo Archeologico Romano-Gallico-Etrusco, Savignano sul Rubicone 22552
Museo Civico, Asolo 21105
Museo Civico, Baranello 21129
Museo Civico, Centuripe 21380
Museo Civico, Cingoli 21426
Museo Civico, Feltre 21541
Museo Civico, Guardiagrele 21727
Museo Civico, Iesi 21733
Museo Civico, Magliano Sabina 21826
Museo Civico, Piazza Armerina 22187
Museo Civico, Sesto Calende 22569
Museo Civico, Tolfa 22657
Museo Civico, Trevignano Romano 22724
Museo Civico, Velletri 22785
Museo Civico Antonino Olmo e Gipsoteche, Savigliano 22550
Museo Civico Archeologico, Canosa di Puglia 21299
Museo Civico Archeologico, Casalmaggiore 21323
Museo Civico Archeologico, Cologna Veneta 21456
Museo Civico Archeologico, Fiesole 21563
Museo Civico Archeologico, Ripatransone 22315
Museo Civico Archeologico Arsenio Crespellani, Bazzano 21146
Museo Civico Archeologico Romano, Chieri 21410
Museo Civico Castello Ursino, Catania 21364
Museo Civico Domenico Mambrini, Galeata 21660
Museo Civico e Foro Romano, Assisi 21107
Museo Civico E. Rogadeo, Bitonto 21173
Museo Civico e Teatro e Serbatoio Romano, Falerone 21535
Museo Civico G.B. Adriani, Cherasco 21401
Museo Correale di Terranova, Sorrento 22594
Museo del Patrimonium, Sutri 22618
Museo del Seminario Vescovile, Bedonia 21147
Museo della Grigna, Esino Lario 21521
Museo dell'Abbazia, Casamari-Veroli 21325
Museo delle Mura, Roma 22376
Museo Diocesano, Sarsina 22537
Museo e Pinacoteca Civici, Vasto 22784
Museo Etrusco, Asciano 21097
Museo Etrusco, San Gimignano 22481
Museo Etrusco di Villa Giulia, Roma 22391
Museo Etrusco Gasparri, Populonia 22242
Museo Etrusco Guarnacci, Volterra 22887
Museo Etrusco Pompeo Aria, Marzabotto 21852
Museo Fondazione C. Faina e Museo Civico Palazzo Faina, Orvieto 22076
Museo Lapidario, Ferrara 21557
Museo Nazionale Archeologico, Sarsina 22538
Museo Nazionale Cerite, Cerveteri 21388
Museo Nazionale della Siritide, Policoro 22229
Museo Nazionale di Villa Guinigi, Lucca 21812
Museo Nazionale Jatta, Ruvo di Puglia 22453
Museo Nazionale Romano-Terme di Diocleziano, Roma 22403
Museo Nicola Antonio Manfroce, Palmi 22123
Museo Nuovo, Roma 22405
Museo Ostiense, Ostia Antica 22081
Museo Palatino, Roma 22407
Museo Paleoveneto, Pieve di Cadore 22198
Museo Provinciale, Catanzaro 21368
Museo Romano, Tortona 22705
Museo Sannitico Provinciale, Campobasso 21295
Museo Torlonia, Roma 22418
Museo Vivico Archeologico e Storico, Bra 21236
Raccolte di Antichità, Bovino 21234
Scavi di Ercolano, Ercolano 21519
Scavi di Oplontis, Torre Annunziata 22698
Scavi di Pompei, Pompei 22234
Scavi e Museo Archeologico di S. Restituta, Napoli 22032
Villa Romana a Mosaici, Desenzano del Garda 21502
Zona Archeologica e Antiquarium, Patti 22137

Malta
Museum of Roman Antiquities, Rabat 24347

Netherlands
Allard Pierson Museum Amsterdam, Amsterdam 24677
Archaeologische Verzameling der Rijksuniversiteit, Utrecht 25554
Delft Volkenkundig Diorama Museum, Delft 24879
Museum onder de N.H. Kerk, Elst 25013
Ouddorps Raad- en Polderhuis, Ouddorp 25375
Oudheidkundig Museum, Sint Michielsgestel 25488
De Romeinen in Velsen, Velsen Zuid 25588
Thermenmuseum, Heerlen 25127

Peru
Museo Nacional de Antropología y Arqueología, Lima 26501

Portugal
Museu Monográfico de Conimbriga, Condeixa-a-Nova 27359
Museu Nacional de Arqueologia, Lisboa 27399

Slovakia
Antická Gerulata v Rusovciach, Bratislava 28195

Spain
Alcázar de los Reyes Cristianos, Córdoba 28974
Conjunto Arqueológico de Carmona, Carmona 28921
Conjunto Arqueológico de Itálica, Santiponce 29689
Museo Arqueológico Monográfico de Cástulo Linares, Linares 29194
Museo Arqueológico Municipal, Alcúdia 28678
Museo Arqueológico Municipal Alejandro Ramos Folqués, Elche 29030
Museo Arqueológico Municipal Camilo Visedo Moltó, Alcoy 28674
Museo Arqueológico Provincial, Badajoz 28755
Museo Catedralicio, Murcia 29387
Museo de Cádiz, Cádiz 28888
Museo de la Comisión Provincial de Monumentos, León 29188
Museo Monográfico de Clunia, Peñalba de Castro 29499
Museo Monográfico y Necrópolis Púnica de Puig des Molins, Eivissa 29027
Museo Municipal, Antequera 28705
Museo Municipal, Jérica 29169
Museu Arqueològic de l'Esquerda, Roda de Ter 29569
Museu d'Arqueología de Catalunya, Barcelona 28788
Museu d'Arqueología de Catalunya-Ullastret, Ullastret 29819
Museu de Badalona, Badalona 28759
Museu Municipal, Tossa de Mar 29803
Museu Nacional Arqueològic de Tarragona, Tarragona 29749

Sweden
Antikenmuseet, Göteborg 30094
Antikmuseet, Lund 30207
Medelhavsmuseet, Stockholm 30361

Switzerland
Historisches Museum der Stadt Baden, Baden 30552
Musée de la Villa Romaine de Pully, Pully 31107
Musée Gallo-Romain d'Octodure, Martigny 30995
Musée Romain, Avenches 30548
Musée Romain, Nyon 31064
Museo di Castelgrande, Bellinzona 30595
Thermen-Museum Juliomagus, Schleitheim 31207
Vindonissa-Museum, Brugg 30660

Tunisia
Musée Archéologique de Makthar, Makthar 31618
Musée d'Institut National de Archéologique d'El-Jem, El-Jem 31608
Musée d'Utique, Utique 31643
Musée National de Carthage, Carthage 31606

Turkey
Afrodisiyas Müzesi, Geyre Köyü Karasu Aydin 31734
Aydin Müzesi, Aydin 31674
Bodrum Sualti Arkeolojisi Müzesi, Bodrum 31686
Çanakkale Müzesi, Çanakkale 31698
Efes Müzesi, Selçuk 31826
Hatay Müzesi, Hatay 31740
Hierapolis Arkeoloji Müzesi, Denizli 31707
Iznik Müzesi, Iznik 31768
Konya Müzesi, Konya 31790
Nigde Müzesi, Nigde 31818
Side Müzesi, Side 31828
Silifke Müzesi, Silifke - Içel 31829
Tire Müzesi, Tire 31843

Ukraine
National Preserve of Tauric Chersonesos, Sevastopol 31949

United Kingdom
Aldborough Roman Town Museum, Boroughbridge 32332
Arbeia Roman Fort and Museum, South Shields 34506
Calleva Museum, Silchester 34489
Castle Museum, Colchester 32652
Castleford Museum Room, Castleford 32551
Chedworth Roman Villa, Yanworth 34901
Chedworth Roman Villa Museum, Cheltenham 32589
Clayton Collection Museum, Chollerford 32621
Corbridge Roman Site Museum, Corbridge 32675
Fishbourne Roman Palace and Museum, Chichester 32608
Hereford City Museum and Art Gallery, Hereford 33254
Housesteads Roman Fort and Museum, Hexham 33268
Lullingstone Roman Villa, Eynsford 32994
Malton Museum, Malton 33883
Ribchester Roman Museum, Ribchester 34298
Richborough Castle - Roman Fort, Sandwich 34422
Roman Army Museum, Greenhead 33162
Roman Legionary Museum, Caerleon 32482
Roman Tainted House, Dover 32807
Roman Villa, Brading 32360
Roman Villa, Newport, Isle of Wight 34049
Segedunum Roman Fort, Bath and Museum, Wallsend 34729
Segontium Roman Museum, Caernarfon 32485
Thurrock Museum, Grays 33148
Ure Museum of Greek Archaeology, Reading 34285
Viroconium Museum, Wroxeter 34898
Wall Roman Site and Museum - Letocetum, Lichfield 33513

Vatican City
Museo Gregoriano Egizio, Città del Vaticano 41397

Yugoslavia
Arheološka Zbirka, Budva 41535

Archaeology, Ibero-American

Argentina
Museo Arqueológico, Gualeguaychú 00351
Museo Arqueológico de Chasicó, Chasicó 00264
Museo Arqueológico de Puerto Esperanza, Puerto Esperanza 00482
Museo Arqueológico de Salta, Salta 00529
Museo Arqueológico de Tilcara, Tilcara 00626
Museo Arqueológico Pío P. Díaz, Cachi 00246
Museo Arqueológico Provincial, San Salvador de Jujuy 00586
Museo Arqueológico Regional Anibal Montes, Río Segundo 00513
Museo Arqueológico Regional Inca Huasi, La Rioja 00387
Museo Arqueológico y Colonial, Fuerte Quemado 00340
Museo de Antropología, Córdoba 00283
Museo de Antropología y Ciencias Naturales, Concordia 00278
Museo de Arqueología de la Universidad Nacional de Tucumán, San Miguel de Tucumán 00572
Museo del Area Fundacional, Mendoza 00428
Museo Florentino Ameghino, Bolívar 00132
Museo Histórico Arqueológico Guillermo Magrassi, Mar del Plata 00418
Museo Pampeano de Chascomús, Chascomús 00263
Museo Provincial Arqueológico Eric Boman, Santa María de Catamarca 00602
Museo Provincial de Arqueología Wagner, Santiago del Estero 00609
Museo Rauzi, Palmira 00456
Museo Regional Dr. Adolfo Alsina, Carhué 00254
Museo Universitario Florentino y Carlos Ameghino, Rosario 00525

Bolivia
Museo Charcas, Sucre 03877
Museo Nacional de Arqueología, La Paz 03869
Museo Universitario, Cochabamba 03863

Brazil
Museu Câmara Cascudo, Natal 03956
Museu Comercial e Arqueológico do Sindicato dos Empregados, Maceió 03950
Museu Lasar Segall, São Paulo 04117
Museu Sitio Arqueológico Casa dos Pilões, Rio de Janeiro 04067

Canada
London Museum of Archaeology, London 05231

Chile
Museo Arqueológico de Chiu Chiu, Chiu Chiu 06365
Museo Arqueológico de La Serena, La Serena 06373
Museo Chileno de Arte Precolombino, Santiago 06383
Museo del Limarí, Ovalle 06377

Colombia
Museo Arqueológico, Mongua 06865
Museo Arqueológico, Pasca 06868
Museo Arqueologico Casa del Marqués de San Jorge, Santafé de Bogotá 06890
Museo Arqueológico Julio César Cubillos, Cali 06834
Museo Arqueológico La Puma de Oro, El Retiro 06846
Museo Arqueológico Nacional, Santafé de Bogotá 06891
Museo del Hombre Tolimense, Ibagué 06849
Museo Maridiaz, Pasto 06870
Parque Arqueológico, San Augustin 06881

Costa Rica
Museo Nacional de Costa Rica, San José 06949

Cuba
Museo Antropológico Montané, La Habana 07141

Dominican Republic
Fortaleza de San Felipe, Santo Domingo 08102
Museo Natural de Historia y Geografía, Santo Domingo 08111
Sala de Arte Prehispánico, Santo Domingo 08112

Ecuador
Museo Antropológico del Banco Central, Guayaquil 08134
Museo Arqueologico Carlos Aiiercado, Esmeraldas 08131
Museo Arqueologico del Banco Central de Bahia, Bahia de Caráciuez 08119
Museo Arqueologico Largacha Ceballos Marlac, Montecristi 08148
Museo Banco del Pacifico, Guayaquil 08135
Museo Carlos Emilio Grijalva, Tulcán 08184
Museo de Sitio de Ingapirca, Azogues 08118
Museo de Sitio del Rumicucho, San Antonio 08183
Museo del Banco Central de Manta, Manta 08147
Museo del Colegio Nacional Pedro Vicente Maldonado, Riobamba 08180
Museo del Colegio Stella Maris, Atacames 08117
Museo Nacional de la Dirección Regional del Banco Central del Ecuador, Quito 08172
Museo Nahim Isaias B., Guayaquil 08142
Museo Sala de Exposición Banco Central de Esmeraldas, Esmeraldas 08132
Museo Santuario Nuestra Señora Natividad del Guayco, La Magdalena 08146
Museo Weilbauer, Quito 08176

Salvador
Museo Nacional David J. Guzmán, San Salvador 08260

France
Musée des Jacobins, Auch 09300

Guatemala
Museo Nacional de Arqueología y Etnología, Guatemala City 19753

Honduras
Museo Arqueológico de Comayagua, Comayagua 19778
Museo Regional de Arqueología Maya, Ciudad de Copán 19777

Italy
Museo Americanistico Federico Lunardi, Genova 21689
Museo Etnografico Castello D'Albertis, Genova 21700

Mexico
Museo Arqueológico de Cuicuilco, México 24418
Museo Arqueológico de Xochimilco, México 24419
Museo Arqueológico de Yucatán, Mérida 24405
Museo Arqueológico del Cerro de la Estrella, México 24420
Museo Arqueológico, Etnográfico e Histórico del Estado, Campeche 24385
Museo de Arte Prehispánico de México Rufino Tamayo, Oaxaca 24491
Museo de El Carmen, México 24433
Museo de la Cultura Huasteca, Ciudad Madero 24391
Museo del Templo Mayor, México 24449

Netherlands
Amerika Museum Nederland, Cuijk 24869

Panama
Parque Arqueológico El Caño, Natá 26435

Peru
Museo Arqueológico Frederico Galvez Durand de la Gran Unidad Santa Isabel, Huancayo 26478
Museo Arqueológico Regional de Ancash, Ancash 26469
Museo Cabrera, Ica 26480
Museo de Arqueología Josefina Ramos de Cox, Lima 26488
Museo de Arqueología y Antropología de la Universidad Nacional Mayor de San Marcos, Lima 26489
Museo de Arte, Lima 26490
Museo de la Universidad, Cusco 26476
Museo de Oro del Perú y Armas del Mundo, Lima 26497
Museo de Sitio de Paracas Julio C. Tello, Pisco 26512

Puerto Rico
Museum of History, Anthropology and Art, San Juan 27466

Spain
Colección de Arqueología y Etnografía Americana, Madrid 29239
Museo Arqueológico Municipal Precolombino, Benalmádena 28840

U.S.A.
Blackwater Draw Museum, Portales 39552
Chaco Culture National Historical Park, Nageezi 38706
El Morro National Monument, Ramah 39680
Salinas Pueblo Missions National Monument, Mountainair 38669

Archaeology, Near and Middle Eastern

France
Musée Arménien de France, Paris 12315
Musée de Bible et Terre Sainte, Paris 12335

Germany
Hilprecht-Sammlung Vorderasiatischer Altertümer der Friedrich-Schiller-Universität Jena, Jena 16600

Iraq
Al Mawsil Museum, Nineveh 20679
Archaeological Site Nimrud (Calah), Nimrud 20678
Babylon Museum, Babylon 20664
Basrah Museum, Basrah 20672
Nasiriya Museum, Nasiriya 20677
Nergal Gate Museum, Mosul 20676
Samarra Museum, Samarra 20680

Israel
Akko Municipal Museum, Akko 20857
Arad Museum, Arad 20861
Archaeological Museum, Kibbutz Ein Dor 20947
Be'eri Archaeological Collection, Be'eri 20867
Beit Miriam-Museum, Kibbutz Palmachim 20956
Bible Lands Museum Jerusalem, Jerusalem 20902
Caesarea Museum, Kibbutz Sedot Yam 20960
Ceramics Museum, Tel Aviv 20994
Golan Archaeological Museum, Qatzrin 20975
Hanita Wall and Tower Museum, Kibbutz Hanita 20950
Hazor Museum, Ayelet-Hashahar 20865
Herbert E. Clark Collection of Near Eastern Antiquities, Jerusalem 20911
Local Museum, Kibbutz Ma'abarot 20955
Local Museum, Kibbutz Sasa 20959
Municipal Museum of Archaeology, History, Art and Malacology, Nahariya 20967
Museum, Ancient Synagogue and Necropolis, Beit Shearim 20870
Museum of Prehistory, Haifa 20890
Nahsholim Museum, Hof Dor 20896
Negev Museum, Be'ersheva 20868
Pères Blancs - Saint Anne, Jerusalem 20926
Reuben and Edith Hecht Museum, Haifa 20893
Saint James Museum and Library, Jerusalem 20929
Samuel Bronfman Biblical and Archeological Museum, Jerusalem 20930
Shrine of the Book, Jerusalem 20932
Skirball Museum of Biblical Archaeology, Jerusalem 20934
Synagogue, Bet Alfa 20871
Tell Qasile Archaeological Site, Tel Aviv 21010
Terra Sancta Museum, Nazareth 20970

Japan
Okayama Shiritsu Oriento Bijutsukan, Okayama 23406

Jordan
Es-Salt Archaeological Museum, Salt 23811
Irbid Archaeological Museum, Irbid 23804
Jarash Archaeological Museum, Jarash 23807
Jordan Archaeological Museum, Amman 23796
Madaba Museum for Archaeology and Folklore, Madaba 23808
Museum of Aqaba Antiquities, Aqaba 23803
Museum of Jordanian Heritage, Irbid 23806
Petra Archaeological Museum, Petra 23809

Lebanon
American University of Beirut Museum, Beirut 24137
Musée National, Beirut 24141

Mexico
Museo de Tabasco, Villahermosa 24522
Museo La Venta Parque, Villahermosa 24523

Netherlands
Bijbels Openluchtmuseum, Heilig Landstichting 25130

Palestine
Musée de l'Ecole Biblique et Archéologique Française, Jerusalem 26432

Turkey
Alacahöyük Arkeoloji Müzesi, Alacahöyük 31654
Anadolu Medeniyetleri Müzesi, Ankara 31659
Elazig Arkeoloji ve Etnografi Müzesi, Elazig 31716
Karatepe Açikhava Müzesi, Kadirli 31769
Türk Seramik Müzesi, Konya 31795
Yazili Kaya Müzesi, Çifteler 31703

United Arab Emirates
Al-Ain Museum, Al-Ain 31965

United Kingdom
Department of Semitic Studies Collection, Leeds 33466
Oriental Museum, Durham 32863

U.S.A.
Elizabeth P. Korn Gallery, Madison 38268
Hellenic Museum and Cultural Center, Chicago 36020

Yemen
Baihan Al Qasab Museum, Wadi Baihan 41498
National Museum, Sanaa 41495
National Museum of Antiquities, Aden 41491

Architecture

Albania
Architecture Museum, Bérat 00010

Australia
Burnett House and Myilly Point Heritage Precinct, Darwin 00959
City of Melbourne Collection, Melbourne 01214
Earlystreet, Norman Park 01315
Elizabeth Farm, Rosehill 01424
Miniature English Village and Brass Rubbing Centre, Flaxton 01013
Palma Rosa Museum, Hamilton, Brisbane 01073
Powder Magazine, Beechworth 00775
Quilpie Museum, Quilpie 01403
Rose Seidler House, Wahroonga 01570

Austria
Architektur im Ringturm, Wien 02802
Architekturzentrum Wien, Wien 02803
Ausstellungszentrum Heft, Hüttenberg 02045
Ausstellungszentrum Heiligenkreuzer Hof, Wien 02809
Ernst Fuchs-Privatmuseum, Wien 02848
Freilicht-Museum Ensemble Gerersdorf, Gerersdorf 01867
Josef Hoffmann-Sanatorium, Purkersdorf 02451
Kunstsammlung des Benediktinerstifts Seitenstetten, Seitenstetten 02633
Lehár-Schlößl, Wien 02895
Minimundus, Klagenfurt 02121
Salvatorianerkloster, Gurk 01969
Studiensammlung historischer Ziegel, Irdning 02076

Bangladesh
Varendra Research Museum, Rajshahi 03059

Belgium
Fondation pour l'Architecture, Bruxelles 03249
Kasteel van Gaasbeek, Gaasbeek 03390
Miniatuurstad, Antwerpen 03109
Musée des Archives d'Architecture Moderne, Bruxelles 03280

Brazil
Fundaçao Oscar Niemeyer, Rio de Janeiro 04002
Museu da Limpeza Urbana - Casa de Banhos de Dom João VI, Rio de Janeiro 04023

Bulgaria
Architekturno-muzeen Rezervat Arbanassi, Veliko Tărnovo 04373
Architekturno-muzeen Rezervat Carevec, Veliko Tărnovo 04374
Muzej Kolju Fičevo, Drjanovo 04178
Nacionalen Architekturno Muzej, Veliko Tărnovo 04379
Okrăžen Istoričeski Muzej, Veliko Tărnovo 04381

Canada
Bellevue House National Historic Site, Kingston 05132
Brubacher House Museum, Waterloo 06225
Canadian Centre for Architecture, Montréal 05359
Jost House Museum, Sydney 05999
Westfield Heritage Village, Rockton 05750

China, People's Republic
Ancient Architecture Museum, Beijing 06415
Hong Kong Haigang Chen Yuan, Shanghai 06689
Sam Tung Uk Museum, Hong Kong 06592
Sheung Yiu Folk Museum, Hong Kong 06593

Croatia
Archaeological Museum, Zadar 07093

Cuba
Museo Arabe, La Habana 07142
Museo Romántico, Trinidad 07189

Czech Republic
Expozice Josef Hoffmann, Brtnice 07267
Muzeum Lidových Staveb, Kouřim 07408
Národopisné Muzeum Třebíz, Třebíz 07671
Obec Architektů, Brno 07262
Státní Galerie ve Zlíně, Zlín 07735
Vila Tugendhat, Brno 07265

Denmark
Den Gamle By, Århus 07754

Egypt
Coptic Museum, Cairo 08205

Estonia
Museum of Estonian Architecture, Tallinn 08269

Finland
Alvar Aalto Museum, Jyväskylä 08436
Hvitträsk, Kirkkonummi 08511
Sederholmin Talo, Helsinki 08379
Suomen Rakennustaiteen Museo, Helsinki 08386

France
Château d'Azay-le-Ferron, Azay-le-Ferron 09379
Ecomusée des Monts d'Arrée, Saint-Rivoal 13240
Ecomusée du Pays de Rennes, Rennes (Ille-et-Vilaine) 12726
Fondation Le Corbusier, Paris 12291
Musée Biochet-Brechot, Caudebec-en-Caux 09907
Musée des Années 30, Boulogne-Billancourt 09661
Musée des Materiaux du Centre de Recherche sur les Monuments Historiques, Paris 12383

Germany
Alt-Rothenburger Handwerkerhaus, Rothenburg ob der Tauber 18238
Architekturmuseum der Technischen Universität München, München 17452
Architekturmuseum Schwaben, Augsburg 14338
Bauhaus-Archiv, Berlin 14679
Befreiungshalle Kelheim, Kelheim 16705
Daniel-Pöppelmann-Haus, Herford 16387
Deutsches Architektur Museum, Frankfurt am Main 15734
Fachwerkbaumuseum im Ständerbau, Quedlinburg 18032
Fagus-Gropius-Ausstellung, Alfeld, Leine 14214
Felsengarten Sanspareil und Morgenländischer Bau, Wonsees 19197
Forum für Angewandte Kunst im Bayerischen Kunstgewerbeverein e.V., Nürnberg 17736
Kathree Häusle, Dettenhausen 15315
Kunstsammlung Lorenzkapelle Rottweil, Rottweil 18255
Museum Altes Land, Jork 16617
Museum der Stadt Waiblingen, Waiblingen 18879
Museumsdorf Bayerischer Wald, Tittling 18716
Museumskirche St. Katharinen, Lübeck 17171
Pelzerhaus, Emden 15561
Prunkräume in der Residenz, Kempten 16718
Regionalmuseum Wolfhagen, Wolfhagen 19179
Schloß Brake - Das Weserrenaissance-Museum, Lemgo 17072
Stiftung Bauhaus Dessau, Dessau 15307
Vitra Design Museum, Weil am Rhein 18966
Walpurgishalle Thale, Thale 18702

Hungary
Ernst Múzeum, Budapest 19813
Magyar Építészeti Múzeum, Budapest 19829

Iceland
Minjasafn Austurlands, Egilsstadir 20092

Ireland
Castletown House, Celbridge 20715

Israel
Islamic Museum, Jerusalem 20915

Italy
Museo Civico, Busseto 21260
Museo Civico, Sulmona 22614
Museo di Architettura Militare, Bologna 21202
Museo di Palazzo Strozzi, Firenze 21613
Oskar Schlemmer Theatre Estate and Collection, Oggebbio 22063
Palazzo Reale, Caserta 21328

Japan
Edo-Tokyo Tatemono-En, Koganei 23178
Hakubutsukan Meiji-Mura, Inuyama 23074
Okugai Hakubutsukan, Gashozukuri Minkaen, Ono 23417
Sankei-en Garden, Yokohama 23767

Kyrgyzstan
Muzej Architektury i Archeologii Vez Burana, Čujsk 23975

Mexico
Museo Nacional de Arquitectura, México 24459

Moldova
Ščusev Museum, Chişinău 24527

Netherlands
Architektuur Centrum Amsterdam, Amsterdam 24681
Modelbouwmuseum, Leiden 25237
Nederlands Architektuurinstituut, Rotterdam 25439
Rietveld Schröderhuis, Utrecht 25567

New Zealand
City Gallery Wellington, Wellington 25929
Society for Preservation of the Kerikeri Stone Store Area Visitor Centre, Kerikeri 25820

Nigeria
Jos National Museum and Museum of Traditional Nigerian Architecture, Jos 25981

Norway
Andøymuseet, Risøyhamn 26263
Kvam Bygdemuseum, Norheimsund 26204
Midttunet, Skei i Jølster 26296
Norsk Arkitekturmuseum, Oslo 26230
Riksantikvaren, Oslo 26242
Stiftsgården, Trondheim 26351
Tuddal Bygdetun, Tuddal 26357
Vennesla Bygdemuseum, Vennesla 26377

Poland
Muzeum Architektury, Wrocław 27280
Muzeum Budownictwa Ludowego - Park Etnograficzny w Olsztynku, Olsztynek 26976
Muzeum Wsi Lubelskiej, Lublin 26918
Muzeum Wsi Opolskiej, Opole 26983

Russia
Gosudarstvennyj Istoriko-architekturnyj i Etnografičeskij Muzej-zapovednik Kiži, Kiži 27758
Gosudarstvennyj Muzej Kolomenskoe, Moskva 27825
Gosudarstvennyj Muzej Zapovednik Petergof, Sankt-Peterburg 28032
Gosudarstvennyj Naučno-issledovatelskij Muzej Architektury im. A.V. Ščuseva, Moskva 27834
Izborskij Gosudarstvennyj Istoriko-architekturnyj i Prirodnij Landšaftnyj Muzej Zapovednik Izborsk, Izborsk 27733
Kostromskij Istoriko-architekturnyj Muzej-zapovednik, Kostroma 27763
Rjazanskij Gosudarstvennyj Istoriko-architekturnyj Muzej-zapovednik, Rjazan 28005
Staročerkasskij Istoriko-architekturnyj Muzej-zapovednik, Staročerkassk 28090
Taganrogskij Gosudarstvennyj Literaturnyj i istoriko-architekturnyj Muzej-zapovednik, Taganrog 28098
Tarskij Istoriko-architekturnyj Muzej, Tara 28104
Vologda Historical, Architectural and Artistic Museum Reserve, Vologda 28134

Spain
Casa-Museu Gaudí, Barcelona 28771
Conjunt Monumental de la Esglésias de Sant Pere, Terrassa 29758
Monasterio de Santa Clara de Tordesillas, Tordesillas 29784
Museo de la Colegiata de Santa Juliana y Claustro, Santillana del Mar 29686
Museo Nacional de Arquitectura, Madrid 29284
Museu d'Arquitectura de la Real Càtedra Gaudí, Barcelona 28789
Real Cartuja de Miraflores, Burgos 28877
Real Monasterio de San Juan de la Peña, San Juan de la Peña 29613

Sweden
Arkitekturmuseet, Stockholm 30333
Friluftmuseet Hallandsgården, Halmstad 30118
Friluftmuseet Skansen, Stockholm 30345
Gunnebo House, Mölndal 30235
Hembygdsgården Rots Skans, Älvdalen 30014

Switzerland
Architekturgalerie Luzern, Luzern 30972
Architekturmuseum, Basel 30563
Baugeschichtliches Archiv der Stadt Zürich, Zürich 31440
Grubenmann-Sammlung, Teufen 31304
Musée d'Architecture, Château-d'Oex 30691

Museum für Gestaltung Zürich, Zürich 31464
Ortsmuseum Eglisau, Eglisau 30740

Thailand
Kamthieng House, Bangkok 31544

Turkey
Ahlat Açik Hava Müzesi, Ahlat 31651

United Kingdom
Ancient High House, Stafford 34540
Blackwell - The Arts and Crafts House, Bowness-on-Windermere 32344
Bramall Hall, Bramhall 32364
Brooking Collection, Dartford 32739
Building of Bath Museum, Bath 32160
Carew Manor and Dovecote, Beddington 32190
Design Museum, London 33629
Farleigh Hungerford Castle, Farleigh Hungerford 33007
Glasgow School of Art - Mackintosh Collection, Glasgow 33078
Guildhall, Leicester 33484
Hill House, Helensburgh 33237
House of Dun, Montrose 33978
Hughenden Manor, High Wycombe 33270
Kufa Gallery, London 33686
Loseley House, Guildford 33170
Mellerstain House, Gordon 33128
Museum of Domestic Design and Architecture MODA, Barnet 32137
Old Merchant's House and Row 111 Houses, Great Yarmouth 33158
Osterley Park House, Isleworth 33344
Royal Incorporation of Architects in Scotland Gallery, Edinburgh 32942
Sainsbury Centre for Visual Arts, Norwich 34088
Scotland Street School Museum, Glasgow 33095
Sir John Soane's Museum, London 33781

U.S.A.
A.D. German Warehouse, Richland Center 39740
Bellamy Mansion Museum of History and Design Arts, Wilmington 41216
Bronck Museum, Coxsackie 36305
Chicago Architecture Foundation, Chicago 36004
Colonel Ashley House, Ashley Falls 35183
The Dana-Thomas House, Springfield 40451
Department of the Treasury Museum, Washington 40958
Edison and Ford Winter Estates, Fort Myers 36937
Ewing Gallery of Art and Architecture, Knoxville 37833
Fairbanks House, Dedham 36434
Frank Lloyd Wright's Pope-Leighey House, Mount Vernon 38665
Frederick Law Olmsted Historic Site, Brookline 35692
The Gardner Museum of Architecture and Design, Quincy 39662
Glessner House Museum, Chicago 36019
Grant-Humphreys Mansion, Denver 36474
Gropius House, Lincoln 38047
Hermann-Grima House, New Orleans 38813
Historic Pullman Foundation, Chicago 36021
The House of the Seven Gables, Salem 40017
Jean Paul Slusser Gallery, Ann Arbor 35119
Koreshan Historic Site, Estero 36743
Lace House Museum, Black Hawk 35521
MAK Center for Art and Architecture, Los Angeles 38160
MAK Center for Art and Architecture, West Hollywood 41112
Museum of American Architecture and Decorative Arts, Houston 37517
National Building Museum, Washington 40982
The Octagon, Washington 40993
Plymouth Antiquarian Society Museum, Plymouth 39507
Ruthmere House Museum, Elkhart 36689
Schifferstadt Architectural Museum, Frederick 37022
Spencer-Peirce-Little Farm, Newbury 38968
Spring Mill State Park Pioneer Village and Grissom Memorial, Mitchell 38557
The Stone House Museum, Belchertown 35409
Strater Hotel, Durango 36582
Van Cortlandt House Museum, Bronx 35684
William Whitley House, Stanford 40483
Wilton House Museum, Richmond 39772
The Wolfsonian, Miami Beach 38466

Vietnam
National Museum of Cham Sculpture, Da-Nang 41459

Arms and Armour

Argentina
Museo de Armas de la Nación, Buenos Aires 00156
Museo de Instituto Magnasco, Gualeguaychú 00352
Museo de la Policía del Chaco, Resistencia 00499
Museo General Lavalle, General Pinto 00347
Museo Tradicionalista El Rancho, Chacabuco 00261

Australia
Firearms Technology Museum, Spring Hill 01466

Austria
Büchsenmacher- und Jagdmuseum, Ferlach 01826
Hexenmuseum, Riegersburg, Steiermark 02496
Hofjagd- und Rüstkammer des Kunsthistorischen Museums, Wien 02869
Landeszeughaus, Graz 01915
Museum der Stadt Steyr, Steyr 02660
Schützenscheibenmuseum, Scheibbs 02606
Waffensammlung Willibald Folger, Bruck an der Mur 01747

Belgium
Brustempoort Museum, Sint-Truiden 03726
Moervarstede, Wachtebeke 03806
Musée d'Armes de Liège, Liège 03545
Musée de la Compagnie Royale des Anciens Arquebusiers de Visé, Visé 03802
Musée de la Porte de Hal, Bruxelles 03269
Musée de la Tour Henri VIII, Tournai 03774
Musée du Fort de Huy, Huy 03480
Musée Français - Armée Française Mai 1940, Cortil-Noirmont 03327
Museum van de Kruisbooggilde Sint-Joris, Brugge 03220

Brazil
Casa de Osório, Rio de Janeiro 03994
Museu Aeroespacial, Rio de Janeiro 04003
Museu de Armas Ferreira da Cunha, Petrópolis 03971
Museu do Instituto Histórico, Carpina 03924
Museu Histórico de Sergipe, São Cristóvão 04100
Museu Histórico do Exército e Forte de Copacabana, Rio de Janeiro 04057
Museu José Bonifácio, São Paulo 04116
Museu Navio Comandante Bauru, Rio de Janeiro 04065
Museu Particular de Armas de Arlindo Pedro Zatti, Porto Alegre 03979

Brunei
Royal Brunei Armed Forces Museum, Bandar Seri Begawan 04136

Canada
Army Museum, Halifax 05003
Evergreen Firearms Museum, Belmont 04533
Lieutenant General Ashton Armoury Museum, Victoria 06198
Murney Tower Museum, Kingston 05143
Royal Military College of Canada Museum, Kingston 05146
Royal Winnipeg Rifles Museum, Winnipeg 06317

China, People's Republic
Minbing Weapon Equipment Display Center, Tongzhou 06745

Colombia
Museo de Armas, Santafé de Bogotá 06893

Croatia
Etnografski Muzej Split, Split 07070

Cuba
Morro-Cabaña Parque Histórico Militar, La Habana 07140
Museo Arabe, La Habana 07142
Museo de la Revolución y Granma Memorial, La Habana 07150

Czech Republic
Východočeské Muzeum, Pardubice 07518

Denmark
Dragon- og Frihedsmuseet, Holstebro 07872
Hjemmevaernsmuseet, Holstebro 07873
Krudttaarnsmuseet, Frederikshavn 07817

Dominican Republic
Museo de las Casas Reales, Santo Domingo 08108

Egypt
Military Museum, Cairo 08216

Ethiopia
War Museum, Addis Ababa 08283

Finland
Ilmatorjuntamuseo, Tuusula 08981

France
Musée de la Guerre au Moyen Age, Castelnaud-la-Chapelle 09897
Musée d'Histoire Militaire, La Cluse-et-Mijoux 10952
Musée du Valois et de l'Archerie, Crépy-en-Valois 10262
Musée Historique, Gourdon (Alpes-Maritimes) 10692
Musée International des Hussards, Tarbes 13651

Germany
Bartholomäus-Schmucker-Heimatmuseum, Ruhpolding 18272
Bayerisches Armeemuseum, Ingolstadt 16563
Burg Meersburg, Meersburg 17304
Burg Neuhaus, Wolfsburg 19183
Burg Stolpen, Stolpen 18606
Burgmuseum, Ortenberg, Hessen 17863
Festungs- und Waffengeschichtliches Museum, Philippsburg 17983
Fürstlich Hohenzollernsche Sammlungen, Sigmaringen 18495
Heimat- und Waffenmuseum, Oberndorf am Neckar 17781
Historisches Waffenmuseum im Zeughaus, Überlingen 18774
Museum im Zwinger, Goslar 16042
Rüstkammer, Dresden 15423
Schloßmuseum Mespelbrunn, Mespelbrunn 17344
Schützenmuseum der Königlich privilegierten Feuerschützengesellschaft Weilheim, Weilheim, Oberbayern 18977
Schützenscheibensammlung, Mainbernheim 17223
Trillarium, Cleebronn 15203
Waffenmuseum Suhl, Suhl 18660

India
Fort Museum, Chennai 20187
Government Museum Vellore, Vellore 20451
Maharaja Banaras Vidya Mandir Museum, Varanasi 20153
Victoria Memorial Hall, Kolkata 20181

Italy
Armeria Reale, Torino 22661
Civico Museo di Guerra per la Pace Diego de Henriquez, Trieste 22734
Collezioni d'Armi e Ceramiche della Rocca Sforzesca, Imola 21736
Museo Civico, Pizzighettone 22223
Museo Civico delle Armi L. Marzoli, Brescia 21240
Museo della Fondazione Fioroni, Legnago 21783
Museo delle Armi Antiche, Milano 21916
Museo di San Michele, Sagrado 22455
Museo Nazionale del Palazzo di Venezia, Roma 22398
Museo Nazionale dell'Arma della Cavalleria, Pinerolo 22207
Museo Nazionale di Castel Sant'Angelo, Roma 22401
Museo Stibbert, Firenze 21626
Museo Storico Italiano della Guerra, Rovereto 22443
Palazzo Ducale, Venezia 22818

Japan
Hirado Castle Donjon, Hirado 23026
Matsuura Shiryo Hakubutsukan, Hirado 23028
Museum of Antique Armour Helmets and Swords, Kyoto 23252
Nihon Token Hakubutsukan, Tokyo 23654
Nishimura Museum, Iwakuni 23093
Oyamazumi-jinja Kokuhokan, Omishima 23415

Malta
Palace Armoury, Valletta 24350

Mexico
Museo de Armas, México 24427

Morocco
Musée d'Armes du Bordj Nord, Fez 24554

Nepal
National Museum of Nepal, Kathmandu 24643

Netherlands
Bussemakerhuis, Borne 24831
Museum van Historische en Moderne Wapens, Enkhuizen 25017

Nigeria
Kanta Museum Argungu, Argungu 25969

Norway
Galtebosamlingen, Spydeberg 26315
Kongsberg Våpenfabrikks Museum, Kongsberg 26142

Peru
Museo de Oro del Perú y Armas del Mundo, Lima 26497

Poland
Muzeum Arsenal, Wrocław 27281
Muzeum Okręgowe, Zamość 27312
Muzeum Pierwszych Piastów na Lednicy, Lednogóra 26875
Muzeum Regionalne, Pyzdry 27054
Muzeum Wojska Polskiego, Warszawa 27239
Muzeum Zbrojownia, Liw 26887

Portugal
Museu Militar de Lisboa, Lisboa 27398

Russia
Centralnyj Voenno-morskoj Muzej, Sankt-Peterburg 28020
Novorossijskij Gosudarstvennyj Istoričeskij Muzej Zapovednik, Novorossijsk 27961

San Marino
Museo delle Armi Antiche, San Marino 28150
Museo delle Armi Moderne, San Marino 28151

Slovakia
Expozícia Zbraní a Mestského Opevnenia, Bratislava 28200

Slovenia
Muzej Novejše Zgodovine Slovenije, Ljubljana 28349

South Africa
Fort Beaufort Historical Museum, Fort Beaufort 28474
Messina Museum, Messina 28543
Museum of Coast and Anti-Aircraft Artillery, Green Point 28490
R.E. Stevenson Museum, Colenso 28449

Spain
Alcázar de Segovia, Segovia 29695
Museo de Armería de Alava, Vitoria-Gasteiz 29930
Museo José Serra Farré, La Riba 29556
Museu Militar, Barcelona 28823
Real Armería, Madrid 29303

Sweden
Livrustkammaren, Stockholm 30358
Vapentekniska Museet, Eskilstuna 30067

Switzerland
Kantonales Museum Altes Zeughaus, Solothurn 31252
Musée d'Histoire, La Neuveville 31058
Musée Militaire Vaudois, Morges 31018
Ortsmuseum Sust, Horgen 30876
Schloßmuseum Thun, Thun 31309
Waffenkammer im Munot-Turm, Schaffhausen 31203

United Kingdom
Border History Museum, Hexham 33266
Cobbaton Combat Collection, Chittlehampton 32620
Dean Castle, Kilmarnock 33381
Delgatie Castle, Turriff 34697
Eastnor Castle, Ledbury 33461
Fawley Court Historic House and Museum, Henley-on-Thames 33248
Fleet Air Arm Museum - Concorde, Yeovilton 34908
Fort Brockhurst, Gosport 33130
Havant Museum, Havant 33218
Infantry and Small Arms School Corps Weapons Collection, Warminster 34744
Museum of Artillery in the Rotunda, London 33714
Preston Hall Museum, Stockton-on-Tees 34571
Ripley Castle, Ripley, North Yorkshire 34309
Royal Armouries, London 33759
Royal Armouries at Fort Nelson, Fareham 33004
Royal Armouries Museum, Leeds 33472
Royal Gloucestershire, Berkshire and Wiltshire Regiment Museum, Salisbury 34410
Royal Marines Museum, Portsmouth 34242
Scottish Infantry Divisional Museum, Penicuik 34159
Warwickshire Yeomanry Museum, Warwick 34755
West Gate Towers, Canterbury 32523

U.S.A.
Daisy International Air Gun Museum, Rogers 39852
Dane G. Hansen Memorial Museum, Logan 38099
General Douglas L. McBride Museum, Roswell 39873
Higgins Armory Museum, Worcester 41294
National Firearms Museum, Fairfax 36780
Remington Firearms Museum and Country Store, Ilion 37572
Saunders Memorial Museum, Berryville 35469
Springfield Armory Museum, Springfield 40462
UDT-SEAL Museum, Fort Pierce 36946

Vatican City
Museo Storico Vaticano, Città del Vaticano 41407

Yemen
Military Museum, Aden 41489

Yugoslavia
Muzej Stara Livnica, Kragujevac 41563
Vojni Muzej Beograd, Beograd 41529

Zimbabwe
Zimbabwe Military Museum, Gweru 41660

Art

Albania
Fine Arts Gallery, Korçë 00024
Fine Arts Gallery, Tiranë 00033

Algeria
Musée Archéologique de Djemila, Wilaya de Setif 00070
Musée Archéologique de Timgad, Timgad 00068
Musée de Constantine, Constantine 00053
Musée de Skikda, Skikda 00064
Musée des Arts Populaires, Alger 00041
Musée National des Beaux-Arts d'Alger, Alger 00044

American Samoa
Jean P. Haydon Museum, Pago Pago 00071

Argentina
Museo de Arte Eduardo Minnicelli, Río Gallegos 00505
Museo de Arte Gauchesco La Recova, San Antonio de Areco 00538
Museo de Bellas Artes de la Boca, Buenos Aires 00163
Museo de Bellas Artes Domingo Faustino Sarmiento, Mercedes 00435
Museo de Bellas Artes Dr. Juan Ramón Vidal, Corrientes 00310
Museo de Calcos y Esculturas Compardas, Buenos Aires 00164
Museo de Historia Reginal San Lorenzo y Galería del Libertador General San Martín, San Lorenzo 00566
Museo Fundación Naum Komp, Buenos Aires 00198
Museo Histórico de Arte, Morón 00448
Museo Judío de Buenos Aires Dr. Salvador Kibrick, Buenos Aires 00212
Museo Municipal de Bellas Artes, Bahía Blanca 00119
Museo Municipal de Bellas Artes, La Calera 00366
Museo Municipal de Bellas Artes, La Paz 00374
Museo Municipal de Bellas Artes, Tandil 00621
Museo Municipal de Bellas Artes Prof. Amelio Ronco Ceruti, Metán 00439

Art, African

Art, American

Art, Asian

Art, Australian

Art, European

Art, Greek and Roman

Art, Latin American

Art, Medieval

Art, Modern and Contemporary

Art, Oriental

Art, Russian

Astronomy

Aviation

Egypt
Airport Museum, Cairo 08201

Finland
Keski-Suomen Ilmailumuseo, Tikkakoski 08945
Luotsitupa, Uusikaupunki 08989
Suomen Ilmailumuseo, Vantaa 09018

France
Musée Aérorétro, Albon 09110
Musée de l'Aviation Légère de l'Armée de Terre, Dax 10295
Musée de l'Invasion Aéroportée, Bénouville 09512
Musée des Troupes Aéroportées, Sainte-Mère-Eglise 13334

Germany
Aeronauticum - Deutsches Luftschiff- und Marinefliegermuseum Nordholz, Nordholz 17722
Ballonmuseum, Gersthofen 15955
Bavaria Airways-Museum, Kirchdorf an der Amper 16743
Deutsche Raumfahrtausstellung, Morgenröthe-Rautenkranz 17414
Deutsches Museum - Flugwerft Schleißheim, Oberschleißheim 17795
Deutsches Segelflugmuseum mit Modellflug, Gersfeld 15953
Dorniermuseum im Neuen Schloß, Meersburg 17305
Erfatal-Museum Hardheim, Hardheim 16290
Flughafen Modellraum, Hamburg 16213
Hermann-Köhl-Museum, Pfaffenhofen an der Roth 17970
Hermann-Oberth-Raumfahrt-Museum, Feucht 15696
Hubschraubermuseum, Bückeburg 15123
Internationales Luftfahrtmuseum, Villingen-Schwenningen 18848
Luftfahrt-Museum Laatzen-Hannover, Laatzen 16921
Otto-Lilienthal-Museum, Anklam 14284
Zeppelin-Museum, Neu-Isenburg 17610
Zeppelin Museum Friedrichshafen, Friedrichshafen 15847
Zeppelin-Museum Meersburg, Meersburg 17313

Ireland
Foynes Flying Boat Museum, Foynes 20773

Italy
Museo Aeronautico, Padova 22088
Museo Aeronautico Caproni di Taliedo, Roma 22354
Museo Aeronautico Caproni di Taliedo, Vizzola Ticino 22880
Museo Storico-Aeronautica Militare, Bracciano 21237

Malaysia
Royal Malaysian Air Force Museum, Kuala Lumpur 24307

Netherlands
Avog's Crash Museum, Lievelde 25256
Dutch Dakota Association Exhibition, Schiphol 25474
Militaire Luchtvaart Museum, Soesterberg 25506
Nationaal Luchtvaart Museum Aviodome, Schiphol 25475
Old Aircraft Museum, Arnemuiden 24761
Space Expo, Noordwijk, Zuid-Holland 25336
Traditiekamer Vliegbasis Twenthe, Enschede 25025
Vliegend Museum Lelystad, Lelystad 25250
Vliegend Museum Seppe, Bosschenhoofd 24833
Westerwolds Crashmuseum, Oude Pekela 25377
Zep/Allon Museeum, Lelystad 25251

New Zealand
Ashburton Aviation Museum, Ashburton 25711
Gore Airforce Museum, Gore 25796
Museum of Aviation, Paraparaumu 25867
New Zealand Fighter Pilots Museum, Wanaka 25922
New Zealand Fleet Air Arm Museum, Auckland 25734
Royal New Zealand Air Force Museum, Christchurch 25754
Vintage Aircraft Museum, Masterton 25832

Peru
Museo Aeronáutico del Perú, Lima 26486

Philippines
Philippine Air Force Museum, Pasay 26578

Poland
Muzeum Lotnictwa Polskiego, Kraków 26835

Portugal
Museu do Ar, Alverca do Ribatejo 27333

Russia
Centralnyj Muzej Aviacii i Kosmonavtiki, Moskva 27792
Gosudarstvennyj Muzej Istorii Kosmonavtiki im. K.E. Ciolkovskogo, Kaluga 27747
Memorialnyj Dom-muzej akademika S.P. Koroleva, Moskva 27840
Memorialnyj Muzej Jurija Gagarina, Gagarin 27725
Memorialnyj Muzej Kosmonavtiki, Moskva 27845
Naučno-memorialnyj Muzej N.E. Žukovskogo, Moskva 27921

South Africa
Pioneers of Aviation Museum, Kimberley 28527
SAAF Museum Durban, Durban 28464
SAAF Museum Port Elizabeth, Port Elizabeth 28569
SAAF Museum Swartkop, Swartkop 28628
SAAF Museum Ysterplaat, Ysterplaat 28646

Spain
Museo de Aeronáutica y Astronáutica, Madrid 29261

Sweden
Landskrona Museum, Landskrona 30183

Switzerland
Flieger-Flab-Museum, Dübendorf 30734
Musée de la Naissance de l'Aviation Suisse, Avenches 30547

United Kingdom
448th Bomb Group Memorial Museum, Seething 34439
Brenzett Aeronautical Museum, Brenzett 32374
Carpetbagger Aviation Museum, Harrington 33196
City of Norwich Aviation Museum, Horsham Saint Faith 33294
Cornwall Aero Park, Helston 33241
Dumfries and Galloway Aviation Museum, Dumfries 32824
Fenland and West Norfolk Aviation Museum, West Walton 34784
Flambards Victorian Village, Helston 33242
De Havilland Aircraft Heritage Centre, Saint Albans 34351
The Helicopter Museum, Weston-super-Mare 34790
Imperial War Museum Duxford, Duxford 32864
Lashenden Air Warfare Museum, Headcorn 33231
Midland Air Museum, Baginton 32106
Midland Warplane Museum, Warwick 34748
Military Aviation Museum, Tangmere 34639
Montrose Air Station Museum, Montrose 33979
Museum of Army Flying, Middle Wallop 33942
Museum of Flight, North Berwick 34067
Newark Air Museum, Newark-on-Trent 34015
Norfolk and Suffolk Aviation Museum, Flixton 33025
North East Aircraft Museum, Sunderland 34614
Percy Pilcher Museum, Lutterworth 33848
Royal Air Force Air Defence Radar Museum, Norwich 34086
Royal Air Force Museum, London 33758
Royal Air Force Museum, Shifnal 34472
Royal Air Force Museum 201 Squadron, Saint Peter Port 34398
Royal Air Force Museum Reserve Collection, Stafford 34541
Shoreham Aircraft Museum, Shoreham 34475
Shuttleworth Collection, Old Warden 34114
Solway Aviation Museum, Crosby-on-Eden 32719
Southampton Hall of Aviation, Southampton 34517
Thameside Aviation Museum, East Tilbury 32884
Tolgos Tin, Redruth 34290
Wellington Aviation Museum, Moreton-in-Marsh 33982
Yorkshire Air Museum, Elvington 32965

Uruguay
Museo Aeronáutico, Montevideo 34931

U.S.A.
Air Force Armament Museum, Eglin Air Force Base 36654
Air Force Flight Test Center Museum, Edwards Air Force Base 36650
Air Heritage Museum of Santa Barbara/Goleta, Goleta 37174
Air Power Park and Museum, Hampton 37324
Air Victory Museum, Medford 38396
Airmen Memorial Museum, Suitland 40567
Airpower Museum, Ottumwa 39218
Alaska Aviation Heritage Museum, Anchorage 35100
Allied Air Force Museum, Allentown 35052
American Airpower Heritage Museum, Midland 38487
American Helicopter Museum Education Center, West Chester 41098
Carolinas Historic Aviation Museum, Charlotte 35945
Clark County Heritage Museum, Henderson 37401
College Park Aviation Museum, College Park 36171
Combat Air Museum, Topeka 40701
EAA AirVenture Museum, Oshkosh 39205
Edward H. White II Memorial Museum, Brooks Air Force Base 35709
Empire State Aerosciences Museum, Glenville 37154
Evergreen Aviation Museum, McMinnville 38251
Fargo Air Museum, Fargo 36805
Frontiers of Flight Museum, Dallas 36360
Glenn H. Curtiss Museum, Hammondsport 37318
Grissom Air Museum, Peru 39335
Hill Aerospace Museum, Hill Air Force Base 37427
International Women's Air and Space Museum, Cleveland 36135
Intrepid Sea-Air-Space Museum, New York 38887
Iowa Aviation Museum, Greenfield 37247
Kalamazoo Aviation History Museum, Kalamazoo 37717
Kansas Aviation Museum, Wichita 41169
Kansas Cosmosphere and Space Center, Hutchinson 37561
Kirkpatrick Science and Air Space Museum at Omniplex, Oklahoma City 39136
Lone Star Flight Museum/Texas Aviation Hall of Fame, Galveston 37089
Louisiana State Museum, Patterson 39296
March Field Museum, Riverside 39794
May Natural History Museum and Museum of Space Exploration, Colorado Springs 36185
Mid-America Air Museum, Liberal 38035
Mitchell Gallery of Flight, Milwaukee 38520
Museum of Aviation at Robins Air Force Base, Warner Robins 40925
Museum of Flight, Seattle 40288
NASA Lewis Research Center's Visitor Center, Cleveland 36136
National Air and Space Museum, Washington 40981
National Model Aviation Museum, Muncie 38677
National Museum of Naval Aviation, Pensacola 39318
National Soaring Museum, Elmira 36707
National Warplane Museum, Horseheads 37501
Neil Armstrong Air and Space Museum, Wapakoneta 40921
New England Air Museum of the Connecticut Aeronautical Historical Association, Windsor Locks 41239
New Mexico Wing-Confederate Air Force, Hobbs 37446
North Carolina Museum of Life and Science, Durham 36590
Oregon Air and Space Museum, Eugene 36752
Parker-O'Malley Air Museum, Ghent 37129
Pearson Air Museum, Vancouver 40840
Pima Air and Space Museum, Tucson 40752
Rhinebeck Aerodrome Museum, Rhinebeck 39734
San Diego Aerospace Museum, San Diego 40086
Santa Maria Museum of Flight, Santa Maria 40206
Science Museum of Virginia, Richmond 39767
Smithsonian Institution, Washington 40999
Southern Museum of Flight, Birmingham 35512
Space Center Houston, Houston 37526
Strategic Air Command Museum, Ashland 35175
Sun'n Fun Fly-In, Lakeland 37906
Texas Air Museum, Rio Hondo 39782
United States Air Force Museum, Wright-Patterson Air Force Base 41306
United States Space and Rocket Center, Huntsville 37554
Virginia Air and Space Center, Hampton 37327
Weeks Air Museum, Miami 38460
Western Aerospace Museum, Oakland 39095
Wings of Freedom, Huntington 37542
Wings of History Air Museum, San Martin 40151
Wonder Works Children's Museum, The Dalles 40671
Wright Brothers National Memorial, Kill Devil Hills 37801
Yankee Air Museum, Willow Run Airport 41203

Venezuela
Museo Aeronáutico Colonel Luis Hernan Paredes, Maracay 41448

Vietnam
Air Force Museum, Ha Noi 41460

Baking and Cookery

Australia
Centennial Bakery Museum, Hurstville 01104
Charles Ferguson Museum, Mentone 01234
Miller Bakehouse Museum, Palmyra 01343
Winns Historic Bakehouse Museum, Coromandel Valley 00934

Austria
Bäckermuseum, Wien 02810
Bezirksmuseum Josefstadt, Wien 02829
Brot- und Mühlen-Lehrmuseum, Gloggnitz 01876
Burgenländisches Brotmuseum, Bad Tatzmannsdorf 01711
Österreichisches Gebäckmuseum, Wels 02785

Belgium
Bakkerijmuseum, Groot-Bijgaarden 03432

Canada
Maison J.A. Vachon, Sainte-Marie 05856
Musée de la Cuisine, Drummondville 04807

France
Musée de la Boulangerie, Bonnieux 09623

Germany
Badisches Bäckereimuseum und Erstes Deutsches Zuckerbäckermuseum, Kraichtal 16859
Bäckerei- und Dorfgeschichtliches Museum, Bremervörde 15080
Deutsches Brotmuseum, Ulm 18788
Europäisches Brotmuseum e.V., Ebergötzen 15477
Lebzelterei- und Wachszieheremuseum, Pfaffenhofen an der Ilm 17968
Museum Alte Pfefferküchlerei, Weißenberg 19021
Passauer Glasmuseum, Passau 17947

Italy
Museo Agricolo Brunnenburg/Landwirtschaftsmuseum, Tirolo di Merano 22647

Netherlands
Bakkerijmuseum, Huizen 25187
Bakkerijmuseum De Grenswachter, Luijksgestel 25260
Caddy's Diner, Purmerend 25395
Museum Bakkerij Mendels, Middelstum 25295
Nederlands Bakkerijmuseum Het Warme Land, Hattem 25113
Oude Bakkerij, Medemblik 25286
Schilder- en Bakkerijmuseum 't Steenhuis, Niebert 25306

Switzerland
La Maison du Blé et du Pain, Echallens 30738
Schweizerisches Gastronomie-Museum, Thun 31311

United Kingdom
Bakelite Museum, Williton 34829
National Museum of Baking, Blindley Heath 32310
Sally Lunn's Refreshment House and Kitchen Museum, Bath 32170

Balneology

Austria
Kurmuseum, Bad Tatzmannsdorf 01713

Croatia
Yaraždinske Toplice Local History Museum, Varaždinske Toplice 07087

Czech Republic
Městské Muzeum, Františkovy Lázně 07321
Muzeum Jáchymovského Hornictví a Lázeňství, Jáchymov 07364
Vlastivědné Muzeum Jesenícka, Jeseník 07368
Zlaty Klíč Muzeum, Karlovy Vary 07387

Germany
Heimatmuseum, Bad Orb 14489
Historische Kuranlagen und Goethe-Theater Bad Lauchstädt, Bad Lauchstädt 14468
Kur- und Stadtmuseum, Bad Ems 14424
Kurmuseum Bad Wildungen, Bad Wildungen 14537
Museum im Alten Rathaus, Bad Brückenau 14407
Salzmuseum, Bad Sülze 14525
Sebastian-Kneipp-Museum, Bad Wörishofen 14550
Stadt- und Bädermuseum, Bad Salzuflen 14507
Stadt- und Bädermuseum Bad Doberan, Bad Doberan 14412

Slovakia
Balneologické Múzeum, Piešťany 28280

Switzerland
Museum Altes Bad Pfäfers, Bad Ragaz 30549

Banks and Banking

Argentina
Museo Históricos del Banco de la Provincia de Buenos Aires, Buenos Aires 00210
Museo Numismático del Banco Nacíonal, Buenos Aires 00225

Australia
ANZ Banking Museum, Melbourne 01210
Bank of Victoria Museum, Yackandandah 01618
Banking and Currency Museum, Kadina 01117
Don Bank Museum, North Sydney 01319
Westpac Museum, Homebush 01096
Westpac Museum, Sydney 01509

Austria
Sparkassen-Museum der Erste Bank, Wien 02961

Canada
Bank of Montreal Museum, Montréal 05353
Farmers Bank of Rustico, Rustico 05763
Old Bank of New Brunswick Museum, Riverside-Albert 05745

Denmark
Sparekassemuseet, Korsør 07947

Finland
Bank Museum of Kansallis-Osake-Pankki, Helsinki 08342
Osuuspankkimuseo, Helsinki 08373

Germany
Sparkassen-Museum, Greding 16068

Haiti
Unité Musée Numismatique, Port-au-Prince 19776

Iran
Sekkeh, Teheran 20659

Israel
Bank Leumi Museum, Tel Aviv 20990

Japan
Sakura Bank Exhibition Room, Kyoto 23268

Mozambique
Museu Nacional da Moeda, Maputo 24580

New Zealand
Westpac Banking Corporation Archive and Museum, Wellington 25949

Peru
Museo del Banco Central de Reserva, Lima 26498

Boats and Shipping

South Australian Maritime Museum, Port Adelaide 01370
Sydney Heritage Fleet, Pyrmont 01397
Treasure Trove Shipwreck Museum, Port Douglas 01374
Western Australian Maritime Museum, Fremantle 01024
Western Australian Museum Geraldton, Geraldton 01035
Whyalla Maritime Museum, Whyalla 01595
Williamstown Historical Museum, Williamstown 01599

Austria
Oberösterreichisches Schiffahrtsmuseum, Grein an der Donau 01934
Schiffahrtsmuseum, Spitz 02646
Schiffleutmuseum, Stadl-Paura 02647

Belgium
Museum voor Binnenscheepvaart, Antwerpen 03117
Nationaal Scheepvaartmuseum, Antwerpen 03120
Scheepvaartmuseum, Bornem 03193

Bermuda
Bermuda Maritime Museum, Mangrove Bay 03856
Bermuda National Trust Museum, Saint George's 03857

Brazil
Espaço Cultural da Marinha, Rio de Janeiro 03997
Museu da Escola Naval, Rio de Janeiro 04017
Museu Naval e Oceanográfico, Rio de Janeiro 04064

Bulgaria
Voenno-morski Muzej, Varna 04369

Canada
Archelaus Smith Museum, Cape Sable Island 04656
Atlantic Statiquarium Marine Museum, Louisbourg 05243
Britannia Heritage Shipyard, Richmond 05728
Campbell River Optical Maritime Museum, Campbell River 04648
CFB Esquimalt Naval Museum and Military Museum, Victoria 06192
Collingwood Museum, Collingwood 04728
Cowichan Bay Maritime Centre, Cowichan Bay 04745
Green Park Shipbuilding Museum and Yeo House, Port Hill 05633
Gulf Museum, Port-aux-Basques 05622
La Have Islands Marine Museum, La Have 05168
HMCS Sackville, Halifax 05011
Lawrence House Museum, Maitland 05264
Marine Museum of Manitoba, Selkirk 05892
Marine Museum of Upper Canada, Toronto 06067
Mariners' Park Museum, Milford 05314
Maritime Command Museum, Halifax 05012
Maritime Museum of British Columbia, Victoria 06200
Maritime Museum of the Atlantic, Halifax 05013
Musée de la Mer, Havre-Aubert 05046
Musée de la Mer, Iles-de-la-Madeleine 05071
Musée de la Mer de Rimouski, Pointe-au-Père 05612
Musée du Navigateur Flottant, Saint-Joseph-de-Sorel 05827
Musée Maritime du Québec, L'Islet-sur-Mer 05217
Muskoka Lakes Museum, Port Carling 05624
Nancy Island Historic Site, Wasaga Beach 06220
Naval Museum of Alberta, Calgary 04636
The Ned Shed Museum, Meldrum Bay 05297
Point Amour Lighthouse, Saint John's 05818
Pointe-Noire - Parc Marin du Saguenay, Baie-Sainte-Catherine 04493
Port Colborne Historical and Marine Museum, Port Colborne 05627
Quaco Museum and Archives, Saint Martins 05837
Saint Mary's River Marine Centre, Sault Sainte Marie 05883
Samson V Maritime Museum, New Westminster 05451
Segwun Heritage Centre, Gravenhurst 04983
Site-Historique du Banc-de-Paspébiac, Paspébiac 05568
Southern Newfoundland Seamen's Museum, Grand Bank 04966
Sunshine Coast Maritime Museum, Gibsons 04943
Trinity Museum, Trinity 06109
Vancouver Maritime Museum, Vancouver 06170
Vancouver Naval Museum, West Vancouver 06249
Voyageur Heritage Centre, Mattawa 05288
West Coast Maritime Museum, Tofino 06029
William D. Lawrence House, Halifax 05023
Yarmouth County Museum, Yarmouth 06344

Chile
Museo Naval de Viña del Mar, Viña del Mar 06407

China, People's Republic
Maritime Museum of Macau, Macau 06644
Oversea Transport Shi Museum, Quanzhou 06683
PLA Naval Museum, Qingdao 06680

Croatia
Orebić Maritime Museum, Orebić 07037
Pomorski i Povijesni Muzej Hrvatskog Primorja, Rijeka 07051
Pomorski Muzej, Zadar 07095
Pomorski Muzej, Dubrovnik 06988
Zavičajni Muzej, Baška 06963

Cyprus Turk
Shipwreck Museum, Girne 07223

Denmark
Aabenraa Museum, Aabenraa 07743
Flaske-Peters-Samling, Ærøskøbing 07749
Fregatten Jylland, Ebeltoft 07788
Handels- og Søfartsmuseet paa Kronborg, Helsingør 07847
Ladbyskibsmuseet, Kerteminde 07901
Limfjordsmuseet, Løgstør 07957
Marstal Søfartsmuseum, Marstal 07967
Orlogsmuseet, København 07931
Skagen By- og Egnsmuseum, Skagen 08041
Søfarts og Fiskerimuseet, Læsø 07951
Søfartssamlingerne i Troense, Svendborg 08070
Strandingsmuseum St. George, Ulfborg 08081
Vikingeskibsmuseet, Roskilde 08029

Egypt
National Maritime Museum, Alexandria 08197
Solar Boats Museum, Giza 08243

Finland
Ålands Sjöfartsmuseum, Mariehamn 08658
Ehrensvärd-Museo, Helsinki 08345
Forum Marinum, Turku 08960
Jakobstads museum, Jakobstad 08417
K.H. Renlundin Museo, Kokkola 08521
Kymenlaakson maakuntamuseo, Kotka 08538
Raahen Museo, Raahe 08818
Rauman Museo, Rauma 08828
Sjöfartsmuseet, Kristiinankaupunki 08550
Sjöhistoriska Institutet vid Åbo Akademi, Turku 08969
Suomen Merimuseo, Helsinki 08385
Uudenkaupungin Kultuurihistoriallinen Museo, Uusikaupunki 08991

France
Château-Musée de Dieppe, Dieppe 10314
Ecomusée de Saint-Nazaire, Saint-Nazaire (Loire-Atlantique) 13161
Espace Maritime et Portuaire des Docks Vauban, Le Havre 11212
Laboratoire Maritime de Dinard, Dinard 10340
Maison du Patrimoine Maritime, Camaret-sur-Mer 09823
Musée à Flot de l'Escorteur d'Escadre, Nantes 12033
Musée Cognacq, Saint-Martin-de-Ré 13133
Musée d'Aquitaine, Bordeaux 09633
Musée d'Art Populaire Régional, Nantes 12035
Musée de la Batellerie, Conflans-Sainte-Honorine 10198
Musée de la Batellerie de l'Ouest, Redon 12706
Musée de la Construction Navale, Noirmoutier-en-l'Ile 12144
Musée de la Marine, Paris 12341
Musée de la Marine, Saint-Brévin-les-Pins 12919
Musée de la Marine de Loire, Châteauneuf-sur-Loire 10034
Musée de la Marine et de l'Économie de Marseille, Marseille 11643
Musée de la Mer, Paimpol 12236
Musée de la Vilaine Maritime, La Roche-Bernard 11020
Musée des Mariniers et de la Batellerie du Rhône, Serrières 13504
Musée des Terre-Neuvas et de la Pêche, Fécamp 10513
Musée d'Histoire de la Ville et d'Ethnographie du Pays Malouin, Saint-Malo (Ille-et-Vilaine) 13120
Musée du Bateau, Douarnenez 10363
Musée Flottant-Architecture Navale, Audierne 09307
Musée Français des Phares et Balises, Ile-d'Ouessant 10852
Musée International du Long Cours Cap Hornier, Saint-Malo (Ille-et-Vilaine) 13121
Musée Maritime, Camaret-sur-Mer 09824
Musée Maritime et Ostréicole, La Tremblade 11063
Musée National de la Marine, Brest 09734
Musée National de la Marine, Paris 12426
Musée National de la Marine, Port-Louis 12631
Musée National de la Marine, Rochefort (Charente-Maritime) 12788
Musée National de la Marine, Saint-Tropez 13275
Musée National de la Marine, Toulon (Var) 13717
Musée Naval de Nice, Nice 12106
Musée Naval Fort Balaguier, La Seyne-sur-Mer 11056

French Polynesia
Musée de Marine, Faranui 14134

Germany
Altes Hafenamt, Dortmund 15377
Altonaer Museum in Hamburg, Hamburg 16204
Atrium an der Schleuse, Brunsbüttel 15112
Binnenschiffahrts-Museum Oderberg, Oderberg, Mark 17817
Buddelschiff-Museum, Wedel 18941
Deutsches Schiffahrtsmuseum, Bremerhaven 15072
Deutsches Sielhafenmuseum in Carolinensiel, Wittmund 19153
Donau-Schiffahrts-Museum-Regensburg, Regensburg 18093
Elbschiffahrtsmuseum mit stadtgeschichtlicher Sammlung, Lauenburg 16992
Fehn- und Schiffahrtsmuseum, Rhauderfehn 18153
Flensburger Schiffahrtsmuseum und Rum-Museum, Flensburg 15713
Heimat- und Schiffahrtsmuseum, Heinsen 16365
Heimatmuseum Haus Morgensonne, Ostseebad Zingst 17907
Informationszentrum am Wasserstraßenkreuz Minden, Minden, Westfalen 17374
Inselmuseum im Alten Leuchtturm, Wangerooge 18924
Kapitän Tadsen Museum, Langeneß 16977
Kieler Stadt- und Schiffahrtsmuseum, Kiel 16728
Klepper-Faltbootmuseum, Rosenheim 18217
Küstenmuseum, Juist 16623
Museum der Deutschen Binnenschifffahrt Duisburg-Ruhrort, Duisburg 15467
Museum der Seefahrt, Geiselhöring 15911
Museum für Antike Schiffahrt des Römisch-Germanischen Zentralmuseums, Mainz 17234
Museumsfeuerschiff Amrumbank/Deutsche Bucht, Emden 15558
Museumslogger AE7 Stadt Emden, Emden 15559
Museumsschiff Mannheim des Landesmuseums für Technik und Arbeit, Mannheim 17247
Museumsschiff STÖR, Holzminden 16495
Neckarschiffahrts-Museum und Weinbau, Heilbronn 16357
Prignitz-Museum Havelberg, Havelberg 16318
Rhein-Museum Koblenz, Koblenz 16775
Rheinmuseum, Emmerich 15565
Schiffahrts- und Schiffbaumuseum, Wörth am Main 19167
Schiffahrtsmuseum auf dem Traditionsschiff, Rostock 18229
Schiffahrtsmuseum der Oldenburgischen Weserhäfen, Brake, Unterweser 15012
Schiffahrtsmuseum Haren (Ems), Haren 16292
Schiffahrtsmuseum mit Nordseeaquarium Nordseeheilbad Langeoog, Langeoog 16981
Schiffahrtsmuseum Nordfriesland, Husum, Nordsee 16532
Schiffahrtsmuseum Rostock, Rostock 18230
SchifffahrtMuseum, Düsseldorf 15456
Schiffs- und Marinemuseum, Senden, Westfalen 18477
Schiffsmuseum Seitenradschleppdampfer "Württemberg", Magdeburg 17217
Technikmuseum U-Boot "Wilhelm Bauer", Bremerhaven 15077
Torfschiffwerftmuseum, Worpswede 19209
Westfälisches Industriemuseum, Waltrop 18915
Wrackmuseum, Cuxhaven 15245

Greece
Aegean Maritime Museum, Mykonos 19573
Maritime Museum of Andros, Andros 19336
Maritime Museum of Thera (Santorini), Oia 19596
Maritime Tradition Museum, Piraeus 19617
Museum of the Merchant Marine, Piraeus 19619
Nautical Museum of Crete, Chania 19430
Nautical Museum of Galaxidi, Galaxidi 19458
Nautikon Mouseiontis Ellados, Piraeus 19620
Oinoussian Maritime Museum, Oinoussai 19597

Iceland
Sjóminjasafn Austurlands, Eskifjördur 20093
Sjóminjasafn Islands, Hafnarfjördur 20097
Sjóminjasafnið á Eyrarbakka, Eyrarbakki 20094

Indonesia
Museum Tni A.L. Loka Jala Crana, Surabaya 20584

Ireland
1796 Bantry French Armada Exhibition Centre, Bantry 20697
Arklow Maritime Museum, Arklow 20685
Foynes Flying Boat Museum, Foynes 20773
Kilmore Quay Maritime Museum, Kilmore Quay 20793
Kilmore Quay Maritime Museum, Wexford 20852
National Maritime Museum of Ireland, Dun Laoghaire 20766

Italy
Civico Museo del Mare, Trieste 22731
Civico Museo Navale, Genova 21682
Civico Museo Navale Didattico, Milano 21897
Galleria Storica del Lloyd Triestino, Trieste 22741
Istituto Policattedra di Ingegneria Navale dell'Università di Genova, Genova 21688
Museo Civico Marinaro 'Gio-Bono Ferrari', Camogli 21291
Museo dei Navigli, Milano 21910
Museo delle Navi, Bologna 21195
Museo delle Navi, Fiumicino 21632
Museo delle Navi Romane, Nemi 22033
Museo Navale, Napoli 22026
Museo Navale Internazionale del Ponente Ligure, Imperia 21748
Museo Storico Navale, Venezia 22815
Museo Tecnico Navale, La Spezia 21764
La Raccolta della Barca Lariana, Pianello del Lario 22186

Jamaica
Fort Charles Maritime Museum, Kingston 22893

Japan
Fune no Kagakukan, Tokyo 23597
Kobe Maritime Museum, Kobe 23164
Tokai Daigaku Kaiyo Kagaku Hakubutsukan, Shimizu 23504
Yokohama Maritime Museum and Nippon-Maru Memorial Park, Yokohama 23775

Korea, Republic
Naval Academy Museum, Jinhae 23894

Malaysia
Maritime Museum, Melaka 24319
Tentera Laut Diraja Malaysia Muzium, Melaka 24325

Malta
Maritime Museum, Vittoriosa 24356
Wickman Maritime Collection, Zabbar 24361

Monaco
Musée Naval, Monaco 24534

Netherlands
Fries Scheepvaart Museum, Sneek 25502
Gemeentemuseum Het Hannemahuis, Harlingen 25109
Marinemuseum, Den Helder 24934
Maritiem Buitenmuseum, Rotterdam 25431
Maritiem en Jutters Museum, Oudeschild 25383
Maritiem Museum Rotterdam, Rotterdam 25432
Maritime Museum Zierikzee, Zierikzee 25683
Minischeepvaartmuseum, Ouwerkerk 25386
Museum Historische Buitenboordmotoren, Zuidhorn 25690
Museum Nanning Hendrik Bulthuis, Leeuwarden 25230
Museumswerf 't Kromhout, Amsterdam 24717
Museumwerf Wolthuis, Sappemeer 25460
Nationaal Reddingmuseum Dorus Rijkers, Den Helder 24935
Nationaal Scheephistorisch Centrum, Leylstad 25255
Nationaal Sleepvaartmuseum, Maassluis 25270
Noordelijk Scheepvaartmuseum, Groningen 25083
Open Haven Museum, Amsterdam 24724
Openlucht Binnenvaartmuseum, Rotterdam 25445
Scheepvaartmuseum, Amsterdam 24733
Scheepvaartmuseum, Gasselternijveen 25042
Zeeuws Maritiem Muzeeum, Vlissingen 25606

New Zealand
Bluff Maritime Museum, Bluff 25741
Museum of Wellington, City and Sea, Wellington 25934
Naval Reserve Association Museum, Dunedin 25776
Whanganui Riverboat Centre Museum, Wanganui 25925
Whangaroa County Museum, Kaeo 25812

Norway
Ålesunds Museum, Ålesund 26004
Berg-Kragerø Museum, Kragerø 26147
Bergens Sjøfartsmuseum, Bergen 26025
Frammuséet, Oslo 26220
Hurtigrutemuseet, Stokmarknes 26327
Kystmuseet Hvaler, Vesterøy 26379
Kystmuseet i Sogn og Fjordane, Florø 26083
Larvik Sjøfartsmuseum, Larvik 26157
Lillesand By-og Sjøfartsmuseum, Lillesand 26166
Marinemuseet, Horten 26121
Museet Kystens Arv, Stadsbygd 26317
Nordnorsk Fartøyvernsenter og Båtmuseum, Gratangen 26098
Norsk Sjøfartsmuseum, Oslo 26233
Sandefjord Sjøfartsmuseum, Sandefjord 26284
Stavanger Maritime Museum, Stavanger 26321
Sunmøre Museum, Ålesund 26005
Svelvik Museum, Svelvik 26335
Vikingskiphuset, Oslo 26248

Peru
Museo Histórico Naval del Perú, Callao 26474

Poland
Centralne Muzeum Morskie, Gdańsk 26696
Muzeum Marynarki Wojennej, Gdynia 26716

Portugal
Colecção Maritima do Comandante Ramalho Ortigão, Faro 27363
Museu de Marinha, Lisboa 27391
Museu Municipal, Alcochete 27330

Russia
Centralnyj Voenno-morskoj Muzej, Sankt-Peterburg 28020
Muzej Morskogo Flota, Moskva 27895

Singapore
Maritime Museum, Singapore 28179

Slovenia
Pomorski Muzej Sergej Mašera, Piran 28375

South Africa
Bartolomeu Dias Museum Complex, Mossel Bay 28547
Clock Tower Maritime Museum, Cape Town 28436
Old Harbour Museum, Hermanus 28496
Port Natal Maritime Museum, Durban 28463
Shipwreck Museum, Bredasdorp 28427
Simon's Town Museum, Simon's Town 28614
South African Maritime Museum, Cape Town 28445

Spain
Archivo-Museo Don Alvaro de Bazán, Viso del Marqués 29927
Museo Marítimo de Asturias, Luanco 29227
Museo Marítimo del Cantábrico, Santander 29667
Museo Marítimo Torre del Oro, Sevilla 29719
Museo Massó, Bueu 28866
Museo Naval, Madrid 29290
Museo Naval - Untzi Museoa, Donostia-San Sebastián 29019

Bones

Books, Book Art and Manuscripts

Museo Marchigiano del Risorgimento G. e D. Spadoni, Macerata 21821

Jordan
School Books Museum, Salt 23813

Liechtenstein
Liechtensteinische Landesbibliothek, Vaduz 24176

Luxembourg
Musée de l'Abbaye, Echternach 24213

Netherlands
Museum Meermanno-Westreenianum, Den Haag 24911
Schriftmuseum J.A. Dortmond, Amsterdam 24734
Scryption, Tilburg 25543

Philippines
Lopez Memorial Museum, Pasig 26582

Poland
Zbiory Muzealne Biblioteki Zakładu Narodowego im. Ossolińskich, Wrocław 27292

Romania
Muzeul a Primei Scoli Româneşti din Şchei Braşovului, Braşov 27503
Muzeul Arhivelor Statului, Bucureşti 27508

Russia
Muzej Knigi, Moskva 27879

Slovenia
Prežihov Spominski Muzej, Ravne na Koroškem 28382

Spain
F.P. Institut d'Estudis Ilerdencs, Lleida 29191
Museo de la Bibliografía Española, Madrid 29268
Museu d'Història de la Ciutat, Sant Feliu de Guíxols 29635

Sweden
Bernadottebiblioteket, Stockholm 30337
Biblioteksmuseet, Borås 30040

Switzerland
Fondation Martin Bodmer, Cologny 30709
Fonds Ancien de la Bibliothèque Cantonale Jurassienne, Porrentruy 31096
Öffentliche Bibliothek der Universität Basel, Basel 30581

Turkey
Türk Vakif Hat Sanatlari Müzesi, Beyazit 31682

United Kingdom
British Library, London 33596
Canterbury Cathedral Archives and Library, Canterbury 32517
Leadhills Miners' Library Museum, Leadhills 33457
Mappa Mundi and Chained Library, Hereford 33256

U.S.A.
Armstrong Browning Library, Waco 40889
Brand Library and Art Galleries, Glendale 37144
Canajoharie Library and Art Gallery, Canajoharie 35816
Center for Book Arts, New York 38851
Chancellor Robert R. Livingston Masonic Library and Museum, New York 38853
Chapin Library of Rare Books, Williamstown 41193
The Collectors Club, New York 38858
Dwight D. Eisenhower Library-Museum, Abilene 34972
Gerald R. Ford Library Museum, Grand Rapids 37208
Hamilton Library and Two Mile House, Carlisle 35841
Herbert Hoover Presidential Library-Museum, West Branch 41097
Historical Museum of the D.R. Barker Library, Fredonia 37036
The Interchurch Center, New York 38885
James Monroe Museum and Memorial Library, Fredericksburg 37028
John F. Kennedy Presidential Library-Museum, Boston 35594
Lyndon Baines Johnson Museum, Austin 35272
Melton Art Reference Library Museum, Oklahoma City 39137
Museum of the Jimmy Carter Library, Atlanta 35224
Pierpont Morgan Library, New York 38930
Rosenbach Museum, Philadelphia 39410
Rutherford B. Hayes Presidential Center, Fremont 37045
Society of Illustrators Museum of American Illustration, New York 38938
State Capital Publishing Museum, Guthrie 37290
The Thoreau Institute at Walden Woods, Lincoln 38048

Yugoslavia
Muzej Orijentalnih Rukopisa, Prizren 41611

Botany

Argentina
Museo Botanico, Buenos Aires 00148
Museo Botánico, Córdoba 00282

Museo de Ciencias Naturales Dr. Amado Bonpland, Corrientes 00311
Museo Farmacobotánica, Buenos Aires 00197

Austria
Biologiezentrum des Oberösterreichischen Landesmuseums, Linz 02220
Kräutermuseum - Naturpark Jauerling Wachau, Maria Laach am Jauerling 02258
Referat Botanik, Graz 01921

Belgium
Musée d'Histoire Naturelle de la Ville de Tournai, Tournai 03777
Natuurhistorisch Museum Provinciaal Domein Zilvermeer, Mol 03601
Schoolmuseum Michel Thiery, Gent 03416

Brazil
Museu Carpológico do Jardim Botânico do Rio de Janeiro, Rio de Janeiro 04010
Museu do Jardim Botânico, Rio de Janeiro 04045
Museu Parque Nacional do Itatiaia, Itatiaia 03941
Museu von Martius, Teresópolis 04124
Sítio Roberto Burle Marx, Rio de Janeiro 04078

Central African Republic
Musée Botanique de Wakombo, M'Baiki 06354

Colombia
Museo de Ciencias Naturales, Duitama 06845

Czech Republic
Botanické Oddělení Národniho Muzea, Průhonice 07615
Mendelianum - Památnik Gregora Mendela, Brno 07256
Muzeum Těšinska, Český Těšín 07289
Rožmberský Dům, Soběslav 07641
Východočeské Muzeum, Pardubice 07518
Západomoravské Muzeum v Třebíči, Třebíč 07670

Denmark
Botanisk Museum, København 07908

Egypt
Scientific Researches Museum, Cairo 08233

Finland
Kasvimuseo, Helsinki 08358
Kasvimuseo, Turun yliopisto, Turku 08961
Kuopion Luonnontieteellinen Museo, Kuopio 08561
Oulun Yliopiston Kasvimuseo, Oulu 08741

France
Exposition Botanique, Villar-d'Arène 13964
Musée d'Histoire Naturelle, Nantes 12040
Musée d'Histoire Naturelle, Nice 12109
Muséum National d'Histoire Naturelle, Paris 12447

Germany
Azaleen-Museum, Bremen 15050
Bonsai Museum Heidelberg, Heidelberg 16330
Botanische Staatssammlung München, München 17459
Botanisches Museum, Hamburg 16205
Botanisches Museum Berlin-Dahlem, Berlin 14686
Fehn- und Schiffahrtsmuseum, Rhauderfehn 18153
Forst- und Jagdmuseum, Hofgeismar 16460
Mooreichensammlung Johann Weber, Göppingen 16010
Museum für Naturkunde der Stadt Gera, Gera 15938
Naturhistorisches Museum, Mainz 17235

Greece
Botanical Museum of the National Gardens, Athinai 19366

Guinea
Musée Botanique, Conakry 19761

India
Botanical Survey of India, Dehradun 20201
Botany Museum, Faizabad 20236
Botany Museum, Gorakhpur 20248
Botany Museum, Jaunpur 20285
Botany Museum, Kanpur 20181
Botany Museum, Lucknow 20339
Central National Herbarium, Haora 20260

Indonesia
Museum Herbarium Bogoriensis, Bogor 20477

Israel
Neot Kedumim, Lod 20962
Ussishkin House, Kibbutz Dan 20946

Italy
Erbario dell'Istituto di Scienze Botaniche dell'Università di Milano, Milano 21901
Istituto ed Orto Botanico Hanbury, Genova 21687
Museo Alpino Duca degli Abruzzi, Courmayeur 21483
Museo Botanico Cesare Bicchi, Lucca 21808
Museo di Storia Naturale Sezione Botanica, Firenze 21616
Museo Friulano di Storia Naturale, Udine 22756

Mali
Musée National du Mali, Bamako 24338

Nepal
Natural History Museum, Kathmandu 24644

New Zealand
New Zealand Fungal Herbarium, Auckland 25735

Society for Preservation of the Kerikeri Stone Store Area Visitor Centre, Kerikeri 25820

Norway
Botanisk Museum, Oslo 26216

Oman
Oman Natural History Museum, Muscat 26386

Pakistan
Botanical Museum, Rawalpindi 26424

Poland
Muzeum Przyrodnicze Uniwersytetu Wrocławskiego, Wrocław 27288

Russia
Botaničeskij Muzej, Sankt-Peterburg 28015

Slovakia
Múzeum Tatranského Národného Parku, Tatranská Lomnica 28309
Ponitrianske Múzeum, Nitra 28272

Slovenia
Prirodoslovni Muzej Slovenije, Ljubljana 28354

South Africa
African Herbalist Shops, Johannesburg 28502
Albany Museum, Grahamstown 28482
National Museum Bloemfontein, Bloemfontein 28421

Spain
Estación Internacional de Biología Mediterránea Carlos Faust, Blanes 28858
Museo de Ciencias Naturales, Onda 29418
Museu de l'Instituto Botánico, Barcelona 28805

Sweden
Botaniksektionen Utställingar, Uppsala 30442
Botaniska Museet, Lund 30208
Linnémuseet, Uppsala 30445
Linnés Hammarby, Uppsala 30446

Switzerland
Botanisches Museum der Universität Zürich, Zürich 31441
Musée de Botanique, Lausanne 30926

United Kingdom
Botanic Gardens Museum, Southport 34529
Falconer Museum, Forres 33034
Kew Palace Museum of the Royal Botanic Gardens, Kew 33372
Museum No 1, Richmond, Surrey 34303
Museum of Garden History, London 33718

Uruguay
Museo y Jardin Botánico Profesor Atilio Lombardo, Montevideo 34956

U.S.A.
Botanical Museum of Harvard University, Cambridge 35785
Edison and Ford Winter Estates, Fort Myers 36937
Museum of Vintage Fashion, Lafayette 37874
Wilderness Park Museum, El Paso 36674

Brewing

Austria
Biermuseum, Laa an der Thaya 02163
Bindereimuseum Hofbräu Kaltenhausen, Hallein 01991
Bräustüberlmuseum, Raab 02453
Brauereimuseum im Stift Göß, Leoben 02199
Braumuseum, Wieselburg an der Erlauf 02991
Erstes Südburgenländisches Schnapsbrennereimuseum, Kukmirn 02161

Belgium
Bocholter Brouwerij Museum, Bocholt 03182
Brouwershuis, Antwerpen 03098
Musée Bruxellois de la Gueuze, Bruxelles 03257
Musée de la Brasserie, Bruxelles 03267
Stedelijk Brouwerijmuseum, Leuven 03534

Czech Republic
Pivovarské Muzeum, Plzeň 07528

Denmark
Fjerritslev Bryggeri- og Egnsmuseum, Fjerritslev 07810

France
Musée de la Bière, Stenay 13580
Musée Français de la Brasserie, Saint-Nicolas-de-Port 13166

Germany
Bayerisches Brauereimuseum Kulmbach, Kulmbach 16907
Brauerei-Kontor, Bochum 14936
Brauerei-Museum, Haßfurt 16300
Brauerei-Museum, Nesselwang 17605
Brauerei Museum Bürger-Bräu Hof, Hof, Saale 16456
Brauereikulturmuseum Gut Riedelsbach, Neureichenau 17658
Brauereimuseum, Aldersbach 14213
Brauereimuseum, Altomünster 14256

Brauereimuseum Bräu im Moos, Tüßling 18766
Brauereimuseum im historischen Kronen-Brauhaus zu Lüneburg, Lüneburg 17185
Brauereimuseum in der Brauerei Franz Xaver Glossner, Neumarkt 17646
Brauhausmuseum, Stadtlauringen 18568
Felsenkeller-Labyrinth im Hirschberg - Brauereimuseum, Beilngries 14636
Fränkisches Brauereimuseum, Bamberg 14577
Hallertauer Hopfen- und Heimatmuseum, Geisenfeld 15912
Heimat- und Brauereimuseum, Pleinfeld 17993
Historische Braustätte der Küppers Brauerei, Köln 16793
Klosterbräu Brauereimuseum, Irsee 16577
Maisel's Brauerei- und Büttnerei-Museum, Bayreuth 14621

Ireland
Guinness Hopestore Museum, Dublin 20742

Netherlands
Biermuseum de Boom, Alkmaar 24652
Brouwerijmuseum Raaf, Heumen 25156
Heineken Experience, Amsterdam 24694
Museumbrouwerij De Roos, Hilvarenbeek 25159

Slovenia
Pivovarski Muzej, Ljubljana 28353

Switzerland
Ortsmuseum, Nürensdorf 31061

United Kingdom
Bass Museum of Brewing, Burton-upon-Trent 32461
Stamford Brewery Museum, Stamford 34547
Tetley's Brewery Wharf, Leeds 33475

Bronzes

France
Collection de Sculptures, Peillon 12480

Italy
Museo Archeologico Mecenate, Arezzo 21082

Japan
Shimane-kenritsu Hakubutsukan, Matsue 23289

Netherlands
Museum Mesdag, Den Haag 24912

United Kingdom
Sion Hill Hall, Thirsk 34662
The Sladmore Gallery of Sculpture, London 33782

Vatican City
Museo Gregoriano Etrusco, Città del Vaticano 41398

Bullfights

Colombia
Museo Taurino de Bogotá, Santafé de Bogotá 06915

Peru
Museo Taurino de la Plaza de Acho, Lima 26507

Portugal
Museu Tauromáquico, Lisboa 27410

Spain
Museo Municipal Taurino, Córdoba 28982
Museo Taurino, Madrid 29297
Museo Taurino, Valencia 29846
Museu Taurí de la Monumental, Barcelona 28826

Buttons

Canada
Wellington Community Historical Museum, Wellington, Ontario 06238

Germany
Deutsches Knopfmuseum, Bärnau 14565

Cabaret → Performing Arts

Calligraphy

China, People's Republic
China Calligraphy Art Museum, Xian 06766
Lin San Zhi Art Display Center, Zhujiang 06808

Calligraphy

Germany
Graphische Sammlung der Universität, Erlangen 15621
Siebold-Museum, Würzburg 19229

Japan
Basho Memorial Museum, Ueno 23734
Imabari City Kono Shiniichi Memorial Culture Hall, Imabari 23069
Jingu Museum of Antiquities, Ise 23078
Masaki Art Museum, Tadaoka 23531
Nihon Shodo Bijutsukan, Tokyo 23653
Ryokan Kinenken, Izumozaki 23098
Saga-kenritsu Hakubutsukan, Saga 23453
Shodo Hakubutsukan, Tokyo 23670
Ueno Royal Museum, Tokyo 23699

Syria
Musée de Calligraphie et Epigraphie Arabe, Damascus 31497

Turkey
İstanbul Divan Edebiyati Müzesi, İstanbul 31752
Türk Vakif Hat Sanatlari Müzesi, Beyazit 31682

United Kingdom
Ditchling Museum, Ditchling 32773

Cameras → Optics

Carpets

Armenia
State Folk Art Museum of Armenia, Erevan 00681

Azerbaijan
State Museum of Azerbaijan Carpets and Applied Art Letif Kerimov, Baku 03036

Brazil
Fundação Eva Klabin Rappaport, Rio de Janeiro 04000

Bulgaria
Izložba na Stari Kotlenski Kilimi, Kotel 04221

Canada
Museum for Textiles, Toronto 06071

Germany
Orientteppich-Museum, Hannover 16282

Iran
Astan-e-Qods-e Razavi Museums, Mashad 20631
Carpet Museum of Iran, Teheran 20643

Turkey
Edirne Arkoloji ve Etnografi Müzesi, Edirne 31713
Vakif Hali Müzesi, İstanbul 31759
Yildiz Şale, İstanbul 31764

Turkmenistan
Carpet Museum, Ašhabad 31860

Carriages and Carts

Argentina
Museo del Carruaje El Tacu, Villa General Belgrano 00659

Australia
Carriage and Harness Museum, Beechworth 00774

Austria
Fiakermuseum, Wien 02852
Kutschen- und Heimatmuseum, Sillian 02639
Kutschen- und Schlittenmuseum, Großraming 01957
Wagenruin im Schloß Schönbrunn, Wien 02967

Belgium
Karrenmuseum, Essen 03375

Bermuda
Carriage Museum, Saint George's 03858

Canada
Clegg's Museum of Horse-Drawn Vehicles, Hamiota 05035
Remington-Alberta Carriage Centre, Cardston 04665

Czech Republic
Vagonářské Muzeum, Studénka 07650

Denmark
Slesvigske Vognsamling - Dansk Vognmuseum, Haderslev 07836
Sparresholm Vognsamling, Holme-Olstrup 07871

Egypt
Royal Carriage Museum, Bulaq-el-Dakrur 08199

France
Musée des Carrosses, Versailles 13933

Musée National de la Voiture et du Tourisme, Compiègne 10184

Germany
Fürst Thurn und Taxis Marstallmuseum, Regensburg 18094
Hessisches Kutschen- und Wagenmuseum, Lohfelden 17131
Kutschen-, Schlitten- und Wagenmuseum Rottach-Egern, Rottach-Egern 18248
Kutschenmuseum, Gaildorf 15891
Kutschenmuseum Hessisches Landgestüt, Dillenburg 15331
Kutschensammlung, Eigeltingen 15522
Marstallmuseum, München 17486
Museum für Kutschen, Chaisen, Karren, Heidenheim an der Brenz 16347
Museum Kutschen-Wagen-Karren, Gescher 15957
Pferde- und Kutschenmuseum, Chieming 15199
Werksmuseum Achse, Rad und Wagen, Wiehl 19094

Italy
Museo del Biroccio, Filottrano 21568
Museo delle Carozze dell'Ottocento, Verona 22840
Museo delle Carrozze, Firenze 21607
Museo delle Carrozze Mario D'Alessandro Marchese di Civitanova, Napoli 22015
Museo Etnografico G. Pitré, Palermo 22112

Netherlands
Agrarisch en Wagenmuseum, De Waal 24877
Kinderwagens van toen, Dwingeloo 24977
Het Koetshuis, Den Haag 24902
Nationaal Rijtuigmuseum, Leek 25220
Oudheidkamer Zijpe, Schagerbrug 25466

Portugal
Museu Nacional dos Coches, Lisboa 27405

Spain
Museo de Carrozas, Madrid 29265

Sweden
Eriksborg Vagnmuseum, Ystad 30489
Livrustkammaren, Stockholm 30358
Vagnmuseet, Malmö 30228

Switzerland
Kutschensammlung Robert Sallmann, Amriswil 30523

United Kingdom
Arlington Court, Arlington 32063
Tyrwhitt-Drake Museum of Carriages, Maidstone 33878

U.S.A.
Cheyenne Frontier Days Old West Museum, Cheyenne 35994

Vatican City
Museo Padiglione delle Carozza, Città del Vaticano 41401

Cartography

Austria
Dokumentationraum Georg Matthäus Vischer, Aigen bei Raabs 01647
Globenmuseum der Österreichischen Nationalbibliothek, Wien 02859
Peter Anich-Museum, Oberperfuss 02360
Vermessungskundliche Sammlung, Linz 02234

Belgium
Mercator Museum, Sint-Niklaas 03719

Brazil
Museu do Colono, Santa Leopoldina 04097

Colombia
Museo de Desarollo Urbano de Bogotá, Santafé de Bogotá 06900

India
Survey Museum, Roorkee 20406

Netherlands
Van de Poll-Stichting, Zeist 25675
Witte's Museum, Axel 24782

Slovenia
Zemljepišni Muzej Slovenije, Ljubljana 28360

Switzerland
Alpineum, Luzern 30970
Gletschergarten, Luzern 30974

United Kingdom
American Museum in Britain, Bath 32153

Carts → Carriages and Carts

Carving, Wood → Wood Carving

Castles and Fortresses

Australia
Fort Scratchley Museum, Newcastle 01307

Austria
Barockjagdschloß Eckartsau, Eckartsau 01777
Befestigungsanlagen von Thunau, Gars am Kamp 01857
Burg Greifenstein, Greifenstein 01933
Burgenkundliches Museum des Steirischen Burgenvereins, Bärnbach 01723
Burgenmuseum Kranichberg, Gloggnitz 01877
Burgmuseum, Güssing 01964
Burgmuseum, Seebenstein 02631
Burgmuseum Clam, Klam 02125
Emperor Maximilian of Mexico Museum, Hardegg 01998
Festung Kniepaß, Unken 02724
Festungsmuseum, Salzburg 02515
Franzensburg, Laxenburg 02189
Gschlößl Leithaprodersdorf-Freilichtanlage, Leithaprodersdorf 02195
Hengistburgmuseum, Hengsberg 02016
Museum Burg Heidenreichstein, Heidenreichstein 02008
Paul Anton Keller-Museum, Lockenhaus 02239
Renaissance Schloss Greillenstein, Röhrenbach 02499
Rittersaalmuseum, Kirchbichl 02103
Sammlungen Burg Bernstein, Bernstein, Burgenland 01728
Sammlungen der Burg Hochosterwitz, Launsdorf 02185
Schloß Naudersberg, Nauders 02327
Schloß Tratzberg mit Sammlungen, Jenbach 02080
Schloßmuseum, Herberstein 02018
Schloßmuseum Rosenburg, Rosenburg am Kamp 02508

Azerbaijan
State Historical and Architectural Museum-preserve Shirvan Shah's Palace, Baku 03035

Bangladesh
Lala Bagh Fort Museum, Dhaka 03054

Belgium
Château de Beloeil, Beloeil 03172
Château de Rixensart, Rixensart 03675
Collection du Château des Princes, Chimay 03323
Musée Baillet-Latour, Latour 03524
Musée de la Chasse, de la Vénerie et de la Protection de la Nature, Lavaux-Sainte-Anne 03525
Musée du Château-Fort, Ecaussinnes-Lalaing 03365
Musée et Parc Archéologiques de Montauban, Buzenol 03311
Stedelijk Museum, Oudenburg 03655

Canada
Bastion, Nanaimo 05423
Castle Hill National Historic Park, Placentia 05605
Château Logue, Maniwaki 05267
Craigdarroch Castle Historical Museum, Victoria 06193
Fort-Numéro-Un de la Pointe-de-Lévy, Québec 05665
Fort Point Museum, La Have 05167
Fort Saint Joseph National Historic Park, Saint Joseph Island 05828
Fort Selkirk, Whitehorse 06265
Fortress of Louisbourg, Louisbourg 05244
Musée du Fort Saint-Jean, Saint-Jean 05795
Old Fort Erie, Niagara Falls 05462
Old Fort William Historical Park, Thunder Bay 06020
Prince of Wales Fort, Churchill 04713

China, People's Republic
Nan Yue Wang Palace Museum, Guangzhou 06549
Pu Ti Temple, Chengde 06496

Czech Republic
Helfštybon Hrad, Týn nad Bečvou 07678
Kinski Castle, Chlumec nad Cidlinou 07293
Muzeum Betlémů, Karlštejn 07388
Náprstek Museum of Asian, African and American Cultures, Liběchov 07431
Švihov Hrad, Švihov 07653
Svojanov Hrad, Polička 07540
Zámecké Muzeum, Opava 07506
Zámek, Hradec nad Moravicí 07352
Zámek, Nové Město nad Metují 07488
Zámek, Vrchotovy Janovice 07709
Zámek Brandýs, Brandýs nad Labem 07246
Zámek Libochovice, Libochvice 07434
Zámek Ličkov, Žatec 07721
Zámek Lysice, Lysice 07452
Zámek Nelahozeves, Nelahozeves 07479
Zámek Sychrov, Sychrov 07655
Zámek Velké Březno, Velké Březno 07693
Zámek Veltrusy, Veltrusy 07697
Zámek Vizovice, Vizovice 07702

Denmark
Borgmuseum, Spøttrup 08062
Jægerspris Slot, Jægerspris 07892
Kronborg Slot, Helsingør 07849
Liselund Gamle Slot, Borre 07773

Palæsamlingerne, Roskilde 08024
Rosenholm Slot, Hornslet 07878
Voergård Slot, Dronninglund 07785

Egypt
Abdeen Palace Museum, Cairo 08200

Finland
Kastleholm Castle, Sund 08906
Linnoitusmuseo, Hanko 08332
Olavinlinna Castle, Olavinlinna 08727
Suomenlinna-Museo, Helsinki 08389
Suomenlinna-Sveaborg, Helsinki 08390
Turun Kaupungin Historiallinen Museo, Turun Linna, Turku 08972

France
Château, Arlay 09241
Château Beaufief, Mazeray 11691
Château de Messilhac, Raulhac 12702
Château de Montmuran, Les Iffs 11326
Château de Rochefort-en-Terre, Rochefort-en-Terre 12790
Château de Talcy, Marchenoir 11586
Château-Musée, Carrouges 09883
Château-Musée, Nemours 12063
Château-Musée d'Art Populaire et Religieux, Clermont (Haute-Savoie) 10134
Château-Musée de Vollore, Vollore-Ville 14077
Château-Musée des Ducs, Duras 10390
Château-Musée du Suscinio, Sarzeau 13412
Château-Musée et Ecuries de Chaumont-sur-Loire, Chaumont-sur-Loire 10063
Château-Musée Mansart, Sagonne 12871
Collections du Château du Breil de Foin, Genneteil 10650
Exposition du Château Fort du Fleckenstein, Lembach 11293
Mini-Château, Amboise 09143
Musée-Château de Haute-Goulaine, Haute-Goulaine 10797
Musée-Château de La Verrerie, Oizon 12181
Musée d'Art et d'Histoire, Schirmeck 13467
Musée des Plans et Reliefs, Paris 12384
Musée du Château, Dinan 10338
Musée du Château, Noirmoutier-en-l'Ile 12145
Musée du Château, Torigni-sur-Vire 13701
Musée du Château de Vincennes, Vincennes 14057
Musée du Château et des Anciennes Écuries, Montbard 11836
Musée du Manoir d'Argentelles, Villebadin 13981
Musée du Tire-Bouchon, Ménerbes 11711
Musée du Vieux Cravant, Cravant-les-Côteaux 10256
Musée National des Châteaux de Versailles et de Trianon, Versailles 13935
Musée National du Château de Fontainebleau, Fontainebleau 10570
Musée National du Château de Pau, Pau 12470

Germany
Allgäuer Burgenmuseum, Kempten 16714
Altes Schloß Schleißheim, Sammlung zur Landeskunde Ost- und Westpreußens, Oberschleißheim 17794
Bergisches Museum Schloß Burg, Solingen 18521
Bettina und Achim von Arnim Museum, Wiepersdorf bei Jüterbog 19096
Burg Lauenstein, Ludwigsstadt 17159
Burg Mildenstein, Leisnig 17067
Burg Pappenheim mit Naturmuseum und Historischen Museum, Pappenheim 17935
Burg Prunn, Riedenburg 18165
Burg Trausnitz, Landshut 16950
Burg Trifels, Annweiler 14289
Burg- und Klosteranlage Oybin, Kurort Oybin 16916
Burg Zwernitz, Wonsees 19196
Burgenmuseum Eisenberg, Eisenberg, Allgäu 15534
Burgmuseum, Höhr-Grenzhausen 16449
Burgmuseum, Kirschau 16754
Burgmuseum, Lisberg 17123
Burgmuseum, Ortenberg, Hessen 17863
Burgmuseum Burg Guttenberg, Haßmersheim 16301
Burgmuseum der Wasserburg Kapellendorf, Kapellendorf 16639
Burgmuseum Grünwald, Grünwald 16130
Burgmuseum Marksburg, Braubach 15023
Dornburger Schlösser, Dornburg, Saale 15369
Ellermeiers Burgmannshof, Hardegsen 16289
Felsenburg Neurathen, Lohmen, Sachsen 17133
Festung Königstein, Königstein, Sächsische Schweiz 16829
Festung Marienberg mit Museum im Fürstenbau, Würzburg 19215
Die Festung Rosenberg - Deutsches Festungsmuseum, Kronach 16882
Festung Wilhelmstein im Steinhuder Meer, Wunstorf 19233
Festungs- und Waffengeschichtliches Museum, Philippsburg 17983
Fürst Thurn und Taxis Schloßmuseum - Museum Kreuzgang, Regensburg 18095
Herzogschloss, Celle 15184
Historische Wehranlage, Mühlhausen, Thüringen 17431
Historisches Kabinett Burgruine Eckartsburg, Eckartsberga 15488
Kaiserburg Nürnberg, Nürnberg 17746
Kaiserpfalzruine, Gelnhausen 15920
Königshaus am Schachen und Alpengarten, Garmisch-Partenkirchen 15898

Ceramics → Porcelain and Ceramics

Chemistry

China (Porcelain) → Porcelain and Ceramics

Cigarettes → Tobacco

Cinematography

Laurel and Hardy Museum, Ulverston 34710

Uruguay
Galeria de Cinemateca, Montevideo 34929

U.S.A.
American Advertising Museum, Portland 39565
The American Film Institute, Los Angeles 38133
The Andy Warhol Museum, Pittsburgh 39459
Ben Keley Art Museum and Pacific Film Archive, Berkeley 35456
Birthplace of John Wayne, Winterset 41258
Film Forum - Film Archives, Collingswood 36175
Hollywood Studio Museum, Hollywood 37462
The Jimmy Stewart Museum, Indiana 37584
McLarty Treasure Museum, Vero Beach 40857
Martin and Osa Johnson Safari Museum, Chanute 35911
Yesteryear Museum, Whippany 41162

Yugoslavia
Muzej Jugoslavenska Kinoteka, Beograd 41516

Circus → Performing Arts

Clocks and Watches → Horology

Clothing and Dress

Argentina
Museo Criollo de los Corrales, Buenos Aires 00153
Museo Nacional de la Histórico del Traje, Buenos Aires 00220

Australia
Benalla Costume and Pioneer Museum, Benalla 00782
Yesteryear Costume Gallery, Ororoo 01337

Belgium
Fashion Museum, Hasselt 03447
Musée du Costume et de la Dentelle, Bruxelles 03288
Poldermuseum, Antwerpen 03127

Brazil
Museo Municipal Barão de Santo Angelo, Rio Pardo 04082

Canada
Costume Museum of Canada, Dugald 04814
Ermatinger, Sault Sainte Marie 05882
Musée Marsil, Saint-Lambert 05830
Ukrainian Catholic Women's League Museum, Edmonton 04853
Ukrainian Museum of Canada, Vancouver 06167
Ukrainian Museum of Canada - Manitoba Branch, Winnipeg 06324
Ukrainian Museum of Canada - Ontario Branch, Toronto 06098

Colombia
Museo Trajes Regionales de Colombia, Cartago 06842

Côte d'Ivoire
Musée National du Costume, Grand Bassam 06957

Croatia
Etnografski Muzej, Zagreb 07100
Etnografski Muzej Split, Split 07070

Czech Republic
Expozice Historického Nábytku 16.-19. a Oděvů 19. Století, Turnov 07676
Klobouřnické Muzeum, Nový Jičín 07492

Denmark
Brede Værk, Lyngby 07961
Fanø Skibsfarts- og Dragtsamling, Fanø 07805

Ethiopia
City Museum, Makale 08286

Finland
Helsinge Hembygdsmuseum, Vantaa 09015
Nukke- ja Pukumuseo, Tampere 08928
Suomen Kansallispukukeskus, Jyväskylä 08441

France
Château Beaufief, Mazeray 11691
Ecomusée du Pays de Montfort, Montfort-sur-Meu 11869
Musée d'Allauch, Allauch 09122
Musée de la Bonneterie, Troyes 13791
Musée de la Mode et du Textile, Paris 12342
Musée Départemental Breton, Quimper 12688
Musée des Arts et Traditions Populaires du Terroir Marseillais, Château-Gombert 10015
Musée du Costume, Château-Chinon 10012
Musée du Costume Trégor-Goëlo, Paimpol 12237
Musée du Folklore et du Vieux Moulin, Moulins (Allier) 11967
Musée du Vieux Honfleur, Honfleur 10828
Musée Galliéra, Paris 12409
Musée Pyrénéen, Lourdes 11478
Pavillon des Arts, Paris 12453

Germany
Deutsches Phonomuseum, Sankt Georgen im Schwarzwald 18305
Fächerkabinett, Bielefeld 14898
Geburtshaus Levi Strauss Museum Jeans und Kult, Buttenheim 15165
Heimat- und Miedermuseum Heubach, Heubach, Württemberg 16415
Heimatmuseum Stade, Stade 18560
Hüttenberger Heimatmuseum, Linden, Hessen 17114
Kostüm-Museum im neuen Schloß Schleißheim, Oberschleißheim 17797
Lippisches Landesmuseum, Detmold 15312
Modemuseum, München 17488
Museum der Deutschen Spielzeugindustrie, Neustadt bei Coburg 17681
von Parish-Kostümbibliothek, München 17507
Regionales Heimatmuseum für das Renchtal, Oppenau 17854
Rheinisches Industriemuseum, Ratingen 18069
Schwarzwälder Trachtenmuseum, Haslach 16299
Siebenbürgisches Museum Gundelsheim, Gundelsheim, Württemberg 16143
Siebenbürgisches Museum Gundelsheim, Gundelsheim, Württemberg 16144
Trachten- und Heimatmuseum, Weiltingen 18981
Trachten- und Heimatstuben, Thierhaupten 18707
Trachtenmuseum, Ochsenfurt 17815
Tuchmuseum Lennep der Anna-Hardt-Stiftung, Remscheid 18137
Württembergisches Trachtenmuseum, Pfullingen 17981

Greece
Ethnological and Folklore Museum, Chios 19432
Folklore and Ethnological Museum of Macedonia and Thrace, Thessaloniki 19672
Folklore Museum, Karditsa 19497
Folklore Museum, Xanthi 19707
Folklore Museum of Thrace, Komotini 19529
Monastery of the Archangel Michael Panormitis, Chora 19435
Nafplion Folklore Museum, Nafplion 19586

Guadeloupe
Musée Municipal de Saint-Barthélemy, Saint-Barthélemy 19740

Hungary
Szombathelyi Képtár, Szombathely 20052

Iceland
Heimilisiðnaðarsafnið Halldórustofa, Blönduós 20087

India
Bharatiya Adim Jati Sevak Sangh Museum, Delhi 20209

Iraq
Baghdad Museum, Baghdad 20668

Ireland
Pighouse Collection, Cornafean 20726

Italy
Casa di Goldoni, Venezia 22789
Galleria del Costume, Firenze 21593
Museo Civico, Amalfi 21057
Museo dei Costumi e Tradizioni locali, Gurro 21732
Museo del Cappello, Alessandria 21049
Museo della Donna, Merano 21878
Museo della Sindone, Torino 22677
Museo Stibbert, Firenze 21626

Japan
Fuzoku Hakubutsukan, Kyoto 23216
Kobe Fashion Museum, Kobe 23163
Sugino Gakuen Isho Hakubutsukan, Tokyo 23674

Jordan
Jordan Folklore and Jewelry Museum, Amman 23797

Korea, Republic
Korean Museum of Contemporary Clothing, Seoul 23932

Malaysia
Museum of Traditional Custumes, Alor Gajah 24277

Mexico
Museo Charrería, Toluca 24513
Museo de la Indumentaria Luis Márquez Romay, México 24441
Museo Serfín de Indumentaria Indígena, México 24475

Netherlands
Drenthe's Veste Stedelijk Museum, Coevorden 24867
Hidde Nijland Museum, Hindeloopen 25164
Huizer Klederdrachtmuseum, Huizen 25188
Kostuummuseum De Gouden Leeuw, Noordlohn 25333
Museum Scheveningen, Den Haag 24913
Politie-Petten Museum, Slochteren 25498
Streekmuseum Ommen, Ommen 25351
Veluws Klederdrachtenmuseum, Epe 25029
Zeeuws Poppen- en Klederdrachten Museum, Zoutelande 25688

New Zealand
Gore Historical Museum and Hokonui Heritage Research Centre, Gore 25797

Norway
Setesdalsmuseet, Rysstad 26276

Philippines
Museum of Philippine Costumes, Manila 26560

Poland
Muzeum w Jarosławiu, Jarosław 26751

Portugal
Museu Nacional do Traje, Lisboa 27404

Russia
Muzej Etnografičeskogo Kostjuma na Kuklach, Moskva 27861

South Africa
Africana Museum, Uitenhage 28632
Bernberg Fashion Museum, Johannesburg 28506
Weenen Museum, Weenen 28641

Spain
Colección de la Casa de Alba, Epila 29039

Sweden
Livrustkammaren, Stockholm 30358

Turkey
Etnografi Müzesi, Antalya 31671
Konya Etnografi Müzesi, Konya 31789

United Kingdom
Bexhill Museum of Costume and Social History, Bexhill-on-Sea 32234
Burton Court, Eardisland 32869
Cavalcade of Costume, Blandford Forum 32305
Chertsey Museum, Chertsey 32594
Churchill House Museum and Hatton Gallery, Hereford 33252
Gallery of Costume, Manchester 33885
Hollytrees Museum, Colchester 32654
Horsham Museum, Horsham 33293
Mansfield Costume Study Centre, Colchester 32655
Museum of Costume, Bath 32165
Museum of Costume, New Abbey 34006
Museum of Costume and Textiles, Nottingham 34097
Nidderdale Museum, Harrogate 33199
Paulise de Bush Costume Collection, Broadclyst 32415
Provost Skene's House, Aberdeen 31989
Royal Ceremonial Dress Collection, London 33761
Saint John's House, Warwick 34751
Totnes Costume Museum, Totnes 34687
Vina Cooke Museum of Dolls and Bygone Childhood, Newark-on-Trent 34020

U.S.A.
First Ladies of Texas Historic Costumes Collection, Denton 36460
The Hermitage, Ho-Ho-Kus 37444
Kent State University Museum, Kent 37776
Mount Mary College Costume Museum, Milwaukee 38521
Museum at the Fashion Institute of Technology, New York 38905
Museum of Vintage Fashion, Lafayette 37874
Philadelphia Mummers Museum, Philadelphia 39402
Reynolda House, Winston-Salem 41252

Coaches → Carriages and Carts

Coffee → Tea and Coffee

Coins → Numismatics

Cookery → Baking and Cookery

Copper

Australia
Geralka Rural Farm, Spalding 01464

Netherlands
Koperslagersmuseum Van de Beele, Horst 25181

Spain
Calcografia Nacional, Madrid 29232

Cosmetics

Bulgaria
Kazanlăshka Roza, Kazanlăk 04211

Canada
Perfume Museum, Niagara-on-the-Lake 05469

France
Château-Promenade des Parfums, Chilleurs-aux-Bois 10097
Musée de la Parfumerie, Paris 12345
Musée de la Parfumerie Fragonard, Grasse 10717
Musée de la Parfumerie Fragonard, Paris 12346
Musée de la Parfumerie Galimard, Grasse 10718
Musée International de la Parfumerie, Grasse 10720

Germany
4711-Museum, Köln 16779
Parfum-Flacon-Museum, München 17506
Wella Museum, Darmstadt 15273

Spain
Museu del Perfum, Barcelona 28808

Switzerland
Parfummuseum, Hochfelden 30873
Schweizer Kamm-Museum, Mümliswil 31029

Costume → Clothing and Dress

Crafts → Handicraft

Criminology

Argentina
División Museo e Investigaciones Históricas de la Policía Federal, Buenos Aires 00138
Museo de Gendarmería Nacional, Buenos Aires 00168
Museo de la Policía del Chaco, Resistencia 00499
Museo Histórico de la Policía de la Provincia de Misiones, Posadas 00475
Museo Histórico de la Policia de Mendoza, Mendoza 00430
Museo Histórico Policial de La Plata, La Plata 00385
Museo Penitenciario Argentino, Buenos Aires 00230

Australia
Adelaide Gaol, Thebarton 01529
Bridgetown Old Gaol Museum, Bridgetown 00824
Fremantle Prison Precinct, Fremantle 01023
Gladstone Gaol, Gladstone, South Australia 01042
Hay Gaol Museum, Hay 01081
Justice and Police Museum, Sydney 01496
Old Dubbo Gaol, Dubbo 00979
Old Gaol and Courthouse, York 01629
Old Gaol Museum and Patrick Taylor Cottage Museum, Albany 00713
Old Jail House, Croydon 00945
Old Melbourne Gaol and Penal Museum, Melbourne 01228
Old Police Station Museum Brookton, Brookton 00843
Police Station and Courthouse, Auburn 00744
Police Station Museum, Mount Barker 01271
Port Arthur Historic Site, Port Arthur 01372
Queensland Police Museum, Brisbane 00833
Richmond Gaol Museum, Richmond, Tasmania 01414
Roebourne Old Gaol Museum, Roebourne 01423
South Australian Police Museum, Thebarton 01530
Stuart Town Gaol Museum, Alice Springs 00728

Austria
Museum des Instituts für gerichtliche Medizin, Wien 02913
Museum für Rechtsgeschichte, Pöggstall 02411
Museum Pfleggerichtshaus, Abfaltersbach 01633
Österreichisches Kriminalmuseum, Scharnstein 02604
Wiener Kriminalmuseum, Wien 02971

Belgium
Centre d'Histoire et de Traditions de la Gendarmerie, Bruxelles 03244
Politiemuseum Oudaan, Antwerpen 03128

Brazil
Museu Biblioteca da Academia de Polícia, Rio de Janeiro 04008
Museu da Companhia Independente do Palácio Guanabara, Rio de Janeiro 04015

Canada
Calgary Police Service Interpretive Centre, Calgary 04625
Correctional Service of Canada Museum, Kingston 05133
Fort Saskatchewan Museum, Fort Saskatchewan 04913
Halifax Police Museum, Halifax 05010
Metropolitan Toronto Police Museum and Discovery Centre, Toronto 06070
Old Carleton County Court House, Woodstock 06338
Ontario Police College Museum, Aylmer 04486
Rotary Museum of Police and Corrections, Prince Albert 05654
Royal Canadian Mounted Police Museum, Regina 05710
Royal Newfoundland Constabulary Museum, Saint John's 05821
Vancouver Police Centennial Museum, Vancouver 06172
Winnipeg Police Museum, Winnipeg 06329

Wood Mountain Ranch and Rodeo Museum, Wood Mountain 06335

China, People's Republic
Police Museum, Hong Kong 06591

Denmark
Fængselshiststoriske Museum, Horsens 07880
Ribe Raadhussamling, Ribe 08013

Egypt
Criminology Museum, Abbasieh 08186
National Police Museum and Ancient Police Museum, Cairo 08227

France
Musée des Collections Historiques de la Préfecture de Police, Paris 12380

Germany
Bayerisches Strafvollzugsmuseum, Kaisheim 16627
Heimatmuseum, Bernau bei Berlin 14871
Historiengewölbe, Rothenburg ob der Tauber 18239
Historische Lochgefängnisse im Alten Rathaus, Nürnberg 17743
Mittelalterliches Kriminalmuseum, Rothenburg ob der Tauber 18241
Polizeihistorische Sammlung Berlin, Berlin 14828
Strafvollzugsmuseum, Ludwigsburg, Württemberg 17149
Zollmuseum, Wegscheid 18948
Zollmuseum Friedrichs, Aachen 14170

India
Jail Training School Museum, Lucknow 20343

Indonesia
Museum Kepolisian Negara Republik Indonesia, Jakarta 20507

Iran
Crime Museum, Teheran 20644

Ireland
Garda Museum, Dublin 20740
Kilmainham Gaol and Museum, Dublin 20748

Italy
Museo Criminologico, Roma 22362
Museo Storico dell'Arma dei Carabinieri, Roma 22415

Japan
Meiji Daigaku Keiji Hakubutsukan, Tokyo 23634

Madagascar
Musée de la Gendarmerie, Toamasina 24270

Malaysia
Muzium Polis Diraja Malaysia, Kuala Lumpur 24303
Sarawak Police Museum, Kuching 24312

Malta
The Old Prison, Victoria 24354

Netherlands
Museum de Gevangenpoort, Den Haag 24909
Museum 't Gevang, Doetinchem 24948
Museum van de Koninklijke Marechaussee, Buren, Gelderland 24862
Nederlands Politie Museum, Apeldoorn 24754
Politiemuseum, Den Haag 24922
Politiemuseum, Zaandam 25668

New Zealand
New Zealand Police Museum, Porirua 25873

Norway
Aurland Bygdetun, Aurland 26019
Trondheim Politimuseum, Trondheim 26354

Philippines
Manila Police Department Museum, Manila 26553

Russia
Muzej Istorii Milicii, Sankt-Peterburg 28054

South Africa
South African Police Service Museum, Pretoria 28595

Spain
Museo de la Escuela General de Policía, Madrid 29269

Sweden
Polishistoriska Museet, Stockholm 30373
Polistekniska Museet, Solna 30326

Switzerland
Kriminalmuseum der Kantonspolizei Zürich, Zürich 31451
Polizeimuseum, Aarau 30496

United Kingdom
Bath Police Museum, Bath 32155
Beaumaris Gaol and Courthouse, Beaumaris 32184
City of London Police Museum, London 33616
Dover Old Town Goal, Dover 32804
Essex Police Museum, Chelmsford 32585
Fire Police Museum, Sheffield 34457
Gloucester Prison Museum, Gloucester 33113
Grampian Police Museum, Aberdeen 31985
Greater Manchester Police Museum, Manchester 33886
HM Prison Service Museum, Rugby 34336
Inveraray Jail, Inveraray 33322
Jedburgh Castle Jail Museum, Jedburgh 33348
Kent Police Museum, Chatham 32576
Metropolitan Police Hospital Museum, London 33709
Mounted Branch Museum, East Molesey 32883
Ripon Prison and Police Museum, Ripon 34312
Sherlock Holmes Museum, London 33780
South Wales Police Museum, Bridgend 32375
Stirling Old Town Jail, Stirling 34566
Tales of the Old Gaol House, King's Lynn 33391
Tetbury Police Museum, Tetbury 34655
Thames Police Museum, London 33793
Tolhouse Museum and Brass Rubbing Centre, Great Yarmouth 33159
West Midlands Police Museum, Birmingham 32281

U.S.A.
Cleveland Police Museum, Cleveland 36130
Houston Police Museum, Houston 37515
Law Enforcement Museum, Roselle 39867
New York City Police Museum, New York 38924
Old Fire House and Police Museum, Superior 40583
The Old Jail Museum, Crawfordsville 36312
The Old Jail Museum, Warrenton 40935
The Old Lincoln County Jail and Museum, Wiscasset 41267
Old Prison Museum, Deer Lodge 36437
Porter County Old Jail Museum, Valparaiso 40834
Yuma Territorial Prison Museum, Yuma 41346

Dairy Products

Denmark
Hjedding Mejerimuseum, Ølgod 08000

Finland
Meijerimuseo, Saukkola 08865

France
Musée du Bocage Normand, Saint-Lô 13108

Germany
Carl-Hirnbein-Museum, Missen-Wilhams 17376
Heimatmuseum Hüttenberg, Hüttenberg 16525
Historische Käsküche, Wiggensbach 19112
Molkerei-Museum, Bernbeuren 14872
Trützschler's Milch- und Reklamemuseum, Hildburghausen 16421

Netherlands
Kaasboerderijmuseum de Weistaar, Maarsbergen 25264

South Africa
Riemland Museum, Heilbron 28495

Switzerland
Milchwirtschaftliches Museum, Kiesen 30889

United Kingdom
National Dairy Museum, Ashurst 32085

Dance → Performing Arts

Decorative and Applied Arts

Algeria
Musée Folklorique de Ghardaia, Ghardaia Oasis 00057

Argentina
Fundación Banco Francés, Buenos Aires 00140
Museo Almacén El Recreo, Chivilcoy 00267
Museo Folklórico Regional de Humahuaca, Humahuaca 00356
Museo Nacional de Arte Decorativo, Buenos Aires 00217
Museo Patria Chica, Realicó 00496
Museo Tornambe de la Universidad Nacional de San Juan, San Juan 00565
Palais de Glace, Buenos Aires 00242

Armenia
State History Museum of Armenia, Erevan 00683

Australia
Johnston Collection, East Melbourne 00986
Powerhouse Museum, Ultimo 01557

Austria
Bardeau'sches Kultur- und Ausstellungszentrum, Feldbach 01816
Heimatmuseum Egg, Egg 01781
Kulturhistorische Sammlung, Graz 01913
Sammlung Bodingbauer, Steyr 02662
Sammlung der Universität für angewandte Kunst Wien mit Oskar Kokoschka Zentrum, Wien 02951
Schloß Loosdorf mit Prunkräumen und Zinnfigurensammlung, Loosdorf, Bez. Mistelbach 02245
Schloß Moosham, Tamsweg 02684

Azerbaijan
State Museum of Azerbaijan Carpets and Applied Art Letif Kerimov, Baku 03036

Belgium
Espace des Saveurs, Herve 03464
Gruuthusemuseum, Brugge 03213
Maagdenhuismuseum, Antwerpen 03108
Maison du Roi, Bruxelles 03254
Musée d'Ansembourg, Liège 03543
Musées Royaux d'Art et d'Histoire, Bruxelles 03306
Stedelijk Museum Ieper, Ieper 03486

Brazil
Açude Museum, Rio de Janeiro 03989
Museu de Arte Popular da Fortaleza dos Reis Magos, Natal 03958
Museu Henriqueta Catharino, Salvador 04096

Bulgaria
Nacionalen Muzej na Dekorativno-priložnite Izkustva, Sofia 04326
Nacionalen Panair i Izložba na Narodnite Chudožestveni Zanajati i Priložnite Izkustva, Selo Orešak 04284

Canada
Canadian Craft and Design Museum, Vancouver 06145
Joseph Schneider Haus, Kitchener 05156
Musée des Arts Décoratifs de Montréal, Montréal 05382
Museum of Cape Breton Heritage, North East Margaree 05488
Nels Berggran Museum, Imperial 05073
Nova Scotia Centre for Craft and Design, Halifax 05016
Oseredok Ukrainian Art Gallery and Museum, Winnipeg 06311
Pavillon Saint-Arnaud, Trois-Rivières 06120
Prescott House Museum, Port Williams 05640
Ross Memorial Museum, Saint Andrews 05772
Whetung Craft Centre and Art Gallery, Curve Lake 04759

Croatia
Muzej za Umjetnost i Obrt, Zagreb 07119
Zbirka Anke Gvozdanović, Zagreb 07126

Cuba
Museo de Artes Decorativas, La Habana 07146
Museo de Artes Decorativas de Santa Clara, Santa Clara 07177

Cyprus Turk
Decorative Arts Museum, Girne 07220

Czech Republic
Design Centrum České Republiky, Brno 07252
Městské Muzeum, Aš 07231
Městské Muzeum, Chotěboř 07298

Denmark
Det Danske Kunstindustrimuseum, København 07912
Davids Samling, København 07913
Michael og Anna Anchers Hus og Saxilds Gaard, Skagen 08040
Museet for Varde By og Omegn, Varde 08086
Museet på Koldinghus, Kolding 07943
Trapholt, Kolding 07944

Estonia
Tarbekunstimuuseum, Tallinn 08272

Finland
Alvar Aalto Museum, Jyväskylä 08436
Edelfelt-Vallgren Museo, Porvoo 08796
Hiekan Taidemuseo, Tampere 08923
Taideteollisuusmuseo, Helsinki 08392

France
Château de Champchevrier, Cléré-les-Pins 10125
Musée Angladon, Avignon 09357
Musée Anne de Beaujeu, Moulins (Allier) 11965
Musée Arménien de France, Paris 12315
Musée Baccarat, Paris 12318
Musée Baron Gérard, Bayeux 09446
Musée Boucher-de-Perthes, Abbeville 09059
Musée Bouilhet-Christofle, Paris 12321
Musée Bourdelle, Paris 12322
Musée d'Art et d'Histoire, Belfort 09499
Musée de la Chapellerie, Esperaza 10457
Musée de la Vie Romantique, Paris 12354
Musée de l'Eventail, Paris 12360
Musée des Années 30, Boulogne-Billancourt 09661
Musée des Arts décoratifs, Lyon 11520
Musée des Arts Décoratifs, Paris 12378
Musée des Beaux-Arts, Blois 09599
Musée des Beaux-Arts, Reims 12714
Musée du Breuil de Saint-Germain, Langres 11118
Musée du Château, Laas 11072
Musée du Château, Siorac-en-Périgord 13532
Musée-Ecole de Laval, Laval (Mayenne) 11151
Musée Historique, Gourdon (Alpes-Maritimes) 10692
Musée Leblanc-Duvernoy, Auxerre 09342
Musée National des Arts Asiatiques Guimet, Paris 12428
Musée Paul Dupuy, Toulouse 13737
Pavillon des Arts, Paris 12453
Prieuré du Vieux Logis, Nice 12111

Germany
Auto- und Motorrad-Museum, Öhringen 17820
Das Berta-Hummel-Museum im Hummelhaus, Massing 17293
Bröhan-Museum, Berlin 14689
Design Center Stuttgart des Landesgewerbeamtes Baden-Württemberg, Stuttgart 18625
Deutsches Drachenmuseum und Stadtmuseum, Furth im Wald 15878
Deutsches Plakat Museum, Essen 15649
Dreikronenhaus, Osnabrück 17870
Ehemaliges Jagdschloß Bebenhausen, Tübingen 18753
Fürstliches Residenzschloß, Detmold 15310
Fugger-Museum, Babenhausen, Schwaben 14370
Gablonzer Archiv Museum, Kaufbeuren 16693
Galerie Handwerk, München 17470
Gewerbemuseum der LGA im Germanischen Nationalmuseum, Nürnberg 17739
Gotisches Haus, Wörlitz 19165
Grassimuseum Leipzig, Leipzig 17037
Heimatmuseum Scheeßel, Scheeßel 18322
Jugendstilmuseum Reissenweber, Brühl, Baden 15105
Kestner-Museum, Hannover 16273
Krippenmuseum, Glattbach 15986
Krippenstube-Heimatstube, Plößberg 17999
Kunstgewerbemuseum, Dresden 15407
Kunstgewerbemuseum, Berlin 14783
Kunstgewerbemuseum im Schloß Köpenick, Berlin 14784
Kunsthandwerk und Plastik Sammlung, Kassel 16677
Kunstsammlungen der Veste Coburg, Coburg 15209
Maximilianmuseum, Augsburg 14349
Museum beim Markt - Angewandte Kunst seit 1900, Karlsruhe 16652
Museum der Dinge-Werkbundarchiv, Berlin 14800
Museum der Stadt Miltenberg und Porzellansammlung Kreis Dux, Miltenberg 17366
Museum der Stadt Zerbst mit Sammlung Katharina II., Zerbst 19270
Museum für Angewandte Kunst, Frankfurt am Main 15758
Museum für Angewandte Kunst, Gera 15937
Museum für Angewandte Kunst, Köln 16806
Museum für Frühislamische Kunst, Bamberg 14583
Museum für schlesische Landeskunde im Haus Schlesien, Königswinter 16830
Museum Hanau, Hanau 16260
Museum Huelsmann, Bielefeld 14902
Museumsberg Flensburg, Flensburg 15714
Die Neue Sammlung, München 17502
Palais Papius, Wetzlar 19084
Plakatmuseum am Niederrhein, Emmerich 15564
Red Dot Design Museum im Design Zentrum Nordrhein Westfalen, Essen 15661
Residenzmuseum, München 17512
Rokokomuseum Schloß Belvedere, Weimar, Thüringen 18998
Schloß Heidelberg, Heidelberg 16342
Schlossmuseum, Langenburg 16974
Schloßmuseum der Stadt Aschaffenburg, Aschaffenburg 14319
Schloßmuseum Mespelbrunn, Mespelbrunn 17344
Schloßmuseum und Königliches Schloss, Berchtesgaden 14653
Schwäbisches Krippenmuseum im Jesuitenkolleg, Mindelheim 17369
Sebnitzer Kunstblumen- und Heimatmuseum Prof. Alfred Meiche, Sebnitz 18449
Spessartmuseum, Lohr am Main 17135
Stadtmuseum Fembohaus, Nürnberg 17759
Stadtmuseum Haus zum Cavazzen, Lindau, Bodensee 17112
Städtisches Museum, Überlingen 18776
Städtisches Museum, Zeulenroda 19273
Vitra Design Museum, Weil am Rhein 18966
Vitra Design Museum Berlin, Berlin 14862
Werdenfelser Museum, Garmisch-Partenkirchen 15901

Greece
Decorative Arts Collection, Rhodos 19639
Konstandoglou Collection, Athinai 19385
Likion Ton Ellinidon Collection, Rethymnon 19636
Museum of Decorative Arts, Athinai 19403

Hungary
Iparművészeti Múzeum, Budapest 19820

India
Crafts Museum, Delhi 20210
Crafts Museum, Kolkata 20181
Dr. Bhau Daji Lad Museum, Mumbai 20179
Government Central Museum, Jaipur, Rajastan 20280
Raja Dinkar Kelkar Museum, Pune 20389

Indonesia
Museum Batik, Yogyakarta 20605
Museum Radya Pustaka, Surakarta 20589

Iran
Astan-e-Qods-e Razavi Museums, Mashad 20631
Pars Museum, Shiraz 20638

Iraq
Mustansiriya School Collections, Baghdad 20671

Ireland
Glebe House and Gallery, Church Hill 20717
Museum of Decorative Arts and History, Dublin 20751

Israel
L.A. Mayer Museum for Islamic Art, Jerusalem 20919

Italy
Museo Civico d'Arte Antica e Palazzo Madama, Torino 22670
Museo Civico Gaetano Filangieri, Napoli 22013
Museo del Corallo, Torre del Greco 22699
Museo del Presepio, Dalmine 21500
Museo dell'Istituto Statale d'Arte, Napoli 22016
Museo Etnologico Missionario, Fiesole 21565
Museo Orientale Ca' Pesaro, Venezia 22814
Oskar Schlemmer Theatre Estate and Collection, Oggebbio 22063
Palazzo Tozzoni, Imola 21744
Raccolte di Palazzo Tursi, Genova 21703

Japan
Fukuoka-shi Bijutsukan, Fukuoka 22974
Tako no Hakubutsukan, Tokyo 23678
Toyota Municipal Museum of Art, Toyota, Aichi 23723

Korea, Republic
Ewha Yoja Taehakkyo Pakmulgwan, Seoul 23919

Latvia
Dekoratīvi Lietišķās Mākslas Muzejs, Rīga 24062

Lebanon
Moussa Castle Museum, Beiteddine 24144

Luxembourg
Villa Vauban, Luxembourg 24232

Malaysia
Muzium Negeri Kedah, Alor Setar 24280

Mexico
Museo Estudio Diego Rivera, México 24452
Museo Franz Mayer, México 24453
Museo Mural Diego Rivera, México 24457

Netherlands
Amsterdams Historisch Museum, Amsterdam 24678
Centraal Museum Utrecht, Utrecht 25555
Collectie A. Veltman, Bussum 24864
Expositieruimte De Weem, Westeremden 25640
Fogelsangh State, Veenklooster 25582
Frans Hals Museum, Haarlem 25091
Hans van Riessen Museum, Vledderveen, Drente 25602
Historisch Museum Deventer, Deventer 24942
Het Kantenhuis, Amsterdam 24699
Kasteel de Haar, Haarzuilens 25100
Museum Grootmoeders Keuken, Wedde 25627
Museum Het Catharina Gasthuis, Gouda 25065
Museum Simon van Gijn, Dordrecht 24965
Nederlands Tegelmuseum, Otterlo 25373
Oudheidkamer in het Stadhuis, Bolsward 24823
Stedelijk Museum, Alkmaar 24654
Stedelijk Museum Roermond, Roermond 25417
Stedelijk Museum Vianen, Vianen 25594
Stedelijk Museum Zutphen, Zutphen 25697
Streekmuseum Het Rondeel, Rhenen 25404
Het Waaierkabinet, Amsterdam 24744

New Zealand
Dowse Art Museum, Lower Hutt 25823

Norway
Kunstindustrimuseet i Oslo, Oslo 26225
Nordenfjeldske Kunstindustrimuseum, Trondheim 26349
Vestlandske Kunstindustrimuseum, Bergen 26037

Philippines
Bayanihan Folks Arts Center, Manila 26548
Museo ng Kalinangang Pilipino, Manila 26557

Poland
Muzeum Kultury Szlacheckiej, Łopuszna 26903
Muzeum Okręgowe w Toruniu, Toruń 27170
Muzeum Plakatu w Wilanowie, Warszawa 27226
Muzeum Sprzętu Gospodarstwa Domowego, Ziębice 27319
Muzeum Sztuk Użytkowych, Poznań 27029
Muzeum Zamoyskich w Kozłówce, Kamionka 26766
Sztuka Dalekiego Wschodu, Toruń 27172

Portugal
Casa de Vitorino Ribeiro, Porto 27420
Casa Museu Guerra Junqueiro, Porto 27421
Exhibition Centre, Lisboa 27379
Fundação Ricardo do Espírito Santo Silva, Lisboa 27380
Museu-Biblioteca da Fundacão de Casa de Bragança, Vila Viçosa 27450
Museu Calouste Gulbenkian, Lisboa 27385
Museu Condes de Castro Guimarães, Cascais 27348
Museu da Quinta das Cruzes, Funchal 27367
Museu Municipal, Pinhel 27417
Museu Municipal de Chaves, Chaves 27351
Museu Nacional de Machado de Castro, Coimbra 27358
Museu Nacional de Soares dos Reis, Porto 27429
Palácio Nacional de Mafra, Mafra 27412

Romania
Muzeul Hrandt Avakian, Bucureşti 27518
Muzeul Judeţean Argeş, Piteşti 27621

Russia
Coasting Hill Pavilion, Lomonosov 27777
Gosudarstvennyj Chudožestvennyj Muzej Altajskogo Kraja, Barnaul 27698
Gosudarstvennyj Muzej Istorii Sankt-Peterburga, Sankt-Peterburg 28028
Gosudarstvennyj Muzej Zapovednik Petergof, Sankt-Peterburg 28032
Muzej Dekorativno-prikladnogo Iskusstva, Sankt-Peterburg 28049
Muzej Palechskogo Remesla, Palech 27982
Oružejnaja Palata, Moskva 27927
Vserossijskij Muzej Dekorativno-Prikladnogo i Narodnogo Iskusstva, Moskva 27943

South Africa
The Design Museum, Cape Town 28437
Melrose House, Pretoria 28583
Roodepoort Museum, Florida Park 28473
Van Gybland-Oosterhoff Collection, Pretoria 28600

Spain
Centro del Diseño, Bilbao 28851
Museo de la Alhambra, Granada 29117
Museu d'Arts Decoratives, Barcelona 28792
Museu Local d'Artesania Terrissaire, Verdú 29881
Museu Romàntic Can Llopis, Sitges 29732
Palacio Real de Madrid, Madrid 29299

Sweden
Hälsinglands Museum, Hudiksvall 30132
Jämtlands Läns Museum, Östersund 30272
Länsmuseet Halmstad, Halmstad 30119
Örebro Läns Museum, Örebro 30266
Röhsska Museet, Göteborg 30103
Skoklosters Slott, Skokloster 30314
Surahammars Bruksmuseum, Surahammar 30415

Switzerland
Abegg-Stiftung, Riggisberg 31132
Bernisches Historisches Museum, Bern 30604
Collection de la Fondation in memoriam Comtesse Tatiana Zoubov, Genève 30802
Froschmuseum, Münchenstein 31031
Haus zum Kirschgarten, Basel 30566
Heimatmuseum und Buchdruckerstube, Beromünster 30623
Historisches Museum Luzern, Luzern 30976
Musée de Design et d'Arts Appliqués Contemporains, Lausanne 30927
Musée d'Histoire, La Chaux-de-Fonds 30695
Musée Eugène Burnand, Moudon 31025
Musee Suisse Schweizerisches Landesmuseum, Zürich 31460
Museum für Gestaltung Basel, Basel 30576
Museum für Gestaltung Zürich, Zürich 31464
Museum in der Burg Zug, Zug 31403
Museum Lindengut, Winterthur 31403
Rathaussammlung, Stein am Rhein 31284
Stadtmuseum Wil, Wil 31388
Stiftung Dr. Edmund Müller, Beromünster 30625

Turkey
Yildiz Şale, İstanbul 31764

United Kingdom
Alfred Dunhill Museum, London 33578
American Museum in Britain, Bath 32153
Art and Design Gallery, Hatfield 33215
Bantock House, Wolverhampton 34867
Belton House, Grantham 33141
Bolton Museum and Art Gallery, Bolton 32320
Bolton Museum and Art Gallery, Bolton 32321
Brighton Museum and Art Gallery, Brighton 32394
Charleston Collection, Firle 33020
Cheltenham Art Gallery and Museum, Cheltenham 32590
Cleveland Crafts Centre, Middlesbrough 33944
Clocktower Museum, Elsham 32963
Clotworthy Arts Centre, Antrim 32053
Coughton Court, Alcester 32008
Cragside House, Rothbury 34326
Design Museum, London 33629
Dimbola Lodge, Freshwater 33044
Doddington Hall, Doddington 32775
Gawsworth Hall, Macclesfield 33863
Gilbert Collection, London 33647
Guild Gallery, Bristol 32407
Guildhall, Bath 32161
Helena Thompson Museum, Workington 34886
Herbert Art Gallery and Museum, Coventry 32687
Holburne Museum of Art, Bath 32162
Kellie Castle, Pittenweem 34192
Little Holland House, London 33691
Lotherton Hall, Aberford 31994
Manchester City Art Gallery, Manchester 33889
Manor House, Sandford Orcas 34415
Merchant Adventurers' Hall, York 34915
Millennium Galleries, Sheffield 34461
Mompesson House, Salisbury 34409
Museum of Domestic Design and Architecture MODA, Barnet 32137
Museum of Farnham, Farnham 33011
Museum of the Order of Saint John, London 33725
Newark Town Treasures and Art Gallery, Newark-on-Trent 34017
Newby Hall, Ripon 34310
Norton Conyers, Ripon 34311
Palace of Westminster, London 33741
Peckover House, Wisbech 34858
Pickford's House Museum, Derby 32758
Polesden Lacey, Great Bookham 33152
Potter's Museum of Curiosity, Bolventor 32325
Powell-Cotton Museum and Quex House, Birchington 32252
Ragley Hall, Alcester 32009
Royal Museum and Art Gallery, Canterbury 32521
Scolton Manor Museum, Haverfordwest 33220
Speke Hall, Liverpool 33544
Sutton Park, Sutton-on-the-Forest 34620
Tatton Park, Knutsford 33428
Usher Gallery, Lincoln 33522
Victoria and Albert Museum, London 33799
Waddesdon Manor, Waddesdon 34718
Warner Archive, Milton Keynes 33960
West Berkshire Museum, Newbury 34024
West Wycombe Park House, West Wycombe 34786
William Morris Gallery and Brangwyn Gift, London 33810

Uruguay
Museo de Arte Industrial, Montevideo 34934

U.S.A.
The 100th Meridian Museum, Cozad 36306
1890 House-Museum and Center for Victorian Arts, Cortland 36285
Adam Thoroughgood House, Virginia Beach 40872
Alleghany Highlands Arts and Crafts Center, Clifton Forge 36147
American Museum of Straw Art, Long Beach 38110
Ash Lawn-Highland, Charlottesville 35952
Asia Society Galleries, New York 38845
Asian Cultures Museum, Corpus Christi 36278
Astor House Hotel Museum, Golden 37166
Atlantic Wildfowl Heritage Museum, Virginia Beach 40873
The Bard Graduate Center for Studies in the Decorative Arts, Design and Culture, New York 38847
Barnes Foundation, Merion 38437
Batsto Village, Hammonton 37320
Bellamy Mansion Museum of History and Design Arts, Wilmington 41216
The Bennington Museum, Bennington 35445
Bergstrom-Mahler Museum, Neenah 38741
Birks Museum, Decatur 36425
Boscobel Restoration, Garrison 37102
Brunnier Art Museum, Ames 35075
Buccleuch Mansion, New Brunswick 38767
California Heritage Museum, Santa Monica 40208
Campbell House Museum, Saint Louis 39957
The Carole and Barry Kaye Museum of Miniatures, Los Angeles 38139
Cincinnati Art Museum, Cincinnati 36074
The Columbian Museum and Art Center, Wamego 40920
Concord Museum, Concord 36238
Cooper-Hewitt National Design Museum, New York 38860
Coral Gables Merrick House, Coral Gables 36262
Crescent Bend Armstrong-Lockett House and William P. Toms Memorial Gardens, Knoxville 37830
The Dana-Thomas House, Springfield 40451
Daughters of the American Revolution Museum, Washington 40956
Decatur House Museum, Washington 40957
Dedham Historical Museum, Dedham 36433
Deming-Luna Mimbres Museum, Deming 36455
Department of the Treasury Museum, Washington 40958
Edsel and Eleanor Ford House, Grosse Pointe Shores 37279
Edward Dean Museum of Decorative Arts, Cherry Valley 35977
Elbert Hubbard-Roycroft Museum, East Aurora 36599
Fenimore Art Museum, Cooperstown 36257
Festival-Institute Museum, Round Top 39876
Fonthill Museum, Doylestown 36555
Fort Hunter Mansion, Harrisburg 37348
Fred Wolf Jr. Gallery, Philadelphia 39378
Frederic Remington Art Museum, Ogdensburg 39125
Gallier House, New Orleans 38812
Goldstein Museum, Saint Paul 39991
Gomez Foundation for Mill House, Marlboro 38352
Harrison Gray Otis House, Boston 35591
Headley-Whitney Museum, Lexington 38014
Henry B. Plant Museum, Tampa 40626
Herbert and Eileen Bernard Museum, New York 38882
Heritage Center of Lancaster County, Lancaster 37919
Hermann-Grima House, New Orleans 38813
Hillwood Museum, Washington 40972
Hinckley Foundation Museum, Ithaca 37633
Historic Cherry Hill, Albany 35000
Historic Hope Foundation, Windsor 41236
The Historic Indian Agency House, Portage 39551
Historical Society of Saratoga Springs Museum, Saratoga Springs 40223
Houston Museum of Decorative Arts, Chattanooga 35964
Indianapolis Museum of Art, Indianapolis 37598
The John and Mable Ringling Museum of Art, Sarasota 40217
Julian H. Sleeper House, Saint Paul 39995
Kansas Museum of History, Topeka 40702
Kearney Mansion Museum, Fresno 37049
Kelton House Museum Garden, Columbus 36229
Kemerer Museum of Decorative Arts, Bethlehem 35477
Kent State University Museum, Kent 37776
Kimberly Crest House, Redlands 39712
Ladew Topiary Gardens Museum, Monkton 38577
Leigh Yawkey Woodson Art Museum, Wausau 41057
Lemon Hill Mansion, Philadelphia 39387
Liberty Hall, Frankfort 37006
Lightner Museum, Saint Augustine 39921
Loudoun Mansion, Philadelphia 39388
Lower Cape Fear Historical Society Museum, Wilmington 41219
McMinn County Living Heritage Museum, Athens 35205
Manchester Historical Society Museum, Manchester 38293
Massee Lane Gardens, Fort Valley 36970
The Mattatuck Museum of the Mattatuck Historical Society, Waterbury 41027
Maymont, Richmond 39764
Memorial Hall Museum, Deerfield 36440
Middleton Place Foundation, Charleston 35936
Mint Museum of Craft and Design, Charlotte 35949
Montpelier Cultur Arts Center, Laurel 37962
Moody Mansion Museum, Galveston 37090
Morris-Butler House Museum, Indianapolis 37600
Morris-Jumel Mansion, New York 38901
Moses Myers House, Norfolk 39014
Mount Clare Museum House, Baltimore 35323
MSC Forsyth Center Galleries, College Station 36173
Muscatine Art Center, Muscatine 38693
Museum of American Architecture and Decorative Arts, Houston 37517
Museum of Decorative Art, Chicago 36033
Museum of Early Southern Decorative Arts, Winston-Salem 41250
Museum of New Hampshire History, Concord 36245
The Museums of Oglebay Institute, Wheeling 41159
New Visions Gallery, Marshfield 38368
Nichols House Museum, Boston 35600
The Old Stone Jail Museum, Palmyra 39264
Osborn-Jackson House, East Hampton 36613
Owensboro Museum of Fine Art, Owensboro 39225
Parry Mansion Museum, New Hope 38796
Patterson Homestead, Dayton 36401
Pittock Mansion, Portland 39571
The Prairie Museum of Art and History, Colby 36166
Raynham Hall Museum, Oyster Bay 39243
Renfrew Museum, Waynesboro 41075
Riverview at Hobson Grove, Bowling Green 35623
Rockwell Museum of Western Art, Corning 36272
Rockwood Museum, Wilmington 41214
Royal Arts Foundation, Newport 38987
Ruthmere House Museum, Elkhart 36689
Sam Bell Maxey House, Paris 39277
Sanford Museum, Sanford 40172
Schuyler-Hamilton House, Morristown 38638
Stamford Historical Society Museum, Stamford 40477
Stan Hywet Hall and Gardens, Akron 34992
The Stephen Girard Collection, Philadelphia 39414
Sterling and Francine Clark Art Institute, Williamstown 41194
Ten Broeck Mansion, Albany 35004
University of Rochester Memorial Art Gallery, Rochester 39818
The Valentine Museum - Richmond History Center, Richmond 39768
Vance Kirkland Museum, Denver 36486
The Vermont State House, Montpelier 38613
Villa Terrace Decorative Arts Museum, Milwaukee 38524
Visual Arts Gallery, Pensacola 39322
Vizcaya Museum, Miami 38459
Warther Museum, Dover 36549
Webster House Museum, Elkhorn 36691
Wichita Center for the Arts, Wichita 41173
Willoughby-Baylor House, Norfolk 39017
Wilton House Museum, Richmond 39772
Winterthur Museum, Winterthur 41261
The Wolfsonian, Miami Beach 38466

Uzbekistan
Bucharskij Gosudarstvennyj Muzej, Buchara 41358

Yugoslavia
Muzej Primenjene Umetnosti, Beograd 41520

Distilling → Wines and Spirits

Dolls and Puppets

Australia
Heirloom Doll Museum, Airlie Beach 00710
Jerilderie Doll World Museum, Jerilderie 01114

Austria
Badener Puppen- und Spielzeugmuseum, Baden bei Wien 01718
Elli Riehl-Puppenmuseum, Treffen bei Villach 02710
Internationale Puppenausstellung, Sankt Wolfgang im Salzkammergut 02595
Puppen- und Spielzeugmuseum, Wien 02945
Puppenmuseum, Einöde 01791
Puppenmuseum Hintermann, Villach 02733
Puppenmuseum Kärntner Eisenwurzen, Hüttenberg 02048
Waldviertler Puppenmuseum, Waldkirchen 02761
Welser Puppenweltmuseum, Wels 02787

Belgium
Musée Marial de Beauraing, Beauraing 03165

Drawing

Ecology

Economics

Economics

Sweden
Bankmuseet, Stockholm 30335
Tullmuseum, Stockholm 30397

Switzerland
Museo Doganale Svizzero, Gandria 30789

United Kingdom
Robert Opie Collection, Gloucester 33116

U.S.A.
Discovery World - The James Lovell Museum of Science, Economics and Technology, Milwaukee 38513

Education

Albania
Museum of Education, Elbasan 00019
Museum of Education, Korçë 00026

Algeria
Musée du Mont Riant, Alger 00042

Argentina
Eureka - Parque de la Ciencia, Mendoza 00424
Museo de Escuela de Educación Técnica Número 1, Dolores 00319
Museo de la E.E.M. Número 3, Dolores 00320
Museo de los Niños Barrilete, Córdoba 00287
Museo y Centro Estudios Históricos de la Facultad de Odontología, Buenos Aires 00240

Australia
Alumny Creek School Museum, Grafton 01056
Andrew Ross Museum, Kangaroo Ground 01123
Frankston Primary Old School Museum, Frankston 01020
Gloucester School Museum, Gloucester 01048
Hale School Museum, Wembley Downs 01588
The Museum of Nursing, Camperdown 00873
Old School Museum, Merimbula 01237
Saint John's Schoolhouse Museum, Reid 01412
Sir Edgeworth David Memorial Museum, Kurri Kurri 01143
Uleybury School Museum, One Tree Hill 01333

Austria
Archiv der Universität Wien, Schausammlung, Wien 02804
Burgenländisches Schulmuseum, Lockenhaus 02238
Kindermuseum Zoom, Wien 02880
Kinderweltmuseum, Vöcklamarkt 02739
Niederösterreichisches Schulmuseum, Asparn an der Zaya 01681
Volksschulmuseum, Maria Taferl 02263

Azerbaijan
Baku Museum of Education, Baku 03031

Belgium
Stedelijk Onderwijsmuseum Ieper, Ieper 03487

Bulgaria
Muzej na Narodnoto Obrazovanie, Gabrovo 04186

Canada
Alex Youck School Museum, Regina 05694
Algonquin College Museum, Nepean 05436
Athol Murray College of Notre Dame Museum, Wilcox 06273
Bleakhouse Museum, Fogo Island 04893
Brocksden Country School Museum, Stratford 05969
Cape Breton Centre for Heritage and Science, Sydney 05997
Century Schoolhouse, Toronto 06047
Children's Own Museum, Toronto 06048
Darlingford School Heritage Museum, Darlingford 04763
East Coulee School Museum, East Coulee 04823
École du Rang II, Authier 04480
Edmonton Public Schools Museum, Edmonton 04838
Enoch Turner Schoolhouse, Toronto 06052
Frontenac County Schools Museum, Kingston 05135
The Hamilton Children's Museum, Hamilton 05027
King Seaman School Museum, River Herbert 05742
Little School Museum, Lockeport 05222
Little White Schoolhouse, Truro 06122
McCulloch House Museum and Hector Exhibit Centre, Pictou 05599
Manitoba Children's Museum, Winnipeg 06305
Metchosin School Museum, Victoria 06201
Morrison Museum of the Country School, Islay 05087
Musée Acadien du Québec, Bonaventure 04552
Musée du College de Lévis, Lévis 05210
Museum of the North American Indian Travelling College, Cornwall 04738
Old Crofton School Museum, Crofton 04751
Oxford County Museum School, Burgessville 04604
Quinte Educational Museum, Bloomfield 04545
River Valley School Museum, Virden 06210
Rocky Lane School Museum, Fort Vermilion 04916
Sesquicentennial Museum, Toronto 06086
Star Mound School Museum, Snowflake 05940
Tupperville School Museum, Bridgetown 04590
University of Alberta Museums, Edmonton 04856
Victoria School Museum, Carleton Place 04669
Victoria School Museum, Edmonton 04857
Wilson MacDonald Memorial School Museum, Selkirk 05893

Chile
Museo Pedagógico Carlos Stuardo Ortiz, Santiago 06393

China, People's Republic
Central Nation University Museum, Beijing 06430
Children's Museum, Shanghai 06685

China, Republic
National Taiwan Science Education Center, Taipei 06823

Colombia
Museo Colegio de la Salle, Envigado 06847

Croatia
Hrvatski Školski Muzej, Zagreb 07109
Hrvatski Sportski Muzej, Zagreb 07110

Cuba
Museo Nacional de la Campana de Alfabetización, La Habana 07156

Czech Republic
Krkonošské Muzeum, Paseky nad Jizerou 07519
Muzeum Komenského v Přerově, Přerov 07606
Okresní Vlastivědné Muzeum Nový Jičín, Příbor 07608
Pedagogické Muzeum Jana Ámoše Komenského, Praha 07592

Denmark
Børnenens Museum, København 07907
Flakkebjerg Skolemuseum, Slagelse 08053

Egypt
Education Museum, Cairo 08207

Finland
Elimäen Koulumuseo, Elimäki 08311
Jyväskylän Lyseon Museo, Jyväskylä 08437
Jyväskylän Yliopiston Museo, Jyväskylä 08438
Koulumuseo, Helsinki 08362
Lastenmuseo, Helsinki 08366
Saukkojärven Kotiseutu- ja Koulumuseo, Ranua 08825
Suomen Koulumuseo, Tampere 08932

France
Musée de l'Ecole Rurale, Trégarvan 13774
Musée National de l'Éducation, Rouen 12843
Musée Valentin Haüy, Paris 12444

Germany
Altdorfer Universitäts-Museum, Altdorf bei Nürnberg 14228
Bayerisches Schulmuseum, Ichenhausen 16537
Deutsches Museum für Schulkunst, Hagen, Westfalen 16161
Dorfschulmuseum, Ködnitz 16777
Erstes Allgäu-Schwäbisches Dorfschulmuseum, Erkheim 15614
Erstes Bayerisches Schulmuseum, Sulzbach-Rosenberg 18662
Exploratorium - Kindermuseum Stuttgart und Region, Stuttgart 18627
Die Franckeschen Stiftungen zu Halle, Halle, Saale 16186
Fröbelmuseum, Keilhau 16703
Gedenkstätte für C.G. Salzmann und J.C.F. GuthsMuths, Schnepfenthal 18368
Hamburger Schulmuseum, Hamburg 16217
Heimatmuseum Hallstadt, Hallstadt 16202
Heimatstube Wendhausen, Schellerten 18327
Johann-Baptist-Graser-Schulmuseum, Bayreuth 14618
Jugendmuseum Schöneberg, Berlin 14767
Das Junge Museum, Bottrop 15005
Kinder- und Jugendmuseum, München 17477
Kinder- und Jugendmuseum im Prenzlauer Berg, Berlin 14771
Kindermuseum, Frankfurt am Main 15755
Kindermuseum, Wuppertal 19240
Kindermuseum, Karlsruhe 16651
Kindermuseum Hamburg, Hamburg 16223
Kleines Museum - Kinder der Welt, Frankfurt/Oder 15781
Labyrinth Kindermuseum Berlin, Berlin 14789
Landschulmuseum Göldenitz, Göldenitz bei Rostock 16004
Memorialmuseum Friedrich Fröbel, Oberweißbach 17809
Mobiles Kindermuseum im Freizeitheim Vahrenwald, Hannover 16277
Museum im Koffer - Kindermuseum Nürnberg, Nürnberg 17751
Museum Industriekultur mit Motorradmuseum, Schulmuseum und Kinderabteilung, Nürnberg 17752
Museum Kindheit und Jugend, Berlin 14812
Museum zum Anfassen, Ostseebad Binz 17900
Ostfriesisches Schulmuseum Folmhusen, Westoverledingen 19073
Sammlungen des Instituts für Hochschulkunde der Deutschen Gesellschaft für Hochschulkunde, Würzburg 19228
Schlossmuseum Reckahn, Reckahn 18084
Schulgeschichtliche Sammlung, Magdeburg 17218
Schulgeschichtliche Sammlung im Main-Taunus-Kreis, Kriftel 16880
Schulheimatmuseum, Asbach-Bäumenheim 14308
Schulhistorische Sammlung Cruismannschule, Bochum 14944
Schulmuseum, Frankfurt/Oder 15783
Schulmuseum des Bezirks Unterfranken, Bad Bocklet 14403
Schulmuseum Friedrichshafen am Bodensee, Friedrichshafen 15846
Schulmuseum Fronau, Roding 18192
Schulmuseum Lilienthal, Lilienthal 17104
Schulmuseum Mozartschule Rheingönheim, Ludwigshafen am Rhein 17155
Schulmuseum Nordwürttemberg in Kornwestheim, Kornwestheim 16856
Schulmuseum Nürnberg, Nürnberg 17757
Schulmuseum und Hallenhaus, Middelhagen, Rügen 17360
Schulmuseum Vechelde, Vechelde 18818
Schulmuseum - Werkstatt für Schulgeschichte Leipzig, Leipzig 17058
Schulmuseum Wildenhain, Wildenhain bei Großenhain, Sachsen 19114
Stadtmuseum Teterow, Teterow 18697
Städtisches Schulmuseum, Lohr am Main 17136
Theodor-Mommsen-Gedächtnisstätte, Garding 15897
Universitätsmuseum Hohenheim, Stuttgart 18649
Wasserwelt Erlebnismuseum, Ostseebad Binz 17904
Westfälisches Schulmuseum, Dortmund 15388

Greece
Athens University Museum, Athinai 19364
Hellenic Children's Museum, Athinai 19379

Guatemala
Museo Universitario de San Carlos, Guatemala City 19758

Hungary
Országos Pedagógiai Múzeum és Könyvtár, Budapest 19849

India
Bal Sangrahalaya, Lucknow 20337
Children's Museum, Bhavnagar 20167
Government Educational Museum, Etawah 20235
National Children's Museum, Delhi 20214
Nehru Children's Museum, Kolkata 20181
Regional Science Centre, Bhopal 20172
Regional Science Centre and Planetarium, Kozhikode 20181
Regional Science Centre Bhubaneswar, Bhubaneshwar 20174
Shri Girdharbhai Sangrahalaya, Amreli 20151

Ireland
Plunket Museum of Irish Education, Dublin 20759

Italy
Museo per la Storia dell'Università di Pavia, Pavia 22145

Japan
Iwata-shi Kyu Mitsukegakko, Iwata, Shizuoka 23095
Muroran-shi Seishonen Kagakukan, Muroran 23337

Jordan
Children's Heritage and Science Museum, Amman 23791
School Books Museum, Salt 23813

Korea, Republic
Andong Teachers College Museum, Andong 23873
Cheju College Museum, Cheju 23876
Chonbuk University Museum, Chonju 23884
Chonnam University Museum, Kwangju 23902
Dan Kook University Museum, Seoul 23916
Dong-a University Museum, Pusan 23910
Gongju College of Education Museum, Gongju 23890
Hansong Womens College Museum, Seoul 23923
Joongang University Museum, Seoul 23926
Kangreung College Museum, Kangreung 23897
Kookmin College Museum, Seoul 23928
Kwangdong College Museum, Kangreung 23898
Kyongnam College Museum, Masan 23907
Myong Ji University Museum, Seoul 23941
Samsung Children's Museum, Seoul 23946
Sangji Vocational College Museum, Andong 23874
Sejong College Museum, Seoul 23947
Sokang University Museum, Seoul 23949
Songsin Teachers College Museum, Seoul 23950
Sung Kyun Kwan University Museum, Seoul 23955
Taegu National University of Education Museum, Taegu 23961
Won Kwang College Museum, Iri 23893
Yeungnam University Museum, Kyongsan 23906

Lithuania
Museum of Pedagogics, Kaunas 24184

Malaysia
Malaysian Youth Museum, Melaka 24318

Mexico
Antiguo Colegio de San Ildefonso, México 24407
Museo Pedagógico Nacional, México 24472
Papalote, Museo del Niño, México 24480

Netherlands
Academisch Historisch Museum der Universiteit Leiden, Leiden 25234
Comenius Museum, Naarden 25301
Historisch Documentatiecentrum voor het Nederlands Protestantisme 1800-Heden, Amsterdam 24695
Joodse Schooltje, Leek 25219
Kindermuseum, Amsterdam 24701
Nationaal Schoolmuseum, Rotterdam 25437
De Ontdekhoek Kindermuseum, Rotterdam 25442
Schoolmuseum, Terneuzen 25529
Schoolmuseum Geleen, Geleen 25047
Schooltijd Schoolmuseum, Terneuzen 25530
Scouting Museum de Ducdalf, Rotterdam 25446
Universiteitsmuseum, Groningen 25084
Universiteitsmuseum De Agnietenkapel, Amsterdam 24740
Van 't Lindenhoutmuseum, Nijmegen 25327

New Zealand
Museum of Childhood, Masterton 25831
Saint Andrews College Museum, Christchurch 25756

Norway
Vestlandske Skolemuseum, Stavanger 26323

Pakistan
Education Museum, Hyderabad 26397

Peru
Museo Didáctico Antonini, Nasca 26511

Philippines
Central Luzon State University Museum, Muñoz 26571
Centro Escolar University Museum and Archives, Manila 26551

Poland
Muzeum Oświatowe, Puławy 27050
Muzeum Oświaty w Bydgoszczy, Bydgoszcz 26652

Puerto Rico
Museo del Niño, San Juan 27465

Russia
Muzej A.S. Makarenko, Moskva 27858
Ogni Moskvy - Muzej Istorii Gorodskogo Osveščenija, Moskva 27925
Učebno-chudožestvennyj Muzej im. I.V. Cvetaeva, Moskva 27941

Slovakia
Museum of Special Educational System, Levoča 28248

Slovenia
Slovenski Šolski Muzej, Ljubljana 28357

South Africa
Edoardo Villa Museum, Pretoria 28577

Spain
Museo del Niño, Albacete 28658

Sweden
Friluftmuseet Hallandsgården, Halmstad 30118
Skolmuseum Bunge, Farösund 30077
Stockholms Skolmuseum, Stockholm 30389

Switzerland
Musée d'Yverdon-les-Bains et sa Région, Yverdon-les-Bains 31422
Schweizer Kindermuseum, Baden 30555

United Kingdom
Andrew Carnegie Birthplace Museum, Dunfermline 32844
Auld Sköll, Fair Isle 32995
Böd of Gremista Museum, Lerwick 33499
Captain Cook's Schoolroom Museum, Great Ayton 33149
Causeway School Museum, Bushmills 32475
Christ's Hospital Museum, Horsham 33291
College Museum, Lancing 33441
Connections Discovery Centre, Exeter 32986
Hands on History, Kingston-upon-Hull 33397
Haslemere Educational Museum, Haslemere 33210
Heriot-Watt University Archive Collections, Edinburgh 32921
Islington Education Artefact Library, London 33676
Livesey Museum for Children, London 33692
Museum of Childhood, Edinburgh 32927
Museum of Eton Life, Eton 32981
Museum of the History of Education, Leeds 33471
Old Grammar School, Castletown 32556
Ragged School Museum, London 33755
Rugby School Museum, Rugby 34339
Scaplen's Court Museum, Poole 34215
Scotland Street School Museum, Glasgow 33095
Staff College Museum, Camberley 32495
Tom Brown School Museum, Uffington 34708

Uruguay
Museo Pedagógico José Pedro Varela, Montevideo 34951

U.S.A.
A.C. Gilbert's Discovery Village, Salem 40024
A.D. Buck Museum of Natural History and Science, Tonkawa 40699
Allen R. Hite Art Institute, Louisville 38185
Arkansas State University Museum, Jonesboro 37699
Austin Children's Museum, Austin 35264
Bay Area Discovery Museum, Sausalito 40235
Brooklyn Children's Museum, Brooklyn 35697
Buffalo and Erie County Naval and Military Park, Buffalo 35737
Capital Children's Museum, Washington 40954
Chicago Children's Museum, Chicago 36006

Egyptology

Electricity

Embroidery → Needlework

Enamel Works

Energy

Madagascar
Musée de l'Université de Tuléar, Tuléar 24272

Russia
Gaz Factory Museum, Nižnij Novgorod 27950
Muzej Istorii Razvitija Mosenergo, Moskva 27873

Switzerland
Kraftwerkmuseum Löntsch, Netstal 31049

Tajikistan
Muzej po Istorii Stroitelstva Gidroelektričeskogo Zavoda v Nurke, Nurek 31512

United Kingdom
Electric Mountain - Museum of North Wales, Llanberis 33550
Ellenroad Engine House, Milnrow 33956
Markfield Beam Engine and Museum, London 33706

U.S.A.
Coolspring Power Museum, Coolspring 36255
National Atomic Museum, Albuquerque 35020
North Anna Nuclear Information Center, Mineral 38527
Texas Energy Museum, Beaumont 35399
World of Energy at Keowee-Toxaway, Seneca 40311

Engraving → Graphic Arts

Entomology → Insects

Epitaphs → Inscriptions and Epitaphs

Ethnology

Albania
District Ethnographic Museum, Elbasan 00017
Ethnographic Museum, Bérat 00012
Ethnographic Museum, Durrës 00016
Ethnographic Museum, Gjirokastër 00022

Algeria
Musée National du Bardo, Alger 00045

Angola
Museu de Etnografia do Lobito, Lobito 00082
Museu Municipal, Nova Lisboa 00094
Museu Nacional de Antropologia, Luanda 00088

Argentina
Centro Mundo Aborigen, Córdoba 00281
Museo Arqueológico de Salta, Salta 00529
Museo Cacique Balata, La Cumbre 00369
Museo de Ciencias Antropológicas y Naturales, Santiago del Estero 00607
Museo de Ciencias Naturales y Misional del Colegio San José, Esperanza 00332
Museo del Indio, Los Toldos 00404
Museo del Mundo, Buenos Aires 00192
Museo Ethnográfico de las Obras Misionales Pontificias, Buenos Aires 00195
Museo Etnográfico Juán B. Ambrosetti, Buenos Aires 00196
Museo Etnográfico Municipal Dámaso Arce, Olavarría 00453
Museo Etnográfico y Archivo Histórico Enrique Squirru, Azul 00115
Museo Histórico Municipal y Colección de Arte Precolombino Arminio Weiss, Rafaela 00490
Museo Independencia, Córdoba 00293
Museo Indigenista, Esquel 00336
Museo Municipal de Lomas de Zamora, Lomas de Zamora 00402
Museo Nacional del Hombre, Buenos Aires 00222
Museo Privado de Arqueología Regional Julio Gironde, Carmen de Patagonés 00256
Museo Regional de Antropología, Resistencia 00502
Museo Runa de Antropología, Tafí del Valle 00619
Museo Salesiano Ceferino Namuncura, Córdoba 00301

Armenia
State History Museum of Armenia, Erevan 00683

Australia
Aboriginal Artefacts Museum, Beachport 00768
Adelaide Lithuanian Museum and Archives, Norwood 01326
Alpenrail Swiss Model Village and Railway, Claremont, Tasmania 00904
Anthropology Museum, Brisbane 00826
Berndt Museum of Anthropology, Nedlands 01302
Chinese Museum, Melbourne 01213
Golden Dragon Museum, Bendigo 00785
Italian Historical Museum, Carlton 00882
J.L. Shellshear Museum of Comparative Anatomy and Physical Anthropology, Sydney 01494
J.T. Wilson Museum of Human Anatomy, Sydney 01495
Macleay Museum, Sydney 01497
Miegunyah Pioneer Women's Memorial House Museum, Bowen Hills 00810
Philippine House Museum, Shepparton 01448
Queensland Museum, South Bank 01456
South Australian Museum, Adelaide 00704
Templin Historical Village, Boonah 00803
Tineriba Tribal Gallery and Museum, Hahndorf 01071
Western Australian Museum, Perth 01358

Austria
Ethnographisches Museum Schloss Kittsee, Kittsee 02108
Haus der Völker, Schwaz 02624
Heimathaus Mörbisch, Mörbisch 02306
Heimatmuseum im Amonhaus, Lunz 02248
Missions-Ethnographisches Museum St. Gabriel, Mödling 02299
Museum - Begegnung der Kulturen, Krenglbach 02154
Museum für Völkerkunde, Wien 02919
Referat Volkskunde, Graz 01925
Richard-Simoncic-Museum, Rabensburg 02456
Volkskundliche Sammlung alter bäuerlicher Geräte, Ludesch 02247

Bangladesh
Bangla Academy Folklore Museum, Dhaka 03049
Chittagong University Museum, Chittagong 03045
Ethnological Museum, Chittagong 03046

Belarus
Muzej Staražytna Belaruskaj Kultury, Minsk 03080

Belgium
Africa-Museum, Tervuren 03755
Etnografisch Museum, Antwerpen 03101
Etnografische Collecties van de Universiteit Gent, Gent 03403
Musée Africain, Namur 03617
Musée de Chine, Bruxelles 03266
Musée de la Vie Wallonne, Liège 03549
Musée de l'Orfevrerie de la Communaute Française, Seneffe 03706
Museum voor Volkskunde, Brugge 03224

Benin
Musée de Cotonou, Cotonou 03845
Musée de Natitingou, Natitingou 03846
Musée Ethnographique, Porto-Novo 03849

Bolivia
Museo Antropológico, Sucre 03876
Museo Nacional de Etnografía y Folklore, La Paz 03871

Bosnia and Herzegovina
Zemaljski Muzej, Sarajevo 03896

Botswana
Kgosi Bathoen II (Segopotso) Museum, Kanye 03907
Supa-Ngwao Museum Centre, Francistown 03904

Brazil
Museu da Cidade, São Paulo 04105
Museu de Antropologia do Instituto Joaquim Nabuco de Pesquisas Sociais, Recife 03982
Museu de Arqueologia e Etnologia da Universidade de São Paulo, São Paulo 04107
Museu de Etnografia Plinio Ayrosa, São Paulo 04112
Museu de Folclore Édison Carneiro, Rio de Janeiro 04033
Museu do Homem, Curitiba 03929
Museu do Índio, Manaus 03952
Museu do Indio, Rio de Janeiro 04043
Museu do Instituto de Antropologia Câmara Cascudo, Natal 03959
Museu do Instituto Nina Rodrigues, Salvador 04095
Museu-Escola Esacro do Estado da Paraiba, João Pessoa 03943
Museu Paranaense, Curitiba 03930

Bulgaria
Ethnographical Museum, Dobrič 04171
Etnografski Muzej, Berkovica 04147
Etnografski Muzej, Elčovo 04179
Etnografski Muzej, Plovdiv 04263
Etnografski Muzej, Silistra 04290
Etnografski Muzej, Varna 04360
Etnografski muzej, Burgas 04158
Etnografski Muzej Dunavski Ribolov i Lodkostroenie, Tutrakan 04357
Etnografski Muzej Oslekova kăšta, Koprivštica 04216
History Museum, Dimitrovgrad 04169
Istoričeski Muzej, Batak 04144
Istoričeski Muzej, Razgrad 04271
Istoričeski Muzej Targovište, Targovište 04353
Istoričeskij Muzej, Tutrakan 04358
Kărpeeva Kašta, Kotel 04222
Okražen Istoričeski Muzej, Veliko Tărnovo 04381

Burkina Faso
Musée National de Burkina Faso, Ouagadougou 04399

Cameroon
Musée de Diamare, Maroua 04415
Musée de Douala, Douala 04411
Musée International de Akum, Bamenda 04409
Musée Municipal de Mokolo, Mokolo 04417

Canada
Arkona Lion's Museum, Arkona 04463
Eskimo Museum, Churchill 04711
Glenbow Museum, Calgary 04628
Haida Gwaii Museum at Qay'llnagaay, Skidegate 05932
Huron-Ouendat Village, Midland 05309
Ksan Historical Village and Museum, Hazelton 05047
McCord Museum, Montréal 05373
Manitoba Museum of Man and Nature, Winnipeg 06307
Musée Canadien des Civilisations, Outaouais 05065
Musée de Baie Comeau, Baie Comeau 04491
Musée de Charlevoix, Pointe-au-Pic 05613
Musée de la Civilisation, Québec 05671
Musée des Abénakis, Odanak 05506
Musée du Bas Saint-Laurent, Rivière-du-Loup 05747
Musée du Château Ramezay, Montréal 05385
Musée et Centre de Transmission de la Culture Daniel Weetaluktuk, Inukjuak 05079
Musée François Pilote, La Pocatière 05169
Musée Kateri Tekakwitha, Kahnawake 05094
Musée Kio-Warini, Loretteville 05241
Museum of Anthropology, Vancouver 06158
Museum of Archaeology and Ethnology, Burnaby 04611
North American Black Historical Museum, Amherstburg 04444
Northern Life Museum and National Exhibition Centre, Fort Smith 04914
Prince of Wales Northern Heritage Centre, Yellowknife 06345
La Pulperie de Chicoutimi, Chicoutimi 04708
Rainy River District Women's Institute Museum, Emo 04871
Royal British Columbia Museum, Victoria 06204
Surrey Museum, Surrey 05992
Transcona Historical Museum, Winnipeg 06323
Ukraina Museum, Saskatoon 05877
Ukrainian Canadian Archives and Museum of Alberta, Edmonton 04852
Ukrainian Cultural Heritage Village, Edmonton 04854
Ukrainian Museum of Canada, Saskatoon 05878
Ukrainian Museum of Canada - Alberta Branch, Edmonton 04855

Central African Republic
Musée Ethnographique Regional, Bouar 06353
Musée National Barthélémy Boganda, Bangui 06352

Chile
Museo Antropológico de Antofagasta, Antofagasta 06361
Museo Antropológico de Iquique, Iquique 06371
Museo Arqueológico San Miguel de Azapa, Arica 06363

China, People's Republic
Anthropological Museum, Beijing 06417
Anthropological Museum of Xiamen University, Xiamen 06762
Museum of the Cultural Palace of National Minorities, Beijing 06455
Peking Man in Zhoukoudian, Beijing 06461

China, Republic
Museum of the Institute of History and Philology, Academia Sinica, Taipei 06819

Colombia
Exposición Permanente de Cerámica Indígena, Manizales 06851
Museo de Ciencias y Antropología, Cartago 06841
Museo de Historia Natural, Santafé de Bogotá 06902
Museo Etnográfico Madre Laura, Medellín 06858
Museo Etnográfico Miguel Angel Builes, Medellín 06859
Museo Nacional de Antropología, Santafé de Bogotá 06912
Museo Nacional de Colombia, Santafé de Bogotá 06913

Congo, Democratic Republic
Musée du Roi de Cuba, Mushenge 06936
Musée National de Kananga, Kananga 06926
Musée National de Lubumbashi, Lubumbashi 06933
Musée Regional, Kisangani 06932

Congo, Republic
Musée Régional André Grenard Matsoua, Kinkala 06939
Musée Régional Ma-Loango Diosso, Pointe-Noire 06940

Côte d'Ivoire
Musée de la Côte d'Ivoire, Abidjan 06952

Croatia
Creski Muzej, Cres 06978
Etnografska Zbirka, Koprivnički 07008
Etnografska Zbirka Franjevačkog Samostana, Zaostrog 07127
Gradski Muzej, Bjelovar 06967
Gradski Muzej Karlovac, Karlovac 07001
Gradski Muzej Makarska, Makarska 07024
Gradski Muzej Virovitica, Virovitica 07090
Knežev Dvor, Cavtat 06975
Memorijalna Zbirka Eugena Kumičića, Brseč 06971
Muzej Džkovštine, Dakovo 06980
Muzej Moslavine, Kutina 07021
Muzejska Zbirka, Čazma 06976
Muzejska Zbirka Krapina i Okolica, Krapina 07017
Narodni Muzej Labin, Labin 07022
Staro Selo Kumrovec, Kumrovec 07020
Zavičajni Muzej, Čazma 06977

Cuba
Museo Antropológico Montané, La Habana 07141
Museo de Etnologia, La Habana 07147
Museo Etnográfico, La Habana 07152

Cyprus
Ethnographical Museum, Paphos 07214

Cyprus Turk
Ethnographical Museum, Lefkoşa 07226
Mevlevi Tekke Museum, Lefkoşa 07228

Czech Republic
Etnografické muzeum, Tovačov 07666
Etnografický Ústav, Brno 07254
Hrdličkovo Muzeum Člověka, Praha 07563
Lesnické, Myslivecké a Rybářské Muzeum, Hluboká nad Vltavou 07335
Městské Muzeum, Úpice 07684
Městské Muzeum, Valašské Klobouky 07688
Moravské Zemské Muzeum, Brno 07260
Muzeum Dr. Aleše Hrdličky, Humpolec 07356
Muzeum Jindřicha Jindřicha, Domažlice 07316
Muzeum Vysočiny, Jihlava 07372
Náprstek Museum of Asian, African and American Cultures, Liběchov 07431
Náprstkovo Muzeum Asijských, Afrických a Amerických Kultur, Praha 07580
Národopisné Muzeum Plzeňska, Plzeň 07527
Slovácké Muzeum, Uherské Hradiště 07681

Denmark
Djurslands Museum - Dansk Fiskerimuseum, Grenå 07827
Grindsted Museum, Grindsted 07830
Kulturhistorisk Museum, Randers 08008
Nordsjaellandsk Folkemuseum, Hillerød 07860
Vendsyssel Historiske Museum, Hjørring 07863

Dominican Republic
Museo del Hombre Dominicano, Santo Domingo 08109

Ecuador
Museo Antropológico, Quito 08152
Museo Arqueología y Etnología, Quito 08153
Museo Azuayo del Folklore, Cuenca 08124
Museo de Etnografía, Quito 08162
Museo Etnografico del Cologio Nacional Mejia, Quito 08167

Egypt
Arabic Museum, Cairo 08203
Ethnological Museum, Cairo 08211

Salvador
Museo Nacional David J. Guzmán, San Salvador 08260

Estonia
Estonian National Museum, Tartu 08275

Ethiopia
City Museum, Makale 08286
City Museum, Yirgalem 08287
Ethnographic Museum, Addis Ababa 08279

Fiji
Fiji Museum, Suva 08291

Finland
Ethnographisches Museum Pöykkölä, Rovaniemi 08844
Karjaan Museo, Karjaa 08464
Kettumäen Ulkomuseo ja Kotiseututalo, Kuusankoski 08571
Kulttuurien Museo, Helsinki 08363
Lapin Maakuntamuseo, Rovaniemi 08845
Liedon Vanhalinna, Vanhalinna 09014
Mäntyharjun Museo, Mäntyharju 08653
Perniön Museo, Perniö 08769
Rautalammin Museo, Rautalampi 08833
Ruokolahden Kotiseutumuseo, Ruokolahti 08849
Tornionlaakson Maakuntamuseo, Tornio 08956
Vanajan Kotiseutumuseo, Hämeenlinna 08324

France
Ecomusée de la Brenne, Le Blanc 11172
Ecomusée de l'Ile de Groix, Ile-de-Groix 10846
Ecomusée de Plein Air du Quercy, Sauliac-sur-Célé 13418
Ecomusée du Pays de Rennes, Rennes (Ille-et-Vilaine) 12726
Musée Alsacien, Haguenau 10784
Musée Arménien de France, Paris 12315
Musée Béarnais, Pau 12465
Musée Camarguais, Arles 09244
Musée d'Art et d'Histoire de Lisieux, Lisieux 11407
Musée Dauphinois, Grenoble 10739
Musée de Cosne, Cosne-Cours-sur-Loire 10219
Musée de la Haute-Auvergne, Saint-Flour (Cantal) 12998
Musée de la Marine, Paris 12341
Musée de la Poupée, Paris 12348
Musée de l'Homme, Paris 12364
Musée Départemental des Hautes-Alpes, Gap 10639
Musée des Arts Africains, Océaniens et Amérindiens, Marseille 11647
Musée des Beaux-Arts, Angoulême 09186
Musée d'Ethnographie de l'Université de Bordeaux II, Bordeaux 09639
Musée d'Histoire Naturelle, Rouen 12837

Ethnology

Musée d'Histoire Naturelle et d'Ethnographie, Colmar 10166
Musée du Biterrois, Béziers 09548
Musée du Bûcheron, Germaine 10654
Musée du Château Saint-Jean, Nogent-le-Rotrou 12136
Musée du Pays de Luchon, Bagnères-de-Luchon 09393
Musée Entomologique, Saint-Quentin (Aisne) 13217
Musée Ethnographique du Donjon, Niort 12131
Musée-Fondation Alexandra David-Néel, Digne 10320
Musée Joseph-Vaylet, Espalion 10453
Musée Napoléonien, Ile-d'Aix 10845
Musée National des Arts et Traditions Populaires, Paris 12430
Musée Portuaire, Dunkerque 10389

Georgia
Kutaisskij Gosudarstvennyj Muzej Istorii i Etnografii, Kutaisi 14147

Germany
Abenteuermuseum Saarbrücken - Sammlung Heinz Rox-Schulz, Saarbrücken 18280
Adelhausermuseum, Natur- und Völkerkunde, Freiburg im Breisgau 15804
Afrika-Museum, Bergen, Kreis Celle 14657
Agrar- und Freilichtmuseum, Crimmitschau 15238
Anthropologische Sammlung der Universität Göttingen, Göttingen 16020
Archäologisch-Ethnographische Lehr- und Studiensammlung des Instituts für Altamerikanistik und Ethnologie der Universität Bonn, Bonn 14968
Brasilienmuseum im Kloster Bardel, Bad Bentheim 14386
Darß-Museum, Ostseebad Prerow 17905
Deutsches Albert-Schweitzer-Zentrum, Frankfurt am Main 15733
Deutsches Märchen- und Wesersagenmuseum, Bad Oeynhausen 14485
Ethnologisches Museum, Berlin 14703
Hamaland-Museum und Westmünsterliche Hofanlage, Vreden 18864
Haus Völker und Kulturen - Ethnologisches Museum, Sankt Augustin 18302
Iwalewa Haus, Bayreuth 14615
JuniorMuseum im Ethnologischen Museum, Berlin 14768
Kindheitsmuseum, Schönberg, Holstein 18371
Landesschau Äthiopien, Neulingen, Enzkreis 17645
Linden-Museum, Stuttgart 18636
Ludwig-Harms-Haus, Hermannsburg 16393
Missionsmuseum, Sankt Ottilien 18312
Missionsmuseum der Mariannhiller Missionare, Würzburg 19222
Missionsmuseum der Spiritaner Knechtsteden, Dormagen 15368
Museum der deutschen Sprachinselorte bei Brünn, Erbach, Donau 15589
Museum Europäischer Kulturen, Berlin 14802
Museum Forum der Völker, Werl 19050
Museum für Archäologie, Völkerkunde und Naturkunde, Mannheim 17245
Museum für Naturkunde und Völkerkunde Julius Riemer, Lutherstadt Wittenberg 17207
Museum für Stadtgeschichte und Volkskunde, Heppenheim 16379
Museum für Völkerkunde, Frankfurt am Main 15765
Museum für Völkerkunde, Witzenhausen 19161
Museum für Völkerkunde der Universität Kiel, Kiel 16732
Museum für Völkerkunde Hamburg, Hamburg 16236
Museum für Völkerkunde zu Leipzig, Leipzig 17050
Naturhistorisches Museum, Nürnberg 17753
Niedersächsisches Landesmuseum Hannover, Hannover 16280
Rautenstrauch-Joest-Museum, Köln 16813
Sammlung Buchheim - Museum der Phantasie, Bernried, Starnberger See 14877
Sammlung Vor- und Frühgeschichte und Völkerkunde, Gießen 15975
Schwarz-Afrika-Museum, Vilshofen 18855
Staatliches Museum für Völkerkunde Dresden, Dresden 15429
Staatliches Museum für Völkerkunde Dresden, Sammlungen, Dresden 15430
Staatliches Museum für Völkerkunde München, München 17524
Übersee-Museum, Bremen 15069
Ungarndeutsches Heimatmuseum Backnang, Backnang 14375
Ur-Wolpertinger-Museum, Kreuth 16877
Völkerkundemuseum der von Portheim-Stiftung, Heidelberg 16344
Völkerkundemuseum Herrnhut, Herrnhut 16406
Völkerkundesammlung, Lübeck 17175
Völkerkundliche Sammlung, Schleswig 18348
Völkerkundliche Sammlung der Philipps-Universität, Marburg 17264
Völkerkundliche Sammlung der Universität, Göttingen 16030
Völkerkundliches exotisches, zoologisches und heimatkundliches Missionsmuseum, Bad Driburg 14414
Volkskundliche Sammlungen, Witzenhausen 19162
Vorderasiatisches Museum, Berlin 14863
Zweigmuseum des Staatlichen Museum für Völkerkunde, Oettingen 17833

Ghana
Institute of African Studies Teaching Museum, Legon 19314

Greece
Ethnographical Historical Museum of Lárissa, Lárissa 19543
Folklore Museum, Pogoniani 19625
Folklore Museum, Vitsa 19701
Folklore Museum of Skyros, Skyros 19656
Museum of Cretan Ethnology, Timbaki 19689

Guatemala
Museo Regional, Chichicastenango 19751

Guinea
Musée Annexe de Kissidougou, Kissidougou 19764
Musée Annexe de Youkounkoun, Youkounkoun 19767
Musée Fédérale Annexe de Koundara, Koundara 19765
Musée National de Conakry, Conakry 19763
Musée Regional de Beyla, Beyla 19759

Guinea-Bissau
Musée da Guine Portugesa, Bissau 19768
Museu Etnografico Nacional, Bissau 19769

Honduras
Museo Antropologia e Historia Valle de Sula, San Pedro Sula 19781

Hungary
Csongrádi Múzeum, Csongrád 19870
Déri Múzeum, Debrecen 19871
Dráva Múzeum, Barcs 19796
Ferenczy Károly Múzeum, Szentendre 20034
Gyoërffy István Nagykun Múzeum, Karcag 19915
Intercisa Múzeum, Dunaújváros 19876
Jfj. Lele J. Néprajzi Gyűjteménye, Szeged 20012
Kanizsai Dorottya Múzeum, Mohács 19948
Kiskun Múzeum, Kiskunfélegyháza 19927
Kiss Pál Múzeum, Tiszafüred 20059
Kossuth Múzeum, Cegléd 19868
Laczkó Dezsoë Múzeum, Veszprém 20071
Matyó Múzeum, Mezőkövesd 19941
Munkácsy Mihály Múzeum, Békéscsaba 19799
Néprajzi Gyűjtemény, Sopron 20000
Néprajzi Kiállítás, Pécs 19977
Néprajzi Múzeum, Budapest 19842
Rábaközi Múzeum, Kapuvár 19914
Rákóczi Múzeum, Sárospatak 19989
Szántó Kovács Múzeum, Orosháza 19960
Szatmári Múzeum, Mátészalka 19940
Thorma János Múzeum, Kiskunhalas 19930
Thury György Múzeum, Nagykanizsa 19952
Türr István Múzeum, Baja 19789
Vármúzeum, Kisvárda 19933
Viski Károly Múzeum, Kalocsa 19909

Iceland
Thjódminjasafn Islands, Gardabaer 20095

India
Anthropological Museum, Gauhati 20241
Anthropology Museum, Delhi 20206
Anthropology Museum, Ranchi 20403
Bharat Itihas Samshodhak Mandal Museum, Pune 20389
Bihar Tribal Welfare Research Institute Museum, Ranchi 20404
Ethnological Museum, Pune 20394
Government Museum, Pudukottai 20391
Jawaharlal Nehru State Museum, Itanagar 20278
Museum of the Department of Anthropology, Lucknow 20345
Prabhas Patan Museum, Prabhas Patan 20390
State Museum, Kohima 20311
Tibet House Museum, Delhi 20226
Tribal Museum, Ahmedabad 20137
Victoria and Albert Museum, Mumbai 20179
Zonal Anthropological Museum, Shillong 20415
Zonal Museum, Dehradun 20203

Indonesia
Museum Negeri Maluku Siwa Lima, Ambon 20457
Museum Negeri Propinsi Nusa Tenggara Timur, Kupang 20530
Museum Negeri Sumatera Utara, Medan 20544
Museum Pemda Balige, Balige 20458
Subak Museum, Banjar Senggulan 20468

Iran
Ethnological Museum of Hammame-e-Ganjalixan, Kerman 20625
Moaven Al- Molk Museum, Kermanshah 20627
Muséyé Mardom Shenassi, Teheran 20654
Rasht Museum, Rasht 20636

Israel
Museum for Beduin Culture, Kibbutz Lahav 20954
Negev Museum, Be'ersheva 20868

Italy
Istituto Geografico Polare Silvio Zavatti, Fermo 21545
Museo Africano Missionari Comboniani, Verona 22835
Museo Calabrese di Etnografia e Folklore, Palmi 22120
Museo Civico Archeologico Etnologico, Modena 21943
Museo Civico di Numismatica, Etnografia e Arti Orientali, Torino 22671
Museo Civico Etnografico, Oleggio 22064
Museo del Po, Monticelli d'Ongina 21998
Museo delle Culture Extraeuropee Dinz Rialto, Rimini 22311
Museo delle Genti d'Abruzzo, Pescara 22165
Museo delle Valli Valdesi, Torre Pellice 22702
Museo di Antropologia, Bologna 21201
Museo di Antropologia dell'Università di Napoli, Napoli 22018
Museo di Antropologia ed Etnografia, Torino 22683
Museo di Antropologia ed Etnologia, Firenze 21612
Museo di Antropologia G. Sergi, Roma 22384
Museo di Arte Cinese ed Etnografico, Parma 22131
Museo e Pinacoteca del Santuario Madonna delle Grazie, Rimini 22312
Museo Etiopico, Frascati 21654
Museo Etnografico, Aprica 21076
Museo Etnografico, Montodine 22000
Museo Etnografico, Parma 22134
Museo Etnografico, Sampeyre 22469
Museo Etnografico, Ultimo 22758
Museo Etnografico, Morigerati 22005
Museo Etnografico Africa Mozambico, Bari 21138
Museo Etnografico Africano, San Lorenzo in Campo 22492
Museo Etnografico Castello D'Albertis, Genova 21700
Museo Etnografico dei Cimbri, Selva di Progno 22558
Museo Etnografico del Carretto Siciliano, Terrasini 22643
Museo Etnografico del Pinerolese, Pinerolo 22206
Museo Etnografico del Ponente Ligure, Cervo 21389
Museo Etnografico della Civiltà Contadina, Colorno 21457
Museo Etnografico della Lunigiana, Villafranca in Lunigiana 22870
Museo Etnografico della Trinità, Botticino 21232
Museo Etnografico delle Alpi Occidentali, Boves 21233
Museo Etnografico G. Fontana, Sappada 22531
Museo Etnografico Romagnolo, Russi 22451
Museo Etnografico Tiranese, Madonna di Tirano 21825
Museo Etnologico della Montagna Pistoiese, Cutigliano 21499
Museo Indiano, Bologna 21211
Museo Nazionale Preistorico ed Etnografico Luigi Pigorini, Roma 22402
Museo Storico Etnografico della Bassa Valsesia, Romagnano Sesia 22434
Museo Storico Etnografico Naturalistico della Valmalenco, Chiesa in Valmalenco 21411
Raccolta Etnografica, Vallo di Nera 22771
Südtiroler Landesmuseum für Volkskunde, Brunico 21252

Japan
Abashiri Kyodo Hakubutsukan, Abashiri 22912
Kokuritsu Minzokugaku Hakubutsukan (Minpaku), Suita 23523

Jordan
The Anthropological National Folklore Museum, Amman 23789

Kazakhstan
Vostočno Kazachstanskij Ėtnografičeskij Muzej, Ust-Kamenogorsk 23845

Kenya
Kitale Museum, Kitale 23851
Meru Museum, Meru 23853

Korea, Democratic People's Republic
Korean Central Ethnographic Museum, Pyongyang 23866

Korea, Republic
Pacific Cultural Museum, Seoul 23944

Kyrgyzstan
Gumbez Manace Literary Ethnographic Museum, Taš-Aryk 23980

Latvia
Turaidas Muzejrezervāts, Sigulda 24108

Lesotho
Morija Museum, Morija 24153

Liberia
Africana Museum, Monrovia 24155
National Museum, Monrovia 24156

Lithuania
Aušros Avenue Mansion, Šiauliai 24187
Aušros Avenue Mansion, Šiauliai 24187
Lietuvos Nacionalinis Muziejus, Vilnius 24199
Šiauliai Aušros Museum, Šiauliai 24193
Žeimelis Žiemgalos Museum, Žeimelis 24201

Luxembourg
Musée d'Art Rustique, Vianden 24238

Macedonia
Muzej i Galeriya Bitola, Bitola 24246
Muzej na Makedonija - Arceološki, Etnološki i Istoriski, Skopje 24252

Malawi
Museum of Malawi, Blantyre 24273

Malaysia
Malay Ethnographic Museum, Kuala Lumpur 24298
Museum of Aboriginal Affairs, Gombak 24282
Museum of Beauty, Melaka 24321
Muzium Negara, Kuala Lumpur 24301
Muzium Rakyat, Melaka 24323
Sabah Museum, Kota Kinabalu 24291
Sarawak Museum, Kuching 24311

Mali
Musée National du Mali, Bamako 24338

Malta
Inquisitor's Palace, Vittoriosa 24355
Ta' Kola Windmill, Xaghra 24359

Mexico
Museo Amparo, Puebla 24498
Museo del Estado de Jalisco, Guadalajara 24397
Museo Nacional de Antropología, México 24458
Museo Nacional de las Culturas, México 24467
Museo Regional de Actopán, Actopán 24384
Museo Regional de Antropología, Mérida 24406
Museo Regional de Antropología Carlos Pellicer Camara, Villahermosa 24524
Museo Regional de Antropologia e Historia de Tepic, Tepic 24511
Museo Universitario de Culturas Populares, Colima 24392

Mongolia
Museum of Mongolian Ethnography, Ulaanbaatar 24542

Morocco
Musée Ethnographique, Tétouan 24573

Myanmar
University of Mandalay Collections, Mandalay 24590

Namibia
National Museum of Namibia, Windhoek 24636

Netherlands
Afrika Centrum, Cadier en Keer 24865
Afrika Museum, Berg en Dal 24804
Expositie Versteend Leven, Drouwen 24975
KIT Tropenmuseum, Amsterdam 24702
Moluks Historisch Museum, Utrecht 25557
Museum Nusantara, Delft 24884
Museum Suriname, Amsterdam 24713
Nederlands Openluchtmuseum, Arnhem 24770
Nijmeegs Volkenkundig Museum, Nijmegen 25326
Rijksmuseum voor Volkenkunde, Leiden 25243
Volkenkundig Museum Gerardus van der Leeuw, Groningen 25085
Volkskundig en Voorhistorisch Museum, Swalmen 25524
Wereldmuseum Rotterdam, Rotterdam 25450

New Zealand
Okains Bay Maori and Colonial Museum, Okains Bay 25852
Otago Museum, Dunedin 25778
Te Awamutu Museum, Te Awamutu 25897
Whanganui Regional Museum, Wanganui 25924

Nigeria
Ataoja, Oba Oyewale Matanmi's Palace, Oshogbo 25991
Gidan Makama Museum, Kano 25984
Museum of the Institute of African Studies, Ibadan 25974
Museum of the Institute of African Studies, Oshogbo 25993

Norway
Etnografisk Museum, Oslo 26217
Kon-Tiki Museum, Oslo 26224
De Kulturhistoriske Samlinger, Bergen 26031
Varjjat Sámi Musea, Varangerbotn 26368

Panama
Museo Antropológico Reina T. de Araúz, Panamá City 26437

Papua New Guinea
J.K. MacCarthy Museum, Goroka 26451
Papua New Guinea National Museum and Art Gallery, Boroko 26450

Paraguay
Museo Etnográfico Andrés Barbero, Asunción 26462

Peru
Museo Nacional de la Cultura Peruana, Lima 26503
Museo y Biblioteca Leoncio Prado, Huánuco 26479

Philippines
Aga Khan Museum, Marawi 26570
Anthropology Museum, Dumaguete 26528
Barangay Museum, Mandaluyong 26545
National Museum, Zamboanga 26608
National Museum of the Philippines, Manila 26562
Palawan Teachers College Museum, Puerto Princesa 26584
Saint Louis University Museum, Baguio 26517
Saint Theresa's College Folklife Museum, Cebu 26525
Sulu Ethnological Museum, Jolo 26533
Tawi-Tawi Ethnological Museum, Tawi-Tawi 26600
University Museum, Cebu 26526
University Museum of Anthropology, Quezon City 26588
University of Santo Tomas Museum of Arts and Sciences, Manila 26569

Poland
Górnośląski Park Etnograficzny, Chorzów 26669
Harcerskie Muzeum Etnograficzne przy Szkole Podstawowej nr 11 w Katowicach, Katowice 26772
Mission and Folklore Museum, Polanica Zdrój 27009
Muzeum Etnograficzne, Kraków 26828
Muzeum Etnograficzne, Toruń 27168
Muzeum Etnograficzne, Wrocław 27282
Muzeum Etnograficzne im. Franciszka Kotuli, Rzeszów 27078
Muzeum Etnograficzne w Zielonej Górze z Siedzibą w Ochli, Ochla 26966
Muzeum Etnograficzny, Tarnów 27158
Muzeum Etnografii, Gdańsk 26703
Muzeum Historyczno-Etnograficzne, Chojnice 26664
Muzeum im. Jana Nikodema Jaronia, Olesno 26971
Muzeum - Kaszubski Park Etnograficzny im. Til Gulgowskich we Wdzydzach, Wdzydze Kiszewskie 27253
Muzeum Kaszubskie, Kartuzy 26771
Muzeum Kultury Ludowej, Kolbuszowa 26797
Muzeum Kultury Ludowej, Węgorzewo 27254
Muzeum Mazurskie, Szczytno 27148
Muzeum Misyjno-Etnograficzne, Pieniężno 26998
Muzeum Pojezierza Łęczyńsko-Włodawskiego, Włodawa 27272
Muzeum Regionalne, Jarocin 26750
Muzeum Regionalne, Myślenice 26938
Muzeum Regionalne im. Marcina Rożka, Wolsztyn 27276
Muzeum Regionalne PTTK im. Hieronima Ławinczaka, Krotoszyn 26861
Muzeum Rzemiosła Tkackiego, Turek 27177
Muzeum Tatrzańskie im. Tytusa Chałubińskiego, Zakopane 27309
Muzeum w Tomaszowie Mazowieckim, Tomaszów Mazowiecki 27164
Muzeum Wisły, Tczew 27162
Muzeum Wsi Kieleckiej, Kielce 26789
Muzeum Wsi Mazowieckiej, Sierpc 27093
Muzeum Zachodnio-Kaszubskie, Bytów 26657
Muzeum Ziemi Puckiej, Puck 27048
Nadwiślański Park Etnograficzny w Wygiełzowie i Zamek w Lipowcu, Wygiełzów 27296
Orawski Park Etnograficzny, Zubrzyca Górna 27325
Ośrodek Budownictwa Ludowego w Szymbarku z filia w Bartnem, Sękowa 27087
Palucka Izba Muzealna, Kcynia 26781
Punkt Etnograficzny w Rogierówku, Rogierówko 27067
Sądecki Park Etnograficzny, Nowy Sącz 26960

Portugal
Museu Antropológico, Coimbra 27352
Museu de Azambuja, Azambuja 27339
Museu de Etnografia e História, Porto 27424
Museu de Olaria, Barcelos 27340
Museu de Roque Gameiro, Minde 27413
Museu Etnográfico da Sociedade de Geografia de Lisboa, Lisboa 27395
Museu Etnográfico e Arqueológico do Dr. Joaquim Manso, Nazaré 27414
Museu Municipal Dr. Santos Rocha, Figueira da Foz 27366
Museu Nacional de Etnologia, Lisboa 27401

Puerto Rico
Turabo University Museum, Gurabo 27456

Qatar
Qatar National Museum, Doha 27472

Romania
Complexul Naţional Muzeal Astra, Sibiu 27646
Ethnographic Museum, Tulcea 27672
Muzeul de de Etnografie şi Artă Populară Orăştie, Orăştie 27615
Muzeul de Etnografie Braşov, Braşov 27505
Muzeul de Etnografie Piatra-Neamţ, Piatra Neamţ 27618
Muzeul de Etnografie şi Artă Populară, Reghin 27631
Muzeul de Istorie şi Etnografie Lugoj, Lugoj 27597
Muzeul Etnografic, Răşinari 27630
Muzeul Etnografic al Moldovei, Iaşi 27589
Muzeul Etnografic al Transilvaniei, Cluj-Napoca 27548
Muzeul Etnografic Beiuş, Beiuş 27492
Muzeul Etnografic Lupsa, Lupsa 27598
Muzeul Etnografic Poiana Sibiului, Poiana Sibiului 27627
Muzeul Etnografic Rădăuţi, Rădăuţi 27628
Muzeul Etnografic Urlaţi, Urlaţi 27677
Muzeul Judeţean de Etnografie şi a Regimentului de Graniţă-Caransebeş, Caransebeş 27538
Muzeul Judeţean de Istorie şi Etnografie, Focsani 27574
Muzeul Judeţean Vilcea, Măldăreşti 27599
Muzeul Tării Oaşului, Negreşti Oaş 27609

Russia
Muzej Antropologii i Etnografii im. Petra Velikogo, Sankt-Peterburg 28046
Naučno-issledovatelskij Institut i Muzej Antropologii im. D.N. Anučina, Moskva 27920
Nižnetagilskij Muzej-Zapovednik Gornozavodskogo Dela Srednego Urala, Nižnij Tagil 27954
Pskovskij Istoričeskij, Architekturnyj i Chudožestnennyj Muzej, Pskov 27998
Rossijskij Ėtnografičeskij muzej, Sankt-Peterburg 28065

Rwanda
Musée de Kabgayi, Kabgayi 28141
Musée National, Butare 28140

Singapore
Asian Civilisations Museum, Singapore 28176

Slovakia
Etnografická Expozícia - Vajnory House, Bratislava 28198
Etnografické Múzeum, Martin 28259
Horehronské múzeum, Brezno 28219
Múzeum, Bardejovské Kúpele 28191
Okresné Vlastivedné Múzeum, Humenné 28236
Vlastivedné Múzeum, Prešov 28286
Vlastivedné Múzeum, Topoľčany 28310
Západoslovenské Múzeum v Trnave, Trnava 28312

Slovenia
Belokranjski Muzej, Metlika 28366
Kurnikova Hiša, Tržič 28394
Loški Muzej, Škofja Loka 28385
Mestni Muzej Idrija, Idrija 28328
Pokrajinski Muzej, Kočevje 28332
Pokrajinski Muzej, Maribor 28363
Pokrajinski Muzej, Murska Sobota 28370
Posavski Muzej Brežice, Brežice 28325
Slovenski Etnografski Muzej, Ljubljana 28355
Tolminski Muzej, Tolmin 28391
Tržiški Muzej, Tržič 28395

Somalia
Somali National Museum, Mogadishu 28403

South Africa
Africana Museum, Mariannhill 28541
Anthropology Museum and Resource Centre, Johannesburg 28503
Duggan-Cronin Gallery, Kimberley 28522
Museum of Anthropology and Archaeology, Pretoria 28584
University Museum, Stellenbosch 28624

Spain
Ecomuseu de les Valls d'Aneu, Esterri d'Aneu 29050
Euskal Arkeologia, Etnografia eta Kondaira Museoa, Bilbao 28852
Museo Africano Mundo Negro, Madrid 29257
Museo Canario, Las Palmas de Gran Canaria 29479
Museo de América, Madrid 29262
Museo de Antropología de Tenerife - Casa de Carta, La Laguna 29176
Museo de Artes y Costumbres Populares, Combarro 28971
Museo de Artes y Costumbres Populares, Piedrafita de El Cebrero 29506
Museo de Artes y Costumbres Populares, Ribadavia 29558
Museo de Bellas Artes, Mahón 29309
Museo de Zaragoza, Zaragoza 29958
Museo del Blat y de la Pagesia, Cervera 28948
Museo del Carro y la Labranza, Tomelloso 29782
Museo do Pobo Galego, Santiago de Compostela 29683
Museo Etnográfico de Azuaga de la Sierra y la Campiña, Azuaga 28754
Museo Etnográfico de Cantabria, Muriedas 29393
Museo Etnográfico de los Valles de Campoo, Canduela 28910
Museo Etnográfico Textil Pérez Enciso, Plasencia 29509
Museo Etnológico de Morella y del Meastrazgo, Morella 29383
Museo Municipal de San Telmo, Donostia-San Sebastián 29018
Museo Municipal Etnológico de la Huerta, Alcantarilla 28667
Museo Nacional de Antropología, Madrid 29282
Museo Nacional de Antropología, Madrid 29283
Museo Parroquial de Arte Sacro y Etnología, Anso 28704
Museo Provincial, Teruel 29762
Museu de la Fusta, Areu 28720
Museu de la Pedra i de l'Estable, Guimerà 29135
Museu de l'Acordió, Arsèguel 28726
Museu de Mallorca, Palma de Mallorca 29471
Museu del Pagès, Castelldans 28932
Museu Diocesà i Comarcal, Solsona 29736
Museu Etnogràfic de Ripoll, Ripoll 29564
Museu Etnològic de Barcelona, Barcelona 28816
Museu Etnologic de Guadalest, Guadalest 29128
Museu Etnològic del Montseny La Gabella, Arbúcies 28712
Museu Etnològic i Arqueològic, Juneda 29173
Museu Parroquial, Vinaixa 29924

Sri Lanka
Colombo National Museum, Colombo 29980
Museum of Ethnology and Folk Art, Ratnapura 29992
Ratnapura National Museum, Ratnapura 29994

Sudan
Ethographical Museum, Khartoum 29999
Halfa Museum, Wadi Halfa 30008

Swaziland
Swaziland National Museums, Lobamba 30012

Sweden
Ajtte - Svenskt Fjäll- och Samemuseum, Jokkmokk 30143
Arboga Museum, Arboga 30024
Disagården, Uppsala 30444
Etnografiska Museet, Stockholm 30343
Fotevikens Museum, Höllviken 30130
Jamtli Historieland, Östersund 30273
Jukkasjärvi Hembygdsgård, Jukkasjärvi 30144
Medelpads Fornminnesförening, Sundsvall 30407
Norbergs Kommuns Museer, Norberg 30246
Ovanakers Hembygdsgard, Edsbyn 30058
Trelleborgs Museum, Trelleborg 30427
Världskulturmuseet, Göteborg 30106

Switzerland
Afrika-Museum, Zug 31486
Ethnographische Sammlung, Fribourg 30778
Musée Cantonal d'Histoire, Sion 31243
Musée d'Ethnographie, Conches 30714
Musée d'Ethnographie, Genève 30812
Musée d'Ethnographie, Neuchâtel 31053
Museum der Kulturen Basel, Basel 30574
Museum für Völkerkunde, Burgdorf 30673
Tibet Songtsen House, Zürich 31478
Völkerkundemuseum der Universität Zürich, Zürich 31481
Völkerkundemuseum Sankt Gallen, Sankt Gallen 31178
Völkerkundliche Sammlung, Winterthur 31411

Togo
Musée d'Histoire et d'Ethnographie, Aneho 31599
Musée National du Togo, Lomé 31602

Tunisia
Musée Dar Jellouli, Sfax 31628
Musée de Mahdia, Mahdia 31617
Musée des Arts et Traditions Populaires Dar Ben Abdallah, Tunis 31640
Musée du Village, Moknine 31621
Musée Régional des Arts et Traditions Populaires, Le Kef 31616

Turkey
Etnografi Müzesi, Ankara 31664
Etnografi Müzesi, Eskişehir 31726
Koyunoglu Müzesi, Konya 31791

Turkmenistan
Historical and Ethnographical Museum, Turkmenabat 31869
Muzej Kizyl-Arvata, Kizyl-Arvat 31865
National Museum of Turkmenistan, Ašhabad 31862

Uganda
Folk Museum, Mbarara 31880
Folk Museum, Soroti 31882

Ukraine
Etnografičeskij Muzej Tavrika, Simferopol 31951
State Historical Museum, Kamenec-Podolskij 31907
State Museum of Ethnography, Arts and Crafts, Lviv 31936

United Kingdom
Brunei Gallery, London 33601
Dunrobin Castle Museum, Golspie 33123
The Eastern Museum, Derby 32757
Gurkha Museum, Winchester 34842
Hancock Museum, Newcastle-upon-Tyne 34029
Hastings Museum and Art Gallery, Hastings 33212
Horniman Museum, London 33671
Liverpool Museum, Liverpool 33537
Museum of Mankind, London 33722
Pitt Rivers Museum, Oxford 34139
Powell-Cotton Museum and Quex House, Birchington 32252
Rhodes Memorial Museum and Commonwealth Centre, Bishop's Stortford 32289
Royal Albert Memorial Museum and Art Gallery, Exeter 32988
Royal Engineers Museum, Gillingham, Kent 33061
Russell-Cotes Art Gallery and Museum, Bournemouth 32339
Saffron Walden Museum, Saffron Walden 34350
Sainsbury Centre for Visual Arts, Norwich 34088
University Museum of Archaeology and Anthropology, Cambridge 32510

Uruguay
Museo del Gaucho, Montevideo 34939

U.S.A.
Abbe Museum, Bar Harbor 35339
Adams State College Luther Bean Museum, Alamosa 34996
Adan E. Treganza Anthropology Museum, San Francisco 40100
African Art Museum of the S.M.A. Fathers, Tenafly 40657
Afro-American Cultural Center, Charlotte 35944
Alabama-Coushatta Indian Museum, Livingston 38090
Alabama Museum of Natural History, Tuscaloosa 40769
Alaska Indian Arts, Haines 37303
Alutiiq Museum and Archaeological Repository, Kodiak 37839
American Museum of Asmat Art, Saint Paul 39989
American Swedish Institute, Minneapolis 38529
The Amerind Foundation, Dragoon 36558
Anasazi Heritage Center, Dolores 36532
Andrew J. Blackbird Museum, Harbor Springs 37336
Anthropology Museum, DeKalb 36442
Appalachian Center for Crafts, Smithville 40386
The Appaloosa Museum and Heritage Center, Moscow 38644
Arizona State Museum, Tucson 40744
Armenian Museum of America, Watertown 41037
The Balch Institute for Ethnic Studies, Philadelphia 39364
Baltimores Black American Museum, Baltimore 35304
Balzekas Museum of Lithuanian Culture, Chicago 36002
Bernice Pauahi Bishop Museum, Honolulu 37474
Brigham Young University Museum of Peoples and Cultures, Provo 39643
Buechel Memorial Lakota Museum, Saint Francis 39936
Burke Museum of Natural History and Culture, Seattle 40279
Cahokia Mounds State Historic Site, Collinsville 36176
California African-American Museum, Los Angeles 38137
California State Indian Museum, Sacramento 39901
Capitol Reef National Park Visitor Center, Torrey 40707
Carnegie Museum of Natural History, Pittsburgh 39463
Carter County Museum, Ekalaka 36656
Castine Scientific Society Museum, Castine 35866
C.E. Smith Museum of Anthropology, Hayward 37385
C.H. Nash Museum-Chucalissa Archaeological Museum, Memphis 38408
Cherokee Heritage Centre, Tahlequah 40612
College of Eastern Utah Prehistoric Museum, Price 39610
Colorado River Indian Tribes Museum, Parker 39282
Colter Bay Indian Arts Museum, Colter Bay Village 36190
Confederated Tribes and Bands of the Yakama Indian Nation - Cultural Heritage Center Museum, Toppenish 40704
Cultural Rights and Protection/Ute Indian Tribe, Fort Duchesne 36898
DePauw University Anthropology Museum, Greencastle 37243
Diablo Valley College Museum, Pleasant Hill 39495
Douglas County Museum of History and Natural History, Roseburg 39865
Durham Center Museum, East Durham 36602
Eastern Arizona Museum and Historical Society of Graham County, Pima 39443
Eastern California Museum, Independence 37574
Edge of the Cedars State Park, Blanding 35528
Eiteljorg Museum of American Indians and Western Art, Indianapolis 37588
Elgin Public Museum, Elgin 36678
Etowah Indian Mounds Historical Site, Cartersville 35854
Evelyn Payne Hatcher Museum of Anthropology, Saint Cloud 39932
Exhibition of the Norwegian-American Historical Association, Northfield 39055
Favell Museum of Western Art and Indian Artifacts, Klamath Falls 37824
Five Civilized Tribes Museum, Muskogee 38699
Florence Hawley Ellis Museum of Anthropology, Abiquiu 34978
Fort Ancient Museum, Oregonia 39189
Fort Fetterman State Museum, Douglas 36539
Fort Recovery Museum, Fort Recovery 36951
Frisco Native American Museum and Natural History Center, Frisco 37051
Grace Hudson Museum and The Sun House, Ukiah 40787
Grand Village of the Natchez Indians, Natchez 38731
Haffenreffer Museum of Anthropology, Bristol 35668
Hartzler-Towner Multicultural Museum, Nashville 38725
Heard Museum, Phoenix 39432
The Heritage Center, Pine Ridge 39447
Heritage Library and Museum, Anchorage 35103
Herrett Center for Arts and Science, Twin Falls 40780
Heym-Oliver House, Russell 39889
High Desert Museum, Bend 35439
Hopewell Culture National Historic Park, Chillicothe 36058
Horry County Museum, Conway 36251
Hudson Museum, Orono 39200
Indian Center Museum, Wichita 41168
Indian City U.S.A., Anadarko 35095
Indian Museum of Lake County-Ohio, Painesville 39256
Indian Museum of North America, Crazy Horse 36314
Indian Museum of the Carolinas, Laurinburg 37965
Indian Temple Mound Museum, Fort Walton Beach 36971
The Institute For American Indian Studies (IAIS), Washington Green 41024
Institute of American Indian Arts Museum, Santa Fe 40194
International Museum of Cultures, Dallas 36361
Iroquois Indian Museum, Howes Cave 37528
Jacques Marchais Museum of Tibetan Art, Staten Island 40492
Jean Lafitte National Historical Park and Preserve, New Orleans 38815
Jensen Arctic Museum, Monmouth 38580
Jesse Peter Museum, Santa Rosa 40211
Ka-Do-Ha Indian Village Museum, Murfreesboro 38684

Expeditions → Scientific Expeditions

Explosives

Eyeglasses → Optics

Faience → Porcelain and Ceramics

Farms and Farming

Fashion → Clothing and Dress

Festivals

Fire Fighting and Rescue Work

Firearms → Arms and Armour

Fishing and Fisheries

Durrell Museum, Durrell 04821
Ellerslie Shellfish Museum, Tyne Valley 06127
Fisheries Museum of the Atlantic, Lunenburg 05250
Fisherman's Life Museum, Halifax 05008
Fisherman's Museum, Musgrave Harbour 05417
Fishermen's Museum, Port-de-Grave 05628
Gulf of Georgia Cannery, Richmond 05729
Margaree Salmon Museum, North East Margaree 05487
Newfoundland Museum, Saint John's 05817
Northumberland Fisheries Museum, Pictou 05600
Port Dover Harbour Museum, Port Dover 05629
Salvage Fisherman's Museum, Salvage 05859
Tehkummah Township Museum, Tehkummah 06010
William Ray House, Dartmouth 04767

Czech Republic
Lesnické, Myslivecké a Rybářské Muzeum, Hluboká nad Vltavou 07335

Denmark
Blåvand Museum, Blåvand 07769
Fiskeri- og Søfartsmuseet, Esbjerg 07794
Fjordmuseet, Jyllinge 07894
Gilleleje Fiskerimuseum, Gilleleje 07822
Museumscenter Hanstholm, Hanstholm 07840
Nordsømuseet, Hirtshals 07862
Søfarts og Fiskerimuseet, Læsø 07951

Egypt
Aquatics Museum - Institute of Oceanography and Fisheries, Suez 08253

Finland
Ålands Jakt och Fiskemuseum, Storby 08900
Langingkoski Imperial Fishing Lodge, Kotka 08539
Merikarvian Kalastusmuseo, Merikarvia 08667
Runebergs stugan, Jakobstad 08419
Skärgårdsmuseet, Lappoby-Åland 08606

France
Ecomusée de la Pêche, Thonon-les-Bains 13677
Maison du Patrimoine Maritime, Camaret-sur-Mer 09823
Musée de la Conserverie Le Gall, Loctudy 11428
Musée de la Mer, Paimpol 12236
Musée de la Pêche, Concarneau 10187
Musée de la Vilaine Maritime, La Roche-Bernard 11020

Germany
Deutsches Jagd- und Fischereimuseum, München 17460
Deutsches Meeresmuseum, Stralsund 18610
Fischer- und Webermuseum Steinhude, Wunstorf 19234
Fischereimuseum, Wassertrüdingen 18939
Jagd- und Fischereimuseum, Adelsdorf 14186
Jagd- und Fischereimuseum Schloß Tambach, Weitramsdorf 19035
Museum für Wattenfischerei, Wremen 19210
Museum im Malhaus, Wasserburg, Bodensee 18938
Museumslogger AE7 Stadt Emden, Emden 15559
Nationalpark-Haus, Butjadingen 15164
Norderneyer Fischerhausmuseum, Norderney 17715
Oberpfälzer Fischereimuseum, Tirschenreuth 18713
Schloß Wolfstein mit Jagd- und Fischereimuseum und Galerie Wolfstein, Freyung 15833

Greenland
Aalisarnermut Piniarnermullu Katersugaasivik, Ilulissat 19716

Iceland
Síldarminjasafnid a Siglufirdi, Siglufjördur 20124
Sjóminjasafn Islands, Hafnarfjördur 20097

India
Museum of the Central Marine Fisheries Research Station, Mandapam Camp 20353

Italy
Museo Ittico, Pescara 22166

Japan
Seto Inland Sea Folk History Museum, Takamatsu, Kagawa 23539

Netherlands
It Earmhus en Oud Friese Greidboerderij, Wartena 25624
Gemeentemuseum Elburg, Elburg 25011
Historische Expositie Klederdracht en Visserijmuseum, Bunschoten Spakenburg 24858
Jan Vissermuseum, Helmond 25142
Museum Arnemuiden, Arnemuiden 24760
Museum 't Fiskershúske, Moddergat 25297
Museum in 't Houtenhuis, De Rijp 24874
Museum Scheveningen, Den Haag 24913
Museum van Egmond, Egmond aan Zee 24995
Visserij- en Cultuurhistorisch Museum, Woudrichem 25657
Visserijmuseum, Breskens 24845
Visserijmuseum, Bruinisse 24852
Visserijmuseum, Vlaardingen 25598
Visserijmuseum Zoutkamp, Zoutkamp 25689
Visserijtentoonstelling Hulp en Steun, Urk 25551
Zee- en Havenmuseum de Visserijschool, Ijmuiden 25191

Norway
Andøymuseet, Risøyhamn 26263
Fiskerimuseet og Kunstsmie i Sund, Sund i Lofoten 26331
Fiskerimuseet på Hjertøya, Molde 26187
Fiskerværsmuseet, Sørvågen 26313
Fossmotunet - Målselv Bygdemuseum, Moen 26185
Grytøy Bygdetun, Lundenes 26176
Kommandør Chr. Christensen's Hvalfangst Museum, Sandefjord 26282
Kystmuseet i Sogn og Fjordane, Florø 26083
Leka Bygdemuseum, Leka 26159
Lenvik Bygdemuseet, Finnsnes 26081
Lofotmuseet, Kabelvåg 26130
Nordkappmuseet, Honningsvåg 26119
Nordlandsmuseet, Bodø 26045
Norges Fiskerimuseet, Bergen 26034
Norsk Hermetikkmuseum, Stavanger 26319
Norsk Skogbruksmuseum, Elverum 26071
Sunnhordland Folkemuseum og Sogelag, Stord 26329
Vestvågøy Museum, Leknes 26160

Poland
Muzeum Rybołówstwa, Hel 26743

Portugal
Museu dos Baleeiros, Lajes do Pico 27374
Museu Oceanográfico, Setúbal 27438

Russia
Muzej-Akvarium, Vladivostok 28129
Muzej Ochoty i Rybolovstva, Moskva 27904

South Africa
Old Harbour Museum, Hermanus 28496

Spain
Arrantzaleen Museoa, Bermeo 28845
Museu de la Pesca de Palamós, Palamós 29451
Museu Marítim de Barcelona, Barcelona 28822

Sri Lanka
National Maritime Museum, Galle 29988

Sweden
Kukkola Fiskemuseum, Haparanda 30121
Nordvärmlands Jakt och Fiskemuseum, Sysslebäck 30417

Switzerland
Fischereimuseum, Ermatingen 30753
Fischereimuseum, Neuhausen am Rheinfall 31056
Musée du Léman, Nyon 31062
Museo della Pesca, Caslano 30680
Seemuseum in der Kornschütte, Kreuzlingen 30905

United Kingdom
Arbuthnot Museum, Peterhead 34176
Brighton Fishing Museum, Brighton 32393
Brixham Museum, Brixham 32413
Buckhaven Museum, Buckhaven 32435
Buckie Drifter Maritime Museum, Buckie 32436
Eyemouth Museum, Eyemouth 32993
Fishermen's Museum, Hastings 33211
Forge Mill Needle Museum and Bordesley Abbey Visitor Centre, Redditch 34288
Golden Hind Museum, Brixham 32414
Hull Maritime Museum, Kingston-upon-Hull 33399
Izaak Walton's Cottage, Shallowford 34453
Lossiemouth Fisheries and Community Museum, Lossiemouth 33827
Maritime Museum for East Anglia, Great Yarmouth 33157
National Fishing Heritage Centre, Grimsby 33165
Scottish Fisheries Museum, Anstruther 32052
True's Yard Fishing Heritage Centre, King's Lynn 33393
Tugnet Ice House, Spey Bay 34538
Whitstable Oyser and Fishery Exhibition, Whitstable 34818

U.S.A.
The American Museum of Fly Fishing, Manchester 38299
Catskill Fly Fishing Center and Museum, Livingston Manor 38092
Clausen Memorial Museum, Petersburg 39341
Cold Spring Harbor Whaling Museum, Cold Spring Harbor 36168
Museum of Biloxi, Biloxi 35499
National Fresh Water Fishing Hall of Fame, Hayward 37388
Sag Harbor Whaling and Historical Museum, Sag Harbor 39915

Yugoslavia
Ribarsko-Biološka Zbirka, Novi Dojran 41579

Folk Art

Argentina
Museo Cooperativo Eldorado, Eldorado 00327
Museo de Artes y Artesanías Enrique Estrada Bello, Santo Tomé 00611
Museo de Motivos Argentinos José Hernández, Buenos Aires 00184
Museo Monseñor José Fagnano, Río Grande 00511

Australia
Bega Valley Regional Art Gallery, Bega 00779
Latvian Museum, Wayville 01586
Man From Snowy River Folk Museum, Corryong 00936
Das Neumann Haus Museum, Laidley 01148
Tiagarra Aboriginal Culture Centre and Museum, Devonport 00967

Austria
Anton-Museum, Zwettl, Niederösterreich 03024
Haus der Völker, Schwaz 02624
Heimatmuseum, Telfs 02692
Museum für Volkskultur Spittal an der Dau, Spittal an der Drau 02645
Österreichisches Museum für Volkskunde, Wien 02933
Private Lebzelt- und Buttermodelabdrucksammlung, Pressbaum 02438
Salzburger Museum Carolino Augusteum, Salzburg 02531
Sammlungen Schloß Moosham, Mauterndorf 02278
Tiroler Volkskunstmuseum, Innsbruck 02075
Walsermuseum Lech-Tannberg, Lech 02192

Bangladesh
Sonargaon Folk Art and Craft Museum, Sonargaon 03061

Belarus
Gallery of Traditional Ornamental Art, Minsk 03075
Grodnenski Gosudarstvennyj Istoričeskij Muzej, Grodno 03071

Belgium
Museum voor Volkskunde, Brugge 03224
Rariteiten- en Ambachtenmuseum 't Krekelhof, Koksijde 03510

Brazil
Museu Casa do Pontal, Rio de Janeiro 04013
Museu de Arte e Cultura Popular Coordenação de Cultura, Cuiabá 03926
Museu de Arte Popular, Salvador 04090

Bulgaria
Nacionalen Etnografski Muzej na Bălgarskata Akademija na Naukite, Sofia 04322

Cameroon
Musée Bamilike, Dschang 04412

Canada
Lower Fort Garry, Selkirk 05891
Musée de Charlevoix, Pointe-au-Pic 05613
Museum of Antiquities, Saskatoon 05872

Chile
Museo de Arte Popular Americano, Santiago 06386
Museo Regional de la Araucania, Temuco 06398

China, People's Republic
Guangdong Folk Arts and Crafts Museum, Guangzhou 06539

Colombia
Museo de Arte y Tradiciones Populares, Santafé de Bogotá 06898

Costa Rica
Museo Indigeno, San José 06948

Croatia
Galerija Hlebine-Muzejska Zbirka, Hlebine 06992
Galerija Zavjetnih Slika Brodova, Dubrovnik 06984
Narodni Muzej, Zadar 07094

Cuba
Museo de Arte Popular, La Habana 07145

Cyprus
Cyprus Folk Art Museum, Nicosia 07202
Folk Art Museum, Limassol 07198
Folk Art Museum, Yeroskipos 07216
Pierides Museum, Larnaka 07196

Cyprus Turk
Folk Art Museum, Girne 07221

Czech Republic
Městské Muzeum, Česká Třebová 07282
Muzeum Beskyd Frýdek-Místek, Frýdek-Místek 07323
Oddělení Oblastního Muzea Jihovychodní Moravy, Zlín, Luhačovice 07450
Vlastivědné Muzeum, Vysoké nad Jizerou 07716

Denmark
Lolland-Falsters Stiftsmuseum, Maribo 07965

Ecuador
Museo de Artesanias Cefa, Quito 08161
Museo de la Inmaculada Concepción, Cuenca 08125
Museo de las Artes Populares Cidap, Cuenca 08126

Finland
Emil Cedercreutzin Museo, Harjavalta 08333
Ilmajoen Museo, Ilmajoki 08408
Muurlan Kotiseutumuseo, Muurla 08687

France
Abbaye-Musée, Airvault 09081
Maison d'Offwiller, Offwiller 12173
Musée Alsacien, Strasbourg 13596
Musée Catalan des Arts et Traditions Populaires, Perpignan 12499
Musée Cévenol, Le Vigan (Gard) 11282
Musée d'Archéologie et d'Art Populaire René-Bauberot, Châteauponsac 10037
Musée d'Art et d'Histoire, Pithiviers (Loiret) 12536
Musée d'Art et Traditions Populaires, Nancy 12020
Musée d'Art Régional, Villiers-Saint-Benoit 14049
Musée d'Arts et Traditions Populaires, La Guérinière 10992
Musée d'Arts et Traditions Populaires Paul Reclus, Domme 10350
Musée de Cerdagne, Sainte-Léocadie 13317
Musée de Dol, Dol-de-Bretagne 10344
Musée de la Passementerie, Jonzieux 10889
Musée Départemental de l'Oise, Beauvais 09484
Musée Départemental des Arts et Traditions Populaires du Perche, Saint-Cyr-la-Rosière 12956
Musée des Arts et des Traditions Populaires des Hautes-Côtes, Reulle-Vergy 12738
Musée des Arts et Métiers, Salles-la-Source 13369
Musée des Arts et Traditions Populaires, Blain 09579
Musée des Arts et Traditions Populaires, Cherves-Mirebeau 10091
Musée des Arts et Traditions Populaires, La Petite-Pierre 11010
Musée des Arts et Traditions Populaires et des Arts Appliqués, Moissac 11786
Musée du Charroi Rural, Salmiech 13370
Musée du Vieux-Château, Laval (Mayenne) 11150
Musée National des Arts et Traditions Populaires, Paris 12430
Musée Régional d'Arts et de Traditions Popoulaires, Grimaud 10754

Gabon
Musée des Arts et Traditions du Gabon, Libreville 14141

Germany
Altonaer Museum in Hamburg, Hamburg 16204
Bauernhaus-Museum, Bielefeld 14897
Buddelschiff-Museum, Neuharlingersiel 17636
Erzgebirgische Volkskunststube, Bermsgrün 14868
Erzgebirgischer Spielzeugwinkel, Obereisenheim 17769
Heimatmuseum, Bad Neustadt an der Saale 14482
Heimatmuseum im Unteren Turm, Leutershausen 17088
Heimatmuseum Schloß Adelsheim, Berchtesgaden 14650
Heimatstube Freest, Freest 15796
Heimatstube Podersam-Jechnitz, Kronach 16885
Missionsmuseum des päpstlichen Missionswerks der Kinder in Deutschland, Aachen 14167
Museum für bergmännische Volkskunst Schneeberg, Schneeberg, Erzgebirge 18367
Museum für Sächsische Volkskunst, Dresden 15418
Museum für Volkskunst, Meßstetten 17348
Museum Knochenstampfe, Zwönitz 19303
Museum Otzberg, Otzberg 17918
Museum Rade am Schloß Reinbek, Reinbek 18122
Museumsdorf Bayerischer Wald, Tittling 18716
Oderlandmuseum, Bad Freienwalde 14430
Siegerlandmuseum mit Ausstellungsforum Haus Oranienstraße, Siegen 18489
Theodor-Zink-Museum und Wadgasserhof, Kaiserslautern 16626
Volkskundemuseum des Bezirks Unterfranken, Bad Bocklet 14404
Vorderasiatisches Museum, Berlin 14863

Greece
Archipelagos Cultural Center, Athinai 19362
Eleftheriadis Collection, Petra 19614
Folk Art Museum of the Metropolis of Kos, Kos 19534
Kyriazopoulos Collection, Thessaloniki 19676
Mouseio Ellinikis Laïkis Technis, Athinai 19389
National Historical Museum, Athinai 19411

Hungary
Naiv Művészek Múzeuma, Kecskemét 19920
Népmüvészeti Tájház, Balatonszentgyörgy 19794
Palóc Múzeum, Balassagyarmat 19790
Szabadtéri Néprajzi Múzeum, Szentendre 20039

India
Ananda Niketan Kirtishala, Haora 20259
Cultural Research Institute, Kolkata 20181
Gurusaday Museum, Kolkata 20322
Kachchh Museum, Bhuj 20175
Lady Wilson Museum, Dharampur 20230
Madhya Pradesh Tribal Research and Development Institute, Bhopal 20171
Museum and Art Gallery, Burdwan 20181
State Tribal Museum, Chhindwara 20191

Indonesia
Museum Negeri Sumatera Barat, Padang 20551

Iran
Sanandaj Museum, Sanandaj 20637

Israel
Mishkan Le'Omanut, Ein Harod 20877

Italy
Casa del Pascoli, San Mauro Pascoli 22495
Museo Carnico delle Arti Popolari Michele Gortani, Tolmezzo 22658
Museo della Comunità di Fiemme, Cavalese 21372
Museo della Cultura Popolare Contadina, Correga Ligure 21470
Museo della Vita e delle Tradizioni Popolari Sarde, Nuoro 22058

Museo delle Arti e Tradizioni Popolari del Gargano Giovanni Tancredi, Monte Sant'Angelo 21978
Museo Etnografico G. Pitrè, Palermo 22112
Museo Etnografico Siciliano Giuseppe Pitrè, Palermo 22113
Museo Ibleo delle Artie e Tradizioni Popolari, Modica 21953
Museo Nazionale delle Arti e Tradizioni Roma, Roma 22399
Museo Pittori Naif Italiani, Luzzara 21819

Japan
Fujii Bijutsu Mingeikan, Takayama 23548
Gotoh Bijutsukan, Tokyo 23602
Hachiro Yuasa Memorial Museum, Mitaka 23314
Kochi-ken Kaitokukan, Kochi 23169
Kumamoto International Folk Art Museum, Kumamoto 23193
Kurashiki Mingeikan, Kurashiki 23200
Kyoto Prefectural Museum, Kyoto 23246
Matsumoto Folk Arts Museum, Matsumoto 23293
Nihon Mingeikan, Tokyo 23652
Okinawa-kenritsu Hakubutsukan, Naha 23363
Osaka Nippon Mingeikan, Suita 23524
Tottori-kenritsu Hakubutsukan, Tottori 23712

Korea, Republic
Cheju-do Folk Craft, Folklore and Natural History Museum, Cheju 23877
Chonju National Museum, Chonju 23886
Duksung Womens College Art Museum, Seoul 23918
Kuknip Minsok Pakmulgwan, Seoul 23935
Kwangju Municipal Museum, Kwangju 23903
Suk Joo-sun Memorial Museum of Korean Folk Arts, Seoul 23953

Latvia
Latvijas Etnogāfiskais Brīvdabas Muzjs, Rīga 24075

Mexico
Museo de Arte Popular, Toluca 24515
Museo de Arte Popular Poblano, Puebla 24500
Museo Nacional de Artes e Industrias Populares, México 24461
Museo Regional de Arte Michoacano, Uruapán 24521
Museo Regional de Artes Populares, Patzcuaro 24496
Museo Regional de Guadalajara, Guadalajara 24398

Morocco
Musée Bert Flint, Marrakech 24558
Musée d'Art Populaire Marocain, Tétouan 24571
Musée Ethnographique, Chefchaouen 24553

Namibia
Shambyu Museum, Shambyu 24626

Netherlands
Gouden Handen, 's-Heerenberg 25119
Huize Nijenstede, Hardenberg 25105
Katwijks Museum, Katwijk aan Zee 25203
Multi Colour Museum, Middelburg 25291
Museum De Vier Quartieren, Oirschot 25343
Muzen Museum voor Creatief Werk, Bergeijk 24808

New Zealand
Rotorua Museum of Art and History, Rotorua 25884
Whakatane District Museum and Gallery, Whakatane 25951

Nigeria
Museum of Antiquities, Oshogbo 25992

Norway
Fylkesmuseet for Telemark og Grenland, Skien 26297
Lågdalsmuseet, Kongsberg 26143
Maihaugen, Lillehammer 26165
Nordfjord Folkemuseum, Sandane 26281
Rjukan og Tinn Museum, Rjukan 26266

Pakistan
Lok Virsa, Islamabad 26400

Peru
Colección de Arte Popular de Elvira Luza, Lima 26484

Philippines
Bontoc Museum, Bontoc 26520
Kailokuan Historical Ilocano Museum, Pasay 26576

Poland
Muzeum Beskidzkie im. A. Podżorskiego, Wisła 27262
Muzeum Budownictwa Ludowego, Sanok 27085
Muzeum Etnograficzne, Poznań 27020
Muzeum Etnograficzne, Włocławek 27267
Muzeum Kultury Ludowej, Osiek nad Notecią 26985
Muzeum Lachów Sądeckich im. Zofii i Stanisława Chrząstowskich, Podegrodzie 27007
Muzeum Pomorza Środkowego, Słupsk 27098
Muzeum Regionalne, Łuków 26921
Muzeum Regionalne, Radomsko 27060
Muzeum Regionalne im. Seweryna Udzieli, Stary Sącz 27115
Muzeum Regionalne Ziemi Zbąszyńskiej PTTK, Zbąszyń 27315
Muzeum Rzemiosła, Krosno 26860

Portugal
Museu de Arte Popular, Lisboa 27390

Puerto Rico
Museo de Las Américas, San Juan 27464

Romania
Complexul Național Muzeal Astra, Sibiu 27646
Muzeul Arhitecturii Populare din Gorj, Bumbești-Jiu 27532
Muzeul de Artă Populară, Constanța 27555
Muzeul de de Etnografie și Artă Populară Orăștie, Orăștie 27615
Muzeul de Etnografie și Artă Populară, Reghin 27631
Muzeul Etnografic Gura Humorului, Gura Humorului 27582
Muzeul Maramureșului, Sighetu Marmației 27649
Muzeul Satului, București 27527

Russia
Municipalnyj Muzej Naivnogo Iskusstva, Moskva 27854
Muzej Narodnogo Iskusstva, Moskva 27899
Ostankinskij Dvorec-muzej, Moskva 27928
Vserossijskij Muzej Dekorativno-Prikladnogo i Narodnogo Iskusstva, Moskva 27943

Slovakia
Historické Múzeum, Bratislava 28203
Múzeum, Ždiar 28315

Spain
Museo Diocesano Regina Coeli, Santillana del Mar 29687
Museo Municipal de Prehistoria, Gandía 29076
Museo Municipal Taurino, Córdoba 28982
Museo Parroquial, Ecija 29024
Museu d'Art Popular, Horta de Sant Joan 29144
Museu de l'Empordà, Figueres 29057
Museu Municipal, Molins de Rei 29361

Sri Lanka
Folk Museum, Anuradhapura 29976

Sweden
Dalarnas Museum, Falun 30074

Switzerland
Historisches Museum Murten, Murten 31041
Musée du Vieux-Pays d'Enhaut, Château-d'Oex 30692
Museo di Vallemaggia, Giumaglio 30829
Museum im Lagerhaus, Sankt Gallen 31174
Schloßmuseum Thun, Thun 31309

Syria
Museé d'Art Populaire du Hauran, Bosra 31496
Popular Traditions Museum Qasrelazem, Damascus 31500

Tunisia
Musée des Arts Populaires et Traditions, Sfax 31629

Ukraine
Kolomya State Museum of Folk Art, Kolomja 31913
Nacionalnij Muzej u Lvovi, Lviv 31935
Ukrainian Museum of Folk and Decorative Art, Kyïv 31925

United Kingdom
Buxton Museum and Art Gallery, Buxton 32478
Polish Cultural Institution Gallery, London 33748

Uruguay
Museo del Indio y del Gaucho, Tacuarembó 34965

U.S.A.
Abby Aldrich Rockefeller Folk Art Museum, Williamsburg 41186
Academy Art Museum, Easton 36625
American Folk Art Museum, New York 38836
American Museum of Straw Art, Long Beach 38110
Americana Museum, El Paso 36664
Art and Culture Center of Hollywood, Hollywood 37464
Art Center of Battle Creek, Battle Creek 35373
Beck Cultural Exchange Center, Knoxville 37827
Bedford Gallery at the Dean Lesher Regional Center for the Arts, Walnut Creek 40909
Birmingham-Bloomfield Art Center, Birmingham 35514
Blue Ridge Institute and Museum, Ferrum 36827
B'nai B'rith Klutznick National Jewish Museum, Washington 40953
Boone County Historical Center, Boone 35570
Branigan Cultural Center, Las Cruces 37947
Brattleboro Museum and Art Center, Brattleboro 35639
Brookings Arts Council, Brookings 35688
Bulloch Hall, Roswell 39872
Center for Cultural Arts, Gadsden 37060
Chase Home Museum of Utah Folk Art, Salt Lake City 40042
Chattahoochee Valley Art Museum, La Grange 37854
Columbus Cultural Arts Center, Columbus 36226
Creative Arts Center, Pontiac 39526
Cuban Museum of Arts and Culture, Miami 38451
Cultural Heritage Center, Dallas 36354
Davis Art Center, Davis 36389
Delta Cultural Center, Helena 37393
Denver Art Museum, Denver 36470
Eide-Dalrymple Gallery, Sioux Falls 40372
Eva and Morris Feld Gallery, New York 38869
Falkirk Cultural Center, San Rafael 40156
Fayette Art Museum, Fayette 36817
Folk Art Center, Asheville 35168
Folk Art Society of America, Richmond 39759
Four Rivers Cultural Center, Ontario 39179
Fowler Museum of Cultural History, Los Angeles 38142
Goschenhoppen Folklife Museum, Green Lane 37238
Grants Pass Museum of Art, Grants Pass 37217
The Greater Reston Arts Center, Reston 39732
Havre de Grace Decoy Museum, Havre de Grace 37380
Hellenic Museum and Cultural Center, Chicago 36020
Henry County Museum and Cultural Arts Center, Clinton 36150
High Museum of Art, Folk Art and Photography Galleries, Atlanta 35219
Hiwan Homestead Museum, Evergreen 36770
Hungarian Folk-Art Museum, Port Orange 39542
Hungarian Heritage Center Museum, New Brunswick 38769
International Institute of Metropolitan Detroit, Detroit 36509
Jaffrey Civic Center, Jaffrey 37656
Jamaica Center for the Performing and Visual Arts, Jamaica 37657
James and Meryl Hearst Center for the Arts, Cedar Falls 35878
Jimmie Rodgers Museum, Meridian 38435
Kentucky Art and Craft Foundation, Louisville 38190
Kentucky Folk Art Center, Morehead 38626
Liberty Village Arts Center and Gallery, Chester 35982
Lyndon House Art Center, Athens 35198
McKissick Museum, Columbia 36206
Marian and Religious Museum, Brooklyn 35702
Mercer Museum, Doylestown 36557
Miles B. Carpenter Museum, Waverly 41062
Mingei International Museum, San Diego 40079
Mission Cultural Center for Latino Arts, San Francisco 40114
Mount Dora Center for the Arts, Mount Dora 38650
Museo Italoamericano, San Francisco 40115
El Museo Latino, Omaha 39167
Museum in the Community, Hurricane 37560
Museum of Craft and Folk Art, San Francisco 40116
Museum of International Folk Art, Santa Fe 40198
National Hall of Fame for Famous American Indians, Anadarko 35096
New England Carousel Museum, Bristol 35665
The Octagon Center for the Arts, Ames 35078
Oscar Howe Art Center, Mitchell 38560
Ozark Folk Center, Mountain View 38668
Parson Fisher House, Blue Hill 35547
Pelham Art Center, Pelham 39307
Pennsylvania Dutch Folk Culture Society Museum, Lenhartsville 37996
Petterson Museum of Intercultural Art, Claremont 36090
Polish American Museum, Port Washington 39548
Polish Museum of America, Chicago 36042
Ralph Milliken Museum, Los Banos 38178
Rialto Museum, Rialto 39736
Richland County Museum, Lexington 38026
Romanian Ethnic Art Museum, Cleveland 36139
Rose Center Museum, Morristown 38641
San Francisco African American Historical and Cultural Society Museum, San Francisco 40121
Schweinfurth Memorial Art Center, Auburn 35240
Scottsdale Museum of Contemporary Art, Scottsdale 40269
Sedona Arts Center, Sedona 40305
Shaker Museum, Old Chatham 39150
Shenandoah Valley Folk Art and Heritage Center, Dayton 36405
Shoshone Tribal Cultural Center, Fort Washakie 36972
Snug Harbor Cultural Center, Staten Island 40494
South Arkansas Arts Center, El Dorado 36659
South Carolina Artisans Center, Walterboro 40914
Southern Ohio Museum and Cultural Center, Portsmouth 39585
Southern Vermont Art Center, Manchester 38301
Stewart Indian Cultural Center, Carson City 35853
Swedish American Museum Association of Chicago Museum, Chicago 36047
Tennessee Valley Art Association, Tuscumbia 40777
Torpedo Factory Art Center, Alexandria 35045
Tucumcari Historical Research Institute Museum, Tucumcari 40759
Ukrainian-American Museum, Warren 40927
Ukrainian Museum, Cleveland 36142
Ukrainian Museum, New York 38948
Ukrainian National Museum, Chicago 36049
Vermont Folklife Center, Middlebury 38475
Virginia Museum of Fine Arts, Richmond 39771
Volcano Art Center, Hawaii National Park 37382
Washington Pavillion of Arts and Science, Sioux Falls 40376
Wendell Gilley Museum, Southwest Harbor 40430
Wheelwright Museum of the American Indian, Santa Fe 40204
White River Museum, Meeker 38404
William Bonifas Fine Arts Center, Escanaba 36736
Worcester Center for Crafts, Worcester 41298

Vietnam
Vietnam Museum of Fine Arts, Ha Noi 41471

Yemen
Crater Folk Museum, Aden 41487

Yugoslavia
Galerija Naivnih Slikara, Kovačica 41562
Gradski Muzej, Foča 41549
Muzej Naivne Umetnosti, Sid 41619

Folklore

Albania
Muzeu i Filmit Shkodër, Shkodër 00031

American Samoa
Jean P. Haydon Museum, Pago Pago 00071

Argentina
Centro Mundo Aborigen, Córdoba 00281
Museo Centro Cultural Pachamama, Amaicha del Valle 00103
Museo de Artesanías Tradicionales Folklóricas, Corrientes 00309
Museo de Esculturas Luis Perlotti, Buenos Aires 00167
Museo de la Artesanía Tradicional Juan Alfonso Carrizo, La Plata 00383
Museo del Traje, La Rioja 00390
Museo El Alero, Aristóbulo del Valle 00108
Museo Etnográfico y Colonial Juan de Garay, Santa Fé 00594
Museo Folklórico, La Rioja 00391
Museo Folklórico Provincial, San Miguel de Tucumán 00576
Museo Gauchesco Ricardo Güiraldes, San Antonio de Areco 00541
Museo Histórico y de la Tradiciones Populares de la Boca, Buenos Aires 00209
Museo La Cinacina, San Antonio de Areco 00542
Museo Molino Nant Fach, Trevelin 00635
Museo Rafael Escriña, Santa Clara de Saguier 00591
Museo Rauzi, Palmira 00456
El Museo Viajero, Buenos Aires 00237
Museo y Archivo Histórico de San Nicolás, San Nicolás de los Arroyos 00583

Australia
Alambee Auto and Folk Museum, Echuca 00988
Albany Residency Museum, Albany 00711
Armidale and District Folk Museum, Armidale 00740
Australian Children's Folklore Collection, Melbourne 01211
Barossa Valley Historical Museum, Tanunda 01513
Bowraville Folk Museum, Bowraville 00812
Brambuk Living Cultural Centre, Halls Gap 01072
Carbethon Folk Museum and Pioneer Village, Crows Nest 00942
Channel Folk Museum, Lower Snug 01178
Clarendon House, Nile 01313
Dawson Folk Museum, Theodore 01531
Daylesford and District Historical Museum, Daylesford 00961
Dowerin District Museum, Dowerin 00973
Dreamtime Cultural Centre, North Rockhampton 01318
Folk Museum, Deloraine 00962
Franklin House, Launceston 01157
Gawler Folk Museum, Gawler 01028
Gippsland Heritage Park, Moe 01252
Gloucester Lodge Museum, Yanchep 01620
Hahndorf Academy Public Art Gallery and Museum, Hahndorf 01070
History House, Armadale, Western Australia 00739
Kadina Heritage Museum, Kadina 01118
Kempsey Historical and Cultural Museum, Kempsey 01130
Latrobe Court House Museum, Latrobe 01155
Mahogany Inn, Mahogany Creek 01184
Mingenew Museum, Mingenew 01248
Mount Laura Homestead Museum, Whyalla Norrie 01596
National Trust Museum, Balaklava 00748
Nor West Bend Museum, Morgan 01264
Old Blythewood, Pinjarra 01360
Old Mornington Post Office Museum, Mornington 01269
Old Newcastle Gaol Museum, Toodyay 01536
Old Wool and Grain Store Museum, Beachport 00769
Penneshaw Maritime and Folk Museum, Penneshaw 01355
Pioneer Settlement Museum, Swan Hill 01484
Port Pirie National Trust Museum, Port Pirie 01386
Redcliffe Historical Museum, Redcliffe 01409
Rockcavern, Beechworth 00776
Settlers Museum, Brewarrina 00822
Tamborine Mountain Heritage Centre, Eagle Heights 00983
Tiboobura Local Aboriginal Land Council Keeping Place, Tiboobura 01534
Wellington Courthouse Museum, Wellington 01587
Wonnerup House and Old School, Busselton 00859
Woodloes Homestead Folk Museum, Cannington 00878
Zara Clarke Folk Museum, Charters Towers 00893

Austria
Gailtaler Heimatmuseum Georg Essel, Hermagor 02019
Heimat- und Landlermuseum, Bad Goisern 01694
Heimathaus mit Photographiemuseum, Mariazell 02265
Heimatkundliche Sammlung Strick, Bad Mitterndorf 01708
Heimatmuseum, Gleisdorf 01872
Heimatmuseum Arzberg, Passail 02377

Food

Forest Products

Fortresses → Castles and Fortresses

Fossils

Fresco Painting → Mural Painting and Decoration

Fur → Hides and Skins

Furniture and Interior

Furniture and Interior

Pałac Radziwiłłów w Nieborowie, Nieborów 26946
Salonik Chopinów, Warszawa 27248
Zamek Królewski na Wawelu - Państwowe Zbiory Sztuki, Kraków 26852

Portugal
Museu Palácio Nacional da Ajuda, Lisboa 27407
Paço dos Duques de Bragança, Guimarães 27372
Palácio Nacional da Pena, Sintra 27442
Palacio Nacional de Queluz, Queluz 27431

Puerto Rico
Casa Blanca Museum, San Juan 27462
Dr. Jose Celso Barbose Museum, Bayamon 27454
Museum of the Puerto Rican Family of the 19th Century, San Juan 27468

Russia
Dvorec-Muzej Petra I, Sankt-Peterburg 28022
Dvorets-muzej Petra III, Lomonosov 27778
Memorialnyj Dom-muzej V.M. Vaznecova, Moskva 27843

Slovakia
Museum of Home Décor, Kežmarok 28238
Múzeum Červený Kameň, Častá 28222
Nábytkové Muzeum, Markušovce 28258
Slovenské Národné Múzeum - Múzeum Betliar, Betliar 28192

Slovenia
Mestni Muzej Ljubljana, Ljubljana 28347

South Africa
Bertram House Museum, Cape Town 28432
Caledon Museum, Caledon 28430
Campbell Collections, Durban 28456
Drostdy Museum, Swellendam 28629
Dunluce House Museum, Kimberley 28523
Gately House, East London 28470
Graaf-Reinet Museum, Graaff-Reinet 28479
Great Fish River Museum, Cradock 28452
Jansen Collection, Pretoria 28580
Koopmans-De Wet House Museum, Cape Town 28439
Macrorie House Museum, Pietermaritzburg 28561
Marie Rawdon Museum, Matjiesfontein 28542
Montagu Museum, Montagu 28546
Museum Old Presidency, Bloemfontein 28419
Natale Labia Museum, Muizenberg 28548
Old House Museum, Durban 28462
De Oude Drostdy, Tulbagh 28630
Oude Kerk Volksmuseum, Tulbagh 28631
Our Heritage Museum, Adelaide 28404
The Paarl Museum, Paarl 28557
Richmond Museum, Richmond 28605
Rudd House Museum, Kimberley 28528
Somerset East Museum, Somerset East 28617
Stellenbosch Museum, Stellenbosch 28622
Temlett House, Grahamstown 28488
Worcester Museum, Worcester 28645

Spain
Casa de Pilatos, Sevilla 29707
Colección Vivot, Palma de Mallorca 29463
L'Enrajolada Casa-Museu Santacana, Martorell 29336
Museu Romantic Can Papiol, Vilanova i la Geltrú 29901

Sweden
Charlotte Berlins Museum, Ystad 30487
Ebbas Hus, Malmö 30219
Friluftmuseet Skansen, Stockholm 30345
Gustav III.'s Paviljong, Solna 30324
Julita Museums, Julita 30146
Krusenstjernska Gården, Kalmar 30150
Läckö Slott, Lidköping 30188
Rosendals Slott, Stockholm 30379
Stjernsunds Slott, Askersund 30033
Svaneholms Slott, Skurup 30315
Ulriksdals Slott, Solna 30327

Switzerland
Château, La Sarraz 31194
Château de Grandson, Grandson 30843
Château et Musée de Valangin, Valangin 31342
Engadiner Museum, Sankt Moritz 31180
Heimatmuseum Allschwil, Allschwil 30513
Heimatmuseum Schanfigg, Arosa 30536
Musée Régional du Vieux-Coppet, Coppet 30716
Museum Bärengasse, Zürich 31461
Museum für Wohnkultur des Historismus und des Jugendstils, Hilterfingen 30870
Museum Langmatt Sidney und Jenny Brown, Baden 30554
Palazzo Castelmur, Stampa 31271
Plantahaus - Chesa Planta, Samedan 31163
Schloß Tarasp, Tarasp 31298
Schloßmuseum, Oberhofen am Thunersee 31069
Unterengadiner Museum, Scuol 31224

Turkey
Osmali Evi, Bursa 31696

Ukraine
Alupka State Palace and Park Preserve, Alupka 31883

United Kingdom
Anne Hathaway's Cottage, Stratford-upon-Avon 34592
Arreton Manor, Arreton 32072
Ascott House, Leighton Buzzard 33494
Astley Hall Museum and Art Gallery, Chorley 32622
Aston Hall, Birmingham 32258
Athelhampton House, Dorchester 32784
Attingham Park Exhibition, Shrewsbury 34478
Audley End House, Saffron Walden 34348
Belgrave Hall and Gardens, Leicester 33482
Belton House, Grantham 33141
Bishops' House Museum, Sheffield 34456
Blackwell - The Arts and Crafts House, Bowness-on-Windermere 32344
Bowling Hall Museum, Bradford 32348
Brodsworth Hall, Doncaster 32778
Buckland Abbey, Yelverton 34904
Building of Bath Museum, Bath 32160
Burton Constable Hall, Kingston-upon-Hull 33395
Chethams's Hospital and Library, Manchester 33884
Church Farmhouse Museum, London 33614
Clarke Hall, Wakefield 34720
Claydon House, Middle Claydon 33941
Clergy House, Alfriston 32023
Cottage Museum, Lancaster 33433
Crathes Castle, Banchory 32127
Croxteth Hall, Liverpool 33534
Dalemain Historic House, Penrith 34161
Dan Winters House - Ancestral Home, Loughgall 33834
Drumlanrig Castle, Thornhill, Dumfriesshire 34669
Dudmaston House, Quatt 34260
Dunham Massey Hall, Altrincham 32040
East Riddlesden Hall, Keighley 33352
Elizabethan House, Plymouth 34195
Eltham Palace, London 33635
Epworth Old Rectory, Epworth 32976
Erddig Agricultural Museum, Wrexham 34892
Fairfax House Museum, York 34913
Felbrigg Hall, Norwich 34081
Fenton House, London 33638
Firle Place, Firle 33021
Florence Court House, Enniskillen 32972
Florence Nightingale Museum, Aylesbury 32097
Ford Green Hall, Stoke-on-Trent 34576
Gainsborough Old Hall, Gainsborough 33049
Geffrye Museum, London 33645
Georgian House, Bristol 32406
The Georgian House, Edinburgh 32918
Glamis Castle, Glamis 33066
Grove Rural Life Museum, Ramsey, Isle of Man 34264
Haddo House, Methlick 33938
Haden Hall, Cradley Heath 32697
Haden Hill House, Cradley Heath 32698
Hall-I'Th'-Wood Museum, Bolton 32323
Hall's Croft, Stratford-upon-Avon 34593
Hampton Court Palace, East Molesey 32882
Hardwick Hall, Chesterfield 32602
Haremere Hall, Etchingham 32979
Harewood House, Harewood 33191
Hauteville House, Saint Peter Port 34397
Heaton Hall, Manchester 33887
Hellen's House, Much Marcle 33989
Hill House, Helensburgh 33237
Hill of Tarvit Mansion House, Cupar 32729
Hinchingbrooke House, Huntingdon 33305
Hopetoun House, South Queensferry 34504
Ickworth House, Horringer 33290
Inveraray Castle, Inveraray 33321
Judges' Lodgings, Lancaster 33434
Kelmscott Manor, Kelmscott 33355
Kirkham House, Paignton 34145
Knebworth House, Knebworth 33424
Knole, Sevenoaks 34448
Lennoxlove House, Haddington 33173
Lydiard House, Swindon 34630
Lytham Hall, Lytham Saint Anne's 33858
Manor House, Donington-le-Heath 32783
Mary Arden's House and the Countryside Museum, Stratford-upon-Avon 34595
Melford Hall, Long Melford 33824
Michelham Priory, Hailsham 33177
Mount Edgcumbe House, Cremyll 32708
Nash's House and New Place, Stratford-upon-Avon 34596
National Portrait Gallery, Montacute 33976
Normanby Hall, Scunthorpe 34433
Nostell Priory, Wakefield 34722
Number 1 Royal Crescent Museum, Bath 32167
Oak House Museum, West Bromwich 34778
Oakwell Hall Country Park, Birstall 32283
Old Bridge House Museum, Dumfries 32827
Old House, Hereford 33257
Osborne House, East Cowes 32874
Packwood House, Lapworth 33446
Plas Newydd, Llangollen 33569
Preston Manor, Brighton 32395
Provan Hall House, Glasgow 33090
Provost Skene's House, Aberdeen 31989
Queen Charlotte's Cottage, Richmond, Surrey 34305
Rainham Hall, Rainham 34262
Red Lodge, Bristol 32411
Revolution House, Chesterfield 32604
Royal Pavilion, Brighton 32397
Rufford Old Hall, Rufford 34335
Scone Palace, Perth 34173
Seaton Delaval Hall, Seaton 34437
Selly Manor Museum, Birmingham 32276
Shakespeare Birthplace Trust, Stratford-upon-Avon 34598
Shibden Hall Museum, Halifax 33186
Shrewsbury Castle, Shrewsbury 34482
Sion Hill Hall, Thirsk 34662
Smithills Hall Museum, Bolton 32324
Southchurch Hall Museum, Southend-on-Sea 34526
Southside House, London 33785
Spencer House, London 33786
Stourhead House, Stourton 34586
Strangers Hall Museum of Domestic Life, Norwich 34090
Stratfield Saye House and Wellington Exhibition, Stratfield Saye 34591
Sulgrave Manor, Sulgrave 34611
Syon House, London 33790
Tenement House, Glasgow 33099
Town House Museum of Lynn Life, King's Lynn 33392
Treasurer's House, York 34918
Trevithick Cottage, Camborne 32499
Tudor House Museum, Southampton 34520
Turton Tower, Turton Bottoms 34700
The Vyne, Basingstoke 32151
Wallington Hall, Cambo 32497
Walmer Castle, Walmer 34730
Wightwick Manor, Wolverhampton 34869
Wilton House, Wilton 34831
Woburn Abbey, Woburn 34864
Wythenshawe Hall, Manchester 33902

U.S.A.
Ace of Clubs House, Texarkana 40667
Alexander Ramsey House, Saint Paul 39988
The Apple Trees Museum, Burlington 35746
Baxter House Museum, Gorham 37184
Beauport-Sleeper-McCann House, Gloucester 37158
Bloom Mansion, Trinidad 40728
Boscobel Restoration, Garrison 37102
Byers-Evans House Museum, Denver 36464
Carpenter Home Museum, Cle Elum 36114
Casa Navarro, San Antonio 40059
Codman House - The Grange, Lincoln 38044
Coffin House, Newbury 38967
Collinsville Depot Museum, Collinsville 36177
Copper King Mansion, Butte 35765
Cranbrook House and Gardens Auxiliary, Bloomfield Hills 35533
Cuneo Museum, Vernon Hills 40855
Darnall's Chance, Upper Marlboro 40803
Dumbarton House, Washington 40962
Dyckman Farmhouse Museum, New York 38865
Edison and Ford Winter Estates, Fort Myers 36937
Fairbanks House, Dedham 36434
Fairlawn Mansion and Museum, Superior 40582
Fall River County Historical Museum, Hot Springs 37504
General Adam Stephen House, Martinsburg 38371
Gracie Mansion, New York 38877
Grier-Musser Museum, Los Angeles 38144
Groton Historical Museum, Groton 37281
Harvey House Museum, Florence 36856
Hill-Hold Museum, Montgomery 38604
The Hill House, Portsmouth 39587
Hillforest House Museum, Aurora 35261
Historic General Dodge House, Council Bluffs 36298
Historical Newton Home, Decatur 36429
John Jay Homestead, Katonah 37749
John Wornall House Museum, Independence 37578
Julian H. Sleeper House, Saint Paul 39995
Kimball House Museum, Battle Creek 35374
Lexington County Museum, Lexington 38027
Loudoun Mansion, Philadelphia 39388
Merchant's House Museum, New York 38898
Merwin House Tranquility, Stockbridge 40520
Molly Brown House Museum, Denver 36476
Montpelier Cultur Arts Center, Laurel 37962
Mount Clare Museum House, Baltimore 35323
Old Hoxie House, Sandwich 40165
Old Westbury Gardens, Old Westbury 39154
Parry Mansion Museum, New Hope 38796
Pearl S. Buck House, Perkasie 39326
Phelps House, Burlington 35748
Pierrepont Museum, Canton 35825
Pointe Coupee Museum, New Roads 38827
Rebecca Nurse Homestead, Danvers 36375
Riordan Mansion State Historic Park, Flagstaff 36841
Rotch-Jones-Duff House and Garden Museum, New Bedford 38756
Sagamore Hill National Historic Site, Oyster Bay 39244
Sam Brown Memorial Park, Browns Valley 35715
The Shadows-on-the-Teche, New Iberia 38798
The Stephen Girard Collection, Philadelphia 39414
Stuart House City Museum, Mackinac Island 38242
Taft Museum of Art, Cincinnati 36082
Tinker Swiss Cottage Museum, Rockford 39834
Turner House Museum, Hattiesburg 37376
United States Department of the Interior Museum, Washington 41005
Victoria Mansion, Portland 39563
Wakefield House Museum, Blue Earth 35546
Wentworth Gardner and Tobias Lear Houses, Portsmouth 39584
White Hall Historic Site, Richmond 39748
The Willard House, Evanston 36765
Winslow Crocker House, Yarmouth Port 41318
Wyck Museum, Philadelphia 39421

Yugoslavia
Stalna Izložba Stilskog Namještaja 18.-19. St., Čelarevo 41540

Games → Toys and Games

Gas → Petroleum Industry and Trade

Gems → Precious Stones

Genealogy

Australia
Australian Institute of Genealogical Studies, Blackburn 00798

Austria
Großer Wappensaal im Landhaus, Klagenfurt 02115
Kammerhofmuseum der Stadt Gmunden, Gmunden 01890

Canada
Alberton Museum, Alberton 04428
Beaconsfield Historic House, Charlottetown 04685

Ireland
Heraldic Museum, Dublin 20743

Latvia
Kurzemes Hercogu Kapenes, Jelgava 24026

Netherlands
Huygens Museum Hofwijck, Voorburg 25609

New Zealand
Albertland and Districts Museum, Wellsford 25950
Waipu Centennial Trust Board, Waipu 25915

South Africa
Huguenot Memorial Museum, Franschhoek 28475

Spain
Museo de Heráldica Alavesa, Mendoza 29351

United Kingdom
Ancient House Museum, Clare 32631
Greenwich Local History Centre, London 33654
Mountbatten Exhibition, Romsey 34323

U.S.A.
Anoka County Historical and Genealogical Museum, Anoka 35132
Bellflower Genealogical and Historical Society Museum, Bellflower 35419
Camden Archives and Museum, Camden 35806
Dyer Memorial Library, Abington 34977
Fryer Memorial Museum, Munnsville 38680
Historical Society of Saint Marys and Benzinger Township Museum, Saint Marys 39984
Historical Society of the Town of Clarence Museum, Clarence 36095
Mayville Area Museum of History and Genealogy, Mayville 38388
Northampton County Historical and Genealogical Society Museum, Easton 36629
Union County Museum, Lewisburg 38004

Geography

Austria
Lungauer Landschaftsmuseum, Mauterndorf 02277

Germany
Universum Science Center Bremen, Bremen 15070

Italy
Museo della Società Geografica Italiana, Roma 22371
Raccolte dell'Istituto di Geografia, Roma 22429

Poland
Muzeum-Dworek Wincentego Pola, Lublin 26912

Russia
Russkij Gosudarstvennyj Muzej Arktiki i Antarktiki, Sankt-Peterburg 28066

Switzerland
Museum Langenthal, Langenthal 30913

United Kingdom
Explorerne Museum, Belleek 32206

U.S.A.
Explorers Hall, Washington 40964

Geology

Angola
Museu de Geológia, Paleontológia e Mineralógia, Luanda 00086

Argentina
Museo Mineralógico Prof. Manuel Tellechea, Mendoza 00432

Dunn-Seiler Museum, Mississippi State University 38548
E.C. Allison Research Center, San Diego 40076
Ed Clark Museum of Missouri Geology, Rolla 39855
Eleanor Barbour Cook Museum of Geology, Chadron 35901
Emporia State University Geology Museum, Emporia 36716
Fiedler Memorial Museum, Seguin 40306
Fort Peck Museum, Fort Peck 36943
Franklin Mineral Museum, Franklin 37012
Fryxell Geology Museum, Rock Island 39825
The Geological Museum, Laramie 37937
Geology Museum, Huntington 37546
Gerald E. Eddy Geology Center, Chelsea 35971
Grand Canyon National Park Museum Collection, Grand Canyon 37194
Greene Memorial Museum, Milwaukee 38514
Lora Robins Gallery of Design from Nature, Richmond 39762
Luzerne County Historical Museum, Wilkes-Barre 41183
McKissick Museum, Columbia 36206
Mammoth Site of Hot Springs, Hot Springs 37505
Mesa Southwest Museum, Mesa 38440
Mississippi Petrified Forest Museum, Flora 36850
Museum of Geology, Rapid City 39692
Museum of the Geological Sciences, Blacksburg 35524
New York State Museum, Albany 35001
Orton Geological Museum, Columbus 36231
Petrified Forest of the Black Hills, Piedmont 39438
Rolla Minerals Museum, Rolla 39856
Ruth Hall Museum of Paleontology, Abiquiu 34979
Schoellkopf Geological Museum, Niagara Falls 39002
Silver River Museum, Ocala 39105
Springfield Science Museum, Springfield 40463
Vermont Marble Exhibition, Proctor 39621
W.M. Keck Museum, Reno 39726

Vietnam
Geology Museum, Ha Noi 41465

Yugoslavia
Zbirka Poduzeća Naftagas, Novi Sad 41589

Glass and Glassware

Australia
City Art Gallery, Wagga Wagga 01567
Colac Otway Shire Hammerton Bottle Collection, Colac 00922
Devonport Gallery and Arts Centre, Devonport 00964
Fusions Gallery, Fortitude Valley 01017
House of Bottles, Kinglake 01137
House of Bottles and Bottle Museum, Tewantin 01523
Wagga Wagga Regional Art Gallery, Wagga Wagga 01568

Austria
Gläsermuseum, Gerersdorf 01868
Glasmuseum Zalto, Nagelberg 02323
Heimathaus Ulrichsberg, Ulrichsberg 02723
Heimatstube Schwarzenberg am Böhmerwald, Schwarzenberg am Böhmerwald 02619
Hinterglasmuseum, Sandl 02535
Museum Freudenthaler Glassammlung, Weißenkirchen im Attergau 02772
Salvador Dalí im Palais Pallavicini, Wien 02950
Sammlung der Neuen Stölzle Kristall, Nagelberg 02324
Stadt-, Glas- und Steinmuseum, Gmünd, Niederösterreich 01887
Steirisches Glaskunstzentrum und Glasmuseum Bärnbach, Bärnbach 01724
Wiener Glasmuseum, Wien 02970

Belgium
Musée du Verre, Liège 03553
Musée du Verre Art et Technique, Charleroi 03319
Musée du Verre chez Val-Saint-Lambert Château, Seraing 03708
Villa 't Eksternest, Roeselare 03683

Canada
Canadian Clay and Glass Gallery, Waterloo 06226
Les Maisons de Bouteilles, Richmond 05730

Czech Republic
Městské Muzeum v Železném Brodě, Železný Brod 07731
Muzeum Skla, Harrachov v Krkonoších 07326
Muzeum Skla a Bižuterie, Jablonec nad Nisou 07360
Muzeum Sklářské Manufactury - Moser, a.s., Karlovy Vary 07386
Muzeum Šumavy, Kašperské Hory 07390
Severočeské Muzeum v Liberci, Liberec 07433
Sklářské Muzeum, Kamenický Šenov 07382
Sklářské Muzeum, Nový Bor 07490
Uměleckoprůmyslové Muzeum v Praze, Praha 07599
Východočeské Muzeum, Pardubice 07518
Východočeské Muzeum, Pardubice 07518

Denmark
Anneberg-Samlingerne, Nykøbing Sjælland 07983
Den Gamle Gaard, Fåborg 07800
Glasmuseet Ebeltoft, Ebeltoft 07789

Finland
Iittalan Tehtaan Museo, Iittala 08406
Pykäri Nuutajärven Lasimuseo, Nuutajärvi 08721
Suomen Lasimuseo, Riihimäki 08840

France
Musée de l'Ecole de Nancy, Nancy 12022
Musée Despiau Wlerick, Mont-de-Marsan 11809
Musée du Verre, Sars-Poteries 13409
Musée du Vitrail, Gordes 10687
Musée International de la Parfumerie, Grasse 10720
Musée National Adrien Dubouché, Limoges 11403

Germany
Erich Mäder-Glasmuseum, Grünenplan 16128
Glas- und Keramikmuseum, Großalmerode 16108
Glasmuseum, Frauenau 15787
Glasmuseum, Immenhausen 16554
Glasmuseum, Warmensteinach 18929
Glasmuseum Boffzen, Boffzen 14963
Glasmuseum Grünenplan, Grünenplan 16129
Glasmuseum Hadamar, Hadamar 16155
Glasmuseum Rheinbach, Rheinbach 18159
Glasmuseum Steina, Bad Sachsa 14498
Glasmuseum Weisswasser, Weisswasser 19033
Glasmuseum Wertheim, Wertheim 19059
Goethe-Museum Stützerbach mit Museum zur Geschichte des technischen Glases, Stützerbach 18619
Heimatmuseum Uelzen mit Gläsersammlung Röver, Uelzen 18779
Historische Fraunhofer-Glashütte, Benediktbeuern 14642
Museum des Kreises Plön mit norddeutscher Glassammlung, Plön 17998
Museum für Glaskunst, Lauscha 17002
Museum für Modernes Glas, Rödental 18194
Museumsdorf und Technisches Denkmal, Klasdorf 16759
Neues Schloss Wallerstein, Wallerstein 18907
Passauer Glasmuseum, Passau 17947
Stadtmuseum Neustadt an der Waldnaab, Neustadt an der Waldnaab 17674
Stadtmuseum Waldkraiburg, Waldkraiburg 18896
Teplitz-Schönauer Heimatmuseum, Frankfurt am Main 15778
Theresienthaler Glasmuseum, Zwiesel 19300
Waldmuseum, Zwiesel 19301

Iran
Abgineh Va Sofalineh, Teheran 20642

Israel
Glass Museum, Tel Aviv 20996

Italy
Museo Vetrario, Venezia 22816

Japan
Notojima Glass Art Museum, Notojima 23395

Mexico
Museo del Vidrio, Monterrey 24485

Netherlands
De Drentse Glasbloazer, Dalen 24872
Glasmuseum, Hoogeveen 25173
Nationaal Glasmuseum, Leerdam 25224
Ontmoetingscentrum de Veldkei, Expositie, Havelte 25115

Poland
Muzeum Okręgowe, Jelenia Góra 26758

Russia
State Museum Pavlovsk Palace and Park, Pavlovsk 27984

Spain
Museo del Castillo de Peralada, Peralada 29503
Museo del Vidrio, San Ildefonso o la Granja 29610
Museu del Vidre, Algaida 28682

Sweden
Glasbruksmuseet i Surte, Surte 30416
Smålands Museum, Växjö 30472

Switzerland
Fondation Neumann, Gingins 30825
Gewerbemuseum, Winterthur 31396
Musée Ariana, Genève 30807
Musée de Design et d'Arts Appliqués Contemporains, Lausanne 30927
Musée du Verrier, Saint-Prex 31156
Museum Bellerive, Zürich 31463

United Kingdom
Bennie Museum, Bathgate 32173
Brierley Hill Glass Museum, Brierley Hill 32388
Broadfield House Glass Museum, Kingswinford 33408
Clevedon Court, Clevedon 32635
Dartington Glass Museum, Torrington 34684
Guildford House Gallery, Guildford 33167
Haworth Art Gallery, Accrington 32006
Himley Hall, Himley 33275
Royal Brierley Crystal Museum, Dudley 32819
Shipley Art Gallery, Gateshead 33056
South Shields Museum and Art Gallery, South Shields 34507
Stained Glass Museum, Ely 32968
Studio Glass Gallery, London 33789
World of Glass, Saint Helens 34372
Yelverton Paperweight Centre, Yelverton 34905

U.S.A.
Cambridge Glass Museum, Cambridge 35798
Corning Glass Center, Corning 36270
Corning Museum of Glass, Corning 36271
Fenton Glass Museum, Williamstown 41196
The Glass Museum, Dunkirk 36579
Greentown Glass Museum, Greentown 37261
The Jones Museum of Glass and Ceramics, Sebago 40297
Museum of American Glass at Wheaton Village, Millville 38505
National Heisey Glass Museum, Newark 38958
National Museum of Ceramic Art and Glass, Baltimore 35327
Neustadt Museum of Tiffany Art, New York 38920
Sandwich Glass Museum, Sandwich 40166

Globes → Cartography

Gold and Silver

Australia
Gold Museum, Ballarat 00752
Gold Treasury Museum, Melbourne 01218

Austria
Gold- und Silberschmiedemuseum, Wien 02860
Kaiserappartments und Ehemalige Hofsilber- und Tafelkammer, Wien 02876
Rauriser Talmuseum, Rauris 02473
Schloß- und Goldbergbaumuseum, Großkirchheim 01950

Belgium
Kasteelmuseum Slot van Laarne, Laarne 03518
Musée Régional d'Histoire et d'Archéologie, Visé 03803
Provinciaal Museum Sterckshof - Zilvercentrum, Antwerpen 03130
Stedelijk Museum, Oudenaarde 03653
Trésor de la Collégiale, Huy 03481
Trésor de la Collegiale Sainte-Waudru, Mons 03608
Trésor du Frère Hugo d'Oignies, Namur 03627

Bermuda
Tucker House Museum, Saint George's 03860

Bolivia
Museo del Oro y Metales Preciosos, La Paz 03867

Bulgaria
Otdel Etnografiya, Istoričeski Muzej, Vraca 04394

Canada
Klondike National Historic Sites, Dawson City 04773
Sherbrooke Village, Sherbrooke, Nova Scotia 05910
Silvery Slocan Museum, New Denver 05441
Soo Line Historical Museum, Weyburn 06258

Colombia
Museo del Oro, Santafé de Bogotá 06908

Costa Rica
Museo de Oro Precolombino, San José 06947

Czech Republic
Regionální Muzeum v Jílovém u Prahy, Jílové u Prahy 07376

Denmark
Tønder Museum, Tønder 08079

France
Collection Charles de l'Escalopier, Amiens 09153
Petit Musée de l'Argenterie, Paris 12455

Germany
Bergbau- und Heimatmuseum, Goldkronach 16033
Deutsches Goldschmiedehaus, Hanau 16257
Grünes Gewölbe, Dresden 15404
Historisches Rathaus, Krempe 16871
Historisches Silbererzbergwerk Grube Samson und Heimatmuseum, Sankt Andreasberg 18301
Ikonenmuseum Schloß Autenried, Ichenhausen 16539
Museum im Goldschmiedehaus, Ahlen 14195
Städtisches Museum Wesel, Wesel 19065
Technisches Museum Silberwäsche, Antonsthal 14295

Italy
Mostra Permanente del Tesoro della Cattedrale, Palermo 22106
Museo Alessi, Enna 21515
Museo Capitolare, Città di Castello 21431
Museo Civico, Lucignano 21815
Museo d'Arte e Storia Antica Ebraica, Casale Monferrato 21322
Museo della Comunità Ebraica di Roma, Roma 22370
Museo della Prepositura, Montecatini Val di Nievole 21982
Museo e Pinacoteca Civica, Todi 22650
Museo Sacro, Pompei 22232
Tesoro del Duomo, Milano 21934

Korea, Republic
Ewha Yoja Taehakkyo Pakmulgwan, Seoul 23919
National Museum of Korea, Seoul 23943

Latvia
Rīgas Vēstures un Kuģniecības muzejs, Rīga 24098

Netherlands
Collectie in het Gemmeentehuis, Brummen 24853
. Nederlands Goud-, Zilver- en Klokkenmuseum, Schoonhoven 25478
Oudheidkamer Beilen, Beilen 24797
Schoonhovens Edelambachtshuys, Schoonhoven 25479

New Zealand
Clyde Historical Museums, Clyde 25759
Maniototo Early Settlers Museum, Naseby 25842

Norway
Norsk Bergverksmuseum, Kongsberg 26144

Portugal
Museu de Alberto Sampaio, Guimarães 27371

Russia
Almaznyj fond, Moskva 27788

Spain
Cámara Santa, Oviedo 29442
Museo de Arte Sacro Antiguo, Villanueva de Lorenzana 29915

Sweden
Gruvmuseet, Sala 30293
Silvermuseet, Arjeplog 30027
Skattkammaren - Uppsala Domkyrkas Museum, Uppsala 30451

United Kingdom
Brodick Castle, Brodick 32424
Goldsmiths' Hall, London 33648
Ickworth House, Horringer 33290
Painters's Hall, London 33740
Treadgolds Museum, Portsmouth 34245

U.S.A.
Big Thunder Gold Mine, Keystone 37795
Custer Museum, Clayton 36110

Vatican City
Museo Storico Artistico, Città del Vaticano 41406

Graphic Arts

Argentina
Museo Municipal de Bellas Artes Lucas Braulio Areco, Posadas 00476
Museo Nacional del Grabado, Buenos Aires 00221

Armenia
M. Sarians Museum, Erevan 00675

Austria
Albertina, Wien 02800
Franz Traunfellner-Dokumentation, Pöggstall 02409
Galerie Loisel Grafik, Pörtschach am Wörther See 02417
Karikaturmuseum Krems, Krems 02147
Kunstsammlungen und Graphisches Kabinett, Furth bei Göttweig 01850
Kupferstichkabinett, Wien 02893
Salvador Dalí im Palais Pallavicini, Wien 02950
Salzburger Museum Carolino Augusteum, Salzburg 02531
Werner-Berg-Galerie der Stadt Bleiburg, Bleiburg 01732

Belgium
Cabinet des Estampes et des Dessins, Liège 03537
Centre de la Gravure et de l'Image Imprimée de la Communauté Française de Belgique, La Louvière 03516
Collections Artistiques de l'Université de Liège, Liège 03538
Stedelijk Prentenkabinet, Antwerpen 03137
Steinmetzkabinet, Brugge 03228

Canada
Galerie de l'UQAM, Québec 05667
Glenhyrst Art Gallery of Brant, Brantford 04587
McMaster Museum of Art, Hamilton 05031
The Station Gallery, Whitby 06261
Yaneff International Art, Caledon East 04618

China, People's Republic
Changshu Engraved Stone Museum, Changshu 06490
Hong Kong Space Museum, Hong Kong 06584
Qijiang Stone Engraving Museum, Gunan 06557
Shandong Stone Engraving Art Museum, Jinan 06615
Stone Engraving Art Museum, Beijing 06467
Stone Engraving Art Museum, Chongqing 06512
Stone Engraving Museum, Fu 06530
Suzhou Engraved Stone Museum, Suzhou 06723
Wuxi Engraved Stone Display Center, Wuxi 06760

Colombia
Museo de Artes Gráficas, Santafé de Bogotá 06899

Gravestones → Tombs

Handicapped

Handicraft

Heimatstuben der Stadt, Titisee-Neustadt 18715
Heimschneidermuseum, Großwallstadt 16124
Historische Handwerkerstuben, Gingst 15980
Historische Spinnerei Gartetal, Gleichen 15990
Historisches Stadtmuseum, Burghausen, Salzach 15152
Kolpings- und Handwerksmuseum im Faltertor, Dettelbach 15314
Kreisheimatmuseum, Demmin 15294
Kreismuseum Gräfenhainichen, Oranienbaum 17856
Kreismuseum Oranienburg, Oranienburg 17859
Kulturhistorisches Museum Rostock, Rostock 18225
Kulturhistorisches Museum Stralsund, Stralsund 18611
Landesmuseum Mainz, Mainz 17232
Lohgerber-, Stadt- und Kreismuseum, Dippoldiswalde 15342
Ludwig-Gebhard-Museum, Tiefenbach, Oberpfalz 18710
Mainfränkisches Museum Würzburg, Würzburg 19219
Museum am Markt / Schubarts Museum, Aalen 14173
Museum der Stadt Colditz, Colditz 15219
Museum Dermbach, Dermbach 15298
Museum des Kreises Plön mit norddeutscher Glassammlung, Plön 17998
Museum ehemalige Klöppelschule Tiefenbach, Tiefenbach, Oberpfalz 18711
Museum für bäuerliches Handwerk und Kultur, Wilhelmsdorf, Württemberg 19119
Museum für Holzhandwerke, Sinzig, Rhein 18511
Museum Göltzsch, Rodewisch 18190
Museum im Alten Schloß, Altensteig 14243
Museum Kloster Asbach, Rotthalmünster 18253
Museum Schloß Ehrenstein, Ohrdruf 17841
Museum Schloss Moritzburg, Moritzburg 17416
Museum Schloß Neu-Augustusburg, Weißenfels 19029
Museum Schloß Wilhelmsburg, Schmalkalden 18359
Museumsscheune Fränkische Schweiz, Hollfeld 16489
Natur-Museum mit Bauerngarten, Goldberg, Mecklenburg 16032
Norddeutsches Handwerkermuseum, Ovelgönne 17919
Oberpfälzer Handwerksmuseum, Rötz 18204
Regionalmuseum Alsfeld, Alsfeld 14226
Schefflenztal-Sammlungen, Schefflenz 18323
Schiefer- und Ziegelmuseum Dörfles-Esbach, Dörfles-Esbach 15352
Schloss Braunfels, Braunfels 15024
Schwäbisches Handwerkermuseum, Augsburg 14355
Siebenbürgisches Museum Gundelsheim, Gundelsheim, Württemberg 16143
Siebenbürgisches Museum Gundelsheim, Gundelsheim, Württemberg 16144
Staatliche Galerie Moritzburg Halle, Halle, Saale 16198
Stadt- und Bergbaumuseum Freiberg, Freiberg, Sachsen 15803
Stadtmuseum Gardelegen, Gardelegen 15896
Städtisches Hutmuseum, Lindenberg im Allgäu 17115
Städtisches Museum Braunschweig, Braunschweig 15040
Straßenbau - einst und jetzt, Waldbüttelbrunn 18885
Südhessisches Handwerksmuseum, Roßdorf bei Darmstadt 18220
Tabakspeicher, Nordhausen 17721
Technik anno dazumal - Museum Kratzmühle, Kinding 16737
Thüringer Museum Eisenach, Eisenach 15532
Voithenberghammer, Furth im Wald 15880
Volkskundliche Sammlung des Fichtelgebirgsvereins, Weidenberg 18956
Wachsstöcklkabinett - Wachzieher- und Lebzelter-Museum, Viechtach 18838
Waldnaabtal-Museum in der Burg Neuhaus, Windischeschenbach 19132
Wannenmachermuseum, Emsdetten 15572
Wegmachermuseum, Wasserburg am Inn 18937
Westfälisches Freilichtmuseum Hagen, Hagen, Westfalen 16166
Zeiselmairhaus, Schrobenhausen 18397

Greece
Ethnological Museum of Pyrsogianni Stonemasons, Konitsa 19530
Vouvalina Museum, Kalymnos 19492

Hungary
Kékfestő Múzeum, Pápa 19967
Kis Géza Ormánság Múzeum, Sellye 19993
Néprajzi Gyűjtemény, Sopron 20000

Iceland
Heimilisidnardarsafnid Halldórustofa, Blönduós 20087
Minjasafnid Burstarfelli, Vopnafjördur 20130

India
Arts and Crafts Museum, Bhavnagar 20165
Government Museum, Thiruvananthapuram 20429
Magan Sangrahalaya Samiti, Wardha 20454
Mahatma Phule Vastu Sangrahalaya, Pune 20395
Sree Moolam Shastyabdapurti Memorial Institute, Thiruvananthapuram 20430
Museum of Arts and Crafts, Lucknow 20344

Italy
Museo della Civiltà Contadina ed Artigiana della Calabria, Monterosso Calabro 21993
Museo dello Spazzacamino, Santa Maria Maggiore 22516
Museo dell'Ombrello e del Parasole, Gignese 21707

Japan
European Folkcraft Museum, Kawakami 23141
Gotoh Bijutsukan, Tokyo 23602
Ishikawa-kenritsu Dento Sangyo Kogeikan, Kanazawa 23124
Japan Handicrafts Museum, Koishihara Branch, Buzen 22947
Kyoto Gion Oil Lamp Museum, Kyoto 23240
Kyoto Museum of Traditional Crafts - Fureaikan, Kyoto 23244
Nagasaki Municipal Museum, Nagasaki 23352
Nihon Token Hakubutsukan, Tokyo 23654
Sapporo Geijutsu no Mori, Sapporo 23474
Tokyo Central Bijutsukan, Tokyo 23683
Tokyo Kokuritsu Kindai Bijutsukan Kogeikan, Tokyo 23689

Jordan
Jordan Museum of Popular Tradition, Amman 23798

Korea, Republic
Straw and Grass Handicraft Museum, Seoul 23952

Kuwait
The Tareq Rajab Museum, Hawelli 23968

Malaysia
Craft Museum, Kuala Lumpur 24297
Legends Heritage Museum, Kuah Langkawi 24292

Morocco
Musée de Dar-El-Jamaï, Meknès 24559

Netherlands
Atelier Na-iem, Gees 25045
Craftselijke Zadelmakerij Museum, Bellingwolde 24799
De Dubbele Palmboom, Rotterdam 25424
Grolsch Museum, Groenlo 25071
Het Hoogeland Museum, Uithuizermeeden 25548
Kantmuseum, Uithuizen 25546
Museum De Grutterswinkel, Leeuwarden 25229
Museum Valkenheide, Maarsbergen 25265
Museum van het Ambacht, Den Haag 24914
Nederlands Centrum voor Handwerken, Breda 24843
't Oude Ambachtshuis, Moordrecht 25300
Streekmuseum Opsterland, Gorredijk 25062

New Zealand
Hawke's Bay Museum, Napier 25841

Niue
Huanki Cultural Centre, Alofi 25997

Norway
Bygdetunet Jutulheimen, Vågåmo 26366
Hardanger Folkemuseum, Utne 26362
Stjørdal Museum KF, Stjørdal 26325
Trastad Samlinger, Borkenes 26048

Poland
Muzeum Dawnego Kupiectwa, Świdnica 27130
Muzeum Miedzi, Legnica 26877
Muzeum Regionalne, Chojnów 26666
Muzeum Regionalne, Krasnystaw 26856
Muzeum Rzemiosł Artystycznych i Precyzyjnych, Warszawa 27230
Państwowe Muzeum Etnograficzne, Warszawa 27247

Romania
Muzeul Tehnicii Populare Bucovinene, Rădăuți 27629

Russia
Gorodeckij Kraevedčeskij Muzej, Gorodec 27727
Novgorodskij Gosudarstvennyj Muzej-zapovednik, Novgorod 27957

Slovakia
Múzeum Umeleckých Remesiel, Bratislava 28212
Múzeum v Kežmarku, Kežmarok 28239

Slovenia
Mestni Muzej Ljubljana, Ljubljana 28347

South Africa
Zululand Historical Museum, Eshowe 28471

Spain
Colección Municipal, Granada 29110
Museo Etnológico de Navarra Julio Caro Baroja, Ayegui 28747

Sweden
Färgargården, Norrköping 30249
Falkenbergs Museum, Falkenberg 30069
Hallands Länsmuseer, Varberg 30474
Läckö Slott, Lidköping 30188
Länsmuseet Gävleborg, Gävle 30086
Lidköpings Hantverks- och Sjöfartsmuseum, Lidköping 30189
Nora Museum, Gyttorp 30113
Skellefteå Museum, Skellefteå 30310
Sundsvalls Hantverksmuseum, Sundsvall 30408

Switzerland
Heimatmuseum, Reinach (Basel-Land) 31121
Historisches Museum Arbon, Arbon 30532
Historisches Museum Blumenstein, Solothurn 31251
Malermuseum Wetzikon, Wetzikon 31381
Musée des Arts et des Sciences, Sainte-Croix 31159
Musée du Vieux-Moudon, Moudon 31024
Musée Paysan et Artisanal, La Chaux-de-Fonds 30698
Museum Wasseramt, Halten 30859
Ortsmuseum, Kaltbrunn 30888
Ziegelei-Museum, Cham 30688

United Kingdom
Abingdon Museum, Abingdon 32004
Bewdley Museum, Bewdley 32231
Castle Park Arts Centre, Frodsham 33046
Cousland Smiddy, Cousland 32684
Crafts Council Collection, London 33622
Cumberland Pencil Museum, Keswick 33365
Devon Guild of Craftsmen Gallery, Bovey Tracey 32342
Fordyce Joiner's Visitor Centre, Fordyce 33030
Friary Art Gallery, Lichfield 33508
Gordon Brown Collection, Ravenshead 34274
Hat Works, Museum of Hatting, Stockport 34567
Hop Farm, Paddock Wood 34142
Jersey Battle of Flowers Museum, Saint Ouen 34392
Mission Gallery, Swansea 34628
Museum of Local Crafts and Industries, Burnley 32451
The Petworth Cottage Museum, Petworth 34182
Ruthin Craft Centre, Ruthin 34343
Saint Ives Museum, Saint Ives, Cornwall 34382
Shepherd Wheel, Sheffield 34464
Shire Hall Gallery, Stafford 34542
Somerset Rural Life Museum, Glastonbury 33103
Stockwood Craft Museum and Mossman Gallery, Luton 33847
Strachur Smiddy Museum, Strachur 34588
Town Museum, East Grinstead 32876
W. Hourston Smithy Museum, Saint Margaret's Hope 34388

U.S.A.
Alleghany Highlands Arts and Crafts Center, Clifton Forge 36147
American Craft Museum, New York 38835
Arrowmont School of Arts and Crafts Collection, Gatlinburg 37106
Brookfield Craft Center, Brookfield 35685
Bunker Hill Museum, Charlestown 35942
Center for Book Arts, New York 38851
Contemporary Crafts Association Museum, Portland 39567
Craft Alliance Gallery, Saint Louis 39960
Crafts Museum, Mequon 38431
Craftsman Farms Foundation, Parsippany 39285
Crowley Art Association and Gallery, Crowley 36329
Cultural Heritage Center, Dallas 36354
Dawson Springs Museum and Art Center, Dawson Springs 36396
Fowler Museum of Cultural History, Los Angeles 38142
Hammond Museum, North Salem 39043
Hand Workshop Art Center, Richmond 39760
Hartzler-Towner Multicultural Museum, Nashville 38725
Kentucky Art and Craft Foundation, Louisville 38190
The London Brass Rubbing Centre in Washington D.C., Gaithersburg 37070
Longboat Key Center for the Arts, Longboat Key 38121
Lyndon House Art Center, Athens 35198
Macalester College Art Gallery, Saint Paul 39996
Mattye Reed African Heritage Center, Greensboro 37257
Mint Museum of Craft and Design, Charlotte 35949
Mississippi Crafts Center, Ridgeland 39777
Museum and Arts Center in the Sequim Dungeness Valley, Sequim 40314
Museum of the American Quilter's Society, Paducah 39250
Pope County Historical Museum, Glenwood 37156
Red Rock Museum, Church Rock 36069
Renwick Gallery of the Smithsonian American Art Museum, Washington 40996
Richard Sparrow House, Plymouth 39508
Schingoethe Center for Native American Cultures, Aurora 35259
School of Nations Museum, Elsah 36708
Snug Harbor Cultural Center, Staten Island 40494
Society for Contemporary Craft Museum, Pittsburgh 39474
South Carolina Artisans Center, Walterboro 40914
Southwest Museum, Los Angeles 38172
Steppingstone Museum, Havre de Grace 37381
Tama County Historical Museum, Toledo 40689
Thomas E. McMillan Museum, Brewton 35650
Western Colorado Center for the Arts, Grand Junction 37202
Worcester Center for Crafts, Worcester 41298
World Kite Museum and Hall of Fame, Long Beach 38116

Yemen
Al-Mukalla Museum, Al-Mukalla 41493
Seiyun in Wadi Hadhramaut Museum, Seiyun 41496

Yugoslavia
Gradski Muzej Sombor, Sombor 41624

Heraldry → Genealogy

Hides and Skins

Canada
Ermatinger, Sault Sainte Marie 05882
Fort Carlton, Regina 05701
Lieu Historique National du Commerce de la Fourrure, Lachine 05174
Nor' Wester and Loyalist Museum, Williamstown 06279
Port Royal National Historic Site, Annapolis Royal 04454
Sturgeon River House, Sturgeon Falls 05977

History

Albania
District Historical Museum, Përmet 00029
Museum of the Struggle for National Liberation, Tiranë 00034
Muzeu Historik Fier, Fier 00021

Algeria
History and Natural History Museum, Alger 00039

Andorra
Museu Casa Rull, Sispony 00076

Angola
Centro Nacional de Documentação e Investigação Histórica, Luanda 00083
Museu da Escravatura, Luanda 00085
Museu do Reino do Koongo, Mbanza Koongo 00092

Argentina
Casa Natal de Sarmiento, San Juan 00560
Fuerte de la Punta del Sauce, La Carlota 00367
Galería Monumento Histórico Nacional a la Bandera, Rosario 00516
Museo Americanista, Lomas de Zamora 00401
Museo de la Administración Federal de Ingresos Públicos, Buenos Aires 00172
Museo de la Casa Histórica de la Independencia Nacional, San Miguel de Tucumán 00574
Museo de la Escuela Normal Alejandro Carbo, Córdoba 00286
Museo de los Corrales Viejos de Parque de los Patricios, Buenos Aires 00181
Museo de los Pioneros, Río Gallegos 00506
Museo General Belgrano, Buenos Aires 00199
Museo Hermanos Nacif Weiss, Rivadavia 00514
Museo Histórico Conventual San Carlos, San Lorenzo 00567
Museo Histórico de la Honorable Cámara de Diputados de la Nación, Buenos Aires 00203
Museo Histórico de la Provincia de Catamarca, San Fernando del Valle de Catamarca 00548
Museo Histórico Nacional, Buenos Aires 00206
Museo Histórico Provincial Colonel Manuel José Olascoaga, Chos Malal 00269
Museo La Cinacina, San Antonio de Areco 00542
Museo Malvinas Argentinas, Río Gallegos 00507
Museo Metropolitano, Buenos Aires 00214
Museo Municipal Paula Florido, 25 de Mayo 00095
Museo Nacional Justo José de Urquiza, Concepción del Uruguay 00276
Museo Parlamentario, Buenos Aires 00228
Museo Ramón Pérez Fernández, Rivadavia 00515
Museo Regional Aníbal Cambas, Posadas 00477
Museo Regional Carlos Funes Derieul, Coronel Dorrego 00306
Museo Regional Dr. José Luro, Pedro Luro 00463
Museo Regional Histórico y de Ciencias Naturales, Coronel Pringles 00308
Museo Regional José G. Brochero, Santa Rosa de Río Primero 00605
Museo Regional Provincial, Puerto Deseado 00481
Museo Rural de la Posta de Sinsacate, Jesús María 00363
Museos Integrales de Antofagasta de la Sierra y Laguna Blanca, San Fernando del Valle de Catamarca 00550
Sala Josefa Rodriguez del Fresno, Santa Fé 00601

Armenia
State History Museum of Armenia, Erevan 00683

Australia
Adelaide Lithuanian Museum and Archives, Norwood 01326
Adelaide Masonic Centre Museum, Adelaide 00693
Australian Stockman's Hall of Fame and Outback Heritage Centre, Longreach 01173
City of Adelaide Civic Collection, Adelaide 00695
Conservation Resource Centre, Glebe 01043
Edith Cowan University Museum of Childhood, Claremont, Western Australia 00906
Edmund Wright House, Adelaide 00697
Griffith Pioneer Park Museum, Griffith 01061
Hyde Park Barracks Museum, Sydney 01493
Melbourne Museum, Carlton 00883
Migration Museum, Adelaide 00700
Monarch Historical Museum, Williamstown 01601

Museum of Chinese in the Americas, New York 38909
Museum of Connecticut History, Hartford 37363
The Museum of East Texas, Lufkin 38212
Museum of Florida History, Tallahassee 40621
Museum of History and Industry, Seattle 40289
Museum of Man in the Sea, Panama City Beach 39270
Museum of Nebraska History, Lincoln 38054
Museum of New Mexico, Santa Fe 40199
Museum of Our National Heritage, Lexington 38022
Museum of Russian Culture, San Francisco 40117
Museum of Science and History of Jacksonville, Jacksonville 37654
Museum of Texas, Waco 40893
Museum of the Albemarle, Elizabeth City 36680
Museum of the American Printing House for the Blind, Louisville 38195
Museum of the Cape Fear Historical Complex, Fayetteville 36823
Museum of the Cherokee Indian, Cherokee 35976
Museum of the Fur Trade, Chadron 35902
Museum of the Mountain Man, Pinedale 39448
Museum of the New South, Charlotte 35950
Museum of the Northern Great Plains, Fort Benton 36875
Napoleonic Society of America, Clearwater 36118
National Afro-American Museum and Cultural Center, Wilberforce 41180
National Border Patrol Museum and Memorial Library, El Paso 36673
National Cowboy and Western Heritage Museum, Oklahoma City 39138
National Cowgirl Museum and Hall of Fame, Fort Worth 36989
National Czech and Slovak Museum, Cedar Rapids 35886
National Frontier Trails Center, Independence 37580
National Hall of Fame for Famous American Indians, Anadarko 35096
National Museum of American History, Washington 40985
National Museum of American Jewish History, Philadelphia 39397
National Museum of Funeral History, Houston 37520
National Museum of the American Indian, New York 38918
National Society of the Children of the American Revolution Museum, Washington 40992
National Yiddish Book Center, Amherst 35085
Native American Exhibit, Fonda 36869
Native American Heritage Museum at Highland Mission, Highland 37423
Naumkeag House, Stockbridge 40522
Nevada Historical Society Museum, Reno 39722
Nevada State Fire Museum and Comstock Firemen's Museum, Virginia City 40881
Nevada State Museum, Carson City 35852
New Echota, Calhoun 35781
New Jersey State Museum, Trenton 40722
New Mexico Farm and Ranch Heritage Museum, Las Cruces 37948
The Newseum, Arlington 35156
Nickels-Sortwell House, Wiscasset 41266
Nobles County Historical Society Museum, Worthington 41302
North Carolina Museum of History, Raleigh 39675
Northeastern Nevada Museum, Elko 36692
Northern Indiana Center for History, South Bend 40405
Norwich University Museum, Northfield 39059
Oakland Museum of California, Oakland 39092
Oaks House Museum, Jackson 37642
O'Fallon Historical Museum, Baker 35286
Ohio Historical Center, Columbus 36230
Oklahoma Territorial Museum, Guthrie 37289
Oktibbeha County Heritage Museum, Starkville 40487
Old Capitol Museum of Mississippi History, Jackson 37643
Old Colony Historical Museum, Taunton 40641
Old Fort Garland, Fort Garland 36901
Old Fort Western, Augusta 35252
The Old Manse, Concord 36240
Old Ordinary Museum, Hingham 37441
Old Spanish Fort and Museum, Pascagoula 39290
Old State House, Boston 35602
Old State House, Hartford 37364
The Old State House Museum, Little Rock 38081
Old Washington Museum, Washington 40945
Old World Wisconsin, Eagle 36594
Olde Colonial Courthouse, Barnstable 35351
Oldest House Museum Complex, Saint Augustine 39922
Oliver House Museum, Saint Martinville 39982
Olmsted County Historical Society Museum, Rochester 39808
Olustee Battlefield, Olustee 39156
Oregon Coast History Center, Newport 38978
Our House State Memorial, Gallipolis 37083
Owens-Thomas House, Savannah 40242
Pacific University Museum, Forest Grove 36870
Pardee Home Museum, Oakland 39093
The Park-McCullough House, North Bennington 39024
Parker Tavern Museum, Reading 39698
Paul H. Karshner Memorial Museum, Puyallup 39659
Paul Revere House, Boston 35603
Paynes Creek Historic State Park, Bowling Green 35620
The Peace Museum, Chicago 36041
Pembina State Museum, Pembina 39309
Pennsylvania Anthracite Heritage Museum, Scranton 40274
Pennsylvania Lumber Museum, Galeton 37079
Peoria Historical Society, Peoria 39324
The Petroleum Museum, Midland 38491
Pierce Manse, Concord 36246
Pioneer Arizona Living History Museum, Phoenix 39435
Pioneer Florida Museum, Dade City 36348
Pioneer Heritage Center, LSU-Shreveport, Shreveport 40349
Pioneer Log Cabin Museum, Manhattan 38306
Pioneer Museum, Watford City 41047
Pioneer Woman Statue and Museum, Ponca City 39524
Pipestone County Historical Museum, Pipestone 39452
Pipestone National Monument, Pipestone 39453
Plimoth Plantation Museum, Plymouth 39506
Plum Grove Historic Home, Iowa City 37613
Polish American Museum, Port Washington 39548
Polish Museum of America, Chicago 36042
Porter-Phelps-Huntington Foundation, Hadley 37297
Portholes Into the Past, Medina 38403
Portsmouth Museums, Portsmouth 39588
Postville Courthouse Museum, Lincoln 38043
Prairie Grove Battlefield, Prairie Grove 39602
President Andrew Johnson Museum, Greeneville 37246
President Benjamin Harrison Home, Indianapolis 37603
The Presidential Museum, Odessa 39117
El Pueblo de Los Angeles Historical Monument, Los Angeles 38168
Putnam Museum of History and Natural Science, Davenport 36386
Railroad and Heritage Museum, Temple 40654
Red River Valley Museum, Vernon 40853
Redwood County Historical Society Museum, Redwood Falls 39717
Rensselaer Russell House Museum, Waterloo 41031
The Rice Museum, Georgetown 37122
Roanoke Island Festival Park, Manteo 38324
Roberson Museum and Science Center, Binghamton 35503
Rochester Museum, Rochester 39815
Rockingham, Princeton 39618
Roniger Memorial Museum, Cottonwood Falls 36294
Rosalie House, Eureka Springs 36759
Rosalie House Museum, Natchez 38732
Roscoe Village Foundation, Coshocton 36291
Rose Hill Plantation State Historic Site, Union 40795
Roseau County Historical Museum, Roseau 39864
Rowan Museum, Salisbury 40035
Royall House, Medford 38394
Ruggles House, Columbia Falls 36214
Rumford Historical Museum, North Woburn 39048
Rutherford B. Hayes Presidential Center, Fremont 37045
Safe Haven, Oswego 39216
Sag Harbor Whaling and Historical Museum, Sag Harbor 39915
Sagamore Hill National Historic Site, Oyster Bay 39244
Saint Augustine Lighthouse and Museum, Saint Augustine 39924
Saint Clements Island-Potomac River Museum, Colton Point 36192
Salem Maritime National Historic Site, Salem 40020
Salem Witch Museum, Salem 40021
Salter Museum, Argonia 35147
Sam Houston Memorial Museum, Huntsville 37555
San Francisco African American Historical and Cultural Society Museum, San Francisco 40121
San Jacinto Museum of History, La Porte 37867
San Joaquin County Historical Museum, Lodi 38098
San Marcos de Apalache Historic Site, Saint Marks 39981
Sanford Museum, Sanford 40172
Santa Fe Trail Museum, Trinidad 40730
Sault de Sainte Marie Historical Sites, Sault Sainte Marie 40231
Schomburg Center for Research in Black Culture, New York 38936
Seminole Nation Museum, Wewoka 41150
Senate House, Kingston 37814
Shaker Museum, New Gloucester 38781
Shaker Museum, South Union 40425
Shawneetown Historic Site, Old Shawneetown 39153
Sheldon Museum, Haines 37304
Shiloh Museum of Ozark History, Springdale 40448
Shirley-Eustis House, Boston 35605
Sibley Historic Site, Mendota 38424
Sinclair Lewis Museum, Sauk Centre 40229
Skirball Cultural Center, Los Angeles 38170
Slavonic Benevolent Order of the State of Texas Museum, Temple 40655
Smith Robertson Museum, Jackson 37644
Smith-Zimmermann Museum, Madison 38271
Smoky Hill Museum, Salina 40030
Society of the Cincinnati Museum, Washington 41000
Sons of the American Revolution Museum, Louisville 38197
Sotterley Plantation Museum, Hollywood 37465
South Carolina Confederate Relic Room and Museum, Columbia 36209
South Carolina Historical Society Museum, Charleston 35939
Southern Ute Indian Cultural Center, Ignacio 37571
Southwestern Michigan College Museum, Dowagiac 36551
Spirit of '76 Museum, Wellington 41086
Spurlock Museum, Urbana 40810
Stagecoach Inn Museum Complex, Newbury Park 38969
Star of the Republic Museum, Washington 41022
Star-Spangled Banner Flag House and 1812 Museum, Baltimore 35330
State Historical Society of Missouri Museum, Columbia 36199
State Museum of History, Oklahoma City 39144
State Museum of Pennsylvania, Harrisburg 37350
Staten Island Ferry Collection, Staten Island 40496
Statue of Liberty National Monument and Ellis Island Immigration Museum, New York 38942
Stearns History Museum, Saint Cloud 39934
Stephen A. Douglas Tomb, Chicago 36046
Stephens Museum, Fayette 36819
Stevens County Gas and Historical Museum, Hugoton 37536
Steves Homestead Museum, San Antonio 40069
Stewart M. Lord Memorial Museum, Burlington 35750
Stockbridge Library Historical Room, Stockbridge 40524
Storrowton Village Museum, West Springfield 41127
Strecker Museum Complex, Waco 40895
Strong Museum, Rochester 39816
Sunwatch Indian Village - Archaeological Park, Dayton 36403
Surratt House Museum, Clinton 36149
Swindler's Ridge Museum, Benton 35448
Tantaquidgeon Indian Museum, Uncasville 40789
Tate House, Portland 39562
Tennessee State Museum, Nashville 38727
Texas City Museum, Texas City 40668
Texas Memorial Museum, Austin 35277
Texas Ranger Hall of Fame and Museum, Waco 40896
Theodore Roosevelt Birthplace, New York 38946
Theodore Roosevelt Inaugural National Historic Site, Buffalo 35742
Thomas Edison Birthplace Museum, Milan 38495
Thomas P. Kennard House, Lincoln 38058
Thomas Wolfe Memorial, Asheville 35172
Thousand Islands Museum of Clayton, Clayton 36113
Tippecanoe Battlefield, Battle Ground 35376
Traverse County Historical Society Museum, Wheaton 41158
Treaty Site History Center, Saint Peter 40003
Tryon Palace, New Bern 38760
Tubman African-American Museum, Macon 38257
Turtle Bay Museums, Redding 39711
Turtle Mountain Chippewa Heritage Center, Belcourt 35410
Tuskegee Institute National Historic Site, Tuskegee Institute 40779
Ukrainian-American Museum, Warren 40927
Ukrainian Museum, Cleveland 36142
Uncle Remus Museum, Eatonton 36631
United States Army Museum of Hawaii, Fort DeRussy 36893
United States Marine Corps Museum, Washington 41007
Utah State Historical Society Museum, Salt Lake City 40050
The Valley Forge Museum, Valley Forge 40830
Valley Forge National Historical Park, Valley Forge 40831
Vandalia State House, Vandalia 40842
Ventura County Museum of History and Art, Ventura 40846
Vikingsholm, Tahoma 40616
Virginia Historical Society Museum, Richmond 39770
Wabasha County Museum, Lake City 37888
Wabasso Historical Society Museum, Wabasso 40888
The Wallace Museum Foundation, Montgomery 38602
Warden's House Museum, Stillwater 40514
Waseca County Historical Society Museum, Waseca 40943
Washington Crossing Historic Park, Washington Crossing 41023
Weir Farm, Wilton 41226
Wells Fargo History Museum, Los Angeles 38176
Wentworth-Coolidge Mansion, Portsmouth 39583
Western Archeological and Conservation Center, Tucson 40758
Western Hotel Museum, Lancaster 37916
Wilber Czech Museum, Wilber 41179
Will Rogers Memorial, Claremore 36094
William Hammond Mathers Museum, Bloomington 35542
William Howard Taft National Historic Site, Cincinnati 36084
William M. Colmer Visitor Center, Ocean Springs 39111
William S. Hart County Park and Museum, Newhall 38976
Willowbrook at Newfield, Newfield 38975
Windham Textile and History Museum, Willimantic 41197
Wing Luke Asian Museum, Seattle 40296
Winnebago Area Museum, Winnebago 41243
Winnie Davis Museum of History, Gaffney 37062
Winona County Historical Museum, Winona 41246
Winston Churchill Memorial and Library in the United States, Fulton 37059
Winterthur Museum, Winterthur 41261
Witte Museum, San Antonio 40070
Women's Heritage Museum, San Francisco 40131
Women's History Museum, West Liberty 41115
Woolaroc Museum, Bartlesville 35356
Workman and Temple Family Homestead Museum, City of Industry 36087
Wright Museum, Wolfeboro 41273
Wyoming State Museum, Cheyenne 35997
Yazoo Historical Museum, Yazoo City 41320
Yorba-Slaughter Adobe Museum, Chino 36062
Yorktown Museum, Yorktown Heights 41331
Yorktown Visitor Center Museum, Yorktown 41330

Uzbekistan

Gosudarstvennyj Muzej Istorii Kultury i Iskusstva Uzbekistana, Samarkand 41374
Historical Museum of Uzbekistan M.T. Oibek, Taškent 41380
Karakalpakskij Istoričeskij Muzej, Nukus 41373
Memorialnyj Muzej Juldaš Ahunbabaev, Margelan 41369
Sergej Borodin Muzej, Taškent 41386
Tashkent Historical Museum of the People of Uzbekistan, Taškent 41387

Venezuela

Casa Natal de El Libertador Simón Bolívar, Caracas 41412
Museo Cristóbal Mendoza, Trujillo 41455
Museo de Historia y Artesanía de la Colonial Tovar, Colonia Tovar 41442

Vietnam

Vien Bao Tang Lich Sa Viet Nam, Ha Noi 41469

Yugoslavia

Jevrejski Istorijski Muzej, Beograd 41511
Muzej Istorije Jugoslavije, Beograd 41515
Narodni Muzej, Beograd 41524
Narodni Muzej, Kragujevac 41565
Narodni Muzej, Leskovac 41571
Narodni Muzej Kruševac, Kruševac 41569
Narodni Muzej Niš, Niš 41578
Spomen Kuća Bitke na Sutjesci, Tjentište 41634
Spomen Muzej Prvog Zasjedanja ZAVNOBiH-a, Mrkonjić Grad 41573

History, Early → Prehistory and Early History

History, Local and Regional

Afghanistan

Bamian Museum, Bamian 00001
Ghazni Museum, Ghazni 00002
Herat Museum, Herat 00003
Kabul Museum, Kabul 00004
Kandahar Museum, Kandahar 00007
Maimana Museum, Maimana 00008
Mazar-i-Sharif Museum, Mazar-i-Sharif 00009

Albania

Butrinti Museum, Butrint 00014
District Historical Museum, Bérat 00011
District Historical Museum, Vlorë 00038
Elbasan Museum, Elbasan 00018
Fier Archaeological Museum, Fier 00020
Gjirokastër Museum, Gjirokastër 00023
Korçë Museum, Korçë 00025
National Historical Museum, Tiranë 00036
Scanderbeg Museum, Kruja 00028
Shkodër Museum, Shkodër 00032

Algeria

Musée Archéologique de Guelma, Guelma 00058
Musée de Béjaia, Béjaia 00049
Musée de Tiemcen, Tiemcen 00067
Musée d'El-Oued, El-Oued 00056
Musée National Cirta, Constantine 00054
Musée National Zabana - Demaeght Museum, Oran 00059
Musée Saharien de Ouargla, Ouargla 00060

American Samoa

Jean P. Haydon Museum, Pago Pago 00071

Andorra

Museu Viladomat d'Escultura, Escaldes-Engordany 00073

Angola

Museu da Pesca, Moçamedes 00093
Museu do Congo, Carmona 00079
Museu do Dundu, Chitato 00080
Museu do Pioneiro, Malange 00091
Museu Regional da Huila, Lumbango 00090
Museu Regional do Planalto Central, Huambo 00081

Argentina

Cartref Taid, Trevelin 00634
Casa de la Cultura, Curuzú Cuatiá 00316
Centro de Exposiciones La Casona de los Olivera, Buenos Aires 00137
Complejo Histórico Chivilcoy, Chivilcoy 00266
Complejo Museológico La Estación, Cruz Alta 00315
Exposición de Gregorio de Laferrere, Gregorio de Laferrere 00349

History, Local and Regional

Musée Municipal Robert Dubois-Corneau, Brunoy 09768
Musée National Archéologique et Site, Nissan-lez-Enserune 12133
Musée Oberlin, Waldersbach 14091
Musée Percheron, Mortagne-au-Perche 11950
Musée Pierre-Gaudin, Puteaux 12674
Musée Pigeard, Magny-en-Vexin 11549
Musée Pillon, Chaumont-en-Vexin 10060
Musée Quentovic, Etaples 10470
Musée Régional Arts et Traditions de l'Orléanais, Beaugency 09469
Musée Régional d'Art Populaire, Guérande 10763
Musée Régional d'Auvergne, Riom 12758
Musée Régional Dupuy-Méstreau, Saintes 13344
Musée Roybet Fould, Courbevoie 10234
Musée Saint-Remi, Reims 12719
Musée Sainte-Croix, Poitiers 12576
Musée Serret et de la Vallée, Saint-Amarin 12889
Musée Suffren et du Vieux Saint-Cannat, Saint-Cannat 12927
Musée Urbain-Cabrol, Villefranche-de-Rouergue 13998
Musée Vauban, Neuf-Brisach 12068
Musée Vendéen, Fontenay-le-Comte 10572
Musée Victor Aubert, Maule 11680
Musée Villeneuvien, Villeneuve-sur-Yonne 14029
Musées de Sens, Sens 13497
Palais Bénédictine, Fécamp 10514
Parc et Château de Valencay, Valençay 13836
Village-Musée, Fos-sur-Mer 10587

French Guiana
Musée Local, Cayenne 14132

French Polynesia
Musée de Tahiti et des Iles, Punaauia 14138
Na Te Ara Museum, Uturoa 14140

Gabon
Musée National du Gabon, Libreville 14142

Georgia
State Museum of Abkhasia, Suchumi 14148

Germany
Abteilung Handwerk und dörfliches Leben des Heimatmuseums Neu-Ulm, Neu-Ulm 17611
Ahler Kråm - Volkskundliche Sammlung, Partenstein 17939
Alexander-Mack-Museum, Bad Berleburg 14394
Allgäu-Museum, Kempten 16713
Alpinmuseum, Kempten 16716
Alt-Arnstorf-Haus, Arnstorf 14305
Alt-Freden-Sammlung, Freden 15795
Alt-Stade im Baumhaus (Privatmuseum), Stade 18558
Alte Oberamtei, Gerabronn 15942
Altes Haus, Greifenstein 16070
Altes Rathaus, Lüneburg 17184
Altonaer Museum in Hamburg, Hamburg 16204
Amrumer Heimatmuseum, Nebel 17590
Amtsturm-Museum, Lüchow, Wendland 17177
Archäologie-Museum, Heilbronn 16353
Archäologische Sammlung mit Heimatvertriebenenstube und Kruk-Sammlung, Königsbrunn 16820
Auberlehaus, Trossingen 18748
August-Holländer-Museum, Emsdetten 15570
Ausstellung Juden in Buttenhausen, Münsingen 17536
Aventinus-Museum, Abensberg 14180
Bachgau-Museum, Großostheim 16118
Bad Schwalbacher Kur-, Stadt- und Apothekenmuseum, Bad Schwalbach 14514
Badhaus Museum und Galerie, Kulmbach 16906
Badisches Landesmuseum Karlsruhe, Karlsruhe 16647
Bartholomäus-Schmucker-Heimatmuseum, Ruhpolding 18272
Bauernhausmuseum Knechtenhofen, Oberstaufen 17802
Berg- und Stadtmuseum, Obernkirchen 17783
Bergbau- und Heimatmuseum, Goldkronach 16033
Bergbaumuseum, Altenberg, Erzgebirge 14235
Bergwinkelmuseum, Schlüchtern 18355
Besucherbergwerk Vereinigt Zwitterfeld zu Zinnwald, Zinnwald-Georgenfeld 19279
Bezirksmuseum, Buchen 15116
Bezirksmuseum Dachau, Dachau 15246
Bezirksmuseum Marzahn-Hellersdorf, Berlin 14684
Bismarck-Museum, Bad Kissingen 14454
Blaues Schloß, Obernzenn 17786
BLM Bauernhaus-Museum Bortfeld, Wendeburg 19039
Bodenheimer Heimatmuseum, Bodenheim 14950
Börde-Heimatmuseum, Lamstedt 16940
Bördenheimatmuseum Heeslingen, Heeslingen 16325
Bomann-Museum Celle, Celle 15182
Braith-Mali-Museum, Biberach an der Riß 14886
Brandenburgisches Textilmuseum, Forst, Lausitz 15725
Braunauer Heimatmuseum, Forchheim, Oberfranken 15721
Braunschweigisches Landesmuseum, Braunschweig 15029
Brensbach Museum und Galerie im alten Rathaus, Brensbach 15087
Breuberg-Museum, Breuberg 15090
Brünner Heimatmuseum, Schwäbisch Gmünd 18403
Brüxer und Komotauer Heimatstuben, Erlangen 15619
Brunnenmuseum, Bad Vilbel 14531
Buchholzer Heimatmuseum, Buchholz in der Nordheide 15119
Burg Beeskow, Beeskow 14634
Burg Hagen, Hagen bei Bremerhaven 16159
Burg-Museum, Parsberg 17938
Burg- und Schloßmuseum Allstedt, Allstedt 14223
Burg- und Stadtmuseum Königstein, Königstein im Taunus 16828
Burg Vischering, Lüdinghausen 17182
Burghofmuseum, Soest 18516
Burgmuseum, Lenzen, Elbe 17082
Burgmuseum, Wolfsegg 19189
Burgmuseum Bad Bodenteich, Bad Bodenteich 14405
Burgmuseum Waldeck, Waldeck, Hessen 18886
Buxtehude Museum für Regionalgeschichte und Kunst, Buxtehude 15169
Christian-Wolff-Haus, Halle, Saale 16185
Curt-Engelhorn-Zentrum, Mannheim 17241
Daniel-Pöppelmann-Haus, Herford 16387
Denkmalhof Rauchhaus Möllin, Möllin 17389
Detlefsen-Museum, Glückstadt 15994
Dithmarscher Landesmuseum, Meldorf 17325
Dörpmuseum Münkeboe, Südbrookmerland 18656
Dokumentation Obersalzberg - Orts- und Zeitgeschichte, Berchtesgaden 14649
Domowniski muzej Dešno, Dissen, Niederlausitz 15347
Dorf- und Heimatmuseum, Winterbach bei Schorndorf 19139
Dorfmuseum, Bad Alexandersbad 14378
Dorfmuseum, Kienberg, Oberbayern 16736
Dorfmuseum Alter Forsthof, Wetter, Hessen 19077
Dorfmuseum Altkirchen, Altkirchen 14246
Dorfmuseum Daniel-Martin-Haus, Rauschenberg 18077
Dorfmuseum Delligsen, Delligsen 15289
Dorfmuseum Günzach, Günzach 16135
Dorfmuseum im Greifenhaus, Hausen, Oberfranken 16314
Dorfmuseum Mertingen, Mertingen 17342
Dorfmuseum Ostheim, Nidderau 17690
Dorfmuseum Tündern, Hameln 16250
Dorfmuseum Weckbach, Weilbach 18969
Dorfmuseum Wilsenroth, Dornburg, Westerwald 15370
Dorfstube Münchholzhausen, Wetzlar 19078
Dotzheimer Museum, Wiesbaden 19097
Dr.-Bauer-Heimatmuseum, Bad Rothenfelde 14497
Dr. Eisenbarth- und Heimatmuseum, Oberviechtach 17808
Dreieich-Museum, Dreieich 15394
Drilandmuseum Gronau, Gronau, Westfalen 16100
Dümmer-Museum, Lembruch 17069
Egerländer-Elbogner Heimatstuben, Illertissen 16546
Egerland-Museum, Marktredwitz 17282
Eichsfelder Heimatmuseum, Heilbad Heiligenstadt 16351
Eidelstedter Heimatmuseum, Hamburg 16210
Eiderstedter Heimatmuseum, Sankt Peter-Ording 18313
Eifelmuseum Blankenheim, Blankenheim, Ahr 14922
Elbschiffahrtsmuseum mit stadtgeschichtlicher Sammlung, Lauenburg 16992
Elsenzer Heimatstuben, Eppingen 15582
Emschertal-Museum der Stadt Herne, Herne 16395
Emslandmuseum Lingen, Lingen 17118
Emslandmuseum Schloß Clemenswerth, Sögel 18513
Erbacher Heimatzimmer, Eltville 15551
Ernst-Moritz-Arndt-Museum, Garz, Rügen 15902
Die Eulenburg, Rinteln 18184
Fehnmuseum Eiland, Großefehn 16112
Felix-Nussbaum-Haus, Osnabrück 17872
Felsberg-Museum, Lautertal, Odenwald 17005
Felsenmeer-Museum, Hemer 16375
Feringa Sach - Ortsgeschichte und heimatkundliche Sammlung, Unterföhring 18799
Festung Marienberg mit Museum im Fürstenbau, Würzburg 19215
Fichtelgebirgsmuseum, Wunsiedel 19232
Fischer- und Webermuseum Steinhude, Wunstorf 19234
Flößer- und Heimatmuseum, Wolfach 19171
Focke-Museum, Bremen 15054
Fossilien- und Heimatmuseum, Messel 17345
Fränkische-Schweiz-Museum, Pottenstein 18014
Fränkisches Bauern- und Handwerkermuseum Kirchenburg Mönchsondheim, Iphofen 16573
Frankenwaldmuseum, Kronach 16884
Franziskanermuseum, Villingen-Schwenningen 18845
Frauen Museum Wiesbaden, Wiesbaden 19099
Freilichtmuseum am Kiekeberg, Rosengarten, Kreis Harburg 18214
Freilichtmuseum "Frelsdorfer Brink", Frelsdorf 15825
Freilichtmuseum Rhöner Museumsdorf, Tann, Rhön 18677
Friesisches Heimatmuseum, Niebüll 17692
Froaschgass-Museum, Wettenberg 19074
Fruchtkasten, Tuttlingen 18767
Fürstenzimmer im Schloß Kirchheim, Kirchheim unter Teck 16748
Fürstlich Leiningensche Sammlungen - Heimatmuseum, Amorbach 14273
Gablonzer Haus mit Isergebirgsmuseum, Kaufbeuren 16694
Gäubodenmuseum, Straubing 18614
Gaildorfer Stadtmuseum im Alten Schloß, Gaildorf 15890
Gartenkunst-Museum Schloß Fantasie, Eckersdorf 15490
Gemeinde-Heimatmuseum Harsum, Harsum 16294
Gemeindemuseum im Historischen Rathaus, Seeheim-Jugenheim 18459
Geroldsecker-Museum im Storchenturm, Lahr, Schwarzwald 16931
Glas-Museum Marienhütte und Teufelsmoor-Museum und Teufelsmoor-Galerie, Gnarrenburg 15997
Glashaus-Derneburg, Holle 16486
Glasmuseum Weisswasser, Weisswasser 19033
Glauberg-Museum, Glauburg 15987
Goethe-Gedenkstätte im Amtshaus, Ilmenau 16551
Goslarer Museum, Goslar 16037
Goslarer Zinnfiguren-Museum, Goslar 16038
Grafschafter Museum im Moerser Schloß, Moers 17401
Grafschaftsmuseum, Wertheim 19060
Graslitzer Gedenk- und Informationsraum, Aschaffenburg 14313
Greifensteiner Burgmuseum, Greifenstein 16072
Grenzland- und Trenckmuseum, Waldmünchen 18898
Grenzlandheimatstuben des Heimatkreises Marienbad, Neualbenreuth 17616
Hällisch-Fränkisches Museum, Schwäbisch Hall 18407
Härtsfeld-Museum, Neresheim 17600
Haidhausen-Museum, München 17472
Hallertauer Heimat- und Hopfenmuseum, Mainburg 17224
Hallertauer Hopfen- und Heimatmuseum, Geisenfeld 15912
Hamaland-Museum und Westmünsterliche Hofanlage, Vreden 18864
Hanauer Museum, Kehl 16702
Haniel Museum, Duisburg 15464
Haus am Kleistpark, Berlin 14741
Haus der Geschichte, Bad Harzburg 14439
Haus der Heimat, Olbernhau 17843
Haus der Ortsgeschichte, Schwäbisch Hall 18409
Haus der Stadtgeschichte, Donauwörth 15358
Haus des Gastes mit heimatkundlicher Sammlung, Gößweinstein 16019
Haus Kickelhain, Mosbach, Baden 17417
Haus Rottels, Neuss 17665
Haus zum Stockfisch - Stadtmuseum, Erfurt 15606
Haus zur Hohen Lilie, Naumburg, Saale 17587
Hausenhäusl, Reit im Winkl 18126
Heidemuseum Dat ole Huus, Bispingen 14916
Heidemuseum Rischmannshof Walsrode, Walsrode 18910
Heiliggeistkirche, Landshut 16951
Heimat-Museum Maintal, Maintal 17227
Heimat- und Bauernmuseum, Bruck, Oberpfalz 15102
Heimat- und Bergbaumuseum, Nentershausen, Hessen 17599
Heimat- und Brauereimuseum, Pleinfeld 17993
Heimat- und Braunkohlemuseum, Steinberg, Oberpfalz 18585
Heimat- und Buddelmuseum, Osten 17882
Heimat- und Dorfmuseum Pfaffenwiesbach, Wehrheim 18949
Heimat- und Grimmelshausenmuseum, Oberkirch 17776
Heimat- und Humboldtmuseum, Eibau 15509
Heimat- und Industriemuseum, Kolbermoor 16843
Heimat- und Industriemuseum, Wackersdorf 18865
Heimat- und Schiffahrtsmuseum, Heinsen 16365
Heimat- und Ski-Museum, Braunlage 15027
Heimat- und Torfmuseum, Gröbenzell 16095
Heimat- und Uhrenmuseum, Villingen-Schwenningen 18846
Heimat- und Wallfahrtsmuseum, Xanten 19254
Heimatdiele Kutenholz, Kutenholz 16920
Heimatecke am Seifenbach, Beierfeld 14635
Heimatgeschichtliches Museum, Modautal 17386
Heimathaus, Nesselwang 17606
Heimathaus Alte Mühle, Schladen 18341
Heimathaus Aying, Aying 14369
Heimathaus De Theeshof, Schneverdingen 18369
Heimathaus der Stadt Lauingen, Lauingen 16999
Heimathaus der Stadt Warendorf, Warendorf 18927
Heimathaus des Rupertiwinkels und Heimatstube der Sudetendeutschen, Tittmoning 18717
Heimathaus des Vereins zur Erhaltung der Rundlinge im Hannoverischen Wendland, Küsten 16903
Heimathaus Dingden, Hamminkeln 16256
Heimathaus Greven Worth, Selsingen 18476
Heimathaus Mehedorf, Bremervörde 15082
Heimathaus Neuchl-Anwesen, Hohenschäftlarn 16476
Heimathaus Pfarrkirchen, Pfarrkirchen 17972
Heimathaus Sittensen, Sittensen 18512
Heimathaus Sonthofen, Sonthofen 18539
Heimathaus Wendelstein, Wendelstein, Mittelfranken 19041
Heimathausanlage Schafstall, Bremervörde 15083
Heimatkabinett Westerholt, Herten 16408
Heimatkundliche Sammlung, Elzach 15554
Heimatkundliche Sammlung, Heideck 16328
Heimatkundliche Sammlung, Heroldsbach 16400
Heimatkundliche Sammlung, Isen 16578
Heimatkundliche Sammlung, Lich 17092
Heimatkundliche Sammlung, Pfronten 17978
Heimatkundliche Sammlung Bergendorf, Holzheim 16493
Heimatkundliche Sammlung des Heimatdienstes Hindelang, Hindelang 16433
Heimatkundliche Sammlung und Ausstellung, Hermannsburg 16392
Heimatkundliches Museum, Friedeburg, Ostfriesland 15838
Heimatmuseum, Adelsdorf 14185
Heimatmuseum, Aidlingen 14203
Heimatmuseum, Aken 14205
Heimatmuseum, Allendorf, Lumda 14220
Heimatmuseum, Angermünde 14281
Heimatmuseum, Arneburg 14301
Heimatmuseum, Bad Gottleuba 14436
Heimatmuseum, Bad Langensalza 14467
Heimatmuseum, Bad Rodach 14496
Heimatmuseum, Bad Schandau 14510
Heimatmuseum, Blindheim 14931
Heimatmuseum, Camburg 15180
Heimatmuseum, Dahlen, Sachsen 15252
Heimatmuseum, Dietenhofen 15324
Heimatmuseum, Dömitz 15351
Heimatmuseum, Eibelstadt 15510
Heimatmuseum, Elsenfeld 15549
Heimatmuseum, Eltmann 15550
Heimatmuseum, Ergoldsbach 15611
Heimatmuseum, Falkensee 15686
Heimatmuseum, Falkenstein, Vogtland 15688
Heimatmuseum, Frankenberg, Sachsen 15729
Heimatmuseum, Friedland bei Neubrandenburg 15840
Heimatmuseum, Gerstungen 15956
Heimatmuseum, Grabow, Mecklenburg 16052
Heimatmuseum, Greußen 16083
Heimatmuseum, Groitzsch bei Pegau 16098
Heimatmuseum, Großengottern 16113
Heimatmuseum, Großröhrsdorf, Oberlausitz 16120
Heimatmuseum, Großzschepa 16126
Heimatmuseum, Haimhausen 16175
Heimatmuseum, Karlstein am Main 16666
Heimatmuseum, Kirchdorf auf Poel 16744
Heimatmuseum, Kölleda 16778
Heimatmuseum, Lengenfeld, Vogtland 17076
Heimatmuseum, Markranstädt 17271
Heimatmuseum, Mering 17339
Heimatmuseum, Möckmühl 17387
Heimatmuseum, Moosburg an der Isar 17413
Heimatmuseum, Osterwieck 17890
Heimatmuseum, Perleberg 17963
Heimatmuseum, Polling, Kreis Weilheim 18003
Heimatmuseum, Pritzwalk 18027
Heimatmuseum, Radeburg 18045
Heimatmuseum, Rattenberg 18070
Heimatmuseum, Reichenau an der Pulsnitz 18114
Heimatmuseum, Sandhausen 18298
Heimatmuseum, Sternberg 18598
Heimatmuseum, Strausberg 18615
Heimatmuseum, Treuenbrietzen 18733
Heimatmuseum, Weisendorf 19017
Heimatmuseum, Wiesenbach, Baden 19104
Heimatmuseum, Mülheim an der Ruhr 17440
Heimatmuseum Ahlem, Hannover 16269
Heimatmuseum Ahrbergen, Giesen 15968
Heimatmuseum Aichach, Aichach 14198
Heimatmuseum Algermissen, Algermissen 14219
Heimatmuseum Alter Pfarrhof, Raisting 18052
Heimatmuseum Altes Rathaus, Angelburg 14279
Heimatmuseum Altomünster, Altomünster 14258
Heimatmuseum Amöneburg, Amöneburg 14272
Heimatmuseum Amt Blankenstein, Gladenbach 15983
Heimatmuseum Aschen, Diepholz 15319
Heimatmuseum Auetal, Auetal 14336
Heimatmuseum Bad Aibling, Bad Aibling 14377
Heimatmuseum Bad Eilsen, Bad Eilsen 14422
Heimatmuseum Bad König, Bad König 14456
Heimatmuseum Bad Laer, Bad Laer 14466
Heimatmuseum Bad Lauterberg, Bad Lauterberg 14469
Heimatmuseum Bad Münder, Bad Münder 14474
Heimatmuseum Bad Oldesloe, Bad Oldesloe 14488
Heimatmuseum Bad Wildungen, Bad Wildungen 14535
Heimatmuseum Balingen, Balingen 14569
Heimatmuseum Bammental, Bammental 14591
Heimatmuseum Battenberg-Laisa, Battenberg, Eder 14598
Heimatmuseum Baunach, Baunach 14600
Heimatmuseum Beratzhausen, Beratzhausen 14647
Heimatmuseum Berching mit Ritter-v.-Gluck-Archiv, Berching 14648
Heimatmuseum Berkatal, Berkatal 14668
Heimatmuseum Betzenstein, Betzenstein 14880
Heimatmuseum Biebesheim, Biebesheim 14894
Heimatmuseum Biebrich, Wiesbaden 19101
Heimatmuseum Bislich, Wesel 19062
Heimatmuseum Blankenau, Hosenfeld 16508
Heimatmuseum Bleicherode, Bleicherode 14929
Heimatmuseum Bockwindmühle, Lebusa 17007
Heimatmuseum Börgerende-Rethwisch, Börgerende 14961
Heimatmuseum Boizenburg, Boizenburg 14966
Heimatmuseum Boxberg, Boxberg, Baden 15008
Heimatmuseum Breckerfeld, Breckerfeld 15042
Heimatmuseum Brigachtal, Brigachtal 15091
Heimatmuseum Brüssow, Brüssow 15111
Heimatmuseum Brunsbüttel, Brunsbüttel 15113
Heimatmuseum Buchenau, Dautphetal 15278
Heimatmuseum Buchenberg, Buchenberg bei Kempten 15117
Heimatmuseum Buchloe, Buchloe 15120
Heimatmuseum Büddenstedt, Büddenstedt 15125
Heimatmuseum Büderich, Wesel 19063
Heimatmuseum Bühl, Baden, Bühl, Baden 15129
Heimatmuseum Bürgeln, Cölbe 15214
Heimatmuseum Burgau, Burgau, Schwaben 15146
Heimatmuseum Carl Swoboda, Schirgiswalde 18338

927

History, Local and Regional

Historisch Museum Hengelo, Hengelo 25143
Historisch Museum Het Burgerweeshuis, Arnhem 24765
Historisch Museum Het Kleine Veenlo, Veenendaal 25579
Historisch Museum Het Palthe Huis, Oldenzaal 25345
Historisch Museum Tweestromenland, Beneden Leeuwen 24801
Home of History, Rotterdam 25427
Huis Verwolde, Laren, Gelderland 25215
Huize Keizer, Denekamp 24937
Kapiteinshuis Pekela, Nieuwe Pekela 25311
Katwijks Museum, Katwijk aan Zee 25203
Kijk en Luister Museum, Bennekom 24802
De Klinze, Oudkerk 25385
De Klomphoek, Beilen 24796
Het Land van Strijen, Strijen 25521
Het Land van Thorn/ Panorama Thorn, Thorn 25531
Liemers Museum, Zevenaar 25679
Limburgs Miniatuurmuseum, Sint Geertruid 25485
Limburgs Openluchtmuseum Eynderhoof, Nederweert Eind 25304
Loosduins Museum De Korenschuur, Den Haag 24905
Maarten Van Rossum Museum, Zaltbommel 25671
Marker Museum, Marken 25282
Middendorpshuis, Den Ham 24932
Minimuseum, Groningen 25078
Museum Arnemuiden, Arnemuiden 24760
Museum De Koloniehof, Frederiksoord 25041
Museum De Schilpen, Maasland 25268
Museum de Stadshof, Zwolle 25702
Museum de Stratemakerstoren, Nijmegen 25322
Museum de Trije Gritenijen, Grouw 25087
Museum Delfzijl, Delfzijl 24891
Museum Dorestad, Wijk bij Duurstede 25641
Museum Elisabeth Weeshuis, Culemborg 24871
Museum Eungs Schöppe, Markelo 25281
Museum Flehite Amersfoort, Amersfoort 24668
Museum Freriks, Winterswijk 25647
Museum Frerikshuus, Aalten 24648
Museum Gesigt van 't Dog, Hellevoetsluis 25137
Museum Havezate Mensinge, Roden 25413
Museum Hertogsgemaal, 's-Hertogenbosch 25147
Museum Het Petershuis, Gennep 25050
Museum in de Toren, Goedereede 25057
Museum in 't Houtenhuis, De Rijp 24874
Museum Kempenland, Eindhoven 25002
Museum Maarssen, Maarssen 25266
Museum Meerenberg, Bloemendaal 24818
Museum Nagele, Nagele 25303
Museum Orvelte, Orvelte 25367
Museum Oud Overschie, Rotterdam 25434
Museum Oud-Rijnsburg, Rijnsburg 25406
Museum Oud Soest, Soest 25505
Museum Rijswijk Het Tollenshuis, Rijswijk, Zuid-Holland 25410
Museum Sint-Paulusgasthuis, Sint Oedenrode 25491
Museum Slag bij Heiligerlee, Heiligerlee 25132
Museum Stad Appingedam, Appingedam 24759
Museum Stedhûs Sleat, Sloten 25499
Museum Striid tsjin it Wetter, Wommels 25651
Museum Swaensteijn, Voorburg 25610
Museum 't Coopmanshûs, Franeker 25039
Museum 't Poorthuis, Leerdam 25223
Museum voor Heemkunde Almelo, Almelo 24656
Museum voor Zuid- en Noord-Beveland, Goes 25058
Museum Wierdenland, Ezinge 25037
Museum Willem van Haren, Heerenveen 25122
Museum Yerseke, Yerseke 25661
Museum Zwaantje Hans Stockman's Hof, Schoonebeek 25477
Museumboerderij, Leens 25222
Museumboerderij Vreeburg, Schagen 25463
Museumboerderij Westfrisia, Hoogwoud 25175
Museumsboerderij Oud Noordwijk, Noordwijk, Zuid-Holland 25335
Museumwinkel Albert Heijn, Zaandam 25666
Nationaal Coöperatie Museum, Schiedam 25469
Natuur Historisch Museum en Heemkunde Centrum, Meerssen 25288
Het Nieuwe Kruithuis, Bourtange 24835
Noorderhuis, Zaandam 25667
Oeteldonks Gemintemuzejum, 's-Hertogenbosch 25152
Olie- en Korenmolen Woldzigt, Roderwolde 25416
Oude Aarde, Giethoorn 25055
Het Oude Raadhuis, Urk 25550
Oude Stadhuis, Hasselt 25111
Oudheidkamer, Den Burg 24892
Oudheidkamer, Enter 25027
Oudheidkamer, Medemblik 25287
Oudheidkamer, Rendswoude 25399
Oudheidkamer, Steenwijk 25515
Oudheidkamer, Vught 25617
Oudheidkamer, Wijngaarden 25642
Oudheidkamer Bleiswijk, Bleiswijk 24817
Oudheidkamer Brederwiede, Vollenhove 25608
Oudheidkamer Doorn, Doorn 24957
Oudheidkamer Geervliet, Geervliet 25044
Oudheidkamer Goor, Goor 25061
Oudheidkamer Leiderdorp, Leiderdorp 25246
Oudheidkamer Lemster Fiifgea, Lemmer 25253
Oudheidkamer Maasdriel, Kerkdriel 25205
Oudheidkamer/ Museum Mr. Andreae, Kollum 25209
Oudheidkamer Reeuwijk, Reeuwijk 25398
Oudheidkamer Renswoude, Renswoude 25402
Oudheidkamer Ridderkerk, Ridderkerk 25405
Pasmans Huus, Ruinen 25454
Poldermuseum, Noorden 25332
Purmerends Museum, Purmerend 25396
't Rieuw, Nuis 25339
Rijssens Museum, Rijssen 25409
Roerstreekmuseum, Sint Odilienberg 25489
De Schotse Huizen, Veere 25583
Slaait'n Hoes, Onstwedde 25352
Sliedrechts Museum, Sliedrecht 25495
Somme Museum, Schagen 25464
Spakenburgs Museum 't Vurhuus, Bunschoten Spakenburg 24859
Stadsmuseum Doetinchem, Doetinchem 24950
Stadsmuseum IJsselstein, IJsselstein 25193
Stadsmuseum Woerden, Woerden 25649
Stadsmuseum Zoetermeer, Zoetermeer 25687
Stedelijk Museum, Amsterdam 24735
Stedelijk Museum Het Domein, Sittard 25493
Stedelijk Museum Zutphen, Zutphen 25697
Stedelijke Oudheidkamer De Roos, Geertruidenberg 25043
Streekhistorisch Centrum, Stadskanaal 25512
Streekmuseum De Vier Craftsen, Hulst 25189
Streekmuseum Goeree en Overflakkee, Sommelsdijk 25507
Streekmuseum Hattem, Hattem 25114
Streekmuseum Het Admiraliteitshuis, Dokkum 24953
Streekmuseum Het Dorp van Bartje, Rolde 25418
Streekmuseum Het Land van Axel, Axel 24781
Streekmuseum Jan Anderson, Vlaardingen 25597
Streekmuseum Land van Valkenburg, Valkenburg 25574
Streekmuseum Leudal, Haelen 25102
Streekmuseum Stevensweert/ Ohé en Laak, Stevensweert 25520
Streekmuseum Volkssterrenwacht, Bergum 24813
Streekmuseum West Zeeuws-Vlaanderen, IJzendijke 25194
Themapark Openluchtmuseum De Spitkeet, Harkema 25108
Het Veenkoloniaal Museum, Veendam 25577
Vestingmuseum Oudeschans, Oudeschans 25382
Visserij- en Cultuurhistorisch Museum, Woudrichem 25657
Volendams Museum, Volendam 25607
Volksbuurtmuseum Wijk, Utrecht 25569
Volkskundig Educatie Museum, Susteren 25523
Wegwijs Museum, Bakkum 24787
Werkspoor Museum, Amsterdam 24745
Westfries Museum, Hoorn 25180
Zaanlandse Oudheidkamer, Zaandijk 25670
De Zaanse Schans, Zaandam 25669
Zandvoorts Museum, Zandvoort 25672
Zo Was 'T, Nieuwleusen 25317
Zuiderzeemuseum, Enkhuizen 25019

Netherlands Antilles
Curaçao Museum, Curaçao 25704

New Zealand
Alexandra Museum, Alexandra 25708
Amuri Historical Museum, Waiau 25907
Ashburton Museum, Ashburton 25712
Auckland Museum and Auckland War Memorial Museum, Auckland 25719
Belfast Museum, Christchurch 25744
Black's Point Museum, Reefton 25881
Brain-Watkins House, Tauranga 25895
Brayshaw Museum Park, Blenheim 25740
Cambridge Museum, Cambridge 25742
Catlins Historical Museum, Owaka 25857
Central Hawke's Bay Settlers Museum, Waipawa 25914
Chatham Islands Museum, Waitangi 25918
Cheviot Museum, Cheviot 25743
Cobblestones Museum, Greytown 25800
Coromandel School of Mines Museum, Coromandel 25762
Cromwell Museum, Cromwell 25763
Cust Museum, Cust 25764
Dargaville Museum, Dargaville 25766
Eketahuna and Districts Museum, Eketahuna 25784
Far North Regional Museum, Kaitaia 25816
Featherston Heritage Museum, Featherston 25785
Featherston Memorabilia Museum, Featherston 25786
Firth Tower Historical Reserve, Matamata 25835
Fletcher House, Dunedin 25774
Forrester Gallery, Oamaru 25850
Foxton Museum, Foxton 25789
Glentunnel Museum, Coalgate 25761
Golden Bay Museum and Gallery, Golden Bay 25794
Gore Historical Museum and Hokonui Heritage Research Centre, Gore 25797
Havelock Museum, Havelock 25804
Hawke's Bay Museum, Napier 25841
Helensville and District Pioneer Museum, Helensville 25807
Hororata Historic Museum, Darfield 25765
Howick Historical Village, Pakuranga 25862
Hurworth Cottage, New Plymouth 25847
Journey's End Cottage and Laishley House, Auckland 25727
Kaiapoi Historical Museum, Christchurch 25751
Kaikohe Pioneer Village and Museum, Kaikohe 25814
Kaikoura District Museum, Kaikoura 25815
Kapiti Coast Museum Waikanae, Wellington 25931
Karamea Museum, Karamea 25818
The Kauri Museum, Matakohe 25834
Kawhia Regional Museum Gallery, Kawhia 25819
Lyttelton Historical Museum, Christchurch 25752
Marton Historic Village Museum, Marton 25829
Mercury Bay and District Museum, Whitianga 25955
Methven Museum, Methven 25836
Morrin Museum, Morrinsville 25838
Motueka District Museum, Motueka 25839
Mount Bruce Pioneer Museum, Masterton 25830
Murchison Museum, Murchison 25840
Nelson Provincial Museum, Nelson 25843
North Otago Museum, Oamaru 25851
Ongaonga Old School Museum, Ongaonga 25853
Opotiki Heritage and Agricultural Society Museum, Opotiki 25854
Otago Peninsula Museum, Dunedin 25779
Otago Settlers Museum, Dunedin 25780
Otakou Marae Museum, Dunedin 25782
Otautau and District Local History Museum, Otautau 25855
Oxford Museum, Oxford 25858
Paeroa and District Historical Society Museum, Paeroa 25859
Pahiatua and District Museum, Pahiatua 25860
Papakura and District Historical Society Museum, Papakura 25866
Pataka Porirua Museum of Arts and Cultures, Porirua 25874
Picton Community Museum, Picton 25870
Pioneer Village, Silverdale 25890
Piopio and District Museum, Piopio 25871
Plains Vintage Railway and Historical Museum, Ashburton 25715
Pleasant Point Railway and Historical Society Museum, Pleasant Point 25872
Port Chalmers Museum, Port Chalmers 25876
Puhoi Historical Society Museum, Puhoi 25877
Raglan and District Museum, Raglan 25879
Rakiura Museum, Stewart Island 25891
Rangiora Museum, Rangiora 25880
Renwick Museum, Renwick 25882
Russell Museum, Russell 25888
Science Centre and Manawatu Museum, Palmerston North 25865
South Canterbury Museum, Timaru 25903
South Taranaki Regional Museum, Patea 25869
Southland Museum and Art Gallery, Invercargill 25811
Sumner/Redcliffs Historical Museum, Christchurch 25757
Switzers Museum, Waikaia 25910
Taieri Historical Museum, Outram 25856
Taihape and District Museum, Taihape 25892
Tairawhiti Museum, Gisborne 25793
Tauranga Historic Village Museum, Tauranga 25896
Tawhiti Museum, Hawera 25806
Te Amorangi Trust Museum, Rotorua 25885
Te Awamutu Museum, Te Awamutu 25897
Te Kuiti and District Historical Society Museum, Te Kuiti 25899
Te Whare Taonga O Akaroa, Akaroa 25707
Te Whare Whakaaro o Pito-one, Lower Hutt 25826
Temuka Courthouse Museum, Temuka 25900
Teviot District Museum, Roxburgh 25886
Tokomairiro Historical Society Museum, Milton 25837
Tuatapere Bushmans Museum, Tuatapere 25906
Upper Waitaki Pioneer Museum and Gallery, Kurow 25821
Vallance Cottage, Alexandra 25709
Wagener Museum, Kaitaia 25817
Waiheke Island Historical Society Museum, Waiheke Island 25908
Waikato Museum of Art and History, Hamilton 25803
Waikouaiti Museum, Waikouaiti 25911
Waipukurau Museum, Waipukurau 25916
Wairarapa Museum and Art Gallery, Masterton 25833
Wairoa District Museum, Wairoa 25917
Wallace Early Settlers Museum, Riverton 25883
Ward Museum, Ward 25926
Warkworth and District Museum, Warkworth 25927
West Coast Historical Museum, Hokitika 25808
Whanganui Regional Museum, Wanganui 25924
Whangarei Museum, Whangarei 25954
Whangaroa County Museum, Kaeo 25812
Woodville Pioneer Museum, Woodville 25956
Wyndham Museum, Wyndham 25957

Nicaragua
Museo Gregorio Aguilar Barea, Chontales 25958
Museo Tenderi, Masaya 25961

Niger
Musée National du Niger, Niamey 25962
Musée Régional de Zinder, Zinder 25963

Nigeria
Aaragon Museum, Ilupeju 25980
Didi Museum, Abuja 25966
Esie Museum, Ilorin 25979
National Museum, Lagos, Lagos 25987
National Museum Makurdi, Makurdi 25988
National Museum of Abeokuta, Abeokuta 25965
National Museum of Akure, Akure 25968
National Museum of Calabar, Calabar 25971
National Museum of Enugu, Enugu 25972
National Museum of Port Harcourt, Port Harcourt 25995
National Museum Uyo, Uyo 25996
Owo Museum, Owo 25994

Norfolk Island
Norfolk Island Museum, Kingston 25998

Norway
Ålen Bygdetun, Ålen 26003
Alta Museum, Alta 26007
Aust-Agder Museet, Arendal 26013
Ballangen Bygdemuseet, Ballangen 26021
Bjarkøy Museet, Bjarkøy 26039
Bjugn Bygdatun, Bjugn 26041
Blokkodden Villmarksmuseet, Engerdal 26073
Bokn Bygdemuseet, Føresvik 26089
Borgarsyssel Museum, Sarpsborg 26287
Brevik Bymuseum, Brevik 26051
Cudrio Kystmuseum, Langesund 26155
Dagali Museum, Geilo 26093
Dalane Folkemuseum, Egersund 26062
Drammens Museum for Kunst og Kulturhistorie, Drammen 26058
Dyrøy Bygdemuseet, Brøstadbotn 26052
Eidsberg og Mysen Historielag, Eidsberg 26066
Eidskog Museum, Eidskog 26067
Eidsvoll Bygdemuseet, Eidsvoll Verk 26069
Eiktunet Kulturhistorisk Museum, Gjøvik 26095
Fedrenes Minne, Hidrasund 26111
Folldal Bygdetun, Folldal 26085
Fosnes Bygdemuseum, Seierstad 26288
Fredrikstad Museet, Fredrikstad 26090
Frosta Bygdemuseet, Frosta 26091
Gamstuggu Nordli, Nordli 26203
Gruetunet, Kirkenær 26136
Guovdageainnu Gilisillju, Kautokeino 26135
Hå Bygdemuseum, Varhaug 26371
Hamarøy Bygdetun, Harmarøy 26105
De Heibergske Samlinger - Sogn Folkemuseum, Kaupanger 26134
Herøy Kystmuseum, Leinøy 26158
Holmestrand Museum, Holmestrand 26114
Hurdal Bygdetun, Hurdal 26126
Iveland og Vegusdal Bygdemuseum, Vatnestrom 26374
Karmsund Folkemuseum, Haugesund 26108
Klepp Bygdemuseum, Kleppe 26138
Krambuvika Bygdemuseum, Tennevoll 26337
Leksvik Bygdesamling, Leksvik 26161
Levanger Museum, Levanger 26163
Lista Museum, Vanse 26367
Lørenskog Bygdetun, Lørenskog 26175
Malla Bleikvasslis Samlinger, Bleikvassli 26042
Meløy Bygdemuseum, Ørnes 26211
Midttunet, Skei i Jølster 26296
Nes Lensemuseum, Skiptvet 26299
Nord-Troms Museum, Sørkjosen 26310
Nordmøre Museum, Kristiansund 26151
Nore og Uvdal Bygdetun, Uvdal i Numedal 26363
Oddentunet, Os i Østerdalen 26213
Ofoten Museum, Narvik 26201
Øksnes Bygdemuseum, Alsvåg 26006
Orkdal Bygdemuseum, Orkanger 26210
Oslo Bymuseum, Oslo 26238
Oslo Kommunes Modellsamling, Oslo 26239
Rabekk Museum, Moss 26192
Rana Museum, Mo i Rana 26182
Rennesøy Bygdemuseum, Rennesøy 26260
Rindal Bygdemuseum, Rindal 26261
Rørosmuseet, Røros 26272
Røyrvik Bygdatun, Limingen 26167
Ryfylkemuseet, Sand 26280
Rygnestadtunet, Rysstad 26275
Salangen Bygdetun, Sjøvegan 26291
Saltdal Bygdetun, Rognan 26268
Sandefjord Bymuseum, Sandefjord 26283
Sandtorg Bygdetun, Sørvik 26314
Singsås Bygdemuseum, Singsås 26290
Skånland Museet, Evenskjer 26074
Skaun Bygdamuseum, Børsa 26049
Skiptvet Bygdemuseum, Skiptvet 26300
Smøla Museum, Smøla 26305
Snåsa Bygdamuseum, Snåsa 26306
Soknedal Museumslag, Soknedal 26309
Sømna Bygdetun, Vik i Helgeland 26380
Sør-Senja Museum, Stonglandseidet 26328
Stavanger Museum, Stavanger 26322
Stokke Bygdetun, Stokke 26326
Straumsnes Museum, Kanestraum 26131
Sunmøre Museum, Ålesund 26005
Sunndal Bygdemuseum, Sunndalsøra 26332
Surnadal Bygdemuseum, Surnadal 26333
Svalbard-Museum, Longyearbyen 26174
Svelvik Museum, Svelvik 26335
Time Bygdemuseum, Undheim 26361
Toten Økomuseum, Kapp 26132
Tresfjord Museum, Tresfjord 26342
Trondarnes Distriktmuseum, Harstad 26106
Tveitens Samlinger, Eggedal 26065
Ullensaker Bygdetun, Jessheim 26129
Vadsø Museum - Ruija Kvenmuseum, Vadsø 26365
Varteig Bygdemuseum, Varteig 26373
Vefsn Museum, Mosjøen 26191
Vega Bygdemuseum, Vega 26375
Vestvågøy Museum, Leknes 26160
Vingelen Kirke- og Skolemuseum, Vingelen 26382
Woksengs Samlinger, Rørvik 26273

Pakistan
Lahore Fort Museum, Lahore 26410
Lahore Museum, Lahore 26411
Sind Provincial Museum, Hyderabad 26399

Panama
Museo Belisario Porras, Panamá City 26438

Papua New Guinea
Madang Museum, Yomba 26452

938

History, Maritime → Boats and Shipping

History, Medieval

History, Modern

History, Social → Social Conditions

Horology

Horses

Horsemanship Museum of Takekoma Shrine,
Natori — 23381

Poland
Muzeum Łowiectwa i Jeździectwa, Warszawa — 27219

Russia
Muzej Konevodstva, Moskva — 27880

Sweden
Nordiska Travmuseet i Årjäng, Årjäng — 30026

Switzerland
Musée du Cheval, La Sarraz — 31195
Pferdekuranstalt, Bern — 30614

United Kingdom
Courage Shire Horse Centre, Maidenhead — 33872
National Horseracing Museum, Newmarket — 34043
Royal Mews, London — 33768
Suffolk Punch Heary Horse Museum,
Woodbridge — 34872
York Racing Museum, York — 34921

U.S.A.
Aiken Thoroughbred Racing Hall of Fame and
Museum, Aiken — 34988
American Royal Museum, Kansas City — 37733
American Saddle Horse Museum, Lexington — 38012
American Work Horse Museum, Lexington — 38028
International Museum of the Horse, Lexington — 38016
Museum of the Horse, Ruidoso Downs — 39884
National Museum of the Morgan Horse,
Shelburne — 40334

Horticulture

Austria
Steirisches Obstbaumuseum, Puch bei Weiz — 02442

Brazil
Sítio Roberto Burle Marx, Rio de Janeiro — 04078

Canada
Lawn Heritage Museum, Lamaline — 05182

Czech Republic
Národní Zemědělské Muzeum v Praze, Úsek Valtice,
Valtice — 07690

Egypt
Agricultural Museum, Giza — 08240

Germany
Deutsches Gartenbaumuseum Erfurt, Erfurt — 15600
Deutsches Kleingärtnermuseum, Leipzig — 17030
Gärtner- und Häckermuseum, Bamberg — 14578
Rosenmuseum Steinfurth, Bad Nauheim — 14478
Wieland-Gartenhaus, Biberach an der Riß — 14888

Norway
Gamle Hvam Museum, Årnes — 26015

United Kingdom
Botanic Gardens Museum, Southport — 34529
British Lawnmower Museum, Southport — 34530
Harlow Carr Museum of Gardening, Harrogate — 33197
National Museum of Gardening, Helston — 33244
Rievaulx Abbay, Rievaulx — 34307

U.S.A.
Barnes Foundation, Merion — 38437

Household Articles

Australia
Cleve National Trust Museum, Cleve — 00912

Austria
Europäisches Museum für Frieden,
Stadtschlaining — 02648
Privatsammlung Hermine Brandstetter,
Ostermiething — 02375

Belgium
Musée Communal, Xhoris — 03833

Canada
Badger Creek Museum, Cartwright — 04674
Heritage Farm Village, North Battleford — 05480
Minnie Thomson Memorial Museum, Stratford — 05971
New Denmark Memorial Museum, New
Denmark — 05439
Sombra Township Museum, Sombra — 05941

Denmark
Ofenmuseum L. Lange Co., Svendborg — 08069

Finland
Lounais-Hämeen Museo, Forssa — 08319
Tuomarinkylän Museo, Helsinki — 08396
Varkauden Museo, Varkaus — 09022

France
Musée d'Art et d'Histoire de Provence, Grasse — 10716

Germany
Besenmuseum, Ehingen, Donau — 15504
Deutsches Pinsel- und Bürstenmuseum,
Bechhofen — 14631
Elektro-Museum, Hilden — 16422
Erstes Nachttopf-Museum der Welt, München — 17464
Feuerstätten-Ausstellung im Lausitzer
Bergbaumuseum, Hoyerswerda — 16510
Miele-Museum, Gütersloh — 16140
Ortsmuseum Ursulastift, Gerstetten — 15954
Sammlung Berger, Amorbach — 14274
Schloß Neunhof, Nürnberg — 17756
Stadtmuseum Lüdenscheid, Lüdenscheid — 17180
Uckermärkische Heimatstuben, Fürstenwerder — 15862
Wäscherei-Museum Omas Waschküche, Berlin — 14864

Greece
Historical and Folklore Museum, Kalamata — 19482

Ireland
Castle Brand Visitor Centre, Nenagh — 20823

Italy
Museo della Civiltà Contadina ed Artigiana,
Ripatransone — 22318
Museo della Civiltà Contadina Romagnola 'Mario
Bocchini', Cesena — 21395
Museo della Fondazione Ugo da Como, Lonato — 21802

Japan
Sanuki Folk Art Museum, Takamatsu, Kagawa — 23538

Korea, Republic
Cheju Folklore Museum, Cheju — 23878

Lebanon
Beiteddine Museum, Shouf — 24151

Netherlands
Aansteker- en Lucifermuseum, Vlijmen — 25605
Gemeentelijk Museum 't Oude Slot, Veldhoven — 25585
Grietje Tump Museum, Landsmeer — 25214
Heemkundekring Willem Van Strijen,
Zevenbergen — 25681
Museum - Herberg de Ar, Westerbork — 25638
Museum voor het Kruideniersbedrijf, Utrecht — 25560
Nederlands Strijkijzer-Museum, Noordbroek — 25331
Oudheidkamer, Bruinisse — 24851

New Zealand
North Otago Museum, Oamaru — 25851
Waimate Historical Museum, Waimate — 25912

Philippines
Museo ng Kalinangang Pilipino, Manila — 26557

South Africa
Voortrekker Museum of the Orange Free State,
Winburg — 28644

Sweden
Sekelskiftesmuseét, Laxå — 30185

Switzerland
Collection d'Etains, Sierre — 31236

United Kingdom
Biscuit Tin Museum, Duns — 32852
Bygones at Holkham, Wells-next-the-Sea — 34771
Dalmeny House, South Queensferry — 34503
Fan Museum, London — 33637
Hornsea Museum of Village Life, Hornsea — 33289
The Museum of the Home, Pembroke — 34155
Priest House, West Hoathly — 34780
Railway Village Museum, Swindon — 34631
Session Cottage Museum, Turriff — 34699
Swinford Museum, Filkins — 33019

Hunting

Austria
Heimat-Jagdmuseum, Prigglitz — 02439
Jagd- und Forstmuseum, Feistritz am Wechsel — 01815
Jagdmuseum Brandhof, Gollrad — 01900
Museum Kaiser Franz Joseph I. und die Jagd,
Neuberg an der Mürz — 02328
Oberösterreichisches Jagdmuseum, Sankt
Florian — 02542
Trophäensaal und Erstes Oberösterreichisches
Falknereimuseum, Altenfelden — 01660

Brazil
Museu Clube dos Caçadores, Rio de Janeiro — 04014

Croatia
Lovački Muzej, Zagreb — 07112

Czech Republic
Lesnické, Myslivecké a Rybářské Muzeum, Hluboká
nad Vltavou — 07335
Muzeum T.G. Masaryk's House, Čejkovice — 07276

Denmark
Dansk Jagt- og Skovbrugsmuseum, Hørsholm — 07884
Fjordmuseet, Jyllinge — 07894
Spillemands-Jagt og Skovbrugsmuseet i Rebild,
Skørping — 08051

Finland
Ålands Jakt och Fiskemuseum, Storby — 08900
Tyrvään Seudun Museo, Vammala — 09012

France
Musée de la Chasse et de la Nature, Paris — 12337
Musée de la Vénerie et des Spahis, Senlis — 13492
Musée International de la Chasse, Gien — 10661

Germany
Agrar- und Forstmuseum, Wittenburg — 19150
Deutsches Jagd- und Fischereimuseum,
München — 17460
Forstliche und Jagdkundliche Lehrschau Grillenburg,
Grillenburg — 16087
Gräfliche Sammlungen und Afrikanisches
Jagdmuseum, Erbach, Odenwald — 15592
Jagd- und Falknereimuseum, Riedenburg — 18167
Jagd- und Fischereimuseum, Adelsdorf — 14186
Jagd- und Fischereimuseum Schloß Tambach,
Weitramsdorf — 19035
Jagd- und Naturkunde Museum, Niederstetten — 17698
Jagd- und Naturkundemuseum, Brüggen,
Niederrhein — 15104
Jagd- und Schloßmuseum Spangenberg,
Spangenberg — 18546
Jagdhaus Gabelbach, Ilmenau — 16552
Jagdkundemuseum, Dischingen — 15346
Jagdmuseum, Buschow — 15162
Jagdschau im Jagdschloss Springe, Springe — 18555
Jagdschloß Granitz, Ostseebad Binz — 17899
Jagdschloß Paulinzella, Paulinzella — 17950
Museum Burg Falkenstein, Pansfelde — 17931
Museum des Oberbergischen Kreises,
Nümbrecht — 17730
Museum für Jagdtier- und Vogelkunde des
Erzgebirges, Augustusburg — 14361
Museum Jagd und Wild auf Burg Falkenstein,
Falkenstein, Oberpfalz — 15687
Museum Jagdschloß Kranichstein, Darmstadt — 15269
Museum Schloss Moritzburg, Moritzburg — 17416
Rhöner Naturmuseum, Tann, Rhön — 18678
Sammlung historischer Jagdwaffen, Kulmbach — 16912
Schloß Ludwigslust, Ludwigslust — 17158
Schloß Wolfstein mit Jagd- und Fischereimuseum und
Galerie Wolfstein, Freyung — 15833
Tier- und Jagdmuseum, Bad Dürrheim — 14421

Hungary
Mátra Múzeum, Gyöngyös — 19887

Netherlands
Landbouw- en Juttersmuseum Swartwoude, Buren,
Friesland — 24860
Museum voor Natuur- en Wildbeheer,
Doorwerth — 24959
Stinzenmuseum, Beers, Friesland — 24795

Norway
Norsk Skogbruksmuseum, Elverum — 26071

Poland
Muzeum Łowiectwa i Jeździectwa, Warszawa — 27219

Russia
Muzej Ochoty i Rybolovstva, Moskva — 27904

Slovakia
Múzeum vo Sv. Antone, Svätý Anton — 28304

Slovenia
Tehniški Muzej Slovenije, Ljubljana — 28358

Spain
Museo Nacional de Caza, Real Bosque de
Riofrío — 29547

Sweden
Nordvärmlands Jakt och Fiskemuseum,
Sysslebäck — 30417

Switzerland
Greb Jagd-Museum, Busswil (Thurgau) — 30676
Museum Alpin, Pontresina — 31095
Schweizer Museum für Wild und Jagd,
Utzenstorf — 31340

United Kingdom
Dog Collar Museum, Maidstone — 33874
Dunrobin Castle Museum, Golspie — 33123

U.S.A.
Atlantic Wildfowl Heritage Museum, Virginia
Beach — 40873

Hygiene → Medicine and Hygiene

Icons

Albania
Onufri Iconographic Museum, Bérat — 00013

Bosnia and Herzegovina
Umjetnička galerija Bosne i Hercegovine,
Sarajevo — 03895

Bulgaria
Alexander Nevski Cathedral - Crypt - Museum of Old
Bulgarian Art, Sofia — 04304
Muzej na Văzroždenskata Ikona, Varna — 04365

Canada
Musée d'Art Néo-Byzantin, Montréal — 05379

Croatia
Biskupska Pinakoteka, Dubrovnik — 06982
Muzej Srpske Pravoslavne Crkve, Dubrovnik — 06987

Cyprus
Byzantine Museum, Paphos — 07213
Byzantine Museum and Art Galleries, Nicosia — 07201

Cyprus Turk
Icon Museum, Gazimagusa — 07216
Icon Museum, Girne — 07222
Icon Museum, Güzelyurt — 07225

Egypt
Coptic Museum, Cairo — 08205

Finland
Ortodoksinen Kirkkomuseo, Kuopio — 08563

Germany
Ikonen-Museum, Recklinghausen — 18085
Ikonen-Museum der Stadt Frankfurt am Main,
Frankfurt am Main — 15753
Ikonenmuseum, Autenried — 14368
Ikonenmuseum Schloß Autenried, Ichenhausen — 16539

Greece
Agathonos Monastery Collection, Ypati — 19709
Agei Saranda Monastery, Spárti — 19658
Agia Lovra Monastery, Kalavryta — 19486
Agios Vissarion Monastery, Trikala — 19694
Andreadis Collection, Athinai — 19360
Anthiros Monastery, Karditsa — 19494
Archeological Collection, Filiatra — 19452
Byzantine Museum, Tinos — 19692
Byzantine Museum of Katapoliani, Paros — 19606
Byzantine Museum of the Metropolis of Samos and
Ikaria, Samos — 19644
Collection of the Evangelismos tis Theotokou,
Skiathos — 19654
Collection of the Mega Spileon Monastery,
Kalavryta — 19487
Collection of the Metropolis of Kefallinia,
Argostolion — 19348
Collection of the Metropolis of Monemvassia and
Spárti, Spárti — 19660
Collection of the Metropolis of Xanthi, Xanthi — 19706
Collection of the Monastery of Saint Ignatios,
Kalloni — 19490
Collection of the Monastery of Saint John the Divine,
Antissa — 19341
Collection of the Saint John the Divine Monastery,
Patmos — 19607
Collection of the Tatarna Monastery,
Karpenission — 19499
Corgialenios Historical and Cultural Museum,
Argostolion — 19349
Ecclesiastical Museum, Komotini — 19528
Ecclesiastical Museum of the Metropolis of Trikki and
Stagoi, Trikala — 19695
Kardamyla Cultural Centre of Michael and Stamatia
Xylas, Ano Kardamyla — 19339
Monastery of the Evangelistria, Skopelos — 19655
Monastery of the Zoodochos Pigi or Agia, Batsi — 19424
Mouseio Mpenaki, Athinai — 19396
Museum of Epirot Folk Art, Metsovon — 19569
Museum of Sacred Icons, Athinai — 19406
Museum of the Metropolis of Messinia,
Kalamata — 19483
Preveli Monastery, Rethymnon — 19637
Profitis Ilias Monastery, Pyrgos — 19632
Thira Ecclesiastical Museum, Thira — 19687

India
Museum of Icons and Art Objects, Gangtok — 20240

Italy
Museo di Dipinti Sacri Ponte dei Greci, Venezia — 22809

Macedonia
Muzej na Makedonija - Arceološki, Etnološki i
Istoriski, Skopje — 24252

Netherlands
Odigia Ikonen-Museum, Den Haag — 24920

Russia
Muzej Izobrazitelnych Iskusstv Karelii,
Petrozavodsk — 27994
Permskaja Gosudarstvennaja Chudožestvennaja
Galereja, Perm — 27989
Uspenskij Sobor, Moskva — 27942

Ukraine
Kiev Museum of Ukrainian Art, Kyïv — 31920
Kiev-Pechersky National Museum, Kyïv — 31921
Muzej Volynskoj Ikony, Luck — 31927

Yugoslavia
Zbirka Crkve Sv. Nikole, Perast — 41595

Incunabula → Books, Book Art and
Manuscripts

South Africa
Queenstown and Frontier Museum, Queenstown 28603

Spain
Museu de Zoologia de Barcelona, Barcelona 28806

Switzerland
Papiliorama-Nocturama Foundation, Marin-Epagnier 30988
Tierwelt-Panorama, Ebikon 30736

Thailand
Forest Entomology Museum, Bangkok 31541

United Kingdom
Booth Museum of Natural History, Brighton 32392
National Dragonfly Biomuseum, Ashton, Oundle 32081
Oxford University Museum of Natural History, Oxford 34137
Worldwide Butterflies and Lullingstone Silk Farm, Sherborne 34469

U.S.A.
Entomology Research Museum, Riverside 39793
Essig Museum of Entomology, Berkeley 35458
The Frost Entomological Museum, University Park 40799
May Natural History Museum and Museum of Space Exploration, Colorado Springs 36185
R.M. Bohart Museum of Entomology, Davis 36393

Instruments of Torture

Austria
Folterkammer mit Heimatmuseum, Pöggstall 02408
Foltermuseum, Wien 02853

France
Tour des Voleurs, Riquewihr 12764

Germany
Burg Stolpen, Stolpen 18606
Hexenmuseum, Ringelai 18183
Museum im Zwinger, Goslar 16042

Spain
Museu de l'Institut de Criminología, Barcelona 28804

Ironwork → Metalwork

Ivory

Belgium
Trésor de la Cathedrale Notre-Dame, Tournai 03779

France
Musée des Ivoires, Yvetot 14123

Germany
Deutsches Elfenbeinmuseum Erbach, Erbach, Odenwald 15591
Domschatz, Trier 18739
Elfenbein-Museum, Michelstadt 17354
Elfenbeinmuseum, Walldürn 18904

Italy
Civiche Raccolte d'Arte Applicata, Milano 21894
Museo del Duomo, Salerno 22462

Jewellery → Precious Stones

Judaica

Argentina
Museo Judío de Buenos Aires Dr. Salvador Kibrick, Buenos Aires 00212

Australia
Jewish Holocaust Centre, Elsternwick 01000
Jewish Museum of Australia, Port Phillip 01383
Sydney Jewish Museum, Darlinghurst 00956

Austria
Jüdisches Museum der Stadt Wien, Wien 02875
Jüdisches Museum Hohenems, Hohenems 02037
Museum Judenplatz Wien, Wien 02922
Österreichisches Jüdisches Museum, Eisenstadt 01799

Bosnia and Herzegovina
Muzej Jevreja Bosne i Hercegovine, Sarajevo 03891

Canada
Beth Tzedec Reuben and Helene Dennis Museum, Toronto 06038
Saint John Jewish Historical Museum, Saint John 05806
Silverman Heritage Museum, Toronto 06088

Czech Republic
Židovské Muzeum v Praze, Praha 07604

France
Musée d'Art et d'Histoire du Judaïsme, Paris 12330
Musée d'Art Juif, Paris 12331
Musée Judéo-Alsacien, Bouxwiller 09704
Musée Juif Comtadin, Cavaillon 09916

Germany
Alte Synagoge, Hechingen 16322
Alte Synagoge, Essen 15646
August-Gottschalk-Haus, Esens 15640
Braunschweigisches Landesmuseum, Braunschweig 15029
Ehemalige Synagoge mit Ausstellung Juden auf dem Lande- Beispiel Ichenhausen, Ichenhausen 16538
Emslandmuseum Lingen, Lingen 17118
Gedenkstätte Synagoge, Dornum 15372
Heine-Haus, Hamburg 16219
Jüdische Gedenkstätte und ehemalige Synagoge, Wallhausen, Württemberg 18908
Jüdisches Kulturmuseum, Augsburg 14346
Jüdisches Kulturzentrum, Fulda 15874
Jüdisches Museum, Frankfurt am Main 15754
Jüdisches Museum, Göppingen 16006
Jüdisches Museum, München 17475
Jüdisches Museum Berlin, Berlin 14766
Jüdisches Museum Franken in Fürth, Fürth, Bayern 15863
Jüdisches Museum Franken in Schnaittach, Schnaittach 18366
Jüdisches Museum im Raschi-Haus, Worms 19199
Jüdisches Museum Rendsburg und Dr.-Bamberger-Haus, Rendsburg 18139
Landesrabbiner Dr. I.E. Lichtigfeld-Museum, Michelstadt 17355
Museum in der Präparandenschule, Höchberg 16443
Museum Jordanbad, Eppingen 15585
Museum Judengasse mit Börnegalerie, Frankfurt am Main 15767
Museum Synagoge Gröbzig, Gröbzig 16096
Museum zur Geschichte der Juden in Kreis und Stadt Heilbronn, Obersulm 17806
Städtische Dauerausstellung zur Geschichte der Aschaffenburger Juden, Aschaffenburg 14321
Synagoge und Jüdisches Museum Ermreuth, Neunkirchen am Brand 17653

Greece
Evraiko Mouseio tis Ellados, Athinai 19376
Jewish Museum of Thessaloniki, Thessaloniki 19675

Hungary
Középkori O-Zsinagóga, Sopron 19998
Országos Zsidó Vallási és Történeti Gyüjtemény, Budapest 19851

Ireland
Irish Jewish Museum, Dublin 20745

Israel
Babylonian Jewry Museum, Or Yehuda 20973
Bar David Museum, Kibbutz Bar Am 20944
Beit-Alfa Ancient Synagogue, Kibbutz Chefzi-bah 20945
Beth Hatefutsoth, Tel Aviv 20992
Capharnaum Ancient Synagogue, Kefar Nahum 20940
Central Archives for the History of the Jewish People, Jerusalem 20904
Israel Museum, Jerusalem, Jerusalem 20918
Mishkan Le'Omanut, Ein Harod 20877
Museum of Ethnography and Folklore, Tel Aviv 21005
Museum of Jewish Art, Jerusalem 20920
Schocken Institute of Jewish Research, Jerusalem 20931
Sir Isaac and Edith Wolfson Museum, Jerusalem 20933
Ticho House, Jerusalem 20935
The U. Nahon Museum of Italian Jewish Art, Jerusalem 20937

Italy
Museo della Comunità Ebraica, Venezia 22806

Latvia
Ebreji Latvijā, Rīga 24063

Netherlands
Joods Historisch Museum, Amsterdam 24698
Synagoge, Bourtange 24836

Poland
Muzeum Dzieje i Kultura Żydów, Kraków 26826
Muzeum Żydowskiego Instytutu Historycznego w Polsce, Warszawa 27245
Stary Cmentarz Żydowski, Wrocław 27291

Portugal
Museu Luso-Hebraico de Albraão Zacuto, Tomar 27444

Slovakia
Múzeum Židovskej Kultúry, Bratislava 28214

South Africa
South African Jewish Museum, Cape Town 28444

Spain
Museo Sefardí, Toledo 29777

Suriname
Stichting Joden Savanna, Paramaribo 30010

Sweden
Judiska Museet i Stockholm, Stockholm 30351

Switzerland
Jüdisches Museum der Schweiz, Basel 30568

United Kingdom
Jewish Museum, London 33679
Jewish Museum Finchley, London 33680
Manchester Jewish Museum, Manchester 33890
Scottish Jewish Museum, Glasgow 33097

U.S.A.
American Jewish Historical Museum, New York 38838
Benjamin and Dr. Edgar R. Cofeld Judaic Museum of Temple Beth Zion, Buffalo 35735
The Ernest W. Michel Historical Judaica Collection, New York 38868
Gershon Rebecca Fenster Museum of Jewish Art, Tulsa 40763
Hebrew Union College-Jewish Institute of Religion Skirball Museum, Cincinnati 36079
Herbert and Eileen Bernard Museum, New York 38882
Jane L. and Robert H. Weiner Judaic Museum, Rockville 39843
The Jewish Museum, New York 38890
Jewish Museum of Maryland, Baltimore 35315
Judah L. Magnes Museum, Berkeley 35459
Judaica Museum of Central Synagogue, New York 38891
Judaica Museum of the Hebrew Home for the Aged at Riverdale, Bronx 35679
Lillian and Albert Small Jewish Museum, Washington 40977
Museum of Jewish Heritage, New York 38910
Museum of the Southern Jewish Experience, Jackson 37641
National Museum of American Jewish Military History, Washington 40986
Philadelphia Museum of Judaica-Congregation Rodeph Shalom, Philadelphia 39404
Sylvia Plotkin Judaica Museum, Scottsdale 40270
Temple Museum of Religious Art, Cleveland 36141

Yugoslavia
Jevrejski Istorijski Muzej, Beograd 41511

Keys → Locks and Keys

Lace → Needlework

Lacquerwork

Germany
Museum für Lackkunst, Münster 17551

Japan
Hachiga Minzoku Bijutsukan, Takayama 23549
Hida Takayama Museum, Takayama 23554
Hida Takayama Shunkei Kaikan, Takayama 23555
Inro Bijutsukan, Takayama 23557
Kaisendo Museum, Kaminoyama 23114

Mexico
Museo de Laca - Coneculta, Chiapa de Corzo 24389

Myanmar
Lacquerware Museum, Pagan 24595

Lamps and Lighting

Australia
Firelight Museum, Leongatha 01163
Lighthouse Keepers Cottage, Carnarvon 00886
Narooma Lighthouse Museum, Narooma 01295

Belgium
Lampenmuseum, Wezemaal 03826

Canada
Cap-de-Bon-Désir, Bergonnes 04534
Cape Bonavista Lighthouse, Bonavista 04554
Mississagi Strait Lighthouse Museum, Meldrum 05296
West Point Lighthouse Museum, O'Leary 05516

Czech Republic
Muzeum Svitidel a Chladičů, Nový Jičín 07493

Denmark
Fyrskib Nr. XVII, København 07915

Germany
Museum Gunnar-Wester-Haus, Schweinfurt 18435
Zentrum für internationale Lichtkunst, Unna 18797

Ireland
Wexford County Museum, Enniscorthy 20771

Mexico
Museo de la Luz, México 24442

Spain
Casita del Príncipe, El Pardo 29488

United Kingdom
Museum of Lighting, Edinburgh 32929
Museum of Scottish Lighthouses, Fraserburgh 33043
Pendeen Lighthouse, Pendeen 34158
Skerryvore Museum, Hynish 33309
Smeaton's Tower, Plymouth 34199
Withernsea Lighthouse Museum, Withernsea 34860

U.S.A.
Bill Baggs Cape Florida State Recreation Area, Key Biscayne 37786
Key West Lighthouse Museum, Key West 37790
Magic Lantern Castle Museum, San Antonio 40063
Neustadt Museum of Tiffany Art, New York 38920
Ponce DeLeon Inlet Lighthouse, Ponce Inlet 39525

Language and Literature

Argentina
Museo Almafuerte, La Plata 00376
Museo Areneo de Estudios Históricos de Nueva Pompeya, Buenos Aires 00146
Museo de Arte Español, Buenos Aires 00157
Museo Histórico José Hernández-Chacra Pueyrredón, Villa Ballester 00651
Museo y Centro Cultural Victoria Ocampo, Mar del Plata 00421

Armenia
Charents Literary Memorial Museum, Erevan 00670
Isahakians Museum, Erevan 00672
Tumanyans Museum, Erevan 00684

Australia
Henry Kendall Cottage and Historical Museum, Gosford 01053
Henry Lawson Centre, Gulgong 01064
Nutcote Museum, Neutral Bay 01305
Palma Rosa Museum, Hamilton, Brisbane 01073
Tom Collins House, Swanbourne 01486

Austria
Adalbert-Stifter-Haus, Linz 02216
Anton Wildgans-Haus, Mödling 02297
Bezirksmuseum Alsergrund, Wien 02819
Bezirksmuseum Döbling, Wien 02821
Franz Xaver Gruber-Gedächtnishaus, Ach 01637
Georg Rendl-Museum, Oberndorf bei Salzburg 02357
Georg Trakl-Forschungs- und Gedenkstätte, Salzburg 02520
Hanrieder-Gedenkraum, Putzleinsdorf 02452
Heimatmuseum und Klöpferhaus, Eibiswald 01789
Hermann Broch-Museum, Teesdorf 02690
Internationales Esperanto-Museum der Österreichischen Nationalbibliothek, Wien 02872
Josef Weinheber-Museum, Kirchstetten 02106
Joseph Misson-Gedenkstätte, Mühlbach am Mannhartsberg 02313
Karl Heinrich Waggerl-Haus, Wagrain 02751
Kernstock-Museum, Bruck an der Lafnitz 01744
Österreichische Nationalbibliothek, Wien 02928
Österreichisches Sprachinselmuseum, Wien 02935
Paul Anton Keller-Museum, Lockenhaus 02239
Paul Ernst-Gedenkstätte, Sankt Georgen an der Stiefing 02545
Peter Handke-Ausstellung, Griffen 01939
Raimund-Gedenkstätte, Gutenstein 01973
Richard Billinger-Gedenkraum, Sankt Marienkirchen bei Schärding 02563
Robert Hamerling - Museum, Kirchberg am Walde 02101
Robert Musil-Literatur-Museum, Klagenfurt 02123
Sterbehaus Ferdinand Raimunds, Pottenstein 02421
Strindberg-Museum Saxen, Saxen 02598
Unser kleines Museum, Gries im Pinzgau 01937

Azerbaijan
Nizami Ganjavi, Baku 03033

Belarus
Litaraturny muzej Janki Kupaly, Minsk 03077
Literary History Museum, Minsk 03078
Maksim Bogdanovich Literature Museum, Minsk 03079

Belgium
Archief en Museum voor het Vlaamse Cultuurleven, Antwerpen 03096
Archives et Musée de la Littérature, Bruxelles 03231
Centre Provincial d'Hébergement Le Caillou, Roisin 03684
Emile Verhaeren Museum, Sint-Amands 03711
Guido Gezelle Museum, Brugge 03214
Literair Museum, Hasselt 03448

Mauritius
Robert Edward Hart Memorial Museum, Souillac 24381

Mongolia
Natsagdorj Museum, Ulaanbaatar 24545

Netherlands
A.M. de Jongmuseum, Nieuw Vossemeer 25309
Bilderdijkmuseum, Amsterdam 24685
Fries Letterkundig Museum, Leeuwarden 25226
It Gysbert Japicxhûs Museum, Bolsward 24822
Letterkundig Museum, Olst 25349
Maarten Maartenshuis, Doorn 24956
Multatuli Museum, Amsterdam 24709
Theo Thijssen Museum, Amsterdam 24739

Norway
Aulestad, Follebu 26087
Bjørgan Prestegård, Kvikne 26153
Garborgheimen - Knudaheio, Bryne 26053
Ibsenhuset og Grimstad Bymuseet, Grimstad 26099
Ibsens Venstøp, Skien 26298
Ivar Aasen-tunet, Hovdebygda 26123
Nørholm, Homborsund 26116
Petter Dass-Museet på Alstahaug, Sandnessjøen 26286
Ratvolden, Røros 26271
Sagstua Skolemuseum, Sagstua 26277
Vinjestova, Vinje 26384

Pakistan
Iqbal Museum, Lahore 26409

Philippines
Ayala Museum, Vigan 26603

Poland
Dom Gerharta Hauptmanna, Jelenia Góra 26757
Jan Kochanowski Muzeum, Czarnolas 26676
Muzeum Andrzeja Struga, Warszawa 27200
Muzeum Biograficzne Władysława Orkana, Poręba Wielka 27012
Muzeum Bolesława Prusa, Nałęczów 26943
Muzeum Emila Zegadłowicza, Gorzeń Górny 26734
Muzeum Henryka Sienkiewicza, Wola Okrzejska 27274
Muzeum Henryka Sienkiewicza w Oblęgorku, Oblęgorek 26965
Muzeum im. Adama Mickiewicza w Śmiełowie, Żerków 27317
Muzeum im. Aleksandra Świętochowskiego, Gołotczyzna 26730
Muzeum Jana Kasprowicza, Zakopane 27306
Muzeum Józefa Ignacego Kraszewskiego, Romanów 27071
Muzeum Kornela Makuszyńskiego, Zakopane 27308
Muzeum Lat Szkolnych Stefana Żeromskiego, Kielce 26786
Muzeum Literackie Henryka Sienkiewicza, Poznań 27024
Muzeum Literackie im. Józefa Czechowicza, Lublin 26915
Muzeum Literatury im. Adama Mickiewicza, Warszawa 27218
Muzeum Literatury im. Jarosława Iwaszkiewicza, Sandomierz 27083
Muzeum Marii Konopnickiej w Żarnowcu, Jedlicze 26755
Muzeum Okręgowe, Suwałki 27126
Muzeum Piśmiennictwa i Muzyki Kaszubsko-Pomorskiej, Wejherowo 27255
Muzeum-Pracownia Literacka Arkadego Fiedlera, Puszczykowo 27053
Muzeum Romantyzmu, Opinogóra 26978
Muzeum Stanisława Staszica, Piła 27000
Muzeum Stefana Żeromskiego, Nałęczów 26944
Muzeum Władysława Broniewskiego, Warszawa 27238
Oddział Literacki im. Marii Dąbrowskiej w Russowie, Russów 27073
Regionalne Muzeum Młodej Polski PTTK Rydlówka, Kraków 26850

Portugal
Casa-Oficina de António Carneiro, Porto 27423

Romania
Expozitia Memoriala Ady Endre, Oradea 27612
Expozitia Memoriala Iosif Vulcan, Oradea 27613
Expozitia Memoriala Mihai Eminescu, Ipoteşti 27595
Expozitia Memoriala Vasile Alecsandri, Mirceşti 27604
Muzeul Brăilei, Brăila 27499
Muzeul Literaturii Române, Bucureşti 27520
Muzeul Literaturii Române, Iaşi 27590
Muzeul Memorial Bojdeuca Ion Creangă, Iaşi 27591
Muzeul Memorial Emil Isac, Cluj-Napoca 27549
Muzeul Memorial George Coşbuc, Coşbuc 27559

Russia
Dom-muzej A.N. Ostrovskogo, Moskva 27805
Dom-muzej I.S. Turgeneva, Spasskoe-Lutovinovo 28088
Dom-muzej M.I. Cvetaevoj, Moskva 27808
Dom-muzej M.Ju. Lermontova, Moskva 27809
Dom-muzej N.S. Leskova, Orël 27970
Dom-muzej N.V. Gogolja, Moskva 27811
Gosudarstvennyj Literaturno-memorialnyj Muzej im. M.Ju. Lermontova, Pjatigorsk 27995
Gosudarstvennyj Literaturnyj Muzej, Moskva 27822
Gosudarstvennyj Literaturnyj Muzej im. I.S. Turgeneva, Orël 27971
Gosudarstvennyj Memorialnyj Muzej V.G. Belinskogo, Belinskij 27700
Gosudarstvennyj Muzej A.M. Gorkogo, Nižnij Novgorod 27951
Gosudarstvennyj Muzej A.S. Puškina, Moskva 27823
Gosudarstvennyj Muzej L.N. Tolstogo, Moskva 27826
Gosudarstvennyj Muzej L.N. Tolstogo, Moskva 27827
Gosudarstvennyj Muzej L.N. Tolstogo "Jasnaja Poljana", Jasnaja Poljana (Tula) 27741
Gosudarstvennyj Muzej V.V. Majakovskogo, Moskva 27832
Kazanskij Memorialnyj Muzej im. A.M. Gorkogo, Kazan 27751
Kirovskij Oblastnoj Kraevedčeskij Muzej, Kirov 27756
Kulturnyj Centr-muzej V.S. Vysockogo, Moskva 27837
Kvartira-muzej N.A. Nekrassova, Sankt-Peterburg 28037
Lermontovskij Gosudarstvennyj Muzej Tarchany, Lermontov 27775
Literaturno-memorialnyj Muzej F.M. Dostoevskogo, Sankt-Peterburg 28038
Literaturnyj Muzej, Penza 27985
Literaturnyj Muzej Instituta Russkoj Literatury, Sankt-Peterburg 28039
Memoralnyj Muzej-kvartira A.S. Puškina, Moskva 27839
Memorialnyj Dom-muzej Gercena, Moskva 27841
Memorialnyj Muzej A.P. Čechova, Melichovo 27783
Memorialnyj Muzej Černyševskogo, Saratov 28075
Moskovskij Gosudarstvennyj Muzej S.A. Esenina, Moskva 27852
Moskovskij Literaturnyj Muzej-Centr K.G. Paustovskogo, Moskva 27853
Muzej A.M. Gorkogo, Moskva 27856
Muzej-čitalnja N.V. Fëdorova, Moskva 27859
Muzej-dača A.S. Puškina, Puškin 28000
Muzej Ekslibrisa, Moskva 27860
Muzej im. N.A. Ostrovskogo, Moskva 27868
Muzej-kvartira A. Puškina, Sankt-Peterburg 28057
Muzej-kvartira A.M. Gorkogo, Moskva 27883
Muzej-kvartira A.N. Tolstogo, Moskva 27884
Muzej-kvartira A.P. Čechova, Moskva 27885
Muzej-kvartira F.M. Dostoevskogo, Moskva 27887
Muzej-kvartira Lunačarskogo, Moskva 27889
Muzej-kvartira V.S. Mejercholda, Moskva 27892
Muzej Licej, Puškin 28001
Muzej Stancionnyj Smotritel, Vyra 28139
Muzej-Usadba L.N. Tolstogo v Chamovnikach, Moskva 27915
Nacionalnyj Muzej Puškina, Sankt-Peterburg 28063
Nižnetagilskij Muzej-Zapovednik Gornozavodskogo Dela Srednego Urala, Nižnij Tagil 27954
Novorossijskij Gosudarstvennyj Istoričeskij Muzej Zapovednik, Novorossijsk 27961
Omskij Gosudarstvennyj Obedinennyj Istoričeski i Literaturnyj Muzej, Omsk 27965
Puškinskij Gosudarstvennyj Zapovednik, Michajlovskoe 27786
Samarskij Memorialnyj Muzej im. A.M. Gorkogo, Samara 28013
Severoossetinskij Literaturnyj Muzej im. K.L. Četagurova, Vladikavkaz 28126
Stalsky Memorial Museum, Ašaga-stal 27690
State Amalgamated Museum of the Writers of the Ural, Ekaterinburg 27722
Taganrogskij Gosudarstvennyj Literaturnyj i istoriko-architekturnyj Muzej-zapovednik, Taganrog 28098
Taganrogskij Muzej im. A.P. Čechova, Taganrog 28100
Vystavočnye Zaly v Dome Aksakovych, Moskva 27944

Samoa
Robert Louis Stevenson Museum, Vailima 28146

Slovakia
Literárna Expozícia - Múzeum Janka Jesenského, Bratislava 28208
Museum of Literature and Music, Banská Bystrica 28185
Múzeum Bábkarských Kutúr a Hračiek Hrad Modrý Kameň, expozícia Dolná Strhová, Dolná Strehová 28225
Múzeum Janka Krála, Liptovský Mikuláš 28252
Múzeum Ľudovíta Štúra, Modra 28267
Oravské Múzeum Pavla Országha Hviezdoslava, Dolný Kubín 28227
Slovanské Múzeum A.S. Puškina, Brodzany 28220
Slovenské Národné Literárne Múzeum, Martin 28262
Vlastivedné a Literárne Múzeum, Svätý Jur 28305

Slovenia
Kurnikova Hiša, Tržič 28394
Prešernov Spominski Muzej, Kranj 28338
Rojstna Hiša Pesnika Otona Župančiča, Vinica 28398
Spominska Zbirka Pisatelja Ivana Cankarja, Vrhnika 28399

South Africa
Afrikaans Language Museum, Paarl 28556
Nasionale Afrikaanse Letterkundige Museum en Navorsingsentrum, Bloemfontein 28420
National English Literary Museum, Grahamstown 28485
Olive Schreiner House, Cradock 28453

Spain
Casa de Cervantes, Valladolid 29851
Casa de Zorrilla, Valladolid 29852
Casa-Museo Antonio Machado, Segovia 29696
Casa-Museo Azorín, Monóvar 29369
Casa-Museo de Lope de Vega, Madrid 29233
Casa-Museo de Unamuno, Salamanca 29594
Casa Museo Federico García Lorca, Fuente Vaqueros 29071
Casa-Museo Menéndez Pelayo, Santander 29665
Casa-Museo Rosalía de Castro, Padrón 29448
Casa-Museo Tomás Morales, Moyá 29384
Casa-Museo Zenobia-Juan Ramón, Moguer 29357
Casa-Museu del Poeta Verdaguer, Folgueroles 29060
Casa Natal de Cervantes, Alcalá de Henares 28663
Centro de Mesonero Romanos, Madrid 29234
Museu Verdaguer, Vallvidrera 29873
Museu Víctor Balaguer, Vilanova i la Geltrú 29902

Sweden
Mårbacka Manor, Sunne 30410
Strindbergsmuseet Blå Tornet, Stockholm 30392

Switzerland
Ausstellung Heinrich Federer, Sachseln 31148
Bibliothèque Publique et Universitaire, Salle Rousseau, Neuchâtel 31050
Dichter- und Stadtmuseum/ Herwegh-Archiv, Liestal 30942
Fondation Martin Bodmer, Cologny 30709
Fondation Rainer Maria Rilke, Sierre 31237
Gotthelf-Stube, Lützelflüh 30961
Institut et Musée Voltaire, Genève 30804
Johanna-Spyri-Museum im Alten Schulhaus, Hirzel 30872
Musée de la Science-Fiction, de l'Utopie et des Voyages Extraordinaires, Yverdon-les-Bains 31421
Musée Jean-Jacques Rousseau, Genève 30816
Musée Jean-Jacques Rousseau, Môtiers 31021
Museo Hermann Hesse, Montagnola 31010
Museum Casa Anatta, Casa Selma und Klarwelt der Seligen, Ascona 30539
Sherlock Holmes-Museum, Meiringen 31001
Thomas-Mann-Archiv, Zürich 31477

Turkey
Aşiyan Müzesi, Bebek 31678
Cahit Sitki Taranci Müzesi, Diyarbakir 31709
İstanbul Divan Edebiyati Müzesi, İstanbul 31752
Sait Faik Müzesi, Burgaz Adasi 31691
Yunus Emre Müzesi, Yunus Emre 31858

Ukraine
Chernigiv M.M. Kotsyubinski Literary Museum, Černigiv 31887
Chernivtsi Yu.A. Fedkovich Memorial Museum, Černivci 31890
Kiev Lesya Ukrainka State Literature Museum, Kyïv 31918
Kiev T.G. Shevchenko State Museum, Kyïv 31922
Literaturno-Memoralnyj Muzej N.A Ostrovskogo, Šepetovka 31947
Literaturno-memorialny Muzei A.S. Puškina i P.I. Čajkovskogo, Kamenka 31908
Literaturno-Memorialny Muzei Lesi Ukrayinky, Kolodjažne 31912
Literaturno-memorialny Muzej Ivana Franko, Lviv 31932
Literaturnyj Muzej "Literaturnoe Pridneprovje", Dnepropetrovsk 31899
Memorial Museum The Grave of T.G. Shevchenko, Kanev 31909
Memorijalnyj Dom-muzej Javornickogo, Dnepropetrovsk 31900
Poltava State Museum, Poltava 31945
T.G. Shevchenko State Memorial Museum, Ševčenkovo 31950
Velikosoročinskij literaturno-memorialnyj muzej im N.V. Gogolja, Velikie Soročintsy 31960

United Kingdom
Abbotsford House, Melrose 33928
Bachelor's Club, Tarbolton 34641
Barrie's Birthplace, Kirriemuir 33420
Bateman's Kipling's House, Burwash 32462
Bleak House, Broadstairs 32416
Book Museum, Bath 32159
Brontë Parsonage Museum, Haworth 33228
Broughton House and Garden, Kirkcudbright 33413
Brownsbank Cottage, Biggar 32241
Burns Cottage Museum, Alloway 32028
Burns House, Dumfries 32822
Burns House Museum, Mauchline 33922
Carlyle's House, London 33607
Ceiriog Memorial Institute, Glyn Ceiriog 33118
Charles Dickens Birthplace Museum, Portsmouth 34231
Charles Dickens Centre, Rochester 34317
Coleridge Cottage, Nether Stowey 34005
Cowper and Newton Museum, Olney 34117
D.H. Lawrence Birthplace Museum, Eastwood 32898
The Dickens House Museum, London 33630
Dickens House Museum Broadstairs, Broadstairs 32418
Dove Cottage and the Wordsworth Museum, Grasmere 33145
Dr. Johnson's House, London 33631
Dylan Thomas Boathouse, Laugharne 33451
Elstow Moot Hall, Bedford 32194
Hardy's Cottage, Higher Bockhampton 33272
Hauteville House, Saint Peter Port 34397
Hill Top, Sawrey 34426
Izaak Walton's Cottage, Shallowford 34453
James Hogg Exhibition, Ettrick 32983
Jane Austen's House, Chawton 32579
Jerome K. Jerome Birthplace Museum, Walsall 34732
John Buchan Centre, Biggar 32245
John Bunyan Museum, Bedford 32195
John Creasey Museum, Salisbury 34408
John Moore Countryside Museum, Tewkesbury 34656
Keats House, London 33681
Michael Bruce Cottage Museum, Kinnesswood 33410
Milton's Cottage, Chalfont Saint Giles 32567
Newstead Abbey, Ravenshead 34276
Richard Jefferies Museum, Swindon 34632
Robert Burns Centre, Dumfries 32828
Ruskin Library, Lancaster 33440
Samuel Johnson Birthplace Museum, Lichfield 33511
Shandy Hall, Coxwold 32696
Shaw's Corner, Ayot-Saint-Lawrence 32098
Shelley Rooms, Bournemouth 32340
Thomas Carlyle's Birthplace, Ecclefechan 32900
Tobias Smollett Museum, Alexandria 32019
Ty Mawr Wybrnant, Dolwyddelan 32777
Vennel Gallery, Irvine 33338
Wordsworth House, Cockermouth 32650
The Writers' Museum, Edinburgh 32954

U.S.A.
Berkshire County Historical Society Museum at Arrowhead, Pittsfield 39477
Curwood Castle, Owosso 39227
Dickinson Homestead, Amherst 35082
Edgar Allan Poe House, Philadelphia 39371
Edgar Allan Poe House and Museum, Baltimore 35308
Edgar Allan Poe Museum, Richmond 39758
Ernest Hemingway House Museum, Key West 37789
John G. Neihardt Center, Bancroft 35334
John Greenleaf Whittier Home, Amesbury 35080
The Kate Chopin House and Bayou Folk Museum, Cloutierville 36158
Limberlost State Historic Site, Geneva 37111
Museum of the Alphabet, Waxhaw 41064
My Old Kentucky Home, Bardstown 35345
National Steinbeck Center, Salinas 40031
Orchard House - Home of the Alcotts, Concord 36241
Robert Louis Stevenson Memorial Cottage, Saranac Lake 40214
Sarah Orne Jewett House, South Berwick 40410
Wadsworth-Longfellow House, Portland 39564
William Cullen Bryant Homestead, Cummington 36341
Wren's Nest House Museum, Atlanta 35230

Uzbekistan
Literaturnyj Muzej Alisher Navoj, Taškent 41381
Literaturnyj Muzej Andižana, Andižan 41356
Literaturnyj Muzej G. Guliama iz Fergana, Kokand 41368
Sadriddin Aini Memorial Museum, Samarkand 41377

Yugoslavia
Memorijalni Muzej Džuro Jakšić, Srpska Crnja 41630
Vukov i Dositejev Muzej, Beograd 41530

Law

Argentina
Museo Notarial Argentino, Buenos Aires 00224

Australia
Beechworth Historic Court House, Beechworth 00772
Chelsea Court House Museum, Chelsea 00894
Justice and Police Museum, Sydney 01496
Melrose Courthouse Museum, Melrose 01233
Old Borroloola Police Station Museum, Borroloola 00807
Old Court House, Croydon 00944
Old Gaol and Courthouse, York 01629
South Australian Police Museum, Thebarton 01530
Stuart Town Gaol Museum, Alice Springs 00728

Belgium
Nationaal Museum en Archief van Douane en Accijnzen, Antwerpen 03119

Canada
Campbell House, Toronto 06039
Old Court House Museum, Guysborough 04996
Old Kings Courthouse Museum, Kentville 05119
Revelstoke Court House, Revelstoke 05721

Finland
Rikosmuseo, Vantaa 09017

Germany
Bayerisches Strafvollzugsmuseum, Kaisheim 16627
Rechtshistorisches Museum, Karlsruhe 16657

Netherlands
Vredespaleis, Den Haag 24930

Philippines
Kalantiaw Shrine, Batan 26518

Poland
Muzeum Adwokatury Polskiej, Warszawa 27198

Slovakia
Múzeum Polície Slovenskej republiky, Bratislava 28210

United Kingdom
Galleries of Justice, Nottingham 34094

HM Prison Service Museum, Rugby 34336
The Judge's Lodging, Presteigne 34250
Old Crown Court and Shire Hall, Dorchester 32789
Tolhouse Museum and Brass Rubbing Centre, Great
Yarmouth 33159

U.S.A.
Birmingham Civil Rights Institute Museum,
Birmingham 35508
King Kamehameha V - Judiciary History Center,
Honolulu 37483
Law Enforcement Museum, Roselle 39867
Mount Pulaski Courthouse, Mount Pulaski 38662
National Border Patrol Museum and Memorial Library,
El Paso 36673
South Carolina Law Enforcement Officers Hall of
Fame, Columbia 36210

Lead and Tin Figures

Austria
Zinngießerhäusl, Mattighofen 02273

Belgium
Tinelmuseum, Sinaai-Waas 03710

Germany
Deutsches Zinnfigurenmuseum, Kulmbach 16908
Museum zur brandenburg-preußischen Geschichte/
Zinnfigurenmuseum, Gusow 16148
Städtisches Turmmuseum Freiburg, Freiburg im
Breisgau 15816
Zinnfigurenmuseum, Herzberg am Harz 16411
Zinnkeller, Weidenberg 18957

Netherlands
Nationaal Tinnen Figuren Museum, Ommen 25350
Speelgoed- en Blikmuseum, Deventer 24943

Switzerland
Zinnfiguren-Museum, Zürich 31482

Leather

Belgium
Musée de l'Ancienne Abbaye, Stavelot 03745

Germany
Deutsches Ledermuseum/ Schuhmuseum Offenbach -
DLM, Offenbach am Main 17834
Weißgerbermuseum, Doberlug-Kirchhain 15349

Poland
Muzeum Cechu Rzemiosł Skórzanych im. Jana
Kilińskiego, Warszawa 27203

United Kingdom
Northampton Central Museum and Art Gallery,
Northampton 34074
Walsall Leather Museum, Walsall 34734

Literature → Language and Literature

Locks and Keys

Austria
Hanns Schell-Collection, Graz 01910

Belgium
Provinciaal Veiligheidsinstituut, Antwerpen 03132

France
Musée Le Secq des Tournelles - Musée de la
Ferronnerie, Rouen 12841

Germany
Deutsches Schloß- und Beschläge-Museum,
Velbert 18822

Netherlands
Lips Slotenmuseum, Dordrecht 24962

United Kingdom
Neville Blakey Museum of Locks, Keys and Safes,
Brierfield 32387
Willenhall Lock Museum, Willenhall 34827

U.S.A.
Lock Museum of America, Terryville 40665

Lumber → Forest Products

Machines and Machinery

Australia
Boiler House Steam and Engine Museum,
Kurwongbah 01144
Booleroo Steam and Traction Museum,
Booleroo 00802
Chinchilla and District Historical Society Museum,
Chinchilla 00902
Cobdogla Irrigation and Steam Museum,
Cobdogla 00919
Corrigin Museum, Corrigin 00935
Manjimup Timber Museum, Manjimup 01194
Morphett's Enginehouse Museum, Burra 00858
National Motor Museum, Birdwood 00796
Rushworth Museum, Rushworth 01429

Belgium
Chemin de Fer à Vapeur des Trois Vallées, Remise des
Locomot ives, Mariembourg 03582
Nationaal Schoeiselmuseum, Izegem 03492
Nationaal Vlas-Kant- en Linnenmuseum,
Kortrijk 03513

Canada
Rocanville and District Museum, Rocanville 05749

Czech Republic
Technické Muzeum v Brně, Brno 07263

Denmark
Arbejder-, Håndværker- og Industrimuseet,
Horsens 07879

France
Musée du Moteur, Saumur 13433
Musée Industriel Corderie Vallois, Notre-Dame-de-
Bondeville 12150

Germany
Bayerisches Moor- und Torfmuseum, Grassau,
Chiemgau 16064
Deutsches Baumaschinen-Modellmuseum,
Weilburg 18971
Gerätemuseum des Coburger Landes, Ahorn, Kreis
Coburg 14196
Industriemuseum Chemnitz, Chemnitz 15193
MAN Museum, Augsburg 14348
Molkerei-Museum, Bernbeuren 14872
Museum Gauselmann, Espelkamp 15644
Museum Industriekultur mit Motorradmuseum,
Schulmuseum und Kinderabteilung,
Nürnberg 17752
Sammlung historischer Maschinen und Geräte,
Calau 15172
Wasserkraftmuseum Leitzachwerk, Feldkirchen-
Westerham 15691
Werksmuseum der MTU, München 17531

Ireland
Irish Steam Preservation Society Museum,
Stradbally 20836
Steam Museum, Straffan 20837

Japan
Kawaguchi-ko Motor Museum, Narusawa 23379

Netherlands
Naaimachine Museum, Dordrecht 24967
Nederlands Stoommachinemuseum,
Medemblik 25285
Noord-Hollands Motoren Museum, Nieuwe
Niedorp 25310
Techniek Museum Delft, Delft 24889

New Zealand
Otago Vintage Machinery Club Museum,
Dunedin 25781
Pigeon Valley Steam Museum, Wakefield 25921
Rockville Machinery Museum, Takaka 25893
Tokomaru Steam Engine Museum, Tokomaru 25905

Norway
Bergens Tekniske Museet, Bergen 26027
Jonas Øglands Bedriftsmuseum, Sandnes 26285

Spain
Museu dels Autòmats, Barcelona 28810

Sweden
Faktorimuseet, Eskilstuna 30064
Fornminnesgården, Eksjö 30060

Switzerland
Musée Suisse de la Machine à Coudre,
Fribourg 30783
Nähmaschinen-Museum, Steckborn 31278
Schweizerisches Dampfmaschinenmuseum
Vaporama, Thun 31310

United Kingdom
Bolton Steam Museum, Bolton 32322
Brunel Engine House, London 33602
Cheddleton Flint Mill, Cheddleton 32582
Coleham Pumping Station, Shrewsbury 34480
Cornish Mines, Engines and Cornwall Industrial
Discovery Centre, Pool 34211
Corris Railway Museum, Machynlleth 33868
Crossness Engines Display, London 33623
Dingles Steam Village, Lifton 33514

Doune Motor Museum, Doune 32799
Etruria Industrial Museum, Stoke-on-Trent 34574
Forncett Industrial Steam Museum, Forncett Saint
Mary 33032
Garlogie Mill Power House Museum, Garlogie 33053
Haynes Motor Museum, Sparkford 34536
Hobbies Museum of Fretwork, Dereham 32761
Hollycombe Steam Collection, Liphook 33528
Kew Bridge Steam Museum, Kew 33371
Lark Lane Motor Museum, Liverpool 33536
Lewis Textile Museum, Blackburn, Lancashire 32293
Middleton Top Engine House, Middleton-by-
Wirksworth 33948
Midland Motor Museum, Bridgnorth 32378
Motor Museum, Ramsgate 34266
Museum of Bath at Work, Bath 32164
Museum of the Welsh Woollen Industry,
Llandysul 33558
National Tramway Museum, Matlock 33919
Newcomen Engine House, Dartmouth 32743
Papplewick Pumping Station, Ravenshead 34277
Pinchbeck Marsh Engine and Land Drainage Museum,
Spalding 34534
Ryhope Engines Museum, Sunderland 34616
Shore Road Pumping Station, Birkenhead 32255
Steam Museum, Penrith 34163
Stretham Old Engine, Stretham 34604
Waterworks Museum - Hereford, Hereford 33260
Welsh Industrial and Maritime Museum, Cardiff 32534
West Wycombe Motor Museum, West
Wycombe 34785
Westonzoyland Pumping Station Museum,
Bridgwater 32381
Workshop and Stores, Grangemouth 33140

U.S.A.
Steam Engine Museum, Mabel 38228

Majolica → Porcelain and Ceramics

Mammals

Australia
Whaleworld Museum, Albany 00715

Canada
Agawa Bay Exhibition Centre, Wawa 06233
Sidney Marine Museum, Sidney 05922

India
Zoology Museum, Lucknow 20349

Italy
Museo di Storia Naturale della Maremma,
Grosseto 21721

Japan
Nihon Monki Senta Hakubutsukan, Inuyama 23077

Netherlands
Natuurmuseum Rotterdam, Rotterdam 25438

Poland
Muzeum Lasu i Drewna przy Lesnym Zakładzie
Doświadczalnym SGGW, Rogów 27068

South Africa
Amathole Museum, King William's Town 28530

Switzerland
Museum Stemmler, Schaffhausen 31201

Man, Prehistoric

Argentina
Museo de Antropología, Córdoba 00283

Brazil
Museu Nacional, Rio de Janeiro 04062

Colombia
Museo Universitario, Medellín 06864

Croatia
Hrvatski Prirodoslovni Muzej, Zagreb 07108

Ecuador
Museo de Sitio Arqueologico el Mongote Real Alto,
Guayaquil 08138

Germany
Neanderthal Museum, Mettmann 17351
Urmensch-Museum, Steinheim an der Murr 18590

Italy
Museo e Grotte dei Balzi Rossi, Ventimiglia 22828

U.S.A.
Wayne State University Museum of Anthropology,
Detroit 36514
Zion National Park Museum, Springdale 40450

Manuscripts → Books, Book Art and Manuscripts

Maps → Cartography

Marine Archaeology

Australia
Museum of Tropical Queensland, Townsville 01545
Western Australian Maritime Museum,
Fremantle 01024

Brazil
Espaço Cultural da Marinha, Rio de Janeiro 03997

Cameroon
Cameroon Maritime Museum, Douala 04410

Canada
Sidney Marine Museum, Sidney 05922

France
Conservatoire Maritime Basque, Ciboure 10112
Musée Conservatoire Maritime et Rural,
Narbonne 12050
Musée d'Istres, Istres 10865

Germany
Nationalpark-Haus, Butjadingen 15164

Israel
National Maritime Museum, Haifa 20891

Italy
Museo Navale Romano, Albenga 21047

South Africa
Port Elizabeth Museum, Port Elizabeth 28568

Spain
Museu d'Arqueològia Submarina, Pals 29484

Sweden
Vasamuseet, Stockholm 30398

Turkey
Bodrum Sualti Arkeolojisi Müzesi, Bodrum 31686

United Kingdom
Dartmouth Museum, Dartmouth 32742
National Maritime Museum, London 33733

Marine Biology → Oceanography

Masks

Belgium
Musée International du Carnaval et du Masque,
Binche 03179

Denmark
Radio- og Motorcykel Museet, Stubbekøbing 08066

Germany
Deutsches Fastnachtmuseum, Kitzingen 16757
Narrenschopf, Bad Dürrheim 14419

Japan
Shishi Kaikan, Takayama 23559

Sri Lanka
Ambalangoda Mask Museum, Ambalangoda 29974

Switzerland
Musée Suisse de la Marionette, Fribourg 30784

Mass Media

Argentina
Museo de Medios de Comunicación,
Resistencia 00500
Museo del las Comunicaciones de Mar del Plata, Mar
del Plata 00417
Museo Radiofónico de la Ciudad de Boulogne,
Boulogne 00133

Australia
City Park Radio Museum, Launceston 01156

Austria
Ars Electronica Center, Linz 02217
Erstes Österreichisches Funk- und Radiomuseum,
Wien 02849
Museum in Progress, Wien 02921

Canada
CBC Museum, Toronto 06045

Medicine and Hygiene

Mills

Mineralogy

Argentina
Centro de Exposiciónes de Geologia y Mineria, Buenos Aires 00136
Museo de Ciencias Naturales Luma, Tanti 00622
Museo de Mineralogía y Geología Dr. Alfredo Stelzner, Córdoba 00288
Museo Municipal de Historia Natural, General Alvear 00343
Museo Provincial de Historia Natural de La Pampa, Santa Rosa 00604

Australia
Ashworths Treasures of the Earth, Home Hill 01095
Bennetts Mineral and Fossil Collection, Shepparton 01447
Crystal Kingdom, Coonabarabran 00931
Echuca Gem Club Collection, Echuca 00989
House of Bottles, Kinglake 01137
School of Earth Sciences Museum, Townsville 01547
West Coast Pioneer's Memorial Museum, Zeehan 01632

Austria
Bergbaumuseum, Hall in Tirol 01987
Bergbaumuseum mit Mineralienschau und Schaubergwerk, Hüttenberg 02046
Felsenmuseum, Bernstein, Burgenland 01727
Heimathaus Richard Eichinger und Steinmuseum, Enzenkirchen 01810
Marmormuseum, Adnet 01643
Mineralien-Museum Zirbenhof, Ebene Reichenau 01772
Museum Bramberg - Wilhelmgut, Bramberg 01736
Paläontologisches Museum, Offenhausen 02370
Referat Mineralogie, Graz 01924
Stadtmuseum Schladming, Schladming 02608

Belgium
Mineralogisch Museum, Schoten 03705
Musée Communal de la Pierre de Sprimont, Sprimont 03743
Musée de Minéralogie et de Géologie, Bruxelles 03278
Schoolmuseum Michel Thiery, Gent 03416

Bolivia
Museo Mineralogico, La Paz 03868

Bosnia and Herzegovina
Zavičajni Muzej, Travnik 03897

Brazil
Museu Amsterdam Suer de Pedras Preciosas, Rio de Janeiro 04004
Museu de Ciências da Terra - DNPM, Rio de Janeiro 04031
Museu H. Stern, Rio de Janeiro 04054

Canada
Bancroft Mineral Museum, Bancroft 04496
Fundy Geological Museum, Parrsboro 05565
Mineral and Gem Geological Museum, Parrsboro 05566
Musée Minéralogique d'Asbestos, Asbestos 04466
Musée Minéralogique et Minier de Thetford Mines, Thetford Mines 06016
Museum of Geology, Edmonton 04845
New Brunswick Mining and Mineral Interpretation Centre, Petit-Rocher 05594
Princeton and District Museum, Princeton 05661
R.B. Ferguson Museum of Mineralogy, Winnipeg 06313

Chile
Museo de Historia Natural de Valparaíso, Valparaíso 06402

China, People's Republic
Dalian Museum of Natural History, Dalian 06514

Colombia
Museo de Minerales del Instituto Geofísico, Santafé de Bogotá 06903
Museo Mineralógico Salón Tulio Ospina, Medellín 06863

Croatia
Hrvatski Narodni Zoološki Muzej, Zagreb 07106
Mineraloško-Petrografski Muzej, Zagreb 07113

Czech Republic
Městské Muzeum, Radnice u Rokycan 07616
Městské Muzeum, Stříbro 07649
Městské Muzeum, Volyně 07706
Městské Muzeum v Mariánských Lázních, Mariánské Lázně 07455
Muzeum Českého Ráje, Turnov 07677
Okresni Muzeum, Most 07472
Okresní Muzeum Sokolov, Sokolov 07643
Okresni Vlastivědné Muzeum, Nový Jičín 07494
Ostravské Muzeum, Ostrava 07511
Rožmberský Dům, Soběslav 07641

Denmark
Geologisk Museum, København 07916

Ecuador
Museo del Colegio Nacional Pedro Vicente Maldonado, Riobamba 08180
Museo Petrográfico del Servicio Nacional de Geología y Minería, Quito 08173

Finland
Geologian Tutkimuskeskuksen Kivimuseo, Espoo 08314
Kivimuseo, Helsinki 08360
Kivimuseo, Tampere 08924
Kultamuseo Tankavaara, Tankavaara 08939

France
Espace Minéralogique Minéraux Couleur Nature, Eymoutiers 10490
Galerie de Minéralogie, Paris 12293
Maison de la Pierre de Volvic, Volvic 14079
Musée de la Mine de Cap Garonne, Le Pradet 11257
Musée de Minéralogie de l'Ecole des Mines de Paris, Paris 12370
Musée d'Histoire Naturelle, Nantes 12040
Musée Minéralogique, Nîmes 12127
Musée Minéralogique de la Société Industrielle, Mulhouse 11996
Musée Municipal, Saint-Dizier 12974
Muséum d'Histoire Naturelle, Le Havre 11217

Germany
Bartholomäus-Schmucker-Heimatmuseum, Ruhpolding 18272
Bergbau- und Mineralienmuseum, Oberwolfach 17812
Geologisches Museum der DSK-Saar, Saarbrücken 18281
Geologisches und Mineralogisches Museum der Christian-Albrechts-Universität, Kiel 16726
GeoMuseum der Universität, Köln 16790
Geosammlung der Technischen Universität Clausthal, Clausthal-Zellerfeld 15201
Heimatmuseum Betzenstein, Betzenstein 14880
Heimatmuseum im Alten Kloster, Erbendorf 15593
Heimatstube Langenaubach, Haiger 16171
Höhlenmuseum Kubacher Kristallhöhle und Freilicht-Steinemuseum, Weilburg 18973
Kali-Bergbaumuseum Volpriehausen, Uslar 18810
Kristallmuseum, Viechtach 18836
Marienglashöhle Friedrichroda, Friedrichroda 15841
Mineralien-Fossilien-Museum, Neckartenzlingen 17597
Mineralien-Kabinett der TU Braunschweig, Braunschweig 15035
Mineralien-Sammlung, Hohenwarth 16481
Mineralien- und Heimatmuseum, Pleystein 17995
Mineralienmuseum Essen, Essen 15658
Mineralienmuseum Pforzheim-Dillweißenstein, Pforzheim 17974
Mineralienschau, Vohenstrauß 18860
Mineralogisch-Geologische Gesteins-Sammlung, Schwarzenfeld 18428
Mineralogische Sammlung, Erlangen 15622
Mineralogisches Museum der Philipps-Universität Marburg, Marburg 17261
Mineralogisches Museum der Universität, Würzburg 19221
Mineralogisches Museum der Universität Bonn, Bonn 14987
Mineralogisches Museum der Universität Hamburg, Hamburg 16229
Mineralogisches Museum (Kristalle und Gesteine), Münster 17549
Museum Barsinghausen, Barsinghausen 14596
Museum für Mineralogie und Geologie, Dresden 15417
Museum für Naturkunde der Humboldt-Universität zu Berlin, Berlin 14806
Museum im Hollerhaus, Dietfurt 15326
Museum Reich der Kristalle, München 17497
Naturkunde-Museum, Bielefeld 14904
Naturkunde-Museum Bamberg, Bamberg 14584
Privatmuseum Hans Klein, Prichsenstadt 18023
Sammlungen im Adelmannschloß, Landshut 16953
Schwarzwälder Mineralienmuseum, Neubulach 17621
Stadthistorisches Museum, Bad Salzdetfurth 14505
Stadtmuseum Nittenau, Nittenau 17705
Stadtmuseum Stadtoldendorf, Stadtoldendorf 18570
Stein- und Fossiliensammlung Albert, Sulzdorf 18667
Urwelt-Museum Oberfranken, Bayreuth 14627
Urweltmuseum Aalen, Aalen 14177
Waldmuseum, Mehlmeisel 17314
Zinngrube Ehrenfriedersdorf, Ehrenfriedersdorf 15508

Greece
Mineralogical Museum of Lavrion, Lavrion 19545
Museum of Mineralogy, Petrology and Geology, Athinai 19404

Hungary
Herman Ottó Múzeum, Miskolc 19944

India
Central College Museum, Bangalore 20155
Geography Museum, Faizabad 20237
Geological Museum, Lucknow 20341
Our India Project Museum, Narendrapur 20377

Ireland
James Mitchell Museum, Galway 20776

Italy
Civico Museo di Storia Naturale, Ferrara 21551
Collezione Mineralogica, Spello 22595
Frasassi- le Grotte, Genga 21678
Mineralogy, Petrography and Vulcanology Museum, Catania 21362
Museo Calderini, Varallo Sesia 22774
Museo Carlo Venturini, Massa Lombarda 21858
Museo Civico, Finale Emilia 21569
Museo Civico A. Klitsche de la Grange, Allumiere 21053
Museo Civico di Storia Naturale, Cremona 21487
Museo Civico di Storia Naturale, Pavia 22139
Museo Comunale A. Mendola, Favara 21539
Museo del Dipartimento di Scienze della Terra, Pavia 22140
Museo della Miniera, Massa Marittima 21863
Museo dell'Istituto di Mineralogia e Petrologia, Modena 21946
Museo di Mineralogia, Massa Marittima 21864
Museo di Mineralogia, Roma 22386
Museo di Mineralogia del Dipartimento di Scienza della Terra, Cagliari 21266
Museo di Mineralogia e Petrografia, Parma 22132
Museo di Mineralogia L. Bombicci, Bologna 21204
Museo di Palazzo San Francesco, Domodossola 21507
Museo di Paleontologia e di Mineralogia, Valdagno 22768
Museo di Storia Naturale Sezione Mineralogia, Firenze 21618
Museo Mineralogico, Iglesias 21735
Museo Mineralogico e delle Zolfare, Caltanissetta 21282
Museo Minerario del'Elba, Rio Marina 22314
Museo Storico Minerario, Perticara 22151
Raccolta dell'Istituto di Mineralogia e Geologia, Sassari 22542
Real Museo Mineralogico, Napoli 22031

Japan
Akita Daigaku Kozangakubu Fuzok u Kogyo Hakubutsukan, Akita 22920
Ikuno Kobutsukan, Ikuno, Hyogo 23067
Tanakami Mineral Museum, Otsu 23448

Luxembourg
Collection Eugène Pesch, Oberkorn 24234

Mexico
Museo Casa del Risco, México 24425

Mozambique
Museu Nacional de Geologia, Maputo 24582

Namibia
Geological Survey Museum, Windhoek 24634

Netherlands
Mineralenexpositie De Siersteen, Oostwold, Leek 25362
Mineralogisch-Geologisch Museum, Delft 24882
Mineralogisch Museum, Grouw 25086

New Zealand
Crystal Mountain - Crystal Mineral Gallery Museum, Auckland 25721
Geology Museum, Auckland 25724
Thames School of Mines and Mineralogical Museum, Thames 25901

Poland
Muzeum Mineralogiczne, Szklarska Poręba 27150
Muzeum Mineralogiczne Instytutu Nauk Geologicznych, Wrocław 27285

Portugal
Museu de História Natural, Porto 27425
Museu Mineralógico e Geológico, Coimbra 27357

Romania
Complexul Muzeal Judeţean Botosani, Dorohoi 27567
Muzeul de Istorie Naturală Iaşi, Iaşi 27588
Muzeul de Mineralogie Baia Mare, Baia Mare 27489

Russia
Gornyj Muzej, Sankt-Peterburg 28023
Gosudarstvennyj Geologičeskij Muzej im V.I. Vernadskogo, Moskva 27819
Mineralogičeskij Muzej im. A.E. Fersmana Akademii Nauk Rossii, Moskva 27849
Natural Science Museum of the Ilmen State Reserve, Miass 27784

Spain
Colección de Geología, Vilajüiga 29894
Museo de Ciencias Naturales, Pontevedra 29519
Museo Geominero, Madrid 29277
Museu Mollfulleda de Mineralogía, Arenys de Mar 28719

Sri Lanka
Museum of Gems and Minerals, Ratnapura 29993

Sweden
Sveriges Geologiska Undersökning, Uppsala 30452

Switzerland
Alpines Museum, Zermatt 31425
Collezione di Minerali e Fossili, Semione 31231
Geologisch-Mineralogische Ausstellung der Eidgenössischen Technischen Hochschule Zürich, Zürich 31443
Kristallmuseum, Guttannen 30855
Mineralien Museum, Seedorf (Uri) 31226
Musée des Minéraux et des Fossiles, Rougemont 31142
Museum Alpin, Pontresina 31095
Museum La Truaisch, Sedrun 31225
Steinmuseum, Solothurn 31256

Tanzania
Mineral Resources Divisional Museum, Dodoma 31523

Thailand
Mineralogy Museum, Bangkok 31545

United Kingdom
Abbey and Stones Museum, Margam 33906
Camborne School of Mines Geological Museum and Art Gallery, Pool 34210
Cornwall Geological Museum, Penzance 34165
Creetown Gem Rock Museum, Creetown 32706
Geological Museum and Art Gallery, Redruth 34289
Planet Earth Museum, Newhaven 34040
Royal Cornwall Museum, Truro 34695
Royal Pump Room Museum, Harrogate 33200
Welsh Slate Museum, Llanberis 33552

U.S.A.
A.E. Seaman Mineral Museum, Houghton 37507
Arizona Mining and Mineral Museum, Phoenix 39428
California State Mining and Mineral Museum, Mariposa 38350
Colburn Gem and Mineral Museum, Asheville 35166
Colorado School of Mines Geology Museum, Golden 37169
Gillespie Museum of Minerals, De Land 36412
Idaho Museum of Mining and Geology, Boise 35560
Lizzadro Museum of Lapidary Art, Elmhurst 36704
Meadowlands Museum, Rutherford 39894
Miles Mineral Museum, Portales 39554
Mineral and Lapidary Museum of Henderson County, Hendersonville 37403
Mineral Museum, Butte 35766
Mineralogical Museum of Harvard University, Cambridge 35792
Mousley Museum of Natural History, Yucaipa 41342
Museum of North Carolina Minerals, Spruce Pine 40475
New Mexico Bureau of Mines Mineral Museum, Socorro 40390
Post Rock Museum, La Crosse 37848
Tri-State Mineral Museum, Joplin 37703
University of Arizona Mineral Museum, Tucson 40755
W.M. Keck Museum, Reno 39726

Vietnam
Geological Museum, Ho Chi Minh City 41473

Yugoslavia
Zbirka Rudnika Majdanpek, Majdanpek 41572

Zimbabwe
Macgregor Museum, Harare 41661

Miniature Painting

France
Collections de l'Ecole Nationale Supérieure des Beaux-Arts, Paris 12281

India
Government Museum and Art Gallery, Chandigarh 20183
M.C. Mehta Gallery, Ahmedabad 20135

Netherlands
Reflex Miniatuurmuseum, Amsterdam 24729

Switzerland
Patek Philippe Museum, Genève 30820

United Kingdom
Microworld, Bath 32163

Mining Engineering

Argentina
Museo del Cielo, Villa Carlos Paz 00652

Australia
Acland Coal Mine Museum, Acland 00688
Burra Mine Open Air Museum, Burra 00857
Emmaville Mining Museum, Emmaville 01004
Grubb Shaft Gold and Heritage Museum, Beaconsfield 00770
Gwalia Historical Museum, Leonora 01164
Gympie and District Historical and Gold Mining Museum, Gympie 01069
Hannans North Tourist Mine, Kalgoorlie 01121
Herons Reef Historic Gold Diggings, Fryerstown 01026
Morphett's Enginehouse Museum, Burra 00858
Richmond Main Mining Museum, Pelaw Main 01353
Sovereign Hill, Ballarat 00755
State Coal Mine Museum, Wonthaggi 01612

Umoona Opal Mine and Museum, Coober Pedy 00928

Austria
Arsenik-Schauhütte des Bezirksheimatmuseums Spittal im Pöllatal, Rennweg 02487
Ausstellungszentrum Heft, Hüttenberg 02045
Bergbau- und Heimatmuseum, Gloggnitz 01875
Bergbaumuseum, Grünbach am Schneeberg 01961
Bergbaumuseum, Mühlbach am Hochkönig 02312
Bergbaumuseum Klagenfurt, Klagenfurt 02113
Bergbaumuseum Leogang, Leogang 02203
Bergbaumuseum mit Mineralienschau und Schaubergwerk, Hüttenberg 02046
Bergbaumuseum Pöllau, Neumarkt in Steiermark 02338
Bergbaumuseum und Schaustollen, Fohnsdorf 01829
Bergbauschaustollen, Pölfing-Brunn 02413
Böcksteiner Montanmuseum Hohe Tauern, Böckstein 01735
Eisenmuseum, Murau 02319
Historische Silbergruben - Schaubergwerk und Museum, Oberzeiring 02367
Museum Bramberg - Wilhelmgut, Bramberg 01736
Rauriser Talmuseum, Rauris 02473
Schaubergwerk Barbarastollen, Leogang 02204
Schaubergwerk Grillenberg, Payerbach 02379
Schaubergwerk Kupferplatte, Jochberg 02083
Schaubergwerk Seegrotte, Hinterbrühl 02025
Schloß- und Goldbergbaumuseum, Großkirchheim 01950
Schwazer Silberbergwerk, Schwaz 02626
Tiroler Bergbau- und Hüttenmuseum, Brixlegg 01743
Untersbergmuseum Fürstenbrunn, Grödig 01941

Belgium
Musée de la Mine et Musée du Clou, Fontaine-l'Evêque 03386

Brazil
Museu do Ouro, Sabará 04083
Museu Mineralógico da Escola de Minas, Ouro Prêto 03968

Canada
Baie Verte Peninsula Miners' Museum, Baie Verte 04494
Barkerville Historic Town, Barkerville 04503
Black Nugget Museum, Ladysmith 05177
British Columbia Museum of Mining, Britannia Beach 04596
Cape Breton Miners' Museum, Glace Bay 04948
Cobalt's Northern Ontario Mining Museum, Cobalt 04722
Elliot Lake Nuclear and Mining Museum, Elliot Lake 04868
Fernie and District Historical Museum, Fernie 04887
Frank Mills Outdoor Mining Machinery Museum, Silverton 05927
Historic Atlas Coal Mine, East Coulee 04824
Inverness Miners Museum, Inverness 05081
Jack Lynn Memorial Museum, Horsefly 05063
Jack Miner Museum, Kingsville 05148
Keno City Mining Museum, Keno City 05113
Leitch Collieries, Crowsnest Pass 04753
Lynn Lake Mining Town Museum, Lynn Lake 05253
Musée Régional des Mines et des Arts de Malartic, Malartic 05265
New Brunswick Mining and Mineral Interpretation Centre, Petit-Rocher 05594
Rossland Historical Museum, Rossland 05756
Saint Lawrence Memorial Miner's Museum, Saint Lawrence 05833
Sandon Museum, New Denver 05440
Silver Ledge Hotel Museum, Ainsworth Hot Springs 04424
Springhill Miner's Museum, Springhill 05953
Stewart Historical Museum, Stewart 05962
Village Minier de Bourlamaque, Val d'Or 06132

Colombia
Museo Siderúrgico de Colombia, Belencito 06831

Croatia
Narodni Muzej Labin, Labin 07022

Czech Republic
Hornické Muzeum OKD, Ostrava 07509
Muzeum Českého granátu, Třebenice 07668
Muzeum Jáchymovského Hornictví a Lázeňství, Jáchymov 07364
Okresní Muzeum Příbram, Příbram 07609
Okresní Muzeum v Kutné Hoře - Hradek, Kutná Hora 07420

Denmark
Søby Brunkulslejer og Brunkulsmuseet, Herning 07856

Finland
Leppävirran Kotiseutumuseo, Leppävirta 08619
Outokummun Kaivosmuseo, Outokumpu 08746

France
Caves Muséalisées Byrrh, Thuir 13688
Maison de Pays, Sainte-Marie-aux-Mines 13323
Mine Témoin d'Alès, Alès 09116
Musée de la Meunerie, Le Molay-Littry 11237
Musée de la Mine, La Machine 11001
Musée de la Mine Lucien-Mazars, Aubin 09293
Musée des Mines d'Argent des Gorges du Fournel, L'Argentière-la-Bessée 11134
Musée du Fer et du Fil, Dompierre (Orne) 10351

Germany
Bad Rappenauer Museum, Bad Rappenau 14491
Bergbau- und Greifenstein-Museum, Ehrenfriedersdorf 15507
Bergbau- und Heimatmuseum Paulushof, Essen 15648
Bergbau- und Industriemuseum Ostbayern, Kümmersbruck 16897
Bergbau- und Stadtmuseum Weilburg, Weilburg 18970
Bergbaudokumentation Hansa Empelde, Ronnenberg 18211
Bergbaumuseum, Hausham 16315
Bergbaumuseum, Oelsnitz, Erzgebirge 17822
Bergbaumuseum Achthal, Teisendorf 18691
Bergbaumuseum im Besucherbergwerk Tiefer Stollen, Aalen 14171
Bergbaumuseum Peißenberg, Peißenberg 17955
Bergbaumuseum Schachtanlage Knesebeck, Bad Grund 14437
Bergisches Museum für Bergbau, Handwerk und Gewerbe, Bergisch Gladbach 14660
Bergmännisches Traditionskabinett mit Besucherbergwerk, Breitenbrunn, Erzgebirge 15048
Bergwerksmuseum, Penzberg 17959
Besucher-Bergwerk Hüttenstollen, Salzhemmendorf 18294
Besucherbergwerk Finstertal, Asbach bei Schmalkalden 14309
Besucherbergwerk Grube Fortuna, Solms 18526
Besucherbergwerk Grube Gustav, Meißner 17324
Besucherbergwerk Schiefergrube Christine, Willingen, Upland 19125
Cornberger Sandsteinmuseum, Cornberg 15221
Deutsches Bergbau-Museum, Bochum 14937
Erzstollen Silbergründle, Seebach, Baden 18450
Feld- und Grubenbahnmuseum, Solms 18527
Fossilien- und Heimatmuseum, Messel 17345
Freiberger Silberbergwerke - Himmelfahrt-Fundgrube, Freiberg, Sachsen 15798
Grube Alte Hoffnung Erbstolln, Mittweida 17383
Haniel Museum, Duisburg 15464
Heimat- und Bergbaumuseum, Lugau, Erzgebirge 17196
Heimat- und Bergbaumuseum, Nentershausen, Hessen 17599
Heimat- und Braunkohlemuseum, Steinberg, Oberpfalz 18585
Heimatmuseum, Markranstädt 17271
Heimatmuseum, Scharfenberg bei Meißen 18319
Heimatmuseum Friedewald, Friedewald, Hessen 15839
Heimatstube Offenbach, Mittenaar 17378
Historischer Schieferbergbau Lehesten, Lehesten, Thüringer Wald 17013
Historisches Bergamt Bad Wildungen-Bergfreiheit, Bad Wildungen 14536
Historisches Erzbergwerk im Silberbergwerk Bodenmais, Bodenmais 14951
Historisches Kabinett - Sammlung für Bergbaukunde, Modellsammlung, Winkler-Gedenkstätte und Karzer, Freiberg, Sachsen 15800
Historisches Schmucksteinbergwerk Silberschacht, Bach an der Donau 14372
Historisches Silberbergwerk "Hella-Glücksstollen", Neubulach 17620
Informationszentrum Schloß Paffendorf, Bergheim, Erft 14659
Institut für Wissenschafts- und Technikgeschichte, Kustodie, Freiberg, Sachsen 15801
Kali-Bergbaumuseum Volpriehausen, Uslar 18810
Landesbergbaumuseum Baden-Württemberg, Sulzburg 18666
Lausitzer Bergbaumuseum Knappenrode, Hoyerswerda 16511
Lehr- und Schaubergwerk Frisch Glück, Johanngeorgenstadt 16615
Lehr- und Schaubergwerk Herkules Frisch Glück, Waschleithe 18933
Maffeischächte der Grube Auerbach-Nitzlbuch, Auerbach, Oberpfalz 14333
Mansfeld-Museum Hettstedt, Hettstedt, Sachsen-Anhalt 16414
Mansfelder Bergwerksbahn e.V., Benndorf 14643
Mineralien-Museum Andreas Gabrys, Lam 16936
Museum der Stadt Aue, Aue, Sachsen 14332
Museum der Stadt Gladbeck, Gladbeck 15981
Museum Huthaus Einigkeit, Brand-Erbisdorf 15016
Museum Industriekultur, Osnabrück 17877
Museum Kalkwerk Lengefeld, Lengefeld, Erzgebirge 17074
Museum Schloß Schwarzenberg, Schwarzenberg 18427
Museum und Besucherbergwerk der Graphit Kropfmühl AG, Hauzenberg 16316
Museum und Besucherbergwerk Rammelsberg, Goslar 16043
Museumspark, Rüdersdorf bei Berlin 18262
Niedersächsisches Bergbaumuseum, Langelsheim 16961
Nordhessisches Braunkohle-Bergbaumuseum, Borken, Hessen 15000
Oberharzer Bergwerksmuseum, Clausthal-Zellerfeld 15202
Oberpfälzer Flußspat-Besucherbergwerk Reichhart-Schacht, Stulln 18620
Saarländisches Bergbaumuseum, Bexbach 14885
Schaubergwerk Büchenberg, Elbingerode, Harz 15541
Schaubergwerk Teufelsgrund, Münstertal 17562
Schaubergwerk Zum Tiefen Molchner Stolln, Pobershau 18000
Schiefermuseum, Ludwigsstadt 17161
Schwarzwälder Mineralienmuseum, Neubulach 17621
Silbereisenbergwerk Gleißinger Fels, Fichtelberg 15702
Silberstollen Geising, Geising 15913
Stadt- und Bergbaumuseum Freiberg, Freiberg, Sachsen 15803
Stadt- und Heimatmuseum, Marienberg 17265
Städtische Museen Zwickau, Zwickau 19298
Städtische Sammlungen Freital, Freital 15824
Steinkohlen-Besucherbergwerk Rabensteiner Stollen, Ilfeld 16545
Technisches Denkmal Tobiashammer, Ohrdruf 17842
Werra-Kalibergbau-Museum, Heringen, Werra 16390
Zinngrube Ehrenfriedersdorf, Ehrenfriedersdorf 15508

Hungary
Alapítvány Érc és Ásványbányászati Múzeum, Rudabánya 19984
Központi Bányászati Múzeum, Sopron 19999
Mecseki Bányászati Múzeum, Pécs 19974
Tatabánya Múzeum, Tatabánya 20058

Italy
La Miniera, Desio 21503

Japan
Nogata-shi Sekitan Kinenkan, Nogata 23394
Sekitan Kinenkan, Ube 23730

Luxembourg
Musée National des Mines Fer Luxembourgeoisie, Rumelange 24237

Namibia
Kolmanskop Museum, Kolmanskop 24614

Netherlands
Industrion Museum for Industry and Society, Kerkrade 25206
Steenkolenmijn Daalhemergroeve, Valkenburg 25573

New Zealand
Alexandra Museum, Alexandra 25708
Coromandel School of Mines Museum, Coromandel 25762
Lakes District Museum, Arrowtown 25710
Switzers Museum, Waikaia 25910
Tuapeka Goldfields Museum, Lawrence 25822
Waihi Arts Centre and Museum Association, Waihi 25909

Norway
Folldal Gruver, Folldal 26086
Gammelgruva, Løkken Verk 26168
Modums Blaafarveværk, Åmot 26009
Norsk Bergverksmuseum, Kongsberg 26144
Sulitjelma Gruvemuseum, Sulitjelma 26330

Poland
Muzeum Geologiczne, Kraków 26830
Muzeum Górnictwa i Hutnictwa Kopalina Złota, Złoty Stok 27323
Muzeum Górnictwa i Hutnictwa Rud Żelaza, Częstochowa 26679
Muzeum Górnictwa Podziemnego, Nowa Ruda 26950
Muzeum Górnictwa Węglowego, Zabrze 27299
Muzeum Górnicze, Bogatynia 26640
Muzeum Żup Krakowskich, Wieliczka 27259
Skansen Górniczy Królowa Luiza, Zabrze 27301

Romania
Muzeul Mineritului, Petroşani 27616

Russia
Gornyj Muzej, Sankt-Peterburg 28023

Slovakia
Banícke Múzeum, Gelnica 28233
Banícke Múzeum, Rožňava 28289
Slovenské Banské Múzeum, Banská Štiavnica 28189

Slovenia
Koroški Muzej Ravne na Koroškem, Ravne na Koroškem 28381
Muzej Jesenice, Jesenice 28329
Zavičajni Muzej, Velenje 28397

South Africa
Barberton Museum, Barberton 28408
Pilgrim's Rest Museum, Pilgrim's Rest 28566

Spain
Museo Histórico-Minero Don Felipe de Borbón y Grecia, Madrid 29278

Sweden
Gruvmuseet, Sala 30293
Långbans Gruvby, Karlstad 30162
Ludvika Gammelgård och Gruvmuseum, Ludvika 30203

Switzerland
Bergbaumuseum, Horgen 30875
Bergbaumuseum Graubünden mit Schaubergwerk, Davos Platz 30721
Gonzen-Museum, Sargans 31185

United Kingdom
Big Pit National Mining Museum of Wales, Blaenavon 32299
Cefn Coed Colliery Museum, Neath 34000
Chatterley Whitfield Mining Museum, Stoke-on-Trent 34573
Dunaskin Open Air Museum, Patna 34149
Durban House Heritage Centre, Eastwood 32899
Elliot Colliery Winding House, New Tredegar 34011
Florence Mine Heritage Centre, Egremont 32957
Geevor Tin Mining Museum, Pendeen 34157
Gloddfa Ganol Slate Mine, Blaenau Ffestiniog 32297
Great Laxey Wheel and Mines Trail, Laxey 33454
Hartham Park - Underground Quarry Museum, Corsham 32681
Killhope, the North of England Lead Mining Museum, Wearhead 34763
Minera Lead Mines, Minera 33962
Morwellham Quay Historic Port Copper Mine, Tavistock 34647
Museum of Lead Mining, Wanlockhead 34739
Museum of Yorkshire Dales Lead Mining, Earby 32868
National Coal Mining Museum for England, Wakefield 34721
National Mining Museum, Haughton 33217
Nenthead Mines Museum, Nenthead 34003
Peak District Mining Museum, Matlock 33920
Poldark Mine and Heritage Complex, Helston 33245
Prestongrange Industrial Heritage Museum, Prestongrange 34254
Scottish Mining Museum, Newtongrange 34059
South Wales Miner's Museum, Port Talbot 34222
Sygun Copper Mine, Beddgelert 32189
Tar Tunnel, Coalport 32643
Threlkeld Quarry and Mining Museum, Threlkeld 34670
Tom Leonard Mining Museum, Skinningrove 34495
Welsh Slate Museum, Llanberis 33552
Woodhorn Colliery Museum, Ashington 32080

Uruguay
Museo de la Dirección Nacional de Minería y Geología, Montevideo 34937

U.S.A.
Alabama Mining Museum, Dora 36533
Arizona Mining and Mineral Museum, Phoenix 39428
Big Thunder Gold Mine, Keystone 37795
Bisbee Mining and Historical Museum, Bisbee 35515
Black Hills Mining Museum, Lead 37981
California State Mining and Mineral Museum, Mariposa 38350
Comer Museum, Morgantown 38628
Coppertown U.S.A., Calumet 35783
Dahlonega Courthouse Gold Museum, Dahlonega 36349
Fort Wilkins Historic Complex, Copper Harbor 36261
Franklin Mineral Museum, Franklin 37012
Grand Encampment Museum, Encampment 36720
Idaho Museum of Mining and Geology, Boise 35560
Iron Mountain Iron Mine, Vulcan 40887
Ironworld Discovery Center, Chisholm 36065
Jerome State Historic Park, Jerome 37682
Lafayette Miners Museum, Lafayette 37875
Miners Foundry Cultural Center, Nevada City 38749
The Mining Museum, Platteville 39489
Museum of Anthracite Mining, Ashland 35181
North Star Mining Museum, Grass Valley 37223
Reed Gold Mine State Historic Site, Stanfield 40481
Sterling Hill Mining Museum, Ogdensburg 39124
Tintic Mining Museum, Eureka 36758
Underhill Museum, Idaho Springs 37570
Vermont Marble Exhibition, Proctor 39621
Wallace District Mining Museum, Wallace 40907
The Walsenburg Mining Museum and Fort Francisco Museum of La Veta, Walsenburg 40912
Western Museum of Mining and Industry, Colorado Springs 36188
World Museum of Mining, Butte 35767

Yugoslavia
Mineraloška Zbirka Rudnika Trepča, Stari Trg 41631
Muzej Rudarstva i Metalurgije, Bor 41533

Zambia
Copperbelt Museum, Ndola 41655

Zimbabwe
National Mining Museum, Kwekwe 41665

Mollusks

Greece
Moschakeion, Athinai 19387

Italy
Museo Zoologico Cambria, Messina 21886

Netherlands
Natuurmuseum Rotterdam, Rotterdam 25438

Spain
Museo Nacional de Ciencias Naturales, Madrid 29286
Museu de Malacologia Cau del Cargol, Vilassar de Dalt 29905
Museu de Zoologia de Barcelona, Barcelona 28806

Monasteries

Austria
Kartause Gaming, Gaming 01855

Bangladesh
Archaeological Museum, Mainamati 03057

Belgium
Musée de l'Abbaye d'Orval, Villers-devant-
Orval 03799
Museum van de Abdij van Roosenberg,
Waasmunster 03805

Bulgaria
Nacionalen Muzej Rilski Manastir, Rilski
Manastir 04274

Cambodia
The Angkor Conservation, Siem Reap 04408

Denmark
Danmarks Kloster Museum, Ry 08033

France
Musée-Abbaye Saint-Germain, Auxerre 09340

Germany
Deutsches Kartausen-Museum, Buxheim bei
Memmingen 15168
Kloster Altenberg, Solms 18528
Kloster Irsee, Irsee 16576
Klosteranlage mit Klostermuseum, Maulbronn 17296
Klostermuseum Heggbach, Maselheim 17291
Klostermuseum Hirsau, Calw 15178
Klostermuseum Jerichow, Jerichow 16609
Kornhaus Georgenthal-Klosterruinen,
Georgenthal 15934
Missionsmuseum, Schwarzach am Main 18423
Museum Abtei Liesborn, Wadersloh 18866
Museum des Landkreises Waldshut - Sankt Blasien,
Sankt Blasien 18303
Museum Höxter-Corvey, Höxter 16455
Museum Kloster Zinna, Kloster Zinna 16768
Museum zur Kloster- und Stadtgeschichte, Steinheim
an der Murr 18589
Prignitz-Museum Havelberg, Havelberg 16318
Prunkräume in der Residenz, Kempten 16718
Sammlungen der Benediktiner-Abtei Braunau, Rohr,
Niederbayern 18207
Schloss Salem, Salem, Baden 18289
Torbogenmuseum, Königsbronn 16819

Greece
Karyes-Protaton, Agion Oros 19319

Ireland
Adare Trinity Museum, Adare 20682

Italy
Museo della Collegiata, Castell'Arquato 21344
Museo dell'Opera di Santa Croce, Firenze 21609

Japan
Treasure House of the Eiheiji Temple, Eiheiji 22963

Netherlands
Museum Kloster Ter Apel, Ter Apel 25526

Norway
Klostertunet, Halsnøy Kloster 26101
Rissa Bygdemuseum, Rissa 26264
Utstein Kloster, Mosterøy 26193

Slovakia
Múzeum Červený Kláštor, Červený Kláštor 28223

Spain
Monasterio de la Encarnación, Madrid 29255
Monasterio de la Santa Cruz, Sahagún 29592
Monasterio de las Descalzas Reales, Madrid 29256
Monasterio de las Huelgas de Burgos, Burgos 28869
Monasterio de San Juan de los Reyes, Toledo 29768
Monasterio de San Pedro, San Pedro de
Cardeña 29623
Monasterio de Sant Cugat, Sant Cugat del
Vallès 29632
Monasterio de Santa María, Ripoll 29563
Monasterio de Santa María, Santa María de
Huerta 29657
Monasterio de Santa María la Real, Nájera 29395
Monasterio de Santes Creus, Santes Creus 29670
Museu de Poblet, Monestir de Poblet 29364
Museu Monàstic, Vallbona de les Monges 29865

Switzerland
Klostermuseum Sankt Georgen, Stein am
Rhein 31282

United Kingdom
Beaulieu Abbey Exhibition of Monastic Life,
Brockenhurst 32421
Bede's World, Jarrow 33347
Glastonbury Abbey Museum, Glastonbury 33101

U.S.A.
Teutopolis Monastery Museum, Teutopolis 40666

Yugoslavia
Manastirska Zbirka-Riznica Manastira Dečane,
Dečane 41546

Manastirski Muzej, Cetinje 41542
Riznica Manastira Studenica, Raška 41614

Money → Numismatics

Mosaics

Greece
Monastery of Ossios Loukas, Steiri 19664

Italy
Antiquarium e Mosaico Romano, Bevagna 21164
Musei Civici agli Eremitani, Padova 22087
Museo del Battistero, Albenga 21045
Museo di Torcello, Venezia 22810
Pinacoteca Comunale Faenza, Faenza 21533

Portugal
Museu Monográfico de Conimbriga, Condeixa-a-
Nova 27359

Spain
Museo Municipal, Alcázar de San Juan 28670

Switzerland
Pro Urba, Orbe 31083

Tunisia
Musée de Sousse, Sousse 31633
Musée National du Bardo, Le Bardo 31615

Turkey
Büyük Saray Mozaik Müzesi, İstanbul 31748
Istanbul Arkeoloji Müzeleri, Gülhane 31735
Silifke Mozaik Müzesi, Narlikuyu 31812

Ukraine
Saint Sophia of Kiev, Kyïv 31923

United Kingdom
Aldborough Roman Town Museum,
Boroughbridge 32332
Roman Villa Museum at Bignor, Bignor 32247

Mummies

Egypt
Elephantine Island's and Aswan Museum,
Aswan 08198

Germany
Bleikeller, Bremen 15051
Petrefaktensammlung, Staffelstein,
Oberfranken 18574

Poland
Muzeum im. Władysława Orkana, Rabka 27055

Mural Painting and Decoration

Belgium
Sint-Baafskathedraal Gent, Gent 03417

Bulgaria
Muzej na Rezbarskoto i Zografsko Izkustvo,
Trjavna 04355

Canada
Canadian Museum of Animal Art, Bolton 04551

France
Musée Palais Lascaris, Nice 12107

Germany
Fürstlich Ysenburg- und Büdingensches
Schloßmuseum, Büdingen 15127
Leitheimer Schloß-Museum, Kaisheim 16628
Museum für Vor- und Frühgeschichte,
Saarbrücken 18283
Torhalle Frauenchiemsee und Vikarhaus,
Chiemsee 15200

Greece
Byzantine Collection, Kerkyra 19512
Byzantine Museum, Zakynthos 19710
Makris Collection, Volos 19703

Italy
Camposanto e Museo dell'Opera, Pisa 22209
Cappella degli Scrovegni, Padova 22086
Cenacolo di Sant'Apollonia, Firenze 21581
Chiesa di Santa Maria Maddalena de Pazzi,
Firenze 21582
Convento dell'ex-Convento di Sant'Onofrio detto di
Fuligno, Firenze 21584
Fondazione Romano nel Cenacolo di Santo Spirito,
Firenze 21586

Libreria Sansoviniana, Venezia 22796
Museo Benedettino Nonantolano e Diocesano di Arte
Sacra, Nonantola 22042
Museo Civico, Sansepolcro 22510
Museo Civico di Schifanoia, Ferrara 21552
Museo Civico Parazzi, Viadana 22851
Museo d'Arte Sacra, Colle di Val d'Elsa 21450
Museo degli Argenti, Firenze 21605
Museo del Castello Colleoni Porto, Thiene 22644
Museo del Duomo Albani, Urbino 22762
Museo della Villa Bettoni, Bogliaco 21177
Museo dell'Opera del Duomo, Prato 22262
Museo di Pittura Murale, Prato 22263
Museo di San Marco, Firenze 21614
Museo Diocesano, Gaeta 21658
Museo e Chiostri Monumentali di Santa Maria Novella,
Firenze 21620
Palazzo Medici Riccardi, Firenze 21628
Palazzo Vecchio, Firenze 21629
Pinacoteca Civica-Palazzo Canonici, Spello 22596
Pinacoteca Comunale, Argenta 21089
Pinacoteca Giralamo di Giovanni, Camerino 21289
Rocca Borromeo, Angera 21067
Villa della Farnesina, Roma 22433

Japan
Nagoya Castle Treasure House, Nagoya, Aichi 23357
Takamatsuzuka Wall Painting Museum, Asuka 22940
Yaegaki-jinja Treasure Storehouse, Matsue 23292

Spain
Museo de Navarra, Pamplona 29485
Museo Diocesano de Huesca, Huesca 29149
Museo Real Colegiata de San Isidoro, León 29191
Museu Diocesà d'Urgell, La Seu d'Urgell 29704

Switzerland
Klostermuseum, Müstair 31036

Turkey
Göreme Açikhava Müzesi, Nevşehir 31813

Ukraine
Saint Sophia of Kiev, Kyïv 31923

United Kingdom
Plas Newydd, Llanfairpwll 33564

U.S.A.
Gallery of Prehistoric Paintings, New York 38874

Yugoslavia
Galerija Fresaka, Beograd 41507

Museology

Brazil
Museu de Arqueologia e Etnologia da Universidade de
São Paulo, São Paulo 04107

Chile
Museo Histórico y Antropológico de la Universidad
Austral de Chile, Valdivia 06400

Music and Musical Instruments

Argentina
Museo Areneo de Estudios Históricos de Nueva
Pompeya, Buenos Aires 00146
Museo de Instrumentos Musicales, Buenos
Aires 00171
Museo de Instrumentos Musicales Emilio Azzarini, La
Plata 00382
Museo de la Partitura Historica, Rosario 00519
Museo de SADAIC Vincente López y Planes, Buenos
Aires 00186
Museo del Tango Roberto Firpo, Salto 00535
Museo del Teatro y la Música de Córdoba Cristobal de
Aguilar, Córdoba 00291
Museo Manuel de Falla, Alta Gracia 00102

Armenia
Khachatrians Museum, Erevan 00674
Spendiarians Museum, Erevan 00680

Australia
Grainger Museum, Parkville, Victoria 01350
Historic and Ethnic Instrument Collection,
Nedlands 01303
McCrae Homestead Museum, McCrae 01208
Miniature English Village and Brass Rubbing Centre,
Flaxton 01013
Das Neumann Haus Museum, Laidley 01148
Organ Historical Trust of Australia, Camberwell,
Victoria 00867
Waltzing Matilda Centre and Qantilda Museum,
Winton 01604

Austria
Anton Bruckner-Museum, Ansfelden 01671
Arnold Schönberg Center, Wien 02805
Beethoven-Gedenkstätte, Wien 02814
Beethoven-Gedenkstätte Eroicahaus, Wien 02815

Beethoven-Gedenkstätte in Floridsdorf, Wien 02816
Beethoven-Wohnung im Pasqualati-Haus,
Wien 02817
Beethovenhaus, Krems 02146
Beethovenhaus " Haus der Neunten", Baden bei
Wien 01719
Blasmusik-Museum, Ratten 02471
Brucknerzimmer, Kronstorf 02157
Franz Daurach-Sammlung, Hadres 01981
Franz von Suppé-Gedenkstätte, Gars am Kamp 01858
Franz Xaver Gruber-Museum,
Lamprechtshausen 02170
Haydn-Geburtshaus, Rohrau 02502
Haydn-Gedenkstätte mit Brahms-Gedenkraum,
Wien 02863
Haydn-Museum, Eisenstadt 01798
Hugo Wolf-Haus, Perchtoldsdorf 02384
Johann Michael Haydn-Gedenkstätte, Salzburg 02521
Johann Strauß-Gedenkstätte, Wien 02873
Johannes Brahms-Museum, Mürzzuschlag 02317
Kammerhofmuseum der Stadt Gmunden,
Gmunden 01890
Komponierstube Gustav Mahlers, Steinbach am
Attersee 02655
Lehár-Villa, Bad Ischl 01701
Lisztmuseum, Raiding 02461
Mozart-Gedenkstätte Figarohaus, Wien 02905
Mozart-Gedenkstätte im Bezirksgericht, Sankt
Gilgen 02549
Mozart Wohnhaus, Salzburg 02523
Mozarts Geburtshaus, Salzburg 02524
Museum des Wiener Männergesang-Vereins,
Wien 02915
Museum Franz Schubert und sein Freundeskreis,
Atzenbrugg 01683
Museum für mechanische Musik und Volkskunst,
Haslach 02003
Musica Kremsmünster, Kremsmünster 02153
Pater Peter Singer-Museum, Salzburg 02526
Pleyel-Geburtshaus, Großweikersdorf 01960
Robert Stolz Museum Graz, Graz 01927
Schönberg-Haus in Mödling, Mödling 02302
Schubert-Gedenkstätte Geburtshaus, Wien 02958
Schubert-Gedenkstätte Sterbewohnung, Wien 02959
Steirisches Uhren-, Musikalien- und
Volkskundemuseum, Arnfels 01674
Stiftssammlungen des Zisterzienserstiftes Rein,
Gratwein 01903
Stille Nacht-Museum, Hallein 01994
Stoani Haus der Musik, Gasen 01865
Wilhelm Kienzl-Museum, Waizenkirchen 02759

Belgium
Archief en Museum voor het Vlaamse Cultuurleven,
Antwerpen 03096
Musée des Instruments de Musique, Bruxelles 03283
Peter Benoitmuseum, Harelbeke 03444
Stedelijk Museum voor Heemkunde en Folklore,
Aarschot 03086
Stedelijke Musea, Sint-Niklaas 03721
Vleeshuis, Antwerpen 03140

Brazil
Centro de Pesquisas Folclóricas, Rio de
Janeiro 03995
Museu Carlos Gomes, Campinas 03919
Museu da Imagem e do Som, Rio de Janeiro 04022
Museu Villa-Lobos, Rio de Janeiro 04070

Canada
Anne Murray Centre, Springhill 05952
Guy Lombardo Museum, London 05229
Hank Snow Country Music Centre, Liverpool 05218
Maison de l'Accordéon, Montmagny 05350
Sounds of Yesteryear, Winnipeg 06322

China, People's Republic
National Museum of Music, Beijing 06459

Colombia
Museo Organológico Folklórico Musical, Santafé de
Bogotá 06914

Croatia
Zbirka Umjetnina KAIROS, Trogir 07085

Cuba
Museo Nacional de Música, La Habana 07158

Czech Republic
Janáčkovo Muzeum, Brno 07255
Muzeum Antonína Dvořáka, Praha 07575
Muzeum Bedřicha Smetany, Praha 07576
Muzeum České Hudby, Litomyšl 07440
Muzeum české hudby, Praha 07577
Muzeum Středniho Pootaví, Strakonice 07646
Muzikologické Pracoviště, Opava 07502
Památník Antonína Dvořáka, Nelahozeves 07478
Památník Antonína Dvořáka, Vysoká u Příbrami 07714
Památník Antonína Dvořáka, Zlonice 07736
Památník Bedřicha Smetany, Jabkenice 07359
Památník Bohuslava Martinů, Polička 07539
Památník Dr. Emila Axmana, Chropyně 07302
Památník Františka Ondříčka a Českého kvarteta,
Brandýs nad Labem 07245
Památník Josefa Suka, Křečovice 07414
Památník Leoše Janáčka, Hukvaldy 07355
Památník W.A. Mozarta a Manželů Duškových,
Praha 07591
Památník Zdeňka Fibicha, Všeborice 07710

Denmark
Carl Nielsen Museet, Odense 07988
Carl Nielsens Barndomshjem, Årslev 07760
Musikhistorisk Museum og Carl Claudius' Samling, København 07927

Ecuador
Museo de Instrumentos Musicales Pablo Traversari, Quito 08163

Estonia
Eesti Teatri-ja Muusikamuuseum, Tallinn 08265

Finland
Ainola, Järvenpää 08415
Sibelius Museum, Turku 08968
Suomen Kansansoitinmuseo, Kaustinen 08480

France
Maison de la Musique Mécanique, Mirecourt 11777
La Maison du Luthier de Jenzat, Jenzat 10878
Musée de la Musique, Paris 12344
Musée de la Musique Mécanique, Crillon-le-Brave 10266
Musée des Instruments de Musique à Vent, La Couture-Boussey 10960
Musée des Musiques Populaires, Montluçon 11885
Musée du Phonographe et de la Musique Mécanique, Sainte-Maxime 13331
Musée Edith Piaf, Paris 12403
Musée Hector Berlioz, La Côte-Saint-André 10956
Musée Maurice Ravel, Montfort-l'Amaury 11868
Musée-Placard d'Erik Satie, Paris 12442
Musée Pyrénéen, Lourdes 11478

Germany
Albert-Schweitzer-Gedenk- und Begegnungsstätte, Weimar, Thüringen 18982
Bach-Gedenkstätte im Schloß Köthen, Köthen, Anhalt 16835
Bachhaus Eisenach, Eisenach 15527
Beatles Museum, Halle, Saale 16184
Beethoven-Haus, Bonn 14973
Brahmshaus, Baden-Baden 14556
Carl-Maria-von-Weber-Museum, Dresden 15397
Carl Orff Museum, Dießen am Ammersee 15321
Deutsches Harmonikamuseum, Trossingen 18749
Deutsches Phonomuseum, Sankt Georgen im Schwarzwald 18305
Ellermeiers Burgmannshof, Hardegsen 16289
Elztalmuseum - Regionalgeschichte und Orgelbau, Waldkirch 18893
Erstes Deutsches Museum für mechanische Musikinstrumente, Rüdesheim am Rhein 18263
Forschungs- und Gedenkstätte im Geburtshaus des Komponisten Heinrich-Schütz-Haus, Bad Köstritz 14460
Franz-Liszt-Museum der Stadt Bayreuth, Bayreuth 14613
Gebrüder-Lachner-Museum, Rain am Lech 18049
Geigenbau-Museum, Bubenreuth 15115
Geigenbau- und Heimatmuseum, Mittenwald 17380
Händel-Haus, Halle, Saale 16191
Harmonium-Museum, Hennef 16377
Heinrich-Schütz-Haus, Weißenfels 19028
Johann-Sebastian-Bach-Museum, Leipzig 17040
Liszthaus - Goethe-Nationalmuseum, Weimar, Thüringen 18992
Little Cavern, Biebelnheim 14892
Louis Spohr-Gedenk- und Forschungsstätte, Kassel 16678
Max-Reger-Gedächtniszimmer, Brand, Oberpfalz 15017
Mozarthaus, Augsburg 14350
Museum Bürgstadt, Bürgstadt 15137
Museum der Stadt Füssen, Füssen 15866
Museum für Blasmusikinstrumente, Kürnbach 16902
Museum Gottfried Silbermann, Frauenstein 15789
Museum mechanischer Musikinstrumente, Königslutter 16827
Museum Mechanischer Musikinstrumente, Bruchsal 15099
Musikhistorische Sammlung Jehle, Albstadt 14209
Musikinstrumenten-Ausstellung des Händel-Hauses, Halle, Saale 16194
Musikinstrumenten-Museum, Markneukirchen 17270
Musikinstrumenten-Museum, Berlin 14818
Musikinstrumenten-Museum der Universität Leipzig (Interim), Leipzig 17052
Musikinstrumenten- und Puppenmuseum, Goslar 16044
Musikinstrumentenmuseum, München 17500
Musikinstrumentenmuseum Lißberg, Ortenberg, Hessen 17864
Musikinstrumentensammlung, Erlangen 15624
Musikinstrumentensammlung der Universität, Göttingen 16026
Neues Schloß und Instrumentenmuseum, Kißlegg 16756
Orgelbaumuseum, Ostheim vor der Rhön 17892
Orgelmuseum Altes Schloß, Valley 18814
Orgelmuseum Borgentreich, Borgentreich 14999
Orgelmuseum Kelheim, Kelheim 16706
Private Sammlung Mechanischer Musikinstrumente, Wohlhausen 19169
Regionalgeschichtliche Sammlung mit Musikinstrumentensammlung Hans und Hede Grumbt Wasserburg Haus Kemnade, Hattingen 16307
Reuterhaus mit Richard-Wagner-Sammlung, Eisenach 15530
Richard-Wagner-Museum, Bayreuth 14625
Richard-Wagner-Museum Graupa, Pirna 17986
Robert-Schumann-Haus Zwickau, Zwickau 19296
Sängermuseum, Feuchtwangen 15701
Sammlung historischer Tasteninstrumente Neumeyer-Junghanns-Tracey, Bad Krozingen 14464
Schumann-Haus, Leipzig 17059
Schwarzwald-Museum, Triberg 18734
Silcher-Museum Schnait, Weinstadt 19014
Stadtgeschichtsmuseum Arnstadt "Haus zum Palmbaum" mit Bachgedenkstätte und Literatenkabinett, Arnstadt 14304
Stadtmuseum im Spital, Crailsheim 15232
Stiftung Kloster Michaelstein/Museum, Blankenburg, Harz 14921
Trompetenmuseum, Bad Säckingen 14502
Werner-Egk-Begegnungsstätte, Donauwörth 15363
Zungeninstrumenten-Sammlung Zwota, Zwota 19305

Greece
Anoyanakis Collection, Athinai 19361
Mouseio Laikon Organon, Athinai 19395

Hungary
Bartók Béla Emlékház, Budapest 19808
Beethoven Emlékmúzeum, Martonvásár 19939
Liszt Ferenc Emlékmúzeum és Kutatóközpont, Budapest 19827
Zenetörténeti Múzeum, Budapest 19865

Iran
Sabā's House, Teheran 20658

Israel
Museum of Musical Instruments, Jerusalem 20921

Italy
Casa di Verdi, Busseto 21259
Casa Museo Toscanini, Parma 22124
Casa Natale di Rossini, Pesaro 22159
Civico Museo Bibliografico Musicale, Bologna 21181
Galleria dell'Accademia, Firenze 21594
House of Music-Parma, Parma 22127
Museo Casa Busoni, Empoli 21511
Museo Casa Natale Giacomo Puccini, Lucca 21809
Museo Civico Belliniano, Catania 21363
Museo degli Strumenti Musicali, Cesena 21392
Museo degli Strumenti Musicali, Milano 21909
Museo degli Strumenti Musicali Meccanici, Savio 22553
Museo degli Strumenti Musicali Sardi Don Giovanni Dore, Tadasuni 22620
Museo di Strumenti del Conservatorio Statale di Musica Giuseppe Verdi, Torino 22686
Museo Donizettiano, Bergamo 21159
Museo Francesco Cilea, Palmi 22122
Museo Nazionale degli Strumenti Musicali, Roma 22397
Museo Pucciniano, Torre del Lago Puccini 22700
Museo Spontiniano, Maiolati Spontini 21828
Museo Storico Musicale, Napoli 22027
Museo Stradivariano, Cremona 21489
Museo Villa Puccini, Viareggio 22852
Tempietto Rossiniano della Fondazione Rossini, Pesaro 22162

Jamaica
Bob Marley Museum, Kingston 22892

Japan
Gakkigaku Shiryōkan, Tachikawa 23530
Kyoto Arashiyama Music Box Museum, Kyoto 23236
Musashino Ongaku Daigaku Gakki Hakubutsukan, Tokyo 23639
Sendai Music Box Museum, Sendai 23491

Kazakhstan
Muzej Narodnych Muzykalnych Instrumentov Kazachstana, Almaty 23817

Korea, Republic
Edison and Gramophone Museum, Kangnung 23896

Luxembourg
Musée d'Instruments Anciens et d'Archives au Conservatoire de Musique, Luxembourg 24228

Netherlands
Christ Boelens Jukeboxen Museum, Sint Oedenrode 25490
Draaiorgelmuseum, Assen 24775
Museum De Speelman, Giethoorn 25054
Museum Musica, Stadskanaal 25510
Muziekinformatie- en Documentatiecentrum Ton Stolk, Vlaardingen 25596
Muziekinstrumentenmakersmuseum, Tilburg 25538
Nationaal Museum van Speelklok tot Pierement, Utrecht 25561
Piano en Pianola Museum, Amsterdam 24727
Popmuseum, Den Haag 24923
Rock 'n Roll Museum Arum, Arum 24772

Norway
Jacob Breda Bullmuseet, Rendalen 26258
Myllargut-Heimen, Rauland 26257
Ringve Museum, Trondheim 26350
Troldhaugen - Edvard Grieg Museum, Paradis 26252

Poland
Biblioteka, Muzeum i Archiwum Warszawskiego Towarzystwa Muzycznego im. Stanisława Moniuszki, Warszawa 27190
Muzeum Feliksa Nowowiejskiego, Barczewo 26613
Muzeum Fryderyka Chopina, Warszawa 27206
Muzeum Fryderyka Chopina w Żelazowej Woli, Sochaczew 27103
Muzeum Instrumentów Muzycznych, Poznań 27023
Muzeum Ludowych Instrumentów Muzycznych, Szydłowiec 27154
Muzeum Piśmiennictwa i Muzyki Kaszubsko-Pomorskiej, Wejherowo 27255
Salon Muzyczny im. Fryderyka Chopina, Antonin 26610
Salonik Chopinów, Warszawa 27248

Portugal
Museu Instrumental, Lisboa 27397

Romania
Expozitia Memoriala George Enescu, Dorohoi 27568
Muzeul Național George Enescu, București 27526

Russia
Dom-muzej F.I. Šaljapina, Moskva 27806
Gosudarstvennaja Kollekcija Unikalnych Muzykalnych Instrumentov, Moskva 27813
Gosudarstvennyj Centralnyj Muzej Musykal'noj Kultury im. M.I. Glinki, Moskva 27816
Gosudarstvennyj Dom-muzej N.A. Rimskogo-Korsakova, Tichvin 28106
Gosudarstvennyj Dom-muzej P.I. Čajkovskogo, Klin 27759
Memorialnyj Muzej A.N. Skrjabina, Moskva 27844
Muzej-kvartira Dirižëra N.S. Golovanov, Moskva 27886
Muzej Moskovskoj Konservatorii, Moskva 27897
Muzej Muzykalnych Instrumentov, Sankt-Peterburg 28059
N.G. Rubinstein Museum, Moskva 27922

Slovakia
Hudobná Expozícia - Rodný Dom J.N. Hummela, Bratislava 28204
Hudobné Múzeum, Bratislava 28205
Museum of Literature and Music, Banská Bystrica 28185
Nábytkové Muzeum, Markušovce 28258

South Africa
National Music Museum, Bloemfontein 28422

Spain
Casa-Museo Manuel de Falla, Granada 29107
Museo de la Gaita, Gijón 29086
Museu de la Música, Barcelona 28800
Museu Pau Casals, El Vendrell 29879

Sweden
Carl Jularbo Museum, Avesta 30034
Hobby- och Leksaksmuseum, Stockholm 30349
Jussi Björlingmuseet, Borlänge 30048
Musikmuseet, Stockholm 30365
Smetanamuseet, Göteborg 30105
Stiftelsen Musikkulturens Främjande, Stockholm 30386

Switzerland
Ausstellung der Schweizerischen Geigenbauschule, Brienz, Bern 30652
Blasinstrumenten-Sammlung, Zimmerwald 31431
Blasinstrumentensammlung Karl Burri, Bern 30605
Fredy's Mechanisches Musikmuseum, Lichtensteig 30939
Harmonium-Museum, Liestal 30944
Mechanisches Musikmuseum, Sursee 31293
Musée Baud, L'Auberson 30543
Musée de Boîtes à Musique et Automates, Sainte-Croix 31158
Musée de Musiques, L'Auberson 30544
Musée Paderewski, Morges 31019
Musée Suisse de l'Orgue, Roche 31134
Museum für Musikautomaten, Seewen 31229
Musikmuseum, Basel 30579
Nostalgisches Musikparadies, Oberhasli 31066
Richard Wagner-Museum, Luzern 30982
Sammlung Heinrich Brechbühl, Steffisburg 31280
Schweizer Jazzmuseum, Uster 31338
Streichinstrumentensammlung, Einsiedeln 30744

Turkey
İstanbul Divan Edebiyati Müzesi, İstanbul 31752

Ukraine
Literaturno-memorialny Muzei A.S. Puškina i P.I. Čajkovskogo, Kamenka 31908
Muzej Igora Stravinskogo, Ustyloog 31958
State Museum of Theatrical, Musical and Cinematographic Art of Ukraine, Kyïv 31924

United Kingdom
Chantry Bagpipe Museum, Morpeth 33984
Dean Castle, Kilmarnock 33381
Edinburgh University Collection of Historic Musical Instruments, Edinburgh 32913
The Elgar Birthplace Museum, Lower Broadheath 33836
Fenton House, London 33638
Finchcocks, Goudhurst 33136
Holst Birthplace Museum, Cheltenham 32591
Horniman Museum, London 33671
Joseph Parry's Cottage, Merthyr Tydfil 33934
Keith Harding's World of Mechanical Music, Northleach 34076
Mechanical Music and Doll Collection, Chichester 32611
Mechanical Music Museum and Bygones, Cotton 32683
Museum of Instruments, London 33720
Museum of Piping, Glasgow 33085
Museum of the Royal Military School of Music, Twickenham 34703
Museum of Victorian Reed Organs and Harmoniums, Shipley 34474
Musical Museum, London 33728
Piano Museum Collection, Hereford 33258
Renishaw Hall Museum, Renishaw 34293
Russell Collection of Early Keyboard Instruments, Edinburgh 32946
Saint Albans Organ Museum, Saint Albans 34355

U.S.A.
Alabama Music Hall of Fame, Tuscumbia 40775
Center for American Music, Stephen Foster Memorial, Pittsburgh 39465
Country Music Hall of Fame and Museum, Nashville 38720
Delta Blues Museum, Clarksdale 36101
Eubie Blake Jazz Museum and Gallery, Baltimore 35309
Fort Morgan Museum, Fort Morgan 36935
Gospel Music Hall of Fame and Museum, Detroit 36508
Graceland, Memphis 38413
Hollywood Bowl Museum, Los Angeles 38146
International Bluegrass Music Museum, Owensboro 39223
Lee Conklin Antique Organ History Museum, Hanover 37333
Liberace Museum, Las Vegas 37957
Louisiana Country Music Museum, Marthaville 38369
Mario Lanza Museum, Philadelphia 39389
Motown Historical Museum, Detroit 36512
Museum of the American Piano, New York 38913
The Music House, Acme 34981
Musical Box Society International Museum, Norwalk 39065
Musical Wonder House, Wiscasset 41265
The Rock and Roll Hall of Fame and Museum, Cleveland 36138
The Roy Rogers-Dale Evans Museum, Victorville 40868
Shrine to Music Museum, Vermillion 40849
Stearns Collection of Musical Instruments, Ann Arbor 35124
Yale University Collection of Musical Instruments, New Haven 38792

Uzbekistan
Mouhtar Ashrafi Museum, Taškent 41382

Naive Art → Folk Art

Natural History

Afghanistan
Science Museum, Kabul 00006

Albania
Muzeu i Shkencave Natyrore, Tiranë 00035

Algeria
History and Natural History Museum, Alger 00039

Angola
Museu Nacional de História Natural, Luanda 00089

Argentina
Museo Argentino de Ciencias Naturales Bernardino Rivadavia, Buenos Aires 00147
Museo de Antropología y Ciencias Naturales, Concordia 00278
Museo de Ciencias Antropológicas y Naturales, Santiago del Estero 00607
Museo de Ciencias Naturales Augusto G. Schulz, Resistencia 00498
Museo de Ciencias Naturales Bartolomé Mitre, Córdoba 00285
Museo de Ciencias Naturales de Oberá, Oberá 00452
Museo de Ciencias Naturales del Departamento San Cristóbal, San Cristóbal 00545
Museo de Ciencias Naturales e Historia, Posadas 00474
Museo de Ciencias Naturales Juan Cornelio Moyano, Mendoza 00427
Museo de Ciencias Naturales Rvdo. P. Antonio Scasso, San Nicolás de los Arroyos 00580
Museo de Ciencias Naturales y Antropológicas Prof. Antonio Serrano, Paraná 00457
Museo de Ciencias Naturales y Misional del Colegio San José, Esperanza 00332
Museo de Historia Natural Dr. Ricardo S. Vadell, Suipacha 00615
Museo de Instituto Antártico Argentino, Buenos Aires 00169
Museo de la Facultad de Ciencias Naturales y del Instituto Miguel Lillo, San Miguel de Tucumán 00575
Museo de la Región de Ansenuza Aníbal Montes, Miramar 00440
Museo de la Selva Juan Forster, Miramar 00441

Museo del Agua y del Suelo, Viedma 00648
Museo del Colegio Nacional Justo José de Urquiza, Paraná 00459
Museo del Parque Nacional Los Alerces, Villa Futalaufquen 00658
Museo El Hombre y la Naturaleza, San Juan 00562
Museo Histórico y Natural de Lavalle, Lavalle Villa Tulumaya 00398
Museo Interactivo de Ciencias Naturales, Ituzaingó 00361
Museo Jorge Pasquini López, San Salvador de Jujuy 00588
Museo Marcelo López del Instituto Hellen Keller, Córdoba 00294
Museo Municipal de Ciencias, Bahía Blanca 00120
Museo Municipal de Ciencias Naturales Carlos Ameghino, Mercedes 00438
Museo Municipal de Ciencias Naturales Carlos Darwin, Punta Alta 00485
Museo Municipal de Historia Natural, San Rafael 00585
Museo Participativo de Ciencias, Buenos Aires 00229
Museo Provincial de Ciencias Naturales Dr. Angelo Gallardo, Rosario 00524
Museo Provincial de Ciencias Naturales Florentino Ameghino, Santa Fé 00600
Museo Provincial de Ciencias Naturales y Oceanográfico, Puerto Madryn 00483
Museo Provincial de Historia Natural de La Pampa, Santa Rosa 00604
Museo Regional de Ciencias Naturales Tomás Santa Coloma, Tres Arroyos 00633
Museo Rocsen, Nono 00451

Australia
Albany Residency Museum, Albany 00711
Australian Museum, Sydney 01489
Lake Broadwater Natural History Museum, Dalby 00952
Museum of Central Australia, Alice Springs 00724
Museum of Tropical Queensland, Townsville 01545
Papua New Guinea Display Centre, Crafers 00938
Queen Victoria Museum and Art Gallery, Launceston 01159
Rottnest Island Museum, Rottnest Island 01427
South Australian Museum, Adelaide 00704
Western Australian Museum Geraldton, Geraldton 01035
Wildlife Wonderlands Giant Worm Museum, Bass 00761

Austria
Lobaumuseum, Wien 02899
Museum der Stadt Mödling, Mödling 02301
Naturhistorisches Museum, Wien 02925
Naturkunde- und Feuerwehrmuseum, Dobersberg 01759
Niederösterreichisches Landesmuseum, Sankt Pölten 02580
Vorarlberger Naturschau, Dornbirn 01765

Bahrain
Bahrain National Museum, Manama 03044

Belarus
Belovežskaja Pušča Muzej, Belovežskaja Pušča 03070

Belgium
Musée de la Montagne Saint-Pierre, Lanaye 03520
Musée de l'Histoire de la Forêt d'Ardenne, Saint-Hubert 03695
Musée d'Histoire Naturelle de Mons, Mons 03605
Natuurwetenschappelijk Museum, Antwerpen 03123

Bermuda
Bermuda Natural History Museum, Flatts 03851

Bolivia
Museo del Litoral Boliviano, La Paz 03866

Bosnia and Herzegovina
Zemaljski Muzej, Sarajevo 03896

Brazil
Museu Civico-Religioso Padre Cicero, Juazeiro do Norte 03944
Museu de Ciência e Técnica da Escola de Minas, Ouro Prêto 03967
Museu de Ciências Naturais, Recife 03984
Museu de História Natural, Campinas 03920
Museu e Biblioteca do Instituto Geográfico e Histórico do Amazonas, Manaus 03953
Museu Nacional, Rio de Janeiro 04062
Museu Paraense Emílio Goeldi, Belém 03909

Brunei
Muzium Brunei, Bandar Seri Begawan 04133

Bulgaria
Nacionalen Prirodonaučen Muzej, Sofia 04329
Prirodonaučen Muzej, Belogradčik 04146
Prirodonaučen Muzej, Kotel 04224
Prirodonaučen Muzej, Plovdiv 04268
Prirodonaučen Muzej, Selo Černi Osam 04281

Burundi
Musée Vivant de Bujumbura, Bujumbura 04401

Canada
Abernethy Nature Heritage Museum, Abernethy 04421
Banff Park Museum, Banff 04498
Big Beaver Nature Centre and Museum, Big Beaver 04536
Biodôme de Montréal, Montréal 05357
B.J. Hales Museum of Natural History, Brandon 04579
Canadian Museum of Nature, Ottawa 05537
Cape Breton Centre for Heritage and Science, Sydney 05997
Centre d'Interpretation du Parc de l'île-Bonaventure-et-du Rocher-Percé, Percé 05580
Centre d'Interprétation du Patrimoine de Sorel, Sorel-Tracy 05943
Centre Muséographique de l'Université Laval, Québec 05664
Chatham-Kent Museum, Chatham, Ontario 04698
Écomusée de la Haute-Beauce, Saint-Evariste 05786
Garden of the Gulf Museum, Montague 05348
Grand Coteau Heritage and Cultural Centre, Shaunavon 05900
Kluane Museum of Natural History, Burwash Landing 04614
Lac La Ronge Museum, La Ronge 05171
Living Prairie Museum, Winnipeg 06304
McLurg Museum, Wilkie 06274
Manitoba Museum of Man and Nature, Winnipeg 06307
Miramichi Natural History Museum, Miramichi 05325
Mountain View Doukhobor Museum, Grand Forks 04973
Musée des Sciences Naturelles, Vaudreuil 06176
Musée du Séminaire de Sherbrooke, Sherbrooke, Québec 05914
Museum of Natural History, Halifax 05015
Ovens Museum, Riverport 05744
Park House Museum, Amherstburg 04445
Point Pelee Natural History Museum, Leamington 05199
Presqu'ile Provincial Park Museum, Brighton 04594
Prince Albert National Park Nature Centre, Waskesiu Lake 06223
Quetico Provincial Park Heritage Pavilion, Atikokan 04474
Rondeau Provincial Park Visitor Centre, Morpeth 05407
Royal British Columbia Museum, Victoria 06204
Royal Saskatchewan Museum, Regina 05711
Sam Waller Museum, The Pas 06015
Saskatchewan Wildlife Federation Museum, North Battleford 05481
Tatla Lake Centennial Museum, Tatla Lake 06008
Transcona Historical Museum, Winnipeg 06323
Whiteshell Natural Historic Museum, Seven Sisters Falls 05896

Chad
Musée National, N'Djamena 06357

Chile
Museo de Historia Natural de Concepción, Concepción 06367
Museo de Historia Natural de San Pedro Nolasco, Santiago 06387
Museo de Historia Natural de Valparaíso, Valparaíso 06402
Museo Dillmann S. Bullock, Angol 06360
Museo Regional Salesiano Maggiorino Borgatello, Punta Arenas 06380

China, People's Republic
Chongqing Natural Museum, Chongqing 06511
Dalian Museum of Natural History, Dalian 06514
Guangxi Natural Museum, Nanning 06667
Jilin Natural Museum, Changchun 06480
Shanghai Natural History Museum, Shanghai 06699
Tianjin Museum of Natural History, Tianjin 06739
Zhejiang Natural Museum, Hangzhou 06568

China, Republic
Taiwan Museum, Taipei 06829

Colombia
Museo de Historia Natural, Popayán 06874
Museo del Instituto de la Salle, Santafé de Bogotá 06906
Museo Universitario, Medellín 06864

Congo, Republic
Musée National, Brazzaville 06938

Croatia
Archeological and Natural History Museum, Brijuni 06970
Prirodoslovni Muzej, Rijeka 07052
Prirodoslovni Muzej, Split 07075

Cuba
Museo de Historia Natural Felipe Poey, La Habana 07148
Tranquilino Sandalio de Noda Museo de Ciencias Naturales, Pinar del Río 07172

Cyprus Turk
Archaeological and Natural Science Museum, Güzelyurt 07224

Czech Republic
Hrad Roštejn, Telč 07658
Jihomoravské Muzeum ve Znojmě, Znojmo 07739
Městské Muzeum a Galerie, Hlinsko v Čechách 07333
Moravské Zemské Muzeum, Brno 07260
Muzeum, Litvínov 07443
Muzeum v Bruntále, Bruntál 07268
Muzeum Východních Čech v Hradci Králové, Hradec Králové 07351
Muzeum Vysočiny, Jihlava 07372
Národní Muzeum, Praha 07582
Okresní Muzeum, Hořovice 07345
Okresní Vlastivědné Muzeum Vsetín, Valašské Meziříčí 07689
Památník Prokopa Diviše, Znojmo 07740
Polabské Muzeum, Poděbrady 07535
Přírodovědecké muzeum, Praha 07594
Přírodovědecké Sbírky, Opava 07504
Středočeské Muzeum, Roztoky u Prahy 07626
Vlastivědné Muzeum v Olomouci, Olomouc 07499
Západočeské Muzeum, Plzeň 07531

Denmark
Wellings Landsbymuseum, Lintrup 07956

Ecuador
Museo del Santuario de la Virgen de Agua Santa, Baños 08121
Museo Ecuatoriano de Ciencias Naturales, Quito 08166
Museo Franciiscos Campos, Guayaquil 08139
Museo La Salle, Quito 08170
Vivarium, Museo de Historia Natural, Quito 08177

Salvador
Museo de Historia Natural de El Salvador, San Salvador 08259

Faroe Islands
Føroya Náttúrugripasavn, Tórshavn 08289

Finland
Forssan Luonnonhistoriallinen Museo, Forssa 08318
Jyväskylän Yliopiston Museo, Jyväskylä 08438
Kuopion Luonnontieteellinen Museo, Kuopio 08561
Luonnonhistoriallinen Museo, Porvoo 08798
Luontotalo Arkki, Pori 08792
Seinäjoen Luonto-Museo, Seinäjoki 08873
Tampereen Luonnontieteellinen Museo, Tampere 08934
Tieteelliset Kokoelmat, Forssa 08320

France
Maison-Musée des Sciences, Lettres et Arts, Cholet 10105
Musée d'Allard, Montbrison 11845
Musée d'Histoire Naturelle, Aix-en-Provence 09089
Musée d'Histoire Naturelle, Angers 09179
Musée d'Histoire Naturelle, Chambéry 09957
Musée d'Histoire Naturelle, Lille 11386
Musée d'Histoire Naturelle, Marseille 11652
Musée d'Histoire Naturelle, Perpignan 12501
Musée d'Histoire Naturelle, Rouen 12837
Musée d'Histoire Naturelle, Toulon (Var) 13712
Musée d'Histoire Naturelle, Troyes 13793
Musée d'Histoire Naturelle, Amnéville-les-Thermes 09158
Musée d'Histoire Naturelle, Dijon 10333
Musée d'Histoire Naturelle et de la Préhistoire, Nîmes 12124
Musée d'Histoire Naturelle et d'Ethnographie, Colmar 10166
Musée d'Histoire Naturelle et d'Ethnographie, La Rochelle 11036
Musée d'Histoire Naturelle et d'Histoire Locale, Elbeuf 10409
Musée d'Histoire Naturelle Gabriel-Foucher, Bourges 09686
Musée d'Initiation à la Nature de Normandie, Caen 09801
Musée du Biterrois, Béziers 09548
Musée du Château des Ducs de Wurtemberg, Montbéliard 11842
Musée du Granit, Saint-Michel-de-Montjoie 13151
Musée Lecoq, Clermont-Ferrand 10133
Musée Municipal des Beaux Arts et d'Histoire Naturelle, Châteaudun 10026
Musée Océanographique, L'Ile-Rousse 11378
Musée Pasteur, Paris 12438
Musée Requien, Avignon 09364
Musée Vivant d'Histoire Naturelle, Nancy 12026
Muséum des Sciences Naturelles, Orléans 12220
Muséum des Sciences Naturelles et de Préhistoire, Chartres 10007
Muséum des Volcans, Aurillac 09321
Muséum d'Histoire Naturelle, Autun 09330
Muséum d'Histoire Naturelle, Blois 09600
Muséum d'Histoire Naturelle, Grenoble 10745
Muséum d'Histoire Naturelle, Lyon 11537
Muséum d'Histoire Naturelle, Nice 12109
Muséum d'Histoire Naturelle de Bordeaux, Bordeaux 09644
Muséum d'Histoire Naturelle de Toulouse, Toulouse 13739
Muséum d'Histoire Naturelle, d'Ethnographie et d'Archéologie, Cherbourg 10089
Nature en Provence, Riez 12753

French Guiana
Musée Départemental, Cayenne 14131

French Polynesia
Musée du Coquillage, Papara 14135

Georgia
State Museum of Adjar, Batumi 14144
State Museum of the South-Ossetian Autonomous District, Chinvali 14145

Germany
Adelhausermuseum, Natur- und Völkerkunde, Freiburg im Breisgau 15804
Agrar- und Forstmuseum, Wittenburg 19150
Alpines Museum des Deutschen Alpenvereins, München 17447
Bayerisches Moor- und Torfmuseum, Grassau, Chiemgau 16064
Bodensee-Naturmuseum, Konstanz 16846
Carl-Schweizer-Museum, Murrhardt 17571
Darß-Museum, Ostseebad Prerow 17905
Dillhäuser Fachwerkhaus im Tiergarten Weilburg, Weilburg 18972
Elbtal-Haus Bleckede, Bleckede 14928
Emsland-Moormuseum, Geeste 15905
Felsendome Rabenstein, Chemnitz 15192
Fuhlrott-Museum, Wuppertal 19237
Harzmuseum, Wernigerode 19054
Haus der Natur, Eichendorf 15513
Haus der Natur, Willingen, Upland 19126
Heimat- und Bauernmuseum, Bruck, Oberpfalz 15102
Heimatmuseum der Insel Hiddensee, Kloster, Hiddensee 16766
Heimatmuseum und Naturalienkabinett, Waldenburg, Sachsen 18889
Informationszentrum und Heimatsammlung, Zell, Oberfranken 19266
Kinder-Akademie Fulda Werkraummuseum, Fulda 15875
Korallen- und Heimatmuseum, Nattheim 17583
Kreis-Heimatmuseum, Bad Frankenhausen 14427
Landesmuseum für Natur und Mensch, Oldenburg, Oldenburg 17850
Landschaftsmuseum Obermain, Kulmbach 16909
Mauritianum, Altenburg, Thüringen 14239
Moor- und Fehnmuseum, Barßel 14597
Moormuseum Moordorf, Südbrookmerland 18657
Müritz-Museum, Waren 18926
Museum am Schölerberg, Osnabrück 17876
Museum Bayerisches Vogtland, Hof, Saale 16457
Museum der heimischen Tierwelt, Nabburg 17575
Museum der Stadt Gladbeck, Gladbeck 15981
Museum für Archäologie, Völkerkunde und Naturkunde, Mannheim 17245
Museum für Naturkunde, Chemnitz 15195
Museum für Naturkunde, Magdeburg 17215
Museum für Naturkunde und Völkerkunde Julius Riemer, Lutherstadt Wittenberg 17207
Museum für Naturkunde und Vorgeschichte, Dessau 15302
Museum im Umweltschutz-Informationszentrum Oberfranken mit Kinder-Erlebnis-Museum, Bayreuth 14623
Museum Mensch und Natur, München 17496
Natureum Niederelbe, Balje 14572
Naturhistorisches Museum, Heilbronn 16356
Naturhistorisches Museum Schloß Bertholdsburg, Schleusingen 18350
Naturkunde-Museum, Coburg 15210
Naturkunde-Museum K.-W. Donsbach, Herborn, Hessen 16383
Naturkundemuseum, Reutlingen 18148
Naturkundemuseum Freiberg, Freiberg, Sachsen 15802
Naturkundemuseum im Marstall, Paderborn 17926
Naturkundemuseum im Ottoneum, Kassel 16682
Naturkundemuseum Leipzig, Leipzig 17053
Naturkundemuseum Niebüll, Niebüll 17693
Naturkundliches Bildungszentrum, Ulm 18790
Naturkundliches Museum, Wiesenfelden 19106
Naturkundliches Museum und Schulungsstätte "Alte Schmiede", Handeloh 16262
Naturmuseum der Stadt Augsburg, Augsburg 14351
Naturmuseum und Forschungsinstitut Senckenberg, Frankfurt am Main 15768
Naturwissenschaftliche Sammlungen, Berlin 14820
Naturwissenschaftliches Museum, Aschaffenburg 14315
Naturwissenschaftliches Museum der Stadt Flensburg, Flensburg 15715
Naturwissenschaftliches Museum Duisburg, Duisburg 15470
Naturzentrum Nordfriesland, Bredstedt 15043
Niedersächsisches Landesmuseum Hannover, Hannover 16280
Pfalzmuseum für Naturkunde - POLLICHIA-Museum, Bad Dürkheim 14417
Potsdam-Museum, Potsdam 18012
Staatliches Museum für Naturkunde, Görlitz 16016
Staatliches Museum für Naturkunde, Karlsruhe 16659
Staatliches Museum für Naturkunde Stuttgart, Stuttgart 18642
Stadtmuseum Schloß Hoyerswerda, Hoyerswerda 16512
Städtisches Naturkundliches Museum, Göppingen 16012
Torfmuseum, Neustadt am Rübenberge 17671
Übersee-Museum, Bremen 15069
Vylym-Hütte, Userin 18808
Waldmuseum, Burg, Dithmarschen 15143
Waldmuseum, Furth im Wald 15881
Waldmuseum Wassermühle, Wingst 19133
Westfälisches Museum für Naturkunde, Münster 17559
Zumsteinhaus mit Römischem Museum und Naturkunde-Museum, Kempten 16719

Greece
Mouseion Goulandri Fysikis Istorias, Kifissia 19519

Museum of Natural History and Historical
Photography, Polygyros 19628
Natural History Museum of Cephalonia,
Argostolion 19350
Natural History Museum of Oeta, Ipati 19470
Zakynthos Museum of the Natural Heritage,
Zakynthos 19712

Guatemala
Museo Nacional de Historia Natural, Guatemala
City 19756

Hungary
Bakonyi Természettudományi Muzeum, Zirc 20080
Janus Pannonius Múzeum Természettudományi
Osztálya, Pécs 19972
Magyar Természettudományi Múzeum,
Budapest 19837
Országos Műszaki Múzeum, Budapest 19848
Savaria Múzeum, Szombathely 20050

Iceland
Byggdasafn Austur-Skaftafellssýslu, Höfn 20098
Fiska- og Náttúrngripasafn Vestmannaeyja,
Vestmannaeyjar 20129
Náttúrufrædaistofnun Islands, Akureyrarsetur,
Akureyri 20084
Náttúrufrædlistofnun Íslands, Reykjavik 20113
Náttúrugripasafnid i Neskaupstad,
Neskaupstadur 20104

India
Baroda Museum and Picture Gallery, Vadodara 20159
Bengal Natural History Museum, Darjeeling 20199
Birbal Sahani Institute of Palaeobotany Museum,
Lucknow 20338
Government Museum, Thiruvananthapuram 20429
Municipal Museum Gwalior, Gwalior 20256
National Museum of Natural History, Delhi 20218
Natural History Museum of Bombay Natural History
Society, Mumbai 20179
Saint Joseph's College Museum,
Tiruchirappalli 20431
State Museum, Trichur 20434

Iran
Science and Technology Museum, Yazd 20662

Iraq
Iraq Natural History Research Centre and Museum,
Baghdad 20669

Ireland
Ballyheigue Maritime Centre, Ballyheigue 20694

Israel
Bet Pinhas Museum of Nature, Haifa 20882
Hebrew University Collections of Natural History,
Jerusalem 20910
Natural Sciences Museum, Hulata 20898
Sharon Museum, Emek Hefer 20879
Sturman Institute Museum of Regional Science,
Afula 20856

Italy
Civico Museo Insubrico di Storia Naturale, Induno
Olona 21750
Domus Galilaeana, Pisa 22212
Musei Civici, Reggio Emilia 22299
Museo Aldrovandiano, Bologna 21187
Museo Andrea Piovene, Lonedo di Lugo 21803
Museo Archeologico e Naturalistico, Imola 21741
Museo Civico, Finale Emilia 21569
Museo Civico, Gallipoli 21665
Museo Civico, Ragogna 22276
Museo Civico A. Klitsche de la Grange,
Allumiere 21053
Museo Civico delle Scienze, Pordenone 22244
Museo Civico di Scienze Naturali, Faenza 21528
Museo Civico di Storia e Scienze Naturali,
Montebelluna 21979
Museo Civico di Storia Naturale, Crocetta del
Montello 21490
Museo Civico di Storia Naturale, Milano 21907
Museo Civico di Storia Naturale, Morbegno 22004
Museo Civico di Storia Naturale, Taino 22623
Museo Civico di Storia Naturale, Trieste 22742
Museo Civico di Storia Naturale, Venezia 22799
Museo Civico di Storia Naturale, Verona 22838
Museo Civico di Storia Naturale de Lucca,
Lucca 21810
Museo del Lupo Appenninico, Civitella
Alfedena 21444
Museo del Parco Nazionale d'Abruzzo,
Pescasseroli 22168
Museo della Bonifica, Argenta 21087
Museo dell'Avifauna Appenninica, Sarnano 22532
Museo delle Scienze della Terra e del Lavoro
Contadino, Piandimeleto 22185
Museo delle Valli d'Argenta, Argenta 21088
Museo di Scienze Naturali, Cesena 21398
Museo di Scienze Naturali, Città della Pieve 21428
Museo di Scienze Naturali, Pavia 22143
Museo di Scienze Naturali Tommaso Salvadori,
Fermo 21547
Museo di Storia Naturale, Follonica 21638
Museo di Storia Naturale, Nervesa della
Battaglia 22034
Museo di Storia Naturale, Perugia 22158
Museo di Storia Naturale, Stroncone 22612
Museo di Storia Naturale Brandolini-Rota e Giol,
Oderzo 22060

Museo di Storia Naturale Don Bosco, Torino 22685
Museo di Storia Naturale e del Territorio, Calci 21274
Museo di Storia Naturale e Museo di Arte e Antichità,
L'Aquila 21769
Museo di Storia Naturale Faraggiana-Ferrandi,
Novara 22048
Museo Didattico di Scienze Naturali, Pinerolo 22205
Museo Friulano di Storia Naturale, Udine 22756
Museo Garda, Ivrea 21757
Museo Missionario Cinese e di Storia Naturale,
Lecce 21778
Museo Missionario Francescano, Rimini 22313
Museo Naturalistica-Archeologico, Vicenza 22858
Museo Naturalistico Provinciale, Sondrio 22592
Museo Ornitologico e di Scienze Naturali,
Ravenna 22290
Museo Pavese di Scienze Naturali, Pavia 22144
Museo Regionale di Scienze Naturali, Saint
Pierre 22458
Museo Regionale di Scienze Naturali, Torino 22692
Museo Sardo di Scienze Naturali, Belvi 21149
Museo Tridentino di Scienze Naturali, Trento 22720

Jamaica
Natural History Museum, Kingston 22903

Japan
Agricultural Museum, Miyazaki, Miyazaki-ken 23326
Ainu Museum, Sapporo 23464
Akiyoshi-choritsu Akiyoshidai Kagaku Hakubutsukan,
Shuuhou 23519
Akiyoshi-dai Museum of Natural History, Akiyo 22924
Aomori Kenritsu Kyodokan, Aomori 22927
Chiba-kenritsu Chuo Hakubutsukan, Chiba 22950
Fuji Visitor Center, Kawaguchiko 23139
Fukui City Natural Science Museum, Fukui 22969
Hiwa Museum for Natural History, Hiwa 23049
Hourai-choritsu Horaiji-san Shizenkagaku
Hakubutsukan, Hourai 23057
Institute of Nature Study, Tokyo 23608
Kagoshima-ken Bunka Center, Kagoshima 23101
Kagoshima-kenritsu Hakubutsukan,
Kagoshima 23102
Kokuritsu Kagaku Hakubutsukan, Tokyo 23620
Mount Horaiji Natural History Museum, Hourai 23058
Nagaoka Municipal Science Museum, Nagaoka 23347
Okinawa-kenritsu Hakubutsukan, Naha 23363
Omachi Alpine Museum, Omachi 23411
Ryuga-Do Cave Museum, Tosayamada 23710
Saga-kenritsu Hakubutsukan, Saga 23453
Saitama-kenritsu Shizenshi Hakubutsukan,
Nagatoro 23353
Towada Natural History Museum, Towadako 23714
The University Museum, Tokyo 23701
Yamaguchi Hakabutsukan, Yamaguchi 23754
Yokosuka-shi Hakubutsukan, Yokosuka 23777

Jordan
Children's Heritage and Science Museum,
Amman 23791
Jordan Natural History Museum, Irbid 23805

Kenya
National Museums of Kenya, Nairobi 23858

Korea, Republic
Cheju-do Folk Craft, Folklore and Natural History
Museum, Cheju 23877
Kuknip Kwahak Pakmulgwan, Seoul 23934
National Science Museum of Korea, Daejeon 23889

Kuwait
Educational Science Museum, Kuwait 23969

Lebanon
Musée de Préhistoire Libanaise, Beirut 24139

Liberia
Natural History Museum of Liberia, Monrovia 24157

Luxembourg
Musée National d'Histoire Naturelle,
Luxembourg 24230

Malawi
Museum of Malawi, Blantyre 24273

Malaysia
Sabah Museum, Kota Kinabalu 24291

Malta
Ghar Dalam Museum, Birzebbuga 24342
Natural Science Museum, Victoria 24353

Mauritius
Natural History Museum, Port Louis 24380

Mexico
Museo de Ciencias Naturales, Toluca 24516
Museo de Historia Natural, México 24436
Museo Nacional de Historia Natural de la Ciudad de
México, México 24463

Mongolia
Natural History Museum, Ulaanbaatar 24546
State Central Museum, Ulaanbaatar 24548

Morocco
Musée National d'Histoire Naturelle, Rabat 24565

Mozambique
Museu de História Natural, Maputo 24578
Museu Monstruário de Manica, Manica 24575

Myanmar
Natural History Museum, Yangon 24607

Namibia
Möwe Bay Museum, Möwe Bay 24618
National Museum of Namibia, Windhoek 24636
Okaukuejo Museum, Okaukuejo 24619
Swakopmund Museum, Swakopmund 24628

Netherlands
Bezoekerscentrum Mijl Op Zeven, Ospel 25368
Centrum voor Natuur en Landschap, West
Terschelling 25635
EcoMare, De Koog 24873
Fort Kijkduin, Castricum 24866
Fries Natuurmuseum, Leeuwarden 25228
Jan Verwey Natuurmuseum, Noordwijk, Zuid-
Holland 25334
Missiemuseum Steijl, Steijl 25516
Museon, Den Haag 24907
Naturalis, Leiden 25240
Natuur Streekmuseum Klif en Gaast,
Oudemirdum 25378
Natuurhistorisch Museum de Peel, Asten 24780
Natuurhistorisch Museum en Aquarium Octopus,
Appelscha 24758
Natuurmuseum, Nes 25305
Natuurmuseum Brabant, Tilburg 25539
Natuurmuseum Enschede, Enschede 25022
Natuurmuseum het Drents-Friese Woud,
Wateren 25625
Natuurmuseum Nijmegen, Nijmegen 25325
De Noordwester, Vlieland 25603
Tute-Natura, Bennekom 24803
Veenmuseum Wester-Haar-Vriezenveensewijk,
Vriezenveen 25615
Veluws Diorama, Nunspeet 25340
Zeeuws Biologisch Museum, Oostkapelle 25360
Zomerkoestal uut 't Wold, Ruinerwold 25458

New Zealand
Canterbury Museum, Christchurch 25745
South Canterbury Museum, Timaru 25903
Te Kauri Lodge Museum, Hamilton 25802
Te Papa, Wellington 25948

Nigeria
Ataoja, Oba Oyewale Matanmi's Palace,
Oshogbo 25991
Natural History Museum, Ife 25977

Norway
Agder Naturmuseum og Botaniske Hage,
Kristiansand 26148
Bergen Museum, Bergen 26024
Naturhistoriske Samlinger, Bergen 26033
Norsk Fjellmuseum, Lom 26171
Rana Museum, Mo i Rana 26183
Sykkylven Naturhistorisk Museum, Sykkylven 26336
Vitenskapsmuseet, Trondheim 26355
Zoologisk Museum, Oslo 26249

Pakistan
Dam Site Museum, Mangla 26416
Natural History Museum, Bhawalpur 26391
Natural History Museum, Karachi 26405
Natural History Museum, Lahore 26413
Pakistan Museum of Natural History,
Islamabad 26401

Panama
Museo Nacional de Panamá, Panamá City 26448

Papua New Guinea
Papua New Guinea National Museum and Art Gallery,
Boroko 26450

Paraguay
Museo de Ciencias Naturales, Asunción 26458
Museo de Historia Natural del Paraquay,
Asunción 26459

Peru
Museo de Historia Natural, Lima 26495

Philippines
Philippine Marine and Terrestrial Fauna, Pasay 26580
Philippine Marine Life and Philippine Shells,
Pasay 26581
University of Santo Tomas Museum of Arts and
Sciences, Manila 26569

Poland
Jacek Malczewski Muzeum, Radom 27057
Muzeum Częstochowskie, Częstochowa 26678
Muzeum Ewolucji Instytutu Paleobiologii PAN,
Warszawa 27205
Muzeum Kościuszkowskie PTTK, Miechów 26923
Muzeum Łowiectwa i Jeździectwa, Warszawa 27219
Muzeum Miejskie, Nowa Sól 26953
Muzeum Przyrodnicze, Jelenia Góra 26759
Muzeum Przyrodnicze, Kazimierz Dolny 26779
Muzeum Przyrodnicze Babiogórskiego Parku
Narodowego, Zawoja 27314
Muzeum Przyrodnicze Bieszczadzkiego Parku
Narodowego, Ustrzyki Dolne 27180
Muzeum Przyrodnicze Karkonoskiego Parku
Narodowego, Jelenia Góra 26760
Muzeum Przyrodnicze Uniwersytetu Łódzkiego,
Łódź 26898
Muzeum Przyrodnicze Wolińskiego Parku Narodowego
im. Prof. Adama Wodziczki, Międzyzdroje 26927

Muzeum Przyrodniczo-Leśne Słowińskiego Parku
Narodowego, Smołdzino 27099
Muzeum Regionalne, Świebodzin 27131
Muzeum w Gorzowie Wielkopolskim, Gorzów
Wielkopolski 26735
Muzeum w Wałbrzychu, Wałbrzych 27187
Muzeum Wiedzy o Środowisku, Poznań 27031
Muzeum Ziemi Piskiej, Oddział Muzem Okręgowego w
Suwałkach, Pisz 27003
Muzeum Zoologiczne Instytutu Zoologii Uniwersytetu
Jagiellońskiego, Kraków 26846
Ośrodek Muzealno-Dydaktyczny Wielkopolskiego
Parku Narodowego, Mosina 26934

Portugal
Museu de História Natural, Coimbra 27355
Museu Nacional de História Natural, Lisboa 27402

Réunion
Muséum d'Histoire Naturelle, Saint-Denis 27476

Romania
Complexul Muzeal de Stiinţe ale Naturii Constanţa,
Constanţa 27553
Complexul Muzeal de Stiintele Naturii Bacău,
Bacău 27487
Complexul Muzeal Judeţean Vrancea, Focsani 27573
Muzeul de Istorie Naturală din Sibiu, Sibiu 27647
Muzeul de Istorie Naturala Grigore Antipa,
Bucureşti 27514
Muzeul de Ştiinţele Naturii, Roman 27636
Muzeul de Ştiinţele Naturii Aiud, Aiud 27482
Muzeul de Ştiinţele Naturii Ploieşti, Ploieşti 27625
Muzeul Judeţean Argeş, Piteşti 27621
Muzeul Judeţean Mureş, Tîrgu Mureş 27667
Natural Science Museum, Tulcea 27674

Russia
Brjanskij Gosudarstvennyj Obedinennyj Kraevedčeskij
Muzej, Brjansk 27707
Darvinovskij Muzej, Moskva 27802
Gosudarstvennyj Istoriko-architekturnyj,
Chudožestvennyj i Prirodnyj Muzej-Zapovednik
Caricyno, Moskva 27821
Lipeckij Oblastnoj Kraevedčeskij Muzej, Lipeck 27776
Museum of History and Art, Kaliningrad 27744
Muzej Gosudarstvennogo Prirodnogo Nacionalnogo
Parka Losinogo Ostrova, Moskva 27865
Muzej-kvartira K.A. Timirjazeva, Moskva 27888
Muzej Zemlevedenija Moskovskogo
Gosudarstvennogo Universiteta M.V. Lomonosova,
Moskva 27919
Nižnetagilskij Muzej-Zapovednik Gornozavodskogo
Dela Srednego Urala, Nižnij Tagil 27954
Novorossijskij Gosudarstvennyj Istoričeskij Muzej
Zapovednik, Novorossijsk 27961
Novosibirskij Oblastnoj Kraevedčeskij Muzej,
Novosibirsk 27963
Pjatigorskij Kraevedčeskij Muzej, Pjatigorsk 27996
Sebežskij Muzej Prirody, Sebež 28078

Senegal
Centre de Recherches et de Documentation du
Sénégal, Saint-Louis 28172

Seychelles
National Museum, Victoria 28173

Slovakia
Městské Muzeum, Sabinov 28292
Městské Múzeum, Zlaté Moravce 28317
Museum Spiša, Spišská Nová Ves 28300
Podtatranské Múzeum, Poprad 28282
Podunajské Múzeum, Komárno 28240
Prírodovedné Múzeum, Bratislava 28215
Tekovské Múzeum, Levice 28247
Turčianske Múzeum Andreja Kmeta, Martin 28264
Vlastivedné Múzeum v Hlohovci, Hlohovec 28234
Záhorské muzeum, Skalica 28295

South Africa
Durban Natural Science Museum, Durban 28458
East London Museum, East London 28469
Natal Museum, Pietermaritzburg 28562
National Museum Bloemfontein, Bloemfontein 28421
Stevenson-Hamilton Memorial Information Centre,
Skukuza 28615

Spain
Colleción de Arte y Ciencias Naturales, Ciudad
Real 28959
Museo de Ciencias Naturales de Alava, Vitoria-
Gasteiz 29933
Museo de Ciencias Naturales de Tenerife, Santa Cruz
de Tenerife 29649
Museo del Colegio Costa y Llobera, Port de
Pollença 29524
Museo del Seminario Diocesano, Burgos 28874
Museo Valenciano de Historia Natural, Valencia 29847
Museu Darder d'Història Natural, Banyoles 28767
Museu de Granollers-Ciències Naturals,
Granollers 29126
Museu Municipal Guilleries, Sant Hilari Sacalm 29637
Museu Regional d'Artá, Artá 28727

Sri Lanka
National Museum of Natural History, Colombo 29984

Sudan
Natural History Museum, Medani 30004
Natural History Museum, Port Sudan 30007

Needlework

Numismatics

Musée Romain, Lausanne 30933

United Kingdom
Bank of England Museum, London 33583
British Museum, London 33597
Fitzwilliam Museum, Cambridge 32503
Museum on the Mound, Edinburgh 32932
Royal Mint Sovereign Gallery, London 33769

U.S.A.
American Numismatic Society Museum, New York 38840
Museum of the American Numismatic Association, Colorado Springs 36186
United States Army Finance Corps Museum, Fort Jackson 36907
United States Mint-Philadelphia, Philadelphia 39417

Yugoslavia
Privatna Zbirka Marija Lukovića, Prčanj 41607

Oceanography

Argentina
Museo del Lago Gutiérrez, Bariloche 00128
Museo Provincial de Ciencias Naturales y Oceanográfico, Puerto Madryn 00483

Canada
Marine Museum of the Great Lakes, Kingston 05140
Sidney Marine Museum, Sidney 05922

Chile
Museo Comparativo de Biología Marina, Viña del Mar 06405

Colombia
Museo del Mar, Santafé de Bogotá 06907

Cyprus
Tornaritis-Pierides Municipal Museum of Marine Life, Aghia Napa 07190

Egypt
Aquatics Museum - Institute of Oceanography and Fisheries, Suez 08253

France
Centre de la Mer, Paris 12265
Musée de la Mer, Biarritz 09552
Nausicaa, Boulogne-sur-Mer 09665
Océanopolis, Brest 09736
Océarium du Croisic, Le Croisic 11200

Germany
Deutsches Meeresmuseum, Stralsund 18610
Internationales Muschelmuseum, Wangerland 18923
Muschel- und Schneckenmuseum, Norden 17711
Nationalpark-Haus, Butjadingen 15164
Nordseemuseum, Bremerhaven 15076

Israel
Red Sea Maritime Museum, Eilat 20876

Italy
Museo Oceanografico dell'Istituto Talassografico, Taranto 22626

Japan
Futtsu Oceanographic Museum of Chiba Prefecture, Kimitsu 23150
Mukaishima Marine Biological Station, Mukaishima 23336
Shima Marineland, Ago 22914
Shimoda Marine Biological Station, Kamo, Izu 23118
Suma Aqualife Museum, Kobe 23167
Umi-no Hakubutsukan, Toba 23572

Lebanon
Lebanon' Marine Wildlife Museum with Collection of Murex, Jdeidet El-Metn 24149

Madagascar
Musée du Centre National de Recherches Océanographiques, Nosy-Bé 24269

Monaco
Musée Océanographique de Monaco, Monaco 24535

Mozambique
Museum of Inhaca Island, Maputo 24583

Netherlands
Miramar Zeemuseum, Vledder 25599
Nationaal Zeebiologisch Museum Scheveningen, Den Haag 24918
Pieter Vermeulen Museum, Ijmuiden 25190

Panama
Museo de Ciencias Naturales, Panamá City 26441

Poland
Muzeum Morskie, Szczecin 27144
Muzeum Oceanograficzne i Akwarium Morskie, Gdynia 26718
Szkolne Muzeum Morskie, Bolesławiec 26645

Portugal
Museu do Mar - Rei D. Carlos, Cascais 27349

Museu Municipal do Funchal (História Natural), Funchal 27369
Museu Oceanográfico, Setúbal 27438

Puerto Rico
Marine Sciences Museum, Mayagüez 27457

Russia
Muzej-Akvarium, Vladivostok 28129
Muzej Mirovogo Okeana, Kaliningrad 27745

Senegal
Musée de la Mer, Gorée 28170

South Africa
Sea World, Durban 28465

Spain
Palacio del Mar/Aquarium, Donostia-San Sebastián 29020

Sweden
Aquaria Vattenmuseum, Stockholm 30332

Tunisia
Musée Océanographique Dar-El-Hout de Salammbô, Salammbô 31625

United Kingdom
Robertson Museum and Aquarium, Millport 33954
Scottish Maritime Museum, Irvine 33337

U.S.A.
Calvert Marine Museum, Solomons 40392
Chesapeake Bay Maritime Museum, Saint Michaels 39987
Custom House Maritime Museum, Newburyport 38971
East Hampton Town Marine Museum, East Hampton 36609
Kendall Whaling Museum, Sharon 40324
Maine Maritime Museum, Bath 35362
Marine Museum at Fall River, Fall River 36797
Marineland Ocean Museum, Marineland 38342
Mel Fisher Maritime Heritage Museum, Key West 37791
The MIT Museum, Cambridge 35794
Museum of Yarmouth History, Yarmouth 41316
North Carolina Maritime Museum, Beaufort 35388
North Wind Undersea Institute, Bronx 35683
Penobscot Marine Museum, Searsport 40278
Ponce DeLeon Inlet Lighthouse, Ponce Inlet 39525
Shore Village Museum, Rockland 39836
South Street Seaport Museum, New York 38941
Suffolk County Vanderbilt Museum, Centerport 35893
Texas Maritime Museum, Rockport 39841
Treasures of the Sea Exhibit, Georgetown 37119
Ventura County Maritime Museum, Oxnard 39239
Virginia Marine Science Museum, Virginia Beach 40879
William Scarbrough House, Savannah 40244

Vietnam
Oceanographic Museum, Nhatrang 41480

Yugoslavia
Ribarsko-Biološka Zbirka, Novi Dojran 41579

Oenology → Wines and Spirits

Office Equipment

Austria
Büromaschinen-Museum, Aspang 01678
Kopiergerätemuseum, Wien 02883

Germany
Büromuseum, Mülheim an der Ruhr 17439
Deutsches Schreibmaschinenmuseum, Bayreuth 14611
Museum der Kommunikations- und Bürogeschichte, Bamberg 14582
Telefonmuseum Hittfelder Bahnhof, Seevetal 18466

Switzerland
Schreibmaschinen-Museum, Pfäffikon (Zürich) 31091
Schreibmaschinenmuseum Baggenstos, Wallisellen 31371

Oil → Petroleum Industry and Trade

Opera → Performing Arts

Optics

Canada
Museum of Visual Science and Optometry, Waterloo 06230

France
Musée de l'Optique, Biesheim 09555
Musée Pierre Marly, Paris 12441

Germany
Holowood - Holographiemuseum Bamberg, Bamberg 14580
Kreismuseum, Rathenow 18066
Leica Stammbaum und Museum, Solms 18529
Museum für Holographie und neue visuelle Medien, Frechen 15794
Optisches Museum, Oberkochen 17777
Optisches Museum der Ernst-Abbe-Stiftung Jena, Jena 16601
Photomuseum CAMERAMA, Bad Soden am Taunus 14520
Sammlung historischer Mikroskope von Ernst Leitz, Wetzlar 19087
Zeiler Foto- und Filmmuseum, Zeil am Main 19260

Netherlands
Universiteitsmuseum Utrecht, Utrecht 25568

Slovakia
Oddelenie Technické Múzeum Košice, Spišská Béla 28299

Switzerland
Musée Suisse de l'Appareil Photographique, Vevey 31358

United Kingdom
British Optical Association Museum, London 33598
Buckingham Movie Museum, Buckingham 32438
Medina Camera Museum, Freshwater 33045

Ornithology → Birds

Painted and Stained Glass

France
Musée de l'Hospice Saint-Roch, Issoudun 10862

Germany
Deutsches Glasmalerei-Museum Linnich, Linnich 17121
Museum für bäuerliche und sakrale Kunst, Ruhpolding 18275
Museum für Zeitgenössische Glasmalerei, Langen in Hessen 16966

Japan
Hamamatsu City Museum of Art, Hamamatsu 23009

Switzerland
Musée Suisse du Vitrail, Romont 31137

Painting

Argentina
Casa Museo Bruzzone, Mar del Plata 00416
Estudio Museo Ramoneda, Humahuaca 00355
El Fogon de los Arrieros, Resistencia 00497
Museo Atelier Antonio Ortiz Echagüe, Carro Quemado 00257
Museo Austral de Pintura Primitiva Moderna Naïf, Esquel 00335
Museo Maurice Minkowski, Buenos Aires 00213
Museo Municipal de Arte Angel María de Rosa, Junín 00364
Museo Municipal de Arte Juan Carlos Castagnino, Mar del Plata 00419
Museo Municipal de Artes Visuales, Quilmes 00355
Museo Municipal de Artes Visuales, Santa Fé 00598
Museo Nacional de Bellas Artes, Buenos Aires 00219
Museo Pedagógico de Arte Visuales, Gálvez 00342
Museo Provincial de Bellas Artes, Corrientes 00314
Museo Provincial de Bellas Artes Dr. Pedro E. Martínez, Paraná 00462
Palacio del Mate, Posadas 00478
Pinacoteca, Córdoba 00303

Armenia
Avetisians Museum, Erevan 00669
Jottos Museum-Workshop, Erevan 00673
M. Sarians Museum, Erevan 00675

Australia
Brauhinia Shire Bicentennial Art Gallery, Springsure 01468
Dalby Regional Gallery, Dalby 00951
Harvery Art Gallery, Harvey 01077
McCrae Homestead Museum, McCrae 01208
Murilla Shire Art Gallery, Miles 01245
National Gallery of Victoria, Melbourne 01226
Tamworth City Gallery, Tamworth 01512
Tweed River Regional Art Gallery, Murwillumbah 01286
Wollongong City Gallery, Wollongong East 01608

Austria
Adalbert Stifter-Gedenkstätte, Wien 02799
Alfons Graber-Museum, Steinach 02652
Ausstellungszentrum Heiligenkreuzer Hof, Wien 02809
Europäisches Museum für Frieden, Stadtschlaining 02648
Franz Zeh-Museum, Heidenreichstein 02006
Galerie Günther Frey, Radenthein 02458
Galerie im Teisenhoferhof der Malschule Motiv Wachau, Weißenkirchen in der Wachau 02773
Gauermann-Museum, Miesenbach 02288
Kunstpromenade Achensee, Achenkirch 01640
Kunstsammlung des Benediktinerstifts Seitenstetten, Seitenstetten 02633
Museum des Augustiner-Chorherrenstifts, Reichersberg 02479
Museum Kaiser Franz Joseph I. und die Jagd, Neuberg an der Mürz 02328
Prof. Eidenberger-Museum, Niederwaldkirchen 02349
Riesenrundgemälde Schlacht am Bergisel, Innsbruck 02069
Sammlung Essl - Kunst der Gegenwart, Klosterneuburg 02132
Schloß Ambras, Innsbruck 02070
Schloßmuseum Niederleis, Niederleis 02346
Stiftsmuseum Praemonstratenser-Chorherren Stift Schlägl, Aigen-Schlägl 01650
Stiftung Aratym, Gutenstein 01974

Belarus
Chagall Museum, Vitebsk 03083

Belgium
Collections Artistiques de l'Université de Liège, Liège 03538
Eugeen Van Mieghem Museum, Antwerpen 03102
Gemeentelijk Museum Gustaaf de Smet, Deurle 03345
Hôpital Notre-Dame de la Rose, Lessines 03530
Koninklijk Museum voor Schone Kunsten, Antwerpen 03106
Maagdenhuismuseum, Antwerpen 03108
Musée Alexandre-Louis Martin, Carnières 03312
Musée Constantin Meunier, Bruxelles 03262
Musée de l'Art Wallon, Liège 03551
Musée de l'Assistance Publique, Bruxelles 03273
Musée des Beaux-Arts Charleroi, Charleroi 03317
Musée des Beaux-Arts de la Ville de Mons, Mons 03604
Musée d'Ixelles, Bruxelles 03285
Musée du Vieux-Cimetière, Soignies 03735
Musée Ducal, Bouillon 03196
Musée Léon de Smet, Deurle 03346
Musée Schott, Bruxelles 03305
Museum Constant Permeke, Jabbeke 03496
Museum Felix de Boeck, Drogenbos 03360
Museum Jakob Smits, Mol 03600
Museum Modest Huys, Zulte 03841
Museum Onze-Lieve-Vrouw ter Potterie, Brugge 03219
Museum Smidt van Gelder, Antwerpen 03112
Provinciaal Museum Stijn Streuvels, Ingooigem 03488
Rockoxhuis, Antwerpen 03133
Stadhuis van Antwerpen, Antwerpen 03136
Stedelijk Ostmuseum, Hoogstraten 03471
Timmermans-Opsomerhuis, Lier 03558

Brazil
Casa de Alfredo Andersen, Curitiba 03927
Coleção do Palácio do Governo de Campos do Jordão, Campos do Jordão 03923
Museu de Arte Contemporânea da Universidade de São Paulo, São Paulo 04108
Museu de Arte Sacra Dom Ranulfo, Maceió 03951
Museu Internacional de Arte Naïf do Brasil, Rio de Janeiro 04061
Museu Nacional de Belas Artes, Rio de Janeiro 04063
Pinacoteca do Estado do São Paulo, São Paulo 04119

Bulgaria
Gradska Chudožestvena Galerija, Sofia 04307
Kartinna Galerija, Varna 04362
Kašta-muzej Stanislav Dospevski, Pazardžik 04246
Okrăžna Chudožestvena Galerija, Burgas 04160
Okrăžna Chudožestvena Galerija, Pleven 04257
Okrăžna Chudožestvena Galerija, Ruse 04277
Okrăžna Chudožestvena Galerija, Veliko Tărnovo 04382
Okrăžna Chudožestvena Galerija, Vidin 04390
Okrăžna Chudožestvena Galerija Vladimir Dimitrov-Maistora, Kjustendil 04214

Canada
Art Gallery of Ontario, Toronto 06035
Art Gallery of Peterborough, Peterborough 05586
Atelier Imago, Moncton 05339
Centre d'Art de Cowansville, Cowansville 04744
Centre d'Exposition l'Imagier, Aylmer 04484
Chapel Gallery, North Battleford 05479
Legislative Building Art Galleries, Regina 05704
Leighton Foundation Collection, Calgary 04632
Oak Hall, Niagara Falls 05461
Perrault's Museum, Val Marie 06133
Vancouver Art Gallery, Vancouver 06168
Ziska Gallery, Bracebridge 04569

Chile
Casa del Arte de la Universidad de Concepción, Concepción 06366
Museo de Bellas Artes, Viña del Mar 06406

Painting

Museo Nacional de Bellas Artes de Santiago de Chile, Santiago 06391
Pinacoteca de la Universidad de Concepción, Concepción 06369

China, People's Republic
Lin San Zhi Art Display Center, Zhujiang 06808
Museum of Fine Arts, Beijing 06451

China, Republic
Hwa Kang Museum, Taipei 06818
Ran-In-Ting Museum, Taipei 06825

Colombia
Museo de Arte Colonial, Santafé de Bogotá 06894
Museo de Arte Colonial, Villa de Leyva 06922
Museo de Arte Contemporáneo, Santafé de Bogotá 06895
Museo de Museos, Tunja 06921
Museo Efrain Martínez, Popayán 06875

Croatia
Galerija Slika, Motovun 07028
Galerija Umjetnina, Split 07071
Ivan Meštrović Gallery, Split 07072
Zavičajni Muzej Grada Rovinja, Rovinj 07054

Cuba
Museo Ignacio Agramonte, Camagüey 07133

Cyprus
Byzantine Museum and Art Galleries, Nicosia 07201

Czech Republic
Expozice Mladý Gustav Mahler a Jihlava, Jihlava 07371
Galerie Antonína Chittussiho, Ronov nad Doubravou 07621
Galerie Felixe Jeneweina, Kutná Hora 07418
Klášter Sv. Anežky České, Praha 07566
Muzeum Aloise Jiráska, Hronov 07354
Památník Adolfa Kaspara, Loštice 07446

Denmark
Ballerup Egnsmuseet, Ballerup 07767
Fåborg Museum for Fynsk Malerkunst, Fåborg 07799
Fanø Kunstsamling, Fanø 07803
Jugendhuset, Varde 08085
Michael og Anna Anchers Hus og Saxilds Gaard, Skagen 08040
Mølsteds Museum, Dragør 07783
Museet på Koldinghus, Kolding 07943
Randers Kunstmuseum, Randers 08009
Skagens Museum, Skagen 08042
Skovgaard Museet i Viborg, Viborg 08096
Statens Museum for Kunst, København 07934
Vejle Kunstmuseum, Vejle 08089

Dominican Republic
Galería Nacional de Bellas Artes, Santo Domingo 08103

Egypt
Museum of Fine Arts and Cultural Center, Alexandria 08195

Finland
Nelimarkka Museo . Etelä-Pohjanmaan Aluetaidemuseo ja Nelimarkka-resedenssi, Alajärvi 08295
Särestöniemi Museo, Kaukonen 08478
Taidemuseo, Kokkola 08523

France
Collections de l'Ecole Nationale Supérieure des Beaux-Arts, Paris 12281
Fondation Le Corbusier, Paris 12291
Fondation Van-Gogh Arles, Arles 09242
Maison-Musée Ted Jacobs, Les Cerqueux-sous-Passavent 11317
Musée Adzak, Paris 12314
Musée Antoine Lécuyer, Saint-Quentin (Aisne) 13216
Musée Arménien de France, Paris 12315
Musée Baron Gérard, Bayeux 09446
Musée Bourdelle, Paris 12322
Musée Condé, Chantilly 09979
Musée d'Art, Senlis 13491
Musée d'Art et d'Archéologie, Aurillac 09319
Musée d'Art et d'Histoire, Dreux 10381
Musée d'Art et d'Histoire Romain Rolland, Clamecy 10119
Musée d'Art Naif, Nice 12097
Musée de Grenoble, Grenoble 10740
Musée de Pont-Aven, Pont-Aven 12592
Musée de Vulliod Saint-Germain, Pézenas 12515
Musée Départemental d'Art Ancien et Contemporain, Épinal 10435
Musée des Arts et Traditions Populaires, Locronan 11426
Musée des Augustins, Toulouse 13731
Musée des Beaux-Arts, Arras 09258
Musée des Beaux-Arts, Bernay 09521
Musée des Beaux-Arts, Béziers 09546
Musée des Beaux-Arts, Blois 09599
Musée des Beaux-Arts, Brest 09731
Musée des Beaux-Arts, Carcassonne 09862
Musée des Beaux-Arts, Chambéry 09955
Musée des Beaux-Arts, Marseille 11649
Musée des Beaux-Arts, Menton 11723
Musée des Beaux-Arts, Mirande 11774
Musée des Beaux-Arts, Nantes 12039
Musée des Beaux-Arts, Quimper 12689
Musée des Beaux-Arts, Rouen 12836
Musée des Beaux-Arts, Saintes 13342
Musée des Beaux-Arts, Strasbourg 13611
Musée des Beaux-Arts, Tourcoing 13747
Musée des Beaux-Arts, Mulhouse 11990
Musée des Beaux-Arts de Dunkerque, Dunkerque 10388
Musée des Beaux-Arts et d'Archéologie, Besançon 09529
Musée des Beaux-Arts et d'Archéologie, Libourne 11367
Musée des Beaux-Arts et d'Archéologie, Rennes (Ille-et-Vilaine) 12730
Musée des Beaux-Arts et de la Dentelle, Calais 09820
Musée des Beaux-Arts Hôtel Fayet, Béziers 09547
Musée du Centre de Recherches sur les Monuments Historiques, Paris 12390
Musée du Château, Flers 10546
Musée du Faouët, Le Faouët 11203
Musée du Louvre, Paris 12396
Musée du Luxembourg, Paris 12397
Musée du Maréchal Foch, Tarbes 13650
Musée Duplessis, Carpentras 09878
Musée en Herbe, Paris 12405
Musée Ernest Hébert, Paris 12406
Musée Eugène Boudin, Honfleur 10829
Musée Fabre, Montpellier 11913
Musée Fesch, Ajaccio 09101
Musée Francisque Mandet, Riom 12757
Musée Garinet, Châlons-en-Champagne 09946
Musée Garret, Vesoul 13938
Musée Grobet-Labadié, Marseille 11655
Musée Historique, Mont-Saint-Michel 11813
Musée Hyacinthe Rigaud, Perpignan 12502
Musée Jeanne d'Aboville, La Fère 10964
Musée Laplace, Beaumont-en-Auge 09476
Musée Magnin, Dijon 10335
Musée Malraux, Le Havre 11216
Musée Morice Lipsi, Rosey 12824
Musée Municipal, Coutances 10248
Musée Municipal, La Roche-sur-Yon 11026
Musée Municipal, Lons-le-Saunier 11443
Musée Municipal, Vire 14062
Musée Municipal de la Chartreuse, Douai 10362
Musée Municipal des Beaux-Arts, Valence (Drôme) 13839
Musée Municipal Paul Lafran, Saint-Chamas 12932
Musée National des Arts Asiatiques Guimet, Paris 12428
Musée Saint-Vic, Saint-Amand-Montrond 12886
Musée Thomas Henry, Cherbourg 10088
Musées de la Cour d'Or, Metz 11743
Pavillon des Arts, Paris 12453

Georgia
Georgian State Picture Gallery, Tbilisi 14152

Germany
Allgäu-Museum, Kempten 16713
Anhaltische Gemäldegalerie, Dessau 15299
August Macke Haus, Bonn 14972
Braith-Mali-Museum, Biberach an der Riß 14886
C.O. Müller-Galerie, Eichstätt 15516
Edwin-Scharff-Museum, Neu-Ulm 17613
Erstes Imaginäres Museum - Sammlung Günter Dietz, Wasserburg am Inn 18934
Friedrich-Eckenfelder-Galerie, Balingen 14568
Fürstliches Schloß mit Gemäldegalerie, Mausoleum, Bückeburg 15122
Gablonzer Archiv Museum, Kaufbeuren 16693
Galerie am Prater, Berlin 14711
Galerie im Alten Rathaus, Prien 18024
Galerie im Ermelerspeicher, Schwedt 18429
Galerie Skell, Schmiedeberg, Osterzgebirge 18362
Gaudnek-Museum, Altomünster 14257
Gemäldegalerie, Berlin 14731
Gemäldegalerie Alte Meister, Kassel 16672
Gemäldesammlung, Erlangen 15620
Gentilhaus, Aschaffenburg 14312
Heimatmuseum Scheeßel, Scheeßel 18322
Heimatmuseum Stadt Starnberg, Starnberg 18575
Herkomer-Museum am Mutterturm, Landsberg am Lech 16945
Hudetz-Turm, Wiesent 19107
Jakob-Philipp-Hackert Ausstellung, Prenzlau 18018
Künstlerhaus Walter Helm, Aschaffenburg 14314
Kulturhaus der Otto-Hellmeier-Stiftung, Raisting 18053
Kunsthaus Boskamp, Hohenlockstedt 16474
Kunsthaus Nürnberg, Nürnberg 17749
Ludwig-Doerfler-Galerie, Schillingsfürst 18333
Mainfränkisches Museum Würzburg, Würzburg 19219
Malerstübchen Willingshausen, Willingshausen 19128
Mansfeld-Galerie, Lutherstadt Eisleben 17198
Museum am Burghof, Lörrach 17127
Museum Burg Falkenstein, Pansfelde 17931
Museum der Stadt Ettlingen, Ettlingen 15676
Museum Folkwang Essen, Essen 15659
Museum Gasteiger-Haus, Holzhausen 16492
Museum Rolf Werner, Seebad Bansin 18453
Neue Residenz, Bamberg 14585
Olaf-Gulbransson-Museum, Tegernsee 18690
Orangerie Benrath, Düsseldorf 15454
Otto-Dill Museum, Neustadt an der Weinstraße 17679
Otto-Dix-Haus, Gera 15940
Paul-Röder-Museum, Marktoberdorf 17279
Podium Kunst, Schramberg 18391
Rathausgalerie, Bad Harzburg 14440
Sammlungen im Adelmannschloß, Landshut 16953
Schloß Weissenstein, Pommersfelden 18004
Schloßmuseum Murnau, Murnau 17570
Schlossmuseum Oranienburg, Oranienburg 17860
Siebenbürgisches Museum Gundelsheim, Gundelsheim, Württemberg 16143
Siebenbürgisches Museum Gundelsheim, Gundelsheim, Württemberg 16144
Staatliche Kunsthalle Karlsruhe, Karlsruhe 16658
Staatsgalerie in der Benediktiner-Abtei, Ottobeuren 17916
Stadtmuseum Bautzen, Bautzen 14604
Städtische Galerie, Schieder-Schwalenberg 18330
Städtische Gemäldegalerie, Füssen 15868
Städtische Kunstgalerie im Deutschordenshaus, Donauwörth 15362
Städtische Wessenberg-Galerie, Konstanz 16851
Strübhaus-Haus der Malkunst, Veringenstadt 18833
Wallraf-Richartz-Museum - Fondation Corboud, Köln 16817

Greece
Alex Mylonas Museum, Athinai 19359
Art Gallery of the Municipality of Larrisa, Lárissa 19542
N. Hadjikyriakos-Ghikas Gallery, Athinai 19410
Oinoussian Maritime Museum, Oinoussai 19597

Guam
Isla Center for the Arts at the University of Guam, Mangilao 19747

Hungary
Hincz Gyula Állandó Gyüjtemény, Vác 20063
Kohán Múzeum, Gyula 19895
Munkácsy Mihály Múzeum, Békéscsaba 19799
Rippl-Rónai Emlékház, Kaposvár 19912
Szönyi István Emlék Múzeum, Zebegény 20079
Zettl Langer gyüjtemény, Sopron 20004
Zichy Mihály Emlékmúzeum, Zala 20075

Iceland
Listasafn Árnesinga -Árnesýsla Art Gallery, Selfoss 20122
Listasafn Einars Jónssonar, Reykjavik 20109

India
Academy of Fine Arts Museum, Kolkata 20181
Bhure Singh Museum, Chamba 20182
Central Museum, Bhopal 20170
Sri Chitra Art Gallery, Thiruvananthapuram 20428
Dogra Art Gallery, Jammu 20282
Folklore Museum, Mysore 20371
Indian Museum, Kolkata 20181
Institute Menezes Braganza, Panaji 20381
Sri Jayachamarajendra Art Gallery, Mysore 20372
Maharaja Fatesingh Museum, Vadodara 20441
Salarjung Museum, Hyderabad 20272
Sangli State Museum, Sangli 20409
Victoria Memorial Hall, Kolkata 20181

Indonesia
Gunarsa Museum, Klungkung 20529
Museum Le Mayeur, Sanur 20567
Neka Museum and Gallery, Gianyar 20490

Ireland
Bantry House, Bantry 20698
Glebe House and Gallery, Church Hill 20717
Limerick City Gallery of Art, Limerick 20804

Israel
Beit Immanuel, Ramat Gan 20977
Beit Uri Ve Rami Nechushtan, Kibbutz Ashdot Yaakov 20943
Glichenstein Museum, Zefat 21021
Mishkan Le'Omanut, Ein Harod 20877

Italy
Casa Museo-Quadreria, Fossombrone 21651
Cenacolo di Sant'Apollonia, Firenze 21581
Civico Museo d'Arte Moderne, Anticoli Corrado 21069
Convento dell'ex-Convento di Sant'Onofrio detto di Fuligno, Firenze 21584
Donazione Palazzina della Meridiana, Firenze 21585
Galleria Civica, Valdagno 22767
Galleria Civica d'Arte Moderna e Contemporanea, Sassoferrato 22546
Galleria dell'Accademia Albertina di Belle Arti, Torino 22667
Galleria di Palazzo Rosso, Genova 21685
Mostra Permanente della Biblioteca Estense, Modena 21941
Musei Civici, Piacenza 22179
Museo Alessi, Enna 21515
Museo Archeologico G. Moretti, San Severino Marche 22502
Museo Berenziano, Cremona 21485
Museo Borromeo, Isola Bella 21754
Museo Carlo Venturini, Massa Lombarda 21858
Museo Civico, Casale Monferrato 21321
Museo Civico, Pordenone 22243
Museo Civico, Rieti 22307
Museo Civico, Sassocorvaro 22544
Museo Civico Ala Ponzone, Cremona 21486
Museo Civico e Diocesano d'Arte Sacra, Colle di Val d'Elsa 21449
Museo Civico e Pinacoteca Basilio Cascella, Pescara 22163
Museo Civico e Pinacoteca del Palazzo Malatestiano, Fano 21536
Museo Civico Il Correggio, Correggio 21471
Museo d' Arte Sacra, San Leo 22488
Museo d'Arte Antica, Milano 21908
Museo degli Affreschi G.B. Cavalcaselle, Verona 22839
Museo del Cenedese, Vittorio Veneto 22878
Museo del Paesaggio, Pallanza 22118
Museo del Palazzo Ducale, Mantova 21842
Museo del Santuario e Museo Baroffio, Varese 22780
Museo del Seminario Vescovile, Rovigo 22447
Museo della Fondazione Giovanni Scaramangà di Altomonte, Trieste 22743
Museo di Capodimonte, Napoli 22019
Museo di Castelvecchio, Verona 22841
Museo di Sant'Agostino, Genova 21698
Museo Diocesano di Arte Sacra, San Miniato 22497
Museo Domenicani, Taggia 22621
Museo e Pinacoteca Civica, Alessandria 21051
Museo e Pinacoteca Civici, Teramo 22633
Museo e Pinacoteca Civici, Vasto 22784
Museo e Pinacoteca del Santuario Madonna delle Grazie, Rimini 22312
Museo Francesco Borgogna, Vercelli 22832
Museo Lodovico Pogliaghi, Varese 22781
Museo Pepoli, Trapani 22709
Museo Pinacoteca A. Salvucci, Molfetta 21959
Museo-Pinacoteca Comunale, Mogliano Marche 21956
Museo Poldi Pezzoli, Milano 21923
Museo Provinciale di Palazzo Attems, Gorizia 21712
Museo Sant'Andrea, Clusone 21445
Museo Storico Aloisiano, Castiglione delle Stiviere 21357
Pinacoteca, Corridonia 21472
Pinacoteca, Massa Marittima 21866
Pinacoteca, Ploaghe 22224
Pinacoteca Capitolina, Roma 22421
Pinacoteca Civica, Cento 21379
Pinacoteca Civica, Forli 21648
Pinacoteca Civica, Imperia 21749
Pinacoteca Civica, Monza 22003
Pinacoteca Civica Carlo Servolini, Collesalvetti 21454
Pinacoteca Communale, Jesi 21759
Pinacoteca Communale, San Ginesio 22483
Pinacoteca Comunale, Cascia 21326
Pinacoteca Comunale, Fermo 21548
Pinacoteca Comunale, Gualdo Tadino 21725
Pinacoteca Comunale, Imola 21746
Pinacoteca Comunale, Pieve di Cento 22200
Pinacoteca Comunale, Prato 22264
Pinacoteca Comunale, Ravenna 22292
Pinacoteca Comunale, Spoleto 22604
Pinacoteca Comunale Alberto Martini, Oderzo 22061
Pinacoteca Comunale Faenza, Faenza 21533
Pinacoteca Comunale Foresiana, Portoferraio 22250
Pinacoteca del Duomo, Cittadella 21435
Pinacoteca della Chiesa di San Francesco, Mercatello sul Metauro 21881
Pinacoteca dell'Abbrazia di San Paolo, Roma 22422
Pinacoteca dell'Opera Pia Ricci, Monte San Martino 21976
Pinacoteca e Biblioteca Rambaldi, Coldirodi di Sanremo 21447
Pinacoteca e Musei Comunali, Macerata 21823
Pinacoteca G.A. Levis, Racconigi 22273
Pinacoteca Giovanni Morscio, Dolceacqua 21506
Pinacoteca M. Cascella, Ortona 22073
Pinacoteca Manfrediana, Venezia 22821
Pinacoteca Nazionale, Cagliari 21270
Pinacoteca Nazionale, Siena 22583
Pinacoteca Parrocchiale di San Tomaso Beckett, Padova 22095
Pinacoteca Repossi, Chiari 21404

Jamaica
Institute of Jamaica, Kingston 22896

Japan
Aichi-kenritsu Geijutsu Daigaku Horyuji Kondo Hekiga Mosha Tenjikan, Nagakute 23340
Akita Prefectural Art Gallery, Akita 22922
Bridgestone Bijutsukan, Ishibashi Zaidan, Tokyo 23581
Chiba City Museum of Art, Chiba 22948
Eisei Bunko Museum, Tokyo 23593
Hiroshima Bijutsukan, Hiroshima 23040
Hokkaidoritsu Asahikawa Bijutsukan, Asahikawa 22933
Ibaraki Daigaku Izura Bijutsu Bunka Kenkyujo, Kitaibaraki 23155
Kuroda Kinenshitsu, Tokyo 23628
Kushiro Art Museum, Kushiro 23207
Kyosai Kawanabe Memorial Museum, Warabi 23749
Meiji Memorial Picture Gallery, Tokyo 23636
Narukawa Bijutsukan, Hakone 23006
Ryushi Memorial Hall, Tokyo 23661
Shinshu-shinmachi Art Museum, Shinshiyuushin 23511
Takasaki-shi Bijutsukan, Takasaki 23547
Tenri Gallery, Tokyo 23680
Tokyo Geijutsu Daigaku Daigaku Bijutsukan, Tokyo 23684
Torajiro Kojima Memorial Hall, Kurashiki 23202
Ueno Royal Museum, Tokyo 23699
Yamagata Museum of Art, Yamagata 23753

Lebanon
Daheshite Museum, Beirut 24138
Gibran Museum, Bsharri 24145

Liechtenstein
Sammlungen des Regierenden Fürsten von Liechtenstein, Vaduz 24179

Painting, 17th C.

Painting, 18th C.

Painting, 19th C.

Painting, 20th C.

Painting, English

Painting, European

Painting, European

Italy
Fondazione Magnani Rocca, Mamiano di Traversetolo 21833
Galleria Civica Anna e Luigi Parmiggiani, Reggio Emilia 22298
Galleria Nazionale d'Arte Antica Palazzo Corsini, Roma 22341
Galleria Spada, Roma 22344

Luxembourg
Jean-Pierre Pescatore Collection Villa Vauban, Luxembourg 24224

Netherlands
Rijksmuseum Twenthe, Enschede 25024
Singraven, Denekamp 24939

Norway
Hagan, Eggedal 26064
Holmsbu Billedgalleri, Holmsbu 26115
Munchs Hus, Åsgårdstrand 26017
Rogaland Kunstmuseum i Stavanger, Stavanger 26320
Trøndelag Kunstgalleri/Trondheim Kunstmuseum, Trondheim 26353

Poland
Galeria Sztuki Polskiej XIX w. w Sukiennicach, Kraków 26817
Jacek Malczewski Muzeum, Radom 27057

Portugal
Casa-Museu dos Patudos, Alpiarça 27332
Museu Nacional de Arte Antiga, Lisboa 27400

Russia
Gosudarstvennyj Eremitage, Sankt-Peterburg 28024
Smolenskij Muzej-Zapovednik, Smolensk 28085

Slovenia
Narodna Galerija, Ljubljana 28350

Spain
Collecio Thyssen-Bornemisza, Barcelona 28776
Museo de Cádiz, Cádiz 28888
Museo de los Reyes Católicos, Granada 29118
Museo Municipal Mateo Hernández, Béjar 28834

Sweden
Göteborgs Konstmuseum, Göteborg 30096
Kungliga Akademien för de Fria Konsterna, Stockholm 30353

Switzerland
Fondazione Thyssen-Bornemisza, Castagnola 30682
Kunstmuseum Basel, Basel 30572
Musée des Beaux-Arts Cantonal, Lausanne 30930
Museo Civico di Belle Arti, Lugano 30966
Museum Briner und Kern, Winterthur 31401
Sammlung Oskar Reinhart am Römerholz, Winterthur 31406

Turkey
Erzurum Resim ve Heykel Müzesi, Erzurum 31722
İzmir Resim ve Heykel Müzesi, İzmir 31767

United Kingdom
The Bowes Museum, Barnard Castle 32136
Buscot Park House, Faringdon 33006
Cooper Gallery, Barnsley, South Yorkshire 32140
Ferens Art Gallery, Kingston-upon-Hull 33396
Glasgow Art Gallery and Museum, Glasgow 33076
Hampton Court Palace, East Molesey 32882
Hatton Gallery, Newcastle-upon-Tyne 34030
National Gallery, London 33731
National Gallery of Scotland, Edinburgh 32933
The New Art Gallery Walsall, Walsall 34733
Tabley House Collection, Knutsford 33427
Walker Art Gallery, Liverpool 33548
Wallace Collection, London 33802
Weston Park, Weston-under-Lizard 34792
York City Art Gallery, York 34920

Painting, French

Belgium
Musée d'Art Moderne et d'Art Contemporain, Liège 03547

Brazil
Estrada do Açude Museum, Rio de Janeiro 03999

France
L'Annonciade, Saint-Tropez 13273
Musée Albert André, Bagnols-sur-Cèze 09396
Musée Baron Martin, Gray 10731
Musée de la Vie Romantique, Paris 12354
Musée de l'École de Barbizon - Auberge Ganne, Barbizon 09418
Musée Départemental de l'Oise, Beauvais 09484
Musée des Beaux-Arts, La Rochelle 11035
Musée des Beaux-Arts, Valenciennes 13842
Musée Jean-Honoré Fragonard, Grasse 10721
Musée-Maison Natale Gustave Courbet, Ornans 12222
Musée Matisse, Nice 12104
Musée Municipal Gautron du Coudray, Marzy 11673
Musée National de l'Orangerie, Paris 12427

Musée National Eugène Delacroix, Paris 12434
Musée National Gustave Moreau, Paris 12435
Musée National Jean-Jacques Henner, Paris 12436
Musée National Message Biblique Marc Chagall, Nice 12105
Musée Picasso, Antibes 09207
Musée Pissarro, Pontoise 12619
Musée Toulouse-Lautrec, Naucelle 12057
Musée Utrillo-Valadon, Sannois 13387
Musée Yves-Brayer, Cordes 10210

Germany
Staatsgalerie in der Residenz, Ansbach 14294

Switzerland
Museum Langmatt Sidney und Jenny Brown, Baden 30554
Petit Palais, Genève 30821

Painting, German

Germany
Angermuseum, Erfurt 15597
Atelier Otto Niemeyer-Holstein, Koserow 16857
Conzen-Sammlung, Düsseldorf 15437
Künstlerhaus Exter, Übersee 18777
Kunsthalle Rostock, Rostock 18227
Museum der Stadt Pasewalk und Künstlergedenkstätte Paul Holz, Pasewalk 17941
Museum Ostdeutsche Galerie, Regensburg 18100
Pahl Museum, Mainhardt 17225
Staatsgalerie im Hohen Schloß, Füssen 15867
Städtische Galerie Peter Breuer, Zwickau 19297
Toni-Merz-Museum, Sasbach bei Achern, Baden 18315

Italy
Museo Hans Multscher e Museo Civico, Vipiteno 22874

Painting, Italian

Austria
Graf Harrach'sche Familiensammlung, Rohrau 02501

France
Musée Départemental de l'Oise, Beauvais 09484
Musée des Beaux-Arts Denys-Puech, Rodez 12795

Germany
Staatsgalerie in der Residenz Würzburg, Würzburg 19230

Italy
Casa Buonarroti, Firenze 21577
Casa del Giorgione, Castelfranco Veneto 21340
Casa Natale di Raffaello, Urbino 22760
Cenacolo del Ghirlandaio, Firenze 21579
Cenacolo Vinciano, Milano 21890
Collezioni Comunali d'Arte, Bologna 21182
Galleria Alberoni, Piacenza 22177
Galleria Colonna, Roma 22336
Galleria Comunale d'Arte, Cagliari 21263
Galleria Comunale d'Arte, Prato 22258
Galleria d'Arte Moderna, Firenze 21591
Galleria d'Arte Moderna Ricci-Oddi, Piacenza 22178
Galleria degli Uffizi, Firenze 21592
Galleria dell'Accademia, Firenze 21594
Galleria dell'Accademia di Belle Arti Tadini, Lovere 21807
Galleria di Palazzo Bianco, Genova 21683
Galleria Doria Pamphilj, Roma 22339
Galleria Estense, Modena 21940
Galleria Municipale, Francavilla al Mare 21653
Galleria Nazionale, Parma 22126
Galleria Nazionale d'Arte Antica Palazzo Barberini, Roma 22340
Galleria Nazionale dell'Umbria, Perugia 22153
Galleria Nazionale di Palazzo Spinola, Genova 21686
Galleria Palatina, Firenze 21596
Galleria Regionale di Palazzo Bellomo, Siracusa 22587
Galleria Sabauda, Torino 22668
Gallerie dell'Accademia, Venezia 22795
Musei Civici, Pesaro 22160
Musei Civici agli Eremitani, Padova 22087
Museo Bandini, Fiesole 21562
Museo Canonica, Roma 22359
Museo Canonicale, Verona 22837
Museo Casa del Mantegna, Mantova 21839
Museo Civico, Bagnacavallo 21127
Museo Civico, Montepulciano 21991
Museo Civico, Pescia 22171
Museo Civico di Barletta, Barletta 21140
Museo Civico e Diocesano d' Arte Sacra, Montalcino 21974
Museo Civico Giulio Ferrari, Carpi 21315
Museo Civico Luigi Bailo, Treviso 22726
Museo Correr, Venezia 22800
Museo de Napoli, Terlizzi 22634

Museo del Risorgimento Vittorio Emanuele Orlando, Palermo 22109
Museo della Collegiata di Santa Andrea Empoli, Empoli 21513
Museo della Fondazione Querini Stampalia, Venezia 22808
Museo della Magnifica Comunità di Cadore, Pieve di Cadore 22197
Museo della Società di Esecutori di Pie Disposizioni, Siena 22579
Museo dell'Accademia dei Concordi, Rovigo 22448
Museo di Bevagna, Bevagna 21165
Museo di Casa Vasari, Arezzo 21083
Museo di Giuseppe Pellizza, Volpedo 22884
Museo di San Giuseppe, Bologna 21207
Museo di Santa Maria delle Grazie, San Giovanni Valdarno 22486
Museo Diocesano, Cortona 21477
Museo Diocesano di Pienza, Pienza 22193
Museo e Pinacoteca Civica del Broletto, Novara 22049
Museo Giannettino Luxoro, Genova 21701
Museo Giovanni Boldini, Ferrara 21556
Museo Regionale, Messina 21885
Museo Renato Brozzi, Traversetolo 22711
Museo Statale di Arte Medioevale e Moderna, Arezzo 21085
Museo Storico-topografico, Firenze 21627
Museo Vanvitelliano, Caserta 21327
Palazzo Ducale, Venezia 22818
Pinacoteca, Castelfiorentino 21337
Pinacoteca Civica, Ascoli Piceno 21102
Pinacoteca Civica, Iesi 21734
Pinacoteca Civica, San Gimignano 22482
Pinacoteca Civica 'Francesco Podesti' e Galleria Comunale d'Arte Moderna, Ancona 21064
Pinacoteca Civica 'Inzaghi', Budrio 21253
Pinacoteca Comunale, Assisi 21112
Pinacoteca Comunale, Cesena 21400
Pinacoteca Comunale, Città di Castello 21433
Pinacoteca Comunale, Massa Fermana 21856
Pinacoteca Comunale, Volterra 22888
Pinacoteca del Pio Monte della Misericordia, Napoli 22029
Pinacoteca dell'Accademia Carrara, Bergamo 21160
Pinacoteca dell'Accademia Zelantea, Acireale 21025
Pinacoteca di Brera, Milano 21930
Pinacoteca e del Museo B.Gigli, Recanati 22295
Pinacoteca e Museo Civico, Bettona 21163
Pinacoteca Giuseppe Stuard, Parma 22136
Pinacoteca Nazionale, Bologna 21215
Pinacoteca Nazionale, Ferrara 21560
Pinacoteca Provinciale di Bari, Bari 21139
Pinacoteca Rizzi, Sestri Levante 22572
Pinacoteca San Francesco, Montefalco 21985
Raccolta d'Arte di San Francesco, Trevi 22721
Sala d'Arte Antica, Chianciano Terme 21403
Scuola Dalmata dei SS. Giorgio e Trifone, Venezia 22822
Scuola Grande Arciconfraternita di San Rocco, Venezia 22823
Scuola Grande Arciconfraternita S.M. del Carmelo, Venezia 22824
Scuola Grande di San Giovanni Evangelista, Venezia 22825

Peru
Museo de Arte Italiano, Lima 26491

Painting, Latin American

Argentina
Museo Municipal de Artes Plásticas, Olavarría 00454
Museo Municipal de Bellas Artes Lucas Braulio Areco, Posadas 00476
Museo Regional de Pintura José Antonio Terry, Tilcara 00628

Bolivia
Museo del Ateneo de Bellas Artes, Sucre 03878

Brazil
Museu Antonio Parreiras, Niterói 03961

Cuba
Centro Wilfredo Lam, La Habana 07137

Mexico
Museo Casa Diego Rivera I.N.B.A., Guanajuato 24401
Museo Casa Estudio Diego Rivera y Frida Kahlo, México 24426
Museo del Palacio de Bellas Artes, México 24448
Museo Frida Kahlo, México 24454
Museo Nacional de Arte, México 24460
Museo-Taller José Clemente Orozco, Guadalajara 24399
Pinacoteca Virreinal de San Diego, México 24482

Puerto Rico
Popular Arts Museum, San Juan 27469

Painting, Medieval

Austria
Alte Galerie, Graz 01904
Museum des Chorherrenstifts Klosterneuburg, Klosterneuburg 02131

Czech Republic
Klášter Sv. Jiří, Praha 07567

France
Musée d'Unterlinden, Colmar 10168

Germany
Staatsgalerie in der Burg, Burghausen, Salzach 15154
Staatsgalerie in der Neuen Residenz, Bamberg 14589

Hungary
Keresztény Múzeum, Esztergom 19882

India
Birla Academy of Art and Culture Museum, Kolkata 20181

Italy
Museo Civico, Pistoia 22217
Museo dell'Opera del Duomo, Orvieto 22075

Macedonia
Umjetnička Galerija, Skopje 24255

Russia
Centralnyj Muzej Drevnerusskoj Kultury i Isskustva im. Andreja Rubleva, Moskva 27793

Spain
Instituto Amatller de Arte Hispánico, Barcelona 28783

Painting, Netherlandish

Belgium
Gemeentelijk Museum en Cultuurhuis Emiel Van Doren, Genk 03395
Jordaenshuis, Antwerpen 03105
Memlingmuseum, Brugge 03217
Musée des Beaux-Arts de Tournai, Tournai 03775
Musée des Beaux-Arts et Céramique, Verviers 03793
Museum Mayer van den Bergh, Antwerpen 03110
Museum van de Sint-Salvatorskathedraal, Brugge 03222
Museum van het Heilig Bloed, Brugge 03223
Museum Wuyts-Van Campen en Baron Caroly, Lier 03557
Rubenshuis, Antwerpen 03135
Stedelijk Museum, Oudenaarde 03653
Stedelijk Museum Van der Kelen-Mertens, Leuven 03535

Germany
Staatsgalerie in der Residenz, Ansbach 14294

Italy
Galleria di Palazzo Bianco, Genova 21683
Galleria Sabauda, Torino 22668

Netherlands
Dordrechts Museum, Dordrecht 24960
Frans Walkate Archief/ SNS Historisch Archief, Kampen 25198
Groninger Museum, Groningen 25077
Jopie Huisman Museum, Workum 25002
Koninklijk Kabinet van Schilderijen, Den Haag 24903
Museum Bredius, Den Haag 24908
Museum Kempenland, Eindhoven 25002
Museum voor Moderne Kunst, Arnhem 24769
Oudheidkundige Verzameling, Sluis 25500
Peter Van den Braken Centrum, Sterksel 25519
Rijksmuseum, Amsterdam 24731
Schilderijenzaal Prins Willem V, Den Haag 24927
Singer Museum, Laren, Noord-Holland 25217
Stedelijk Museum De Lakenhal, Leiden 25244
Stedelijk Museum Het Prinsenhof, Delft 24887
Ton Smits Huis, Eindhoven 25008

South Africa
Groot Constantia Manor House and Wine Museum, Constantia 28451

United Kingdom
Breamore House, Breamore 32368
Ferens Art Gallery, Kingston-upon-Hull 33396
Raby Castle, Darlington 32738
Shipley Art Gallery, Gateshead 33056
Talbot Rice Gallery, Edinburgh 32953

Painting, Renaissance

Belgium
Da Vinci-Museum, Tongerlo 03766

Canada
Imhoff Art Gallery, Saint Walburg 05850

France
Musée du Clos-Lucé, Amboise 09145

Germany
Albrecht-Dürer-Haus, Nürnberg 17732
Burg Trausnitz, Landshut 16950
Staatsgalerie im Schloß Johannisburg, Aschaffenburg 14320
Städtisches Museum Schloß Rheydt, Mönchengladbach 17398

Italy
Casa Natale di Tiziano Vecellio, Pieve di Cadore 22196
Castello d'Issogne, Issogne 21755
Cenacolo di San Salvi, Firenze 21580
Galleria Nazionale delle Marche, Urbino 22761
Pinacoteca Comunale, Sarnano 22534

Portugal
Museu de Setúbal - Convento de Jesus - Galeria de Arte Quinhentista, Setúbal 27437

Painting, Spanish

Austria
Graf Harrach'sche Familiensammlung, Rohrau 02501

France
Musée Goya, Castres 09904

Spain
Casa-Museo José Benlliure, Valencia 29831
Casa Natal de Goya, Fuendetodos 29067
Casa y Museo de El Greco, Toledo 29767
Colección de Arte Carmen Rodríguez Acosta, Granada 29108
Colección de la Facultad de Filosofía y Letras, Madrid 29242
Colección del Banco de España, Madrid 29246
Colección Veri, Marratxinet 29335
Museu Barrau, Santa Eulària des Riu 29652
Museo de Bellas Artes, Badajoz 28757
Museo de Bellas Artes, Córdoba 28979
Museo de Bellas Artes, Granada 29116
Museo de Bellas Artes de Santander, Santander 29666
Museo de Reproducciones de El Greco, Yecla 29943
Museo Evaristo Valle, Gijón 29088
Museo Gustavo de Maeztu, Estella 29047
Museo Jovellanos, Gijón 29089
Museo Julio Romero de Torres, Córdoba 28981
Museo Municipal Mariano Benlliure, Crevillente 29000
Museo Nicanor Piñole, Gijón 29090
Museo Romántico, Madrid 29294
Museo Sorolla, Madrid 29296
Museo Zabaleta, Quesada 29543
Museu Nacional d'Art de Catalunya, Barcelona 28824
Panteón de Goya, Madrid 29300

United Kingdom
Pollok House, Glasgow 33089

Paleontology → Fossils

Paper

Australia
Tamworth City Gallery, Tamworth 01512

Canada
Centre d'Exposition sur l'Industrie des Pâtes et Papiers, Trois-Rivières 06112

Czech Republic
Papírna Muzeum, Velké Losiny 07695

Denmark
Bruunshåb Gamle Papfabrik, Viborg 08092

Finland
Myllysaaren Museo, Valkeakoski 09009
Verlan Tehdasmuseo, Verla 09030

France
Musée du Papier Le Nil, Angoulême 09187
Musée du Papier Peint, Rixheim 12768
Musée Historique du Papier, Ambert 09136

Germany
Firmenmusemum Novatech, Reutlingen 18145
Museum Papiermühle Homburg, Triefenstein 18736
Papiergeschichtliche Sammlung, Bergisch Gladbach 14662
Papiermuseum, Düren 15436
Rheinisches Industriemuseum Bergisch Gladbach, Bergisch Gladbach 14663

Italy
Museo Civico della Carta, Cairate 21271
Museo della Carta, Amalfi 21058
Museo della Carta e della Filigrana, Fabriano 21524

Japan
Kami no Hakubutsukan, Tokyo 23614

Malaysia
Kite Museum, Melaka 24317

Netherlands
Museum van Knipkunst, Westerbork 25639

Poland
Muzeum Papiernictwa, Duszniki Zdrój 26692

Spain
Museo Molino Papelero de Capellades, Capellades 28915

Switzerland
Basler Papiermühle, Basel 30565

United Kingdom
Heron Corn Mill and Museum of Papermaking, Beetham 32196
Whitworth Art Gallery, Manchester 33901

U.S.A.
Robert C. Williams American Museum of Papermaking, Atlanta 35227

Peasant Life and Traditions

Australia
Blacksmith's Cottage, Bacchus Marsh 00746
Blundell's Cottage, Parkes 01344
Caboolture Historical Village and Museum, Caboolture 00863
Chiverton House Museum, Northampton 01322
City of Gosnells Museum, Gosnells 01054
Clifton and District Historical Museum, Clifton 00915
Hunter Valley Museum of Rural Life, Scone 01441
Kalamunda History Village, Kalamunda 01119
Murchison Settlement Museum, Mullewa 01279

Austria
Alte Wassermühlen und Museum Des Bauern Sach und Zeug, Maria Luggau 02259
Bauernmühle-Dorfmuseum, Finkenstein 01827
Bauernmuseum Großklein, Großklein 01951
Bauernmuseum Guntersdorf, Guntersdorf 01967
Bauernmuseum Lanzenkirchen, Lanzenkirchen 02180
Bauernmuseum Osternach, Ort im Innkreis 02371
Bauernmuseum Spannberg, Spannberg 02642
Bergbauernmuseum, Wildschönau 02996
Denkmalhof Arler, Abtenau 01636
Familienmuseum im Altbauernhaus, Göstling an der Ybbs 01895
Freilichtmuseum Historische Volkskunde Kalte Kuchl, Rohr im Gebirge 02500
Freilichtmuseum Tiroler Bauernhöfe, Kramsach 02143
Heimathaus Litzelsdorf, Litzelsdorf 02237
Holzknechtmuseum im Salzkammergut, Bad Goisern 01695
Holzknechtmuseum Trübenbach im Naturpark Ötscher-Tormäuer, Wienerbruck 02990
Mentlhof-Bergbauernmuseum, Heiligenblut 02012
Museum für bäuerliche Arbeitsgeräte, Imst 02050
Museum Humanum, Waldkirchen 02760
Museum im Tabor, Feldbach 01817
Oberösterreichisches Freilichtmuseum Sumerauerhof, Sankt Florian 02541
Paznauner Bauernmuseum, Mathon 02270
Tiroler Bauernhausmuseum, Kitzbühel 02110
Volkskundlich-Landwirtschaftliche Sammlung, Stainz 02649
Waldviertler Bauernhaus-Museum, Weitra 02779
Waldviertler Bauernhof-Museum, Gföhl 01870

Belgium
Musée de la Vie Paysanne, Dampicourt 03336
Musée de la Vie Rurale en Wallonie, Saint-Hubert 03694
Zwischen Venn und Schneeifel, Saint-Vith 03699

Canada
Fishermen's Life Museum, Jeddore Oyster Ponds 05090
Red Deer and District Museum, Red Deer 05690
Whitchurch-Stouffville Museum, Gormley 04961

Czech Republic
Valašské Muzeum v Přírodě, Rožnov pod Radhoštěm 07625

Denmark
Ærø Museum, Ærøskøbing 07748
Als Hjemstavnsmuseum, Hadsund 07838
Frilandsmuseet, Lyngby 07962
Sorø Amts Museum, Sorø 08060
Stenstrup Museum, Højby 07867

Finland
Herttoniemen Museo, Helsinki 08355
Hollolan Kotiseutumuseo, Hollola 08400
Juvan Museo, Juva 08435
Kainuun Museo, Kajaani 08448
Kangasniemen Museo, Kangasniemi 08457
Kokemäen Ulkomuseo, Kokemäki 08518
Merimiehen Koti, Uusikaupunki 08990
Museokylä Kalluntalo, Laukaa 08609
Nivalan Museo Katvala, Nivala 08710
Orimattilan Kotiseutumuseo, Orimattila 08730
Oriveden Paltanmäen Museo, Orivesi 08734
Pielaveden Kotiseutumuseo, Pielavesi 08777
Porlammin Kotiseutumuseo, Lapinjärvi Porlammi 08595
Rovaniemen Kotiseutumuseo, Rovaniemi 08847
Saamelaismuseo Siida, Inari 08413
Saloisten Kotiseutumuseo, Arkkukari 08299
Seurasaaren Ulkomuseo, Helsinki 08380
Talomuseo, Kuortane 08566
Työväenasuntomuseo, Helsinki 08397
Vihannin Kotiseutumuseo, Vihanti 09033
Ypäjän Kotiseutumuseo, Ypäjä 09057

France
Ecomusée d'Alsace, Ungersheim 13814
Ecomusée de la Vie Rurale, Hannonville-sous-les-Côtes 10787
Maison de l'Eclusier, Saint-Malo-de-Guersac 13118
Musée Alice Taverne, Ambierle 09137
Musée Conservatoire Maritime et Rural, Narbonne 12050
Musée d'Arts et Traditions Populaires, Marmoutier 11619
Musée de Kerhinet, Saint-Lyphard 13113
Musée de la Ferme d'Antan, Jugon-lès-Lacs 10899
Musée de la Goubaudière, Cholet 10107
Musée de la Vie Rurale, Steenwerck 13579
Musée du Charroi Rural, Salmiech 13370
Musée du Monde Rural, Rettel 12736
Musée Rural, Saint-André-d'Embrun 12895
Musée Rural de la Sologne Bourbonnaise, Beaulon 09472
Musée Rural du Porzay, Plomodiern 12554

Germany
Ackerbürgermuseum Haus Leck, Grebenstein 16066
Agrarmuseum Wandlitz, Wandlitz 18917
Bäuerliches Museum im Achentaler Heimathaus, Rohrdorf 18208
Bauern- und Handwerker-Museum, Malgersdorf 17238
Bauernhaus-Museum, Wolfegg 19173
Bauernhausmuseum, Bad Füssing 14431
Bauernhausmuseum Altburg, Calw 15176
Bauernhausmuseum Hohenstein, Württemberg, Hohenstein, Württemberg 16480
Bauernmuseum Schniderlihof, Oberried 17790
Bauernmuseum Blankensee, Blankensee bei Luckenwalde 14923
Bauernmuseum Inzigkofen, Inzigkofen 16572
Bauernmuseum Zabeltitz, Zabeltitz 19257
BLM Bauernhaus-Museum Bortfeld, Wendeburg 19039
Börde-Museum, Ummendorf 18794
Brandenburgisches Freilichtmuseum Altranft, Altranft 14260
Bürger- und Bauernmuseum, Hilzingen 16430
Dorfmuseum Ahnenhaus, Pliezhausen 17996
Dorfmuseum Buchenberg, Königsfeld im Schwarzwald 16824
Dorfmuseum Deckenpfronn, Deckenpfronn 15279
Dorfmuseum Dettingen/Iller, Dettingen an der Iller 15317
Fränkische Hopfenscheune mit heimatkundlicher Sammlung, Neunkirchen am Sand 17654
Fränkisches Freilandmuseum Fladungen, Fladungen 15711
Freilichtmuseum Beuren, Beuren bei Nürtingen 14881
Freilichtmuseum Dorfstube Ötlingen, Weil am Rhein 18962
Freilichtmuseum Neuhausen ob Eck, Neuhausen ob Eck 17639
Fürstenbergerhof, Zell am Harmersbach 19263
Heimatmuseum, Buttstädt 15166
Heimatmuseum, Höpfingen 16453
Heimatmuseum, Neckargerach 17595
Heimatmuseum, Nellingen 17598
Heimatmuseum, Neukirch, Lausitz 17640
Heimatmuseum, Schöneiche bei Berlin 18377
Heimatmuseum Altmannstein, Altmannstein 14248
Heimatmuseum Flacht, Weissach, Württemberg 19020
Heimatmuseum Ihringen, Ihringen 16544
Heimatmuseum im Vogteigebäude, Hüttlingen 16526
Heimatmuseum Mehrstetten, Mehrstetten 17315
Heimatmuseum Obere Mühle, Loßburg 17143
Heimatmuseum Seßlach, Seßlach 18481
Heimatmuseum Untergrombach, Bruchsal 15097
Heimatstube Fischbach, Niedereschach 17697
Heimatstube Mühlhausen, Villingen-Schwenningen 18847
Heimatstube Neuhaus-Schiernitz, Neuhaus-Schierschnitz 17638
Heimatstuben, Waldbronn 18882
Heimatstuben der Csávolyer im Beinsteiner Torturm, Waiblingen 18878
Hohenloher Freilandmuseum, Schwäbisch Hall 18410
Karpatendeutsches Museum, Karlsruhe 16650
Kreisheimatmuseum, Grimma 16089
Mönchguter Museum, Göhren, Rügen 16003
Museum, Mühlacker 17425
Museum Alte Lateinschule Großenhain, Großenhain, Sachsen 16114
Museum im Adler, Benningen 14644
Museum Im Dorf, Reutlingen 18147
Museum im Seelhaus, Bopfingen 14996
Museum Kalt-Heiß, Deckenpfronn 15280
Museumsdorf Bayerischer Wald, Tittling 18716
Museumsdorf Cloppenburg, Cloppenburg 15205
Museumshof, Bad Oeynhausen 14486
Museumshof auf dem Braem, Gescher 15958
Niederlausitzer Heidemuseum, Spremberg 18553
Niederrheinisches Freilichtmuseum, Grefrath 16069
Odenwälder Freilandmuseum, Walldürn 18905
Ostfriesisches Freilichtmuseum Pewsum, Krummhörn 16894
Reubacher Heimatmuseum, Rot 18231
Rheinisches Freilichtmuseum und Landesmuseum für Volkskunde Kommern, Mechernich 17300
Rhön-Museum, Fladungen 15712
Rieser Bauernmuseum, Maihingen 17222
Schwäbisches Bauern- und Technikmuseum, Eschach 15631
Schwarzwälder Freilichtmuseum Vogtsbauernhof, Gutach, Schwarzwaldbahn 16149
Stadtmuseum Oschatz, Oschatz 17867
Städtische Museen Wangen im Allgäu, Wangen im Allgäu 18922
Städtisches Museum, Korbach 16854
Stormarnsches Dorfmuseum, Altes Bauernhaus am Thie, Hoisdorf 16485
Ungarn-deutsche Heimatstuben, Langenau, Württemberg 16970
Vilstaler Bauernmuseum, Eichendorf 15514
Vogtländisches Freilichtmuseum Landwüst/Eubabrunn, Landwüst 16957
Volkskunde-Museum, Rudolstadt 18260
Volkskunde- und Freilichtmuseum, Konz 16852
Waldhufen-Heimatmuseum Salmbach, Engelsbrand 15576
Westfälisches Freilichtmuseum Detmold, Detmold 15313

Hungary
Göcseji Falumúzeum, Zalaegerszeg 20076
Sóstói Múzeumfalu, Sóstógyógyfürdő 20005
Szabadtéri Néprajzi Gyűjtemény, Szenna 20030
Szabadtéri Néprajzi Múzeum, Szentendre 20039
Vasi Múzeumfalu, Szombathely 20053

Italy
Casa Museo, Palazzolo Acreide 22101
Mostra della Civiltà Contadina, Massa Marittima 21859
Museo Contadino, Varese Ligure 22782
Museo del Lavoro Contadino, Campobello di Mazara 21296
Museo del Lavoro e della Tradizioni Popolari della Versilia Storica, Seravezza 22563
Museo della Canape e della Vita Contadina, Bentivoglio 21152
Museo della Civiltà Contadina, Dozza 21510
Museo della Civiltà Contadina, Moio della Civitella 21957
Museo della Civiltà Contadina, Montecorice 21984
Museo della Civiltà Contadina, Novellara 22053
Museo della Civiltá Contadina, Piandimeleto 22184
Museo della Civiltà Contadina della Valpadana, Cremona 21488
Museo della Civiltà Contadina dell'Alto Monferrato e della Bassa Langa, Castagnole delle Lanze 21333
Museo della Civiltà Rurale del Vicentino, Malo 21832
Museo della Vita Contadina "Diogene Penzi", San Vito al Tagliamento 22506
Museo dell'Agricoltura e del Mondo Rurale, San Martino in Rio 22494
Museo delle Contadinerie, Costigliole d'Asti 21481
Museo di Civiltà Contadina, Castelnuovo Calcea 21349
Museo di Storia e Cultura Contadina, Genova 21699
Museo Etnografico Coumboscuro della Civiltà Provenzale in Italia, Sancto Lucia de Coumboscuro 22507
Museo Etnografico Romagnolo Benedetto Pergoli, Forlì 21645
Museo Ettore Pomarici Santomasi, Gravina di Puglia 21717

Lebanon
Saint Sharbel Museum, Annaya 24136

Netherlands
Openluchtmuseum Het Hoogeland, Warffum 25622
Themapark Openluchtmuseum De Spitkeet, Harkema 25108

Norway
Agatunet, Nå 26196
Bø Bygdemuseet, Bø i Telemark 26043
Hemnes Bygdetun, Bjerka 26040
Inderøy Bygdemuseum, Sakshaug 26278
Oppdal Bygdemuseum, Oppdal 26207
Rollag Bygdetun, Rollag 26269
De Samiske Samlinger, Karasjok 26133
Søgne Bygdemuseum, Søgne 26308
Stor-Elvdal Museum, Koppang 26146
Sunnhordland Folkemuseum og Sogelag, Stord 26329
Tingvoll Bygdemuseum, Tingvoll 26339
Tynset Bygdemuseum, Tynset 26360
Valdres Folkemusem, Fagernes 26077

Poland
Muzeum Przyrodniczo-Leśne Świętokrzyskiego Parku Narodowego, Święty Krzyż 27134

Romania
Peasant Farm Museum, Sarichioi 27639

Spain
Museu dels Raiers, El Pont de Claverol 29516

Sweden
Ekehagens Forntidsby, Åsarp 30031
Hägnan Friluftsmuseet i Gammelstad, Gammelstad 30090
Örnsköldsviks Museum, Örnsköldsvik 30270

Switzerland
Bauernhaus-Museum, Muttenz 31042
Bauernmuseum Althus, Gurbü 30853
Bauernmuseum Wohlenschwil, Wohlenschwil 31416
Heimatmuseum, Oberweningen 31073
Heimatmuseum Bucheggberg, Buchegg 30664
Heimatmuseum der Albert-Edelmann-Stiftung, Ebnat-Kappel 30737
Heimatmuseum Stammheimertal, Unterstammheim 31334
Musée Paysan et Artisanal, La Chaux-de-Fonds 30698
Museo della Civiltà Contadina del Mendrisiotto, Stabio 31266
Museum zur Ronmühle, Schötz 31214
Orts- und Wohnmuseum, Marthalen 30989
Ortsmuseum Hinwil, Hinwil 30871
Ortsmuseum zur Hohlen Eich, Wädenswil 31366
Schweizerisches Freilichtmuseum für ländliche Kultur, Brienz, Bern 30653

United Kingdom
Auchindrain Museum of Country Life, Inveraray 33319
Blists Hill Victorian Town Open Air Museum, Madeley 33870
Breamore Countryside Museum, Breamore 32367
Calbourne Water Mill and Rural Museum, Calbourne 32487
Cotswold Heritage Centre, Northleach 34075
Glenesk Folk Museum, Brechin 32370
Great Barn Museum of Wiltshire Rural Life, Avebury 32092
Lackham Museum of Agriculture and Rural Life, Lacock 33431
Mesolithic Museum, Abinger Common 32005
Mullach Ban Folk Museum, Mullach Ban 33991
Museum of East Anglian Life, Stowmarket 34587
Museum of Kent Life, Sandling 34418
Perry's Cider Mills, Ilminster 33315
Rural Life Centre, Farnham 33012
Stanmer Rural Museum, Brighton 32398
Usk Rural Life Museum, Usk 34714
Wayside Folk Museum, Zennor 34925
White House Museum of Buildings and Country Life, Aston Munslow 32087

U.S.A.
Ashland Logging Museum, Ashland 35174
Blue Ridge Institute and Museum, Ferrum 36827
Coggeshall Farm Museum, Bristol 35667
Forest Capital State Museum, Perry 39328
Fred Dana Marsh Museum, Ormond Beach 39197
Georgia Agrirama-19th Century Living History Museum, Tifton 40681
Lum and Abner Museum and Jot 'Em Down Store, Pine Ridge 39446
Midway Village and Museum, Rockford 39831
Mountain Life Museum, London 38107
Naper Settlement Museum, Naperville 38711
Patten Lumberman's Museum, Patten 39295
President Calvin Coolidge State Historic Site, Plymouth Notch 39513
The Spanish Quarter Museum, Saint Augustine 39925
Storrowton Village Museum, West Springfield 41127
Stuttgart Agricultural Museum, Stuttgart 40563
Volo Antique Auto Museum and Village, Volo 40886
Watson Farm, Jamestown 37666

Performing Arts

Argentina
Museo de Instituto Nacional de Estudios de Teatro, Buenos Aires 00170
Museo de la Casa del Teatro, Buenos Aires 00174
Museo del Teatro Colón, Buenos Aires 00194
Museo del Teatro y la Música de Córdoba Cristobal de Aguilar, Córdoba 00291

Australia
Performance Space, Redfern 01410
Performing Arts Collection of South Australia, Adelaide 00703
Performing Arts Museum, Melbourne 01229

Austria
Kinder-Knürstl-Museum, Götzis 01897
Museum der Wahrnehmung, Graz 01918
Museum Sensenwerk, Deutschfeistritz 01754
Österreichisches Circus- und Clown-Museum, Wien 02929
Österreichisches Theatermuseum, Wien 02936
Puppentheatermuseum, Mistelbach an der Zaya 02293

Azerbaijan
State Museum of the Dzabarey Theatre, Baku 03037

Belgium
Archief en Museum voor het Vlaamse Cultuurleven, Antwerpen 03096
Archives et Musée de la Littérature, Bruxelles 03231
Musée du Théâtre Royal de la Monnaie, Bruxelles 03293

Brazil
Museu dos Teatros do Rio de Janeiro, Rio de Janeiro 04051
Museu Teatro, Rio de Janeiro 04068

Bulgaria
Muzej na Naroden Teatar Ivan Vazov, Sofia 04318
Muzej na Narodnata Opera, Sofia 04319

China, People's Republic
Beijing Animation Art Museum, Beijing 06420
Beijing Opera Museum, Beijing 06428
Tianjin Drama Museum, Tianjin 06736

Costa Rica
Galeria Teatro Nacional Enrique Echandi y Joaquín García Monge, San José 06943

Cyprus
Nikos Nikolaides Theatrical Archives, Limassol 07200

Czech Republic
Měnínská Brána, Brno 07257
Moravské Zemské Muzeum, Brno 07260

Denmark
Teatermuseet, København 07935

Estonia
Eesti Teatri-ja Muusikamuuseum, Tallinn 08265

Finland
Teatterimuseo, Helsinki 08393

France
Bibliothèque-Musée de la Comédie-Française, Paris 12260
Manoir de Veygoux, Scénomusée des Combrailles, Charbonnières-les-Varennes 09988
Musée de l'Opéra National de Paris, Paris 12367
Musée du Cirque, Vatan 13884
Musée du Théâtre, Couilly-Pont-aux-Dames 10227
Musée Kwok-On, Paris 12417

Georgia
State Theatrical Museum, Tbilisi 14158

Germany
Augsburger Puppentheatermuseum Die Kiste, Augsburg 14339
Brecht-Weigel-Gedenkstätte, Berlin 14688
Circus-, Varieté- und Artistenarchive, Marburg 17257
Curt-Engelhorn-Zentrum, Mannheim 17241
Deutsches Theatermuseum, München 17462
Ekhof-Theater, Gotha 16045
Erstes Circusmuseum in Deutschland, Preetz, Holstein 18016
Fastnachtsmuseum, Herbstein 16386
Filmmuseum Bendestorf, Bendestorf 14639
Freiburger Fasnetmuseum, Freiburg im Breisgau 15808
Historische Kuranlagen und Goethe-Theater Bad Lauchstädt, Bad Lauchstädt 14468
König Ludwig II.-Museum, Herrenchiemsee 16401
Markt- und Schaustellermuseum, Essen 15657
Museum für Kunst-, Stadt-, Theater- und Musikgeschichte, Mannheim 17246
Museum für Puppentheater, Lübeck 17170
Neuberin-Museum, Reichenbach, Vogtland 18118
Puppentheatersammlung, Radebeul 18043
Stadtmuseum Rottweil, Rottweil 18257
Theatergeschichtliche Sammlung und Hebbel-Sammlung, Kiel 16734
Theatermuseum der Landeshauptstadt, Düsseldorf 15459
Theatermuseum Hannover, Hannover 16285
Theatermuseum in der Reithalle, Meiningen 17320
Theaterwissenschaftliche Sammlung, Köln 16816
Valentin-Karlstadt Musäum, München 17529
Zirkus und Varieté Archivsammlung Reinhard Tetzlaff, Hamburg 16248

Greece
Hellenic Theatre Museum and Study Center, Athinai 19381
Panos Aravantinos Theatrical Museum of Painting and Stage Design, Piraeus 19621

Hungary
Bajor Gizi Emlékmúzeum, Budapest 19806
Országos Színháztörténeti Múzeum és Intézet, Budapest 19850

Israel
Israel Goor Theater Archive and Museum, Jerusalem 20917
Israel Theater Museum, Tel Aviv 20998

Italy
Civico Museo Teatrale di Fondazione Carlo Schmidl, Trieste 22739
Collezione Titta Ruffo, Pisa 22210
Museo Biblioteca dell'Attore, Genova 21690
Museo del Teatro, Faenza 21529
Museo del Teatro, Spoleto 22602
Museo del Teatro Municipale, Piacenza 22181
Museo dell'Opera, Buggiano 21254
Museo Romagnolo del Teatro, Forlì 21647
Museo Teatrale alla Scala, Milano 21926
Raccolta di Disegni Teatrali, Spoleto 22605
Raccolta Teatrale del Burcardo, Roma 22425

Japan
Waseda Daigaku Tsubouchi Hakushi Kinen Engeki Hakubutsukan, Tokyo 23702

Netherlands
Clown Pepie Museum, Spijkenisse 25509
Kermis- en Circusmuseum Steenwijk, Steenwijk 25514
Theater Museum, Amsterdam 24738
Ut Hoes met de Kiekdoes, Maastricht 25279

Norway
Teatermuseet i Oslo, Oslo 26245

Poland
Muzeum Teatralne, Warszawa 27234
Muzeum Teatralne, Kraków 26842

Portugal
Museu Nacional do Teatro, Lisboa 27403

Romania
Muzeul Teatrului, Iaşi 27593
Muzeul Teatrului National, Bucureşti 27529

Russia
Dom-muzej F.I. Šaljapina, Moskva 27806
Dom-muzej K.S. Stanislavskogo, Moskva 27807
Dom-muzej M.N. Ermolovoj, Moskva 27810
Gosudarstvennyj Centralnyj Teatralnyj Muzej im. Bachrušina, Moskva 27818
Gosudarstvennyj Muzej Detskich Teatrov, Moskva 27824
Gosudarstvennyj Muzej Teatralnogo i Musykalnogo Iskusstva, Sankt-Peterburg 28030
Kulturnyj Centr-muzej V.S. Vysockogo, Moskva 27837
Museum of the Mussorgsky State Academic Opera and Ballet Theatre, Sankt-Peterburg 28044
Muzej Cirkovogo Iskusstva, Sankt-Peterburg 28048
Muzej Etnografičeskogo Kostjuma na Kuklach, Moskva 27861
Muzej Gosudarstvennogo Akademičeskogo Bolšogo Teatra Rossii, Moskva 27862
Muzej Gosudarstvennogo Akademičeskogo Malogo Teatra, Moskva 27863
Muzej Gosudarstvennogo Akademičeskogo Marijnskogo Teatra Opery i Baleta, Sankt-Peterburg 28051
Muzej-kvartira Dirižëra N.S. Golovanov, Moskva 27886
Muzej-kvartira V.I. Nemiroviča-Dančenko, Moskva 27891
Muzej-kvartira V.S. Mejercholda, Moskva 27892
Muzej Moskovskogo Chudožestvennogo Akademičeskogo Teatra, Moskva 27896
Muzej Moskovskoj Konservatorii, Moskva 27897
Muzej Teatra Operetty, Moskva 27912
N.G. Rubinstein Museum, Moskva 27922

Slovenia
Slovenski Gledališki Muzej, Ljubljana 28356

South Africa
National Theatre Museum, Bloemfontein 28423

Spain
Museo del Teatro, Almagro 28689
Museu de les Arts Escèniques, Barcelona 28802

Sweden
Dansmuseet, Stockholm 30341
Gripes Modeltheatremuseum, Nyköping 30260
Marionettmuseet, Stockholm 30360
Sveriges Teatermuseum, Nacka 30244

Switzerland
Schweizerische Theatersammlung, Bern 30617

Ukraine
State Museum of Theatrical, Musical and Cinematographic Art of Ukraine, Kyïv 31924

United Kingdom
Collection of Portraits and Performance History, London 33618
Ellen Terry Memorial Museum, Tenterden 34652
Georgian Theatre Royal Museum, Richmond, North Yorkshire 34299
Greenwich Theatre Art Gallery, London 33655
Mander and Mitchenson Theatre Collection, London 33705
Museum of Entertainment, Whaplode 34802
Royal Shakespeare Company Collection, Stratford-upon-Avon 34597
Scottish Traditions of Dance, Edinburgh 32951
Shakespeare's Globe Exhibition, London 33779
Theatre Museum, London 33794
University of Bristol Theatre Collection, Bristol 32412

U.S.A.
American Museum of Magic, Marshall 38359
Arts and Science Center for Southeast Arkansas, Pine Bluff 39444
Barnum Museum, Bridgeport 35654
Bloomington Art Center, Bloomington 35543
Center for Puppetry Arts, Atlanta 35214
Central City Opera House Museum, Central City 35894
Charles B. Goddard Center for Visual and Performing Arts, Ardmore 35145
Circus City Festival Museum, Peru 39334
Circus World Museum, Baraboo 35342
Emmett Kelly Historical Museum, Sedan 40303
Ford's Theatre, Washington 40967
Hampden-Booth Theatre Museum, New York 38880
Hertzberg Circus Museum, San Antonio 40062
Hocking Valley Museum of Theatrical History, Nelsonville 38744
Hollywood Bowl Museum, Los Angeles 38146
International Clown Hall of Fame and Research Center, Milwaukee 38516
The John and Mable Ringling Museum of Art, Sarasota 40217
Marcella Sembrich Opera Museum, Bolton Landing 35565
The Museum of Vision, San Francisco 40118
National Museum of Dance, Saratoga Springs 40224
New York Public Library for the Performing Arts, New York 38926
Palm Springs Desert Museum, Palm Springs 39261
Rose Museum at Carnegie Hall, New York 38933
Tabor Opera House Museum, Leadville 37983
Vent Haven Museum, Fort Mitchell 36932
Visual Arts Center, Portsmouth 39590
Western Gallery, Bellingham 35421
Wexner Center for the Arts, Columbus 36233
Yerba Buena Center for the Arts, San Francisco 40132

Yugoslavia
Muzej Pozorišne Umetnosti, Beograd 41519

Petroleum Industry and Trade

Argentina
Museo Nacional del Petróleo, Comodoro Rivadavia 00273

Australia
Sagasco Historical Group Museum, Brompton 00840

Austria
Erdölmuseum, Neusiedl an der Zaya 02344
Freilichtmuseum Erdöl- und Erdgaslehrpfad, Prottes 02441

Canada
Oil Museum of Canada, Oil Springs 05510
Petrolia Discovery, Petrolia 05595
Ralph Allen Memorial Museum, Oxbow 05561
Turner Valley Gas Plant, Turner Valley 06123

France
Musée du Pétrole, Merkwiller-Pechelbronn 11733

Germany
Deutsches Erdölmuseum, Wietze 19110
ESWE-technicum an der Fasanerie, Wiesbaden 19098
Gaseum, Essen 15652
Heimatstube Hänigsen, Uetze 18783

Hungary
Magyar Olajipari Múzeum, Zalaegerszeg 20078

Netherlands
Tweewielermuseum Tankstop, Workum 25655

Poland
Muzeum Przemysłu Naftowego w Bóbrce, Chorkówka 26667

Romania
Muzeul National al Petrolului, Ploieşti 27626

Switzerland
Öle-Museum, Münsingen 31033

United Kingdom
Aberdeen Maritime Museum, Aberdeen 31978
Biggar Gasworks Museum, Biggar 32240
Carrickfergus Gasworks, Carrickfergus 32546
Fakenham Museum of Gas and Local History, Fakenham 32996
The National Gas Museum Trust, Leicester 33491

U.S.A.
Butler County Museum and Kansas Oil Museum, El Dorado 36660
California Oil Museum, Santa Paula 40210
East Texas Oil Museum at Kilgore College, Kilgore 37800
Historic Pithole City, Pleasantville 39501
Oil Patch Museum, Russell 39890

Pets

Austria
KiK - Kultur im Kloster, Klostermarienberg 02128

Netherlands
Hondenmuseum, Bergeijk 24807
Katten Kabinet, Amsterdam 24700

United Kingdom
Dog Collar Museum, Maidstone 33874

Pewter

Czech Republic
Okresní Muzeum, Mladá Boleslav 07463

France
Musée des Arts et Traditions Populaires du Terroir
Marseillais, Château-Gombert 10015

Germany
Heimatmuseum im Wachtturm, Geyer 15965
Kreismuseum Zons, Dormagen 15367
Torhaus Dölitz, Leipzig 17063
Völkerschlachtdenkmal und Forum 1813, Museum zur
Geschichte der Völkerschlacht, Leipzig 17065
Weygang-Museum, Öhringen 17821

Netherlands
Het Zakkendragershuisje, Rotterdam 25452

Pharmacy

Argentina
Museo de la Farmacia Dra. D'Alessio Bonino, Buenos
Aires 00178

Australia
Medical History Museum, Melbourne 01224

Austria
Destillier- und Drogenmuseum, Pernegg 02388
Grazer Stadtmuseum, Graz 01909

Belgium
Hôpital Notre-Dame de la Rose, Lessines 03530
Museactron, Maaseik 03573

Brazil
Museu Antonio Lago, Rio de Janeiro 04006
Museu da Farmácia, Rio de Janeiro 04018

Canada
Niagara Apothecary, Niagara-on-the-Lake 05466
Saskatchewan Pharmacy Museum, Regina 05714

Cuba
Museo Farmacéutico, Matanzas 07167

Finland
Qwensel ja Apteekkimuseo, Turku 08967

France
Ancienne École de Médecine Navale, Rochefort
(Charente-Maritime) 12783
Musée de la Pharmacie Albert Ciurana,
Montpellier 11904
Musée de Pharmacie, Paris 12373
Musée d'Histoire de la Médecine et de la Pharmacie,
Lyon 11528
Pharmacie-Musée de l'Hôtel Dieu le Comte,
Troyes 13796

Germany
Apotheken-Museum, Schiltach 18335
Apothekenmuseum, Hofgeismar 16459
Bad Schwalbacher Kur-, Stadt- und
Apothekenmuseum, Bad Schwalbach 14514
Deutsches Apotheken-Museum im Heidelberger
Schloß, Heidelberg 16331
Drogerie-Museum, Weißenstadt 19032
Löwen-Drogerie und Museum, Oelsnitz,
Vogtland 17824
Niederlausitzer Apothekenmuseum, Cottbus 15229
Stiftung Kohl'sche Einhorn-Apotheke, Weißenburg in
Bayern 19026

Hungary
Arany Sas Patika, Budapest 19804
Fekete Sas Patikamúzeum, Székesfehérvár 20019
Patikamúzeum, Kőszeg 19935

Italy
Farmacia Conventuale, Venezia 22791
Museo della Farmacia, Parma 22130

Japan
Health Science Museum, Hiroshima 23038
Naito Kinen Kusuri Hakubutsukan, Kawashima,
Gifu 23147

Netherlands
Nederlands Drogisterij Museum, Maarssen 25267

New Zealand
Ernest and Marion Davis Medical History Museum,
Auckland 25722

Norway
Ibsenhuset og Grimstad Bymuseet, Grimstad 26099
Norsk Farmasihistorisk Museum, Oslo 26231

Poland
Muzeum Farmacji, Kraków 26829
Muzeum Historii Medycyny i Farmacji,
Szczecin 27142

Romania
Muzeul de Istorie a Farmaciei Cluj-Napoca, Cluj-
Napoca 27547

Russia
Farmacevtičeskij muzej, Moskva 27812

Slovakia
Farmaceutická Expozícia, Bratislava 28201

Slovenia
Pharmaceutical and Medical Museum of Bohuslav
Lavička, Ljubljana 28352

South Africa
Adler Museum of Medicine, Johannesburg 28501

Spain
Museo Arqueológico y de Historia Natural, Santo
Domingo de Silos 29692
Museo de Farmacia, Llivia 29216
Museo de Farmacia, Peñaranda de Duero 29500
Museo de la Farmacia Hispana, Madrid 29270
Museo Retrospectivo de Farmacia y Medicina, El
Masnou 29338
Museu Farmàcia de l'Hospital de Santa Catarina,
Girona 29099
Real Cartuja, Valldemosa 29867

Sweden
Stranda Hembygdsförening, Mönsterås 30237

Switzerland
Pharmazie-Historisches Museum der Universität
Basel, Basel 30582

United Kingdom
Museum of the Royal Pharmaceutical Society of Great
Britain, London 33726
Pharmaceutical Society Museum, Edinburgh 32939

U.S.A.
New Orleans Pharmacy Museum, New Orleans 38819

Philately → Postage Stamps

Philosophy

Austria
Gsellmanns Weltmaschine, Edelsbach bei
Feldbach 01778
Ludwig Wittgenstein-Dauerausstellung, Kirchberg am
Wechsel 02102
Sigmund Freud-Museum, Wien 02960

Belgium
Maison d'Erasme, Bruxelles 03253

Czech Republic
Památník Jana Ámoše Komenského, Bílá
Tremešná 07237
Památník Jana Ámoše Komenského, Horní
Branná 07343
Památník Jana Ámoše Komenského, Fulnek 07325
Pamětní Síň Jana Ámoše Komenského, Brandýs nad
Orlicí 07247

France
Musée Jean-Jacques Rousseau, Montmorency 11892

Germany
Albert-Schweitzer-Gedenk- und Begegnungsstätte,
Weimar, Thüringen 18982
Deutsches Freimaurermuseum, Bayreuth 14610
Ernst-Bloch-Zentrum, Ludwigshafen am Rhein 17151
Freimaurer-Museum, Berlin 14709
Freimaurermuseum der Großen Landesloge der
Freimaurer von Deutschland, Sankt
Michaelisdonn 18310
Friedrich-Engels-Haus, Wuppertal 19236
Hegelhaus, Stuttgart 18632
Karl-Marx-Haus, Trier 18741
Museum Barockschloß Rammenau,
Rammenau 18054
Nietzsche-Archiv, Weimar, Thüringen 18995
Novalis-Museum, Wiederstedt 19093
Wilhelm-Ostwald-Gedenkstätte, Großbothen 16111

Greece
Theophilos Kairis Museum, Andros 19338

Lebanon
Gibran Museum, Bsharri 24145

Netherlands
Het Spinozahuis, Rijnsburg 25407

Spain
Museo Balmes, Vic 29884

Switzerland
Museum Casa Anatta, Casa Selma und Klarwelt der
Seligen, Ascona 30539
Nietzsche-Haus, Sils in Engadin 31239

Turkey
Ziya Gökalp Müzesi, Diyarbakir 31712

United Kingdom
Museum of Freemasonery, London 33716

U.S.A.
Orchard House - Home of the Alcotts, Concord 36241

Uzbekistan
Memorialnyj Muzej Abu Ali Ibn Sina, Afčona 41354

Photography

Argentina
Museo de la Fotografía, Rafaela 00489
Museo Municipal Histórico Fotográfico de Quilmes,
Quilmes 00488

Australia
Australian Centre for Photography, Paddington 01340
Beatties Historic Photograph Museum, Taroona 01518
Centre for Contemporary Photography, Fitzroy 01011
City Exhibition Space, Sydney 01491
Eric Thomas Galley Museum, Queenstown 01402
Horsham Regional Art Gallery, Horsham 01098
Latrobe Court House Museum, Latrobe 01155
Monash Gallery of Art, Wheelers Hill 01594

Austria
Albertina, Wien 02800
Bild- und Tonarchiv, Graz 01905
Fotoforum, Innsbruck 02057
Oberösterreichische Fotogalerie, Linz 02232
Palais Palffy, Wien 02939
Photomuseum des Landes Oberösterreich, Bad
Ischl 01703

Belgium
Archives et Musée de la Littérature, Bruxelles 03231
Provinciaal Museum voor Fotografie,
Antwerpen 03131

Botswana
Phuthadikobo Museum, Mochudi 03908

Canada
Canadian Museum of Contemporary Photography,
Ottawa 05536
Centre for Art Tapes, Halifax 05006
Photographers Gallery, Saskatoon 05874
Presentation House Gallery, North Vancouver 05493
Saint Marys Museum, Saint Marys 05838
VU Centre de Diffusion et de Production de la
Photographie, Québec 05680

Chile
Sala Sergio Larrain, Santiago 06396

Cuba
Fototeca de Cuba, Habana Vieja 07164

Czech Republic
České Centrum Fotografie, Praha 07549
Uměleckoprůmyslové Muzeum v Praze, Praha 07599

Denmark
Danmarks Fotomuseum, Herning 07853
Museet for Fotokunst, Odense 07997
Det Nationale Fotomuseum, København 07928

Finland
Helsingin Kaupungin taidemuseo, Mejlahti,
Helsinki 08349
Suomen Valokuvataiteen Museo, Helsinki 08388

France
Centre National de la Photographie, Paris 12267
Centre Photographique d'Ile-de-France, Pontault-
Combault 12610
Centre Régional de la Photographie Nord-Pas-de-
Calais, Douchy-les-Mines 10367
Galerie Municipale du Château d'Eau, Toulouse 13722
Musée Adzak, Paris 12314
Musée Arménien de France, Paris 12315
Musée de la Photographie, Mougins 11959
Musée du Centre de Recherches sur les Monuments
Historiques, Paris 12390
Musée Français de la Photographie, Bièvres 09559
Musée Municipal, La Roche-sur-Yon 11026
Musée National des Arts Asiatiques Guimet,
Paris 12428
Pavillon des Arts, Paris 12453

Germany
Agfa Photo-Historama, Köln 16780
Deutsches Film- und Fototechnik Museum,
Deidesheim 15284
Foto-Museum, Essen 15651
Fotogalerie Alte Feuerwache, Mannheim 17242
Fotografie Forum international, Frankfurt am
Main 15738
Fotomuseum im Münchner Stadtmuseum,
München 17468

Haus der Fotografie - Dr. Robert-Gerlich-Museum,
Burghausen, Salzach 15151
Heimatmuseum Glonn, Glonn 15992
Holowood - Holographiemuseum Bamberg,
Bamberg 14580
Industrie- und Filmmuseum Wolfen, Wolfen 19174
Kamera- und Fotomuseum Leipzig, Leipzig 17041
Kunstsammlungen der Ruhr-Universität Bochum,
Bochum 14940
Kupferstich-Kabinett, Dresden 15410
Münchner Stadtmuseum, München 17493
Museum Folkwang Essen, Essen 15659
Museum für Gegenwartskunst Siegen, Siegen 18488
Museum für Photographie, Braunschweig 15037
Museum Galgenhaus, Berlin 14810
Photographisch-optisches Museum,
Biedenkopf 14896
Solinger Fotoforum, Solingen 18525
Städtische Galerie Iserlohn, Iserlohn 16582
Städtische Galerie Schwarzes Kloster, Freiburg im
Breisgau 15815

Hungary
Magyar Fotográfiai Múzeum, Kecskemét 19919

India
Gandhi Museum, Bhavnagar 20168

Italy
Gabinetto Fotografico, Firenze 21589
Istituto di Fotografia Alpina Vittorio Sella, Biella 21167
Museo dell'Immagine, Cesena 21397
Museo di Storia della Fotografia Fratelli Alinari,
Firenze 21615
Museo e Centro di Documentazione Fotografica,
Venezia 22812
Museo Nazionale del Cinema, Torino 22688

Japan
Ken Domon Museum of Photography, Sakata 23460
Kiyosato Museum of Photographic Arts,
Kitakoma 23157
Kushiro Art Museum, Kushiro 23207
Nakagawa Photo Gallery, Kyoto 23255
Nara City Museum of Photography, Nara 23369
Nihon Camera Hakubutsukan, Tokyo 23648
Tokyo-to Shashin Bijutsukan, Tokyo 23694

Lithuania
Photography Museum, Šiauliai 24190

Luxembourg
Musée Municipal, Dudelange 24212
Villa Vauban, Luxembourg 24232

Mexico
Museo de la Fotografía, Pachuca 24495

Netherlands
Huis Marseille, Amsterdam 24697
Museum Kempenland, Eindhoven 25002
Museum Radiotron, Emmen 25016
Nederlands Foto Instituut, Rotterdam 25441
Omroepmuseum en Smalfilmmuseum,
Hilversum 25162
Oudheidkamer/ Museum Mr. Andreae, Kollum 25209
Prentenkabinet der Universiteit Leiden, Leiden 25241
Spaarnestad Fotoarchief, Haarlem 25097
Stedelijk Museum Het Domein, Sittard 25493

New Zealand
Albertland and Districts Museum, Wellsford 25950
City Gallery Wellington, Wellington 25929
Nelson Provincial Museum, Nelson 25843
New Zealand Centre for Photography,
Wellington 25937

Norway
Levanger Museum, Levanger 26163
Norsk Museum for Fotografi - Preus Fotomuseum,
Horten 26122

Poland
Gdańska Galeria Fotografii, Gdańsk 26700
Jadernówka, Mielec 26928
Muzeum Historii Fotografii, Kraków 26832

Russia
Moskovskij Dom Fotografii, Moskva 27851

Slovenia
Arhitekturni Muzej Ljubljana, Ljubljana 28341

South Africa
Bensusan Museum of Photography,
Johannesburg 28504

Spain
Museo de Dibujo Castillo de Larrés,
Sabiñánigo 29588
Museo de Reproducciones Artísticas, Bilbao 28854

Sweden
Bildens Hus, Sundsvall 30406
Erna och Victor Hasselblads Fotografiska Centrum,
Göteborg 30095
Fotomuséet i Osby, Osby 30275
Moderna Museet, Stockholm 30363

Switzerland
Centre de la Photographie Genéve, Genève 30798
Fotogalerie, Bern 30607
Fotomuseum Winterthur, Winterthur 31395
Musée de l'Elysée, Lausanne 30929

Photography (continued)

Museum für Gestaltung Zürich, Zürich 31464
Museum im Bellpark, Kriens 30906

United Kingdom
British Photographic Museum, Totnes 34686
Ferens Art Gallery, Kingston-upon-Hull 33396
Fox Talbot Museum, Lacock 33430
Impressions Gallery of Photography, York 34914
Jersey Photographic Museum, Saint Helier 34376
Kodak Museum, London 33685
National Museum of Photography, Film and Television, Bradford 32353
Nelson Tower, Forres 33035
Open Eye Photography Gallery, Liverpool 33543
Peacock, Aberdeen 31988
Photographers Gallery, London 33746
Postcard Museum, Holmfirth 33282
The Royal Photographic Society Octagon Galleries, Bath 32169
Sutcliffe Gallery, Whitby 34807
Viewpoint Photographic Gallery, Salford 34406
Vintage Museum of Photography, London 33800

U.S.A.
Abrons Arts Center, New York 38831
The African American Museum in Philadelphia, Philadelphia 39357
Agnes Gallery, Birmingham 35506
The Albin O. Kuhn Gallery, Baltimore 35295
Arthur Griffin Center for Photographic Art, Winchester 41231
Baldwin Photographic Gallery, Murfreesboro 38686
Blue Sky, Portland 39566
Burden Gallery, New York 38849
California Museum of Photography, Riverside 39792
Center for Creative Photography, Tucson 40745
Center for Photography at Woodstock, Woodstock 41284
The Friends of Photography at the Ansel Adams Center, San Francisco 40109
High Museum of Art, Folk Art and Photography Galleries, Atlanta 35219
Historical Society of Oak Park and River Forest, Oak Park 39082
International Center of Photography, New York 38886
International Museum of Photography and Film, Rochester 39812
J. Paul Getty Museum, Los Angeles 38148
Japanese American National Museum, Los Angeles 38149
Kirkpatrick Center Museum Complex, Oklahoma City 39135
The Lyons Redstone Museum, Lyons 38224
Main Gallery of Henry Street Settlement, New York 38895
The Museum of Contemporary Photography, Chicago 36032
Museum of Photographic Arts, San Diego 40083
Photographic Investments Gallery, Atlanta 35226
Photographic Resource Center, Boston 35604
Ruddell Gallery, Spearfish 40438
Santa Ana College Art Gallery, Santa Ana 40179
Silver Eye Center for Photography, Pittsburgh 39473
Society for Contemporary Photography, Kansas City 37743
Southeast Museum of Photography, Daytona Beach 36409
Video Museum and Theater, Grass Valley 37224
Visual Arts Museum, New York 38949

Physics

Argentina
Fundación Solar Rietti, Buenos Aires 00142
Museo de Física de la Universidad Nacional de La Plata, La Plata 00381

Belgium
Atomium, Bruxelles 03232
Museum voor de Geschiedenis van de Wetenschappen, Gent 03411

Canada
Ontario Science Centre, Toronto 06075

Germany
Naturkundliche Sammlung, Altusried 14263
Röntgen-Gedächtnisstätte, Würzburg 19227

Israel
Bloomfield Science Museum Jerusalem, Jerusalem 20903

Italy
Domus Galilaeana, Pisa 22212
Museo di Fisica, Bologna 21203
Museo Torricelliano, Faenza 21532
Tempio Voltiano, Como 21463

Poland
Muzeum Marii Skłodowskiej-Curie, Warszawa 27221

Portugal
Museu de Física, Coimbra 27354

United Kingdom
Aberdeen University Natural Philosophy Museum, Aberdeen 31980
Fox Talbot Museum, Lacock 33430
Liverpool Museum, Liverpool 33537
Michael Faraday's Laboratory and Museum, London 33710

U.S.A.
Louisville Science Center, Louisville 38193
Science Discovery Center of Oneonta, Oneonta 39174

Pipes, Tobacco → Tobacco

Plaster Casts

Germany
Abgußsammlung antiker Plastik, Berlin 14670
Gipsformerei, Berlin 14733
Knauf-Museum, Iphofen 16574
Museum Kloster Asbach, Rotthalmünster 18253

India
Government Educational Museum, Deoria 20228

Italy
Gipsoteca Canoviana e Casa del Canova, Possagno 22252
Gipsoteca del Castello Svevo, Bari 21133
Gipsoteca Istituto d'Arte, Firenze 21599
Gipsoteca Libero Andreotti, Pescia 22170

Spain
Museo del Azulejo, Onda 29419
Museo del Castillo de Odna, Onda 29420

Switzerland
Gipsmuseum Oberwiesen, Schleitheim 31205

United Kingdom
House of the Binns, Linlithgow 33525

Uruguay
Museo del Azulejo, Montevideo 34938

Playing Cards

Belgium
Nationaal Museum van de Speelkaart, Turnhout 03787

France
Musée du Vieux Marseille, Marseille 11654

Germany
Deutsches Spielkartenmuseum, Leinfelden-Echterdingen 17017
Schloß- und Spielkartenmuseum, Altenburg, Thüringen 14240

Spain
Museo Fournier de Naipes de Alava, Vitoria-Gasteiz 29935

Police → Criminology

Politics and Government

Argentina
Antiguo Recinto del Congreso Nacional, Buenos Aires 00134
Museo de la Casa de Gobierno, San Miguel de Tucumán 00573
Museo de la Casa Rosada, Buenos Aires 00175
Museo Nuestra Señora de Carrodilla, Luján de Cuyo 00410
Museo Parlamentario, Buenos Aires 00228
Museo Roberto Noble, Buenos Aires 00232

Australia
Chifley Home, Bathurst 00765
Government House, Sydney 01492
Hawke House, Bordertown 00805
Museum of Sydney, Sydney 01500
Old Government House, Belair 00780
Old Government House, Brisbane 00830
Old Parliament House, Parkes 01345
School of Political and Social Inquiry Museum, Clayton 00911
Vaucluse House, Vaucluse 01564

Austria
Zeitreise - Renner Villa Gloggnitz, Gloggnitz 01879

Benin
Musée d'Histoire, Ouidah 03847

Bulgaria
Kašta-muzej Dimităr Blagoev, Sofia 04309
Kašta-muzej Georgi Kirkov, Sofia 04312
Kašta-muzej Laëš Košut, Šumen 04346
Kašta-muzej Vasil Kolarov, Šumen 04349
Muzeen Kat Parva Socialističeska Sbirka, Veliko Tărnovo 04377
Nacionalen Muzej Georgi Dimitrov, Sofia 04325

Canada
Bellevue House National Historic Site, Kingston 05132
Commissariat House, Saint John's 05813
Cossit House Museum, Sydney 05998
Diefenbaker House, Prince Albert 05650
Domaine Cataraqui, Sillery 05925
Government House Museum, Regina 05703
Haliburton House Museum, Windsor, Nova Scotia 06282
John G. Diefenbaker Replica Law Office, Wakaw 06215
Musée Laurier, Victoriaville 06206
Old Government House, Fredericton 04928
Rutherford House, Edmonton 04849
Vancouver Holocaust Education Centre, Vancouver 06169
William Henry Steeves House, Hillsborough 05054

China, People's Republic
Museum at the Site of the First National Congress of the Communist Party of China, Shanghai 06693
Museum of the former Residence of Comrade Mao Zedong at Shaoshan, Shaoshan 06707
Old Zhi National Government, Wuhan 06753
Rongyu Guan, Jiangyin 06606

Colombia
Museo Casa Rafael Núñez, Cartagena 06837
Museo de Arte Colonial, Villa de Leyva 06922

Denmark
Reventlow-Museet Pederstrup, Horslunde 07886

Egypt
Museum of the People's Assambly, Cairo 08223

France
Musée Georges Clemenceau, Paris 12410

Germany
Deutsch-Deutsches Museum Mödlareuth, Töpen 18719
Ehemaliges Reichsparteitagsgelände, Nürnberg 17735
Grenzland-Museum Bad Sachsa, Bad Sachsa 14499
Grenzmuseum, Bad Königshofen 14457
Reichstagsmuseum, Regensburg 18102
Residenz Ellingen, Ellingen, Bayern 15543

Greece
Alexandros Papanastassiou Museum, Levidion 19547

Hungary
Bajcsy-Zsilinszky Emlékmúzeum, Veszprém 20069
Széchenyi Emlékmúzeum, Nagycenk 19951
Szoborpark, Budapest 19859
Vay Adám Múzeum, Vaja 20065

India
Chandradhari Museum, Darbhanga 20197
Gandhi Memorial Museum, Madurai 20350
Gandhi Museum, Bhavnagar 20168
Gandhi Museum, Lucknow 20340
Gandhi Smarak Sangrahalaya, Barrackpur 20160
National Gandhi Museum and Library, Delhi 20216
Netaji Museum, Kolkata 20181
V.K. Krishna Menon Museum and Art Gallery, Kozhikode 20335

Ireland
Avondale House, Rathdrum 20826

Israel
Ben-Gurion House, Tel Aviv 20991

Italy
Domus Mazziniana, Pisa 22213

Japan
Gaimusho, Gaiko Shiryokan, Tokyo 23598
Osaka Human Rights Museum, Osaka 23431
Parliamentary Memorial Museum, Tokyo 23660

Malaysia
Tuan Yang Terutama Yang di-Pertua Negeri, Melaka 24326

Mexico
Casa de Juárez, Oaxaca 24490
Museo Legislativo, México 24456

Netherlands
Oud Raadhuis, Beek en Donk 24794
Theo Thijssen Museum, Amsterdam 24739

Philippines
Carlos P. Garcia Memorabilia, Manila 26549
Quezon Memorial Shrine, Quezon City 26587
Rizal Shrine, Intramuros 26531

Poland
Muzeum Hymnu Narodowego, Nowy Barkoczyn 26957

Puerto Rico
Casa Blanca Museum, San Juan 27462
Luis Muñoz Rivera Museum, Barranquitas 27453

Russia
Centralnyj Muzej MVD Rossii, Moskva 27795
Podpolnaja Tipografija CK RSDRP, Moskva 27933

South Africa
Goetz/Fleischack Museum, Potchefstroom 28570
Kruger Museum, Pretoria 28581
President Pretorius Museum, Potchefstroom 28572
Rhodes Cottage Museum, Muizenberg 28549

Spain
Casa-Museo León y Castillo, Telde 29754
Museo Documental, Guernica y Luno 29134
Museo Histórico de la Administración Española, Alcalá de Henares 28666

Sri Lanka
Bandaranaike Museum, Colombo 29979

Turkey
Anitkabir Müzesi, Ankara 31660
Atatürk Evi, Trabzon 31845
Atatürk Müzesi, Bursa 31692
Atatürk Müzesi, Diyarbakir 31708
Atatürk Müzesi, İzmir 31765
Atatürk Müzesi, Konya 31787
Atatürk Müzesi, Samsun 31823
Atatürk ve Etnografya Müzesi, Akşehir 31652
Ataürk Müzesi, Şişli 31834
Dolmabahçe Palace, İstanbul 31750
Eskişehir Atatürk ve Kültür Müzesi, Eskişehir 31724

United Kingdom
Arthur Cottage, Ballymena 32117
Ballance House, Glenavy 33104
Benjamin Franklin House, London 33590
Cabinet War Rooms, London 33604
Chartwell House, Chartwell 32573
Commonwealth Institute, London 33620
Cromwell Museum, Huntingdon 33304
Greenhill Covenanter's House, Biggar 32244
Hughenden Manor, High Wycombe 33270
Lloyd George Museum and Highgate, Llanystumdwy 33572
Milton's Cottage, Chalfont Saint Giles 32567
Old House of Keys, Castletown 32557
Pankhurst Centre, Manchester 33898
Rhodes Memorial Museum and Commonwealth Centre, Bishop's Stortford 32289
War and Peace Exhibition, Oban 34111
Washington Old Hall, Washington, Tyne and Wear 34758
Wellington Museum, London 33805

U.S.A.
Andrew Johnson National Historic Site, Greeneville 37244
First Territorial Capitol of Kansas, Fort Riley 36952
Franklin D. Roosevelt Library-Museum, Hyde Park 37565
Georgia Capitol Museum, Atlanta 35216
Historical Society of Quincy and Adams County Museum, Quincy 39663
Humphrey Forum, Minneapolis 38533
McConnell Mansion, Moscow 38645
Meadow Garden, Augusta 35247
Museum of American Political Life, West Hartford 41107
Old South Meeting House, Boston 35601
Sewall-Belmont House, Washington 40997
The White House, Washington 41012
Woodrow Wilson Birthplace and Museum, Staunton 40505

Yugoslavia
Muzej Istorije Jugoslavije, Beograd 41515

Porcelain and Ceramics

Australia
Colac Otway Shire Hammerton Bottle Collection, Colac 00922
Devonport Gallery and Arts Centre, Devonport 00964
Erica Underwood Gallery, Bentley 00787
Fusions Gallery, Fortitude Valley 01017
National Museum of Australian Pottery, Wodonga 01606
Northcote Pottery, Thornbury 01532
Orange Regional Gallery, Orange 01336
Shepparton Art Gallery, Shepparton 01449

Austria
Mühlviertler Keramikwerkstätte Hafnerhaus, Leopoldschlag 02207
Novum Forum, Neumarkt in Steiermark 02339
Schloß Weyer, Gmunden 01892
Sommerhuber-Kachelofenmuseum, Steyr 02663
Töpfermuseum, Stoob 02675
Wiener Porzellanmanufaktur Augarten, Wien 02973
Zsolnay-Keramik-Porzellan-Museum, Potzneusiedl 02423

Cleveland Crafts Centre, Middlesbrough 33944
Clifton Park Museum, Rotherham 34327
Coalport China Museum, Coalport 32642
Collection of Martinware Pottery, Southall 34509
Croydon Museum, Croydon 32770
De Morgan Centre, London 33626
Gladstone Pottery Museum, Stoke-on-Trent 34577
Glynn Vivian Art Gallery, Swansea 34626
Goss and Crested China Centre, Horndean 33288
Guildford House Gallery, Guildford 33167
Guildhall Museum, Carlisle 32538
Harlow Museum, Harlow 33193
Hastings Museum and Art Gallery, Hastings 33212
Hull University Art Collection, Kingston-upon-Hull 33400
Jackfield Tile Museum, Jackfield 33346
Kirkcaldy Museum and Art Gallery, Kirkcaldy 33412
Martinware Pottery Collection, London 33707
Melrose Abbey Museum, Melrose 33929
Mill Green Museum and Mill, Hatfield 33216
Museum of the Royal Pharmaceutical Society of Great Britain, London 33726
Museum of Worcester Porcelain, Worcester 34883
Nantgarw China Works Museum, Nantgarw 33995
Percival David Foundation of Chinese Art, London 33744
Peter Scott Gallery, Lancaster 33438
Pitshanger Manor and Gallery, London 33747
The Potteries Museum and Art Gallery, Stoke-on-Trent 34579
Raby Castle, Darlington 32738
Roman Villa Museum at Bignor, Bignor 32247
Royal Crown Derby Museum, Derby 32760
School of Art Gallery and Museum, Aberystwyth 32003
Sherborne Castle, Sherborne 34467
Sion Hill Hall, Thirsk 34662
Sir Henry Doulton Gallery, Stoke-on-Trent 34580
Spode Museum, Stoke-on-Trent 34581
Sunderland Museum and Art Gallery, Sunderland 34618
Upton House, Banbury 32125
Wedgwood Museum, Stoke-on-Trent 34582
Wisbech and Fenland Museum, Wisbech 34859

U.S.A.
A.L. Fetterman Educational Museum, Fort Valley 36969
Central Iowa Art Museum, Marshalltown 38366
China Institute Gallery, New York 38856
The Jones Museum of Glass and Ceramics, Sebago 40297
Museum of Ceramics at East Liverpool, East Liverpool 36619
National Museum of Ceramic Art and Glass, Baltimore 35327
Pewabic Pottery Museum, Detroit 36513
The Ross C. Purdy Museum of Ceramics, Westerville 41133
The Scein-Joseph International Museum of Ceramic Art, Alfred 35046
The World Organization of China Painters, Oklahoma City 39145

Portraits

Denmark
Det Nationalhistoriske Museum på Frederiksborg, Hillerød 07859

Germany
Burg Hohenzollern, Bisingen 14915
Stiftung Schloß Eutin, Eutin 15683

Italy
Quadreria Comunale, Prato 22265

Netherlands
Hofje Van Gratie, Delft 24880
Occo Hofje, Amsterdam 24723

New Zealand
New Zealand Portrait Gallery, Wellington 25938

Spain
Galerie de Catalans Illustres, Barcelona 28782

Sweden
Svenska Statens Porträttsamling, Mariefred 30232

United Kingdom
Beningbrough Hall, York 34910
The Blairs Museum, Aberdeen 31982
Bodelwyddan Castle Museum, Bodelwyddan 32312
Collection of Portraits and Performance History, London 33618
Djanogly Art Gallery, Nottingham 34093
Fyvie Castle, Fyvie 33048
Goodwood House, Chichester 32609
National Portrait Gallery, London 33734
Parham Elizabethan House Gardens, Pulborough 34257
Scottish National Portrait Gallery, Edinburgh 32949

U.S.A.
The Gilbert Stuart Museum, Saunderstown 40234
John Jay Homestead, Katonah 37749

Redwood Library and Athenaeum, Newport 38986

Yugoslavia
Zbirka Eparhije Banatski, Vršac 41643

Postage Stamps

Brazil
Museu Numismático e Filatélico, Rio de Janeiro 04066

Canada
Musée Canadien de la Poste, Outaouais 05065

China, People's Republic
China Stamp Museum, Beijing 06438

Cuba
Museo Postal Cubano, La Habana 07161

Egypt
Postal Museum, Cairo 08230

France
Musée de la Poste, Paris 12347

Germany
Archiv für Philatelie der Museumsstiftung Post und Telekommunikation, Bonn 14969
Berliner Hundemuseum, Ostseebad Binz 17897
Briefmarkenmuseum im Kloster Bardel, Bad Bentheim 14387

Greece
Tahydromiko Moyseio, Athinai 19419

Hungary
Bélyegmúzeum, Budapest 19809

India
National Philatelic Museum, Delhi 20219

Iran
Museum of Post and Telecomunication Mokhaberat, Teheran 20653

Italy
Gabinetto delle Stampe, Roma 22334
Gabinetto Stampe e Disegni, Venezia 22792
Museo della Stampa, Soncino 22591

Japan
Kitte no Hakubutsukan, Tokyo 23617

Liechtenstein
Postmuseum des Fürstentums Liechtenstein, Vaduz 24178

Monaco
Musée des Timbres et des Monnaies, Monaco 24532

Norway
Postmuseet, Oslo 26241

San Marino
Museo Postale, Filatelico-Numismatico, San Marino 28155

Spain
Museo Postal y Telegráfico, Madrid 29293

Switzerland
Philatelistisches Museum der Vereinten Nationen, Genève 30822

U.S.A.
National Postal Museum, Washington 40991
Spellman Museum of Stamps and Postal History, Weston 41144

Zambia
National Archives of Zambia, Lusaka 41653

Postal Services

Andorra
Museu Postal d'Andorra, Ordino 00075

Argentina
Museo de Telecomunicaciones, Buenos Aires 00187
Museo Postal y Telegráfico Doctor Ramon J. Carcano, Buenos Aires 00231

Australia
Telstra Museum Brisbane, Clayfield 00909
Wireless Hill Telecommunications Museum, Applecross 00734

Belgium
Musée Postal, Bruxelles 03302

Botswana
Postal Museum Botswana, Gaborone 03906

Brazil
Museu do Telephone, Rio de Janeiro 04049
São Paulo Telephone Museum, São Paulo 04120

Canada
Bell Canada Telephone Historical Collection, Montréal 05356
Maison de la Poste, Montréal 05374
Musée Canadien de la Poste, Outaouais 05065
Poste de Traite Chauvin, Tadoussac 06005
Ross House Museum, Winnipeg 06315
Telephone Historical Collection, Halifax 05021
Telephone Pioneer Museum, Saint John 05808
Telorama, Regina 05717
Toronto's First Post Office, Toronto 06096

China, People's Republic
Beijing Telephone History Museum, Donghuang 06524

China, Republic
Postal Museum, Taipei 06824

Colombia
Museo Filatélico del Banco de la República, Medellín 06860

Croatia
Hrvatski Muzej Pošte i Telekomunikacija, Zagreb 07105

Czech Republic
Poštovní Muzeum, Praha 07593
Poštovní Muzeum, Vyšší Brod 07717

Denmark
Post Tele Museum, København 07932
Telefonmuseet, Hellerup 07845

Finland
Postimuseo, Helsinki 08374

France
Musée de la Diligence, Riquewihr 12761
Musée de la Poste, Paris 12347
Musée de la Poste des Pays de Loire, Nantes 12036
Musée d'Histoire des PTT d'Alsace, Riquewihr 12762
Musée Postal du Relais Henri IV, Saint-Macaire 13116

Germany
Museum für Kommunikation Berlin, Berlin 14805
Museum für Kommunikation Frankfurt, Frankfurt am Main 15761
Museum für Kommunikation Hamburg, Hamburg 16234
Museum für Kommunikation Nürnberg, Nürnberg 17750
Museumsstiftung Post und Telekommunikation, Bonn 14988
Philipp-Reis-Gedächtnisstätte, Friedrichsdorf, Taunus 15843
Postmuseum Rheinhausen, Oberhausen-Rheinhausen 17772
Telefonmuseum Hittfelder Bahnhof, Seevetal 18466

Greece
Museum of Telecommunications, Néa Kifissia 19592

Hungary
Postamúzeum, Balatonszemes 19793
Postamúzeum, Budapest 19854

Iran
Museum of Post and Telecomunication Mokhaberat, Teheran 20653

Italy
Museo Storico delle Poste e Telecomunicazioni, Roma 22416

Korea, Republic
Postal Museum, Seoul 23945

Latvia
Lattelekom Muzejs, Rīga 24071

Luxembourg
Musée des Postes et Telecommunications, Luxembourg 24225

Malawi
Mtengatenga Postal Museum, Namaka 24276

Mauritius
Mauritius Postal Museum, Port Louis 24379

Mexico
Museo de las Telecomunicaciones, México 24444
Museo Postal, México 24473

Morocco
Musée Postal, Rabat 24566

Netherlands
Museum Radiotron, Emmen 25016
Museum voor Communicatie, Den Haag 24915

New Zealand
New Zealand Post Collection Museum, Wellington 25939

Norway
Kjerringøy Gamle Handelssted, Bodø 26044

Peru
Museo Postal y Filatélico de Correos del Perú, Lima 26506

Poland
Muzeum Poczty i Telekomunikacji, Wrocław 27287

Muzeum Poczty i Telekomunikacji Oddział w Gdańsku, Gdańsk 26706

Portugal
Museu das Comunicações, Lisboa 27389

Russia
Centralnyj Muzej Svjazi im. A.S. Popova, Sankt-Peterburg 28018

South Africa
Stampwise Info Square, Pretoria 28597

Spain
Museo Postal y Telegráfico, Madrid 29293
Museu Gabinet Postal, Barcelona 28819

Sweden
Postal Museum, Stockholm 30374

Switzerland
Musée des Téléphones de Genève, Plan-les-Ouates 31094
Museum für Kommunikation, Bern 30612
Telefonmuseum im Greuterhof, Islikon 30884

Tunisia
Musée Postal, Tunis 31642

United Kingdom
Bath Postal Museum, Bath 32156
British Telecom Museum, Oxford 34129
Heritage Services Consignia, London 33667
IBTE Museum of Telecommunication, Worksop 34887
Museum of Communication, Bo'ness 32329
National Wireless Museum, Seaview 34438
Timeball Tower, Deal 32750

U.S.A.
Arkansas Post National Memorial, Gillett 37132
Fort Leavenworth Historical Museum and Post Museum, Fort Leavenworth 36919
National Postal Museum, Washington 40991
Spellman Museum of Stamps and Postal History, Weston 41144

Yugoslavia
PTT Muzej Zajednice Jugoslovenskih Pošta, Telegrafa i Telefona, Beograd 41527

Posters

Finland
Julistemuseo, Lahti 08581

Germany
Kleines Plakatmuseum, Bayreuth 14619
Puppentheatermuseum, Kaufbeuren 16698

Pottery, Earthenware → Porcelain and Ceramics

Precious Stones

Argentina
Museo de Mineralogía y Geología Dr. Alfredo Stelzner, Córdoba 00288

Australia
Australian Pearling Exhibition, Darwin 00958
Berlins Gem and Historical Museum, South Nanango 01459
Griffith Regional Art Gallery, Griffith 01062
Kealley's Gemstone Museum, Nannup 01291
Opal and Gem Museum, Ballina 00757
Port Stephens Shell Museum, Corlette 00933

Austria
Perlmuttdrechslerei, Riegersburg, Niederösterreich 02495
Schmuckmuseum Gablonzer Industrie, Enns 01809
Swarovski Kristallwelten, Wattens 02767

Belgium
Diamantmuseum, Grobbendonk 03431
Musée Curtius, Liège 03542
Provinciaal Diamantmuseum, Antwerpen 03129

Brazil
Museu Amsterdam Suer de Pedras Preciosas, Rio de Janeiro 04004
Museu do Diamante, Diamantina 03931
Museu H. Stern, Rio de Janeiro 04054

Costa Rica
Museo de Jade, San José 06945

Croatia
Etnografski Muzej Split, Split 07070

Cyprus
Cyprus Jewellers Museum, Nicosia 07204

Czech Republic
Městské Muzeum Klenotnice, Nová Paka 07483
Muzeum Českého Ráje, Turnov 07677

Egypt
Palace of Royal Jewelleries, Zizinia 08258

Finland
Jalokivi Galleria, Kemi 08486

France
Musée Minal, Héricourt 10811

Germany
Deutsches Edelsteinmuseum, Idar-Oberstein 16540
Grünes Gewölbe, Dresden 15404
Kristallmuseum Riedenburg, Riedenburg 18168
Museum Idar-Oberstein, Idar-Oberstein 16541
Technisches Museum der Pforzheimer Schmuck- und Uhrenindustrie, Pforzheim 17977

Greece
Gouriotis Collection, Lárissa 19544
Ilias Lalaounis Jewelry Museum, Athinai 19383
Mouseio Kompologiou, Nafplion 19585

Iran
Javaherat, Teheran 20649

Israel
Harry Oppenheimer Diamond Museum, Ramat Gan 20978

Jordan
Jordan Folklore and Jewelry Museum, Amman 23797

Morocco
Musée des Oudaïa, Rabat 24564

Netherlands
Edelsteenslijperij de Steenarend, Eindhoven 24999
Museum voor Moderne Kunst, Arnhem 24769

Poland
Muzeum Kamieni Szlachetnych, Polanica Zdrój 27010

Russia
Almaznyj fond, Moskva 27788

Sweden
Porfyrmuseet, Älvdalen 30015

Switzerland
Musée de l'Horlogerie et de l'Emaillerie, Genève 30811

United Kingdom
The Crypt - Town Hall Plate Room, Oxford 34132
Her Majesty Tower of London, London 33666
Jewellery Quarter Discovery Centre, Birmingham 32271
Town and Crown Exhibition, Windsor 34856

U.S.A.
The Bead Museum, Prescott 39604
Crater of Diamonds State Park Museum, Murfreesboro 38683

Prehistory and Early History

Argentina
Museo Municipal C.I.P.A.S., Salto 00536
Museo Paleontológico, Arqueológico e Histórico de la Ciudad de Deán Funes, Deán Funes 00318
Museo Paleontológico Egidio Feruglio, Trelew 00630

Australia
Hawkesbury Museum, Windsor 01603

Austria
Archäologisches Museum, Globasnitz 01874
Archiv für die Waldviertler Urgeschichtsforschung, Horn 02043
Ateliersammlung Herbert Hiesmayr, Sankt Thomas am Blasenstein 02584
Ausgrabungsdokumentation 6000 Jahre Wohnberg Oberleis, Ernstbrunn 01811
Burgmuseum für Vor- und Frühgeschichte, Deutschlandsberg 01756
Grenzlandmuseum Raabs an der Thaya, Raabs an der Thaya 02455
Heimatmuseum Steyregg, Steyregg 02666
Höbarth- und Madermuseum der Stadt Horn, Horn 02044
Keltenmuseum, Hallein 01992
Kulturerbe Hallstatt, Hallstatt 01996
Museum für Frühgeschichte des Landes Niederösterreich, Traismauer 02705
Museum für Ur- und Frühgeschichte, Stillfried 02669
Museum für Ur- und Frühgeschichte, Wieselburg an der Erlauf 02992
Museum für Urgeschichte, Koblach 02135
Museum für Urgeschichte des Landes Niederösterreich, Asparn an der Zaya 01680
Museum Großklein, Großklein 01952
Österreichisches Felsbildermuseum, Spital am Pyhrn 02643
Salzburger Museum Carolino Augusteum, Salzburg 02531
Stadtmuseum Wiener Neustadt, Wiener Neustadt 02988
Tiroler Landesmuseum Ferdinandeum, Innsbruck 02074
Ur- und frühgeschichtliche Eisenindustrie im Bezirk Oberpullendorf - Schauraum, Oberpullendorf 02361
Urgeschichtliche Sammlung, Engerwitzdorf 01807
Urzeitmuseum Nußdorf ob der Traisen, Traismauer 02706

Belgium
Archeologisch Museum van de Universiteit, Gent 03398
Domus Romana, Aubechies 03152
Heemkundig Museum Slag van Lafelt, Vlijtingen 03804
Musée Archéologique Régional d'Orp-le-Grand, Orp-le-Grand 03650
Musée de la Préhistoire, Gesves 03426
Musée de la Préhistoire en Wallonie, Flémalle 03384
Musée d'Ourthe-Ambléve, Comblain-au-Pont 03324
Musée Historique et Préhistorique Van den Steen, Jehay-Amay 03498
Musée Régional d'Histoire et d'Archéologie, Visé 03803
Ondergronds Museum, Kanne 03503
Voorhistorisch Museum, Zonhoven 03837

Brazil
Museu de Arqueologia e Artes Populares, Paranaguá 03969

Bulgaria
Earth and Man Museum, Sofia 04306

Canada
MacBride Museum, Whitehorse 06266
Musée d'Archéologie de l'Université du Québec à Trois-Rivières, Trois-Rivières 06115
Musée d'Histoire et d'Archéologie, La Sarre 05172
Powell River Historical Museum, Powell River 05645

China, People's Republic
Regional Museum, Xinhui 06782

Congo, Democratic Republic
Musée de Préhistoire, Kinshasa 06929

Croatia
Arheološki Muzej Zagreb, Zagreb 07097

Czech Republic
Archeologické Pracoviště, Opava 07501
Melicharovo Městské Muzeum, Unhošt 07683
Regionální Muzeum K.A. Polánka, Žatec 07720

Denmark
Esbjerg Museum, Esbjerg 07793
Haderslev Museum, Haderslev 07835
Hollufgård - Arkeologi og Landskab, Odense 07995
Moesgård Museum, Højbjerg 07866
Ringkøbing Museum, Ringkøbing 08015
Skive Museum, Skive 08045
Skjern-Egvad Museum, Skjern 08049
Søllerød Museum, Holte 07877
Vesthimmerlands Museum, Års 07759

Egypt
National Museum for Civilization, Cairo 08226

Equatorial Guinea
Museo Etnológico Misional C.M.F., Santa Isabel 08261

Finland
Ålands Museum, Mariehamn 08657

France
Ecomusée des Traditions et Arts Populaires, Esse 10459
Exposition de la Préhistoire, Mazières-en-Mauges 11696
Musée Archéologique, Martizay 11670
Musée d'Art et d'Histoire, Saint-Antonin-Noble-Val 12902
Musée de la Pierre à Fusil, Meusnes 11749
Musée de la Préhistoire, Les Matelles 11330
Musée de la Préhistoire à Saint-Guenole, Penmarch 12485
Musée de l'Avallonnais, Avallon 09352
Musée de Paléontologie Humaine de Terra Amata, Nice 12099
Musée de Préhistoire, Aurignac 09318
Musée de Préhistoire, Cabrerets 09787
Musée de Préhistoire d'Île-de-France, Nemours 12064
Musée de Préhistoire James Miln-Zacharie le Rouzic, Carnac 09872
Musée de Préhistoire Régionale, Menton 11722
Musée Départemental Breton, Quimper 12688
Musée Départemental de la Préhistoire, Le Grand-Pressigny 11208
Musée Départemental de Préhistoire, Solutré-Pouilly 13546
Musée du Vieil Auvillar, Auvillar 09337
Musée Municipal de Préhistoire, Roquefort-sur-Soulzon 12814
Musée Municipal des Beaux Arts et d'Histoire Naturelle, Châteaudun 10026
Musée National de Préhistoire, Les Eyzies-de-Tayac-Sireuil 11323
Musée Préhistorique, Le Mas-d'Azil 11230
Musée Sundgauvien, Altkirch 09129
Parc de Préhistoire de Bretagne, Malansac 11564

Germany
Altmärkisches Museum, Stendal 18594
Archäologische Staatssammlung München, München 17451
Archäologisches Landesmuseum, Wünsdorf 19212
Archäologisches Museum des Historischen Vereins für Oberfranken, Bayreuth 14608
Archäologisches Museum Neu-Ulm, Neu-Ulm 17612
Archäologisches Zentrum Hitzacker, Hitzacker 16437
Audorfer Museum im Burgtor, Oberaudorf 17766
Austellung zur Erd- und Vorgeschichte, Breitscheid, Hessen 15049
Bachmann-Museum, Bremervörde 15079
Braith-Mali-Museum, Biberach an der Riß 14886
Braunschweigisches Landesmuseum, Wolfenbüttel 19175
Dischinger Heimatmuseum, Dischingen 15345
Dr.-Carl-Haeberlin-Friesen-Museum, Wyk auf Föhr 19252
Ehemalige Erzbischöfliche Kanzlei, Bremervörde 15081
Felix-Nussbaum-Haus, Osnabrück 17872
Festungsanlage-Museum Senftenberg, Senftenberg 18478
Geschichtlich-heimatkundliche Sammlung, Aschheim 14327
Goldberg-Museum, Riesbürg 18178
Haffmuseum Ueckermünde, Ueckermünde 18778
Heimat- und Handfeuerwaffenmuseum, Kemnath 16710
Heimat- und Torfmuseum, Gröbenzell 16095
Heimatmuseum, Allensbach 14222
Heimatmuseum, Camburg 15180
Heimatmuseum, Grabow, Mecklenburg 16052
Heimatmuseum, Prieros 18026
Heimatmuseum Blaubeuren, Blaubeuren 14924
Heimatmuseum der Stadt Rerik, Ostseebad Rerik 17906
Heimatmuseum Ebersbach in der Humboldt-Baude, Ebersbach, Sachsen 15483
Heimatmuseum Garbsen, Garbsen 15893
Heimatmuseum Gensungen, Felsberg 15695
Heimatmuseum Maßbach, Maßbach 17292
Heimatmuseum Osterhofen, Osterhofen 17886
Heimatmuseum Riedlingen, Riedlingen 18170
Heimatmuseum Uelzen mit Gläsersammlung Röver, Uelzen 18779
Helms-Museum, Hamburg 16220
Herborner Heimatmuseum, Herborn, Hessen 16382
Hürten-Heimatmuseum, Bad Münstereifel 14476
Jesuitenkolleg, Mindelheim 17368
Karl-Wagenplast-Museum, Schwaigern 18413
Kreisheimatmuseum Weißes Haus, Rotenburg an der Fulda 18232
Kulturgeschichtliches Museum Osnabrück, Osnabrück 17874
Kulturhistorisches Museum Schloß Merseburg, Merseburg 17341
Landesmuseum für Natur und Mensch, Oldenburg, Oldenburg 17850
Landesmuseum für Vorgeschichte, Dresden 15411
Landesmuseum für Vorgeschichte Sachsen-Anhalt, Halle, Saale 16192
Lobdengau-Museum, Ladenburg 16926
Ludwig-Roselius-Museum für Ur- und Frühgeschichte, Worpswede 19208
Museum Alzey, Alzey 14265
Museum Burg Eisenhardt, Belzig 14638
Museum Burg Ranis, Ranis 18056
Museum der Stadt Lauffen am Neckar, Lauffen am Neckar 16998
Museum der Stadt Schkeuditz, Schkeuditz 18340
Museum der Stadt Wolgast, Wolgast 19190
Museum des Ohrekreises, Wolmirstedt 19193
Museum für die Archäologie des Eiszeitalters, Neuwied 17686
Museum für Dithmarscher Vorgeschichte, Heide, Holstein 16327
Museum für Naturkunde des Zittauer Landes, Zittau 19284
Museum für Naturkunde und Vorgeschichte, Dessau 15302
Museum für Ur- und Frühgeschichte, Freiburg im Breisgau 15814
Museum für Ur- und Frühgeschichte, Eichstätt 15520
Museum für Ur- und Frühgeschichte Thüringens, Weimar, Thüringen 18993
Museum für Vor- und Frühgeschichte, Egeln 15496
Museum für Vor- und Frühgeschichte, Gunzenhausen 16146
Museum für Vor- und Frühgeschichte, Langenau, Württemberg 16969
Museum für Vor- und Frühgeschichte, Berlin 14809
Museum für Vor- und Frühgeschichte, Saarbrücken 18283
Museum für Vor- und Frühgeschichte - Archäologisches Museum, Frankfurt am Main 15766
Museum im Kräuterkasten, Albstadt 14208
Museum im Marstall, Winsen, Luhe 19138
Museum im Vorderen Schloss, Mühlheim an der Donau 17437
Museum Reichenfels, Hohenleuben 16473
Museum Schloss Hellenstein, Heidenheim an der Brenz 16349
Museum Schloß Klippenstein, Radeberg 18041
Museum Schloß Moritzburg, Zeitz, Elster 19262
Museumsdorf Düppel, Berlin 14817
Niederbayerisches Vorgeschichtsmuseum, Landau an der Isar 16942
Niedersächsisches Landesmuseum Hannover, Hannover 16280
Oderlandmuseum, Bad Freienwalde 14430
Peter-Wiepert-Museum, Burg auf Fehmarn 15142
Pfahlbaumuseum Unteruhldingen, Uhldingen-Mühlhofen 18787
Prähistorische Siedlung Pestenacker, Weil am Lech 18961
Prähistorisches Heimatmuseum, Veringenstadt 18832
Quadrat Bottrop, Bottrop 15006
Rheinisches Landesmuseum Trier, Trier 18743
Roemer- und Pelizaeus-Museum, Hildesheim 16426
Römermuseum Kastell Boiotro, Passau 17948
Römermuseum Weißenburg, Weißenburg in Bayern 19023
Römisch-Germanisches Zentralmuseum, Mainz 17236
Römische Villa Rustica Möckenlohe, Adelschlag 14184
Sammlung Irmgard Friedl, Griesbach im Rottal 16086
Sammlung Vor- und Frühgeschichte und Völkerkunde, Gießen 15975
Schloßmuseum, Quedlinburg 18038
Schloßmuseum Neuburg, Neuburg an der Donau 17623
Siegerlandmuseum mit Ausstellungsforum Haus Oranienstraße, Siegen 18489
Spengler-Museum, Sangerhausen 18300
Spreewald-Museum Lübbenau/Lehde, Lübbenau 17163
Stadtmuseum Erlangen, Erlangen 15626
Stadtmuseum Mutzschen, Mutzschen 17573
Stadtmuseum Tharandt, Tharandt 18705
Städtisches Heimatmuseum, Taucha bei Leipzig 18682
Städtisches Museum, Bad Reichenhall 14495
Städtisches Museum Ludwigsburg, Ludwigsburg, Württemberg 17148
Städtisches Zentrum für Geschichte und Kunst, Riesa 18177
Steinsburg-Museum, Römhild 18201
Steinzeitmuseum, Korb 16853
Südschwäbisches Vorgeschichtsmuseum im Jesuitenkolleg, Mindelheim 17371
Uffenheimer Gollachgaumuseum, Uffenheim 18784
Ulmer Museum, Ulm 18792
Ur- und Frühgeschichtliche Sammlung, Erlangen 15628
Urgeschichtliches Museum, Blaubeuren 14927
Volkskundemuseum, Schönberg, Mecklenburg 18374
Vonderau-Museum, Fulda 15876
Vor- und Frühgeschichte Sammlung, Kassel 16688
Vor- und Frühgeschichtliches Museum, Thalmässing 18703
Vorgeschichtsmuseum der Oberpfalz, Amberg, Oberpfalz 14267
Vorgeschichtsmuseum im Grabfeldgau, Bad Königshofen 14458

Greece
Archeological Collection, Liknades 19548
Archeological Collection, Maroneia 19557
Archeological Collection, Siatista 19649
Museum of Atlantis, Athinai 19401

Guinea
Musée Annexe de Kissidougou, Kissidougou 19764
Musée Annexe de Youkounkoun, Youkounkoun 19767
Musée National de Conakry, Conakry 19763

Hungary
Vértesszőllősi Bemutatóhelye, Vértesszőllős 20068

India
Archaeological Museum, Pune 20392
Archaeological Museum, Udaipur 20435
Archaeology Museum, Allahabad 20144
Baripada Museum, Baripada 20159
University Museum of Science and Culture, Aligarh 20142

Israel
Bet Gordon, Deganya Aleph 20873
Huleh Valley Regional Prehistoric Museum, Ma'ayan Barukh 20964
Museum of Prehistory, Jerusalem 20923
Museum of Prehistory, Sha'ar Hagolan 20986

Italy
Antiquarium Forense, Roma 22327
Centro Camuno di Studi Preistorici, Capo di Ponte 21303
Centro di Studi Preistorici ed Archeologici, Varese 22778
Civiche Raccolte Archeologiche e Numismatiche di Milano, Milano 21893
Istituto Italiano di Paleontologia Umana, Roma 22346
Mercati Dr. Traiano, Roma 22349
Museo Archeologico Eoliano, Lipari 21789
Museo Archeologico G. Moretti, San Severino Marche 22502
Museo Archeologico Romano, Isernia 21753
Museo Archeologico Statale, Ascoli Piceno 21099
Museo Archeologico U. Granafei, Mesagne 21884
Museo Civico, Erba 21518
Museo Civico, Mazara del Vallo 21871
Museo Civico, Sassoferrato 22548
Museo Civico, Termini Imerese 22637

Press → Mass Media

Printing

Prints → Graphic Arts

Prisons → Criminology

Puppets → Dolls and Puppets

Radio → Mass Media

Railroads

Rare Books → Books, Book Art and Manuscripts

Religious Art and Symbolism

Museo della Propositura di San Pietro, Montecatini Terme e Tettuccio 21981
Museo delle Cripte, Poggiardo 22226
Museo dell'Opera del Duomo, Perugia 22157
Museo di Arte Religiosa, Oleggio 22065
Museo di Arte Sacra, Ponzone 22241
Museo di Arte Sacra, San Gimignano 22480
Museo di Arte Sacra e Tempietto Robbiano, Montevarchi 21996
Museo di San Domenico, Bologna 21206
Museo di San Petronio, Bologna 21208
Museo di Santa Maria di Castello, Genova 21697
Museo di Sant'Antonino, Piacenza 22182
Museo Diocesano, Acerenza 21024
Museo Diocesano, Albenga 21046
Museo Diocesano, Andria 21065
Museo Diocesano, Arezzo 21084
Museo Diocesano, Ascoli Piceno 21101
Museo Diocesano, Bari 21137
Museo Diocesano, Bitonto 21174
Museo Diocesano, Cassano Ionio 21332
Museo Diocesano, Empoli 21514
Museo Diocesano, Gubbio 21729
Museo Diocesano, Imola 21743
Museo Diocesano, L'Aquila 21770
Museo Diocesano, Mantova 21845
Museo Diocesano, Mazara del Vallo 21872
Museo Diocesano, Montalcino 21975
Museo Diocesano, Piazza Armerina 22188
Museo Diocesano, Pistoia 22221
Museo Diocesano, Recanati 22294
Museo Diocesano, Rossano 22437
Museo Diocesano, Trani 22707
Museo Diocesano, Velletri 22786
Museo Diocesano Antonio Bergamaschi, Pennabilli 22148
Museo Diocesano d'Arte Sacra, Agrigento 21035
Museo Diocesano d'Arte Sacra, Bergamo 21158
Museo Diocesano d'Arte Sacra, Brescia 21243
Museo Diocesano d'Arte Sacra, Lodi 21801
Museo Diocesano di Arte Sacra, Mileto 21935
Museo Diocesano di Arte Sacra, Nicotera 22036
Museo Diocesano di Arte Sacra, Orte 22071
Museo Diocesano di Arte Sacra, Palermo 22111
Museo Diocesano di Arte Sacra, Volterra 22886
Museo Diocesano di Arte Sacra San Gregorio Barbarigo, Padova 22093
Museo Diocesano di Osimo, Osimo 22077
Museo Diocesano e Gallerie del Tiepolo, Udine 22755
Museo Diocesano Inercomunale di Arte Sacra, Castignano 21360
Museo Diocesano Inercomunale di Arte Sacra, Monalto Marche 21961
Museo Diocesano Inercomunale di Arte Sacra, Rotella 22438
Museo Diocesano Intercomunale di Arte Sacra, Comunanza 21464
Museo Diocesano Intercomunale di Arte Sacra, Grottammare 21724
Museo Diocesano Intercomunale di Arte Sacra, Monteprandone 21990
Museo Diocesano Intercomunale di Arte Sacra, Ripatransone 22319
Museo Diocesano Teatino, Chieti 21414
Museo Diocesano Tridentino, Trento 22717
Museo e Archivio Capitolare, Assisi 21109
Museo e Chiostri Monumentali di Santa Maria Novella, Firenze 21620
Museo e Pinacoteca Diocesana, Camerino 21288
Museo Francescano, Gubbio 21731
Museo Francescano, Roma 22393
Museo Orientale, Tagliacozzo 22622
Museo Parrocchiale, Castell'Arquato 21347
Museo Parrocchiale, Mogliano Marche 21955
Museo Parrocchiale della Chiesa Collegiata, Mercatello sul Metauro 21880
Museo Parrocchiale di Arte Sacra, Ponte in Valtellina 22235
Museo Parrocchiale di Santa Maria delle Grazie, Salerno 22463
Museo Piersanti, Matelica 21869
Museo Pio IX e Pinacoteca d'Arte Sacra Senigallia, Senigallia 22561
Museo Sacro, Caorle 21300
Museo Sacro, Archivio della Cattedrale di S. Rufino, Assisi 21110
Museo-Tesoro Basilica di S. Francesco, Assisi 21111
Museo Tesoro della Collegiata di San Lorenzo, Chiavenna 21408
Museo Tipologico del Presepio, Macerata 21822
Pinacoteca Comunale, Castiglion Fiorentino 21354
Pinacoteca Parrocchiale, Buonconvento 21257
Raccolta d'Arte, Roccalbegna 22325
Raccolta d'Arte Diocesano, Città della Pieve 21429
Raccolta dell'Opera del Duomo, Oristano 22070
Tesoro della Cattedrale, Aosta 21073
Tesoro della Collegiata di Sant'Orso, Aosta 21074

Japan

Amanosan Kongo-ji Treasure House, Kawachi-Nagano 23136
Amida-ji Treasure Storehouse, Hofu 23050
Atsuta-Jingu Museum, Nagoya, Aichi 23355
Byodo-in Treasure House, Uji, Kyoto 23738
Chikubushima Treasure House, Shiga 23502
Chikurin-ji Treasure House, Kochi 23168
Chishaku-in Treasure Hall, Kyoto 23210
Chusonji Sankozo, Hiraizumi 23030
Daigo-ji Treasure Hall, Kyoto 23211
Daihoon-ji Treasure House, Kyoto 23212
Hakone-Jinja Homotsuden, Hakone 23004
Hiraizumi Museum, Hiraizumi 23031
Hommyo-ji Treasure House, Kumamoto 23191
Horyuji Daihozoden Treasure Museum, Ikoma 23065
Hotoko Ninomiya Jinja Homotsuden, Odawara 23397
Ichijo-ji Treasure House, Kasai 23130
Itsukushima-jinja Homotsukan, Hatsukaichi 23013
Izumo Taisha Shrine Treasure, Taisha 23534
Izumo Taisha Treasure House, Izumo 23097
Kakurin-ji Treasure House, Kakogawa 23106
Kamakura Kokuhokan, Kamakura 23108
Kamakuragu Homotsu Chinretsujo, Kamakura 23109
Kanshin-ji Reihokan, Kawachi-Nagano 23137
Kashima-jingu Treasure House, Kashima, Ibaraki 23134
Kasuga Taisha, Nara 23366
Katori-jingu Treasure House, Sawara 23484
Kikuchi-Rekishikan, Kikuchi 23149
Kitano Temman-gu Treasure House, Kyoto 23228
Kofukuji Kokuhokan, Nara 23367
Koryu-ji Reihoden, Kyoto 23233
Koyasan Reihokan, Koya 23189
Kumano Nachi Taisha Treasure House, Nachikatsuura 23339
Kyoto Kokuritsu Hakubutsukan, Kyoto 23241
Minobusan Homotsukan, Minobu 23308
Mishima Taisha Treasure House, Mishima 23312
Motsu-ji Storage House, Hiraizumi 23032
Munakata Taisha Shinpōkan, Genkai-Machi 22984
Myôhôin, Kyoto 23254
Naritasan History Museum, Narita 23377
Nata-dera Homotsukan, Komatsu 23185
Nikko Futarasan Jinja Hakubutsukan, Nikkou 23387
Nikko Toshogu Treasure House, Nikkou 23388
Ninna-ji Temple Treasure House, Kyoto 23257
Nyoirin-ji Treasure House, Yoshino 23784
Oyamazumi-jinja Kokuhokan, Omishima 23415
Rinno-ji Jokodo Treasure House, Nikkou 23389
Rokuharamitsu-ji Treasure House, Kyoto 23265
Rokuonji, Kyoto 23266
Saikyo-ji Treasure Hall, Hirado 23029
Sanjusangendo, Kyoto 23269
Senko-ji Treasure House, Ono 23418
Shido-dera Treasure House, Shido 23500
Shido-ji Homotsukan, Shido 23501
Shingen-Ko Treasure House, Enzan 22964
Shiogama Shrine Museum, Shiogami 23512
Shoren-in Treasure House, Kyoto 23274
Shosoin Treasure Repository, Nara 23373
Sumiyoshi-jinja Treasure House, Shimonoseki 23509
To-ji Homotsukan, Kyoto 23275
Todai-ji Treasure Hall, Nara 23374
Toshodai-ji Treasure House, Nara 23375
Tsurugaoka Hachiman-gu Treasure House, Kamakura 23113
Uesugi Shrine Treasure House, Yonezawa 23782
Yahiko-jinja Treasure House, Yahiko 23750
Yakushi-ji Treasure House, Nara 23376
Yamaguchi Hoshun Memorial Hall, Hayama 23014
Yamanouchi-jinja Treasure History Hall, Kochi 23172
Yogen-In, Kyoto 23278
Yutoku Shrine Museum, Kashima, Saga 23135
Zenko-ji Tendai Sect Treasure House, Nagano 23345
Zuigan-ji Hakabutsukan, Matsushima 23299

Korea, Republic

Moka Buddhist Art Museum, Kangchon 23895

Lebanon

Qozhiah Museum, Ehden 24148

Malta

Sanctuary of our Lady of Graces Museum, Zabbar 24360

Mongolia

Museum of Religious History, Ulaanbaatar 24543

Myanmar

The Buddhist Art Museum, Yangon 24603
Museum of the Shwenawdaw Pagoda, Bago 24586

Netherlands

Breda's Museum, Breda 24840
Gemeentemuseum voor Religieuze Kunst, Weert 25630
Kerkmuseum De Klokkengieterij, Vries 25613
Kerkmuseum Janum, Janum 25195
Museum Amstelkring, Amsterdam 24710
Museum in de Stiftkerk, Thorn 25532
Museum Van Gerwen-Lemmens, Valkenswaard 25575
Museum voor Devotieprentjes en andere Devotionalia, Maastricht 25273
Museum voor Kerkelijke Kunst, Workum 25653
Museum voor Religieuze Kunst, Uden 25544
Schatkamer van de Basiliek van Onze Lieve Vrouwe, Maastricht 25275
Schatkamer van de Sint-Servaasbasiliek, Maastricht 25276
Sint Jansmuseum De Bouwloods, 's-Hertogenbosch 25154
Sint-Plechelmusbasiliek met Schatkamer, Oldenzaal 25347
Stoottroepen Museum, Assen 24778
Wilhelmietenmuseum, Huijbergen 25186
Zwanenbroedershuis, 's-Hertogenbosch 25155

Norway

Heddal Bygdetun, Notodden 26206
Oslo Middelalderpark, Oslo 26240
Sør-Varanger Museum, Kirkenes 26137
Stiklestad Nasjonal Kultursenter, Verdal 26378

Panama

Museo de Arte Religioso, Parita 26449
Museo de Arte Religioso Colonial, Panamá City 26440

Paraguay

Museo Iconográfico, Itaugua 26467
Museo Mons Juan Sinforiano Bogarin, Asunción 26464

Peru

Museo de Arte Religioso de la Basílica Catedral, Lima 26492
Museo del Convento de los Descalzos, Lima 26499

Philippines

Barasoain Historical Landmark, Malolos 26543
San Agustin Museum Intramuros, Intramuros 26532
Xavier University Museum (Museo de Oro), Cagayan de Oro 26522

Poland

Muzeum Archidiecezjalne, Katowice 26773
Muzeum Archidiecezjalne, Poznań 27017
Muzeum Archidiecezjalne, Przemyśl 27038
Muzeum Archidiecezjalne Lubelskie, Lublin 26910
Muzeum Archidiecezjalne we Wrocławiu, Wrocław 27279
Muzeum Diecezjalne, Pelplin 26997
Muzeum Diecezjalne, Tarnów 27157
Muzeum Diecezjalne Sztuki Kościelnej, Sandomierz 27081
Muzeum Katedralne Jana Pawła II, Kraków 26834
Muzeum Klasztorne OO Cystersów, Szczyrzyc 27147
Muzeum Parafialne, Dobra 26687
Muzeum Parafialne, Krynica 26864
Muzeum Sztuki Sakralnej, Bardo 26614
Parafia Ewangelicko - Augsburska Wang, Karpacz 26770
Zabytkowa Cerkiew w Bartnem, Bartne 26616
Zbiory Sztuki na Jasnej Górze, Częstochowa 26681

Portugal

Museu Antonino, Faro 27364
Museu de Arte Sacra da Universidade, Coimbra 27353
Museu de Aveiro, Aveiro 27338
Museu de São Roque, Lisboa 27392
Museu Diocesano de Arte Sacra, Funchal 27368
Museu Nacional de Machado de Castro, Coimbra 27358
Palácio Nacional de Mafra, Mafra 27412
Tesouro da Sé Primaz, Braga 27343

Russia

Archangelskij Sobor, Moskva 27789
Blagoveščenskij Sobor, Moskva 27790
Centralnyj Muzej Drevnerusskoj Kultury i Isskustva im. Andreja Rubleva, Moskva 27793
Cerkov Pokrova v Filjach, Moskva 27799
Cerkov Rispoloženija, Moskva 27800
Gosudarstvennaja Tretjakovskaja Galerja, Moskva 27814
Isaakievskij Sobor, Sankt-Peterburg 28036
Novodevičij Monastyr, Moskva 27924
Patrijaršie Palaty, Moskva 27932
Pokrovskij Sobor-chram Vasilija Blažennogo, Moskva 27934
Svjato-Troickij Sobor, Sankt-Peterburg 28068
Svjatogorskij Monastyr, Puškinskie Gory 28002

Spain

Arxiu del Monestir, Sant Joan de les Abadesses 29638
Casa de las Dueñas, Sevilla 29706
Colección Parroquial, Colmenar Viejo 28970
Colección Parroquial, Gascueña 29081
Colección Parroquial, San Mateo 29619
Colección Parroquial, Traiguera 29804
Colleción Parroquial, Albocácer 28661
Hospital-Santuario de Nuestra Señora de la Caridad, Illescas 29156
Monasterio de Dominicas, Quejana 29542
Monasterio de la Encarnación, Osuna 29435
Monasterio de San Millán de Suso, San Millán de Suso 29621
Monasterio de Santa Clara, Zafra 29944
Museo Arciprestal, Morella 29382
Museo Catedral, Palma de Mallorca 29469
Museo Catedralicio, Almería 28691
Museo Catedralicio, Avila 28738
Museo Catedralicio, Badajoz 28756
Museo Catedralicio, Burgo de Osma 28868
Museo Catedralicio, Burgos 28870
Museo Catedralicio, Cádiz 28887
Museo Catedralicio, Ciudad Real 28960
Museo Catedralicio, Eivissa 29026
Museo Catedralicio, Guadix 29130
Museo Catedralicio, Jaén 29162
Museo Catedralicio, León 29186
Museo Catedralicio, Málaga 29313
Museo Catedralicio, Palencia 29454
Museo Catedralicio, Santo Domingo de la Calzada 29691
Museo Catedralicio, Segovia 29698
Museo Catedralicio, Sigüenza 29726
Museo Catedralicio, Tortosa 29800
Museo Catedralicio, Tui 29812
Museo Catedralicio-Diocesano, León 29187
Museo Conventual, Medina de Pomar 29343
Museo das Peregrinacións, Santiago de Compostela 29674
Museo de Arte Sacro, Monforte de Lemos 29365
Museo de Arte Sacro, Osuna 29437
Museo de Arte Sacro de la Colegiata de Iria Flavia, Padrón 29449
Museo de la Catedral de Santiago de Compostela, Santiago de Compostela 29678
Museo de la Colegiata, Belmonte 28837
Museo de la Colegiata, Medinaceli 29347
Museo de los Caminos, Astorga 28732
Museo de los Corporales, Daroca 29007
Museo de Semana Santa, Zamora 29947
Museo Diocesano, Lleida 29191
Museo Diocesano, Lugo 29229
Museo Diocesano, Pamplona 29486
Museo Diocesano, Tudela 29811
Museo Diocesano-Catedralicio, Cuenca 29006
Museo Diocesano-Catedralicio, Ourense 29440
Museo Diocesano-Catedralicio, Segorbe 29693
Museo Diocesano-Catedralicio, Valladolid 29859
Museo Diocesano-Catedralicio, Barbastro 28769
Museo Diocesano Catedralicio de Arte Sacro, Orihuela 29427
Museo Diocesano de Arte Antiguo, Sigüenza 29727
Museo Diocesano de Arte Sacro, Las Palmas de Gran Canaria 29481
Museo Diocesano de Arte Sacro, Teruel 29761
Museo Municipal, Xàtiva 29938
Museo Parroquial, Alquezar 28696
Museo Parroquial, Barco de Avila 28832
Museo Parroquial, Bocairente 28860
Museo Parroquial, Celanova 28945
Museo Parroquial, Medina de Rioseco 29346
Museo Parroquial, Roda de Isábena 29568
Museo Parroquial, Santa Gadea del Cid 29654
Museo Parroquial, Santa María del Campo 29660
Museo Parroquial de San Félix, Girona 29093
Museo Parroquial de Santa Eulalia, Paredes de Nava 29490
Museo Parroquial de Zurbarán, Marchena 29333
Museo Parroquial Santa María La Real, Xunqueira de Ambia 29940
Museo Sor María de Jesús de Agreda, Agreda 28651
Museo-Tesoro Catedralicio, Córdoba 28983
Museo-Tesoro Catedralicio, Lugo 29231
Museo-Tesoro Catedralicio, Plasencia 29510
Museo-Tesoro Catedralicio, Toledo 29780
Museo-Tesoro de la Basílica de la Macarena, Sevilla 29721
Museo-Tesoro de la Cofradía de la Expiración, Málaga 29318
Museo-Tesoro de la Santina, Covadonga 28997
Museo-Tesoro del Templo del Cristo del Gran Poder, Sevilla 29722
Museo-Tesoro Parroquial, Arcos de la Frontera 28714
Museo-Tesoro Parroquial de Santiago, Orihuela 29428
Museo Virgen de la Portería, Avila 28744
Museu-Arxiu de Santa María de Mataró, Mataró 29341
Museu Capitular, Lleida 29191
Museu d'Art, Girona 29096
Museu Diocesà de Barcelona, Barcelona 28812
Museu Diocesà de Mallorca, Palma de Mallorca 29472
Museu Històric de la Seu, Manresa 29327
Museu Parroquial, Castelló d'Empúries 28933
Museu Parroquial, Santa Pau 29661
Museu Parroquial Palau Solitar, Palau de Plegamans 29452
Museu-Tresor Parroquial, Verdú 29882
Palau Ducal, Gandía 29077
Real Casa del Labrador, Aranjuez 28710
Real Monasterio de Santa María de El Puig, El Puig de Santa María 29540
Valle de los Caídos, Valle de Cuelgamuros 29868

Switzerland

Dommuseum, Chur 30702
Domschatz Sankt Ursen Kathedrale, Solothurn 31250
Kirchenschatz, Bremgarten (Aargau) 30650
Kirchenschatz, Glarus 30830
Kirchenschatz-Museum, Baden 30553
Kirchenschatz Sankt Pelagius Kirche, Bischofszell 30639
Klostermuseum Disentis, Disentis 30731
Musée de Payerne et Abbatiale, Payerne 31087
Musée du Grand Saint-Bernard, Le Grand-Saint-Bernard 30842
Musée sur l'Ordre de Malte, Compesières 30713
Museo di Santa Maria degli Angioli, Lugano 30968

Tunisia

Musée d'Art Islamique du Ribat, Monastir 31622
Musée Raccada, Kairouan 31613

United Kingdom

The Blairs Museum, Aberdeen 31982
Cathedral Treasury Museum, Carlisle 32537
Christ Church Cathedral Treasury, Oxford 34130
Guildford Cathedral Treasury, Guildford 33166
Lincoln Cathedral Treasury, Lincoln 33517
Rievaulx Abbay, Rievaulx 34307
Saint Andrews Cathedral Museum, Saint Andrews 34360
Saint Augustine's Abbey, Canterbury 32522
Saint Mungo Museum of Religious Life and Art, Glasgow 33094
Saint Peter Hungate Church Museum, Norwich 34089

Religious History and Traditions

Reptiles

**Rescue Equipment → Fire Fighting and
Rescue Work**

Rocks → Mineralogy

Salt

Sarcophagi → Tombs

Scientific Apparatus and Instruments

Edison and Ford Winter Estates, Fort Myers 36937
Everhart Museum, Scranton 40272
Explora Science Center and Children's Museum, Albuquerque 35014
The Exploratorium, San Francisco 40108
Fernbank Science Center, Atlanta 35215
Flandrau Science Center, Tucson 40749
Fontenelle Forest Association Museum, Bellevue 35415
Fort Worth Museum of Science and History, Fort Worth 36984
The Franklin Institute, Philadelphia 39377
Geology Museum, Huntington 37546
Harbor Branch Oceanographic Institution, Fort Pierce 36944
Hicksville Gregory Museum, Hicksville 37418
Houston Museum of Natural Science, Houston 37514
Insights - El Paso Science Center, El Paso 36670
Iredell Museum of Arts Heritage, Statesville 40501
Kansas City Museum, Kansas City 37737
Kauai Children's Discovery Museum, Kapaa 37747
Lakeview Museum of Arts and Sciences, Peoria 39323
Louisiana Arts and Science Center, Baton Rouge 35365
McAllen International Museum, McAllen 38229
McKinley Museum and McKinley National Memorial, Canton 35829
McWane Center, Birmingham 35510
Maryland Science Center, Baltimore 35321
Maxwell Museum of Anthropology, Albuquerque 35018
Miami Museum of Science, Miami 38458
Monte L. Bean Life Science Museum, Provo 39644
Museum of Arts and Sciences, Macon 38254
Museum of Discovery and Science, Fort Lauderdale 36917
Museum of Geology, Rapid City 39692
Museum of Robotics, Orinda 39190
Museum of Science, Boston 35598
Museum of Science and History of Jacksonville, Jacksonville 37654
National Inventors Hall of Fame, Akron 34991
National Museum of Natural History, Washington 40988
New Mexico Museum of Natural History and Science, Albuquerque 35021
New York Hall of Science, Flushing Meadows 36865
North Carolina Museum of Life and Science, Durham 36590
The North Museum of Natural History and Science, Lancaster 37925
Omnisphere and Science Center, Wichita 41171
The Oyster and Maritime Museum of Chincoteague, Chincoteague 36061
Pacific Science Center, Seattle 40292
Paterson Museum, Paterson 39294
Petaluma Wildlife and Natural Science Museum, Petaluma 39339
Porter Thermometer Museum, Onset 39176
Reading Public Museum and Art Gallery, Reading 39702
Red River Valley Museum, Vernon 40853
Reuben H. Fleet Science Center, San Diego 40085
Roberson Museum and Science Center, Binghamton 35503
Rochester Museum, Rochester 39815
Roper Mountain Science Center, Greenville 37268
Saint Louis Science Center Museum, Saint Louis 39978
Sci-Port Discovery Center, Shreveport 40352
Sci-Tech Center of Northern New York, Watertown 41040
Science Center of Connecticut, West Hartford 41110
Science Center of Iowa, Des Moines 36493
Science Museum, Upton 40808
Science Museum of Long Island, Manhasset 38303
Science Museum of Minnesota, Saint Paul 40000
Science Museum of Virginia, Richmond 39767
Science Museum of Western Virginia, Roanoke 39804
Science Spectrum, Lubbock 38207
Science Station Museum, Cedar Rapids 35887
Sciencenter, Ithaca 37634
SciTech Museum, Aurora 35260
Sony Wonder Technology Lab, New York 38940
South Dakota Discovery Center, Pierre 39440
Southwest Museum of Science and Technology, Dallas 36365
Southwestern Michigan College Museum, Dowagiac 36551
Virginia Living Museum, Newport News 38993
Weather Discovery Center, North Conway 39030
Yesteryear Museum, Whippany 41162

Yugoslavia
Galerija Nauke i Technike Srpske Akademije Nauka i Umetnosti, Beograd 41508
Muzej Nikole Tesle, Beograd 41518

Scientific Expeditions

Australia
Australian Antarctic Division Display, Kingston 01139
Bligh Museum of Pacific Exploration, Bruny Island 00847
Sturt House, Grange 01059

Austria
Heinrich Harrer-Museum, Hüttenberg 02047

Belgium
Africa-Museum, Tervuren 03755

Canada
Champlain Trail Museum, Pembroke 05575

Czech Republic
African Safari and Veteran Car Museum, Dvůr Králové nad Labem 07319
Památník Dr. Emila Holuba, Holice v Čechách 07340

Denmark
Hauchs Physiske Cabinet, Sorø 08059
Knud Rasmussens Hus, Hundested 07888

France
Musée des Sciences, Laval (Mayenne) 11148

Germany
Abenteuermuseum Saarbrücken - Sammlung Heinz Rox-Schulz, Saarbrücken 18280
Alfred-Wegener-Gedenkstätte, Zechlinerhütte 19259

Kyrgyzstan
Memorialnyj Muzej N.M. Prževalskogo, Prževalsk 23978

Latvia
Gaidu un Skautu Muzejs, Ogre 24049

New Zealand
Canterbury Museum, Christchurch 25745

Norway
Olav Bjaalandmuseet, Morgedal 26189
Polarmuseet, Andenes 26011
Roald Amundsens Hjem Uranienborg, Svartskog 26334
Roald Amundsens Minne, Borge Sarpsborg 26046

South Africa
Hartenbos Museum, Hartenbos 28493

Spain
Casa-Museo de Colón, Valladolid 29853
Monasterio de Santa María de la Rábida, Palos de la Frontera 29483
Museo Casa de Colón, Las Palmas de Gran Canaria 29480

Sweden
Äventyret Ostindiefararen Götheborg, Göteborg 30093
Andréemuseet, Gränna 30109

United Kingdom
Captain Cook Birthplace Museum, Middlesbrough 33943
Captain Cook's Schoolroom Museum, Great Ayton 33149
David Livingstone Centre, Blantyre 32307
Discovery Museum, Newcastle-upon-Tyne 34028
Gilbert White's House and the Oates Museum, Selborne 34440
John McDouall Stuart Museum, Dysart 32867
Royal Research Ship Discovery, Dundee 32841
Scott Polar Research Institute Museum, Cambridge 32508

Uruguay
Museo de Descubrimiento, Montevideo 34935

U.S.A.
Captain Nathaniel B. Palmer House, Stonington 40529
Lawrence L. Lee Scouting Museum, Manchester 38296
Martin and Osa Johnson Safari Museum, Chanute 35911
North Star Scouting Memorabilia, West Saint Paul 41123

Sculpture

Argentina
El Fogon de los Arrieros, Resistencia 00497
Museo al Aire Libre, Buenos Aires 00145
Museo Casa de Yrurtia, Buenos Aires 00152
Museo Municipal de Bellas Artes Lucas Braulio Areco, Posadas 00476

Australia
City of Melbourne Collection, Melbourne 01214

Austria
Anton Hanak-Museum, Langenzersdorf 02177
Atelier Augarten - Zentrum für zeitgenössische Kunst der Österreichischen Galerie Belvedere, Wien 02808
Dokumentation des ehemaligen Heilbades, Bad Pirawarth 01709
Freilichtmuseum Römersteinbruch, Sankt Margarethen 02560
Galerie im Bildhauerhaus und Skulpturenwanderweg, Einöde 01790
Künstlergarten Alfred Kurz, Lichtenau 02209
Kunstpromenade Achensee, Achenkirch 01640
Museum des Augustiner-Chorherrenstifts, Reichersberg 02479
Museum für zeitgenössische Metallplastik, Sankt Pantaleon 02572
Othmar Jaindl-Museum, Villach 02731
Salvador Dalí im Palais Pallavicini, Wien 02950
Schloß und Gurschner Museum, Pram 02430
Schloßmuseum Niederleis, Niederleis 02346
Schwarzenberger Skulpturenpark, Schwarzenberg am Böhmerwald 02620
Siegfried Charoux-Museum, Langenzersdorf 02179
Skulpturenpark Kramsach, Kramsach 02145
Tiroler Kunstpavillon Kleiner Hofgarten, Innsbruck 02073

Belgium
Monumental Gallery Sculpturama, Bornem 03192
Musée Communal de Jette, Bruxelles 03260
Musée Constantin Meunier, Bruxelles 03262
Musée de l'Art Wallon, Liège 03551
Musée de l'Assistance Publique, Bruxelles 03273
Musée des Beaux-Arts de la Ville de Mons, Mons 03604
Musée du Vieux-Cimetière, Soignies 03735
Musée en Plein Air du Sart-Tilman, Liège 03554
Musée Schott, Bruxelles 03305
Musées Royaux d'Art et d'Histoire, Bruxelles 03306
Museum Mayer van den Bergh, Antwerpen 03110
Museum van de Sint-Salvatorskathedraal, Brugge 03222
Museum voor Stenen Voorwerpen, Gent 03415
Openluchtmuseum voor Beeldhouwkunst Middelheim, Antwerpen 03125
Stedelijk Museum Het Toreke, Tienen 03761
Taxandriamuseum, Turnhout 03789

Brazil
Museu de Arte Contemporânea da Universidade de São Paulo, São Paulo 04108
Museu Internacional de Arte Naïf do Brasil, Rio de Janeiro 04061

Canada
Arnold Mikelson Mind and Matter Gallery, White Rock 06263
Art Gallery of York University, Toronto 06036
Dofasco Gallery, Dundas 04817
Galerie des Sculptures, Beauport 04523
John Weaver Sculpture Museum, Hope 05061
Robert Tait McKenzie Memorial Museum and Mill of Kintail, Carleton Place 04668
Toronto Sculpture Garden, Toronto 06095
Ziska Gallery, Bracebridge 04569

Congo, Democratic Republic
Musée des Beaux-Arts, Kinshasa 06930

Croatia
Atelier Ivan Meštrović, Zagreb 07098
Galerija Antuna Augustinčića, Klanjec 07003
Ivan Meštrović Gallery, Split 07072
Umjetnička Galerija, Dubrovnik 06990

Cyprus Turk
Lapidari Museum, Lefkoşa 07227

Czech Republic
Klášter Sv. Anežky České, Praha 07566
Městské Muzeum a Galerie, Hořice v Pokrkonoší 07342
Městské Muzeum a Galerie Otakara Spaniela a Josefa Wágnera, Jaroměř 07365
Sbirka Českého Sochařstvi, Zbraslav nad Vltavou 07724
Státní Galerie Výtvarného Umění, Cheb 07292

Denmark
Fåborg Museum for Fynsk Malerkunst, Fåborg 07799
Hammerichs Hus, Ærøskøbing 07750
Louisiana Museum of Modern Art, Humlebæk 07887
Ny Carlsberg Glyptotek, København 07930
Randers Kunstmuseum, Randers 08009
Rudolph Tegners Museum, Dronningmølle 07786
Statens Museum for Kunst, København 07934
Thingbaek Kalkminer Bundgaards Museum, Skørping 08052
Thorvaldsens Museum, København 07936
Thorvaldsens Samlingen på Nysø, Præstø 08007
Vejen Kunstmuseum, Vejen 08088

Egypt
Mukhtar Museum, Cairo 08217

Finland
Emil Wikström Museo, Valkeakoski 09007
Gösta Serlachiuksen Taidemuseo, Mänttä 08652
Huittisten Museo, Huittinen 08401
Lapinlahden Taidemuseo ja Eemil Halonen Museo, Lapinlahti 08597
Mikkelin Taidemuseo, Mikkeli 08674
Wäinö Aaltosen Museo, Turku 08976
Walter Runebergin Veistoskokoelma, Porvoo 08801
Yrjö Liipolan Taidekokoelma, Koski 08536

France
Château de Fleurigny, Thorigny-sur-Oreuse 13683
Collections de l'Ecole Nationale Supérieure des Beaux-Arts, Paris 12281
Espace Salvador Dalí, Paris 12287
Fondation François-Brochet, Auxerre 09339
Fondation Le Corbusier, Paris 12291
Musée Adzak, Paris 12314
Musée Arménien de France, Paris 12315
Musée Bartholdi, Colmar 10164
Musée Boleslaw Biegas, Paris 12319
Musée Bouchard, Paris 12320
Musée Bourdelle, Paris 12322
Musée Calvet, Avignon 09358
Musée d'Art et d'Archéologie, Aurillac 09319
Musée d'Art et d'Histoire, Meudon 11744
Musée d'Art Naïf Max-Fourny, Paris 12333
Musée de la Société Archéologique et Historique de la Charente, Angoulême 09185
Musée de la Vie Romantique, Paris 12354
Musée de Provins et du Provinois, Provins 12666
Musée de Vendôme d'Art et d'Histoire, Vendôme 13906
Musée Départemental d'Art Ancien et Contemporain, Épinal 10435
Musée Départemental de l'Oise, Beauvais 09484
Musée des Amis de Thann, Thann 13661
Musée des Années 30, Boulogne-Billancourt 09661
Musée des Arts Décoratifs, Saumur 13430
Musée des Augustins, Toulouse 13731
Musée des Beaux-Arts, Angers 09178
Musée des Beaux-Arts, Arras 09258
Musée des Beaux-Arts, Béziers 09546
Musée des Beaux-Arts, Marseille 11649
Musée des Beaux-Arts, Pau 12468
Musée Despiau Wlerick, Mont-de-Marsan 11809
Musée du Centre de Recherches sur les Monuments Historiques, Paris 12390
Musée du Luxembourg, Paris 12397
Musée du Prieuré de Graville, Le Havre 11215
Musée François-Pompon, Saulieu 13420
Musée Garinet, Châlons-en-Champagne 09946
Musée Henri Chapu, Le Mée-sur-Seine 11233
Musée Institut Tessin, Paris 12414
Musée-Jardin Paul-Landowski, Boulogne-Billancourt 09662
Musée Lapidaire, Avignon 09362
Musée Lapidaire, Mozac 11984
Musée Lapidaire de la Cité, Carcassonne 09864
Musée Morice Lipsi, Rosey 12824
Musée Municipal, Lons-le-Saunier 11443
Musée Municipal de la Chartreuse, Douai 10362
Musée Municipal Nicolas Poussin, Les Andelys 11300
Musée National Auguste Rodin, Meudon 11745
Musée National des Arts Asiatiques Guimet, Paris 12428
Musée P. Dubois-A. Boucher, Nogent-sur-Seine 12139
Musée Rude, Dijon 10336
Musée Zadkine, Paris 12445
Pavillon des Arts, Paris 12453

Germany
Akademisches Kunstmuseum der Universität, Bonn 14967
Albrechtsburg, Meißen 17321
Alf Lechner Museum, Ingolstadt 16561
Antiken- und Abgußsammlung des Archäologischen Seminars, Marburg 17255
Edwin-Scharff-Museum, Neu-Ulm 17613
Ernst Barlach Haus, Hamburg 16211
Ernst Barlach Museum Altes Vaterhaus, Ratzeburg 18072
Ernst Barlach Stiftung Güstrow, Güstrow 16137
Europäischer Skulpturenpark, Willebadessen 19123
Fritz-Best-Museum, Kronberg 16887
Galerie der Sammlung Berthold-Sames, Oberaudorf 17767
Gaudnek-Museum, Altomünster 14257
Gerhard-Marcks-Haus, Bremen 15056
Heimatmuseum Stadt Starnberg, Starnberg 18575
Karl-Seckinger-Ausstellung, Karlsruhe 16649
Kulturzentrum Sinsteden des Kreises Neuss, Rommerskirchen 18209
Kunsthalle Bremen, Bremen 15061
Kunsthalle Würth, Schwäbisch Hall 18411
Kunsthaus Nürnberg, Nürnberg 17749
Kunstmuseum Kloster Unser Lieben Frauen, Magdeburg 17212
Kunstsammlung Lorenzkapelle Rottweil, Rottweil 18255
Kunstsammlungen der Ruhr-Universität Bochum, Bochum 14940
Lapidarium, Berlin 14790
Mainfränkisches Museum Würzburg, Würzburg 19219
Museum Bad Arolsen, Bad Arolsen 14379
Museum für Abgüsse Klassischer Bildwerke, München 17495
Museum für Kunst in Steatit, Frankfurt am Main 15762
Museum Gasteiger-Haus, Holzhausen 16492
Museum Würth, Künzelsau 16899
Nationalgalerie Friedrichswerdersche Kirche - Schinkelmuseum, Berlin 14819
Prof.-Fritz-Behn-Museum, Bad Dürrheim 14420
Sammlung Mittelalterliche Kunst in Thüringen, Eisenach 15531
Sammlungen des Archäologischen Instituts der Universität, Göttingen 16028
Schloß Seehof mit Ferdinand Tietz-Sammlung, Memmelsdorf 17332
Schlossmuseum Oranienburg, Oranienburg 17860
Skulpturenmuseum, Heilbronn 16358
Skulpturenmuseum Glaskasten Marl, Marl, Westfalen 17285
Skulpturenmuseum im Hofberg, Landshut 16954
Skulpturensammlung, Dresden 15427

Skulpturensammlung und Museum für Byzantinische
  Kunst, Berlin 14841
Städtische Galerie im Rathauspark, Gladbeck 15982
Städtische Galerie Liebieghaus, Frankfurt am
  Main 15774
Städtisches Museum Simeonstift, Trier 18746
Stiftsmuseum der Stadt Aschaffenburg,
  Aschaffenburg 14323
Stiftung Hans Arp und Sophie Taeuber-Arp e.V.,
  Remagen 18133
Stiftung Wilhelm Lehmbruck Museum,
  Duisburg 15472
Suermondt-Ludwig-Museum, Aachen 14169
Von der Heydt-Museum, Wuppertal 19243
Walhalla, Donaustauf 15356

Greece
A. Sohos Museum, Tinos 19690
Alex Mylonas Museum, Athinai 19359
Archeological Collection, Drama 19441
Archeological Collection, Monemvassia 19572
Archeological Collection, Serrai 19647
Archeological Collection, Symi 19665
Archeological Collection, Tanagra 19666
Archeological Collection, Tilos 19688
Christos Capralos Museum, Agrinion 19325
Christos Capralos Museum, Athinai 19369
Foundation Skironio Museum Polychronopoulos, Néa
  Kifissia 19591
Historical Museum of Crete, Iráklion 19472
Museum of Contemporary Art, Andros 19337
Museum of Sculpture and Figurines of Loukia
  Georganti, Athinai 19407
N. Hadjikyriakos-Ghikas Gallery, Athinai 19410
Nikolaos Perantinos Museum of Sculpture,
  Athinai 19413

Guam
Isla Center for the Arts at the University of Guam,
  Mangilao 19747

Hungary
Finta Múzeum, Túrkeve 20062
Hincz Gyula Állandó Gyüjtemény, Vác 20063
Szoborpark, Budapest 19859

Iceland
Ásmundarsafn, Reykjavik 20107
Listasafn Einars Jónssonar, Reykjavik 20109
Sigurjón Ólafsson Museum, Reykjavik 20119

India
Akshaya Kumar Maitreya Museum, Darjeeling 20198
Archaeological Museum, Konarak 20332
Archaeological Museum, Vaisali 20444
Archaeological Museum, Varanasi 20447
Assam State Museum, Gauhati 20243
Bangiya Sahitya Parisad Museum, Kolkata 20181
Belkhandi Museum, Belkhandi 20161
Bhagalpur Museum, Bhagalpur 20162
Birla Museum, Bhopal 20169
Bundelkhand Chhatrasal Museum, Banda 20154
District Museum, Guntur 20253
District Museum, Shivpuri 20419
Dr. Raj Bali Pandey Puratatva Sangrahalaya,
  Deoria 20227
Government Museum, Bharatpur 20164
Government Museum, Kodagu 20310
Government Museum, Mathura 20356
Government Museum, Mount Abu 20360
Government Museum and Art Gallery,
  Chandigarh 20183
Himachal State Museum, Shimla 20416
History Museum, Ahmednagar 20138
I.V.K. Rajwade Sanshodhan Mandal Museum,
  Dhule 20233
Khajana Buildings Museum, Hyderabad 20270
Khiching Museum, Khiching 20306
Mahatma Gandhi Hindi Sangrahalaya, Kalpi 20296
Mahatma Gandhi Memorial College Museum,
  Udupi 20438
Museum and Saraswati Bhandar, Kotah 20333
Puratatva Sangrahalaya, Gorakhpur 20249
Purvattatva Sangrahalaya Madhya Pradesh Shasan,
  Damoh 20196
Rani Laxmi Bai Palace Sculpture Collection,
  Jhansi 20290
Sahitya Parishad Museum, Midnapore 20359
Sikar Museum, Sikar 20421
Sir Choturam Memorial Museum, Sangaria 20408
Thanjavur Art Gallery, Thanjavur 20426
Tulsi Sangrahalaya Ramvan, Satna 20414
Watson Museum, Rajkot 20402
Zilla Samgrahasala, Purulia 20398

Italy
Antiquarium Nazionale, Minturno 21937
Antiquarium Sestinale, Sestino 22567
Casa Buonarroti, Firenze 21577
Casa Museo Fantoni, Rovetta 22444
Cripta e Museo di Sant'Anastasio, Asti 21114
Fondazione Magnani Rocca, Mamiano di
  Traversetolo 21833
Galleria d'Arte Moderna Carlo Rizzarda, Feltre 22140
Galleria dell'Accademia, Firenze 21594
Galleria e Mostra del Presepe nel Mondo, Santuario di
  Montevergine 22530
Galleria Regionale di Palazzo Bellomo,
  Siracusa 22587
Galleria Rinaldo Carnielo, Firenze 21597
Giardino di Boboli, Firenze 21598

Musei Civici, Pavia 22138
Musei Civici agli Eremitani, Padova 22087
Museo Arcivescovile, Ravenna 22287
Museo Bardini, Firenze 21604
Museo Barracco, Roma 22358
Museo Canonica, Roma 22359
Museo Canonicale, Verona 22837
Museo Civico, Siena 22578
Museo Civico Antonio Cordici, Erice 21520
Museo d'Arte Antica, Milano 21908
Museo degli Affreschi G.B. Cavalcaselle,
  Verona 22839
Museo del Duomo, Milano 21913
Museo delle Statue - Stele Lunigianesi,
  Pontremoli 22240
Museo dell'Opera di Santa Maria del Fiore,
  Firenze 21610
Museo di Castelvecchio, Verona 22841
Museo di Sant'Agostino, Genova 21698
Museo di Villa Carlotta, Tremezzo 22714
Museo Dupré, Fiesole 21564
Museo Enrico Butti, Viggiù 22867
Museo Galleria di Villa Borghese, Roma 22394
Museo Lapidario del Duomo, Modena 21949
Museo Lapidario Marsicano, Avezzano 21122
Museo Lodovico Pogliaghi, Varese 22781
Museo Michelangelo, Caprese 21306
Museo Nazionale del Bargello, Firenze 21625
Parco dei Mostri, Bomarzo 21222
Parco Monumentale di Pinocchio, Collodi 21455
Pinacoteca dell'Accademia di Belle Arti,
  Carrara 21319
Raccolta Amici di Manzù, Ardea 21081
Sale della Prepositura, Casole d'Elsa 21331

Japan
Asakura Sculpture Gallery, Tokyo 23579
Chokoku no Mori Bijutsukan, Hakone 23003
Iwate-kenritsu Hakubutsukan, Morioka 23332
Museum of Contemporary Sculpture, Tokyo 23640
Rokuzan Bijutsukan, Hotaka 23056
Sapporo Sculpture Museum, Sapporo 23476
Utsukushigahara Kogen Bijutsukan, Chisagata 22956

Lebanon
Rachana Open Air Museum, Rachana 24150

Liberia
Tubman Centre of African Culture, Cape Mount 24154

Liechtenstein
Sammlungen des Regierenden Fürsten von
  Liechtenstein, Vaduz 24179

Lithuania
Europos Parkas, Vilnius 24197

Malaysia
Ibrahim Hussein Foundation Museum, Pulau
  Langkawi 24329

Mexico
Galería de la Escuela Nacional de Artes Plásticas,
  México 24414
Museo de Historia en la Alhondiga de Granaditas,
  Guanajuato 24402
Taller de Artes Plásticas Rufiho Tamayo,
  Oaxaca 24493

Nepal
Woodwork Museum, Bhaktapur 24641

Netherlands
Beelden aan Zee, Den Haag 24893
Museum Jacobs van den Hof, Amersfoort 24669
Odapark, Venray 25593
Pier Pander Museum, Leeuwarden 25232

Nigeria
National Museum - House of Images Esie, Esie 25973

Norway
Anders Svors Museet, Hornindal 26120
Anne Grimdalens Minne, Dalen i Telemark 26056
Erkebispegården, Trondheim 26348
Vigeland-Museet, Oslo 26247

Portugal
Casa-Museu Teixeira Lopes e Galerias Diego de
  Macedo, Porto 27422
Museu de Alberto Sampaio, Guimarães 27371
Museu Municipal de Santarém, Santarém 27432

Puerto Rico
Museo de Arte de Ponce, Ponce 27459
Popular Arts Museum, San Juan 27469

Romania
Muzeul Cecilia şi Frederic Storck, Bucureşti 27509
Muzeul de Artă, Tîrgu Jiu 27662
Muzeul de Istorie şi Artă al Municipiului Bucureşti,
  Bucureşti 27516

Russia
Gosudarstvennyj Muzej-masterskaja Skulptora A.S.
  Golubkinoj, Moskva 27828
Gosudarstvennyj Muzej Vadima Sidura,
  Moskva 27831
Memorialnyj Muzej-Masterskaja Skulptora S.T.
  Konenkova, Moskva 27847
Meždunarodnyj Centr-Muzej im. N.K. Rericha,
  Moskva 27848
Muzej Skulptury, Sankt-Peterburg 28061

Slovakia
Galéria Mesta Bratislavy, Bratislava 28202

Slovenia
Gorenjski Muzej Kranj, Kranj 28337

South Africa
Rembrandt Van Rijn Art Gallery, Stellenbosch 28620

Spain
Museo Antón, Candás 28908
Museo del Sacromonte, Granada 29119
Museo Diocesano-Catedralicio, Astorga 28734
Museo Municipal, Ayllón 28748
Museo Nacional de Escultura, Valladolid 29861
Museo Salzillo, Murcia 29392
Museu Clarà, Barcelona 28787
Museu d'Art, Girona 29096
Museu Frederic Marès, Barcelona 28817

Sudan
Merowe Museum, Merowe 30005

Sweden
Carl Eldhs Ateljémuseum, Stockholm 30340
Döderhultarmuseet, Oskarshamn 30276
Eskilstuna Konstmuseet, Eskilstuna 30063
Gustav III.'s Antikmuseum, Stockholm 30346
Millesgården, Lidingö 30187
Vitlycke Museum - Rock Art Centre,
  Tanumshede 30420

Switzerland
Antikensammlung, Bern 30603
Kunstmuseum Winterthur, Winterthur 31399
Lapidarium, Sankt Gallen 31172
Museo Vela, Ligornetto 30948
Museum der Klosterruine mit Lapidarium,
  Rüeggisberg 31143
Museum Kleines Klingental, Basel 30578
Skulpturhalle Basel, Basel 30588

Turkey
Resim ve Heykel Müzesi, İstanbul 31754

Ukraine
Chudožestvennyj Muzei, Sevastopol 31948

United Kingdom
Andrew Logan Museum of Sculpture, Berriew 32217
Barbara Hepworth Museum and Sculpture Garden,
  Saint Ives, Cornwall 34379
Ferens Art Gallery, Kingston-upon-Hull 33396
Furness Abbey, Barrow-in-Furness 32145
Henry Moore Institute, Leeds 33467
New Art Centre, East Winterslow 32885
The New Art Gallery Walsall, Walsall 34733
William Lamb Memorial Studio, Montrose 33981
Winchester Cathedral Triforium Gallery,
  Winchester 34849
Wysing Arts, Bourn 32336
Yorkshire Sculpture Park, West Bretton 34777

U.S.A.
DeCordova Museum and Sculpture Park,
  Lincoln 38045
Gallery II, Kalamazoo 37716
Gallery of Art, Overland Park 39220
Grounds For Sculpture, Hamilton 37310
International Sculpture Center, Hamilton 37311
Krasl Art Center, Saint Joseph 39946
Laumeier Sculpture Park and Museum, Saint
  Louis 39969
Mitchell Museum at Cedarhurst, Mount Vernon 38664
Nathan Manilow Sculpture Park, University
  Park 40798
The North Shore Arts Association, Gloucester 37161
Umlauf Sculpture Garden and Museum, Austin 35278

Vatican City
Museo Gregoriano Profano, Città del Vaticano 41399

Vietnam
National Museum of Cham Sculpture, Da-Nang 41459

Yugoslavia
Galerija Matice Srpske, Novi Sad 41582
Galerija Srpske Akademije Nauka i Umetnosti,
  Beograd 41509

Shells

Australia
Big Shell Museum, Tewantin 01522
Griffiths Sea Shell Museum and Marine Display, Lakes
  Entrance 01150
Port Stephens Shell Museum, Corlette 00933
Rosewall Memorial Shell Museum, Port Lincoln 01379

Brazil
Museu Oceanográfico Prof. Eliézer de C. Rios, Rio
  Grande 04081

China, People's Republic
Lushun Snakes Dao Natural Museum, Dalian 06517

Croatia
Malakološki Muzej, Makarska 07025

Germany
Buddelschiff-Museum, Wedel 18941
Internationales Muschelmuseum, Wangerland 18923
Muschel- und Schneckenmuseum, Norden 17711

Greece
Museum of Shells of the Greek Seas, Néa
  Moudiana 19594

Japan
Chiba-shi Kasori Kaizuka Hakubutsukan, Chiba 22951

Mozambique
Museu Ferreira de Almeida, Nampula 24585

Netherlands
Miramar Zeemuseum, Vledder 25599
Schelpen Museum, Zaamslag 25662

New Zealand
Picton Community Museum, Picton 25870

Oman
Oman Natural History Museum, Muscat 26386

Philippines
Carfel Seashell Museum, Malate 26542

United Kingdom
Glandford Shell Museum, Glandford 33067

Shipping → Boats and Shipping

Shoes

Austria
Stiefelmachermuseum, Rechnitz 02476

Belgium
Nationaal Schoeiselmuseum, Izegem 03492

Canada
Bata Shoe Museum, Toronto 06037

Czech Republic
Obuvnické Muzeum, Zlín 07734

France
Ecomusée du Sabotier, Soucht 13559
Musée de la Chaussure et d'Ethnographie Régionale,
  Romans-sur-Isère 12803

Germany
Deutsches Ledermuseum/ Schuhmuseum Offenbach -
  DLM, Offenbach am Main 17834
Deutsches Schustermuseum, Burgkunstadt 15157
Heimatmuseum Buchenberg, Buchenberg bei
  Kempten 15117
Historisches Schuhmuseum, Landsberg am
  Lech 16946

Italy
Museo della Calzatura, Vigevano 22866

Japan
Japan Footwear Museum, Fukuyama 22981

Mexico
Museo del Calzado, México 24446

Netherlands
Klompen Museum, Keijenborg 25204
Klompenmuseum De Platijn, Best 24814
Klompenmuseum Gebr. Wietzes, Eelde 24987
Nederlands Leder- en Schoenenmuseum,
  Waalwijk 25618
Scherjon's Klompenmakerij en Museum,
  Noordbergum 25329

Spain
Museo del Calzado, Elda 29035

Sweden
Skoindustrimuseet, Kumla 30176

Switzerland
Bally Schuhmuseum, Schönenwerd 31211

United Kingdom
Northampton Central Museum and Art Gallery,
  Northampton 34074
Rossendale Footware Heritage Museum,
  Rawtenstall 34278
Shoe Museum, Street 34603

Silk

China, People's Republic
China Silk Museum, Hangzhou 06559
Suzhou Silk Museum, Suzhou 06726

France
Musée des Vallées Cévenoles, Saint-Jean-du-
  Gard 13070

Musée du Tissage et de la Soierie, Bussières 09779

Germany
Stadtmuseum Pirna, Pirna 17987

Italy
Civico Museo della Seta Abegg, Garlate 21672

Japan
Okaya Sericultural, Equipment and Literature and Silk Museum, Okaya 23402
Silk Hakubutsukan, Yokohama 23769

Netherlands
Zijdemuseum, Grijpskerke 25070

Spain
Museo del Tejido Sedero Valenciano, Valencia 29840

United Kingdom
David Evans World of Silk, Crayford 32704
Macclesfield Silk Museum, Macclesfield 33865
Paradise Mill Silk Museum, Macclesfield 33866
Whitchurch Silk Mill, Whitchurch, Hampshire 34811
Working Silk Museum, Braintree 32363

U.S.A.
Wistariahurst Museum, Holyoke 37469

Silver → Gold and Silver

Skeletons → Bones

Social Conditions

Angola
Museu da Escravatura, Luanda 00085

Argentina
De los Viejos Colonos, Bariloche 00126
Museo Comunitario de Villa Regina, Villa Regina 00664
Museo Histórico Comunal y de la Colonización Judía Rabino Aaron H. Goldman, Moisés Ville 00443
Museo Social Argentino de Universidad, Buenos Aires 00235

Australia
ANZAC Memorial, Sydney 01487
History House, Portland 01389
Hou Wang Miau, Atherton 00743
Immigration Museum, Melbourne 01222
Meroogal House, Nowra 01327
Mulgrave Settlers Museum, Gordonvale 01052
Mundubbera and District Historical Museum, Mundubbera 01281
National Museum of Australia, Canberra 00876
National Pioneer Women's Hall of Fame, Alice Springs 00725
School of Political and Social Inquiry Museum, Clayton 00911
Vaucluse House, Vaucluse 01564
Wangaratta Exhibitions Gallery, Wangaratta 01574

Austria
Erstes Österreichisches Museum für Alltagsgeschichte, Neupölla 02342
Museum Arbeitswelt Steyr, Steyr 02659
Museum der Gewerkschaft Agrar-Nahrung-Genuß, Wien 02910
Museum im Hof, Sankt Pölten 02578
Österreichisches Gesellschafts- und Wirtschaftsmuseum, Wien 02932

Belgium
Archief en Museum van het Vlaams Leven te Brussel, Bruxelles 03230
Daensmuseum en Archief de Vlaamse Sociale Strijd, Aalst 03084
Museum van het Vlaams Studentenleven, Leuven 03531
Pelgrom Museum Poorterswoning, Antwerpen 03126
Sint-Dimpna en Gasthuismuseum, Geel 03391

Benin
Musée d'Histoire, Ouidah 03847

Bulgaria
Okrăžen Istoričeski Muzej, Plovdiv 04266

Burkina Faso
Musée des Civilisations du Sud Ouest, Gaoua 04398

Canada
Hanna Pioneer Museum, Hanna 05038
Salvation Army George Scott Railton Heritage Centre and Museum, Toronto 06084
Westfield Heritage Village, Rockton 05750

China, People's Republic
Museum of Dr. Sun Yat-Sen, Zhongshan 06803

Croatia
Muzej Grada Splita, Split 07073

Czech Republic
Muzeum a Pojizerská Galerie, Semily 07635

Denmark
Památnik Selského Povstáni, Rtyně v Podkrkonoší 07627

Denmark
Arbejdermuseet, København 07906

Finland
Amurin Työläismuseokortteli, Tampere 08921
Kauppilanmäen Museo, Valkeakoski 09008
Teollisuustyöväen Asuntomuseo, Imatra 08412
Työväen Keskusmuseo, Tampere 08938

France
CEDIAS Musée Social, Paris 12264
Maison de l'Outil et de la Pensée Ouvrière, Troyes 13788
Musée d'Histoire 1939-1945 L'Appel de la Liberté, Fontaine-de-Vaucluse 10561
Musée du Travail Charles-Peyre, Montfermeil 11863
Musée Municipal Marcel Migrenne, Guise 10775

Germany
Badisches Landesmuseum Karlsruhe, Karlsruhe 16647
Friedrich-Engels-Haus, Wuppertal 19236
Hans-Böckler-Geburtshaus, Trautskirchen 18726
Heimatmuseum, Friedland bei Neubrandenburg 15840
Heimatmuseum, Herbrechtingen 16384
Historisches Museum Bielefeld, Bielefeld 14900
Industriemuseum Chemnitz, Chemnitz 15193
Karl-Marx-Haus, Trier 18741
Löhe-Zeit-Museum, Neuendettelsau 17629
Museum der Arbeit, Hamburg 16230
Museum der Stadt Rüsselsheim, Rüsselsheim 18267
Museum Malerwinkelhaus, Marktbreit 17274
Museum Schloss Lichtenberg, Fischbachtal 15709
Rheinisches Industriemuseum, Ratingen 18069
Schnarch-Museum Alfeld, Alfeld, Leine 14218
Schulze-Delitzsch-Haus, Delitzsch 15288
Speicherstadtmuseum, Hamburg 16244
Werra-Kalibergbau-Museum, Heringen, Werra 16390
Westfälisches Industriemuseum, Dortmund 15387

Hungary
Nógrádi Történeti Múzeum, Salgótarján 19988

Italy
Museo dell'Uomo e dell'Ambiente, Terra del Sole 22640

Japan
Nagaoka Municipal Science Museum, Nagaoka 23347

Korea, Republic
Independence Hall of Korea, Chonan 23882

Lithuania
Lithuanian State Museum, Vilnius 24200

Mauritius
Folk Museum of Indian Immigration, Moka 24375

Mexico
Museo Nacional de las Populares, México 24469

Namibia
Alte Feste, Windhoek 24633
Owela Display Centre, Windhoek 24637

Netherlands
Amev Verzekeringsmuseum, Utrecht 25553
Burger Weeshuis, Zierikzee 25682
Museum Jannink, Enschede 25021
Nationaal Vakbondsmuseum De Burcht, Amsterdam 24719
Woonbootmuseum, Amsterdam 24747

New Zealand
Catlins Historical Museum, Owaka 25857
Engine House, Dunedin 25773
Museum of Wellington, City and Sea, Wellington 25934
Otago Settlers Museum, Dunedin 25780
South Canterbury Museum, Timaru 25903

Norway
Kongsvinger Museum, Kongsvinger 26145
Norsk Industriarbeidermuseet, Rjukan 26265
Trastad Samlinger, Borkenes 26048
Vesterålen Bygdemuseum, Melbu 26180

Philippines
Ayala Museum, Makati 26538

Poland
Muzeum Okregowe, Żyrardów 27326

Russia
Centralnyj Muzej Vserossijskogo Obščestva Slepych, Moskva 27798
Muzej Obščestva Krasnogo Kresta Rossii, Moskva 27901
Muzej Obščestvennogo Pitanija, Moskva 27903
Ogni Moskvy - Muzej Istorii Gorodskogo Osveščenija, Moskva 27925

Senegal
Maison des Esclaves, Gorée 28169

Slovenia
Muzej Ljudske Revolucije Trbovlje, Trbovlje 28392

South Africa
Kimberley Mine Museum, Kimberley 28524

Spain
Museo Comarcal, Zalduondo 29945

Sweden
Arbetets Museum, Norrköping 30248

United Kingdom
Beamish, North of England Open Air Museum, Beamish 32182
Bexhill Museum of Costume and Social History, Bexhill-on-Sea 32234
Blaise Castle House Museum, Bristol 32402
Buckleys Yesterday's World, Battle 32178
Castleford Museum Room, Castleford 32551
Cogges Manor Farm Museum, Witney 34862
Cookworthy Museum of Rural Life in South Devon, Kingsbridge 33394
East Carlton Steel Heritage Centre, East Carlton 32873
Elizabethan House Museum, Great Yarmouth 33155
Epping Forest District Museum, Waltham Abbey 34737
Heatherbank Museum of Social Work, Glasgow 33079
Iona Heritage Centre, Isle-of-Iona 33341
Lancaster City Museum, Lancaster 33436
Landmark Forest Heritage Park, Carrbridge 32545
Luton Museum and Art Gallery, Luton 33846
Millgate Museum, Newark-on-Trent 34014
Montrose Museum and Art Gallery, Montrose 33980
Museum of Liverpool Life, Liverpool 33542
Museum of Local Life, Worcester 34881
Museum of Smuggling History, Ventnor 34716
National Museum of Labour History, Manchester 33897
Pembroke Lodge Family History Centre and Museum, Birchington 32251
People's History Museum, Manchester 33899
People's Story Museum, Edinburgh 32938
Pickford's House Museum, Derby 32758
Powysland Museum and Montgomery Canal Centre, Welshpool 34774
Prescot Museum, Prescot 34249
Ragged School Museum, London 33755
Saint John's House, Warwick 34751
Salvation Army International Heritage Centre, London 33776
Scaplen's Court Museum, Poole 34215
Summerlee Heritage Park, Coatbridge 32645
Swaledale Folk Museum, Reeth 34291
Tain and District Museum, Tain 34637
Town House Museum of Lynn Life, King's Lynn 33392
Ulster-American Folk Park, Omagh 34118
Waterfront Museum, Poole 34216
West Berkshire Museum, Newbury 34024
West Somerset Rural Life Museum, Allerford 32024
Weymouth Museum, Weymouth 34800

U.S.A.
Birmingham Civil Rights Institute Museum, Birmingham 35508
Black Heritage Museum, Miami 38450
Chesapeake and Ohio Canal Tavern Museum, Sharpsburg 40327
The David Davis Mansion, Bloomington 35535
Prudence Crandall Museum, Canterbury 35822
The Sandor Teszler Gallery, Spartanburg 40435
Stone's Tavern Museum, Ligonier 38039
Wapello County Historical Museum, Ottumwa 39219
Wenham Museum, Wenham 41092
Yesteryear Museum, Whippany 41162

Yugoslavia
Muzej Kulturne Istorije, Požarevac 41605

Speleology

Austria
Höhlenmuseum, Obertraun 02363
Höhlenmuseum Eisensteinhöhle, Bad Fischau 01691
Höhlenmuseum in der Lurgrotte, Peggau 02380
Karst- und Höhlenkundliche Abteilung, Wien 02879
Obir-Tropfsteinhöhlen, Bad Eisenkappel 01689

Belgium
Natuurhistorisch Museum Boekenbergpark, Antwerpen 03122

Bulgaria
Muzej na Rodopskija Karst, Čepelare 04161

France
Grotte de Rouffignac, Rouffignac-Saint-Cernin 12846
Grottes d'Azé, Azé 09382
Musée Français de Spéléologie, Gagny 10632

Germany
Höhlenkundemuseum Dechenhöhle, Iserlohn 16580
Höhlenmuseum, Frasdorf 15786
Museum für Höhlenkunde, Laichingen 16934
Saalfelder Feengrotten, Saalfeld, Saale 18278

Italy
Museo Civico Geo-Speleologico, Garessio 21670
Museo di Speleologia, Borgo Grotta Gigante 21227
Museo di Speleologia Vincenzo Rivera, L'Aquila 21768

New Zealand
Waitomo Museum of Caves, Waitomo Caves 25919

Slovakia
Slovenské Múzeum Ochrany Prírody a Jaskyniarstva, Liptovský Mikuláš 28254

Slovenia
Notranjski Muzej Postojna, Postojna 28376

Switzerland
Höhlenmuseum, Sundlauenen 31292
Musée Suisse de Spéléologie, Chamoson 30689

United Kingdom
Dan-yr-Ogof Showcaves Museum, Abercrave 31974
Llechwedd Slate Caverns, Blaenau Ffestiniog 32298
Wookey Hole Cave Diving and Archaeological Museum, Wookey Hole 34878

Spirits → Wines and Spirits

Sports and Recreation

Argentina
Museo del Deporte Pierre de Coubertin, La Falda 00371
Museo Municipal del Deporte, San Fernando del Valle de Catamarca 00549
Primer Museo Permanente del Boxeo Argentino, Buenos Aires 00243

Australia
Australian Gallery of Sport and Olympic Museum, Jolimont 01115
Golf Australia House, Melbourne 01219
Museum of Western Australian Sport, Claremont, Western Australia 00907
National Motor Racing Museum, Bathurst 00766

Austria
Alpenverein-Museum, Innsbruck 02053
Eisstockmuseum, Sankt Georgen im Attergau 02547
Internationales Wintersport- und Heimatmuseum, Mürzzuschlag 02316
Jenbacher Museum, Jenbach 02079
Österreichisches Olympia- und Sportmuseum, Wien 02934
Österreichisches Wandermuseum, Alpl 01655
Salzburger Landes-Skimuseum, Werfenweng 02792
Ski- und Heimatmuseum, Sankt Anton 02538

Belgium
Sportmuseum Vlaanderen, Leuven 03533

Brazil
Museu de Esportes Mané Garrincha, Rio de Janeiro 04032

Bulgaria
Centralen Muzej na Fizičeskata Kultura i Sport, Sofia 04305

Canada
Alberta Sports Hall of Fame and Museum, Red Deer 05688
British Columbia Golf House Museum, Vancouver 06140
British Columbia Sports Hall of Fame and Museum, Vancouver 06143
Canada's Sports Hall of Fame, Toronto 06040
Canadian Baseball Hall of Fame, Toronto 06041
Canadian Football Hall of Fame and Museum, Hamilton 05025
Canadian Golf Hall of Fame, Oakville 05502
Canadian Golf Museum, Aylmer 04483
Canadian Lacrosse Hall of Fame, New Westminster 05448
Canadian Scouting Museum, Ottawa 05538
Canadian Ski Museum, Ottawa 05539
Glengarry Sports Hall of Fame, Maxville 05289
Hockey Hall of Fame, Toronto 06061
International Ice Hockey Federation Museum, Kingston 05136
Manitoba Sports Hall of Fame and Museum, Winnipeg 06308
Musée Gilles-Villeneuve, Berthierville 04535
Museum of Canada, Aquatic Hall of Fame, Winnipeg 06309
New Brunswick Sports Hall of Fame, Fredericton 04927
Northwestern Ontario Sports Hall of Fame, Thunder Bay 06019
Olympic Hall of Fame and Museum, Calgary 04638
Royal Saint John's Regatta Museum, Saint John's 05822
Saint John Sports Hall of Fame, Saint John 05807
Saskatchewan Baseball Hall of Fame and Museum, Battleford 04519
Saskatchewan Sports Hall of Fame and Museum, Regina 05716
Sports Hall of Memories, Trail 06103
Temple de la Renommée Olympique du Canada, Ottawa 05550

China, People's Republic
China Sports Museum, Beijing 06437

Croatia
Hrvatski Sportski Muzej, Zagreb 07110

Cyprus
Cyprus Olympic Committee Museum, Nicosia 07207

Czech Republic
Muzeum Tělovýchovy a Sportu, Praha 07579

Estonia
Estonian Sports Museum, Tartu 08276

Finland
Hiihtomuseo, Lahti 08580
Suomen Jääkiekko-Museo, Tampere 08931
Suomen Urheilumuseo, Helsinki 08387

France
Musée des Ballons, Balleroy 09404
Musée des XVIes Jeux Olympiques d'Hiver, Albertville 09108
Musée National du Sport, Paris 12433

Germany
Billardmuseum, München 17457
Deutsches Skimuseum, Planegg 17989
Deutsches Sport- und Olympia-Museum, Köln 16782
Fischinger Heimathaus mit Schimuseum, Fischen im Allgäu 15710
Frankfurter Sportmuseum, Frankfurt am Main 15742
Friedrich-Ludwig-Jahn-Museum, Freyburg 15829
Grünauer Wassersportmuseum, Berlin 14736
Heimat- und Ski-Museum, Braunlage 15027
Motor-Sport-Museum Hockenheimring, Hockenheim 16441
Museum im Klösterle, Peiting 17956
Schwäbisches Schützenmuseum, Kronburg 16890
Ski- und Heimatmuseum, Kurort Oberwiesenthal 16915
Ski- und Heimatmuseum Upfingen, Sankt Johann, Württemberg 18308
Skimuseum, Oberreute 17789
Sportmuseum Berlin, Berlin 14842
Sportmuseum Leipzig, Leipzig 17060
Stadtmuseum Teterow, Teterow 18697
Tennismuseum Gasber, Oberhausen, Rheinland 17775

Hungary
Testnevelési és Sportmúzeum, Budapest 19860

India
Mountaineering Museum, Darjeeling 20200
National Sportsmuseum, Patiala 20383

Israel
International Jewish Sports Hall of Fame, Netanya 20971
Pirre Gildesgame Maccabi Museum, Ramat Gan 20981

Italy
Museo Nazionale della Montagna Duca degli Abruzzi, Torino 22690

Japan
Chichibunomiya Kinen Sports Hakubutsukan, Tokyo 23583
Museum of Winter Sports, Sapporo 23473
Sports Car Museum of Japan, Gotemba 22987
Sumo Hakubutsukan, Tokyo 23675
Yakyu Taiiku Hakubutsukan, Tokyo 23705

Latvia
Latvijas Sporta Muzejs, Rīga 24081

Liechtenstein
Skimuseum, Vaduz 24180

Mexico
Museo Casa de la Bola, México 24422

Netherlands
Ajax Museum, Amsterdam 24676
Het Eerste Friese Schaatsmuseum, Hindeloopen 25163
Kaatsmuseum, Franeker 25038
Max Euwe Centrum, Amsterdam 24707
Nationaal Schaakmuseum, Den Haag 24917
Het Nederlands Sportmuseum, Biddinghuizen 24815
Nederlands Sportmuseum, Lelystad 25248
Schaatsmuseum, Venhuizen 25589

New Zealand
Bowls New Zealand Museum, New Plymouth 25845
National Cricket Museum, Wellington 25935
National Racing Museum, Auckland 25733
National Scout Museum, Kaiapoi 25813
Olympic Museum, Wellington 25941
Rugby Museum, Palmerston North 25864

Nigeria
Aaragon Museum, Lagos 25985

Norway
Kongsberg Ski Museum, Kongsberg 26141
Skimuseet, Oslo 26243
Sondre Nordheimstova, Morgedal 26190

Philippines
Phillipines Sports Hall of Fame, Intramuros 26530

Poland
Muzeum Sportu i Turystyki, Łódź 26899
Muzeum Sportu i Turystyki, Warszawa 27233
Muzeum Sportu i Turystyki Regionu Karkonoszy, Karpacz 26768
Muzeum Sportu i Turystyki Ziemi Gdańskiej, Gdańsk 26707

Russia
Muzej Grebnych Vidov Sporta, Moskva 27866
Muzej Obščestva Sporta Dinamo-Moskva, Moskva 27902
Muzej Sporta v Lužnikach, Moskva 27909

South Africa
Rugby Museum, Newlands 28550

Spain
Museu Futbol Club Barcelona President Núñez, Barcelona 28818
Museu i Centre d'Estudis de l'Esport Dr. Melcior Colet, Barcelona 28821

Sweden
Idrottsmuseet, Göteborg 30098
Idrottsmuseet, Malmö 30220
Nordiska Travmuseet i Årjäng, Årjäng 30026
Sveriges Riksidrottsmuseum, Farsta 30078
Västerbottens Museum med Svenska Skidmuseet, Umeå 30440

Switzerland
Alpines Ballonsport-Museum, Mürren 31035
Musée Olympique, Lausanne 30932
Schweizerisches Alpines Museum, Bern 30618
Schweizerisches Schützenmuseum, Bern 30619
Schweizerisches Sportmuseum, Basel 30587
Wintersport-Museum, Davos Platz 30724

Turkey
Turkish Sports Museum, Şişli 31835

United Kingdom
Artemis Archery Collection, Oldland 34116
British Cycling Museum, Camelford 32513
British Golf Museum, Saint Andrews 34358
Deep Sea Adventure and Diving Museum, Weymouth 34797
Donington Grand Prix Collection, Castle Donington 32549
James Gilbert Rugby Football Museum, Rugby 34337
Jim Clark Room, Duns 32854
Leicestershire CCC Museum, Leicester 33487
Manchester United Museum and Tour Centre, Manchester 33894
MCC Museum, London 33708
Millwall FC Museum, London 33711
Museum of Rugby, Twickenham 34702
River and Rowing Museum, Henley-on-Thames 33249
Rugby Art Gallery and Museum, Rugby 34338
Rugby School Museum, Rugby 34339
Scottish Football Museum, Glasgow 33096
Scottish Rugby Union Museum, Edinburgh 32950
Somerset Cricket Museum, Taunton 34645
Wimbledon Lawn Tennis Museum, London 33812

U.S.A.
Aiken Thoroughbred Racing Hall of Fame and Museum, Aiken 34988
American Quarter Horse Heritage Center and Museum, Amarillo 35070
American Sport Art Museum and Archives, Daphne 36381
Babe Ruth Birthplace and Baseball Center, Baltimore 35298
Black Legends of Professional Basketball Museum, Detroit 36497
College Football Hall of Fame, South Bend 40403
Colorado Ski Museum, Vail 40820
Don Garlits Museum of Drag Racing, Ocala 39104
Golf Museum, Far Hills 36802
Green Bay Packer Hall of Fame, Green Bay 37234
Greyhound Hall of Fame, Abilene 34973
Harness Racing Museum and Hall of Fame, Goshen 37187
Huntington Beach International Surfing Museum, Huntington Beach 37548
Indiana Basketball Hall of Fame, New Castle 38776
Indianapolis Motor Speedway Hall of Fame Museum, Indianapolis 37597
International Bowling Museum and Hall of Fame, Saint Louis 39966
International Swimming Hall of Fame, Fort Lauderdale 36915
International Tennis Hall of Fame Museum, Newport 38980
Kentucky Derby Museum, Louisville 38191
The Lacrosse Museum and National Hull of Fame, Baltimore 35317
Michigan Sports Hall of Fame, Detroit 36511
Naismith Memorial Basketball Hall of Fame, Springfield 40461
National Art Museum of Sport, Indianapolis 37601
National Baseball Hall of Fame and Museum, Cooperstown 36258
National Football Museum, Canton 35830
National Fresh Water Fishing Hall of Fame, Hayward 37388
National Museum of Polo and Hall of Fame, Lake Worth 37902

National Museum of Racing and Hall of Fame, Saratoga Springs 40225
National Museum of Roller Skating, Lincoln 38055
National Museum of the Morgan Horse, Shelburne 40334
The National Soccer Hall of Fame, Oneonta 39173
National Softball Hall of Fame and Museum Complex, Oklahoma City 39139
National Wrestling Hall of Fame, Stillwater 40517
New England Ski Museum, Franconia 37000
Paul W. Bryant Museum, Tuscaloosa 40773
Peter J. McGovern Little League Baseball Museum, South Williamsport 40426
Pro Rodeo Hall of Fame and Museum of the American Cowboy, Colorado Springs 36187
San Diego Hall of Champions Sports Museum, San Diego 40088
Sanford Museum, Sanford 40172
Schwartz Collection of Skiing Heritage, San Rafael 40158
South Carolina Tennis Hall of Fame, Belton 35434
South Dakota Amateur Baseball Hall of Fame, Lake Norden 37894
The Sports Museum of New England, Boston 35606
State of Oregon Sports Hall of Fame, Portland 39574
Sun'n Fun Fly-In, Lakeland 37906
Texas Sports Hall of Fame, Waco 40897
United States Hockey Hall of Fame, Eveleth 36769
United States National Ski Hall of Fame and Museum, Ishpeming 37626
Virginia Sports Hall of Fame, Portsmouth 39589
Water Ski Hall of Fame, Polk City 39520
World Figure Skating Museum and Hall of Fame, Colorado Springs 36189
World Golf Hall of Fame, Saint Augustine 39926

Stained Glass → Painted and Stained Glass

Stelae → Tombs

Stoves

Belgium
Musée Gaumais, Virton 03801

Germany
Egge-Museum Altenbeken, Altenbeken 14234
Eisenkunstgußmuseum, Witzenhausen 19160
Museum für Eisenkunstguß, Hirzenhain 16436

Netherlands
Haags Openbaar Vervoer Museum, Den Haag 24898

Norway
Bakke Bygdeminnelag, Skotselv 26302

Stucco

Germany
Schloss Salem, Salem, Baden 18289

Sugar

Austria
Österreichisches Zuckermuseum, Tulln 02717

Barbados
Sir Frank Hutson Sugar Museum, Saint James 03066

Canada
British Columbia Sugar Museum, Vancouver 06144
Maple Sugar Museum, Art Gallery and Pioneer Home, Sundridge 05989
Redpath Sugar Museum, Toronto 06080

Germany
Zucker-Museum, Berlin 14867

Guadeloupe
Ecomusée de Marie Galante, Grand Bourg 19733

U.S.A.
The Judah P. Benjamin Confederate Memorial at Gamble Plantation, Ellenton 36696

Tapestries

Belgium
Musée de la Tapisserie, Enghien 03371
Stedelijk Museum, Oudenaarde 03653
De Wit - Royal Manufacturers of Tapestries, Mechelen 03593

France
Château d'Angers, Angers 09172
Château de Langeais, Langeais 11114
Château-Musée de la Grange, Manom 11575
Château-Musée du XVe et XVIIIe Siècle, Commarin 10179
Galerie Nationale de la Tapisserie et de l'Art Textile, Beauvais 09483
Musée d'Arts et d'Histoire, Hesdin 10817
Musée de la Tapisserie Contemporaine, Angers 09175
Musée de la Tapisserie de Bayeux, Bayeux 09447
Musée Départemental de la Tapisserie, Aubusson 09295
Musée Leblanc-Duvernoy, Auxerre 09342
Musée Réattu, Arles 09247
Musée Sobirats, Carpentras 09880
Villa et Jardins Ephrussi de Rothschild, Saint-Jean-Cap-Ferrat 13052

Germany
Schloß Bruchsal, Bruchsal 15100

Italy
Museo degli Arazzi Fiamminghi, Marsala 21850
Museo Pinacoteca Santa Casa, Loreto 21805
Pinacoteca Civica Bruno Molajoli, Fabriano 21525

Netherlands
Museumboerderij New Greenwich Village, Zuidwolde, Drenthe 25693
Vierschaar Museum, Veere 25584

Spain
Museo Catedralicio, Lleida 29191
Museo Catedralicio, Zamora 29946
Museo Catedralicio de la Seo, Zaragoza 29953
Museo de Tapices, Oncala 29417
Museo Diocesano de Albarracín, Albarracín 28659
Museo Parroquial, Pastrana 29493
Real Fábrica de Tapices, Madrid 29304

Switzerland
Schloßmuseum Thun, Thun 31309

United Kingdom
Hampton Court Palace, East Molesey 32882
Lanhydrock, Bodmin 32317
Lyme Hall, Disley 32770
Occupation Tapestry Gallery and Maritime Museum, Saint Helier 34377
Upton House, Banbury 32125

Vatican City
Galleria degli Arazzi, Città del Vaticano 41394

Tea and Coffee

Angola
Museu do Café, Luanda 00087

China, People's Republic
China Tea Museum, Hangzhou 06560
Flagstaff House Museum of Tea Ware, Hong Kong 06575

Germany
Museum für Kaffeetechnik, Emmerich 15563
Museum Zum Arabischen Coffe Baum, Leipzig 17051
Das Ostfriesische Teemuseum und Norder Heimatmuseum, Norden 17712

Ireland
Bewley's Café Museum, Dublin 20734

Netherlands
Geels Co. Koffie- en Theemuseum, Amsterdam 24691
Historische Kruidenierswinkel Fa. Wijlhuizen, Velp 25586
Koffie- en Winkelmuseum, Pieterburen 25393
Museum Joure, Joure 25196
De Theefabriek, Houwerzijl 25185

Switzerland
Johann Jacobs Museum, Zürich 31450

United Kingdom
Bramah Tea and Coffee Museum, London 33593

Technology

Telecommunications → Postal Services

Television → Mass Media

Terracotta

Textiles

Theatre → Performing Arts

Tin Figures → Lead and Tin Figures

Tobacco

Tombs

Tools

Tourism

Toys and Games

Trades and Guilds

Forwarders' Museum, Prescott 05649
Hyman and Sons General Store, Gaspé 04939
Site-Historique du Banc-de-Paspébiac, Paspébiac 05568

Czech Republic
Expozice Řemesel, Moravské Budějovice 07469

Denmark
Roskilde Museums Købmandsgård, Roskilde 08027
Slagelse Museum for Handel, Håndværk og Industri, Slagelse 08055
Slagterbutikken anno 1920, Roskilde 08028

Finland
Hotelli- ja Ravintolamuseo, Helsinki 08356
Jakobstads museum, Jakobstad 08417
Kurikan Museo, Kurikka 08567
Naantalin Museo, Naantali 08695

Germany
Bäckereimuseum, Rimpar 18181
Bauern- und Handwerker-Museum, Malgersdorf 17238
Christophs Friseur-Museum, Leipheim 17022
Deutsches Fleischermuseum, Böblingen 14954
Drechsler- und Metalldrücker-Museum, Wendelstein, Mittelfranken 19040
Fränkisches Museum, Feuchtwangen 15699
Freiburger Fasnetmuseum, Freiburg im Breisgau 15808
Gildehaus Bardowick, Bardowick 14593
Handwerksmuseum am Mühlenberg, Suhlendorf 18661
Haus zur Hohen Lilie, Naumburg, Saale 17587
Heimat-und Handwerkermuseum, Leutershausen 17087
Heimatmuseum Calau, Calau 15171
Heimatmuseum der Stadt Herrnhut, Herrnhut 16405
Heimatmuseum der Stadt Ketzin, Ketzin 16721
Heimatstube Ansprung, Zöblitz 19286
Historische Gesellenherberge, Blankenburg, Harz 14919
Historischer Saal der Fischerzunft, Würzburg 19218
Historisches Museum Bamberg, Bamberg 14579
Kreismuseum, Finsterwalde 15707
Krell'sche Schmiede, Wernigerode 19055
Kulturgeschichtliches Museum Wurzen mit Ringelnatzsammlung, Wurzen 19246
Lechflößermuseum, Lechbruck 17008
Museum auf der Osterburg, Weida 18952
Museum der Stadt Mittweida "Alte Pfarrhäuser", Mittweida 17384
Museum in der Burg, Coppenbrügge 15220
Museumsstadl, Bernried, Niederbayern 14875
Schmiede Burg Schlitz, Burg Schlitz 15144
Schmiedemuseum Arfeld, Bad Berleburg 14398
Schwarzwald-Museum, Triberg 18734
Stadtmuseum im Hermansbau und Heimatmuseum Freundenthal, Memmingen 17333
Stadtmuseum Pforzheim, Pforzheim 17976
Steinhauermuseum, Randersacker 18055

Italy
Raccolte dell'Museo di Merceologia, Roma 22432

Malta
Gharb Folklore Museum, Gharb 24343

Netherlands
Stadhuismuseum, Zierikzee 25684
Tattoo Museum, Amsterdam 24737

Norway
Samvirkemuseet, Gjettum 26094

Slovakia
Považské Múzeum, Žilina 28316

United Kingdom
Blake's Lock Museum, Reading 34280
Elvaston Castle Working Estate Museum, Elvaston 32964
Guildhall Museum, Rochester 34318
Guinness Archives, London 33659
Her Majesty Customs and Excise National Museum, Liverpool 33535
History of Advertising Trust Archive, Raveningham 34273
Museum of Net Manufacture, Dorset 32796
Museum of Shops, Eastbourne 32887
Museum of Witchcraft, Cornwall 32678
National Fairground Museum, Northampton 34073
Orkney Museum, Kirkwall 33418
Stephens Collection, London 33787
Stockwood Craft Museum and Mossman Gallery, Luton 33847
Mr. Straw's House, Worksop 34888
W.H. Smith Museum, Newtown, Powys 34064

U.S.A.
Blacksmith Shop Museum, Dover-Foxcroft 36550
Forts Folle Avoine Historic Park, Danbury 36372
Grand Island Trader's Cabin, Munising 38679
Hubbell Trading Post National Historic Site, Ganado 37092
Old Market House, Galena 37073
South Sutton Old Store Museum, South Sutton 40424
Wells Fargo History Museum Old Sacramento, Sacramento 39911

Transport

Argentina
Museo de los Subterraneos, Buenos Aires 00183
Museo de Transportes, Luján 00407
Museo Histórico del Transporte Carlos Hillner Decoud, Quilmes 00486

Australia
Australian Electric Transport Museum, Saint Kilda, South Australia 01432
Brisbane Tramway Museum, Ferny Grove 01010
D.A. Wurfel Grain Collection, Pinnaroo 01361
Museum of Transportation and Rural Industries, Boyanup 00814
Victoria's Tramway Museum, Bylands 00861

Austria
Gipfelmuseum, Ehrwald 01787
Mödlinger Stadtverkehrsmuseum, Mödling 02300
Weinviertler Oldtimermuseum Poysdorf, Poysdorf 02426
Wiener Straßenbahnmuseum, Wien 02976

Belgium
Musée du Transport Urbain Bruxellois, Bruxelles 03294
Vlaams Tram- en Autobusmuseum, Berchem 03174

Brazil
Museu do Bonde, Rio de Janeiro 04040

Bulgaria
Transporten Muzej, Ruse 04278

Canada
1910 Boomtown, Saskatoon 05864
Cumberland House, Regina 05697
History of Transportation, Moose Jaw 05398
Pouce Coupe Museum, Pouce Coupe 05643
Yukon Transportation Museum, Whitehorse 06268

China, People's Republic
Xian Highway Display Center, Xian 06775

China, Republic
Chung-Cheng Aviation Museum, Taipei 06817

Czech Republic
Muzeum Silnic a Dálnic ČR, Velké Meziřiči 07696
Ústecká Bus Historické Muzeum, Chlumec u Ústi nad Labem 07295

Denmark
Lolland-Falsters Traktor- og Motormuseum, Eskildstrup 07796

Egypt
Transportation Museum, Cairo 08236

Finland
Keski-Suomen Tieliikennemuseo, Kintaus 08509
Mobilia, Kangasala 08455
Raitioliikennemuseo, Helsinki 08376
Saimaan Kanavan Museo, Lappeenranta 08603

France
Musée de la Poste et des Voyages, Amboise 09144
Musée des Transports, du Tourisme et des Communications, Toulouse 13732

Germany
Bremerhavener Versorgungs- und Verkehrsmuseum, Bremerhaven 15071
DB Museum im Verkehrsmuseum Nürnberg, Nürnberg 17734
Deutsches Straßenmuseum, Germersheim 15946
Deutsches Technikmuseum Berlin, Berlin 14699
Eisenbahnmuseum Lehmann, Hofheim, Unterfranken 16464
Emslandmuseum Papenburg, Papenburg 17933
Flößerei- und Verkehrsmuseum, Gengenbach 15928
Hannoversches Straßenbahn-Museum, Sehnde 18467
Heimat- und Flößermuseum Calmbach, Bad Wildbad 14534
Historisches Straßenbahn-Depot Sankt Peter, Nürnberg 17744
Museum Industriekultur mit Motorradmuseum, Schulmuseum und Kinderabteilung, Nürnberg 17752
Technik Museum Speyer, Speyer 18550
Technik- und Verkehrsmuseum, Stade 18564
Unterfränkisches Verkehrsmuseum, Gemünden am Main 15927
Verkehrsmuseum Dresden, Dresden 15433
Verkehrsmuseum Karlsruhe, Karlsruhe 16662
Verkehrsmuseum Schwanheim der Verkehrsgesellschaft Frankfurt am Main, Frankfurt am Main 15779

Hungary
Közlekedési Múzeum, Budapest 19825
Millenniumi Földalatti Vasúti Múzeum, Budapest 19838
Városi Tömegközlekedési Múzeum, Budapest 19863

Italy
Museo Europeo dei Trasporti Ogliari, Ranco 22282

Japan
Chikatetsu Hakabutsukan, Tokyo 23585
Kotsu Hakubutsukan, Tokyo 23623
Kotsu Kagaku Hakubutsukan, Osaka 23425
Umekoji Steam Locomotive Museum, Kyoto 23276

Lithuania
Bicycle Museum, Šiauliai 24188

Luxembourg
Musée des Tramway et Autobus, Luxembourg 24226

Namibia
Transnamib Museum, Windhoek 24639

Netherlands
Amsterdams Openbaar Vervoer Museum, Amsterdam 24679
Openbaar Vervoer Museum, Borculo 24828
Openbaar Vervoer Museum, Rotterdam 25444
Rijdend Tram Museum, Ouddorp 25376
Tram Museum Rotterdam, Rotterdam 25449

New Zealand
Dunedin Museum of Transport and Technology, Dunedin 25770
East Coast Museum of Technology, Gisborne 25792
Ferrymead Heritage Park, Christchurch 25750
Museum of Transport and Technology, Auckland 25732
National Trolleybus Museum, Foxton 25791
Yaldhurst Museum of Transport and Science, Christchurch 25758

Norway
Haldensvassdragets Kanalmuseum, Ørje 26209
Norsk Vegmuseum, Fåberg 26076

Poland
Okręgowe Muzeum Techniki Drogowej i Mostowej Okręgu Lubelskiego przy Zarządzie Dróg w Zamościu, Zamość 27313

Portugal
Museu do Carro Eléctrico, Porto 27427

Russia
Muzej Istorii Moskovskogo Metropolitena, Moskva 27870
Muzej Morskogo Flota, Moskva 27895

South Africa
Heidelberg Motor Museum, Heidelberg 28494
James Hall Museum of Transport, Johannesburg 28512
Outeniqua Railway Museum, George 28478

Sweden
Holmgrens Volkswagenmuseum, Pålsboda 30279
Kanalmuseet Skantzen, Hallstahammar 30117
Norrbottens Järnvägsmuseum, Luleå 30204

Switzerland
Verkehrshaus der Schweiz, Luzern 30983

United Kingdom
Aston Manor Transport Museum, Birmingham 32259
Aycliffe and District Bus Preservation Society, Newton Aycliffe 34057
Birkenhead Tramways and Taylor Street Large Object Collections, Birkenhead 32254
Bournemouth Transport Museum, Bournemouth 32338
Bury Transport Museum, Bury, Lancashire 32465
Castle Point Transport Museum, Canvey Island 32524
City of Portsmouth Preserved Transport Depot, Portsmouth 34233
Cobham Bus Museum, Cobham 32647
Cotswold Motoring Museum and Toy Collection, Bourton-on-the-Water 32341
Dover Transport Museum, Whitfield 34814
East Anglia Transport Museum, Carlton Colville 32540
Grampian Transport Museum, Alford, Aberdeenshire 32021
Ipswich Transport Museum, Ipswich 33332
Launceston Steam Railway, Launceston 33452
Lincolnshire Road Transport Museum, Lincoln 33518
Llangollen Motor Museum, Llangollen 33568
London's Transport Museum, London 33702
Manchester Museum of Transport, Manchester 33892
Museum of Transport, Glasgow 33086
National Motor Museum, Brockenhurst 32422
Nottingham Transport Heritage Centre, Ruddington 34332
Oxford Bus Museum Trust, Long Hanborough 33823
Pendon Museum of Miniature Landscape and Transport, Long Wittenham 33825
Sandtoft Transport Centre, Doncaster 32782
Sheffield Bus Museum, Sheffield 34462
Snibston Discovery Park, Coalville 32644
Springburn Museum, Glasgow 33098
Stondon Museum, Lower Stondon 33838
Streetlife, Kingston-upon-Hull 33403
Ulster Folk and Transport Museum, Holywood 33286
War Room and Motor House Collection, Harrogate 33201
Workshop and Stores, Grangemouth 33140

U.S.A.
American Bicycle and Cycling Museum, Santa Fe 40189
Atchinson, Topeka and Santa Fe Depot, Alden 35026
Baltimore Streetcar Museum, Baltimore 35303
Carriage House Museum, Colorado Springs 36180
Central Texas Museum of Automotive History, Rosanky 39863
Cole Land Transportation Museum, Bangor 35336
Connecticut Trolley Museum, East Windsor 36623
Cookeville Depot Museum, Cookeville 36253
Delaware and Hudson Canal Historical Society Museum, High Falls 37420
Estes-Winn Antique Automobile Museum, Asheville 35167
Forney Transportation Museum, Denver 36473
The Franklin Museum, Tucson 40750
Genesee Country Village and Museum, Mumford 38673
Hollenberg Pony Express Station Museum, Hanover 37332
Indiana Transportation Museum, Noblesville 39008
Lake Waccamaw Depot Museum, Lake Waccamaw 37899
Long Island Museum of American Art, History Cariages, Stony Brook 40531
Michigan State Trust for Railway Preservation, Owosso 39228
Michigan Transit Museum, Mount Clemens 38648
Miracle of America Museum, Polson 39521
Museum of Transportation, Brookline 35695
Museum of Transportation, Saint Louis 39974
National Road/Zane Grey Museum, Norwich 39071
New York Museum of Transportation, West Henrietta 41111
New York Transit Museum, Brooklyn 35703
Orange Empire Railway Museum, Perris 39327
Owls Head Transportation Museum, Owls Head 39226
Patee House Museum, Saint Joseph 39951
Pioneer Auto Museum, Murdo 38682
Portholes Into the Past, Medina 38403
Railways to Yesterday, Rockhill Furnace 39835
R.E. Olds Transportation Museum, Lansing 37935
Seashore Trolley Museum, Kennebunkport 37766
Shore Line Trolley Museum, East Haven 36614
Sloan Museum, Flint 36849
Southern Museum of Flight, Birmingham 35512
Stanley Museum, Kingfield 37806
Steamtown National Historic Site, Scranton 40275
Studebaker National Museum, South Bend 40407
Swigart Museum, Huntingdon 37540
Transportation Exhibits, Nevada City 38751
Travel Town Museum, Los Angeles 38173
United States Army Transportation Museum, Fort Eustis 36900
Virginia Museum of Transportation, Roanoke 39805
Wade House and Wesley Jung Carriage Museum, Greenbush 37242
Wells Fargo History Museum, Minneapolis 38540
Wells Fargo History Museum, Sacramento 39910
West Chicago City Museum, West Chicago 41101
Wheels O' Time Museum, Peoria 39325
Whitewater Canal Historic Site, Metamora 38444
Wisconsin Automotive Museum, Hartford 37367
Yankee Candle Car Museum, South Deerfield 40413

Venezuela
Museo del Transporte Guillermo José Schael, Caracas 41433

Travel → Tourism

Treasuries

Austria
Museum und Schatzkammer des Deutschen Ordens, Wien 02924

Belgium
Krypte en Schatkamer van de O.L.V. Basiliek, Halle 03436
Trésor de la Cathedrale Notre-Dame, Tournai 03779
Trésor de la Collegiale Sainte-Begge, Andenne 03090

Croatia
Riznica Franjevačkog Samostana Split, Split 07076
Riznica Katedrala, Dubrovnik 06989

Denmark
Rosenborg Slot, København 07933

France
Musée-Trésor d'Église - Art Sacré, Charroux 10003
Musées de Sens, Sens 13497
Palais du Tau, Reims 12721

Germany
Domschatz, Trier 18739
Domschatzmuseum, Regensburg 18092
Kirchenschatz im Sankt Fridolinsmünster, Bad Säckingen 14501
Schatzkammer der Residenz München, München 17516

Italy
Capitolo del Duomo, Chieri 21409
Museo del Tesoro del Duomo, Monza 22002
Museo del Tesoro del Duomo, Vigevano 22865
Museo del Tesoro della Cattedrale, Anagni 21061
Museo del Tesoro della Cattedrale di San Lorenzo, Genova 21695

Treasuries

Museo Tesoro dell'Arcivescovado, Cosenza 21480
Tesoro del Duomo, Enna 21517
Tesoro del Duomo, Messina 21887
Tesoro del Duomo, Rieti 22308
Tesoro del Duomo di San Giorgio, Ragusa 22280
Tesoro della Cattedrale, Veroli 22833
Tesoro della Chiesa di San Pietro, Calascibetta 21273

Japan
Honda Museum, Kanazawa 23120
Meiji Jingu Homotsuden, Tokyo 23635
Suifu Meitokukai Foundation Tokugawa Museum, Mito 23322

Netherlands
Schatkamer van de Kathedrale Basiliek Sint-Bavo, Haarlem 25096

Russia
Almaznyj fond, Moskva 27788

Spain
Museo Catedralicio, Granada 29115
Museo-Tesoro Catedralicio y Diocesano, Calahorra 28892
Museu-Tresor Parroquial, Olot 29415
Tresor de la Catedral, Girona 29101

Sweden
Skattkammaren, Stockholm 30381

Switzerland
Klostermuseum, Muri (Aargau) 31039
Museum Münster, Münster 31034
Trésor de la Cathédrale Notre-Dame-du-Glarier, Sion 31246

Turkey
Topkapi Sarayi Müzesi, İstanbul 31757

United Kingdom
Christ Church Cathedral Treasury, Oxford 34130
Durham Cathedral Treasures of Saint Cuthbert, Durham 32858

Yugoslavia
Riznica Srpske Pravoslavne Crkve u Kotoru, Kotor 41561

Typography → Books, Book Art and Manuscripts

Uniforms, Military

Australia
W.A. Scout Museum, West Perth 01590

Belgium
Bastogne Historical Center, Bastogne 03159
Museum Slag der Zilveren Helmen, Halen 03433

Brazil
Museu da Força Expedicionária Brasileira - FEB, Rio de Janeiro 04021
Museu do Monumento Nacional aos Mortos da Segunda Guerra Mundial, Rio de Janeiro 04046

Canada
Battlefield House Museum, Stoney Creek 05963
Black Watch of Canada Regimental Memorial Museum, Montréal 05358
Canadian Force Base Gagetown Military Museum, Oromocto 05521
Canadian War Museum, Ottawa 05540
Jamieson Museum, Moosomin 05402
Lord Strathcona's Horse Museum, Calgary 04633
Military Communications and Electronics Museum, Kingston 05141
Queen's Own Cameron Highlanders of Canada Regimental Museum, Winnipeg 06312
Royal Canadian Artillery Museum, Shilo 05917
The Royal Canadian Regiment Museum, London 05235
Royal Military College of Canada Museum, Kingston 05146

Denmark
Forsvarsmuseet på Bornholm, Rønne 08022
Tøjhusmuseet, København 07937

Finland
Mannerheim Museo, Helsinki 08367
Ratsuväkimuseo, Lappeenranta 08602

France
Musée de la Gendarmerie, Melun 11707

Germany
Ordenmuseum, Neuffen 17635
Städtisches Museum Abtshof, Jüterbog 16622

Ghana
Ghana Armed Forces Museum, Kumasi 19311

India
Army Medical Corps Centre Museum, Lucknow 20336
Fort Museum, Chennai 20187

Indonesia
Museum Abri Satriamandala, Jakarta 20500

Ireland
Mullingar Military Museum, Mullingar 20822

Italy
Museo della Battaglia, San Martino della Battaglia 22493
Museo dell'Istituto Storico e di Cultura dell'Arma del Genio, Roma 22380
Museo Storico della Fanteria, Roma 22411

Netherlands
Collectie Militaire Traditie, Oosterhout 25357
Historisch Museum Grenadiers en Jagers, Arnhem 24764
Marinemuseum, Den Helder 24934
Somme Museum, Schagen 25464
Traditiekamer Regiment Stoottroepen, Ermelo 25032

New Zealand
Queen Elizabeth II Army Memorial Museum, Waiouru 25913

Pakistan
Pakistan Army Museum, Rawalpindi 26425

Poland
Muzeum Bitwy Grunwaldzkiej, Stębark 27116

Puerto Rico
Museum of Military and Naval History, San Juan 27467

Russia
Centralnyj Voenno-morskoj Muzej, Sankt-Peterburg 28020

South Africa
Castle Military Museum, Cape Town 28435

Thailand
Royal Thai Navy Museum, Samut Prakan 31587

United Kingdom
Aldershot Military Museum and Rushmoor Local History Gallery, Aldershot 32013
Argyll and Sutherland Highlanders Regimental Museum, Stirling 34560
Bankfield Museum, Halifax 33179
Border Regiment and King's Own Royal Border Regiment Museum, Carlisle 32536
Cheshire Military Museum, Chester 32596
Duke of Cornwall's Light Infantry Museum, Bodmin 32316
Durham Light Infantry Museum and Durham Art Gallery, Durham 32860
East Lancashire Regiment Museum, Blackburn, Lancashire 32292
Fusiliers' Museum Lancashire, Bury, Lancashire 32466
Herefordshire Light Infantry Regimental Museum, Hereford 33255
Household Cavalry Museum, Windsor 34853
Kent and Sharpshooters Yeomanry Museum, Edenbridge 32903
King's Own Scottish Borderers Regimental Museum, Berwick-upon-Tweed 32221
Military Museum of Devon and Dorset, Dorchester 32788
National War Museum of Scotland, Edinburgh 32935
Queen's Own Hussars Museum, Warwick 34749
Regimental Museum of The Queen's Own Highlanders, Seaforth Highlanders and The Queen's Own Cameron Highlanders, Inverness 33328
Royal Army Veterinary Corps Museum, Aldershot 32017
Royal Corps of Transport Museum, Aldershot 32018
Royal Irish Fusiliers Museum, Armagh 32069
Royal Scots Regimental Museum, Edinburgh 32944
Royal Signals Museum, Blandford Forum 32306
Royal Sussex Regiment Museum, Eastbourne 32890
Royal Ulster Rifles Regimental Museum, Belfast 32203
Somerset Military Museum, Taunton 34646
South Wales Borderers and Monmouthshire Regimental Museum of the Royal Regiment of Wales, Brecon 32372
Wiltshire Regiment Museum, Devizes 32765
Winchcombe Folk and Police Museum, Winchcombe 34835
Worcestershire Yeomanry Cavalry Museum, Worcester 34885

U.S.A.
Military Historians Museum, Westbrook 41129

Yugoslavia
Muzej Stara Livnica, Kragujevac 41563

Vehicles

Andorra
Museu Nacional de l'Automòbil, Encamp 00072

Argentina
Museo Argentino de Motos Antiguas, Mendoza 00425
Museo del Automóvil, Buenos Aires 00189
Museo del Automóvil, Luján 00408
Museo del Automóvil Club Argentino, Buenos Aires 00190
Museo del Automóvil de Santa Teresita, Santa Teresita 00606
Museo del Automovilismo Juan Manuel Fangio, Balcarce 00121
Museo Ramos Generales, Villa María 00662

Australia
Alambee Auto and Folk Museum, Echuca 00988
Australian Electric Transport Museum, Saint Kilda, South Australia 01432
Binalong Motor Museum, Binalong 00792
Canberra Bicycle Museum, Dickson 00968
Chiltern Motor Museum, Chiltern 00900
Cobb and Co Museum, Toowoomba 01538
Gippsland Heritage Park, Moe 01252
H. B. Lamb Early Transport Buggy Museum, Camperdown 00872
Latrobe Bicycle Race Club Museum, Latrobe 01154
Motorcycle Haven, Adelaide River 00709
National Automobile Museum of Tasmania, Launceston 01158
National Motorcycle Museum, Mitchell 01251
Pine Ridge Car Museum, Main Ridge 01185
Powerhouse House and Car Museum, Portland 01392
Raverty's Motor Museum, Echuca 00991
Serpentine Vintage Tractors and Machinery Museum, Serpentine 01444
Tasman Antique Motor Museum, Ranelagh 01406

Austria
Automobil-Museum Siegfried Marcus, Stockerau 02671
Automobil- und Motorradmuseum Austria, Mitterndorf an der Fischa 02295
Automobilhistorisches Museum, Linz 02219
Automobilmuseum, Aspang 01677
Fahrradmuseum, Ybbs 03012
Kutschenmuseum, Laa an der Thaya 02165
Motorrad-Museum Krems-Egelsee, Krems 02150
Motorradmuseum, Neunkirchen, Niederösterreich 02341
Motorradmuseum, Sulz 02681
Museum Fahrzeug-Technik-Luftfahrt, Lauffen 02184
Nostalgie auf Rädern - Fahrzeugmuseum, Großklein 01953
Das Österreichische Motorradmuseum, Eggenburg 01785
Österreichisches Straßenbahn- und Lokalbahnbetriebsmuseum, Mariazell 02266
Oldtimer-Museum, Gmunden 01891
Oldtimermuseum, Ardagger 01673
Oldtimermuseum im Schloß, Blindenmarkt 01733
Porsche Automuseum Helmut Pfeifhofer, Gmünd, Kärnten 01884
Radmuseum anno dazumal, Altmünster 01664
Tauernstraßen-Museum, Eben im Pongau 01770
Traktorveteranensammlung Dorf an der Pram, Wendling 02788
Villacher Fahrzeugmuseum, Villach 02734

Barbados
Mallalieu Motor Museum, Christ Church 03064

Belgium
Automuseum Old Timer, Lo-Reninge 03563
Autoworld, Bruxelles 03233
Nationaal Wielermuseum, Roeselare 03679

Canada
Canadian Automotive Museum, Oshawa 05524
Car Life Museum, Bonshaw 04557
Cosmodôme, Laval 05192
Gervais Wheels Museum, Alida 04431
Gratton's Weldwood Museum, London 05227
Heaman's Antique Autorama, Carman 04672
Manitoba Automobile Museum, Elkhorn 04867
Musée Automobile, Saint-Jacques 05793
Musée Jean-Hotte, Saint-Eustache 05785
Reynolds Museum, Wetaskiwin 06254
Spoke Wheel Car Museum, Charlottetown 04694
Streetcar and Electric Railway Museum, Milton 05319
Trev Deeley Motorcycle Museum, Richmond 05734

Chile
Auto Museum Moncopulli, Osorno 06375

China, People's Republic
Grand Prix Museum, Macau 06641

Cuba
Depósito del Automóvil, La Habana 07138

Czech Republic
African Safari and Veteran Car Museum, Dvůr Králové nad Labem 07319
Automuseum E.R. Prihoda, Praha 07547
Muzeum Bicyklů, Rokycany 07619
Muzeum Historických Motocyklů, Kašperské Hory 07389
Muzeum Motocyklů, Lesná u Znojma 07428
První České Muzeum Velocipédů, Chotěboř 07299
Škoda Auto Museum, Mladá Boleslav 07464
Technické Muzeum Tatra, Kopřivnice 07404
Ústecká Bus Historické Muzeum, Chlumec u Ústi nad Labem 07295

Denmark
Aalholm Automobil Museum, Nysted 07985
Danmarks Cykelmuseum, Ålestrup 07751
Egeskov Veteranmuseum, Kværndrup 07948
Jysk Automobilmuseum, Gjern 07824
Radio- og Motorcykel Museet, Stubbekøbing 08066

Finland
Tiemuseo, Helsinki 08395

France
Collection Schlumpf, Mulhouse 11987
Espace Automobiles Matra, Romorantin-Lanthenay 12806
Manoir Automobile, Lohéac 11431
Musée Auto Moto Vélo, Châtellerault 10045
Musée de l'Automobile, Grenoble 10742
Musée de l'Automobile, Valençay 13835
Musée de l'Automobile, Velaine-en-Haye 13897
Musée de l'Automobile du Mans, Le Mans 11224
Musée de l'Automobile Française, Reims 12713
Musée de l'Automobile Miniature, Fontenay-sur-Mer 10574
Musée de l'Automobiliste, Mougins 11960
Musée de Voitures Anciennes et Sellerie, Menetou-Salon 11714
Musée des Arts et Metiers, Paris 12379
Musée Henri Malartre, Rochetaillée-sur-Saône 12791
Musée Militaire, Clères 10126
Musée National de la Voiture et du Tourisme, Compiègne 10184

Germany
August Horch Museum Zwickau, Zwickau 19294
Auto Museum Dr. Carl Benz, Ladenburg 16925
Auto-Museum Fritz B. Busch, Wolfegg 19172
Auto-Sammlung Gut-Hand, Aachen 14160
Auto Technik Museum, Sinsheim 18507
Auto- und Motorradmuseum, Witzenhausen 19159
Auto- und Spielzeugmuseum Boxenstop, Tübingen 18752
Automobil-Museum, Asendorf bei Bruchhausen-Vilsen 14328
Automobil-Veteranen-Salon, Gundelfingen an der Donau 16142
Automuseum Engstingen, Engstingen 15580
Automuseum Störy, Bockenem 14946
AutoMuseum Volkswagen, Wolfsburg 19182
Auwärter-Museum, Stuttgart 18623
BMW Museum, München 17458
Deutsches Automuseum Schloss Langenburg, Langenburg 16971
Deutsches Zweirad- und NSU-Museum, Neckarsulm 17596
EFA Museum für Deutsche Automobilgeschichte, Amerang 14270
Erstes Deutsches Motorroller-Museum, Aschaffenburg 14311
Erstes Niederbayerisches Automobil- und Motorrad-Museum, Adlkofen 14189
Fahrradmuseum der Fahrrad-Veteranen-Freunde-Dresden 1990, Dresden 15400
Fahrzeugmuseum, Egelsbach 15497
Fahrzeugmuseum Marxzell, Marxzell 17290
Fahrzeugmuseum Suhl, Suhl 18659
Heinrich-Büssing-Haus, Wolfsburg 19184
Historische Fahrzeugsammlung, Simmelsdorf 18499
Horster Motorrad-Museum, Gelsenkirchen 15922
Landwirtschaftliches Museum Wetzlar, Wetzlar 19083
Mercedes-Benz Museum, Stuttgart 18637
Motor-Sport-Museum Hockenheimring, Hockenheim 16441
Motorrad-Museum, Augustusburg 14360
Motorrad Museum, Ibbenbüren 16535
Motorradmuseum, Michelstadt 17356
Museum für Kutschen, Chaisen, Karren, Heidenheim an der Brenz 16347
Museum Mobile, Ingolstadt 16568
Niederrheinisches Motorradmuseum, Moers 17402
Niedersächsisches Kutschenmuseum, Lilienthal 17103
Norddeutsches Auto- und Motorrad-Museum, Bad Oeynhausen 14487
Oldenburger Fahrradmuseum, Oldenburg, Oldenburg 17852
Porsche Museum, Stuttgart 18640
Rosso Bianco-Auto Museum, Aschaffenburg 14317
Rübesams Da Capo Oldtimermuseum, Leipzig 17054
Schlepper-, Auto- und Gerätemuseum Hesse, Aidhausen 14201
Schnauferlstall, Ruhpolding 18276
Werksmuseum Achse, Rad und Wagen, Wiehl 19094
Westfalia-Auto-Museum, Rheda-Wiedenbrück 18156

Ireland
An Dun Transport and Heritage Museum, Ballinahown 20689
Celbridge Motor Museum, Celbridge 20716
Fethard Park and Folk Museum, Fethard 20772
Museum of Irish Transport, Killarney 20791
National Transport Museum, Dublin 20755
Rathgory Transport Museum, Dunleer 20768

Italy
Centro Storico Fiat, Torino 22664
Museo della Carrozza, Macerata 21820
Museo dell'Automobile Carlo Biscaretti di Ruffia, Torino 22679
Museo delle Carrozze, Maser 21853
Museo delle Carrozze, Trani 22706

Japan
Ferrari Museum, Gotemba 22986

Veterinary Medicine

Viticulture → Wines and Spirits

**Voyages of Discovery → Scientific
Expeditions**

Wallpaper

Water

Wax, Molded

Weapons → Arms and Armour

Weaving

Webereimuseum, Breitenberg, Niederbayern 15047
Weberhausmuseum, Schauenstein 18321
Wirker- und Strickermuseum, Apolda 14299

Greece
Municipal Ethnographic Museum, Ioannina 19467
Nomikos Collection, Pyrgos 19631
Vlachos Collection, Mytilini 19583

Kuwait
Sadu House, Kuwait 23971

Netherlands
Museumboerderij, Staphorst 25513
Museumboerderij Vreeburg, Schagen 25463

Norway
Hadeland Folkemuseum, Jaren 26128

Poland
Muzeum Okręgowe, Bielsko-Biała 26631

Sweden
Textilmuseet, Borås 30045

Switzerland
Weberei- und Heimatmuseum Ruedertal, Schmiedrued 31209

United Kingdom
Bancroft Mill Engine Trust, Barnoldswick 32138
Mill Trail Visitor Centre, Alva 32041
Newtown Textile Museum, Newtown, Powys 34061
Paisley Museum and Art Gallery, Paisley 34147
Weaver's Cottage, Kilbarchan 33377
Weavers Cottage Museum, Airdrie 32007

U.S.A.
Handweaving Museum and Arts Center, Clayton 36112
Watkins Woolen Mill, Lawson 37975

Weights and Measures

Germany
Adam-Ries-Museum, Annaberg-Buchholz 14285
Stadtmuseum Oschatz, Oschatz 17867
Zirkelmuseum, Wilhelmsdorf, Mittelfranken 19117

Netherlands
NMI-Museum IJkwezen, Delft 24886

Poland
Muzeum Miar - Zbiory Metrologiczne Głównego Urzędu Miar, Warszawa 27222

United Kingdom
Avery Historical Museum, Smethwick 34500
Westgate Museum, Winchester 34848

Whaling → Fishing and Fisheries

Wines and Spirits

Australia
Grapevine Museum, Chiltern 00901
Pioneer Rum Museum, Beenleigh 00778
Tasmania Distillery Museum, Hobart 01093

Austria
Bezirksmuseum Döbling, Wien 02821
Brennereimuseum am Hitzlhammer, Sankt Oswald bei Freistadt 02568
Galerie und Weinmuseum Schloß Gamlitz, Gamlitz 01856
Heimatmuseum, Grafenwörth 01901
Kellermuseum, Falkenstein 01813
Mostmuseum, Neumarkt im Mühlkreis 02337
Mostmuseum, Sankt Leonhard am Forst 02559
Österreichs größter historischer Weinkeller, Retz 02489
Pulkautaler Weinbaumuseum, Hadres 01982
Schlumberger Wein- und Sektkellerei, Wien 02957
Stadtmuseum mit Weinmuseum, Bad Vöslau 01714
Weinbau- und Landwirtschaftsmuseum, Hadersdorf 01980
Weinbaumuseum, Reidling 02483
Weinbaumuseum, Güssing 01965
Weinmuseum Kitzeck, Kitzeck im Sausal 02111
Weinmuseum Prellenkirchen, Prellenkirchen 02436
Weinstadtmuseum Krems, Krems 02151
Winzerhaus, Poppendorfberg 02419

Belgium
Nationaal Jenevermuseum, Hasselt 03451

Canada
The Wine Museum, Kelowna 05112

China, People's Republic
Macau Wine Museum, Macau 06643

France
Château du Clos de Vougeot, Vougeot 14084
Collection Vini-Viticole et de Tonnellerie, Zellenberg 14130
Ecomusée de la Distillerie et du Pays Fougerollais, Fougerolles (Haute-Saône) 10596
Musée de la Distillerie, Pontarlier 12609
Musée de la Distillerie Combier, Saumur 13428
Musée de la Pomme et du Cidre, Pleudihen-sur-Rance 12547
Musée de la Tonnellerie et du Vin, Aloxe-Corton 09128
Musée de la Tradition Champenoise, Épernay 10431
Musée de la Vigne, Gornac 10688
Musée de la Vigne et du Vin, Lézignan-Corbières 11359
Musée de la Vigne et du Vin, Lods 11430
Musée de la Vigne et du Vin de Franche-Comté, Arbois 09220
Musée de l'Armagnac, Condom 10196
Musée des Vins de Touraine, Tours 13759
Musée du Château de Cassaigne, Cassaigne 09887
Musée du Cidre, Montaure 11830
Musée du Vignoble et des Vins d'Alsace, Kientzheim 10912
Musée du Vignoble Nantais, Le Pallet 11245
Musée du Vin, Paris 12401
Musée du Vin, Saint-Hilaire-de-Loulay 13040
Musée du Vin dans l'Art, Pauillac 12474
Musée du Vin de Bourgogne, Beaune 09481
Musée du Vin de Champagne Piper-Heidsieck, Reims 12715
Musée du Vin de la Batellerie et de la Tonnellerie, Bergerac 09518
Musée Municipal d'Archéologie et du Vin de Champagne, Épernay 10433
Musée Régional du Cidre et du Calvados, Valognes 13862
Musée Viticole Charles-Bernard, Fixin 10542

Germany
Baierweinmuseum, Bach an der Donau 14371
Brennereimuseum Haselünne, Haselünne 16296
Dampfkornbranntweinbrennerei-Museum, Wildeshausen 19115
Deutsches Weinbaumuseum, Oppenheim 17855
Dorfmuseum, Pfaffenweiler 17971
Dorfmuseum Hanweiler, Winnenden 19134
Erstes Korkenziehermuseum der Welt, Kreuth 16874
Frankfurter Äpfelwein-Museum, Frankfurt am Main 15739
Heimat-Museum Maintal, Maintal 17227
Heimatmuseum Dornstetten, Dornstetten 15371
Historisches Museum der Pfalz, Speyer 18548
Hohenloher Freilandmuseum, Schwäbisch Hall 18410
Kaiserstühler Weinbaumuseum, Vogtsburg 18858
Kelter- und Weinbaumuseum, Niederstetten 17699
Kupferberg-Museum, Mainz 17231
Markgräfler Museum Müllheim, Müllheim 17444
Mittelmoselmuseum im Barockhaus Böcking, Traben-Trarbach 18721
Museum Bürgstadt, Bürgstadt 15137
Museum für Weinbau und Stadtgeschichte, Edenkoben 15491
Museum für Weinkultur, Deidesheim 15285
Neckarschiffahrts-Museum und Weinbau, Heilbronn 16357
Rheingauer Weinmuseum Brömserburg e.V., Rüdesheim am Rhein 18266
Schnapsmuseum, Kötzting 16839
Schwäbisches Schnapsmuseum, Bönnigheim 14960
Sieben-Keltern-Museum, Metzingen 17352
Stadtmuseum Herrenmühle, Hammelburg 16255
Tauberländer Dorfmuseum, Weikersheim 18960
Vinarium, Cleebronn 15204
Wein- und Heimatmuseum, Durbach 15473
Weinbau- und Heimatmuseum, Klingenberg am Main 16763
Weinbaumuseum, Flörsheim-Dalsheim 15718
Weinbaumuseum Alte Kelter, Erlenbach, Kreis Heilbronn 15629
Weinbaumuseum der Winzergenossenschaft, Ortenberg, Baden 17862
Weinbaumuseum im Herrenhof, Neustadt an der Weinstraße 17680
Weinbaumuseum Meersburg, Meersburg 17312
Weinbaumuseum Stuttgart-Uhlbach, Stuttgart 18650
Weinmuseum, Vaihingen 18813
Weinmuseum Schlagkamp-Desoye Senheim, Senheim 18480
Winzermuseum Rauenberg, Rauenberg 18075

Hungary
Présház, Tokaji 20060
Tokaji Múzeum, Tokaji 20061

Ireland
Locke's Distillery Museum, Kilbeggan 20783
The Old Jameson Distillery, Dublin 20757

Italy
Enoteca Regionale Permanente la Serenissima, Gradisca d'Isonzo 21714
Museo Atesino del Vino, Caldaro 21275
Museo del Vino, Quaranti 22269
Museo del Vino, Torgiano 22659
Museo della Vite e del Vino della Val di Sieve, Rufina 22450
Museo delle Contadinerie Bersano, Nizza Monferrato 22037

Museo dell'Enoteca Regionale Piemontese, Grinzane Cavour 21718
Museo di Storia dell'Agricoltura, Cesena 21399
Museo Martini di Storia dell'Enologia, Pessione 22176
Museo Ratti dei Vini di Alba, La Morra 21761
Raccolta Bersano delle Stampe sul Vino, Nizza Monferrato 22038

Luxembourg
Freilichtmuseum Schwebsingen, Bech-Kleinmacher 24202
Musée du Vin, Ehnen 24215

Netherlands
Nationaal Likeur- en Frisdrankenmuseum Isidorus Jonkers, Hilvarenbeek 25160
Nederlands Gedistilleerd Museum De gekroonde Branduskatel, Schiedam 25470
Nederlands Wijnmuseum, Arnhem 24771
Het Wijnkopersgildehuys, Amsterdam 24746
Wijnmuseum, Lent 25254
Wijnmuseum De Keyser onder 't Boterhuys, Delft 24890

Poland
Muzeum Ziemi Lubuskiej, Zielona Góra 27320

Portugal
Museu Rural e do Vinho do Concelho, Cartaxo 27347

Slovakia
Malokarpatské Vinohradnicke Múzeum, Pezinok 28278

South Africa
Groot Constantia Manor House and Wine Museum, Constantia 28451

Spain
Cortijo Bacardi, Málaga 29312

Sweden
Vin- och Sprithistoriska Museet Stiftelsen, Stockholm 30399

Switzerland
Argauisch Kantonales Weinbaumuseum, Tegerfelden 31299
Haus zum Torggel, Berneck 30621
Heimat- und Rebbaumuseum, Spiez 31260
Musée de la Vigne et du Vin, Aigle 30506
Musée International de l'Etiquette, Aigle 30507
Musée Régional d'Histoire et d'Artisanat du Val-de-Travers, Môtiers 31023
Musée Valaisan de la Vigne et du Vin, Muraz 31038
Orts- und Weinbaumuseum, Neftenbach 31047
Ortsmuseum Höngg, Zürich 31469
Rebbaumuseum am Bielersee, Ligerz 30947
Schaffhauser Weinbaumuseum, Hallau 30858
Walliser Reb- und Weinmuseum, Salgesch 31161
Weinbau-Museum, Chur 30705
Weinbaumuseum am Zürichsee, Au, Zürich 30542
Weinbaumuseum Jenins, Jenins 30886

United Kingdom
Cider Museum, Hereford 33253
Glenfarclas Distillery Museum, Ballindalloch 32115
Glenfiddich Distillery Museum, Dufftown 32820
Harvey's Wine Museum, Bristol 32223
Lindisfarne Wine and Spirit Museum, Berwick-upon-Tweed 32223
Scotch Whisky Heritage Centre, Edinburgh 32947
Sheppy's Farm and Cider Museum, Bradford-on-Tone 32356

U.S.A.
Oscar Getz Museum of Whiskey History, Bardstown 35346
Rodgers Tavern, Perryville 39332
Wine Museum of Greyton H. Taylor, Hammondsport 37319

Wood → Forest Products

Wood Carving

Armenia
State Folk Art Museum of Armenia, Erevan 00681
State Fretwork Museum, Erevan 00682

Belgium
Musée du Bois - Musée de la Vie Rurale, Mettet 03598

Bulgaria
Muzej na Rezbarskoto i Zografsko Izkustvo, Trjavna 04355

Canada
Musée des Anciens Canadiens, Saint-Jean-Port-Joli 05797

France
Musée National Picasso La Guerre et la Paix, Vallauris 13849

Germany
Städtische Galerie, Traunstein 18725

Städtische Galerie Peter Breuer, Zwickau 19297

Greece
Folklore Museum, Thessaloniki 19673
Nikou Collection, Mytilini 19581

Iceland
Listasafn Árnesinga -Árnesýsla Art Gallery, Selfoss 20122

Ireland
Clonfert Diocesan Museum, Loughrea 20809

Italy
Mostra Permanente di Xilografia di Pietro Parigi, Firenze 21601
Museo della Xilografia Italiana Ugo da Carpi, Carpi 21316
Museo Diocesano e Collezione dei Presepi, Bressanone 21246

Japan
Hida Kaiun-no-mori, Takayama 23550

Netherlands
Museumboerderij New Greenwich Village, Zuidwolde, Drenthe 25693

New Zealand
Museum of Woodwork and Ornamental Turning, Ashburton 25714
Puke Ariki - Taranaki Museum, New Plymouth 25848

Nigeria
National Museum, Oron, Oron 25990

Russia
Permskaja Gosudarstvennaja Chudožestvennaja Galereja, Perm 27989

Switzerland
Ausstellung der Kantonalen Schnitzerschule, Brienz, Bern 30651

Thailand
Kamthieng House, Bangkok 31544

Turkey
Vakif İnşaat ve Sanat Eserleri Müzesi, İstanbul 31760

United Kingdom
Florence Nightingale Museum, Aylesbury 32097
Little Moreton Hall, Congleton 32667
Thomas Bewick's Birthplace, Mickley 33940
William Lamb Memorial Studio, Montrose 33981

U.S.A.
Alaska Indian Arts, Haines 37303
Barnegat Bay Decoy and Baymen's Museum, Tuckerton 40739
Crafts Museum, Mequon 38431
Hoo-Hoo International Forestry Museum, Gurdon 37288
Jim Savage Art Gallery and Museum, Sioux Falls 40373
Longboat Key Center for the Arts, Longboat Key 38121
National Museum of Woodcarving, Custer 36347
Trinity Heights - Saint Joseph Center-Museum, Sioux City 40369
Wendell Gilley Museum, Southwest Harbor 40430

Zoology

Argentina
Museo de Animales Venenosos, Buenos Aires 00155
Museo de Zoología, Córdoba 00290
Museo Histórico Municipal Alfredo E. Múlgura, General Belgrano 00344
Museo Municipal de Ciencias Naturales Lorenzo Scaglia, Mar del Plata 00420
Museo Natural Dr. Carlos A. Marelli, Colón 00272

Armenia
Zoological Museum of the Institute of Zoology, Erevan 00686

Australia
Tasmanian Museum and Art Gallery, Hobart 01094
Western Australian Museum, Perth 01358
Zoology Museum, Brisbane 00836

Austria
Biologiezentrum des Oberösterreichischen Landesmuseums, Linz 02220
Kynologisches Museum, Wien 02894
Naturhistorisches Museum, Admont 01642
Referat Zoologie, Graz 01926
Robert Hytha-Museum, Oberwölbling 02365

Belgium
Aquarium Dubuisson et Musée de Zoologie de l'Université de Liège, Liège 03536
Koninklijke Maatschappij voor Dierkunde van Antwerpen, Antwerpen 03107
Musée de Zoologie Auguste Lameere, Bruxelles 03279
Musée d'Histoire Naturelle de la Ville de Tournai, Tournai 03777
Musée d'Histoire Naturelle de Mons, Mons 03605

Brazil
Museu de Zoologia, São Paulo 04113

Canada
Aasland Museum Taxidermy, Cranbrook 04747
Adams Igloo Wildlife Museum, Smithers 05933
Cowan Vertebrate Museum, Vancouver 06149
Frames Northern Museum, Creighton 04749
Grizzly Bear Prairie Museum, Wanham 06218
International Fox Museum, Summerside 05987
Museum of Zoology, Edmonton 04847
UBC Fish Museum, Vancouver 06166
University of Calgary Museum of Zoology,
Calgary 04641
Zoology Museum, Winnipeg 06330

Colombia
Museo de Ciencias Naturales del Colegio de San José,
Medellín 06856

Croatia
Hrvatski Narodni Zoološki Muzej, Zagreb 07106

Cuba
Museo y Biblioteca de Zoología, La Habana 07162

Czech Republic
Biskupský Dvůr, Brno 07251
Lesnické, Myslivecké a Rybářské Muzeum, Hluboká
nad Vltavou 07335
Muzeum Úsov, Úsov 07685
Rožmberský Dům, Soběslav 07641

Denmark
Zoologisk Museum, København 07939
Zoologisk Museum Svendborg, Svendborg 08074

Ecuador
Museo Zoológico, Ambato 08116

Egypt
Giza Zoological Museum, Giza 08241
Scientific Researches Museum, Cairo 08233

Ethiopia
Natural History Museum, Addis Ababa 08282

Finland
Eläinmuseo, Helsinki 08347
Kuopion Luonnontieteellinen Museo, Kuopio 08561
Ostrobothnia Australis, Vaasa 08996
Oulun Yliopiston Eläinmuseo, Oulu 08739
Turun Biologinen Museo, Turku 08971

France
Atelier d'Art Animalier, La Chapelle-Thouarault 10947
Musée d'Anatomie Normale, Strasbourg 13598
Musée de la Vallée de l'Ubaye, Barcelonnette 09419
Musée d'Histoire Naturelle, Nantes 12040
Musée Océanographique, Arcachon 09224
Musée Zoologique de l'Université Louis Pasteur et de
la Ville de Strasbourg, Strasbourg 13617
Muséum-Aquarium de Nancy, Nancy 12027
Muséum d'Histoire Naturelle, Nice 12109
Muséum National d'Histoire Naturelle, Paris 12447

Germany
Berliner Hundemuseum, Ostseebad Binz 17897
Brehm-Gedenkstätte, Renthendorf 18142
Dillhäuser Fachwerkhaus im Tiergarten Weilburg,
Weilburg 18972
Dinosaurier-Freilichtmuseum Münchehagen, Rehburg-
Loccum 18112
Dr.-Carl-Haeberlin-Friesen-Museum, Wyk auf
Föhr 19252
Ernst-Haeckel-Haus, Jena 16596
Fehn- und Schiffahrtsmuseum, Rhauderfehn 18153
Forst- und Jagdmuseum, Hofgeismar 16460
Jagd- und Naturkunde Museum, Niederstetten 17698
Münchner Tiermuseum, München 17494
Museum der Natur, Gotha 16047
Museum der Stadt Alfeld (Leine), Alfeld, Leine 14217
Museum für Naturkunde der Humboldt-Universität zu
Berlin, Berlin 14806

Museum für Naturkunde der Stadt Gera, Gera 15938
Museum für Tierkunde, Dresden 15419
Naturhistorisches Museum, Mainz 17235
Naturkunde-Museum Bamberg, Bamberg 14584
Naturkundemuseum Erfurt, Erfurt 15610
Phyletisches Museum, Jena 16602
Rhöner Naturmuseum, Tann, Rhön 18678
Staatlicher Schloßbetrieb Schloß Nossen / Kloster
Altzella, Nossen 17727
Staatliches Naturhistorisches Museum,
Braunschweig 15039
Tiermuseum, Lenggries 17080
Waldmuseum Herfa, Heringen, Werra 16389
Zoologische Sammlungen des Institutes für Zoologie,
Halle, Saale 16200
Zoologische Schausammlung, Tübingen 18764
Zoologische Staatssammlung, München 17534
Zoologisches Forschungsinstitut und Museum
Alexander Koenig, Bonn 14993
Zoologisches Museum der Universität, Kiel 16735
Zoologisches Museum der Universität,
Göttingen 16031
Zoologisches Museum der Universität Hamburg,
Hamburg 16249
Zoologisches Museum der Universität Heidelberg,
Heidelberg 16345
Zoologisches und Tiermedizinisches Museum der
Universität Hohenheim, Stuttgart 18654

Ghana
Zoology Museum, Legon 19316

Greece
Zoological Museum, Athinai 19422

Guatemala
Museo Nacional y Zoológico La Aurora, Guatemala
City 19757

India
Government J.T.C. Museum, Faizabad 20238
Madras Christian College Museum, Chennai 20189
Mahatma Gandhi Museum, Mangalore 20354
Zoological Museum, Dehradun 20204
Zoological Museum, Faizabad 20239
Zoological Museum, Gorakhpur 20250
Zoological Museum, Hardwar 20264
Zoological Museum, Jaunpur 20286
Zoological Museum, Meerut 20358
Zoology Department Museum, Allahabad 20147
Zoology Museum, Annamalai Nagar 20153
Zoology Museum, Kanpur 20181
Zoology Museum, Muzaffarnagar 20370

Indonesia
Museum Kebun Raya Bogor, Bogor 20478
Museum Komodo, Jakarta 20508
Museum Taman Laut Ancol, Jakarta 20517

Iran
Zoological Museum, Karaj 20623

Ireland
Museum of Natural History, Dublin 20752
University College Zoological Museum, Cork 20725
Zoological Museum, Dublin 20765

Israel
Bet Gordon, Deganya Aleph 20873
Ussishkin House, Kibbutz Dan 20946
Zoological Museum, Tel Aviv 21011

Italy
Civico Museo di Storia Naturale, Ferrara 21551
Museo Alpino Duca degli Abruzzi, Courmayeur 21483
Museo Civico di Storia Naturale, Pavia 22139
Museo Civico di Storia Naturale G. Doria,
Genova 21692
Museo Civico di Zoologia, Roma 22361
Museo del Cervo, Villavallelonga 22872
Museo del Dipartimento di Zoologia dell'Università di
Bari, Bari 21135
Museo dell'Istituto di Zoologia, Bologna 21197

Museo di Anatomia Comparata Battista Grassi,
Roma 22381
Museo di Storia Naturale dell'Accademia dei
Fisocritici, Siena 22582
Museo di Storia Naturale, Sezione Zoologica La
Specola dell'Università degli Studi di Firenze,
Firenze 21619
Museo di Zoologia, Napoli 22022
Museo di Zoologia della Università di Palermo,
Palermo 22110
Museo Didattico Zoologico, Oria 22068
Museo Zoologico, Catania 21367
Museo Zoologico dell'Istituto Nazionale per la Fauna
Selvatica, Ozzano dell'Emilia 22084
Museo Zoologico dell'Università di Torino,
Torino 22694
Museo Zoologico G. Scarpa, Treviso 22729
Raccolta Didattica di Animali dell'Istituto di Zoologia,
Sassari 22543

Jamaica
Zoology Museum, Kingston 22904

Japan
Hieizan Natural History Museum, Kyoto 23221
Meguro Kiseichukan, Tokyo 23632
Odawara Crustacea Museum, Tokyo 23657

Jordan
Animal Museum, Amman 23788

Korea, Republic
Kuknip Kwahak Pakmulgwan, Seoul 23934

Madagascar
Musée d' ORSTOM, Antananarivo 24262

Mexico
Museo Zoologico Cesar Domínguez Flores, Tuxtla
Gutiérrez 24519

Netherlands
Kikkermuseum, Den Haag 24901
Schoonewelle, Zwartsluis 25699
Zoölogisch Museum Amsterdam, Amsterdam 24748

New Zealand
Kahutara Canoes and Taxidermy Museum,
Featherston 25788
Otago Museum, Dunedin 25778

Nigeria
Zoology Museum, Ibadan 25975

Pakistan
Islamia College Museum, Peshawar 26420
Zoological Museum, Lahore 26415

Philippines
National Museum, Zamboanga 26608

Poland
Muzeum i Instytut Zoologi PAN, Warszawa 27211
Muzeum Lasu i Drewna przy Lesnym Zakładzie
Doświadczalnym SGGW, Rogów 27068
Muzeum Przyrodnicze Instytutu Systematyki i Ewolucji
Zwierząt PAN, Kraków 26840
Muzeum Przyrodnicze Uniwersytetu Wrocławskiego,
Wrocław 27288

Portugal
Museu de História Natural, Porto 27425

Romania
Complex Muzeal de Stiintele Naturii, Galaţi 27575
Muzeul de Istorie Naturala Grigore Antipa,
Bucureşti 27514
Muzeul Zoologic al Universităţii Babeş-Bolyai, Cluj-
Napoca 27552

Russia
Gosudarstvennyj Muzej Životnovodstva im Akademika
E.F. Liskuna, Moskva 27833
Muzej Košek, Moskva 27881

Zoologičeskij Muzej Akademii Nauk, Sankt-
Peterburg 28072
Zoologičeskij Muzej Moskovskogo Gosudarstvennogo
Universiteta M.V. Lomonosova, Moskva 27945

Slovakia
Múzeum Tatranského Národného Parku, Tatranská
Lomnica 28309
Ponitrianske Múzeum, Nitra 28272

South Africa
Albany Museum, Grahamstown 28482
Museum of Natural History, Pretoria 28585
Port Elizabeth Museum, Port Elizabeth 28568
South African Museum, Cape Town 28446
Zoology Museum, Johannesburg 28521

Spain
Museo de Historia Natural, Santiago de
Compostela 29677
Museo Nacional de Ciencias Naturales, Madrid 29286

Sweden
Zoologiska Museet, Lund 30215
Zoologiska Utställingar, Uppsala 30458

Switzerland
Hasenmuseum, Bubikon 30661
Musée Cantonal de Zoologie, Lausanne 30925
Musée de Grenouille, Estavayer-le-Lac 30759
Tierwelt-Panorama, Ebikon 30736
Zoologisches Museum der Universität Zürich,
Zürich 31483

Uganda
Department of Zoology Museum, Kampala 31874
Murchison Falls National Park Museum, Murchison
Falls 31881
Queen Elizabeth National Park Museum, Lake
Katwe 31879
Wildlife Education Centre, Entebbe 31873

Ukraine
Benedykt Dybowsky Zoological Museum, Lviv 31931

United Kingdom
Bell Pettigrew Museum, Saint Andrews 34357
Birmingham Nature Centre, Birmingham 32264
Cole Museum of Zoology, Reading 34281
Grant Museum of Zoology and Comparative Anatomy,
London 33652
Loch Ness 2000 Exhibition, Drumnadrochit 32814
Natural History Museum, Bangor, Gwynedd 32131
Natural History Museum, Belfast 32199
Oxford University Museum of Natural History,
Oxford 34137
University Museum of Zoology, Cambridge 32511
Walter Rothschild Zoological Museum, Tring 34693
Zoology Museum, Glasgow 33100

Uruguay
Museo Zoológico Dámaso A. Larrañaga,
Montevideo 34957

U.S.A.
Museum of Vertebrate Zoology, Berkeley 35462
Museum of Zoology, Amherst 35084
Museum of Zoology, Ann Arbor 35123
National Museum of Wildlife Art, Jackson 37646
New Bedford Whaling Museum, New Bedford 38755
Palo Alto Junior Museum, Palo Alto 39266
Philip L. Wright Zoological Museum, Missoula 38554
Space Farms Zoological Park and Museum,
Sussex 40590
Toledo Museum of Science, Toledo 40691
University of North Dakota Zoology Museum, Grand
Forks 37197
University of Wisconsin Zoological Museum,
Madison 38277

Zimbabwe
Natural History Museum of Zimbabwe,
Bulawayo 41659

List of Advertisers